INDEX

Covers All 1953 Through 1961 Models
Foreign Car Tune Up Data ... 1146

D1106545

CAR CHAPTER SECTIONS

NAME OF CAR	PAGE	NAME OF CAR	PAGE	NAME OF CAR	PAGE
Buick	378	Dodge Dart	642	Oldsmobile	852
Buick Special	419	Edsel	696	Oldsmobile F-85	880
Cadillac	449	Falcon	582	Plymouth	912
Chevrolet	478	Ford	696	Pontiac	963
Chrysler	530	Hudson	1041	Pontiac Tempest	1008
Comet	582	Imperial	530	Rambler	1041
Continental	775	Jeep	1110	Studebaker	1075
Corvair	601	Lancer	754	Thunderbird	696
Corvette	478	Lincoln	775	Valiant	754
De Soto	530	Mercury	805	Willys	1110
Dodge	642	Nash	1041		

GENERAL SERVICE SECTION

SUBJECT	PAGE		PAGE
Air Conditioning	177	Non-Slip Differentials	109
Alternators	57	Overdrives	100
Brakes, Hydraulic	112	Rear Axles, General Service	102
Brakes, Power	128	Starter Switches	83
Dash Gauges	85	Starting Motors	77
Distributors	46	Steering Gears, Power	145
Fuel Pumps	96	Trouble Shooting	3
Generators & Regulators	62	Tune Up, General Service	38
Ignition Systems	46		

AUTOMATIC TRANSMISSION SECTION

How to Push and Tow Automatic Drive Cars .... Inside Front Cover

NAME OF UNIT	PAGE	NAME OF UNIT	PAGE
Borg Warner Drive, Studebaker	179	Hydra-Matic, Single Coupling Type	283
Buick Dynaflow	210	Hydra-Matic, Dual Coupling Type	263
Buick Twin Turbine	210	Hydra-Matic, Three Speed	1132
Buick Flight Pitch	191	Hydra-Matic, Olds. F-85	892
Buick Triple Turbine	191	Merc-O-Matic	240
Buick Special	431	Multi-Drive, Mercury	240
Comet Drive	253	Pontiac Tempest	
Cruise-O-Matic, Ford & T-Bird	240	Powerflite, Chrysler	
Edsel Mile-O-Matic	253	Powerglide, Chevrolet	
Edsel Dual-Power	240	Powerglide, Corvair	
Flashomatic, Rambler	233	Torqueflite 6, Chrysler	
Flightomatic, Studebaker	240	Torqueflite V8, Chrysler	
Ford-O-Matic, Three Speed	240	Twin Range Turbo-	
Ford-O-Matic, Two Speed	253	Turbo-Drive, Lincoln	
		Turboglide, Chevrolet	

MOTOR
AUTO REPAIR MANUAL

Second Vintage Car Edition

24th Edition, Fourth Printing, 1981

Ralph Ritchen

Editor

Louis Forier • Wallace Norde

Associate Editors

Robert DiFazio

Editorial Assistant

Published by
MOTOR

224 West 57th St., New York, N.Y. 10019

The Automotive Business Magazine

Printed in the U.S.A. © Copyright MCMLXI by The Hearst Corporation
Library of Congress Catalog Number: 81-81681

ISBN 0-87851-546-1

TROUBLE SHOOTING
INDEX OF SYMPTOMS

ENGINE TROUBLES

Starting a stalled engine.................. 4
Engine won't start...................... 5
Hard starting 5
Engine stalls 6
Engine starts but won't drive car........ 6
Engine misfires 6
Lack of power......................... 7
Poor high speed performance........... 7
Rough engine idle..................... 7
Spark knock 7
Pre-ignition 7
Engine kickback 7
Backfire 7
Muffler explosion 7
After-burning 7
Flat spot 8
Engine overheats 8
Engine oil leakage.................... 8
High oil consumption.................. 9
Oil pressure relief valve leaks.......... 9
Engine oil dilution.................... 9
No oil pressure 9
Low oil pressure 9
High oil pressure 9
Engine noises 9

ELECTRICAL TROUBLES

Battery requires frequent recharging...... 10
Starter won't rotate or rotates slowly....... 11
Starter spins but won't engage flywheel.... 11
Starter pinion jammed into flywheel gear... 11
Starter pinion disengages slowly.......... 11
Starter pinion won't release............. 11
Starter noise 11
Generator does not charge.............. 12
Generator noise 12
Generator brush noise 12
Alternator troubles 12
Lights flicker 12
Lamps fail to burn.................... 12
Lights flare up when engine is speeded up.. 12
Stop light troubles 12
Turn signal troubles................... 12

CLUTCH TROUBLES

Clutch drags 13
Clutch slips 13
Clutch grabs 13
Clutch chatters 13
Clutch pedal pulsates.................. 13
Clutch rattles 13
Noise when pedal is depressed........... 13
Noise when pedal is released............ 13
Bearing noise 13

SYNCHROMESH TRANSMISSION TROUBLES

Slips out of high or second.............. 14
Slips out of second slowly............... 14
Slips out of low or reverse.............. 14
Gears clash when shifted................ 14

Transmission leaks oil..................... 14
Leakage at torque tube.................. 14

OVERDRIVE TROUBLES

Overdrives Without Relay

Trans. won't operate in O.D............. 14
Trans. fails to kickdown................. 14

Overdrives With Relay

Overdrive won't engage................ 14
Overdrive won't kickdown.............. 15
Trans. won't shift into reverse, etc........ 16
Engine cuts out....................... 16

Mechanical

O.D. won't drive unless locked up manually. 16
Overdrive does not engage or lock-up
   does not release.................... 16
Overdrive engages with severe jolt or noise. 16
Free-wheels at speeds above 30 mph....... 16

AUTOMATIC TRANSMISSION TROUBLES

Buick Special 432
Buick Twin Turbine types............... 16
Buick Triple Turbine types.............. 18
Chevrolet Powerglide 19
Chevrolet Turboglide 20
Comet Drive 25
Corvair Powerglide 632
Edsel Mile-O-Matic 25
Edsel Dual-Power Drive................ 24
Flightomatic 24
Ford-O-Matic three speed.............. 24
Ford-O-Matic two speed................ 25
Ford Cruise-O-Matic 24
Hydra-Matic, single coupling type........ 25
Hydra-Matic, two coupling type 28
Hydra-Matic, three speed type 1144
Merc-O-Matic 24
Multi-Drive 24
Oldsmobile F-85 906
Pontiac Tempest 1024
Powerflite 21
Rambler Flashomatic 30
Studebaker Automatic Drive............. 29
Torqueflite 23
Turbo-Drive 24

REAR AXLE TROUBLES

Noise when pulling straight ahead........ 31
Noise when coasting in gear............. 31
Intermittent noise 31
Knocks or clicks 31

Noise on turns........................ 31
Oil leak at axle ends.................. 31
Oil leak at pinion shaft................. 31

BRAKE TROUBLES

Brake pedal goes all the way to floor..... 31
No pedal after hard usage.............. 31
Brakes drag at all wheels.............. 31
Brake drags at one wheel.............. 31
Car pulls to one side.................. 31
Springy pedal action................... 32
Excessive pedal pressure necessary to stop.. 32
Too light pedal pressure
   (Brake action severe)............... 32
Brakes squeak when applied............. 32

POWER BRAKE TROUBLES

Hard pedal (no assist)................. 32
Brake pedal chatters.................. 32
Brakes grab 32
Slow release, drag, no release.......... 32
Spongy pedal, excessive pedal travel..... 33
Brakes apply when engine is started....... 33
Pedal kicks back with engine running....... 33

FRONT END & STEERING TROUBLES

Hard steering 33
Excessive play or looseness in steering...... 33
Erratic steering when brakes are applied... 33
Car pulls to one side.................. 33
Scuffed tires 33
Cupped tires 33
Front wheel shimmy................... 33
Front wheel tramp.................... 33
Car wanders 33
Road shocks 33

POWER STEERING TROUBLES

Chrysler Coaxial Type.................. 34
Chrysler Constant Control Type.......... 34
Ford Torsion Bar Type................. 35
Saginaw Offset and In Line Types........ 35
Saginaw Rotary Valve Type............. 35

POWER TOP, WINDOW & SEAT TROUBLES

Hydro-Lectric Type

Top will not operate................... 36
Top operates in one direction only........ 36
Window lift inoperative................. 36
Windows operate slowly upward......... 36
Windows operate slowly downward...... 36
Window raises when top or seat is operated 36
Two windows operate from one switch..... 36
Seat adjuster inoperative............... 36

Seat operates slowly...................... 36
All units operate slowly.................... 36
Power unit inoperative on any control switch 36

Electric Type for Windows & Seats

Window won't operate from main switch only 36
Window won't operate from main or
door switch 36

Window won't operate in one direction only
from main or door switch.............. 36
Circuit breaker in door clicks on and off
continuously and window won't operate... 36
Main or door switch operates window in
wrong direction 36
Window operates sluggishly............. 36
All windows do not operate.............. 36
Seat regulators inoperative.............. 36
One seat regulator inoperative........... 37

Seat regulator operates in one direction only 37
Seat regulator operates sluggishly......... 37

WINDSHIELD WIPER TROUBLES

Electric type 37
Vacuum type 40

Engine Troubles

STARTING A STALLED ENGINE

When an engine fails to start the chances are that 90 per cent of the cases will involve the ignition system and seldom the fuel system or other miscellaneous reasons. If a systematic procedure is followed the trouble can almost always be found without the use of special equipment.

To begin with, turn on the ignition switch and if the ammeter shows a slight discharge (or if the telltale lamp lights) it indicates that current is flowing. A glance at the gas gauge will indicate whether or not there is fuel in the tank.

Operate the starter and if the engine turns over freely, both the battery and starter are functioning properly. On the other hand, if the starter action is sluggish it may be due to a discharged or defective battery, loose, corroded or dirty battery terminals, mechanical failure in the starter, starter switch or starter drive. If the starter circuit is okay, skip this phase of the discussion and proceed to ignition.

Starter Circuit Checkout

To determine which part of the starter circuit is at fault, turn on the light switch and again operate the starter. Should the lights go out or become dim, the trouble is either in the battery, its connections or cables. A hydrometer test of the battery should indicate better than 1.250 specific gravity, while a voltmeter, placed across the positive and negative posts, should indicate about 6 volts for a 6-volt battery and 12 volts for a 12-volt system. If either of these tests prove okay, clean and then the battery connections and cable terminals or replace any cable which is doubtful.

If the lights remain bright when the starter is operated, the trouble is between the battery and the starter, or the starter itself is at fault, since it is evident that there is no electrical connection between the points. If these connections are good and tight, it is safe to assume that the starter or starter switch is defective.

Primary Ignition Checkout

Let's assume that the battery and starter are doing their job, and that fuel is reaching the carburetor, but the car does not start, then the trouble must be somewhere in the ignition circuit. But first, before starting your diagnosis, it is advisable to give the whole system a visual inspection which might uncover obvious things such as broken or disconnected wires etc.

The best way to start tracking down ignition troubles is to begin with the primary circuit since this is where troubles show up most frequently. First remove the distributor cap and block the points open with a piece of cardboard, then turn on the ignition and with a test bulb or voltmeter check to see if there is current at the terminal on the distributor. If you do not get a reading at this point, the current is cut off somewhere in the connections leading back to the ignition switch or it may be that the condenser has an internal short to the ground. The latter possibility can be eliminated if you can restore current at the distributor terminal by disconnecting the condenser from the distributor plate so that its outside shell is not grounded. With the possibility of a bad condenser out of the way, work toward the ignition switch and test for current at each connection until you get to one where you get a reading. Between this connection and the distributor lies the trouble.

On the other hand, if the test equipment shows a current reading at the distributor terminal, it is safe to assume that the trouble is in the unit itself, most likely burned or dirty breaker points. A final positive test for defective breaker points can be made very simply by removing the cardboard from between the points, and positioning the distributor cam by turning the engine to where the points are closed. With the points closed there should be no current at the distributor terminal. If there is current, renew the points.

In an emergency, the points can be cleaned by using the sanded side of a match box, a knife blade, or a sharp edge of a screwdriver to scrape the scale from the contact faces. After cleaning the points, and a gauge is not availiable to set the gap, a quick adjustment can be made by using four layers of a piece of newspaper. The thickness of the paper is equivalent to about .020", which is the approximate gap setting for most distributors. Of course, at the earliest opportunity, a precise point adjustment should be made.

If the procedure outlined under "Primary Ignition Checkout" does not uncover the trouble then it will be necessary to continue the tests into the secondary ignition circuit.

Secondary Ignition Checkout

First of all, remove the wire from one of the spark plugs, turn on the ignition and operate the starter. While the engine is cranking, hold the terminal of the spark plug wire about ¼" away from the engine or spark plug base. If the spark is strong and jumps the gap, the trouble is confined to either the spark plugs or lack of fuel. Before going any further, wipe the outside of the plugs to remove any dirt or dampness which would create an easy path for the current to flow, then try to start the engine again. If it still fails to start, remove one of the spark plugs and if it is wet around the base, it indicates that the fuel system is okay, so it naturally follows that the spark plugs are at fault. Remove all the plugs, clean them and set the gaps. An emergency adjustment of spark plug gaps can be made by folding a piece of newspaper into five layers. When changing the gap, always bend the side (ground) electrode and never the center one as there is danger of breaking the insulation.

Fuel System Checkout

If the spark plug that was removed showed no indication of dampness on its base, check the fuel system. A quick check can be made by simply removing the carburetor air cleaner and looking down into the carburetor. Open and close the throttle manually and if fuel is present in the carburetor, the throttle will operate the accelerating pump, causing it to push gasoline through the pump jet. If it does, check the choke valve. If the engine is cold, the choke valve should be closed. If the choke won't close, the engine can be started by covering the carburetor throat with your hand while the engine is cranking, provided, of course, that fuel is reaching the carburetor.

Check the operation of the fuel pump by disconnecting the fuel lines from the pump to the carburetor. Crank the engine and if the pump is working, fuel will pulsate out of the line. If not, either the pump isn't working or the line from the tank to the pump is clogged. Before blaming the pump, however, disconnect the line at the inlet side of the pump which leads to the tank and, while a companion listens at the tank, blow through the line. If a gurgling sound is heard back in the tank, the line is open and the trouble is in the pump. Remove the sediment bowl and clean the screen, then replace the bowl and screen, being sure that you have an air-tight fit. If the pump still refuses to function, it should be removed and repaired.

The foregoing discussion will, in most cases, uncover the cause of why an engine won't start. However, if further diagnosis is necessary, the following list will undoubtedly provide the answer.

ENGINE WON'T START

Due to Open Primary Ignition Circuit

1. Burned or oxidized ignition points.
2. Primary circuit resistance unit burnt or open (12-volt systems).
3. Ignition points not closing.
4. Breaker arm binding on pivot post, preventing closing of points.
5. Breaker arm spring weak or broken.
6. Breaker arm distorted or bent.
7. Dirty ignition points.
8. Primary lead connection loose at distributor or coil.
9. Primary windings in coil broken.
10. Open ignition switch circuit.

Due to Grounded Primary Ignition Circuit

A grounded coil primary winding, a grounded ignition switch, or a grounded switch-to-coil primary lead will cause excessive current flow and will usually cause wires to burn.

1. Ignition points not opening or closing due to improper adjustment.
2. Ignition points not opening due to worn rubbing block on breaker arm.
3. Faulty insulating bushing in breaker arm.
4. Cracked or faulty insulator at distributor primary terminal.
5. Grounded condenser.
6. Distributor-to-coil lead grounded.
7. Primary coil winding grounded.

Due to Faulty Secondary Ignition Circuit

1. Corroded spark plug cable terminals.
2. Chafed or cracked insulation on cables.
3. Ignition coil weak or inoperative.
4. Moisture on ignition coil, terminals, distributor cover, spark plug porcelains, or in distributor
5. Improper type of spark plugs.
6. Cracked distributor cap or a burned carbon track from distributor cap center terminal to distributor housing.
7. Improper installation of spark plug cables (not correct for engine firing order).
8. Spark plugs damaged, dirty or wet, porcelains cracked, or gaps improperly spaced.
9. Rotor contact spring bent or broken.
10. Distributor rotor grounded.
11. Distributor cap center terminal (inner) broken or missing.
12. Broken or burned out radio suppressor in distributor cap.

Due to Battery

1. Battery run down.
2. Terminals loose or badly corroded.
3. Improper ground.
4. Battery cables frayed or undersize.

Due to Starter Motor

1. Not operating properly.
2. Congealed engine oil due to use of too heavy a grade of oil or to the formation of sludge.
3. Starter gear binding in flywheel gear.
4. Defective starter switch.
5. Faulty neutral safety switch on cars with automatic transmission.

Due to Excessive Fuel Supply (Flooding)

The engine is said to be flooded with fuel when a quantity of liquid fuel collects in the intake manifold, and perhaps also in the cylinders. This condition gives a mixture that is much too rich to ignite.

If the carburetor has a provision for opening the choke valve when the throttle is fully open, crank the engine with the throttle open until engine starts. It will start as soon as the extra fuel is pumped out.

If the choke valve is not designed to open when the throttle is fully opened, tie or block the choke valve open and crank the engine until it starts.

Flooding may also occur on the road. If the carburetor supplies too rich a mixture at full throttle, the intake manifold may be flooded with liquid fuel, with the result that when the engine is stopped, heat evaporates the fuel and thus provides an over-rich incombustible mixture. The engine won't start until the rich mixture is pumped out by cranking.

1. Choke not operating properly.
2. Automatic choke not properly set.
3. Carburetor unloader linkage (if equipped) not properly set.
4. Float level set too high.
5. Dirty, worn or faulty needle valve and seat.
6. Float sticking or rubbing against side of fuel bowl.
7. Leak in float, allowing fuel to get inside.
8. Fuel pump pressure too great.

Due to Insufficient Fuel Supply

1. Carburetor inlet needle stuck in its seat, due to gum in fuel.
2. Float level too low.
3. Clogged inlet screen at carburetor.
4. Faulty fuel pump or one of insufficient capacity.
5. Fuel pump strainer clogged.
6. Faulty fuel pump bowl gasket.
7. Flexible line (if used) twisted, deteriorated or restricted.
8. Fuel line to tank clogged, kinked, restricted or leaking.
9. Vent in fuel tank filler cap clogged or restricted.
10. Worn fuel pump camshaft lobe.

HARD STARTING

When Engine is Hot

This condition is usually caused by an over-supply of fuel due to any of the items listed under *Engine Won't Start Due to Excessive Fuel Supply*. In rare cases, an ignition coil may lose its efficiency when it is hot and cause ignition failure.

When Engine is Cold

Many of the conditions enumerated under *Engine Won't Start* also may cause hard starting in cold weather. Of particular importance, however, are the following:

1. Choke setting too lean.
2. Fuel may have kerosene in it or water, or ice in bottom of tank.
3. Ice in fuel filter bowl.
4. Ice in fuel lines.
5. Engine is cranked too slowly or won't turn over because: (a) engine oil is too thick in sub-zero weather; (b) battery weak due to extremely low temperature.
6. Another possibility, although remote, is that the water pump is jammed with ice, which will interfere with cranking engine if fan belt is tight.

Due to Vapor Lock

The term vapor lock means the flow of fuel to the mixing chamber in the carburetor has been stopped (locked) by the formation of vaporized fuel pockets or bubbles caused by overheating the fuel by hot fuel pump, hot fuel lines or hot carburetor.

The more volatile the fuel the greater the tendency for it to vapor lock. Vapor lock is encouraged by high atmospheric temperature, hard driving, defective engine cooling and high altitude.

A mild case of vapor lock will cause missing and hard starting when engine is warm. Somewhat more severe vapor lock will stop the engine which cannot be started again until it has cooled off enough so that any vaporized fuel has condensed to a liquid.

Due to Percolation

When fuel boils in the carburetor it is said to percolate. The boiling fuel, of course, comes under the head of Vapor Lock. Percolation results in a very lean or rich mixture which may cause power loss if lean or hard starting if rich.

On some carburetors the possibility of this trouble is avoided by adding an anti-percolating valve to the carburetor design. The valve is sometimes linked to the throttle and opens when the throttle is closed allowing gasified fuel to escape to the atmosphere.

If the anti-percolating linkage is so adjusted that the valve opens early, air may be drawn in and this may cause a "flat spot" the next time the throttle is opened.

If the valve fails to open when the throttle is closed and the engine shut off, the intake manifold may be flooded, causing hard starting.

After Long Storage

1. The more volatile components in the fuel have evaporated and those remaining are not sufficiently volatile to provide a combustible mixture.
2. Low or run-down battery.

3. Corrosion of engine parts may result in so much friction that starter cannot crank engine at proper speed, if at all.
4. Pistons, etc. may be stuck fast by gummy oil.
5. Engine valves may stick open due to gummy deposits.
6. There is the possibility that any small part essential to the running of the engine may be stuck due to gummy film or to corrosion.
7. Some of these troubles are most likely to occur in hot, humid climate and near salt water.

ENGINE STALLS

Many troubles which prevent smooth running at idle may cause stalling. The list includes almost everything that may cause hard starting or missing. Some of the more common causes are:
1. Engine idle speed set too low.
2. Large air leaks in intake manifold such as a disconnected windshield wiper vacuum line.
3. Ignition points need attention.
4. Engine valves leaking.
5. Vapor lock.
6. Over-supply of fuel (flooding).
7. Valves set too tight.

If carburetor is equipped with a fast idle cam, which increases engine speed when the choke is in operation during the warm-up period, the engine may stall if the fast idle device fails to open the throttle due to sticking or need for adjustment.

On some cars equipped with a fluid coupling or torque converter, if the throttle is closed quickly the engine stalls. To avoid this trouble, most cars have a device which retards the speed of the throttle closing; this is called a dashpot and is usually mounted on the carburetor. It consists of a piston or diaphragm and a spring-closed check valve. If the linkage is out of adjustment or the check valve leaks, the engine will stall.

If the engine quits smoothly when car is in operation, the trouble is often caused by sudden lack of fuel due to:
1. Fuel tank empty.
2. Vapor lock.
3. Flooding.
4. Water in fuel.
5. Frozen fuel line.

Carburetor Icing

The carburetor discharges liquid fuel into the air stream in the form of an atomized spray which evaporates readily. The heat required to evaporate the gasoline is drawn from the entering air, thereby lowering its temperature. The cooler air chills the interior of the carburetor and may cause the moisture in the air to condense into droplets.

Under certain conditions of atmospheric temperature and humidity, the liberated moisture actually collects and freezes on the chilled carburetor surfaces, especially on the throttle plate and surrounding throttle body. When the throttle is almost completely closed for idling, this ice tends to bridge the gap between the throttle plate and throttle body, thereby cutting off the air supply and causing the engine to stall. Opening the throttle for restarting breaks the ice

bridge but does not eliminate the possibility of further stalling until the engine and carburetor has warmed up.

For carburetor icing to occur, the outside air must be cool enough so that the refrigerating effect of fuel evaporation in the carburetor will lower the temperatures of the throttle plate and body below both the dew point of moist air and the freezing point of water. The air must also contain sufficient moisture for appreciable condensation of water to occur when it is chilled in the carburetor.

Generally speaking, carburetor icing occurs when winter grade gasoline (more volatile than summer grade) is used and when the atmospheric temperature ranges from 30° to 50° F. at relative humidities in excess of 65%.

Carburetor icing problems can be reduced by the use of anti-icing additives, such as alcohols, in the fuel. Some fuel refiners use anti-stalling additives in their gasolines which have proved effective in combating carburetor icing.

Another form of carburetor icing has been observed in some engines during high-speed driving on cool, moist days. When certain cars are driven steadily at 60 to 80 mph, the large quantities of cool air passing through the carburetor may result in gradual ice formation within the carburetor's venturi. Since this ice restricts the venturi passage, the resultant increased vacuum in the venturi tends to increase the rate of fuel flow. The fuel-air mixture thus becomes excessively rich, causing loss of power and high fuel consumption.

ENGINE STARTS BUT WON'T DRIVE CAR

1. Broken part in the drive line anywhere from clutch to rear axle shaft.
2. No oil or not enough oil in fluid coupling or torque converter.
3. Some defect in automatic transmission causes binding or dragging of clutches or slipping bands.
4. Engine develops only enough power to run itself due to: (a) extremely lean or rich mixture; (b) excessive engine friction; (c) throttle does not open; (d) very dirty air cleaner; (e) clogged exhaust system.
5. Oil in fluid coupling or torque converter is semi-solid due to zero temperature. This trouble is unlikely if the recommended oil is used.

ENGINE MISFIRES

At All Speeds

1. Fouled spark plug or broken porcelain.
2. Faulty spark plug cables.
3. Low battery voltage.
4. Low generator voltage.
5. Burned or pitted ignition points.
6. Incorrect ignition point gap.
7. Faulty condenser or coil.
8. Weak spark or no spark in one or more cylinders.

9. Faulty distributor cap or rotor.
10. Primary circuit restricted or open intermittently.
11. Primary circuit detoured by short intermittently.
12. Secondary circuit restricted or open intermittently.
13. Secondary circuit detoured by short intermittently.
14. Blown cylinder head gasket between cylinders. This can be noted when missing occurs in two adjacent cylinders.
15. Sticking valves.
16. Hydraulic tappet holds valve open slightly.
17. Broken valve spring.
18. Leak at intake manifold gaskets.
19. Mixture too rich or too lean.
20. High tension wire shorted in metal manifold.

At High Speed

1. Hot spark plugs. Change to colder type but note that a hot plug may be due to loose installation or lack of a plug gasket (if gasket is called for).
2. Ignition point gap much too wide.
3. Breaker arm binding or sticking.
4. Breaker arm spring weak.
5. Sticking engine valves.
6. Valve springs too weak to close valves promptly.
7. Valve springs broken.
8. Valve springs shimmy.
9. Intermittent delivery of fuel to carburetor so that momentarily the mixture is too weak for combustion.
10. Mild vapor lock.
11. Weak spark.
12. Exhaust manifold clogged with carbon.
13. Exhaust manifold, muffler or tail pipe restricted.
14. Improper ignition timing.
15. Centrifugal advance not functioning properly.
16. Manifold heater valve held closed.
17. Dirty carburetor air cleaner.
18. Choke valve not completely open.
19. Carburetor throttle lever loose on shaft.
20. Improper fuel pump operation.
21. Preignition.
22. Incorrect valve timing.

At Low or Idle Speeds

1. Faulty spark plugs.
2. Spark plugs gaps too narrow.
3. Dirty or corroded secondary circuit connections or faulty ignition cables.
4. Cracked or faulty distributor cap. Radial contacts in cap burned or worn.
5. Dirty air cleaner.
6. Leaky valves.
7. Ignition point gap too narrow.
8. Faulty carburetion due to: (a) float level too high or too low; (b) float valve leaking; (c) incorrect or loose jets; (d) restricted or partially clogged idle air passage or jet; (e) air leak occurring between upper and lower carburetor body; (f) air leak occurring around carburetor throttle shaft.
9. Air leaks in intake manifold or carburetor resulting from: (a) loose manifold connections or leaks occurring in vacuum lines; (b) loose manifold nuts or capscrews; (c)

broken or damaged intake manifold or carburetor gaskets; (d) cracked manifold; (e) warped or damaged manifold contacting surface.

10. Slight leaks occurring at fuel pump check valves.
11. Air leak occurring around intake valve stem because of excessive valve stem-to-guide clearance.

When Car is Accelerated

If the engine misses when car is accelerated but does not miss when idling the reason is that the spark plugs stop firing because of increased compression pressure caused by:

1. Weak spark.
2. Plug gaps too wide.
3. Plug fouled or damp.
4. Plug porcelain below par.

LACK OF POWER OR HIGH SPEED PERFORMANCE

It should be noted that the altitude at which the car is operated has a decided effect on performance. A car adjusted for normal altitudes will lack performance at high altitudes, whereas a car which operates normally at high altitudes may have a lean carburetor adjustment and show signs of preignition when operated at sea level.

1. Ignition timing incorrect.
2. Centrifugal governor advance not operating properly.
3. Vacuum advance not operating properly.
4. Ignition points burned, pitted, sticking or bouncing (due to weak breaker arm spring).
5. Faulty spark plugs.
6. Faulty ignition cables.
7. Faulty ignition coil.
8. Faulty carburetion.
9. Lack of engine compression.
10. Preignition.
11. Inoperative manifold heater valve (stuck closed).
12. Restricted carburetor inlet resulting from dirty air cleaner or choke valve not fully open.
13. Carburetor throttle lever loose on shaft.
14. Throttle linkage not properly adjusted.
15. Carburetor throttle valve not completely open.
16. Carburetor accelerating pump not functioning properly.
17. Improper fuel pump operation.
18. Partially restricted exhaust pipe, muffler or tail pipe.
19. Clutch slippage.
20. Excessive rolling resistance resulting from (a) dragging brakes, (b) tight wheel bearings, (c) misalignment of power transmitting units, (d) misalignment of rear axle, (e) underinflated tires.
21. Incorrect rear axle gear ratio.
22. Oversize tires.
23. Incorrect valve timing.
24. Inaccurate speedometer (gives impression of lack of performance).

ROUGH IDLE

The term "rough idle" means that the engine does not run smoothly when idling. The most likely cause is an over-rich mixture but any defect which produces uneven explosions or missing will cause a rough idle. The most common causes are:

1. Dirty idle jets and passages.
2. Rich idle adjustment.
3. Dirty air cleaner.
4. Float level too high.
5. Choke set too rich.
6. Fuel volatility too high or too low.
7. Substantial air leak into intake manifold.
8. Fuel pump pressure too high or too low.
9. Clogged carburetor jets.
10. Ignition point gap too narrow or much too wide.
11. Spark plug gaps too narrow or too wide.
12. Sticking breaker arm.
13. Weak spark which permits some missing.
14. Leaky engine valve.
15. Sticking valve or rocker.
16. Broken valve spring.
17. Insufficient tappet clearance.
18. Hydraulic tappet holds valve open.

SPARK KNOCK, PING, DETONATION

All three expressions mean the same thing. It is a sharp metallic knock caused by vibration of the cylinder head and block. The vibration is due to split-second high-pressure waves resulting from almost instantaneous abnormal combustion instead of the slower normal combustion.

The ping may be mild or loud. A mild ping does no harm but a severe ping will reduce power. A very severe ping may shatter spark plugs, break valves or crack pistons.

Pinging is most likely to occur on open throttle at low or moderate engine speed. Pinging is encouraged by:

1. Overheated engine.
2. Low octane fuel.
3. Too high compression.
4. Spark advanced too far.
5. Hot mixture due to hot engine or hot weather.
6. Heavy carbon deposit which increases the compression pressure.

Tendency to ping increases with mixture temperature including high atmospheric temperature; intake manifold heater valve "on" when engine is warm; hot cooling water; hot interior engine surfaces due to sluggish water circulation or water jackets clogged with rust or dirt especially around exhaust valves. Some of these troubles may be confined to one or two cylinders.

If an engine pings objectionably because of too low octane fuel, retard the spark setting but first be sure that the cooling system is in good condition, the mixture not too lean and the combustion chambers free of carbon deposit.

PRE-IGNITION

Pre-ignition means that the mixture is set on fire before the spark occurs, being ignited by a red hot spot in the combustion chamber such as an incandescent particle of carbon; a thin piece of protruding metal; an overheated spark plug, or a bright red hot exhaust valve. The result is reduction of power and overheating accompanied by pinging. The bright red hot exhaust valve may be due to a leak, to lack of tappet clearance, to valve sticking, or a weak or broken spring.

Pre-ignition may not be noticed if not severe. Severe pre-ignition results in severe pinging. The commonest cause of pre-ignition is a badly overheated engine.

When the engine won't stop when the ignition is shut off, the cause is often due to red hot carbon particles resting on heavy carbon deposit in a very hot engine.

ENGINE KICKBACK

If ignition is set too far advanced, spark may occur before top dead center when engine is cranked. The first (and only) explosion runs the engine backward. A kickback may jam the starter or break the starter drive housing.

BACKFIRE

Backfiring is a subdued explosion in the intake manifold. Causes are:

1. Lean mixture (often due to dirt or water in fuel).
2. Engine cold and choke too lean.
3. Leaky or sticking intake valve or weak or broken intake valve spring.
4. Leakage of current across distributor cap may cause backfire by enabling spark to occur in a cylinder which is on its intake stroke. Two mixed-up spark plug wires may also cause this trouble.
5. Popping back is synonymous with backfire.

MUFFLER EXPLOSION

This is a sharp, gun-like report caused by temporary cessation of ignition. If this trouble occurs frequently, once it starts, the most likely causes are:

1. Intermittent open circuit in primary (ammeter needle swings further away from zero when generator is charging).
2. Intermittent short circuit in primary (ammeter needle swings toward zero when generator is charging).
3. Short circuit in coil or in secondary wire from coil to distributor.
4. If just a couple of explosions are heard and then no more for a time (even for days) the trouble may be due to a gradually failing condenser.

AFTER-BURNING

A subdued put-putting at the exhaust tail pipe may be due to leaky exhaust valves which permit the mixture to finish combustion in the muffler. If exhaust pipe or muffler is red hot, better let it cool, as there is some danger of setting the car on fire. Most likely to occur when mixture is lean.

FLAT SPOT

If an engine does not respond promptly when the throttle is opened quickly it (or the carburetor) is said to have a flat spot. This is usually caused by any of the following:

1. Accelerator pump piston (or diaphragm) leaks.
2. Accelerator pump valves leak.
3. Accelerator pump stroke too short.
4. Accelerator pump passages restricted.
5. Fuel volatility too low or too high.
6. Float level too low.
7. Fuel pump pressure too low.
8. The anti-percolating valve (on some carburetors) may open too soon when throttle is closed. If so, carburetor may have flat spot next time throttle is opened when engine is hot.
9. Fuel too hot due to hot engine and hot weather (see Vapor Lock).
10. If carburetor has a metering pin operated by throttle linkage and also a vacuum piston linked to the throttle to give a rich mixture at part throttle and moderate engine speed, a flat spot will be noted if the device fails to function properly because of stuck piston, vacuum leakage or restricted vacuum passages.
11. If carburetor has vacuum piston which provides richer mixture at part throttle and moderate engine speed by opening an additional passage or jet within carburetor, a flat spot will occur if fuel valves fail to work, or fuel passages are restricted, or if piston does not function because it is sticking, vacuum leakage or restricted vacuum passages.
12. Late ignition timing.

ENGINE OVERHEATS

Water is used to cool the engine and air is used to cool the water. Anything which prevents this water-air system from working properly will cause overheating. Oil or grease in the water will reduce the ability of the water to absorb heat from the block and to transfer heat in the water to the radiator. There are six basic causes of overheating:
1. Water does not cool engine.
2. Air does not cool water.
3. Slow combustion.
4. Pre-ignition.
5. Pinging.
6. Excessive friction in engine or elsewhere in power transmitting units.
7. Excessive back pressure in exhaust system.

Water Too Hot

1. Slipping fan belt.
2. Not enough water in system.
3. Carburetor mixture too lean.

4. Clogged exhaust system.
5. Late ignition timing.
6. Centrifugal advance fails to advance spark as engine speed increases because weights stick or because of sticking elsewhere in mechanism.
7. Pre-ignition.
8. Pinging.
9. Water circulation impeded by installation of wrong cylinder head gasket.
10. Cylinder head gasket installed incorrectly, blocking off water holes.
11. Leaky cylinder head gasket permits exhaust gas to enter water. The gas bubbles interfere with the ability of the water to cool the engine.
12. Water circulation slowed down by rust, scale or dirt in water jackets.
13. Water distributing tube (when used) within cylinder block rusted out, dented or improperly installed so that not enough water reaches some cylinders, thus causing local overheating.
14. Local overheating at one cylinder (or more) due to heavy deposit of rust, scale or dirt in water jacket around cylinder or exhaust valve port.
15. Water circulation impeded by thermostat which fails to open fully or sticks closed.
16. Water temperature increased by thermostat which fails to open at correct temperature. Or the installation of a thermostat which opens at too high a temperature.
17. Any water hose which has rotted on inside, allowing loosened strips of rubber to impede water circulation.
18. The baffle in top tank may be bent in such a way as to interfere with free discharge of water from the hose.
19. Vertical water passages in radiator are partially clogged with dirt, rust, corrosion or scale (mineral salts in hard water).
20. Exterior of radiator clogged with dirt, leaves or insects.
21. Rotting of water hose may weaken it so that pump suction causes it to collapse when engine is running fast, thus throttling the water flow.
22. If water pump seal leaks, air may be drawn into the water. Air bubbles in cooling water reduce the cooling ability of the water.
23. Water pump impeller loose on its shaft or impeller blades badly corroded.
24. Overheats due to alcohol type antifreeze during mild weather.

Water Leakage

Cylinder Head
1. Loose attaching bolts.
2. Dirty, corroded or burred surface prevents tight fit.
3. Warped surface does not fit tight against gasket.
4. Cracked due to freezing or excessive heat.
5. On overhead valve head, exhaust valve seats may be cracked, allowing water to leak into cylinders and crankcase.

Cylinder Block
1. Dirty, corroded or burred surface prevents tight fit.

2. Warped surface does not fit tight against gasket.
3. Cracked due to freezing or excessive heat.
4. If L-head design, excessive heat may crack exhaust valve seats, allowing water to leak into crankcase.
5. Block cracked due to use of cylinder head bolt which is too long.
6. Leaky expansion plugs or pipe plugs in water jacket.

Cylinder Head Gasket
1. Dirty, corroded or broken.
2. Loose because cylinder head bolts are loose.
3. Leaks because it cannot make tight contact between head and block.

Water Pump
1. Loose pump.
2. Faulty gasket.
3. Improper installation.
4. Warped pump body or dirty metal surfaces.
5. Hole or crack in pump body.
6. Worn seal.
7. Seal improperly installed.
8. Bent pump shaft.
9. Loose bearings or bushings or worn pump shaft.

Radiator
1. Leaks due to freezing or corrosion.
2. Strain due to improper attachment to car.
3. Fan striking radiator.
4. Drain plug or petcock leaks.
5. Radiator baffle bent so that water is directed into overflow pipe.
6. Clogged radiator causing water to pile up in upper tank which causes coolant to flow out overflow pipe.

Hose
1. Hose clamps loose.
2. Hose improperly installed.
3. Hose rotted through.

Heater: See that all heater connections are tight and that its radiator does not leak.

ENGINE OIL LEAKAGE

1. Oil pan drain plug loose or gasket missing.
2. Crack or hole in oil pan.
3. Oil pan gasket leaks due to: (a) loose screws; (b) damaged gasket; (c) improperly installed gasket; (d) bent oil pan flange.
4. Timing case cover gasket leaks due to: (a) loose screws; (b) damaged gasket; (c) improperly installed gasket; (d) bent cover flange; (e) leakage at engine support plate.
5. Front crankshaft oil seal leaks due to: (a) worn oil seal; (b) seal not properly installed; (c) rough surface on crankshaft, or fan pulley or damper; (d) damper or pulley loose; (e) seal or cover not centered on crankshaft; (f) oil return passage to crankcase clogged up (if provided).
6. Rear main bearing oil seal leaks due to: (a) worn oil seal; (b) improper oil seal installation; (c) worn rear main bearing; (d) rough crankshaft

surface.

7. Oil return passage to crankcase clogged.
8. Expansion plug in block at rear of camshaft leaks due to poor fit, careless installation, or corrosion.
9. Leakage at any external piping.
10. Plugs at ends of oil passages in cylinder block leak.
11. Oil filter leaks.
12. Leakage at distributor housing.
13. Valve cover leaks due to loose screws, defective gasket, improperly installed gasket or bent cover flange.
14. Rocker arm cover or push rod cover leaks because of loose screws, defective gasket, improper gasket installation or bent cover flange.
15. Pipe connections loose on oil gauge or oil filter lines.
16. Loose oil pump or faulty gasket (if pump is on outside of block).
17. Clogged breather and/or crankcase ventilating discharge pipe, permits increase in pressure within engine, thus causing oil to be forced out past any oil seals or gaskets.
18. If oil pressure relief valve is mounted on outside of block, leakage may occur if unit is loose or its gasket defective.

HIGH OIL CONSUMPTION

1. External oil leaks.
2. Leaky piston rings due to wear.
3. Leaky piston rings due to sticking caused by gummy deposit. Try to free up with suitable solvent poured in fuel tank. Blue smoke at tail pipe indicates badly leaking rings.
4. Worn pistons and cylinders.
5. Cylinder block distorted by tightening cylinder head bolts unevenly.
6. Excessive clearance between intake valve stems and guides allows oil mist to be sucked into cylinders.
7. Punctured vacuum pump diaphragm permits oil from crankcase to be sucked into intake manifold.
8. Worn main or rod bearings allow excessive leakage from bearings. Result is cylinder walls are flooded with oil.
9. Oil pressure too high due to faulty action of oil pressure relief valve, or clogged relief passage.
10. If pressure lubricated, loose piston pins may permit excessive leakage to cylinder walls.
11. Grade of oil used is too light. A poor quality oil may become far too thin when engine is hot. Hard driving on hot days will also consume more oil.

OIL PRESSURE RELIEF VALVE LEAKS

1. Relief valve needs tighter adjustment.
2. Relief valve spring weak or broken.
3. Valve seat worn or distorted.
4. Plunger type valve face worn.

5. Plunger type valve stuck open.
6. Ball type valve damaged.
7. Pump discharge pipe or passages leak.

ENGINE OIL DILUTION

1. Oil contains foam caused by presence of water in oil. Water may be due to condensation within crankcase or to a leaky cylinder head gasket.
   Extreme dilution of oil by fuel may add enough liquid to oil to mislead. In extreme cases, oil level may increase. Dilution is greatest when frequent stops are made in cold weather.

NO OIL PRESSURE

1. Oil pressure gauge defective.
2. Pipe to oil pressure gauge stopped up.
3. Not enough oil in crankcase.
4. Oil pump broken.
5. Oil pressure relief valve stuck open.
6. Oil passages on discharge side of pump stopped up.
7. Oil screen or passages on intake side of pump stopped up.

LOW OIL PRESSURE

1. Oil pressure gauge inaccurate.
2. Pipe to pressure gauge restricted.
3. Oil too thin due to dilution, poor quality, or too light a grade used.
4. Oil pressure relief valve adjustment too light.
5. Relief valve spring weak.
6. Oil pump gears worn.
7. Oil pump cover worn.
8. Oil pump body or cover loose.
9. Oil pump gasket damaged, improperly installed or too thick.
10. Air leak in oil intake pipe (if oil level is low).
11. Air leak in top of floating screen (if used).
12. Oil intake pipe or screen clogged with water, sludge, gummy oil, dirt or ice.
13. Oil leak in discharge pipe.
14. Loose connections in oil lines.
15. Worn main, rod or camshaft bearings.

HIGH OIL PRESSURE

1. Oil pressure gauge defective.
2. Oil too heavy.
3. Oil pressure relief valve adjustment too heavy.
4. Relief valve spring too stiff.
5. Oil pressure relief passage clogged.
6. Plunger type relief valve stuck by gummy oil or plunger is too tight a fit.
7. Main oil passages on pressure side of pump clogged.

ENGINE NOISES

Loose Main Bearing

A loose main bearing is indicated by a powerful but dull thud or knock when the engine is pulling. If all main bearings are loose a noticeable clatter will be audible.

The thud occurs regularly every other revolution. The knock can be confirmed by shorting spark plugs on cylinders adjacent to the bearing. Knock will disappear or be less when plugs are shorted. This test should be made at a fast idle equivalent to 15 mph in high gear. If bearing is not quite loose enough to produce a knock by itself, the bearing may knock if oil is too thin or if there is no oil at the bearing.

Loose Flywheel

A thud or click which is usually irregular. To test, idle the engine at about 20 mph and shut off the ignition. If thud is heard, the flywheel may be loose.

Loose Rod Bearing

A metallic knock which is usually loudest at about 30 mph with throttle closed. Knock can be reduced or even eliminated by shorting spark plug. If bearing is not loose enough to produce a knock by itself, the bearing may knock if oil is too thin or if there is no oil at the bearing.

Piston Pin

Piston pin, piston and connecting rod noises are difficult to tell apart.

A loose piston pin causes a sharp double knock which is usually heard when engine is idling. Severity of knock should increase when spark plug to this cylinder is short-circuited. However, on some engines the knock becomes more noticeable at 25 to 35 mph on the road.

Piston pin rubs against cylinder wall, caused by lock screw being loose or snap ring broken.

Piston & Rings

1. Excessive clearance between pistons and cylinders (piston slap).
2. Out-of-round or tapered bores.
3. Top piston ring strikes ridge at top of cylinder bore.
4. Carbon deposit on top of piston strikes cylinder head.
5. Piston rubs against cylinder head gasket.
6. Broken piston ring.
7. Excessive side clearance of ring in groove.
8. Worn or broken piston ring lands.
9. Broken piston.

Valves

1. Valve click due to too much tappet clearance, hydraulic tappet not working properly, warped valve, sticking valve, binding rocker arm.
2. Insufficient oil to valve mechanism, especially overhead valves.
3. Worn or scored parts anywhere in valve mechanism.
4. Broken valve springs.
5. Weak valve springs.
6. Cocked valve springs.
7. Excessive tappet guide clearance.
8. Lower end of tappet scored, chipped,

9. Very rough surface on cams.
10. Excessive valve stem-to-guide clearance.
11. Valve face not concentric with valve stem.
12. Valve seat face not concentric with valve stem.
13. Valve covers on overhead valve engines tightened excessively will amplify normal valve noise.

Hydraulic Lifters

The malfunctioning of a hydraulic valve lifter is almost always accompanied by a clicking or tapping noise. More or less hydraulic lifter noise may be expected when the engine is cold but if lifters are functioning properly the noise should disappear when the engine warms up.

If all or nearly all lifters are noisy, they may be stuck because of dirty or gummy oil.

If all lifters are noisy, oil pressure to them may be inadequate. Foaming oil may also cause this trouble. If oil foams there will be bubbles on the oil level dipstick. Foaming may be caused by water in the oil or by too high an oil level or by a very low oil level.

If the hydraulic plungers require an initial adjustment, they will be noisy if this adjustment is incorrect.

If one lifter is noisy the cause may be:
1. Plunger too tight in lifter body.
2. Weak or broken plunger spring.
3. Ball valve leaks.
4. Plunger worn.
5. Lock ring (if any) improperly installed or missing.
6. Lack of oil pressure to this plunger.

If ball valve leaks, clean plunger in special solvent such as acetone and reinstall. Too often, plungers are condemned as faulty when all they need is a thorough cleaning.

Gum and dirty oil are the most common causes of hydraulic valve lifter trouble. Engine oil must be free of dirt. Select a standard brand of engine oil and use no other. Mixing up one standard brand with another may cause gummy oil and sticking plungers. Do not use any special oils unless recommended by the car manufacturer and change oil filter or element at recommended intervals.

Timing Gears

1. Gears loose on hubs or shafts.
2. Gears misaligned.
3. Excessive gear backlash.
4. Eccentric gear, usually due to high key.
5. Teeth meshed too tight (new oversize gear).
6. Too much end play in camshaft or crankshaft.
7. Front crankshaft bearing clearance excessive.
8. Chipped tooth usually on camshaft gear.

Timing Chain

1. Chain loose due to wear.
2. Sprocket teeth worn.
3. Sprockets loose on hubs or shafts.
4. Sprockets misaligned.
5. Front camshaft bearing clearance excessive.
6. Front main bearing clearance excessive.
7. Loose vibration damper or drive pulley.

Loose Engine Mountings

Occasional thud with car in operation. Most likely to be noticed at the moment the throttle is opened or closed.

Excessive Crankshaft End Play

A rather sharp rap which occurs at idling speed but may be heard at higher speeds also. The noise should disappear when clutch is disengaged.

Water Pump

1. Water pump shaft pulley loose.
2. Impeller loose on shaft.
3. Too much end play in pump shaft.
4. Too much clearance between shaft and bearings.
5. Impeller blades rubbing against pump housing.
6. Impeller pin sheared off or impeller broken.
7. Rough bearing.
8. Pump seal too hard.

Fan Belt

1. Belt worn or burned.
2. Wrong belt. Does not fit pulley grooves properly.
3. Belt too tight. Squeaks.
4. Belt or pulley dirty or sticky with gummy oil.
5. Pulley bent, cracked or broken.
6. Belt pulleys misaligned.
7. Belt loose; squeaks when engine is accelerated.

Fan

1. Fan blades bent.
2. Fan blades loose on hub.
3. Fan out of balance when made.
4. Fan blades strike radiator.
5. Fan shaft end play excessive.
6. Fan shaft loose on its bearings.
7. Defective fan bearings.
8. Bearings need lubrication.

Engine Vibration

1. Unequal compression in cylinders.
2. Missing at high speed.
3. Unbalanced fan or loose fan blade.
4. Incorrect adjustment of engine mounts, or damaged mounts.
5. Loose engine mounts.
6. Engine support loose on frame or cylinder block.
7. Unbalanced or sprung crankshaft.
8. Excessive engine friction due to tight pistons, etc.
9. Defective vibration damper.

Electrical Troubles

NOTE—Ignition troubles are included in the *Engine Troubles* section under the various operating difficulties these troubles could cause.

BATTERY REQUIRES FREQUENT RECHARGING

Insufficient Current Flow to Battery
1. Glazed or burned generator commutator.
2. Incorrect voltage regulator setting.
3. Regulator contacts oxidized or burned.
4. Sulphated battery.
5. Corroded battery terminals.
6. Regulator not grounded.
7. Loose connections or grounds in lighting or ignition circuits.
8. Slipping fan belt.

9. Wrong size generator drive pulley.

Excessive Starting Load Causing Abnormal Current Flow From Battery
1. Frequent use of starting motor.
2. Excessive use of starting motor due to difficulty in starting.
3. Faulty starting motor.
4. Excessive engine friction due to tight pistons, etc., or heavy engine oil.

Excessive Lighting Load
1. Car operation confined largely to night driving.
2. Tail and stop light wires reversed.
3. Stop light switch inoperative (closed at all times).
4. Unnecessary use of head lamps while parking.
5. Ground or short in lighting circuit.

Abnormal Accessory Load
1. Radio.
2. Heater.
3. Windshield defroster.
4. Cigar lighter.
5. Spotlights.

Internal Discharge of Battery
1. Plates badly sulphated.
2. Cell leak due to cracked jar or sealing compound.
3. Water level not maintained at proper height.
4. Plate separators ineffective.
5. Exterior of battery covered with corrosion and acid-soaked dirt which forms a path to ground for current.

Miscellaneous
Radio supressor connected to generator or regulator field terminal.

STARTER WON'T ROTATE OR ROTATES SLOWLY

If lights become dim or go out when the starter switch is closed, the battery may be too weak to operate the starter. In this case, the engine may be started by pushing the car.

NOTE—Buick Special 1961, 1959 Triple Turbine transmission and 1959-61 Hydra-Matics cannot be started by pushing because these transmissions have no rear oil pump to drive the engine through the transmission. In such cases, a fully charged battery should be installed or a "jumper" circuit should be used from another charged battery.

Due to Starter Circuit

1. Low battery. Lights grow very dim or go out when starter switch is closed.
2. Connections loose, dirty, corroded or broken at battery terminals, starter switch terminal, battery ground strap.
3. Short circuit across starter terminal.

Due to Starter Switch

1. Starter pedal (if any) stuck.
2. Starter switch stuck.
3. Pedal linkage fails to close starter switch (older cars).
4. Defective solenoid.
5. Neutral safety switch on cars with automatic transmissions out of adjustment or defective.
6. Starter switch makes poor contact due to dirt, corrosion, bent parts, weak contact spring.
7. Starter switch fails to close circuit because of sticking or broken contact parts.

Due to Armature & Field Circuits

1. Armature windings burned out, shorted, grounded or open-circuited.
2. Short circuit in armature winding or brush pigtail lead.
3. Broken wire in armature winding or brush pigtail lead.
4. Loose, dirty or corroded connections in armature circuit, including ground.
5. Field coils burned out, shorted or grounded.
6. Broken wire in field winding or broken lead.
7. Loose, dirty or corroded connections in field circuit.

Due to Commutator & Brushes

1. Brush pigtail leads loose or broken.
2. Starter brushes cracked crosswise (prevents flow of current).
3. Arm type brush holder sticks.
4. Brush sticks in sliding brush holder.
5. Bent brush holder misaligns brush and causes poor contact.
6. Starter brushes badly worn.
7. Brush leads shorted or have loose, dirty, corroded or broken connections.
8. Poor brush contact due to weak or broken springs.
9. Brushes coated with oil.
10. High mica between commutator segments prevents brush contact.
11. Commutator bars loose and/or solder melted.
12. Commutator dirty, corroded or burned.

Due to Armature Binding

1. Loose field poles.
2. Armature shaft frozen in bearings.
3. Loose end plates.
4. Windings thrown out of armature slots.
5. Armature locked magnetically to field poles because of loose bearings or worn or bent armature shaft.
6. Bendix spring retaining screws loose (jammed against housing).
7. Cracked or distorted drive housing.
8. Starter misaligned.
9. Starter jams because of burred teeth on drive pinion or flywheel gear.
10. Starter pinion (sliding gear type) jams because of incorrect endwise clearance.

Due to Engine Resistance

1. Piston sticking to cylinders in overheated engine.
2. Pistons stuck to cylinders because of gummy oil.
3. Pistons binding in cylinders because of corrosion after long lay-up.
4. Jammed generator armature.
5. Combustion chamber full of water.
6. Solid ice in water pump.
7. Broken part in engine causes jamming.
8. Excessive engine friction, due to cold weather and too heavy oil.

Due to Improper Engine Repairs

1. New rings too tight.
2. New pistons too tight.
3. Main or rod bearings too tight.
4. New camshaft bearings too tight.

STARTER SPINS BUT WON'T ENGAGE FLYWHEEL GEAR

Bendix Type

1. Bendix pinion stuck on shaft due to dirty or gummy shaft or bent shaft.
2. Bendix spring broken.
3. Bendix spring bolt broken.
4. Pinion housing cracked.
5. Drive key sheared.
6. Pinion teeth broken off.
7. Starter ring gear has several teeth missing.
8. Armature shaft broken.

Sliding Gear Type

1. Weak or broken meshing spring.
2. Fault in sliding gear linkage.
3. Fault in solenoid.
4. Over-running clutch worn out or lubricant caked or gummy.

5. Drive key sheared.
6. Pinion teeth broken off.
7. Flywheel ring gear has several teeth missing.
8. Armature shaft broken.

STARTER PINION JAMMED INTO FLYWHEEL GEAR

1. Burred teeth on pinion or ring gear.
2. Misalignment of starter or armature shaft.
3. If engine kicks back when being started, Bendix pinion may jam. Loosen starter to free pinion.

STARTER PINION DISENGAGES SLOWLY

Bendix Type

The most probable cause is a dirty Bendix drive shaft. Or the pinion may bind on its shaft due to a bent shaft or too tight a fit between pinion and splines.

Sliding Gear Type

1. Pinion binds on its shaft due to too tight a fit or due to bent or burred shaft.
2. Pinion shaft sticky or dirty.
3. Sliding gear operating linkage sticking or binding.
4. Solenoid does not operate properly.

STARTER PINION WON'T RELEASE

Sliding Gear Type

If solenoid operated, the solenoid may be defective. If pedal operated, the shift linkage may be binding or sticking. May also be caused by a defective starting switch on cars with key-starter switch.

STARTER NOISE

1. Loose pole pieces rubbing against armature.
2. Gear noise due to defective teeth.
3. Flywheel ring gear untrue.
4. Starter drive housing loose on flywheel housing.
5. Starter motor loose on drive housing.
6. Commutator end plate loose.
7. Armature shaft bent.
8. Worn armature shaft, bearings or bushings.
9. Drive pinion shaft bent.
10. Worn drive pinion shaft, bearings or bushings.
11. Misalignment caused by dirt or burrs on mating surfaces.

TROUBLE SHOOTING

GENERATOR DOES NOT CHARGE

1. Fan belt broken or slips badly.
2. Belt pulley slips on armature shaft.
3. Cutout relay fails to close.
4. Armature won't rotate because of seized bearing, etc.
5. External wiring from generator to starter switch terminal short-circuited or circuit is open because of detached wire or very dirty or corroded connection.
6. Voltage regulator inoperative.
7. Open circuit or short circuit in armature or field windings.
8. Brushes stuck.
9. Brushes coated with oil.
10. Brush lead connections dirty or disconnected.
11. Improperly seated brushes.
12. Weak brush springs.
13. Very dirty commutator.
14. Burned or corroded commutator.
15. Commutator bars short-circuited.
16. High mica on commutator.
17. Solder melted at commutator bar connections.

GENERATOR NOISE

1. Generator loose on engine.
2. Generator end plates loose.
3. Armature shaft bent.
4. Armature shaft worn.
5. Bushing or bearing worn or needs lubrication.
6. Armature shaft end play excessive.
7. Generator pulley loose on its shaft.
8. Generator or pulley misaligned.
9. Bent, cracked or partially broken pulley.
10. Generator fan rubs on generator.

GENERATOR BRUSH NOISE

1. High mica between commutator bars.
2. Sprung armature shaft.
3. Rough, dirty or glazed commutator.
4. Worn or loose brushes.
5. Commutator out of round.
6. Brushes not seating properly.
7. Too little or too much brush spring tension.

CHRYSLER ALTERNATOR

Alternator Fails To Charge

1. Drive belt loose.
2. Brushes sticking.
3. Open charging circuit.
4. Open in stator winding circuit.

5. Faulty soldered connections at output terminal stud.
6. Rectifiers open circuited.

Low Unsteady Charging Rate

1. Drive belt loose.
2. High resistance at battery terminal posts.
3. Loose connections.
4. Poor ground between engine and body ground wire.
5. Resistance in charging circuit.
6. Open stator windings.

Low Output

1. Grounded stator.
2. Shorted rectifier.
3. Voltage regulator faulty.

Excessive Charging Rate

1. Voltage regulator faulty.
2. Open circuited rectifier.

Noisy Alternator

1. Misaligned belt or pulley, or loose pulley.
2. Shorted rectifier.
3. Worn bearings.
4. Rotor shaft sprung.

Regulator Points Oxidized

1. Poor ground connections.
2. Improper voltage regulator air gap setting.
3. Shorted field in alternator.
4. Voltage regulator setting too high.

Burned Points or Coil Windings In Regulator

1. Voltage regulator setting too high.

Voltage Regulator Points Stuck

1. Poor ground connections between alternator and regulator.

LIGHTS FLICKER

Circuit Breaker Vibrates

When the circuit breaker vibrates and causes lights to flicker it indicates a short in one of the lighting circuits, which may be traced as follows:

1. Pull switch successively to each lighting position. If circuit breaker vibrates in all positions except "off" the trouble should be found in the tail lamp and license lamp circuit, or instrument, map light, or clock light circuits.
2. If circuit breaker vibrates in parking lamp position only, look for a short in the parking lamp circuit.
3. If circuit breaker vibrates in head-lamp position only, inspect head-lamp wiring circuit and lamp assemblies. If both filaments in head-lamps burn at the same time, replace headlamp unit.

LAMPS FAIL TO BURN

1. Burned out bulb.
2. An open circuit in wiring.
3. A defective switch.
4. Burned out fuse.

LIGHTS FLARE UP WHEN ENGINE IS SPEEDED UP

This condition is caused by high voltage in the electrical system due to one or more of the following:

1. Electrolyte in battery low or weak.
2. High resistance in circuit between generator and battery due to loose or dirty connections.
3. Poor ground between generator and engine.
4. Voltage regulator adjusted too high.
5. Voltage regulator inoperative.

STOP LIGHT TROUBLES

1. If only one stop light fails to burn, check lamp bulb, socket and wiring.
2. If both stop lights fail to burn also check stop light switch and fuse.
3. If stop light burns when brake pedal is released, check stop light switch, brake pedal clearance and for dragging brakes.
4. If compensating port in brake master cylinder is plugged by foreign material, or is covered by the piston primary cup when brake pedal is released, high pressure will be maintained in hydraulic system and stop light switch will remain closed.

TURN SIGNAL TROUBLES

1. If signals are inoperative on both turns, look for a blown fuse or a defective flasher.
2. If stop lights burn, the fuse and rear signal lamp bulbs are okay.
3. An inoperative right signal light may be caused by a burned out bulb at the right indicator or a right signal lamp. The opposite applies for an inoperative left signal light.
4. If bulbs are okay, look for an open circuit or defective switch.
5. If indicator light on dash burns steady when lever is placed in a turn position, check for burned out bulb in park or stop light. If park and stop light bulbs are okay, check for faulty flasher.
6. If indicator light on dash does not burn when lever is in a turn position, check for burned out bulb or a faulty flasher.
7. If switch fails to cancel after completion of turn, remove steering wheel and check for worn or broken mechanism.

Clutch Troubles

CLUTCH DRAGS

Clutch drag means that when the clutch pedal is depressed fully the clutch disc is not completely released. In consequence it does not come to rest but continues to rotate, being dragged around by the rotation of the engine. Clutch dragging causes clashing of gears, especially when shifting from neutral to low or reverse.

1. Pedal cannot disengage clutch because of excessive free pedal travel. Pedal linkage should be adjusted so that the pedal shank is about 1" from the under side of the toe-board.
2. Worn clutch linkage.
3. Release levers need adjustment.
4. Clutch disc warped out of true.
5. High spots on clutch facing.
6. Broken or loose facings.
7. Loose rivet in facing.
8. Clutch disc hub binds on splined clutch shaft due to bent shaft, tight fit, burred splines or splines covered with gummy oil or dirt.
9. Clutch disc wobbles because of broken springs in hub.
10. Clutch disc hub out of true.
11. Clutch shaft bent.
12. Clutch shaft out of true because of worn bearings.
13. Transmission is not in alignment with flywheel housing.
14. Clutch pressure plate warped, thus throwing release levers out of adjustment.
15. Flange of clutch cover not in alignment with flywheel because of loose attaching screws, bent flange, dirt between flange and flywheel.
16. Grease on clutch facings.
17. Engine misaligned due to deteriorated or broken engine mounts.
18. Loose flywheel housing-to-engine attaching bolts.
19. Release fork pivot worn.

CLUTCH SLIPS

The clutch disc slips whenever the clutch pressure plate fails to hold it tight against the face of the flywheel. If clutch slippage is severe, the engine speed will rise above normal on full throttle in high gear. Slight but continuous slippage may go unnoticed until the clutch facings are ruined by excessive temperature caused by friction.

In a very high percentage of cases, clutch slippage is due to less than zero clearance between the shank of the pedal and the toe-board because of failure to have the pedal adjusted in time. The consequence is worn and burned clutch facings. Before the clutch starts slipping, the normal wear of the facings causes a gradual reduction in clutch pedal free play. When there is no free play of the

pedal the clutch starts slipping.

Other causes of clutch slippage are:
1. Driving with foot resting on pedal.
2. Binding or sticking of pedal or its linkage.
3. Binding or sticking of clutch disc hub on clutch shaft.
4. Binding of release levers.
5. Release bearing sleeve sticks.
6. Weak or broken clutch pressure springs.
7. Worn clutch facings.
8. Facings covered with grease or oil.
9. Facings burned.
10. Release levers improperly adjusted.
11. Pressure plate sticks.

CLUTCH GRABS

A clutch is said to grab when it engages too abruptly. The usual causes are:
1. Loss of tension in cushioning plates in the rim of the steel clutch disc. These plates cause the clutch facings to bulge outward slightly. The resulting springy action of the facings aids in producing a smooth, gentle clutch engagement.
2. Use of wrong type of clutch facing.
3. Grease or oil on facings.
4. Clutch springs too stiff.
5. Momentary binding in clutch linkage while clutch is being engaged.
6. Exposed rivet heads due to excessively worn facings or loose rivets.

CLUTCH CHATTERS

If a clutch chatters while it is being engaged, the trouble is caused by rapid gripping and slipping. The usual causes are:
1. Somewhat sticky clutch friction surfaces due to gummy lubricant.
2. Clutch friction surfaces damp or wet.
3. Weak clutch springs.
4. Slight binding in clutch linkage during engagement.
5. Slight binding of pressure plate during engagement.
6. Loose engine mounts.

CLUTCH PEDAL PULSATES

Clutch pedal pulsation has often been termed a nervous pedal. When a slight pressure is applied on the pedal, with the engine running, the pedal will vibrate or bounce with every revolution of the engine. As the pressure on the pedal is increased, the pulsation will cease.
1. Loose or improperly adjusted engine mounts.
2. Collar on clutch release sleeve does

not run true due to a bent clutch shaft, or the clutch shaft misaligned because of misalignment between crankshaft and transmission.
3. Clutch release levers not adjusted to uniform height.

CLUTCH RATTLES

This condition will occur when the engine is idling with transmission in neutral.
1. Excessive clearance at pressure plate driving lugs.
2. Anti-rattle springs or retractor springs on release levers (or release bearing) weak, broken or disconnected.
3. Looseness in clutch pedal operating linkage.

NOISE WHEN PEDAL IS DEPRESSED

1. Clutch release bearing worn, dirty, damaged, broken or inadequately lubricated.
2. Clutch shaft bearing or bushing in crankshaft worn, damaged, broken or inadequately lubricated.
3. Clutch shaft rear bearing at front end of transmission, worn, dirty or lacks lubricant.

NOISE WHEN PEDAL IS RELEASED

1. Misalignment of transmission with engine causing slight wobble of clutch disc hub—noticeable with engine idling or at low road speed.
2. Disc hub loose fit on splined clutch shaft.
3. Disc damper springs weak or broken.
4. No pedal play.
5. Weak or broken pedal return spring.
6. Weak or broken release sleeve spring.
7. Clutch linkage sticks.
8. Clutch pedal sticks.
9. Clutch release sleeve sticks.
10. Clutch release fork binds.

BEARING NOISE

Clutch Release Bearing:—With engine idling, there is a high-pitched rubbing noise when foot rests on clutch pedal.

Clutch Pilot Bearing:—Fairly high-pitched noise when clutch pedal is fully depressed with engine idling.

Manual Shift Transmission Troubles

SLIPS OUT OF HIGH OR SECOND

1. Motion of shifter linkage incomplete because of wear or need of adjustment.
2. Transmission not aligned with engine.
3. Lock balls for shift rails fail to hold because:
   a) Ball spring is weak or broken.
   b) Ball worn or broken.
   c) Notch for ball is worn.
4. Clutch shaft front bearing or bushing in crankshaft worn.
5. Main drive gear bearing worn.
6. Mainshaft bearings worn, front or rear.
7. Broken snap ring or bearing retainer.
8. Shifter fork worn.
9. Shifter fork set screws (if any) worn.
10. Splines on mainshaft worn.
11. Splines on hub of synchronizer clutch gear worn.
12. Synchronizer clutch teeth worn.
13. Main drive gear clutch teeth or second speed gear clutch teeth worn.
14. Excessive end play in clutch shaft.
15. Excessive end play in mainshaft.

SLIPS OUT OF SECOND ONLY

Look for excessive end play in countershaft gear cluster or worn second speed gears. Synchronizer clutch teeth for engaging second gear are worn. Also the mating clutch teeth on second gear.

SLIPS OUT OF LOW OR REVERSE

1. Motion of shifter linkage incomplete because of wear or need of adjustment.
2. Lock ball for low and reverse fails to hold gear in mesh because:
   a) Ball spring is weak or broken.
   b) Ball is worn or broken.
   c) Notch for ball is worn.

GEARS CLASH WHEN SHIFTED

1. Clutch drags.
2. Synchronizer friction surfaces scored, worn, burred or gummed up.
3. Front or rear mainshaft bearing worn.
4. Synchronizer clutch gear hub loose on splined mainshaft due to wear.
5. Lubricant too thick or too cold.
6. Clutch shaft bearing worn.
7. Clutch shaft not true because transmission is not aligned with engine or crankshaft.

TRANSMISSION LEAKS OIL

1. Oil too thin.
2. Oil level too high.
3. Poor quality oil foams excessively.
4. Leakage at front or rear oil seal because of wear or loose bearing.
5. Main drive gear bearing retainer loose or gasket damaged.
6. Rear main bearing retainer loose or gasket damaged.
7. Transmission cover loose or gasket damaged.
8. Leakage at shifter cross shaft at side of transmission.
9. Breather or vent (if used) clogged.
10. Speedometer drive gasket loose.
11. Oil return passage (if used) at front or rear of transmission clogged.
12. Gearshift lever oil seal worn.
13. Drain plug loose or damaged.
14. Crack or sand hole in transmission case.

LEAKAGE AT TORQUE TUBE

1. Oil return hole from ball housing to transmission stopped up.
2. Scored universal joint or bushing.
3. More than .006" clearance between front torque tube bushing and propeller shaft.
4. Worn or damaged oil seal in torque tube.

Overdrive Troubles

OVERDRIVES WITHOUT RELAY

Studebaker 1958-60

In this system, Fig. 1, the relay has been eliminated from the electrical circuit and the circuit is connected directly to the starter solenoid. The circuit is energized when the car speed is sufficiently high enough to close the governor points, thus grounding the circuit. To check the overdrive electrical circuit, proceed as follows:

Transmission Fails to Operate In Overdrive

1. Check and replace fuse as required.
2. Check all connections at starter solenoid, fuse holder, kickdown switch, overdrive solenoid and governor.
3. Ground the governor wire at the solenoid. If the solenoid clicks, replace or repair the governor. If the solenoid fails to click, check current from kickdown switch to solenoid and replace the kickdown switch or solenoid as required.

Transmission Fails to Kickdown

1. Check for loose connections at the solenoid, kickdown switch and distributor.
2. Check current from kickdown switch to solenoid and replace kickdown switch or solenoid as required.

OVERDRIVES WITH RELAY

In checking electrical troubles on these units, refer to Fig. 2. Then proceed as follows:

Overdrive Won't Engage

1. Check fuse in overdrive circuit.
2. With the ignition on, ground No. 1 terminal on the relay with a jumper wire. This will close the relay and energize the solenoid. The proper functioning of the circuit will be evidenced by a "click" which will be heard as the solenoid engages. If the solenoid does not engage under the conditions outlined in step 2, then proceed to step 3.
3. Remove jumper wire between ground and No. 1 terminal. With three terminal relay, leave ignition on and connect terminals 2 & 3 with a jumper lead. With four terminal relay and ignition on or off, connect terminals 2 & 3 with a jumper lead. In either case, if the solenoid engages then the relay is at fault and should be replaced. If the solenoid does not engage, proceed to next step.
4. Ignition may be turned off for this test. Remove jumper lead from terminals 2 & 3. Attach one end of a long jumper wire to No. 4 terminal on the solenoid (terminal with heavy

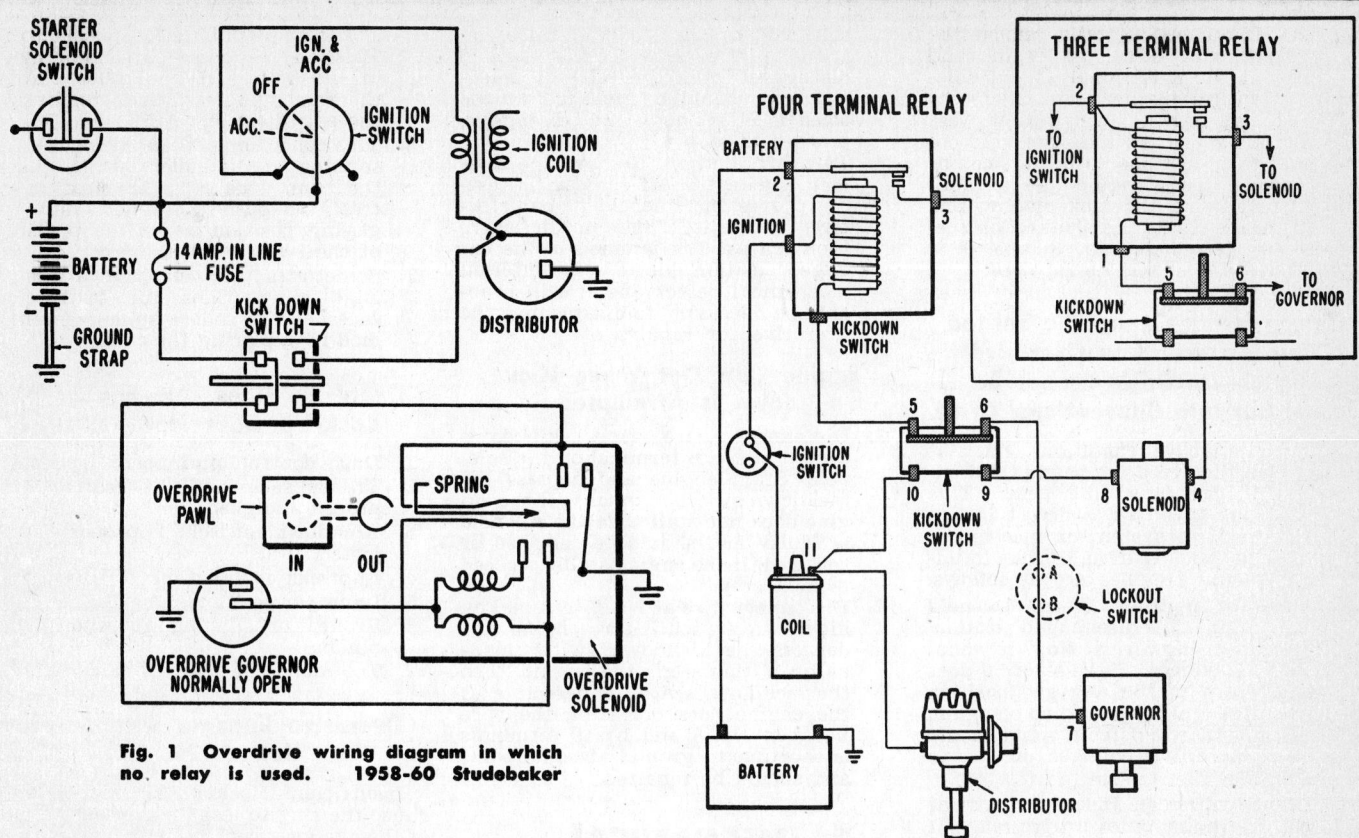

Fig. 1 Overdrive wiring diagram in which no relay is used. 1958-60 Studebaker

Fig. 2 Overdrive circuit diagram which may be used for systems using three - and four - terminal relays

wire), and touch the other end of this wire to a convenient source of current. If the solenoid now engages, there is a bad connection between terminals 3 & 4 and the wire in the harness should be replaced or the terminals cleaned or tightened. However, if the solenoid still does not engage, it should be removed for a bench test. If the solenoid checks okay off the car it means that the overdrive needs internal repairs (see "Mechanical Troubles"). If the relay, solenoid and connecting wires are okay as determined in steps 1-4 and the overdrive still does not function properly on the road, then proceed to the next step.

5. With the ignition on, first ground No. 5 then No. 6 terminal on the kickdown switch, the solenoid should engage both times. If the solenoid engages with No. 5 terminal grounded and fails to do so when terminal No. 6 is grounded, the kickdown switch is defective and should be replaced. If the solenoid does not engage when either terminal is grounded then the connection between No. 1 and No. 5 terminals is bad and must be repaired. If you have not yet located the trouble, proceed to step 6.

6. *On cars equipped with lockout switch:*
With ignition on, push overdrive manual control all the way in. Ground terminal A on lockout switch with a jumper lead. The solenoid should now engage. If it does not, then the connection between terminals A and 6 is defective and should be repaired. Now remove ground from terminal A

and place it on terminal B. If the relay does not engage then either the lockout switch is defective or the manual control cable does not move the shift lever all the way into overdrive because of improper adjustment. If lockout switch and control cable adjustment is found to be okay then move the jumper lead to No. 7 terminal on the governor and ground. If the solenoid now moves into the engaged position, the governor is the unit giving the trouble and should be replaced. If the solenoid still does not engage, there is a bad connection between terminals 6 and 7.

On cars without lockout switch:
With ignition on, ground No. 7 terminal on governor. If the solenoid engages, the governor is probably defective. If the solenoid does not engage then there is a poor connection between terminals 6 and 7.

Overdrive Won't Kick Down

1. With ignition on, place jumper lead between No. 7 terminal on governor and ground, solenoid will click into the engaged position. D e p r e s s plunger on the kickdown switch manually, this should cut off the current to the solenoid which will click again as it moves to the disengaged position. If the kickdown circuit checks out okay when the

switch is operated manually but fails to operate under driving conditions, then check the throttle linkages and make the necessary adjustments to give the kickdown switch full travel. If the kickdown does not operate either manually or while driving, then replace the kickdown switch. While checking the kickdown circuit, do not overlook the possibility of bad wiring or connections which might upset the accuracy of your diagnosis. If any wires are frayed or without proper insulation, replace them. If step 1 does not uncover any trouble which would prevent the transmission from having a kickdown, proceed to step 2.

2. With engine running, hook a jumper lead between No. 8 terminal on the solenoid and ground, depress the kickdown switch manually, the engine should stop. If it does not stop, proceed to step 3 to isolate the faulty unit.

3. With engine running, place a jumper lead between terminal No. 10 on the kickdown switch and ground. If this does not stop the engine, the connection between terminals 10 and 11 is defective and should be repaired. If the engine stalls, as it should, then remove the jumper lead and start the engine again. Ground No. 9 terminal on the kickdown switch with a jumper lead and depress the switch manually. If the engine does not stall, the kickdown switch is defec-

tive. If the engine stalls, remove the jumper wire, start the engine and ground No. 8 terminal on the solenoid with a jumper lead. If the engine now stalls when you depress the kickdown switch, the solenoid is at fault and should be serviced or replaced. If the engine does not stall by depressing the kickdown switch, it means that the connection between terminals No. 8 and 9 is broken and should be repaired.

Transmission Cannot Be Shifted Into Reverse And Overdrive Button On Dash Cannot Be Pulled Out Into Conventional Drive.

When the above conditions exist, it means that the overdrive pawl is still engaged with the balk ring gear. This could be due to either a defect in the electrical control system or mechanical difficulty in the overdrive. Checks to uncover electrical troubles are as follows:

1. Turn off ignition. If the solenoid "clicks" into the disengaged position, disconnect the wire at No. 7 terminal on the governor. If the solenoid does not return to the engaged position when the ignition is turned on again, the governor is defective and should be replaced. If it engages, proceed to step 2.
2. Leave ignition on. Disconnect wire at No. 1 terminal on overdrive relay. If the solenoid disengages then the wire from the relay to the governor is grounded at some point. Or it may be that the kickdown switch itself is shorted to ground. If the solenoid does not disengage in step 2 then proceed to step 3.
3. With ignition still on, disconnect

solenoid wire at No. 3 terminal on the overdrive relay. If the solenoid disengages then the relay is defective and should be replaced. If the solenoid still does not disengage, proceed to step 4.
4. Turn off ignition. Remove the solenoid and test it off the car. If testing proves the solenoid to be defective, replace it. If it is not defective then the pawl is jammed in the engaged position due to some internal mechanical defect and it will probably be necessary to disassemble the overdrive for repairs.

Engine Cuts Out When Kickdown Is Attempted

1. Disconnect wire from kickdown switch at No. 8 terminal on the solenoid. Start engine and depress the kickdown switch manually. If the engine does not stall then the solenoid is faulty and should be replaced or repaired. If the engine stalls, proceed to next step.
2. Disconnect wire at No. 9 terminal on kickdown switch. Start engine and depress the kickdown switch manually. If this stalls the engine, then the kickdown switch is defective. If the engine does not stall, the wire between No. 8 and No. 9 terminals is shorting to ground at some point and should be repaired.

MECHANICAL TROUBLES

Overdrive Won't Drive Unless Locked Up Manually

1. Occasionally the unit may not drive the car forward in direct drive unless

locked up by pulling the dash control. This may be caused by one or more broken rollers in the roller clutch, the remedy for which is to replace the entire set of rollers.
2. This condition may also be caused by sticking of the roller retainer upon the cam. This retainer must move freely to push the rollers into engaging position under the pressure of the two actuating springs.
3. Sometimes this condition is due to slight indentations, worn in the cam faces by the rollers spinning, remedied by replacing the cam.

Overdrive Does Not Engage or Lock-Up Does Not Release

1. Dash control improperly connected.
2. Transmission and overdrive improperly aligned.
3. Kickdown switch improperly adjusted.
4. Improper installation of solenoid.
5. Improper positioning of blocker ring.
6. Broken or slipping governor drive pinion.
7. Too much end play in mainshaft.

Overdrive Engages with Severe Jolt or Noise

Insufficient blocker ring friction may cause the ring to lose its grip on the hub of the sun gear control plate.

Free-Wheels At Speeds Over 30 MPH

If cam roller retainer spring tension is weak the unit will free-wheel at all times.

Buick Dynaflow Troubles

TWIN TURBINE TYPES

Engine Stalls While Decelerating Car with Brakes Applied

1. Improper adjustment of throttle dashpot.
2. Engine not properly tuned up.

Transmission Oil Foams and Spews Out of Breather

1. Transmission overfilled. If transmission is overfilled, check for blackened condition of oil, indicating leakage of rear axle lubricant into transmission due to defective propeller shaft seals. Check for low oil level in rear axle housing. Correct cause of leakage and completely drain and refill transmission.
2. Water in transmission, indicated by overfilled condition and brown color

of transmission oil. Water in transmission usually comes from a leaking oil cooler. In this case there may be excessive oil accumulation in top tank of engine radiator. Correct cause of leakage and completely drain and refill transmission.
3. Air leak into hydraulic system at rear oil pump gaskets.

Car Will Not Move In Any Range—Rear Wheels Free

1. If car will not move for 1 to 8 minutes after standing overnight, park car for several hours with engine stopped and then check front oil pump pressure. A zero reading until such time as car will move indicates that front pump loses its prime due to excessive clearances. Inspect front pump. If condition has existed for

some time it is advisable to inspect clutch and bands for excessive wear due to slippage at low apply pressure.
2. If car will not move in any range after extended operation in Reverse it indicates air leakage into pump suction line and suction and excessive clearance at front oil pump. Front oil pump pressure will be very low during period when car will not move. Inspect for air leaks at rear oil pump gaskets. Inspect front oil pump and cover for excessive clearances.

Car Will Not Move In Any Range—Rear Wheels Locked

1. Parking lock engaged or parking brake applied.
2. Lock up due to broken part in rear axle or transmission.

Car Will Not Move In Direct Drive Only

1. If front oil pump and high accumulator pressures are okay, remove and inspect clutch assembly.
2. If front oil pump pressure is okay but high accumulator pressure is low and accumulator body gasket is not leaking internally, inspect for leaks in reaction flange gasket. If gasket is satisfactory, inspect clutch piston outer seal and ball check, also oil sealing rings on hubs of reaction shaft flange and low drum.

Car Will Not Move In Reverse Only

1. Reverse servo inoperative.
2. Band improperly adjusted or band operating strut has dropped out of place.

Excessive Slip In All Ranges

1. If condition occurs only after operation in Reverse, see Condition 2 under *Car Will Not Move in Any Range—Rear Wheels Free.*
2. Low oil level.
3. Manual control linkage improperly adjusted.
4. If front oil pump pressure is low, remove and inspect pressure regulator valve and all valve and servo body gaskets. If cause is not found remove and inspect front oil pump for wear or excessive clearances. Inspect pump cover and reaction shaft flange gaskets for leaks.

Excessive Slip In Direct Drive Only

1. Manual control linkage improperly adjusted.
2. Leak at high accumulator gasket, indicated by low oil pressure at high accumulator.
3. If above items are okay, remove and inspect clutch plates, sealing rings and clutch piston. Inspect for stuck check ball in piston.

Excessive Slip In Low Only

1. Manual control linkage improperly adjusted.
2. Low band improperly adjusted.
3. If pressure at low accumulator is low, check for leak at accumulator body gasket. If gasket is okay remove valve and servo body and check for gasket leaks and condition of low servo piston seal.
4. Low band and drum scored or worn.

Excessive Slip In Reverse Only

1. Manual control linkage improperly adjusted.
2. Reverse band improperly adjusted. Check for strut out of place or broken anchor.
3. If front oil pump pressure is low remove valve and servo body and check for gasket leaks and condition of reverse servo piston seal.
4. Reverse band and ring gear scored or worn.

Car Creeps In Neutral

1. Manual control linkage improperly adjusted.

2. Remove valve and servo body and check for low servo piston sticking up.
3. Remove clutch and inspect for sticking, warped or improperly assembled clutch plates. Note whether "dish" of steel plates is in same direction on all plates. If creep occurs only when engine is accelerated to about 2500 rpm, pay particular attention to condition of check balls at vents in clutch piston and reaction shaft flange.

Car Creeps Forward In Reverse or Backward In Low

Manual control linkage improperly adjusted.

Low-To-Direct Shift Abnormally Rough, or Slip Occurs

1. If high accumulator pressure is low, remove accumulator and check body gaskets. Check for accumulator piston sticking down. Top land of piston must be fully visible through top port in body.
2. If accumulator and gasket are okay, inspect for leaks in valve and servo body gaskets.
3. Low band improperly adjusted.
4. Binding or worn clutch plates.

Excessive Chatter or Clunk When Starting In Low or Reverse

NOTE—A very slight chatter just as car starts to move in reverse, which disappears as soon as car is in motion, may be considered normal. A slight clunk when shifting into Low or Reverse is also normal.

1. Check engine and transmission mountings for tightness. Inspect for broken rubber thrust pad at transmission mounting.
2. Low or Reverse band improperly adjusted.
3. If conditions 1 and 2 do not correct the trouble, direct drive clutch may be dragging. Remove clutch and inspect for sticking, warped, or improperly assembled clutch plates. Note whether "dish" of steel plates is in same direction on all plates.
4. Inspect for excessive wear of reverse ring gear bushing. Check for foreign matter in planet pinion needle bearings.

Hard Shifting Out of Parking

This condition is caused by binding of transmission shift rod in shift idler lever. If a burr exists on shift rod where it enters idler lever, remove burr with a file. If idler lever is distorted, replace the lever.

TRANSMISSION NOISES

When diagnosing abnormal noises in the transmission, consideration should be given to the parts that are in motion when the noise occurs. The presence or absence of noise in each range should be noted so that the parts which cause the

noise can be determined by a process of elimination.

Hum or Low Whine In Neutral or Parking

A hum or low whine in neutral or parking is normal since all planetary gears are free to rotate without the steadying effect of a load. Some hum also may be expected in Low and Reverse.

Low Growl In Transmission

A low growl in transmission which disappears in several minutes after engine is started, following extended parking in extremely cold weather is caused by cavitation of the cold oil. This is a normal condition which requires no correction.

Buzzing Noise

A buzzing noise can be caused by low oil level, or by the front pump delivery check valve seating on the edge of the gasket between valves and servo bodies.

A buzzing noise, noticeable in Parking and Neutral, may be caused by excessive clearance of pressure regulator valve in valve body or an oversize orifice in valve land. Correction requires replacement of valve.

Clicking Noise In All Ranges

This may be caused by a foreign object going through the converter. A clicking noise only when car is in motion may be caused by the parking lock pawl contacting the ratchet wheel due to improper manual control linkage adjustment.

Abnormal Hum or Whine In All Ranges

This condition may be attributed to worn parts or excessive clearances in the front oil pump. Noise caused by the front pump will increase in Low and will diminish at car speeds above 45 mph in Direct Drive. It increases and decreases with engine speed in all ranges. When excessive clearances exist in front oil pump, a pressure test will usually indicate low front pump pressure.

Abnormal Hum or Whine In All Ranges but Direct Drive

This may be attributed to conditions in the planetary gear train since these gears are locked in Direct Drive but either idling or transmitting power in all other ranges.

Squealing or Screeching

Squealing or screeching immediately following installation of front oil pump parts indicates that the driving gear has been installed backwards. This condition should be corrected without further operation of the transmission as severe damage will result.

Whistling Noise

A whistling noise which occurs during low speed acceleration in Drive, Low and Reverse, accompanied by unsatisfactory transmission performance indicates cavi-

TROUBLE SHOOTING

tation of oil due to incomplete filling of torque converter. Remove valve and servo body assembly and check for restrictions in passages leading to torque converter. If these passages are clear,

check passages in reaction shaft flange.

A whistling noise during low speed acceleration in Drive, Low and Reverse but with otherwise satisfactory transmission performance may be caused by

thin, weak, or cracked turbine vanes, or vanes which are bent over at the exit edges. Such vanes will vibrate under load, causing a whistle. Replacement of the turbine is required for correction.

Buick Triple Turbine Types

Car Will Not Move In Any Range

1. Linkage incorrectly adjusted.
2. Low or no front pump pressure due to:
   (a) Low oil level.
   (b) Oil screen clogged.
   (c) Worn or scored front pump and/or reaction flange.
   (d) Case and/or valve body gaskets not sealing and allowing air to enter hydraulic units.
   (e) Pressure regulator valve binding and sticking.

Car Will Not Move In Forward Range Only

1. Forward and neutral clutches not operating.
2. Rear sprag and neutral clutch not operating.
3. Reverse clutch stuck in applied position.

Car Will Not Move In Reverse Only

1. Reverse clutch not operating.
2. Forward clutch stuck in applied position.
3. Grade retard clutch stuck in applied position.
4. Front sprag slipping.

No Grade Retard Operation Only

1. Grade retard clutch not operating.
2. Will not shift into "G" detent position because of binding in parking pawl slide and roller.

Excessive Slippage In Forward and Reverse

1. Low oil level.
2. Linkage not properly adjusted.
3. Forward and neutral clutches slipping.
4. Low front pump pressure.
5. Front sprag slipping.
6. Front sprag and/or rear sprag slipping.
7. Stator control linkage not properly adjusted.
8. Converter anti-leakdown valve not operating properly or missing.
9. Pressure regulator valve stuck in by-pass position.

Excessive Slippage At High Throttle and No Top Speed Forward

1. Neutral clutch not applying.
2. Neutral clutches slipping.
3. Stator control linkage not properly adjusted.

Car Creeps Forward In Neutral

1. Linkage not properly adjusted.
2. Neutral clutch and/or forward clutch not releasing or not assembled properly.
3. Grade retard clutch not releasing or not assembled properly.

Car Will Not Hold In Park or Will Not Go In Park

1. Linkage not properly adjusted.
2. Parking pawl slide and roller binding.
3. Parking pawl broken.
4. Grade retard backing plate retainer ring not in groove or missing.

Forward Clutch Does Not Operate Properly

1. Low or no apply pressure due to:
   (a) Valve body and/or case gaskets not sealing.
   (b) O-rings on adapter sleeve damaged or missing.
   (c) Piston outer seal and/or inner oil ring damaged or missing.
   (d) Porous output shaft support.
   (e) Modulator valve and/or limit valve sticking due to burrs, dirt, etc.
   (f) Neutral clutch apply circuit has excessive leak.
2. Piston and/or output shaft support damaged or burred causing piston not to apply or release.
3. Piston outer seal lip turned over causing piston to stick.
4. Clutch plates warped or worn.
5. Clutch plates not properly installed.

Neutral Clutch Does Not Operate Properly

1. Low or no apply pressure due to:
   (a) Valve body and/or case gaskets not sealing.
   (b) O-rings on adapter sleeve damaged or missing.
   (c) The two rear oil rings on grade retard reaction shaft damaged or missing.
   (d) The two front oil rings on output shaft damaged or missing.
   (e) Any one or all first turbine shaft oil rings damaged or missing.
   (f) Piston outer seal and/or inner seal damaged or missing.
   (g) Forward clutch apply circuit has excessive leak.
2. Piston and/or front carrier damaged or burred causing piston not to apply or release.
3. Piston outer seal lip turned over causing piston to stick.
4. Clutch plates warped or worn.

5. Clutch backing plate retaining ring not properly installed or missing.

Reverse Clutch Does Not Operate Properly

1. Low or no apply pressure due to:
   (a) Valve body and/or case gaskets not sealing.
   (b) Porus apply channel in case.
   (c) Reaction flange gasket not sealing.
   (d) Reaction flange and/or case mating surfaces irregular.
   (e) Piston outer seal and/or inner seal damaged or missing.
2. Piston and/or reaction flange damaged causing piston to stick.
3. Piston outer seal lip turned over causing piston to stick.
4. Clutch plates warped or worn.
5. Clutch plates not properly installed.
6. Clutch pressure plate not properly installed.

Grade Retard Clutch Does Not Operate Properly

1. Low or no apply pressure due to:
   (a) Valve body and/or case gaskets not sealing.
   (b) Adapter sleeve O-rings damaged or missing.
   (c) Piston outer seal and/or inner seal damaged or missing.
   (d) Porous output shaft support.
2. Piston and/or output shaft support damaged causing piston to stick.
3. Piston outer seal lip turned over causing piston to stick.
4. Clutch backing plate retaining ring not properly installed or missing.
5. Clutch plates warped or worn.
6. Clutch plates not properly installed.

Stator Does Not Operate Properly

1. Linkage not properly adjusted.
2. Stator piston control valve stuck due to roughness of rear carrier bore, dirt, etc.
3. Low or no apply pressure due to:
   (a) Valve body and/or case gaskets not sealing.
   (b) Porous apply channel in case.
   (c) Reaction flange gasket not sealing.
   (d) Reaction flange and case mating surfaces irregular.
   (e) Second turbine shaft rear oil ring damaged or missing.
   (f) The two front oil rings on second turbine shaft damaged or missing.
   (g) Any one of three oil rings on reaction shaft damaged or missing.
   (h) One or both of the front oil

rings on second turbine shaft damaged or missing.
(i) Stator modulator valve stuck.
(j) Limit valve stuck.
4. Stator piston ring damaged or missing or incorrect ring and gap.
5. Stator blades not rotating freely due to:

(a) Piston stuck in bore or carriers because of burrs, dirt, etc.
(b) Stator blade ring damaged.
(c) Stator blades damaged.
(d) Front and/or rear carrier damaged, dirty, etc.
6. Stator piston retaining ring improperly installed or missing.

7. Stator piston control valve not gauged properly or shims below spring not laying flat in bore.
8. Stator piston control valve retainer not in proper position or missing.
9. Stator free wheel rollers not properly installed or roller spring damaged or missing.

Chevrolet Powerglide Troubles

Transmission Oil Foams and Spews Out of Filler Tube

1. Oil level too high.
2. Damaged suction pipe seal.
3. Ears on suction pipe retainer bent.
4. Bore for suction pipe in housing too deep.
5. Sand hole in suction bore in transmission housing or case.
6. Sand hole in suction cavity in valve body.
7. Water in transmission, indicated by overfilled condition and brown color of transmission oil. Water in transmission usually comes from a leaking oil cooler. In this case there may be excessive oil accumulation in top tank of radiator. Correct cause of leakage and completely drain and refill transmission.

Check Points For Oil Leaks and High Oil Consumption

1. Transmission housing side cover.
2. Low drive valve body and transmission case.
3. Servo cover and transmission case.
4. Transmission housing and transmission case.
5. Front of flywheel housing.
6. Transmission case extension and transmission case.
7. Oil cooler pipe connections.
8. Transmission case oil seal.
9. Ruptured diaphragm in vacuum modulator assembly (1950-54 & (1958-60).
10. "O" ring seal between converter cover and pump assembly.
11. Front pump "O" ring seal.
12. Front pump oil seal.
13. Oil drain in front pump plugged.
14. Oil leak between oil pump and converter cavity due to sand hole in transmission housing.

Transmission Overheats

1. Low coolant level.
2. Defective transmission thermostat.
3. Defective oil cooler.
4. Excessive slippage of clutch or low band.

Car Will Not Move In Any Range—Rear Wheels Free

1. If car will not move in any range after extended operation in reverse, it indicates air leakage into suction lines and excessive clearance at front oil pump. Front pump pressure will be very low during period when car will not move. Inspect for air leaks at rear oil pump stand.
2. If car will not move for several minutes after standing overnight, park car for several hours with engine stopped and then check front oil pump pressure. A zero reading until such time as car will move indicates that front pump loses its prime due to excessive clearances. If condition has existed for some time it is advisable to inspect clutches and bands for excessive wear due to slippage.
3. Broken internal parts.

Car Will Not Move In Any Range - Rear Wheels Locked

1. Parking lock pawl engaged.
2. Parking brake applied.
3. Lock up due to broken part in transmission or rear axle.

Car Will Not Move In Reverse Only

1. Low band needs adjusting.
2. Clutch relief valve stuck.
3. Clutch plates binding in hub or flange.
4. Clutch plates not properly installed.
5. Clutch piston stuck.
6. Reverse band strut broken.

Excessive Slip In All Ranges

1. Low oil level.
2. Manual control linkage improperly adjusted.
3. Oil suction pipe damaged or not seating properly, allowing air to be sucked into pumps.
4. Oil suction screen clogged.
5. Front oil pump worn or damaged.
6. Faulty pressure regulator valve or gasket.
7. On 1950-52 units, free wheeling stator rollers or secondary pump not properly assembled.

Excessive Slip In Manual Low & First Gear In Drive Range

1. Improper linkage adjustment.
2. Improper low band adjustment or broken band.
3. Modulator piston stuck (to 1954).
4. Accumulator valve stuck.
5. Broken low servo piston ring.
6. Worn clutch drum.
7. Defective servo-to-case gasket.
8. Defective valve body gaskets.

Excessive Slip In Reverse Only

1. Improper linkage adjustment.
2. Improper reverse band adjustment, or broken band.
3. No oil pressure due to stuck accumulator valve, stuck modulator lever or piston (to 1954).
4. Broken reverse servo piston ring.
5. Defective valve body gaskets.

Car Creeps In Neutral

1. Improper linkage adjustment.
2. Low band adjusted too tight.
3. Clutch inoperative due to:
(a) Clutch plates not properly assembled.
(b) Clutch plates sticking.
(c) Clutch relief valve stuck closed.
(d) Defective valve body gasket.
(e) Control lever not attached to manual valve inside transmission.

Car Creeps Forward In Reverse or Backward In Low

1. Improper manual linkage adjustment.

Low-To-Direct Shift Abnormally Rough

1. Improper low band adjustment.
2. Worn clutch plates.
3. Clutch plates binding in drum or flange.
4. Modulator piston stuck (to 1954).
5. Inoperative accumulator dump valve.
6. Modulator vacuum line leaking (1953-54 & 1958-60).
7. Vacuum modulator valve stuck (1958-59).
8. Throttle linkage misadjusted (1955-57).

Engine Races On Low-To-Direct Shift

1. Clutch plates worn or burned.
2. Modulator spring weak (1953-54 & 1958-60).
3. Oil passage to clutch restricted.
4. Throttle linkage misadjusted (1955-57).

Rough Shift, Direct To Low

1. Improper low band adjustment.
2. Modulator piston stuck (to 1954).
3. Vacuum modulator valve stuck (1958-60).
4. Throttle linkage misadjusted (1955-57).

No Upshift In Drive Range

1. Defective governor.

TROUBLE SHOOTING

2. Stuck shift valve.
3. Clutch plates worn or burned.

No Down Shift From Direct-To-Low With Accelerator Floored

1. Throttle linkage misadjusted.
2. Sticky shifter valve.

Rough Shift, Neutral to Reverse

1. Accumulator piston stuck closed.
2. Improper reverse band adjustment.
3. Modulator piston stuck (to 1954).
4. Engine idling speed too high.
5. Excessive end play in transmission. mainshaft.

Chatter In Manual Low & First Gear Drive Range

1. Improper low band adjustment.
2. Worn low band or drum.
3. Defective clutch plates.
4. Clutch piston stuck.
5. Clutch relief valve stuck.

Chatter In Reverse

1. Improper reverse band adjustment.
2. Worn reverse band or drum.
3. Worn or damaged reverse ring gear bushing.
4. Worn or damaged transmission case rear bushing.

Buzzing In All Ranges

1. Low oil level.
2. Front and/or rear pump not functioning properly.

Ringing Noise In Converter

1. Low oil level.
2. Oil suction pipe damaged or not seating properly.
3. Defective pressure regulator valve.
4. Front oil pump worn.

Chevrolet Turboglide Troubles

No Drive In Any Range

1. Low oil level.
2. Front pump defective or assembled backwards.
3. Front pump priming ball not seating (1959-60).
4. Defective converter pump.

No Drive Except In Grade Retard

1. Both overrun clutches assembled backwards.

No Drive Except In Grade Retard and Reverse. Cannot Load Engine In Drive

1. Outer overrun clutch assembled backwards.
2. Forward and neutral clutch not applied due to severe leakage in forward clutch hydraulic circuit.

Drive Is Poor At Low Speeds, No Reverse, Grade Retard Normal

1. Inner overrun clutch assembled backwards.
2. Stator overrun clutch not holding.

Car Drives Very Slightly In Neutral, Reverse Normal

1. Neutral clutch not released.

Car Drives Normal In Neutral and Drive At Low Speeds, No Reverse

1. Forward clutch not released.

Transmission Will Not Shift To Performance Stator Angle

1. Stator control linkage out of adjustment.

2. Converter charging pressure is low for one of the following reasons:
   (a) Leakage which will reduce line pressure enough to cause pressure regulator valve to shut off converter "in" line.
   (b) Leakage in converter circuit.
   (c) Discharge orifice in transfer plate plugged.
   (d) Damaged or leaking seal rings on second turbine shaft. Damage to front ring allows converter "out" pressure to leak to stator passage. Damage to middle ring allows neutral pressure to leak to converter "out" passage.

Unable To Push Start

1. Rear oil pump drive pin broken or missing.

Clutch Slippage On Wide Open Throttle Starts

1. Low oil pressure due to leakage. Especially check forward pressure tube O-ring seal.
2. Mechanical interference which will prevent forward piston from fully applying.
3. Forward clutch facing failure.

Grade Retard Slow To Apply

1. Control linkage out of adjustment preventing manual valve getting into grade retard position.
2. Low pressure resulting from leakage. Check pressure tube O-ring seals and other O-ring seals.
3. Mechanical interference of grade retard piston.

4. Glazed grade retard plates.

No Drive, Reverse Normal, No Grade Retard

1. Reverse clutch not disengaged.

Grade Retard Brakes Violently

1. Vacuum hose disconnected.
2. Vacuum modulator diaphram ruptured or hose disconnected.
3. Forward clutch not disengaging.

Shifts From Standstill Very Slowly

1. Check linkage to ascertain that shift lever is positioned by transmission detents.
2. Accumulator control valve stuck closed (1957).
3. Leakage in hydraulic system. Check pressure tube O-ring seals and other seals and gaskets.
4. Front pump priming ball seating poorly (1959-60).
5. Front pump side clearance excessive.

Shifts From Standstill Very Harsh and Fast

1. Accumulator control valve spring too strong or valve stuck open (1957).
2. Vacuum modulator diaphragm ruptured.
3. Vacuum hose disconnected.
4. Excessively high idle speed.
5. Defective neutral accumulator spring (1959-60).
6. Kinked vacuum to modulator supply hose.

Excess Vibration In Neutral

1. Converter and flywheel not in proper alignment.

Chrysler Powerflite Troubles

POOR SHIFT QUALITY

Harsh Shift from Neutral to Reverse

1. Reverse band adjustment.
2. Reverse piston, sleeve, etc.
3. Reverse band, lever, strut, etc.
4. Incorrect engine idle speed.

Harsh Shift from Neutral to Drive

1. Throttle linkage adjustment.
2. Kickdown piston, guide, etc.
3. Incorrect engine idle speed.

Delayed Shift from Neutral to Drive

1. Kickdown band adjustment.
2. Kickdown band, lever, strut, etc.
3. Oil level too low.

Runaway on Upshifts

1. Oil level too low.
2. Throttle linkage adjustment.
3. Regulator valve or spring.
4. Valve body mating surface leaks.
5. Throttle valve, cam, spring.
6. Kickdown piston, guide, etc.
7. Regulator body mating surfaces leak.
8. Reaction shaft seal.
9. Input shaft seal rings.
10. Reaction shaft bore.
11. Clutch retainer bushing.
12. Reaction shaft seal rings.
13. Clutch discs, plates.
14. Clutch piston, seal rings.
15. Clutch check valve ball.

Runaway on Upshifts Light Throttle Only

1. Front pump worn.

Harsh Upshifts

1. Throttle linkage adjustment.
2. Regulator valve, spring.
3. Valve body mating surface leaks.
4. Manual valve, lever.
5. Kickdown piston, guide, etc.
6. Regulator body mating surfaces leak.
7. Direct clutch spring.
8. Clutch spring retainer snap ring.

Harsh Lift Foot Shifts

1. Throttle linkage adjustment.
2. Valve body mating surface leaks.
3. Throttle valve, cam, spring.
4. Servo pressure bleed valve.
5. Shuttle valve, plug, etc.

Runaway on Downshifts at Part Throttle

1. Oil level low.
2. Gearshift linkage adjustment.
3. Throttle linkage adjustment.
4. Valve body mating surface leaks.
5. Manual valve, lever.
6. Servo restrictor valve.

Harsh Downshift

1. Throttle linkage adjustment.
2. Valve body mating surface leaks.

3. Throttle valve, cam, spring.
4. Servo restrictor valve.
5. Clutch discs, plates.
6. Clutch piston, seal rings.
7. Thrust washers worn.

Runaway on Kickdowns

1. Kickdown band adjustment.
2. Regulator valve, spring.
3. Valve body mating surface leaks.
4. Servo restrictor valve.
5. Shuttle valve, plug, etc.
6. Kickdown piston, guide, etc.
7. Governor assembly.
8. Rear pump assembly.

Harsh Kickdowns

1. Kickdown band adjustment.
2. Regulator valve, spring.
3. Servo pressure bleed valve.
4. Shuttle valve, plug, etc.
5. Kickdown piston, guide, etc.
6. Regulator body mating surfaces leak.
7. Reaction shaft seal.
8. Governor assembly.
9. Rear pump assembly.
10. Input shaft seal rings.
11. Reaction shaft bore.
12. Direct clutch spring.
13. Clutch spring retainer snap ring.
14. Clutch disc, plates.
15. Clutch piston, seal rings.

Shudder During Shifts

1. Shift valve or spring.

IMPROPER RESPONSE TO SHIFT LEVER POSITION

No Detent Feel

1. Manual valve or lever.

Detent Not With Pointer

1. Gearshift linkage adjustment.
2. Manual valve or lever.

Gate Not With Pointer

1. Gearshift linkage adjustment.
2. Kickdown band adjustment.
3. Valve body mating surface leaks.
4. Shift valve or spring.
5. Kickdown piston, guide, etc.
6. Regulator body mating surfaces leak.
7. Reaction shaft seal.
8. Input shaft seal rings.
9. Reaction shaft bore.

Moves Forward In Neutral

1. Clutch spring retainer snap ring.
2. Clutch discs or plates.
3. Planet pinion shafts.

Moves Forward In Neutral At High Engine Speeds

1. Clutch check valve ball.

Moves Backward In Neutral

1. Gearshift linkage adjustment.

2. Manual valve or lever.
3. Reverse band adjustment.
4. Reverse piston, sleeve, etc.
5. Reverse band, lever, strut, etc.
6. Output shaft support.

No Drive

1. Oil level low.
2. Gearshift linkage adjustment.
3. Regulator valve or spring.
4. Oil strainer clogged.
5. Manual valve or lever.
6. Front pump drive sleeve.
7. Front pump pinion.
8. Front pump assembly worn.
9. Regulator body mating surfaces leak.
10. Planet pinion shafts.
11. Output shaft support.

No Drive In Drive or Low

1. Throttle valve, cam or spring.
2. Output shaft support.

EXCESSIVE SLIP CONDITIONS

Slips In All Ranges

1. Low oil level.
2. Regulator valve or spring.
3. Converter control valve.
4. Valve body mating surface leaks.
5. Front pump drive sleeve.
6. Front pump assembly worn.
7. Regulator body mating surfaces leak.
8. Input shaft seal rings.
9. Reaction shaft bore.

Kickdown Band Slips

1. Throttle linkage adjustment.
2. Kickdown band adjustment.
3. Valve body mating surface leaks.
4. Throttle valve, cam or spring.
5. Valve body end cover plug.
6. Shuttle valve, plug, etc.
7. Kickdown piston, guide, etc.
8. Kickdown band, lever, strut, etc.

Kickdown Band Slips Over 25 MPH

1. Valve body end cover plug.
2. Shuttle valve, plug, etc.

Slips In Drive

1. Valve body mating surface leaks.
2. Kickdown piston, guide, etc.
3. Clutch retainer bushing.
4. Reaction shaft seal rings.
5. Clutch discs or plates.
6. Clutch piston or seal rings.
7. Clutch check valve ball.

Reverse Band Slips

1. Valve body mating surface leaks.
2. Reverse band adjustment.
3. Reverse piston, sleeve, etc.
4. Reverse band, lever, strut, etc.

Slips On Steep Grades

1. Low oil level.

TROUBLE SHOOTING

DRAGGING BANDS, CLUTCHES OR BRAKES

Drag In All Ranges

1. Hand brake adjustment.
2. Shift valve or spring.
3. Clutch spring retainer snap ring.

Drag In Drive And Low

1. Reverse band adjustment.
2. Reverse piston, sleeve, etc.
3. Reverse band, lever, strut, etc.
4. Output shaft support.

Drag In Reverse, Drive And Low

1. Valve body mating surface leaks.
2. Regulator body mating surfaces leak.
3. Reaction shaft seal.
4. Input shaft seal rings.
5. Reaction shaft bore.
6. Clutch discs or plates.
7. Clutch piston or seal rings.

Drag In Drive Only

1. Valve body mating surface leaks.
2. Kickdown sun gear snap ring.

Drag In Reverse And Drive

1. Kickdown piston, guide, etc.

ABNORMAL SHIFT PATTERNS

No Upshift

1. Low oil level.
2. Gearshift linkage adjustment.
3. Valve body mating surface leaks.
4. Manual valve or lever.
5. Shift valve or spring.
6. Kickdown piston, guide, etc.
7. Governor assembly.
8. Rear pump assembly.
9. Clutch check valve ball.

Upshift Pattern Low

1. Throttle linkage adjustment.
2. Valve body mating surface leaks.
3. Throttle valve, cam or spring.
4. Shift valve or spring.
5. Governor assembly.
6. Rear pump assembly.

Upshift Pattern Low At Heavy Throttle Only

1. Regulator valve or spring.

All Upshifts 10-15 MPH

1. Throttle valve, cam or spring.
2. Throttle pressure check ball.

Upshift Pattern High

1. Throttle linkage adjustment.
2. Valve body mating surface leaks.

3. Throttle valve, cam or spring.
4. Shift valve or spring.
5. Governor assembly.
6. Rear pump assembly.

Shifts Erratically

1. Low oil level.
2. Valve body mating surface leaks.
3. Shift valve or spring.
4. Output shaft support gaskets.

No Downshift

1. Shift valve or spring.
2. Governor assembly.

Low Downshift Speed

1. Shift valve or spring.

High Downshift Speed

1. Gearshift linkage adjustment.
2. Leaks at valve body mating surface.
3. Manual valve or lever.
4. Kickdown valve ball or rod.

Kickdown At Part Throttle

1. Gearshift linkage adjustment.
2. Leaks at valve body mating surface.
3. Manual valve or lever.
4. Kickdown valve ball or rod.

No Kickdown

1. Throttle linkage adjustment.
2. Leaks at valve body mating surface.
3. Throttle valve, cam or spring.
4. Kickdown valve ball or rod.
5. Shift valve or spring.

Kickdown Limit Low

1. Regulator valve or spring.
2. Leaks at valve body mating surface.
3. Governor assembly.
4. Rear pump assembly.

OTHER DIFFICULTIES

Starter Won't Energize

1. Gearshift linkage adjustment.
2. Neutral starter switch.
3. Manual valve or lever.

Shifts Hard Into Neutral

1. Neutral starter switch.

Shifts Hard Into Reverse

1. Back-up light switch.

Accelerator Pedal Sticks At Closed Throttle

1. Throttle linkage adjustment.
2. Throttle valve, cam or spring.

Hard To Fill Transmission

1. Breather restricted.
2. Output shaft support gaskets.

Oil Foams From Filler

1. Oil level.

2. Breather restricted.
3. Output shaft support gaskets leak.

Oil Leaks At Seals

1. Breather.
2. External seals.
3. Output shaft support gaskets.

Transmission Overheats

1. Kickdown band adjustment.
2. Converter control valve.
3. Reverse band adjustment.
4. Reverse piston, sleeve, etc.
5. Reverse band, lever, strut, etc.
6. Regulator body mating surfaces leak.
7. Reaction shaft seal.
8. Rear pump assembly.
9. Input shaft seal rings.
10. Reaction shaft bore.
11. Plugged lubrication holes.
12. Kickdown sun gear snap ring.
13. Clutch spring retainer snap ring.
14. Clutch disc or plates.
15. Thrust washers worn.

Impossible to Start Engine by Pushing

1. Output shaft support gaskets leak.
2. Rear pump assembly.

NOISES

Grating Noise With Car Moving

1. Defective speedometer pinion.
2. Rear bearing or snap ring.

Buzzing

1. Oil level.
2. Regulator body mating surfaces leak.

Squealing After Installing Transmission

1. Front pump drive sleeve.
2. Front pump pinion.

Whistling In All Ranges

1. Converter control valve.
2. Front pump drive sleeve.

Rubbing

1. Worn front pump.
2. Thrust washers worn.

Rubbing In Drive Only

1. Kickdown sun gear snap ring.

Excessive Gear Noise

1. Rear pump assembly.
2. Kickdown carrier bushing.
3. Planet pinion shafts.
4. Output shaft support or bushing.

Grinding

1. Oil collector rings.

Chrysler Torqueflite Troubles

SHIFT DIFFICULTIES

Harsh N to D or N to R

1. Pressure checks, line lube, etc.
2. Low-reverse band adjustment.
3. Engine idle.
4. L-R servo band or linkage.
5. Accumulator.
6. Front clutch.
7. Rear clutch.

Delayed N to D

1. Oil level.
2. Pressure checks, line lube, etc.
3. Valve body—bolts, mating surfaces.
4. Accumulator.
5. Air pressure check.
6. Front pump.
7. Front clutch.

Runaway on Upshift & 3-2 Kickdown

1. Oil level.
2. Throttle linkage adjustment.
3. Pressure checks, line lube, etc.
4. Kickdown band adjustment.
5. Kickdown servo band or linkage.
6. Valve body—bolts, mating surfaces.
7. Accumulator.
8. Air pressure check.
9. Rear clutch.

Harsh Upshift & 3-2 Kickdown

1. Throttle linkage adjustment.
2. Pressure checks, line lube, etc.
3. Kickdown band adjustment.
4. Kickdown servo band or linkage.
5. Valve body—bolts, mating surfaces.
6. Accumulator.
7. Rear clutch.

No Upshift

1. Oil level.
2. Throttle linkage adjustment.
3. Pressure checks, line lube, etc.
4. Kickdown band adjustment.
5. Kickdown servo band or linkage.
6. Valve body—bolts, mating surfaces.
7. Accumulator.
8. Air pressure check.
9. Governor.
10. Rear clutch.

No Kickdown or Normal Downshift

1. Oil level.
2. Throttle linkage adjustment.
3. Gearshift control cable adjustment.
4. Pressure checks, line lube, etc.
5. Kickdown band adjustment.
6. Kickdown servo band or linkage.
7. Valve body—bolts, mating surfaces.
8. Accumulator.
9. Air pressure check.
10. Governor.
11. Overrunning clutch.

Shifts Erratically

1. Oil level.
2. Throttle linkage adjustment.
3. Gearshift control cable adjustment.
4. Pressure checks, line lube, etc.
5. Engine idle.

6. Regulator valve or spring (V8).
7. Output shaft rear bearing (V8).
8. Oil strainer.
9. Valve body—bolts, mating surfaces.
10. Air pressure check.
11. Governor.
12. Front pump—drive sleeve.

OPERATING DIFFICULTIES

Slips in Forward Drive Position

1. Oil level.
2. Pressure checks, line lube, etc.
3. Valve body—bolts, mating surfaces.
4. Accumulator.
5. Air pressure check.
6. Regulator valve body, gasket, mating surfaces (V8).
7. Front clutch.
8. Rear clutch.
9. Overrunning clutch.

Slips in L-R Only

1. Pressure checks, line lube, etc.
2. Low-reverse band adjustment.
3. Low-reverse servo band or linkage.
4. Valve body—bolts, mating surfaces.
5. Air pressure check.
6. Regulator valve body, gasket, mating surfaces (V8).

Slips in All Positions

1. Oil level.
2. Pressure checks, line lube, etc.
3. Regulator valve or spring (V8).
4. Valve body—bolts, mating surfaces.
5. Air pressure check.
6. Front pump.
7. Regulator valve body, gasket, mating surfaces (V8).
8. Converter (6).

No Drive in Any Position

1. Oil level.
2. Pressure checks, line lube, etc.
3. Regulator valve or spring (V8).
4. Oil strainer.
5. Valve body—bolts, mating surfaces.
6. Air pressure check.
7. Front pump.
8. Regulator valve body, gasket, mating surfaces (V8).

No Drive in Forward Ranges

1. Pressure checks, line lube, etc.
2. Kickdown band adjustment.
3. Kickdown servo band or linkage.
4. Valve body—bolts, mating surfaces.
5. Accumulator.
6. Air pressure check.
7. Front clutch.
8. Rear clutch.
9. Overrunning clutch.

No Drive in R

1. Pressure checks, line lube, etc.
2. Low-reverse band adjustment.
3. Low-reverse servo band or linkage.
4. Air pressure check.
5. Rear clutch.
6. Governor (6).
7. Valve body (6).

Drives in N

1. Gearshift control cable adjustment.
2. Valve body—bolts, mating surfaces.
3. Front clutch.

MISCELLANEOUS

Drags or Locks

1. Kickdown band adjustment.
2. Low-reverse band adjustment.
3. Hand brake adjustment.
4. Kickdown servo band or linkage.
5. Low-reverse servo band or linkage.
6. Front clutch.
7. Rear clutch.
8. Planetary gear set.
9. Overrunning clutch.

Grating, Scraping Noise

1. Hand brake adjustment.
2. Output shaft rear bearing (V8).
3. Governor.
4. Rear pump.
5. Front pump.
6. Front clutch.
7. Rear clutch.
8. Planetary gear set.

Buzzing Noises

1. Oil level.
2. Regulator valve or spring (V8).
3. Converter control valve (V8).
4. Regulator valve body, gasket, mating surfaces (V8).
5. Valve body (6).

Trans. Hard to Fill—Oil Blows Out Fill Tube

1. Oil level.
2. Regulator valve or spring (V8).
3. Converter control valve (V8).
4. Breather.
5. Oil strainer.
6. Front pump (V8).
7. Regulator valve body, gasket, mating surfaces (V8).

Trans. Overheats

1. Oil level.
2. Kickdown band adjustment.
3. Low-reverse band adjustment.
4. Hand brake adjustment.
5. Regulator valve or spring (V8).
6. Converter control valve (V8).
7. Torque converter cooling (V8).
8. Rear pump.
9. Front pump.
10. Regulator valve body, gasket, mating surfaces (V8).
11. Front clutch.
12. Rear clutch.
13. Convertor (6).

Impossible to Push

1. Oil level.
2. Pressure checks, line lube, etc.
3. Low-reverse band adjustment.
4. Low-reverse servo band or linkage.
5. Valve body—bolts, mating surfaces.
6. Rear pump.

Starter Won't Energize

1. Gearshift control cable adjustment.
2. Starting switches.

TROUBLE SHOOTING

Cruise-O-Matic • Edsel Dual-Power Drive • Flightomatic Ford-O-Matic 1952-58 and 3 Speed '59 • Merc-O-Matic • Multi-Drive • Turbo-Drive Troubles

Severe Engagement In Low, Drive or Reverse

1. Improper idle speed.
2. Throttle linkage adjustment.
3. Incorrect oil pressure.
4. Defective valve body.
5. Oil pressure regulator.
6. Rear band adjustment.

Rough Start In Reverse

1. Improper idle speed.
2. Throttle linkage adjustment.
3. Incorrect oil pressure.
4. Defective valve body.
5. Oil pressure regulator.
6. Rear band adjustment.

Shift Points from 1-2 and 2-3 Too High, Too Low or Erratic

1. Throttle linkage adjustment.
2. Defective governor.
3. Defective valve body.
4. Leakage in hydraulic system.

Severe Shift from Intermediate to Drive

1. Throttle linkage adjustment.
2. Front band adjustment.
3. Defective valve body.
4. Defective front servo.
5. Oil pressure regulator.

Engine Races from Intermediate to Drive

1. Throttle linkage adjustment.
2. Defective valve body.
3. Hydraulic system leaks.

No Downshift from Drive to Intermediate when Accelerator is Depressed

1. Throttle linkage adjustment.
2. Improper oil pressure.
3. Defective valve body.

Severe Shift from Drive to Intermediate with Throttle Closed

1. Throttle linkage adjustment.
2. Improper idle speed.
3. Defective valve body.

Excessive Creeping

1. Engine idle speed too high.

Slippage or Chatter in Intermediate

1. Throttle linkage adjustment.
2. Front band adjustment.
3. Improper oil pressure.
4. Defective valve body.
5. Oil pressure regulator.
6. Defective front servo.
7. Defective front clutch.
8. Hydraulic system leaks.

Slippage or Chatter in Low

1. Throttle linkage adjustment.
2. Rear band adjustment.
3. Improper oil pressure.
4. Defective valve body.
5. Oil pressure regulator.
6. Defective rear servo.
7. Defective front clutch.
8. Hydraulic system leaks.

Slippage or Chatter In D1 Only

1. Defective planetary one-way clutch.

Slippage or Chatter in Reverse

1. Throttle linkage adjustment.
2. Rear band adjustment.
3. Improper oil pressure
4. Defective valve body.
5. Oil pressure regulator.
6. Defective rear servo.
7. Defective rear clutch.
8. Hydraulic system leaks.

Car Won't Move in D or D2

1. Front band adjustment.
2. Defective valve body.
3. Defective front servo.
4. Defective front clutch.
5. Hydraulic system leaks.

Car Won't Move In D1 Only

1. Defective planetary one-way clutch.

Car Won't Move in Low or Reverse

1. Worn or defective rear band.
2. Inoperative rear servo.
3. Defective valve body.

Car Won't Move in Any Range

1. Low oil level.
2. Broken parking lock.
3. Defective valve body.
4. Oil pressure regulator.
5. Hydraulic system leaks.
6. Broken converter hub.

Locks in Reverse

1. Defective front clutch.
2. Check parking linkage.
3. Front band applied.

Locks in Low or Drive

1. Defective rear clutch.
2. Check parking linkage.
3. Broken parking pawl.

Parking Lock Will Not Hold

1. Manual linkage adjustment.
2. Check parking linkage.
3. Broken pawl operating lever.

Engine Won't Rotate When Car is Pushed

1. Oil pressure regulator.
2. Defective rear oil pump.
3. Hydraulic system leaks.

Transmission Overheats

1. Restricted converter cooling air passage.
2. Rear band adjustment.
3. Oil pressure regulator.
4. Defective converter clutch.
5. Front band adjustment.

Engine Runaway on Forced Downshift

1. Defective valve body.

Noise in Neutral

1. Converter cover bolts striking.
2. Defective front pump.
3. Interference in converter.
4. Check parking linkage.

Noise in Low, Intermediate or Reverse

1. Defective planetary assembly.
2. Defective front clutch.
3. Defective rear clutch.

Noise when Coasting in Neutral at 20-30 MPH, Engine off

1. Defective rear pump.

Noise in Converter

1. Converter cover bolts striking.
2. Interference in converter.

Comet Drive • Ford-O-Matic 2 Speed • Mile-O-Matic

Harsh Initial Engagement In D, L and R

1. Engine idle speed.
2. Throttle linkage.

Slips or Chatters In D or L

1. Fluid level.
2. Throttle linkage.
3. Control pressure check.
4. Low band adjustment.
5. Air pressure check.
6. Engine—transmission mounts.
7. Low servo and band.
8. Rear pump.

Slips or Chatters in R

1. Fluid level.
2. Throttle linkage.
3. Control pressure check.
4. Reverse band adjustment.
5. Air pressure check.
6. Engine—transmission mounts.
7. Reverse servo and band.
8. Leakage in reverse servo apply circuit.

Creeps Excessively in D

1. Engine idle speed.

Engine Overspeeds During 1-2 Shift

1. Fluid level.
2. Fluid odor—check for burned clutch plates.
3. Throttle linkage.
4. Control pressure check.
5. Low band adjustment.
6. Air pressure check.
7. Control valve body.
8. Leakage in clutch apply or low servo release circuit.
9. High clutch.
10. Planetary gears.

Momentary Lockup During 1-2 Shift

1. Fluid level.
2. Throttle linkage.
3. Control pressure check.
4. Low band adjustment.
5. Low servo and band.
6. High clutch.
7. Low servo piston return spring.

Severe 2-1 Downshift During Coast-Down

1. Engine idle speed.
2. Throttle linkage.
3. Control valve body.
4. Control pressure check.

No 1-2 Shift in D

1. Fluid level.
2. Fluid odor—check for burned clutch plates.
3. Throttle linkage.
4. Manual linkage.
5. Governor.
6. Leakage in control pressure main circuit.
7. High clutch.
8. Low servo and band.

Delayed 1-2 Shift

1. Throttle linkage.
2. Governor.
3. Leakage in control pressure main circuit.

Slips Continuously After 1-2 Shift

1. Fluid odor—check for burned clutch plates.
2. Fluid level.
3. Throttle linkage.
4. Control pressure check.
5. Air pressure check.
6. High clutch.
7. Leakage in clutch apply or low servo release circuit.

No 2-1 Forced Downshift (Kickdown)

1. Throttle linkage.
2. Control valve body.
3. Leakage in control pressure main circuit.

No 2-1 Shift During Coast-Down

1. Control valve body.
2. Governor.

Fluid Forced Out Filler Tube or Vent

1. Fluid check for engine coolant contamination.
2. Transmission external vent.
3. Fluid aeration check.

Transmission Overheats

1. Control pressure check.
2. Cooler flow check.

Acceleration Normal But Maximum Speed About 45 MPH

1. Converter one-way clutch.

Acceleration Very Poor—Operation Normal Above 30 MPH at Steady Throttle

1. Converter one-way clutch.

Engine Won't Start By Pushing Car

1. Fluid level.
2. Manual linkage.
3. Control valve body.
4. Rear pump.
5. Leakage in control pressure main circuit.

Parking Lock Won't Hold or Binds

1. Manual linkage.
2. Reverse band adjustment.

Hydra-Matic Drive Troubles

SINGLE COUPLING TYPE

UPSHIFT DIFFICULTIES

Upshifts Too High

1. Transmission throttle rear rod too short.
2. Plug missing in parking brake bracket.
3. Leak between parking brake bracket and case.
4. Leak between governor rings and oil delivery sleeve.

Upshifts Too Low

1. Transmission throttle rear rod too long.

Upshifts Vary

1. Binding linkage may cause engine idle speed to vary and may cause shift patterns to vary.
2. Intermittent oil pressure.
3. Excessive oil pressure caused by sticking pressure regulator valve, sticking front pump slide, or blocked passage in vane type pump.

No Upshifts (Operates In 1st Only)

1. Check operation of front clutch and front band release with air pressure. Excessive leak would prevent front unit from shifting into direct drive.
2. Sticking governor plungers.

3. Plug missing in parking brake bracket.
4. Leak in governor feed passages.
5. Worn governor rings or ring lands.
6. Leak between parking brake bracket and case.
7. Leak between governor rings and oil delivery sleeve.

2-3 Shift Occurs Too Close to 1-2 Shift

1. Shorten transmission throttle rear rod to give more throttle pressure.
2. Clean and inspect control valve assembly. If condition persists, try a new control valve assembly.

No 2-3 or 3-4 Upshift With Full Throttle

1. Excessive oil pressure.
2. Defective pressure regulator valve.
3. Defective front pump.
4. Insufficient governor pressure.

Shudder or Chatter on 2-3 Shift

1. Transmission throttle rear rod too long.
2. Improper band adjustment.
3. Low oil pressure.
4. Remove oil pan, side cover and valve body and test operation of transmission with air pressure, especially band release passages, rear clutch apply passage and compensator passage.
5. Sticking TV or TV regulator valve.
6. Defective control valve assembly.

DOWNSHIFT DIFFICULTIES

Improper Throttle Downshift

1. Shorten transmission throttle rear rod to provide more throttle pressure.
2. Insufficient pressure at full throttle may prevent TV or TV regulated pressure from overcoming governor pressure to give proper downshifts on a heavy pull.
3. Disassemble and clean control valve assembly, especially to the TV valve and TV regulator valve.

No Forced Downshift

1. Accelerator pedal rod too short, causing accelerator pedal to hit floor before throttle is wide open.
2. Transmission throttle rear rod too long.
3. Defective control valve assembly.
4. Leak in clutch apply oil circuit in front units.

Hunts Between 3rd & 4th with Light Throttle

1. Transmission throttle rear rod excessively short.
2. Sticking TV valve or TV regulator valve.

Rough 3-2 or 3-1 Downshift

1. Binding throttle linkage causing engine to idle too fast.

2. Defective control valve assembly.
3. Check passages in case under control valve.
4. Restricted exhaust hole in case or restriction in control valve body may delay application of rear servo until after car has stopped, causing severe downshift after stopping.
5. Disassemble rear servo and check for broken accumulator check valve or sticking check valve plunger.
6. Check to see that rear servo exhaust valve operates freely in its bore. Interference between exhaust valve and servo gasket may cause exhaust valve to stick open.

Severe Downshift After Car Is Stopped

1. Fast carburetor idle adjustment.
2. Binding throttle linkage.
3. Blocked or restricted exhaust hole in case.
4. Transmission throttle rear rod too short.
5. Accumulator valve in rear servo stuck open.

Acts Like Neutral on Forced 4-3 Downshift

1. If transmission runs free on a 2-3 shift above 25 mph or on a forced 4-3 downshift, check for a blocked by-pass passage around the 4-3 downshift valve in front servo.
2. On 1953 models, see that 4-3 downshift valve spring retainer is in place and that orifice in valve is not blocked.

SLIPPING DIFFICULTIES

Slips In All Ranges

1. Low oil pressure.
2. Sticking TV or TV regulator valves.
3. Defective control valve assembly.
4. Defective torus members.

Slips In 1st, 2nd & 3rd

1. Both bands need adjusting.
2. Blocked, restricted or interconnected compensator passage in case.
3. Stuck compensator valve.
4. Stuck throttle valve.

Slips In 1st, 3rd & Reverse

1. Loose adjustment or defective front band.
2. Low oil pressure.
3. Excessive oil leak, restriction or interconnected passages in front servo apply circuit.
4. Restricted or blocked compensator passage.
5. Excessive leak between servo and case, or between servo body and release cylinder, or by binding pistons.

Slips In 1st & 2nd

1. Improper rear band adjustment.
2. Low oil pressure.
3. Excessive leak from rear servo.
4. Blocked compensator passage in rear servo.
5. Broken oil rings in rear servo.

6. Weak or broken rear servo spring.
7. Blocked or interconnected rear servo passages.
8. Binding rear servo pistons.

Slips In 2nd & 4th

1. Slipping of front clutch may be caused by a blocked, restricted or interconnected clutch apply passage in case.
2. Excessive leak past oil delivery sleeve rings.
3. Defective annular piston seals.
4. Worn clutch plates.
5. Improper number of clutch plates in unit.
6. Improper annular piston installed.
7. Weak or distorted clutch release springs.

Slips In 3rd & 4th

1. Excessive leak around oil delivery sleeve.
2. Restricted, leaking or interconnected passages.
3. Leakage around control valve assembly.
4. Worn rings on oil delivery sleeve.
5. Worn clutch plates.
6. Worn annular piston seals.
7. Improper number of clutch plates in unit.
8. Weak or distorted clutch release springs.
9. See that steel clutch plate is next to annular piston.

Slips During 2-3 Shift

1. Transmission throttle rear rod too long.
2. Improper band adjustment.
3. Low oil pressure.
4. Check transmission with air pressure, especially both band release passages, rear band apply passage and compensator passage.
5. Remove servos and check for restricted passage with 1/8" welding rod.
6. Sticking TV or TV regulator valves.
7. Defective control valve assembly.
8. If slip occurs under 25 mph, front servo 4-3 downshift valve may be stuck closed.

No Drive In Reverse Only (Slips)

1. Low oil pressure in reverse only.
2. Check to see that pressure regulator reverse pipe is in place and that passages in case are not blocked.
3. See that reverse clutch pipe fits properly in valve body and case, and that reverse passage in case and rear bearing retainer is open.
4. Disassemble and inspect reverse unit. Check especially for seized reverse piston or excessively worn cone clutch surfaces.

Slips In Reverse Only

1. Low oil pressure in reverse.
2. Check for restricted or leaking reverse apply oil passage in rear bearing retainer, defective reverse piston seals, or sticking reverse piston.
3. Loose, blocked or restricted reverse clutch pipe.

Slips In Drive Right On Coast

1. Sticking front servo overrun control valve.

Slips Momentarily After Car Has Been Standing

1. Check for leaking torus check valve.

OTHER DIFFICULTIES

No Drive In Any Range

1. Check for disconnected linkage.
2. If no detent is felt even though transmission outer shift lever moves, inner detent lever may have come loose on shaft.
3. Low or no oil pressure.
4. Defective pressure regulator.
5. Front pump intake pipe loose.
6. "O" ring out of position in intake bore of front pump body.
7. Front pump discharge pipe not fitting properly in pump and front servo.
8. Check main line exhaust valve to see that it is not stuck in exhaust position.
9. Check for plugged line exhaust port in case.
10. Check for excessive leaks in oil circuits of control valve.
11. Check front pump, and see if pump drive key is installed in front drive gear.
12. Check for broken manual valve.
13. Broken front band.

Operates In 2nd & 4th Only

1. Front planetary locked up may cause transmission to miss 1st and 3rd by slipping front drum inside band. Would also cause low engine speed on stall test.

Operates In 1st, 3rd & Reverse Only

1. May be caused by excessive leak in oil circuit which releases front band and applies front clutch. Loss of pressure in this circuit would prevent band from releasing and would allow clutch to slip. Thus front unit would operate in reduction at all times.

No 4th Speed At Any Time

1. Check case passages under control valve body. Blocked or restricted exhaust passage may cause governor pressure to be trapped behind 3-4 shift valve and governor plug.
2. Sticking governor plungers.
3. Worn governor rings and ring lands.
4. Worn oil delivery sleeve.
5. Improperly fitting feed and delivery pipes.
6. See that parking brake bracket fits flat against case.
7. Inspect control valve assembly, especially for sticking 3-4 shift valve, governor plug, regulator plug, sticking TV regulator valve or TV valves.

No 4th Speed When Warm or Downshifts to 1st When Warm

1. Check for missing locating ball in governor and rear pump drive gear. When this ball is missing, the transmission will usually operate normally while cold but will not upshift after it is warmed up or will downshift to 1st speed while driving along the highway.

Rough or Violent Shifts

1. Completely readjust throttle control linkage. If shifts are still violent after linkage adjustment, try changing the length of the transmission rear rod slightly in either direction to see if shifts are improved.
2. May be caused by either too much or not enough oil pressure.
3. May be caused by sticking valves. If condition persists after cleaning control valve assembly, try a new control valve assembly since rough shifts may be caused by excessive leakage.

Starts In 2nd, 3rd or 4th In Drive Range

1. Governor plungers sticking part way open.
2. If large governor weight (G-1) is stuck open this will be accompanied by not being able to shift to Reverse unless engine is shut off.
3. Check for worn governor rings or ring lands.
4. Parking brake bracket cracked or there is a pin hole between the two blocker piston bores.
5. Inoperative shift valves.

Acts Like Neutral Above 2nd

1. Slipping or no drive may be caused by excessive leak around oil delivery sleeve, restricted, leaking or interconnected passages.
2. If transmission runs free on a 2-3 shift above 25 mph or on a forced 4-3 downshift, check for a blocked by-pass passage around the 4-3 downshift valve in the front servo. On 1953 models, see that the 4-3 downshift valve spring retainer is in place and that orifice in valve is not blocked.
3. Check rings on oil delivery sleeve, clutch plates and annular piston seals.
4. Slippage may be caused by improper number of clutch plates in unit, or weak or distorted release springs which have caused clutch to drag and wear excessively.
5. Check to see that steel clutch plate is located next to annular piston.

Engine Momentarily Speeds Up, Band Apply Rough

1. Usually noticeable on light to medium throttle shifts. Transmission throttle rear rod too long.
2. Bands adjusted too loose.
3. Low oil pressure.
4. Remove side cover, bottom pan and control valve and check for excessive oil leak with air pressure.
5. Remove servos and use ⅛" welding rod to check for restrictions in passages.
6. Remove front servo and disassemble to check for worn parts, or leaking, restricted or interconnected passages.

Shifts Above 2nd In Low Range

1. Check selector lever linkage adjustment to see if indicator and detent lever on transmission are properly indexed.
2. Defective control valve assembly.

Moves Forward In Reverse with Light Throttle

1. Check for rear unit clutches bound up. This would cause rear unit internal gear to turn at the same speed and in the same direction as the intermediate shaft, thus driving the reverse unit forward.

Locks Up On Reverse Coast

1. Try lengthening gearshift control rod about two turns.
2. Check for cause of low oil pressure in Reverse.

Jumps Out of Reverse

1. Caused by detent lever on transmission not being properly indexed when selector lever is in R. Adjust selector lever linkage.

Cannot Move Selector to Reverse

1. If lever moves to reverse with engine shut off, but not with engine running, check governor for sticking G-1 plunger, worn rings or lands, or worn governor oil delivery sleeve.
2. If lever will not move to reverse with engine shut off or running, check for stuck reverse blocker piston or binding reverse crank on parking brake bracket.

Locks Up In Forward Ranges After Driving in Reverse

1. Caused by reverse cone clutch hanging up. This condition can usually be corrected by (a) place selector lever in reverse position and apply brakes firmly; (b) speed up engine and place selector lever in Drive Right range; (c) when shift is complete return to idle; (d) repeat not more than five times until transmission is free.

Clashes When Shifted to Reverse

1. Extremely low pressure may allow parking blocker piston to retract so that parking pawl engages when selector lever is shifted to R.
2. Excessively low engine idle.
3. Sticking parking blocker piston.
4. Parking pawl worn.
5. Excessive clearance between parking pawl and blocker piston when piston is extended.

Unable to Start Engine By Pushing

1. No rear pump pressure.

Parking Pawl Will Not Engage With Engine Shut Off

1. Check for stuck parking blocker piston.

2. Parking pawl crank binding.

NOISES

1. Noise in neutral and all gears whenever engine is running is caused by a defective front pump.
2. Noise in neutral only (disappears when shifted to Drive) is caused by defective rear unit planetary gears.
3. Noise in neutral, 1st and 2nd speeds only is caused by defective rear unit planetary gears.
4. Noise in neutral, 1st, 3rd and reverse speeds only is caused by defective front unit planetary gears.
5. Noise in reverse gear on acceleration only is caused by defective reverse unit planetary gears.
6. Noise in reverse on deceleration only is caused by rear unit planetary gears.
7. A metallic scraping at front of transmission is caused by excessive backlash or torus members.
8. Noise when coasting at 20-35 mph, engine not running and selector lever in neutral is caused by defective rear oil pump gears.

Hydra-Matic Drive Troubles

TWO COUPLING TYPE

Car Moves Forward In "N"

1. Manual linkage incorrectly adjusted.
2. Neutral clutch not releasing properly.
3. Rear unit clutch not releasing properly.
4. Overrun band not fully released.

Car Moves Rearward in "Drive"

1. Governor boost valve stuck open.

Car Reverses In "N"

1. Stationary cone sticking.
2. Reverse piston not fully released.

Car Won't Move In "Gear"

1. Front sprag clutch slipping.
2. Front sprag clutch incorrectly installed.
3. Rear sprag clutch slipping.
4. Rear sprag clutch incorrectly installed.
5. Neutral clutch apply restricted or leaking.
6. Manual linkage incorrectly adjusted.
7. Manual valve not engaged with drive pin.
8. Low oil pressure.

Car Won't Move In "Gear" (Stalls)

1. Stationary cone sticking.
2. Reverse piston not fully released.
3. Front sprag clutch broken.
4. Rear sprag clutch broken.

Neutral Condition In "R"

1. Reverse piston apply restricted or leakage.
2. Stationary cone key missing.

Locked-Up Condition In "R"

1. Neutral clutch not releasing properly.
2. Rear unit clutch not releasing properly.
3. Overrun band not fully released.
4. Rear sprag clutch incorrectly installed.

No Reverse Drive (Slips)

1. Reverse piston apply restricted or leakage.
2. Low oil pressure.
3. Manual linkage incorrectly adjusted.

4. Manual valve not engaged with drive pin.
5. Front sprag clutch slipping.
6. Front sprag clutch broken.

Selector Lever Won't Go Into "R"

1. Governor valves sticking.
2. Broken governor oil seal rings.
3. Reverse blocker piston stuck open.

Slips In 1st and 3rd In "Dr-4"

1. Front sprag clutch slipping.
2. Front sprag clutch broken.

Slips In or Misses 2nd and 4th

1. Front unit coupling cover seals leaking.
2. Front unit coupling cover exhaust valves sticking or missing.
3. Front unit coupling cover feed restriction or leak.
4. Front unit coupling cover signal restriction or leak.
5. Low oil pressure.
6. Coupling valve sticking.
7. Sticking valve or dirt in valve body.

Slips In 1st and 2nd (All Drive Ranges)

1. Neutral clutch slipping or burned.
2. Neutral clutch apply restricted or leaking.
3. Incorrect number of clutch plates.
4. Rear sprag clutch slipping.
5. Rear sprag clutch broken.
6. Low oil pressure.

Slips in 3rd and 4th In "Dr-3" and "Dr-4"

1. Rear unit clutch slipping or burned.
2. Rear unit clutch apply restricted or leaking.
3. Incorrect number of clutch plates.

Slips In 3rd In "Dr-3" On Coast

1. Overrun clutch slipping or burned.
2. Overrun clutch apply restricted or leaking.
3. Sticking valve or dirt in valve body.

Slips In 1st and 2nd In "Lo" On Coast

1. Servo apply restricted or leaking.

2. Overrun band not anchored to case or broken.
3. Servo piston binding in case or in servo or accumulator body.
4. Overrun band facing worn or loose.

Slips In 1st In All Drive Ranges

1. Front sprag clutch slipping.
2. Front sprag clutch broken.
3. Front sprag clutch incorrectly installed.
4. Rear sprag clutch slipping.
5. Rear sprag clutch broken.
6. Rear sprag clutch incorrectly installed.
7. Neutral clutch slipping or burned.
8. Neutral clutch apply restricted or leaking.
9. Incorrect number of clutch plates.

No Upshifts

1. Governor valves sticking.
2. Broken governor oil seal rings.
3. Sticking valve or dirt in valve body.

Misses 2nd

1. Amplifier valve sticking.
2. Transition valve sticking.
3. Sticking valve or dirt in valve body.

Misses 3rd

1. Transition valve sticking.
2. Sticking valve or dirt in valve body.

Rough 2-3 Shift

1. Trimmer valve stuck.
2. Accumulator piston stuck.
3. Accumulator gasket broken or leaking.
4. Restricted or leaking oil passages.
5. Broken accumulator spring.
6. Broken or leaking accumulator piston oil seal ring.

Locks Up In 3rd and 4th

1. Rear sprag clutch broken.

Locks Up In 2nd and 4th

1. Front sprag clutch broken.

Upshifts High

1. Governor valves sticking.
2. Leaking or restricted main line feed to governor.
3. Broken governor oil seal rings.
4. Throttle linkage adjusted short.
5. Sticking valve or dirt in valve body.

Upshifts Low

1. Governor valves sticking.
2. Broken governor oil seal rings.
3. Throttle linkage adjusted long.
4. Sticking valve or dirt in valve body.

Studebaker Automatic Drive Troubles

Car Won't Move In Any Range

1. Selector linkage disconnected.
2. Low or no fluid.
3. Worn front pump.
4. Damaged front pump drive fingers on converter.
5. Excessive oil leakage.
6. Blocked oil passage.
7. Broken fins in converter.
8. Main relief valve stuck open.
9. Accumulator valve stuck.

Car Won't Move In Forward Ranges

1. Low or no forward servo pressure.
2. Broken forward drive band.
3. Excessively worn forward drive band lining.
4. Incorrect band adjustment.
5. Stuck forward servo.
6. Damaged forward drive freewheel unit.
7. Reverse band stuck in applied position.

Car Won't Move In Reverse

1. Low or no reverse servo pressure due to stuck reverse interlock valve.
2. Broken band.
3. Excessively worn lining.
4. Incorrect band adjustment.
5. Stuck reverse servo.
6. Reverse freewheel unit slipping.
7. Low or forward band stuck in applied position.

Ineffective Engine Braking for Deceleration In Manual Low

1. Low band slipping.
2. Incorrect band adjustment.
3. Broken band.
4. Excessively worn lining.
5. Low servo pressure.
6. Stuck low servo.
7. Reverse freewheel unit slipping.

Slips During Acceleration In Drive Intermediate

1. Multiple disc clutch slipping.
2. Worn disc facings.
3. Stuck clutch piston.
4. Excessive oil leakage in clutch circuit.
5. Blocked passage to clutch.
6. Governor valve sleeve out of position in housing.
7. Mislocated oil distributor tube.

Won't Shift to Direct Drive or Slips After Direct Drive Clutch is Engaged

1. Damaged governor.
2. Governor sticking on shaft.
3. Governor valve stuck in intermediate or automatic low position.
4. Low direct drive clutch pressure in direct drive cylinder due to blocked passage, leaking direct drive clutch piston seals O ring, leaking seal ring at front ring gear or mainshaft.
5. High converter pressure due to sticking converter reverse or direct valve, leaking seals in converter, mainshaft bronze lubricator valve loose and twisted out of correct position.
6. Improper clutch operation due to sticking or distorted direct drive clutch piston, or excessive lining wear or direct drive clutch plate.
7. Oil level too high, interfering with governor.

Engine Won't Start By Pushing

1. Damaged or excessively worn rear pump.
2. Damaged rear pump drive mechanism.
3. Blocked passage in extension housing, case, or valve block.
4. Excessive leakage of rear pump pressure.

Car Moves With Lever In Park

1. Parking pawl does not engage properly.
2. Incorrect adjustment of hand control linkage.
3. Incorrect adjustment of parking linkage.
4. Parking interlock piston stuck in locked position.
5. Parking pawl or linkage broken.

Engine Stalls When Lever is Shifted to Drive

1. Governor stuck in direct drive position.
2. Hydraulic detent stuck, holding governor in direct drive.
3. Governor sticking on shaft.
4. Governor valve sleeve out of position in housing.

Engine Stalls When Car is Stopped After Being In Direct Drive

1. Governor stuck in drive position.
2. Hydraulic detent stuck, holding governor in direct drive.
3. Governor sticking on shaft.
4. Governor sleeve out of position.
5. Blocked governor valve drain passage.
6. Damaged or sticking direct drive clutch in converter.

Will Not Downshift At Kickdown

1. Incorrect accelerator linkage adjustment.
2. Interference between linkage and other parts such as floor pan, transmission case, etc.
3. Damaged governor.
4. Governor sticking on shaft.
5. Governor control cam stop screw out of adjustment.
6. Blocked governor valve drain passage.
7. High oil level, interfering with governor.

Engine Labors, Transmission Overheats In Forward Ranges

1. Incorrect reverse band adjustment.
2. Distorted reverse band.
3. Internal oil leakage in valve block.
4. Reverse servo piston stuck in applied position.

Engine Labors, Transmission Overheats In Drive & Reverse

1. Incorrect low band adjustment.
2. Distorted low band.
3. Low brake piston sticking in applied position.
4. Internal oil leakage in valve block.

Engine Labors In Reverse

1. Incorrect forward band adjustment.
2. Internal oil leak in valve block.
3. Forward servo piston sticking.
4. Damaged or distorted forward band.

Engine Labors In Automatic Low, Low & Reverse

1. Multiple disc clutch dragging.
2. Internal oil leakage in valve block.
3. Multiple disc clutch piston sticking.
4. Broken or damaged multiple disc clutch release springs.

Engine Labors On Take-Off

1. Torque converter stator freewheel unit slipping.

TROUBLE SHOOTING

Transmission Overheats, Low Top Speed

1. Torque converter stator freewheel unit stuck.

Stalls In Drive When Shift from Automatic Low to Intermediate is Made

1. Stuck relay valve not allowing release of low band.

Starts In Intermediate Instead of Low

1. Governor valve fails to return to low position when car comes to a stop.
2. Governor sticking on shaft.
3. Governor valve or detent sticking.
4. Second speed drive mechanism sticking in locked position.
5. Weak or wrong governor spring.
6. Booster spring too strong.

Transmission Noisy When Standing Still In Drive

1. Low fluid level.
2. Front pump inlet screen clogged.
3. Fluid level too high.
4. Damaged front pump drive fingers on converter.
5. Air leaks in front pump intake circuits.

6. Improper main relief or converter shuttle valve action.
7. Broken converter fins.
8. Loose direct drive clutch backing plate or drive fingers in converter.

Severe Clunk In D, L & R Ranges

1. Accumulator valve stuck open.

Severe Clunk In D Range

1. Oil passage to outer forward servo cylinder not restricted — incorrect servo plate.

Severe Clunk In Reverse

1. Oil passage to outer reverse servo cylinder not restricted—wrong servo plate.

Noisy When Car Moves Forward

1. Damaged or excessively worn rear pump or rear pump drive mechanism.
2. Damaged or excessively worn speedometer drive gear or pinion.
3. Damaged mainshaft assembly or excessively worn gears, bearings, etc.

Brakes Drag After Being Applied & Released

1. Anticreep pressure switch inoperative.

2. No or low rear pump pressure.

Brakes Drag At All Times

1. Anticreep solenoid valve sticking.

Brakes Drag When Starting from Standstill

1. Anticreep switch grounded or sticking closed.
2. Anticreep solenoid valve-to-release switch wire grounded.
3. Anticreep solenoid valve grounded or sticking.

Anticreep System Inoperative

1. Carburetor throttle valve sticking slightly open.
2. Anticreep release switch incorrectly adjusted.
3. Anticreep release switch sticking open.
4. Anticreep system fuse burned out.
5. Open circuit between anticreep system fuse and ignition switch.
6. Open circuit between anticreep pressure switch and fuse.
7. Anticreep pressure switch sticking open.
8. Open circuit between anticreep solenoid valve and pressure switch.
9. Open circuit in anticreep solenoid valve.

Rambler Flashomatic Troubles

Initial Engagement Too Rough

1. Idle speed too high.
2. Control pressure too high.

Initial Engagement Delayed

1. Fluid level low.
2. Rear band loose.
3. Control pressure too low at idle speed.

Inoperative In All Ranges

1. Fluid level low.
2. Manual linkage disconnected.
3. No control pressure.
4. Rear band and/or servo inoperative.
5. Converter failure.

No Drive In D1 Or L Position

1. Fluid level low.
2. Manual linkage not properly adjusted.
3. Control pressure low.
4. Front clutch will not apply.
5. Rear band will not apply.
6. Transition valve stuck.

No Drive In D1 Only

1. Defective one-way clutch.

No Drive In R Position

1. Fluid level low.
2. Manual linkage not adjusted properly.

3. Control pressure low.
4. Rear clutch will not apply.
5. Rear band will not apply.
6. Transition valve stuck.

Locks Up In D1 or L Position

1. Rear clutch applied.
2. Front band applied.

Locks Up In D1 or D2 Position (2nd Gear)

1. Rear band applied.
2. Rear clutch applied.
3. One-way clutch applied (V8).

Locks Up In D1 or D2 Position (3rd Gear)

1. Rear band applied.
2. Front band applied.
3. One-way clutch applied (V8).

Locks Up In R Position

1. Front clutch applied.
2. Front band applied.

Slips In D1 Or L Position

1. Fluid level low.
2. Control pressure low.
3. Rear servo travel limited.
4. Front clutch slips.
5. Rear pump check valve stuck open.

Locks Up In D1 Only (V8)

1. Defective one-way clutch.

Slips In R Position

1. Fluid level low.
2. Control pressure low.
3. Rear servo travel limited.
4. Rear clutch slips.
5. Rear pump check valve stuck open.

1-2 Upshift Rough

1. Control pressure too high.
2. Band adjustments.
3. Governor valve stuck.

1-2 Upshift Slips

1. Control pressure low.
2. Band adjustments.
3. Governor valve stuck.
4. Front servo piston travel limited.
5. Fluid leakage.

No 1-2 Upshift

1. Governor valve stuck.
2. 1-2 shift valve stuck.

1-2 Upshift Too Early

1. Governor valve stuck.

1-2 Upshift Too Late

1. Governor valve stuck.

2. Leak in governor circuit.
3. Control pressure too high.

2-3 Upshift Rough

1. Control pressure too high.
2. Band adjustments.
3. Governor valve stuck.

2-3 Upshift Slips

1. Control pressure low.
2. Front band adjustment.
3. Governor valve stuck.
4. Internal leaks.

No 2-3 Upshift

1. Governor valve stuck.
2. 2-3 shift valve stuck.

2-3 Upshift Early

1. Governor valve stuck.

2-3 Upshift Late

1. Governor valve stuck.
2. Leak in governor circuit.
3. Throttle vacuum control misadjusted.

3-2 Downshift Rough (Closed Throttle)

1. Throttle vacuum control misadjusted.
2. Orifice control valve stuck.

3-2 Kickdown Early

1. Throttle vacuum control misadjusted.

No Kickdown

1. Throttle vacuum control misadjusted.
2. No current through kickdown switch.

2-1 Downshift Rough (Closed Throttle)

1. Throttle linkage misadjusted.
2. Rear servo check valve stuck.

No Push Start

1. Rear pump inoperative.
2. Pressure regulator valve stuck.

No Park Position

1. Manual linkage misadjusted.
2. Damaged internal linkage.
3. Damaged park pawl.

Rear Axle Troubles

Noise When Pulling Straight Ahead

1. Not enough oil.
2. Wrong grade of oil.
3. Poor quality oil.
4. Ring gear and pinion have excessive backlash.
5. Ring gear and pinion worn.
6. Pinion shaft bearings worn or loose.
7. Pinion shaft end play excessive.
8. Ring gear and pinion misaligned because of bent axle housing or distorted differential case.
9. Ring gear warped.
10. Differential bearings worn or loose.
11. Ring gear rivets or screws loose.
12. Ring gear and pinion not matched set.

Noise When Coasting In Gear

Any axle noise which is heard when the engine is pulling the car is likely to be heard when coasting although not as loud as when pulling.

If ring gear and pinion are meshed too tight, the noise will be greater when decelerating. The noise will disappear when the engine is pulling unless the gears are very tight.

Excessive end play of pinon shaft due to loose pinion nut or incorrect adjustment.

Intermittent Noise

1. Warped ring gear.
2. Loose ring gear rivets or screws.
3. Ring gear improperly installed on differential case due to dirt or burrs between the two.

Knocks or Clicks

1. Flat spot on ring gear or pinion tooth, or tooth chipped, or particle of metal lodged on tooth.
2. Flat spot on bearing.
3. Loose axle shaft key.
4. Loose splined shafts.

Noise On Turns

1. Differential pinions or side gears chipped, scuffed or teeth broken.
2. Differential pinions binding on pinion shaft.
3. Differential pinions or side gears loose due to worn bushings or shaft.
4. Excessive backlash between pinions

and side gears.
5. Excessive axle shaft end play.
6. Contacting surfaces between side gear and differential case burred, scored or otherwise damaged.

Oil Leak At Axle Ends

1. Oil level too high.
2. Oil too light or poor quality.
3. Axle shaft oil seals worn.
4. Axle shaft bearing retainer loose.
5. Cracked rear axle housing.
6. Vent (if any) clogged.

Oil Leak At Pinion Shaft

1. Oil level too high.
2. Oil too light or poor quality.
3. Pinion oil seal worn.
4. Pinion oil seal retainer distorted, loose in housing or improperly installed.
5. Oil return passage in carrier housing restricted.
6. Universal joint companion flange hub rough, scored or out of round.
7. Universal joint companion flange loose on pinion shaft.

Brake Troubles

Brake Pedal Goes All Way Down to Toeboard

1. Normal wear on linings.
2. No fluid in reservoir.
3. Leaks in brake system.
4. Air in brake system which causes a springy, rubbery action of brake pedal.
5. Rubber cups damaged or shrunken by excessive heat.
6. Rubber cups shrunken or swollen by mineral oil in system, or wrong type of brake fluid.

No Pedal After Hard Usage

1. Excessive heat causes fluid to vaporize.

2. Brake drum material too thin due to machining drum beyond safe limits.

Brakes Drag At All Wheels

1. By-pass port hole in master cylinder blocked.
2. Mineral oil in brake system.

Brake Drags On One Wheel

1. Brake shoes too close to drum.
2. Weak or broken shoe return spring.
3. Cylinder cups distorted.
4. Brake hose restricted.
5. Drag or binding in emergency brake cable.
6. Loose or defective wheel bearings.

Car Pulls to One Side When Brakes Are Applied

1. Tires not properly inflated.
2. Loose or defective wheel bearings.
3. Badly misaligned wheels.
4. Steering gear out of adjustment.
5. Loose brake backing plate.
6. Anchor adjustment uneven between left and right sides.
7. Oil or brake fluid on linings.
8. Different makes of lining used between left and right sides.
9. Scored or out-of-round brake drums.
10. Drums have different friction between left and right sides.

Springy Pedal Action

1. Brake shoes improperly adjusted.
2. Air in brake system.
3. New lining improperly fitting brake drums.
4. Flexible lines expand under pressure due to deterioration of material.

Excessive Pedal Pressure Necessary to Stop Car

1. Brake shoes improperly adjusted.

2. Brake pedal or linkage binds.
3. Lining making only partial contact with drum.
4. Incorrect linings used.
5. Lining glazed.

Too Light Pedal Pressure (Brake Action Severe)

1. Brake shoes improperly adjusted.
2. Loose brake backing plate.
3. Oil or fluid on linings.
4. Linings damaged by excessive heat.

5. Scored brake drums.

Brakes Squeak On Application

1. Dampening spring (when used) missing or insulated from drum.
2. Improper brake adjustment.
3. Lining hard or glazed.
4. Lining making poor contact with drum.
5. Brake lining cracked.
6. Rivets loose.

Power Brake Troubles

To determine quickly whether the power unit is functioning, shut off the engine and apply the brakes several times to eliminate all vacuum from the system. Then apply the brakes, holding a light pressure on the brake pedal, and start the engine. If the power unit is operating, the brake pedal will move forward slightly and less pedal pressure will be required to apply the brake.

If no vacuum assist is felt on the pedal, insert a vacuum gauge in series between the vacuum line and power unit to check the vacuum supply to the unit. An internal leak in the power unit can usually be heard or checked with a vacuum gauge. An optional method of checking for an internal leak is to apply and hold the brake pedal and stop the engine. After one minute there should be enough vacuum to provide pedal assist for several applications, provided there are no internal or external leaks.

The hydraulic system can be checked for leaks by applying the brake pedal with constant pressure. If the pedal moves slowly toward the floor, a leak in the hydraulic system is indicated. If there is a spongy action when the brake pedal is depressed, bleed the system to remove air from the lines.

The cause of power brake problems in general as they apply to the different makes and type of power units are as follows:

Hard Pedal (No Assist)

1. Air cleaner element clogged.
2. Leak or obstruction in vacuum line or fittings.
3. Vacuum check valve stuck or leaking.
4. Vacuum reserve tank leaking.
5. Internal or external leak in power unit.
6. Vacuum cylinder piston jammed (piston type).
7. Vacuum cylinder piston packing defective (piston type).
8. Interference between bellows and dash or mat (bellows type).
9. Defective diaphragm (diaphragm type).
10. Wheel or master cylinder cups swollen by improper fluid.
11. Bound up pedal linkage.
12. Dented vacuum cylinder (piston type).
13. Defective or kinked flexible hydraulic line.
14. Control valve defective (Bendix Hydrovac).

Bendix Master-Vac:
1. Leak between power and master cylinders.
2. Internal vacuum hose leaking or restricted.
3. Control valve jammed.
4. Improperly adjusted stop light switch (Pontiac).

Kelsey-Hayes Diaphragm Type:
1. Air valve seat jammed in power piston.
2. Blocked air passage in power piston guide sleeve.

Kelsey-Hayes Round Bellows Type:
1. Improperly adjusted valve eccentric.
2. Improperly adjusted push rod.
3. Bent pedal trigger.

Kelsey-Hayes Oval Bellows Type:
1. Vacuum passage in valve housing blocked.
2. Vacuum valve binding in guide from defective spring or dry seal.
3. Valve operating rod binding.
4. Pedal linkage bent or improperly adjusted.
5. Inspection screw or gasket loose or missing.

Moraine Diaphragm Type:
1. Leak between power and master cylinders.
2. Bend or distortion causing bind in lever mechanism or reaction plate.
3. Internal vacuum hose leaking or restricted.
4. Jammed air valve.

Midland:
1. Slave cylinder piston sticking.

Brake Pedal Chatters

1. Air in brake lines or hydraulic cylinder.
2. Pedal trigger arm incorrectly adjusted. (Bendix Power-Vac piston type).
3. Residual check valve defective (Bendix Hydro-Vac).

Kelsey-Hayes Round Bellows Type:
1. Incorrectly adjusted valve adjusting eccentric.
2. Incorrectly adjusted push rod eccentric.

Kelsey-Hayes Oval Bellows Type:
1. Brake pedal push rod incorrectly adjusted.
2. Power brake trigger bent or incorrectly adjusted.

3. Power brake trigger pivot rubber collar defective.
4. Guide sleeve bearing seal binding on guide sleeve.

Brakes Grab

1. Foreign material on brake lining.
2. Brakes improperly adjusted.
3. Scored brake drums.

Bendix Treadle-Vac:
1. Counter reaction spring broken.
2. Vacuum poppet valve sticking.
3. Internal hydraulic leaks.

Bendix Master-Vac:
1. Vacuum cylinder dented.
2. Valve plunger sticking.
3. Vacuum check valve defective.
4. Loose vacuum connections.
5. Faulty pedal linkage.

Kelsey-Hayes Diaphragm Type:
1. Dirt lodged between reaction piston and insert under reaction piston dome cup.

Kelsey-Hayes Oval Bellows Type:
1. Power linkage binding.
2. Power unit seals binding.

Moraine Diaphragm Type:
1. Sticking air valve.
2. Reaction diaphragm leakage.
3. Diaphragm passage restricted.
4. Reaction spring broken.
5. Reaction levers dislodged.

Slow Release, Drag, No Release

1. Pedal or linkage binding.
2. Brakes binding or improperly adjusted.
3. Compensator port plugged.
4. Clogged air filter.
5. Defective return spring on pedal in power unit.
6. Defective or kinked flexible hydraulic line.

Bendix Treadle-Vac Hydraulic Type:
1. Restricted air passage.
2. Excessive hydraulic seal friction.
3. Residual check valve defective.
4. Valve plunger or compensating valve sticking.
5. Atmospheric poppet valve stuck in closed position.

Bendix Hydro-Vac:
1. Control valve not functioning.
2. Power piston sticking.
3. Hydraulic piston yoke not releasing sticking ball check.

Kelsey-Hayes Diaphragm Type:
1. Air valve "O" ring dry.
2. Inspection screw and gasket loose.
3. Misaligned cylinder.
4. Defective reaction spring, or control springs.
5. Plugged compensating hole near end of sleeve in power piston.
6. Air cleaner cover sleeve section not concentric with power piston guide sleeve.

Kelsey-Hayes Round Bellows Type:
1. Incorrect push rod eccentric adjustment.
2. Incorrect master cylinder push rod adjustment.
3. Restricted air passage in bracket tube from engine compartment.

Kelsey-Hayes Oval Bellows Type:
1. Push rod improperly adjusted.
2. Guide sleeve bearing seal binding on guide sleeve.

Moraine Diaphragm Type:
1. Power piston air passage blocked.
2. Air valve stuck in closed position.
3. Air valve spring broken.

Midland Hy-Power:
1. Push rod too long.
2. Control valve plunger sticking.
3. Diaphragm housing dented or leaking.
4. Control valve spring defective.
5. Control piston sticking.
6. Check valve sticking.

Spongy Pedal, Excessive Pedal Travel
1. Air in brake hydraulic system.

2. Brakes need adjustment.
3. Internal or external leak in brake hydraulic system.
4. Reservoir fluid level low.
5. Improperly adjusted push rod (Kelsey-Hayes bellows type).

Brakes Apply When Engine Is Started

Bendix Hydro-Vac:
1. Control valve piston sticking.
2. Atmospheric poppet return spring defective.

Pedal Kicks Back With Engine Running

Midland Hy-Power:
1. Leak in check valve.
2. Leak in slave cylinder piston cup.

Front End & Steering Troubles

Hard Steering
1. Low or uneven tire pressure.
2. Steering gear or connections adjusted too tight.
3. Insufficient or incorrect lubricant used.
4. Excessive caster.
5. Suspension arms bent or twisted.
6. Front spring sagged.
7. Frame bent or broken.
8. Steering knuckle bent.
9. Kingpin galled or frozen in bushing.

Excessive Play or Looseness In Steering
1. Steering gear connections adjusted too loose or worn.
2. Steering knuckle bushings worn.
3. Front wheel bearings incorrectly adjusted or worn.

Erratic Steering On Application of Brakes
1. Oil or brake fluid on lining.
2. Brakes improperly adjusted.
3. Front spring weak.
4. Low or uneven tire pressure.
5. Insufficient or uneven caster.
6. Steering knuckle bent.

Car Pulls to One Side
1. Low or uneven tire pressure.
2. Incorrect or uneven caster or camber.
3. Wheel bearings adjusted too tight.
4. Front springs sagged.
5. Toe-in incorrect.
6. Oil or brake fluid on brake lining.
7. Brakes incorrectly or unevenly adjusted.
8. Steering knuckle or knuckle support bent.
9. Frame bent or broken.

10. Shock absorbers inoperative.
11. Rear wheels not tracking with front wheels.
12. Rear axle shifted (spring U bolts loose or center bolt sheared).

Scuffed Tires
1. Tire improperly inflated.
2. Toe-in incorrect.
3. Excessive wheel or tire run-out.
4. Steering knuckle bushings worn.
5. Uneven camber.
6. Incorrect toe-out on turns.
7. Suspension arms bent or twisted.
8. Steering knuckle bent.
9. Excessive speed on turns.

Cupped Tires
1. Improper toe-in.
2. Tires improperly inflated.
3. Wheels, tires or brake drums out of balance.
4. Dragging brakes.
5. Worn steering knuckle bushings.
6. Wheel bearings incorrectly adjusted or worn.
7. Uneven camber.
8. Steering knuckle bent.
9. Excessive mileage without rotating tires.

Front Wheel Shimmy
1. Low or uneven tire pressure.
2. Wheels, tires or brake drums out of balance.
3. Excessive wheel or tire run-out.
4. Shock absorbers inoperative.
5. Steering connections incorrectly adjusted or worn.
6. Steering gear incorrectly adjusted.
7. Front wheel bearings incorrectly adjusted or worn.
8. Incorrect or uneven caster.
9. Steering knuckle bushings worn.

10. Toe-in incorrect.
11. Steering knuckle bent.
12. Eccentric or bulged tires.
13. Stabilizer inoperative.

Front Wheel Tramp
1. Wheels, tires or brake drums out of balance.
2. Wheel or tire not concentric.
3. Shock absorbers inoperative.
4. Stabilizer inoperative.

Car Wanders
1. Low or uneven tire pressure.
2. Steering gear or connections adjusted too loose or worn.
3. Steering gear or connections adjusted too tight.
4. Steering knuckle bushings worn.
5. Improper toe-in.
6. Incorrect or uneven caster or camber.
7. Steering knuckle bent.
8. Kingpin bent.
9. Rear axle shifted (spring U bolts loose or center bolt sheared).
10. Stabilizer inoperative.
11. Kingpins or bushings tight.
12. Bind in lower or upper control arm shaft.
13. Bind in rear spring shackles or dry rear springs.
14. Excessive backlash in steering gear.

Road Shocks
1. High air pressure in tires.
2. Steering gear or connections incorrectly adjusted.
3. Excessive caster.
4. Shock absorbers inoperative.
5. Front springs weak or sagged.
6. Wrong type or size of tires used.
7. Steering knuckle bent.

Power Steering Troubles

CHRYSLER COAXIAL TYPE

Squealing Noise

1. Slipping upper generator drive belt.
2. Slipping lower fan belt.
3. Vibration set up by control valve rod.

Hissing Noise (No Load)

1. Low oil level in reservoir.
2. Inoperative pressure control valve in lower piston rod.

Hissing Noise (Right Turn Only)

1. Oil leakage by lower piston rod gear housing oil seal.

Hissing Noise (Left Turn Only)

1. This noise when accompanied by loss of oil through vent in upper housing may be caused by oil leakage by upper piston rod housing head oil seal.

Cracking Noise On Turns

1. Loose gear-to-frame mounting bolts.

Snapping Noise

1. Loose steering gear-to-frame bolts.
2. Front suspension springs not properly seated.
3. Camber adjusting bushing set screw loose.
4. Center link and tie rods not in alignment.

Chuckle Noise

1. Steering gear arm loose.
2. Loose front wheel bearings.
3. Gear shaft adjustment too loose.
4. Excessive kingpin end play.
5. Steering tube coupling screw loose.
6. Worm bearing pre-load adjustment too loose.
7. Excessive worm shaft end play in connector assembly.

Steering Wanders

1. Gear shaft adjustment too loose.
2. Worm bearing pre-load adjustment too loose.
3. Excessive worm shaft end play in connector assembly.
4. Steering gear arm nut loose.
5. Loose front wheel bearings.
6. Worn or loose steering linkage.
7. Front wheel alignment.
8. Binding at pivot points in front suspension.

Poor Recovery of Wheels to Straight-Ahead Position (Both Directions)

1. Low tire pressure.
2. Binding in front suspension parts.
3. Front wheel alignment.
4. Steering wheel-to-column jacket interference.

5. Steering column jacket bearing.
6. Gear shaft adjustment too tight.
7. Worm bearing pre-load adjustment too tight.

Poor Recovery of Wheels to Straight-Ahead Position (One Direction Only)

1. Same checks as for poor recovery in both directions (see above).
2. If above does not solve problem, center control valve until equal torque readings are obtained in each direction.

Unequal Steering Effort

1. Control valve adjustment.
2. Upper piston rod movement in piston.
3. Connector nut.
4. Control valve loose on rod.
5. Upper piston rod nut loose.
6. Upper piston rod.
7. Reaction assembly.

Lack of Assistance In One Direction

1. Damaged neoprene piston ring.
2. Housing head oil seal.
3. Valve rod lower "O" ring.
4. Piston rod "O" rings.

Lack of Assistance in Both Directions

1. Tire pressure too low.
2. Upper and lower fan and generator belts slipping.
3. Low fluid level in reservoir.
4. Lack of pump pressure.

CHRYSLER CONSTANT CONTROL TYPE

Hard Steering

1. Tires not properly inflated.
2. Low oil level in reservoir.
3. Loose pump belt.
4. Oil on pump belts.
5. Steering linkage needs lubrication.
6. Power steering pump output low.
7. Cross shaft adjustment too tight.
8. Pressure control valve stuck in closed position.
9. External oil leaks.
10. Defective or damaged valve lever.
11. Dirt or chips in steering gear.
12. Damaged column support worm shaft bearings.
13. Damaged thrust bearings or excessive preload adjustment.
14. Rough or hard to turn worm and piston assembly.
15. Excessive internal leakage.

Poor Recovery From Turns

1. Tires not properly inflated.
2. Steering linkage binding.
3. Improper wheel alignment.
4. Damaged or defective steering tube bearings.
5. Steering column jacket and steering

gear not properly aligned.
6. Improper cross shaft mesh adjustment.
7. Pressure control valve piston stuck open.
8. Column support spanner nut loose.
9. Defective or damaged valve lever.
10. Improper worm thrust bearing adjustment.
11. Burrs or nicks in reaction ring grooves in cylinder head or column support.
12. Defective or damaged cylinder head worm shaft seal ring.
13. Dirt or chips in steering gear unit.
14. Rough or catchy worm and piston assembly.

Self-Steering or Leads to Either Side

1. Tires not properly inflated.
2. Improper wheel alignment.
3. Steering wheel off center when car is traveling straight ahead.
4. Valve body out of adjustment.
5. Valve lever damaged.
6. Column support spanner nut loose.

Temporary Increase In Effort When Turning Steering Wheel

1. Low oil level.
2. Loose pump belt.
3. Oil on pump belts.
4. Binding steering linkage.
5. Engine idle too slow.
6. Defective power steering pump.
7. Air in system.
8. External adjustment.
9. Improper cross shaft adjustment.
10. Excessive internal leakage.

Excessive Steering Wheel Free Play

1. Improper cross shaft adjustment.
2. Column support spanner nut loose.
3. Improper worm thrust bearing adjustment.

Lack of Assistance In One Direction

1. Oil leaking past worm shaft cast iron seal ring or ferrule "O" ring.

Lack of Assistance In Both Directions

1. Broken "O" ring on worm piston.
2. Piston end plug loose.
3. Pump belt slipping.
4. Pump output low.

Noises

1. Buzzing noise in neutral only is caused by sticking pressure control valve.
2. Noisy power pump.
3. Damaged hydraulic lines.
4. Pressure control valve sticking.
5. Improper sector shaft adjustment.
6. Air in system.

FORD TORSION BAR TYPE

Hard Steering

1. Low or uneven tire pressure.
2. Improper gear adjustment.
3. Improper wheel alignment.
4. Low fluid level.
5. Twisted or bent suspension parts, frame and linkage components.
6. Tight wheel bearings.
7. Steering spindle bent.
8. Pump belt out of adjustment.
9. Pump output low.
10. Air in system.
11. Valve spool out of adjustment.
12. Valve spool sticking.
13. Steering linkage binding.

Hard Steering Straight Ahead

1. Steering adjustment too tight.
2. Steering gear shaft binding.

Hard Steering While Turning or Parking

1. Oil level low.
2. Pump pressure low.
3. Pressure loss in steering gear due to leakage past "O" rings.
4. Pressure loss between valve spool and sleeve.
5. Pressure loss past piston ring or scored housing bore.

Loose Steering

1. Loose wheel bearings.
2. Loose tie rod ends or linkage.
3. Worn ball joints.
4. Worn suspension parts.
5. Insufficient mesh load.
6. Insufficient worm bearing preload.
7. Valve spool out of adjustment.

Erratic Steering

1. Oil or brake fluid on brake lining.
2. Out of round brake drums.
3. Improperly adjusted brakes.
4. Under-inflated tires.
5. Broken spring or other details in suspension system.
6. Improper caster adjustment.
7. Fluid level low.

Binding or Poor Recovery

1. Steering gear shaft binding.
2. Steering gear out of adjustment.
3. Steering linkage binding.
4. Valve spool binding due to dirt or burred edges.
5. Valve spool out of adjustment.
6. Interference at sector shaft and ball stud.

Loss of Power Assist

1. Pump inoperative.
2. Hydraulic lines damaged.
3. Power cylinder damaged.
4. Valve spool out of adjustment.

Loss of Power Assist In One Direction

1. Valve spool out of adjustment.

Noisy Pump

1. Air being drawn into pump.

2. Lines touching other parts of car.
3. Oil level low.
4. Excessive back pressure caused by obstructions in lines.
5. Excessive wear of internal parts.

Poor Return of Steering Gear to Center

1. Valve spool sticking.
2. Valve spool out of adjustment.
3. All items given under "Binding or Poor Recovery".

Steering Wheel Surge While Turning

1. Valve spool sticking.
2. Excessive internal leakage.
3. Belt slippage.

SAGINAW OFFSET & IN LINE TYPES

Steering Knocks While Turning

1. Improper pitman shaft adjustment.
2. Improper power rack adjustment (offset type).
3. Improper thrust bearing adjustment (offset type).

Steering Wheel Surges or Jerks While Turning

1. Loose pump belt.

Noisy Pump After Refilling Reservoir

1. Check belt adjustment and all fittings and bolts to insure tightness.
2. Make sure all hoses are not touching any other parts of car, particularly sheet metal.
3. Air in system.

Hard Steering When Parking

1. Pump drive belt adjustment.
2. Lack of lubrication in steering gear, linkage and front suspension.
3. Tires improperly inflated.
4. Tight steering gear adjustments.
5. Leakage in steering gear or hydraulic lines.
6. Low pump pressure.

SAGINAW ROTARY VALVE TYPE

Hard Steering

1. Frozen steering shaft bearings.
2. Lower coupling flange rubbing against adjuster.
3. Steering adjustment tight.

Poor Return of Steering

1. Frozen steering shaft bearings.
2. Lower coupling flange rubbing against adjuster.
3. Tires not inflated properly.
4. Incorrect caster and toe-in.
5. Tight steering linkage.
6. Steering gear misalignment.

7. Tight suspension ball joints.
8. Steering adjustment tight.
9. Thrust bearing adjustment tight.
10. Tight sector-to-rack piston adjustment.
11. Rack piston nut and worm preload too tight.
12. Sticky valve spool.

Car Leads to One Side

1. Front end misalignment.
2. Unbalanced or badly worn valve.

Momentary Increase In Effort When Turning Wheel Fast

1. Low oil level in pump.
2. Pump belt slipping.
3. High internal leakage.

External Oil Leaks

1. Loose hose connections.
2. Damaged hose.
3. Side cover O-ring seal.
4. Pitman shaft seals.
5. Housing end plug seal.
6. Adjuster plug seals.
7. Torsion bar seal.

Steering Gear Noise

1. A rattle or chuckle noise caused by loose over-center adjustment.
2. A hissing sound caused by gear being loose on frame.

Excessive Wheel Kickback or Loose Steering

1. Lash in steering linkage.
2. Air in system.
3. Excessive lash between pitman shaft sector and rack piston.
4. Loose thrust bearing adjustment.
5. Ball nut and worm preload.

Wheel Surges or Jerks

1. Loose pump belt.

Hard Steering When Parking

1. Loose pump belt.
2. Low oil level in reservoir.
3. Lack of lubrication in linkage or front suspension.
4. Tires not properly inflated.
5. Insufficient oil pressure.
6. Low oil pressure due to restriction in hoses.
7. Low oil pressure due to worn piston ring or scored housing bore.
8. Pressure loss due to leakage at valve rings, valve body-to-worm seal or rack piston end plug seal.
9. Pressure loss due to loose fit of spool in valve body or leaky valve body.

Valve Squawk

1. Cut or worn dampener ring on valve spool.
2. Loose or worn rotary valve parts.

No Effort Required to Turn

1. Broken torsion bar.

Power Top, Window & Seat Troubles

HYDRO-LECTRIC TYPE

Top Will Not Operate

1. Mechanical interference due to luggage or other objects.
2. Hold down strap not removed.
3. Top not free from windshield header studs.
4. Electrical shorts or loose connections in control switch circuit.
5. Dirty control switch contacts.
6. Inoperative power unit motor.
7. Hydraulic fluid low.
8. Power unit pump inoperative.
9. Stoppage in fluid pipes.
10. Faulty hydraulic control valve.
11. Broken port plate in hydraulic pump.

Top Operates in One Direction Only

1. Mechanical interference due to luggage or other objects.
2. Hold down strap not removed.
3. Top not free from windshield header studs.
4. Electrical shorts or loose connections in control switch circuit.
5. Dirty control switch contact.
6. Improperly adjusted control rod.
7. Hydraulic power cylinder faulty.
8. Stoppage in fluid pipes.
9. Faulty hydraulic control valve.

Window Lift Inoperative

1. Mechanical interference from door arm rest screw.
2. Misaligned glass run channel or window guide.
3. Window lift not connected to lower sash channel.
4. Electrical short or loose connection in battery, motor or cylinder circuit.
5. Cylinder solenoid inoperative.
6. Power unit motor inoperative.
7. Hydraulic fluid low.
8. Hydraulic hoses crimped.
9. Stoppage in fluid pipes.
10. Pump pressure relief valve stuck.
11. Cylinder piston rod disconnected.
12. Broken port plate in pump.

Windows Operate Slowly Upward

1. Mechanical binding due to misalignment.
2. Glass run channels excessively wet.
3. If window does not fully close, stops are improperly adjusted or there is insufficient hydraulic fluid.
4. Electrical failure due to low battery.
5. Hydraulic failure due to stuck pump pressure relief valve.
6. Top control rod improperly adjusted so that control valve is held partially open to allow fluid to enter top lines.

Windows Operate Slowly Downward

1. If a window moves slowly downward when control switch is in neutral po-

sition, the solenoid valve in window lift cylinder is leaking.
2. Mechanical binding due to misalignment.
3. Glass run channels excessively wet.
4. Window lift return spring broken.
5. Hydraulic fluid old, congealed or too heavy for prevailing temperatures.
6. Pump pressure relief valve stuck.

Window Raises When Top or Seat Is Operated

1. Electrical control circuit crossed due to switch "CYL" terminal touching "BAT" terminal.
2. Hydraulic pressure too high if more than one window raises.
3. Solenoid valve in window cylinder leaking.

Two Windows Operate From One Switch

1. Electrical control circuit crossed due to switch "CYL" terminals touching.
2. Hydraulic pressure too high.
3. Solenoid valve in window cylinder leaking.

Seat Adjuster Inoperative

1. Mechanical interference from object under seat.
2. Seat adjuster misaligned.
3. Seat adjuster not attached to seat frame or floor.
4. Electrical short or loose connection in battery, motor or cylinder circuit.
5. Cylinder solenoid inoperative.
6. Power unit motor inoperative.
7. Hydraulic fluid low.
8. Hydraulic hoses crimped.
9. Stoppage in fluid pipes.
10. Pump pressure relief valve stuck.
11. Cylinder piston rod disconnected.
12. Broken port plate in pump.

Seat Operates Slowly

Note: Same as windows operating slowly upward or downward.

All Units Operate Slowly

1. Mechanical interference due to misalignment.
2. Electrical fault due to low battery.
3. Hydraulic fluid too heavy.
4. Pump pressure relief valve stuck.
5. Crimped fluid hoses.
6. Stoppage in fluid pipes.

Power Unit Inoperative on Any Control Switch

Note: When running, the power unit has a clearly audible whirring sound.
1. Battery low.
2. Wiring connections between ignition switch and solenoid relay switch loose, dirty or disconnected.

3. Circuit breaker inoperative.
4. Solenoid relay switch inoperative.
5. Power unit motor inoperative.

ELECTRIC TYPE FOR WINDOWS & SEATS

Note: In addition to the electrical troubles listed below, look for the same mechanical troubles given under the *Hydro-Lectric Type*.

Window Won't Operate from Main Switch Only

1. Broken wire between relay and remote switch.
2. Defective switch in master switch group.
3. Break in wire where it enters door opening.

Window Won't Operate from Main or Door Switch

1. Burned out motor or relay.
2. Defective circuit breaker.
3. Break in battery feed wire from starter solenoid to circuit breaker.

Window Operates In One Direction Only from Main or Door Switch

1. Defective relay.
2. Defective switch.
3. Broken ground wires.
4. Burned out motor.
5. Broken control wire.

Circuit Breaker In Door Clicks On and Off Continuously and Window Won't Operate

1. Control wire grounded.
2. Defective switch.
3. Relay points stuck.

Main Or Door Switch Operates Window In Wrong Direction

1. Lead wires are not connected to proper terminals.

Window Operates Sluggishly

1. Binding window regulator.
2. Broken wires or loose connections.
3. Worn motor brushes.

All Windows Do Not Operate

1. Circuit breaker open in control circuit.
2. Circuit breaker open in power circuit.

Seat Regulators Inoperative

1. Circuit breaker open in control circuit.

2. Circuit breaker open in power circuit.

One Seat Regulator Inoperative

1. Defective wiring between relay and circuit breaker.
2. Defective motor.
3. Defective wiring between switch and

circuit breaker.
4. Defective relay.

Seat Regulator Operates in One Direction Only

1. Defective wiring between switch and relay that applies to direction of travel desired.

2. Defective toggle switch.

Seat Regulator Operates Sluggishly

1. Binding mechanism.
2. Defective wiring.
3. Loose connectors or poor ground.
4. Worn or dirty brushes in motor.

Windshield Wiper Troubles

GENERAL INSPECTION

Before deciding that a windshield wiper needs servicing it might be well to consider some of the external factors which affect their operation.

It must be remembered that windshield wipers will operate more slowly when they do their work on dry glass. This is specially true on cars with curved windshields. You will also find that wiper blades may chatter or fail to travel a complete arc on dry glass. It is therefore obvious that any testing of windshield wiper operation should be done after the windshield has been sprayed with water.

Windshield wipers that chatter or do not wipe the glass clean under normal operating conditions (wet windshield) may need only replacement of the wiper arms or blades instead of more extensive service. This can be determined by visual inspection and most replacements can be made simply without the aid of any special tools.

Uneven movement of the wiper arms with respect to one another is usually caused by cables, pivots or cranks that are out of adjustment in the windshield wiper transmission system.

ELECTRIC TYPE

All passenger car electric windshield wiper circuits, regardless of manufacturer, include a control switch, a small shunt wound motor, and the wiring connecting these units to the battery. A circuit breaker or fuse may be mounted as a separate unit or incorporated in the control switch itself. A worm gear on the motor armature shaft drives one or two gears mounted on crankshafts for wiper operation.

A parking switch is mounted on the motor and actuated by a cam on one of the cranks. The parking switch, connected to the battery through a control switch, keeps the motor in operation for a brief period after the control switch has been shut off, allowing the wiper blades to return to the parked position.

Both single and multiple speed motors are used, the latter incorporating one or several resistors in the field circuit. The resistors may be located either in the parking switch housing or in the control switch.

In the following text you will find a list of the conditions you are likely to encounter when faced with a repair job on electric wipers. By consulting these

possibilities you will simplify the job of locating the source of trouble. But before going further a few words of caution are in order: After you have made your diagnosis and are ready to make repairs, disconnect the battery to avoid damage under the dash or possible personal injury from accidental shorts. Also, on models which use off-glass parking windshield wipers, never remove or disassemble the motor while in "park" position.

Wipers Won't Operate

1. Discharged battery.
2. Blown fuse or faulty circuit breaker.
3. No power to control switch.
4. Faulty control switch.
5. Faulty parking switch.
6. Binding pivots, cranks or linkages.
7. Poor connection at switch.
8. No ground at motor.
9. Faulty motor.

Wipers Won't Park

1. Incorrect adjustment of parking switch lever.
2. Open circuit in lead feeding parking switch.
3. Faulty parking switch.
4. Faulty control switch.
5. No ground at control switch (variable speed wipers).
6. Motor crank and parking switch improperly assembled.
7. Cams in linkage reversed or binding (variable speed wipers).

Wipers Operate Slowly

1. Discharged battery.
2. Binding pivots, cranks or linkages.
3. Faulty motor windings.
4. High resistance connections or wiring.
5. High resistance in control switch contacts.
6. No ground at control switch (variable speed wipers).
7. Faulty resistance unit (if only high speed is affected).
8. Dirty commutator or sticking brushes.
9. Worn or damaged motor.

Multiple Speed Wipers Operate Only at Single Speed

1. Short or open in motor wiring harness.
2. Incorrect connections at control switch.
3. Faulty control switch.

4. Faulty resistance unit.
5. No ground at control switch.
6. Open shunt field in motor.

VACUUM TYPE

For satisfactory windshield wiper operation, it is necessary to have an adequate supply of vacuum. On some cars the vacuum is made available by tapping directly into the intake manifold. With this type of arrangement it is considered normal for the wipers to slow down or stop entirely while going up a hill or during acceleration, since under those conditions the manifold vacuum would drop below the 8"-10" needed to operate the wipers. These conditions are almost completely eliminated on cars equipped with a vacuum booster pump. The purpose of this pump is to maintain enough vacuum to work the wipers under any driving condition.

Some of the conditions which prevent satisfactory windshield wiper operations are listed in the following text and may be used as a guide to help you locate the source of trouble. Always disconnect the battery when working under the dash.

Wipers Won't Operate

1. No vacuum supply to motor due to pinch, restriction or leak in the windshield wiper hose. A vacuum leak or a disconnected hose can easily be located because a hissing sound will be heard whenever the engine is running.
2. Faulty vacuum booster pump.
3. Wiper control switch inoperative or disconnected at motor.
4. Faulty wiper motor.
5. Frozen or binding pivots and linkages.
6. Linkages or cables improperly installed.

Wipers Operate Slowly

1. Low vacuum due to pinch or partial restriction in the wiper hose.
2. Loss of vacuum due to leaks at joints, fittings or in the wiper hose itself.
3. Faulty vacuum booster pump.
4. Faulty wiper motor.
5. Wiper control switch does not move operating valve on the motor to full "ON" position due to improper adjustment.
6. Air intake on motor (breather port) clogged.
7. Binding pivots, cranks, linkages or

binding or frozen idler pulleys on cable tensioners.

8. Cables adjusted too tight.

Wipers Won't Park
1. Faulty parking valve on motor.
2. Wiper control switch out of adjust-

ment.

3. Wiper arms not positioned properly on pivots.

TUNE UP

SATISFACTORY performance of modern engines requires scientific testing equipment in order to restore the engine to the original condition in which it operated when new. In conjunction with this testing equipment, the manufacturer's specifications should be closely followed when making all necessary adjustments in order to obtain smooth performance of the engine with economical results.

The fundamentals of engine tune up are (1) compression, (2) ignition, (3) carburetion. Since compression does not depend in any way upon either ignition or carburetion, it should be checked first.

COMPRESSION

The engine cannot be tuned to develop maximum power and give smooth performance unless normal compression pressure is obtained in each cylinder on every compression stroke. In order to have uniform and maximum compression, the following conditions must be present:
1. Cylinder head bolts must be uniformly tight.
2. Cylinder head and spark plug gaskets must seal securely.
3. Piston rings must seal properly throughout the entire piston stroke.
4. Intake and exhaust valves must be properly adjusted and must seat tightly.

Cylinder Head Bolts

On overhead valve engines, cylinder head bolts not tightened sufficiently will cause changes in valve lash and may permit leakage past the gasket. And on all type engines, uneven or excessively tightened bolts may distort the cylinder bores, causing compression loss and excessive oil consumption.

Tighten all cylinder head bolts to the values given in the *Tune Up* chart in the car chapters, using a torque wrench to compress the head gasket evenly and avoid distortion of head and cylinder bores. The bolts should be tightened in the sequence shown in the illustrations in the car chapters. If no diagram is given, start tightening at the center and work from side to side outward toward the ends.

Installing Spark Plugs

When installing either new or used spark plugs, always blow away dirt from around plug holes, and use new gaskets to insure tight seals without excessive tightening. Excessive tightening may change the gap between electrodes and may crack the insulator.

Make sure the gasket surfaces on spark plugs and cylinder head are clean. Screw the plugs down by hand into firm contact with the gaskets, then tighten them ¼ turn more.

Valve Adjustment

Oil, water and engine temperatures must be stabilized or brought to normal operating temperatures before the valves can be properly adjusted for normal lash. This applies to all engines where the manufacturer specifies that the lash should be adjusted when the engine is warm. Some car companies, Studebaker for example, recommend that the adjustment be made when the engine is cold, which means at normal room temperature.

When an engine is warmed up by running without load in the shop, the oil, water and engine temperatures level off at different points than those obtained on the road; therefore, a wider lash adjustment is required. Thus, if the manufacturer specifies a *road operating clearance* of .015 inch, best results will be obtained by setting the lash at .017 inch if the engine is warmed up in the shop. Of course, if the adjustment is being made after the car has made a hard run on the road, the clearance of .015 inch should be adhered to.

Some car companies recommend an additional .002 inch clearance for exhaust valves on cars that are operated continuously at high speeds.

COMPRESSION TESTS FOR LEAKY CYLINDERS

In using a compression gauge the location of the combustion chamber must be taken into consideration. Except for the new engines introduced in 1958 in which the combustion chamber is formed in the block, all other engines have the combustion chamber in the cylinder head. When checking pressure on engines with cylinder head combustion chambers, it must be realized that the compression pressures in the cylinders in such an engine in perfect condition are not uniform. Car company engineers will tell you that the pressures in the different cylinders of an engine may vary up to 20 lbs. The variation in pressure in some makes of engines is small and large in others. The variation is due principally to lack of uniformity in combustion chamber volumes since it is impossible to make all the combustion chambers in a cylinder head exactly the same size.

In a given engine with a 7 to 1 compression ratio with all combustion chambers the same volume, the compression pressure might be about 120 lbs. However, if the combustion chamber is ⅓ cubic inch too small the pressure will be 126 lbs. and if ⅓ cubic inch too large it will be 114 lbs. This is a variation of 12 lbs.

In the new engines introduced in 1958, this variation is largely eliminated because the underside of the cylinder head is flat except for slight recesses which provide for valves and spark plugs. And inasmuch as the combustion chamber which is formed in the block and piston head forms a smooth machined surface, combustion chamber volumes are naturally more uniform and, therefore, not subject to possible variations as are cast cylinder head combustion chambers.

Compression Pressures and Ratios

Just to satisfy the reader's curiosity, below is a table showing the approximate relationship between compression ratio and compression pressure at cranking speeds:—

Ratio	Pressure
6.5	110
7.0	120
7.5	130
8.0	140

Various design factors affect the compression pressure. Therefore this table may apply to some engines but not to all. Note also that a carbon deposit will raise the compression pressure at any given ratio by reducing the combustion chamber volume. The greater the deposit the higher the pressure.

Compression Gauge Accuracy

However, even if a table such as this could be trusted, there is the question of gauge accuracy. A gauge passes inspection at the factory if it is not more than 2 pounds high or low when the pressure is 100 pounds. Thus there is a possible error of as much as 4 pounds to begin with (98 to 102) although of course some of the gauges will be almost perfectly accurate.

But even if the gauge is accurate when made it is not likely to remain so. It is a delicate instrument and the first time it is dropped it may read 5 pounds too high or too low.

How to Use Compression Gauge

A compression test should be made with all the spark plugs out. When this is done it is unnecessary to remove the air cleaner or to hold the throttle open because there are always two or more intake valves open when the engine is being cranked and the engine consequently gets ample air at cranking speed without opening the throttle or removing the air cleaner.

Get the Maximum Reading

When testing the compression of a cylinder, hold the gauge in place until the hand reaches a maximum reading, even though this may require cranking the engine through 10 revolutions or so. The pressure in the curved tube within the gauge builds up slowly because the compressed air must pass through a small orifice at the entrance to the tube. Without this orifice, the gauge would be damaged by the sudden application of high pressure.

Precaution with Oil Test

Note that if a compression test is made after putting oil in the cylinder to seal the rings, the compression reading may be much too high because the oil reduces the volume of the combustion chamber. When taking this test, the gauge will first reach a maximum reading. Then keep on cranking until the hand falls to a steady position.

Bad Cylinder Is 25 Pounds Low

If any cylinder in an engine is 25 pounds (or more) lower than the highest cylinder it is probable that the valves in that cylinder are leaking. It does not make any difference whether this test is made with engine warm or cold.

It is a mistake to assume that a cylinder which is 5 to 10 pounds lower than the highest has leaky valves because, as previously stated, the variation with tight valves may be much more than 10 pounds.

A Test for Leaky Cylinders

A positive method is to apply air pressure to the cylinders one by one and then listen for leakage. This is an old and tried method although not well known. Remove the porcelain from an old spark plug shell and install a tire valve in the shell by brazing.

Remove all spark plugs in the engine. Bring No. 1 piston up to top dead center on the compression stroke. Screw the device just described into the spark plug hole. Apply air pressure. If necessary have an assistant hold the air chuck on the valve throughout the test.

The piston must not move from its top dead center position while making test with air pressure. It won't move if the crankpin is within about 5 degrees before or after top dead center. The fact that it is not necessary to have the piston exactly on center will speed up the work.

When the air is applied, listen for a hiss:—

1. At the muffler tail pipe for a leaking exhaust valve.
2. At the air cleaner for a leaking intake valve.
3. At the oil filler opening for leaking rings.
4. Remove the filler cap on the radiator and look for bubbles which indicate a leaking cylinder head gasket.

Bring No. 2 piston up to top dead center on the compression stroke and repeat the tests—and so on for the other cylinders.

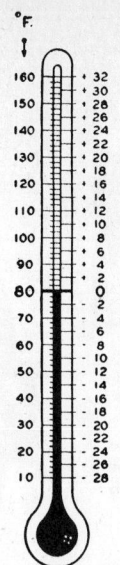

°F.

IGNITION PRIMARY CIRCUIT

Battery

Since the battery is the source of all electrical energy, its efficiency must first be checked, since starting and idle performance are always poor if the battery and its connections are not up to standard. Besides, a low or defective battery will cause inaccuracies in any tests to the starter, generator or ignition systems.

Specific gravity of the electrolyte must be tested *before adding water* as water does not mix immediately and a true reading will not be obtained.

When a hydrometer is used for testing the condition of a battery, a correction must be made for the temperature of the electrolyte, because hydrometer readings are correct only when the electrolyte is at 80 deg. F. For each 5 deg. *decrease* below 80 deg. the specific gravity *lowers* 2 points (.002) of gravity. Likewise, for each 5 deg. *increase* above 80 deg. the specific gravity *rises* .002.

Take the temperature of the electrolyte in each cell with a thermometer. Take the specific gravity of the electrolyte in each cell with a hydrometer. Ob-

tain the actual specific gravity by changing the hydrometer reading by the amount shown on the right side of the scale, Fig. 1, opposite the temperature of the electrolyte. For example, if the temperature of the electrolyte is 60 deg., and the hydrometer reading is 1.290, the actual specific gravity is 1.282 because the correction at 60 deg. is .008 (1.290 minus .008 equals 1.282).

A battery in good condition should have specific gravity of not less than 1.250 in seasons when freezing of water may occur, or 1.235 in seasons when freezing of water is unlikely. The battery must be recharged if the specific gravity is less than the above values.

Add pure distilled water to bring level of electrolyte to ¼ inch above the plates in each cell. Do not fill higher as the electrolyte may overflow and cause damage. Turn filler caps down finger tight.

Battery Cables & Terminals

Inspect the battery cable and ground strap for broken insulation, corroded or broken strands, and loose or corroded terminals.

Repair broken or chafed insulation with loom or tape. If cable strands are broken, corroded, or loose in the terminals, the cables should be replaced, being sure the new cable has ample capacity to carry the current.

Since loose terminals are usually corroded, disconnect loose terminals and thoroughly clean contact surfaces by scraping until bright or by washing with a strong soda solution. Coat cleaned contact surfaces of battery post and terminal with vaseline to retard corrosion. Connect the terminal and tighten securely.

Starter Circuit

A voltmeter should be used to determine the condition of the starter circuit under actual operation.

On cars that cannot be cranked with the starter without turning on the ignition, ground the distributor primary terminal to prevent the spark plugs from firing.

Attach the negative voltmeter test lead to the engine for the ground connection, and the positive lead to the starting motor switch, where the cable from the battery fastens, for the positive connection. (This hook-up is used when the negative post of the battery is

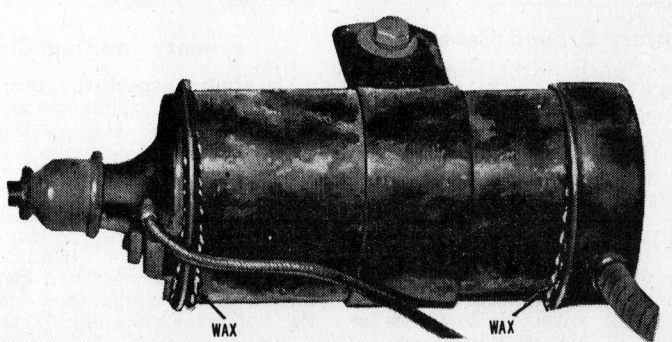

WAX   WAX

Fig. 2 **Example of wax leaking from ignition coil. This does not necessarily mean the coil is bad as it may be due to an abnormal heat condition which melted the wax but did not effect the coil's internal structure**

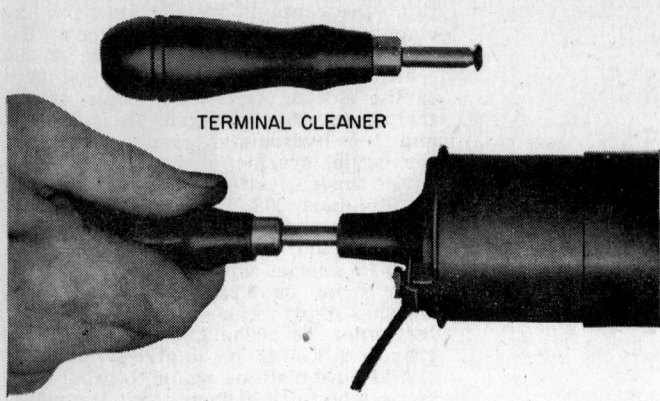

TERMINAL CLEANER

Fig. 3 Cleaning high tension terminal socket of coil with special cleaner made for the purpose. This tool is also used for cleaning out distributor cap cable sockets. Sandpaper wrapped around a pencil will also do an adequate job

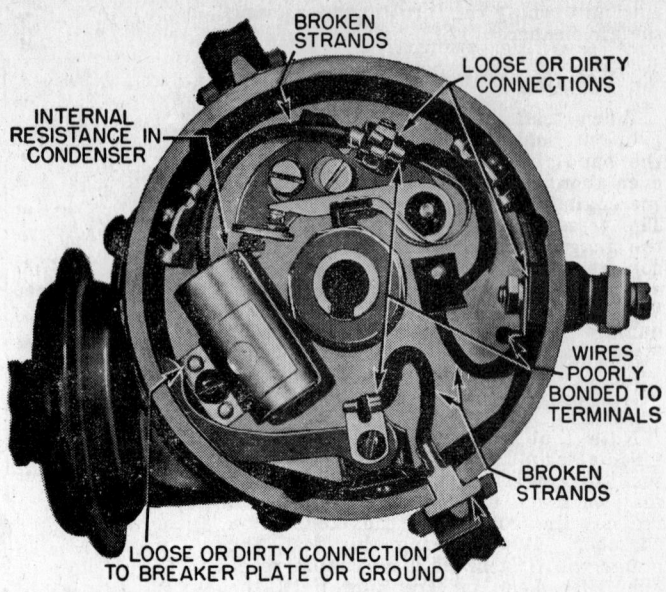

BROKEN STRANDS

LOOSE OR DIRTY CONNECTIONS

INTERNAL RESISTANCE IN CONDENSER

WIRES POORLY BONDED TO TERMINALS

BROKEN STRANDS

LOOSE OR DIRTY CONNECTION TO BREAKER PLATE OR GROUND

Fig. 4 What to look for when checking for high resistance in the primary circuit of the distributor. In addition to the points indicated, look for external circuit high resistance at ignition switch terminals, ammeter terminals, coil terminals and broken or poorly insulated wires in this circuit

grounded; reverse the connections if the opposite is true.)

By cranking the engine with the starter, a discharge load will be put on the starter circuit. If the starter turns the engine at a good rate of speed, the average voltage reading should be between 4½ to 5 volts (double for 12-volt) for a normal operating circuit.

When the starting switch is closed, the starter should crank the engine for 15 seconds, during which the normal voltage reading should be 4½ to 5 volts (double for 12-volt) without any appreciable drop because of the drain on the battery. If the circuit meets the demands for this test, further tests are unnecessary; if not, further testing is required.

Starter Solenoid Switch Test

Connect the voltmeter positive lead to the positive terminal on the solenoid switch. Turn on the ignition and crank the engine for 15 seconds while observing voltmeter reading. If the voltmeter reads more than 1/10th volt, the switch should be repaired or replaced.

Battery Cable Test

Connect the positive voltmeter test lead to the positive battery post and the negative test lead to the battery cable terminal on the starter switch. Crank the engine for 15 seconds while observing the voltmeter reading. If the reading is more than 2/10s of a volt, recheck for loose or dirty terminals. If terminals are clean and tight, replace the cable.

Battery Ground Cable

This test is made in the same manner as the battery cable test except that the negative voltmeter lead should be connected to the engine (or transmission) terminal of the ground cable or strap, and the positive voltmeter lead connected to the negative battery post.

Generator

The tune up job will not remain satisfactory for an extended period of service if the generator output is low because the battery will soon fall below a safe state of charge and ignition then will be starved when the total current draw is heavy.

Remove the cover band and carefully inspect the interior of the generator for (1) worn, rough, or dirty commutator; (2) high mica between commutator segments; (3) thrown solder, which indicates loose connections between the armature windings and commutator segments. These conditions will cause low generator output.

On generators not having a cover band, the unit may be accessible enough to make an inspection with the aid of a mirror; otherwise the generator will have to be disassembled to make the inspection.

If the commutator is in good condition but dirty, clean off all grease with a cloth soaked with cleaning fluid. Then polish the commutator with a strip of fine sandpaper placed over a wooden block having a smooth, square end. Carefully blow out all dust and replace the cover band.

If inspection indicates that the armature requires turning down and undercutting of the mica, this should be done.

Tighten all wiring connections at the generator, regulator, and ammeter.

Primary Ignition Circuit

Carefully inspect the terminals, connections, and visible portions of the following wires: (1) Starter switch to ammeter; (2) ammeter to ignition switch; (3) ignition coil to terminal on distributor housing.

The wires must be securely attached to the terminals and the insulation must be in good condition. If any connections are loose, disconnect and clean the terminals thoroughly, then connect and tighten securely. Turn the ignition switch on and off a few times to be certain it is making positive contact.

Faulty ignition coil operation can be caused by moisture, grease or dirt on

the outside shell. Wax leaking to the outside of the coil, Fig. 2, does not indicate that the coil is defective; it may have been caused by an abnormal heat condition which did not affect the internal structure of the coil.

The high tension terminal socket may be corroded as a result of arcing caused by previous failure to insert properly the end of the cable into the socket. Corrosion also may develop in sea coast areas due to salt air.

Any corrosion will cause resistance to the flow of current. Therefore, the socket should be thoroughly cleaned out with a terminal cleaner, sandpaper or a stiff wire brush, and cable terminal should be cleaned with sandpaper.

All parts of the distributor which affect the primary circuit must be inspected and tested, and worn and defective parts must be replaced to insure satisfactory ignition.

The contact points may be cleaned and adjusted without removing the distributor, but if the interior is dirty or saturated with oil, or new parts are to be installed, the distributor should be removed from the engine.

Centrifugal Advance

This mechanism must operate freely and the springs must return the advance weights to the full retard position during idle speed operation.

Sticking advance weights will result in poor acceleration, whereas weak springs will cause a too rapid spark advance, causing the engine to ping, resulting in engine roughness and a decrease in gasoline economy. Sticking weights can be cleaned but weak springs must be replaced.

To test the action of the weights, turn the rotor in the direction required to advance the weights to their fully extended position. Then release the rotor and allow the springs to return the weights to retard position—which will be indicated by a metallic click when the weights strike the stop.

Vacuum Advance

This unit may be inoperative due to a broken diaphragm or spring. To determine whether this condition exists, crank the engine with the starter and hold the choke closed and throttle open. If the distributor plate will advance and return, the parts are not broken. But the breaker plate will not advance if the diaphragm is broken. If it advances but does not return, the spring is broken.

A leak at the vacuum advance connection will allow excess air to enter the carburetor, which may result in poor gasoline economy through fixed throttle intermediate speeds because of incorrect operation of the vacuum advance mechanism.

If the pigtail leads are broken at any point, or if the distributor housing is worn so that the breaker plate can shift sidewise as it is oscillated by the vacuum advance mechanism, the ignition will be erratic enough to cause flat spots or ignition miss. This condition will usually occur at idle speed or up to 15 m.p.h.

To detect this trouble, disconnect the vacuum line at the distributor. If the trouble disappears, test the pigtail leads, and also check the groove in the distributor housing where the breaker plate "floats."

Condenser

There are several good condenser testers commercially available and when making tests, the condenser must be at normal operating temperature.

The resistance test, measured in microhms, is to determine if there is a high series resistance in the condenser circuit caused by the conditions shown in Fig. 3.

The capacity test, measured in microfarads, is to determine if the condenser capacity is actually within specification limits.

The insulation test, measured in megohms, is to determine if the condenser insulation will hold a charge satisfactorily.

Breaker Points

Carefully examine the points for burns, pits, dirt, and see that they are not sticking on the pivot. Check to see that they are properly spaced and have the correct spring tension. Point spring tension too weak or too strong will limit high speed performance, either by the point "floating", which is due to a weak spring, or "bouncing", which is caused by a spring with too much tension. Consult the *Distributor Specifications* tables in the car chapters for the correct spring tension and the *Ignition* chapter for method of measuring same.

Breaker points in service for some time will appear dull and gray. This condition is normal, and points should not be replaced or filed if full contact of the mating surfaces is obtained.

If points do not meet squarely, align the contact surfaces by bending the contact arm.

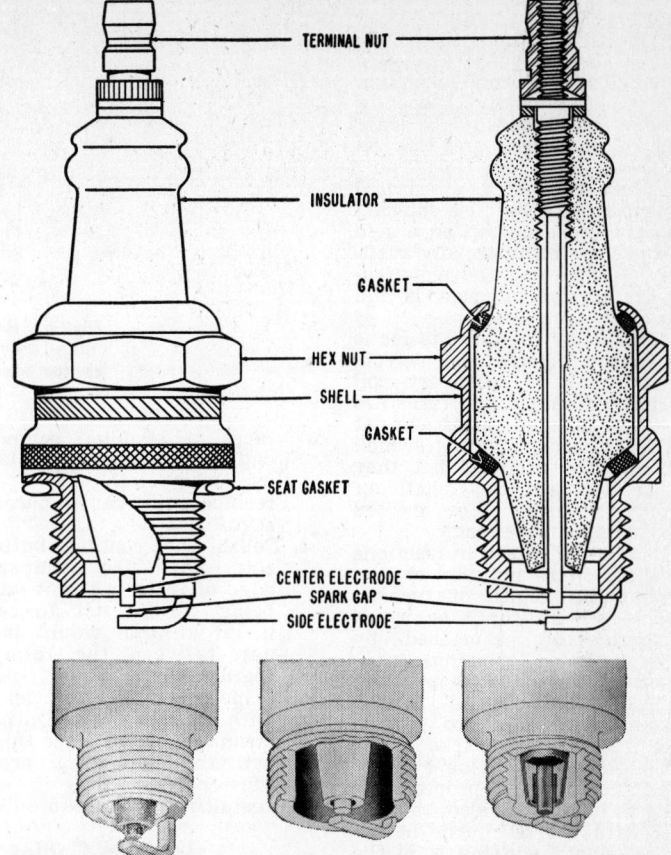

DEPOSIT FORMATION IS RETARDED BY HIGHER OPERATING TEMPERATURE OF THIS PROTRUDING-TIP PLUG. COOL INCOMING MIXTURE PREVENTS OVERHEATING AT HIGH SPEED

FUEL CHARGE CAN CIRCULATE MORE FREELY BETWEEN TIP AND SHELL OF THIS PLUG DUE TO GREATER CLEARANCE. DEPOSITS MUST COLLECT OVER WIDER AREA TO CAUSE FOULING

A THIRD PLUG HAS RECESSED TIP FOR LONGER FOULING PATH. QUICK WARM-UP OF TIP PREVENTS BUILD-UP OF DEPOSITS DURING LOW SPEED OPERATION

Fig. 5 Typical spark plugs

Delco-Remy recommends that points that are blackened or slightly burned or pitted may be cleaned with a special stone or a clean point file. Auto-Lite, on the other hand, claim that their points are so hard that they should never be filed because minute pieces of file are broken off and imbed themselves in the contact surfaces, causing greater concentration of heat and welding of the steel to the contacts.

In filing points, remove the high spots only — it is not necessary to remove all traces of build-up or pit. Do not use emery cloth or sandpaper to clean points as the residue left on the points causes them to burn.

Excessively burned, pitted or worn points cannot be cleaned up and aligned satisfactorily. Therefore, they must be replaced to insure good ignition.

Resistance Test Through Primary Circuit

Any abnormal resistance in the primary circuit of the distributor may be tested with a low-reading voltmeter. To do this, remove the distributor cap and turn over the engine until the breaker arm rubbing block is midway between any two cam lobes, which closes points.

Connect the positive voltmeter lead to the distributor primary terminal, and the negative lead to ground on the engine. With ignition switch on, a reading of more than 1/10th of a volt indicates abnormal resistance at some point in the circuit.

Locate the source of any abnormal resistance by progressively eliminating parts of the circuit, Figs. 3 and 4, noting the result on the voltmeter. To do this, unclip the test lead from the primary terminal and connect it successively to all terminals and connections.

Source of resistance can be caused by dirty or corroded points, bad points, poor contact between the breaker plate and distributor housing, and between housing and engine. Remove the source of resistance by cleaning and tightening loose or corroded connections, or by replacement of parts as required.

For a description of ignition coil resistors used with 12-volt systems, see the *Ignition Systems* Chapter.

IGNITION SECONDARY CIRCUIT

This circuit consists of the coil, high tension wires, rotor, distributor cap and spark plugs.

Coil

The ignition coil terminals should be inspected to be sure they are tight and in good condition, the coil insulation checked for burned or chipped places or cracks, the coil case checked for loose seams, dents or punctures, and the coil tested electrically.

The coil must be tested at normal operating temperature because internal defects often fail to show up on a cold test. Coil testers are commercially available for this purpose and the manufacturers of such equipment provide full instructions as to their use.

The high frequency type coil tester is valuable in that it detects such defects as shorted primary or secondary coil turns, especially if only a few turns are shorted. A few shorted turns do not markedly affect the peak voltage which an ignition coil can produce, but they will seriously decrease the length of time each spark lasts, since shorted turns have a dampening effect.

In other words, the length in fractions of an inch of the spark may not change noticeably, but the length of time in fractions of a second that the spark lasts is considerably shortened by shorted turns in the coil windings.

Thus, a coil with shorted turns, while it could produce sparks of normal length, might not be able to provide good ignition because the sparks do not last long enough in the engine cylinder to ignite the fuel mixture properly.

It must be remembered, also, that an ignition coil with shorted turns in the primary or secondary winding is on the road to failure, since these shorted turns tend to overheat the coil, causing additional turns to become shorted. Finally, enough turns are shorted to cause complete coil failure. The high frequency coil tester, therefore, serves to detect ignition coils that are still good enough to operate the engine, but will very likely soon fail—possibly on the road.

Distributor Cap & Rotor

Corrosion in the terminal sockets and on the segments of the distributor cap, or on the contact button and segment of the rotor, will cause high resistance in the secondary circuit and a weak spark at the plugs.

Widening of the gap between the rotor and cap segments, due to burning of these parts, will also cause high resistance. If they cannot be cleaned satisfactorily or if they are burned excessively, they should be replaced, using the following procedure:

1. Mark the location of the No. 1 cable on the distributor cap, remove the cap from the distributor and pull the cables from the cap.
2. Thoroughly inspect the cap for cracks and for carbon streaks caused by arcing of current between segments through moisture on the cap. Discard the cap if damaged or cracked. Remove carbon streaks by polishing with fine sandpaper and coating the cleaned area with distributor varnish.
3. Clean the inside of the cap terminal sockets, using sandpaper or a brush made for the purpose. Blow all dust out of sockets.
4. Clean corrosion from contact sur-

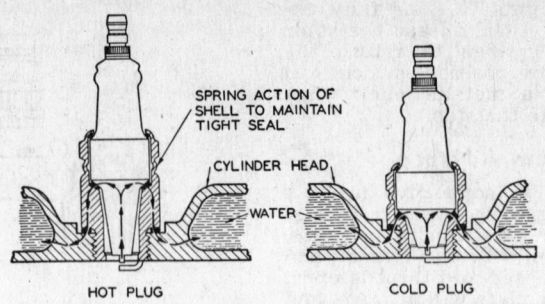

SPRING ACTION OF SHELL TO MAINTAIN TIGHT SEAL

CYLINDER HEAD

WATER

HOT PLUG   COLD PLUG

Fig. 6 Heat range of spark plug is determined by the distance heat must travel from the center electrode to the cylinder head coolant.

faces of terminal segments inside cap by scraping with a knife. Don't use emery cloth or sandpaper as the residue may cause burning of the segments.
5. Polish the contact button of the rotor with fine sandpaper. Clean edge of rotor segment with a knife, being careful not to remove any metal as this would increase the gap between the rotor and cap segments.
6. Wipe rotor and cap clean, and dry with a clean cloth. Do not wash in cleaning solvent since this will damage the insulating properties of these parts.
7. Install rotor and cap on distributor.

Ignition Cables

Cracked, swollen or deteriorated cable insulation permits leakage of high voltage current, which causes weak sparks and loss of power. Such cables should be replaced, but be sure the new cables have ample current carrying capacity. It is advisable to install a complete new set, since the old cables will be deteriorated to about the same extent.

Wipe the cables with cloth moistened with kerosene. Bend the cables to check for cracks or loose or swollen insulation. Thoroughly inspect the terminals for corrosion, looseness or poor contact with wire strands.

If the cables are in good condition, clean any terminals that are corroded, and replace any terminals that are broken or distorted. Replace any broken or deteriorated rubber nipples.

Wash all oil out of recesses around spark plugs with kerosene or other solvent and blow out with air to dry thoroughly. Then install the cables in the following manner:

Starting with No. 1 cable in terminal socket previously marked for No. 1, install the cables in the distributor cap according to the firing order of the engine. If the distributor operates clockwise, install the cables in the distributor cap clockwise; if counter-clockwise, install cables thus. Push the ends of all cables into the terminal sockets.

Push rubber nipples (if equipped) down into place to seal the connections against entrance of moisture, which would cause corrosion of terminals. If the nipples grip the cables too close to the end so that they buckle when installed, they may pull the cables partially out of the sockets and cause arc-

ing and corrosion.

Some cars have ignition cables with carbon cores instead of copper. This type of cable acts as a suppressor for radio interference. Extra care should be taken when handling this type of cable since the carbon cores are easily damaged by stretching or kinking.

Spark Plugs

Under normal operating conditions, spark plugs, Fig. 5, must be cleaned and adjusted every 3,000 to 5,000 miles. Ignition failure may result from using spark plugs too long before cleaning, or the space between shell and insulator may become so tightly packed with carbon or lead oxide deposits that proper cleaning is impossible.

Carbon or oxide deposits are conductors of electricity and may cause intermittent or steady missing, particularly at high speeds and on hard pulls.

Formation of hard carbon or oxide deposits on spark plugs is a normal operating condition, since they are products of combustion resulting from burning of the fuel. The hard carbon is usually black or gray, while the lead oxide deposits may be red, brown or yellow. Both may be accompanied by blistered spots on the insulator.

Slow speed driving during the new car "break-in" period, combined with oil leakage past the rings before they are worn to a good seat, may cause formation of soft carbon in the inner end of the spark plugs. Therefore, it is usually necessary to clean the plugs at the 1,000 and 2,000 mile inspection periods.

Excessive carbon formation after the "break-in" period may be caused by an over-rich carburetor or choke, faulty ignition, worn or scored piston rings, or by continuous slow speed driving. If slow speed driving is the cause, it is advisable to install a "hotter" plug.

If the car is driven continuously at high speeds the engine may operate better and give longer spark plug life with a "colder" plug.

Spark plug manufacturers provide for these conditions of continuous slow or high speed driving by making plugs with longer insulators for use in slow speed driving and shorter insulators for high speed driving, Fig. 6.

When removing or replacing spark plugs, use a wrench which fits the plug snugly. An oversize or worn wrench may distort the spark plug shell and crack

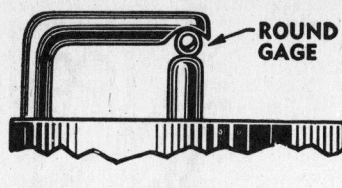

RIGHT

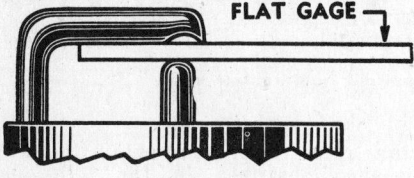

WRONG

Fig. 7 Correct and incorrect spark plug gauges

the insulator. If a socket wrench is allowed to press against the outer end of the plug, the insulator will be cracked or broken.

Carefully inspect the insulators and electrodes of all spark plugs. Replace any plug which has a cracked or broken insulator, or with loose electrodes. If the insulator is worn away around the center electrode, or if the electrodes are burned or worn so they cannot be adjusted for proper gap, the plug is worn out and should be discarded.

Never use resistor type spark plugs with carbon core resistor ignition cables.

Plugs which are in good condition except for carbon or oxide deposits should be thoroughly cleaned and adjusted.

To clean plugs, soak them in a carburetor cleaning solvent from 15 to 30 minutes. Thoroughly dry the interior of plugs with compressed air, then scrape out all carbon and oxide deposits from the shells and insulators with a pointed steel scraper. Blow out all scrapings and use sand-blasting equipment to complete the job. Manufacturers of sand blasters furnish complete instructions as to their use.

When adjusting spark plugs, use a round wire feeler gauge of the diameter specified by the manufacturer and as listed in the *Tune Up* chart in the car chapter. Flat feeler gauges will not give the correct measurement if the electrodes are worn (see Fig. 7). Adjust the gap by bending the side electrode only; bending the center electrode will crack the insulator.

Before installing a spark plug, make sure that the spark plug seat in the cylinder head is clean and free from obstructions. It is strongly recommended that a new seat gasket be used each time a plug is installed because the old gasket has been flattened and very likely will not provide the proper seal if used again. The plug should be screwed into the cylinder head to fully compress the gasket. The following is the recommended procedure for installing spark plugs:

1. Adjust the electrode gap according to specifications (see *Tune Up Data* in each car chapter).
2. Thoroughly clean the cylinder head gasket seating surface.

3. Screw the spark plug in by hand as far as it will go.
4. Carefully fit a socket of the correct size over the plug and pull on the wrench very lightly until you feel contact with the seat gasket.
5. Slowly increase the pull on the wrench until the resistance to pull suddenly becomes very great, indicating that the seat gasket has been fully compressed.

CAUTION—The smaller the size of the plug the less pull on the wrench handle is required to fully compress the seat gasket. For instance, a 14 MM plug requires less pull on the wrench handle than a ⅞″ plug. This is particularly important in the case of 10 MM plugs where only just enough pull should be exercised on the wrench to compress the seat gasket. To avoid the possibility of damage to the plug, use a wrench handle not over 4″ long when installing 10 MM plugs.

Installation of plugs in aluminum heads require particular care, as there is danger of stripping the threads in the cylinder head. Do not use graphite or other lubricating compounds on the threads as lubricants will retard heat transfer by separating the metal of the threads and reduce friction between the threads which may result in stripping the threads in the cylinder head. Spark plugs in aluminum heads should be tightened while the engine is cool. With cast iron heads, tighten the plugs while the engine is at normal operating temperature.

For most satisfactory results when using a torque wrench, refer to specifications given in the car chapters for proper torque.

Ignition Timing

The use of a timing light, Fig. 8, is recommended for checking and setting ignition timing. Timing that is set back as much as six degrees from the best setting will definitely decrease acceleration and top speed performance. See the car chapters for ignition timing details.

CARBURETION

Since carburetion is dependent in several ways on both compression and ignition, it should always be checked last when tuning an engine. See the *Carburetor* chapter for adjustments for the unit you are interested in.

Before adjusting the carburetor, consider the factors outlined below and which definitely affect engine performance.

Carburetor Flange

Check the flange for looseness on the manifold. If one of the flange nuts is loose as little as one-half turn, a sufficient amount of air will enter the intake manifold below the throttle plate to destroy engine idle and all engine performance.

If a tight fit cannot be obtained by tightening the nuts, install a new gasket but be sure that all the old gasket material has been removed.

Throttle Linkage

If the throttle linkage is adjusted so that the accelerator pedal will strike the floor board before the throttle plate is wide open, it will result in low top speed.

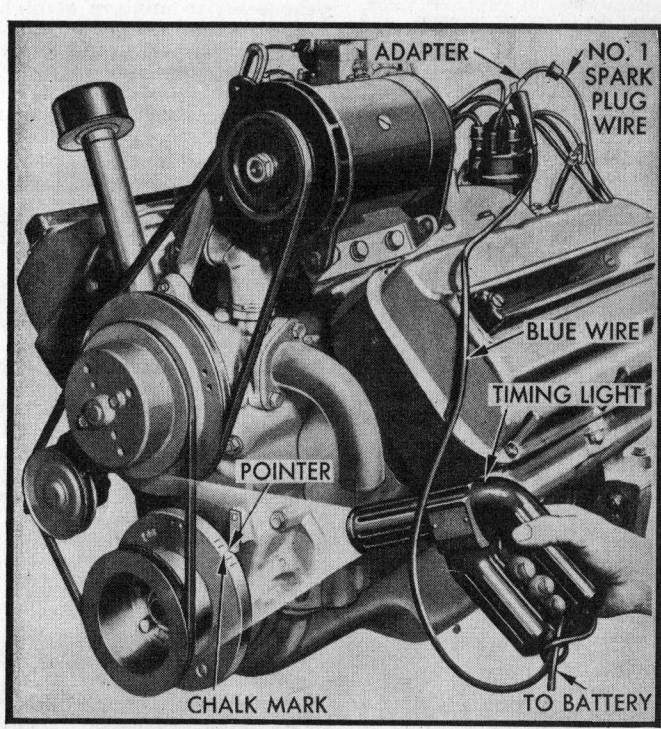

Fig. 8 Checking ignition timing with timing light

Fuel Lines

A restriction of the fuel line will result in an apparent vapor lock action or a definite cut-off of gasoline. This can generally be corrected by blowing out the line with compressed air. In some cases, it may be necessary to replace the line.

Fuel Pump

The pump should be tested to make sure that it will draw an adequate supply of fuel from the tank and deliver it to the carburetor under all conditions of operation. If the pump functions inefficiently, proper adjustment and operation of the carburetor is impossible because the fuel will not be maintained at the prescribed level in the idle passages and main discharge jet (or jets) of the carburetor under all operating conditions.

Fuel Tank

The fuel tank should not be overlooked as a possible source of trouble with carburetion. A shortage of fuel at the fuel pump or carburetor may be caused by pieces of filling station pump hose or other material obstructing the mouth of the feed pipe in the tank, or by a restriction of the air vents in the filler cap and neck.

An unusual amount of dirt, water or gum in the fuel filter indicates that the tank is contaminated with these substances, which should be cleaned out to prevent future failure of the pump or carburetor.

Heat Control Valve

The heat control valve performs an important function in carburetion during the warm-up period, Fig. 9. Carbon or rust formation around the shaft may cause the valve to stick or become sluggish in operation.

A valve sticking in the open position will cause slow engine warm-up, excessive spitting and sluggish engine operation when cold. A valve sticking in the closed position will cause overheating, loss of power and hard starting when the engine is hot, and may also cause warped or cracked manifolds. Sticking in either position* will adversely affect fuel economy.

Grasp the counterweight and rotate the valve through its entire range. The valve must rotate freely and the shaft must have a slight end play. If the shaft is frozen in the manifold, free it up by gently tapping on the ends with a light hammer, and by rotating the counterweight at the same time.

Lubricate the shaft with a thin mixture of powdered graphite and alcohol or kerosene while moving the counterweight back and forth to work the lubricant into the bearings. *Do not use oil as this will form carbon and cause sticking of the valve.*

Inspect the thermostat and the anti-rattle spring to make sure they are properly assembled.

Intake Manifold Leaks

Leakage of air into the intake manifold at any point will affect carburetion

 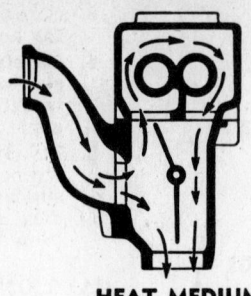 

HEAT ON **HEAT MEDIUM** **HEAT OFF**

Fig. 9 Operation of a typical manifold heat control valve

and general engine performance. Air may leak into the manifold through the joints at the carburetor or cylinder head, cracks in the manifold, cracks or poor connections in the windshield wiper or windshield washer hose lines, or the connections of any accessories which may be connected to the manifold. All such joints should be tested for leaks.

To test the intake manifold for leaks, apply oil from an oil can along the gasket joints with the engine idling. An air leak is indicated when oil is drawn past the gaskets by the suction of the engine. Tighten the nuts or cap screws holding the manifold to the engine and retest for leaks. If tightening fails to stop the leaks, replace the manifold gaskets. If the new gaskets fail to stop the leaks, carefully inspect the manifold for cracks and test any suspicious area with oil.

Air Cleaner

An air cleaner with a dirty element, or with oil that is dirty, too heavy, or too high in the sump, will restrict the air flow through the carburetor and cause a rich mixture at high speeds. In such a condition the air cleaner likewise will not properly remove dirt from the air, and the dirt entering the engine will cause rapid formation of carbon, sticking valves, and wear of piston rings and cylinder bores.

Automatic Choke

The choke mechanism must be inspected and cleaned to make sure it is operating freely. Sluggish action or sticking of the choke will cause excessive fuel consumption, poor performance during warm-up, and possibly hard starting.

The choke thermostat should be set in accordance with the average air temperature as well as the volatility of the fuel being used. It is desirable to have the thermostat set as lean as operating conditions permit in order to avoid an over-rich mixture during engine warm up.

PERFORMANCE TEST

After an engine has been tuned up, the car should be given a thorough and systematic road test to make certain that engine power and performance are up to standard under all operating conditions. The gasoline used in making the test must be of good quality and proper octane rating in order to obtain the performance described in the following tests.

Engine Warm Up

On cars with automatic chokes, a cold engine should operate on fast idle for two to five minutes, depending upon air temperature.

At 32 deg. F. the fast idle cam should move to the slow idle position in approximately ½ to ¾ mile of driving. At higher temperatures, it should move to the slow idle position in a correspondingly shorter distance.

If the engine loads excessively or runs rich on warm up due to a rich choke setting, excessive fuel consumption, carbon formation, and spark plug fouling will result.

An engine which is adjusted for smooth idling in cold outside temperature will not idle smoothly for any length of time in a warm building, since the required carburetor adjustment will cause richness of mixture in the warmer atmosphere.

Gradual Acceleration Test

Starting at idling speed in high gear, gradually open the throttle to increase smoothly the speed of the car through the entire range. Note any roughness, flat spots, or surging in engine performance during acceleration, and the speed at which the unusual condition occurs.

Roughness or poor performance at speeds below 20 m.p.h. indicates improper carburetor idle adjustment, restriction in idle passages in carburetor, tight valve lash or sticking valves, or faulty ignition.

Faulty ignition usually causes a more pronounced roughness than imperfect compression or carburetion.

Roughness or poor performance at speeds above 20 m.p.h. indicates restriction or improper settings in the high speed circuit of the carburetor, or faulty ignition.

Wide Open Throttle Acceleration Test

With the car running at idling speed in high gear, quickly press the accelerator pedal to the floor and hold it there, meanwhile noting the performance of the engine as the car is accelerated. Repeat the acceleration test, starting at different constant speeds throughout speed range of car. The car should accelerate smoothly without hesitation, spitting, or loading of the engine.

A hesitation, spitting, or a flat spot indicates that the accelerating pump is not discharging sufficient gasoline into the engine. Sluggishness or loading indicates that the accelerating pump is adjusted too rich.

Constant Speed Test

Hold the car speed constant at various points through the speed range and note engine performance. The engine should operate smoothly without hesitation or surging under load at all constant speeds.

At some point between 15 and 22 m.p.h. with the car rolling along on a level road or slight upgrade, a slight leanness, surging or missing may be detected. Depressing or releasing the accelerator pedal slightly will eliminate this condition and no attempt should be made to correct it by altering carburetion or ignition. This condition seldom appears in the normal operation of the car.

With Carter carburetors, a surging or loss of power at 55 to 65 m.p.h. constant speed indicates that the metering rod adjustment is too lean. This may occur even though top speed performance is satisfactory.

With Stromberg carburetors, surging at 75 to 80 m.p.h. constant speed indicates that the power jet is stopped up or the vacuum piston is sticking.

Spark Knock

Light detonation or spark knock will occur when operating with part throttle on a hard pull, even though the ignition is properly timed and Ethyl or other high octane fuel is used. Light detonation also will occur when accelerating with fully opened throttle on a hard pull. These operating conditions are normal and no attempt should be made to eliminate light detonation by retarding the ignition timing.

If regular or low octane fuel is used, detonation will probably be excessive with the standard ignition timing, and it may be necessary to retard the timing, which will reduce fuel economy and over-all performance.

Extreme heavy detonation is injurious to any automobile engine. A car driven continuously under conditions and fuels which produce heavy detonation will overheat and lose power, with the possibility of damage to pistons and bearings.

Valve Noise

With the valves adjusted uniformly to specifications, the noise level should be very low as observed in the car while driving. The sound of valve action should be audible, however, when the hood is raised or when the engine is operating on fast idle during warm up.

The valve lash should not be reduced below specifications in an attempt to eliminate valve noise, as this will cause formation of carbon on valve seats and stems, which will then increase valve noise and lower the engine performance.

Sticking valves usually are indicated by an intermittent loudness of action, although the valves will be unusually noisy at all times if they are sticking badly. Sticking valves will cause irregular operation or missing on a low speed pull.

Noisy Hydraulic Lifters

The easiest method for locating a noisy valve lifter is by the use of a piece of garden hose approximately 4 feet in length. Place the end of the hose near the end of each intake and exhaust valve with the other end of the hose near the ear. In this manner, the sound is localized, making it easy to determine which lifter is at fault.

Another method is to place a finger on the face of the valve spring retainer. If the lifter is not functioning properly, a distinct shock will be felt when the valve returns to its seat.

In most cases where noise exists in one or more lifters, all lifter units should be removed and cleaned. If dirt, varnish, carbon, etc. is found to exist in one unit, it more than likely exists in all the units.

Plungers are not interchangeable as they are selectively fitted at the factory. Should a plunger or lifter body become damaged, it is necessary to replace the entire unit.

MINOR TUNE UP

A minor engine tune up is intended as a preventive measure for engines which are in fairly normal condition. It is usually good on cars having low mileage or on those which have traveled 5,000 miles or so since having a major tune up. The frequency of use depends upon the conditions under which the car is operated. A minor tune up should include the following items:

1. Check battery electrolyte specific gravity and level.
2. Inspect battery terminals and cables.
3. Inspect primary wires and ignition switch.
4. Clean coil and terminal socket.
5. Inspect distributor automatic advance weight mechanism.
6. Inspect distributor vacuum control.
7. Clean and adjust distributor contact points, lubricate cam wick and rubbing block.
8. Reset ignition timing.
9. Inspect and clean distributor cap and rotor.
10. Inspect ignition cables.
11. Clean and adjust spark plugs, or install new plugs if required.
12. Clean fuel strainer and filters.
13. Inspect and lubricate manifold heat control valve.
14. Check for intake manifold air leaks.
15. Clean and/or refill air cleaner.
16. Inspect and set choke thermostat.
17. Check fast idle cam and choke unloader adjustments.
18. Lubricate carburetor countershaft (Carter).
19. Check starter vacuum switch timing (if equipped).
20. Adjust throttle linkage.
21. Adjust carburetor.
22. Inspect and adjust fan belt.
23. Inspect water pump, radiator and car heater hose connections, and radiator water level.
24. Clean oil filler cap.
25. Test performance after tune up.

12 VOLT ELECTRICAL SYSTEMS

The 12-volt electrical system, adopted on some cars starting in 1953, is used for two main reasons:

1. To provide adequate electrical power to feed the ever-growing number of electrical accessories used on present day cars.
2. To provide greater available voltages in the ignition system for the new high speed, high compression engines.

Generator Requirements

In 1935 or thereabouts, passenger car generators were designed to produce about 20 amperes. In 1952, generator capacity was increased to over 50 amperes in some cases and even this high output was found to be insufficient to supply the electrical needs of all the accessories used on some cars.

For all practical purposes, the limit of generator output was reached in 1952 with a 6-volt system as generators had become bulky and wiring heavy and clumsy. With a 12-volt system, the same amount of electrical power can be delivered with half the amperage, because power is measured in watts, which are simply amperes multiplied by volts. In other words, when a generator is required to deliver 600 watts, this amount of power can be delivered in two ways: 100 amperes at 6 volts or 50 amperes at 12 volts. In each case the amperes multiplied by the volts produces the same number of watts (600).

As it is the current in amperes flowing through a conductor that determines the required size or gauge of the wire, it is obvious that with a 12-volt system, smaller size wires can be used to deliver the same amount of power as the larger sizes would deliver in a six-volt system.

Ignition System Requirements

Turning to the ignition system, the postwar trend to high compression 8-cylinder engines has made it more difficult to maintain adequate ignition voltage for all engine operating conditions.

Compression in the combustion chamber of the gasoline engine bears the same relation to the firing of a spark plug as does resistance in an electrical conductor to the passage of current through it. The higher the resistance of the conductor, the less current can flow through it. The higher the compression ratio, the weaker the spark. More current can be forced through a conductor of a certain resistance value by increasing the voltage across the conductor. By the same token, the strength of the spark can be increased by increasing the voltage across the spark plug. This is one reason for increasing the system voltage from 6 to 12 volts.

Another factor is the higher speeds developed by the new type engines. With higher speeds, the 6-volt ignition coil does not get sufficient time to become thoroughly saturated and therefore can-

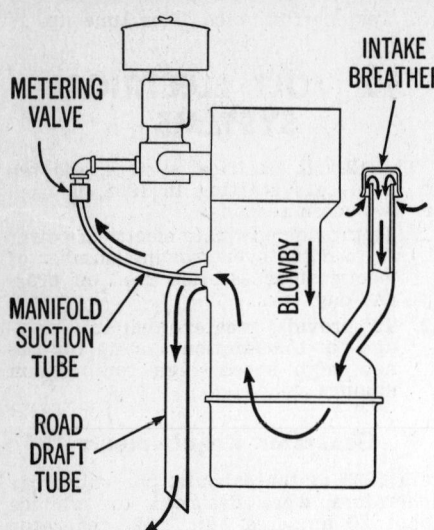

Fig. 10 Schematic drawing showing how either the road draft or manifold suction systems of crankcase ventilation operate

CRANKCASE VENTILATION

Crankcase ventilation has an important function in controlling sludge and keeping the engine lubricating system in good condition. Ineffective or inoperative crankcase ventilators are responsible for lubricating troubles serious enough in some cases to cause engine failure.

Crankcase ventilation originally was developed to correct premature corrosion and wear of engine parts, such as timing chains, piston pins and cylinder walls. This trouble was traced to presence in the engine oil of acids which originated from sulphur in the fuel and entered the crankcase from the combustion chamber.

By sending a steady flow of air through the engine, the water which carried the acids was removed as vapor before it had a chance to condense and collect in the oil. In recent years better gasoline refining has eliminated much of the acid-forming sulphur compounds but the need remains for efficient ventilation in automobile engines.

Two methods of crankcase ventilation are in use, the road-draft system and manifold vacuum system, both shown schematically in the same drawing in Fig. 10.

Fig. 11 shows a typical road draft type. As indicated by the direction of the arrows, air is driven into the crankcase by fan draft through a copper gauze filter in the oil filler cap. It then circulates around the inside of the engine and is discharged through the ventilator outlet pipe, carrying with it the water vapor which collects in the crankcase, particularly in cold weather. Whenever the oiling system is cleaned, the filler and outlet pipes should be removed and flushed out thoroughly. The gauze filters should also be washed in clean gasoline or kerosene.

The manifold vacuum system of crankcase ventilation is standard equipment on 1961 cars to be used in California, and optional equipment on all others. The correct operation of this system depends upon a free flow of air from the carburetor air cleaner through the oil filler tube and engine to the control valve mounted on the intake manifold, Fig. 10. The arrows indicate the direction of the flow of air.

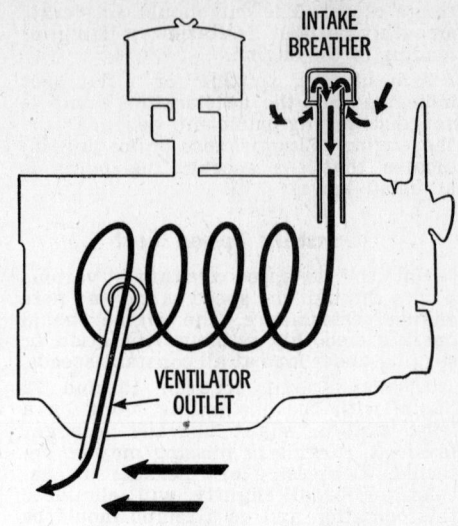

Fig. 11 Road draft system of crankcase ventilation

The vacuum control consists of a springloaded lightweight valve, the spring acting against manifold vacuum. Above about 6" of vacuum, the valve tends to close and the tapered seat progressively restricts the opening. At 12" to 13" of vacuum, the valve is fully closed and a fixed opening through the valve then controls the flow for higher vacuum.

Although the metering valve is reasonably trouble-free in service, it is well to disassemble and clean it occasionally. And always after a valve job the valve should be cleaned. Be sure there is no air leakage at the tube connections between the air cleaner and the oil filler tube. And see that the oil filler tube cap gasket is in good condition. Always keep the cap locked securely in place.

If the control valve becomes clogged with carbon or other foreign matter the ventilation system will not operate and a slight pressure will build up in the crankcase which may cause oil leakage at the rear main bearing or by the piston rings. And should the valve fail to seat it will be impossible to make the engine idle satisfactorily.

not produce enough energy to create a good spark. The 12-volt system is one way of putting more energy into the coil at high speeds without overloading and burning the breaker points at the lower speeds.

Comparing the available outputs of 6 and 12-volt coils at 3600 rpm engine speed, the 6-volt coil will produce 16,000 volts whereas the 12-volt coil will produce 19,000 volts. Thus, at high engine speeds the 12-volt coil produces adequate voltages for this type of operation where the 6-volt coil frequently fails.

Electrical System Changes

With a 12-volt system, many changes had to be made in the electrical units of the car. The battery, starter, generator, ignition coil, the various electrical motors, the light bulbs—all had to be redesigned for 12-volt use but their basic construction remains the same as the 6-volt units. *However, the ignition distributor, breaker points and condenser remain the same as in the 6-volt system.*

IGNITION SYSTEMS

THE IGNITION SYSTEM on all passenger cars can be divided as follows, Fig. 1.

1. Battery to supply current.
2. Ignition wiring to carry current to the units in the system.
3. Ignition switch to control the circuit.
4. Ignition coil to increase the voltage delivered to the spark plugs.
5. A distributor to distribute current

to each cylinder.
6. Spark plugs to ignite the fuel in each cylinder.

But inasmuch as the *Tune Up* chapter deals with such service as comes within the province of tuning up an engine—such as batteries, spark plugs, testing procedures, etc.—this chapter will discuss the functions and service requirements of the distributor itself, together with any additional data not included in the *Tune Up* chapter.

AUTO-LITE & CHRYSLER DISTRIBUTORS

These distributors as used on passenger cars, Figs. 2 and 3, contain two controls which provide automatic advance of ignition timing according to engine speed and load. The centrifugal governor in the distributor body regulates ignition timing according to speed. The vacuum control unit attached to the

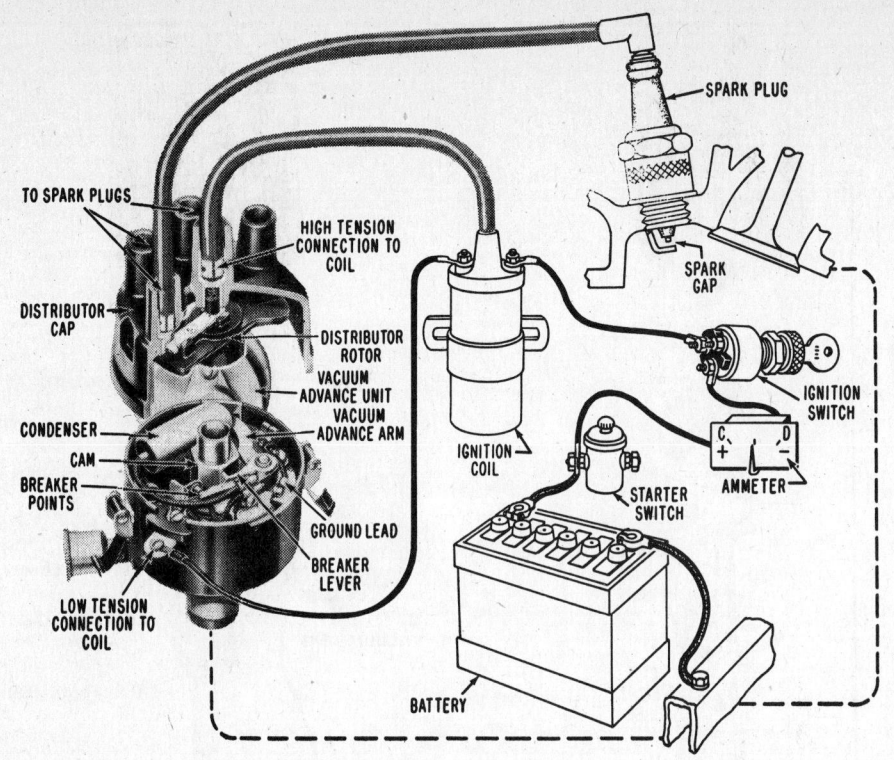

TO SPARK PLUGS

SPARK PLUG

HIGH TENSION CONNECTION TO COIL

SPARK GAP

DISTRIBUTOR CAP

DISTRIBUTOR ROTOR

VACUUM ADVANCE UNIT

VACUUM ADVANCE ARM

CONDENSER

CAM

BREAKER POINTS

BREAKER LEVER

GROUND LEAD

LOW TENSION CONNECTION TO COIL

IGNITION COIL

IGNITION SWITCH

AMMETER

STARTER SWITCH

BATTERY

Fig. 1 Typical ignition system

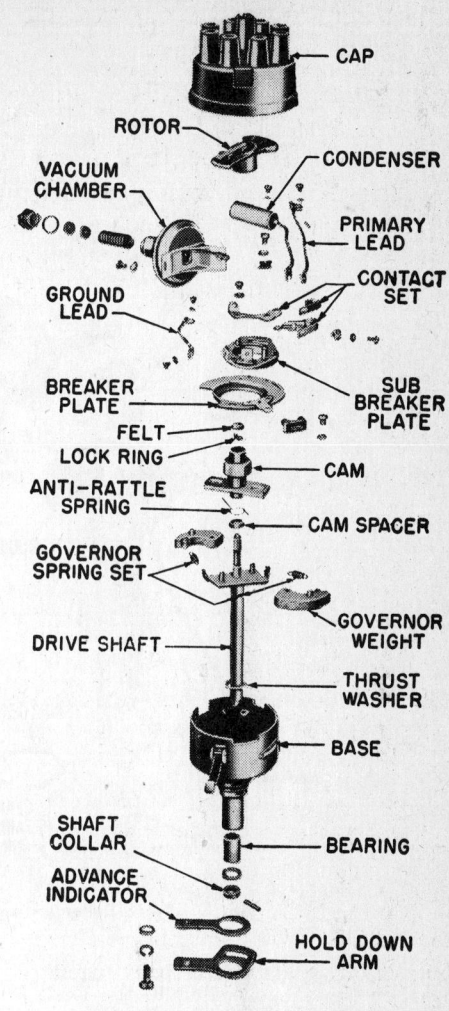

CAP

ROTOR

VACUUM CHAMBER

CONDENSER

PRIMARY LEAD

CONTACT SET

GROUND LEAD

BREAKER PLATE

SUB BREAKER PLATE

FELT

LOCK RING

CAM

ANTI-RATTLE SPRING

CAM SPACER

GOVERNOR SPRING SET

DRIVE SHAFT

GOVERNOR WEIGHT

THRUST WASHER

BASE

SHAFT COLLAR

BEARING

ADVANCE INDICATOR

HOLD DOWN ARM

Fig. 2 Exploded view of typical Auto-Lite distributor

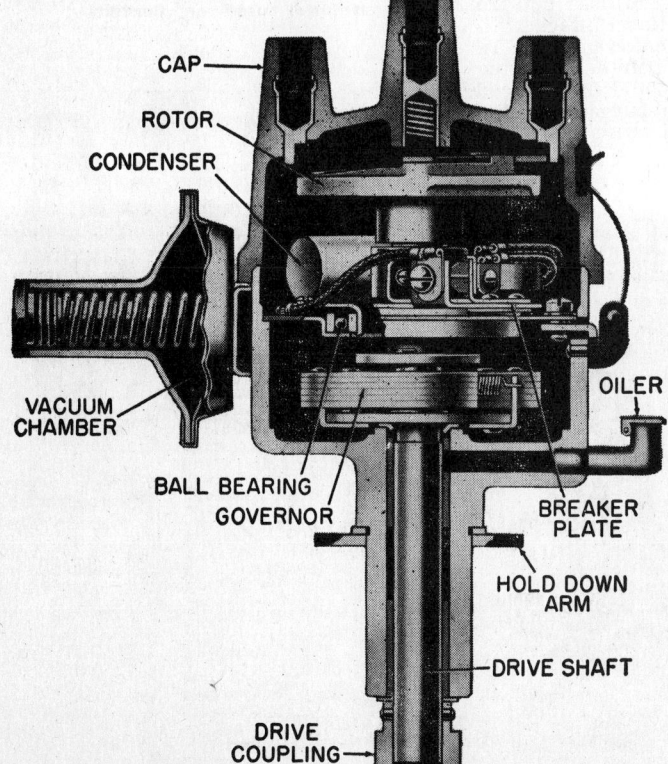

CAP

ROTOR

CONDENSER

VACUUM CHAMBER

OILER

BALL BEARING

GOVERNOR

BREAKER PLATE

HOLD DOWN ARM

DRIVE SHAFT

DRIVE COUPLING

Fig. 3 Sectional view of typical Auto-Lite distributor

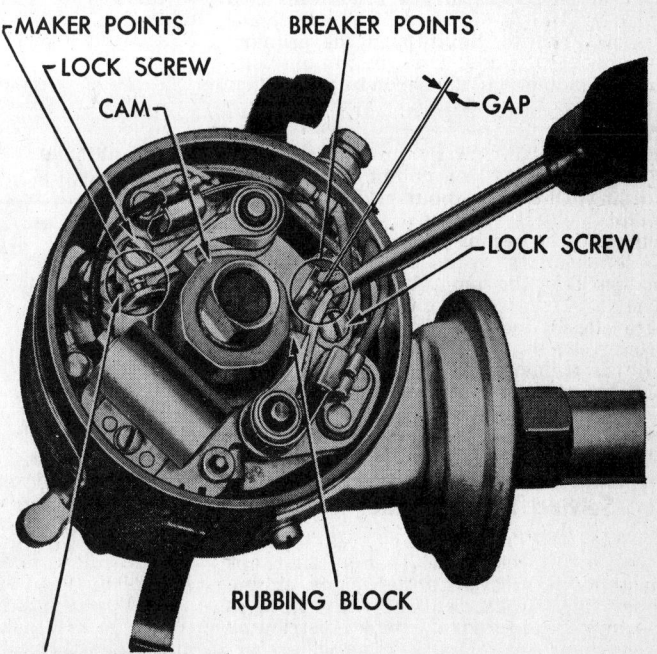

MAKER POINTS

LOCK SCREW

CAM

BREAKER POINTS

GAP

LOCK SCREW

RUBBING BLOCK

STATIONARY PLATE

Fig. 4 Auto-Lite dual point distributor

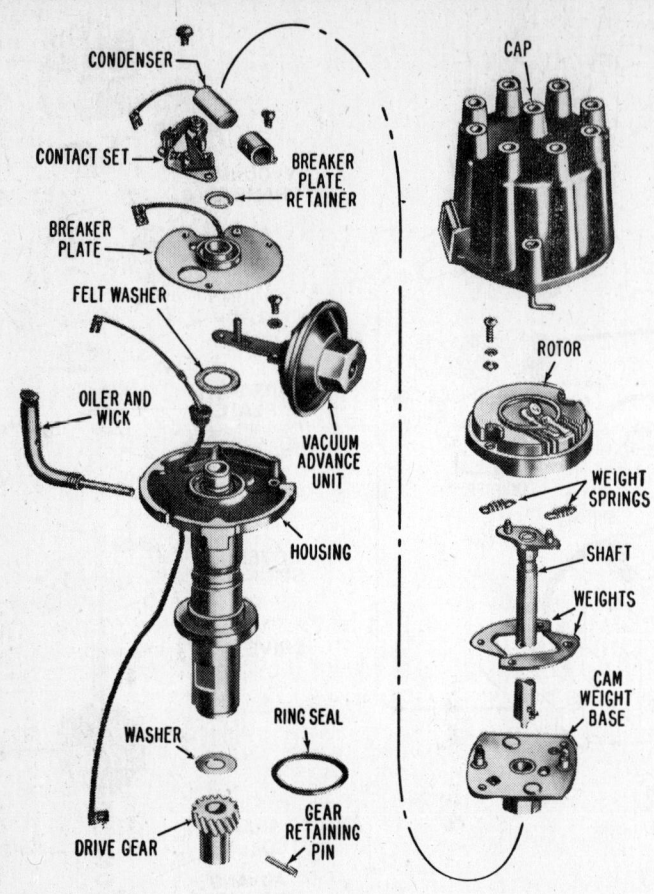

Fig. 5 Delco-Remy external adjustment distributor

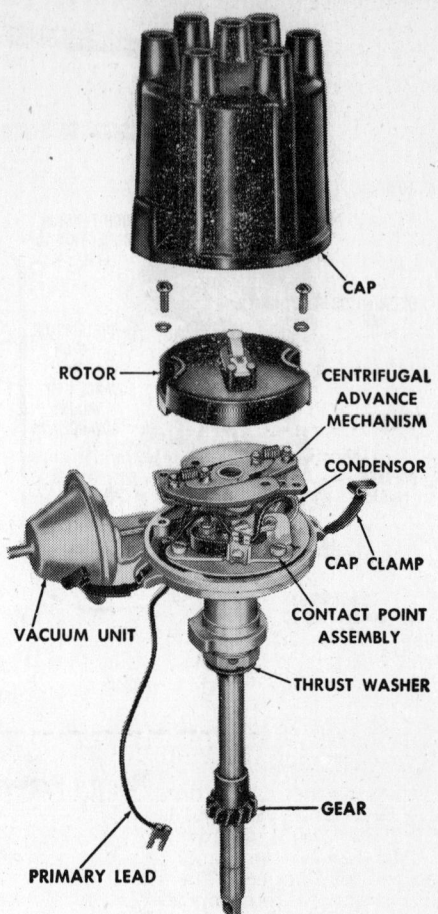

Fig. 6A Delco-Remy distributor used on Corvair

outside of the distributor body regulates ignition timing according to the load.

Dual Point Distributor

The distributor on some late model Chrysler Corporation cars contains two sets of points, Fig. 4, which permit additional current build-up in the primary winding of the coil. Thus, maximum voltage is induced in the secondary winding.

The two sets of points are connected in parallel and are positioned in relation to the 8-lobe cam so as to provide a 7-degree overlap of points opening and closing. One set of points (circuit *maker* points) closes the primary circuit in the coil and the second set of points (circuit *breaker* points) opens the circuit, causing a spark at the plug. Immediately after the spark occurs, the circuit *maker* points are closed ahead of the circuit *breaker* points, thus providing a circuit to build-up the primary winding. As the cam rotates further, the secondary points close and just before the secondary points open, the primary points open 7 degrees ahead.

Setting Dual Breaker Points

Since the "make" and "break" points are timed to close and open at the exact instant necessary for efficient engine operation, adjustment of the points is an important factor in correct distributor operation.

New points can be adjusted with a feeler gauge. If points are used but are still clean and make flat contact with each other, a dial indicator tool can be used satisfactorily. If points are pitted or badly worn, they should be replaced because metal may be burned, causing a resistance that would cause poor point operation.

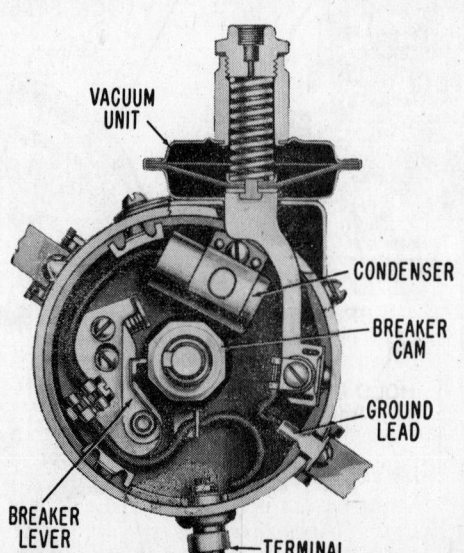

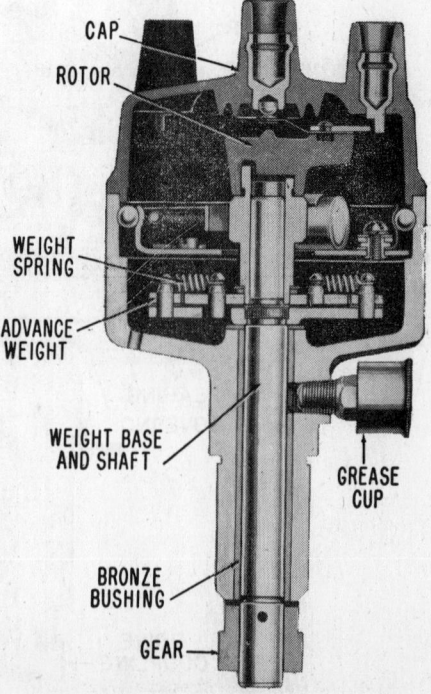

Fig. 6 Sectional view of a Delco-Remy internal adjustment distributor

Feeler Gauge or Dial Indicator Method— Rotate the distributor shaft until the breaker arm rubbing block of one set of points is on the high spot of the cam. Then, with a screwdriver blade in the triangular opening, close or open the points to the proper clearance by turning the screwdriver blade against the stationary point plate. Check the clearance with a clean feeler gauge or dial indicator. Then turn the distributor shaft until the rubbing block of the second set of points is on the high spot of the cam and adjust the second set of points in the same manner.

Dwell Meter Method— If this method is used *block one set of points open* with a piece of wrapping paper or calling card. Then adjust the other set of points to the correct cam angle. Now block open the first set of points and adjust the second set. After both sets of points have been adjusted, allow them to operate together while checking that their total dwell angle measures up to manufacturer's specifications.

DELCO-REMY DISTRIBUTORS

Like Auto-Lite distributors, Delco-Remy units used on passenger cars contain two controls which provide automatic advance of ignition timing according to engine speed and load, Figs. 5 and 6. The centrifugal governor in the distributor body regulates ignition timing according to speed. The vacuum control unit regulates ignition timing according to load.

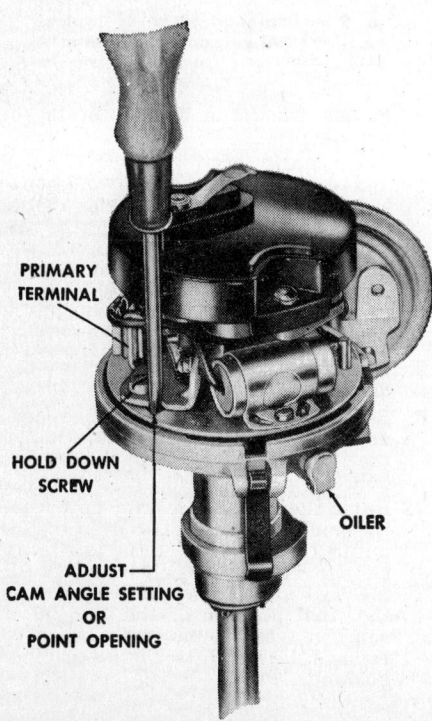

PRIMARY
TERMINAL

HOLD DOWN
SCREW

OILER

ADJUST
CAM ANGLE SETTING
OR
POINT OPENING

Fig. 6B Adjusting breaker points or cam dwell on Corvair distributor

Corvair Distributor

This unit, Fig. 6A, has the breaker plate located below the centrifugal advance mechanism and uses the outer diameter of the main shaft bushing for its bearing surface. The contact set is attached to the movable breaker plate and is serviced as a complete assembly. An opening in the point set assembly allows easy dwell angle or breaker point adjustment as shown in Fig. 6B.

The position of the vacuum control unit when mounted on the distributor housing determines the location of the breaker plate. Note the calibrated scale stamped on the top of the breaker plate, Fig. 6C. To correctly position the breaker plate during assembly at the factory, a mark on the calibrated scale is located opposite the edge of the slot in the distributor housing. This position should not be changed unless there is evidence that the plate has been moved from its original setting.

External Adjustment Type Distributor

This type of unit, Figs. 5 and 7, has a cap with a window which provides easy access for adjusting breaker point gap while the cap is in a mounted position. The circuit breaker plate is located below the centrifugal advance mechanism and uses the outer diameter of the distributor shaft bushing for its bearing surface. The movable plate is held in position by a retainer clip in the upper shaft bushing. The breaker points are attached to the movable breaker plate, the points and plate being furnished as one complete assembly. The vacuum control unit is mounted under the breaker plate to the distributor housing. The molded rotor serves as a cover for the centrifugal advance mechanism.

Adjusting Breaker Points

With the engine running at idle, the point gap is adjusted by first raising the window provided in the cap and inserting a "hex" wrench into the adjusting screw as shown in Fig. 8.

Turn the adjusting screw in (clockwise) until the engine begins to misfire. Then give the wrench one-half turn in the opposite direction.

If a cam angle meter is to be used, turn the adjusting screw until the correct cam angle is obtained.

HOLLEY DISTRIBUTORS

"Full Vacuum" Type

Used on Ford Company cars, this distributor, Figs. 9 and 10, is regulated entirely by the vacuum differential at the carburetor. The spark advance characteristics are controlled by two breaker plate springs working against the distributor vacuum control diaphragm. The amount of spark advance is determined by the amount of vacuum supplied to the distributor and by adjustment of the breaker plate springs.

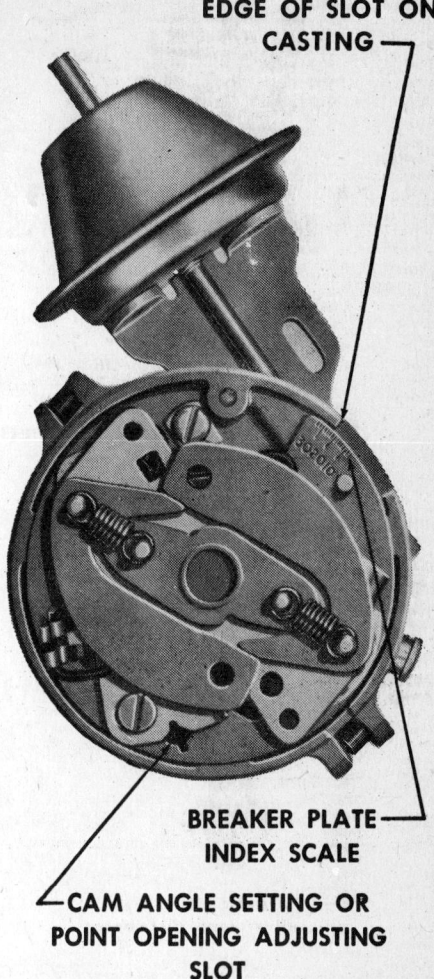

EDGE OF SLOT ON
CASTING

BREAKER PLATE
INDEX SCALE

CAM ANGLE SETTING OR
POINT OPENING ADJUSTING
SLOT

Fig. 6C Corvair distributor showing calibrated scale stamped on top of breaker plate. Mark on scale is located opposite edge of slot in distributor housing. When reassembling a distributor, line up mark on housing with 23° mark on scale

On all 8-cylinder distributors, a vacuum-operated spark control valve is attached to the carburetor throttle body to control manifold vacuum to the distributor and regulate spark advance, Fig. 11.

The 1956 8-cylinder distributors used with 4-barrel carburetors incorporate a double diaphragm for better control of breaker plate advance characteristics, Fig. 11. The purpose of the second diaphragm is to provide a rapid spark retard at the acceleration tip-in point. The primary spark control diaphragm operates in the same manner as the single type diaphragm.

Adjusting Vacuum Advance

The two vacuum advance springs are precision set at the factory with special stroboscopic equipment. This equipment is available for adjustment purposes in the field. Shops having conventional distributor testers can include a mercury column to take care of the setting of

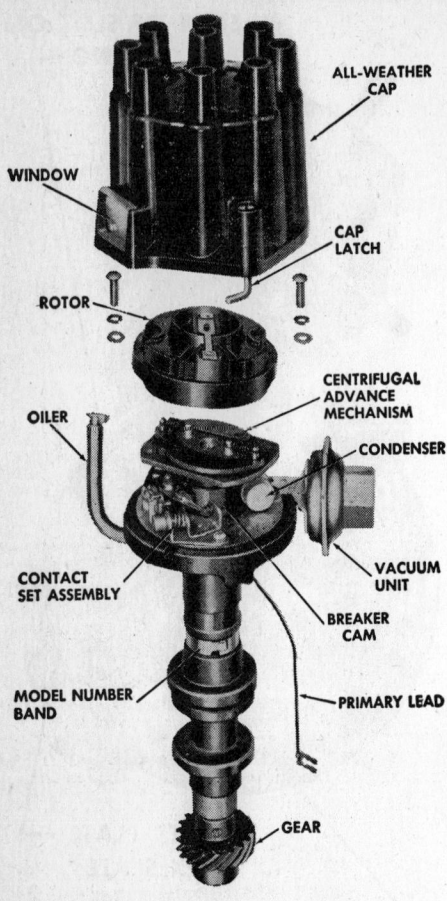

Fig. 7 Delco-Remy external adjustment distributor

these springs as the ordinary vacuum gauge will not provide the required accuracy.

Taking a typical distributor as an example, set the distributor speed at 500 rpm and apply a vacuum of ½". Then turn one spring clockwise until the spark falls within ½ to 1½ degrees advance. With one spring adjusted thus, increase distributor speed to 1000 rpm and apply a vacuum of 2". Adjust the second spring until the spark occurs at about 5 degrees advance.

Centrifugal Advance Distributor

Used on 1957 and later Ford V8s, this distributor, Figs. 12 and 13, is basically the same as the conventional Auto-Lite and Delco-Remy units, the chief difference being that the centrifugal advance mechanism can be adjusted through a slot in the breaker plate as follows:

With the distributor mounted in a test machine, and with the vacuum hose disconnected, operate the distributor in the direction of its normal rotation and increase the rpm until the mechanism begins to advance. Reduce the speed to where there is no advance and zero the advance scale. Increase the speed to the value specified for the first advance reading listed in the specifications (see car chapters). If the correct advance is not indicated at this rpm, stop the distributor and bend the primary spring bracket with a screwdriver as shown in Fig. 14 to change its tension. Bend the

bracket away from the distributor shaft to decrease advance and toward the shaft to increase it.

The primary spring is the spring that is under tension when the distributor shaft is not rotating. To determine which spring is under tension, insert a hook into the adjusting slot and move each spring. The secondary spring will be under less tension than the primary spring.

Check the minimum advance point again, then operate the distributor at the specified rpm to give an advance just below the maximum. If this advance is not to specifications, stop the distributor and bend the secondary spring bracket to give the correct advance.

DISTRIBUTOR SERVICE

Distributor Removal

If the inspections and tests given in the *Tune Up* chapter indicate that the distributor requires cleaning or the installation of new parts, remove the distributor from the engine so that the work can be done properly.

(See Car Chapters for details on removing and installing distributors.)

Each time a distributor is removed and reinstalled, or when a new one is installed, it is essential that it be properly timed. Determine whether the timing mark is on the flywheel, on the vibration damper or on the lower fan pulley. To make it easily visible, clean the mark and trace a narrow line on it with chalk or white paint.

1. Remove the spark plugs to relieve the compression and crank the engine to the firing position for No. 1 cylinder.
2. Trace the No. 1 spark plug wire to its terminal in the distributor cap.
3. Mark the distributor housing directly under this terminal, either by scratching with a screw driver or by a chalk mark so that the rotor position for No. 1 cylinder will be

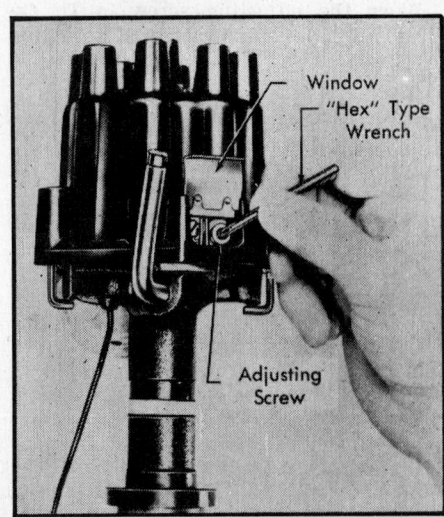

Fig. 8 Adjusting breaker gap through window in distributor cap

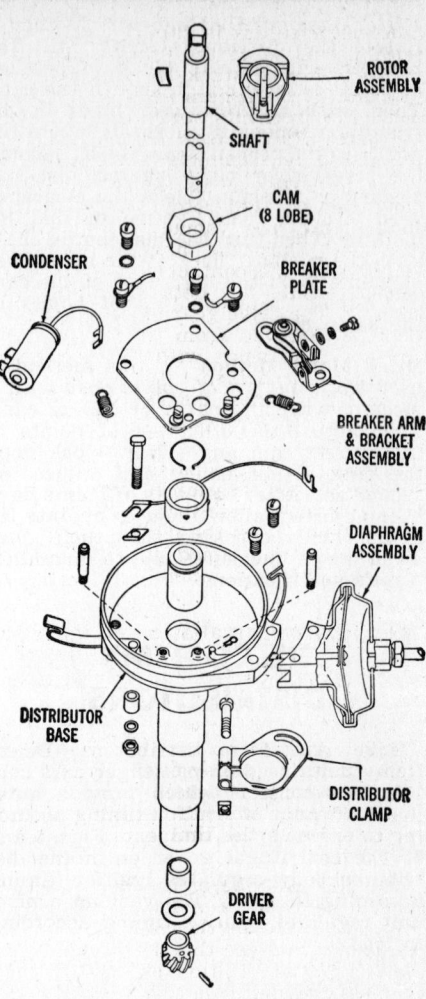

Fig. 9 Exploded view of typical Holley "full vacuum" distributor

known when the distributor is reinstalled.

4. Release the distributor cap clamps and raise the cap (with wires attached) and note the position of the rotor. Its segment should be directly over the mark previously made on the distributor housing. If not, the distributor drive shaft gear or coupling is broken or the drive pin sheared.
5. Disconnect the primary wire at the distributor terminal.
6. Remove the vacuum advance connection (if equipped) and remove the distributor clamp hold-down bolt.
7. Raise the distributor as a unit from its mounting. On gear-driven distributors, the position of the shaft will change as the gear comes out of mesh with the camshaft gear. Unless the final position of the distributor shaft is noted, it may be difficult to replace the distributor in its original position.

Distributor Disassembly

The disassembly procedure on any of

these distributors is fairly obvious and easy. On some of the units, there is a rather complex stack-up of insulating, flat and lock washers at the terminals, but a few moments study of this before the parts are detached from each other will aid in reassembling them correctly.

The first step in disassembly is to remove the cap and rotor, if not already done. Next, the vacuum advance mechanism. Then the breaker plate together with the contact points and condenser should be detached from the housing. The drive gear or coupling may then be removed from the drive shaft, and the drive shaft with its centrifugal governor mechanism lifted from the housing. Further disassembly of the breaker plate and governor mechanism is obvious.

At this time, the parts should be inspected, tested, assembled and adjusted in the manner described in subsequent paragraphs. Then the distributor should be installed and timed with the engine in the following manner.

Distributor Installation & Timing

(See Car Chapters for details on installation and timing.)

Before installing the distributor, check the timing mark on the flywheel, vibration damper or pulley to be certain that the engine has not been rotated while the distributor was off, and that it still remains set on the timing mark for No. 1 cylinder.

If a new distributor is being installed, scratch or chalk a mark on it to correspond to the mark made on the old distributor and use this mark as a guide for the initial position of the rotor as the new distributor is temporarily set in place.

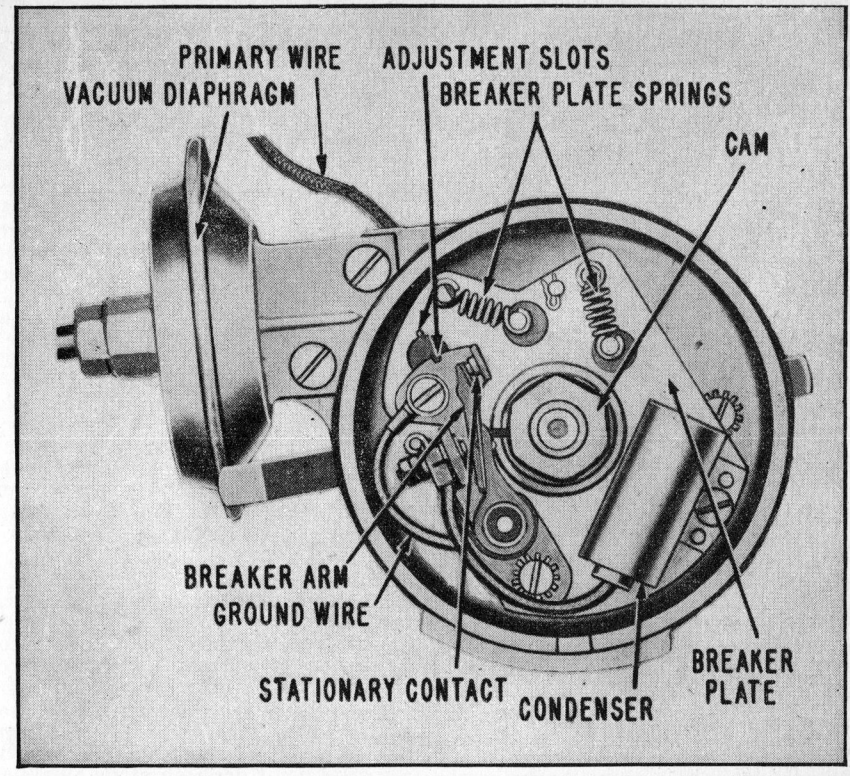

Fig. 10 Breaker plate details of Holley distributor for 6-cylinder engines

Temporarily set the distributor in its mounting with cap removed, being careful to see that the primary terminal and the vacuum control (if used) are in position to connect to the wire and pipe, respectively. However, do not connect them at this time.

With the rotor in approximately the same position as when the distributor was installed (in line with the mark on the distributor housing), allow the distributor to settle down to its permanent position in the mounting, being certain that the screw hole for the clamp hold-

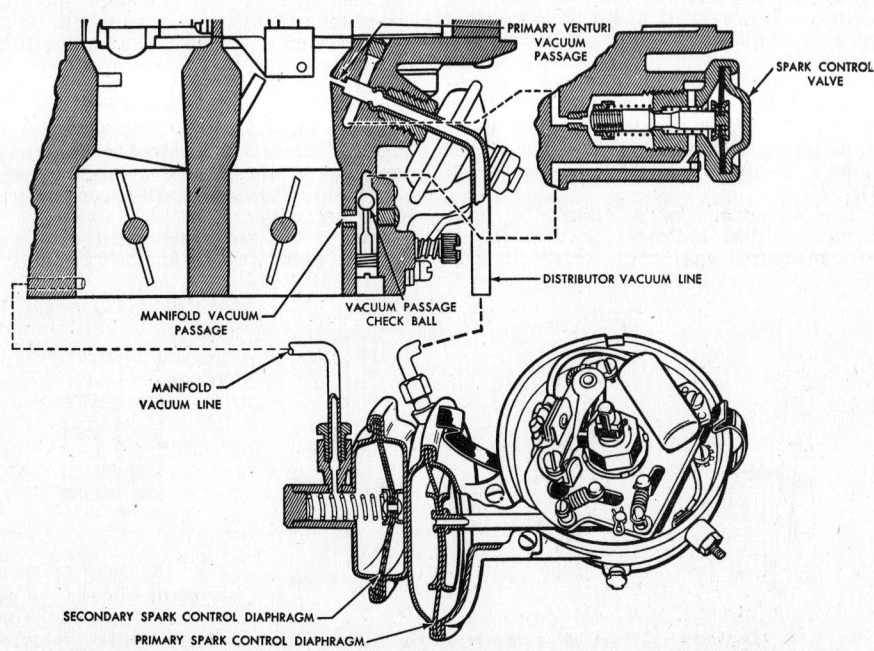

Fig. 11 Distributor vacuum controls used on 1956 Continental, Ford, Lincoln and Mercury with four-barrel carburetors. Note the double vacuum diaphragm which is used for better control of breaker plate advance characteristics

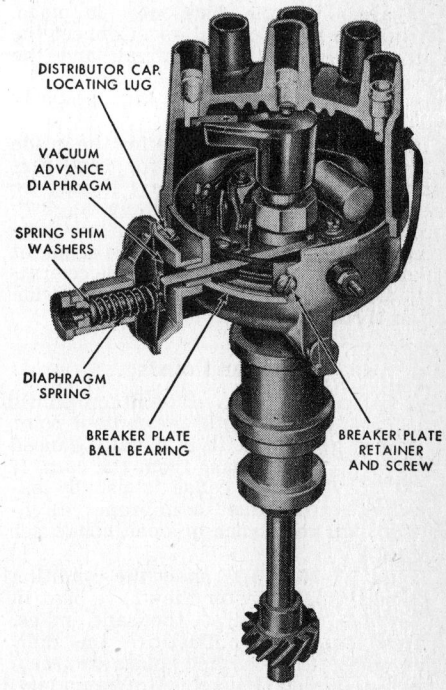

Fig. 12 Holley centrifugal advance distributor

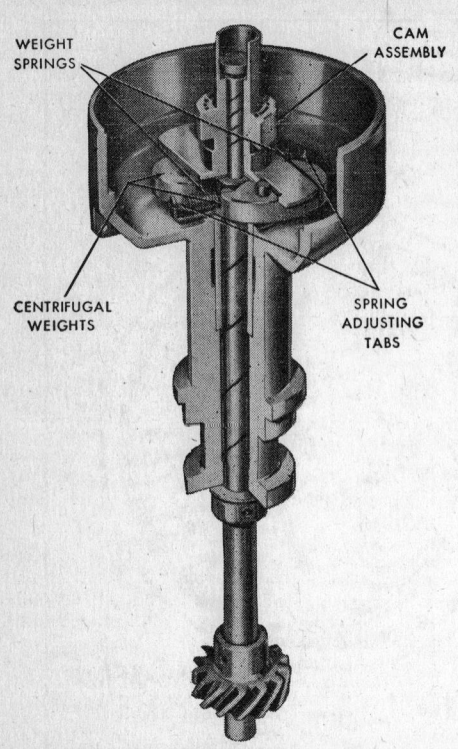

Fig. 13 Holley distributor centrifugal advance mechanism

down bolt is in the center of the clamp slot.

In the case of a gear-driven distributor, notice that the rotor will move from the position in which it was set as the distributor is moved into position. When this occurs, raise the distributor and turn the rotor just far enough beyond the desired position to allow for the change made by the gear movement, and again set the distributor in place. Install the hold-down screw. Connect the primary wire to its terminal, and the vacuum pipe to the vacuum control. The distributor should now be properly timed.

However, to compensate for the grade of fuel being used, and for best performance and fuel economy, it may be necessary to alter the timing slightly from the original setting. The best setting is one which will produce a slight spark knock or "ping" when accelerating from about 10 M.P.H. with wide open throttle.

Breaker Points

The normal color of contact points should be light gray. If the contact point surfaces are black, it is usually caused by oil vapor, or grease from the cam. If they are blue, the cause is usually excessive heating due to improper alignment, high resistance or open condenser circuit.

Figs. 15, 16 and 17 show the condition of contact points after they have been in operation for several thousand miles. These illustrations illustrate the difficulty of setting contact points correctly with a feeler gauge. Unfortunately, points do not wear evenly, and with each thousand miles of operation, the sur-

faces deviate from being parallel with each other. Fig. 15 shows what happens when points are not in correct alignment—they lap over each other.

Fig. 16 shows uneven wear of the contact surfaces, while Fig. 17 pictures the development of a crater and projection, usually caused by a metal transfer from one point to the other.

Fig. 18 shows an enlarged view of a new set of contact points. The right-hand contact has a convex surface, while the left-hand point has a flat surface. This convexity is scarcely visible to the naked eye as it amounts to approximately .002 inch from the center of the point to its outside extremity. The advantage claimed for this design is that the contact of surfaces which break the arc will be nearer to the mass of metal in the two contacts, which gives better heat radiation. A further advantage is that should the points be misaligned, more metal will be in contact when a convex point is used than if both points were flat.

Auto-Lite is strongly against filing of contact points, because the cutting surface of the file produces high spots on the contact surfaces, which means concentration of current and heat in extremely small areas.

Delco-Remy recommends that contact points which are blackened or slightly burned or pitted should be cleaned with a special point dressing stone or a clean contact point file. In dressing the points, remove the high spots only, as it is not necessary to remove all traces of build-up or pit.

Sandpaper or emery cloth should never be used to clean up points, since particles of sand or emery may imbed in the points and cause rapid burning and wear.

Specifications for contact point opening, *as measured with a wire gauge,* are given in the *Tune Up* table in each car chapter. However, if at all possible, this opening should be set on a distributor test fixture or a dial indicator, Figs. 19 and 20. This not only eliminates the possibility of a wrong gap setting, but if the points are slightly rough but otherwise in alignment, there is the danger of obtaining an incorrect gap, as shown in Fig. 21.

The advantage of a distributor test fixture or dial indicator is that it not only measures cam angle or dwell, Fig.

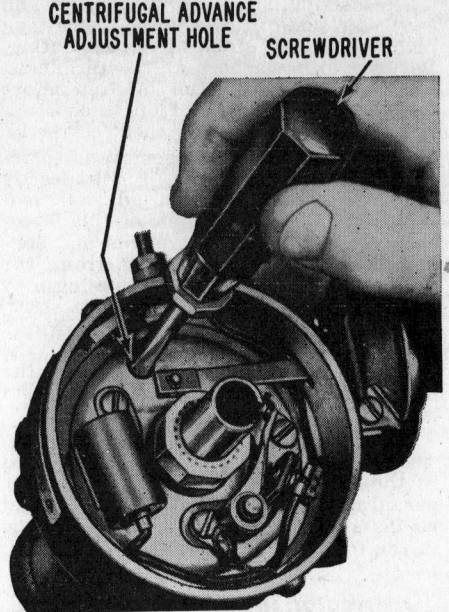

Fig. 14 Centrifugal advance adjustment

22, but it also uncovers irregularities between cam lobes, bouncing of contact points, alignment or rubbing block with cam, alignment of contacts, and breaker arm spring tension. Manufacturers of such equipment furnish complete instructions as to their use.

If the contacts develop a crater or depression on one point and a high spot of metal on the other, the cause is an electrolytic action transferring metal from one contact to the other, Fig. 23. This can be the result of some unusual operation of the car. A slow speed driver in city traffic or door-to-door delivery vehicles will be one extreme, and high speed long distance driving would be the other extreme. It may also be due to an unbalanced ignition system, which can sometimes be improved by a slight change in the condenser capacity.

If the mound is on the positive point, Fig. 24, install a condenser of greater capacity; if the mound is on the negative point, Fig. 25, install a condenser of lesser capacity.

One of the most prevalent causes of contact point failure is the presence of

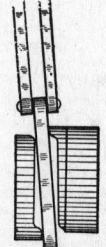

Fig. 15 Contacts out of alignment. A flat .020″ gauge spaces contacts .030″ to .040″

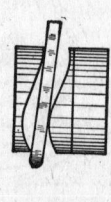

Fig. 16 Contacts worn unevenly. A flat .020″ gauge spaces contacts .030″ to .050″

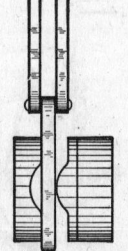

Fig. 17 Contacts pitted. A flat .020″ gauge spaces contacts .040″ to .050″

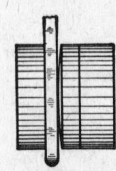

Fig. 18 Only Contacts correctly aligned can be correctly spaced with gauge. New contacts are usually made up of one convex surface operating against one with a flat surface

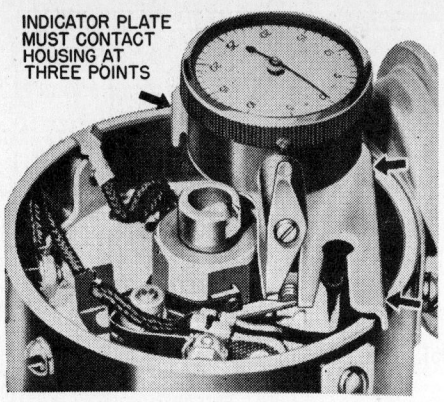

INDICATOR PLATE MUST CONTACT HOUSING AT THREE POINTS

Fig. 19 Dial indicator for measuring contact point opening on Delco-Remy internal adjustment distributors

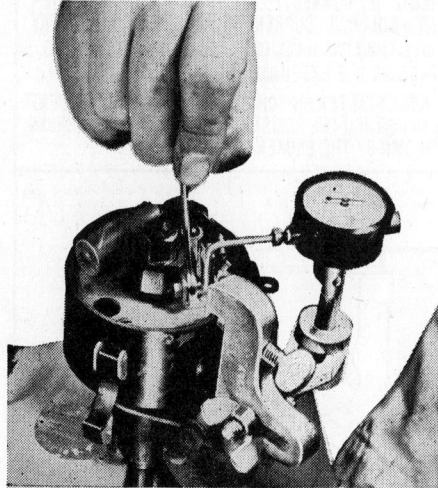

Fig. 20 Dial indicator for measuring contact point opening on Auto-Lite distributors

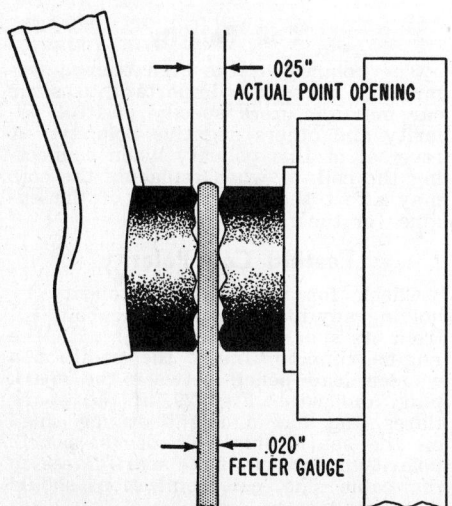

.025" ACTUAL POINT OPENING

.020" FEELER GAUGE

Fig. 21 Why flat feeler gauge will not provide accurate point spacing if points are rough

CAM ANGLE

POINTS CLOSE   POINTS OPEN

Fig. 22 Cam angle or dwell is the number of degrees of breaker cam rotation from the time the points close until they open again

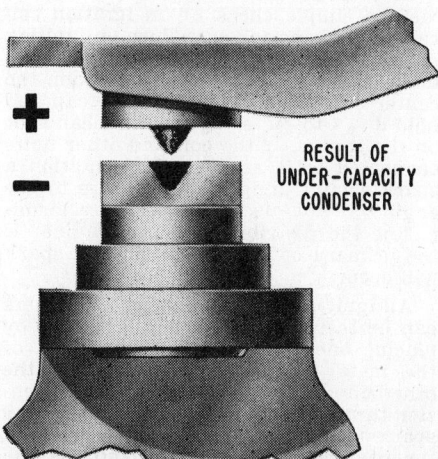

+ −

RESULT OF UNDER-CAPACITY CONDENSER

Fig. 24 Mound on positive point

Fig. 23 Showing how metal from one contact transfers to the other

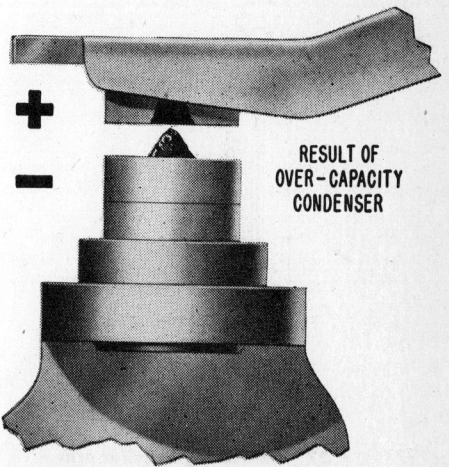

+ −

RESULT OF OVER-CAPACITY CONDENSER

Fig. 25 Mound on negative point

oil or grease on the contact surfaces, usually from over-lubrication of the wicks at the top of the cam, or too much grease on the rubbing block. This condition is indicated by a smudgy line on the point support and breaker plate, Fig. 26. If caught in time the contacts can be cleaned and the residue left on them can be wiped off by drawing a piece of lint-free tape between the contacts.

When new contacts are installed, the breaker arm should be free on the hinge pin, the contacts lined up with the outside diameters registering perfectly, and contact made in the center of the contact surfaces. This can be done by bending the contact support. Never bend the contact arm between the rubbing block and contact.

The rubbing block should be lined up with the cam by using a thin strip of white paper and carbon paper, held between the rubbing block and cam. By rotating the cam against the paper, a carbon impression will be made, showing which way the arm should be bent between the hinge pin and rubbing block to obtain correct alignment. When a straight-line impression is obtained from

top to bottom of the rubbing block against the cam, even though it may be on only one edge of the block, it will be unnecessary to "run in" the block to improve the contact.

Breaker arm spring tension is extremely important. If the tension is too great, the arm will bounce, causing an interruption of the current in the coil and missing in the engine. If the spring tension is not sufficient, the rubbing block will not follow the cam, causing a variation in the cam angle. The spring tension should always be set at the high limit given in the *Distributor Specification* tables, as it will be reduced as the rubbing block wears. Fig. 27 illustrates how the tension is measured.

Condenser

A condenser should not be condemned because the points are burned or oxidized. Oil vapor, or grease from the cam, or high resistance may be the cause of such a condition.

Condensers should be tested with a good condenser tester for leakage, break-down, capacity, and resistance in series in the condenser circuit. Manufacturers of condenser testers furnish complete instructions as to their use.

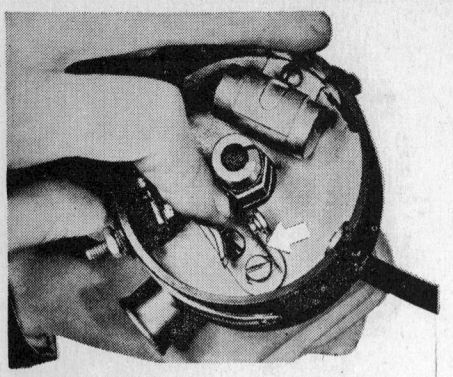

Fig. 26 Oil on contact points shown by smudgy line on point support and breaker plate

Ignition Coil

If poor ignition performance is obtained and the coil is suspected, it may be tested on the car or it may be removed for the test.

Ignition coils are often condemned when the trouble is actually in the ignition switch. A completely defective ignition switch will produce an open primary circuit, giving the same indications as if the coil were completely dead. A partly defective ignition switch will cause a weak spark. Both of these conditions are often blamed on the coil.

By cutting the ignition switch out of the circuit, it can easily be determined whether or not the coil is defective or whether fault lies with ignition switch.

In the case of lockswitch coils, Fig. 28, the coil end cover should be removed and a temporary wire connected directly from the battery (or the nearest live battery connection) to the coil terminal that is normally under the coil end cover. In the case of coils without the lockswitch feature, a similar temporary wire should be connected to the terminal of the coil to which the battery wire is normally connected. In either case, this temporary connection jumps the ignition switch. If the trouble is eliminated when the engine is started, it is obvious that

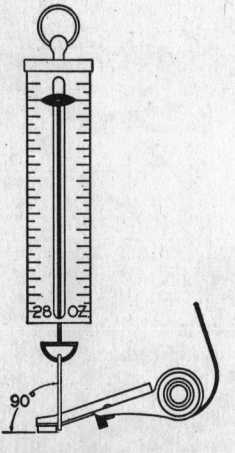

Fig. 27 Measuring breaker arm spring tension

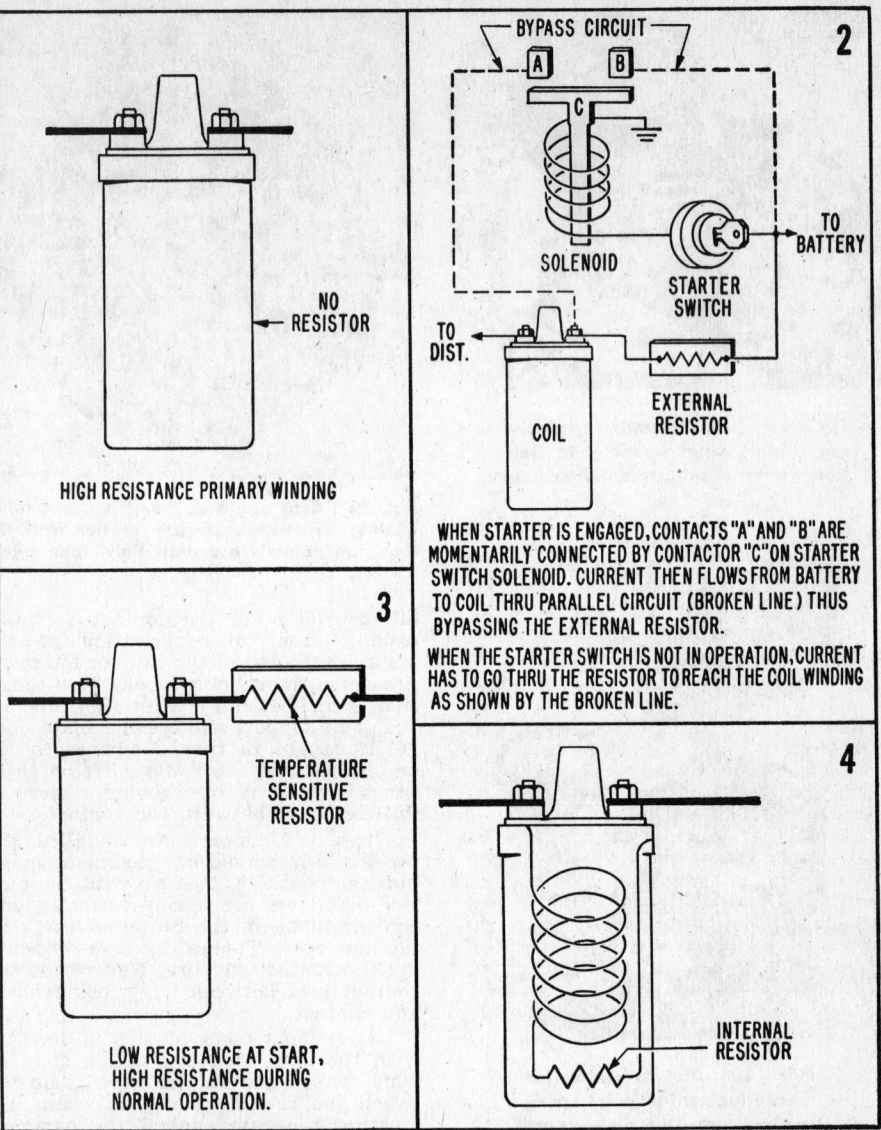

NO RESISTOR

HIGH RESISTANCE PRIMARY WINDING

2

BYPASS CIRCUIT

A   B

C

SOLENOID

STARTER SWITCH

TO BATTERY

TO DIST.

COIL

EXTERNAL RESISTOR

WHEN STARTER IS ENGAGED, CONTACTS "A" AND "B" ARE MOMENTARILY CONNECTED BY CONTACTOR "C" ON STARTER SWITCH SOLENOID. CURRENT THEN FLOWS FROM BATTERY TO COIL THRU PARALLEL CIRCUIT (BROKEN LINE) THUS BYPASSING THE EXTERNAL RESISTOR.

WHEN THE STARTER SWITCH IS NOT IN OPERATION, CURRENT HAS TO GO THRU THE RESISTOR TO REACH THE COIL WINDING AS SHOWN BY THE BROKEN LINE.

3

TEMPERATURE SENSITIVE RESISTOR

LOW RESISTANCE AT START, HIGH RESISTANCE DURING NORMAL OPERATION.

4

INTERNAL RESISTOR

Fig. 28 Twelve volt coil and resistor circuits

the ignition switch was the offender—not the coil.

In the absence of any testing equipment a simple check of an ignition coil can be made as follows: Turn on ignition switch with breaker points closed. Remove the high tension cable from the center socket of the distributor cap and hold it ¼" to ⅜" away from a clean spot on the engine. If the coil and other units connected to it are in good condition a spark should jump from the wire to the engine. If not, use a jumper wire terminal of the distributor to the engine; if the primary is in good condition a spark will occur.

All ignition coils with metal containers can be tested for grounded windings by placing one test clip on a clean part of the metal container and touching the other clip to the primary and high tension terminals. If the lamp lights or tiny sparks appear at the points of contact, the windings are grounded and the coil should be replaced.

Coil Polarity

The polarity of the high tension terminal of the coil is important, as some car manufacturers specify positive polarity and others negative polarity. A reversal of this polarity when connecting the coil, or when replacing the coil, may affect the performance of the engine (or the radio).

Testing Coil Polarity

Check for reversed coil polarity by holding any high tension wire about ¼" from its spark plug terminal with the engine running. Insert the point of a wooden lead pencil between the spark plug and wire, Fig. 29. If the spark flares and has a slight orange tinge on the spark plug side of the pencil, polarity is correct. If the spark flares on the cable side, coil connections should be reversed.

When coils have plus or minus markings near the terminals, with a negative grounded system the negative terminal

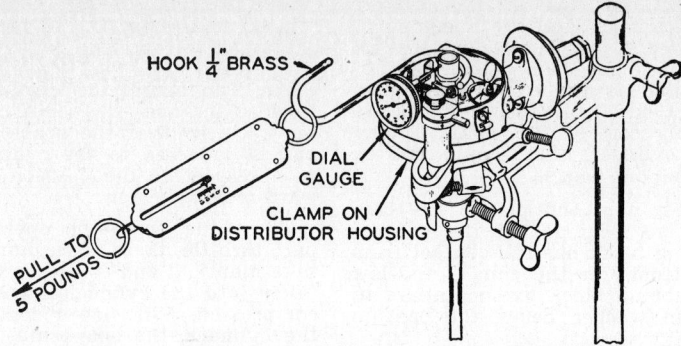

Fig. 30 Auto-Lite recommendation for checking side play of cam. With 5 pounds pull on scale, side play should not exceed .005 inch as indicated on dial gauge

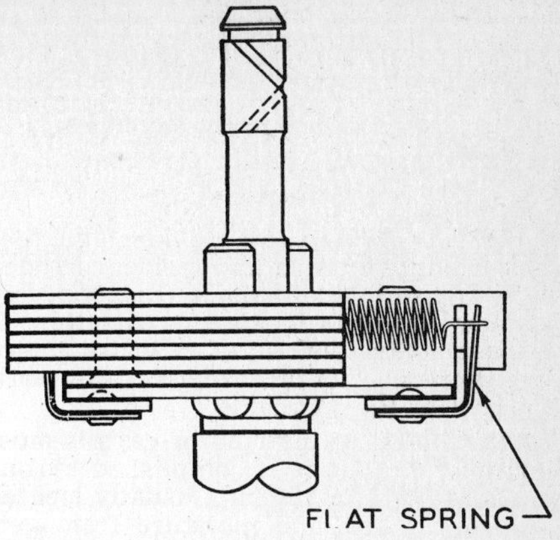

Fig. 32 Flat spring used on some governors to provide a rapid spark advance

wire should be connected to the distributor. With a positive-grounded system, the positive terminal wire should be connected to the distributor.

12 Volt Coil and Ignition Resistor

In order to improve ignition performance during cranking, and to permit the 12-volt ignition coil to be assembled into a container no larger than the one used for 6-volt coils, an external resistance is used with the ignition coil. This external resistance is connected in series with the primary circuit between battery and coil.

Unlike the methods illustrated in Fig. 28, the resistance used on some cars starting with 1960 consists of a high resistance wire incorporated in the instrument panel wiring harness. The wire used with Delco-Remy systems is stainless wire, plastic coated and covered with a glass braid. A similar wire is used on Ford Company cars.

Regardless of whether a resistor unit or a resistance wire is used, they greatly improve starting performance at low temperatures in that the resistance is by-passed during cranking, thereby connecting the ignition coil directly to the battery. This makes full battery voltage available to the coil and thus keeps ignition voltage as high as possible during cranking.

The four 12-volt coil and resistor set-ups in use are shown in the wiring diagrams, Fig. 28.

No. 1 circuit shows a 12-volt coil without any resistor in the primary circuit. The primary winding, however, has a high resistance value.

No. 2 circuit shows the most common Delco-Remy type. It has an external resistor which does not change with temperature. The primary winding of the coil is similar to that of a 6-volt coil but it has a higher resistance value. Note that in this set-up the ignition circuit is wired so that the external resistor is shorted out while the starter switch is operating.

No. 3 circuit is the most common Auto-Lite type. It uses an external resistor whose resistance value changes with temperature. When the car is being started, the cold resistor permits a higher current through the coil primary, resulting in easy starting. As the resistor warms up, its resistance increases to cut down the primary current through the coil for normal operation.

No. 4 circuit shows an Auto-Lite coil with the resistor incorporated within the coil housing. This type is used only on Chrysler 1953-55 Imperial.

Use Correct Coil

1. If a 6-volt coil is used with 1 and 4 systems, the coil will burn out and very often the coil housing will burst. Also the breaker points will burn.

2. If a No. 1 system coil is used with 2 or 3 systems, the coil will not function properly or will not operate at all, causing very hard or no starting.

3. If a 2 or 3 type coil is used in 1 and 4 circuits, the points will burn and the coil housing may burst.

4. If a 6-volt coil is used in any 12-volt system the coil will be permanently damaged and the points will be subject to burning and short life.

5. If an open-circuited resistor is left in circuits 2 or 3, there will be no ignition.

6. If a short-circuited resistor is left in circuits 2 or 3, the coil may burst or the coil winding may burn out.

Checking Resistors

Before installing a new coil to replace one that has burst open, check the external resistor as follows:

1. Connect one terminal of a voltmeter to the battery side of the resistor and the other voltmeter lead to a good ground.

2. Turn on the ignition but don't start the engine.

3. The voltmeter should indicate very close to the battery voltage.

4. Leave voltmeter lead connected to ground and move the other voltmeter lead to the coil side of the resistor.

5. The voltmeter should now read several volts lower than before.

6. If the voltmeter reading is the same or almost the same in both instances, the resistor is short-circuited. Discard it and install a new one.

7. Be sure to install the correct resistor and coil for each system as they have been designed in matching units for maximum performance. *Resistors used with Auto-Lite,*

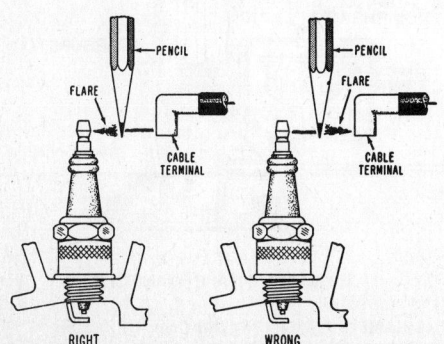

Fig. 29 Checking coil polarity

Fig. 31 Top view of Delco-Remy distributor with breaker plate removed to show centrifugal governor mechanism

Delco-Remy and Ford coils must not be used interchangeably for to do so can result in burned points, overheated coils, misfiring, lower coil output and poor operation.

Distributor Cap

Inspect the cap for cracks, high tension leakage outside and inside, corroded high tension terminals and excessively burned segments inside the cap. Note if the segments show signs of spark jumping on the horizontal instead of the vertical part of the segments.

Ventilation of distributor caps is most important. This is accomplished by one or more holes in the cap, usually located to prevent dirt and moisture from getting inside the cap. If the vent holes are clogged, the ozone gas created by the high tension spark inside the cap could not escape, and in combination with moisture, form an acid which would corrode the metal parts.

Distributor Rotor

Examine the end of the metal strip of the rotor to see that the spark is jumping from the outside end and not the top. If the rotor is too short, the spark will jump from the top instead of the end. Do not file the end of the rotor, even though it may be black from spark action. Clean it with gasoline or other suitable cleaning fluid. Examine the rotor insulation for cracks and leakage.

Inspect the condition of the carbon brush in the center of the cap which rests on the rotor. This should be clean and free to move in and out of the segment so that it will make good contact with the rotor.

Distributor Cam

Examine the cam lobes for excessive wear. This can best be checked with a distributor test fixture. Excessive wear will be indicated by a difference in degrees between the contact opening for each cylinder. A few degrees variation in the cam angle for each cylinder is not so important as the exact spacing of the contact break for each cylinder. As this spacing controls the spark timing for each cylinder, this should not be greater than one degree.

Check for cam end play. The cam should be so located that the breaker arm rubbing block has full contact from top to bottom. If the cam is too low so that rubbing block extends above it, add a thin washer below the cam to raise it.

Side play of the cam with respect to the distributor housing can be checked as shown in Fig. 30. This should not be more than .005 inch with five pounds pull on the cam. If more than .005 inch, the cam and governor weight assembly should be removed and the shaft and bushing checked. Excessive side play can usually be corrected by installing new bushings in the distributor housing, or by replacing the cam, although replacement of both cam and bushing is sometimes necessary.

Automatic Advance Mechanism

Except for Holley "full vacuum" type all other distributors utilize an automatic advance mechanism which functions by virtue of centrifugal weights. Some distributors employ both centrifugal and vacuum advance mechanisms while others make use of only the centrifugal mechanism.

When engine speed increases, the spark must be introduced in the cylinder earlier in the cycle in order that the fuel charge can be ignited and will have time to burn and deliver its power to the piston. To provide this spark advance based on engine speed, the centrifugal governor mechanism is used.

This mechanism, Fig. 31, consists of centrifugal advance weights which throw out against spring tension as the engine speed increases. This movement imparts, through a toggle arrangement, rotational motion to the breaker cam, causing it to rotate a number of degrees with respect to the distributor drive shaft. This causes the lobes on the cam to close and open the contacts earlier in the cycle so that the spark is induced and is delivered to the cylinder earlier with respect to the position of the upward moving piston.

When the engine is operated under part throttle, there is vacuum in the intake manifold and consequently the fuel taken into the cylinder is not so highly compressed. With lower compression in the cylinder, the spark must enter the cylinder earlier so that the mixture can be ignited, burn, and give up its power to the piston.

Lower compression means a slower rate of flame spread in the cylinder as the spark occurs. If the spark occurs earlier in the cycle, that is, if there is some additional spark advance, full burning of the fuel and maximum economy is achieved. This additional advance is obtained by a vacuum advance mechanism—about which see below.

In servicing the distributor, all weights should be removed from the hinge pins, cleaned and checked for excessive wear, either in the weights or pins, or the plate which is slotted for the movement of the pins on top of the governor weights. Replacement should be made if there is any appreciable wear in the slots, as any wear at this point would change the characteristic of the spark advance.

If these parts are in good condition, the hinge pins should be lubricated before being reassembled, by greasing the hinge pins and filling the pockets in the governor weights with grease. Do not use vaseline for this purpose as its melting point is comparatively low.

When installing new centrifugal governor assemblies, it is important that the spacer washers between the housing and shaft be installed correctly. If incorrectly installed, the governor assembly will be too high, causing it to rub

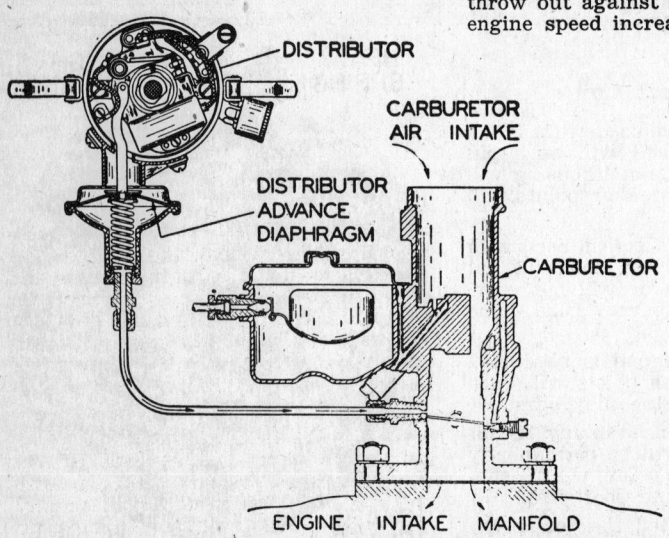

Fig. 33 Auto-Lite vacuum advance mechanism of the type which is mounted on the side of the distributor. Breaker plate is supported on a ball bearing, and the breaker plate alone rotates in the housing as vacuum conditions change

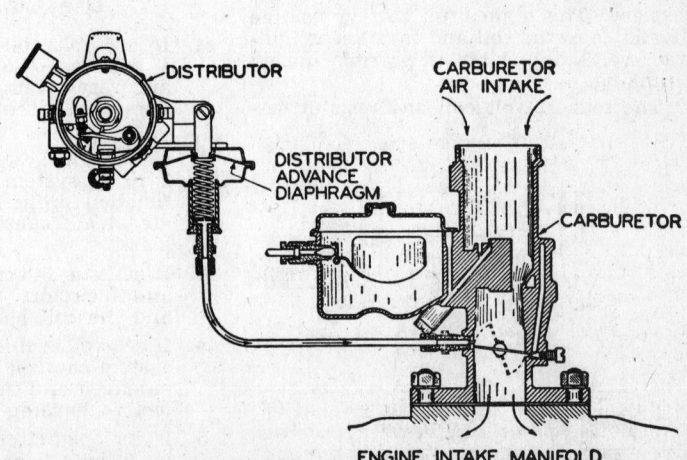

Fig. 34 Auto-Lite vacuum advance mechanism of type which is clamped around the distributor so that the entire distributor is rotated as vacuum conditions change

against the bottom of the breaker plate.

On some distributors, both springs are alike, while on others there is one heavy and one light spring, as in Fig. 31. Another combination that may be found is an additional flat spring on the outside of the outer spring posts, Fig. 32. As the governor speed is increased, the flat springs are first pulled against the posts by the eyes of the coil springs to provide a rapid spark advance of a few degrees before the coil springs pull against the spring posts.

Vacuum Advance Mechanisms

The two types of vacuum advance mechanisms used are illustrated in Figs. 33 and 34. Both types make use of a spring-loaded diaphragm which is connected through linkage to the distributor. The spring loaded side of the diaphragm is air tight and is connected through a vacuum line to the carburetor or intake manifold.

When the throttle is open, vacuum from the intake manifold is introduced into the vacuum advance mechanism and the diaphragm is pulled against the spring, causing the distributor to advance.

In Fig. 33 the mechanism is attached to the distributor breaker plate so that the breaker plate rotates. In Fig. 34 the mechanism is connected to the distributor body so that the entire distributor moves. In both cases, the rotational movement carries the contact points around to an advanced position so that the breaker cam closes and opens the points earlier in the cycle.

Auto-Lite IBP Distributors

Used on some late model Chrysler Corp. cars, this distributor uses a very different type vacuum spark advance. Unlike other systems which either rotate the breaker plate or the entire distributor when manifold vacuum is high, the IBP breaker plate is pivoted in such a way

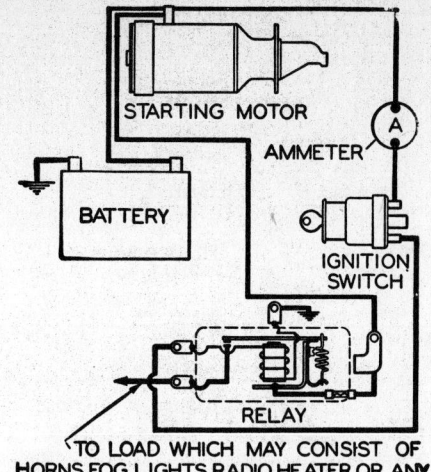

INSTALLED AS ACCESSORY LOAD RELAY TO RELIEVE LOAD ON IGNITION SWITCH

Fig. 35 Showing relay connected in ignition circuit to prevent overloading of ignition switch when accessories are connected through the switch

that the points swing in an arc about the cam when the vacuum advance unit is in operation. Thus, cam angle and breaker point gap change as high manifold vacuum advances the spark. For this reason cam angle should be checked with the vacuum line disconnected and the point gap checked or adjusted when the vacuum advance unit is in full retard position.

Ignition Wiring

The current carrying capacity of all ignition wiring should not be less than that specified by the car manufacturers. All terminals should be securely soldered to the wires and all joints and connections should be clean and tightened with lock washers.

The connecting leads in the distributor should be installed so that the terminals are screwed down tight and in such a manner that they will not interfere with the cap or rotor.

When testing the leads for open circuits, a slight tension should be placed on them, or they should be moved back and forth to find broken wires inside the insulation, which may make contact temporarily during the test.

All leads inside the distributor should be bent away from contact with the housing or other moving parts so that the insulation will not chafe and cause failure due to rubbing or vibration.

The high tension wiring is subjected to high voltage and, therefore, insulation is important. Leakage may exist without being visible, causing poor engine performance. See the *Tune Up* chapter for inspecting and testing data. Special attention should be given to any part of the cables surrounded by metal manifolds or brackets, as any weakness of the insulation inside the metal would cause current leakage and cross-firing, resulting in poor engine performance, especially in wet weather.

Metal manifolds and metal cable brackets should be grounded to the engine. Troublesome engine missing has sometimes been corrected by a good ground connection for these metal parts.

Ignition Switch

Ignition switches are usually designed to carry the ignition circuit only. When accessories such as heater, radio, fan, defroster, etc. are connected through the ignition switch, the switch is overloaded, causing overheating of the switch, which results in the reduction of the energy delivered to the ignition circuit.

When it is desirable to connect accessories to the ignition switch to prevent their being accidentally left on—which would discharge the battery — they should be connected through a relay, Fig. 35, to prevent overloading and consequent ignition switch trouble.

ALTERNATOR SYSTEMS

Alternators, otherwise known as A.C. (alternating current) generators, are used mainly in buses, refrigerated trucks, trucks used in stop-and-go city delivery service, and other vehicles such as police cars, ambulances, and taxicabs equipped with telephones. In all such vehicles the conventional D.C. generator is unable to supply sufficient current for the heavy duty electrical loads required.

To understand how the A.C. system overcomes these limitations it may be helpful to review briefly the operation and construction of the conventional D.C. system.

It may come as a surprise to some that the D.C. generator actually produces alternating current. As the armature rotates through the magnetic field produced by the field coils, alternating current is induced in the armature coil, then flows through the commutator and brushes, where it is converted to direct current. With this design, cooling can be a serious problem under high-output, low-speed conditions. Low speed output can be increased and satisfactory cooling secured by changing the drive ratio (using smaller pulley) to turn the generator faster at low engine rpm. This scheme works fine if engine speed can be limited, but the generator will turn at excessive rpm if the vehicle is operated at cruising speed on the highway. The result is likely to be thrown armature windings and rapid wear of commutator and brushes.

The electrical system of a motor vehicle cannot use alternating current because the battery, ignition system and other electrical devices are designed for direct current use. Although the A.C. generator produces alternating current, direct current is provided by means of the rectifier as we shall soon see.

Alternator System Components

The alternator is composed of the same functional parts as a D.C. generator; however, they operate differently. The field is called a rotor and is the turning portion of the unit. A generating part, called a stator, is the stationary member (comparable to the armature in a D.C. generator). The rectifier, which changes alternating current to direct

ALTERNATOR SYSTEMS

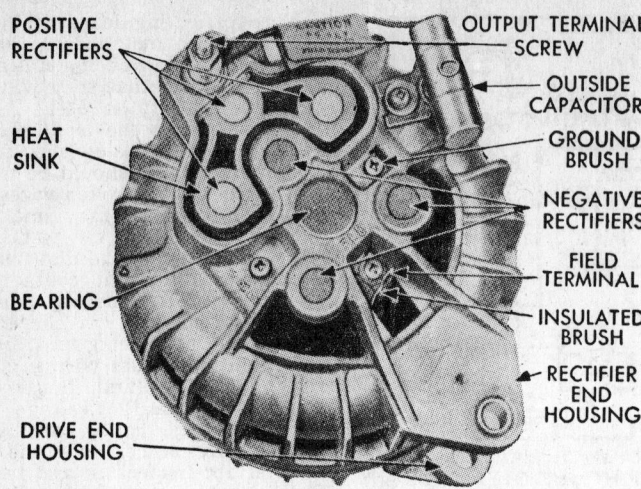

Fig. 1 Chrysler alternator

current, can be compared to the commutator and brushes in a D.C. generator. The regulator, similar to those used in a D.C. system, regulates the output of the generator-rectifier system.

The power source of the system is the alternator. Current is transmitted from the field terminal of the regulator through a slip ring to the field coil and back to ground through another slip ring. The strength of the field regulates the output of the alternating current. This alternating current is then transmitted from the alternator to the rectifier where it is converted to direct current.

Alternator systems are currently manufactured by Delco-Remy, Leece-Neville and Chrysler. However, inasmuch as only the Chrysler system is used as standard equipment on passenger cars, we will confine this chapter to it.

CHRYSLER SYSTEM

This system consists of an alternator, Fig. 1, that generates alternating cur-

rent with six rectifiers to convert alternating current to direct current, and a regulator to limit the direct current voltage.

Alternator

The main components of the alternator are the two end housings, the stator, the rotor and the rectifiers. The two end housings are held together by three through bolts. The housings are vented at both ends and around the outer diameter. Cool air is drawn through the ends and out over the stator windings through the outer diameter vents. The stator assembly, Fig. 2, is sandwiched between the two end housings.

The rotor, Fig. 3, consists of a dough-nut-shaped field coil encased between the six-fingered, overlapping sections which are the pole pieces. The rotor produces an effective 12-pole rotating magnetic field. The ends of the field coil are connected to slip rings. The battery is connected to the field windings through the regulator, the brushes, and the slip rings.

The rotor shaft is supported at the drive end by a pre-lubricated ball bearing. At the opposite end the rotor shaft is supported by a pre-lubricated roller bearing.

Rectifiers

In the alternator, the alternating current is converted to direct current through six silicon diode rectifiers, Fig. 2. Three of the rectifiers have negative polarity cases and are pressed into the die cast aluminum end housing. These rectifiers are in the ground side of the system. The remaining three rectifiers have positive polarity cases and are pressed into the die cast heat sink. The heat sink is electrically insulated from the end housing but has sufficient area to absorb the heat from the rectifiers that are pressed into it.

The chemical composition of a diode is such that it will allow current to flow through itself in only one direction. Therefore, with the proper polarity, the low resistance allows current to flow from the alternator to the battery. The high resistance prevents current from flowing from the battery to the alternator.

Caution: Always be sure the negative post of the battery only is connected to ground when installing a battery. A battery that is installed and connected backwards may result in burning out the rectifiers.

Voltage Regulator

The Chrysler system is protected by a conventional type voltage regulator. No circuit breaker is needed for this system since current can flow through the silicon diode rectifiers in only one direction. Current regulation is automatically controlled by the self-limiting characteristic of the alternator; the inherent reactance within the stator windings impedes and limits the output to the capacity of the system, therefore, no current regulator unit is necessary.

In the voltage regulator, the contacts open when the voltage becomes too high, causing the field current to flow through

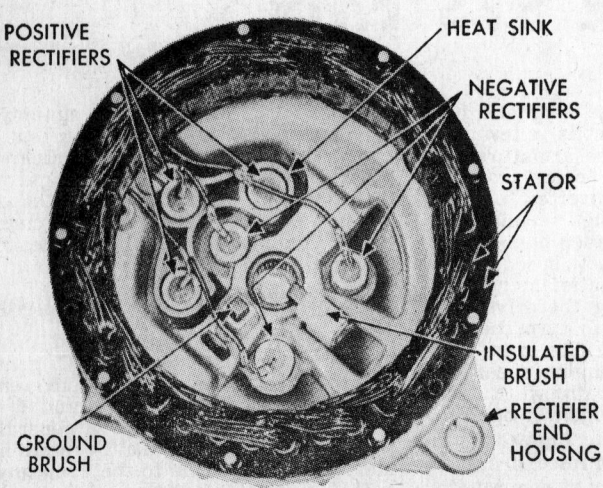

Fig. 2 Stator and rectifier end housing assembly

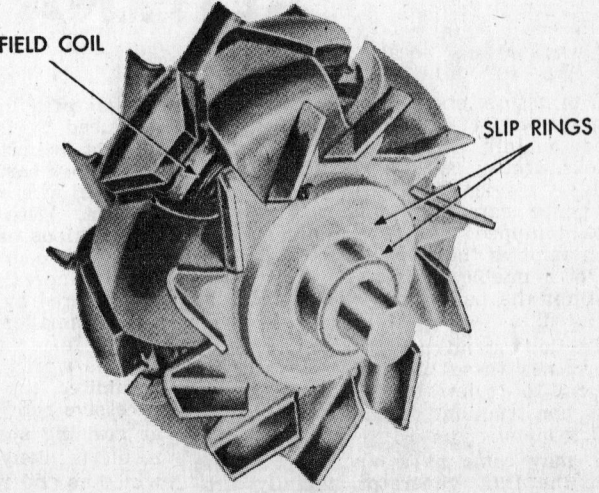

Fig. 3 Rotor assembly

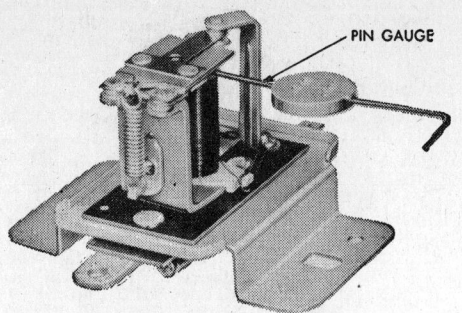

Fig. 4 Checking regulator armature air gap

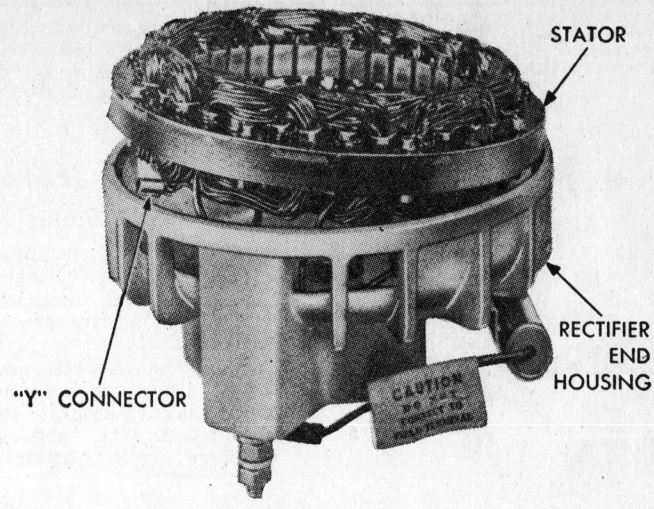

Fig. 6 Separating stator and end housing to expose connector

a resistor. This, of course, reduces the strength of the field and so lowers the voltage output of the alternator.

TESTING THE SYSTEM

Installed In Vehicle

With the battery fully charged and in good condition and engine at normal operating temperature, test the system as follows after first checking the fuse between the regulator and ignition switch.

Caution: Never ground the field circuit between the alternator and regulator as this will result in damage to the voltage regulator.

Charging Circuit Resistance Test Current Output Test

1. Remove the output lead from the alternator battery terminal and connect a D.C. ammeter between the terminal and the disconnected lead.
2. Connect a D.C. voltmeter positive lead to the output lead that was disconnected from the alternator and connect the volmeter negative lead to the battery positive post.
3. Start the engine and adjust its speed to produce 10 amperes from the alternator. The voltage reading should not exceed .2 volt. If there is a higher voltage drop, clean and tighten all connections in the charging circuit and recheck. A voltage drop test across each connection will locate any bad connections.

Current Output Test

1. Disconnect field lead at alternator and at regulator.
2. Install a D.C. ammeter in series with the alternator battery terminal and the wire disconnected from the alternator output terminal.
3. Connect a jumper between the battery terminal and the alternator field terminal.
4. Connect a carbon pile rheostat across the battery.
5. Connect a voltmeter positive lead to the alternator battery terminal and ground the voltmeter negative lead to the alternator housing.
6. Install a tachometer, start the engine and adjust engine speed to 1250 rpm.
7. Adjust carbon pile to obtain 40 amperes while making tests. Turn off immediately when test is completed. The current output should be as specified in the *Alternator Specifications* tables in the car chapters. *If the output is low, the stator or a rectifier is shorted.*
8. Adjust engine speed to 2200 rpm. If output is excessive a rectifier is open. If output is low a rectifier is shorted.

Voltage Regulator Test

1. Disconnect the lead from the alternator output terminal. Connect an ammeter between the battery terminal and the disconnected wire.
2. Connect a D.C. voltmeter positive lead to the alternator battery output terminal and ground the voltmeter negative lead to the alternator housing or regulator base.
3. Start the engine and adjust its speed to 1400 rpm and with ammeter reading 10 amperes by turning on lights, etc. Operate engine for 15 minutes to stabilize temperature

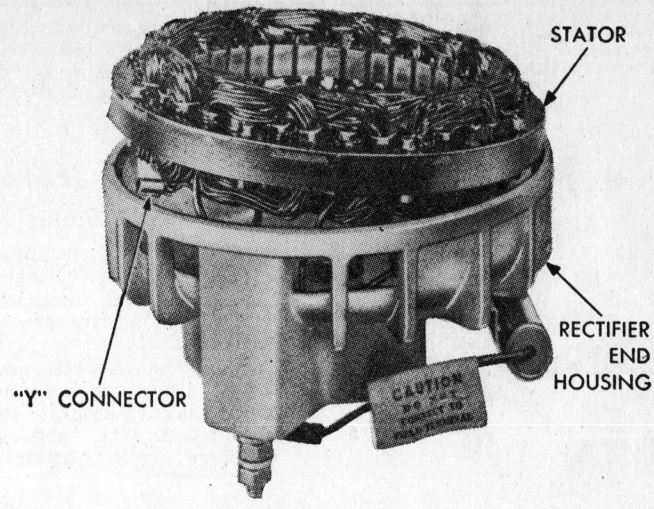

INSULATOR SLEEVE
CONTACT POINTS
ARMATURE
BENDING TOOL
IGNITION SWITCH
SPRING HANGERS
FIELD

Fig. 5 Adjusting spring tension to obtain correct voltage

(regulator cover in place). Check temperature with a thermometer two inches from regulator cover. Adjust engine speed to 1250 rpm. With 15 amperes flowing in the circuit, the voltage should be as given in the specification table in the car chapters.
4. Then increase engine speed to 2200 rpm with five amperes flowing. Voltage should not exceed previous readings by more than .7 volt.
5. If the voltage specifications are not met, remove the regulator for adjustment.

Voltage Regulator Adjustments

In making adjustments, do not short circuit between spring hanger and base or spring. Grounding the spring hanger will damage the regulator.

Armature Air Gap

1. Check air gap with a test lamp connected between ignition and field terminals on the regulator.
2. Insert the .048″ wire gauge, Fig. 4.
3. Press armature plate down (not contact spring). Contacts should open and test lamp should go dim.
4. Insert the .052″ gauge in same position and depress armature plate. Upper contacts should be closed and test lamp should remain lighted.
5. Bend upper contact support as necessary to obtain proper adjustment.

Point Gap

Set lower contact gap to .015″ (plus or minus .001″) by bending lower contact arm. Press the armature plate down so that the armature rests on the nylon stop. Release and recheck gap.

Spring Tension

Always make this adjustment by bending the lower spring hanger, Fig. 5. If the voltage was found to be too high, bend the lower hanger *up*. If the voltage was low, bend the lower hanger down

Install the regulator and repeat the

Fig. 7 Removing or installing insulated brush

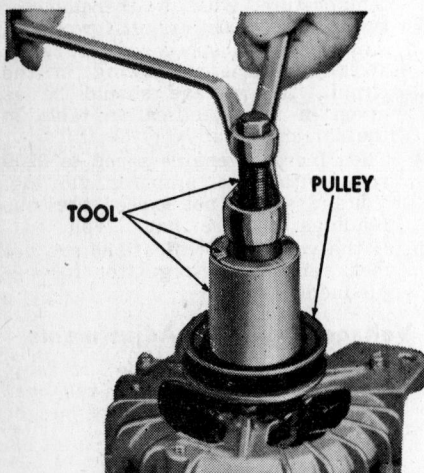

Fig. 8 Removing pulley

Fig. 9 Removing bearing from rotor shaft

tests outlined previously. If further adjustment is necessary, adjust spring tension only. *If adjustment is attempted on the car, do not short circuit between spring hanger and base as regulator will be damaged.*

BENCH TESTS
Field Circuit

1. Disconnect field terminal wire at alternator and at voltage regulator.
2. Connect a D.C. ammeter positive lead to the alternator battery output terminal.
3. Connect the ammeter negative lead to the alternator field terminal.
4. The field current draw should be as specified in the table in the car chapters while turning the rotor shaft manually.

Testing Rectifiers

1. Disassemble alternator as outlined further on and separate the wires at the connector at stator, Fig. 6.
2. Test rectifiers with a #67 bulb test lamp.
3. Connect one side of the test lamp to the positive battery post. Connect the other side of the lamp to a test probe. Connect another test probe to the negative battery post.
4. Touch the outer case of the rectifier with one probe and the other probe to the wire in the center of the rectifier.
5. Reverse the probes.
6. If the test lamp lights in one direction the rectifier is good. If lamp lights in both directions the rectifier is shorted. If lamp does not light in either direction the rectifier is open. *The usual cause of an open or shorted rectifier is a defective capacitor (condenser) or a battery that has been installed in reverse polarity.*

Testing Stator

1. Disconnect rectifiers from stator leads.
2. Inspect stator connections.
3. Test from stator leads to stator core, using 110-volt test lamp. If lamp lights stator is grounded, in which case replace stater.

Excessive Ammeter Fluctuation

If this condition shows up, and is accompanied by flickering headlamps or inferior lights, it may be caused by high resistance in the field circuit to the alternator, or an improperly set voltage regulator.

To correctly diagnose this condition, disconnect the lead at the "IGN" terminal of the regulator. Connect a jumper lead from the positive post of the battery to the "IGN" terminal of the regulator. This will by-pass the car wiring harness circuit to the regulator.

Start and operate the engine at 1250 rpm and observe the lights and ammeter pointer. If the pointer is now normal and the lights do not flicker the cause of the

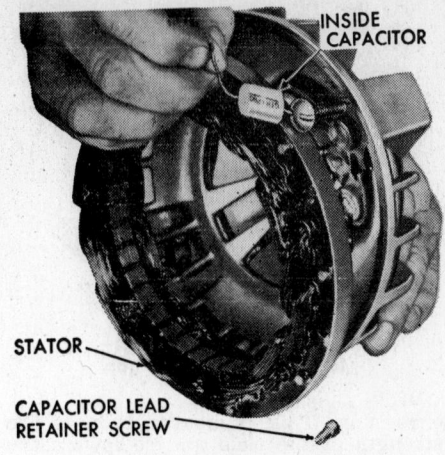

Fig. 10 Removing or installing inside capacitor

fluctuation is corrosion or other high resistance in the field circuit, connectors or the "in-line" fuse holder.

Remove the jumper lead. Clean the connections and tighten the connectors if necessary. Tape the fuse holder completely to prevent moisture and dirt from entering the holder.

If the jumper lead did not correct the excessive ammeter fluctuation the regulator is improperly adjusted and should be corrected as outlined previously.

Excessive ammeter fluctuation should not be confused with the normal action of the regulator and ammeter in any car whether it has an alternator or D.C. generator in which the ammeter may normally show small irregular movements when the regulator just begins to regulate.

Battery Charging

In all cases where a "quick charge" battery charger is used without removing the battery, both car battery cables must be disconnected from the battery before the charger is connected to the battery. *Do not use a "quick charge" to provide starting voltage.*

If it becomes necessary to use a booster battery to start the car, be sure to connect the negative cable of the booster battery to the negative terminal of the car battery and the positive cable of the booster battery to the positive terminal of the car battery.

ALTERNATOR REPAIRS
Service Note

Whenever the alternator is disassembled for servicing, it is recommended that the two long rectifier-to-stator leads be located between the rectifiers in the heat sink and cemented to the rectifier end housing using weatherstrip adhesive. This is especially important if a replacement is made of an early type diode rectifier. The cementing of the leads will reduce vibration of the leads with resultant longer life of the rectifiers and leads.

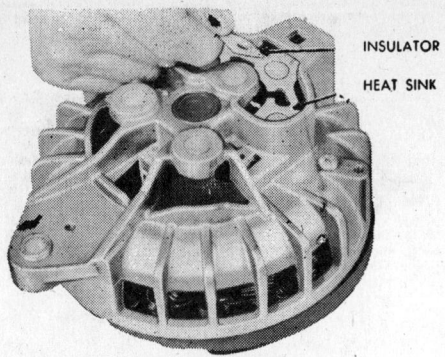

Fig. 11 Removing or installing heat sink insulator

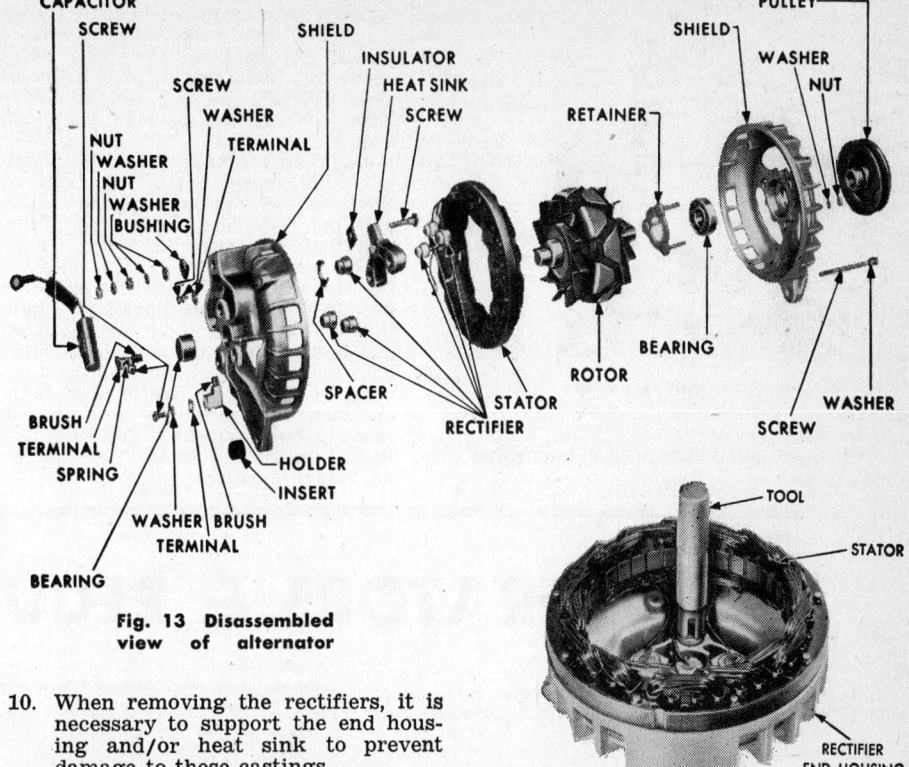

Fig. 13 Disassembled view of alternator

Disassembly

To prevent possible damage to the brush assemblies, Fig. 7, they should be removed before proceeding with the disassembly of the alternator. The insulated brush is mounted in a plastic holder that positions the brush vertically against one of the slip rings.

1. Remove the field terminal and related parts and lift the plastic holder containing the spring and brush from the end housing.
2. The ground brush is positioned horizontally against the remaining slip ring and is retained in a holder that is integral with the end housing. Remove the retaining screw and lift the clip, spring and brush from the end housing. *Stator is laminated; do not burr stator or end housings.*
3. Remove through bolts and pry between stator and drive end housing with a thin blade screwdriver. Carefully separate drive end housing, pulley and rotor from stator and rectifier housing.
4. Remove pulley with a puller, Fig. 8.
5. Remove three nuts and washers and, while supporting end frame, tap rotor shaft with a plastic hammer and separate rotor and end housing.
6. Remove drive end bearing with a puller, Fig. 9.
7. Remove D.C. output terminal screw and inside capacitor or condenser (on units so equipped), Fig. 10.
8. The heat sink, Fig. 11, is held in place by a terminal screw.
9. Remove the insulator.

10. When removing the rectifiers, it is necessary to support the end housing and/or heat sink to prevent damage to these castings.
11. Refer to "Rectifier Testing," and if the rectifiers must be replaced, proceed as follows: Cut rectifier wire at point of crimp. Support rectifier housing on Tool C-3771. This tool is cutaway and slotted to fit over the wires and around the bosses in the housing. Make sure that the bore of the tool completely surrounds the rectifier, then press the rectifier out of the housing, using Tool SP-3380, Fig. 12.

Reassembly, Fig. 13

1. Check rectifier identification to make sure correct rectifier is being used. Identifying part numbers are stamped on the case of the rectifier. They may also be identified by paint marks: red for positive and black for negative.
2. Start new rectifier into case squarely and press rectifier into casting, Fig. 14.
3. Crimp new rectifier wire to wires disconnected at removal.
4. Press bearing into end housing, Fig. 15.
5. Insert bearing in drive end housing and install bearing plate, washers and nuts to hold bearing in place.
6. Position bearing and drive end housing on rotor shaft and, while supporting the base of rotor shaft, press bearing and housing into position on rotor shaft, Fig. 16. Bearing must contact shoulder on rotor shaft.
7. Install pulley on rotor shaft, Fig. 17. Shaft of rotor must be supported in a manner so that all pressing force is on pulley hub and rotor shaft. Bearing should just contact bearing inner race, and bearing

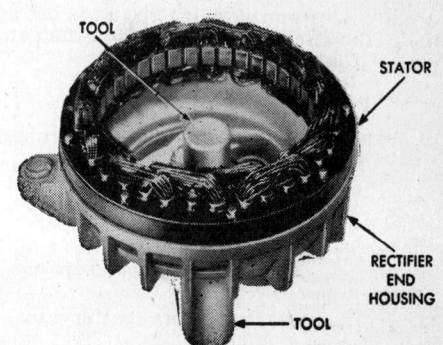

Fig. 14 Installing a rectifier

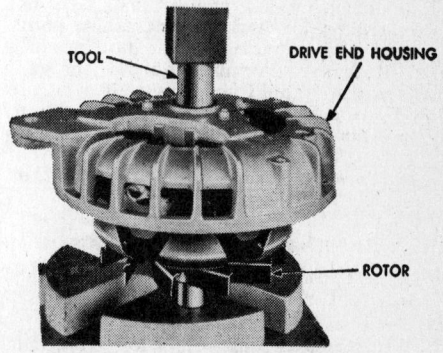

Fig. 15 Installing rectifier end housing bearing

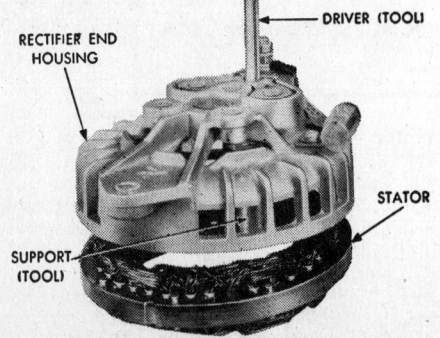

Fig. 12 Removing a rectifier

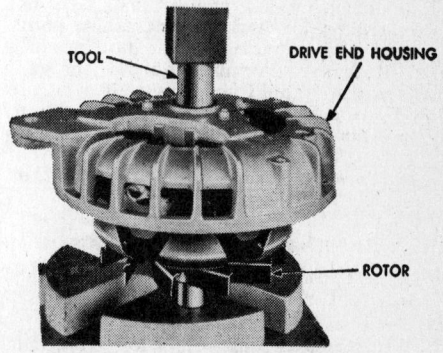

Fig. 16 Installing drive end housing and bearing on rotor shaft

ALTERNATOR SYSTEMS

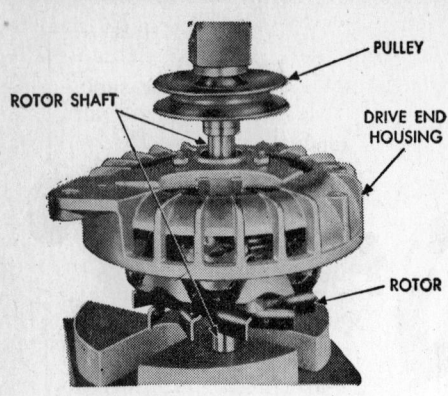

Fig. 17 Installing pulley

should contact shoulder on rotor shaft.

8. If alternator is equipped with an internal capacitor (condenser). make sure heat sink insulator is in place.
9. Install output terminal screw with capacitor attached through heat sink and end housing. Install insulating washers, lockwashers and lock nuts.
10. Position stator on rectifier end housing. Make sure that all of the rectifier connectors and phase leads will not interfere with rotor fans and that capacitor lead has clearance.
11. Position rotor in rectifier end housing and drive end housing. Align through-bolt holes in stator, rectifier end housing and drive end housing.
12. Enter shaft in rectifier end housing bearing. Compress stator and both end housings manually and install through-bolts, washers and nuts.
13. Install insulating brush and terminal attaching screw.

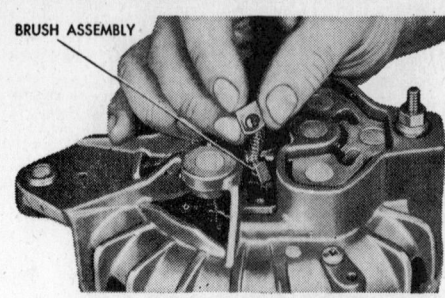

Fig. 18 Installing ground brush

14. Install ground brush and attaching screw, Fig. 18.
15. Rotate pulley slowly to make sure rotor fans do not hit rectifier and stator connectors.

GENERATORS & REGULATORS

GENERATOR OUTPUT TEST

Before making this test, consult the *Generator and Regulator Specifications* table in the vehicle chapter to determine whether the generator is grounded externally in the regulator or if it is grounded internally within the generator. Having determined which circuit is used, make the current output test on the car as follows:

External Ground Systems

1. Make sure all lights and accessories are turned off.
2. Disconnect lead from field terminal of regulator and ground this lead, Fig. 3. *If this in not done on Delco-Remy double contact regulators the upper set of contacts will burn instantly.*
3. Disconnect lead from battery terminal of regulator.
4. Start engine and gradually increase its speed until the ammeter indicates at least 25% above the rated generator output. This will indicate that the generator is in good condition provided the brushes are not arcing excessively at this point. If the generator does not produce its rated maximum output, the generator should be checked further to determine the cause of low output. *Disconnect the test leads as soon as the test is completed to prevent overheating the generator and then stop the engine.*

Internal Ground Systems

1. Referring to Fig. 4, disconnect armature and field wires at generator.
2. Connect a jumper wire from the generator armature terminal to the generator field terminal.

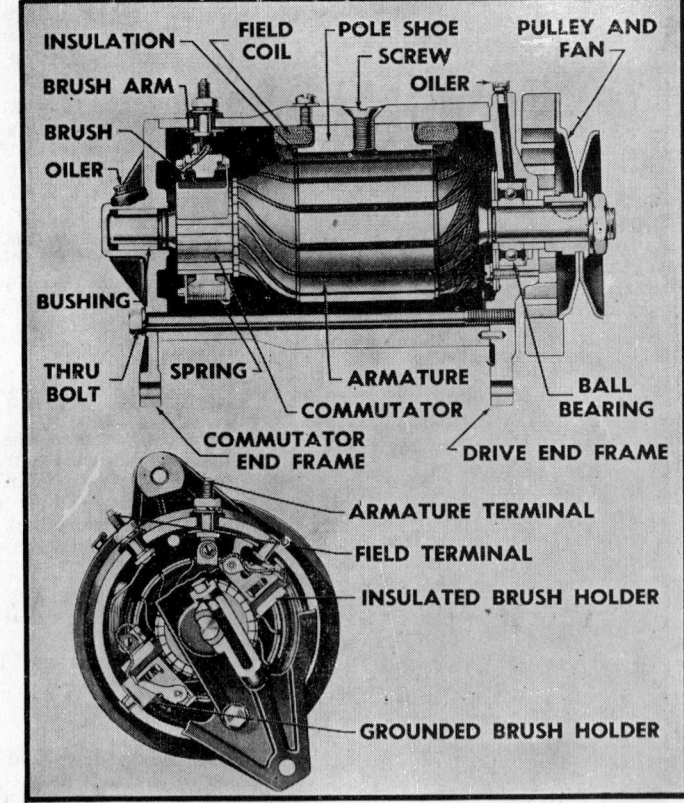

Fig. 1 Typical automobile generator driven by a fan belt

3. Connect the positive lead of a test ammeter to the generator armature terminal.
4. Start the engine and while it is idling, connect the ammeter negative lead to the positive terminal of the battery.
5. Run the engine at a fast idle speed (1500 rpm) and read the current output on the ammeter. If the rated maximum output is not indicated on the ammeter, the generator should be checked further. *Disconnect the test leads as soon as the test is completed to prevent overheating the generator and then stop engine.*

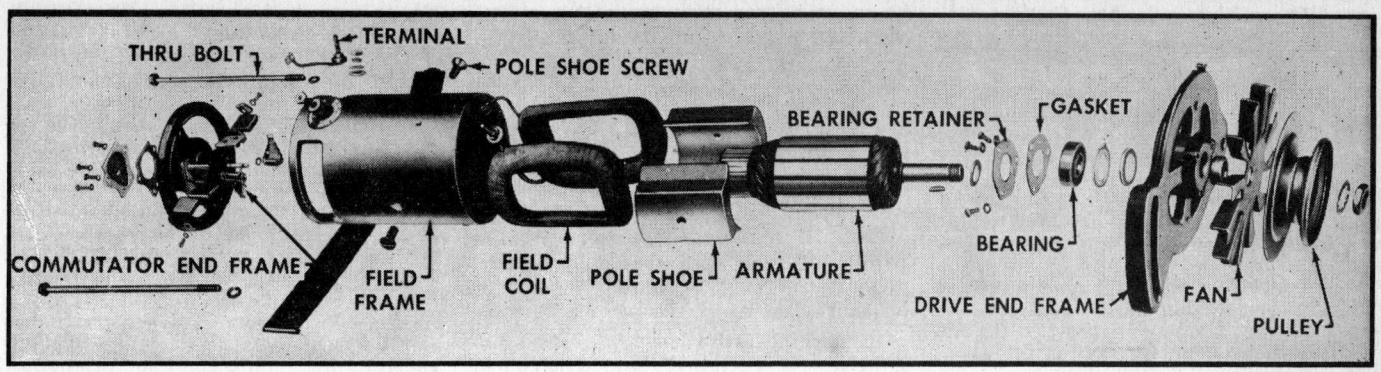

Fig. 2 Exploded view of generator similar to that shown in Fig. 1

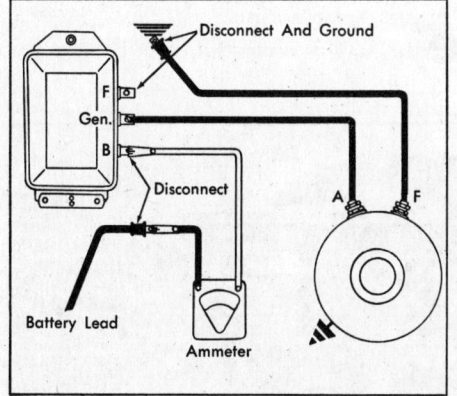

Fig. 3 Generator current output test connections for external ground systems. It is imperative to disconnect and ground the field lead on Delco-Remy double contact voltage regulators, otherwise the upper set of contacts will burn up instantly

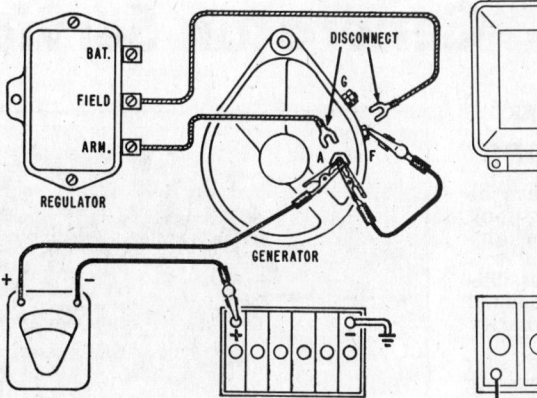

Fig. 4 Generator current output test connections for internal ground systems

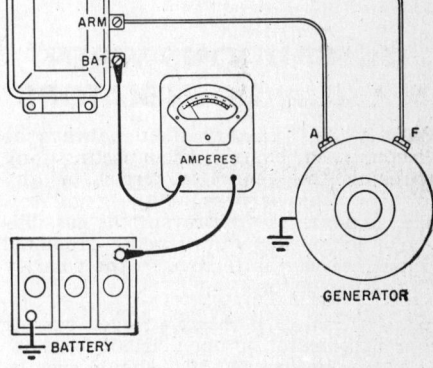

Fig. 6 Ammeter connected in circuit for testing purposes when isolating conditions causing too high or too low charging rates

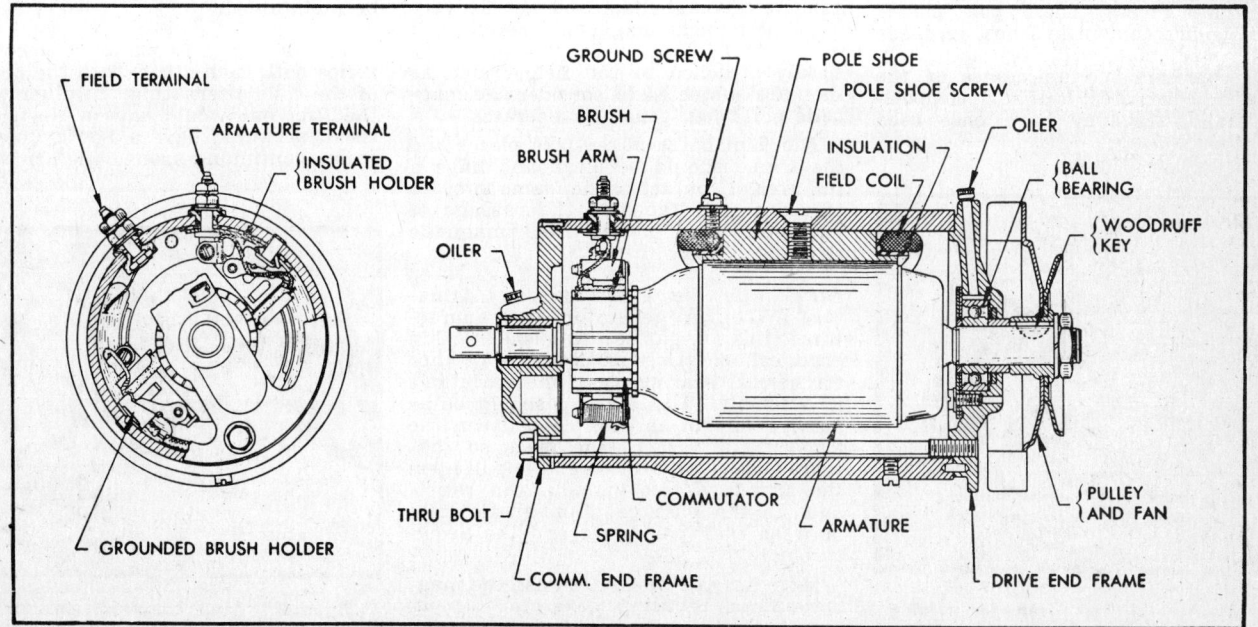

Fig. 5 Construction of Delco-Remy generator with an extruded frame. There is no cover band so inspection is made through openings in commutator end frame. The use of a mirror will aid in the inspection

When There Is No Output

The first step is to inspect the interior of the generator for:
1. Sticking brushes.
2. Worn, rough or dirty commutator.
3. Commutator out of round.
4. High mica between commutator segments.
5. Thrown solder which indicates an open circuit between armature windings and commutator segments (see Figs. 1, 2 and 5).
6. Test and service the generator as outlined further on.

When Charge Is Too High or Too Low

Quick checks on these conditions can be made by inserting an accurate test ammeter in the circuit as in Fig. 6.

If the charging rate is too high, it indicates that the charging rate is not being reduced when it should be. To localize the trouble, run the engine at a fast idle. Remove the wire from the regulator field terminal. If the charging rate now drops to zero, the regulator is at fault. If high charging rate continues with the field wire disconnected, the generator is faulty or there is a grounded or shorted wire in the wiring harness.

If charging rate is too low, a preliminary check of the battery and cables must be made. After the battery has been checked and the terminals and cables cleaned, proceed as follows on all units *except those equipped with the Delco-Remy double contact voltage regulator.*

Run the engine at a fast idle and temporarily place a jumper wire between the proper points to eliminate the regulator from the circuit. If the charging rate increases appreciably, the trouble is in the voltage regulator. If the charging rate remains low, the trouble is either in the generator or in some other connection in the charging circuit. *Do not overlook the possibility of a loose drive belt.*

Caution—On vehicles equipped with Delco-Remy double contact regulator, test as outlined for *No Output Test* for these units.

Generator Service

PRECAUTIONS WHEN SERVICING GENERATORS

Battery—The battery should always be disconnected before disconnecting any wires in the generator circuit or any wires in the harness at the regulator. This is necessary to prevent the possibility of loose connections being grounded in such a way as to reverse the polarity of the generator.

Open Circuit Operation—Never run or test a generator on open circuit for more than a few seconds. If it should ever be necessary to operate the generator with the battery disconnected, the generator must be grounded and both the armature and field wires disconnected from the generator. The brushes should also be raised from the commutator or both the generator and regulator will be damaged.

Field Pole Pieces—These pole pieces, otherwise known as pole shoes, are made of soft steel machined very accurately to fit the inner circumference of the frame. The soft steel is of such composition that after they have once been

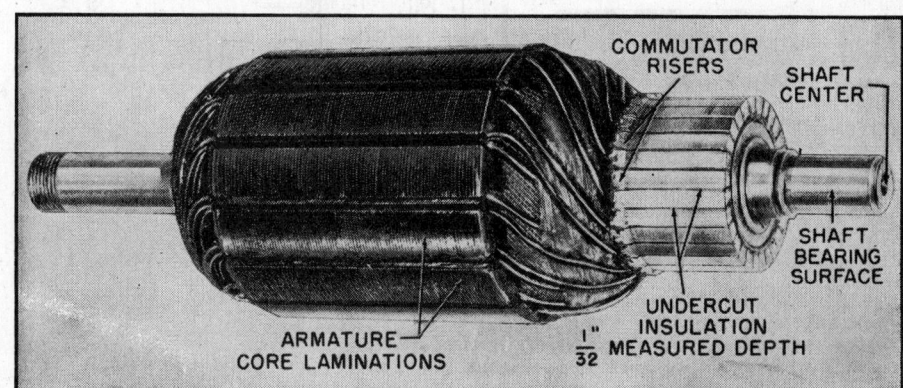

Fig. 7 Typical generator armature

magnetized, they will retain a small amount of magnetism and act as very weak permanent magnets. Therefore, it is important that these pole pieces be rigidly attached to the field frame as they are subjected to considerable magnetic pull when generator operates.

The joint between the pole pieces and the frame should be clean and have a full area of contact to the frame in order to reduce resistance to the passage of magnetic lines in the field magnetic circuit.

Air Gap Between Pole Pieces and Armature—When a generator is manufactured, this air gap is established within practical operating limits with allowance for normal bearing wear and variations in assembly. This air gap should be as nearly uniform as possible between the armature and each pole piece so that there will be uniform magnetic pull upon the armature core and uniform resistance to the passage of magnetic lines between each pole piece and the armature core.

More air gap would decrease the magnetic lines, reducing generator output, and less air gap would increase the magnetic lines. Therefore, if the bearings are in the least doubtful, they should be replaced in order that a uniform air gap be maintained.

Field Coils—Field coils are connected in series with each other, with the polarity of the coils alternating. In other words, the first one would have a North Pole, the next would have a South Pole, and so on, continuing around the armature.

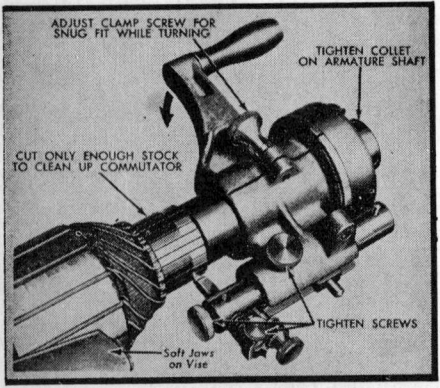

Fig. 8 Special tool used for turning commutator. If a lathe is used for this operation be sure to mount the armature on the bearing surfaces, not on shaft centers

Fig. 9 After turning commutator, mount armature in V blocks and check commutator for runout with dial gauge. Runout should not exceed .001"

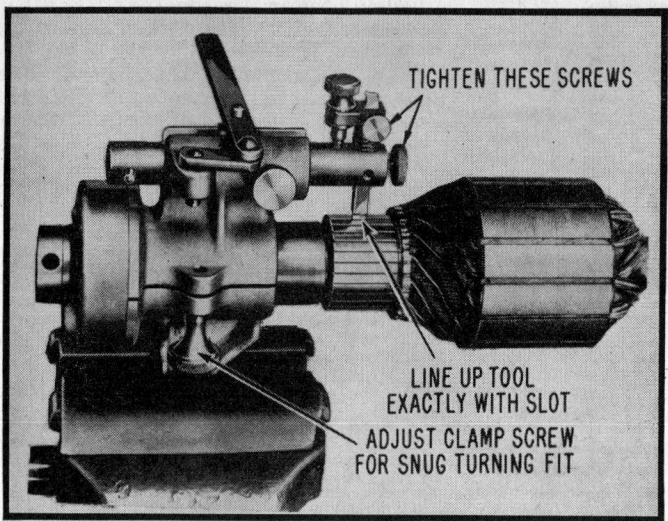

TIGHTEN THESE SCREWS

LINE UP TOOL
EXACTLY WITH SLOT

ADJUST CLAMP SCREW
FOR SNUG TURNING FIT

Fig. 10 Commutator mica insulation should be undercut 1/32″ measured depth

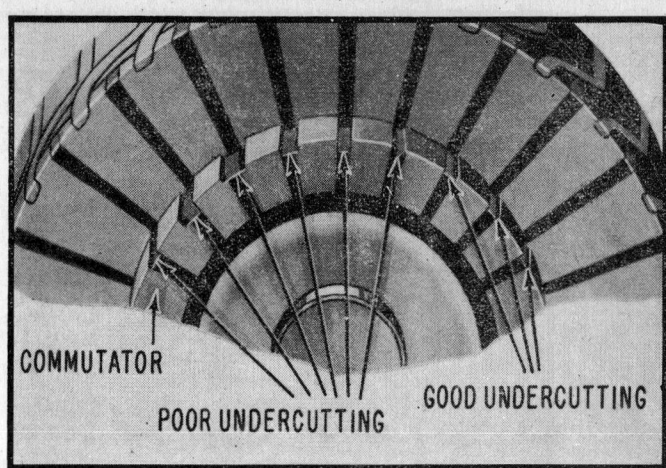

COMMUTATOR

POOR UNDERCUTTING

GOOD UNDERCUTTING

Fig. 11 Examples of proper and improper undercutting

If there is any doubt about the correctness of the assembly, it can easily be checked with an ordinary compass, and with normal voltage in the field circuit. This could happen, for example, in the case of someone trying to save money by replacing only one field coil and obtaining it from a salvage establishment. Not only is the danger of the coil being of the wrong polarity present but it may be one having more or less turns than the field coil designed for the generator. Therefore, whenever one field coil requires replacement, the safest thing to do is to replace the set.

Armature—The armature core is made up of soft steel laminations in which slots are stamped on the outer circumference to carry the armature windings.

The surface of these laminations, Fig. 7, is treated to form an oxidized coating which serves as an insulation between the laminations, thereby reducing the stray currents which otherwise would be present. This coating serves also to lower the temperature of the core and increases the efficiency of the generator. Therefore, armature cores should never be turned or filed, as such treatment would cause short circuits between core laminations, increasing its operating temperature and reducing the efficiency of the generator.

Commutators—It is important that commutators be turned concentric with the armature shaft bearing surfaces. Armatures are manufactured with a concentricity of less than .0005″ for the brush surfaces in relation to the shaft bearing surfaces.

Therefore, turn commutators by mounting them on the shaft bearing surfaces, not on the shaft centers. The bearings do not run on the shaft centers in the generator, Fig. 7.

Commutators should be turned at a speed of approximately 1200 rpm with a sharp tool set exactly on center, Fig. 8, so that a dead smooth surface can be produced with very little sandpapering.

When sandpaper is applied to a commutator, use a strip of 00 about 10″ long. Hold the ends of the paper and let the center of the paper strip rub on the commutator surface. It is not good practice to hold the sandpaper directly against the commutator with the fingers.

After turning the commutator, its concentricity can be checked with a dial gauge, Fig. 9.

The mica insulation between commutator bars should be undercut $\frac{1}{32}$″ measured depth, Figs. 10 and 11. Do not permit the undercutter shaft to rub on the commutator bars as this would produce flat spots on the commutator, reducing the contact area of the brushes.

The saw for undercutting should be

Bulb

6v Battery

Armature
Commutator Bars

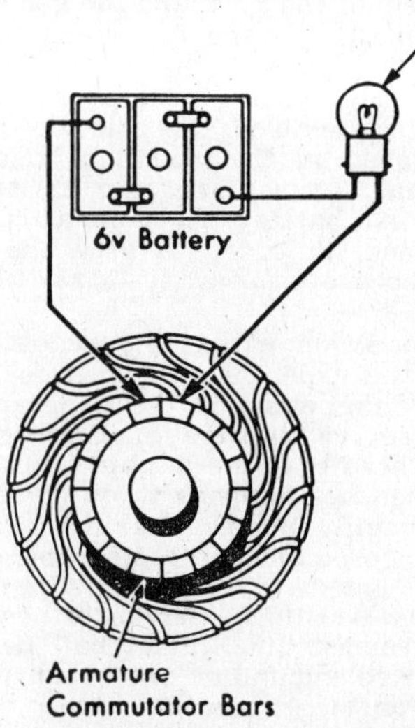

Fig. 12 Hook-up for testing armature for open circuit. When checking against commutator bars, no light will indicate open-circuited armature coils. With a 12-volt system, use a 12-volt battery and 12-volt bulb.

about .002″ wider than the insulation between the bars to insure a complete cutting of the insulation.

After undercutting, any burrs left on the edges of the bars should be cleaned off with a narrow scraper that can be drawn the full length of the undercut groove. Then the armature should be checked for short circuits and open circuits in a growler, Figs. 12 and 13.

Brush Holders—The proper alignment of brush holders is important to obtain maximum generator output with minimum arcing at the brushes. An easy way of checking the alignment of opposite brush holders is to lay a hacksaw blade across both brush holders. Press down on the center of the blade and note if both sides of both brush holders touch the blade. Correction can be made by bending the holder with a screwdriver between the end frame and holder.

Place the commutator end frame on the armature and install new brushes. The edges of the brushes should be parallel with the commutator bars.

Brushes—The seating of brushes is extremely important as it is recommended that brushes be fitted to the commutator with 00 sandpaper, drawn between the brush and commutator, *against the brush holder,* as shown in Fig. 14.

The general practice of placing a band of sandpaper on the commutator and turning the commutator in the direction of its normal rotation is not recommended, as in some generators the brush holders are mounted so that some brushes may operate against rotation and other brushes with rotation. In this case, one brush would be properly seated and the other would have a rounded contact surface, causing arcing. Usually, a strip of 00 sandpaper, approximately 10″ long, pulled through once in the direction to move the brush against the brush holder results in a satisfactory brush seat.

Brushes should be carefully sandpapered to obtain as nearly as possible a full area of contact between the brush and commutator, otherwise it may be difficult to obtain normal output of the

HACKSAW BLADE

OPEN CORE TRANSFORMER (GROWLER)

Fig. 13 Checking armature for short circuit with a growler. As armature is rotated by hand, steel strip (hacksaw blade) will vibrate if short circuit exists

generator. The brushes and brush leads should be free to move in the brush holders to follow the commutator with uniform pressure as the brushes wear.

Brush spring tension should be measured with a good spring scale and adjusted according to the specifications of the generator. If the specifications call for a minimum and maximum limit, they should be adjusted to the maximum pressure so that as the brushes wear, any reduction in pressure will be within limits for a long period of time.

When measuring brush spring tension, use a strip of paper between the brush and commutator, maintaining a slight pull on the paper. Very gradually pull on the scale until the paper can be slipped from under the brush and take a reading on the scale.

Fig. 15 shows the relationship between typical brush holder spring tension arms and brush leads. The brush spring tension arm should rest on top of the brush as shown. If new brushes are too long, the commutator end should be sandpapered until the brush is shortened sufficiently for the spring tension arm to rest on top of the brush. Any filing or notching of the top of the brush is not recommended.

Generator Magnetism—After a generator is built at the factory, the first time it is run it will not generate current. It is necessary, therefore, to apply current from a battery to the field windings to provide magnetic lines to generate the current. After the field coils have been excited, the soft steel pole pieces will retain a small amount of magnetism

(called residual magnetism) which makes them very weak permanent magnets.

After this procedure, when the generator armature starts to rotate, the residual magnetism in the field pole pieces is sufficient to generate a voltage in the armature conductors. This voltage applied to the field circuit increases the magnetism of the field, and the generator builds up the voltage for which it was designed.

Sometimes when a generator is completely disassembled, the pole pieces are not replaced in their original relation, and it may be necessary to excite the fields with a battery, the same as is originally done, in order to give the pole pieces the proper polarity in relation to each other.

In connection with the foregoing remarks, the pole pieces can lose their residual magnetism if the generator is bumped severely against another generator or other heavy metal object. In fact, this sometimes happens when a generator is roughly bumped against another generator on a shelf in a stockroom.

Generator Bearings—Generator bearings usually consist of a radial ball bearing on the drive end and an obsorbent bronze bushing on the commutator end.

Ball bearings should not have in excess of .001" clearance between the outer race and housing in which it is installed and not more than .001" play between the balls and races. The balls should be round and there should be no tight spots when the outer race is held stationary and the inner race is rotated.

Plain bearings should not have in excess of .002" clearance between the shaft and bearing.

When assembling absorbent bronze bearings, always use the right size arbor as these arbors are designed to give the proper bearing fit. This is most necessary because absorbent bronze bearings must not be reamed because to do so will reduce their capacity to hold lubricant.

When assembling bearings or end frames that are equipped with oil wicks, always remove the wick and replace it only after the armature and end frame are assembled.

Lubrication—When a generator is disassembled and cleaned, the absorbent bronze bearing should be soaked in medium engine oil before assembling, and the ball bearing should be packed one-half full with a high melting point grease. Care must be taken not to overlubricate any bearings, as the surplus oil will get on the commutator and brushes, which would seriously affect the operation of the generator.

Nearly all generators are provided with oilers at both ends. Hinged top oilers are located over the bearing and should be given 5 to 10 drops of medium engine oil every 5000 miles. Swinging type oilers are used only on the commutator end cap cover and should be filled with medium engine oil every 5000 miles. Cup-and-wick oilers is found under the bearing. The cup should be removed and filled with medium oil every 5000 miles.

Disassembling Generator

In servicing a generator, the normal procedure is to disassemble it only so far as is necessary to make repair or replacement of defective parts. For example, if the field coils are not short- or open-circuited or grounded, they should not be removed. However, the following procedure assumes that the generator requires complete disassembly.

1. Remove the nut from the end of the armature shaft which holds the pulley in place. It is bad practice to hold the generator in a vise while performing this operation as there is danger of distorting the generator frame. Instead, a suitable strap wrench can be made to hold the pulley by riveting and 18" length of a used fan belt to a piece of pipe. Wrap the belt around the pulley groove and hold it stationary while applying pressure with the pipe.

2. Use a suitable puller to remove the pulley.

3. Remove the screws holding the commutator end frame in place.

4. Take off the end frame and disconnect the field lead attached to one of the brush holders so that the end frame can be completely removed from the generator frame.

5. Remove the drive end frame together with the armature, being careful not to damage the armature windings or commutator by striking it against the pole shoes or field frame.

6. Remove the screws which hold the drive end bearing in place.

7. Remove the drive end frame by slip-

ping it over the bearing. It is not advisable to remove the bearing from the shaft until after it has been examined. If the bearing is found to be in good condition, do not remove it from the shaft.

8. If the bearing is not in good condition, remove the pulley key from the shaft by raising it out of the keyway with a pair of diagonal cutting pliers. Then remove the bearing by pressing it off in an arbor press, being careful not to damage the armature winding.

9. If it is necessary to remove the field coils, the tools shown in Fig. 16, or their equivalent, should be used.

10. Check the commutator end bearing for wear and, if necessary, press the old bearing out and the new one in with the proper arbor. Never ream or scrape absorbent bronze bearings as to do so will reduce their capacity to retain lubricant.

Inspection & Assembly

In the following procedure, some of the operations are mentioned without giving any details because these details have already been covered under "Precautions When Repairing Generators".

1. Clean all parts with a cloth dampened with a suitable cleaning fluid and then dry them with compressed air. Do not immerse field coils, armature, felt washer or insulating parts in fluid or dry them with heat. Never steam clean a generator.

2. Examine all parts for wear or damage.

3. Examine all electrical connections for poor soldering or broken wires.

4. Examine the armature for damage to the core or windings. Examine particularly the core and slot fillers for indications of the armature rubbing the pole pieces. If the core fillers only have been rubbing, drive them into the slots with a narrow piece of copper or fibre. Then coat the fillers with shellac or insulating varnish to hold them in place.

5. If the armature core has been rubbed, filed or turned so that the laminations are short-circuited, the armature should be replaced.

6. Check the armature for short circuits in a growler, Fig. 13.

7. Turn the commutator, Figs. 8, 9.

Fig. 18 Checking brush spring tension on Delco-Remy generator with special type spring scale

8. Undercut the mica, Figs. 10, 11.

9. Use a thin scraper to clean out all chips and remove burrs between commutator bars.

10. Place the armature in a lathe and use 00 sandpaper to remove any scratches from the commutator brush surface.

11. Blow out dust and chips with compressed air.

12. Check the armature for short circuits in a growler to make sure that the armature is still O.K. after the turning and undercutting operations.

13. Check the insulated brush holder for a ground.

14. Check the armature terminal and field terminal for ground.

15. Check the brush holders for alignment with a hacksaw blade.

16. Place the drive end of the armature shaft in a wood block to hold the armature vertical and place the commutator end frame on the shaft.

17. Install new brushes. This can easily be done by using a hook made of stiff wire to hold the brush spring tension arm up while installing the brushes.

18. Adjust the spring tension by bending the brush spring to the high limit of the specifications for the generator being serviced. Use a suitable spring scale to measure the pressure of the brush on the commutator. With a thin strip of paper placed between the brush and commutator, pull up on the spring scale and slightly pull on the paper. When the pressure of the brush is reduced enough to allow the paper to be pulled out, read the indication on the scale.

NOTE—Fig. 17 illustrates the details of the commutator end frame on Delco-Remy generator with extruded frame (see Fig. 5). Brush spring tension on this type generator is accomplished with the specially constructed spring scale shown in Fig. 18. Hook the end of the scale under the end of the brush tension arm and check the tension. Correct if necessary by bending the spring top or by installing a new spring.

19. Check the alignment of the brushes with the commutator bars. The trailing edge of the brushes should be exactly parallel with the bars.

20. Check the spacing of the brushes on the commutator. For a two-pole generator, they should be exactly 180° apart; for a four-pole generator, 90° apart. Count the commutator bars for spacing.

21. Fit the brushes to the commutator by using a 10" strip of 00 sandpaper approximately the width of the commutator. Pull the sandpaper between the brush and commutator (see Fig. 14) in a direction against the brush holder. Be sure the sandpaper conforms to the shape of the commutator to obtain 100% brush contact.

22. The brush spring tension arm should rest on top of the brush (see Fig. 15). If new brushes are too long, the commutator end should be sandpapered until each is shortened

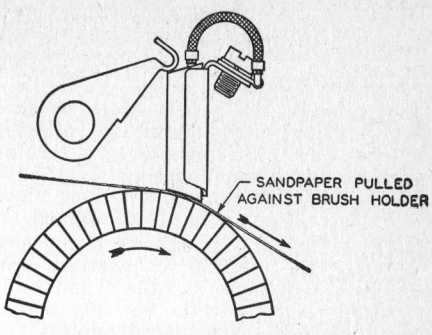

Fig. 14 Recommended method of seating generator brushes

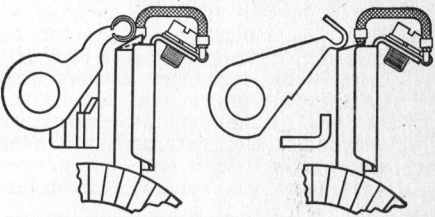

Fig. 15 Relationship between typical reaction type brush holder spring tension arms and brush leads. Tension arm should rest on top of brush

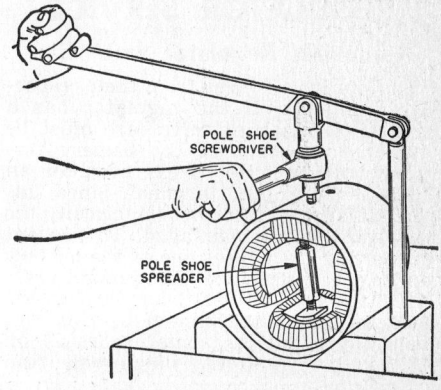

Fig. 16 Using pole shoe spreader and pole shoe screwdriver to remove and install pole shoes and field coils

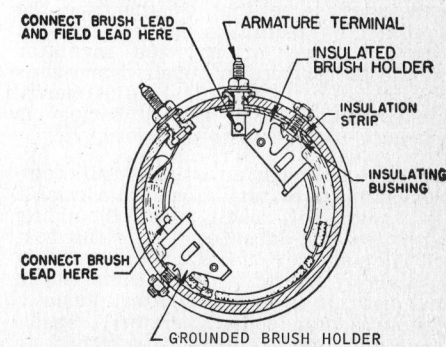

Fig. 17 Details of commutator end frame on Delco-Remy extruded frame generator. This generator is shown in Fig. 5

enough for the spring tension arm to be properly located on top of the brush. Do not file or notch the top of the brushes.

23. For third brush generators, be sure the third brush mountings are free to move for adjusting generator output. This mounting must have sufficient friction to hold it in place after adjustments are completed.

24. Assemble the generator, being sure that all internal connections are clean and tight, and the armature is free to rotate in the bearings before the brushes are placed against the commutator.

25. Be sure the brush leads are bent so they will follow the brushes as they wear shorter. Be sure also that the leads do not run against any part of the armature.

26. Run the generator as a motor by connecting the ground side of a battery to the generator housing, and connect the ungrounded side of the battery to the generator armature terminal. On externally-grounded generators fields, connect a jumper wire from the generator field terminal to ground; for internally-grounded units, connect the jumper wire from the armature terminal to the field terminal. While motoring, the armature should rotate slowly; if it does not, something is wrong with the assembly, which must be corrected before placing the generator in service.

27. After running the generator for a few minutes, stop it and lift the brushes to examine the contact surfaces. If the brush shows that it is wearing in on one side only, slightly twist the brush tension arm to equalize the pressure on the brush to obtain uniform wear.

28. If a generator test bench is available, mount the generator on it, being sure the pulleys are in alignment. For a third brush type generator, no regulator is necessary. For a shunt type generator, connect it to a regulator of the same specifications it will have when on the car, being sure the polarity is correct. Run the generator at maximum speed, same as when on the vehicle. Then adjust the voltage and ampere output according to the highest voltage the specifications call for. Note the action of the brushes; if sparking occurs, check the brush seat, spring tension and brush spring tension arm. Make any necessary adjustment to obtain satisfactory commutation.

NOTE—If a generator test stand is not available, install the generator on the vehicle, being sure the pulleys are in perfect alignment. Then check the output in the same manner as you would on a test stand, adjusting the current and voltage as described later on.

Polarizing Generator

After the generator is installed, it must be polarized. Consult the vehicle chapter to determine whether the generator being serviced has the generator field externally or internally grounded.

For internally-grounded systems, disconnect the field wire from the regulator and momentarily flash this wire to the regulator battery terminal. For externally-grounded units, connect a jumper wire from the "hot" side of the battery to the generator armature terminal.

Regulator Service

REGULATOR SERVICE

Removing Regulator from Car

Disconnect all wires from their respective terminals. If the regulator has a ground terminal, extreme care must be exercised to see that the battery terminal wire does not touch, even for an instant, the ground terminal. Since this will produce a direct short circuit, the regulator will be damaged. To prevent this, either disconnect one of the battery cables or disconnect the ground wire last. Likewise, do not touch the battery wire to the field terminal as this will burn the regulator armature reeds on Auto-Lite regulators, which will ruin the regulator.

Inspecting Regulator

If the following procedure is made in the step-by-step manner in which it is given, it will uncover any trouble as you progress so that by the time the preliminary tests are made, you will know whether or not the regulator should be replaced or repaired and thus save time in making final adjustments. No equipment other than a battery is required for the tests described.

NOTE—Although practically all component parts of regulators are available (although not readily) for rebuilding purposes, the labor cost plus the cost of the parts for such a major operation is scarcely warranted when compared to the cost of a new regulator. From a practical standpoint, therefore, repairs to regulators are usually confined to replacing contacts, springs and resistors.

Remove regulator cover and inspect for any indication that the regulator has been damaged, such as a dented cover, burned paint on inside of cover, terminals in bad condition, any evidence of burning or poor soldering in any part of the regulator.

Tighten the nuts on the bottom of Auto-Lite and Ford regulators, Fig. 19. These nuts, if loose, will create high resistance in the circuit, affecting the performance of the regulator.

If the regulator is equipped with carbon resistors, Fig. 19, remove them from the base as they can be checked for cracks that do not show when on the regulator. When installing, be sure to attach them to their proper places and with the marked numerals facing you.

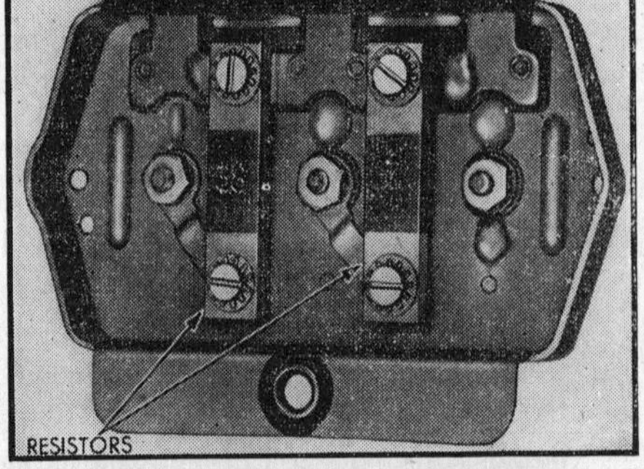

Fig. 19 Bottom view of Auto-Lite regulator with carbon resistors. The three nuts shown must be tight to eliminate high resistance. Resistors must not be cracked and the attaching screws and connections must be clean and tight for the same reason

These numerals indicate the nominal resistance in Ohms, and the one with the higher number belongs on the voltage regulator side of the base. Also, make certain the contact surfaces are clean, and tighten the screws securely.

If the foregoing inspection shows that the regulator appears to be serviceable, the next step is to make a continuity test of the windings. To do this, all you need is a battery of the proper voltage and a small light bulb connected in series with it.

To check the continuity of the series winding, clip one lead to the armature terminal and the other to the battery terminal, Fig. 20. With this hook-up, the bulb should not light. But by closing the circuit breaker contacts by hand, the bulb should light. If it does not, replace the regulator.

To check the continuity of the voltage regulator shunt winding, move the lead from the battery terminal and ground it to the regulator base, Fig. 21. With this hook-up, the voltage regulator contacts should move. If they do not, replace the regulator.

Without changing the connections, lightly touch the circuit breaker armature with one of your fingers. If the assist of the finger closes the circuit breaker contacts, it proves that the shunt winding of the circuit breaker is continuous. If the contacts do not close, replace the regulator.

To check the efficiency of the insulators on the strap which connects the voltage regulator to the current regulator, connect one lead to the field terminal and ground the other to the regulator base, Fig. 22. With this hook-up, the bulb should light. But when the voltage regulator contacts are opened

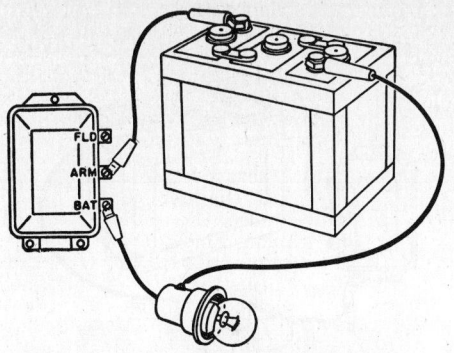

Fig. 20 Hook-up for checking continuity of series winding. Bulb should not light. Bulb should light when circuit breaker contacts are closed by hand. If it doesn't, replace regulator

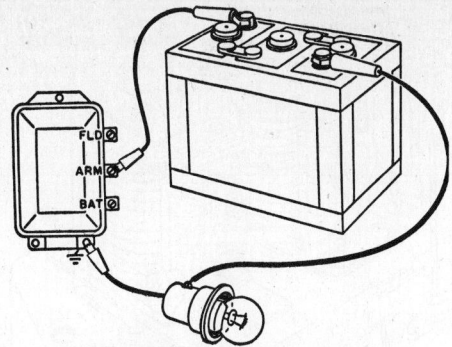

Fig. 21 Hook-up for checking continuity of voltage regulator shunt winding. Voltage regulator contacts should move. If they do not, replace the regulator

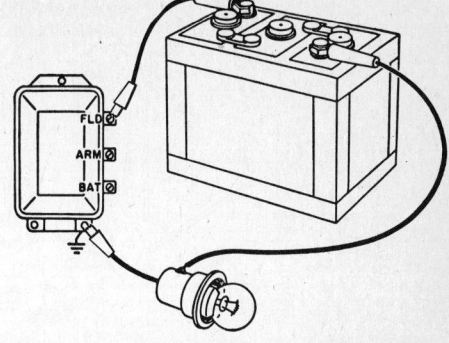

Fig. 22 Hook-up for checking efficiency of insulators on strap which connects current and voltage regulator units. Bulb should light. When the voltage regulator contacts are opened (by hand) light should go out. Closing current regulator contacts should cause light to go out or dim

(by hand) the light should go out. Similarly, when the current regulator contacts are closed, the light should dim or go out. If the conditions do not coincide with the foregoing, either the insulators are no good or they are improperly positioned. Figs. 23, 24, 25 show how these parts should be installed on Delco-Remy regulators, and Fig. 26 illustrates the arrangement on Auto-Lite regulators. (Ford regulators have riveted construction.)

If the regulator checks O.K. thus far, the next step is to clean the contacts and to make the necessary mechanical adjustments.

AUTO-LITE MECHANICAL ADJUSTMENTS

Fig. 27 is a layout of the tools needed to adjust all Auto-Lite regulators.

Cleaning Regulator Contacts

Although it can be done without removing the contacts, a more thorough job can be done by removing the stationary contacts and cleaning each one separately.

Remove the screws which fasten the connecting strap to the stationary contact brackets. Note that the insulator

on the current regulator goes between the strap and contact bracket, and the insulator on the voltage regulator belongs between the strap and flat metal washer, Fig. 26.

If the contacts are burned or rough, carefully dress them with a fine thin cut ignition point file. All filing should be done parallel with the length of the armature, Fig. 28. This will avoid mechanical interlocking, as the contacts have a slight wiping movement when in action.

If there has been metal transfer, creating a crater on one contact and a projection on its mate, file off the projection so that the contact is smooth. Also file a smooth surface on the contact with the crater.

After filing, reinstall the contacts so they just touch each other. Then clean them with a narrow strip of clean lintless tape saturated with an approved cleaning fluid (carbon tetrachloride, for example) applied to the tape with an eye dropper. Draw the wet portion of the tape back and forth across the contact surfaces to remove any oil, grease or dirt. Then draw a dry piece of the tape between the contacts to remove any residue that may remain. Open the contacts to remove the tape so that the pressure on the contacts will not retain small threads between them.

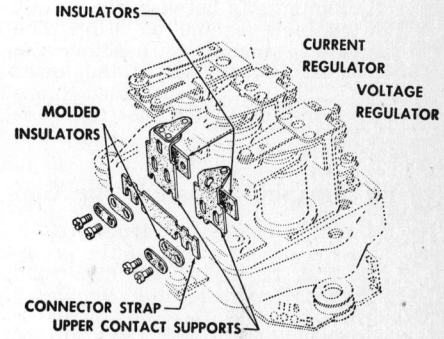

Fig. 24 Relationship of insulators and connector strap on late model Delco-Remy units with single contact voltage regulator

Fig. 23 Relationship of insulator and connector strap on some Delco-Remy regulators

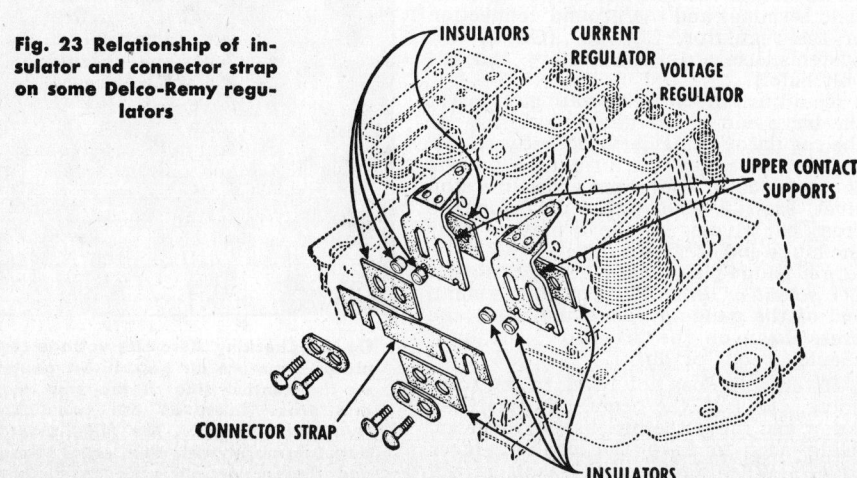

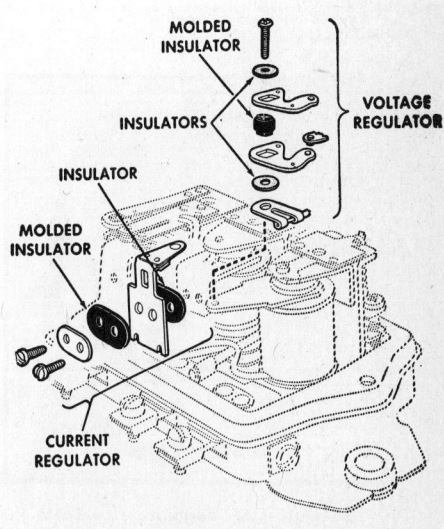

Fig. 25 Regulator contact mounting on Delco-Remy units with double contact voltage regulator

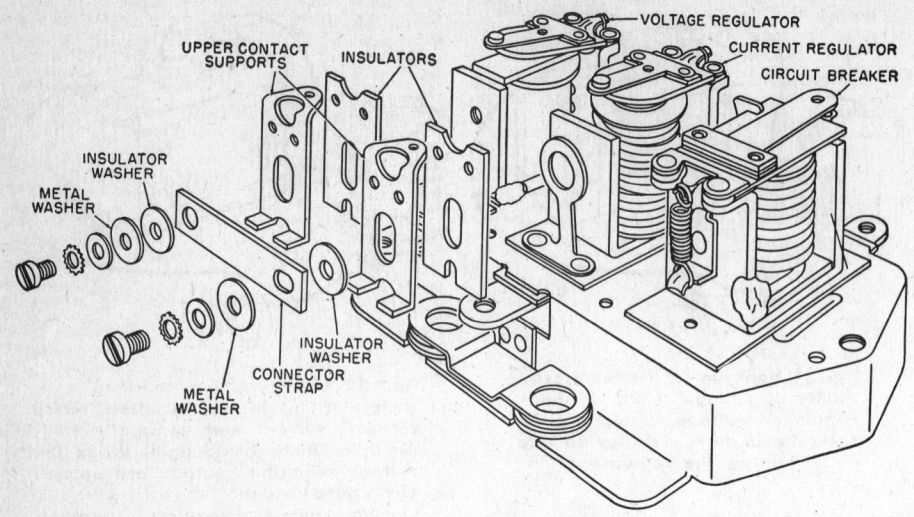

Fig. 26 Relationship of insulators and connector strap on Auto-Lite regulators

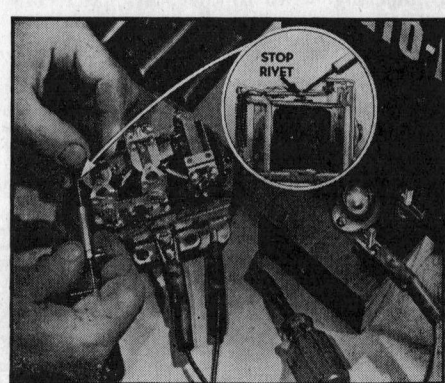

Fig. 29 Checking Auto-Lite voltage regulator armature air gap with the aid of a battery and lamp bulb of the proper voltage connected in series

Circuit Breaker Contact Gap

The minimum gap between the circuit breaker contacts should be .015". The adjustment is made by bending the bridge which is attached to the lower contact. This will be discussed more fully when we make the electrical adjustments.

Circuit Breaker Armature Air Gap

Set the circuit breaker armature air gap with the proper gauge of the group shown in Fig. 27, and to the dimension given in the *Generator and Regulator Specifications* table for the regulator being serviced. With the flat side of the gauge up, between the armature and magnet core, and the edge of the gauge against the ends of the bimetal hinges, the air gap should permit the gauge to just slide in. Adjustment is made by bending the armature stop, which should be so located that it will not interfere with the operation of the armature.

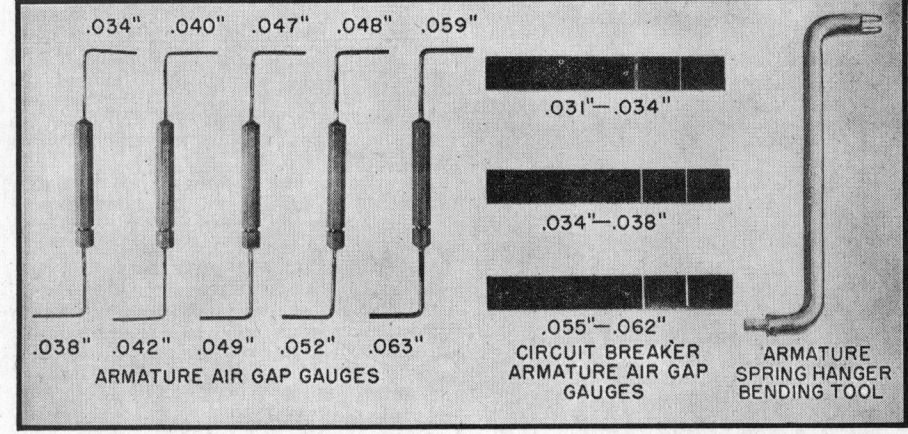

Fig. 27 Tool kit for adjusting the complete line of Auto-Lite regulators

Voltage Regulator Armature Air Gap

The most accurate way to check the voltage regulator air gap is with a 3 candlepower, 6-8 volt bulb connected in series with a six-volt battery, across the field terminal and the ground connection of the regulator, Fig. 29. (On 12-volt systems, use a 12-volt battery and 12-volt bulb.)

To adjust the armature air gap, insert the large end of the gauge specified for the regulator being serviced between the magnet core and the armature on the contact side of the brass armature stop rivet, Fig. 30. Then press down on the cross bar riveted to the armature near the hinge end of the armature. With the larger gauge placed thus, the *light should not go out or dim.* Then place the small end of the gauge at the same place and press down on the armature; the light should go out or dim.

If the bulb does not react to the foregoing, loosen the contact attaching screw and move the bracket up or down, being sure to keep the contact faces square. When the desired result is ob-

tained, securely tighten the attaching screw and again check the gap.

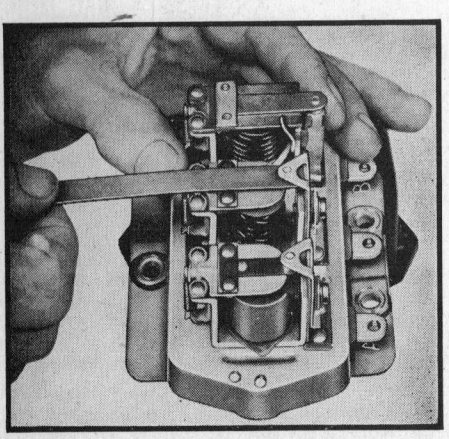

Fig. 28 Auto-Lite regulator contacts should be filed parallel with the length of the armature since they produce a wiping movement when in action

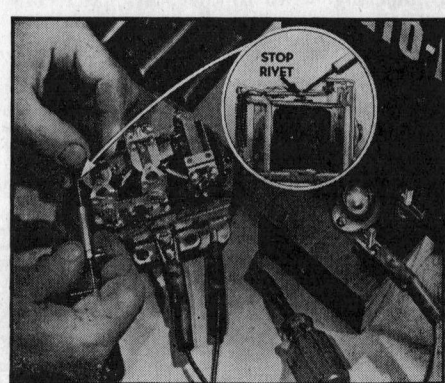

Fig. 30 Checking Auto-Lite voltage regulator armature air gap. Insert gauges on the contact side of the stop rivet and press down on the two hinge rivets as shown. The light should burn normally with the larger gauge and dim or go out with the smaller

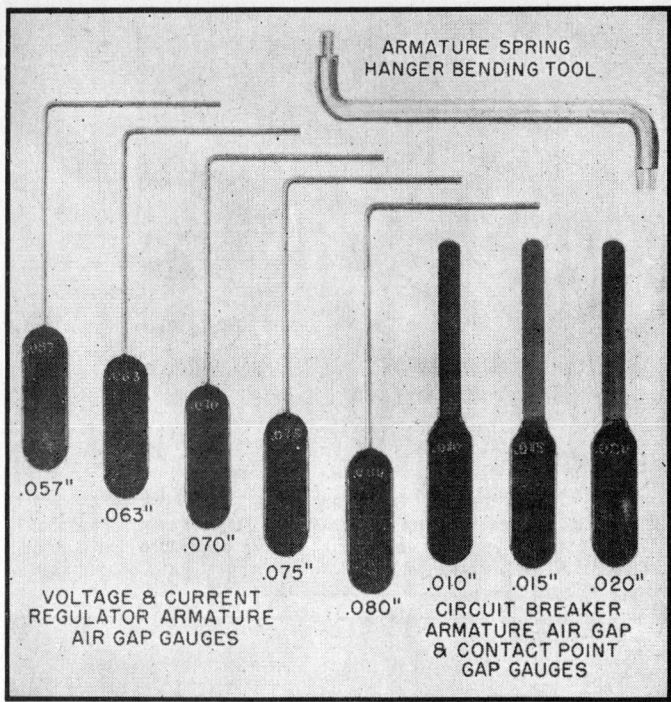

ARMATURE SPRING HANGER BENDING TOOL

.057"
.063"
.070"
.075"
.080"
VOLTAGE & CURRENT REGULATOR ARMATURE AIR GAP GAUGES

.010" .015" .020"
CIRCUIT BREAKER ARMATURE AIR GAP & CONTACT POINT GAP GAUGES

Fig. 31 Tool kit for adjusting complete line of Delco-Remy regulators

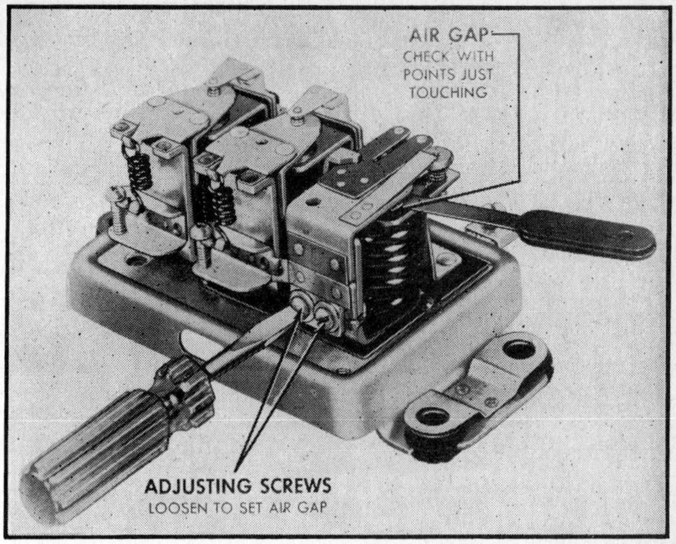

AIR GAP—CHECK WITH POINTS JUST TOUCHING

ADJUSTING SCREWS
LOOSEN TO SET AIR GAP

Fig. 33 Checking and adjusting Delco-Remy circuit breaker armature air gap

Current Regulator Armature Air Gap

This air gap is checked and adjusted in the same manner as for the voltage regulator and according to the specifications given in the *Generator and Regulator Specifications* table.

DELCO-REMY MECHANICAL ADJUSTMENTS

Fig. 31 illustrates a complete tool kit for adjusting Delco-Remy regulators.

Cleaning Contacts

The current and voltage regulator flat points should be cleaned with a spoon or riffler file, Fig. 32. To reach the contacts, loosen the contact bracket mounting screws and tilt the bracket to one side to allow cleaning of points.

When cleaning the lower (or armature) contacts, inspect the upper contacts in the support bracket as well, as they may require cleaning. A thin fine cut ignition point file should be used and the upper rounded points should not be filed excessively. For greater accessibility in cleaning, the contact support brackets may be removed. However, great care must be exercised to install them properly.

Circuit Breaker Armature Air Gap

To check the air gap, place a finger on the armature directly above the winding core and move the armature down until the contacts just close, Fig. 33. Measure the air gap between the armature and the center of the core with a feeler gauge. Do not press on the

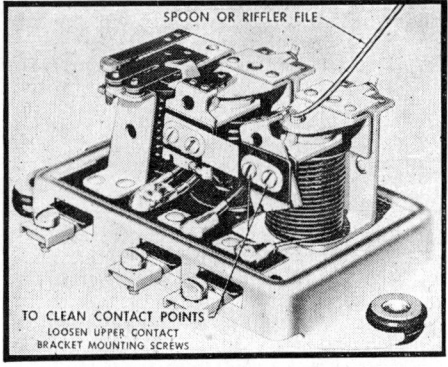

SPOON OR RIFFLER FILE

TO CLEAN CONTACT POINTS
LOOSEN UPPER CONTACT BRACKET MOUNTING SCREWS

Fig. 32 Cleaning Delco-Remy regulator contacts. To reach the contacts, loosen the contact bracket mounting screws and tilt the bracket to one side

armature any harder than is necessary to just close the points. If both sets of points do not close at the same instant, bend the spring fingers on the armature slightly until both sets do meet simultaneously, Fig. 34.

To adjust the air gap, loosen the two adjusting screws at the back of the circuit breaker and raise or lower the armature as required to bring the gap opening to the specification given in the *Generator and Regulator Specifications* table. After adjustment, securely tighten the adjusting screws, making sure the contacts align properly.

Circuit Breaker Contact Gap

This adjustment, which usually calls for .020", is made as follows: With the armature at rest against the upper armature stop, measure the contact opening, Fig. 35. If not according to

Fig. 34 Delco-Remy circuit breaker contacts should close at the same instant. If they do not, bend the spring fingers on the armature until they do

specifications, bend the upper armature stop with the tool shown. To increase the opening, bend the stop up, or down to increase it.

Single Contact Voltage Regulator

Armature Air Gap (1959 and earlier)—To check the gap, Fig. 36, push down the armature until the contacts open. Then slowly release until they barely touch. With the contacts just touching, measure the air gap between the center of the magnet core and the armature with the pin gauge of the specified size given in the *Generator and Regulator Specifications* table in the car chapter.

If adjustment is required, loosen the contact mounting screws slightly to allow movement of the contact support. Insert the feeler gauge and press the armature down against the gauge. Adjust the contact support up or down until the contacts barely touch. Secure the adjustment by tightening the two mounting screws.

Armature Air Gap (1960-61 units)—This regulator features nylon nuts on top of the voltage and current regulator elements to make for easier and more ex-

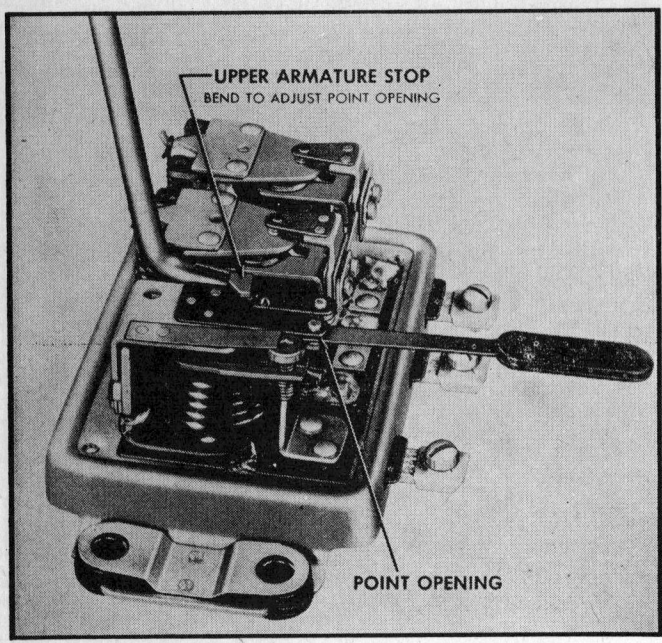

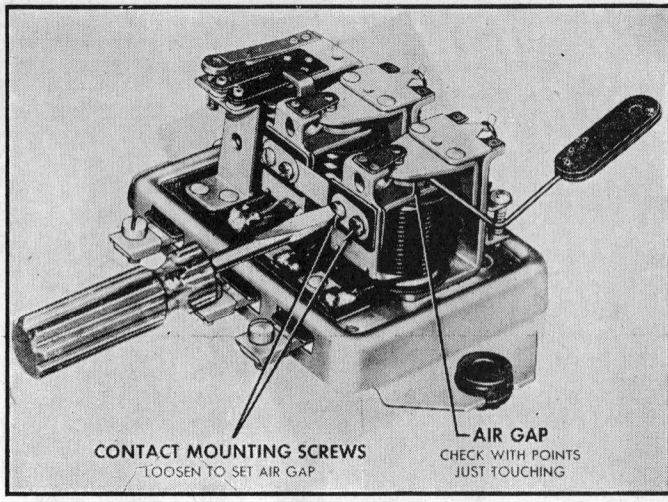

Fig. 36 Checking and adjusting Delco-Remy (before 1960) single contact voltage regulator armature air gap. Check and adjust current regulator in exactly the same way

Fig. 35 Checking and adjusting Delco-Remy circuit breaker point gap. If necessary, bend upper armature stop with tool shown

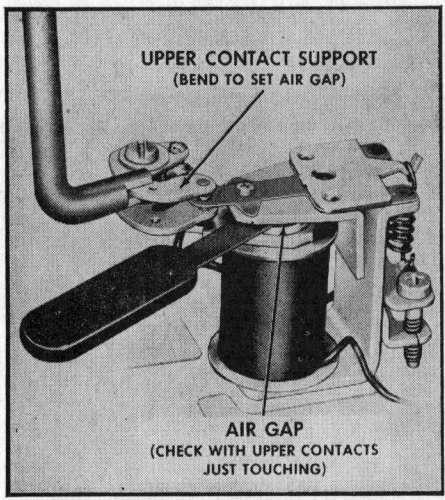

Fig. 38 Checking and adjusting Delco-Remy double contact voltage regulator armature air gap

act adjustment of the armature air gaps. As shown in Fig. 37, push down on armature until contacts are just touching and measure the air gap between armature and magnet core. Adjust the air gap by turning the nylon nut up or down as required.

Dual Contact Voltage Regulator

Armature Air Gap—Make sure the air gap adjusting screw on top of the armature is turned all the way in a clockwise direction before checking the gap. Then with the upper contacts just touching, measure the air gap between the armature and winding core as shown in Fig. 38. Adjust by bending the upper contact support.

Point Opening—Push the armature down until the lower set of contacts are just touching and measure point opening between the upper set of contacts, Fig. 39. Adjust by bending the lower contact support.

ELECTRICAL TESTS & ADJUSTMENTS

After completing the mechanical adjustments, the regulator must be set up electrically either on the car or on a regulator test stand. A number of reliable and accurate test stands are commercially available and the manufacturer of each one furnishes complete instructions as to its use. We will discuss how the job is done on the car for each make regulator.

The first step, of course, is to install the regulator on the car in its proper position. Be sure to observe the precautions for installing them as outlined later on in this chapter. Then, before

commencing the tests, we must reproduce as nearly as possible the same conditions under which the regulator will operate on the car. These include:

1. Run the engine at about 20 mph for at least 15 minutes to bring the regulator up to normal operating temperature. The current flowing through the windings at this engine speed will provide enough heat to accomplish this.
2. The regulator must be mounted in the proper position on the car. If the regulator is being tested on a test stand, it must be mounted in the same position as when on the car.
3. The cover and cover gasket must be

Fig. 37 Checking and adjusting Delco-Remy 1960-61 single contact voltage regulator armature air gap. Check and adjust current regulator in exactly the same manner

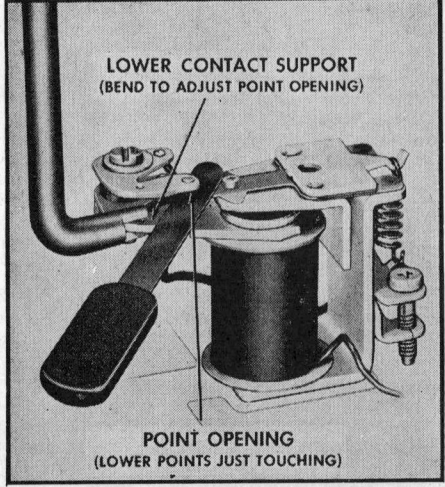

Fig. 39 Adjusting Delco-Remy double contact voltage regulator point opening

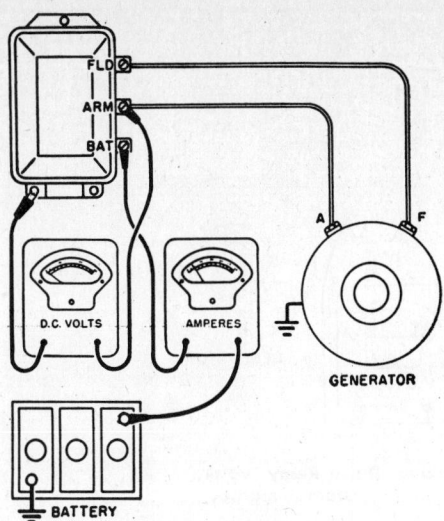

Fig. 40 Hook-up for testing Auto-Lite circuit breaker

in place. The cover, which forms part of the magnetic circuit, must be on because there is a difference of from .2 to .4 of a volt with the cover off and on. Therefore, always have the cover on when final tests are made.

4. Make sure the units are correctly hooked up and check the ground polarity of the battery. Consult the regulator specifications for the correct polarity as regulators must not be used on systems with the polarity opposite to that for which they were designed. Most regulators have different materials for the contacts in each set. Reversing the polarity of the system reverses the direction of the current flow and causes transfer of metal from one contact to the other. Also on some of the high output Auto-Lite regulators using a rectifier in the field circuit, incorrect polarity would make the regulator inoperative (more about rectifiers later).

5. Check the part numbers stamped on the name plates of the generator and regulator to make sure the correct regulator is installed. Regulators are designed for use with a generator having a specified field draw, output, internal connections and speed range, and may not function properly if an incorrect substitution is made.

6. Make sure the battery is fully charged and otherwise in good condition. An old battery, one partially discharged or one subjected to excessive heat will cause high charging rate, while one subjected to excessive cold, hard plates, high resistance separators or sulphation will cause low charging rate. If the battery is not up to operational standards, substitute temporarily for test purposes a fully charged battery in good condition of the same type and capacity.

7. Make sure the generator operates correctly without the regulator in

the circuit. Remove the armature and battery leads from the regulator and connect an ammeter between them. This will cause a discharge through the generator and the engine should be *immediately operated at idle speed.* Remove the field lead from the regulator and, *while operating at idling speed,* touch the field lead to the regulator base. *(On Delco-Remy units with dual contact points on the voltage regulator, never ground the generator field with the regulator connected to the generator as the lower set of contacts will burn instantaneously.* An output check requires that the "GEN" lead to the regulator be disconnected *before* the field is grounded. Then increase the speed slowly, noting the charging rate. *Do not increase the output above the rated output of the generator* because, if prolonged, would burn up the armature. If the generator will not build up to its rated output, inspect the wiring for shorts, opens and incorrect connections, and remove the generator for an overhaul. Also make a voltage drop test of the wiring.

Use of Headphone—An accurate method of noting the exact instant the circuit breaker contacts open and close is to connect a suitable headphone (2000 ohms or more) to the battery and armature terminals of the regulator. When the contacts open and close, a click will be heard.

In using the headphone to obtain an accurate indication of the operation of the voltage regulator contacts, it should be connected between the regulator field terminal and regulator base. The clicks which indicate the opening and closing of the contacts should be regular and clear without missing. If not, it indicates that the contacts are dirty, misaligned or otherwise need attention.

AUTO-LITE ELECTRICAL ADJUSTMENTS

The following describes how these regulators are tested and adjusted on the car. In the accompanying diagrams, only the instruments required are illustrated. Bear in mind, too, that the specifications given in the text are only approximate and are given merely as a guide. Consult the data for each model regulator listed in the *Generator and*

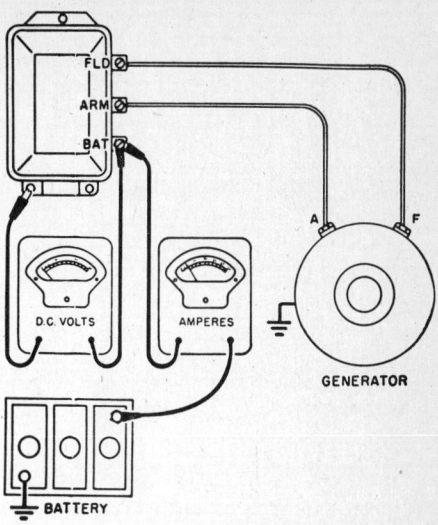

Fig. 41 Hook-up for testing Auto-Lite voltage and current regulators

Regulator Specifications table and adjust accordingly.

Circuit Breaker

Connect a test ammeter and voltmeter into the circuit as shown in Fig. 40. Slowly increase engine speed and observe the voltage when the contacts close—which should be about 6.5 volts. (12.8 on 12-volt systems). Now slowly decrease engine speed and observe the discharge amperage just before the contacts open — which should be 4 to 6 amperes.

To adjust the closing voltage, change the armature spring tension by bending the lower hanger. Increase the spring tension (bend hanger down) to raise the closing voltage, and bend it up to lower the closing voltage.

To adjust the opening amperage, raise or lower the stationary contact, keeping the contacts perfectly aligned. Change the gap by expanding or contracting the stationary contact bridge. But in no case must the gap be less than .015″. Increasing the gap lowers the opening amperage and lessening the gap raises it.

Voltage Regulator

Shift the voltmeter lead from the armature terminal to the battery terminal, Fig. 41. Run the engine at one-half maximum generator output for 15 minutes to make sure the regulator is at

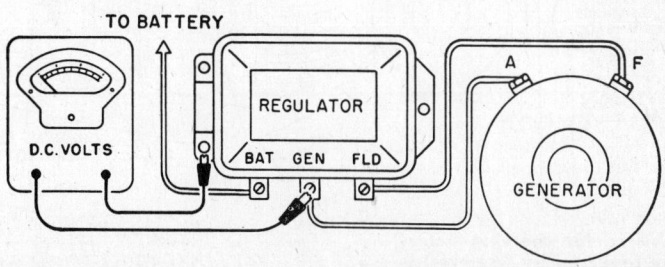

Fig. 42 Hook-up for checking closing voltage on Delco-Remy regulators

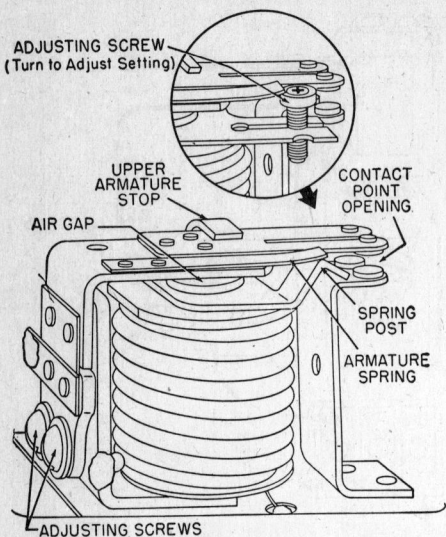

Fig. 43 Closing voltage on some Delco-Remy regulators is adjusted by bending the spring post on which the armature spring rests. On later units adjustment is made by turning the screw shown in the inset

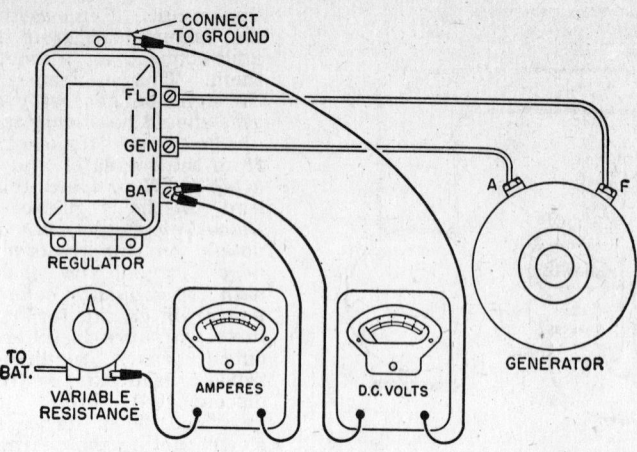

Fig. 45 Hook-up for checking Delco-Remy voltage regulator by the variable resistance method

normal operating temperature. Have the cover on the regulator during the warm-up period and when taking readings.

Reduce engine speed to break the field circuit. Then increase it to 20 mph. Turn on enough lights and accessories to obtain slightly more than one-half the maximum output of the generator. At this point, the voltage should be a steady 7.3 volts (14.5 on 12-volt systems).

NOTE—The purpose of reducing the engine speed before taking the voltage reading is because we want to reproduce the conditions present when the car is operating. To accomplish this, therefore, we must start from scratch by getting rid of *almost* all of the magnetism in the generator before we speed up the engine again in order to build up magnetism and to get a true voltage reading. (The only remaining magnetism is the residual magnetism present in the generator field

pole pieces.) The field current is broken, of course, when the circuit breaker contacts open.

CAUTION—There are some generators designed to charge when the engine is idling, as, for example, those found on many door-to-door delivery vehicles. Reducing engine speed to break the field circuit cannot be accomplished because the circuit breaker contacts will not open. The only alternative, therefore, is to stop the engine and then restart it again to build up the magnetism.

To adjust the voltage regulator, bend the hangar at the lower end of the armature spring. Bending the hangar up decreases voltage and bending it down increases voltage.

After each adjustment, reduce engine speed to open the circuit breaker contacts. Then speed it up and check the voltage.

Current Regulator

With the regulator and instruments

still connected as for the voltage regulator test, Fig. 41, crank the engine with the starter and with the ignition off for not more than 30 seconds at a time (allowing the starter to cool off each time) to partly discharge the battery. Then run the engine fast enough, with lights and accessories turned on, to allow the generator to operate at its full maximum output during the test. If the ammeter does not indicate the full rated output of the generator, proceed as follows:

Adjust the operating amperage by changing the spring tension on the current regulator in the same manner as for the voltage regulator. After each adjustment, reduce engine speed until the circuit breaker contacts open. Then speed it up and take a reading.

If the current regulator is temperature compensated, operate at full charge for 15 minutes before checking. At the end of this period, amperage should have fallen to within one ampere of the hot maximum.

DELCO-REMY ELECTRICAL ADJUSTMENTS

The following procedure describes how Delco-Remy regulators are adjusted on the car. The regulator must be at operating temperature before taking a voltage or current reading. Operating temperature may be assumed to exist after not less than 15 minutes continuous operation with a charging rate of about 10 amperes.

Circuit Breaker

To check and adjust the closing voltage of the circuit breaker, connect a voltmeter as shown in Fig. 42. Start the engine and slowly increase speed, noting the voltage at the instant the circuit breaker contacts close (voltage when ammeter begins to slow reading). If the reading is not within specifications adjust as follows:

Units Without Adjusting Screw—The closing voltage is adjusted on these units, Fig. 43, by bending the spring post on which the armature spring rests. Bending

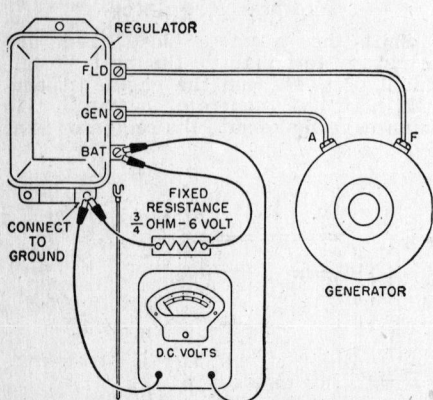

Fig. 44 Hook-up for checking Delco-Remy voltage regulator by fixed resistance method. Note that the fixed resistance is used in place of the battery

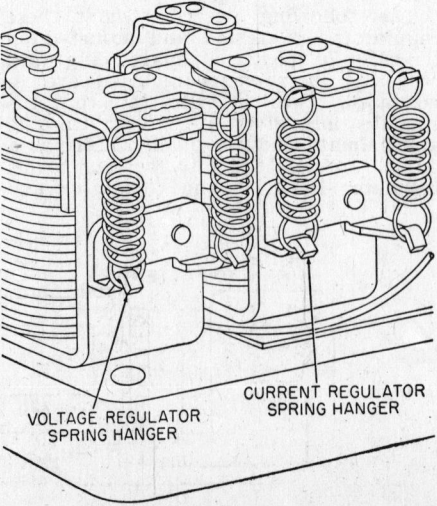

Fig. 46 Setting is adjusted by bending spiral spring hanger of one spring

Fig. 47 Turning the adjusting screw clockwise increases voltage setting. The same method is used to set the current regulator (center unit). Turning screw clockwise increases current setting

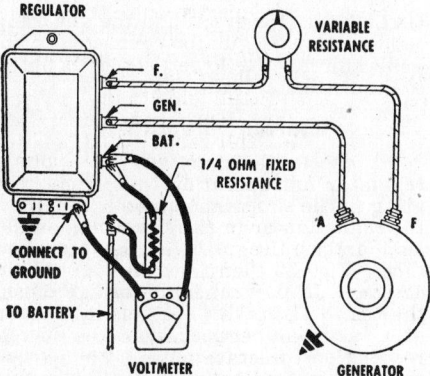

Fig. 48 Connections for checking voltage on Delco-Remy double contact voltage regulator

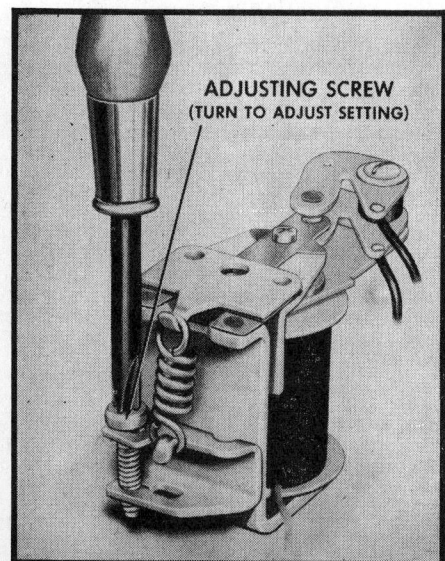

Fig. 49 Adjusting voltage regulator setting (lower contacts)

the spring post upward increases closing voltage, and bending it downward decreases voltage.

Units With Adjusting Screw—The manner of adjusting the closing voltage on these units is shown in the inset in Fig. 43. The spring rests on a left-hand thread, cross-headed screw. Turning the screw to the right increases closing voltage, and turning it to the left decreases the voltage.

Voltage Regulator Single Contact Type

There are two methods of testing Delco-Remy voltage regulators, the fixed resistance method, and the variable resistance method. With the fixed resistance method, the resistance takes the place of the battery in the circuit. With the variable resistance method, the resistance is inserted in the circuit between the battery and test ammeter.

Fixed Resistance Method—On 1118300 and 1118700 series regulators, substitute a ¾ ohm resistance capable of carrying 10 amperes and having a constant resistance with temperature changes for the external charging circuit. As shown in Fig. 44, disconnect the wire from the "BAT" terminal of the regulator and connect the fixed resistance between this "BAT" terminal and ground in parallel with the voltmeter. (On 1118800 series and later units regulators, connect a ¼ ohm fixed resistor into the charging circuit at the "Bat" terminal of the regulator.)

Start the engine and operate at a speed where the generator will be running 25% over the rated output speed (which is about 1500 engine rpm.) Take the reading with the cover on. If the reading is not within specifications adjust as outlined below. After each adjustment and before taking another voltage reading, reduce speed until the circuit breaker contacts open (breaking field circuit). Then bring engine back to speed again and take a reading.

Variable Resistance Method—Remove the wire from the "BAT" terminal of the regulator, Fig. 45, and connect an ammeter and a ¼ ohm variable resistance in series with the "BAT" terminal as shown. Attach the wire removed from

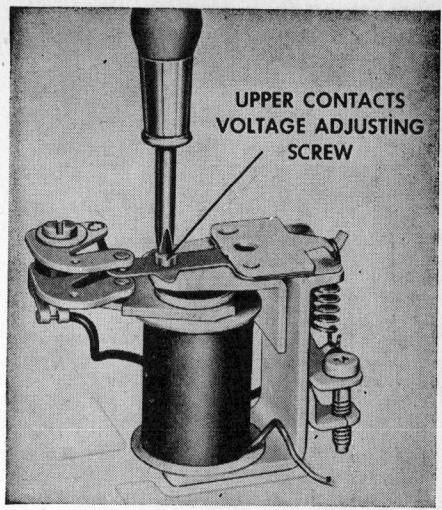

Fig. 50 Adjusting voltage setting of upper contacts

the regulator to the other terminal of the resistance unit. Connect a voltmeter from the "BAT" terminal to ground.

To make the test, start the engine and increase its speed to where the generator will be running at 25% over the rated output speed, which would be about 1500 engine rpm.

If less than 8 amperes is indicated on the ammeter, turn on lights to increase generator output. Cut in the resistance until output is reduced to 8-10 amperes. Then reduce engine speed until circuit breaker contacts open, increase speed again and note the voltage. If the voltage is not within specifications adjust as described below.

NOTE—In using the variable resistance method, it is necessary to readjust the resistance after each voltage adjustment, and then reduce and increase generator speed before taking a voltage reading. Current flow must be about 10 amperes when reading is taken.

Spring Hanger Adjusted Regulators

Fig. 46, the voltage setting is adjusted by bending the spiral spring hanger of

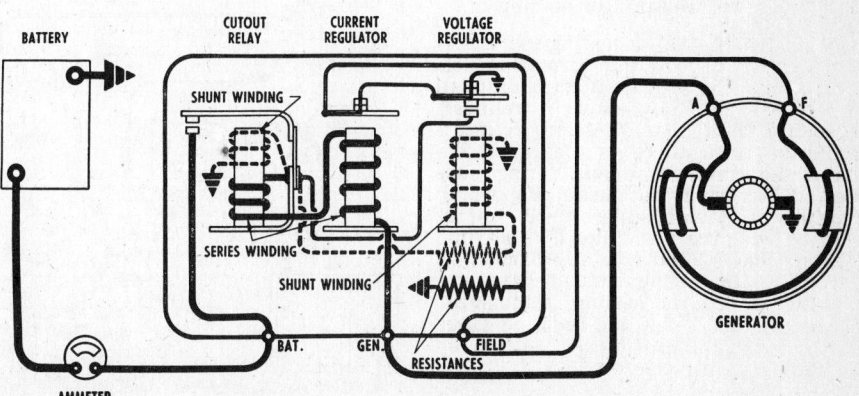

Fig. 51 Wiring diagram of Delco-Remy unit with double contacts on voltage regulator

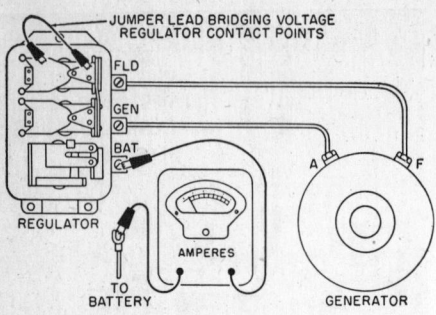

Fig. 52 Hook-up for checking current regulator on Delco-Remy regulators

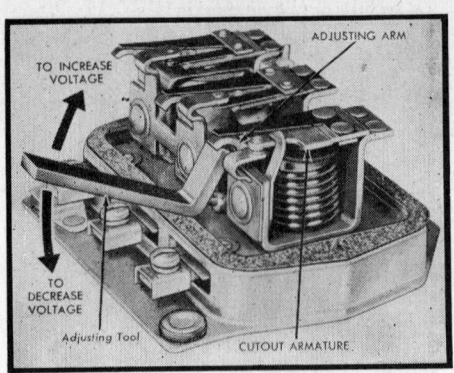

Fig. 54 Adjusting closing voltage on Ford 1950 and later units

one spring down to increase the voltage setting, or up to decrease it. Normally, all adjustments must be confined to one spring only and the other spring should not be touched. This reduces the possibility of throwing the two springs out of balance. Each spring should carry approximately half the total spring tension required.

NOTE—If the regulator is badly out of adjustment, remove one spring and, with a voltmeter connected from the regulator base to the "GEN" terminal, increase generator speed to 3500 rpm. Then adjust the spring hanger until the regulator is operating at approximately two-thirds of the specified setting. Install the second spring and reconnect the voltmeter lead to the regulator "BAT" terminal, with the other lead still connected to ground on the regulator base. Then operate the generator at the specified speed and, confining all adjustments to the second spring, adjust the voltage to the specified setting. The regulator, of course, must be at operating temperature for checks and adjustments and the cover must be in place when voltage readings are taken.

Screw Adjusted Regulators, Single Contact Type

The voltage setting is changed by means of an adjusting screw, Fig. 47. Turning the screw clockwise increases voltage setting and counterclockwise decreases it. After each adjustment, reduce engine speed until the circuit breaker contacts open and then bring it up to speed again before taking a reading.

CAUTION—If the adjusting screw is turned down beyond the normal adjustment range, the spring support may fail to return when the pressure is relieved. In such a case, turn the screw counterclockwise until there is clearance between the screw head and spring support. Then bend the spring support up carefully with small pliers until contact is made with the screw head. The final setting always should be approached by increasing the spring tension, never by reducing it. If the setting is too high, adjust the unit below the required value and then raise it to the exact setting by increasing spring tension.

Dual Contact Voltage Regulator

1. To adjust this type of regulator the battery must be fully charged to

limit the charge rate to 1 to 10 amperes. If above 10 amperes, insert a ¼ ohm resistor in series with the battery, Fig. 48.
2. Connect a voltmeter from regulator "BAT" terminal to ground.
3. Connect a 25-ohm (25 watt) variable resistance (which has an "open" position) between the regulator "F" terminal and the field lead from the generator. (Connections to the variable resistance should be made so that all the resistance can be inserted into the circuit before opening the circuit.)
4. With variable resistance turned out, operate generator at medium speed so that the voltage regulator is operating on the lower set of contacts. Continue to operate for 15 minutes to establish operating temperature of voltage regulator.
5. Cycle the generator by turning the variable resistance to the "open" position momentarily, then slowly cut out all the resistance. Regulator should be operating on the lower contacts at the voltage given in the *Specifications* chart (in car chapters). The setting may be adjusted in the conventional manner by turning the screw to adjust spring tension, Fig. 49.
6. Increase the resistance slowly until the regulator begins to operate on the upper contacts. The voltmeter should indicate a slight drop in voltage of .3 to .5 volts. This differential voltage may be increased by turning the air gap adjusting screw, Fig. 50, in a clockwise direction and decreased by turning it counterclockwise. Air gap adjustment should seldom be necessary on this type regulator. However, if the adjustment screw is turned, it will also affect the setting of the regulator so that the voltage adjustment procedure must be repeated. The regulator must be cycled each time before taking voltmeter readings, as previously described.
7. If the condition ever exists where the voltage setting of the upper contacts is higher than that of the

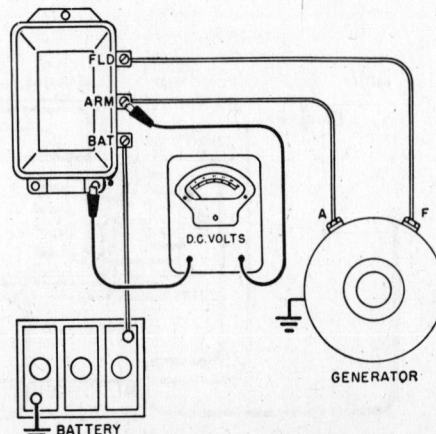

Fig. 53 Hook-up for checking circuit breaker closing voltage on Ford regulators

lower contacts, turn the air gap adjusting screw in a clockwise direction. If adjustment is taken up, it is necessary to reset the nominal air gap by bending the contact supports. Fig. 51 shows a wiring diagram of this type regulator.

CAUTION—Never ground the generator field with the regulator connected to the generator as the lower set of contacts will burn instantaneously.

Current Regulator

To check this setting, the voltage regulator must be prevented from operating. The simplest method is to remove the regulator cover and connect a jumper lead across the voltage regulator contacts, Fig. 52. Turn on lights and accessories to prevent high voltage during the test. Then with the generator operating at medium speed, note the current reading on the ammeter. If the current output is not within specifications, make the adjustment in the same manner outlined for the voltage regulator, Fig. 50.

FORD ELECTRICAL ADJUSTMENTS

The following describes the procedure for testing Ford regulators on the car. The accompanying diagrams show only the instruments needed for each test.

Circuit Breaker

Connect a voltmeter across the regulator armature terminal to the regulator base, Fig. 53. Slowly increase engine speed and observe the voltage when the contacts close—which should be about 6.5 volts (12.8 on 12-volt system). If an adjustment is indicated, proceed as follows:

For 1950 and later model regulators, Fig. 54, the adjustment is made by bending the adjusting arm. Bending the arm upward increases voltage and bending it downward decreases voltage.

Voltage Regulator

Shift the voltmeter lead from the armature terminal to the battery terminal, Fig. 55. Run the engine at one-half maximum generator output for at least 15 minutes to make sure the

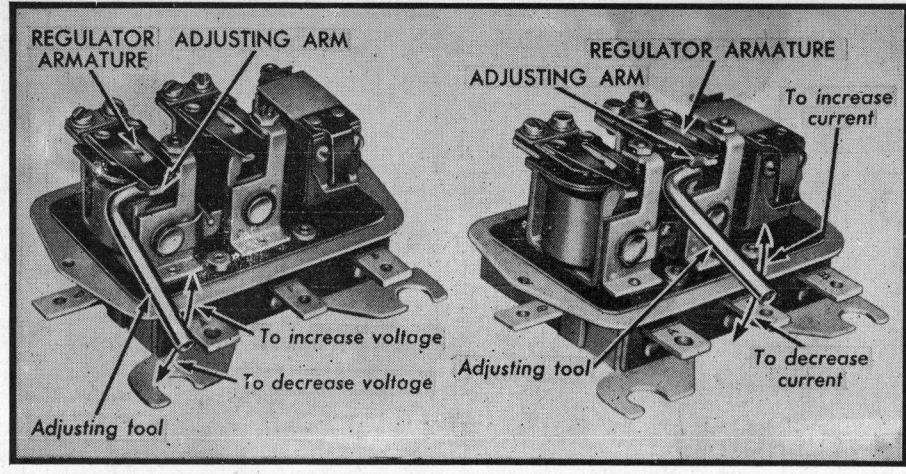

Fig. 56 Adjusting voltage regulator (left) and current regulator (right) on Ford units

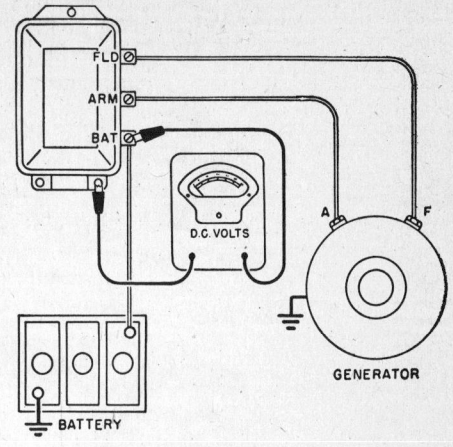

Fig. 55 Hook-up for testing voltage regulator on Ford units

regulator is at normal operating temperature. Have the cover on the unit during the warm-up period and when taking readings.

Reduce engine speed until the circuit breaker contacts open—which breaks the field circuit. Then increase engine speed to about 20 mph. Turn on enough lights and accessories to obtain slightly more than one-half the maximum output of the generator. At this point, the voltage should be a steady 7.3 volts (14.5 on 12-volt system).

NOTE—If the generator is one which is designed to charge even when the engine is idling—such as a door-to-door delivery vehicle—it will be necessary to stop the engine in order to break the field circuit.

To adjust the voltage setting, increase the spring tension by bending the adjusting arm upward to increase voltage, Fig. 56. To decrease voltage, bend the adjusting arm downward. This adjustment is the same for both early and late model regulators.

Current Regulator

With the regulator and instruments still connected as for a voltage regulator test, Fig. 55, crank the engine with the starter (ignition off) for not more than 30 seconds at a time to partly discharge the battery. Then run the engine fast enough, with lights and accessories turned on, to allow the generator to operate at full charge during the test. If the ammeter does not indicate the full rated output of the generator, adjust as follows:

If the current limit is less than specified, increase the spring tension by bending the adjusting arm upward, Fig. 56. To decrease the current, bend the adjusting arm downward. This adjustment is the same for both early and late model regulators.

STARTING MOTORS

WHEN TROUBLE develops in the starting motor circuit, and the starter cranks the engine slowly or not at all, several preliminary checks can be made to determine whether the trouble lies in the battery, in the starter, in the wiring between them, or elsewhere. Many conditions besides defects in the starter itself can result in poor cranking performance.

To make a quick check of the starter system, turn on the headlights. They should burn with normal brilliance. If they do not, the battery may be run down and it should be checked with a hydrometer.

If the battery is in a charged condition so that the lights burn brightly, operate the starting motor. Any one of three things will happen to the lights: (1) They will go out, (2) dim considerably or (3) stay bright without any cranking action taking place.

If Lights Go Out

If the lights go out as the starter switch is closed, it indicates that there is a poor connection between the battery and starting motor. This poor connection will most often be found at the battery terminals. Correction is made by removing the cable clamps from the terminals, cleaning the terminals and clamps, replacing the clamps and tightening them securely. A coating of corrosion inhibitor (vaseline will do) may be applied to the clamps and terminals to retard the formation of corrosion.

If Lights Dim

If the lights dim considerably as the starter switch is closed and the starter operates slowly or not at all, the battery may be run down, or there may be some mechanical condition in the engine or starting motor that is throwing a heavy burden on the starting motor. This imposes a high discharge rate on the battery which causes noticeable dimming of the lights.

Check the battery with a hydrometer. If it is charged, the trouble probably lies in either the engine or starting motor itself. In the engine, tight bearings or pistons or heavy oil place an added burden on the starting motor. Low temperatures also hamper starting motor performance since it thickens engine oil

and makes the engine considerably harder to crank and start. Also, a battery is less efficient at low temperatures.

In the starting motor, a bent armature, loose pole shoe screws or worn bearings, any of which may allow the armature to drag, will reduce cranking performance and increase current draw.

In addition, more serious internal damage is sometimes found. Thrown armature windings or commutator bars, which sometimes occur on over-running clutch drive starting motors, Fig. 1, are usually caused by excessive over-running after starting. This is the result of such conditions as the driver keeping the starting switch closed too long after the engine has started, the driver opening the throttle too wide in starting, or improper carburetor fast idle adjustment. Any of these subject the over-running clutch to extra strain so it tends to seize, spinning the armature at high speed with resulting armature damage.

Another cause may be engine backfire during cranking which may result, among other things, from ignition timing being too far advanced.

To avoid such failures, the driver

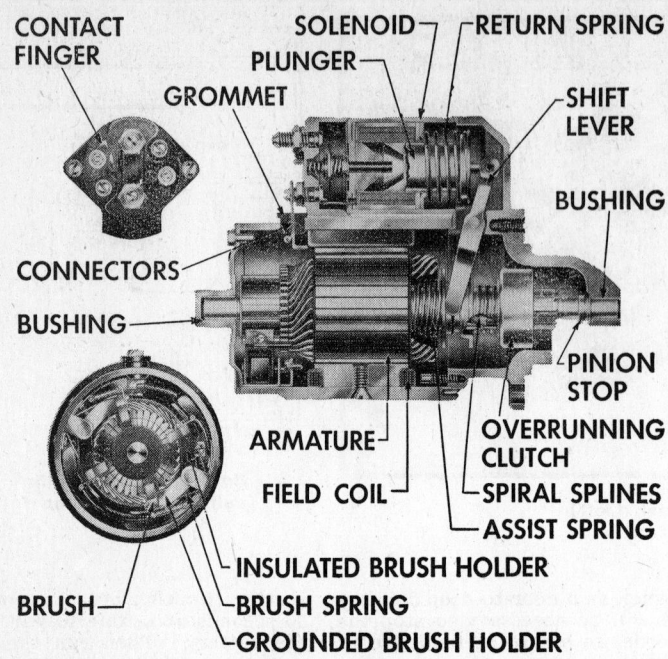

CONTACT FINGER
SOLENOID
RETURN SPRING
PLUNGER
GROMMET
SHIFT LEVER
BUSHING
CONNECTORS
BUSHING
PINION STOP
ARMATURE
OVERRUNNING CLUTCH
FIELD COIL
SPIRAL SPLINES
ASSIST SPRING
INSULATED BRUSH HOLDER
BRUSH
BRUSH SPRING
GROUNDED BRUSH HOLDER

Fig. 1 Sectional view of starter with overrunning clutch drive

Fig. 2 Checking voltage drop between car frame and grounded battery terminal post

Fig. 3 Checking voltage drop between car frame and starting motor field frame

Fig. 4 Checking voltage drop between insulated battery terminal post and starting motor terminal stud (or battery terminal on solenoid, if so equipped)

should pause a few seconds after a false start to make sure the engine has come completely to rest before another start is attempted. In addition, the ignition timing should be reset if engine backfiring has caused the trouble.

Lights Stay Bright, No Cranking Action

This condition indicates an open circuit at some point, either in the starter itself, the starter switch or control circuit. If the car is equipped with a solenoid starting switch, the solenoid control circuit can be eliminated momentarily by placing a heavy jumper lead across the solenoid main terminals to see if the starter will operate. This connects the starter directly to the battery and, if it operates, it indicates that the control circuit is not functioning normally. The wiring and control units must be checked to locate the trouble.

If the starter does not operate with the jumper attached, it will probably have to be removed from the engine so it can be examined in detail.

Checking Circuit With Voltmeter

Excessive resistance in the circuit between the battery and starter will reduce cranking performance. The resistance can be checked by using a voltmeter to measure voltage drop in the circuits while the starter is operated. There are three checks to be made:

1. Voltage drop between car frame and grounded battery terminal post (not cable clamp), Fig. 2.
2. Voltage drop between car frame and starting motor field frame, Fig. 3.
3. Voltage drop between insulated battery terminal post and starting motor terminal stud (or the battery terminal stud of the solenoid), Fig. 4.

Each of these should show no more than one-tenth (0.1) volt drop when the

starting motor is cranking the engine. Do not use the starter for more than 30 seconds at a time to avoid overheating it.

If excessive voltage drop is found in any of these circuits, make correction by disconnecting the cables, cleaning the connections carefully, and then reconnecting the cables firmly in place. A coating of vaseline on the battery cables and terminal clamps will retard corrosion.

NOTE—On some cars, extra long battery cables may be required due to the location of the battery and starter. This may result in somewhat higher voltage drop than the above recommended 0.1 volt. The only means of determining the normal voltage drop in such cases is to check several of these vehicles. Then when the voltage drop is well above the normal figure for all cars checked, abnormal resistance will be indicated and correction can be made as already explained.

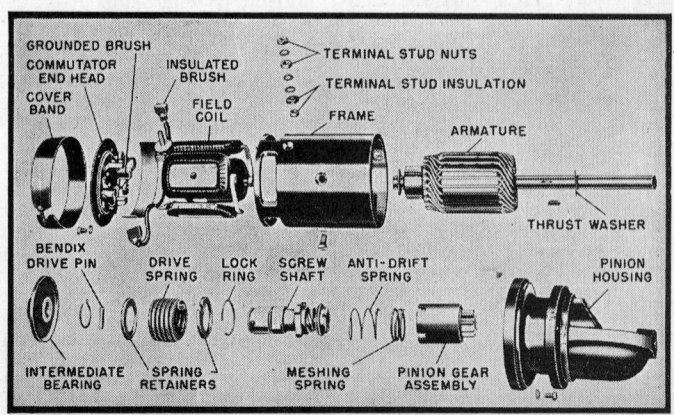

GROUNDED BRUSH
COMMUTATOR END HEAD
COVER BAND
INSULATED BRUSH
FIELD COIL
TERMINAL STUD NUTS
TERMINAL STUD INSULATION
FRAME
ARMATURE
THRUST WASHER
BENDIX DRIVE PIN
DRIVE SPRING
LOCK RING
SCREW SHAFT
ANTI-DRIFT SPRING
PINION HOUSING
INTERMEDIATE BEARING
SPRING RETAINERS
MESHING SPRING
PINION GEAR ASSEMBLY

Fig. 5 Exploded view of starting motor with barrel type Bendix drive

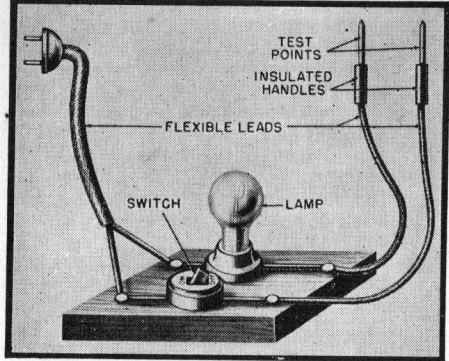

Fig. 6 A simple tester for use in making continuity and ground tests on armature and field windings

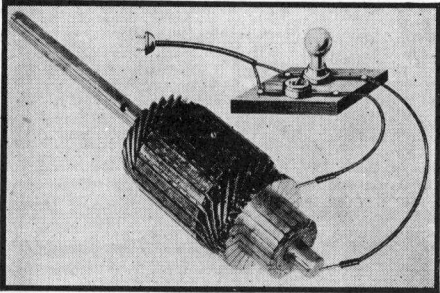

Fig. 7 Checking armature for grounds. If lamp lights armature is grounded and should be replaced

Fig. 8 Measuring commutator runout with dial indicator. Mount shaft in V blocks and rotate commutator. If runout exceeds .003", commutator should be turned in a lathe to make it concentric

Fig. 9 Turning commutator in a lathe. Take light cuts until no worn or bad spots appear. Then remove burrs with 00 sandpaper

STARTING MOTOR SERVICE

To obtain full performance data on a starting motor or to determine the cause of abnormal operation, the starting motor should be submitted to a no-load and torque test. These tests are best performed on a starter bench tester with the starter mounted on it.

From a practical standpoint, however, a simple torque test may be made quickly with the starter in the car. Make sure the battery is fully charged and that the starter circuit wires and terminals are in good condition. Then operate the starter to see if the engine turns over normally. If it does not, the torque developed is below standard and the starter should be removed for further checking.

Removing Starter from Engine

The general procedure for removing a starter from the engine is as follows: Disconnect the leads from the starter. (When the switch is mounted on the motor, the battery lead should be covered with friction tape or a short piece of hose to prevent it from short-circuiting against any metal surface.) Disconnect any pedal linkage directly connected to the starting motor or yoke. Then take out the mounting bolts and lift the starter from the engine.

Disassembling Starting Motor

The disassembly procedure to be followed will vary according to the type and construction of the starting motor. Normally, disassembly should proceed only so far as it is necessary to make repair or replacement of defective parts. For example, the field coils should be checked for opens or grounds and if found to be in normal condition, they should not be removed from the field frame.

1. If the brush holders are of the box type, lift the spring with a hook made of stiff wire and take the brushes out of the holders. On swinging type brushes, disconnect the field coil lead from the insulated brush and slightly tighten the screw to keep the brush in place.

2. Before disassembling commutator end heads that are fastened by a number of screws into the end of the field frame, scratch a mark on the frame and head so that they can be reassembled in their original position. This is not necessary on motors using through bolts to hold the heads and having a dowel pin to locate the commutator end head position.

3. Take out the through bolts or commutator end head and drive end housing attaching screws. If necessary, tap the commutator end head lightly with a rubber or plastic hammer and remove the head.

4. Lift off the drive end head (or pinion housing) and the armature. On types having an intermediate bearing, the armature will remain in the pinion housing. On most motors, this bearing assembly is a press fit in the pinion housing and can be forced out with an arbor press bearing on the drive end of

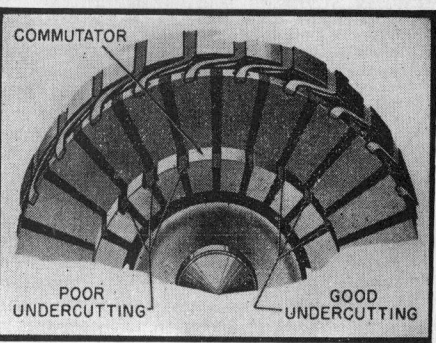

Fig. 10 Good undercutting should be .002" wider than the mica, 1/64" deep and exactly centered so that there are no burrs on the mica

Fig. 11 This illustrates the use of an open core transformer (growler) and a steel strip to test the armature for shorts. Turn armature slowly and if a short is present the steel strip will vibrate rapidly

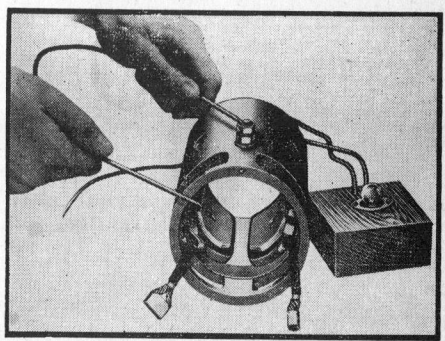

Fig. 12 Testing field coils for grounds. A six-volt test lamp is shown but the test lamp illustrated in Fig. 6 may also be used. If a ground is present, the lamp will light

the shaft. A few types of motors use a screw or a lock ring to hold the intermediate bearing in place. These must be removed before pressing the armature out of the pinion housing. Gear reduction motors require the removal of the intermediate housing screws to complete their disassembly.

Armature Inspection & Service

1. Visually inspect the armature for mechanical defects such as a worn or bent shaft, worn commutator, scored core laminations, and to see that all windings are properly in place in the core slots.
2. Inspect for evidence of excessively high speeds which would throw the windings outward at the ends and may even cause them to leave the core slots.
3. Inspect to see that all windings are properly staked and soldered to the commutator. Resolder if necessary, being careful not to short between coils and commutator bars.
4. With test clips or points such as are illustrated in Fig. 6, test the armature for grounds by touching the shaft with one point and the commutator with the other, Fig. 7. Do not touch the test points to the bearing or brush surfaces as an arc would burn the smooth finish. If the lamp lights, the armature is grounded and should be replaced.
5. Clean the commutator with 00 sandpaper and remove all dirt from between the bars.
6. Place the armature shaft bearing surfaces on V blocks, Fig. 8, and mount a dial indicator against the commutator as shown.
7. Turn the armature slowly and read the total runout as indicated on the dial gauge. If runout exceeds .003", the commutator should be turned down with a lathe to make it concentric.
8. Mount the armature in the lathe by the shaft bearing surfaces (not shaft centers), Fig. 9, and take light cuts until the commutator is completely cleaned up. Remove all burrs with 00 sandpaper. This trueing up of the commutator should also be done if it is rough, burned or if the mica extends above the surface of the copper. Recheck runout after turning the commutator.
9. Undercut the mica $\frac{1}{64}$" measured depth, Fig. 10. This cut should be exactly centered on the mica and the cutting tool used should be .002" wider than the mica. The undercut should be clean and square.
10. If the burrs on the copper after undercutting are not large they can

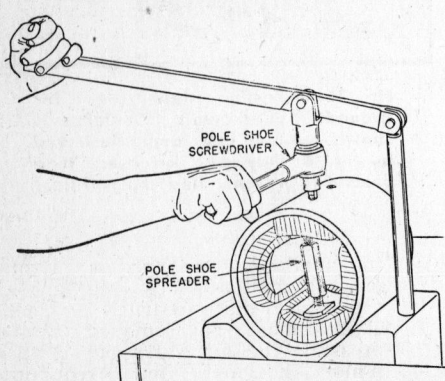

Fig. 13 Recommended equipment for installing field coils and pole shoes

POLE SHOE SCREWDRIVER

POLE SHOE SPREADER

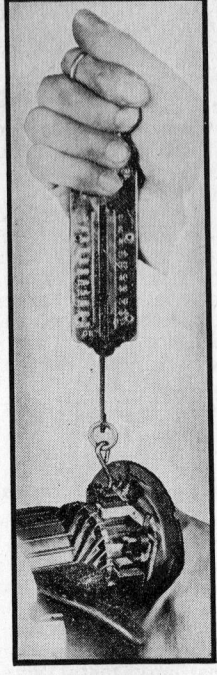

Fig. 14 Measuring brush spring tension on units with box type holders. Hook scale under brush spring and pull parallel to sides of brush. Place a strip of paper between brush and commutator. While holding a slight tension on paper, take scale reading just as paper can be slipped from under brush

be left on the commutator to help seat the brushes after assembly. However, be sure to remove the burrs with 00 sandpaper before completing the overhaul.

11. Place the armature on an open core transformer, otherwise known as a growler, Fig. 11, and hold a hacksaw blade on the core as shown. Rotate the armature slowly and if the armature is shorted the hacksaw blade will become magnetized and vibrate.
12. If a short is present, inspect the commutator risers and bars for copper chips or solder that may be shorting between the bars. If shorts cannot be found, replace the armature.

Frame & Field Service

1. Clean the frame and field with a cloth dampened in cleaning solvent but do not soak insulation or brushes.
2. Inspect for faulty insulation and stripped threads.
3. With a test lamp, check for grounds by touching the terminal stud with one test point and an unpainted spot on the frame with the other test point, Fig. 12. Be sure brushes or leads are not in contact with the frame. If the lamp lights, there is a ground in the field circuit.
4. If a ground is present, remove the terminal stud nuts and if the stud

is removable, press it out of the frame. Then recheck the field coils for grounds as before.
5. If the terminal stud is soldered to the field coils or if the field coils are grounded, remove the pole shoe screws and take the coils out of the frame. It is good practice to mark one end of the frame and also the shoes before disassembly so that they can be installed in their original position.
6. Replace any faulty or damaged parts, making sure all connections are tightly clinched and soldered to be sure that no high resistance connections are present.
7. When installing field coils and shoes, the tools shown in Fig. 13 or their equivalent should be used to insure a tight installation of the coils and shoes.
8. Be sure the pole shoes are installed in the same location and direction as they were originally. On some motors, the shoes are bored after assembly and when they are interchanged they may interfere with the armature. On other motors, the two tips of the shoes are not alike. However, on this type, the long tip is always the trailing edge.
9. If the brushes are oil soaked or are worn to less than ½ their original length they should be replaced.
10. To remove the brushes, unsolder and unclinch the lead from the field coil or connector.
11. Insert the new brush lead to its full depth and insert the equalizer lead (if used).
12. Clinch tightly and solder to make a low resistance connection. Do not use acid for soldering flux as it will damage the insulation. Use a rosin or alcohol solution.

Commutator End Head Service

1. Clean the commutator end head, be-

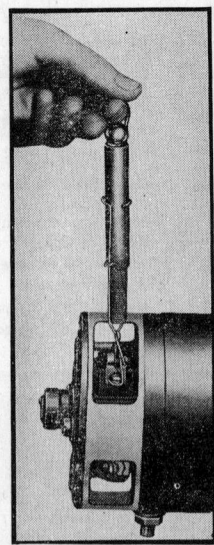

Fig. 15 Measuring brush spring tension on units with swinging type holders. Hook scale under brush screw tight against brush and pull parallel to sides of brush. Use paper as in Fig. 14

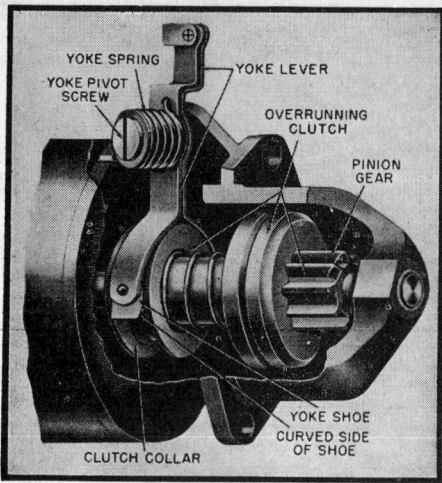

Fig. 16 Assembly of overrunning clutch and yoke shifting lever. Make sure curved sides of yoke shoes are toward gear end of clutch. Reversed yoke shoes can cause improper meshing of pinion

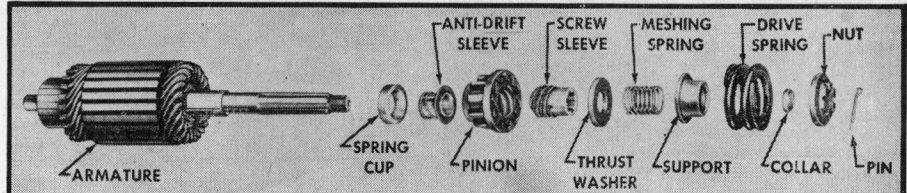

Fig. 18 Layout of compression spring type Bendix drive parts

ing careful not to soak the brushes in solvent.

2. Inspect for a cracked, bent or distorted head and replace if these conditions are present.

3. Place the armature in a padded vise and install the commutator end head on the end of the armature shaft.

4. Do not clamp the armature tightly as this distorts the laminated core.

5. Feel the fit of the bearing on the shaft. If side play is excessive, the bearing or shaft is worn and should be replaced. Where the bearing is replaceable, it should be pressed into place with the correct arbor, as the arbor determines the inside diameter of the bearing. If the bearing is not removable, replace the complete head.

6. With the head mounted on the armature, install a spare brush in one of the holders.

7. Inspect to make sure the brush is parallel to the commutator segments and that it moves freely in the holder.

8. To align the brush it is necessary to install a new arm on swinging type holders, or to replace the complete head or brush plate if the brush holders are of the box type.

9. Measure the brush spring tension with a spring scale hooked under the brush spring, Fig. 14, or brush screw, Fig. 15, near the end. Pull the scale on a line parallel to the edge of the brush and take the reading just as the spring leaves the brush, Fig. 14, or just as the brush leaves the commutator, Fig. 15.

10. Adjust the tension by bending the brush spring at the point where it is clamped by the brush holder.

11. Repeat this brush alignment, movement and tension inspection for all brushes.

12. Be sure to remove the brushes from the holders before taking the head off the armature as they may become chipped or cracked if they are allowed to snap off the commutator.

13. If the brush leads are broken or frayed or if the brushes are oil soaked, chipped, cracked or worn less than ½ their original length, the brushes should be replaced.

14. Brushes that are soldered to the field coils or connectors should be replaced as outlined under Frame and Field Service. Brushes that have the ground terminal riveted under the brush holder should have the lead unsoldered and the terminal unclamped.

15. Insert the lead to its full length in the terminal and clamp tightly. Solder it to make a strong and electrically tight connection, using a high temperature solder and a rosin flux. Do not use acid.

Drive End Head Service

1. Thoroughly clean the head or pinion housing and inspect for cracks.

2. Try the fit of the armature shaft in the bearing and replace the bearing if the side play is excessive.

3. When installing a new bearing, be sure to support the housing so that it does not twist or damage the bearing.

4. Install a new bearing, using the correct arbor, as it is designed to give the proper inside diameter of the bearing without the necessity of reaming or scraping.

5. Soak the bearing in SAE 10 engine oil and remove the excess oil from the housing or head.

STARTER DRIVE SERVICE

Starter drives fall into one or the other of two basic groups, the type that uses the principle of the over-running clutch, Fig. 16, and the Bendix, which uses the spinning nut principle, Figs. 17, 18 and 19.

Starter drive troubles are easy to diagnose and they usually cannot be confused with ordinary starter difficulties. If the starter does not turn over at all or if it drags, look for trouble in the starter or electrical supply system. Concentrate on the starter drive or ring gear if the starter is noisy, if it turns but does not engage the engine, or if the starter won't disengage after the engine is started. After the starter is removed, the trouble can usually be located with a quick inspection.

Worn or chipped ring gear or starter pinion are the usual causes of noisy operation. Before replacing either or both of these parts try to find out what caused the damage. With the Bendix type drive, incomplete engagement of the pinion with the ring gear is a common cause of tooth damage. The wrong pinion clearance on starter drives of the over-running clutch type leads to poor meshing of the pinion and ring gear and to rapid tooth wear.

A less common cause of noise with either type of drive is a bent starter armature shaft. When this shaft is bent, the pinion gear alternately binds and then only partly meshes with the ring gear. Most manufacturers specify a maximum of .003" radial run-out on the armature shaft.

When Clutch Drive Fails

The over-running clutch type drive seldom becomes so worn that it fails to engage since it is directly activated by a fork and lever, Fig. 16. The only thing that is likely to happen is that, once engaged, it will not turn the engine because the clutch itself is worn out. A much more frequent difficulty and one that rapidly wears ring gear and teeth is partial engagement. Proper meshing of the pinion is controlled by the end clearance between the pinion gear and the starter housing or the pinion stop, if one is used.

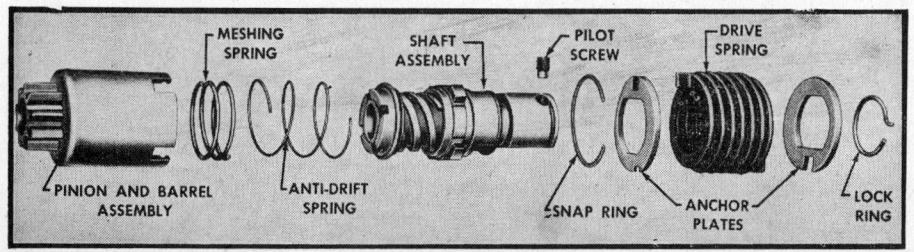

Fig. 17 Layout of barrel type Bendix drive parts

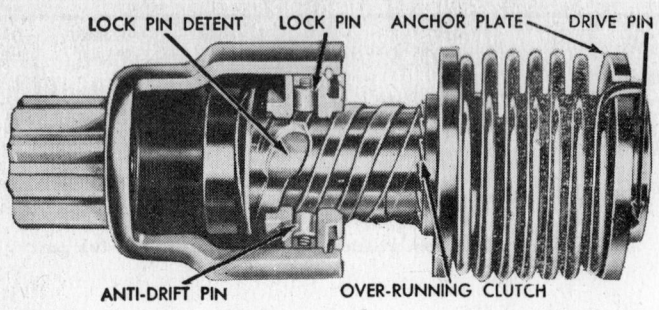

LOCK PIN DETENT   LOCK PIN   ANCHOR PLATE   DRIVE PIN

ANTI-DRIFT PIN   OVER-RUNNING CLUTCH

Fig. 19 Bendix Folo-Thru starter drive

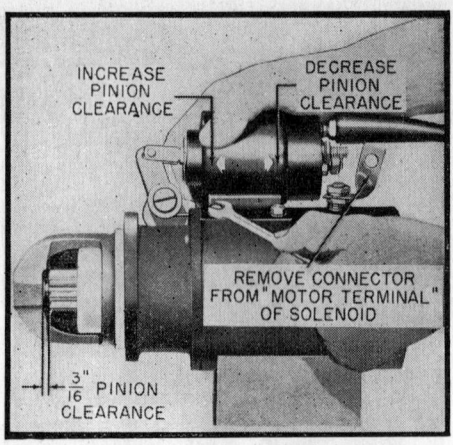

INCREASE PINION CLEARANCE   DECREASE PINION CLEARANCE

REMOVE CONNECTOR FROM "MOTOR TERMINAL" OF SOLENOID

3/16" PINION CLEARANCE

Fig. 21 Adjusting pinion clearance on over-running clutch motor equipped with solenoid having a non-adjustable plunger stud

The clearance is set with the starter off the car and with the drive in the engaged position. To check the clearance, supply current to the starter solenoid with the electrical connection between starter and solenoid removed. Supplying current to the solenoid but not the starter will prevent the starter from rotating during the test. Take out all slack by pushing lightly on the starter drive clutch housing while inserting a feeler gauge between pinion and housing or pinion stop, Fig. 20.

On a number of late model cars, starting with 1957, the solenoids are completely enclosed in the starter housing and the pinion clearance is not adjustable, see Fig. 1. If the clearance is not correct, the starter must be disassembled and checked for excessive wear of solenoid linkage, shift lever mechanism, or improper assembly of parts.

On cars where the solenoid is exposed, the clearance can be adjusted either by loosening the screws holding the solenoid to the starting and moving the solenoid forward and backward, Fig. 21, or by screwing or unscrewing the link attached to the soleniod plunger.

Failure of the over-running clutch drive to disengage is usually caused by binding between the armature shaft and the drive. If the drive, particularly the clutch, shows signs of overheating it indicates that it is not disengaging immediately after the engine starts. If the clutch is forced to over-run too long, it overheats and turns a bluish color. For the cause of the binding, look for rust or gum between the armature shaft and the drive, or for burred splines. Excess oil on the drive will lead to gumming, and inadequate air circulation in the flywheel housing will cause rust.

Over-running clutch drives cannot be overhauled in the field so they must be

replaced. In cleaning, never soak them in a solvent because the solvent may enter the clutch and dissolve the sealed-in lubricant. Wipe them off lightly with kerosene and lubricate them sparingly with SAE 10 or 10W oil.

When Bendix Drive Fails

When a Bendix type drive doesn't engage the cause usually is one of three things: either the drive spring is broken, one of the drive spring bolts has sheared off, or the screwshaft threads won't allow the pinion to travel toward the flywheel.

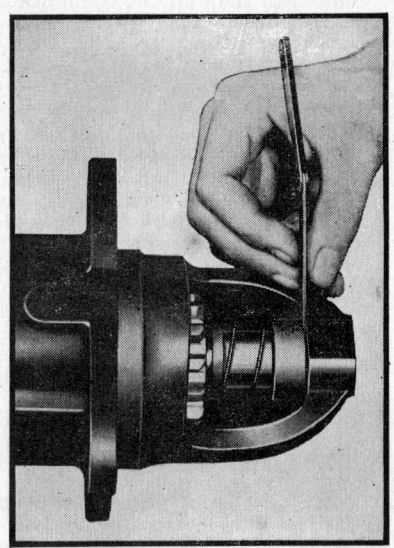

Fig. 20   Measuring Bendix drive stop clearance. Do not compress spring as this will give an incorrect reading

In the first two cases, remove the drive by unscrewing the set screw under the last coil of the drive spring and replace the broken parts. Gummed or rusty screwshaft threads are fairly common causes of Bendix drive failure and are easily cleaned with a little kerosene or steel wool, depending on the trouble. Here again, as in the case of over-running clutch drives, use light oil sparingly, and be sure the flywheel housing has adequate ventilation. There is usually a breather hole in the bottom of the flywheel housing which should be kept open.

The failure of a Bendix drive to disengage or to mesh properly is most often caused by gummed or rusty screwshaft threads. When this is not true, look for mechanical failure within the drive itself.

Bendix Folo-Thru Drive

This type of drive, Fig. 19, is in wide use on late model cars. It incorporates a device that keeps the pinion engaged to the flywheel until the engine reaches a specified rpm. When replacing one of these drives, be sure that you have the correct drive for the car. The drives are rated differently and the correct one must be used for the car being serviced. The Folo-Thru, incidentally, is not supposed to be repaired in the field because of the danger of incorrectly assembling the carefully calibrated springs in the pinion head.

STARTING SWITCHES

MAGNETIC and SOLENOID SWITCHES are designed to perform mechanical jobs electromagnetically such as closing a heavy circuit or shifting the starter drive pinion with the engine flywheel ring gear for cranking. Switches of this type consist basically of contacts and a winding (or windings) around a hollow cylinder containing a movable core or plunger. When the winding (or windings) is energized by the battery through an external control circuit the plunger is pulled inward, producing the necessary mechanical movement.

MAGNETIC SWITCHES

Figs. 1 and 2 illustrate two typical Delco-Remy switches. The switch shown in Fig. 1 is not designed for disassembly and must be replaced if defective.

In the switch shown in Fig. 2 the terminals are assembled into a molded terminal ring which is held in place on the switch case by the cover and screws. Gaskets on both sides of the ring seals the contact compartment as a protection against moisture and dirt. The winding assembly is not removable from the case on this unit although the contact disk, plunger and plunger return spring can be removed after the cover is taken off.

Fig. 3 is a heavy duty magnetic switch. It is completely serviceable and easy to disassemble and assemble. To disassemble, remove the four terminal plate nuts and washers and take off the terminal plate assembly. The contact disk may be removed by taking off the castellated nut. It is necessary to remove the spring and washers on the plunger rod only when the plunger rod needs to be disassembled. To remove the plunger, unscrew the large metal cover, take out the cotter pin in the plunger shaft, remove spring retainer washer and spring, and withdraw the plunger. The winding and switch case is an integral assembly. The only parts that can be removed are the switch terminals. Before removing the switch terminals, the winding leads must be unsoldered from the terminal studs. Whenever the switch is disassembled, upon reassembly, locate the contact disk properly by turning the castellated nut on the disk in or out as required to obtain the dimension shown in Fig. 3 between the contact disk and edge of housing.

SOLENOID SWITCHES

The solenoid switch on a cranking motor not only closes the circuit between the battery and the cranking motor but also shifts the drive pinion into mesh with the engine flywheel ring gear. This is done by means of a linkage between the solenoid switch plunger and the shift lever on the cranking motor. Some linkages are adjustable while others are not (see *Starting Motors* chapter). The linkage is not adjustable on the type shown in Fig. 4 but adjustment of the entire assembly is made by moving the switch on the motor frame.

Fig. 4 shows two views of a solenoid switch used on vehicles with 12-volt systems. Like other solenoid switches, this type is energized by the battery through a separate starting switch. Note, however, that the switch includes an additional small terminal and contact finger. This terminal has no functional duty in relation to the switch, but is used to complete a special ignition circuit during the cranking cycle only. When the solenoid is in the cranking position, the finger touches the contact disk and provides a direct circuit between the battery and ignition coil.

Fig. 5 is an exploded view of the 12-volt solenoid switch shown in Fig. 4. When reassembling the switch the contact finger should be adjusted to touch the contact disk before the disk makes contact with the main switch terminals.

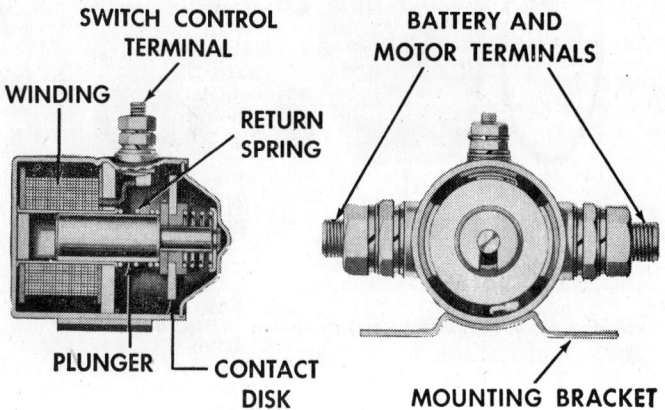

Fig. 1 End and sectional views of a typical magnetic switch

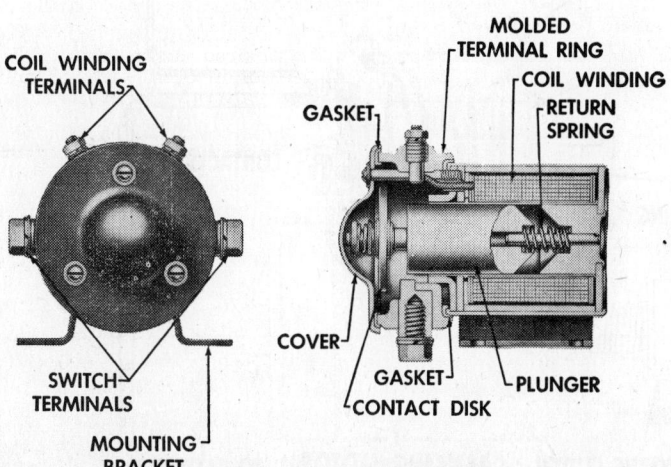

Fig. 2 End and sectional views of a sealed type magnetic switch which uses gaskets to seal the contact compartment

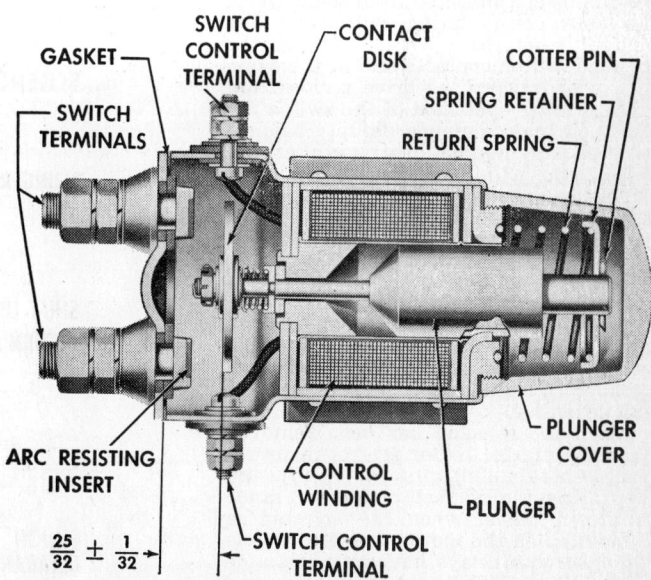

$$\frac{25}{32} \pm \frac{1}{32}$$

Fig. 3 Sectional view of heavy duty sealed type magnetic switch. To adjust the location of the contact disk turn the nut on the disk in or out as required to obtain the dimension shown

STARTING SWITCHES

There should be $\frac{1}{16}''$ to $\frac{3}{32}''$ clearance between the contact disk and the main terminals when the finger touches.

Fig. 6 is a wiring circuit of a typical solenoid switch. There are two windings in the solenoid; a pull-in winding (shown as dashes) and a hold-in winding (shown dotted). Both windings are energized when the external control switch is closed. They produce a magnetic field which pulls the plunger in so that the drive pinion is shifted into mesh, and the main contacts in the solenoid switch are closed to connect the battery directly to the cranking motor. Closing the main switch contacts shorts out the pull-in winding since this winding is connected across the main contacts. The magnetism produced by the hold-in winding is sufficient to hold the plunger in, and shorting out the pull-in winding reduces drain on the battery. When the control switch is opened, it disconnects the hold-in winding from the battery. When the hold-in

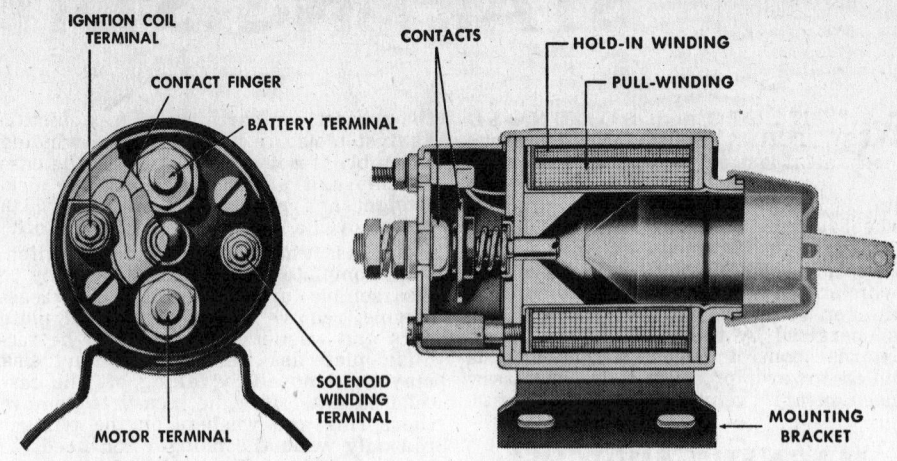

Fig. 4 End and sectional views of a typical solenoid switch. The additional terminal and contact finger are used on 12-volt passenger car applications

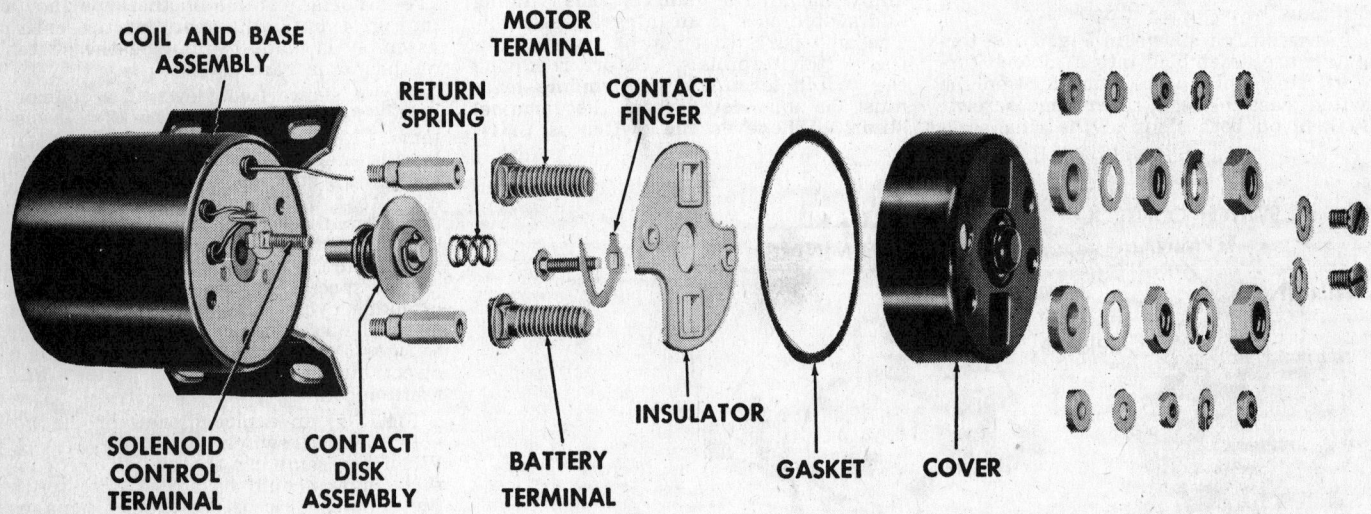

Fig. 5 Exploded view of solenoid switch shown in Fig. 4

winding is disconnected from the battery, the shift lever spring withdraws the plunger from the solenoid, opening the solenoid switch contacts and at the same time withdrawing the drive pinion from mesh. Proper operation of the switch depends on maintaining a definite balance between the magnetic strength of the pull-in and hold-in windings.

This balance is established in the design by the size of the wire and the number of turns specified. *An open circuit in the hold-in winding or attempts to crank with a discharged battery will cause the switch to chatter.*

To disassemble the solenoid, remove nuts, washers and insulators from the switch terminal and battery terminal. Remove cover and take out the contact disk assembly.

When the solenoid has been removed from the starter motor for repair or replacement, the linkage must be adjusted to provide the correct pinion clearance or pinion travel when the solenoid is remounted on the motor. Some solenoids equipped with relays have an adjustable plunger stud, but others must be moved on the motor frame to adjust pinion travel.

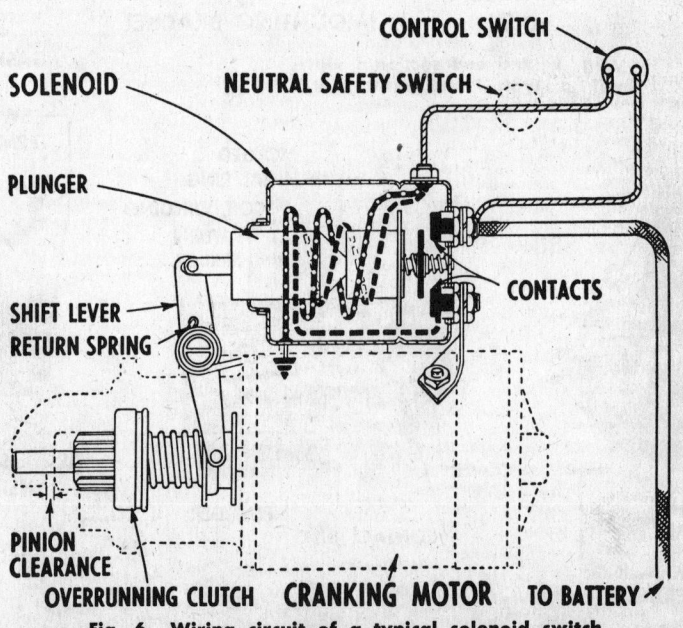

Fig. 6 Wiring circuit of a typical solenoid switch

DASH GAUGES

KING-SEELEY CONSTANT VOLTAGE GAUGES

First introduced on some 1957 cars, the constant voltage system incorporates a voltage regulator as well as "senders" that are different from those used in previous systems, Fig. 1A. The new system can easily be tested with a voltmeter having a range up to 15 volts and with a fuel-gauge sending unit.

Responsible for the greater ease of testing is the greater simplicity of the new system. Essentially, it consists, in addition to the new-type senders, of a voltage regulator which changes the variable input from the car battery and charging system to a constant output of the gauges. When the ignition is turned on, the regulator current flows through a heating coil which encircles a bimetallic arm. Resulting heat causes the arm to bend and separate the contacts. Repeated making and breaking of the circuit supplies current at a pulsating 5 volt pressure to the gauges.

Senders for the fuel and oil-pressure gauges are rheostats. In the fuel-tank unit, the sliding contact brings full resistance into the circuit when the tank is empty and only a small amount of current flows through the dash-gauge heating coil. The bimetallic arm deflects the gauge pointer to "Empty." As the tank fills, the float arm moves the contact, decreasing resistance. As more current flows to the dash heating coil the pointer deflects toward "Full."

In the oil line, a contact, attached to the diaphragm, moves as pressure increases or decreases, varying the resistance in the circuit, and deflecting the gauge needle accordingly.

The sender for the temperature gauge contains an element in which resistance to the flow of electrical current increases with cold. As the engine warms up, resistance falls and the fuller flow of current to the gauge moves the pointer toward "Hot."

Trouble Shooting

When trouble develops, you can quickly put your finger on the cause through the use of the voltmeter and the fuel-gauge sending unit already mentioned. The latter should have a short ground lead and clip.

A word of caution about grounding: When testing or making replacement of a unit under the dash, be careful not to ground the wires to the gauges, sending units or regulator. A full flow of current through the regulator to ground will burn out this unit.

All the trouble that can develop in a constant-voltage gauge system falls into the following four distinct classes: 1. All gauges read too high; 2. All gauges read

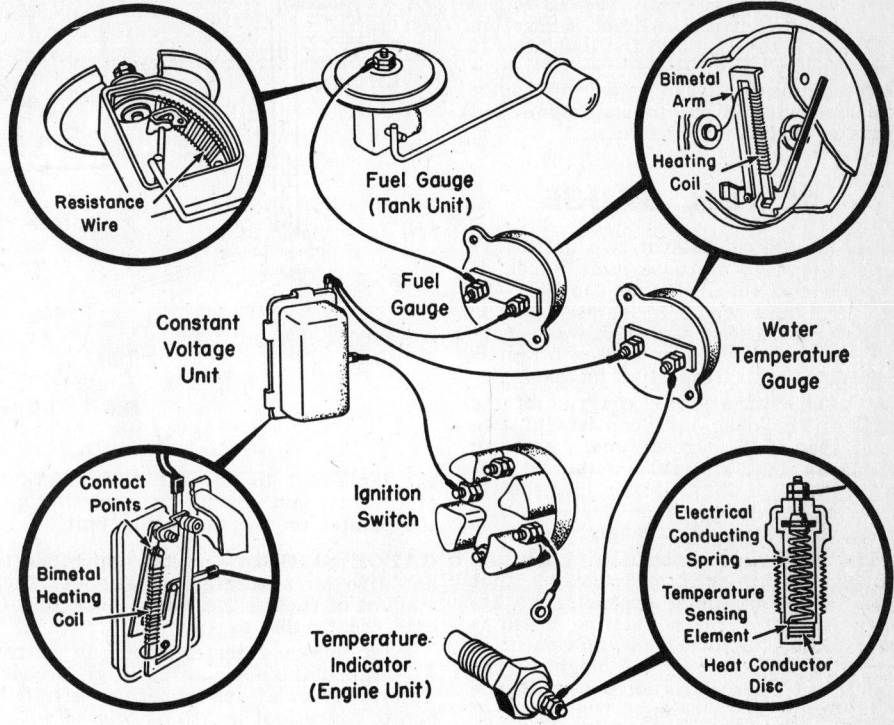

Fig. 1A King-Seeley constant-voltage system with units enlarged to show their construction

at high limit; 3. All gauges read too low; 4. One gauge is inaccurate or erratic.

When All Gauges Read Too High

When all gauges read too high, you will usually find that the voltage regulator is not properly grounded. To be sure, make a quick check with a jumper connected from the regulator case to the sheet metal of the instrument panel. Clean the mounting area to provide a good ground.

When All Gauges Read At High Limit

When all gauges read at the maximum of the needle travel, look for the trouble in stuck points or an open winding in the heating coil in the voltage regulator.

In checking for this trouble, connect the voltmeter to the regulator output terminal and to ground. This will show the output voltage of the regulator. If output shows a steady unregulated voltage equal to the battery voltage, the regulator is defective and should be replaced. A normally operating regulator will cause the voltmeter needle to fluctuate between zero and 7 volts with a 12 volt input.

(While this method does not give an absolutely accurate voltmeter reading, it does indicate whether the regulator is functioning and can be relied upon as a quick service test.)

When All Gauges Read Too Low

There are three possible reasons for all gauges to read too low. Regulator input may be less than the required 5.5 volts, the circuit to regulator may be open or there may be an open circuit in the regulator itself.

This fault is quite simple to check. Test the input to regulator. If battery voltage is normal, regulator is defective and must be replaced.

Single Gauge Trouble

When only one gauge is inaccurate or erratic, the trouble is simple to trace. The cause can only be a loose connection, poor ground, or a defective dash gauge or sending unit.

To pinpoint the trouble, first disconnect the wire from terminal on fuel-level, oil-pressure or temperature sender unit. Connect the wire to the terminal on a new gas tank unit and ground the unit housing with a jumper, Fig. 1B.

With the float in the "Empty" position and the ignition switch turned on, the gauge should read at the low end of the scale. Move the float to the "Full" position, allow the gauge a minute to react and the panel indicator should swing to the top of the scale. If the indicator responds correctly, both the wire to the gauge and the gauge are normal and the sending unit is either defective or not properly grounded.

When a suspected tank unit is being tested, it must be grounded to the tank and the tank to the body and frame. If a jumper wire connected between the tank unit housing and the frame or body does not restore normal gauge action, replace the defective tank unit.

If the indicator does not respond accurately, disconnect the lead wire to the indicator and make a direct connection of the new tank unit to the indicator. If the "Empty" and "Full" tests now give normal indicator action, repair or replace the lead wire. If the indicator does not register accurately, replace it.

AC FUEL GAUGE

The gauge consists of two units: (1) The indicating or dash unit which is mounted on the instrument panel; (2) the tank unit which is installed in the fuel tank. These two units are connected by a single wire and each unit is grounded in its respective location.

Fig. 1 shows a wiring diagram of the gauge. The dash unit consists of two coils spaced 90 degrees apart with an armature and integral pointer at the intersection of the coil axis. An inertia dampener is provided on the armature to prevent vibration on rough roads.

The tank unit consists of a housing enclosing a rheostat or resistance unit with a brush which contacts the resistance unit. This contacting brush is actuated by the float arm—movement of which is controlled by the height of the fuel in the tank. Variations in resistance (height of fuel) change the value of the indicating unit coils so that the pointer indicates fuel availability. A calibrated friction brake is included in

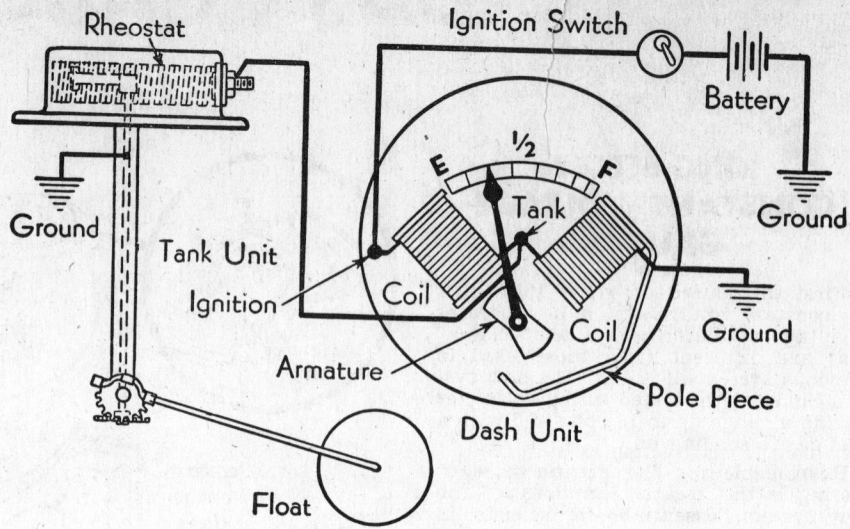

Fig. 1   AC electric fuel gauge

the tank unit to prevent wave motion of the fuel in the tank from oscillating the pointer on the indicating unit.

GAUGE SERVICE—If the gauge does not give an accurate indication of the amount of fuel in the tank, check to locate the trouble as follows:

First, make a tester using an extra AC tank unit known to be in good condition. Then attach a spring terminal clip to a five-foot length of *colored* wire. Connect the other end of this wire to the binding post of the tank unit. Next, attach two spring terminal clips to a similar piece of *black* insulated wire and the tester is ready for use.

Testing Dash Unit—

1. Turn off the ignition switch.
2. Disconnect one of the battery cables.
3. Disconnect the wire which leads to the tank unit.
4. Using the spring clip, connect your *colored* tester wire to the binding post from which the wire was removed.
5. Connect the *black* wire to the flange of the tester and to any convenient ground—such as the unpainted part of the instrument panel.
6. Turn on the ignition switch.
7. Connect the battery cable. Move the arm of the tester back and forth slowly, Fig. 2. If the dash unit is okay, the pointer will move from "Empty" to "Full" freely. If the pointer doesn't move, or only moves part way, the dash unit is defective and a new AC dash unit must be installed.

Test Wiring from Dash to Tank—

1. Turn off ignition switch. Disconnect battery and reconnect wire to dash unit.
2. Follow wire from tank unit to "bayonet connection" or the terminal junction block. Disconnect the wire at this point and clean wire contacts by scraping with a knife or sandpaper, Fig. 3.
3. Attach the *colored* wire of the end of the wire which runs to the instru-

ment panel. Attach the *black* tester wire to the car frame for a ground.

4. Connect the battery cable and turn on the ignition switch. Move the arm of the tester back and forth. If the wiring is okay, the pointer on the dash unit will move from "Empty" to "Full" freely. If the pointer doesn't move or only moves part way, the trouble is in the wire from the dash unit to the tank.

5. If the pointer *does* move correctly, the trouble is in the tank unit or the wire which runs from it to the "bayonet connection", Fig. 3, or terminal junction block. If the connections are all clean and tight, and there are no breaks or chafes in the wire from the bayonet connection to the tank, then a new AC tank unit must be installed.

AUTO-LITE FUEL GAUGES

Thermostatic Type

Figs. 4 and 5—With this type gauge two wires are used to connect the dash unit with the tank unit. The dash unit contains two thermostatic strips heated by resistance wires wound around the strips. The two bimetal strips that are not heated take care of variations in temperature.

The two terminals of the dash unit marked "1" and "2" are connected by separate wires to the tank unit terminals marked "1" and "2".

Movement of the float arm in the tank, due to changes in fuel level, moves a contact arm across a resistance winding in the tank unit. This varies the resistance in the windings of the dash unit, raising and lowering the temperature of the bimetal strips. The strips bend, depending upon the amount of heat they receive, moving the gauge pointer.

Due to the heating of the bimetal strips, the thermostatic type fuel gauge action is slow, and the pointer does not react to sudden changes in fuel level due to sloshing of the gasoline in the tank.

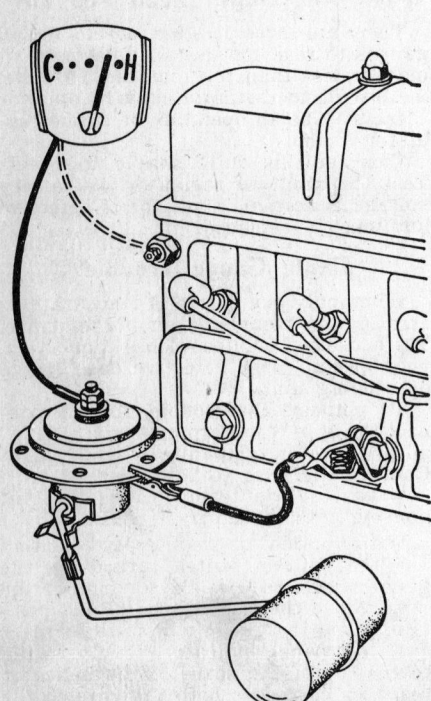

Fig. 1B   When tank unit is used to test temperature gauge, raising float through arc should swing needle of dash unit over toward "hot" side

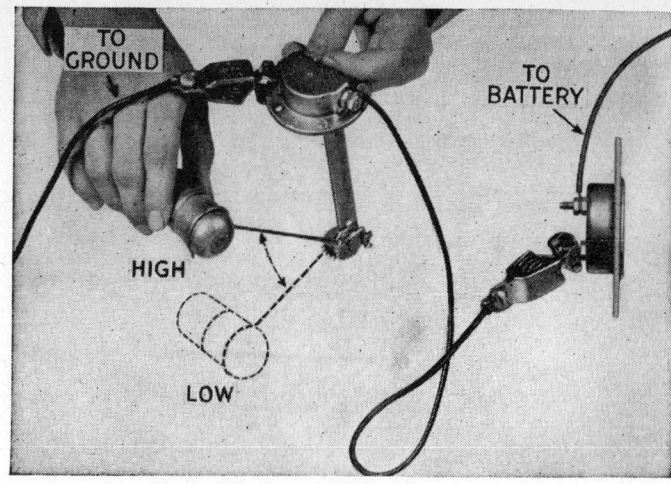

Fig. 2 Showing use of spare tank unit to check operation of dash unit

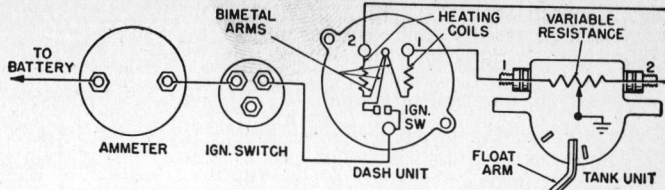

Fig. 5 Wiring diagram of Auto-Lite thermostatic type fuel gauge

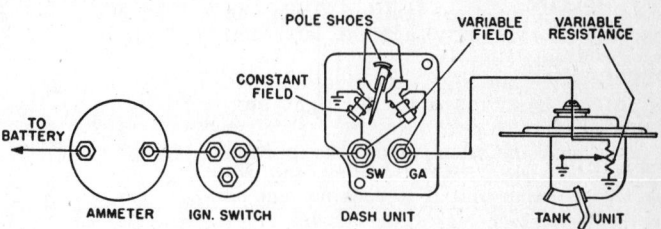

Fig. 6 Wiring diagram of Auto-Lite magnetic type fuel gauge

SERVICE—The gauge can be tested by using a spare tank unit known to be in good condition. The procedure is as follows:

1. Disconnect wires from terminals marked "1" and "2" on the tank unit.

2. Connect the disconnected wires to the corresponding terminals of the spare tank unit.

3. Then, connect a third wire to the frame of the spare tank unit to any good grounding point on the car.

4. Turn on ignition switch. Allow about one minute for the dash unit to heat, then operate the float arm of the spare tank unit (see Fig. 2).

5. If dash unit does not indicate correctly, install a new Auto-Lite dash unit. If dash unit works properly, the fault is in either the wiring or the tank unit.

6. If the dash unit is okay, reconnect the wires to the terminals and disconnect the wires from the tank unit. Ground the No. 1 wire and allow approximately one minute for the dash unit to reach its indication—which should be above the "Full" position.

Then ground both wires and the gauge should return slowly to the "½ Full" position. If the indications are not as described it indicates a grounded or open-circuited wire which should be repaired.

7. By elimination, if the gauge operates correctly in the above tests, the tank unit can be regarded as the cause of the original inoperation.

8. When reconnecting the leads to the dash or tank units, be careful not to interchange them as this would reverse the indications.

9. Erratic or incorrect indications may be caused by a loose connection or ground in the wiring or terminals. A fluctuating pointer is usually caused by dirty contacts in the dash unit. Sticking pointers may be caused by a bent pointer or frame or by interference between the gauge and dash panel. Remove the gauge from the panel and inspect for a bent pointer or pointer bearings. Check to see that there is a slight amount of end play in the pointer shaft and that the pointer turns freely. Clean the contacts by drawing a strip of clean bond paper between them.

Magnetic Type

Fig. 6—The dash unit has two magnetic circuits, each having a separate winding to produce two distinct magnetic fields. One of the windings is grounded internally, and sets up a constant pull toward the "Empty" indication when the ignition switch is turned on. The other winding, called the variable field winding, is grounded through the tank unit. This winding pulls the pointer across the gauge dial to indicate the amount of fuel in the tank.

The tank unit contains a resistor and a contact arm which moves as the float moves. The tank unit case is grounded to complete the fuel gauge circuit.

The magnetic field around the variable winding changes with a change in the amount of the fuel in the tank. As the float in the tank moves from "Full" to "Empty", the strength of the magnetic field is gradually reduced. When the float moves from "Empty" to "Full", the strength of the magnetic field is increased.

The pointer is mounted on a magnetic vane which is attracted by the two lower magnetic poles and assumes a posi-

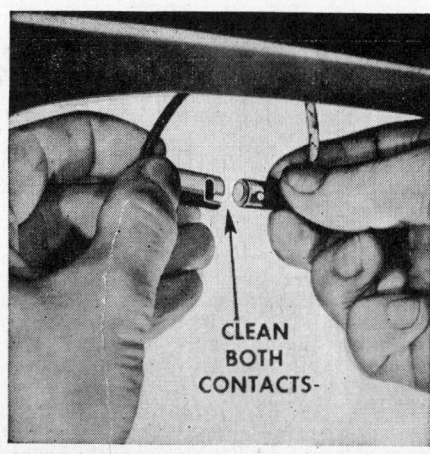

Fig. 3 AC fuel gauge connections

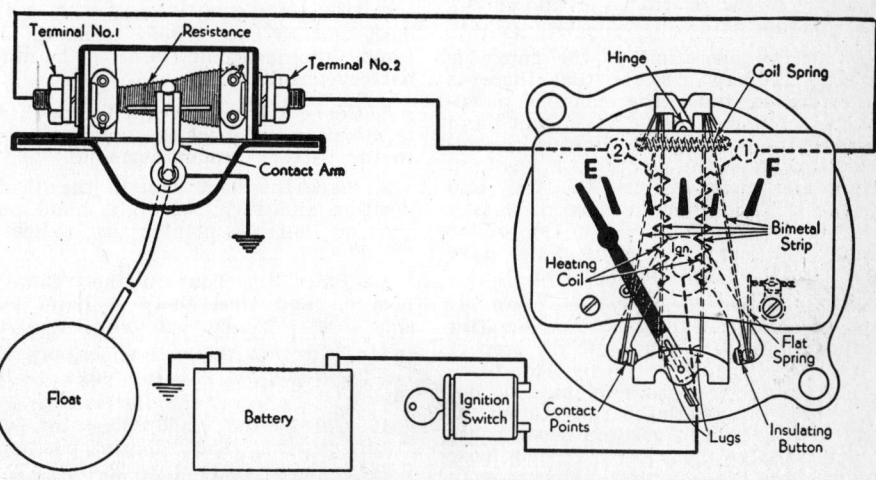

Fig. 4 Auto-Lite thermostatic fuel gauge

tion between them depending upon the combined magnetic field. A counterweight is mounted on the pointer to bring the reading back to "Empty" whenever the ignition is turned off.

SERVICE—If the gauge does not give an accurate indication of the amount of fuel in the tank, check to locate the trouble as follows:

1. Disconnect the lead from the "GA" terminal on the back of the dash unit.

2. Turn on the ignition and the pointer should stay against left stop pin ("Empty").

3. Ground the "GA" terminal and the pointer should move to the right stop pin ("Full").

4. Check the wiring from the ignition switch to the "SW" terminal and replace the dash unit if it does not act as described.

5. Reconnect the lead to the "GA" terminal and disconnect the lead from the tank unit. The gauge should stay against the left stop pin when the ignition is turned on. If it indicates "Full", look for a ground in the wiring between the dash and tank units.

6. Ground the lead at the tank unit. If the gauge does not move to the right pin, look for open circuit in wire.

NOTE—The above tests checked for faults in the dash unit variable field winding and for opens or grounds in the connecting wires, but did not check the constant field winding or tank unit. To test these parts, proceed as follows:

1. Connect a spare tank unit, known to be in good condition, to the "GA" terminal on the dash unit and ground the tank unit case.

2. Operate the float arm manually and observe the readings. If the dash unit indications are incorrect, remove and calibrate the dash unit; if the dash unit indicates correctly, replace the tank unit.

3. If no spare tank unit is available to make this check, remove the tank unit and use it for the above check. If the dash unit constant field winding is open or grounded, the gauge will read "Full" over a large part of the float arm movement. If the tank unit is faulty, the gauge will be erratic or will not operate at all.

4. If the operation of the gauge is erratic it may indicate that there is interference with the pointer movement. Remove the dash unit and inspect the pointer and armature assembly. Straighten the pointer if it has been bent and rubs against the dial and frame. Check to make sure there is a slight amount of end play in the pointer shaft and that the bearing plates have not been bent out of alignment.

5. Make sure bearings are clean. If the adjustable bearing is loose, or after adjusting the end play, apply a drop of air drying varnish to prevent the bearing from turning. Later gauges do not have this adjustable bearing screw; the shaft being held in position between the bearing plates, the upper one being loose and held in place by the dial screws. In no case should varnish be applied to

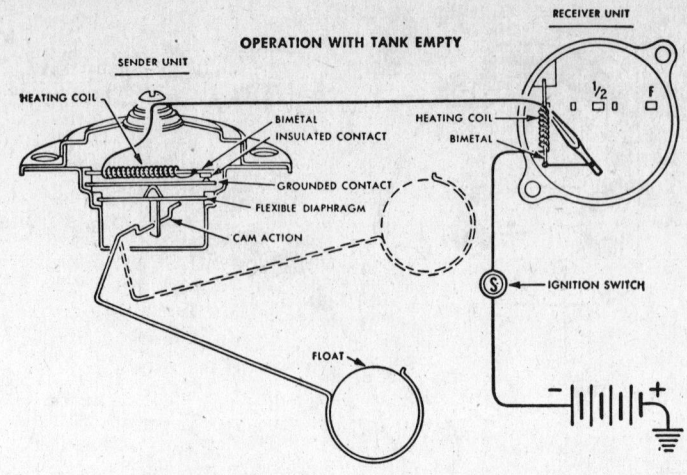

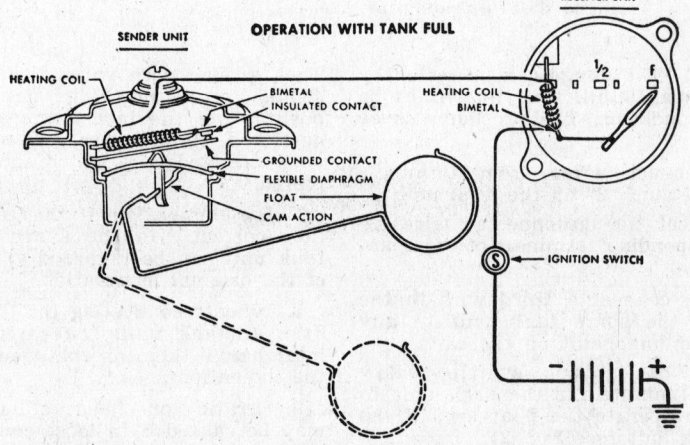

Fig. 7 Ford and King-Seeley fuel gauges (prior to 1957)

this type bearing and adjustment is not necessary.

6. To calibrate the dash gauge, remove it from the panel and mount it in the same position. Check to make sure the pointer turns easily and returns to the left hand stop (empty) from any position. The pointer should return promptly and have a very slight bank against the stop.

7. Connect the "SW" terminal on the dash unit to one battery terminal and ground the dash unit frame to the other battery terminal.

8. Connect the tank unit to the "GA" terminal and connect the tank unit case to the battery ground terminal.

9. Place the float arm in the "Full" position and turn the right hand pole shoe so that the pointer just indicates "Full".

10. Place the float in the "Empty" position and turn the left hand pole shoe to give the correct indication.

11. To rotate the pole shoes, pry the U-shaped lug on the top edge of the shoe.

12. Check the indications at the "Full", "½ full" and "Empty" positions.

13. When calibrating, it may be necessary to spread or reduce the indicator

movement. This is done by bending the upper shoe to increase or decrease the air gap between the pole and armature.

14. After all adjustments are completed, apply a drop of air drying varnish to each shoe to prevent slipping.

KING-SEELEY & FORD FUEL GAUGES
Prior to 1957

Fig. 7—This type gauge consists of a receiver and sender unit. The sender, of course, is the tank unit whereas the receiver is the dash unit.

The sender unit contains a heating coil formed around a bimetal strip, and an external float which varies the height of a grounded spring contact, which in turn increases or decreases the tension of the bimetal strip.

The receiver unit contains a similar heating coil and bimetal strip, linked to a pointer. The receiver unit is series connected to the ignition switch and, therefore, operates only when the ignition switch is turned on.

When the fuel tank is empty, the float of the tank unit is at the bottom of its movement and the two contacts are just touching. With the ignition switch

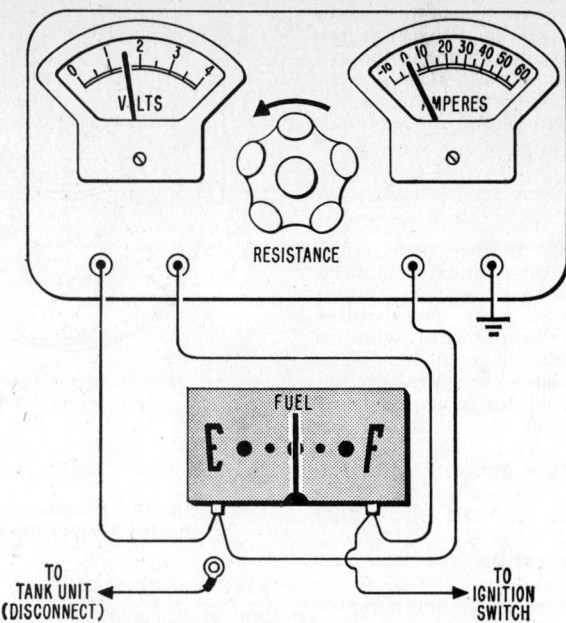

Fig. 7A Testing fuel gauge dash unit with volt-ammeter test set

turned on, current flows through the circuit and heat is generated in the heating coil, causing the bimetal strip to bend. Bending of the bimetal opens the contacts and the circuit is broken. The heating coil and bimetal then cools and the spring returns to its former position where contact is again made.

Since the heating coils of the two units are connected in series, a similar slight bending of the bimetal strip in the dash unit takes place, which is just sufficient to pull the pointer to the "Empty" position.

When the fuel tank is filled, the action of the float and eccentric shaft (some units have cams) raises the grounded contact against the insulated bimetal contact, bending the bimetal strip in the dash unit.

With the bimetal strip under tension, a greater amount of current is required to bend it sufficiently to break contact. A similar increased bending of the bimetal strip in the dash unit occurs and this action pulls the needle over the "Full" position on the dial. The cycle of opening and closing of the contacts is continuously repeated.

Because the bimetal strips heat and cool slowly, sudden changes of fuel level caused by the sloshing of gasoline in the tank are dampened and a steady reading of the average fuel level in the tank is indicated.

SERVICE—Trouble in the units or circuits may cause the gauge to indicate "Empty" at all times or the pointer may constantly rest beyond the "Full" mark.

Gauge Does Not Indicate — When the dash unit does not indicate the fuel level with ignition switch turned on, check the dash unit and wire to the tank unit as follows:

1. With ignition switch turned off, connect a jumper wire from the tank unit terminal to a convenient ground.

2. Turn the ignition switch on momentarily. Then if the dash unit gives an indication, the tank unit is defective and must be replaced.

3. If the dash does not show any indication after completing step 2, ground the tank-to-dash wire at the dash unit terminal.

4. Turn ignition on momentarily. If the dash unit now indicates, then the wire to the tank unit is defective and must be repaired or replaced. However, if the dash unit fails to indicate, then the dash unit is defective.

CAUTION—In making tests, be sure to turn off the ignition switch before the pointer reaches the full end of the scale, otherwise damage to the dash unit will result. A defective tank unit or wiring may have damaged the dash unit. After installing a new dash unit, observe its action after turning on the ignition switch momentarily. If the pointer moves beyond the "Full" mark, then the tank unit or wiring is defective and must be replaced.

In rare cases, a false indication of fuel level would be obtained if a leak developed in the tank unit float. If this condition is found, replace the complete tank unit.

Gauge Indicates Beyond "Full" Mark—When this condition occurs, regardless of the quantity of fuel in the tank, make the following tests to determine the source of the trouble. Before each test, be sure to turn on the ignition switch momentarily to energize the units.

1. If the tank unit is equipped with a radio condenser, disconnect the condenser. Then if the dash unit indicates correctly, the condenser is shorted and a new one should be installed.

2. The next step is to check the wiring between the gauges. Do this by dis-connecting the existing wire and substitute a jumper wire between the gauges. If the dash unit now checks OK, obviously the wiring is defective.

3. If the wiring proved OK use a spare tank unit and operate the float by hand, first being sure to ground the tank unit housing. Then if the dash unit indicates correctly, the tank unit is the source of the trouble.

4. If the dash unit still fails to indicate properly after making the above tests, obviously it is defective and should be replaced.

Using Volt-Ammeter Test Set

If a volt-ammeter test set is available, perhaps it is quicker to test the dash gauge first.

1. Disconnect tank unit wire at dash gauge.

2. With the ignition switch *off*, connect volt-ammeter test set and dash gauge as shown in Fig. 7A.

3. Turn rheostat knob to maximum resistance.

4. Turn ignition switch on.

5. Decrease resistance until voltmeter reads 1.5 volts. If the dash gauge is functioning properly, the fuel gauge will indicate about ½. If it does not the gauge is defective.

6. If the dash gauge indicates properly according to the above test, then check out the radio condenser and dash-to-tank unit wiring as directed above. If these check out all right, obviously the tank unit is defective.

AC TEMPERATURE GAUGES

Vapor Pressure Type

This type gauge consists of a metal case, enclosing a dial, a frame and mechanism assembly. Hermetically attached to the frame socket is a capillary tube (connector) and immersion bulb. The immersion bulb contains a liquid, such as ether, whose vapor pressure is proportional to the temperature.

The expanded gas is directed up the capillary tube, and into the curved bourdon tube (C shaped) which has one end fastened to the mechanism frame. The applied pressure has a straightening effect on the bourdon tube and results in its free end moving outward in proportion to the pressure. Since the free end is connected to the pointer by a linkage, the bourdon tube movement is transferred to an indication on the dial. Because the vapor pressure is constant for any given temperature, the dial is calibrated directly in degrees Fahrenheit.

SERVICE—Vapor pressure gauge troubles are of three kinds: (1) The pointer movement is sticky, jumpy or uneven. (2) The pointer does not move at all. (3) The pointer shows temperatures which are obviously incorrect.

Most automotive engines are designed to operate at temperatures between 140 and 180 degrees. Should the gauge read consistently higher than normal operating temperatures, the engine may be overheating due to one or more of the following:

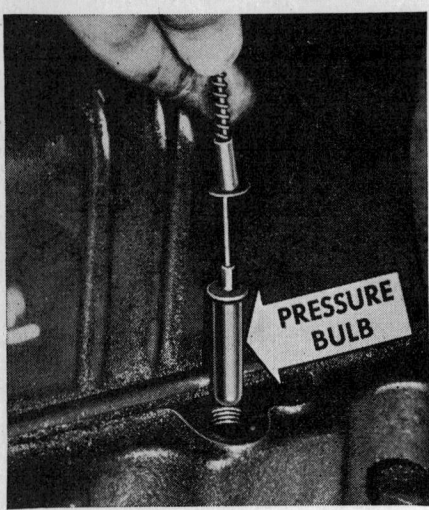

Fig. 8   Removing vapor pressure
bulb from engine block

1. Broken or loose fan belt.
2. Collapsed radiator hose.
3. Frozen radiator.
4. Obstruction in front of radiator, such as dirt or insects.
5. Thermostat out of order.
6. Radiator pressure cap (if fitted) not operating properly.
7. Poor engine lubrication.
8. Low water level in radiator and cooling system.

After the cooling system is thoroughly checked, test the temperature gauge to make sure that nothing is wrong with it. The procedure is as follows:

1. Drain water from radiator.
2. Loosen plug which holds vapor pressure bulb in engine block.
3. Remove the vapor pressure bulb from the engine, Fig. 8.
4. Place the vapor pressure bulb in a pail of hot water, Fig. 9. Also place a thermometer which reads up to 200 degrees F. or higher, and which is reasonably accurate in the hot water. Leave them in about three minutes.
5. If the temperature gauge is okay, the pointer should register the same temperature as the thermometer.
6. If this test shows that the trouble is in the gauge itself, the entire gauge should be replaced with a new unit.
7. When reinstalling one of these gauges in the engine block, don't use a wrench with too long a handle, and don't turn the bulb down too hard. A water-tight fit is all that is needed.

AC Electric Type

This type gauge, Fig. 10, consists of a dash unit and engine unit. These two units are connected by a single wire and each unit is grounded in its respective location.

The indicating unit consists principally of two coils spaced 90 degrees apart with an armature and integral pointer at the intersection of the coil axis. An inertia dampener is provided on the armature assembly to prevent vibration of the pointer on rough roads. The dial has a scale graduated in degrees Fahrenheit.

The engine unit has no moving parts and is essentially an electrical resistor which changes resistance with changes in temperature. The unit has a high resistance value when cold and a low resistance value when hot.

The change in engine unit resistance modifies the strength of the indicating unit coils and causes proper indication of the pointer.

SERVICE—Electric temperature gauge troubles are of four kinds: (1) The pointer doesn't move when the ignition switch is turned on. (2) The pointer indicates a high temperature whether the engine is hot or cold. (3) The pointer does not show temperature accurately. (4) The pointer indicates a low temperature whether the engine is hot or cold.

In addition to the above, any of the cooling system troubles listed under vapor pressure gauges can also affect the electrical unit.

Incorrect temperature readings are checked as follows:

1. Disconnect wire from binding post on end of engine unit.
2. Turn ignition switch on.
3. Hold end of wire away from all wires or other metal.
4. Check dash unit. The needle should point to the low mark or "100"
5. Touch the bare end of the wire to the engine block.
6. Check dash unit again. The needle should then point to over "212" or the high mark.
7. If the dash unit reads as described in steps 4 and 6, it indicates reasonable performance of the dash unit and the connecting wire. In this event, the engine unit should be checked as described below. But if the dash unit does not indicate properly, then first check the wire. If it is okay, replace the dash unit.
8. To check the engine unit, drain the water from the radiator.
9. Disconnect the wire which is attached to the engine unit, Fig. 11.
10. Loosen the engine unit and lift it out.
11. Reconnect the lead wire to the engine unit. Ground the threaded por-

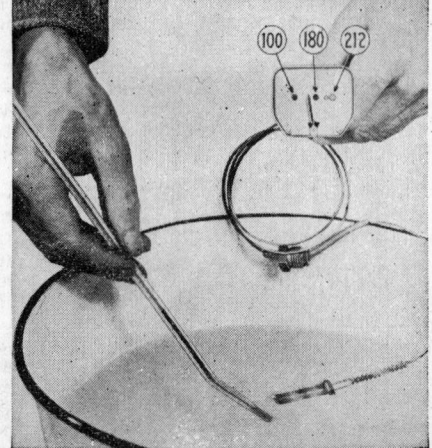

Fig. 9   Testing vapor type
temperature gauge

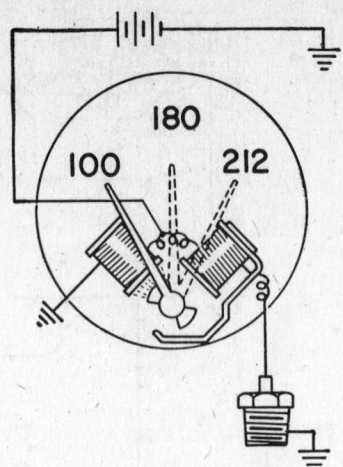

Fig. 10   Diagram of an AC
electric temperature gauge

tion to a convenient point on the car with suitable wire and clamps.
12. Get a pail or other suitable recepticle and fill it with hot water. Also a thermometer having a reading of 200 degrees F. or higher which is known to be reasonably accurate. Place the threaded end of the engine unit *part way* down into the hot water. Place the thermometer in also. Leave them in the water for about three minutes. Do not let any water get above the threads on the engine unit as to do so may ruin the unit.

13. If the dash unit is okay, the pointer should indicate the same temperature as the thermometer. If the pointer does not indicate correctly, replace the engine unit.

AUTO-LITE TEMPERATURE GAUGES

Vapor Pressure Type

This type gauge operates and is serviced in the same manner as described for AC vapor pressure gauges.

Electric Type

This type gauge, Fig. 12, includes two units. The dash unit has three magnetic poles, two of which have windings. One of these windings is connected to the ignition switch and to ground and creates a steady magnetic pull toward the low mark on the scale. The other winding is also connected to the ignition switch but it is grounded by the engine unit. It creates a magnetic pull toward the maximum temperature position the strength of which is dependent upon the amount of resistance inserted in the circuit by the engine unit.

The engine unit is actuated thermally without moving parts. The resistance unit in the engine unit is made of special metal oxides in the form of a flat disc that changes resistance as its temperature varies. When it is hot, the re-

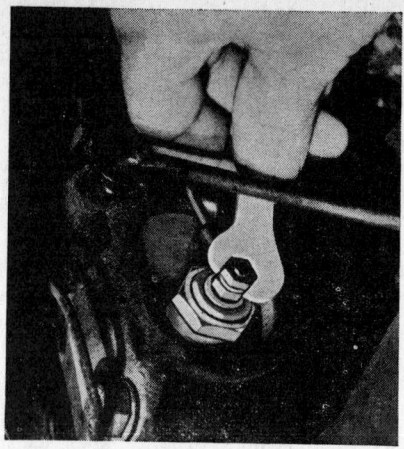

Fig. 11 Disconnecting wire from electric type temperature gauge

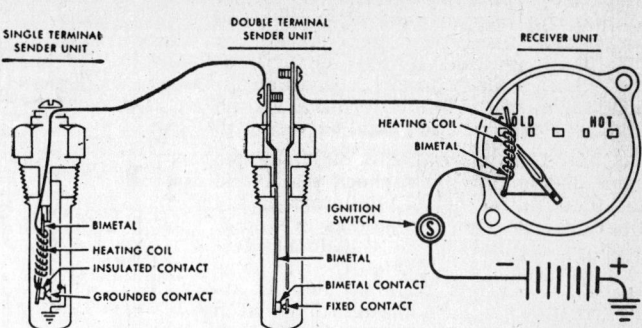

OPERATION WITH LOW WATER TEMPERATURE

OPERATION WITH HIGH WATER TEMPERATURE

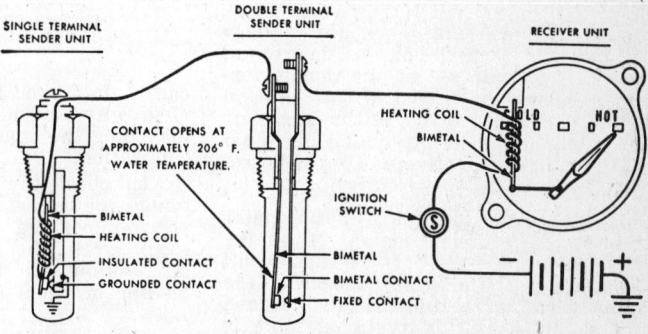

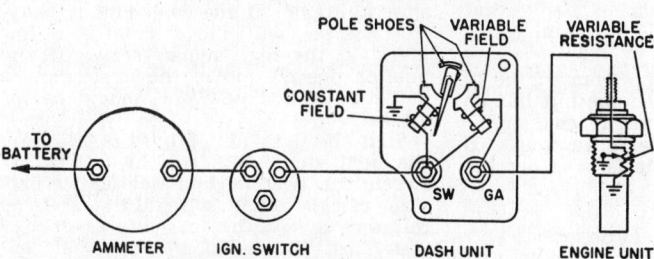

Fig. 12 Wiring diagram of Auto-Lite electric temperature gauge

Fig. 13 Ford and King-Seeley temperature gauges. The diagrams show the installation on 1952-53 Ford and Mercury V8 and Lincoln 1949-51 V8 engines in which two engine units are used, one in each cylinder head

sistance inserted in the variable field circuit is reduced and the pointer is attracted toward the "Hot" position.

The pointer on the dash unit is mounted on a magnetic vane which is attracted by the two lower magnetic poles and assumes a position between them depending upon the combined magnetic field. A counterweight is mounted on the pointer to bring the reading back to zero whenever the ignition is turned off.

SERVICE — The procedure for testing these gauges is the same as described for the AC electric temperature gauge.

KING-SEELEY & FORD TEMPERATURE GAUGES

Prior to 1957

These units, Fig. 13, consists of a sender unit located in the cylinder head and series connected to the receiver or dash unit. The illustrations show the two engine units, one for each cylinder head on the models listed in the caption. When only one sender unit is used, as is the case with an "In-Line" engine the single terminal sender unit is used.

The single terminal sender unit consists of a heating coil formed around a bimetal strip, insulated from the grounded frame. A grounded contact is attached to the frame in alignment with the bimetal contact.

The double terminal sender unit is similar in outward appearance to the single terminal unit with two terminals provided to allow series connection between the receiver unit and the single terminal unit in the opposite cylinder head. As shown in the illustration, this unit consists of a bimetal strip with a contact point, insulated from a supporting frame. The frame also supports a phosphor bronze spring with a contact point in alignment with the bimetal contact, both insulated from ground.

The bimetal assemblies of both sender units are sealed in their respective waterproof casings. The receiver and sender units are both calibrated at the factory and if either one become defective, it should be replaced with a new one.

OPERATION — The dash unit is connected to the ignition switch and to the series connected engine unit (or units). The dash unit will indicate water temperature only when the ignition switch is turned on. When the ignition is turned off, the pointer will register at the "Hot" position. This does not indicate that the cooling system is overheated but that the pointer is at its normal at rest position.

The dash unit, operated by a heater wire on a bimetal strip, is connected to a bulb in the cylinder head (or one bulb in each cylinder head as in Fig. 13.) The bulbs have similar bimetal strips as the dash unit. When the ignition is turned on, current will pass through the dash unit and the engine unit (or units). The

single terminal engine unit is normally grounded. However, as the current passes through the engine unit (or units), heat is generated in the single terminal engine unit bimetal, causing it to bend and open the contact to ground. Flow of current is then stopped, permitting the bimetal to cool and return to its normal, grounded position and the cycle is again repeated.

The same amount of current passes through the dash and engine units since they are connected in series with each other. This current also causes the bimetal in the dash unit to become heated and pull the pointer over to the left or right, depending on the temperature of the water. The cycle of opening and closing of the engine unit contact points is repeated continuously.

When the temperature of the water increases, the heat from the circulating water around the single terminal engine unit supplements the heat generated by the current passing through the units, reducing the amount of current necessary to cause the bimetal to draw away from the fixed contact. With less current flowing through the engine unit (or units), less current likewise flows through the dash unit and deflection or bending of the bimetal in the dash unit is lessened.

SERVICE — When the dash unit does not register with the ignition switch turned on, check the engine unit (or units) and wires as follows:

1. With the ignition switch turned

off, short out the single terminal engine unit by clipping one end of a jumper wire to its terminal and the other end to ground.

2. Turn ignition switch on momentarily. If the dash unit now gives an indication, then the single terminal engine unit is defective and must be replaced.

3. On Lincoln and Mercury engines using two engine units, check the double terminal engine unit as follows: If the dash unit does not register as in step 2, ground terminal "2" of the double terminal engine unit to which the wire connecting the single terminal unit is attached, Fig. 14. Turn the ignition switch on momentarily and observe if the dash unit registers. If it does, then the wire connecting the two engine units is defective.

4. If the dash unit does not register as in step 3, move the clip of the ground wire to terminal "3" of the double terminal engine unit. Turn the ignition switch on momentarily. If the dash unit now registers, then the double terminal engine unit is defective and must be replaced.

5. If the dash unit does not register as in step 4, ground terminal "4" at the dash unit, Fig. 14. If the dash unit registers, then the wire connecting the double terminal engine unit to the dash unit is defective. If the dash unit is still inoperative after the preceding tests, replace the dash unit.

WARNING—In making the above tests, turn off the ignition before the pointer reaches the end of the scale, otherwise the dash unit will become damaged or burned out.

AC OIL PRESSURE GAUGES

Pressure Expansion Type

This type gauge is similar in principle to the vapor-pressure type of water temperature gauge previously decribed. In this unit, however, oil under pressure passes from the engine unit up the connecting tube to the dash unit. As the pressure builds up it has a tendency to straighten out the C-shaped bourdon tube in the dash unit and thus move the pointer attached to the free end of the tube.

As with the water temperature gauges, engine factors should be considered when checking oil gauge operation. Engine oil should be brought to normal temperature. Pressure at idling speed will vary from 3 to 15 lbs. depending on the make of car. Above 30 mph engine speed the gauge should show between ½ and ¾ distance across the dial.

If the gauge is jumpy, sticky or uneven in its operation it must be replaced. If it is suspected of being off its calibration, another gauge known to be accurate can be connected to the oil line and checked. If the new gauge indicates correctly, it proves that the old gauge is defective.

Occasionally the operation of the unit

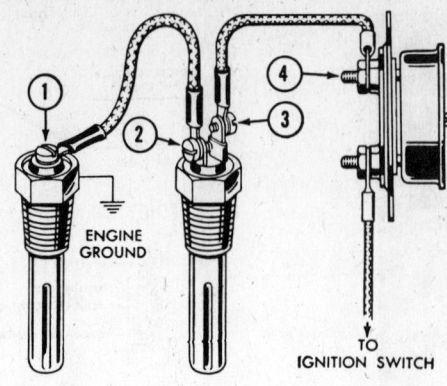

Fig. 14 Check points for testing Ford and King-Seeley temperature gauges when two engine units are used

can be improved by using a fine wire to clear any accumulation of oxide that may plug the small hole in the oil gauge connection.

Also check the oil line from engine to gauge for leaks. Loosen the nut but do not remove the oil line at the engine block while the engine is running. If oil runs out, the trouble is in either the oil line or dash unit.

Electrical Type

This gauge, Fig. 15, consists of a dash and engine unit connected by a single wire. Each unit is grounded in its respective location.

The indicating unit consists principally of two coils spaced 90 degrees apart with an armature and integral pointer at the intersection of the coil axis. An inertia dampener is provided on the armature to prevent vibration of the pointer on rough roads. The dial has a scale graduated in pounds per square inch.

The engine unit consists of a housing enclosing a diaphragm and linkage which moves a contact over a resistance proportional to oil pressure. The change in engine unit resistance modifies the strength of the indicating unit coils and causes proper indication of the pointer.

SERVICE — Electrical oil pressure gauges are subject to five kinds of troubles:

1. The pointer will not move when the ignition switch is on. Probable causes are (a) defective dash unit, (b) break or poor connection between battery and dash unit, (c) dash unit not grounded.

2. The pointer indicates "high" all the time: Probable causes are (a) defective engine unit, (b) break in dash to engine unit wire, (c) engine unit improperly grounded.

3. The pointer indicates "low" all the time: Probable cause is a short to ground at engine unit terminal or in dash-to-engine unit wire.

4. The pointer never indicates low and is always too high: Probable causes are (a) loose or dirty connections, (b) defective dash unit, (c) defective engine unit.

5. The pointer never indicates high

and is always too low: Probable causes are (a) partial ground at engine unit terminal or in dash-to-engine unit wire, (b) defective dash unit, (c) defective engine unit.

To locate the trouble, use the same testing apparatus pictured in Fig. 2 for testing AC fuel gauges, and proceed as follows:

1. Turn off ignition switch.

2. Disconnect one of the battery cables.

3. Disconnect the wire from the oil gauge dash unit which runs to the engine unit.

4. Using the spring clip, connect the colored tester wire to the binding post from which the wire was removed.

5. Connect the black tester wire to the flange of the tester and to any convenient ground—such as the unpainted part of the instrument panel.

6. Turn on the ignition switch.

7. Connect the battery cable. Move the arm of the tester back and forth slowly, Fig. 2. If the dash unit is okay, the pointer will move from the low mark to the high mark freely. If the pointer doesn't move, the dash unit is defective and a new one should be installed.

8. If the dash unit proves to be okay, the next step is to test the wiring between the dash and engine unit. This also can be done with the tester as follows:

9. Turn the ignition switch off and disconnect one battery cable.

10. Follow the wire from the dash to the engine unit, and disconnect the wire at the engine unit.

11. Attach the colored tester wire to the end of the wire which runs to the dash unit. Attach the black tester wire to any convenient ground, such as an unpainted part of the engine.

12. Connect the battery cable. Move the arm of the tester back and forth. If the wiring is okay, the pointer on the dash unit will move from the low mark to the high mark freely. If the pointer doesn't move, or only moves part way, the trouble is in the wire from

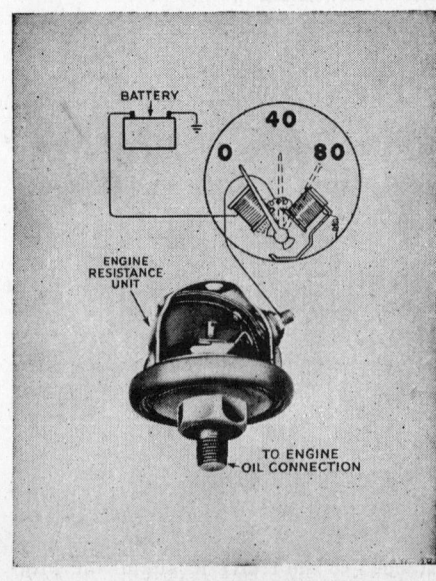

Fig. 15 AC electric oil pressure gauge

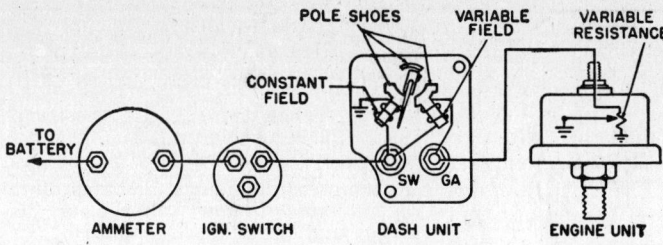

Fig. 16 Auto-Lite electric oil pressure gauge wiring diagram

OPERATION WITH LOW OIL PRESSURE

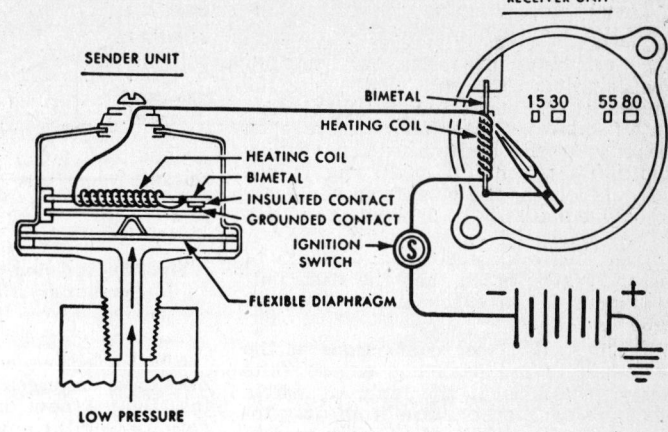

the dash to engine unit. Repair or replace the wire.

13. If the pointer does move correctly, then the trouble is in the engine unit. If the connection at the engine unit is clean, then a new engine unit must be installed.

AUTO-LITE OIL PRESSURE GAUGES

Pressure Expansion Type

This type gauge is similar to the one described for AC and service is performed in the same manner.

Electric Type

This type gauge, Fig. 16, consists of a dash and engine unit. The dash unit has three magnetic poles, two of which have windings. One of these windings is connected to the ignition switch and to ground and creates a steady magnetic pull towards the "zero" position when the ignition switch is turned on. The other winding is also connected to the ignition switch but is grounded by the engine unit. It creates a magnetic pull toward the maximum pressure position, the strength of which is dependent upon the amount of resistance inserted in the circuit by the engine unit.

The engine unit has a resistance with a sliding contact which is actuated by the oil pressure. When pressure is applied to the diaphragm in the engine unit, resistance is shorted out.

The pointer is mounted on a magnetic vane which is attracted by the two lower magnetic poles and assumes a position between them depending upon the combined magnetic field. A counterweight is mounted on the pointer to bring the reading back to zero whenever the ignition is turned off.

SERVICE—To test a gauge which does not give true indications of the oil pressure, make sure electricity is reaching the dash unit. This can be checked as follows: With ignition switch turned on, connect a test lamp from the "SW" terminal on the dash unit to a ground. If the lamp does not light it indicates no current is reaching the gauge, and the ignition switch, ammeter and wiring should be thoroughly inspected.

If current is reaching the gauge, disconnect the lead from the engine unit and again turn on the ignition. The pointer should stay against the left stop pin (no pressure side). Ground the engine unit lead and the pointer should

OPERATION WITH HIGH OIL PRESSURE

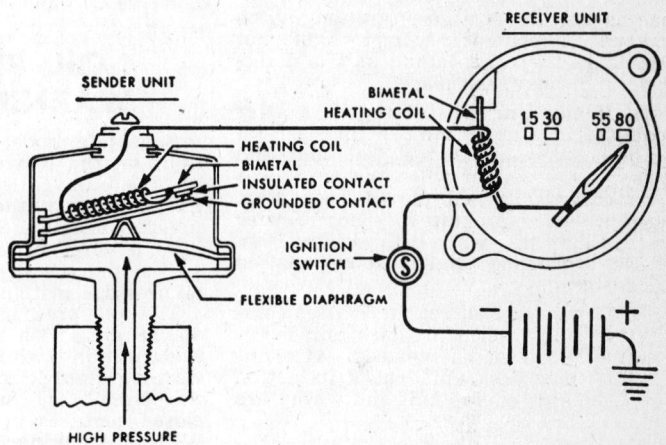

Fig. 17 Ford and King-Seeley electric oil pressure gauge (prior to 1957)

stay against the right stop pin (high pressure side).

If the test results are not as described above, the source of the trouble may be found by following the same procedure outlined for AC electric oil pressure gauge, but using an Auto-Lite fuel gauge tank unit.

KING-SEELEY & FORD OIL PRESSURE GAUGES

Prior to 1957

These gauges, Fig. 17, consist of a dash unit and engine unit. The dash unit is connected to the ignition switch and in series with the engine unit. When the ignition switch is turned off, the pointer will rest at the extreme left position.

The engine unit contains a diaphragm which is deflected in proportion to the pressure of the oil in the line. When the diaphragm is deflected, an electrical circuit is closed, allowing current to flow through a heating coil wound

around a bimetal strip. Heat, generated in this coil, deflects the bimetal to the point where the contact is opened. The bimetal then cools and returns to its original position, which again closes the electrical circuit. This cycle of opening and closing is repeated continuously.

The dash unit contains a similar heating coil formed around a bimetal, connected in series with the coil in the engine unit. As heating takes place in the engine unit, heating also takes place in the dash unit, causing the bimetal strip in each unit to deflect simultaneously.

The pointer indicator is linked to the bimetal strip and oil pressure is indicated by the amount of deflection actuating the pointer.

Increased oil pressure causes greater deflection of the diaphragm in the engine unit, therefore a greater amount of current is required to open the heating coil circuit. This increased current is transmitted to the dash unit, causing a corresponding increased bending of the dash unit bimetal and resultant indication of increased oil pressure.

The heating coil in the engine unit

is shunted by a calibrating resistor at the time of assembly to assure accuracy of the unit.

SERVICE—If the oil pressure gauge is not functioning properly, make the following tests in the order given until the source of trouble is found. If the dash unit pointer indicates oil pressure upon turning on the ignition switch (engine not running) contacts in the engine unit may be frozen, the wire from the dash-to-engine unit may be shorted to ground, or the dash unit may be defective. If this condition existed for any length of time, it is probable that the dash unit is damaged. To check the gauge, proceed as follows:

1. Check for loose connections at the terminals of the dash and engine units and connections at the ignition switch. Inspect condition of wire from dash-to-engine units and wire from dash unit to ignition switch.

2. Remove wire from engine unit terminal. If pointer of dash unit now remains at zero position (ignition switch turned on momentarily and engine not running) then the engine unit is defective and must be replaced.

3. If the pointer still registers after completing step 1, remove the dash-to-engine unit wire at the dash unit and observe the pointer when the ignition is momentarily turned on (do not start engine). If dash unit does not register now, then the wire between the two units is grounded and must be repaired or replaced.

4. If pointer still registers after completing step 2, then the dash unit is defective and must be replaced. After installing new dash unit, check its action to make sure engine unit and wiring are satisfactory.

If dash unit does not indicate oil pressure with ignition on and engine running, connections and wiring appearing satisfactory, test as follows:

1. With ignition switch turned off, short out the engine unit at the terminal. Use a jumper wire with clips for this purpose. Clip one end to the terminal screw of the engine unit and the other end to engine ground.

2. Turn ignition on momentarily. If dash unit now registers, then the engine unit is defective and must be replaced.

WARNING—Turn ignition off before pointer of dash unit reaches the highest pressure mark on the scale. In this test the full voltage of the battery is placed on the dash unit and if allowed to remain for a longer period of time, the unit will burn out.

3. If the dash unit fails to register with the engine unit shorted out as in step 2, either the dash unit or the wire running to the engine unit is defective. Turn ignition switch off and check the wire by clipping one end of the jumper wire to the dash unit terminal and the other end to ground. **CAUTION** — Be sure grounding wire is not connected to ignition side of dash unit.

4. Turn ignition on momentarily. If dash unit fails to register, then the **dash** unit is defective.

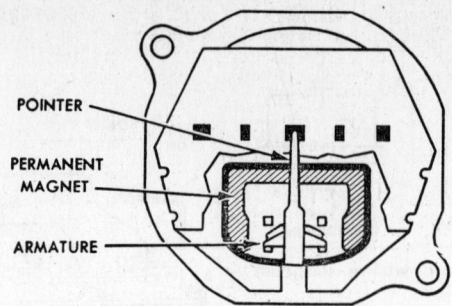

Fig. 18 Drawing of a typical ammeter or battery charge indicator

5. A defective engine unit or wiring may have damaged the dash unit. After installing a new dash unit, observe its action after turning ignition on momentarily. If the indicator moves beyond the point of normal oil pressure, the engine unit or wiring is defective and must be checked.

OIL PRESSURE WARNING LIGHT

Some late model cars utilize a warning light on the instrument panel in place of the conventional dash indicating gauge to warn the driver when the oil pressure is dangerously low. The warning light is wired in series with the ignition switch and the engine unit—which is an oil pressure switch.

The oil pressure switch contains a diaphragm and a set of contacts. When the ignition switch is turned on, the warning light circuit is energized and the circuit is completed through the closed contacts in the pressure switch. When the engine is started, build-up of oil pressure compresses the diaphragm, opening the contacts, thereby breaking the circuit and putting out the light.

Trouble Shooting

The oil pressure warning light should go on when the ignition is turned on. If it does not light, disconnect the wire from the engine unit and ground the wire to the frame or engine block. Then if the warning light still does not light when the ignition switch is on, replace the light bulb.

If the warning light goes on when the wire is grounded to the frame or cylinder block, the engine unit should be checked for being loose or poorly grounded. If the unit is found to be tight and properly grounded, it should be removed and a new one installed. (The presence of sealing compound on the threads of the engine unit will cause a poor ground.)

If the warning light remains lit when it normally should be out, the wire from the light to the engine unit may be grounded. To check for this condition, disconnect the wire at the engine unit and if the light remains lit a ground is indicated. If the light goes out, then the engine unit is at fault and it should be replaced.

The warning light sometimes will light up or will flicker when the engine is idling, even though the oil pressure is adequate. However, the light should go

out when the engine is speeded up. There is no cause for alarm in such cases; it simply means that the pressure switch is not calibrated precisely correct.

AMMETERS

Automotive ammeters indicates direction of current flow (charge or discharge) and the relative amount of current flow. The center point of the dial, Fig. 18, is the point of zero current flow and the two extremes of pointer travel indicate maximum charge and discharge. Therefore, the indicator must not be read for the amount of current charge or discharge but only for charge condition of the generating system.

The typical ammeter consists of a frame to which is attached a permanent magnet. The frame also supports an armature and pointer assembly. When no current flows through the ammeter, the magnet holds the pointer armature so that the pointer stands in the center of the dial. When current passes in either direction through the ammeter, the resulting field attracts the armature away from the effect of the permanent magnet, thus giving a reading proportional to the current strength.

SERVICE—When the ammeter apparently fails to register correctly, there may be trouble in the wiring which connects the ammeter to the generator and battery, or in the generator and battery themselves. There are only a few simple things to check in order to find the cause:

1. Loose connections on the back of the ammeter.

2. Loose connections at the back of the ignition switch, or at the battery. (Ammeters are not grounded to the instrument panel.)

3. Spots on the wiring where the insulation has been chafed, burned or broken.

To check the connections, first tighten the two binding posts on the back of the ammeter. Then, following each wire from the ammeter, tighten all connections on the ignition switch, battery and generator. Chafed, burned or broken insulation can be found by following each ammeter wire from end to end.

After checking and repairing the wiring, tighten all connections and turn the ignition switch on. The pointer should point to the discharge side of the dial slightly. Start the engine and speed it up to about 30 mph. The pointer should then move to the charge side of the dial and its movement should be smooth.

If the pointer does not behave correctly the ammeter itself is out of order and must be replaced with a new one.

GENERATOR TELLTALE LIGHT

Some late model cars utilize a light on the instrument panel in place of the conventional ammeter to indicate to the driver when the generator is charging the battery. The telltale element is a panel-mounted window (usually red) behind which is mounted a small lamp bulb. The bulb lights whenever the ignition switch is turned on and the generator not charging.

Auto-Lite System

When the ignition switch is turned on the circuit is completed from the ignition switch, through the bulb, to a special terminal on the voltage regulator, to the insulated contacts on top of the circuit breaker, to the grounded strap of the circuit breaker.

As the engine is started and generator speed is increased to a car speed of approximately 10 mph, the generator develops sufficient voltage to pull down the circuit breaker armature, closing the main contact points and opening the telltale contacts, causing the light to go out.

If the lamp bulb does not light when the ignition is turned on, ground the telltale terminal *to the engine* (not to another regulator terminal). If the bulb still does not light, check for loose connections or a burned out telltale bulb. If the lamp lights when the telltale terminal is grounded, the main circuit breaker contacts are probably fused (stuck closed) or the armature coil spring is weak or broken.

Delco-Remy System

In this system the generator telltale light is connected in a circuit with the battery and generator. When the generator begins to charge, the voltage build-up in the circuit opposes the battery voltage to the telltale light. As the differential between these two voltages decreases, the light goes out.

If the light stays on after the engine is started and running a little above idling speed, the generator should be checked.

If the light does not go on when the ignition switch is turned on before the

engine is started, the telltale bulb should be checked. If the bulb is OK, check the entire telltale circuit for loose connections or for an open circuit.

SPEEDOMETERS

The following material covers only that service on speedometers which is feasible to perform by the average service man. Repairs on the units themselves are not included as they require special tools and extreme care when making repairs and adjustments and only an experienced speedometer mechanic should attempt such servicing.

The speedometer has two main parts —the indicating head and the speedometer drive cable. When the speedometer fails to indicate speed or mileage, the cable or cable housing is probably broken.

SPEEDOMETER CABLE—Most cables are broken due to lack of lubrication, or a sharp bend or kink in the housing.

A cable might break because the speedometer head mechanism binds. If such is the case, the speedometer head should be repaired or replaced before a new cable or housing is installed.

A "jumpy" pointer condition, together with a sort of scraping noise, is due, in most instances, to a dry or kinked speedometer cable. The kinked cable rubs on the housing and winds up, slowing down the pointer. The cable then unwinds and the pointer "jumps".

To check for kinks, remove the cable, lay it on a flat surface and twist one end with the fingers. If it turns over smoothly the cable is not kinked. But if part of the cable flops over as it is twisted, the cable is kinked and should be replaced.

LUBRICATION—The speedometer cable should be lubricated with special cable

lubricant every 10,000 miles. At the same time, put a few drops of the lubricant on the wick in the speedometer head.

Fill the ferrule on the upper end of the housing with the cable lubricant. Insert the cable in the housing, starting at the upper end. Turn the cable around carefully while feeding it into the housing. Repeat filling the ferrule except for the last six inches of cable. Too much lubricant at this point may cause the lubricant to work into the indicating hand.

INSTALLING CABLE—During installation, if the cable sticks when inserted in the housing and will not go through, the housing is damaged inside or kinked. Be sure to check the housing from one end to the other. Straighten any sharp bends by relocating clamps or elbows. Replace housing if it is badly kinked or broken. Position the cable and housing so that they lead into the head as straight as possible.

Check the new cable for kinks before installing it. Use wide, sweeping, gradual curves where the cable comes out of the transmission and connects to the head so the cable will not be damaged during its installation.

Arrange the housing so it does not lean against the cylinder head because heat from the engine may dry out the lubricant.

If inspection indicates that the cable and housing are in good condition, yet pointer action is erratic, check the speedometer head for possible binding.

The speedometer drive pinion should also be checked. If the pinion is dry or its teeth are stripped, the speedometer may not register properly.

The transmission mainshaft nut must be tight or the speedometer drive gear may slip on the mainshaft and cause slow speed readings.

FUEL PUMPS

FUEL PUMP PRESSURE, LBS.

BUICK
1953-55 .... 4 —5
1956-57 .... 4 —6½
1958-61 .... 5¼—6½

BUICK SPECIAL
1961 .... 4 —5½

CADILLAC
1953-54 .... 3½—5¼
1955 .... 4 —5¼
1956-58 .... 4 —6½
1959-61 .... —5¼—6½

CHEVROLET
1953-56 Six .... 3½—4½
1955-56 V8 .... 4 —5¼
1957-61 Six .... 3½—4½
1957-58 V8 .... 4 —5¼
1959-61 V8 .... 5¼—6½

CHRYSLER & IMPERIAL
1953 .... 3½—5
1954 .... 3½—5½
1955 .... 4½—6½
1956-59 .... 6 —7
1960 .... 4 —5

COMET
1960-61 .... 3½—5½

CONTINENTAL
1956 .... 4 —6
1957 .... 4½—5½
1958 .... 4½—6½
1959-60 .... 5 —6

CORVAIR
1960-61 .... 5¼—6½

DE SOTO
1953-55 .... 3½—5½
1956-59 .... 6 —7
1960 .... 4 —5

DODGE & DART
1953-54 .... 3½—5½
1955-56 .... 4½—6½
1957 Six .... 4 —6
1957 V8 .... 6 —7
1958-60 .... 6 —7
1961 .... 4 —5

EDSEL
1958 .... 5 —6
1959-60 Six .... 4 —5
1959-60 V8 .... 4½—5½

FALCON
1960 .... 4 —5

FORD & THUNDERBIRD
1953 Six .... 4 —5
1953 V8 .... 3½—4½
1954-57, 1959-60 Six .. 4 —5
1958, 1959-60 V8 ...... 4½—5½
1961 Six .... 3½—5½
1961 V8 .... 4 —6

HUDSON
1953-56 .... 3½—5
1957 .... 4 —5½

JEEP
1953-60 .... 2½—3¾

LANCER
1961 .... 3½—5

LINCOLN
1953-54 .... 3½—4½
1955 .... 4 —5
1956 .... 4 —6
1957 .... 4½—5½
1958 .... 4½—6½
1959-61 .... 5 —6

MERCURY
1954-55 .... 4 —5
1956-57 .... 3½—5½
1958 .... 4½—6½
1959-60 312 Eng. .... 4½—5½
1959-60 383, 430 Eng. . 5 —6
1961 Six .... 3½—5½
1961 V8 .... 4 —6

NASH
1953-56 Six .... 3½—5¼
1955-56 V8 .... 3½—5
1957 .... 4 —5½

OLDSMOBILE F-85
1961 .... 4 —5¼

OLDSMOBILE
1953-54 .... 4 —5
1955-56 .... 4 —5¼
1957-61 .... 5 —6

PLYMOUTH
1953-56 Six .... 4 —5½
1955-56 V8 .... 5 —6½
1957 Six .... 4 —6
1957 V8 .... 6 —7
1958-61 .... 6 —7

PONTIAC
1953-57 .... 4 —5
1958-61 .... 5¼—6½

RAMBLER
1953-56 .... 3½—5¼
1957-60 .... 4 —5½

STUDEBAKER
1953-54 .... 4 —5
1955 .... 4 —5½
1956 .... 3½—5
1957-60 .... 3½—5½
1957-58 Supercharged .. 6 —7

TEMPEST
1961 .... 4 —5¼

VALIANT
1960 .... 6 —7
1961 .... 4 —5

WILLYS
1960 .... 6 —7

Fig. 1 illustrates a schematic drawing of a typical fuel system in which a combination fuel and vacuum pump is incorporated. All fuel pumps used on passenger cars are of the diaphragm type, Figs. 2 and 3. Fig. 4 differs in that the pump has a vacuum booster section. The booster section has nothing to do with the fuel system except that it is operated by the pump arm.

Fuel Pump Operation

During the first or suction stroke, the rotation of the eccentric on the camshaft actuates the pump operating arm which pulls the lever and diaphragm downward against the pressure of the diaphragm spring, producing a suction in the pump chamber. The suction holds the outlet valve closed and pulls the inlet valve open, making the fuel flow from the supply tank through the inlet up through the filter screen and down through the inlet valve into the pump chamber. During the return stroke, the diaphragm is forced up by the diaphragm spring, the inlet valve closes and the outlet valve is forced open, allowing the fuel to flow through the outlet to the carburetor.

Vacuum Section Operation

The vacuum section of combination pumps operates the windshield wipers at almost constant speed. The rotation of the camshaft eccentric in this type pump also operates the vacuum booster section by actuating the pump arm which pushes a link and bellows diaphragm downward, expelling the air in the vacuum chamber through its exhaust valve out into the intake manifold of the engine. On the return stroke of the pump arm, the diaphragm is moved upward, producing a suction in the vacuum chamber. This suction operates the vacuum section and draws air through the inlet passage from the windshield wiper.

Fuel Pump Performance

It is essential that the fuel pump deliver sufficient fuel to supply the requirements of the engine under all operating conditions and that it maintain sufficient pressure in the line between the pump and carburetor to keep the fuel from boiling and to prevent vapor lock.

Excessive fuel pump pressure holds the carburetor float needle valve off its seat, causing high gasoline level in the float chamber which in turn increases gasoline consumption.

The pump usually delivers a minimum of ten gallons of gasoline per hour at top engine speeds, under an operating pressure of from 2 to 6 psi (see table). The highest operating pressure will be attained at idling speed and the lowest at top speed.

Fuel Pump Tests

The fuel pump can be tested on the car with a pressure gauge, a hose and a pint measuring can. With this equipment, it is possible to check the fuel pump to see if it is delivering the proper amount of gasoline at the correct pressure.

Pressure Test

To make the pressure test, disconnect the fuel pipe at the carburetor inlet and attach the pressure gauge and hose between the carburetor inlet and the disconnected fuel pipe, Fig. 5. Take the pressure reading with the engine running. The pressure should be within the limits given in the chart, depending on the pump model and the car on which it is installed. The pressure should remain constant or return very slowly to zero when the engine is stopped.

Capacity Test

To make this test, connect the hose so the pump will deliver gasoline into the pint measure held at carburetor level. Run the engine at idle speed and note the time it takes to fill the measure. On the average it should take from 20 to 30 seconds, depending on the pump tested.

When Pressure Is Low

Low pressure indicates extreme wear on one part, small wear on all parts, ruptured diaphragm, dirty valve or gummy valve seat.

Wear in the pump usually occurs at the rocker arm pivot pin and on the contacting surfaces of the rocker arm and links. Due to the leverage design, wear at these points is multiplied five times in the movement of the diaphragm.

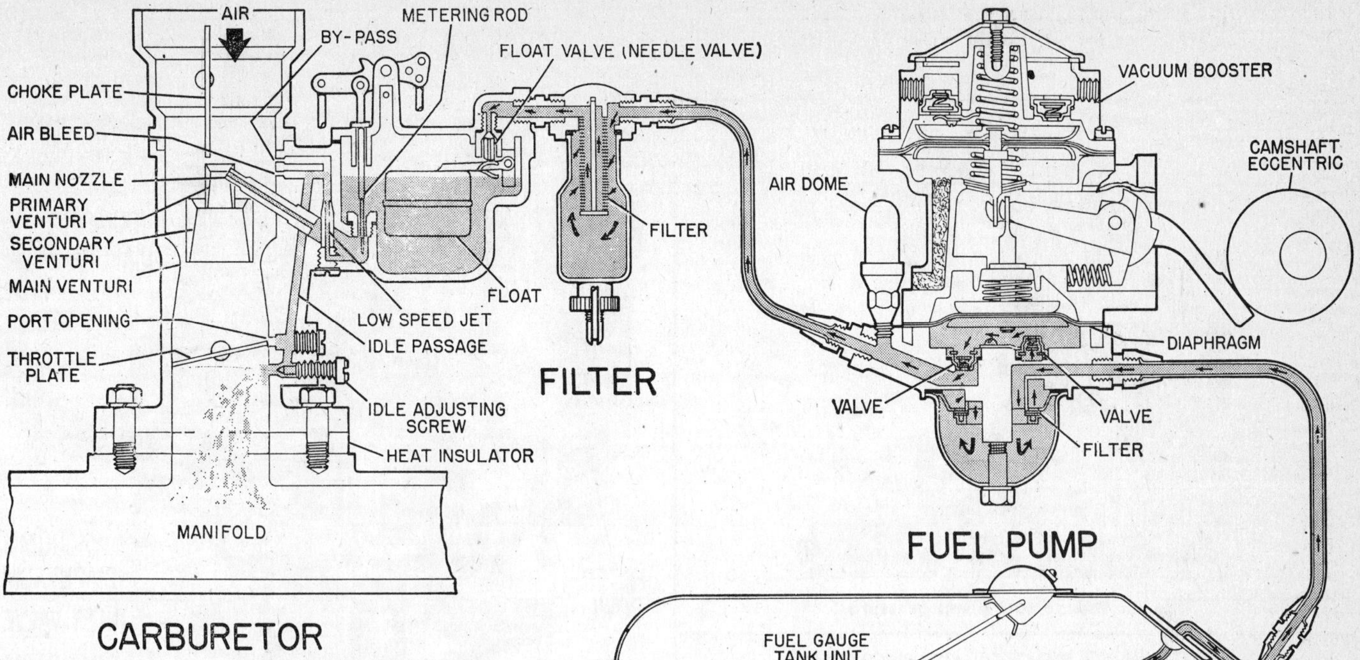

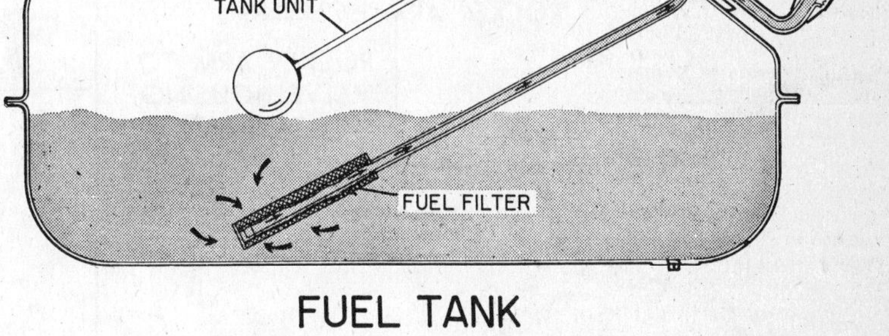

CHOKE PLATE
AIR BLEED
MAIN NOZZLE
PRIMARY VENTURI
SECONDARY VENTURI
MAIN VENTURI
PORT OPENING
THROTTLE PLATE

AIR
BY-PASS
METERING ROD
FLOAT VALVE (NEEDLE VALVE)

FILTER

FLOAT
LOW SPEED JET
IDLE PASSAGE
IDLE ADJUSTING SCREW
HEAT INSULATOR

MANIFOLD

FILTER

CARBURETOR

Fig. 1 Diagram of fuel system in operation when engine is idling

VACUUM BOOSTER
CAMSHAFT ECCENTRIC
AIR DOME
VALVE
DIAPHRAGM
VALVE
FILTER

FUEL PUMP

FUEL GAUGE TANK UNIT
FUEL FILTER

FUEL TANK

It is apparent therefore, that very little wear will materially reduce the stroke of the diaphragm. The worn parts must be replaced for a satisfactory correction.

The diaphragm pull rod has an oil seal around it which prevents the hot oil vapors from the crankcase coming in contact with the diaphragm. If this seal is damaged, the oil vapors have a tendency to shorten the life of the diaphragm.

The first three conditions—extreme wear on one part, small wear on all parts, and ruptured diaphragm—are brought about by usage, while dirty and/or poor fuel is usually the cause of valve trouble.

When Pressure Is High

High pressure is caused by a tight diaphragm, fuel between diaphragm layers, diaphragm spring too strong, pump link frozen to rocker arm.

A tight diaphragm will stretch slightly on the down stroke. As the pump operates, the diaphragm will rebound on the up stroke beyond its normal position, much as a stretched rubber band when it is suddenly released. This rebound will cause a higher than normal pressure in the pump chamber.

A loose diaphragm retainer nut or poor riveting on the diaphragm assembly may allow fuel to seep between the diaphragm layers. This will cause a bulge in the diaphragm and have the same effect as a diaphragm that is too tight.

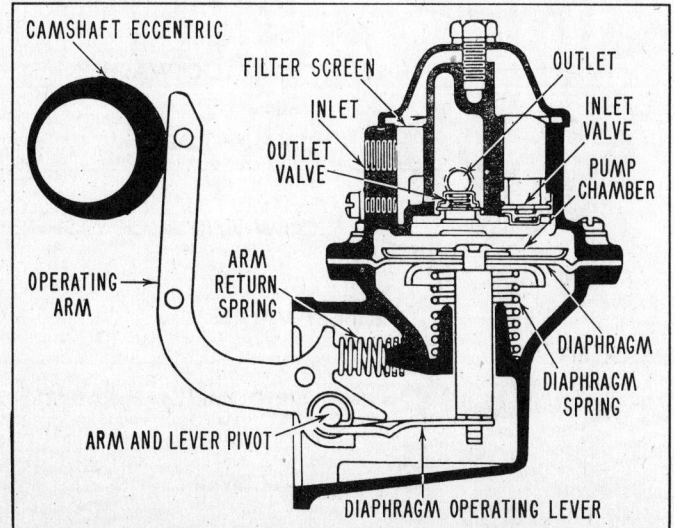

CAMSHAFT ECCENTRIC
FILTER SCREEN
INLET
OUTLET VALVE
OUTLET
INLET VALVE
PUMP CHAMBER
OPERATING ARM
ARM RETURN SPRING
DIAPHRAGM
DIAPHRAGM SPRING
ARM AND LEVER PIVOT
DIAPHRAGM OPERATING LEVER

Fig. 2 Fuel pump with built-in fuel filter

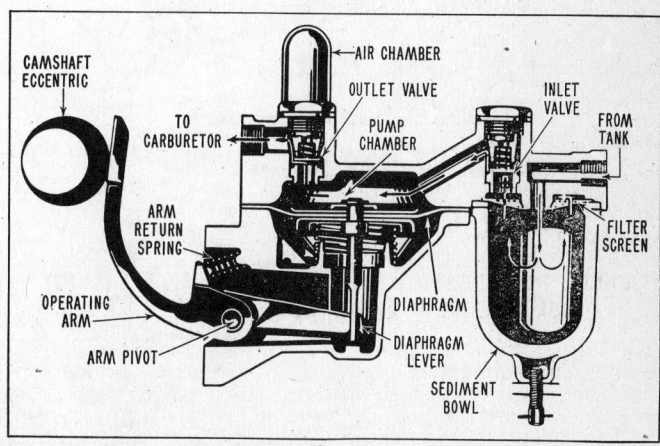

CAMSHAFT ECCENTRIC
TO CARBURETOR
AIR CHAMBER
OUTLET VALVE
PUMP CHAMBER
INLET VALVE
FROM TANK
ARM RETURN SPRING
FILTER SCREEN
OPERATING ARM
DIAPHRAGM
ARM PIVOT
DIAPHRAGM LEVER
SEDIMENT BOWL

Fig. 3 Fuel pump with separate fuel filter

Fig. 4 Fuel pump with fuel filter and vacuum booster for windshield wiper operation

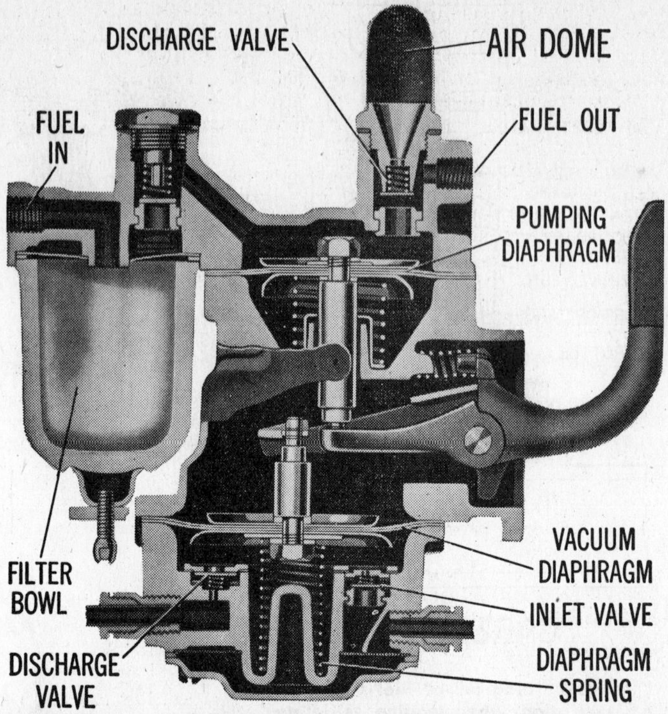

Fig. 5 Testing fuel pump pressure

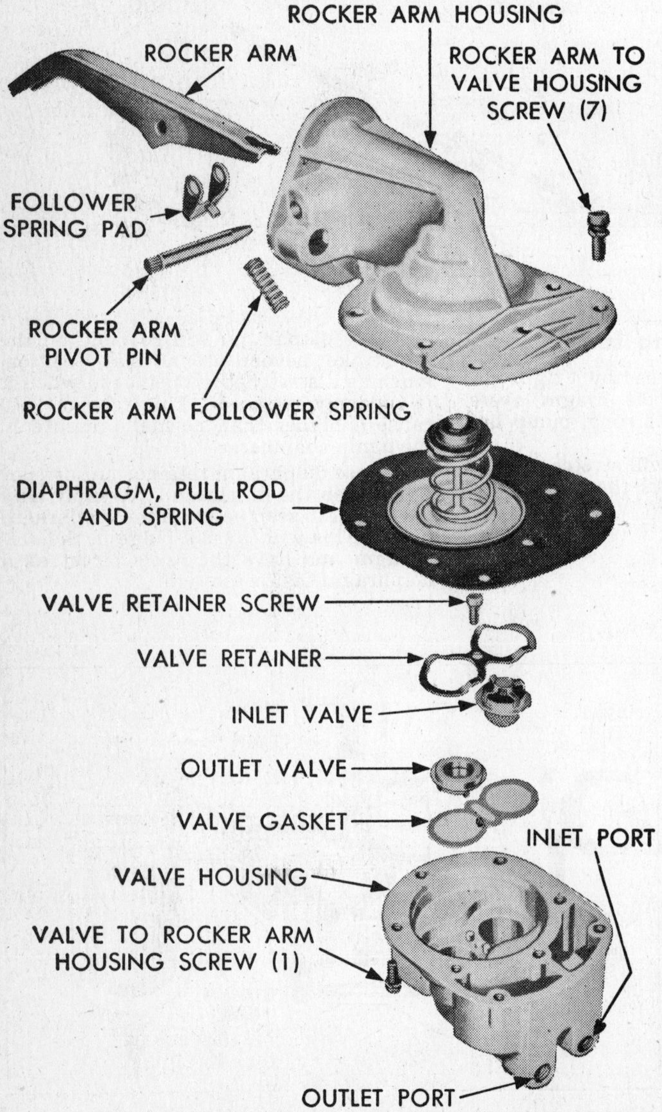

DISCHARGE VALVE

AIR DOME

FUEL IN

FUEL OUT

PUMPING DIAPHRAGM

VACUUM DIAPHRAGM

INLET VALVE

FILTER BOWL

DISCHARGE VALVE

DIAPHRAGM SPRING

ROCKER ARM HOUSING

ROCKER ARM

ROCKER ARM TO VALVE HOUSING SCREW (7)

FOLLOWER SPRING PAD

ROCKER ARM PIVOT PIN

ROCKER ARM FOLLOWER SPRING

DIAPHRAGM, PULL ROD AND SPRING

VALVE RETAINER SCREW

VALVE RETAINER

INLET VALVE

OUTLET VALVE

VALVE GASKET

INLET PORT

VALVE HOUSING

VALVE TO ROCKER ARM HOUSING SCREW (1)

OUTLET PORT

Fig. 6 Auto-Lite fuel pump

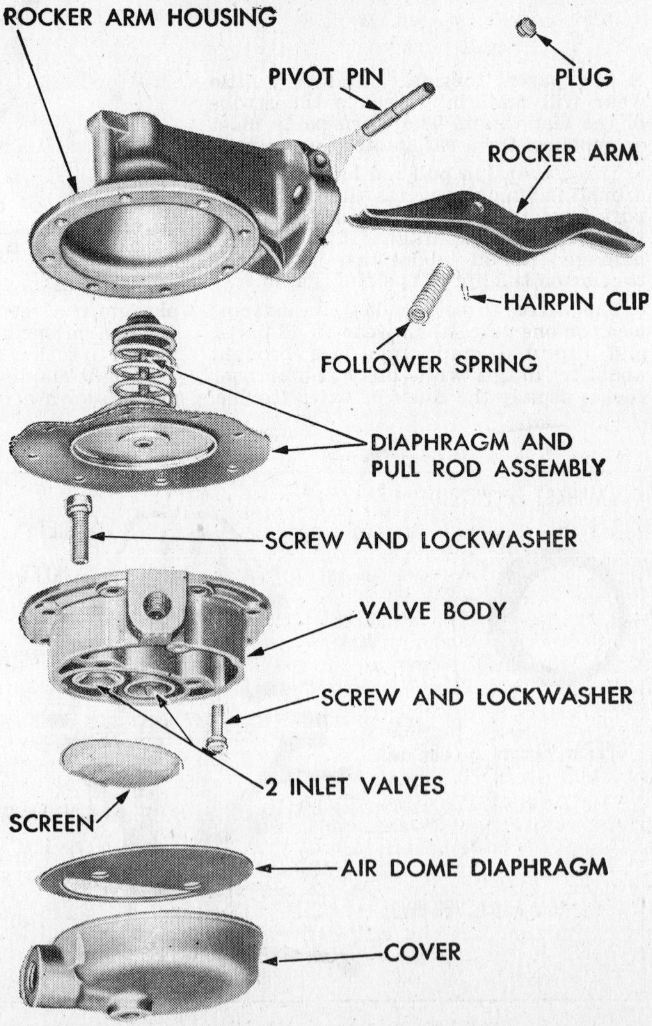

ROCKER ARM HOUSING

PIVOT PIN

PLUG

ROCKER ARM

HAIRPIN CLIP

FOLLOWER SPRING

DIAPHRAGM AND PULL ROD ASSEMBLY

SCREW AND LOCKWASHER

VALVE BODY

SCREW AND LOCKWASHER

2 INLET VALVES

SCREEN

AIR DOME DIAPHRAGM

COVER

Fig. 7 Carter fuel pump

A diaphragm spring that is too strong also causes a high pressure for the diaphragm will operate longer before pressure of the fuel on the diaphragm will overcome the diaphragm spring.

On a combination pump there are times when the operating parts may become badly corroded and the links freeze to the rocker arm. In this condition the pump operates continually, resulting in a very high pressure and a flooding carburetor.

The remedy for all these conditions is to remove the pump for replacement or repair, using a repair kit.

When Capacity Is Low

A pump is extra efficient and will never starve the engine when it supplies fuel equal to or above the capacity of the pump. The pressure, of course, must be within specifications.

Low capacity is usually caused by an air leak in the intake pipe at these points: fuel pipe fitting at pump, bowl flange or diaphragm flange, fuel bowl. (It is assumed that the conditions of too little fuel have already been checked and the pump is the cause of the difficulty.)

An air leak at fuel pipe fittings indicates either poor installation of pump or a defective fitting. The fitting should be tightened or replaced.

A leak at the diaphragm flange may be caused by a warped cover casting, loose diaphragm cover screws or foreign material between cover casting and diaphragm.

A leak at the bowl flange of the cover casting can usually be corrected by the installation of an extra gasket. A warped top cover indicates that the pump must be replaced.

A chipped glass or bent metal bowl may cause a leak at the bowl flange as may a defective gasket or foreign material between gasket and bowl or cover casting. A chipped glass bowl must be replaced while a dented metal bowl can be straightened.

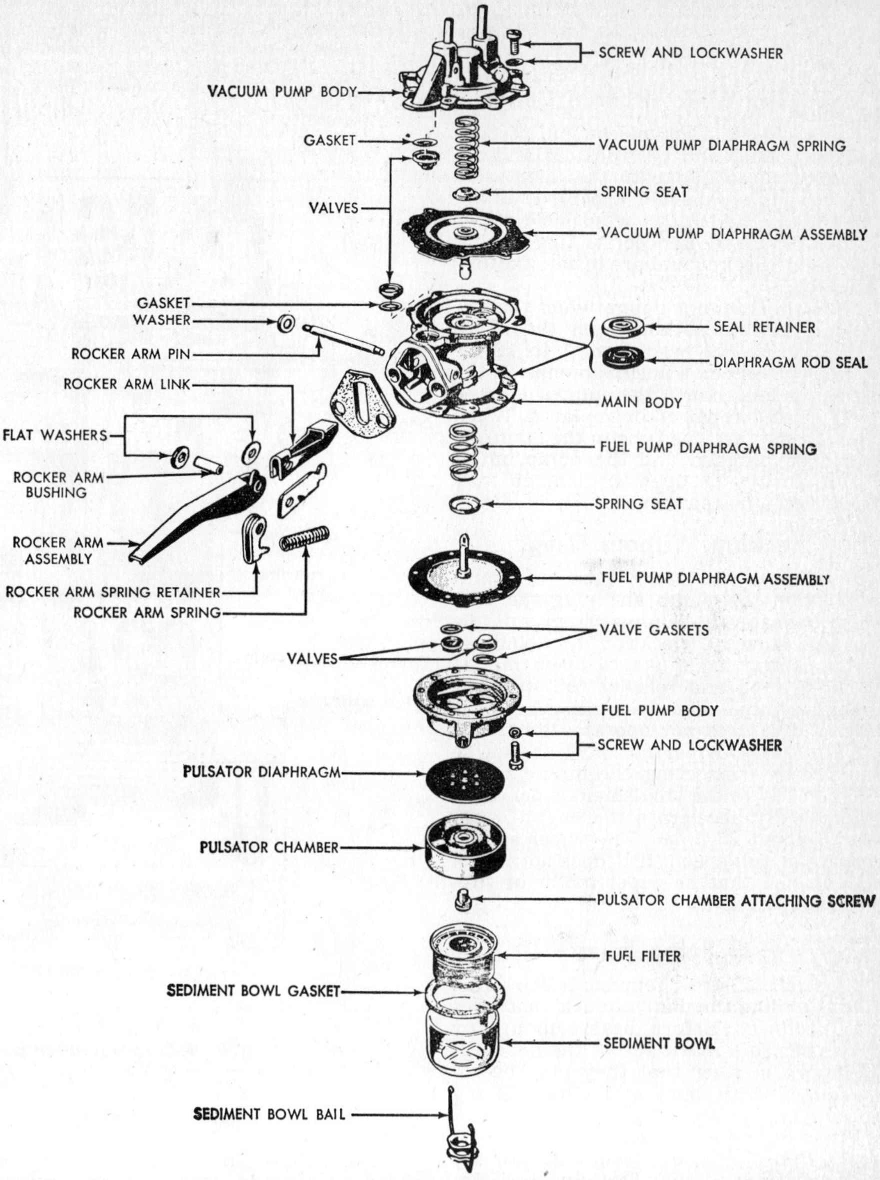
SCREW AND LOCKWASHER
VACUUM PUMP BODY
GASKET
VACUUM PUMP DIAPHRAGM SPRING
SPRING SEAT
VALVES
VACUUM PUMP DIAPHRAGM ASSEMBLY
GASKET
WASHER
SEAL RETAINER
ROCKER ARM PIN
DIAPHRAGM ROD SEAL
ROCKER ARM LINK
MAIN BODY
FLAT WASHERS
FUEL PUMP DIAPHRAGM SPRING
ROCKER ARM BUSHING
SPRING SEAT
ROCKER ARM ASSEMBLY
FUEL PUMP DIAPHRAGM ASSEMBLY
ROCKER ARM SPRING RETAINER
ROCKER ARM SPRING
VALVE GASKETS
VALVES
FUEL PUMP BODY
SCREW AND LOCKWASHER
PULSATOR DIAPHRAGM
PULSATOR CHAMBER
PULSATOR CHAMBER ATTACHING SCREW
FUEL FILTER
SEDIMENT BOWL GASKET
SEDIMENT BOWL
SEDIMENT BOWL BAIL

Fig. 8 A.C. combination pump with four vacuum valves and built-in fuel filter

Vacuum Pump Troubles

To assist the manifold vacuum to operate the windshield wiper at a uniform rate under any engine load is the only function of the vacuum pump. Of course, "uniform rate" infers a wet windshield and not one covered with snow or ice. Failure to do the above indicates difficulty in either the vacuum system of the pump, windshield wiper motor, or tubes and connections.

Symptoms of trouble in the vacuum section show up in four ways: oil consumption, slow windshield wiper action, poor idle, noise.

In some cases it has been found that an engine which has given very good oil mileage suddenly appears to be using oil. Upon investigation, it will often be found that the vacuum booster has a ruptured diaphragm and is drawing oil fumes from the crankcase into the intake manifold. This can be checked by removing the cover of the vacuum section.

When the windshield wiper slows down excessively under engine load, it usually is an indication of a ruptured vacuum diaphragm or defective valve in the vacuum pump. This condition may not be discovered immediately as the windshield wipers may not be used for long intervals.

Oil will be evidenced in the cover casting recesses if the diaphragm is ruptured. The pump should be removed and the diaphragm replaced.

On some cars the engine will idle very poorly when the vacuum diaphragm is ruptured. This is true when the tube from the vacuum pump is connected to one end of the intake manifold. The air leak through the vacuum section will give those cylinders on the end a lean mixture which results in a miss or poor idle. In many cases, this leads one to believe the valves of the engine are sticking; but if they are ground, the miss or poor idle remains.

This condition can be checked by removing the vacuum pump tube at the manifold and plugging the hole. If the miss or rough idle disappears, the trouble is an air leak through the pump or tube connections. The pump should be removed and repaired or the connections tightened to eliminate this trouble.

Sometimes a combination pump will give off a peculiar grunting sound on idle. In some cases this can be remedied by stuffing curled horse hair into the pump breather.

Vacuum Pump Test

With a combination fuel and vacuum pump the windshield wiper should operate at 80 to 100 strokes per minute through all ranges of car speed and load.

FUEL PUMPS

The windshield should be wet when the test is made, otherwise the action will be slow.

Checking With Vacuum Gauge

To check the vacuum section, disconnect both inlet and outlet tubes and attach a vacuum gauge to the inlet (side that goes to windshield wiper). It is assumed that the engine, windshield wiper motor and blade, and connecting tubing have been checked and are in satisfactory condition.

Read the vacuum gauge when the engine is running at 1000 rpm (about 20 mph). It should read from 7 to 12 inches of vacuum on a normal pump. If the reading is less than 7, the pump should be removed and repaired or replaced. When making this test, the tube to the manifold should be plugged and the pump outlet should always be open or damage may result to the mechanism.

Checking Without Gauge

Disconnect the outlet tube (to manifold) from the pump and plug the end. Then operate the engine from an idle through slow acceleration to about 40 mph. If the wiper starts operating at about 15 mph and reaches full speed at about 40 mph, the vacuum section is okay. If it does not operate, it may be the windshield wiper motor. This can be checked by connecting the intake manifold directly to the windshield wiper tube. Then slowly accelerate the engine from idle to about 25 mph. The wiper should operate at full speed. If it does not it can be assumed that he wiper motor or tubing is defective.

Fuel Pump Service

Illustrated are representative fuel pumps among the many models that have been produced. Before disassembling any pump, scribe a mark across the housings in such a manner that they may be reassembled with inlet and outlet fitting holes in correct location.

When disassembled, clean all parts (except diaphragms) in solvent and blow dry with compressed air. Examine the diaphragm for cracks, torn screw holes or ruptures. If deteriorated, install new diaphragm and pull rod assembly. Check the strainer screen and if found to be corroded or clogged, install a new screen. Check the rocker arm for wear or scoring on that portion that contacts the camshaft eccentric. If arm is scored or worn install a new one.

When reassembling a pump, do not use shellac or other adhesive on a diaphragm.

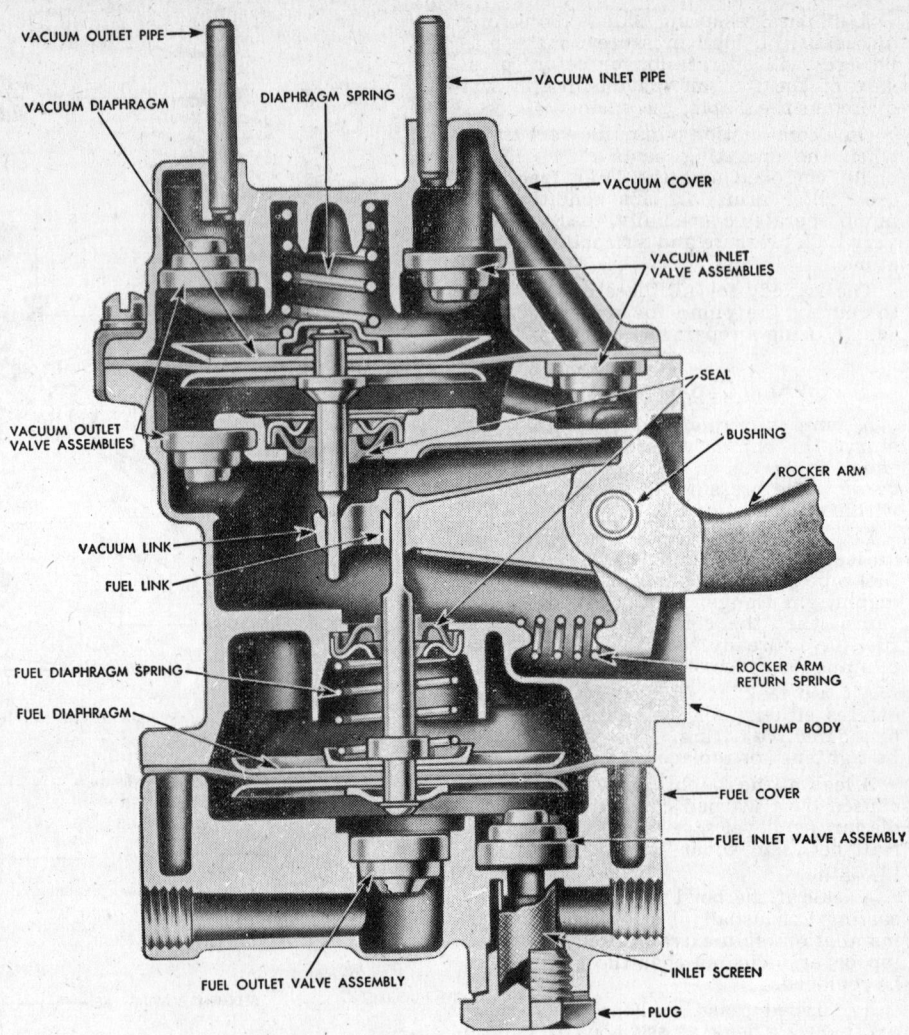

Fig. 9 A.C. combination pump with four vacuum valves

OVERDRIVE

See Trouble Shooting Chapter For Diagnosis Procedure On These Units

OVERDRIVE UNITS are essentially automatic two-speed planetary transmissions attached to the rear of conventional three-speed transmissions. As shown in Fig. 1, the heart of the overdrive is the planetary unit consisting of sun gear, planetary pinions and internal (ring) gear. In overdrive, the pinions are connected to the mainshaft, and revolve around the sun gear which holds against rotation. The internal gear, connected to the tailshaft, is thus forced to rotate at a speed greater than the mainshaft. The engagement of the gearset may be controlled at either the pinions, internal gear or sun gear. In fact, all three methods have been used since the automatic overdrive was adopted in 1934. However, present types are controlled by coupling the internal gear to the tailshaft, or holding the sun gear stationary, or by a combination of the two methods.

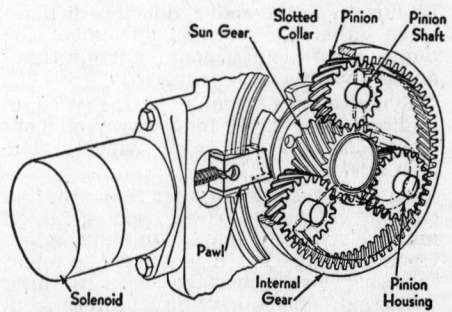

Fig. 1 Through the planetary unit shown, the overdrive provides a higher gear ratio, and when in operation, engine speed is approximately 30 per cent slower than when operating in conventional high gear

Fig. 3 Remove companion flange and governor. Also lockout switch if so equipped

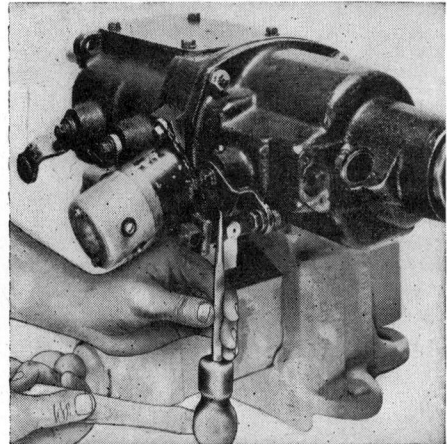

Fig. 4 After driving out locating pin, pull shift shaft as far as possible to disengage operating cam from shift rail. Remove overdrive housing. Tap end of shaft to prevent its coming off with housing and spilling free wheel rollers. Parts inside housing may then be removed

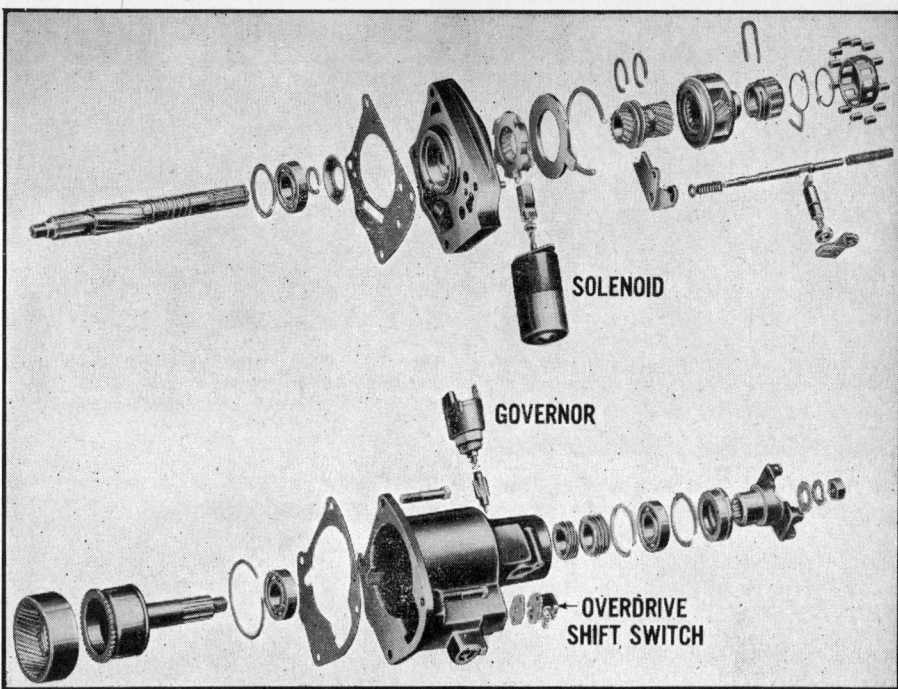

SOLENOID

GOVERNOR

OVERDRIVE SHIFT SWITCH

Fig. 2 Second version of full-electric overdrive with centrifugal governor. This unit is similar to the first version except the design of the second version is more compact. Some models do not use the shift (lockout) switch

FULL-ELECTRIC TYPE

Fig. 2 shows the parts that make up the second version of the full-electric type overdrive. It is more compact than the first version. By following the procedure shown pictorially in Figs. 3 through 12, no difficulty should be experienced in servicing either the first or second versions of these units.

Fig. 7 Separate pinion cage from free wheel unit by removing retaining clip

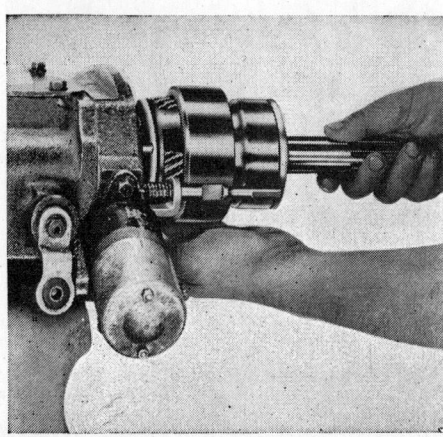

Fig. 5 Hold the adapter plate to the transmission case with one screw and remove the overdrive shaft, catching the free wheel rollers as shown. Removing snap ring permits ring gear to be taken off shaft

Fig. 6 Remove retaining clip and take off free wheel unit and pinion cage

Fig. 8 Remove overdrive sun gear and shift rail

Fig. 9 Remove attaching screws, rotate solenoid ¼ turn and take off

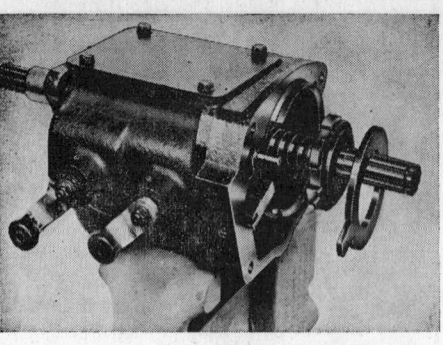

Fig. 10 After releasing snap ring from adapter plate, remove sun gear cover plate, blocker and solenoid pawl

Fig. 11 At this point, if repairs are to be made on the transmission, remove the mainshaft, adapter plate, gears and synchronizer as a unit

Fig. 12 Reverse the order of disassembly to assemble the unit. After inserting the pawl with the notched side up as shown, install blocker assembly and cover plate, being sure blocker ring and pawl are properly positioned. Then install large snap ring in adapter plate

REAR AXLES

NOTE: Specific Service Procedure Covered In Car Chapters

CONTENTS

General Instructions 102
Disassembly Procedure 102
Inspection of Parts 103
Reassembly Procedure 105
Non-Slip Differentials 109

General Instructions

In rear axle service work, there are minor and major operations. Minor operations, such as the removal of axle shafts, bearings and oil seals, can be performed in most cases, without removing the differential carrier from the axle housing.

Major operations, such as the replacement of ring gear and pinion, must be performed with the differential carrier removed from the axle housing. The preliminary work required to remove the differential carrier depends upon the construction employed. In some cases, a removable cover is attached to the back of the axle housing, while in others it is welded to the housing. (Procedure for removing differential carriers and axle assemblies is given in the car chapters.)

Disassembly

Before dismantling the carrier, bear in mind that the factory adjustment of ring gear and pinion sets should not be disturbed unless absolutely necessary. For example, should it become necessary to tear down a differential to replace some part other than a ring gear and pinion, do not disturb the drive pinion adjustment in either disassembling or assembling the unit—assuming of course that it was correct beforehand. Instead, only adjust the ring gear when assembling the unit— which will increase the chances of securing a setting precisely the same as the original setting. In addition, backlash between the ring gear and pinion should be checked and noted before dismantling the unit in order that the gear may be adjusted to the original backlash when making the final adjustments.

It should be remembered that ring gears and pinions are matched at the factory and should remain matched in service. Many times, when one member of a ring gear and pinion set is divorced from the other, the new combination results in a certain amount of noise and an abnormal amount of wear and strain on the teeth. Because of this, service replacements are furnished in matched sets.

With the differential carrier mounted in a vise or fixture, the next step consists of removing the ring gear and differential from the carrier. Before proceeding, however, scratch a mark on each differential adjusting nut and bearing cap, Fig. 1. These marks not only locate on which side of the carrier the adjusting nuts and

Fig. 1 Marking differential adjusting nuts and bearing caps before dismantling assembly

bearing caps are mounted but they show the number of threads exposed on each adjusting nut, and the exact position of the nuts with relation to the bearing caps. If the same ring gear and pinion are to be used again, these marks will serve to bring the original adjustment into being with a minimum of time and effort. (If the differential bearings are

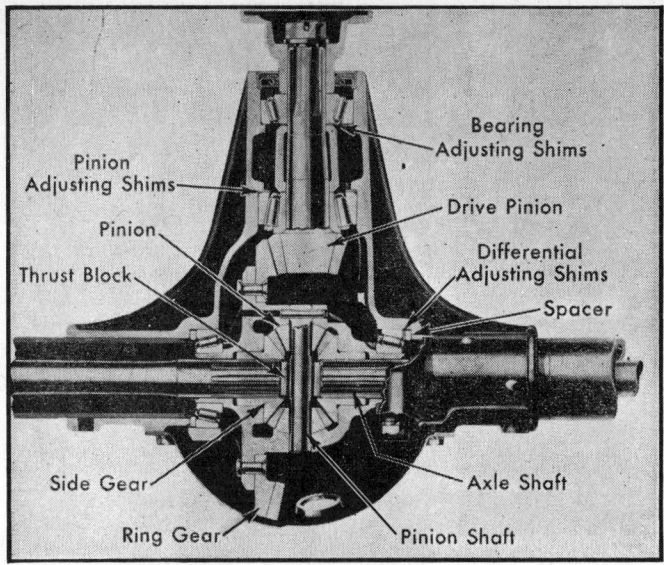

Fig. 2 Showing differential carrier of type having shims for adjusting differential bearings

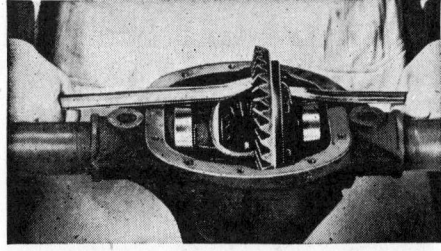

Fig. 3 Method of removing differential from carrier on type having shim-adjusted bearings

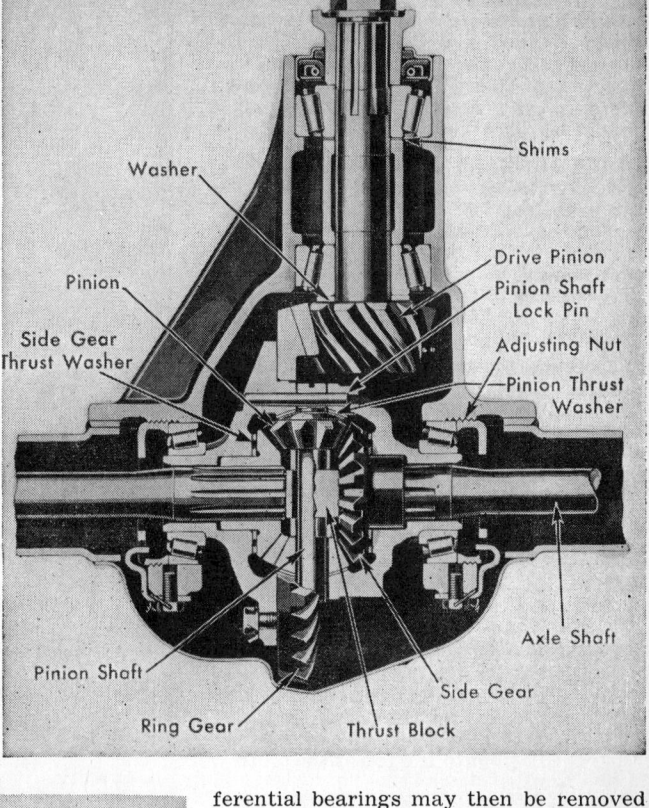

Fig. 5 Details of typical differential unit

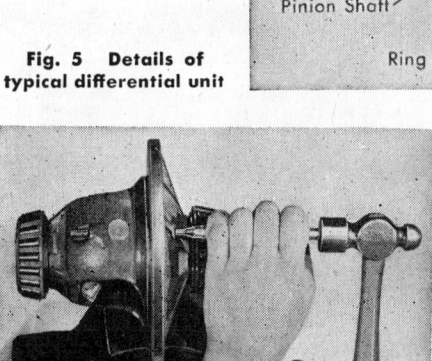

Fig. 4 Removing differential pinion shaft lock pin

Fig. 6 Removing differential bearings with puller

adjusted by shims, Fig. 2, simply tie each set of shims together and carefully lay them aside until needed.)

After removing the differential bearing cap screws, take off the caps and adjusting nuts and lift the differential out of the carrier. Where shims are used for adjusting differential bearings, remove the caps from the bearings and pry the differential out of the carrier, Fig. 3.

The first step in the disassembly of the differential is to remove the ring gear. After removing the attaching cap screws, drive the gear off the differential case by tapping lightly with a soft-faced hammer or mallet. Drive out the differential pinion shaft lock pin, Fig. 4, and push out the shaft (sometimes a lock screw is used). The side gears, pinions, thrust washers, thrust block (if used) and spacers will then be loose and may be picked out of the differential case, Fig. 5. (Specific data concerning special installations are given under the car name.) The dif-

ferential bearings may then be removed from the case with a puller of the type shown in Fig. 6.

The next step is to disassemble the drive pinion. However, it should be removed and disassembled only when it is necessary to replace a part, or to examine closely all parts in connection with a major inspection and overhaul operation. To disassemble, follow the procedure for each type pinion arrangement as given under the car name.

In this connection, however, if the differential carrier was satisfactory from the standpoint of noise before being taken apart, or if it is disassembled for the replacement of a part other than a ring gear and pinion, the location and quantity of shims should be noted. The shims then should be cleaned, tagged and tied together and carefully hung on a hook or set to one side so that, upon reassembly, the original setting may be obtained without delay.

When removing and replacing pinion oil seals, care should be taken to avoid cutting the seal on the sharp edges of the pinion shaft threads, keyway or splines. If the seal is cut and is not replaced, serious leakage of lubricant is almost certain to result.

The best way to guard against cutting the seal is to wrap a piece of shim stock around the pinion shaft so that the oil seal will not come in contact with any sharp edges when the seal is slid off and on. Be sure to blunt or dull the edges of the shim stock so it will not cut the seal.

Inspection of Parts

BEARINGS—Before inspecting bearings, each one should be cleaned by swishing it around in a pail of clean gasoline or kerosene until it is entirely free from grease and oil. Then blow dry with compressed air (if available) rotating the bearing slowly by hand—not by the air pressure. When cleaned and dried, lubricate the bearing with clean engine oil, rotate it by hand, and check for wear and rough spots. If any defects are discovered, it should be discarded.

DIFFERENTIAL PARTS—All parts of the differential, including gears, differential case, carrier, and the axle housing, should be washed thoroughly in clean gasoline or kerosene. Particular attention should be given to remote corners and recesses in the carrier and axle housing to be sure that all muck, grit, gear chips and old grease are removed.

Examine the ring gear and pinion for cracked, chipped or scored teeth. Inspect the bearing surfaces, also the side gears and differential pinion surfaces of the differential case for evidence of roughness or scoring. Inspect the thrust faces of the differential pinions and check their fit on the pinion shaft. Inspect the thrust surfaces of the side gears and check their fit on the axle shafts. Any gears showing any of the above conditions should be scrapped. If the case is equipped with side gear and pinion gear thrust washers, inspect the washers and replace if worn.

Score marks on the contact face of gear teeth show up as light colored areas which are caused by instantaneous fusing of the mating gear teeth, and usually run from the bottom to the top of the tooth.

Fig. 7 Checking run-out of ring gear pilot on differential case

Fig. 8 Use of guide screws for ring gear installation

Fig. 9 Checking run-out of back face of ring gear

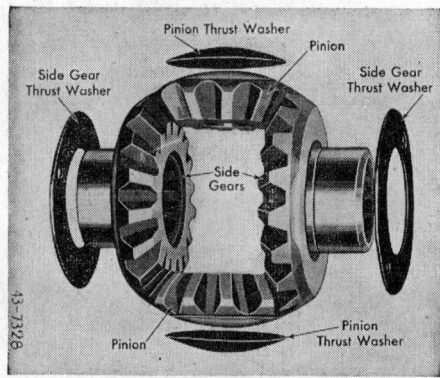

Fig. 10 Layout of differential parts

Fig. 11 Installing axle shaft thrust block and differential pinion shaft

Fig. 12 Installing differential bearings

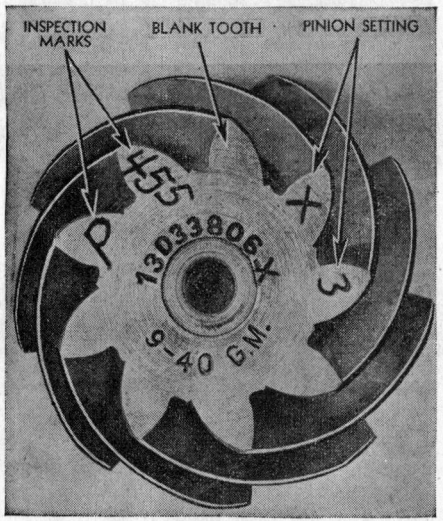

Fig. 13 Example of pinion depth markings

A scoring condition may be the result of insufficient lubrication, the improper lubricant for the load required for the gears, dirty lubricant, or improper tooth contact. The gears in the differential which usually cause noisy operation from these conditions are the ring gear and pinion. The side gears and differential pinions rarely give trouble. In fact, they can be badly worn without affecting the operation of the differential, as they are used only when one rear wheel travels faster than the opposite rear wheel. In spite of this, however, worn side gears and differential pinions should always be replaced during an overhaul operation. If

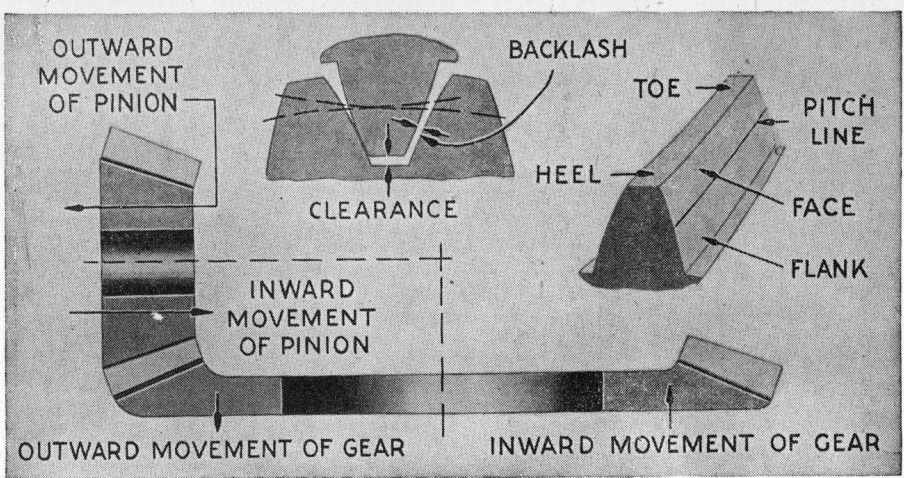

Fig. 14 Showing gear movement and tooth terminology

Fig. 17 "Dialocator" as used with hypoid gear installation

not, the condition will become worse and eventually, through failure of these parts, another tear-down will be required.

Reassembly

The sequence of operations in assembling any piece of mechanism is usually performed in the reverse order from which it was disassembled. Differential carrier units are no exception although the sequence given below may be changed to suit shop conditions. For example, instead of starting with the differential case and ring gear, the drive pinion may be set up and adjusted in the carrier first.

CHECKING DIFFERENTIAL CASE RUN-OUT—Mount the differential case on V blocks, Fig. 7, and check the run-out of the ring gear pilot and case flange. To make this check, mount the dial indicator as shown, with the indicator needle set to zero and the contacting pin just touching the surface to be checked.

Rotate the differential case in the V blocks for one complete revolution and note the amount of deflection on the needle. If the deflection is in excess of the maximum allowable run-out (usually .002 inch) replace the differential case or true it up on a lathe.

RING GEAR, INSTALL — If the ring gear is the bolt-on type, cut the heads from five or six 1½ inch cap screws having the same thread as the ring gear cap screws. (These are to be used as guide pins and can be kept for future jobs.) Cut screwdriver slots in the end of these guide pins and screw them in every other hole in the ring gear, Fig. 8. Be sure the back face of the ring gear and differential flange face are clean and free from nicks and burrs, and any rust preventive film that may be present.

Slip the ring gear with the guide pins on the differential case and tap it in place with a mallet. Install the regular cap screws in the open holes and draw them up evenly and tightly. Remove the guide pins and install the other cap screws. New lock washers should be used and if the cap screw heads are drilled, use new wire to lock them in place.

Mount the assembly in V blocks, Fig. 9, and check the run-out of the back face of

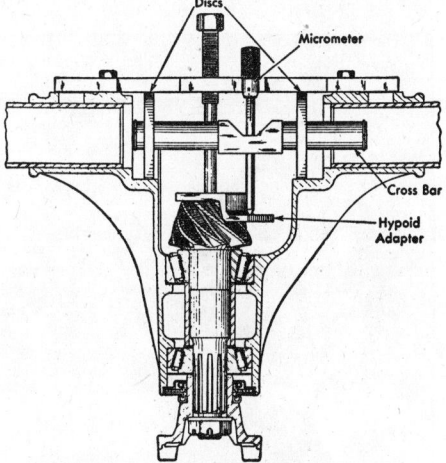

Fig. 15 Micrometer type pinion setting gauge

Fig. 16 "Dialocator" as used with spiral bevel gear installation

Fig. 18 Checking end play of drive pinion

Fig. 19 Adjusting differential bearings on units having adjusting nuts

the ring gear in the same manner as described above for the differential case. If the deflection of the needle is in excess of the maximum allowable run-out (usually .006 inch) the ring gear may not be bolted evenly against the flange face. Sometimes this check is made with the side bearings mounted on the differential case hubs. If so, and the run-out is excessive, the bearings may be mounted incorrectly or they may be cocked on the hubs.

If the ring gear is riveted on the case, it should be removed and replaced in the following manner: Drill through the head of each rivet, using a drill slightly larger than the hole in the case. When the drill penetrates through the case, the head will come off and the rivet can then be driven out. Always drill rivets from the differential case flange side. Do not cut them off with a chisel as this distorts the case. Remove any burrs from around the rivet holes, and check the run-out of the case as described above.

Before riveting on the new gear, bolt it to the case through every other hole and draw down tight to prevent the rivets being squeezed out between the ring gear and the case. Use cold rivets and a riveting machine, if possible and always head the rivets on the ring gear flange—never on the back of the differential case.

The use of hot rivets, headed over by hand, is only recommended as a last resort when cold riveting equipment is not available. This is because when hot rivets cool off, they contract and very often are loose in the holes, with the result that when the gear is under load, the rivets shear off.

Head over one rivet, turn the differential case halfway around and head a rivet at this point. Then head over a rivet between the two already installed, working successively from one side of the gear to the other until all open holes are filled. Remove the temporary bolts and install the rivets in these holes in the same manner.

When the job is completed, mount the assembly in V blocks and check the run-out on the back face of the gear in the manner described above. If excessive, the ring gear may not be riveted evenly against the flange face. If this is the case, remove the rivets and make the installation correctly.

ASSEMBLY OF DIFFERENTIAL — When installing the differential gears and thrust washers (if used), Fig. 10, coat these parts with differential lubricant to facilitate holding them in place while replacing the differential pinion shaft.

Slip the side gear thrust washers and side gears in the differential case. Roll the differential pinions in place, rotating the side gears until the hole through the center of the pinions is in line with the hole for the pinion shaft in the case. Install the axle shaft thrust block (if used) Fig. 11, and push the pinion shaft in place so that the hole in the shaft for the lock pin or screw registers with the hole in the case. Install the lock pin and peen over the outside edge of the hole to prevent the pin from coming loose in service. If a lock screw is used, install a new lock washer and set the screw up tight.

DIFFERENTIAL BEARINGS, INSTALL —Install the differential side bearings, Fig. 12, with the thick side of the inner races toward the case. Be sure they are not cocked and that the inner races seat squarely against the hubs of the differential case. This completes the assembly of the differential unit.

DRIVE PINION, INSTALL—Due to the fact that all gears are not made on the same machine, a definite setting for pinion depth to bring the ring gear and pinion exactly on the cone centers is determined in manufacture by testing each ring gear and pinion set. These setting marks are etched on the toe end of the pinion and read zero (0), or plus (+) or minus (—) a nominal amount, in thousandths of an inch. Fig. 13 is an example showing a pinion marked plus .003 inch (+3).

Fig. 20 Checking backlash between ring gear and pinion

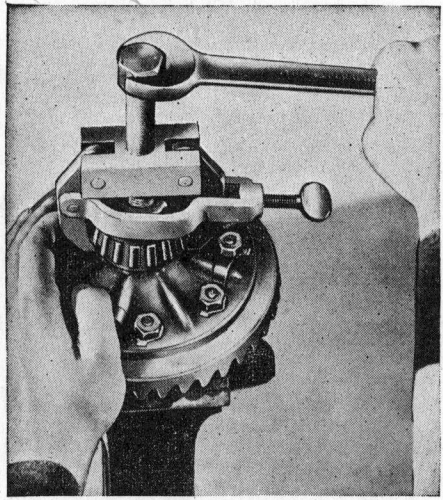

Fig. 21 Using puller to remove differential bearings

A plus mark indicates that the pinion is to be set outward from the center line of the axle. A minus mark indicates that the pinion is to be set inward to the center line of the axle. (Fig. 14 explains gear movements and tooth terminology.)

In order to make these depth settings in accordance with the marks on the pinion, a pinion setting gauge is essential. There are several of these gauges available commercially, each differing in detail but not in principle. Measurements are taken either by a micrometer or a dial indicator.

As shown in Figs. 15, 16 and 17, these gauges are provided with a measuring rod for setting the pinion, and are made adjustable to accommodate all width differential carriers. Different diameter discs are also provided to fit all differential side bearing bores in the carriers. Manufacturers of these gauges usually provide complete instructions for their use, and tables giving the nominal dimension for the various model pinions used on all motor vehicles on which the gauge can be used.

Using the micrometer type gauge, Fig. 15, first install the pinion in the carrier according to the instructions given under

Fig. 22 Checking clearance between bearing cup and differential case on shim-adjusted differential bearings

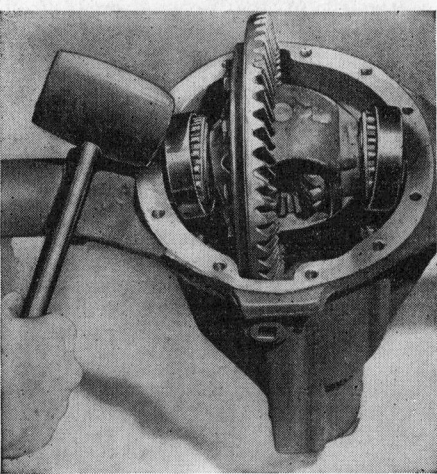

Fig. 23 Installing differential and bearing cups in units with shim-adjusted bearings

the car make, using the shims from the old pinion. Check the pinion shaft end play and make the necessary corrections.

To check the end play, place a dial indicator on the end of the pinion, Fig. 18, work the pinion in and out and note the amount of end play indicated by the movement of the needle. If the job calls for a pre-load of .002 inch, for example, and the indicated end play is .004 inch, .006 inch of shimming should be removed to give the required pre-load of .002 inch.

After the correct pre-load is established, mount the pinion setting gauge in the carrier with the proper size bearing discs, being sure that both discs are seated on the bearing surfaces and do not come in contact with the threads.

To locate the pinion, adjust the micrometer pointer to the nominal setting of the pinion. Then move the pointer to

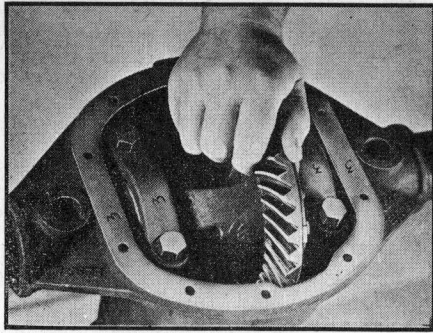

Fig. 24 Showing how bearing caps should be installed according to numerals on shim-adjusted differential units

Fig. 25 Checking run-out of ring gear

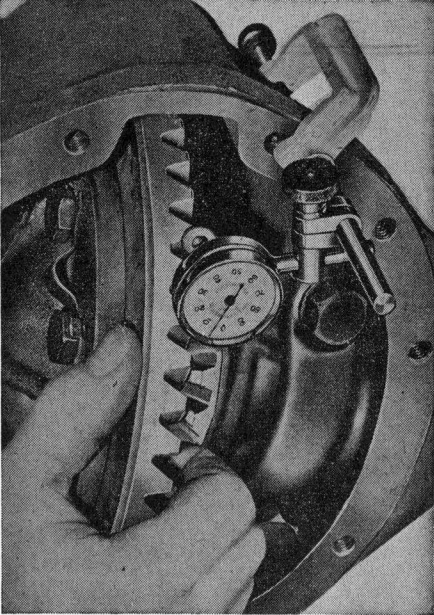

Fig. 26 Checking backlash between ring gear and pinion

the number of thousandths of an inch etched on the end of the pinion. If a plus mark is shown, adjust the pointer away from the center line of the axle. If a minus mark is shown, adjust the pointer toward the center line of the axle. In other words, a plus mark indicates that the pinion is to be moved toward the front of the car; a minus mark toward the rear of the car. Add or remove shims as required until the pinion is located at the nominal depth, plus or minus the amount etched on the end of the pinion.

Where a pinion setting gauge is not available, assemble the differential in the carrier and adjust the backlash between the ring gear and pinion. Then check the tooth contact in the manner described in a later paragraph.

DIFFERENTIAL BEARINGS, ADJUST—Upon completion of the pinion setting operation, assemble the differential unit in the carrier and proceed as follows:

If the same ring gear and pinion are being used again, and if the adjustment

was correct before the unit was dismantled, adjust the bearings according to the marks, Fig. 1, that were scratched on the bearing caps and adjusting nuts. If the differential bearings are adjusted by shims, assemble the unit with the same quantity of shims used originally.

If a new ring gear and pinion are being used, or if an adjustment of the old gears was necessary, proceed as follows, being sure to leave off the drive pinion bearing oil seal to eliminate any drag from this source when making adjustments.

To make the adjustment on units having adjusting nuts, place the differential in the carrier and install the adjusting nuts, taking care to slide these nuts alongside the bearings so that the threads on the nuts fit properly into the threads of the carrier. Install the bearing caps, being sure the marks on the caps line up with the marks on the carrier. Start the cap screws and drop the bearing caps on the adjusting nuts, using the screws as a pilot so as not to cross the threads. Tighten the cap screws and then loosen them from 1 to 1½ turns.

Loosen the right adjusting nut, Fig. 19, until the ring gear and differential case are loose in the bearings—usually four to five notches. Tighten the left-hand nut against the bearing race, removing all backlash between the ring gear and pinion, then back off three or four notches.

Tighten the right-hand nut until the bearing race starts to turn—indicating tension on the bearing. Continue to tighten one to two notches more, then back off the nut until the bearing race stops turning. Retighten this same nut until the bearing race again starts to turn, continuing for two notches more and whatever further tightening is necessary to bring the slot in the nut in line with the bearing cap lock, Fig. 20. Tighten the bearing cap screws and

check the ring gear and pinion backlash.

To check the backlash, mount a dial indicator on the carrier, Fig. 20. To assure an accurate reading, make sure the dial indicator is square with the face of the gear tooth it contacts, and that the pointer is set to zero.

CAUTION—When making this or any other adjustment of the ring gear, tighten the cap screws of the differential bearing caps after each adjustment has been made. This will avoid "creeping" of the ring gear in any direction during the process. However, do not lock the cap screws or adjusting nuts until all adjustments have been completed.

Check the backlash by rocking the ring gear back and forth and noting the amount indicated on the gauge. If the backlash is not within the limits specified by the car manufacturer (usually .005 to .010 inch) an adjustment is required. If the backlash is greater than the allowable maximum, loosen the right-hand nut one notch and tighten the left-hand nut one notch. If the lash is less than the allowable minimum, loosen the left-hand nut one notch and tighten the right-hand nut one notch.

When the adjustment is correct, tighten the bearing caps securely, then recheck the backlash. Install the adjustment nut locks. If the cap screw heads are drilled, lock them with new wire. If nut locks are employed, Fig. 20, be sure to set the ears against the sides of the cap screw heads. Use new lock washers if this locking method is used.

If the differential bearings are adjusted by shims, Fig. 3, the adjustment is obtained by the shims located at each side of the case between the shoulder of the case and the inner race of the bearing. These shims also establish the ring gear position with the pinion. Therefore, backlash must be checked whenever a bearing adjustment is made.

The correct bearing adjustment is one which will provide an .008 inch pinch fit when the differential unit is assembled into the carrier. To make an adjustment, remove the bearing cones and shims, using a puller of the type shown in Fig. 21. Reinstall the bearing cones without the shims and place the assembly in the housing with the bearing cups. Force the unit to one side and check the clearance between the bearing cup and differential case with a feeler gauge, Fig. 22. When the clearance is determined, add .008 inch of shimming—which will give the proper bearing adjustment.

Remove the differential bearings and install equal thicknesses of shims on each side and replace the bearings. Reinstall the differential unit in the housing. This operation is made easier by cocking the differential bearing cups slightly when the differential is placed in the housing and then tapping them lightly with a mallet, Fig. 23. During this operation, be sure the ring gear teeth mesh with the pinion teeth before tapping the bearings in place. After the cups are in position, install the bearing caps. The caps and the gasket surface of the housing are usually marked on one side with a horizontal numeral and on the other side with a vertical numeral, Fig. 24. The position of the nu-

Fig. 27 Method of correcting backlash between ring gear and pinion on shim-adjusted units

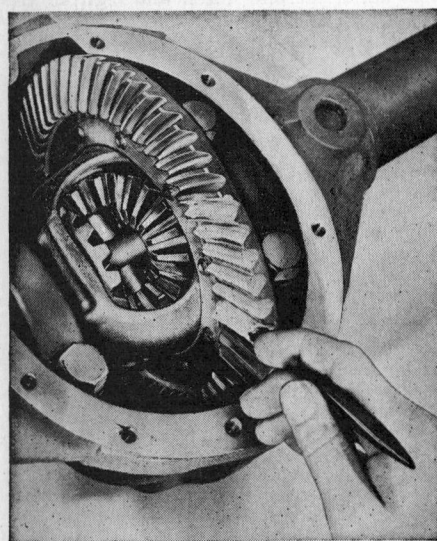

Fig. 28 Painting ring gear teeth to check tooth contact

Fig. 29 Contact too high and narrow. Pinion should be moved toward center of axle

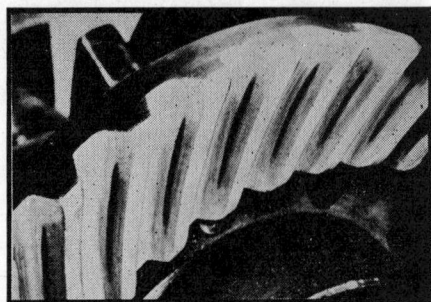

Fig. 30 Contact too low and narrow. Pinion should be moved away from center of axle

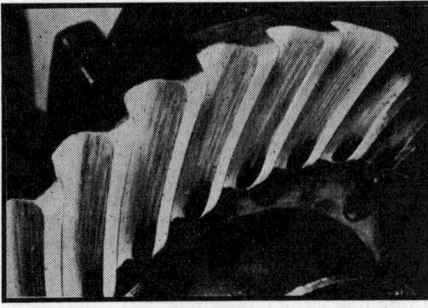

Fig. 31 Short toe contact. Move ring gear away from pinion

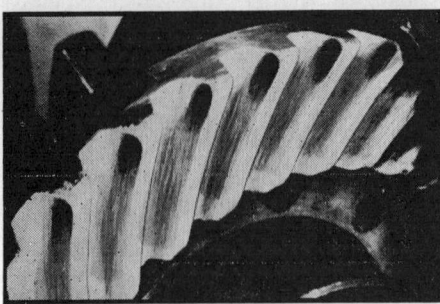

Fig. 32 Short heel contact. Move ring gear toward pinion

Fig. 33 Correct tooth contact. Gears making contact as shown give best results for quiet operation and long life

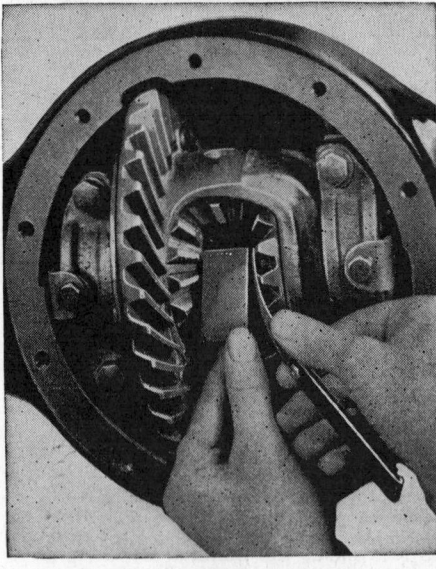

Fig. 34 Checking end play between axle shaft and thrust block

merals should coincide when installing the bearing caps.

Tighten the bearing caps securely and if there is any backlash between the ring gear and pinion, check the back face of the ring gear for run-out, Fig. 25, in a manner already described. If the total indicator reading is in excess of .003 inch, it indicates a sprung differential case or an improperly installed ring gear. In either case, the assembly must be taken apart and rechecked thoroughly.

Mount the backlash gauge indicator on the carrier, Fig. 26, and start checking the backlash between the ring gear and pinion. In the event the lash is not within the proper limits (usually .005 to .007 inch) it will be necessary to change the arrangement of the shims back of the bearings—which are supplied in thicknesses of .003, .005, .010 and .030 inch, any combination of which may be used to obtain the desired result.

Make corrections in backlash according to Fig. 27, bearing in mind that shims removed from one side must be installed at the opposite side so that the total shim thickness of the right and left side will remain unchanged, and the bearing adjustment undisturbed.

NOTE—If a pinion setting gauge was not used to locate the pinion, tooth contact between the ring gear and pinion should be checked at this time, and in the following manner:

GEAR TOOTH CONTACT—Paint about 12 teeth of the ring gear, Fig. 28, with red or white lead of suitable consistency and use it sparingly. When the pinion is rotated, the paint is squeezed away by contact of the teeth, leaving bare areas showing the exact size, shape and location of the contacts. Sharper contact can be obtained by applying a small amount of resistance to the ring gear when rotating the pinion. This is done by holding a block of wood against the back of the ring gear, and using a wrench to rotate the pinion. By examining the contact marks, it can be determined whether contact is too high or too low, or too near the heel or toe.

If the contact is high and narrow, Fig. 29, add shims so as to move the drive pinion in toward the toe of the gear teeth (toward the center of axle) to lower the contact area. This adjustment will decrease the backlash between

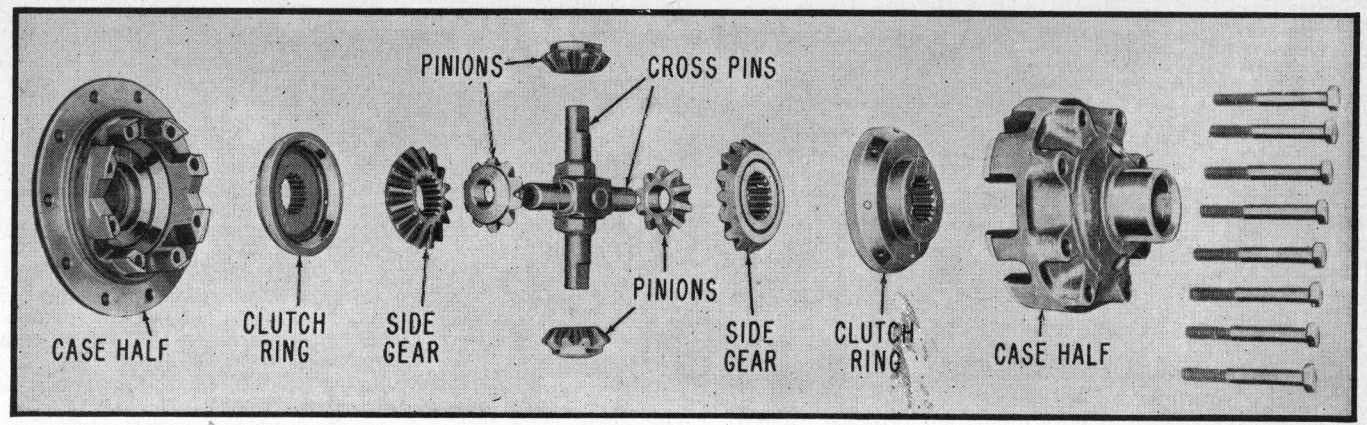

Fig. 35 Spicer non-slip differential of the cone clutch type

the ring gear and pinion, which can be corrected by moving the gear away from the pinion. Several adjustments of both ring gear and pinion may be necessary before correct contact and backlash are secured, whether it is this one or those described below.

A low, narrow contact, Fig. 30, requires the removal of shims to move the pinion out from the gear (away from the center of the axle) a sufficient amount to move the contact area to the proper location. To obtain correct backlash, move the ring gear in toward the pinion.

Fig. 31 shows a short toe contact which is corrected by moving the ring gear away from the pinion. After establishing the correct contact, the proper backlash is obtained by moving the pinion in toward the toe of the ring gear teeth (toward center of axle).

Fig. 32 shows a short heel contact which is corrected by moving the ring gear in toward the pinion. Correct backlash is then obtained by moving the pinion out toward the heel of the ring gear teeth (away from center of axle).

When adjustments have been properly made, the contact shown in Fig. 33 will be secured. This adjustment provides a quiet operating gear set which, because the load is distributed over the teeth within the proper area, will provide normal service.

Tighten the bearing caps securely, then recheck the backlash. If correct, install the adjusting nut locks, lock the adjustment and install the differential carrier unit in the axle housing, being sure the gasket is in good condition.

Some manufacturers provide thrust blocks of several thicknesses to maintain correct axle shaft end play. Where this construction is used, install the axle shafts and check the clearance as shown in Fig. 34. If the clearance does not come within the allowable limits, a new thrust block should be installed.

LUBRICATION—The differential carrier should be lubricated with the exact quantity, grade and type lubricant recommended by the manufacturer of the particular unit being serviced. The housing should never be filled above the level of the bottom of the filler plug hole.

Over-filling causes blown grease seals at the wheels, resulting in leakage and

an accumulation of dirt and grease around the wheels, tires and brakes. On the other hand, if the lubricant is not kept up to the proper level, gears and bearings may run dry, resulting in excessive wear and noise.

SERVICE NOTE—All the foregoing is general information for servicing differential carrier units used on passenger cars included in this manual. To complete the picture, however, specific data such as specifications, drive pinion set-ups, special differential designs, propeller shaft installations on torque tube drive cars pertaining to each make of car are given in the car chapters.

NON-SLIP DIFFERENTIALS

The main purpose of these differentials is that they supply a greater percentage of torque to the wheel with better traction and still furnishes to the wheel with poorer traction as much torque as it is able to

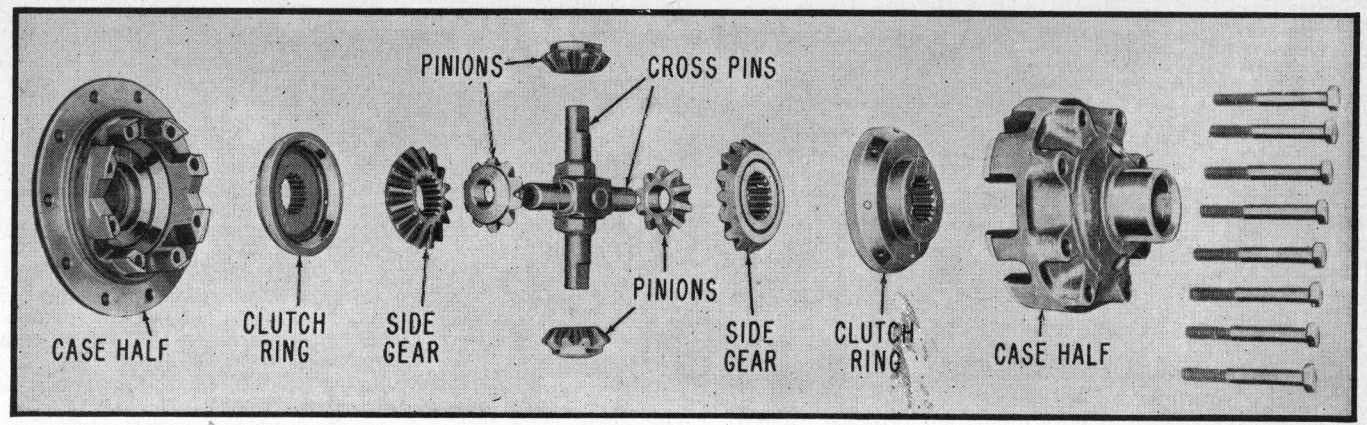

Fig. 36 Spicer non-slip differential of the clutch plate type

absorb under the circumstances.

In the conventional differential the wheel easiest to turn receives the power. Therefore, when traction conditions under the rear wheels are not the same, the driving force is limited by the wheel with the poorer traction (easiest to turn) even though one wheel is on good traction surface.

These non-slip differentials do not permit shock loads or full engine torque to be transmitted to one axle shaft. They provide power to both rear wheels and maintain the differential action that is necessary when the vehicle is turning a corner to permit the outer wheel to turn faster than the inner wheel.

Service Note

"On car" type wheel balancers are not recommended for use on rear wheels of cars equipped with a non-slip differential. The rear wheel will drive if in contact with the ground or with a block even though the opposite wheel is raised. *However, this type of wheel balancer may be used by removing the wheel opposite of the one being balanced with the complete assembly raised.*

SPICER TYPE

Fig. 35 shows the cone clutch type whereas Fig. 36 illustrates the plate clutch type. Each assembly consists of two case halves, two cross pins held together by a thrust block, differential pinions, side gears, and clutch rings (Fig. 35) or clutch plates (Fig. 36).

The cross pins are made with a movable joint at the center to permit each one to move independently while in continuous engagement. The pin ends are made in the form of a V, and a similar V is machined in each case half to provide a ramped cam surface.

In Fig. 35, the clutch ring is fitted over each bevel side gear and mates with a cone surface machined in each half of the differential case.

In Fig. 36, the clutch plates operate between the flat surface on the clutch retainer and the machined surface in each half of the differential case.

Operation

As the vehicle is put in motion, the

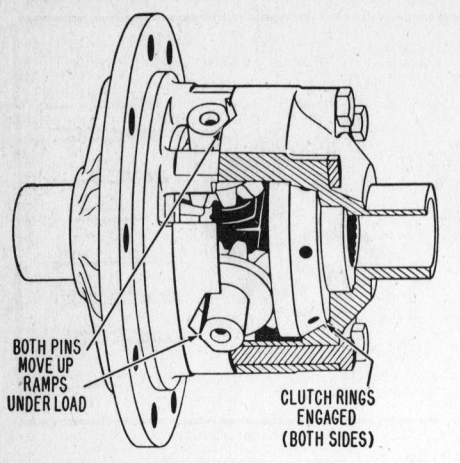

Fig. 37 Differential action when moving straight ahead

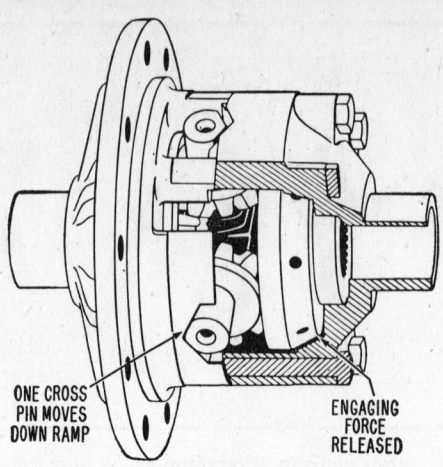

Fig. 38 Differential action when turning a corner

driving force moves the cross pin up the ramp of the cam surface, applying a load to the clutches and restricts turning of the differential through the friction of the clutches on the mating surfaces in the differential case, Fig. 37. This provides a torque ratio between the axle shafts which is based on the amount of friction in the differential and the amount of load that is being applied to the differential.

When turning a corner this process is, in effect, partially reversed, Fig. 38. The differential gears become a planetary gear set, with the gear on the inside of the curve becoming the fixed gear of the planetary. The outer gear of the planetary overruns as the outside wheel on the curve has a further distance to travel. With the outer gear overrunning and the inner gear fixed, the differential pinions are caused to rotate, but since they are restricted by the fixed gear, they must first move the cross pins back down the cam surface, relieving the thrust load of the clutch on its mating surface in the differential case. Thus when turning a corner, the differential, for all practical purposes, is similar to a conventional differential and the wheels are free to rotate at different speeds.

With non-slip differentials, certain characteristics must be taken into consideration. Under average driving conditions, such as straight ahead, reverse, extreme right and left turns, the operation will be the same as with the conventional differential. However, a little more backlash may be noticed due to the lateral movement of the differential cross pins. In addition, a slight chatter may occur under surge torque with one wheel on a slippery surface. These conditions are considered normal.

CAUTION—Do not attempt to spin a wheel under power with a jack under only one side; both wheels must be clear of the ground. If one wheel remains in contact with the ground, there is a possibility that when spinning the other wheel, friction of the clutch rings or clutch dics may set the vehicle in motion.

Servicing Cone Clutch Type

This type differential, Fig. 35, must be replaced as a unit as individual parts are not available. It is furnished less ring gear and side bearings.

Servicing Plate Clutch Type

Before disassembling the differential, scribe a line across the differential case halves for alignment upon reassembly. Then, after removing the attaching bolts, separate the case halves and remove the differential parts.

Inspect all parts. See that there are no worn, cracked or distorted clutch plates. All parts must be free of nicks, burrs or any imperfections that will reduce the efficient operation of the unit.

1. Assemble differential as suggested

in Figs. 39 and 40.
2. Make sure the side gear retainer will rotate with a slight drag when in the case. Repeat for opposite side.
3. Install side gear on ring gear flange half.
4. With ring gear flange half in a vertical position, install one shaft and gears, making certain that notch in shaft is up.
5. Install side gear in other half of case.
6. Hold the remaining case half through the bearing trunnion and install it on the ring gear flange half, being sure scribed mark made previously is in alignment.
7. Tighten attaching bolts evenly to 35-45 lb. ft. torque to avoid distorting the case.
8. Check clearance between pinion mate shaft and the V of the case, Fig. 41. Do this by placing shim stock or feeler gauges on both ends of the same shaft and on opposite sides of the V. The clearance should be as follows:

Buick 1959	.030" Max.
1960-61	None
Chevrolet 1957-59	.015" Max.
1960-61	None
Chrysler Line	.020" Max.
Continental	.045" Max.
Lincoln	.045" Max.
Oldsmobile	.010" Max.
Pontiac	.020" Max.
Rambler V8, 1958-59	.030" Max.
1960-61	None
Studebaker	.020" Max.

Installation Note

Make sure the spline end of the axle shaft does not interfere with the pinion mate shafts. This can be checked with a steel tape by measuring from the bottom of the axle shaft bearing bore to the pinion mate shafts. Then measure the axle shafts from the corresponding point of the bearing to the end of the spline. The minimum clearance required is ⅛". Grind off the spline end of the axle shaft if it is too long. Check the other axle shaft in the same manner.

FORD TYPE

Disassembly

1. Referring to Fig. 42, mark one differential bearing cap and the mating support to help position the parts properly during assembly of the carrier.
2. Remove bearing adjusting nuts and lift differential assembly out of carrier.
3. Remove differential bearings.
4. Loosen *alternate* drive gear attaching bolts evenly to release the spring pressure between differential case and cover.
5. Remove differential case cover and then the drive gear.
6. Remove clutch plates.
7. Remove two Belleville springs.
8. Remove clutch hub, side gear and thrust washer.
9. Drive out differential pinion shaft lock pin.
10. Drive out differential pinion shaft. Then remove pinion gears and thrust washers.

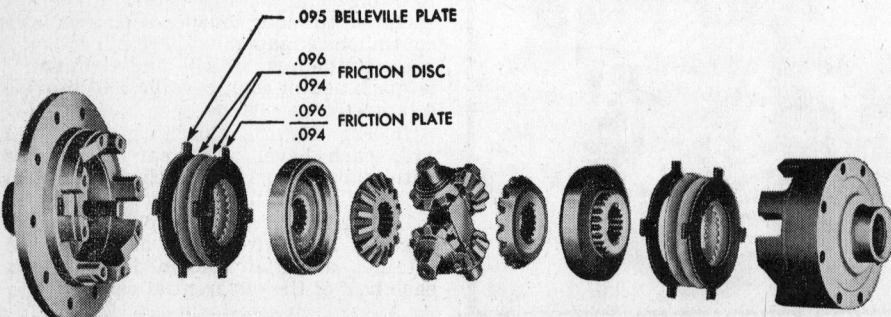

.095 BELLEVILLE PLATE
.096 FRICTION DISC
.094
.096 FRICTION PLATE
.094

Fig. 39 Plate clutch type of non-slip differential (4-stack unit)

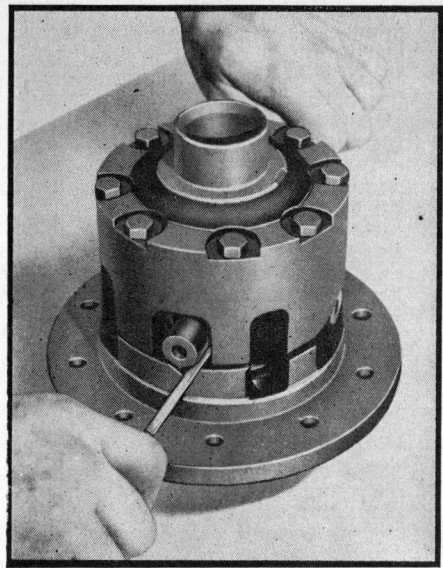

Fig. 41 Checking clearance between pinion mate shaft and V in case. Feeler gauges must be inserted on both ends of same shaft and on opposite sides of V.

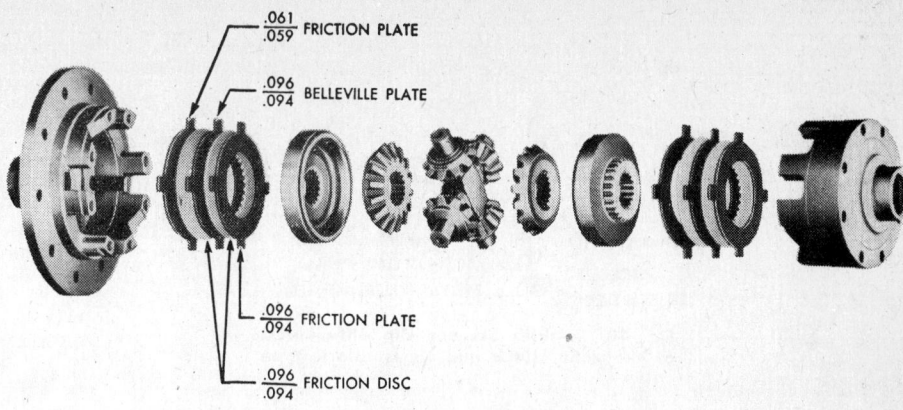

Fig. 40 Plate clutch type of non-slip differential (5-stack unit)

Assembly

1. Lubricate all parts during assembly. Referring to Fig. 42, place side gear and thrust washer in differential case.
2. With soft-faced hammer, drive pinion shaft into case only far enough to retain a pinion thrust washer and pinion gear.
3. Place a second pinion and thrust washer in position, and drive pinion shaft into place. *Carefully line up pinion shaft retainer holes.*
4. Place second pinion and thrust washer in position. Drive pinion shaft into place. Install pinion shaft retainer. *The retainer must not extend beyond the machined surface of the case.*
5. Insert two 2"x$\frac{7}{16}$" bolts through differential flange and thread them 3 or 4 turns into the drive gear as a guide in aligning drive gear bolt holes. Press or tap drive gear into position.
6. Clamp differential case in a vise. Install differential side gear on pinion gears. Place clutch hub on side gear and place thrust washer on hub.
7. Insert two $\frac{3}{16}$"x2" dowel pins into differential case. Place a steel plate on differential case so that slots in dog ears straddle dowel pins. *Lubricate all differential parts so that an accurate torque check can be made.*
8. Place a bonded plate on steel plate. Make sure bonded plate inner spline teeth properly engage hub spline. Assemble remaining plates: a steel plate, a bonded plate and lastly a steel plate.
9. Place two Belleville springs on the top steel plate. Both springs are assembled with concave sides down.
10. Place differential case cover on case and start bolts.
11. Tighten bolts evenly and alternately across the diameter of drive gear.

As the bolts are tightened the Belleville springs are compressed and the case and cover are pulled together.
12. Torque the bolts to 65-75 lb. ft.
13. Check torque required to rotate one side gear while the other side gear is held. Ignore the torque required to start the side gear turning. The torque required to keep it moving steadily should be between 155 and 195 lb. ft. If not within these limits, check for improper assembly.
14. Install differential in carrier.

RAMBLER 6 TYPE

In this type, Fig. 43, the locking action is accomplished by two spring-loaded thrust blocks which bear against each side gear, which in turn are seated in a tapered cone that clutches inside each case half. The spring load is calibrated to be rendered ineffective by variable torque; that is, when turning corners, the torque created on one wheel by differential action will overcome the spring load of the thrust blocks on the side gears.

Service Check

To avoid unnecessary disassembly, the effectiveness of the unit may be checked as follows:

Place the transmission in neutral with the engine turned off and jack up one rear wheel only. Turn the raised wheel in a forward motion with a socket and torque wrench on the axle shaft nut. A torque reading of 80 to 120 ft. lbs. should be attained before the wheel will slip. If reading falls within this range, the assembly is in proper operating condition.

Servicing The Unit

The non-slip differential will be serviced only as a complete unit assembly. When replacement is required, follow the service procedure for the conventional type axle except when working on the differential unit itself. To service the differential unit, proceed as follows, referring to Fig. 43.

1. Separate case halves and inspect parts. The cone seat in the case should be slightly grooved. The male cone surface should be grooved similar to a transmission synchronizer friction ring. Excessive wear or damaged cone surfaces warrants replacement. *Caution: When reassembling the unit, use axle shafts as mounting tools to assure proper gear and cone spline alignment. Do not ignore this procedure as it will be impossible to install shafts at final assembly. Attempting to force the shafts into position may result in*

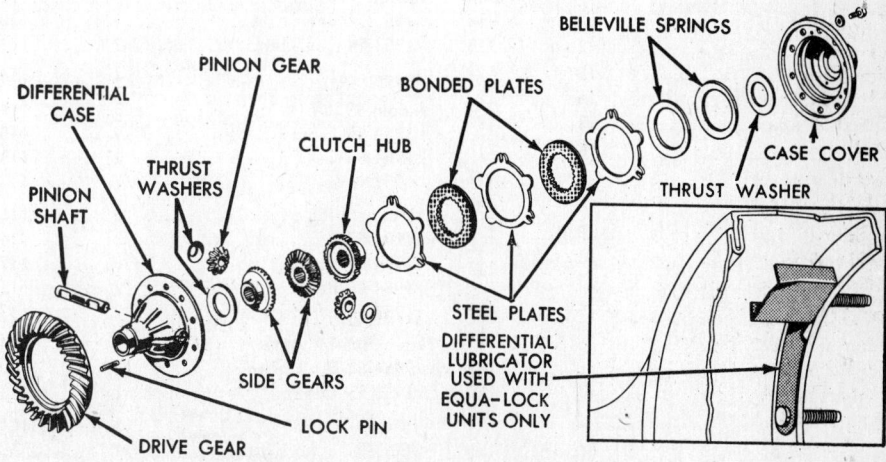

Fig. 42 Ford type non-slip differential

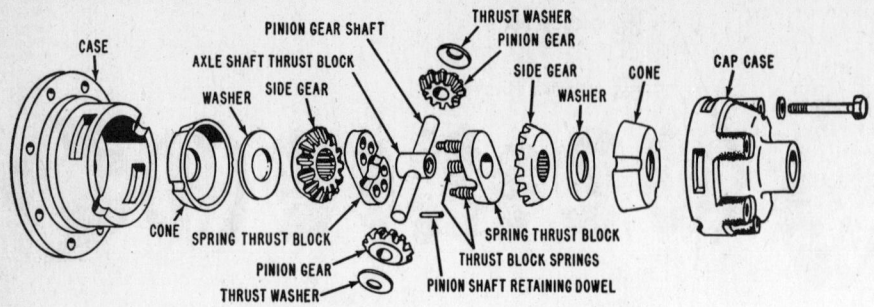

CASE — PINION GEAR SHAFT — THRUST WASHER — PINION GEAR — SIDE GEAR — CONE — CAP CASE — AXLE SHAFT THRUST BLOCK — WASHER — SIDE GEAR — WASHER — CONE — SPRING THRUST BLOCK — PINION GEAR — THRUST WASHER — SPRING THRUST BLOCK — THRUST BLOCK SPRINGS — PINION SHAFT RETAINING DOWEL

Fig. 43 Rambler Six non-slip differential of the cone clutch and thrust block type

breakage of the spring thrust blocks.

2. Clamp one axle shaft vertically in a vise, allowing 3" to extend above vise jaws.

3. Place ring gear flange side of differential case over extended axle shaft with interior of case facing up.

4. Note that cones are stamped "flange" and "cap" on back side. The tapers and surfaces are match fitted.

5. Install cone stamped "flange" into flange half of case over axle shaft splines into proper position.

6. Place washer and side gear over axle shaft and allow it to seat on cone mounting face.

7. One spring thrust block is then placed in position over gear face in alignment with pinion gear shaft grooves. Install pinion shaft, axle shaft thrust block, pinion gears, and thrust washers into flange half of differential case in such a manner that the pinion shaft retaining dowel can be inserted through the pinion gear shaft and into differential case. This prevents the pinion shaft from sliding out and causing damage to the carrier assembly.

8. Insert springs into spring pockets and place second thrust block over springs.

9. Align second side gear to mesh with pinion gears face down on thrust block.

10. Place side gear washer and remaining cone stamped "cap" over side gear.

11. Install cap side of differential assembly over cone in proper position and insert two bolts 180° apart to finger tightness.

12. Install other axle shaft through cap side of differential case, turning it to enter cone splines and then side gear splines. Leaving the axle shaft in this position, insert remaining bolts and torque to 15-18 ft. lbs.

13. Remove the axle shafts. A slight tapping on the shafts with a soft hammer may be necessary to overcome the binding action of the splines during assembly. The shafts can then be readily installed without spline interference at the proper point in final assembly.

14. Install the unit in the axle housing as you would with a conventional differential.

Service Note

After the unit is installed in the housing, do not attempt to rotate one axle shaft until both are in position. Rotation of one axle shaft without the other shaft installed will result in misalignment of cone and side gear splines and prevent entry of the second axle shaft.

HYDRAULIC BRAKES

BRAKE ADJUSTMENT INDEX

Car & Model	Brake Type	Page
Buick 1953-61	2	113
Buick Special 1961	4	114
Cadillac 1960-61	8	117
1957-59 Front	7	116
1957-59 Rear	2	113
1956	2	113
1953-55	1	113
Chevrolet 1955-61	3	114
1953-54	2	113
Chrysler 1956-61	15	122
1953-55 Front	16	122
1953-55 Rear	13	120
Comet 1960-61	5	115
Corvair 1960-61	4	114
Corvette 1955-61	3	114
De Soto 1956-61	15	122
1953-55 Front	16	122
1953-55 Rear	13	120
Dart 1960-61	15	122
Dodge 1957-61	15	122
1953-56 Front	16	122
1953-56 Rear	13	120
Edsel 1958-60	6	116
Falcon 1960-61	5	115

Car & Model	Brake Type	Page
Ford 1961	6	116
1956-60	3	114
1954-55 Rear	2	113
1955 Front	10	118
1954 Front	9	118
1953	2	113
Hudson 1955-57	3	114
1953-54 Jet	12	120
1953-54 (ex. Jet)	2	113
Lancer 1961	4	114
Lincoln 1956-61	3	114
1954-55 Front	9	118
1954-55 Rear	2	113
1953	2	113
Mercury 1958-61	6	116
1956-57	3	114
1954-55 Front	8	117
1954-55 Rear	2	113
1953	2	113
Nash 1955-57 Amb.	3	114
1954-56 Statesman	12	120
1953-55 Others	2	113
Oldsmobile 1959-61	3	114
1953-58	1	113

Car & Model	Brake Type	Page
Oldsmobile F-85, 1961		
Packard 1955-58	3	114
1953-54	1	113
Plymouth 1957-61	15	122
1953-56 Front	16	122
1953-56 Rear	13	120
Pontiac 1953-61	1	113
Pontiac Tempest 1961	4	114
Rambler 1958-61 Amb.	3	114
1960-61 American	5	115
1959 Six-cyl	11	119
1958-59 American	12	120
1958-60 V8 (some)	6	116
1957-58 Six-cyl (late)	12	120
1953-57 (early)	11	119
Studebaker 1954-61	12	120
1953	14	120
Thunderbird 1961		
1956-60	3	114
1955 Rear	2	113
1955 Front	10	118
Valiant 1960-61	4	114
Willys 1953-61	11	119

Brake Adjustments

TYPE ONE

Bendix Brake With Adjustable Eccentric Anchor

This type of brake, Fig. 1, has an eccentric anchor pin which can be turned to raise or lower the brake assembly in the drum for proper centralization. The end of the anchor pin on the backing plate side is bevelled to indicate the low side of the eccentric. If at any time the anchor is removed, reinstall it so the high point of the eccentric is toward the rear of the car, Fig. 2. This should put the anchor at the middle of its adjustment so that turning the anchor in the direction of forward wheel rotation raises the brake assembly in the drum.

Minor Adjustment

1. Jack up car and release parking brake.
2. Check master cylinder push rod adjustment. Allow at least 1/32″ clearance between end of rod and master cylinder piston.
3. Check anchor pin nut with a 16″ wrench to make sure it is tight. Torque to 60-80 ft. lbs. If anchor pin nut is found loose, adjust anchor as outlined below under Major Adjustments.
4. Expand brake shoes by turning star wheel adjuster, moving end of adjusting tool toward the axle as shown in Fig. 3 until wheel and brake drum can just be turned with both hands. Back off adjuster (moving end of tool away from axle) 12 to 14 notches.
5. Make this adjustment at all four wheels. If there is a drag between shoes and drum adjust pin as outlined below.

Major Adjustment

NOTE—The anchor pin must always be adjusted after each brake reline. Failure to do so may cause erratic brake action, noise, low pedal or rapid wear.

1. Disconnect each parking brake cable at the cross shaft by removing the clevis pins. If cables are sticking or frozen, free and lubricate them, or replace them if necessary.
2. With drum and wheel in position, expand brake shoes by turning star wheel adjuster until a slight to medium drag is felt when turning the wheel by hand.
3. Loosen anchor pin lock nut at least one-half turn. Slowly rotate anchor in the direction of forward wheel rotation until point of least drag is reached.
4. Hold anchor pin securely and tighten lock nut to 60-80 ft. lbs. torque.
5. Take up on star wheel adjuster until the wheel can just barely be turned, using both hands. Then back off adjuster 12 to 14 notches.
6. Make this adjustment at all four wheels.

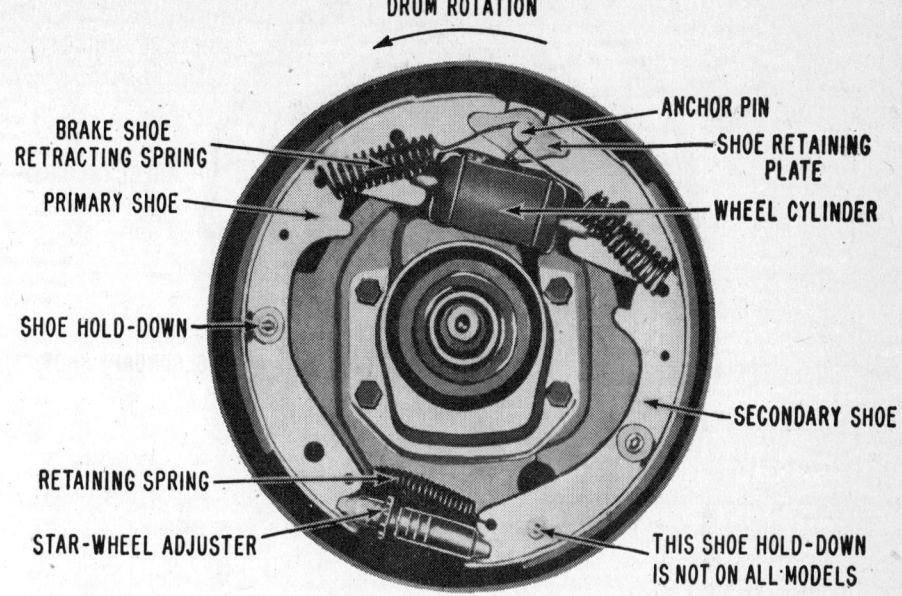

Fig. 1 Bendix brake (Type 1) with adjustable eccentric type anchor

Parking Brake Adjust

Adjust parking brake cables by removing all slack or sag in cables *being careful not to shorten cables to the extent where brake shoes are forced away from the anchor pin.* Rear wheels should turn freely after making a cable adjustment.

TYPE TWO

Bendix Brake With Adjustable Sliding Anchor

This brake, Fig. 4, has a slot in the backing plate to permit centralization of the brake shoes by sliding the anchor pin radially. *The Minor Adjustments are the same as outlined for Type One brakes.* Because of the different anchor arrangement the major adjustments differ.

Major Adjustments

1. Disconnect parking brake cables at cross shaft by removing clevis pins.
2. With drum and wheel in position, loosen anchor pin nut one full turn so that anchor pin can shift in the elongated hole in the backing plate.
3. Turn star wheel adjuster, Fig. 3, until a heavy drag is felt on the drum when attempting to turn the wheel with both hands.
4. Tap anchor pin and backing plate with an 8-oz. ball peen hammer to allow shoes to center in drum. If drag on drum changes, tighten star wheel adjuster and again tap anchor pin and backing plate. Repeat this operation until drag remains constant.

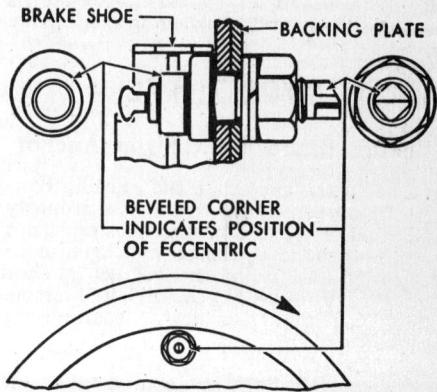

Fig. 2 Eccentric anchor for Type 1 Bendix brake

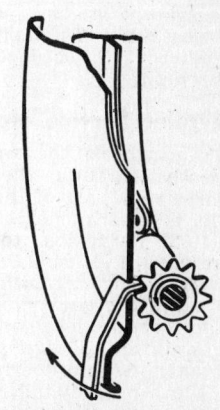

Fig. 3 Turning star wheel adjuster to expand brake shoes

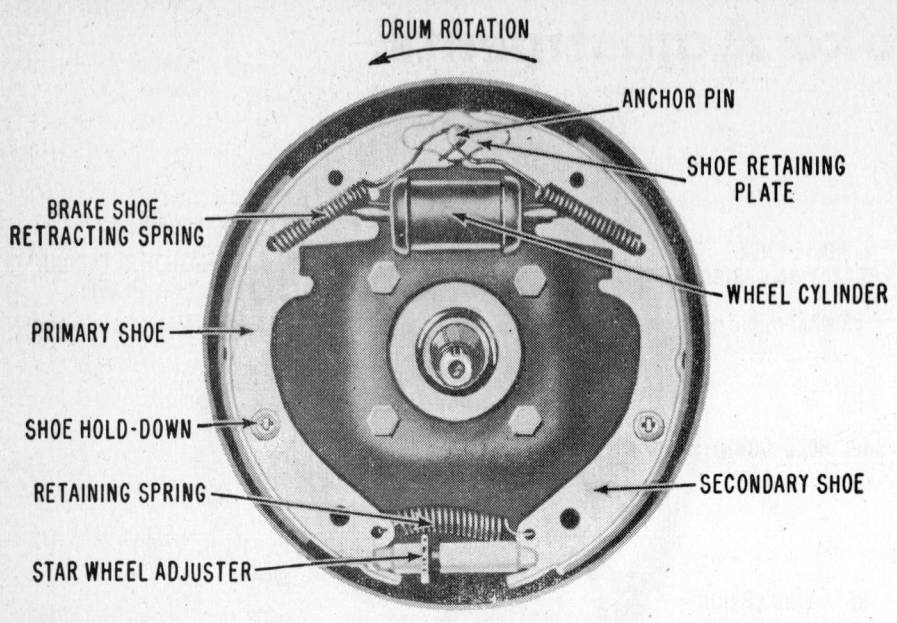

DRUM ROTATION

ANCHOR PIN

SHOE RETAINING PLATE

BRAKE SHOE RETRACTING SPRING

WHEEL CYLINDER

PRIMARY SHOE

SHOE HOLD-DOWN

SECONDARY SHOE

RETAINING SPRING

STAR WHEEL ADJUSTER

Fig. 4 Bendix brake (Type 2) with adjustable sliding type anchor

5. Tighten anchor pin nut to 60-80 ft. lbs. torque. Then back off star wheel adjuster 12 to 14 notches.
6. Make this adjustment on all four wheels and adjust parking brake as outlined for *Type One* brakes.

TYPE THREE

Bendix Brake With Fixed Anchor

Due to the fact that the anchors cannot be adjusted and to have a properly adjusted brake, the brake shoes must not only be ground to the correct drum contour but also from the correct anchor location. Failure to do this will cause pulling, grabbing, spongy pedal action or noise.

Care must be exercised if the drums are turned. A light cut can be taken on drums without difficulty but if it is necessary to remove .020" from the drum diameter, it is advisable to turn the drum .050" and use oversize brake shoes.

When proper brake shoes are installed on this type brake, a minor adjustment is all that is necessary. To make the adjustment, follow the procedure outlined for Type One brakes.

Chevrolet Service Note

On the front wheels the anchor bolt screws directly through the backing plate into the upper part of the steering knuckle, Fig. 5. The anchor bolt should be checked to 80-100 ft. lbs. torque each time the brakes are relined. *Be sure the wheel cylinder is parallel with the road before tightening the anchor bolt as the wheel cylinder casting does not have any dowel pins for locating purposes.* Loose anchors or anchors improperly torqued will allow the wheel cylinder to shift during brake application resulting in erratic action.

On the rear wheels the fixed anchor is bolted directly to the backing plate

and should be torqued to 60-80 ft. lbs.

Chevrolet since 1957 have used retracting springs of two different tensions on front brakes. The springs are painted different colors in order to distinguish them. The primary brake shoe retracting spring is painted gray and has a 40-lb. tension. The secondary retracting spring is painted black and has a 50-lb. tension. The retracting springs are properly installed when the gray or primary spring is attached first, followed by the black or secondary spring. Regardless of the type of springs, always install the primary shoe retracting spring first, followed by the secondary spring. If this is not done, erratic brake action will result.

Ford & Mercury Service Notes

On the front wheels of 1956 Ford and Mercury, the fixed anchor is bolted directly to the backing plate and the anchor nut should be torqued to 60-80 ft. lbs.

On Ford and Mercury after 1956, the front wheel brake assembly is basically the same as that used on 1956 models. However, to insure added strength to the non-adjustable anchor pin and backing plate assembly, the anchor pin is secured to the steering knuckle. The anchor pin also secures the front wheel cylinder to the backing plate.

To reduce the possibility of erratic brake action on this brake system, it is important to torque the following items:
1. Upper arm ball joint 60-80 ft. lbs.
2. Lower arm ball joint 70-90 ft. lbs.
3. Spindle bolt 70-90 ft. lbs.
4. Anchor nut 80-100 ft. lbs.

If upper and lower ball joints show any signs of looseness after they are torqued, replace both ball joints. Failure to do this will result in erratic brake action.

Ford 1960 Service Note

For standardization and interchange-

ability, the adjusting slot in the left rear carrier plate is located rearward of the vertical centerline instead of forward of the centerline. *This change reverses the position of the adjusting screw and also reverses the adjusting screw rotation for the left rear wheel only.*

Helper Springs

Ford, Lincoln and Mercury cars since 1957 have used a helper spring attached to the bottom of both brake shoe retracting springs in the front brakes only, Fig. 5. This spring encourages a more positive release of the brake shoes, and also allows the brake shoes to hold a better released position. *Never discard these helper springs.*

Swedged Type Anchor

As shown in Fig. 5, this type anchor (when used) is pressed through the backing plate and swedged. If this anchor is ever found to be loose, replace the complete backing plate and anchor as an assembly. Do not attempt to weld the anchor pin to the backing plate.

Parking Brake Adjust

Follow the procedure for adjusting the parking brake as outlined for *Type One* brake.

TYPE FOUR

Bendix Brake With Fixed Anchor

As shown in Fig. 6, the anchor pins in the front brakes secure and position the wheel cylinders to the backing plates and screw into the steering knuckle in back of the backing plate. The anchor pins in the rear brakes are secured to the backing plates by means of a lock nut and washer on the back side of the backing plate. When servicing or relining these brakes, torque all anchor pin nuts to 60-80 ft. lbs.

Due to the fact that the anchors cannot be adjusted, and to have a properly adjusted brake, the brake shoes must not only be ground to the correct drum contour but also from the correct anchor location.

The diameter of the anchor pins is 5/8", which is smaller than other Bendix type anchor pins and a special grinding fixture is required in order to grind the lined brake shoes for proper lining and brake drum contact.

Brake Adjustments

Because of the fixed anchor design no major brake adjustment is required after relining.
1. Jack up car and release hand brake.
2. Check master cylinder push rod adjustment, allowing at least $\frac{3}{32}$" clearance between end of push rod and master cylinder piston. Lubricate pedal linkage.
3. Expand brake shoes by turning star wheel adjuster, moving tool toward axle until wheel and brake drum can just be turned with both hands. Then back off adjuster 10 to 12 notches. Make this adjustment on all four wheels.

The front brakes on Corvair and

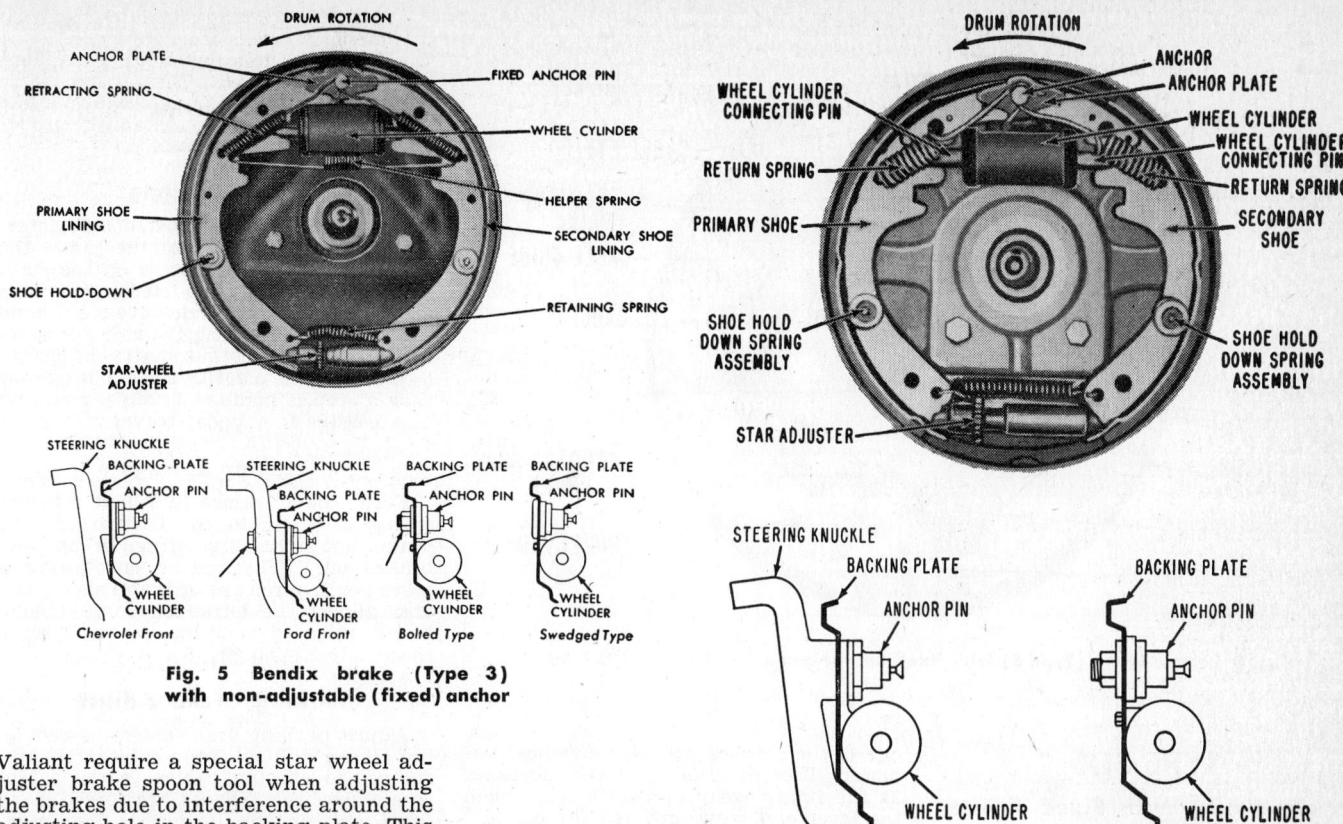

Fig. 5 Bendix brake (Type 3) with non-adjustable (fixed) anchor

Fig. 6 Bendix brake (Type 4) with fixed anchor used on Corvair

Valiant require a special star wheel adjuster brake spoon tool when adjusting the brakes due to interference around the adjusting hole in the backing plate. This special tool has the proper radius and angle and must be used from an off-center angle when turning the star wheel.

Parking Brake Adjust

Adjust parking brake cables by removing all slack or sag in the cables, *being careful not to shorten cables to the extent where the brake shoes are* *forced away from the anchor pin seat.* Be sure to free up or replace any sticking cable. Rear wheels should turn freely after making a cable adjustment.

TYPE FIVE

Bendix Brake With Fixed Anchor

This type brake has a non-adjustable swedged type anchor, Fig. 7. The anchor pin is pressed through the backing plate and swedged. If this anchor is ever found to be loose, replace the complete backing plate and anchor as an assembly. Do not attempt to weld the anchor pin to the backing plate.

Since the anchors cannot be adjusted, a properly adjusted brake requires that the brake shoes must not only be ground to the correct drum contour but also from the correct anchor location.

The diameter of the anchor pins is 11/16" which is smaller than anchor pins used on larger cars, and requires a special grinding fixture in order to grind the lined shoes for proper lining to drum contact.

A new type brake shoe hold-down spring is used at the center of the brake shoe webs. The springs are located between the backing plates and shoe web and require a special tool for removing and installing in order to prevent damaging the spring.

Brake Adjustments

Since the anchors cannot be adjusted, no major adjustment is required. To adjust the brakes follow the procedure outlined for *Type Four* brakes.

Fig. 7 Bendix brake (Type 5) with fixed anchor. Note that no anchor plate is used

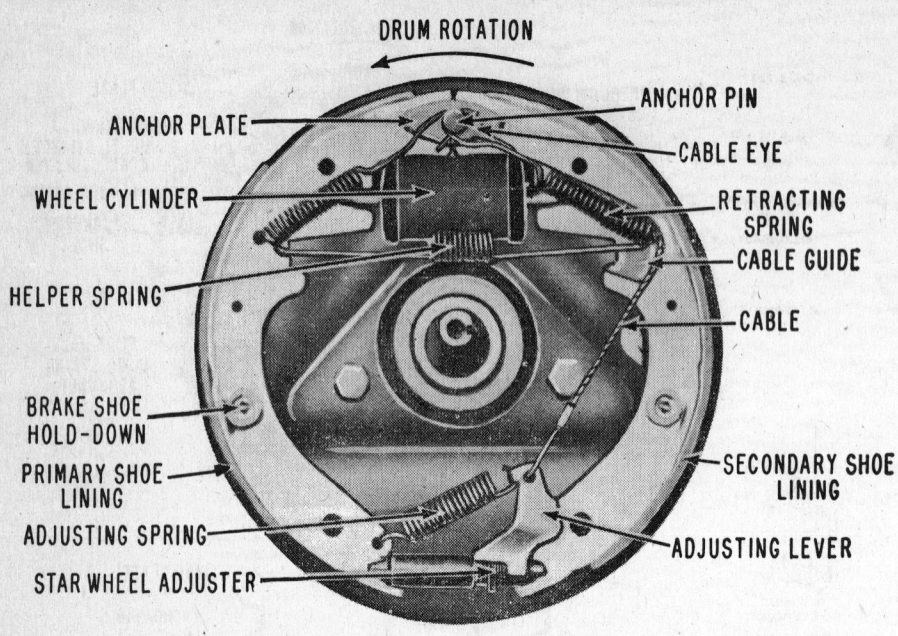

Fig. 8 Bendix brake (Type 6) with fixed anchor and self-adjuster. 1958-59

TYPE SIX

Bendix Brake With Fixed Anchor And Self-Adjuster

In this type brake, Figs. 8 and 9, the self-adjusting mechanism is attached to the secondary brake shoes in all four wheels. The mechanism consists of a cable eye, cable, cable guide which is attached to the secondary shoe, adjusting lever, and spring.

The cable eye is fastened over the anchor pin between the two brake shoe retracting springs. The cable wraps around the cable guide on the secondary brake shoe and continues down to the adjusting lever. The star adjuster spring connects the primary shoe to the adjusting lever instead of to the secondary shoe as in brakes with no automatic adjusters.

The automatic adjusters operate only when the brakes are applied with the car moving in reverse direction, and only if the secondary brake shoe moves away from the anchor toward the brake drum beyond a predetermined point. In other words, whenever the clearance between the lining and drum has increased sufficiently through lining wear to result in excessive travel of the secondary shoe.

The movement of the secondary brake shoe away from the anchor pin allows the cable to pull the adjusting lever in an upward direction against the end of one of the notches on the star wheel adjuster. The travel of the lever increases as the lining wear increases and, when the lever can move upward far enough, it passes over the end of the notch and engages into the next one. When the brakes are released after the car comes to a complete stop, the spring at the star adjuster pulls the adjusting lever in a downward direction, turning the star wheel and expanding the brake shoes.

1960 Mercury Brakes

As shown in Fig. 9, the design, length and location of the primary shoe return springs have been changed. The primary springs are red in color, shorter in length and have larger diameter coils than the secondary springs. This type of spring hook-up helps to prevent raising of the primary shoe in the brake assembly when the brakes are first applied in a forward motion for smoother brake application.

Brake Adjustments

The only adjustments on this type of brake system are made at the star wheel adjusters after installing new brake linings.

1. Jack up car and release parking brake.
2. Check master cylinder push rod adjustment, allowing at least $\frac{1}{32}$" clearance between end of rod and master cylinder piston. Lubricate pedal linkage.
3. Expand brake shoes by turning star wheel adjuster, moving handle of adjusting tool *toward the floor*. Continue to turn star wheel until there is a heavy drag when turning the wheel and drum with both hands.
4. Insert a small screwdriver or ice pick through the star wheel adjusting hole and raise the adjusting lever away from the star wheel. Back off 16 notches on the star wheel adjuster with the adjusting tool, moving the handle of the tool upward.
5. Complete the adjustment by making enough stops with the car moving in reverse to allow the automatic brake shoe adjusters to establish proper lining-to-drum clearance.

Star Adjusters

The star adjusters must not be interchanged from one side of the car to the other as the star adjusters on the right side of the vehicle have left hand threads and those on the left side have right hand threads. Interchanging the star adjusters would cause the automatic adjusting levers to back off the assemblies every time a stop is made in reverse, resulting in excessive foot pedal travel.

Helper Springs

Ford products since 1957 have a helper spring attached to the bottom of both brake shoe retracting springs in the front brakes only. This spring encourages a more positive release of brake shoes, and also allows the brake shoes to hold a better released position. Never discard these helper springs.

Parking Brake Adjust

Adjust parking brake cables by removing all sag or slack from cables. Be careful not to shorten cables to the extent where the brakes shoes are forced away from their anchor. Be sure to free or replace any sticking cable. Rear wheels should turn freely after making a cable adjustment.

TYPE SEVEN

Bendix Brake With Two Point Adjustable Anchor

This type of brake, Figs. 10 and 11, has a two point solid forged anchor assembly which pivots as a unit to raise or lower the brake assembly in the drum. As shown in Fig. 11, bolt "B" acts as the pivot point, permitting bolt "A" to move up or down in an elongated hole in the backing plate. The nuts on both bolts must be loosened to adjust this type of anchor.

Minor Adjustments

1. Jack up car and release parking brake.
2. Check master cylinder push rod adjustment, allowing at least 1/32" clearance between end of push rod and master cylinder piston.
3. Check both anchor pin nuts with a 16" wrench to make sure they are tight. Torque to 60-80 ft. lbs. If an anchor pin nut is found loose, adjust anchor as outlined below under Major Adjustments.
4. Remove front wheels from their hubs and revolve brake drum until adjusting hole in drum is opposite the star wheel adjuster at the bottom of the brake assembly. Inserts the adjusting tool through the hole in the drum and contact the star wheel with the adjusting tool. Move the handle of the tool *downward* to expand the brake shoes. Continue to turn the star wheel

Fig. 9 Bendix brake (Type 6) with fixed anchor and self-adjuster. 1960-61

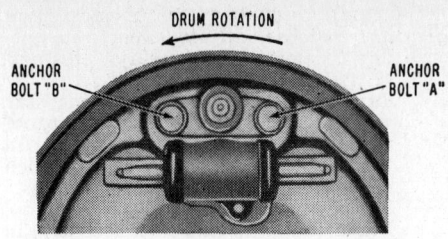

Fig. 11 Two point adjustable anchor used with Types 7 and 8 brakes

until there is a heavy drag on the drum then back off the star wheel 14 to 16 notches. The brake drum should now be absolutely free. If the drum does not spin freely, it may be out of round or the anchor only may be in need of adjustment. Adjust anchor as outlined below.

5. Adjust rear wheels through the backing plate by turning the star wheel adjuster, moving the adjusting tool *upward* until wheel and brake drum can just be turned with both hands. Then back off the adjuster 14 to 16 notches. Wheel and drum should then turn freely. If there is a drag, adjust anchor pin.

Major Adjustment For Front Wheels

NOTE—For rear wheels, refer to "Type Two" Adjustable Sliding Anchor.

1. For front wheels, with drum on and wheel off, loosen both anchor nuts, Fig. 11, so anchor unit can shift in the elongated hole in backing plate.
2. Insert star wheel adjusting tool through hole in drum and expand brake shoes by moving handle of tool *downward*.
3. Expand shoes until a heavy drag is felt on the drum when attempting to turn it with both hands.
4. Tap anchor pin "A" and the backing

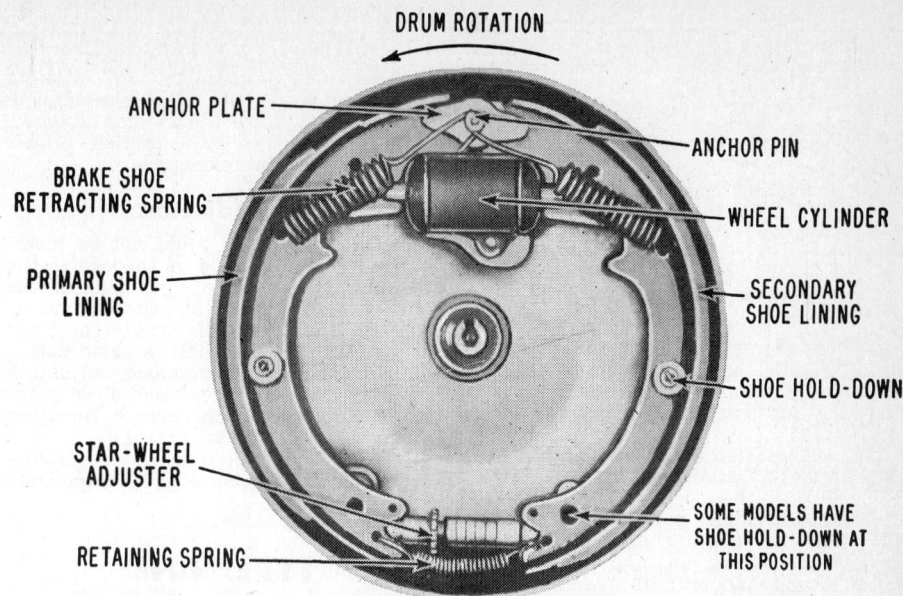

Fig. 10 Bendix brake (Type 7) with two point adjustable anchor

plate with a small ball-peen hammer to allow shoes to center in the drum. If the drag on the drum changes, tighten the star wheel adjuster and again tap anchor pin and backing plate. Repeat this operation until drag remains constant. Tighten anchor pin nut to 60-80 ft. lbs. torque. Then back off star wheel adjuster 14 to 16 notches.

Parking Brake Adjust

Adjust parking brake cables by removing all sag or slack. Be careful not to shorten cables to the extent where the brake shoes are forced away from the anchor pin seat. Free up or replace any sticking cable. Rear wheels should turn freely after making a cable adjustment.

TYPE EIGHT

Bendix Brake With Two Point Adjustable Anchor and Self-Adjuster

This type brake, Fig. 12, is used on the front wheels while the rear wheels use the "Type Two" brake with the adjustable sliding type anchor plus the same type of automatic brake shoe adjuster.

The automatic adjuster mechanism consists of a link, actuating lever, pawl and pawl return spring. The looped end of the link is attached to the anchor pin, and the hooked end to the actuating lever. The actuating lever is held against the secondary brake shoe by means of hold-down cup and spring assembly. The pawl is connected to the actuating lever and held in position by the pawl return spring.

The automatic adjusters operate only when the brakes are applied with the car moving in reverse direction. The wrapping action of the brake shoes following the drum forces the upper end of the primary shoe against the anchor pin and the secondary shoe away from the anchor pin.

The link holds the top of the actuating lever stationary thus forcing the lever to pivot on the secondary shoe hold-down pin. The pivoting action forces the pawl downward against the end of a tooth on the star wheel.

If the lining-to-drum clearance is normal, the downward movement of the pawl will stop before the star wheel is turned. But if the lining-to-drum clearance becomes greater due to wear, the secondary shoe will travel further and the pawl will move downward far enough to turn the star wheel one notch and decrease lining-to-drum clearance.

With the car moving forward when brakes are applied, the self-adjuster will not operate because the wrapping action of the brake shoe forces the secondary shoe and not the primary shoe against the anchor pin.

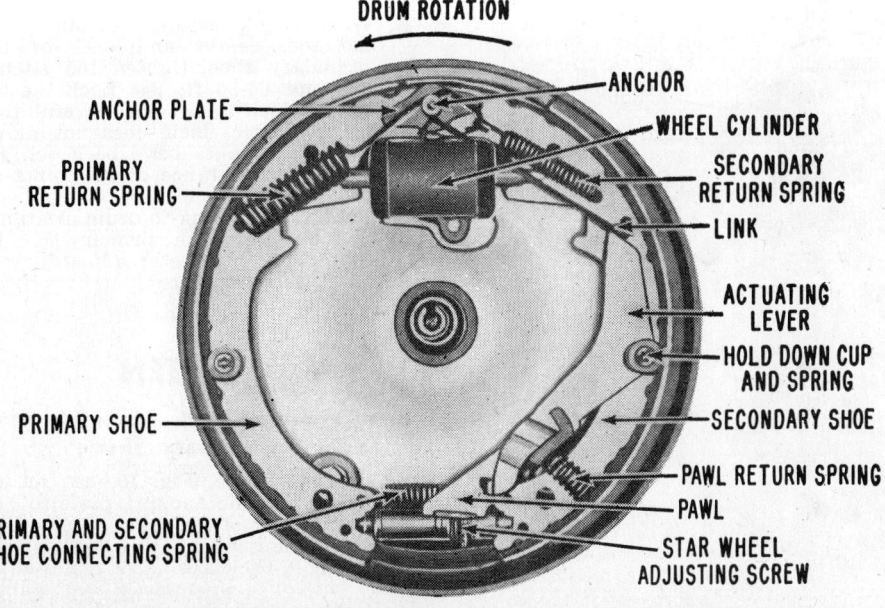

Fig. 12 Bendix brake (Type 8) with two point adjustable anchor and self-adjuster

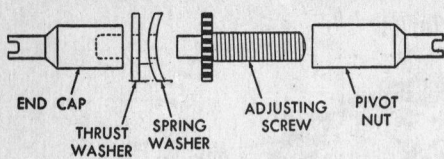

END CAP
THRUST WASHER
SPRING WASHER
ADJUSTING SCREW
PIVOT NUT

Fig. 13 Star wheel adjuster for Type 8 brake; also used on some Type 7 brakes

Brake Adjustments

The only adjustments required on this type of brake system are made after installing new brake lining or if the anchors are found to be loose.

1. Jack up car and release parking brake.
2. Check master cylinder push rod adjustment, allowing at least $\frac{1}{32}$" clearance between end of rod and master cylinder piston.
3. *For Front Brake Only:*
   a. With drum on and wheel off, loosen anchor nuts "A" and "B" (see Fig. 11) so anchor unit can shift in the elongated hole in the backing plate.
   b. Insert star wheel adjusting tool through hole in brake drum and expand brake shoes by moving handle of tool *upward.* Continue to turn star wheel until there is a heavy drag when turning the drum with both hands.
   c. Tap anchor pin "A" and backing plate with a small ball-peen hammer to allow shoes to center in the drum. If the drag on the drum changes, tighten the star wheel and again tap anchor pin and backing plate. Repeat this operation until the drag remains constant. Tighten anchor pin nut to 60-80 ft. lbs. torque. Then back off star wheel 14 to 16 notches.
4. *For Rear Brakes Only:* Use Major Adjustment procedure outlined for

"Type Two" brake. However, be sure to move star wheel adjusting tool downward to expand shoes.
5. Complete adjustment by making enough stops with the car moving in reverse to allow the automatic brake shoe adjusters to establish proper lining-to-drum clearance.

Star Adjusters

The star adjusters must not be interchanged from one side of the car to the other as those on the right side of the vehicle have left hand threads while those on the left side have right hand threads. Interchanging the star adjusters would cause the automatic adjusting levers to *back off* the assemblies every time a stop is made in reverse, resulting in excessive foot pedal travel.

Care must be taken when assembling star adjusters to have the components as shown in Fig. 13.

TYPE NINE

Bendix Brake With Eccentric Stop On Secondary Shoe

The front brake assemblies are rotated about three inches toward the rear of the car as shown in Fig. 14. A short return spring and an eccentric adjuster are added to the brake assembly to prevent the secondary shoes from dragging when released.

Minor Adjustments

(For rear wheels follow procedue outlined for "Type Two" brakes.)

1. Jack up car.
2. Check master cylinder push rod adjustment, allowing at least $\frac{1}{32}$" clearance between end of rod and master cylinder piston.
3. Check anchor pin nut with a 16" wrench to make sure it is tight.

Torque to 60-80 ft. lbs. If anchor pin nut is loose, adjust anchor as outlined below under "Major Adjustments".
4. Expand brake shoes by turning star wheel adjuster, moving handle of tool upward until the brake drum can just be turned with both hands. Then back off adjuster 12 to 14 notches.
5. Loosen lock nut on eccentric stop, Fig. 14, slightly and turn eccentric in direction of forward wheel rotation until a drag is felt on the wheel; then back off the eccentric in the opposite direction until the wheel is free. At this point, hold the eccentric with a suitable wrench and tighten lock nut, being sure eccentric does not turn while tightening lock nut.
6. If a minor adjustment is made with the wheel off and the drum on, insert a .010" feeler gauge through the slot in the brake drum and adjust the eccentric to allow .010" clearance between lining and drum at the center of the secondary brake shoe. Obtain .010" clearance at the center of the primary shoe by taking up on the star adjuster.

Note—The eccentric stop on 1955 Lincoln and Mercury does not have a lock nut; instead the eccentric is spring loaded. However, the adjustment procedure remains the same.

Major Adjustments

(For rear brakes, follow procedure outlined for "Type Two" brake.)

1. With drum on and wheel off, loosen eccentric lock nut and anchor lock nut. *Do not over-loosen anchor lock nut as anchor will tilt in backing plate and adjustment will change when nut is tightened.*
2. Obtain .010" lining-to-drum clearance at the center of the secondary shoe by turning the eccentric in the direction of forward wheel rotation.
3. Obtain .010" lining-to-drum clearance at the heel and toe ends of the secondary shoe by tapping the anchor pin up or down with a small ball-peen hammer.
4. When .010" clearance is obtained at the toe, center and heel of the secondary shoe, tighten the anchor lock nut 60-80 ft. lbs. Lock the eccentric lock nut, being careful that the eccentric itself does not move. After both nuts have been set, re-check the clearance at all points on the secondary shoe.
5. Obtain .010" lining-to-drum clearance at the center of the primary shoe by taking up on the star adjuster.
6. Make this adjustment at both front wheels.

TYPE TEN

Bendix Brake With Eccentric Stop On Primary Shoe

This type brake, Fig. 15, has an eccentric stop in the backing plate to ride against the web of the primary shoe. The primary shoe rests on the eccentric stop and no hold-back spring is required on either shoe. The assembly is held against the stop by its own weight.

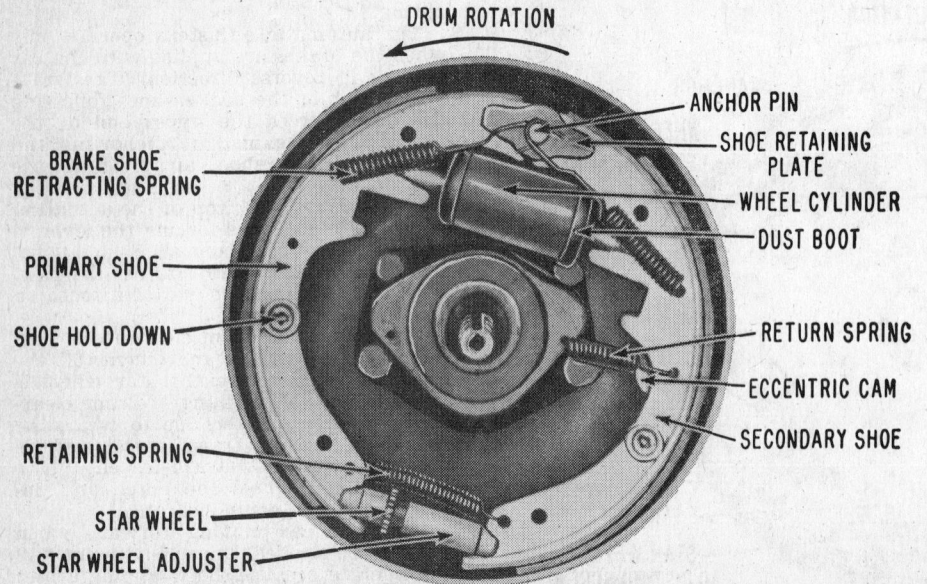

DRUM ROTATION

BRAKE SHOE RETRACTING SPRING
PRIMARY SHOE
SHOE HOLD DOWN
RETAINING SPRING
STAR WHEEL
STAR WHEEL ADJUSTER
ANCHOR PIN
SHOE RETAINING PLATE
WHEEL CYLINDER
DUST BOOT
RETURN SPRING
ECCENTRIC CAM
SECONDARY SHOE

Fig. 14 Bendix brake (Type 9) with eccentric stop on secondary shoe

Minor Adjustments

(For rear brakes, follow procedure outlined for "Type Two" brake.)

1. Jack up car.
2. Check master cylinder push rod adjustment, allowing at least $\frac{3}{32}$" clearance between end of rod and master cylinder piston.
3. Check anchor pin nut with a 16" wrench. If loose, adjust anchor as outlined below under "Major Adjustments". Torque anchor nut to 60-80 ft. lbs.
4. Expand brake shoes by turning star wheel adjuster, moving handle of adjusting tool upward until wheel and brake drum can just be turned with both hands. Then back off adjuster 12 to 14 notches.
5. Turn primary shoe eccentric in the direction of forward wheel rotation until a drag is felt on the brake drum. Back off eccentric until wheel is free. Being spring loaded, the eccentric does not have a lock nut.
6. Make this adjustment at both front wheels.

Major Adjustments

(For rear brakes, follow procedure outlined for "Type Two" brake.)

1. With drum and wheel in position, loosen anchor pin nut one full turn so that the pin can shift in the elongated hole in the backing plate.
2. Turn the star wheel adjuster until a heavy drag is felt on the drum when attempting to turn the wheel with both hands.
3. Tap the anchor pin and backing plate with a small hammer to allow the shoes to center in the drum. If the drag on the drum changes, tighten the star wheel adjuster and again tap the anchor pin and backing plate. Repeat this operation until the drag remains constant. Tighten anchor pin nut to 60-80 ft. lbs. Then back off star wheel adjuster 12 to 14 notches.
4. Turn primary shoe eccentric in the direction of forward wheel rotation until a drag is felt on the brake drum. Then back off eccentric until wheel is free.
5. Make this adjustment on both front wheels.

TYPE ELEVEN

Bendix Brake With Self-Centering Shoes

With this brake, Fig. 16, the brake shoes are held in position by a brake shoe retracting spring and hold-down clips. A retaining spring holds both brake shoes against the abutment block or anchor assembly at the heel ends of the shoes. Brake shoe adjusting cams are used to obtain proper lining-to-drum clearance.

When the brakes are applied with the car moving forward, the shoe contacts the drum and is wrapped into it. The anchor end of the shoe slides along the abutment block in the anchor assembly. The reverse shoe is also self-centering but contributes very little braking action when the car is moving forward.

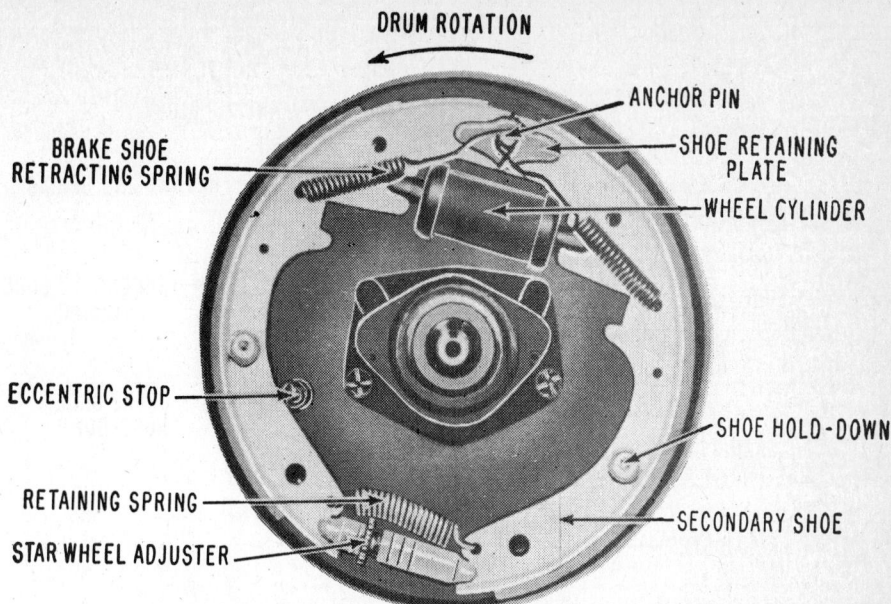

Fig. 15 Bendix brake (Type 10) with eccentric stop on primary shoe

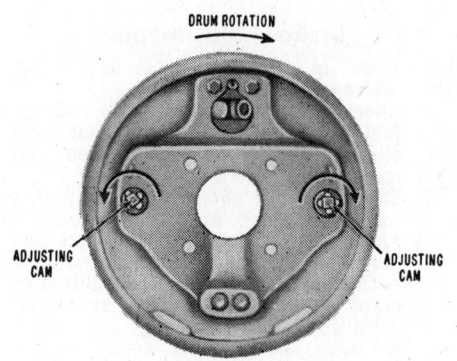

Fig. 17 Type 11 brakes are adjusted by turning cams in directions indicated

Brake Adjustments

Because of the self-centering feature, only minor adjustments are required on this type brake.

1. Jack up car and release parking brake.
2. Check master cylinder push rod clearance, allowing at least $\frac{3}{32}$" clearance between end of rod and master cylinder piston.
3. Expand brake shoes by turning adjusting cams, Fig. 17. If adjustment cams have lock nuts, loosen them. Spin the wheel while turning the adjusting cams until a heavy drag is present and then back off gradually until the wheel is free to turn. Make this adjustment on all four wheels.

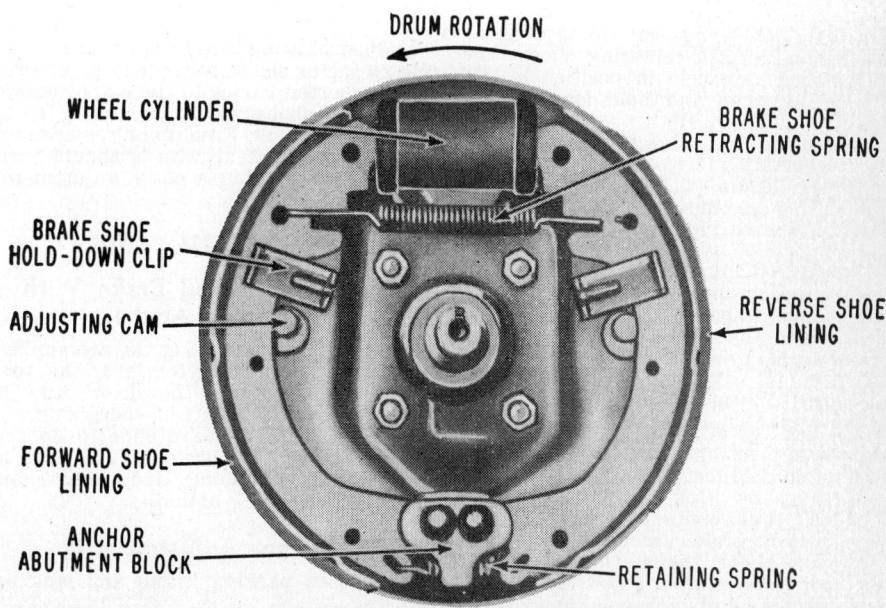

Fig. 16 Bendix brake (Type 11) with self-centering shoes

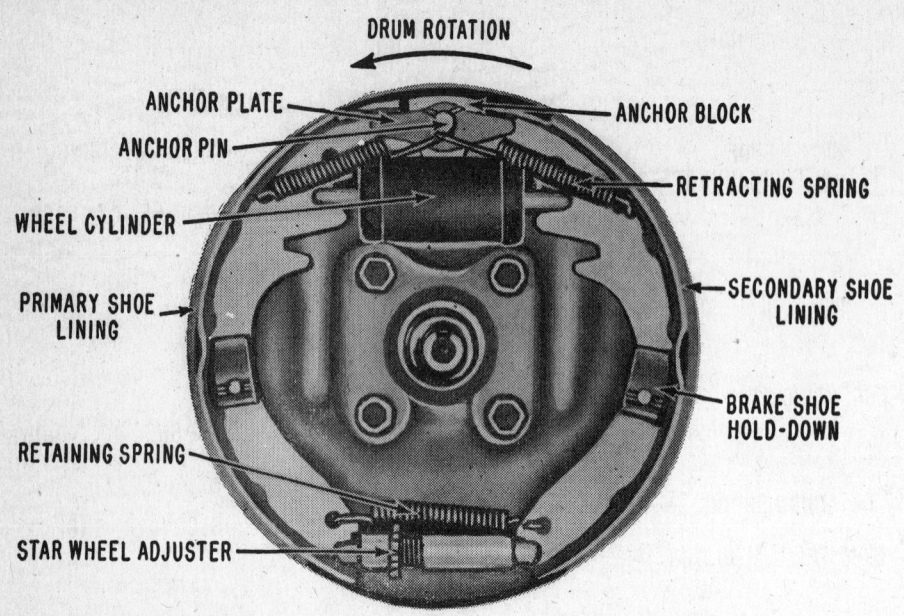

Fig. 18 Wagner brake (Type 12) with self-centering shoes

4. Apply the brake pedal firmly a few times and check all wheels to be sure all wheels can turn freely. If drag is present, readjust as necessary.

Parking Brake Adjust

Adjust parking brake cables by removing all sag or slack. Be careful not to shorten cables to the extent where the brake shoes are forced away from the adjusting cams. Rear wheels should turn freely after making cable adjustment.

TYPE TWELVE

Wagner Brake With Self-Centering Shoes

This brake system, Figs. 18 and 19, is similar to the Bendix type, the outstanding difference being that the type under discussion has self-centering shoes. The brake shoes are held in position by retracting springs and hold-down spring clips.

When the brake is applied, the entire shoe assembly moves as a unit against the brake drum. The braking force is transferred from the primary shoe through the star wheel adjuster to the secondary shoe which, in turn, is pushed against the anchor block. The toe end of the secondary shoe slides along the keystone-shaped anchor block, Fig. 19, and centralizes the shoe assembly in the brake drum.

Anchor Block

The self-centering anchor block must be free to pivot on the stationary anchor pin. Be sure to install it with the curved side (arrow on block) facing the front of the car, thus contacting the primary shoe in each brake assembly.

Always check the stationary anchor pin for looseness; if loose, the entire backing plate and anchor assembly must be replaced.

Brake Adjustments

1. Jack up car and release parking brake.
2. Check master cylinder push rod adjustment, allowing at least $\frac{1}{32}''$ clearance between end of rod and master cylinder piston.
3. Expand brake shoes by turning star wheel adjuster, moving end of adjusting tool upward until wheel and brake drum can just be turned with both hands. Then back off adjuster eight notches. If brake drag is not released after backing off eight notches, apply brake pedal several times to centralize brake shoes in the drum and readjust as necessary.
4. Make this adjustment on all four wheels.

Parking Brake Adjust

Adjust parking brake cables by removing all sag or slack from them. Be careful not to shorten cables to the extent where the brake shoes are forced away from the anchor block. Free up or replace any sticking cable. Rear wheels should turn freely after making a cable adjustment.

TYPE THIRTEEN

Wagner Lockheed Brake With Adjustable Anchors

When these brakes, Fig. 20, are applied with the car moving forward, the forward shoe contacts the drum and is wrapped into it. This self-energizing action causes the forward shoe to do the major share of the braking. The reverse shoe is non-wrapping and contributes very little braking action.

Minor Adjustment

1. Release parking brake and jack up car.
2. Check master cylinder push rod ad-

justment allowing at least $\frac{1}{32}''$ clearance between end of rod and master cylinder piston.
3. Expand brake shoes by turning adjusting cams in the directions indicated in Fig. 21. Spin wheel while turning adjusting cam until a heavy drag is reached, then back off the cam gradually in the opposite direction until the wheel turns freely. Make this adjustment to each brake shoe at all wheels which have this type of brake.

Major Adjustment

The anchor pins must be adjusted after each reline of brakes of this type. A spindle grinder or a brake anchor gauge must be used to obtain correct lining-to-drum clearance when making a major adjustment.

1. With drums and wheels removed, measure the brake drum diameter. Set the spindle grinder to .030" under the drum diameter; if brake gauge is used, set the gauge radius to exactly ½ actual drum diameter.
2. Install spindle grinder or the anchor gauge on the axle.
3. Back off adjusting cams.
4. Check arrows on anchor pins for proper position; they should be facing one another before starting an adjustment.
5. Adjust the cams until center of brake shoes are just touching the anchor gauge pin or sanding disc.
6. If using an anchor gauge, adjust anchor pins until .007" clearance is obtained at toe and heel ends of each shoe. If using a spindle grinder, grind the lining until the sanding disc touches all points of the lining surface.
7. Perform the above operations on all wheels having this type of brake.

Parking Brake

Transmission-mounted parking brake adjustments are covered elsewhere in this chapter (see "Index").

TYPE FOURTEEN

Wagner Self-Centering, Self-Adjusting Brake

This brake assembly, Fig. 22, incorporates two automatic features: the self-centering anchor and the self-adjusting forward brake shoe.

Constant lining-to-drum clearance is maintained on the forward brake shoe by the use of a contact plug which extends through a hole in the shoe and lining, Fig. 23. As the lining wears, the plug is

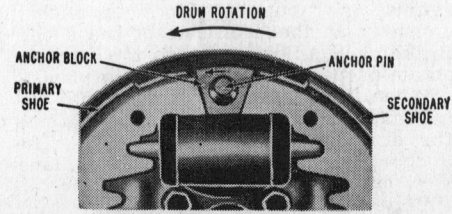

Fig. 19 Details of anchor block for Type 12 brake

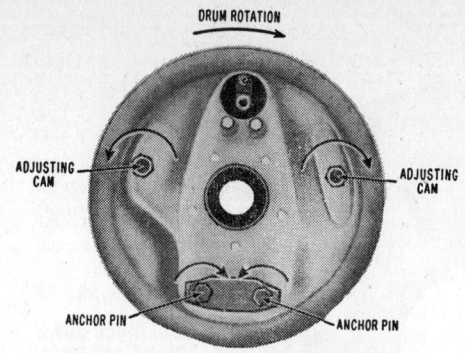

Fig. 21 Type 13 brakes are adjusted by turning cams and anchor pins in directions indicated

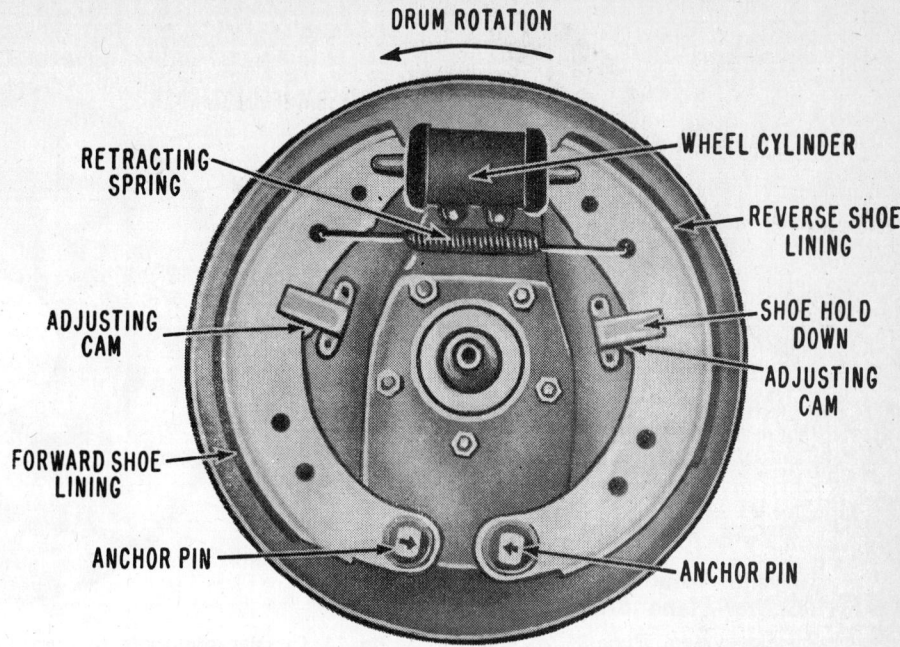

Fig. 20 Wagner-Lockheed brake (Type 13) with adjustable anchors

pushed into the adjusting mechanism which operates a sliding wedge, bringing the shoe and lining closer to the brake drum. The automatic adjusting device will keep the forward shoe in proper adjustment until the lining is worn down to the rivets. Beyond this point, adjustments would have to be made manually (for example, in the case of bonded-on lining).

When the brakes are applied with the car moving forward, the anchor ends of the shoes slide along the abutment block in the anchor assembly and the shoes are thus centered in the brake drum. The forward brake shoe is self-energizing and does about 70% of the braking.

Inspecting Self-Adjusting Device

Exert light pressure on the contact plug and completely retract adjusting wedge, Fig. 23, Remove pressure on contact plug, thus allowing the locking device to hold the wedge in position. Push inward on contact plug, noting whether adjusting wedge advances.

To test contact plug spring pressure, fully retract adjusting wedge, hold and apply inward pressure on contact plug, releasing at intervals to see if spring is operating correctly and returning the plug outward.

When relined shoes are ready to be installed on the car, make sure that the adjusting wedge is in fully retracted position. When the wedge is in this position, the contact plug should be level to .005" (the thickness of an ordinary piece of wrapping paper) above the lining. If the contact plug is more than .005" above the level of the lining, filing is recommended.

Brake Adjustments

Because of the self-adjusting feature of this brake, manual adjustments only have to be made after installing new brake lining.

1. Release parking brake.
2. Check master cylinder push rod adjustment, allowing at least $\frac{1}{32}$" clearance between end of rod and master cylinder piston.
3. With brake drum and wheels in place, place proper wrench on cam adjuster and expand shoes by moving wrench downward until there is a decided drag, then back off until

the wheel turns freely. *In order that the shoes be centralized, the drums must be rotated forward while adjusting the forward shoe and rotated backward while adjusting the reverse shoe.* Repeat procedure on all four wheels.

4. Apply brake pedal firmly several times and repeat procedure outlined above. Make sure wheel turns freely after completing adjustment.

Parking Brake Adjust

Adjust parking brake cables by removing all sag or slack in cables. Be careful not to shorten cables to the extent where the brake shoes are forced away from the adjusting cams. Be sure to free any sticking cable. Rear wheels should turn freely after making a cable adjustment.

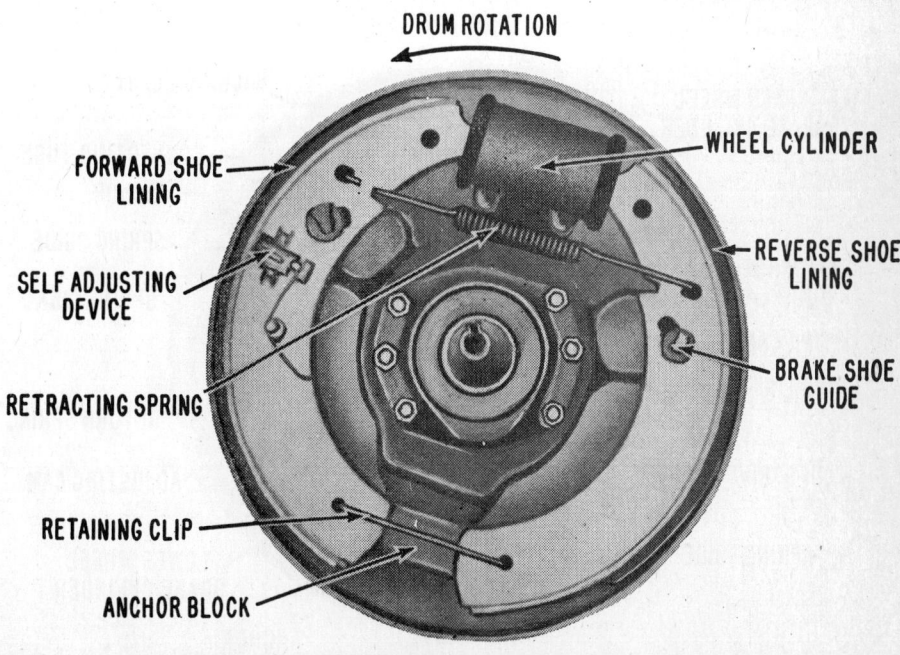

Fig. 22 Wagner self-centering, self-adjusting brake (Type 14)

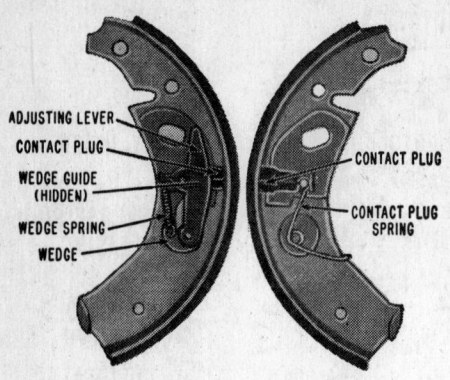

Fig. 23 Details of self-adjusting device on Type 14 brake

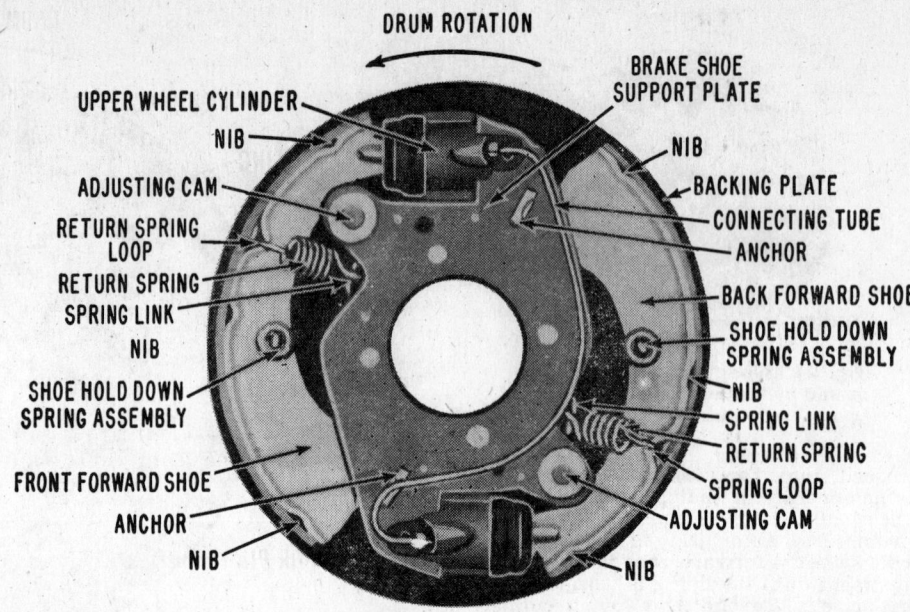

Fig. 25 Chrysler total contact center-plane brake (Type 15). Late 1959, 1960-61

TYPE FIFTEEN

Chrysler Total Contact Center-Plane Brake

In this brake system, Figs. 24, 25, each front brake assembly has two forward acting shoes, while each rear brake assembly has one forward acting shoe and one reverse acting shoe. When the brake is applied with the car moving forward, each forward shoe contacts the drum and is wrapped into it. The reverse acting shoes contribute very little braking work when the car is moving in a forward direction.

Brake Adjustment

When adjusting the front brakes, turn each adjusting cam in the direction of forward wheel rotation, Fig. 26. Turn one cam at a time until the brake shoe locks the wheel. Then turn the cam in the

direction until the wheel is free of any drag. Repeat at all four shoes of the front wheels.

When adjusting the rear brakes, turn the forward shoe adjusting cam in the direction of forward wheel rotation until the brake shoe locks the wheel, then turn the cam in the opposite direction until the wheel turns freely. Make the same adjustment on the reverse shoe.

After completing the adjustment, depress the brake pedal a few times and turn wheels to make sure they are free of drag.

Rear Brake Howl, 1960

A slight brake howl may be encountered at relatively low speeds, particularly on station wagons. If such a condition is encountered it is recommended that rear spring insulators be installed to eliminate this condition. If the insulators fail to correct the brake noise completely it may be necessary to inspect the brakes. Part No. for upper insulator is 1731797, and 1731798 for lower insulator.

TYPE SIXTEEN

Chrysler Lockheed Two Forward Shoe Brake With Two Single-End Wheel Cylinders

In this brake system, Fig. 27, when the brakes are applied with the car moving forward, both brake shoes contact the drum and are wrapped into it. This self-energizing action allows both shoes to do the same amount of braking. The brake shoes are not effective when braking in the reverse direction because the shoes are being applied in the opposite direction of drum rotation.

Minor Adjustment

1. Jack up car.
2. Check master cylinder push rod adjustment, allowing at least $\frac{1}{32}$" clearance between end of rod and master cylinder piston.
3. Expand brake shoes by turning adjusting cams, Fig. 28. Spin the wheel while turning the adjusting cam in the proper direction until a heavy drag is reached; then back the cam off gradually in the opposite direction until the wheel turns freely.
4. Make this adjustment at each brake shoe at both front wheels.

Major Adjustment

A spindle grinder or a brake anchor

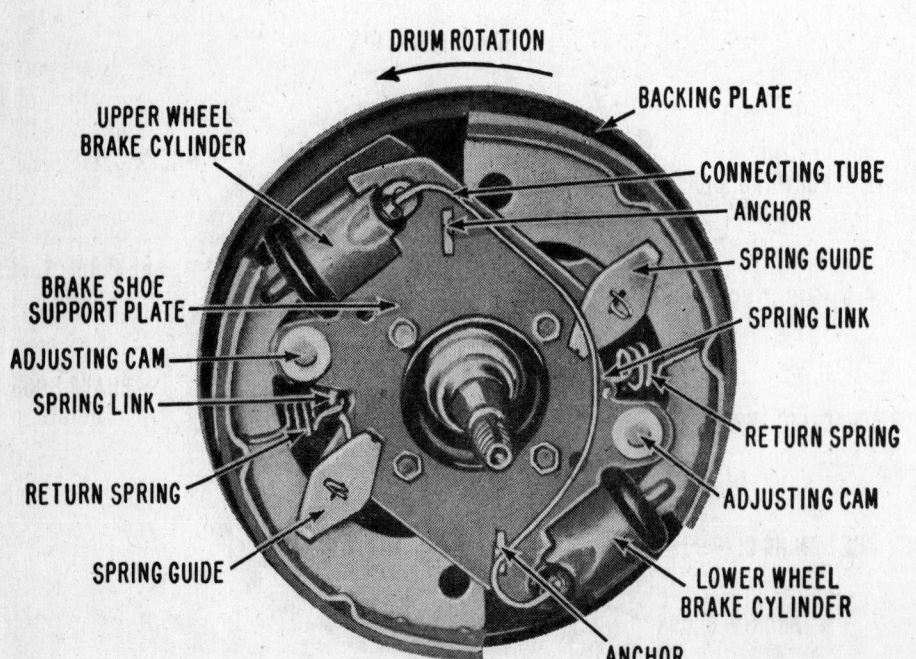

Fig. 24 Chrysler total contact center-plane brake (Type 15). 1956-59

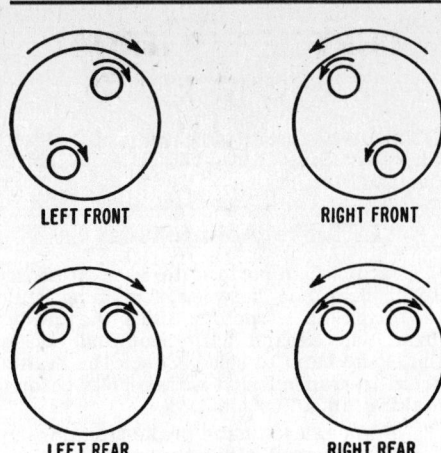

Fig. 26 Diagram for adjusting Type 15 brakes

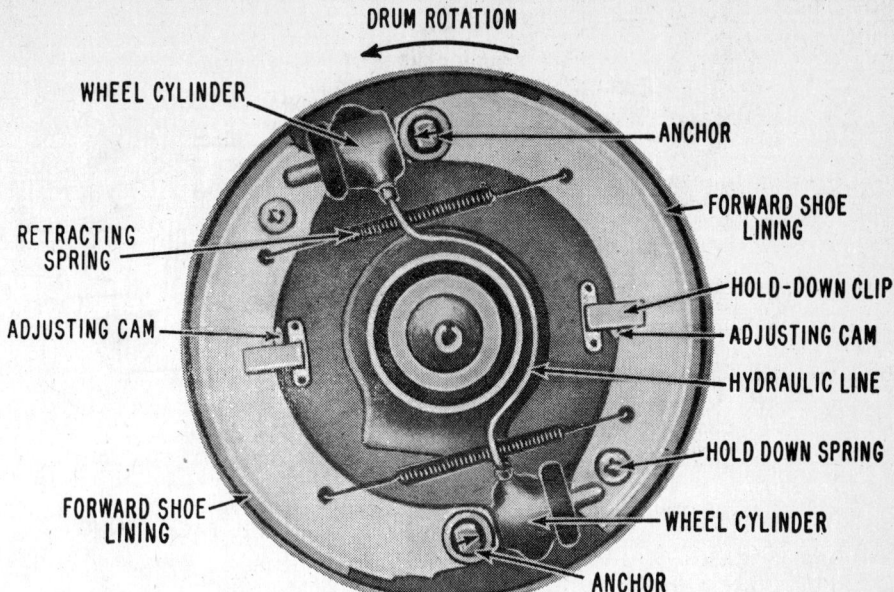

Fig. 27 Chrysler Lockheed two forward shoe brake with two single-end wheel cylinders (Type 16)

gauge must be used to obtain correct lining-to-drum clearances when making major adjustments.

1. With the drums and wheels removed, measure the brake drum diameter. Set the spindle grinder to .030" under the drum diameter. If a brake is used, set the gauge radius to exactly ½ actual drum diameter.
2. Install either the spindle grinder or anchor gauge on front axle spindle.
3. Back off adjusting cams, Fig. 28.
4. Check arrows on anchor pins for proper direction. The arrows should point to the adjacent wheel cylinder before starting the adjustment.
5. Adjust the cams until the center of the brake shoes are touching the anchor gauge pin or the sanding disc.
6. If using the anchor gauge, adjust the anchor pins until .007" clearance is obtained at the toe and heel ends of each shoe. If using a spindle grinder, grind lining until sanding disc touches all points of lining surface.
7. Perform above operations on both front wheels.

CHRYSLER INTERNAL PARKING BRAKE

This type brake, Fig. 29, is mounted at the rear of automatic transmissions. The adjustment of this brake is important because the automatic transmission controls do not have a parking lock.

Brake Adjustments

1. Fully release hand brake from inside the car and place the shift lever or button in the neutral position.
2. Disconnect front end of drive shaft so brake drum can be turned by hand.
3. Remove adjusting screw cover in lower part of brake and loosen clamp bolt.
4. Back off cable adjusting nut.
5. Disconnect cable and check for freeness in housing; sticking cables can usually be freed with a few drops of oil at the upper end of the cable. Cables that cannot be freed should be replaced.
6. Take up on hand brake shoe adjusting nut until a slight drag is felt on the brake drum.

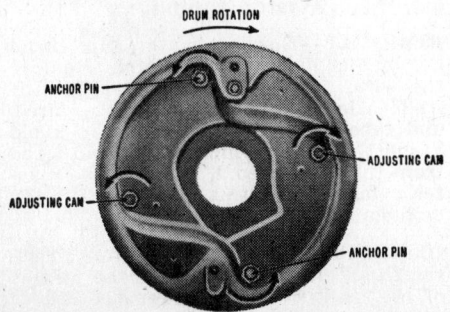

Fig. 28 Type 16 brakes are adjusted by turning cams and anchor pins as indicated

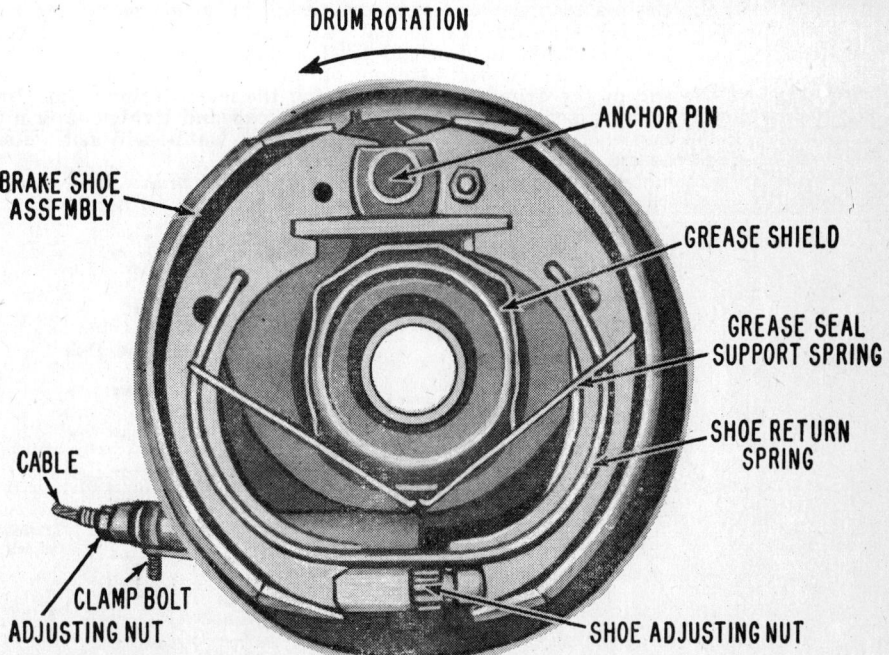

Fig. 29 Chrysler internal parking brake used with automatic transmissions

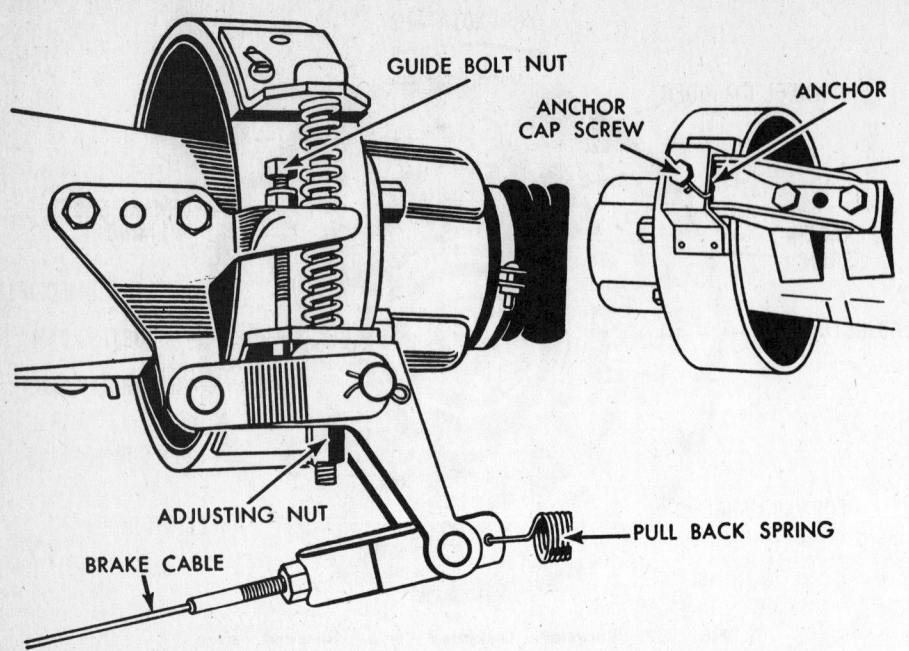

Fig. 30 Chrysler external parking brake used with manual shift transmissions

CHRYSLER EXTERNAL PARKING BRAKE

This type brake, Fig. 30, is used on Chrysler Corp. cars with manual shift transmission.

Brake Adjustments

It is most important to have at least .025″ clearance between the lining and the drum at all points, since the brake drum will expand with heat and cause the brake band to seize. Check the brake drum-to-transmission flange bolts before making an adjustment.

1. Fully release hand brake from inside the car and place the shift lever in neutral.
2. Remove pull back spring and disconnect brake cable.
3. Remove lock wire at anchor cap screw and adjust to obtain .025″ clearance between band and drum at anchor.
4. Adjust guide bolt nut to obtain .025″ clearance between lining and drum at lower half of band.
5. Turn adjusting nut to obtain .025″ clearance between lining and drum at upper half of band.
6. Recheck all clearances.
7. Install new wire lock at anchor and tighten locknut at guide bolt.
8. Adjust cable length so clevis pin fits snugly in cable yoke.
9. Install cotter pin in clevis and hook up pull back spring.

7. Back off one notch or more to obtain .010″ clearance between lining and drum.
8. Turn cable adjusting nut against cable clamp housing until .010″ clearance is obtained between brake shoe cable and brake shoe operating lever.
9. Tighten clamp bolt and replace adjusting cover.
10. Attach propeller shaft and then apply brake lever in car four to six notches; the brake should be firmly applied.

Hydraulic System

FLUID LEVEL—Before checking the fluid level, examine the master cylinder and reservoir, Fig. 31, for evidence of fluid leaks, especially at the brake fluid pipe connection. Examine the rubber boot located at the end of the cylinder. A fluid leak at this point indicates that the master cylinder cup washer is leaking, in which case the cylinder must be removed and disassembled for correction.

Before removing the reservoir filler cap, clean away all dirt so none will fall into the reservoir when the cap is removed. After removing the cap, if the fluid level is more than ⅜″ below the bottom of the filler neck, add sufficient fluid to bring the level to this point. Install the filler cap and tighten it firmly so that dirt and water will not enter the cylinder.

Use only approved brake fluid; never use engine oil or other mineral oils as to do so will ruin the rubber parts of the hydraulic system.

BRAKE PEDAL FREE PLAY—Check the amount of free pedal travel by applying a light finger pressure to the pedal. A slight resistance will be felt when the pedal travel has reached the point where it operates the master cylinder piston. This free travel should be approximately ½″, Fig. 33. Adjustment is made by loosening the push rod lock nut and adjusting the travel of the push rod the necessary amount to obtain the desired pedal free play.

Master Cylinder

REMOVAL—Disconnect the pipe from the master cylinder connection. Remove the wires from the stop light switch, if its location is such that this is required, and tape each wire separately to avoid a short circuit. Unfasten the push rod from the brake pedal. Remove the master cylinder mounting bolts and lift the cylinder from the car.

DISASSEMBLE—Fig. 34. Before disassembling, clean all dirt from the outside of the master clyinder, then proceed as follows:

1. Remove filler cap and gasket.
2. Remove end plug and valve seat

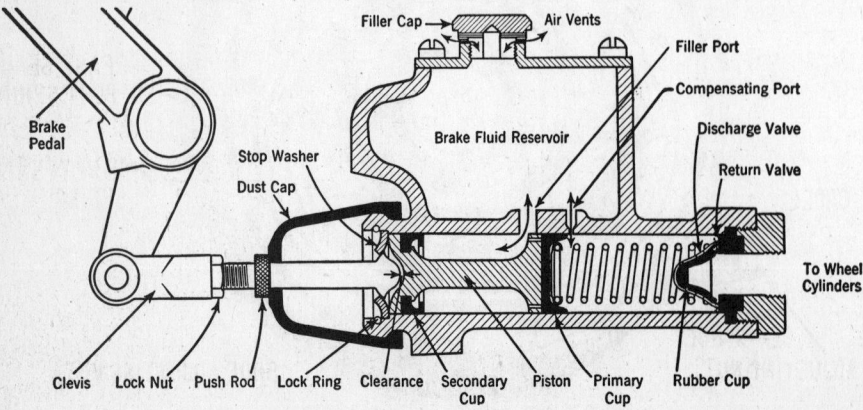

Fig. 31 Hydraulic master cylinder (typical)

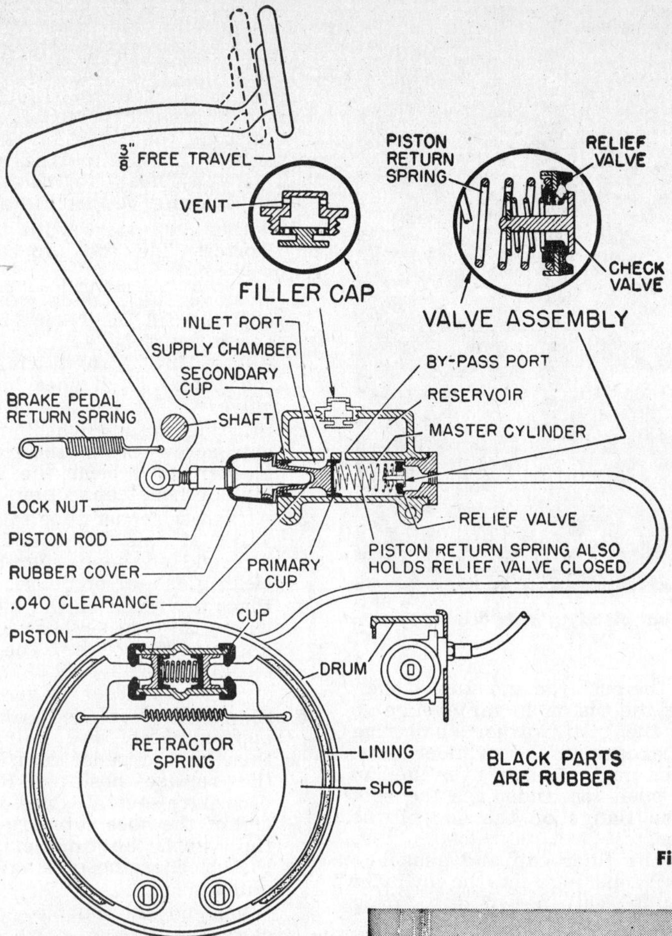

3/8" FREE TRAVEL

PISTON RETURN SPRING

RELIEF VALVE

VENT

CHECK VALVE

FILLER CAP

VALVE ASSEMBLY

INLET PORT

SUPPLY CHAMBER

SECONDARY CUP

BY-PASS PORT

RESERVOIR

BRAKE PEDAL RETURN SPRING

SHAFT

MASTER CYLINDER

LOCK NUT

PISTON ROD

RUBBER COVER

PRIMARY CUP

RELIEF VALVE

PISTON RETURN SPRING ALSO HOLDS RELIEF VALVE CLOSED

.040 CLEARANCE

CUP

PISTON

DRUM

RETRACTOR SPRING

LINING

SHOE

BLACK PARTS ARE RUBBER

Fig. 33 Brake pedal adjustment for free play. This free play is required to prevent hydraulic pressure being applied to the master cylinder piston when brakes are released

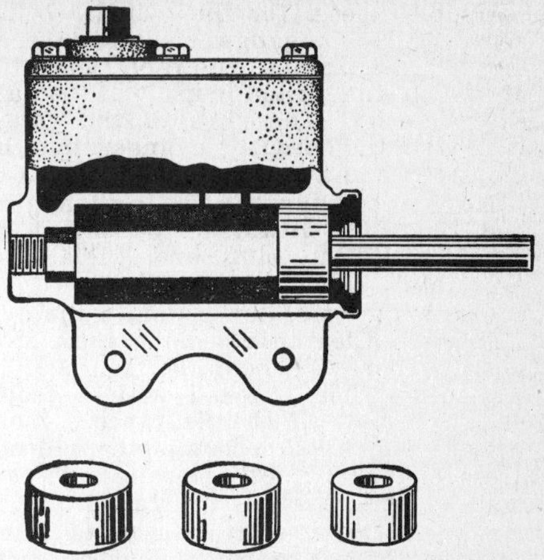

washer from end of cylinder barrel.

3. Remove rubber boot.

4. Remove pedal stop snap ring with a screwdriver and take out the pedal stop and push rod.

5. Remove piston with secondary cup.

6. Remove primary cup.

CLEANING—Immerse all parts of the master cylinder in alcohol and wash thoroughly to remove old hydraulic fluid. Wipe small parts dry with clean cloth. Inside of cylinder and reservoir may be blown dry with compressed air. Do not use gasoline or kerosene for cleaning master cylinder parts.

INSPECTION—Examine cylinder walls. If found to be scored or rusted, cylinder must be reconditioned by honing, Fig. 35. A hone of the proper size should be placed in the chuck of an electric drill. Work the hone back and forth a few times, then inspect the cylinder to see if walls are cleaned up. Do not hone away any more than is required to remove scores and smooth up the cylinder. Remove burrs caused by honing from around the intake and compensating ports.

If available, try a No-Go gauge in cylinder, Fig. 36, using a collar of the

Fig. 36 Using No-Go gauge when inspecting master or wheel cylinder (master cylinder shown)

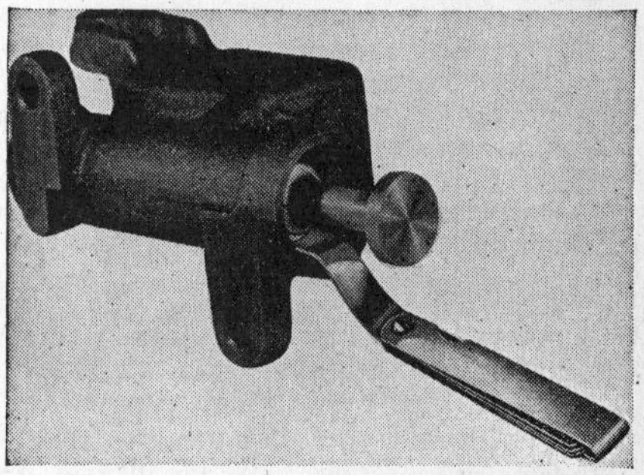

Fig. 37 Checking master cylinder piston fit with feeler gauge

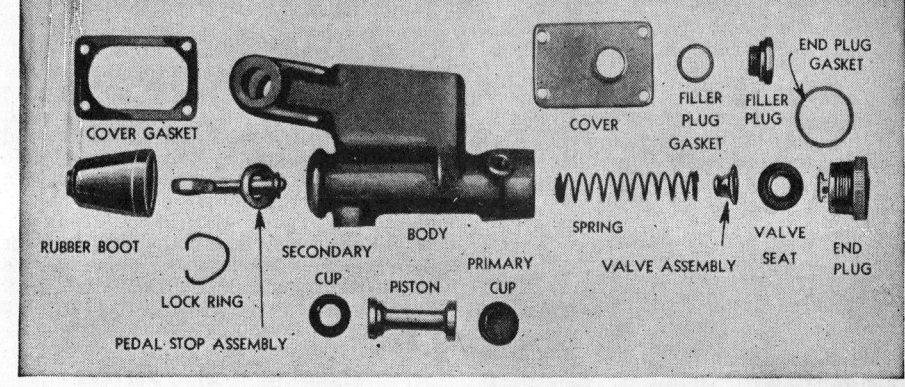

COVER GASKET

RUBBER BOOT

LOCK RING

PEDAL STOP ASSEMBLY

SECONDARY CUP

PISTON

PRIMARY CUP

BODY

COVER

FILLER PLUG GASKET

FILLER PLUG

END PLUG GASKET

SPRING

VALVE ASSEMBLY

VALVE SEAT

END PLUG

Fig. 34 Exploded view of typical master cylinder

Fig. 35 Using hone to clean up master or wheel cylinder (wheel cylinder shown)

correct diameter for the cylinder being serviced. No-Go gauge is slightly larger than the maximum allowable diameter at which the piston cups will operate satisfactorily. Therefore, if the gauge will enter the bore, the cylinder must be discarded and a new one installed.

Inspect the check valve seat on the end plug. If found to be pitted or swollen, replace plug and valve seat assembly.

Check the fit of the piston in the cylinder bore. Clearance between the piston and cylinder wall should be from .001 to .005 inch when checked with a feeler gauge, Fig. 37. If the clearance is more than .005 inch and a new piston will not provide the correct clearance, a new housing will have to be installed.

Always use new rubber parts when reconditioning a cylinder. Rubber parts which are swollen or damaged will seriously impair the proper function of parts. Repair kits which contain all the parts usually required for reconditioning master cylinders, are available. While all the parts contained in the kit may not appear to be in need of replacement, experience has proved that the added safety and braking efficiency provided by replacing these parts will offset the slight cost of the parts.

ASSEMBLY — Before assembling the master cylinder, dip all internal parts in hydraulic brake fluid, then proceed as follows:

1. Install the end plug and washer in the end of the cylinder barrel and tighten securely.
2. Install the check valve assembly in the open end of the piston return spring and insert the valve and spring into the cylinder barrel with the check valve at the outlet end.
3. Install the primary piston cup into the cylinder with the lip of the cup toward the outlet end and over the piston return spring. Insert the piston and secondary cup with the open end of the piston away from the outlet end of the cylinder.

Fig. 38 Adding fluid to master cylinder, using valve controlled filler

Fig. 39 Manual bleeding of hydraulic system

4. Install the push rod and stop washer, forcing the piston in far enough to install the stop washer snap ring in the groove in the cylinder bore.
5. Slide the push rod boot over the end of the push rod and place the boot over the flange on the end of the cylinder.
6. Install the filler cap and gasket.
7. Plug all openings in the cylinder against the entrance of dirt during installation.

INSTALLATION—Place the master cylinder in position and install and tighten the bracket bolts so the cylinder is held firmly to the bracket and in line with the pedal push rod. Fasten the push rod to the brake pedal. Connect the brake fluid pipe to the master cylinder and firmly tighten the union to prevent a fluid leak. Remove the tape from the stop light wire terminals and connect them to the stop light switch. Fill the cylinder reservoir with brake fluid, Fig. 38, bleed the brake system and test the brake pedal clearance.

Bleeding Brake System

Bleeding, or expelling air from the hydraulic system, is necessary each time the fluid becomes so low in the master cylinder that air enters the system. This condition occurs whenever the master cylinder, or a wheel cylinder, or a brake fluid pipe or hose has been replaced or disconnected. There are two methods of bleeding a hydraulic brake system, (1) manual and (2) pressure.

Manual Bleeding Method

Most authorities recommend that the system be bled by starting with the longest line and working successively to the shortest; other authorities prefer the opposite method, that is, by starting with the shortest line and finishing up with the longest. Actually, there is no particular reason why it is necessary to bleed the system in any particular order

except in the case of certain power brake units which must be bled first. There is some possible advantage in bleeding the longest line first on long wheelbase vehicles in that it may be possible to remove a greater percentage of air in this manner and possibly this is the reason why most authorities recommend that the cylinder furthest from the master cylinder be bled first.

Whether you start with the longest or shortest line the procedure is as follows:

1. Remove the master cylinder filler cap and fill the reservoir. The reservoir must be kept full or nearly full of brake fluid while bleeding the system. Each wheel has a bleeder valve.
2. Starting at one wheel, remove the cap screw from the end of the bleeder valve near the brake fluid pipe or hose connection, Fig. 39.
3. Attach a bleeder tube to the bleeder valve at this point and place the free end of the bleeder tube into a clean glass jar or bottle.
4. Place a wrench on the bleeder valve where the bleeder hose is connected and turn the valve to the left (counterclockwise) ½ to ¾ turn. This opens the bleeder valve.
5. Slowly depress the brake pedal to approximately the halfway point; then let the pedal return slowly to the release position. Repeat this procedure several times, keeping the end of the hose submerged in brake fluid until the fluid expelled from the bleeder hose is free of air bubbles.
6. When no air bubbles are visible, close the bleeder valve by turning it clockwise and remove the bleeder hose.
7. Install and tighten the cap screw in the end of the valve and test the valve to be certain that it is seated firmly.
8. Add new fluid to the master cylinder reservoir and repeat the bleeding process on the other wheels in turn. Never use the fluid drained from the brake system if there is any

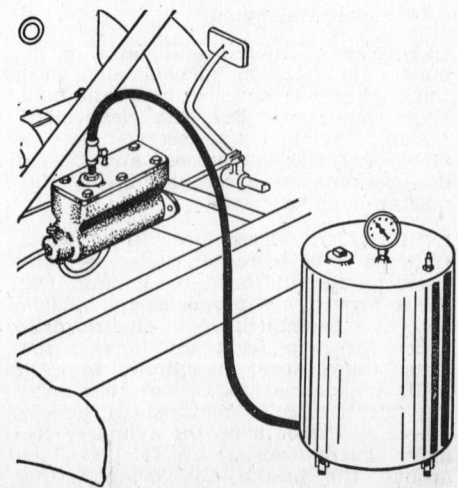

Fig. 40 Pressure bleeding of hydraulic system

doubt about its being clean and free from dirt.

Pressure Bleeding Method

This method of bleeding is accomplished in the same manner as manual bleeding except that the fluid is forced through the lines by air pressure in a tank containing hydraulic fluid.

A typical application of this equipment is shown in Fig. 40. With hydraulic fluid in the tank, charge the tank with 10 to 20 pounds of air pressure. Clean all dirt from around the master cylinder filler cap, remove the cap and attach the hose from the bleeder tank to the master cylinder filler cap opening. Open the bleeder hose valve.

Remove the screw from the bleeder valve at the wheel cylinder. Screw the bleeder hose into the bleeder valve and place the free end of the bleeder hose in a glass jar containing brake fluid, following the same procedure as in manual bleeding. Open the bleeder valve at the wheel cylinder and watch the flow of fluid at the end of the hose. As soon as air bubbles stop, close the valve tightly. Remove the bleeder hose and repeat the process at the other wheels.

Hydraulic Lines

A fluid leak at some point is indicated when the master cylinder reservoir requires the addition of fluid at frequent intervals. When this happens, inspect the pipes, connections, and cylinders for leaks while pressure is applied to the brake pedal. If a leak is evident at a tube or hose, replace the part. A leaky wheel cylinder may be indicated by the presence of fluid on the brake support plate, in which case the cylinder must be removed and overhauled.

FLARING BRAKE TUBING — When necessary to replace brake tubing, always use special metal tubing which is especially designed to withstand high pressure and resist corrosion. For this reason, ordinary copper tubing is not satisfactory and should not be used.

The important thing in connection with making up hydraulic brake pipes is the proper flaring of the ends of the tubing for the compression couplings. Unless the tubing is properly flared the couplings will leak and the brakes will become ineffective.

This tubing must be double-lap flared at the ends in order to produce a strong, leak-proof joint. The tool shown in Fig. 41 is used to form the double-lap flare.

Fig. 42 shows two pieces of tubing—one with a single-lap flare "A" and the other with a double-lap flare "B." Note that the single-lap flare split the tubing while the one shown in "B" has a well formed joint.

To flare the tubing, cut it to the desired length, using the tube cutter, Fig. 43, to prevent flattening the tubing. Square off the end with a fine cut mill file, then ream the sharp edges with a reamer blade provided on the tube cutter.

Place new compression coupling nuts on the tubing. Dip the end of the tubing to be flared in hydraulic brake fluid. This lubrication results in a better formation of the flare. Loosen the clamping nuts on the flaring tool and insert the finished end of the tubing in the channel of the die until it bears against the stop pin, Fig. 44.

Tighten the clamping nuts by hand and place the fixture in a bench vise. Then tighten down the clamping nuts firmly with a wrench and remove the stop pin from the die. The tubing is now firmly gripped in the die and ready for the first flare forming operation.

Using the flare forming tool having the concave die, insert the forming tool in the die and strike firm blows with a one pound hammer until the shoulder of the tool contacts the top of the die.

Next, use the flare forming tool having the 45-degree die at its lower end. Insert the tool in the die and strike firm blows until the shoulder of the tool contacts the top of the die. The resulting double-lap flare is shown in Fig. 44.

To install, position the tube and start each connection by hand to be certain that the coupling threads are properly aligned. Then securely tighten each coupling with a wrench. Install and tighten the tube holding clips, then bleed the brake system.

Wheel Cylinder

REMOVAL—Block the brake pedal in the released position, Fig. 45, to prevent its being moved accidentally while the

Fig. 41   Flaring tool for hydraulic brake tubing

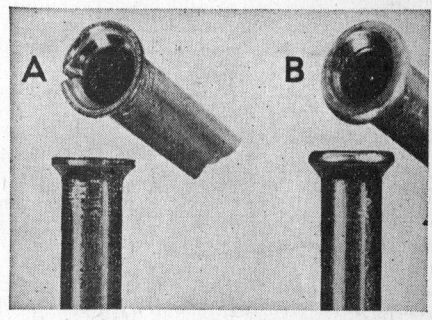

Fig. 42   Showing advantage of double lap flare (B) over single lap flare (A) on hydraulic brake tubing

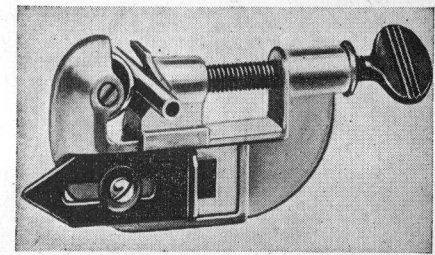

Fig. 43   Special cutting tool for hydraulic brake tubing

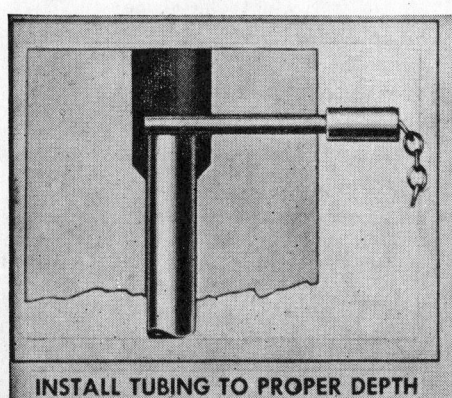

INSTALL TUBING TO PROPER DEPTH

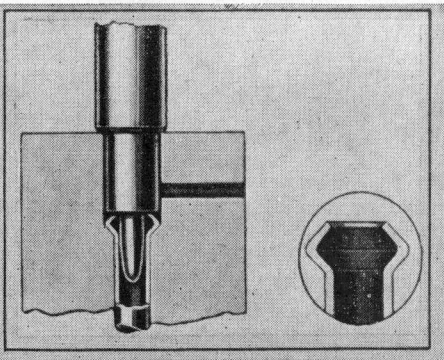

FIRST FLARING OPERATION

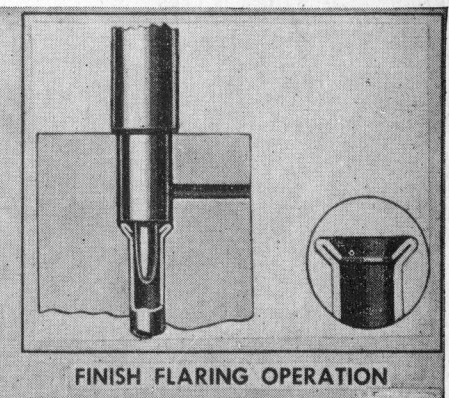

FINISH FLARING OPERATION

Fig. 44   Method of forming double lap flare in brake tubing

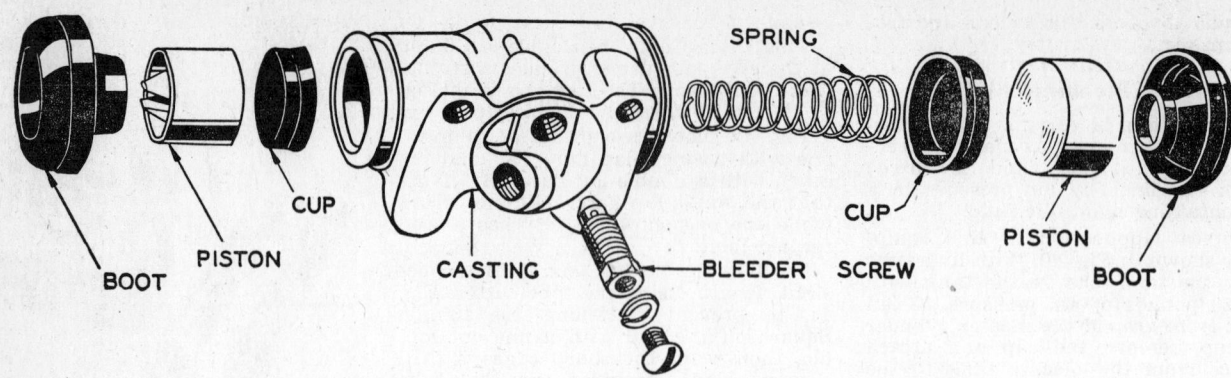

Fig. 46 Exploded view of wheel cylinder with rubber end covers or boots

cylinder is off, thus avoiding the loss of brake fluid.

Jack up the car and remove the wheel and brake drum. Unfasten the brake hose or pipe from the wheel cylinder connection. Unhook the brake shoe retracting spring to permit the shoes to be moved away from the cylinder.

At this point, if step bore cylinders are used, note carefully in which direction the larger bore is facing. On some cars the larger bore faces the rear while on others it faces the front.

Remove the two screws which fasten the cylinder to the brake support plate and take off the cylinder.

DISASSEMBLY—Fig. 46 is an exploded view of a typical wheel cylinder used with Bendix and Lockheed brakes.

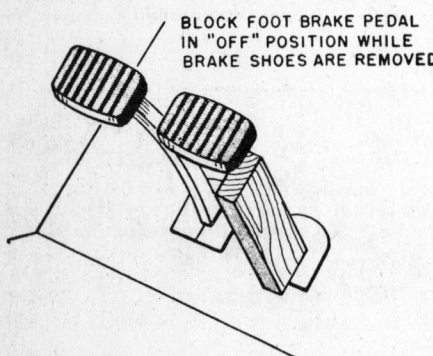

Fig. 45 Method of blocking brake pedal to avoid loss of brake fluid while hydraulic system is open

To disassemble, remove the end covers and push out the pistons, rubber cups and spring. Wash all parts in clean alcohol, but before doing so, wash your hands with soap and water to avoid the possibility of mineral oil or gasoline coming in contact with the parts during assembly.

INSPECTION—Examine cylinder walls. If found to be scored or rusted, the cylinder must be reconditioned by honing, Fig. 35. A hone of the proper size should be placed in the chuck of an electric drill. Work the hone back and forth a few times, then inspect the cylinder to see if the wall is cleaned up. Do not hone any more than is required to remove scores and smooth up the cylinder.

If available, try a No-Go gauge in the cylinder, Fig. 36, using a collar of the correct diameter for the cylinder being serviced. No-Go gauge is slightly larger than the maximum allowable diameter at which the piston cups will operate satisfactorily. Therefore, if the gauge will enter the bore the cylinder must be discarded and a new one installed.

Check the fit of the pistons in the cylinder. Clearance between the pistons and cylinder wall should be from .002 to .004" when checked with a feeler gauge, Fig. 47. If the clearance is more than .004" and new pistons will not provide the correct clearance, a new housing will have to be installed.

Always use new rubber parts when reconditioning a cylinder. Rubber parts which are swollen or damaged will seriously impair the proper function of the brakes. Repair kits are available which contain all parts usually required for re-

conditioning wheel cylinders.

REASSEMBLY & REPLACEMENT — Dip pistons and rubber cups in brake fluid. Place the spring in the center of the housing, the rubber cups at each end of the spring, with their cupped sides to the spring and the flat face of the cups flush with the piston. (On step bore cylinders the spring is tapered, therefore, be sure to place the small tapered end against the smaller piston.) Replace the end covers.

Assemble the wheel cylinder to the brake support plate, connect the fluid pipe or hose and hook the brake shoe retracting spring. Install the brake drum and wheel, and bleed the entire brake system.

Fig. 47 Checking wheel cylinder piston fit with feeler gauge

POWER BRAKES

THE SECRET of power brake service and repair work is a good understanding of the operation of the different brakes available on today's cars.

Mechanical assist units employ a power unit that is connected only to the brake pedal or linkage and helps push the pedal down. Hydraulic assist types, on the other hand, are inserted in the hydraulic system and directly increase

hydraulic fluid pressure. In the hydraulic assist unit known as the integral type, the power unit is attached to the master cylinder; in the other, it is attached to an auxiliary slave cylinder.

Power units are similar in operation and get their energy by opposing engine vacuum to atmospheric pressure. A piston and cylinder, flexible diaphragm or bellows utilize this energy to provide

brake assistance. The fundamental difference between the different types lies simply in how the power unit is suspended when the brakes are not in use.

It is obviously important to know whether a power unit is air suspended or vacuum suspended. Air-suspended units are under atmospheric pressure until the brakes are applied. Then engine vacuum is admitted, causing the piston or diaphragm to move or the bellows to collapse. Vacuum-suspended types are balanced with engine vacuum until the brake pedal is depressed, allowing atmospheric pressure to unbalance the unit and apply force to the brake system.

General Service

Regardless of whether the brakes are air or vacuum suspended, or have integral or auxiliary hydraulic cylinders, certain general service procedures apply. Only top quality, clean brake fluid should be used in power brakes. More seals and valves are used with power brake systems than with ordinary brakes, so an inferior brake fluid will do much more damage. For the same reason, be sure all dirt is kept out of the system.

The fact that brakes will operate even if the power unit fails gives us a clue to successful power brake service. This means the conventional brake system is left intact and a power unit is simply added to the existing system. Trouble-shooting is then exactly the same until we get to the power unit. As with conventional hydraulic brakes, a spongy pedal with power brakes still means air in the system and grease on the linings will still make the brakes grab. Keep in mind, however, that power brakes give a higher line pressure, thus making leaks more critical.

Power units do not require adjustment. Either they work or they don't. If they don't, the various valves and connections are simply replaced. The only exception is that the power units themselves sometimes have an adjustable connection to the brake pedal or linkage.

Another thing that is helpful in power brake overhaul is the manner in which the units wear. Repairs are infrequent until the unit has been in service for a long time. Then, when a malfunction does occur, it means the whole unit should be overhauled. Complete overhaul kits are available and all the parts in the kit should be used in the overhaul.

Trouble Diagnosis

Complaints about power brake operation should be handled as if two separate systems exist. Check for faults in the regular brake system first. If it is O.K., start looking over the power brake circuit. For a quick check of proper power unit operation, press the brake pedal firmly and then start the engine. The pedal should fall away slightly and less pressure should be needed to maintain the pedal in any position. On vacuum-suspended power units, air will rush into the air intake when the brakes are applied.

Another check begins with removal of the stoplight switch and installation of a pressure gauge. Take a reading with the engine off and the power unit not operating. Maintaining the same pedal height, start the engine and take another reading. There should be a substantial pressure increase in the second reading.

Pedal free travel and total travel are critical on cars equipped with power brakes. As a general rule, brakes should be adjusted or relined if the pedal is closer than 1½ in. from the floor with the

POWER BRAKE INDEX

BENDIX:	Index No.
Hydro-Vac	1
Power-Vac	2
Master-Vac	3
Treadle-Vac:	
Poppet Valve Type	4
Hydraulic Reaction Type	5
KELSEY-HAYES:	
Diaphragm Type	6
Bellows Type	7
Piston Type	8
MIDLAND Hy-Power	9
MORAINE:	
Piston Type	10
Diaphragm Type	11

Power Brake Application

Car Make	Index Unit No.	Page
Buick 1953-56	8	136
1957-59	10	143
1957-59	5	130
1960	11	144
Cadillac 1953-55	1	130
1956 and 1958	4	130
1956-58	10	143
1957	1	130
1959-61	3	134
1959-61	11	144
Chevrolet 1955-56	4	130
1957	1	130
1957-58	5	130
1958	10	143
1959-60	3	134
1959-60	11	144
Chrysler 1955	6	138
1956	2	133
1956-60	7	139
1957-60	2	133
Continental 1956-58	4	130
1959-60	5	130

Car Make	Index Unit No.	Page
De Soto 1955	6	138
1956	7	139
1956-60	2	133
Dodge 1955	6	138
1956	7	139
1957-60	2	133
Edsel 1958-60 V8	5	130
1959-60 Six	7	139
Ford 1955-56	9	142
1957-60	7	139
1960-61	3	134
Imperial 1956-60	7	139
Lancer 1961	3	134
Lincoln 1956-58	4	130
1959-60	5	130
1961	3	134
Mercury 1956	4	130
1956-58	5	130
1959-61	3	134
Oldsmobile 1955-59	5	130
1955-59	10	143
1960	3	134
1960	11	144
Plymouth 1955-56	6	138
1956	8	136
1957-58	2	133
1957-61	7	139
Pontiac 1954-56	4	130
1954-58	10	143
1957-58	5	130
1959-60	11	144
1959-60	3	134
Rambler 1956	4	130
1957-60	5	130
Studebaker 1955-60	1	130
1961	3	134
Thunderbird 1955-57	9	142
1958-60	7	139
1960-61	3	134
Valiant 1960-61	3	134

brakes applied. Free travel should be kept strictly to specifications.

Take a manifold vacuum reading if the power unit isn't giving enough assistance. Remember, though, that some of the new V-8's have less than 15 in. of vacuum at idle. If manifold vacuum is abnormally low, tune the engine and then try the power brakes again. Naturally, loose vacuum lines and clogged air intake filters will cut down power brake efficiency. Most units have a check valve that retains some vacuum in the system when the engine is off. A vacuum gauge check of this valve will tell you when it is restricted or stuck open or closed.

Failure of the brakes to release in nine out of 10 cases is caused by a tight or misaligned connection between the power unit and the brake linkage. If this connection is free, look for a broken piston, diaphragm or bellows return spring. The power unit will have to be disassembled for this check and, if the spring is in good condition, continue going through the power unit, checking the fluid, air and vacuum valves.

A simple check of the hydraulic system should be made before proceeding. Loosen the connection between the power unit and the wheel cylinder lines. If the brakes release, the trouble is in the power unit hydraulic circuit. If the brakes still will not release, look for a

restricted brake line or similar difficulties in the regular hydraulic circuit.

A residual pressure check valve is usually included immediately under the brake line connection on hydraulic assist power brakes. This valve maintains a slight hydraulic pressure on the brake lines and wheel cylinders to give better pedal response. If it is sticking, the brakes may not release.

Power brakes that have a hard pedal are usually suffering from a milder form of the same ills that cause complete power unit failure. Collapsed or leaking vacuum lines or insufficient manifold vacuum, as well as punctured diaphragms or bellows and leaky piston seals, all lead to weak power unit operation. A steady hiss when the brake is held down means a vacuum leak that will cause poor power unit operation.

Do not immediately condemn the power unit if the brakes grab. First look for all the usual causes, such as greasy linings or scored drums. Then investigate the power unit. When the trouble has been traced to the power unit, check for a damaged reaction control. The reaction control is usually made up of a diaphragm, spring and valving that tends to resist pedal action. It is put in the system to give the pedal "feel" and deceive your foot into believing it is doing all the work.

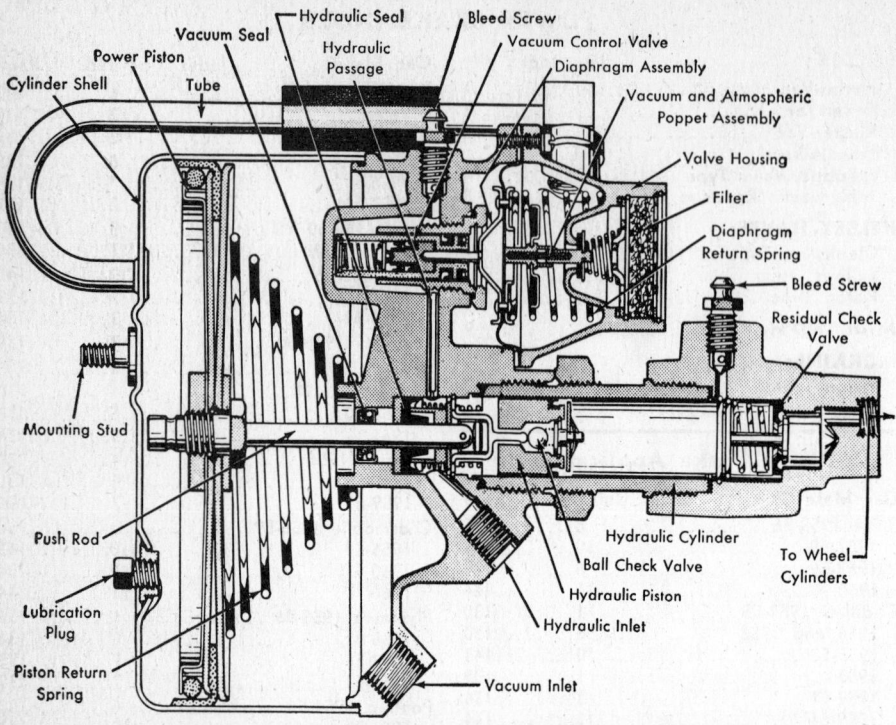

Fig. 1 Bendix Hydrovac. Cadillac 1957

BENDIX HYDROVAC

Index No. 1

This unit, Figs. 1, 2, is a vacuum-suspended system in which vacuum exists on both sides of the power piston in the unapplied stage when the engine is running. The power brake utilizes engine manifold vacuum in its operation.

Operation

As the brake pedal is depressed, the hydraulic pressure developed within the master cylinder is transmitted to the hydraulic piston of the control valve and to the hydraulic slave cylinder. With pressure applied to the control valve piston, the vacuum valve closes and the atmospheric valve opens to admit air to the control side of the vacuum power cylinder. As air is admitted, the forces acting upon the vacuum power cylinder piston are transmitted directly to the hydraulic piston through the push rod. As the hydraulic piston starts to move, the piston check valve closes, trapping fluid under pressure ahead of the piston.

As the brake pedal is released, the pressure within the control valve hydraulic piston chamber is reduced, allowing the atmospheric poppet to close and reopen the vacuum poppet. The vacuum power cylinder piston is again balanced in vacuum and returns to release position. When the hydraulic piston nears the release end of its stroke, its check valve reopens, thus permitting the full release of the brakes.

Bleeding Hydraulic System

To bleed the entire hydraulic brake system, the Hydrovac unit must be bled at both bleeder valves before attempting to bleed at the wheel cylinders. *The entire bleeding operation must be performed with the engine shut off and no vacuum in the power system.*

1. Remove filler plug from brake main cylinder and fill it with hydraulic brake fluid.
2. Attach a bleeder drain hose to the hydraulic cylinder bleeder valve, keeping the end of the drain hose below the surface of fluid in the drain jar.
3. Loosen the hydraulic cylinder bleeder valve ½ to ¾ turn.
4. Depress the brake pedal slowly by hand to expel air. When the pedal has reached the toe board, close the bleeder valve before returning the pedal to its released position.
5. Repeat the procedure until air bubbles cease to appear at the end of the bleeder drain hose in the jar and the stream is a solid fluid mass. Then tighten the bleeder valve and remove the drain hose.
6. After the hydraulic cylinder has been bled, bleed at the vacuum control valve and then proceed to bleed at the wheel cylinders, following the procedure outlined in the *Hydraulic Brake System* chapter.

Maintenance

The outside of the Hydrovac unit should be cleaned thoroughly every six months. All hose clamps should be tightened and all pipe fittings and hydraulic connections should be checked for looseness. One ounce of Bendix Vacuum Cylinder Oil should be added to the power cylinder at the lubrication plug at 10,000 mile intervals or each six-month period, especially prior to the start of cold weather. The air cleaner should be removed, disassembled and cleaned at least twice a year. If the car is operating under dusty conditions, the air cleaner should be cleaned more frequently.

Hydrovac Repairs

When it becomes necessary to dismantle the Hydrovac unit for repairs the following precautions should be taken:

1. Thoroughly wash all parts in clean alcohol.
2. Keep all hydraulic system parts away from mineral oils and greases. Do not handle hydraulic system parts with greasy hands.
3. Use new rubber seals and cups when reassembling the unit.
4. If possible use an air hose to blow dirt and cleaning fluid out of all internal passages and to dry all parts.
5. Inspect vacuum cylinder bore for deep scoring or dents. Small imperfections may be smoothed out by using fine crocus cloth. If rust or corrosion is found in the cylinder bore, it can be removed with fine emery cloth.
6. Inspect bore of hydraulic cylinder for scoring or points of excessive wear. Check gasket sealing surface at ends of cylinder and in hydraulic cylinder end cap.
7. Inspect ball seat in end of hydraulic piston for scoring and scratches.
8. Check push rod surface for score marks.
9. Inspect vacuum and atmospheric rubber poppets in valve housing for wear or deterioration.
10. Check bore of vacuum control valve fitting for scoring and corrosion.
11. Check all springs for distortion and loss of tension.
12. In reassembling the power unit, use all the parts furnished with the repair kit and see Figs. 1 and 2.

BENDIX TREADLEVAC

Index Nos. 4 and 5

These units, Figs. 3 and 5, are of the air suspended type, meaning that atmospheric pressure is present on both sides of the piston in the unapplied stage. The power brake unit replaces the master cylinder only. Other parts of the brake system are the same as with conventional brakes.

Two external lines connect to the power brake unit: one is the vacuum connection to the intake manifold or carburetor (and vacuum reservoir); the other is a hydraulic connection into the hydraulic brake system.

The power unit has no bleeder valve, the entire brake system being bled in the conventional manner as outlined in the Hydraulic Brake System chapter. However, when bleeding the system the engine should be shut off.

Poppet Valve Type—Index No. 4

With this type power unit, as the brake pedal is depressed, the atmosphere poppet closes, then the vacuum poppet opens. Thus vacuum is on the left side of the diaphragm and on the right side of the power piston. This condition creates a force which moves the power piston to the right, compressing the return spring.

With vacuum on the left side of the diaphragm and atmospheric pressure on the right side, a reaction force is obtained which pushes back to the left against the push rod and plunger. As the power piston moves to the right, the hydraulic plunger moves to the right in the hydraulic cylinder.

The initial movement of the plunger allows the compensating valve to seat, trapping fluid in the hydraulic cylinder. Thus fluid under pressure is forced past the residual pressure check valve and through the lines to the wheel cylinders.

Hydraulic Reaction Type—
Index No. 5

When the brakes are applied in this type power brake, the atmosphere port closes and then the vacuum port opens. Thus the right side of the vacuum piston is open to vacuum through the passages in the piston. With a partial vacuum on the right side of the piston and atmosphere on the left side, a force is created which moves the piston with the hydraulic plunger to the right. The initial movement of the hydraulic plunger allows the compensating valve to seat and close off the passage between the fluid reservoir and hydraulic piston.

As pressure is developed within the hydraulic cylinder, fluid is forced through the residual check valve and brake lines to the wheel cylinders. *This same pressure acting against the rubber membrane at the end of the hydraulic plunger transmits a force through the reaction rod and counter reaction spring to the left against the valve plunger which tends to close the vacuum port and bring the power piston to rest.* Since the reaction force is in proportion to the hydraulic pressure developed with the hydraulic cylinder and wheel cylinders, it

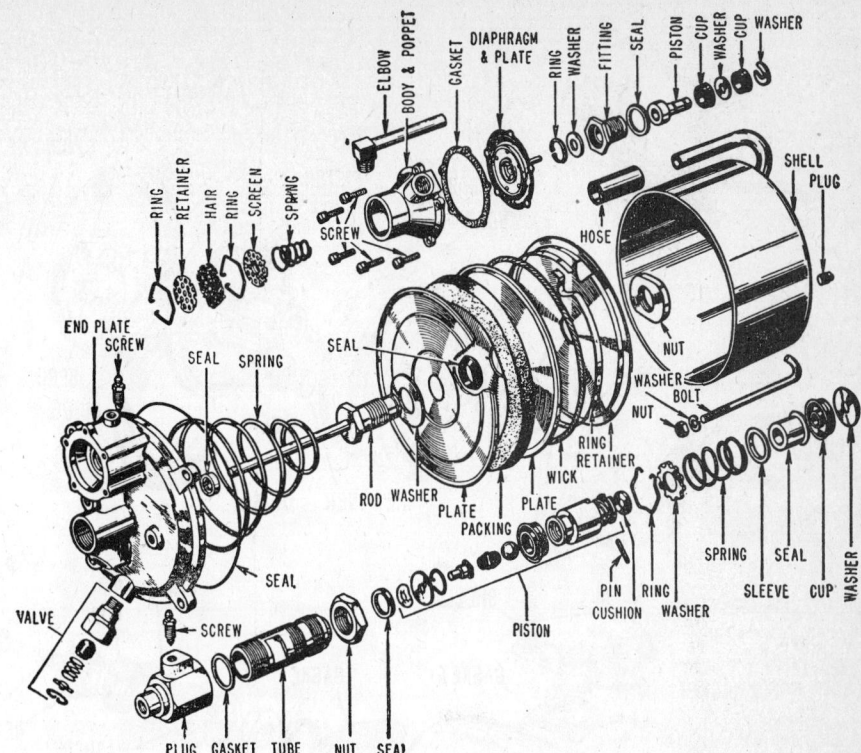

Fig. 2 Bendix Hyrovac. Cadillac 1953-55, Chevrolet 1957, Studebaker 1955-60

gives the driver a "feel" of the amount of braking.

Power Brake Repairs

When it becomes necessary to disassemble these units for repairs, refer to Figs. 4 and 6. The overhaul kit contains all necessary replacement parts for the unit. Use all the new parts in the kit regardless of the condition of the old ones. In addition, replace any other parts

which inspection indicates to be unfit for use.

Before disassembling either of these units, scribe a mark across the vacuum and power cylinders to be sure they are reassembled as originally installed. Also scribe a mark for reassembly purposes across the hydraulic cylinder and cover.

Inspection of Parts

When disassembled, wash all parts in clean alcohol and keep all hydraulic system parts away from mineral oils, greases and greasy hands.

Vacuum Cylinder Shell—Inspect the shell for scoring, pitting, dents or nicks; also for damaged threads in nuts or mounting flanges.

Hydraulic Cylinder Casting—Examine the bore down one inch from the open end. For the hydraulic cup to seal properly, this portion of the bore must be free from scores, deep scratches or corrosion. The sealing surfaces at the reservoir cover, compensating port and hydraulic outlet port must be free of scoring, pitting, dents and nicked edges. Also check casting for cracks and damaged threads.

Hydraulic Port Fitting—The surface of the small end of the fitting must be free of scoring or corrosion which might prevent sealing with the rubber cup of the residual check valve.

Compensating Port Fitting—Inspect surface around port opening, inside threaded end of fitting, for scoring or corrosion which might prevent the fit-

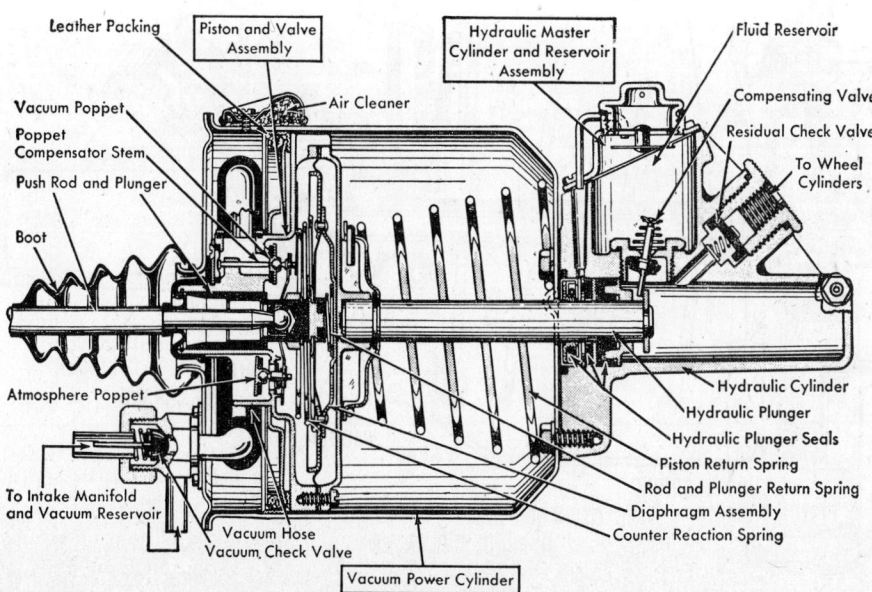

Fig. 3 Bendix Treadlevac, poppet valve type

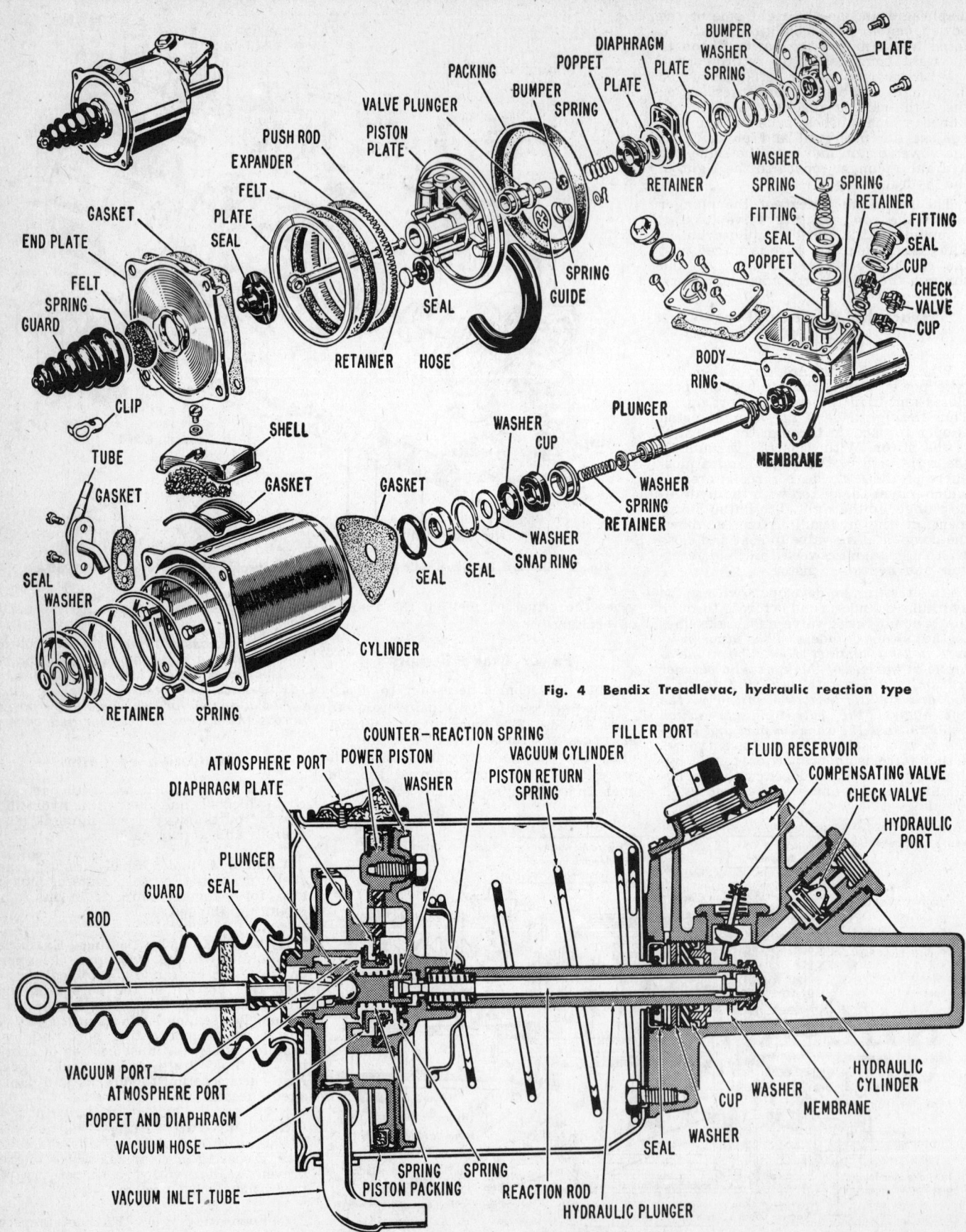

Fig. 4 Bendix Treadlevac, hydraulic reaction type

Fig. 5 Bendix Treadlevac, hydraulic reaction type

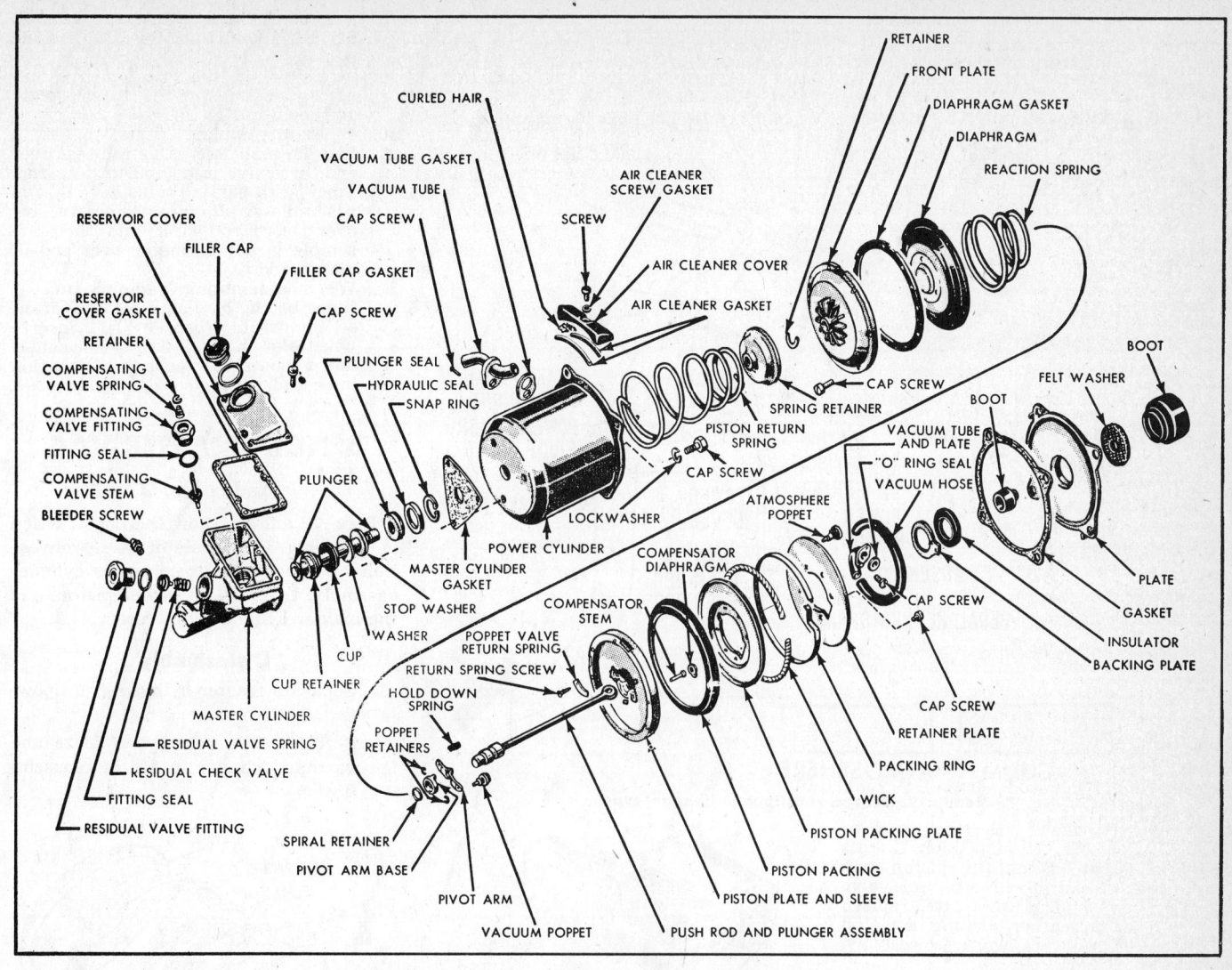

Fig. 6 Bendix Treadlevac, poppet valve type

ting from sealing properly with the compensating valve.

Vacuum Supply Tube—Make sure the tube braze is secure and the tube plate is not distorted.

Piston Plates—Examine plates for cracks and damaged threads. Inspect plunger bore in rear piston plate and poppet seats for scratches and nicks. *Do not attempt to refinish bore;* replace with a new plate if necessary.

Hydraulic Plunger—Inspect the polished surface for scoring, pitting or dents. *Do not* attempt to refinish plunger surface; replace with a new assembly if necessary.

Push Rod and Plunger—The rod must pivot freely in the plunger without any noticeable end play. Inspect plunger for scoring, pitting or dents on the outside diameter polished surface. *Do not* attempt to refinish plunger surface; replace with new assembly if necessary.

Vacuum Cylinder End Plate—Examine end plate for distortion.

BENDIX POWERVAC

Index No. 2

These power brake units, Figs. 7, 8 and 9, are connected mechanically to the brake pedal linkage through the power unit push rod. The power cylinder contains the power piston which is attached to the piston rod and operates against a return spring. Attached to the cylinder is an air cleaner and a vacuum inlet tube. The inlet vacuum tube is attached to the piston by a flexible hose. Operating within the piston and piston rod are a valve rod poppet assembly and valve rod balancing diaphragm pin and diaphragm.

The brake pedal pivots at a point which is rigidly supported under the dash panel. The trigger arm, which is an integral part of the upper portion of the brake pedal, is in contact with the end of the valve rod of the cylinder piston. The power lever, shown behind the brake pedal lever, pivots on the brake pedal lever. The lower end of the power lever is attached to the master cylinder push rod. The upper end of the power lever contains a pin which is free to slide to the right in the forked clevis rod, which is integral with the piston rod.

The brake pedal cam pin is free to move in the slot of the power lever. The cam pin is designed for use in adjusting the position of the trigger arm so as to give equal travel to the released and applied positions. The brake pedal, valve rod and master cylinder push rod are held in the released position by a spring.

Power Unit Repairs

When it becomes necessary to disassemble the unit for repairs, wash all parts in clean alcohol. Do not allow rubber parts to come in contact with mineral oil or grease or dirty hands.

Use compressed air to blow out dirt and cleaner fluid from recesses and internal passages. Place washed parts on clean paper or lintless cloth.

When overhauling the power unit, use all parts in the repair kit. Inspect all other parts and replace damaged or excessively worn parts.

If the inside of the cylinder is rusted

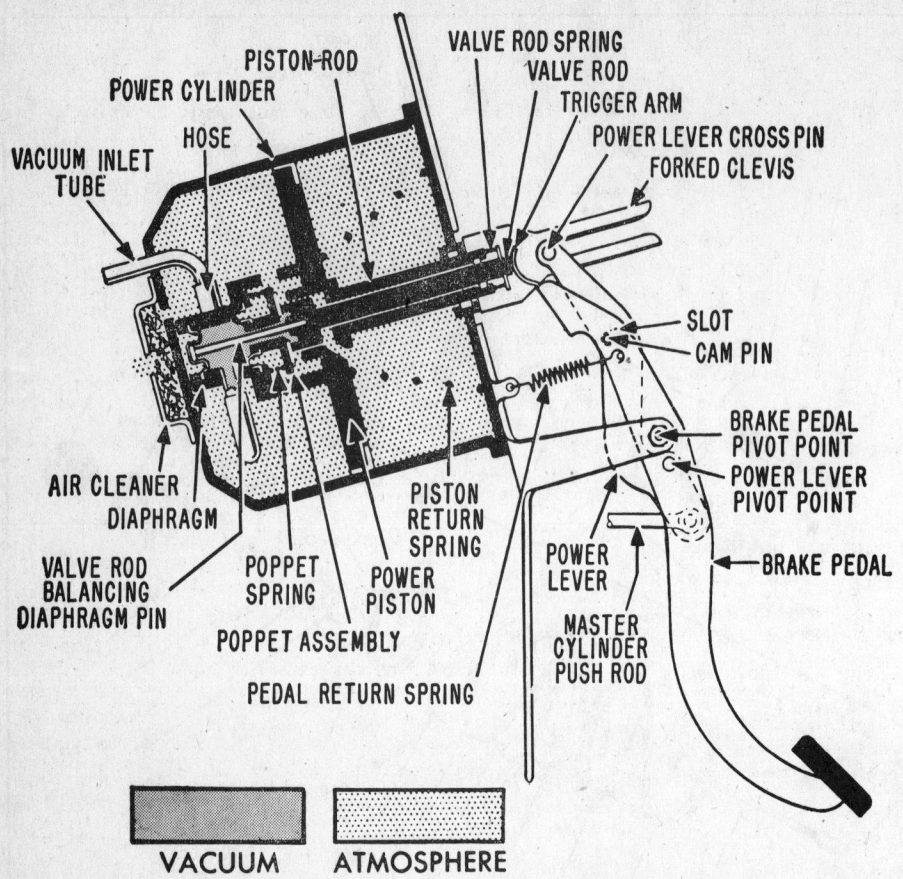

Fig. 7 Bendix Powervac, reactionary linkage type

or corroded, polish with steel wool or fine emery cloth. If inspection reveals nicks or scratches on the piston rod, valve seat at end of valve rod, or valve seat at center of piston plate, replace parts. If piston leather packing or piston rod leather seal are worn excessively, replace.

In servicing one of these units, refer to Figs. 7, 8 and 9 and observe the following precautions:

1. Before removing the unit from the vehicle, place a wood wedge between the power brake lever and the forward edge of the triangular hole in the pedal bracket. This will prevent the trigger arm from extending beyond the extremities of the bracket.
2. Scribe a mark across the air cleaner cover, vacuum tube and plate and cylinder shell as a guide to correct reassembly.
3. Scribe a mark across the cylinder flange and end plate as a guide for reassembly.
4. Scribe a mark across the tube plate and piston plate to insure correct reassembly.
5. Scribe a mark across mounting ring and end plate to assure correct assembly.
6. Assemble piston plate with threaded hole side up.
7. Assemble leather packing on piston with lip side up.
8. Coil cotton wick inside of packing lip and cut wick to required length. Remove and dip wick in Bendix

Vacuum Cylinder Oil. Let excess oil drip off and again coil wicking inside packing.

9. Assemble piston, piston retainer spring and piston rod to end plate as shown in Fig. 10.
10. When assembling parts shown in Fig. 13, assemble valve rod seal over end of valve rod and piston rod. Turn seal partially inside out and assemble small diameter end of seal over valve rod first and then assemble larger diameter over end of piston rod.
11. When assembling vacuum tube it must be in the lower left quadrant as shown in Fig. 11 (left insert) when slot in push rod is horizontal and vacuum test port is at location indicated, *regardless of scribe marks.*

BENDIX MASTER-VAC

Index No. 3

Figs. 12 and 13 show the construction of this unit. It consists of three conventional parts: the vacuum power cylinder assembly, the vacuum power piston, and the master cylinder with reservoir.

Disassembly

1. Separate master cylinder from power cylinder.
2. Scribe a line across end plate and vacuum cylinder to aid in reassembly.

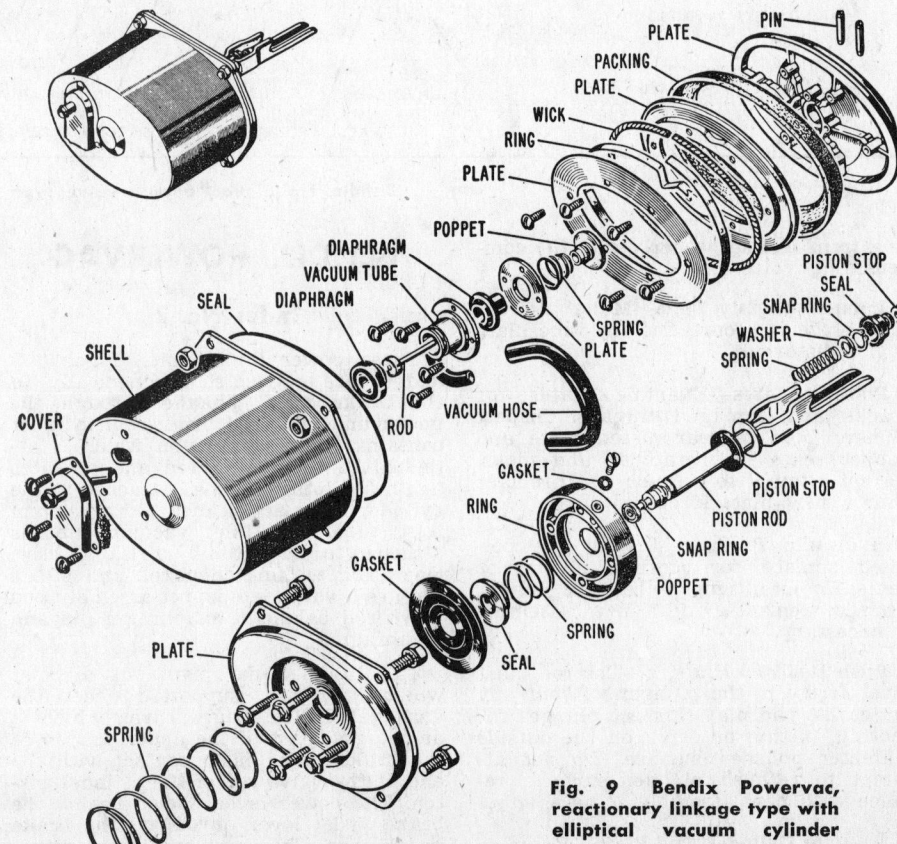

Fig. 9 Bendix Powervac, reactionary linkage type with elliptical vacuum cylinder

3. Scribe a line across face of piston to register with scribe marks on end plate and vacuum cylinder.
4. Remove end plate, Fig. 13.

Inspection

1. Remove air cleaner element and replace if dirty or cracked.
2. Inspect vacuum cylinder for scoring, pitting, dents or nicks. Small imperfections may be smoothed out by using fine crocus cloth. Replace if badly damaged.
3. Examine hydraulic push rod for nicks, corrosion or abrasion. If damaged in any way replace with a new push rod.

Assemble

1. Refer to Figs. 13, 14 and 15. Then assemble air cleaner element over vacuum tube of air cleaner and attach assembly to end plate.
2. Slide vacuum hose onto vacuum tube inlet of air cleaner.
3. Install push rod, being certain rubber reaction disc is in place in front piston plate.
4. Apply a thin coat of shock absorber fluid to base of vacuum cylinder and to piston leather.
5. Center small diameter of piston return spring in vacuum cylinder with large diameter facing piston.
6. Insert vacuum piston into cylinder, aligning scribe marks on face of piston with scribe marks on end plate and vacuum cylinder.

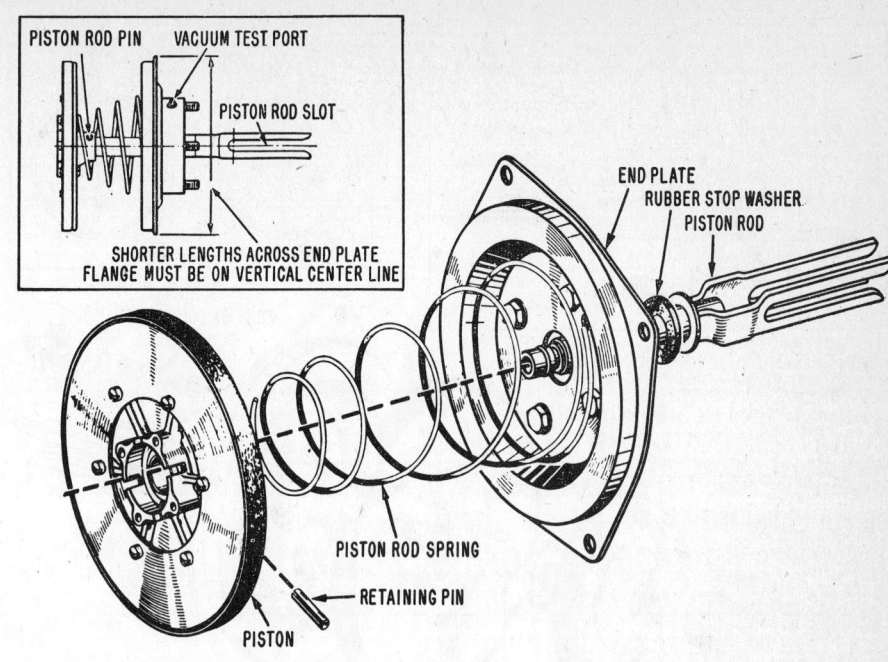

Fig. 10 Assembly of piston, piston retainer spring and piston rod

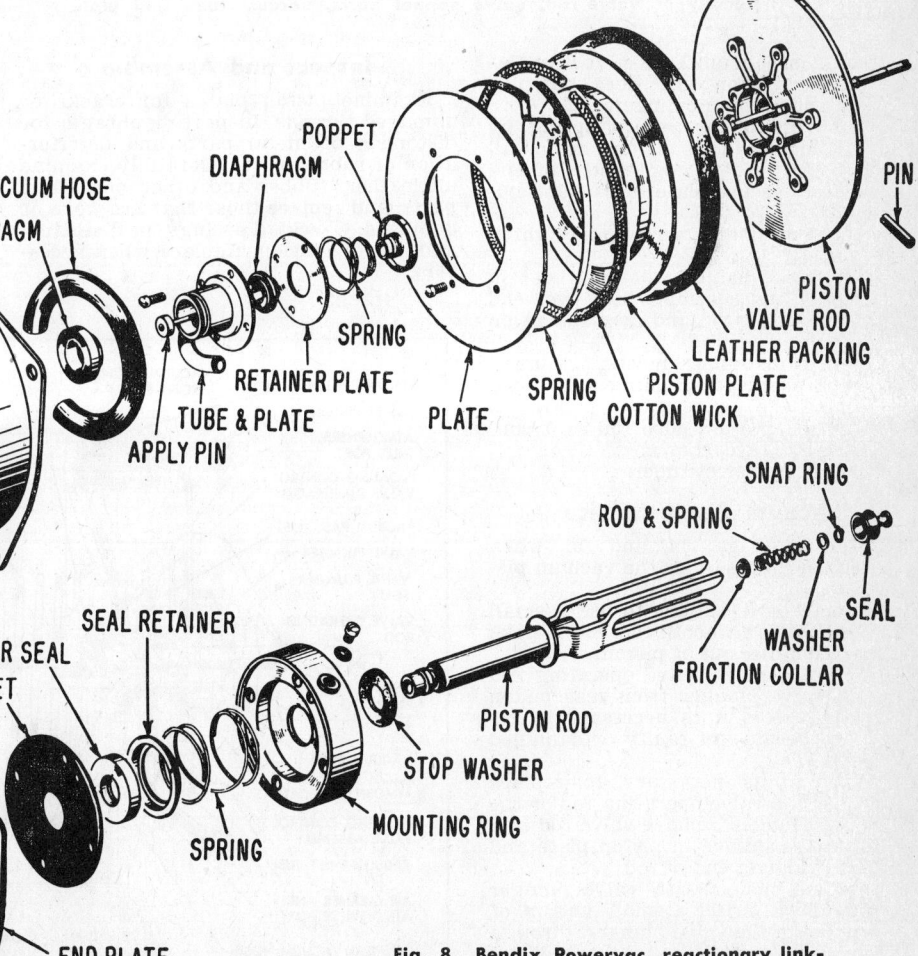

Fig. 8 Bendix Powervac, reactionary linkage type with round vacuum cylinder

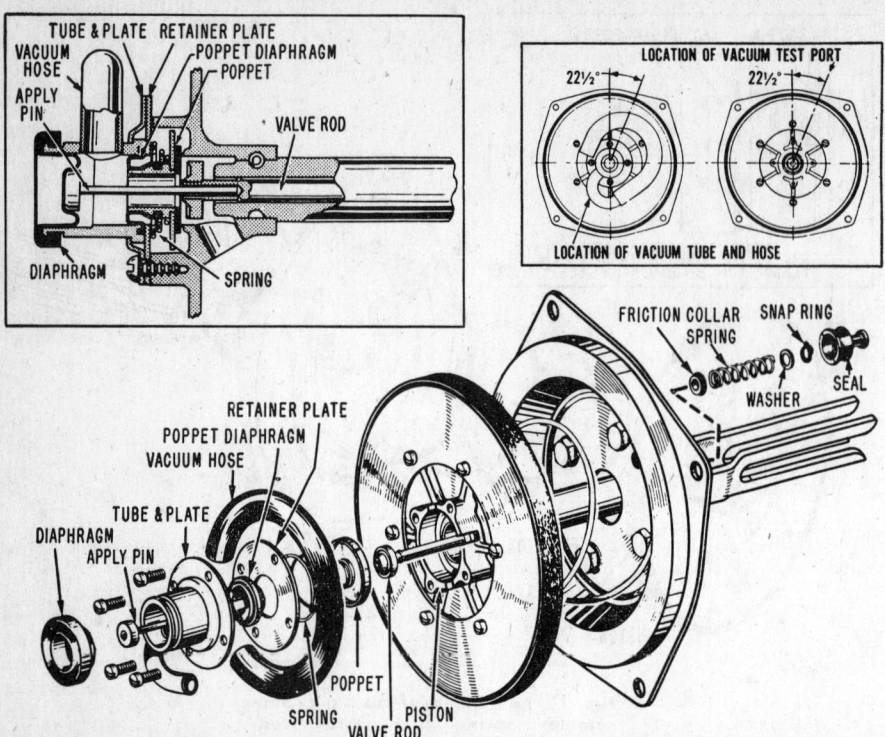

Fig. 11 Assembly of valve rod, valve poppet parts, vacuum tube and plate

7. Position vacuum hose so it lays flat against piston and does not rub against vacuum cylinder.

8. Compress piston return spring by pressing down on piston and install two screws at opposite sides of end plate to secure plate to vacuum cylinder.

9. Install remaining screws and tighten securely.

10. Dip small diameter of dust boot in alcohol and assemble boot over end of operating rod and over flange on end plate.

11. Before installing master cylinder, check push rod adjustment by positioning the gauge shown in Fig. 16 over rod. Adjust push rod so it contacts gauge as shown.

12. Install master cylinder.

Vacuum Piston Service

1. Refer to Figs. 14 and 15 when necessary to service the vacuum piston.

2. It may be necessary to use a small rod having a smooth flat end to push reaction disc out of piston.

3. Do not remove valve operating rod and valve plunger from rear piston plate unless it is necessary to replace because of faulty or damaged parts.

4. When it is necessary to replace either the valve operating rod or the valve plunger, remove valve rod seal from the groove in piston plate and pull seal over end of rod.

5. Holding piston with valve plunger side down, inject a small amount of alcohol in the valve plunger, through opening around valve rod, to wet the rubber lock in the plunger, then drive or pry valve plunger off valve rod.

Inspect and Assemble

Examine piston plates for cracks or damaged threads. Inspect diaphragm for distortion of metal parts and deterioration of rubber parts. Carefully examine all leather, rubber and other perishable parts, and replace those that are worn or damaged. Check all springs for distortion and loss of tension. Replace when necessary.

Reverse the disassembly procedure to assemble the piston, referring to Figs. 14 and 15. If valve operating rod and valve plunger are to be replaced, make certain ball end of rod is locked in valve plunger.

KELSEY HAYES

Piston Type—Index No. 8

This unit, Figs. 18 to 21, is a vacuum suspended system which means that vacuum exists on both sides of the power piston in the unapplied stage when engine or vacuum pump is running. The power brake utilizes engine manifold vacuum in its operation, therefore it is connected to the intake manifold through pipes and flexible connections.

Vacuum Pump

A vane type vacuum pump, driven by an electric motor, is installed in the line between the power brake cylinder and the engine intake manifold to furnish an auxiliary source of vacuum for power brake application whenever the engine is not operating. The pump contains a check valve which maintains a reserve vacuum in the cylinder sufficient for two brake applications with normally light pedal pressure.

The pump receives its current through the ignition switch and a cutout relay. When the engine is not running, the relay contacts are closed so that when the ignition switch is turned on the pump will operate to supply vacuum for brake application. When the engine is started, voltage supplied by the generator energizes the relay coil which then separates the contacts to cut out operation of the pump.

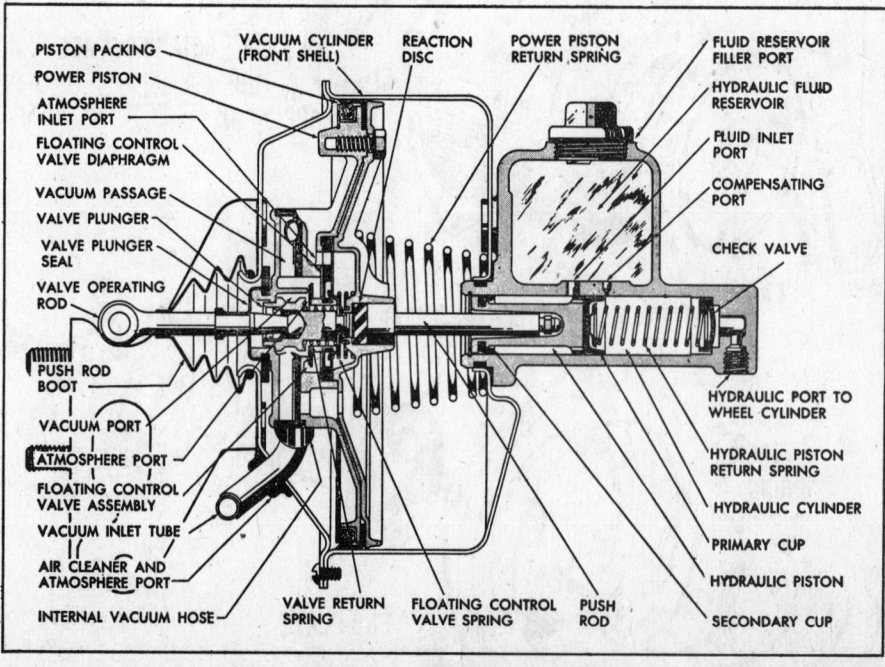

Fig. 12 Bendix Master-Vac

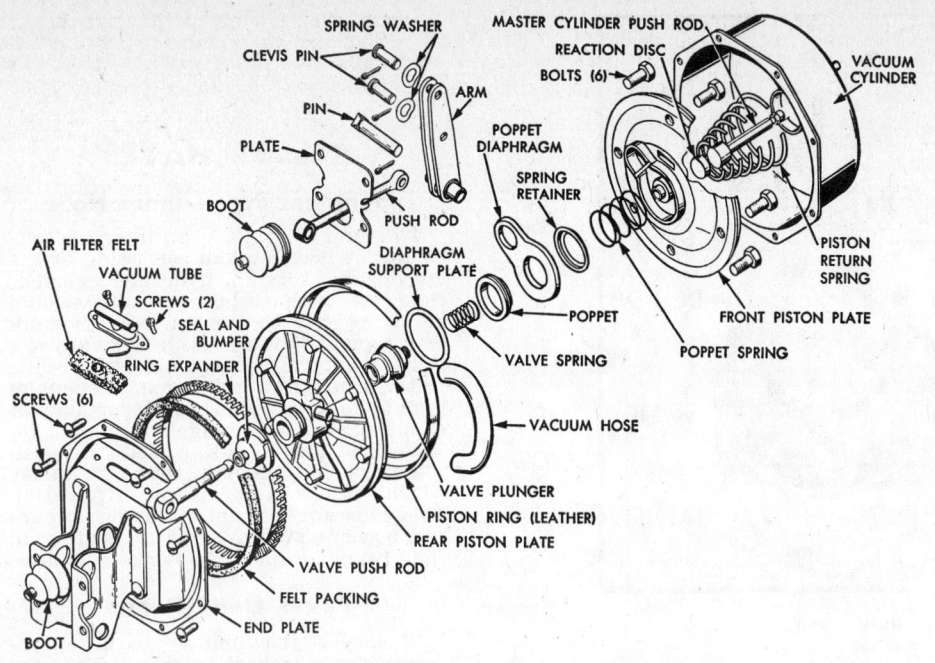

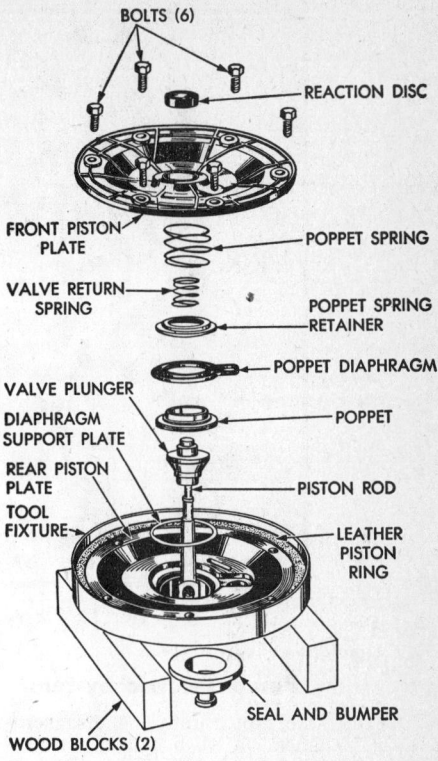

Fig. 13 Exploded view of Bendix Master-Vac

Fig. 14 Bendix Master-Vac power unit piston

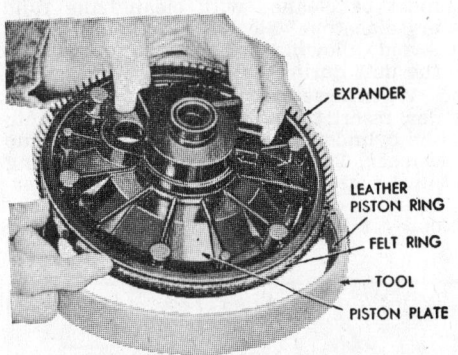

Fig. 15 Assembling piston ring, felt and expander

Vacuum Pump Lubrication

Power brake vacuum pumps are filled at the factory with one ounce of special lubricating oil which provides for 5000 miles of normal operation. The oil supply should be checked every 5000 miles by removing the filler screw on the top surface of the pump.

Maintain the oil level at ¼" below the top of the cover in the Morvac pump, Fig. 19, and with 1" in the Trico pump, Fig. 20.

Vacuum Pump Repairs

When it becomes necessary to dis-

assemble the power brake vacuum pump for inspection or repairs, thoroughly clean all dirt from the exterior, then remove the filler screw and drain the oil from the reservoir. Removal of the cover screws will permit easy disassembly of either type pump. Figs. 19 and 20 show all parts and how they should be placed when pumps are reassembled.

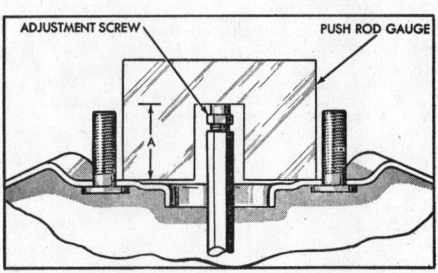

Fig. 16 Adjusting master cylinder push rod.

Dimension "A" applies as follows:

Cadillac 1959	1.180-1.200"
Cadillac 1960-61	1.833-1.844"
Chevrolet 1959-61	1.195-1.200"
Ford 1960-61	.962- .967"
Lincoln	1.175-1.180"
Mercury 1959-61	.990- .995"
Oldsmobile 1960-61	1.833-1.844"
Pontiac 1959-61	1.195-1.200"
Thunderbird 1960-61	.962- .967"
Studebaker 1961	1.195-2.000"
Valiant 1960-61	1.195-1.200"

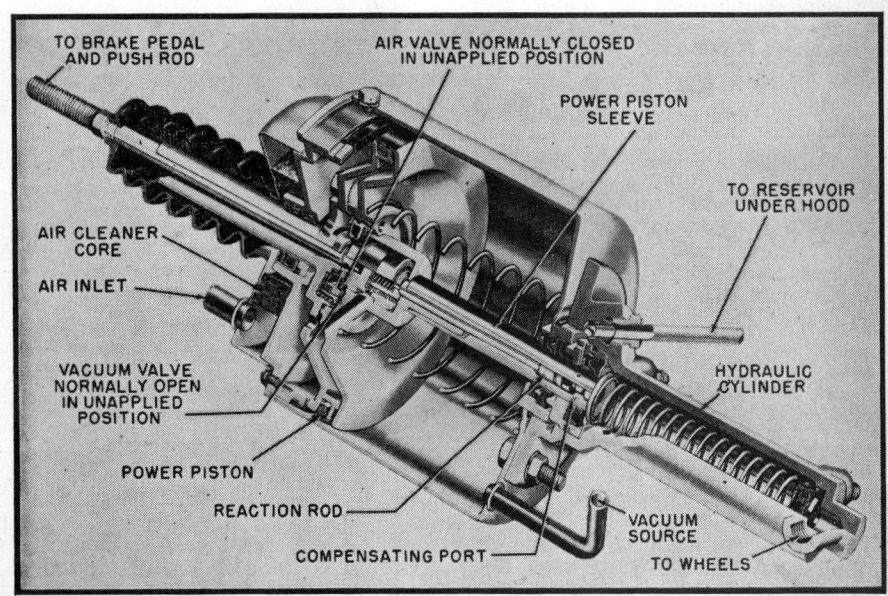

Fig. 18 Kelsey Hayes piston type

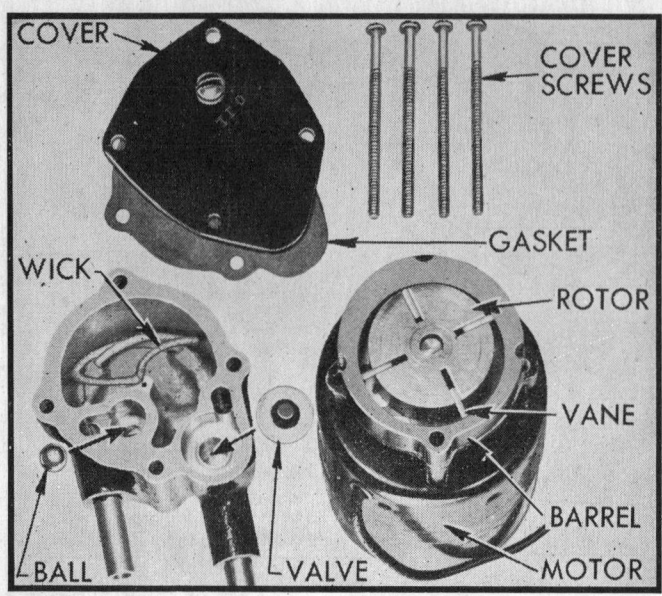

Fig. 19 Morvac vacuum pump

Vacuum Pump Electric System

The electric motor may be disassembled for inspection of brushes, commutator and windings by removing the two long screws and carefully tapping the cover loose from the field frame.

When adjusting the relay, set the point opening at .017"-.033". The relay opening voltage should be adjusted to 5.7-7.2 volts. After excitation of 12-15 volts, points must re-close at not more than 3 volts.

Power Unit Repairs

When it becomes necessary to disassemble the power brake unit for repairs, refer to Fig. 21 and observe the precautions outlined as follows:

1. As an aid in determining the cause of improper power brake operation, wipe fluid from all rubber parts, the residual check valve, the floating control valve and air valve seat. Then carefully examine these parts for nicks, cuts or other damage. After examination, *discard* all these parts.
2. Thoroughly clean the remaining parts in an approved type of alcohol or clean brake fluid.
3. Carefully examine the cleaned parts for nicks, burrs, stripped threads or other damage.
4. Make certain that the small compensating ports in the end of the power piston sleeve are clear. If these holes are plugged, clean them thoroughly and flush the hydraulic system to remove all dirt.
5. If the power piston guide sleeve, outer surface of piston sleeve, or inner surface of sleeve where reaction piston operates show evidence of abrasion, polish out light scores with crocus cloth or very fine polishing paper, then wash and dry thoroughly.
6. If any parts indicate that heavy abrasive action has resulted from

severe contamination of the brake fluid, replace damaged parts and be sure to flush the reservoir and wheel cylinder lines.

7. The power brake cylinder overhaul kit contains all necessary replacement parts for the unit. When reassembling the brake cylinder use all the new parts regardless of whether the old parts appear fit for use. In addition, replace any other parts which inspection indicates to be unfit for use.
8. Before installation, wet all O-rings and rubber cups with clean brake fluid, except where O-ring or seal is pre-greased. *Do not destroy this application of silicone grease.*

KELSEY HAYES

Diaphragm Type—Index No. 6

This unit, Fig. 22, is an integral, self-contained power brake consisting of the air-vacuum housing, hydraulic cylinder, fluid reservoir, air cleaner and vacuum check valve. No vacuum reserve tank or a remote fluid reservoir are required.

The unit is connected to the brake pedal through a push rod. Pendulum type linkage provides the proper amount of mechanical advantage for the driver. When the pedal is depressed, the push rod moves into the unit, actuating valves which create a pressure differential. This causes movement of the diaphragm and power piston assembly, resulting in fluid being forced to the wheel cylinders.

Power Unit Repairs

Whenever the unit is to be disassembled for inspection or repairs, refer to Fig. 23 and observe the precautions outlined for reassembly. Before any part of the unit is reassembled, all metal parts must be cleaned with clean bake fluid or diacetone alcohol and wiped dry. Avoid allowing grit or dirt to get into the unit during reassembly.

When assembling the hydraulic cylinder, insert the power piston bearing into the cylinder on top of the secondary cup washer. The notched face of the bearing must face upward and it must be centered in the cylinder bore. Place the primary cup retainer into the cylinder with the

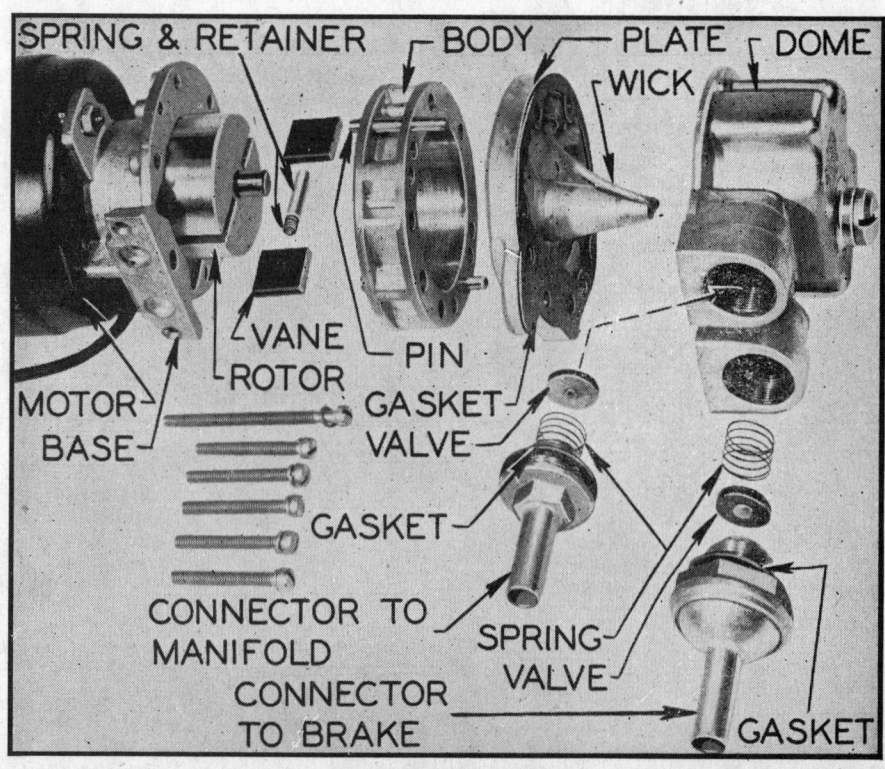

Fig 20 Trico vacuum pump

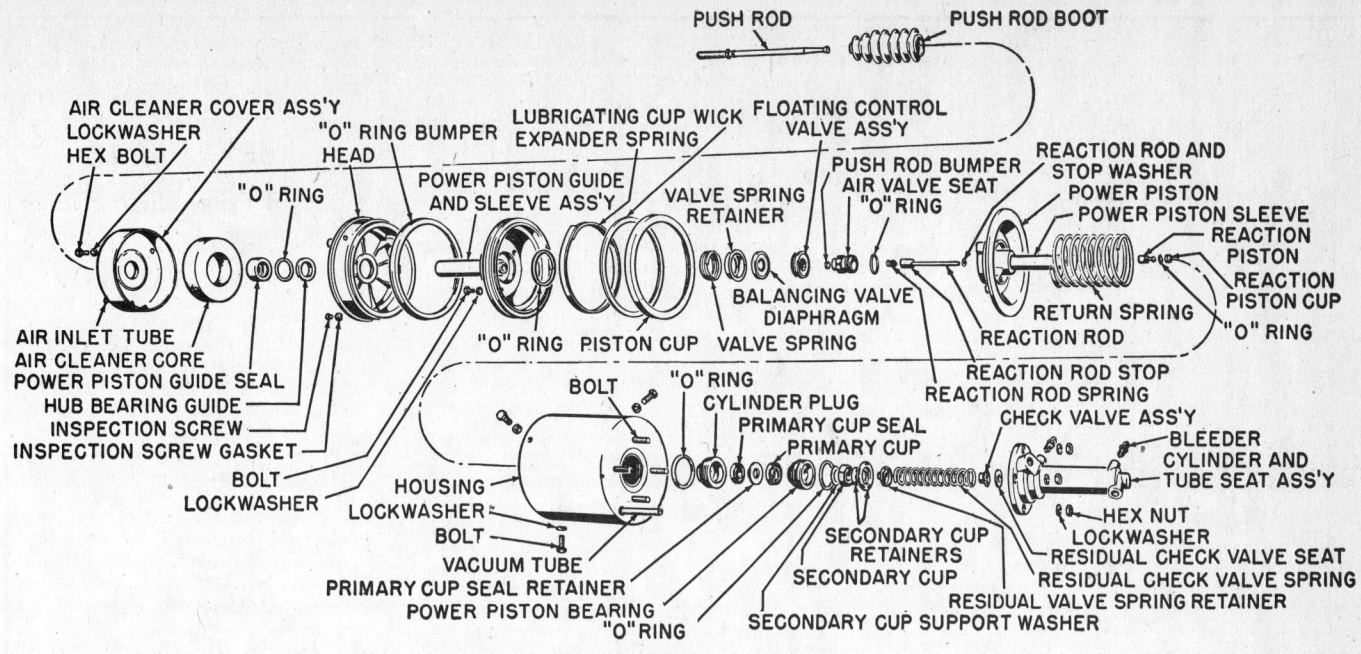

Fig. 21 Kelsey Hayes piston type

notched end down, centering it on the notched surface of the power piston bearing. *This is very important as the retainer will otherwise be damaged when the cylinder plug is installed.*

When assembling the power piston and guide, press the reaction piston and dome cup into the sleeve (dome out). Work carefully to avoid damaging the cup. Press the dome cup firmly down into the sleeve until it bottoms. Check to see that the outer diameter of the reaction cup is not obstructing the compensating ports and that all of these port holes are clean and open.

Install the complete air valve seat assembly in the center of the power piston cavity, over the control spring, reaction spring and reaction rod stop. Use a twisting motion as the seal enters the bore of the power piston. Use thumb pressure to test the air valve seat against the springs for freedom of movement. *The air valve is steel and the cavity is aluminum; therefore, work with care to avoid damaging parts, especially the aluminum vacuum seat.*

When assembling the rubber guide return bumper over the guide sleeve, be sure to install a bumper of the same thickness as the one removed, as the repair kit contains two bumpers, each of a different thickness.

When assembling the cylinder side of the body, insert the floating valve assembly, being sure that the bonded rubber seal is facing downward against the seat.

During the final assembly, while holding the power piston and guide downward, position the flange of the valve side of the body over the edge of the diaphragm and flange of the cylinder side of the body. Press firmly into position. The two sides of the body must be assembled with the notches on one side mated with the keys on the other and the cutaway portions of the flange match.

KELSEY HAYES

Bellows Type—Index No. 7

This type power brake, Fig. 24, is an air-vacuum bellows mounted on the engine side of the dash panel. It is connected mechanically to brake pedal linkage through the power unit push rod. The unit is air suspended and therefore requires a vacuum reserve tank which is mounted on the engine side of the front fender splash shield.

Brake linkage exists only when the unit is assisting in a brake application. With a loss of engine vacuum the brake pedal is free to move completely, independent of the power unit, to apply the brakes in the conventional manner.

Power Unit Repairs

When it becomes necessary to disassemble the unit for repairs, refer to Fig. 24 and observe the following:

When removing the unit from the vehicle, depress and block the pedal to prevent the trigger arm from extending beyond the extremities of the bracket. If the pedal linkage is allowed to extend through the hole in the dash panel, the trigger arm may be damaged. When withdrawing the unit from the dash panel, use care to prevent loss of the nylon bushing on the pedal linkage cross pin.

After disassembling the unit, clean all parts (except bellows, bearing and air filter) in solvent and blow dry with compressed air. If necessary, the bellows may be washed with warm water and mild soap. Inspect all parts for wear or damage and check the air valve for signs of scoring or wear. If the valve body or valve is scored or worn, install new parts as required. Always use new rubber parts, regardless of the condition of the old ones. When reassembling the unit, be sure to observe the following:

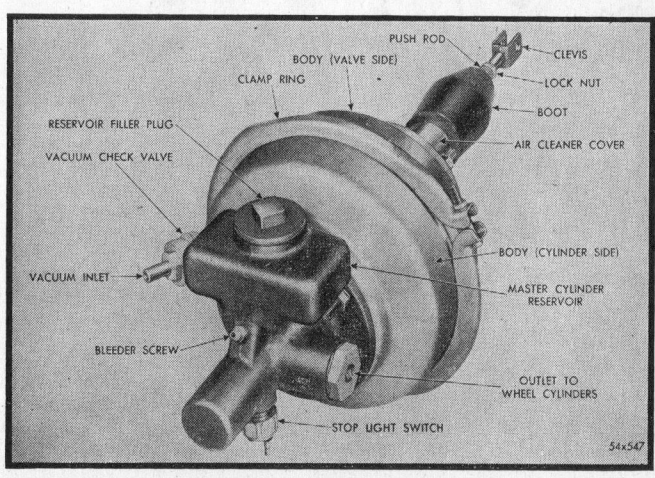

Fig. 22 Kelsey Hayes diaphragm type

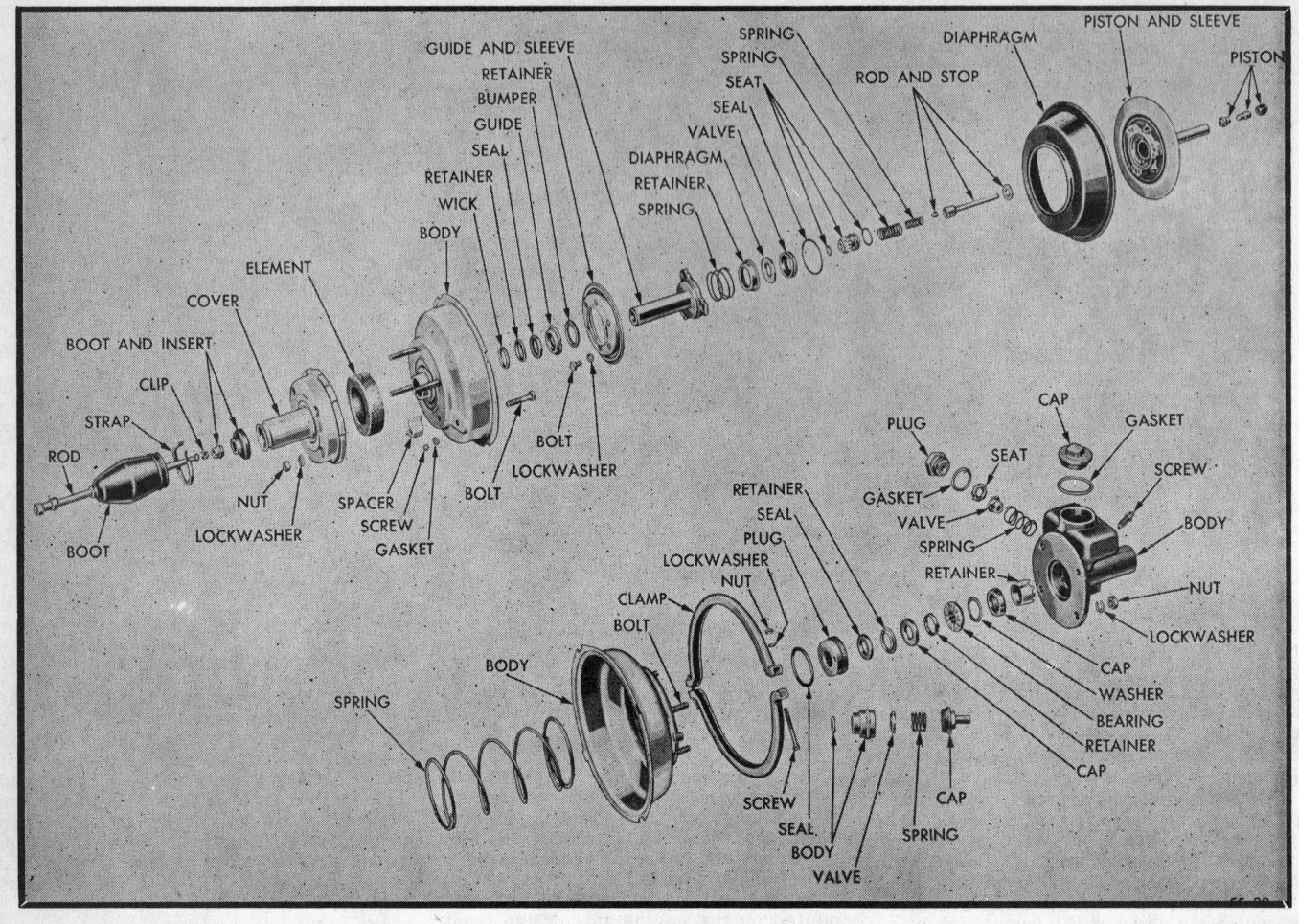

Fig. 23   Kelsey Hayes diaphragm type

1. The vacuum valve seal should be installed in the guide bore with the lip of the seal toward the bottom of the bore.
2. When installing the guide against the valve body, make certain the tapered portion of the vacuum valve enters the seal evenly.
3. If a new bellows is being installed, position the supports in the bellows so they are centered in the three accordion folds and aligned with the bellows and each other. Using holding fixture (made from piece of 4" pipe) to support guide and valve assembly, install bellows, *being sure arrows on edge of bellows and housing are aligned.*
4. With assembly in holding fixture, lightly coat outer surface of air valve with *silicone grease* (no other) and insert into the bore of housing with small end first. Use finger pressure to test for free movement of valve against vacuum valve spring.
5. When installing the valve body cover over the valve housing, do so with the notch in the edge of the cover matching the arrow on the bellows. Be sure air valve spring nestles on dimple in center of cover.
6. When installing the guide spring, place the spring retainer and inner mounting plate over the spring, being sure arrow stamped on plate is in line with arrow on edge of bellows.
7. Using silicone grease only, lubricate inside of bearing and slide it over guide, while compressing bellows. *Bearing must be installed with lip of seal facing out.* Push bearing down over guide and into pocket of plate. Release bellows and bearing will ride up guide with plate into position.
8. The notch on the edge of the outer mounting plate must be in line with

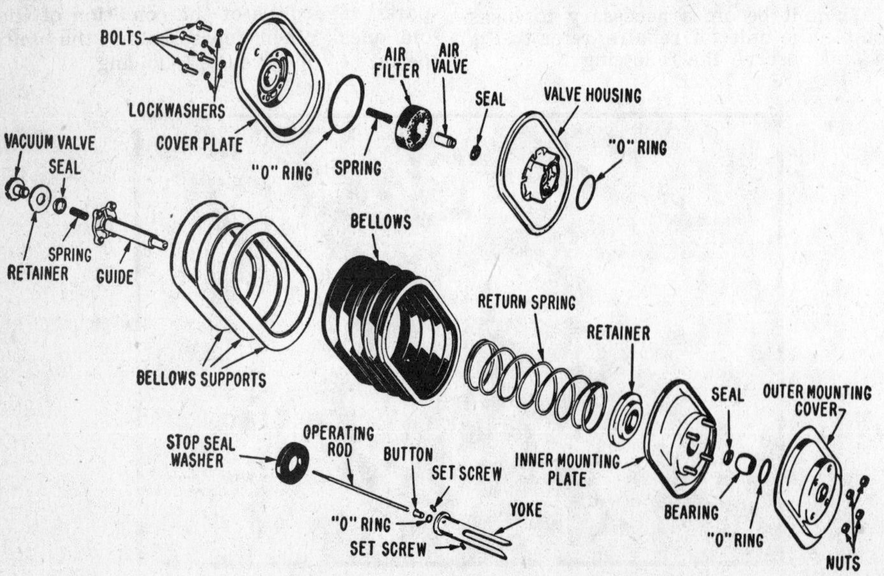

Fig. 24   Kelsey Hayes bellows type power brake

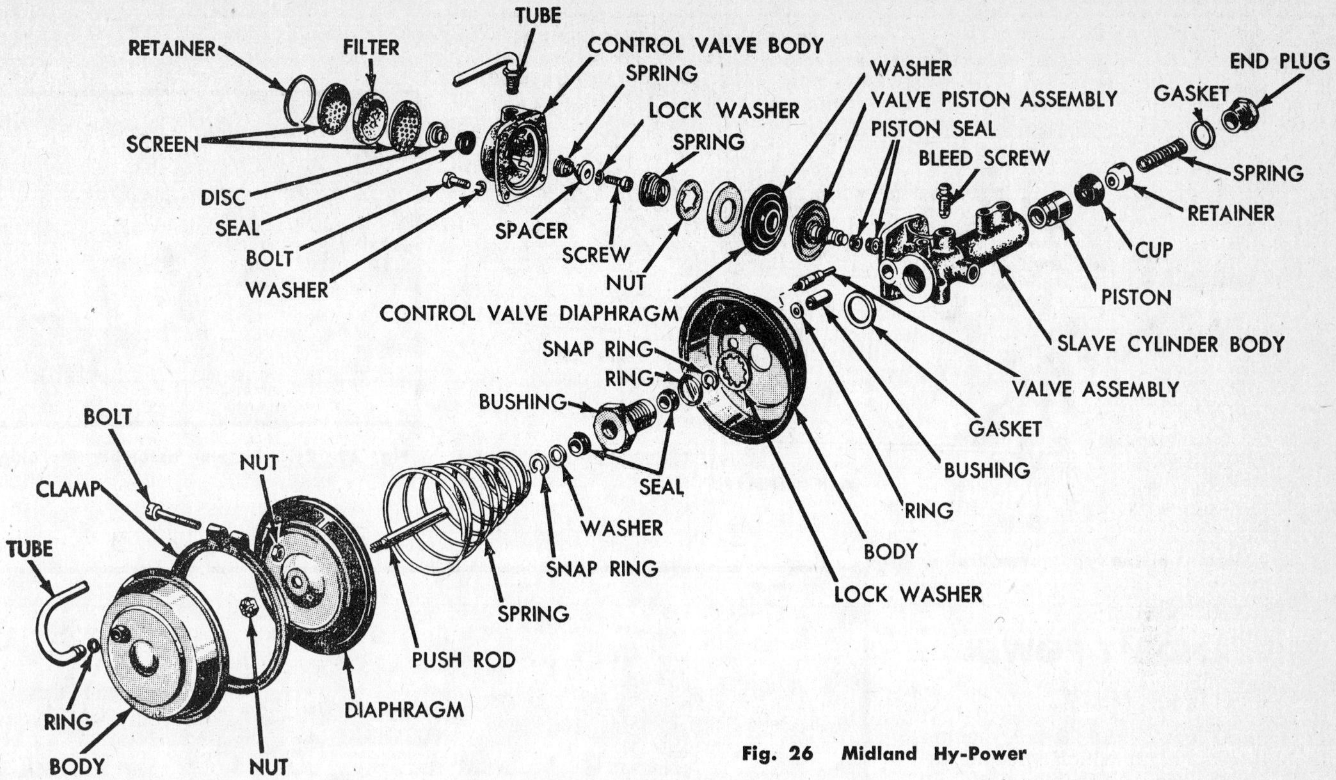

RETAINER   FILTER   TUBE   CONTROL VALVE BODY
SPRING
SCREEN   LOCK WASHER   WASHER   END PLUG
SPRING   VALVE PISTON ASSEMBLY   GASKET
DISC   PISTON SEAL   SPRING
SEAL   BLEED SCREW   RETAINER
BOLT   SPACER   SCREW   CUP
WASHER   SCREW   PISTON
NUT   SLAVE CYLINDER BODY
CONTROL VALVE DIAPHRAGM   VALVE ASSEMBLY
SNAP RING   GASKET
RING   BUSHING
BUSHING   RING
RING   BODY
SEAL   LOCK WASHER
WASHER
BOLT   SNAP RING
NUT   SPRING
CLAMP   PUSH ROD
TUBE   DIAPHRAGM
RING
BODY   NUT

Fig. 26   Midland Hy-Power

arrow on bellows.

9. When the operating rod is installed, press on its end to test for free movement of air and vacuum valves. A "two-step" movement should be felt when the rod is depressed and released fully.

10. When installed, the hub of the yoke must be down snug against the shoulder of the guide with set screws aligned with tapered holes in guide.

11. When installing the power unit on the car, as the yoke passes through the dash panel, be sure that it engages the pedal linkage correctly by sliding over nylon bushings on power brake lever cross pin.

Pedal Linkage Adjustments

If the pedal pressure releases slowly, adjust by rotating the adjustment screw, in a counterclockwise direction.

A time delay, noted during a fast brake application, can be corrected by making a *clockwise* adjustment on the adjustment screw.

Should the pedal vibrate (booster chatter) turn the adjustment screw *counterclockwise*.

Rotation of the adjustment screw should be limited to plus or minus 90 degrees about the original setting.

Pedal Free Play Adjustment

A pedal free play adjustment check should be made after the booster, master cylinder and pedal linkage are installed. When checking, there should be no vacuum in the system; removing the vacuum hose and pressing the brake pedal several times will aid in obtaining a no vacuum condition.

Insert the blade of a screwdriver between the rubber collar of the trigger pivot and the rear side of the elongated hole in the brake lever, forcing them apart. If these parts are not forced apart, a false free play setting, which includes booster valve travel, will be measured at pad end of pedal.

Check free play with linkage in this position by pushing lightly at pad end of pedal. Free pedal travel should be $\frac{1}{32}"$ to $\frac{1}{8}"$. Adjustment is made by lengthening or shortening the push rod as required.

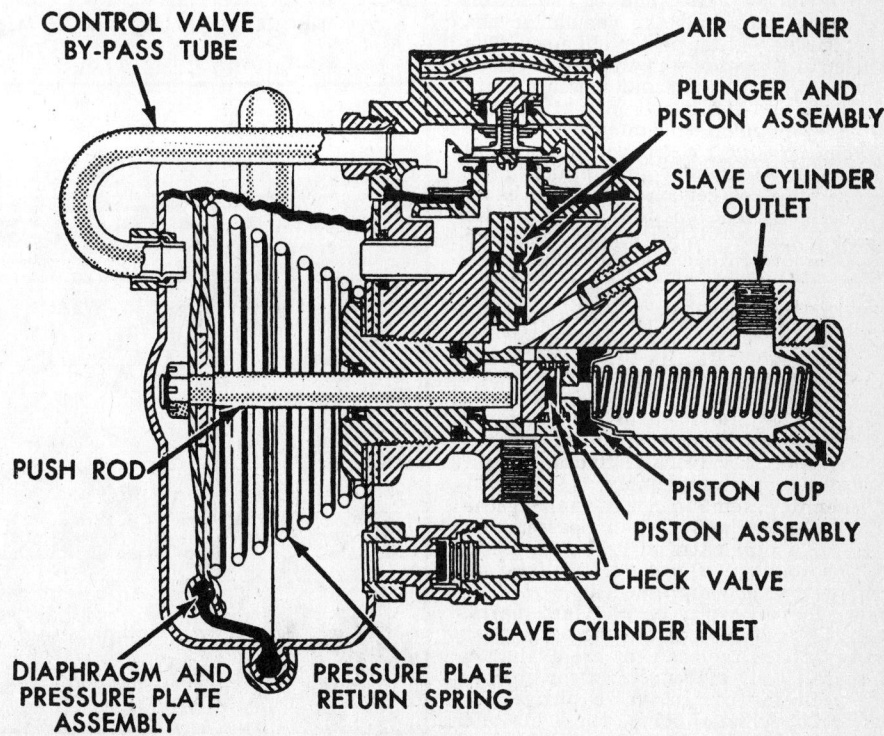

CONTROL VALVE BY-PASS TUBE   AIR CLEANER
PLUNGER AND PISTON ASSEMBLY
SLAVE CYLINDER OUTLET
PUSH ROD   PISTON CUP
PISTON ASSEMBLY
CHECK VALVE
DIAPHRAGM AND PRESSURE PLATE ASSEMBLY   PRESSURE PLATE RETURN SPRING   SLAVE CYLINDER INLET

Fig. 25   Midland Hy-Power

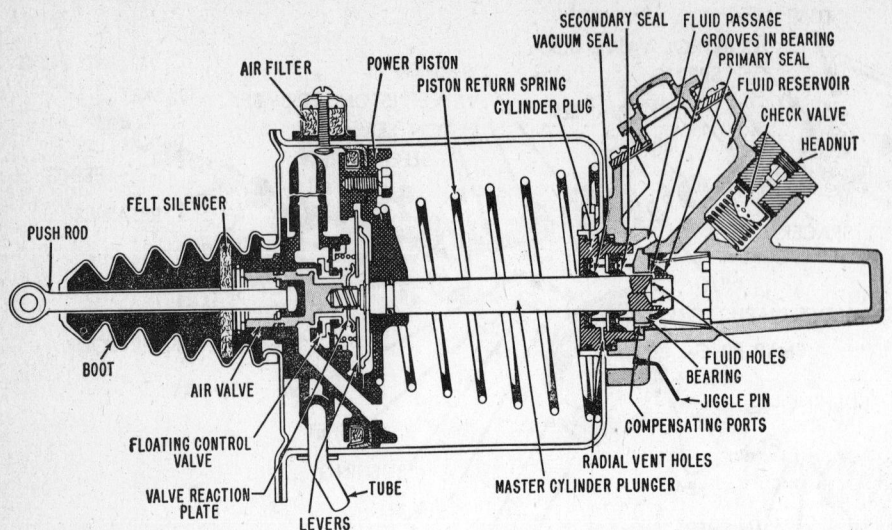

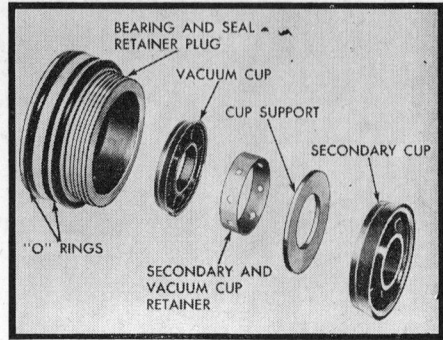

Fig. 29 Cylinder plug assembly. Moraine

Fig. 27 Moraine piston type power brake

MIDLAND HY-POWER

Index No. 9

This unit, Figs. 25 and 26, is a vacuum suspended system in which vacuum exists on both sides of the diaphragm in the unapplied stage when the engine is running.

When the brake pedal is depressed, fluid passes from the master cylinder through the slave cylinder piston openings to the control valve plunger and piston, around the slave cylinder check valve, and through the piston and cup orifices into the brake lines.

As the hydraulic line pressure builds up, the control valve plunger and piston moves out and seals the vacuum in the rear section of the power chamber. The atmospheric pressure in the front section forces the diaphragm and pressure plate assembly and the push rod back toward the slave cylinder. This movement causes the check valve to seal the brake fluid in the slave cylinder and brake lines. As the push rod continues to move back, the slave cylinder piston and cup also moves back and builds up the hydraulic line pressure to operate the brakes.

Power Unit Repairs

When necessary to disassemble the power brake unit for repairs, first mark both bodies of the booster chamber so they can be assembled in their original position. Also punch-mark the flanges of the control valve and hydraulic cylinder for proper reassembly.

When disassembling or assembling the unit, refer to Fig. 26. When disassembled wash all metal parts in brake fluid and dry thoroughly. Blow out all internal passages with compressed air.

Replace all worn or damaged parts. Repair kits which contain the parts most likely to need replacement are available. If there is any evidence of wear or corrosion in the control valve plunger or hydraulic cylinder bores, the hydraulic cylinder body should be replaced.

The push rod must be perfectly smooth

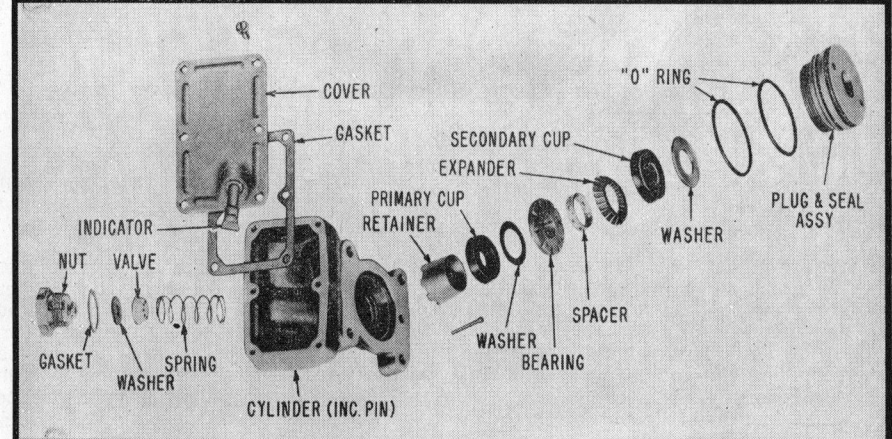

Fig. 28 Exploded view of Moraine power brake master cylinder

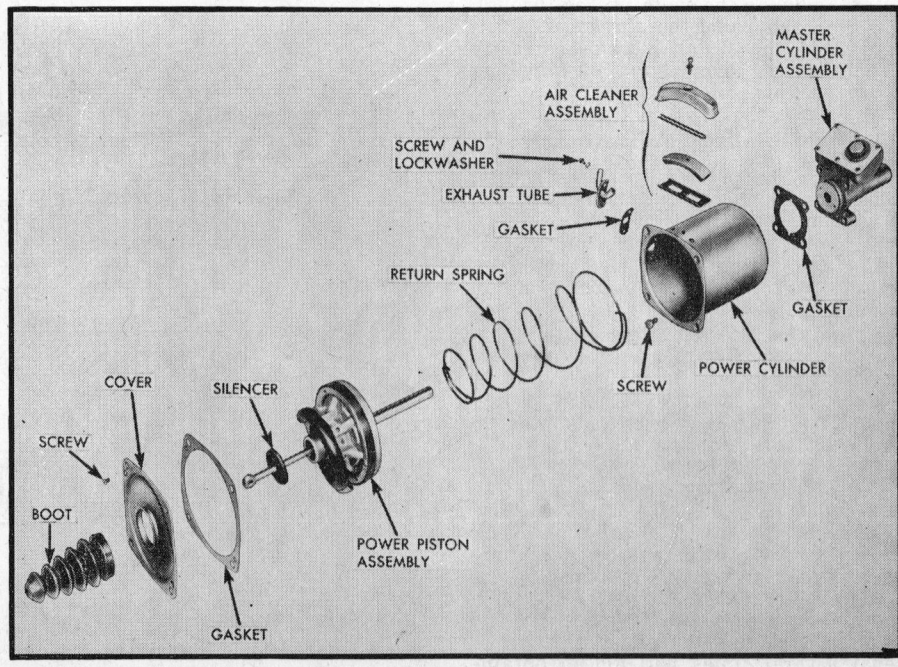

Fig. 30 Exploded view of Moraine power piston

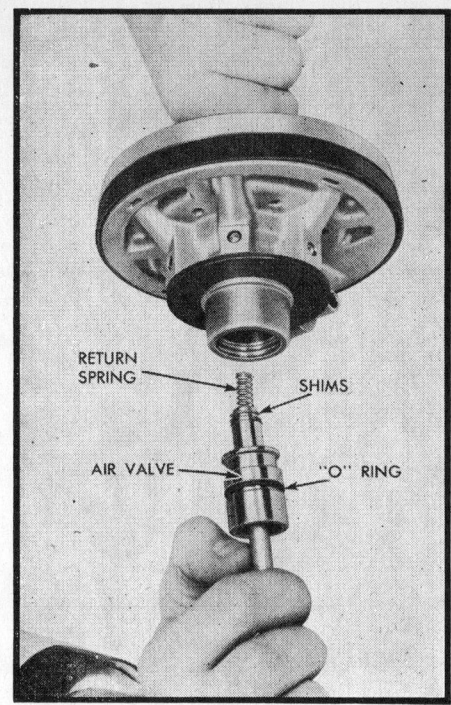

Fig. 31 Installing air valve in power piston. Moraine

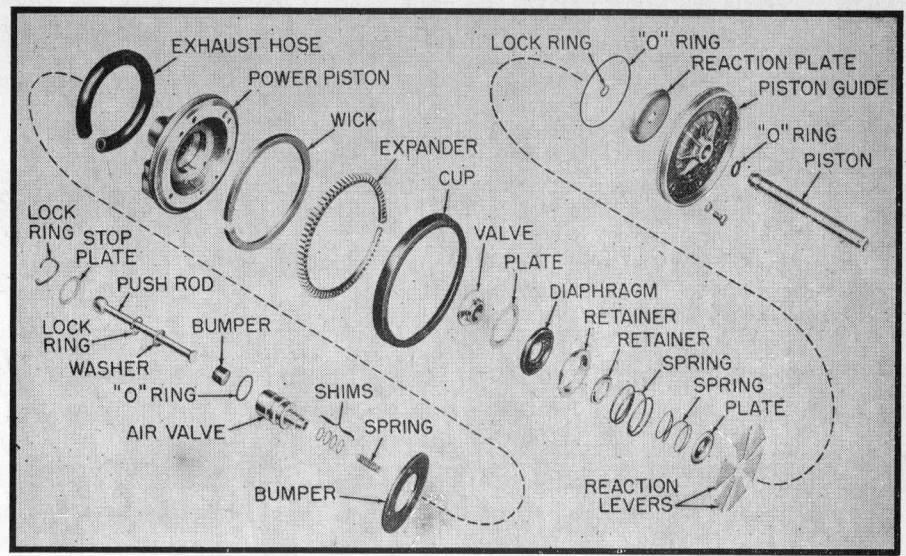

Fig. 32 Exploded view of Moraine power brake master cylinder

and must show no wear to avoid leakage at the seal. Replace the control valve diaphragm, all rubber cups and seals, and the spring. If the control valve seat is damaged, replace the control valve body. Clean the air cleaner screen and blow out with compressed air.

MORAINE

Piston Type—Index No. 10

This unit, Fig. 27, is an air suspended power brake, meaning that atmospheric pressure is present on both sides of the power piston when the brakes are released. The system utilizes intake manifold vacuum and atmospheric pressure for its operation. The power brake unit replaces the master cylinder only. Other parts of the brake system are the same as with conventional brakes.

Two external lines connect to the power brake unit. One is a vacuum connection to the intake manifold (and vacuum reservoir); the other is a hydraulic connection into the hydraulic brake system.

Power Unit Repairs

When it becomes necessary to disassemble the unit for repairs, refer to Figs. 27 to 32 and observe the precautions outlined below before reassembling.

The power cylinder overhaul kit contains all necessary replacement parts for the unit. Use all the new parts in the kit regardless of whether the old parts appear fit for use. In addition, replace any other parts which inspection indicates to be unfit for use.

Inspection of Parts

When the unit has been disassembled,

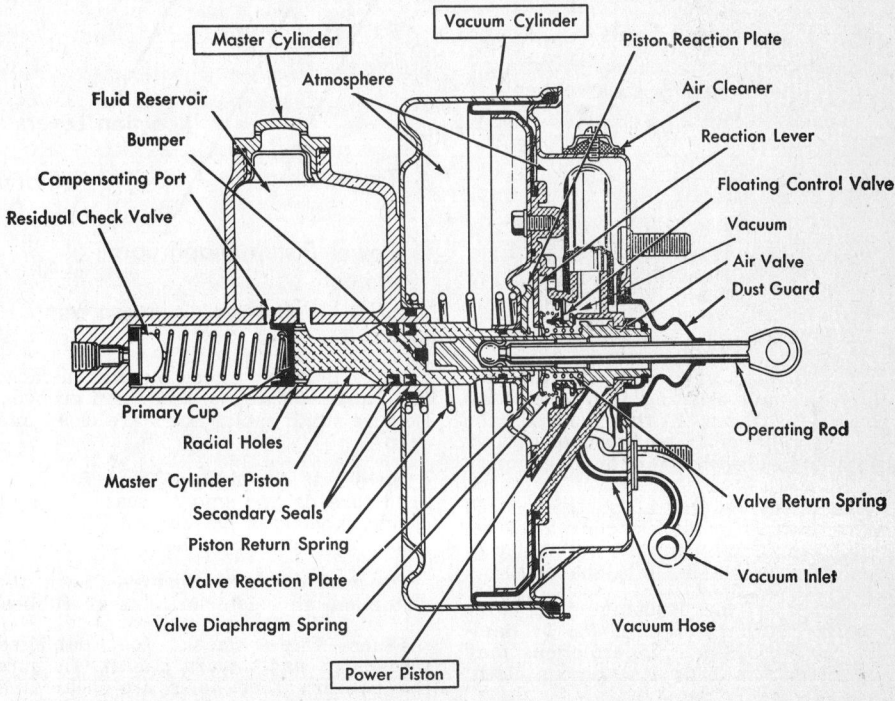

Fig. 33 Moraine diaphragm type

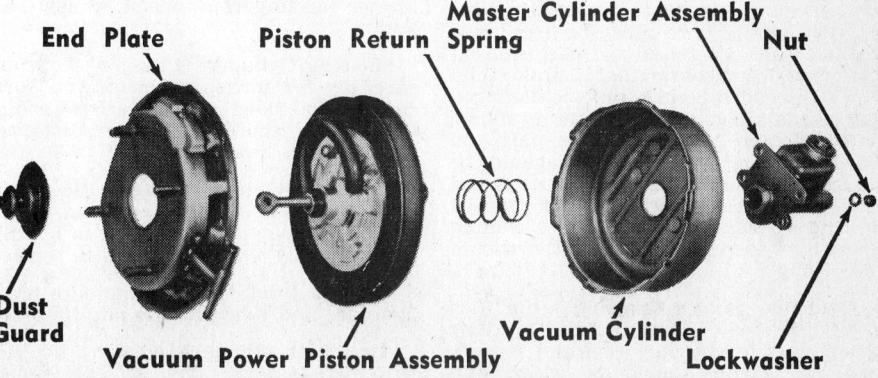

Fig. 34 Moraine diaphragm type

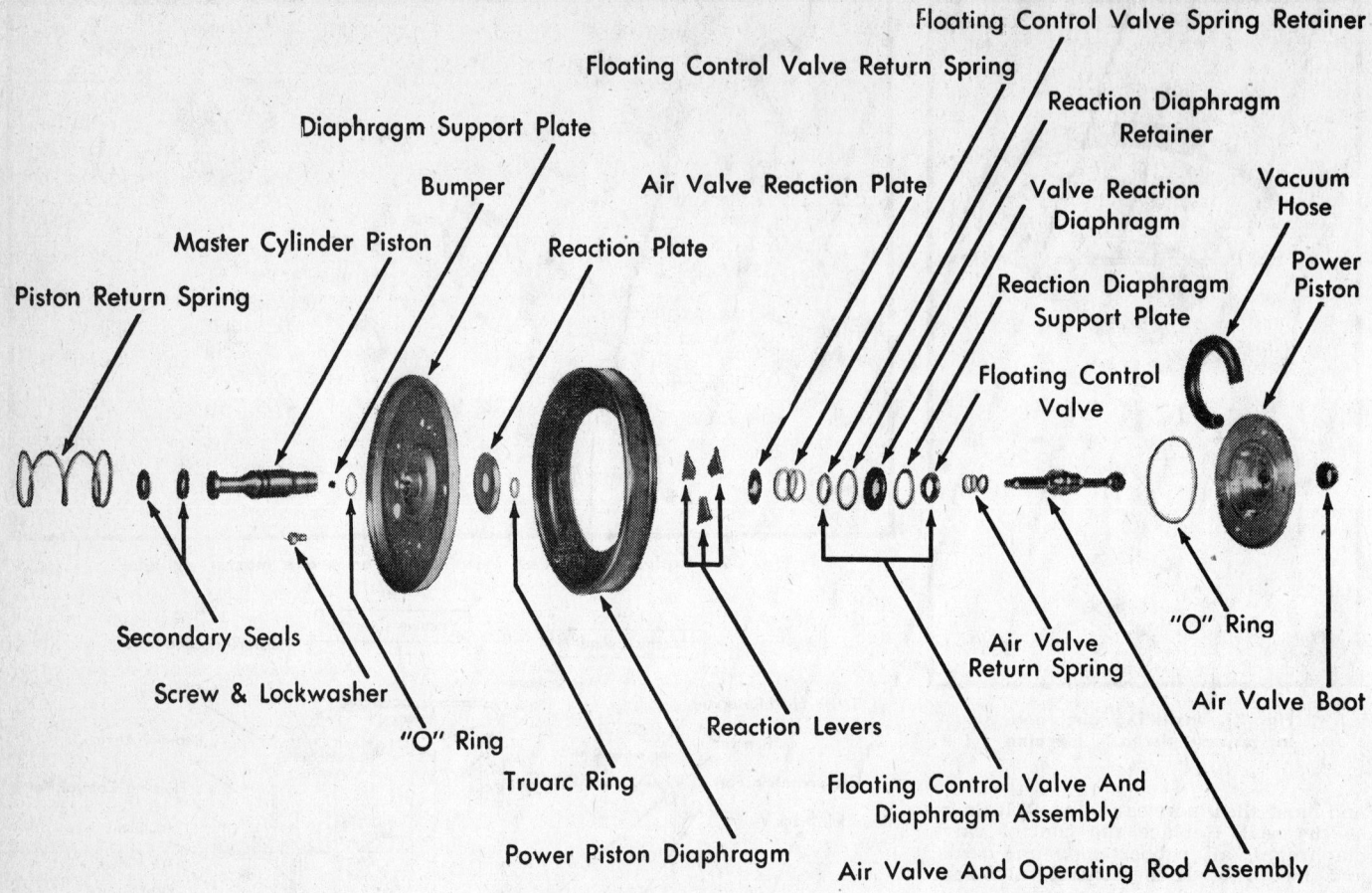

Fig. 35 Moraine diaphragm type

wash all parts in alcohol and air dry. Blow dirt and cleaning fluid out of all internal passages. If the inside of the vacuum cylinder is corroded or rusted, clean with crocus cloth or fine emery cloth.

It is important that all parts be placed on clean paper or lintless cloth after being cleaned to prevent the possibility of dirt being assembled into the unit.

Vacuum Cylinder Housing—Inspect for scoring, pitting, dents, nicks, or damaged threads. Small imperfections may be smoothed out by fine crocus cloth; replace if badly damaged.

Hydraulic Cylinder Casting—Examine bore down one inch from open end. For the primary cup to seal properly, this portion of the bore must be free from scores, deep scratches and corrosion. If it appears that contaminated brake fluid has damaged the bore, replace damaged parts and flush out hydraulic system.

Gasket surfaces under filler plug and head nut and around bore should be clean and smooth. Check for cracks and damaged threads. Jiggle pin should ride free in a clean vent hole. Holes leading from bore to reservoir and outlet should be clean.

Cylinder Plug Assembly—Cavities should be free of imperfections to allow good seats for vacuum seal and secondary cup. Bore should be clean and smooth so it will not score the master cylinder plunger. Check outside surfaces for damaged threads, and clean grooves. Be sure small radial holes are clean and open.

Head Nut Assembly—Check for damaged threads and smooth seat. Use new check valve seat washer and head nut gasket if necessary when reassembling.

Check Valve and Spring—Check for distortion and deterioration of rubber.

Filler Cap—Check for damaged threads or badly worn gasket. Be sure the two breather holes are clean and open.

Cover Plate—Examine plate and screws for imperfections. Use new gasket.

Master Cylinder Plunger—Examine carefully for nicks, corrosion and abrasion. Radial holes in counterbore should be open. If scored, pitted or distorted, replace with new plunger.

Master Cylinder Plunger Bearing—Grooves and holes must be clean. Check fit of master cylinder plunger in bearing bore; if badly worn or damaged, replace.

Vacuum Inlet Tube—Make sure braze is secure and tube plate is not distorted.

Air Filter—Replace element if filled with dirt, or is damaged. Replace rubber gasket.

Air Valve—Check for scratches, dents, distortion or corrosion on both outside and inside surfaces. Check seat for smoothness and flatness. Should have free sliding fit when inserted in power piston bore.

Floating Valve Assembly—Check for distortion of metal parts and deterioration or abrasions of rubber parts.

Power Piston and Guide—Check for cracks, damaged threads, pitted or rough holes, distortion, damage to lever seats, chipping, and rough or uneven seat for floating valve. Be sure all openings and passageways are clean and open.

Seals, Springs, Cups—Carefully examine all rubber, leather and other perishable parts and replace if they are damaged or worn. Check all springs for distortion and loss of tension. Check levers and reaction plates for scuffing or distortion.

MORAINE

Diaphragm Type—Index No. 11

This power brake assembly, Fig. 33, consists of three conventional units: the power cylinder, the power piston and the master cylinder.

Separate the individual units of the assembly by referring to Fig. 34. To separate the end plate from the vacuum cylinder, use two suitable bars against the studs as a prying means to rotate the end plate counterclockwise. Protect the stud threads with small pieces of heater hose.

When disassembled, wash all parts in alcohol to protect rubber parts. Inspect all parts for damage and replace as necessary.

Assemble in reverse order of disassembly. As the master cylinder piston enters the bore of the master cylinder, be cer-tain that the primary cup is in proper position.

Vacuum Piston

When necessary to service the vacuum piston, refer to Fig. 35.

Care must be taken when handling the power piston diaphragm as it must be guarded against grease, oil or foreign matter, and must be protected against nicks or cuts.

Wash parts in alcohol as protection for rubber parts. Examine all parts carefully for damage and replace as required.

When assembling the unit, check that the rubber diaphragm is not distorted as the assembly is pressed into the power piston.

The snap ring that holds the master cylinder to the support plate must be positioned so the lobes are located between the reaction levers.

POWER STEERING

NOTE: See Car Chapters For Linkage Type Power Steering

CAR APPLICATION

	Type	Page		Type	Page
Buick 1953-55	Saginaw Offset	163	Edsel 1958-60	Ford Torsion Bar	157
1956-58	Saginaw In Line	168	Lancer 1961	Chrysler Constant Control	153
1959 Le Sabre [1]	Saginaw In Line	168	Lincoln 1953-55	Saginaw Offset	163
1959-61	Saginaw Rotary Valve	172	1956-58	Saginaw In Line	168
Cadillac 1953-55	Saginaw Offset	163	1958-61	Ford Torsion Bar	157
1956-58	Saginaw In Line	168	Oldsmobile 1953-55	Saginaw Offset	163
1959-61	Saginaw Rotary Valve	172	1956-58	Saginaw In Line	168
Chevrolet 1953-54	Saginaw Offset	163	1959-61	Saginaw Rotary Valve	172
Chrysler 1953-54	Gemmer Hydraguide	161	Plymouth 1955-58	Chrysler Coaxial	145
1954-58	Chrysler Coaxial	145	1958-61	Chrysler Constant Control	153
1958-61	Chrysler Constant Control	153	Pontiac 1953-55	Saginaw Offset	163
Continental 1956-58	Saginaw In Line	168	1956-58	Saginaw In Line	168
1958-61	Ford Torsion Bar	157	1959-61	Saginaw Rotary Valve	172
Dart 1960-61	Chrysler Constant Control	153	Studebaker 1954-59	Saginaw Offset	163
De Soto 1953-54	Gemmer Hydraguide	161	Thunderbird 1961	Ford Torsion Bar	157
1955-58	Chrysler Coaxial	145	Valiant 1961	Chrysler Constant Control	153
1958-61	Chrysler Constant Control	153			
Dodge 1955-58	Chrysler Coaxial	145			
1958-61	Chrysler Constant Control	153			

[1] With standard brakes and automatic transmission.

Chrysler Coaxial Type

This power steering unit, Figs. C1 and C2, incorporates two basic gear mechanisms: a worm and worm connector, and a rack and sector gear. The hydraulic system of the power steering gear consists of a double-acting piston, a valve which fits inside the piston, and hydraulic reaction chamber which gives the driver the "feel" of the road. Axial positioning of the valve directs high pressure oil to one side or the other of the double-acting piston. Other components of the hydraulic system are the oil pump with pressure relief and flow control valve filter and oil reservoir.

Power Steering Repairs

Cleanliness throughout the entire disassembly and assembly procedure cannot be over-emphasized. The unit should be thoroughly cleaned in a suitable solvent when removed from the vehicle. When disassembling, each part should be placed in solvent, washed and dried by compressed air. Crocus cloth may be used to remove small nicks provided it is used carefully. When used on the valve spool, *use extreme care not to round off the sharp edge portion.* The sharp edge portion is vitally important to this type of valve as it helps to prevent dirt and foreign matter from getting between the valve and bore, thus reducing the possibility of sticking.

Remove and discard all O rings and other seals, using new ones lubricated with Lubriplate when assembling.

After removing the power steering unit from the vehicle as outlined in the car chapters, repair the unit as directed in the accompanying illustrations.

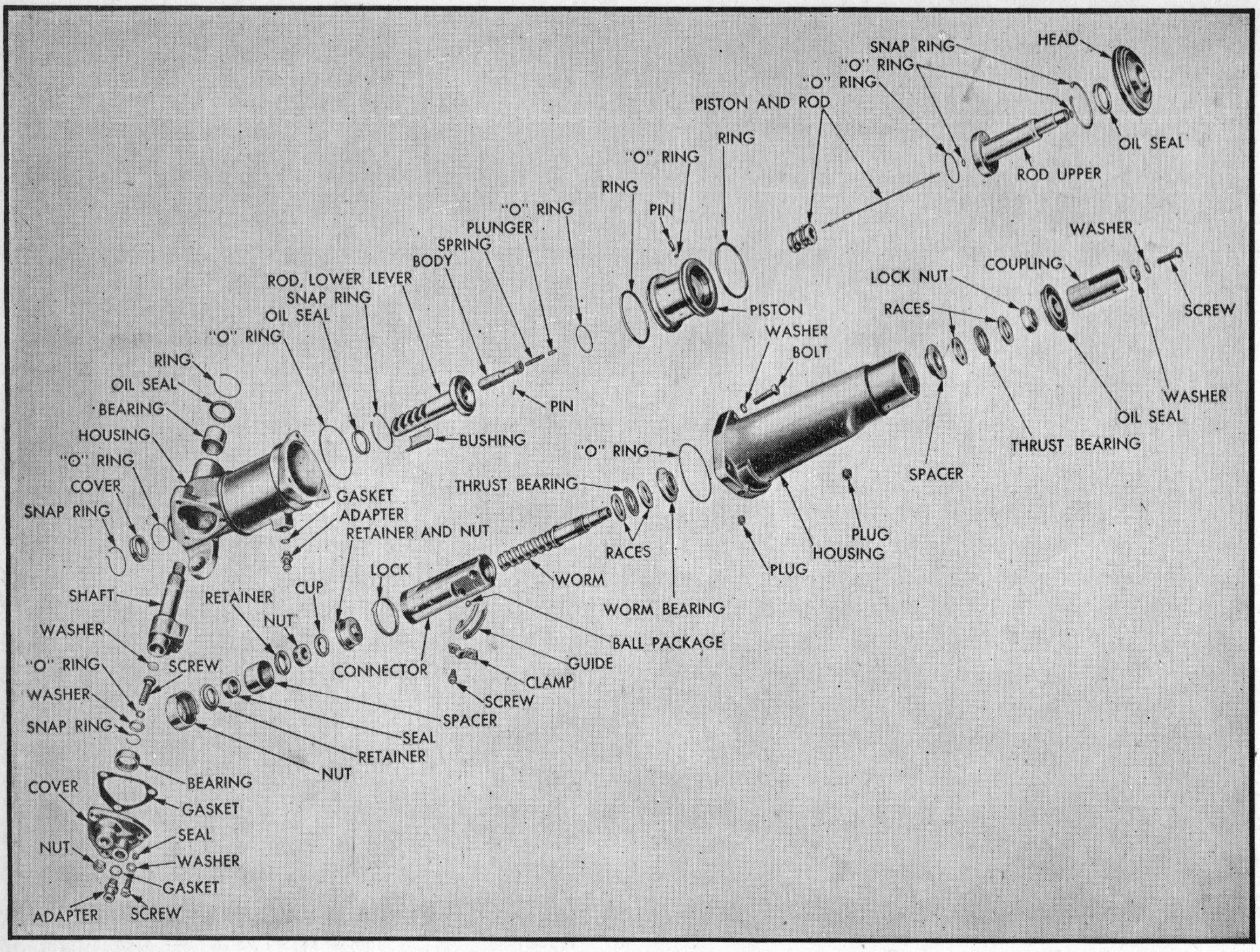

Fig. C1 Coaxial power steering unit used on Chrysler and De Soto

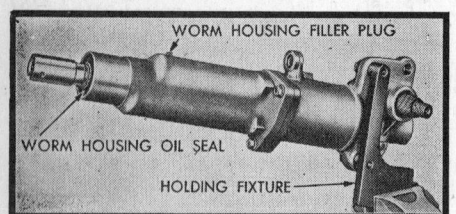

Fig. C3 Drain lubricant from filler hole, attach holding fixture and place unit in vise

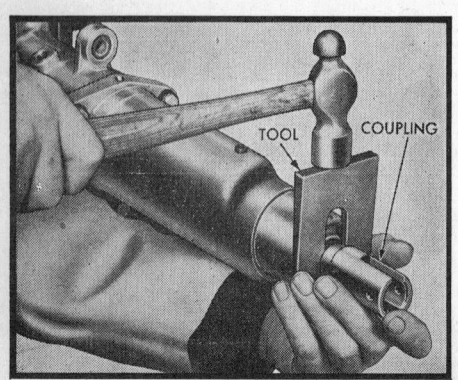

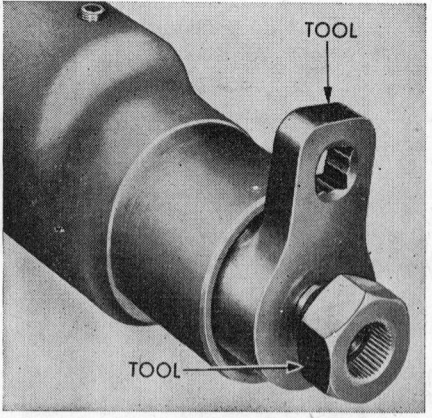

Fig. C5 With tools mounted as shown, remove worm bearing adjusting nut, lockwasher and thrust washer as shown in Fig. C6

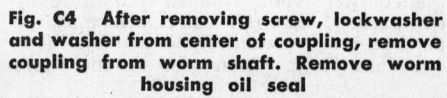

Fig. C4 After removing screw, lockwasher and washer from center of coupling, remove coupling from worm shaft. Remove worm housing oil seal

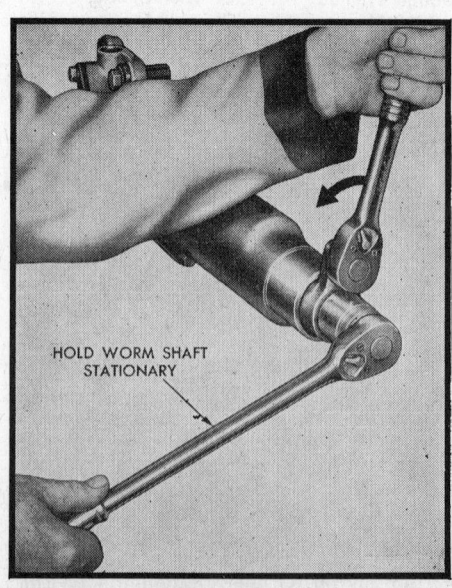

Fig. C6 Removing worm housing bearing adjusting nut

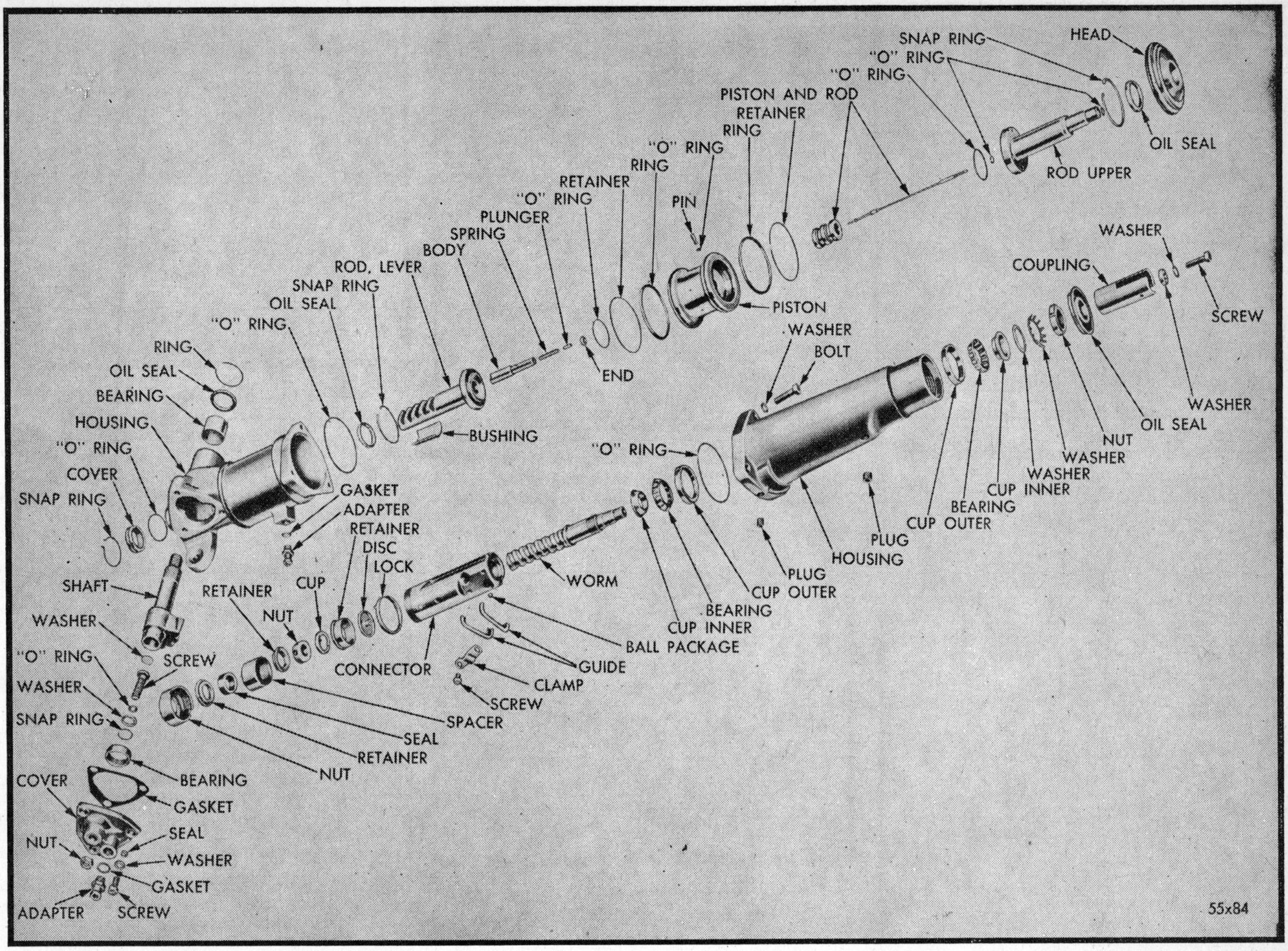

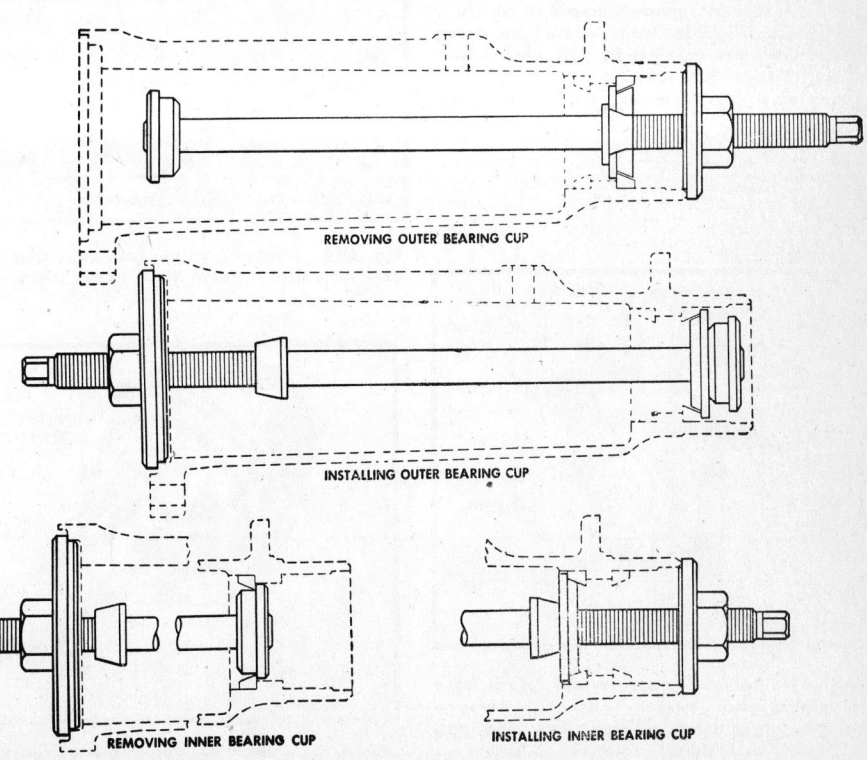

Fig. C2 Coaxial power steering unit used on Dodge and Plymouth. This unit differs from Fig. C1 chiefly in that a retainer is used in front of the upper piston ring

Fig. C7   Removing worm housing

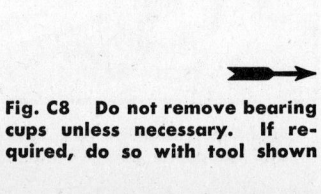

Fig. C8   Do not remove bearing cups unless necessary. If required, do so with tool shown

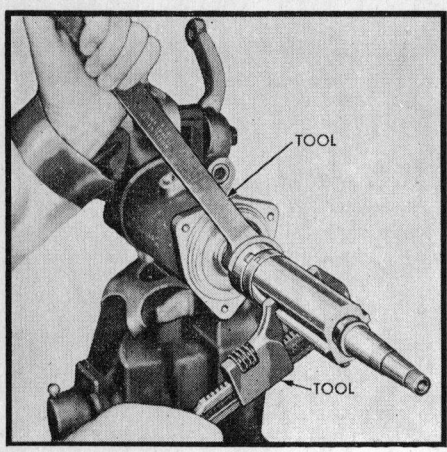

Fig. C9   Removing worm connector nut

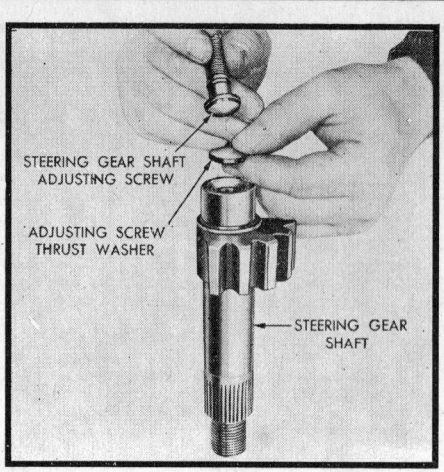

Fig. C12   After removing steering gear shaft from housing, remove adjusting screw retainer snap ring and take out screw, thrust washer and washer

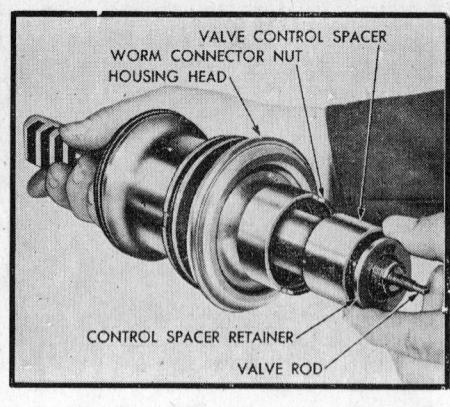

Fig. C16   Removing valve control spacer seal and seal retainers

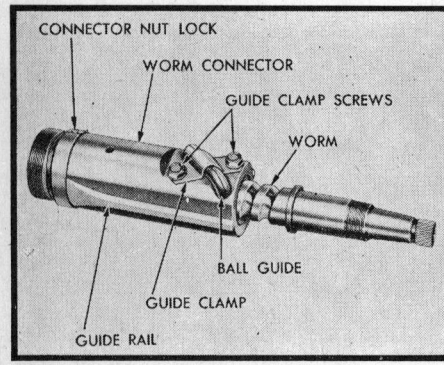

Fig. C10   Remove guide clamp and carefully remove ball guide from worm connector. Worm balls are a select fit with each other; if any of them are damaged it is recommended that a complete set (40) be installed

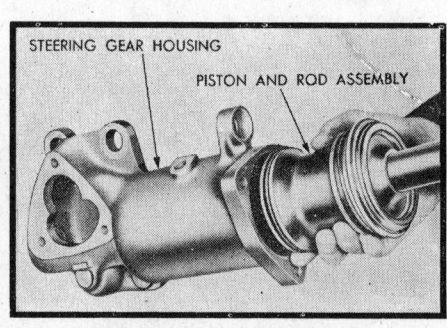

Fig. C13   Removing piston and rods from gear housing

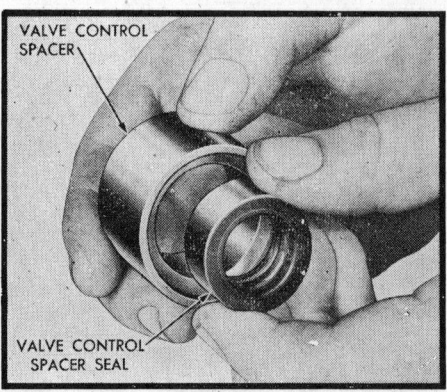

Fig. C17   Remove spacer seal retainers from spacer, and slide seal from valve control spacer

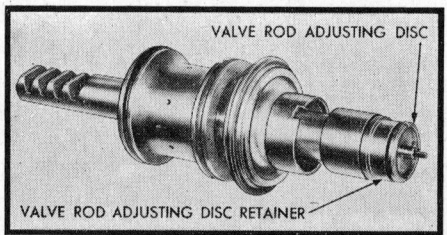

Fig. C14   Remove valve rod adjusting disc and slide disc retainer from upper piston rod

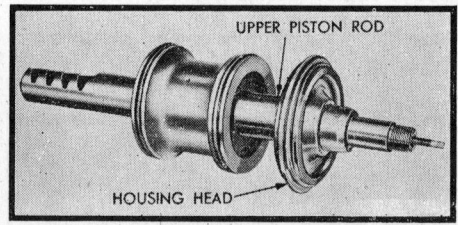

Fig. C18   Remove worm connector nut and slide housing head off upper piston rod. Remove housing "O" ring. Remove rod seal from housing head

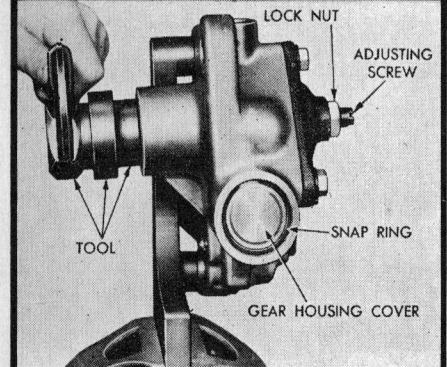

Fig. C11   Remove pressure and return hose adapters and copper gaskets. Remove steering gear shaft oil seal lock ring and with tool shown, remove oil seal

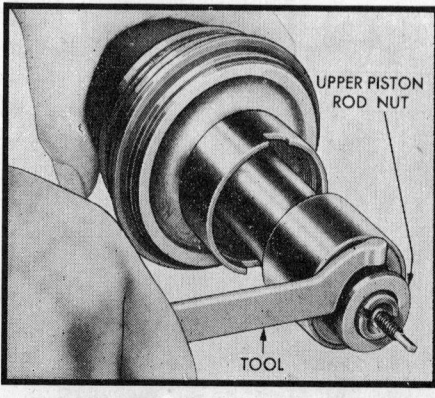

Fig. C15   Removing upper piston rod nut

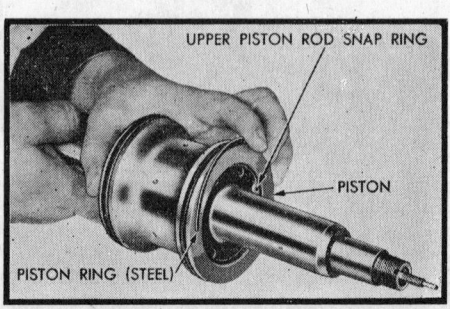

Fig. C19   Remove two backup (steel) and neoprene piston rings from piston

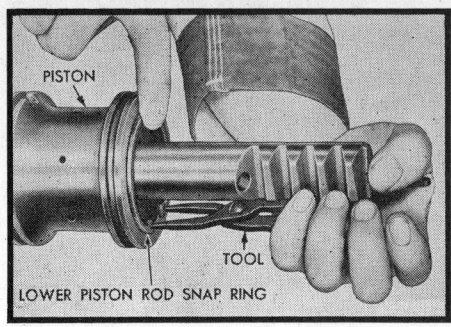

Fig. C20   Removing lower piston rod snap ring

Fig. C24   Remove upper piston rod snap ring and remove piston rod from piston

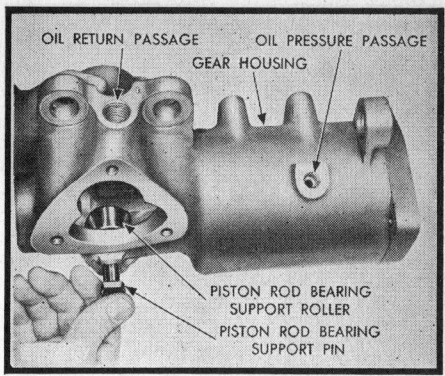

Fig. C28   Remove snap ring and slide bearing support pin out of gear housing and remove roller support

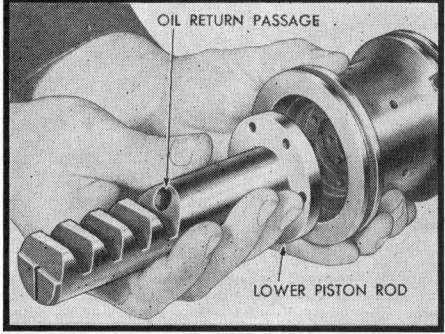

Fig. C21   Slide out lower piston rod

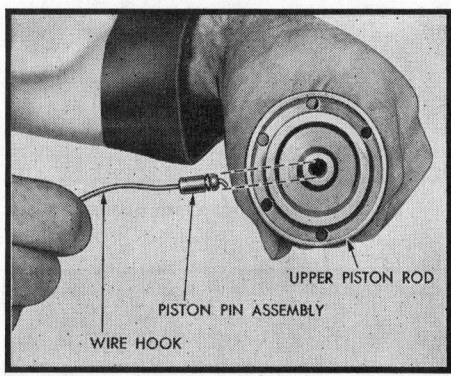

Fig. C25   With wire hook remove piston pin and "O" ring from piston rod

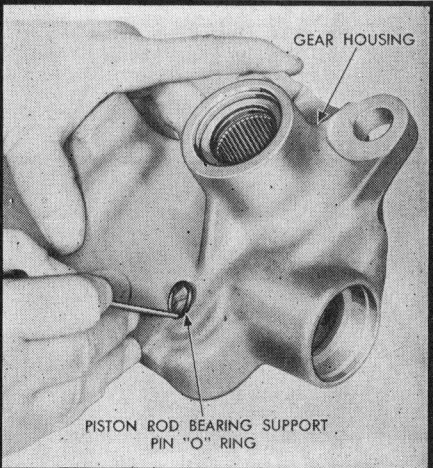

Fig. C29   Remove two bearing support "O" rings located in each side of gear housing

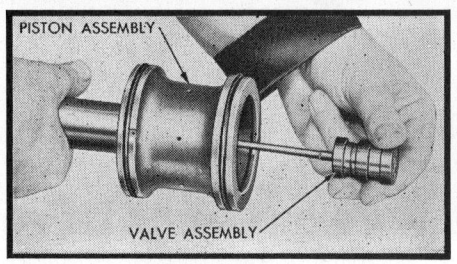

Fig. C22   Using care not to bend valve adjusting rod, slide valve from piston

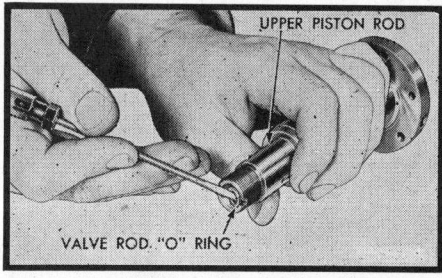

Fig. C26   Remove "O" rings (one in each end of piston rod)

Fig. C23   Drive piston pin into upper piston rod

Fig. C27   Remove upper piston rod "O" ring, and lower piston rod "O" ring

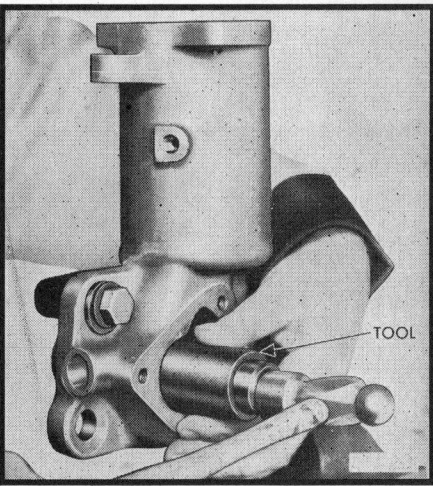

Fig. C30 If necessary, remove steering gear housing needle bearing and remove seal from housing

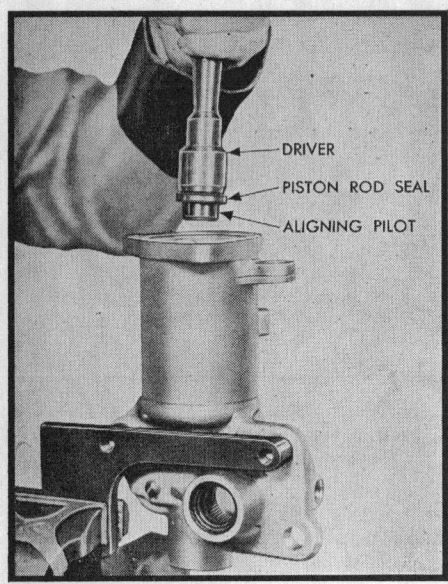

Fig. C31 Installing piston rod seal in gear housing

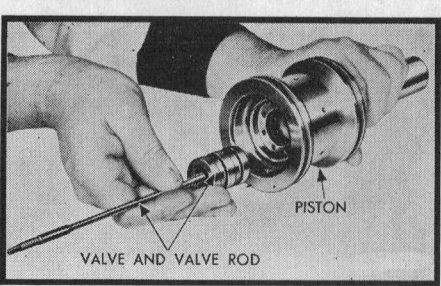

Fig. C34 Installing valve assembly

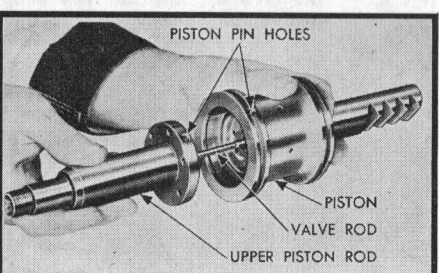

Fig. C35 Installing upper piston rod

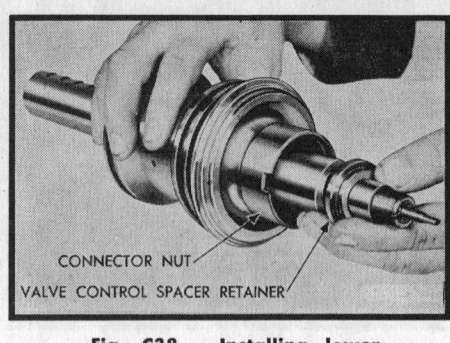

Fig. C38 Installing lower valve control spacer retainer

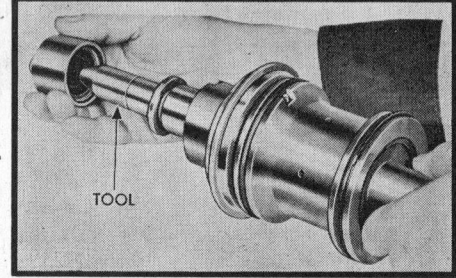

Fig. C39 Installing valve control spacer and seal

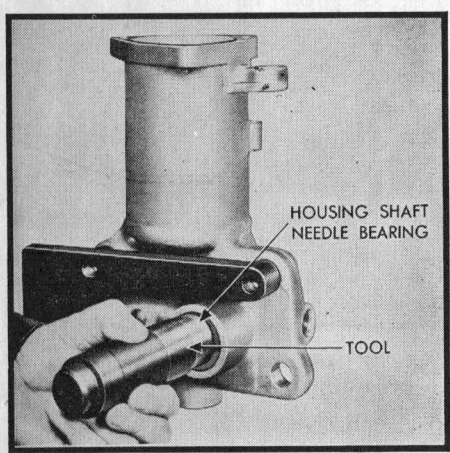

Fig. C32 Installing steering gear shaft needle bearing. Always drive on letter side of bearing

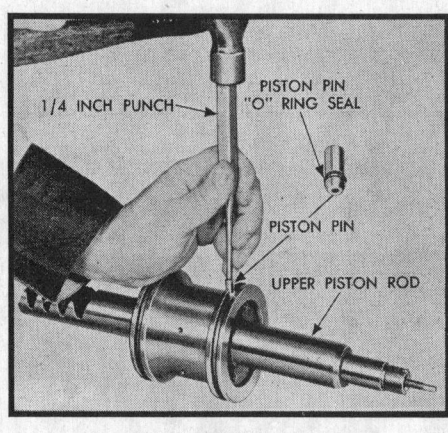

Fig. C36 Installing piston pin

Fig. C40 Locking upper piston rod nut lock cap

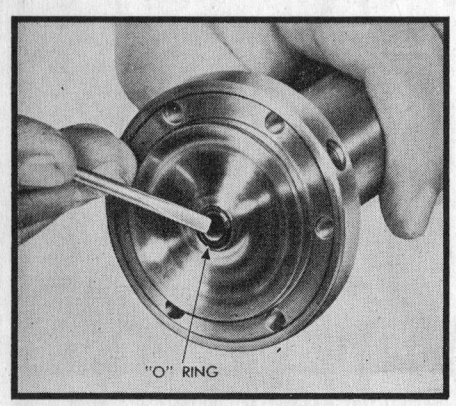

Fig. C33 Installing valve rod "O" rings

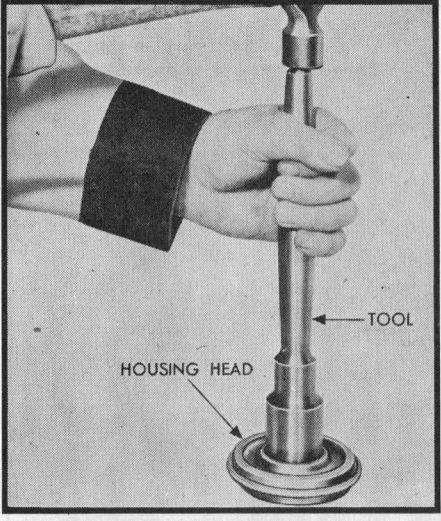

Fig. C37 Installing upper piston rod seal in housing head

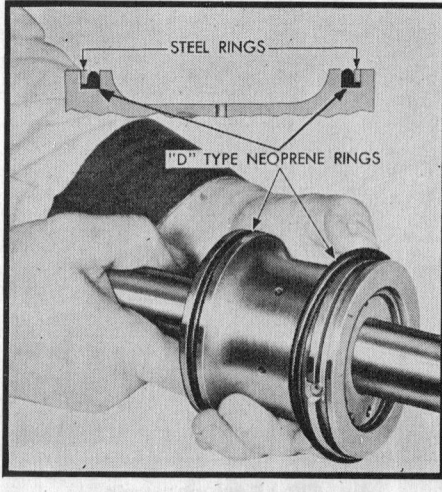

Fig. C41 Installing piston rings

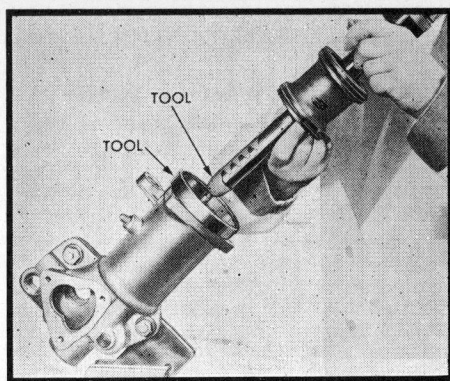

Fig. C42 Installing piston and rod assembly

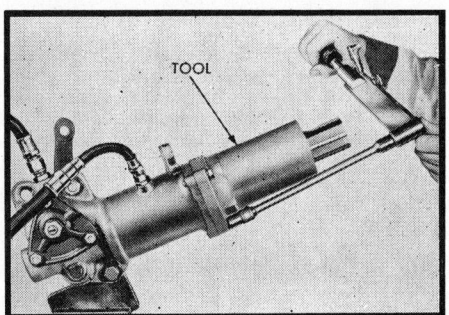

Fig. C43 Installing short dummy housing

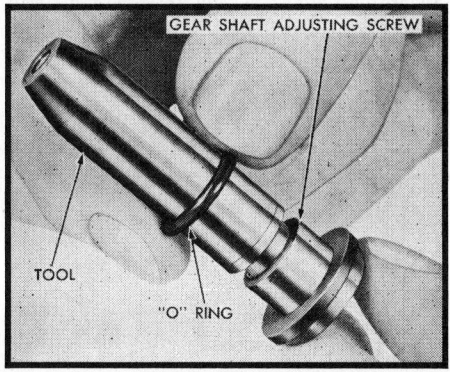

Fig. C44 Installing gear shaft adjusting screw "O" ring

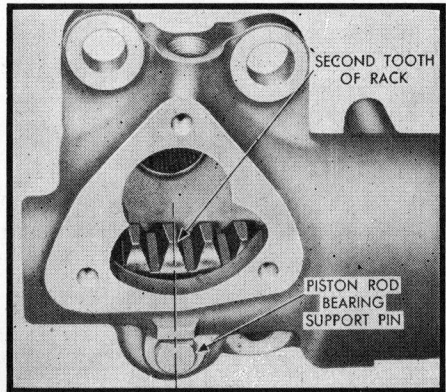

Fig. C45 Centering rack teeth of lower piston tyrod

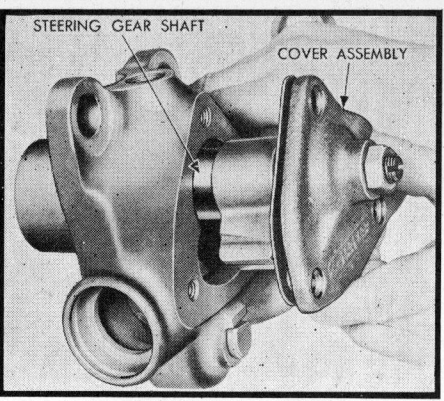

Fig. C46 Installing steering gear shaft and cover

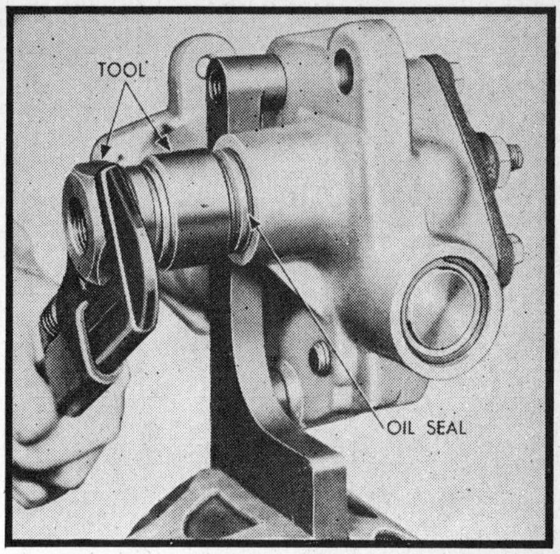

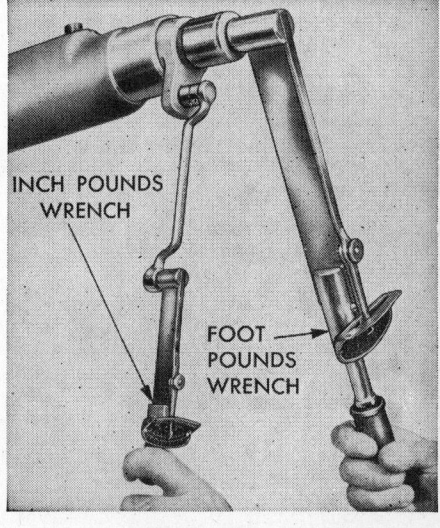

Fig. C47 Installing gear shaft oil seal

Power Steering Adjustments

The three adjustments, all of which can be made without removing the assembly from the car, should be made as follows: Worm bearing, adjustment, piston valve adjustment, and gear lash adjustment. Since a considerable amount of work is involved in making either the worm bearing adjustment or piston valve adjustment in the car, it is suggested that you make definitely sure they are causing the difficulty. If all other possibilities have been checked, make the adjustments without removing the assembly from the car as follows:

Remove steering wheel, steering column jacket and tube. Remove the coupling from the worm shaft and worm housing oil seal. Remove steering connecting rod (drag link) from steering gear arm. Back off gear lash adjusting screw until the lash is maximum.

Worm Shaft Bearing Adjustment

With the tools in Fig. C48 attached as shown, turn steering gear to full left turn and hold in this position with the left torque wrench.

Substitute left wrench shown in Fig. C48 with the combination shown in Fig. C49. Then, while holding five pounds tension with the large wrench, loosen the nut with the small wrench and adjust to exactly five *inch* pounds. Remove the tools with extreme care so as not to move the adjusting nut. Then crimp the ring section of the adjusting nut into the keyway in the worm shaft, being careful not to move the adjusting nut. Install worm housing seal.

Piston Valve Adjustment

Start the engine and run at medium idle speed. Allow steering gear to reach normal operating temperature. Attach a small tap handle (or equivalent) to flat on end of special tool C-3445. Insert tool through worm shaft over end of piston valve rod. With foot-pound torque wrench on steering arm nut, read tension while turning the steering gear to full right and full left at moderate rate. Wrench

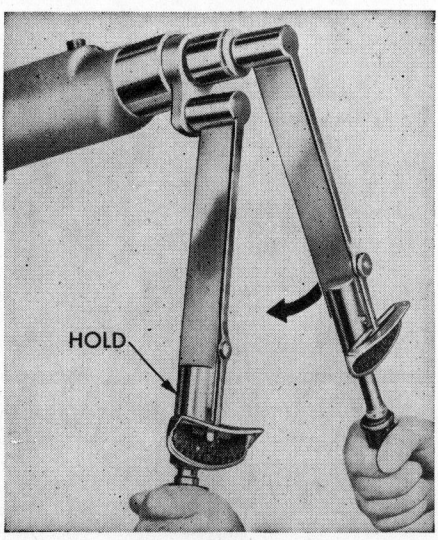

Fig. C48 Adjusting worm housing bearings (outer)

Fig. C49 Final worm housing bearing adjustment

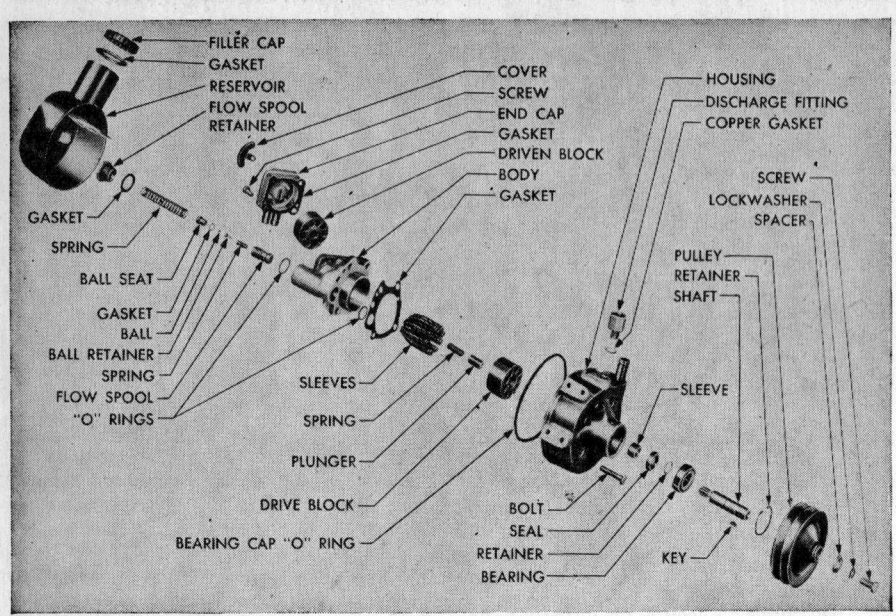

Fig. C50 Power steering sleeve type oil pump

movement should be smooth. Turn piston valve in direction necessary to produce the same torque reading in both directions. Torque reading must be equal and under 40 lb. ft.

If torque reading is less than 25 lb. ft. a much more accurate adjustment can be made with a 300 inch lb. torque wrench, using same procedure.

Gear Lash Adjustment

With engine running and steering gear at normal operating temperature, turn steering gear to straight ahead position. Using a very light finger tip touch at end of steering gear arm, turn gear shaft adjusting screw clockwise until all gear lash has been eliminated. Turn adjusting screw 3/4 turn tighter (clockwise) and tighten lock nut. Stop engine. Install worm housing oil seal with lip of seal down.

With gear still in straight-ahead position, install coupling on worm shaft with slot in up-and-down position. Install drag link, steering tube and wheel.

Lubrication

Since there is no hydraulic connection between the worm and gear housing, the power steering has two separate fluid levels. The reservoir fluid level should be checked every 1000 miles or 30 days. Make sure top of reservoir is absolutely clean. Remove cover or filler cap to check oil level.

An oil level mark is stamped on the inside of the reservoir or on dipstick of style using the filler cap. Replenish as necessary with Automatic Transmission Fluid. When temperatures are consist-

ently below —10 degrees F., it is permissible to drain the hydraulic system and refill with SAE 5W-20 engine oil. The total capacity of the hydraulic system is approximately two quarts; this does not include the worm housing.

The worm housing oil level does not require periodic checking unless leakage occurs. Should the steering gear assembly be removed, however, it should be checked at that time. The oil should be level with the filler plug opening when the gear is in the installed position. Re-

plenish as necessary with Automatic Transmission Fluid.

Draining Hydraulic System

Should it become necessary to drain the hydraulic system, extreme care should be taken to prevent dirt from entering the reservoir while cover or filler cap is removed.

Disconnect the high pressure (small) hose at the gear housing and jack up front end of car. Place hose in a suitable container. While holding hose in container start engine and allow to idle. Turn steering wheel from one extreme to the other until all fluid is forced from unit. *As soon as fluid starts to show large quantities of air bubbles stop engine.* Connect hose and refill.

Refilling Hydraulic System

Fill the reservoir slightly higher than normal. Start engine and allow to run for a short time to circulate oil through hoses. With engine running at idle speed, turn steering wheel back and forth several times from one extreme to the other to bleed all air out of the system. Check fluid level in reservoir and add as required.

Power Steering Pumps

Fig. C50 illustrates the sleeve type pump while Fig. C51 shows the rotor type. When necessary to disassemble either type pump, do so in clean surroundings. After the pump has been disassembled, wash the parts in solvent and blow dry. *Do not immerse the shaft and bearing of the sleeve type pump in solvent as the lubricants sealed in the bearing may become diluted by the solvent; merely wipe with clean cloth.*

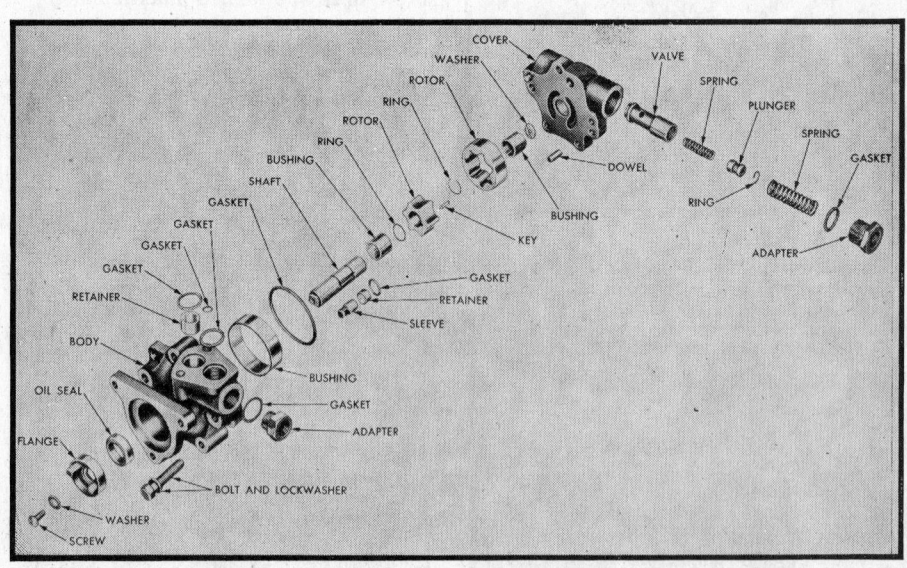

Fig. C51 Power steering rotor type oil pump

Chrysler Constant Control Type

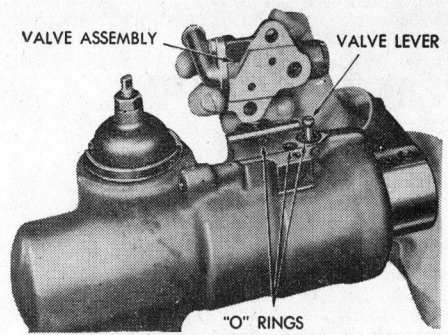

VALVE ASSEMBLY — VALVE LEVER

"O" RINGS

Fig. CC1 Removing or installing valve body assembly

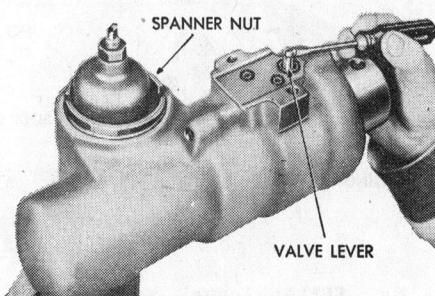

SPANNER NUT

VALVE LEVER

Fig. CC2 Removing valve lever

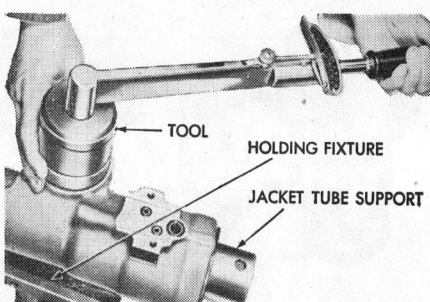

TOOL

HOLDING FIXTURE

JACKET TUBE SUPPORT

Fig. CC3 Removing or installing gear shaft cover nut

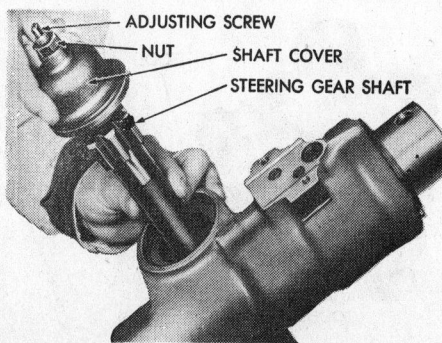

ADJUSTING SCREW

NUT — SHAFT COVER

STEERING GEAR SHAFT

Fig. CC4 Removing or installing gear shaft and cover

The Constant Control Full Time Power Steering consists of a hydraulic pressure pump, a power steering gear and connecting hoses. The power steering gear consists of a gear housing, containing a gear shaft and sector shaft; a power piston with gear teeth milled into the side of the piston which is in constant mesh with the gear shaft sector teeth; and a worm shaft which connects the steering wheel to the power unit piston through a coupling.

Steering Gear Repairs

Prior to disassembly, clean the gear assembly thoroughly in a suitable solvent. Crocus cloth may be used to remove small nicks and burrs provided it is used carefully. When used on the steering gear valve, use extreme care not to round off the sharp edge portions of the two lands located between the valve drilled holes. Remove and discard all "O" ring seals, using new ones lubricated with petrolatum when reassembling.

Disassemble

1. Drain steering gear through pressure and return connections by turning the steering tube coupling from one extreme of travel to the other.
2. Drive out coupling pin and remove coupling.
3. Remove valve body and three "O" rings, Fig. CC1.
4. Remove valve lever by prying under spherical head, Fig. CC2. *Use care not to collapse slotted end of valve lever as this will destroy bearing tolerances of head.*
5. Remove gear shaft cover nut, Fig. CC3.
6. Rotate worm shaft to full right turn, reverse rotation of worm shaft until piston is at center of travel. Then remove gear shaft and cover, Fig. CC4.
7. Remove steering column support nut, Fig. CC5. Turn worm shaft to full right position to compress parts and back off as necessary to align holes in column support and worm shaft.
8. Enter a piece of drill rod through holes in jacket support and worm shaft to keep parts from turning and remove power train, Fig. CC6.
9. Disassemble power train after removing thrust bearing nut.
10. Remove worm shaft upper oil seal, Fig. CC7, and disassemble column jacket support. Reaction seal may be removed from groove in face of jacket support by blowing air pressure into ferrule chamber. Make sure passage from ferrule chamber to upper reaction chamber is unobstructed.

Column Jacket Support, Asemble

Install worm shaft upper oil seal with sealing lip toward bearing, Fig. CC8. Tool C-3650 should be used to drive seal

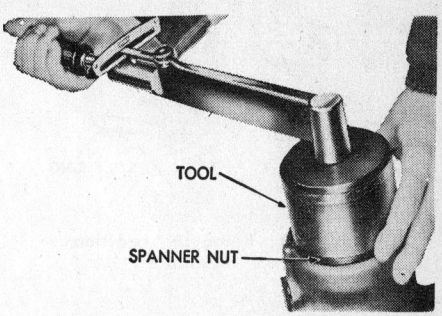

TOOL

SPANNER NUT

Fig. CC5 Removing steering column support nut

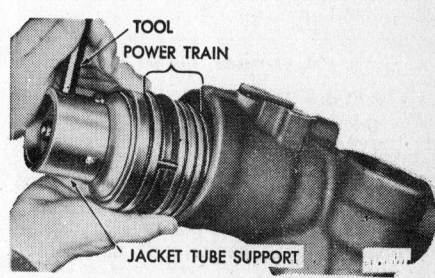

TOOL
POWER TRAIN

JACKET TUBE SUPPORT

Fig. CC6 Removing or installing power train

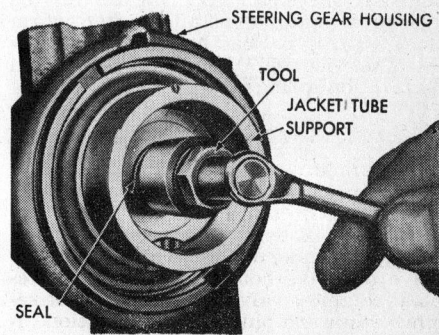

STEERING GEAR HOUSING

TOOL
JACKET TUBE SUPPORT

SEAL

Fig. CC7 Removing worm shaft upper oil seal

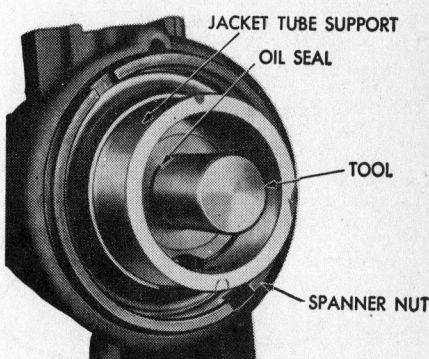

JACKET TUBE SUPPORT
OIL SEAL

TOOL

SPANNER NUT

Fig. CC8 Installing worm shaft upper oil seal

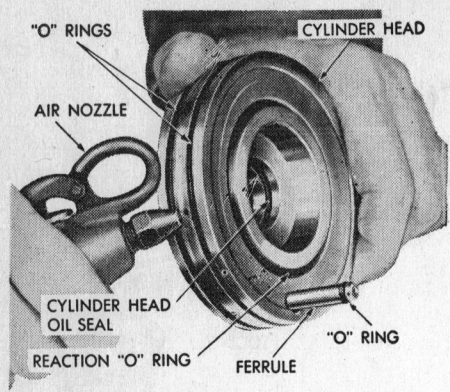

Fig. CC9 Removing reaction ring from cylinder head

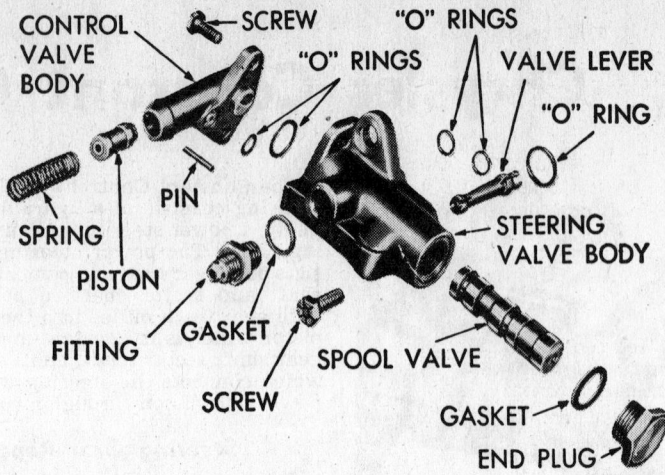

Fig. CC11 Control valve disassembled. 1958 (early)

until tool bottoms on casting to obtain proper compression of rubber seal. Lubricate reaction seal and install in groove in face of column jacket support with flat side of seal out.

Cylinder Head

Disassemble—Remove two "O" rings in outer grooves in head. Remove "O" ring in groove in face of cylinder head with air pressure into oil hole located in groove between two "O" ring grooves, Fig. CC9. Replace cylinder head seal if necessary, Fig. CC10. Check oil passage in ferrule for obstruction. Check lands of cylinder head for burrs.

Assemble — Lubricate and install two large "O" rings in grooves on head. Install lower reaction seal in groove in face of head. The small "O" ring for ferrule groove should be installed after worm shaft bearing preload has been established, otherwise "O" ring will be damaged by reaction springs.

Steering Valve

Disassemble — Compress control valve spring and remove spring retainer pin, spring and pressure control piston. Remove valve body (2 screws) from steering valve. Shake out valve piston. If spool valve or valve housing is damaged, replace complete valve assembly. Do not remove valve end plug unless inspection indicates a leak at seal.

Assemble—Figs. CC11 and CC11A. Install steering valve in housing. Valve lever hole should align with steering gear valve lever opening in bottom of valve housing. Valve must fit smoothly in housing without striking or binding. If valve end plug was removed install new seal and tighten plug to 50 lb. ft. torque. Lubricate pressure control valve piston and slide it into valve body (nose end first). Install spring on top of piston. Compress pin and install pin through both holes at top of control valve body. Assemble control valve body to steering valve body and torque attaching screws to 10 lb. ft. Install new copper sealing gasket and fitting in threaded hole on top of valve body and torque to 30 lb. ft.

Gear Shaft

Disassemble — Remove adjusting screw lock nut and unscrew cover from adjusting screw. Remove screw and washer from, "T" slot in end of gear shaft. Remove small "O" ring from top of cover and large "O" ring from base of cover.

Assemble — Place adjusting screw washer over screw and slide both into "T" slot of shaft. Screw cover into adjusting screw until gear shaft bottoms in cover. Install small "O" ring over adjusting screw into position at top of cover. Install lock nut on adjusting screw but do not tighten. Install large "O" ring in groove on lower face of gear cover.

Steering Gear Housing

Disassemble — The equipment shown in Fig. CC12 should be used for this operation. After removing the oil seal snap ring and back-up ring, remove the oil seal by sliding the threaded porton of the tool's adapter over end of gear shaft and install nut section of tool (C-3350) on shaft. Maintain pressure on adapter with nut of tool while turning adapter, forcing it into seal until it has bottomed in seal. Apply two half rings and retainer over both portions of tool. As hex nut is removed from shaft seal will be pulled from housing.

Assemble—Install gear shaft oil seal in housing (lip of seal toward needle bearing) using Tool C-3350. Place adapter

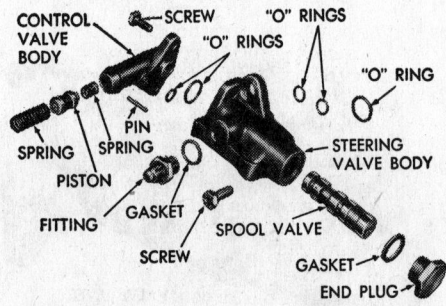

Fig. CC11A Control valve disassembled. Late 1958 and later models

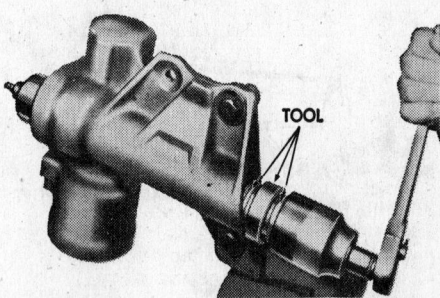

Fig. CC12 Removing gear shaft oil seal

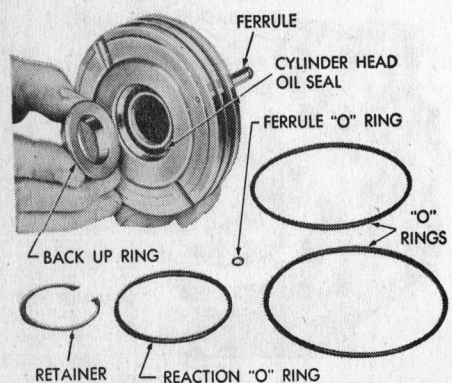

Fig. CC10 Removing cylinder head seal

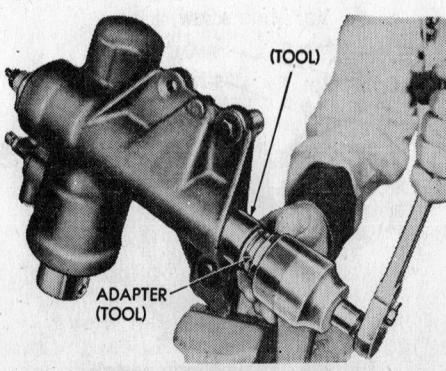

Fig. CC13 Installing gear shaft oil seal

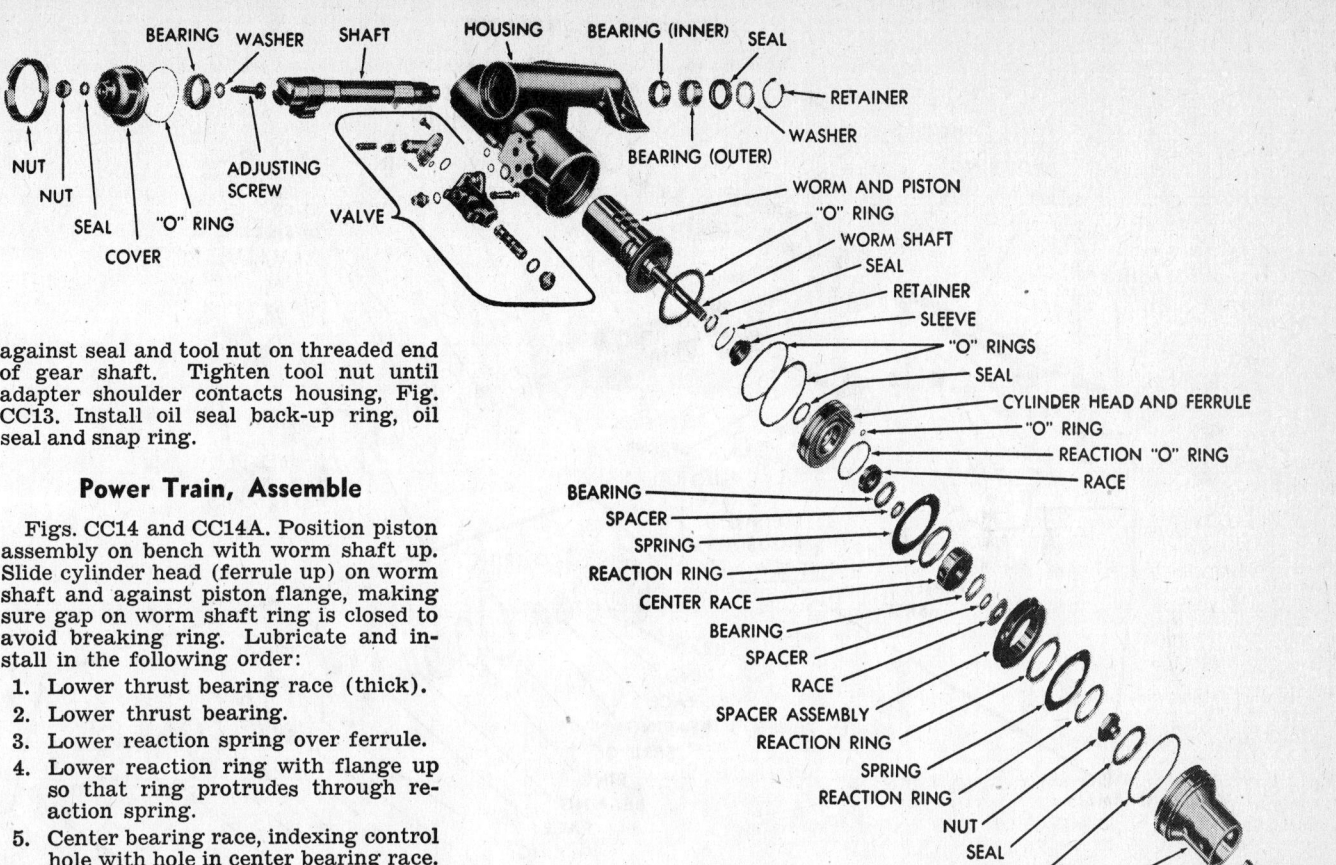

Fig. CC14 Steering gear disassembled. 1958 (early)

against seal and tool nut on threaded end of gear shaft. Tighten tool nut until adapter shoulder contacts housing, Fig. CC13. Install oil seal back-up ring, oil seal and snap ring.

Power Train, Assemble

Figs. CC14 and CC14A. Position piston assembly on bench with worm shaft up. Slide cylinder head (ferrule up) on worm shaft and against piston flange, making sure gap on worm shaft ring is closed to avoid breaking ring. Lubricate and install in the following order:

1. Lower thrust bearing race (thick).
2. Lower thrust bearing.
3. Lower reaction spring over ferrule.
4. Lower reaction ring with flange up so that ring protrudes through reaction spring.
5. Center bearing race, indexing control hole with hole in center bearing race.
6. Install outer spacer, upper thrust bearing, upper thrust bearing race (thin) and new worm shaft thrust bearing nut.
7. Tighten nut as follows: Turn worm shaft counterclockwise ½ turn and hold shaft in this position while tightening nut to 10 lb. ft. torque. *If worm shaft is turned more than ½ turn cylinder head seal will clear oil ring on worm shaft.*
8. Always check position of worm shaft oil ring before bottoming cylinder head against worm piston shoulder to avoid damaging oil ring.
9. Rotate worm center bearing race several turns to position all parts; then loosen adjusting nut.
10. Retighten worm bearing adjusting nut to give a bearing torque of 8 to 16 oz. Check by placing rounds of cord around center bearing race. Make a loop in one end and hook the loop of a spring scale in the cord loop. Pulling on cord will cause bearing race to rotate.
11. If adjusting nut is tightened properly, reading on scale will be 8 to 16 oz. Stake flange of adjusting nut into depression in worm shaft to lock securely.
12. The 8 to 16 oz. torque must remain after nut is locked.
13. Install center bearing spacer over bearing race to engage dowel pin with slot in center bearing race. *Make sure valve lever hole in center bearing race and center spacer are properly aligned.*
14. After installing balance of parts, align parts of power train so that

valve lever hole in center bearing spacer is 90 deg. counterclockwise from piston rack teeth and lock all parts to worm shaft by entering a drill rod through jacket support and worm shaft holes.

Steering Gear, Assemble

1. With steering gear housing fastened in holding fixture in approximate car position, lubricate bore of housing with petrolatum and install power train assembly (Fig. CC5) with center bearing spacer valve lever hole in "up" position to line up with lever clearance hole in gear housing.
2. Place a .0015" feeler gauge to cover aligning notch in gear housing to protect "O" ring sealer when installing gear train. Make sure cylinder head is bottomed on housing shoulder. Do not remove power train locking pin until all parts are positioned in steering gear housing.
3. Align valve lever hole in center bearing spacer exactly with clearance hole in housing with aligning tool, Fig. CC15. *Tool should not be*

removed until spanner nut is securely tightened.

4. Install column support nut and tighten to 150 lb. ft. torque (see Fig. CC5).
5. Set piston at center of travel and install gear shaft and cover so that sector teeth index with piston rack teeth. Install cover nut and torque to 100 lb. ft. (see Fig. CC3).
6. Install valve lever (double bearing end first) into center bearing spacer through hole in steering housing so that slots in valve lever are parallel to worm shaft in order to engage anti-rotation pin in center bearing race, Fig. CC16.
7. Install valve body on housing, making sure valve lever enters hole in piston (see Fig. CC1). Tighten screws to 30 inch lbs.

Tests and Adjustments

1. Fill reservoir to level mark.
2. Connect test hoses to hydraulic pump on car with pressure gauge installed between pump and steering gear to register pressures.
3. Start engine and operate at idle to

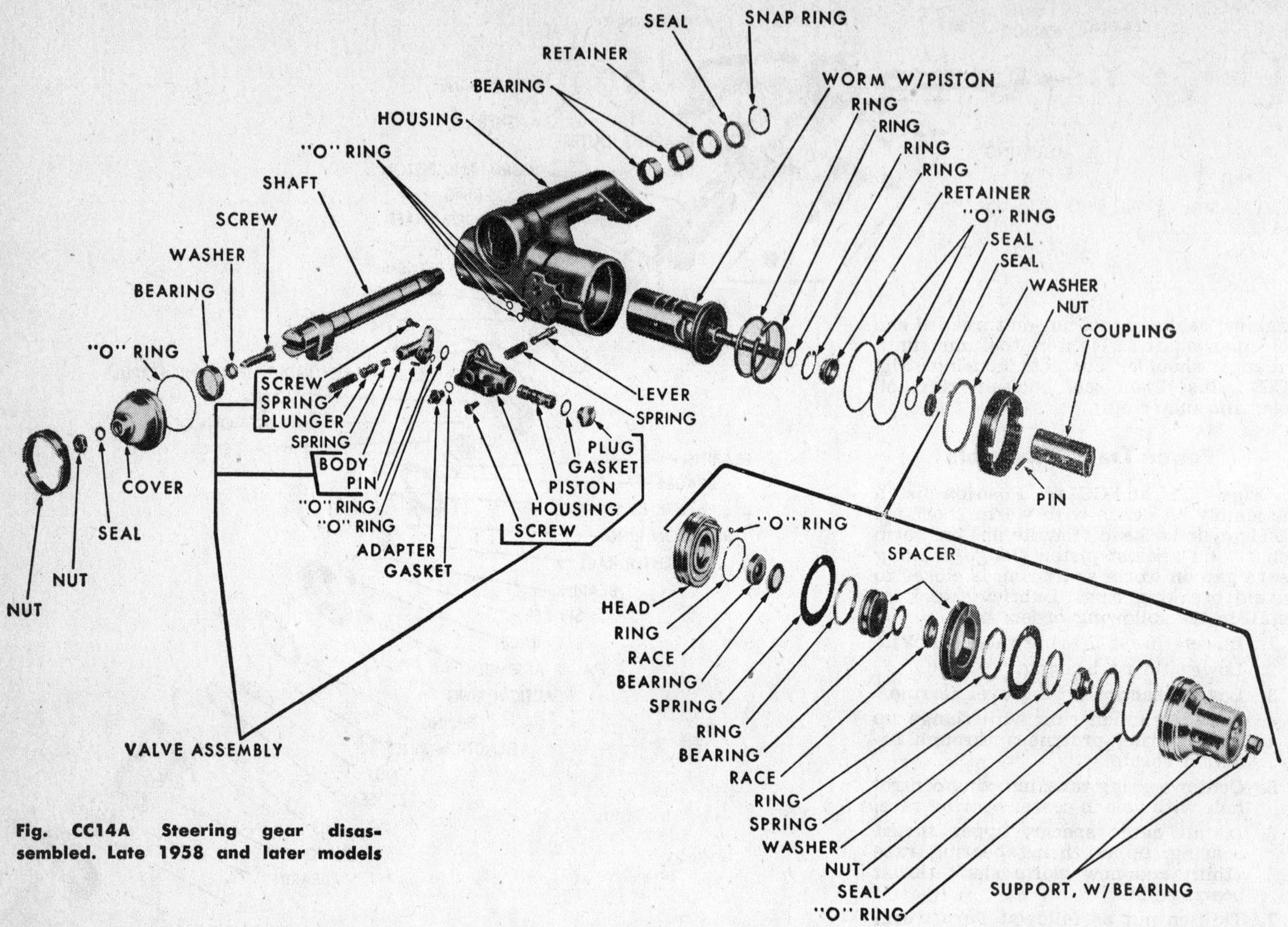

SEAL
SNAP RING
RETAINER
BEARING
WORM W/PISTON
HOUSING
RING
RING
"O" RING
RING
RING
SHAFT
RETAINER
"O" RING
SCREW
SEAL
SEAL
WASHER
WASHER
BEARING
NUT
COUPLING
"O" RING
SCREW
SPRING
PLUNGER
LEVER
SPRING
SPRING
PLUG
GASKET
BODY
PIN
PISTON
COVER
"O" RING
HOUSING
"O" RING
SCREW
PIN
SEAL
ADAPTER
GASKET
"O" RING
NUT
SPACER
NUT
HEAD
RING
RACE
BEARING
SPRING
RING
BEARING
RACE
RING
SPRING
WASHER
NUT
SEAL
"O" RING
SUPPORT, W/BEARING
VALVE ASSEMBLY

Fig. CC14A Steering gear disassembled. Late 1958 and later models

bring steering gear to normal operating temperature.

4. Expel all air from system by turning steering wheel several complete turns from one extreme to the other.

TORQUE WRENCH
WRENCH (TOOL)
TOOL

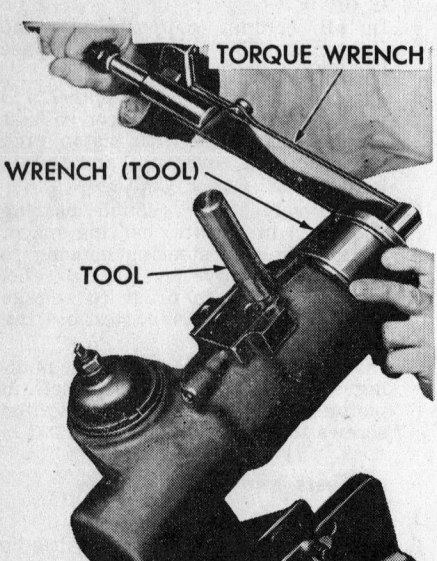

Fig. CC15 Alignment of bearing spacer and center bearing race

5. Refill reservoir.
6. Turn gear shaft adjusting screw outward to assure no mesh adjustment preload for this phase of the test.
7. Tighten steering valve body attaching screws to a torque of 7 lb. ft.
8. Apply oil pressure to complete unit and position steering valve by tapping lightly on one of the pressure control valve screws or on valve end plug to position valve up or down on housing to give equal gear shaft torque within 5 lb. ft., not to exceed 20 lb. ft. in either direction when gear shaft is turned slowly. *Perform this operation carefully or a lockup will occur in steering gear.*
9. With gear shaft on center, tighten gear shaft adjusting screw until backlash just disappears. Tighten 1¼ turns from this position and, while holding adjusting screw in this position, tighten lock nut.
10. Turn off hydraulic power unit.
11. Operate unit manually for a minimum of 180 deg. from center in either direction, measured at worm shaft.
12. Turn on hydraulic power unit.
13. Operate unit through a minimum of one complete cycle. Operate unit through another cycle, this time holding unit at extreme travel in each direction while watching oil pressure gauge. Gauge reading

VALVE LEVER
SPANNER NUT
"O" RINGS

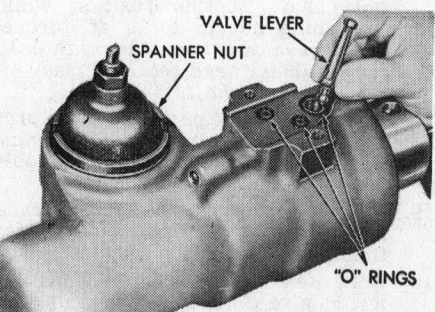

Fig. CC16 Installing valve lever

ADJUSTING SCREW
COVER
NUT

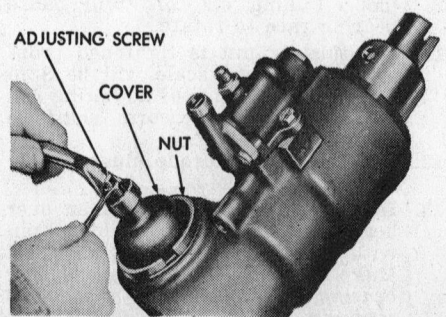

Fig. CC17 Adjusting gear shaft adjusting screw

should be equal in each drection; if not it indicates excessive internal leakage.

14. With oil temperature between 150 to 170 deg. (checked with thermometer in reservoir) oil pressure should be 850 to 950 psi for satisfactory steering operation.

15. With gear shaft on center (plus or minus 2 deg.) readjust gear shaft backlash. Tighten adjusting screw until backlash disappears; continue to tighten ⅜ to ½ turn from this position and tighten lock nut to 50 lb. ft. torque, Fig. CC17.

16. Start from a point at least one full turn of the worm shaft either side of center.

17. The torque at gear shaft required to turn unit through center at 2 rpm in each direction should not exceed 20 lb. ft. and not vary more than 5 lb. ft. from left to right.

18. Position steering valve to obtain equal torque and tighten valve body attaching screws to maintain this setting.

19. With unit under power, but with no load, the torque required to rotate the worm shaft through an included angle at 180 deg. (90 deg. either side of center) should be 5 to 9 inch lbs.

20. Disconnect test equipment.

21. Place steering gear worm at center of travel and install worm connector.

22. Install unit in car.

Power Steering Pumps

Two types of pumps have been used: the sleeve type pump and the slipper type pump. The sleeve type pump is the

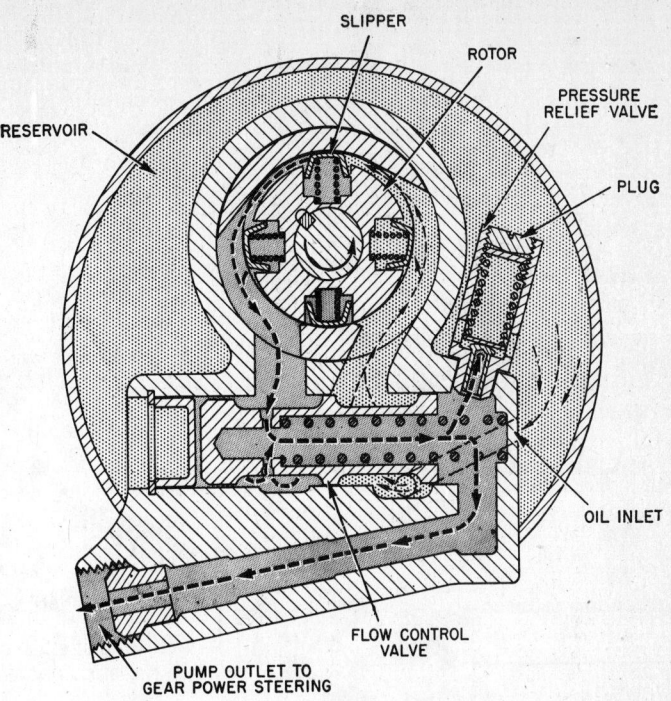

Fig. CC18   Slipper type power steering pump

same design as used on the Coaxial Power Steering unit (illustrated in Fig. C50).

The slipper-type pump, Fig. CC18, is a constant replacement type, bracket-mounted to the engine water pump housing and belt-driven by the engine fan pulley. Elimination of pulsation in oil flow is achieved by the cam surface of the pressed-in insert which evens out oil flow through the pump. Recirculation of oil from the rotor outlet to rotor inlet results in a reduction of torque required to drive the pump and thus reduces the amount of engine horsepower necessary to drive the pump.

Ford Torsion Bar Type

The power steering gear is designed with all components in one housing, Fig. F1. This makes possible internal oil passages between the valve and cylinder, thus eliminating all external lines and hoses, except the pressure and return hoses between the pump and gear.

The power cylinder is an integral part of the housing. The piston is of the double acting type in that oil pressure may be applied to either side of the piston. The one-piece piston and power rack is meshed to the sector shaft.

The hydraulic control valve, actuated by the torsion bar, is composed of a sleeeve and valve spool. The spool is an open center type "4-way" valve. The spool is held in neutral position by the torsion bar and spool actuator. The spool is actuated by the torsion bar. The amount of twisting of the torsion bar depends on the reaction load of the worm and ball nut. The greater the load the greater the twisting of the torsion bar. The torsion bar moves the valve spool which allows pressure to be directed to either side of the power piston, depending upon directional rotation of the steering

wheel, to give power assist.

Two types of pumps have been used: Fig. F2 shows the pulley driven type while Fig. F3 illustrates the type which is mounted at the front of the crankshaft.

Disassemble Steering Gear

1. Remove steering shaft coupling.
2. Remove snap ring and cylinder cap from piston bore; then remove cylinder cap "O" ring.
3. Turn steering shaft all the way to stop and back off 2⅛ turns.
4. Loosen sector shaft adjusting screw, remove cover screws and tap sector shaft out of housing.
5. Remove adjusting screw from cover.
6. Working through sector shaft bore and piston rack, pry piston out.
7. Remove piston "O" ring and piston rack bore "O" ring.
8. Loosen valve sleeve lock screw.
9. Remove valve spool adjuster cap and remove "O" ring from cap.
10. Remove thrust bearing lock nut and control valve sleeve adjuster nut.
11. Remove torsion bar and sleeve as-

sembly by tapping on lower end of torsion bar.

12. Remove sector shaft seal retaining ring and gear housing snap ring.

Disassemble Torsion Bar and Sleeve

1. Position ball nut in vise, using cloth to protect ball nut.
2. Remove valve spool sleeve from torsion bar, and "O" ring from sleeve.
3. Remove adjuster lock nut from lower end of torsion bar. Then remove valve spool adjuster from torsion bar and "O" ring from adjuster.
4. Remove torsion bar, valve spool and actuator from worm shaft.
5. Remove worm thrust bearing and cup from gear housing.
6. Separate valve spool and actuator from torsion bar, using turning motion.
7. Remove snap ring and take valve spool from actuator.
8. Do not disassemble ball nut unless there is evidence of binding or rough spots.

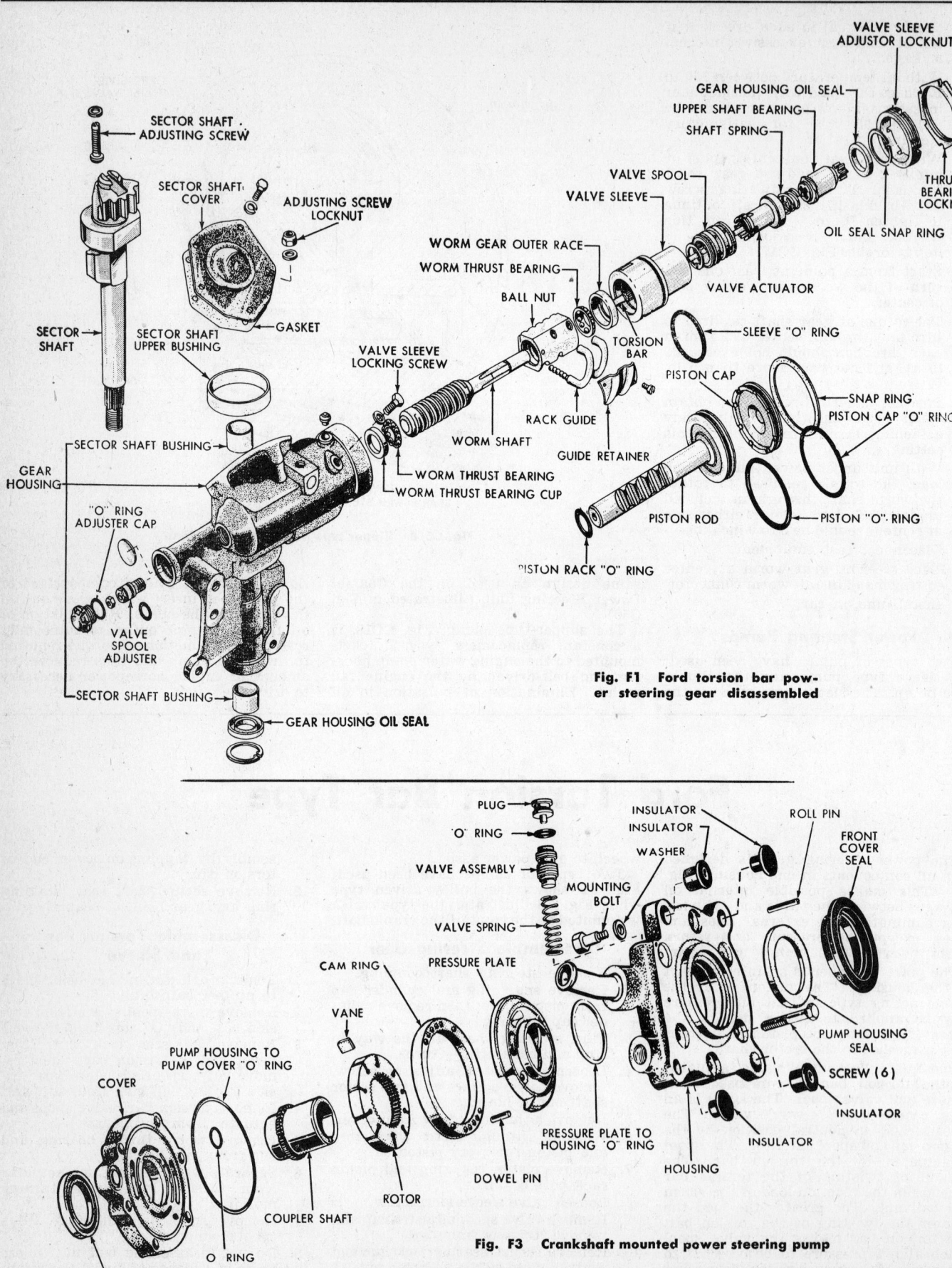

Fig. F1 Ford torsion bar power steering gear disassembled

Fig. F3 Crankshaft mounted power steering pump

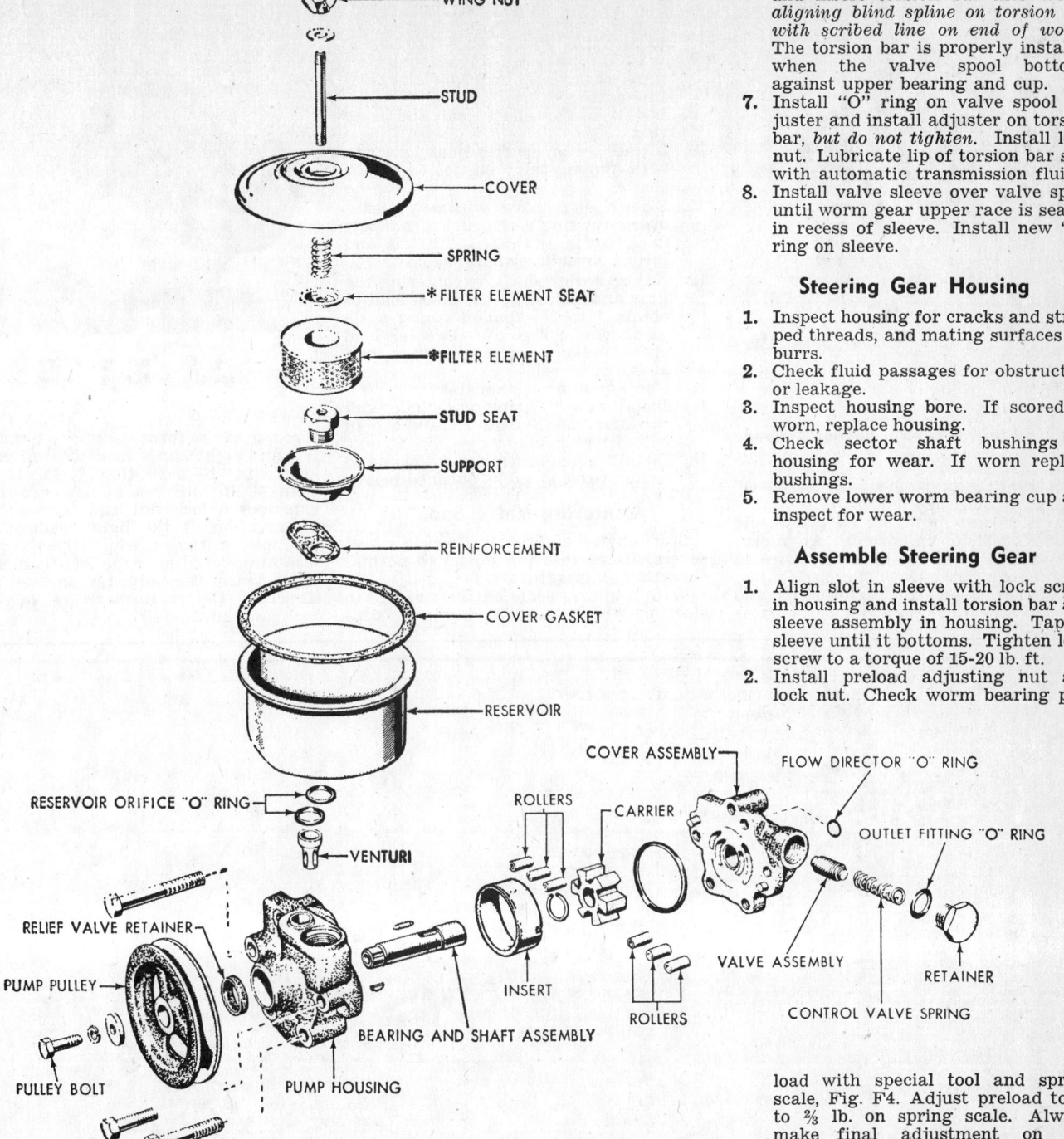

*USED IN EARLY PRODUCTION

Fig. F2   Power steering pump disassembled

and insert torsion bar into worm, *aligning blind spline on torsion bar with scribed line on end of worm.* The torsion bar is properly installed when the valve spool bottoms against upper bearing and cup.

7. Install "O" ring on valve spool adjuster and install adjuster on torsion bar, *but do not tighten.* Install lock nut. Lubricate lip of torsion bar seal with automatic transmission fluid.

8. Install valve sleeve over valve spool until worm gear upper race is seated in recess of sleeve. Install new "O" ring on sleeve.

Steering Gear Housing

1. Inspect housing for cracks and stripped threads, and mating surfaces for burrs.
2. Check fluid passages for obstruction or leakage.
3. Inspect housing bore. If scored or worn, replace housing.
4. Check sector shaft bushings in housing for wear. If worn replace bushings.
5. Remove lower worm bearing cup and inspect for wear.

Assemble Steering Gear

1. Align slot in sleeve with lock screw in housing and install torsion bar and sleeve assembly in housing. Tap on sleeve until it bottoms. Tighten lock screw to a torque of 15-20 lb. ft.
2. Install preload adjusting nut and lock nut. Check worm bearing preload with special tool and spring scale, Fig. F4. Adjust preload to ½ to ⅔ lb. on spring scale. Always make final adjustment on the tighten stroke of adjuster.
3. Install valve spool centering wrench, Fig. F5, on spool adjuster and center valve spool until only the valley between the lands can be seen through the pressure port. Hold torsion bar with tool shown in Fig. F4 while turning centering wrench. Lock centering screw. This is only a preliminary adjustment; make final adjustment on car.
4. Center ball nut with centerline of sector shaft opening.
5. Install "O" ring in piston rack bore of housing and lubricate.
6. Carefully hone all edges of piston rack teeth with a hand stone to pre-

9. Inspect all parts for damage and replace as necessary.

Assemble Torsion Bar and Sleeve

1. Install torsion bar bearing in sleeve.
2. Install torsion bar bearing seal.
3. Install snap ring and check bearing rotation.

4. Check fit of worm gear outer race to insure that it is a hand fit. Then install bearing and race on worm shaft.
5. Install valve spool on actuator and retain with new snap ring. Check valve spool for free rotation.
6. Install torsion bar spring and actuator on torsion bar. *Turn lower shaft so that two identifying punch marks are aligned.* Hold assembly together

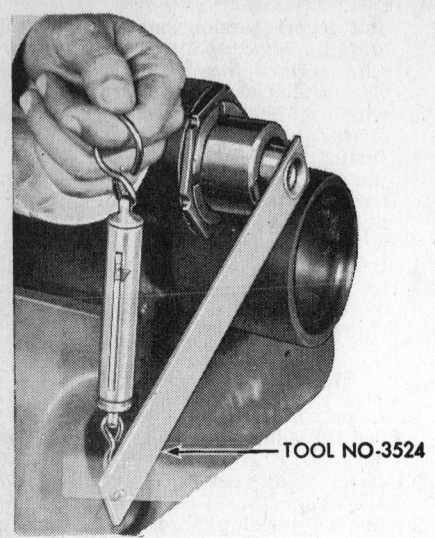

Fig. F4   Checking worm bearing preload

vent cutting piston rack bore "O" ring during installation.

7. Install new "O" ring on piston and install piston in housing. Align center rack teeth with sector bore in housing (3rd groove in rack).

8. Grease splines on sector shaft and install. Make sure sector shaft is centered by installing tool shown in Fig. F4 on torsion bar and rotate worm shaft. Count turns from one stop to the other. There should be at least four turns. If less than four turns remove sector shaft and reinstall correctly.

9. Install sector shaft seal and snap ring.

10. Install sector shaft adjusting screw with proper shim in slot in sector shaft.

11. Place housing cover with new gasket over adjusting screw and turn screw until cover is seated. Install and torque cover screws 15-50 lb. ft.

12. Adjust sector shaft by centering the gear and adjusting the mesh load to obtain 1 to 1½ lbs. on spring scale as shown in Fig. F4. Greater load should be on high point rather than at end of travel.

13. Check piston rack backlash.

14. Install new "O" ring on cylinder end cap and install cap. Retain cap in cylinder with snap ring.

15. Install gear assembly in car and center valve spool as outlined below.

Centering Valve Spool

Start engine and rotate steering wheel several times to bring oil up to normal operating temperature.

With a spring scale on the rim of the steering wheel, and steering gear cen-

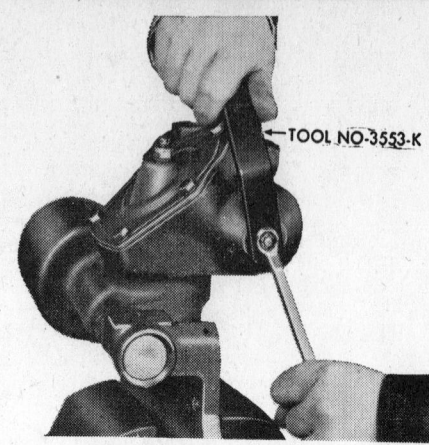

Fig. F5   Locking valve spool centering screw

tered, read the force necessary to make a left and right hand turn. The difference should not be more than ½ lb. If more than ½ lb. difference remove adjuster cap, loosen lock nut and turn adjuster in direction of the light reading. For example, if the steering wheel requires less force to turn to the left than to the right, turn the adjuster in the same direction (left). Recheck reading and lock jam nut. Install cap.

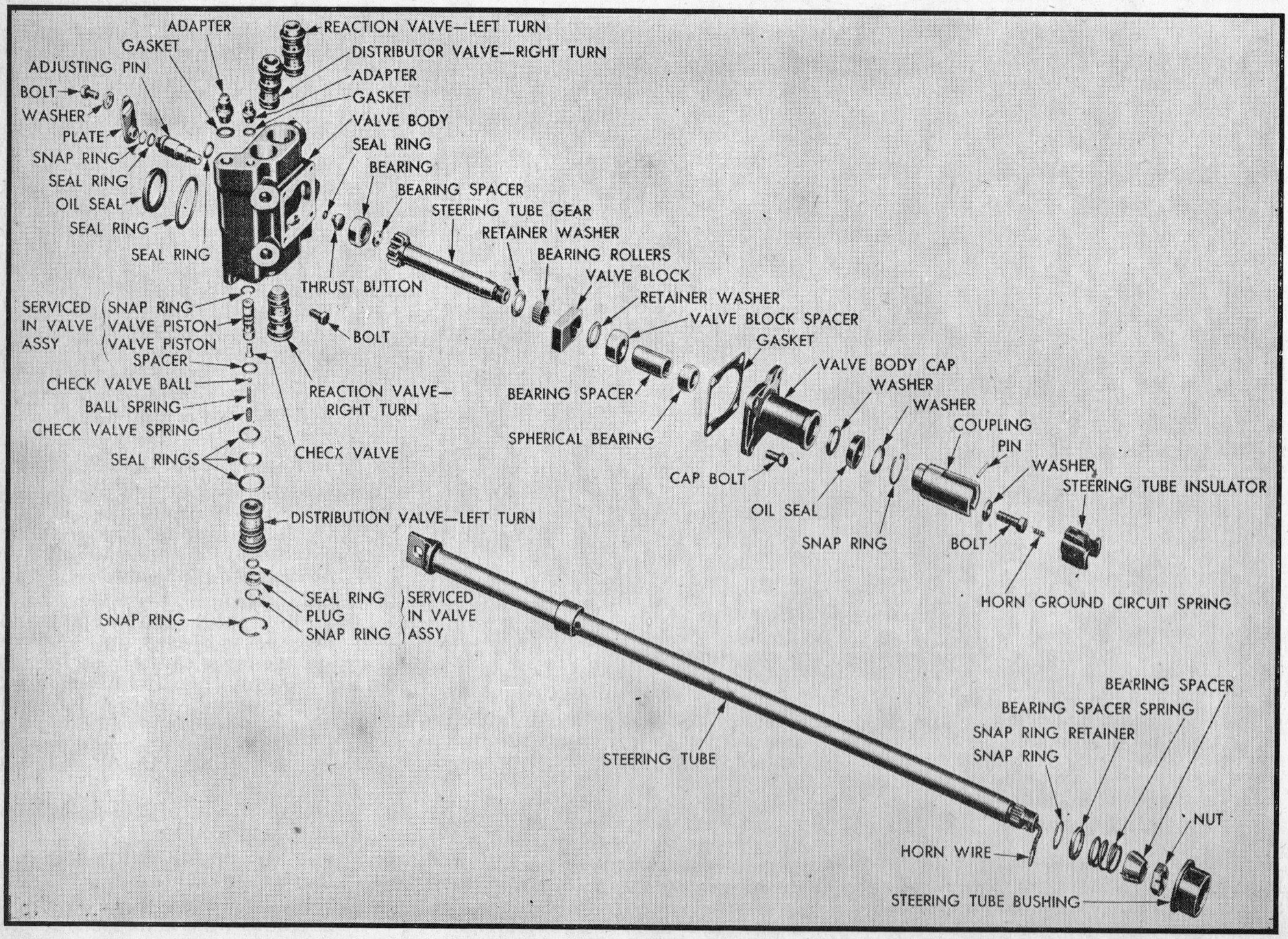

Gemmer Hydraguide

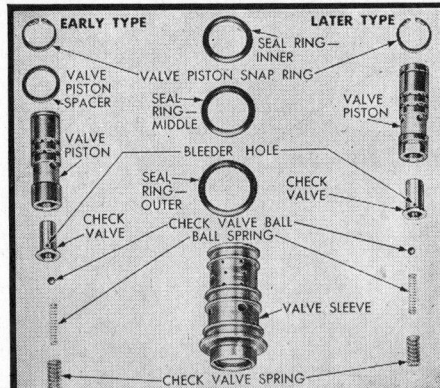

Fig. G2   Gemmer distribution and reaction control valves

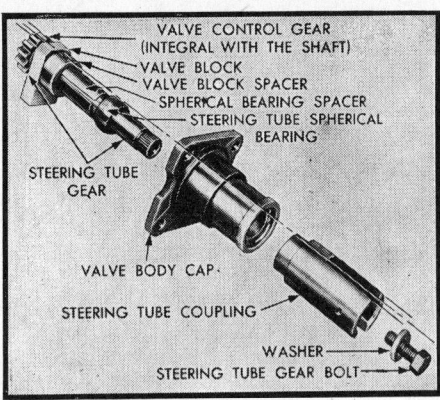

Fig. G3   Gemmer steering tube coupling and lever shaft

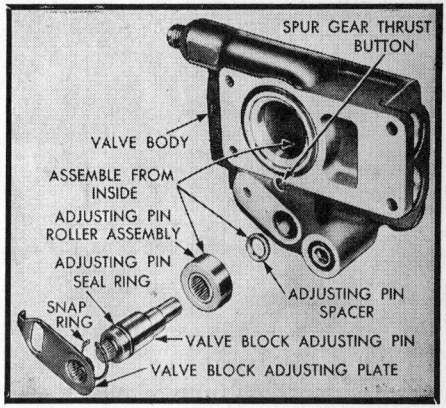

Fig. G4   Gemmer valve body

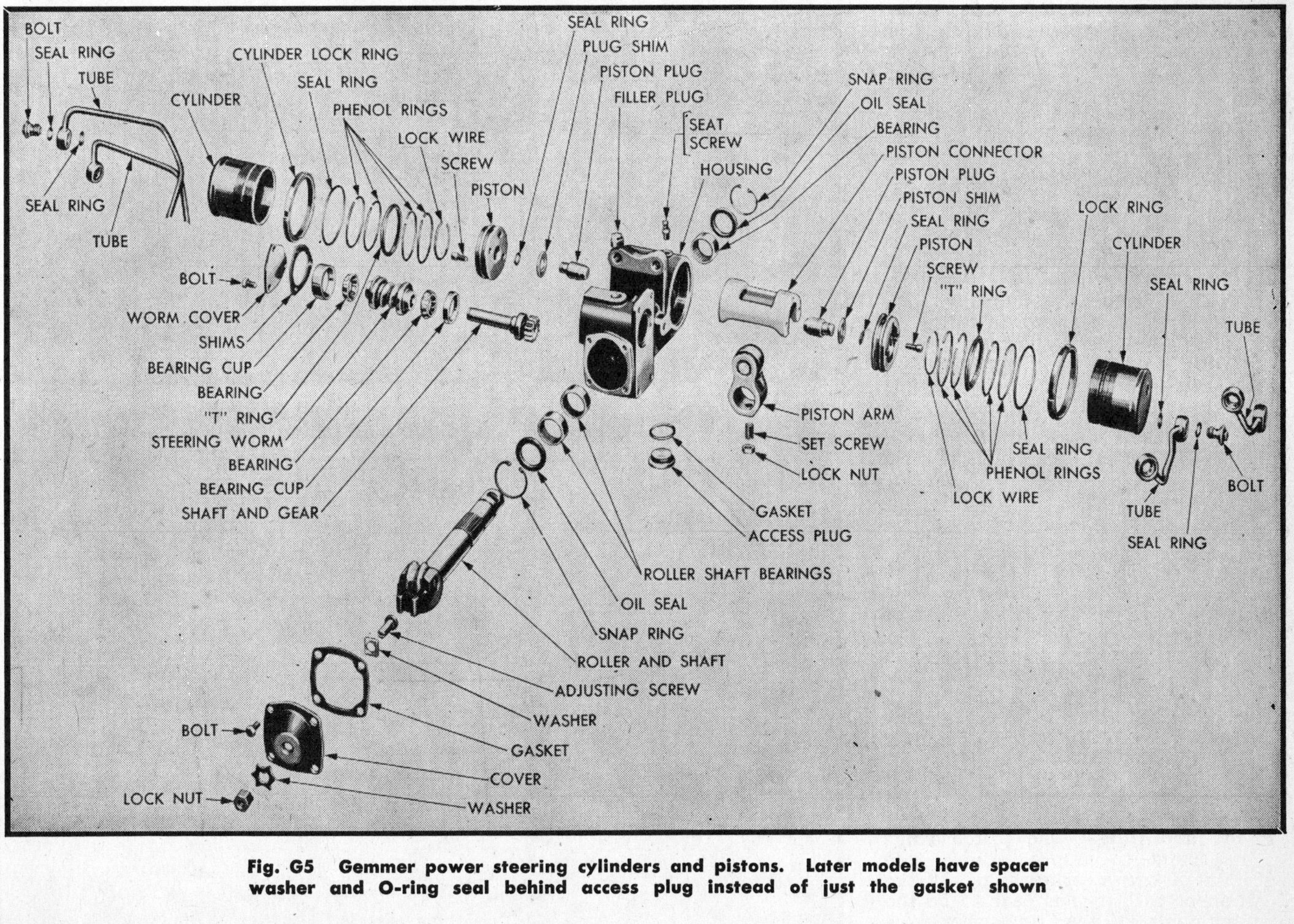

BOLT
SEAL RING
TUBE
CYLINDER LOCK RING
SEAL RING
CYLINDER
PHENOL RINGS
LOCK WIRE
SCREW
SEAL RING
PLUG SHIM
PISTON PLUG
FILLER PLUG
SEAT SCREW
HOUSING
PISTON
SEAL RING
TUBE
BOLT
WORM COVER
SHIMS
BEARING CUP
BEARING
"T" RING
STEERING WORM
BEARING
BEARING CUP
SHAFT AND GEAR
SNAP RING
OIL SEAL
BEARING
PISTON CONNECTOR
PISTON PLUG
PISTON SHIM
SEAL RING
PISTON
SCREW
"T" RING
LOCK RING
CYLINDER
SEAL RING
TUBE
SEAL RING
PHENOL RINGS
LOCK WIRE
BOLT
TUBE
SEAL RING
PISTON ARM
SET SCREW
LOCK NUT
GASKET
ACCESS PLUG
ROLLER SHAFT BEARINGS
OIL SEAL
SNAP RING
ROLLER AND SHAFT
ADJUSTING SCREW
WASHER
GASKET
COVER
WASHER
BOLT
LOCK NUT

Fig. G5   Gemmer power steering cylinders and pistons. Later models have spacer washer and O-ring seal behind access plug instead of just the gasket shown

Fig. G1   Gemmer power steering valve body

This power steering unit, Fig. G1, contains an hydraulic system of two axially opposed power cylinders and a valve body assembly incorporating four valves —two distribution and two reaction. Power is transmitted from the power cylinders to the steering gear shaft through a power arm. Other components of the hydraulic system are a generator-driven oil pump incorporating a pressure relief valve and flow control valve, and a filter within the oil reservoir. The flow control valve limits the flow in the hydraulic system to a pre-determined maximum and thus limits the hydraulic pressure drop in the system. As a result, the horsepower required to drive the pump is kept to a minimum.

By careful design these elements have been combined into two compact units which are connected with a pair of flexible hoses. One unit contains the hydraulic power cylinders, valve body assembly, spur gears and worm-and-roller drive; the other incorporates the reservoir and the oil pump with its valves.

Power Steering Repairs

Before disassembling any of the component parts of the power steering unit, clean the outside surface of the assembly thoroughly. Extreme care should be exercised in disassembly and assembly of these units to prevent dirt from getting into the hydraulic system. Some of the clearance and orifices in the assembly are so small that the presence of a small particle of dirt may prevent the steering assembly from functioning properly.

During the disassembly and reassembly procedure, refer to the illustrations for guidance and be sure to observe the following precautions:

Valve Assemblies—The valve body is made of die cast aluminum. Handle it carefully to prevent damaging the cover or its mating surfaces. Each valve body port boss is marked to aid in the reassembly of the valves in the correct position. Work carefully when removing valves as their internal parts may become dislocated and fall into the housing. To prevent the possibility of improper assembly, units of the valve assembly should be cleaned separately and kept in separate containers. Valve parts are a select fit with each other and are not interchangeable.

Valve Position—The valve position identification marks on the valve body port bosses also indicate the number of O-ring seals used on each valve.

Valve Block Adjusting Pin—When assembling the valve block adjusting pin in the valve body, locate the offset side of the pin away from the steering tube gear. The adjusting plate should not be installed on the adjusting pin until the unit is completely assembled.

Piston and Rings—The piston rings are important to assure trouble free operation of the steering gear. If the condition of the rings appear to be the least bit doubtful, new rings should be installed.

New O-ring seals, gaskets, copper and nylon washers should be used each time

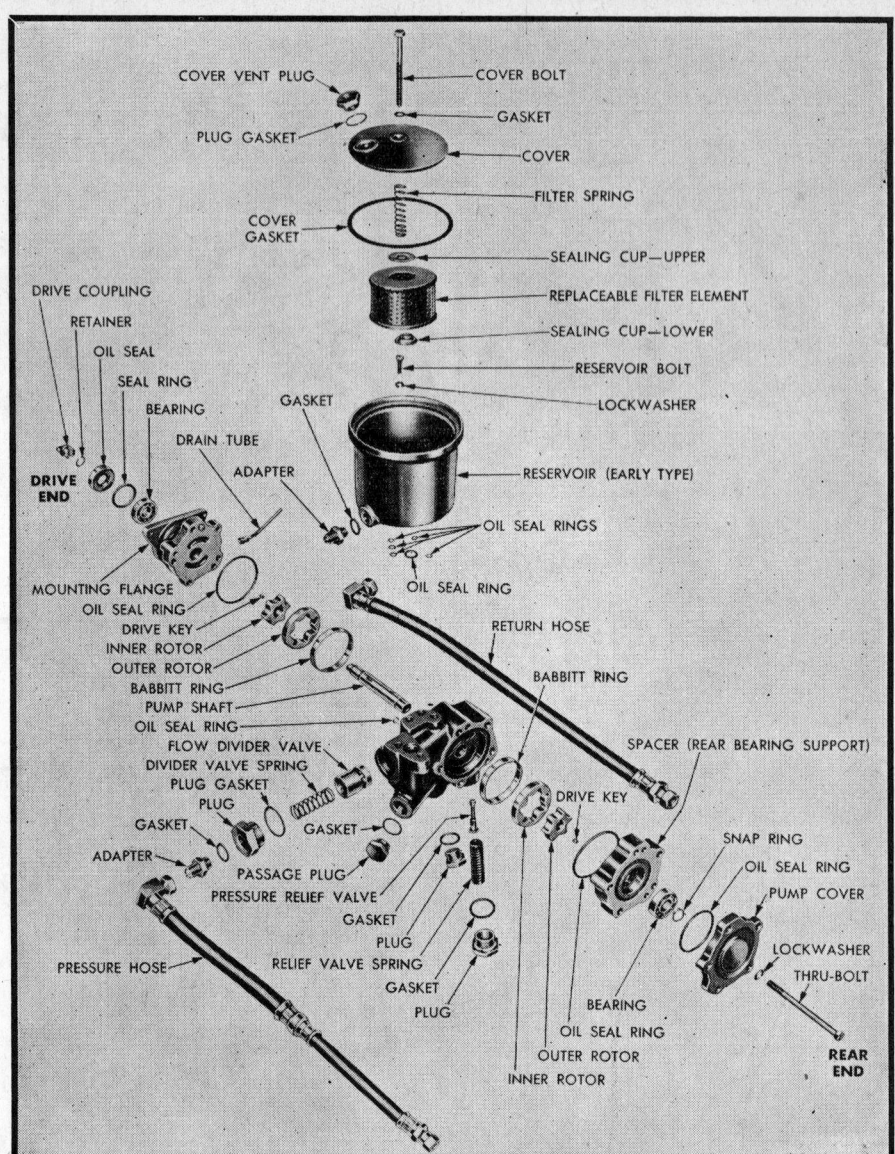

Fig. G6 Gemmer power steering pump and reservoir. Later model pumps have a single set of rotors (see Fig. G7)

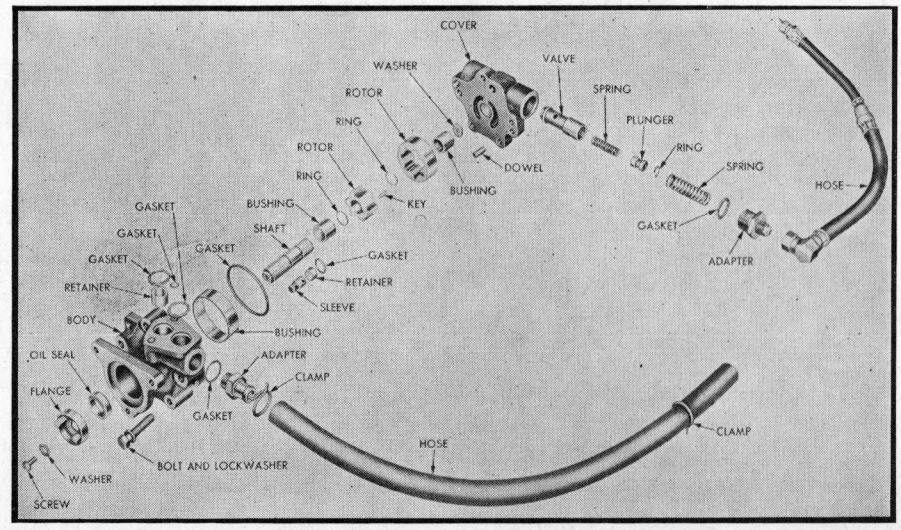

Fig. G7 Single rotor hydraulic oil pump. 1953-54

the assembly is disassembled to prevent leakage.

The tapered side of the thrust ring fits against the tapered side of the piston ring groove.

Worm Shaft Bearing Adjustment— Turn the adjusting screw clockwise until the worm rotates freely without binding from one extreme to the opposite extreme. The worm gear, when properly adjusted, should rotate freely in the bearing cones without binding. The gear should also be sufficiently tight to eliminate any free play between shaft and bearing.

Hold the adjusting screw and tighten the lock nut to 25 lb. ft. torque. After tightening the nut, recheck the adjustment.

Steering Gear Shaft Adjustment— When making this adjustment, always remove the power arm access plug and loosen the power arm set screw before attempting to adjust the cross shaft.

Set the worm gear and piston arm at the center position. Hold the worm at center with one hand. With the other hand on the pitman arm, check the backlash between worm and gear in both directions. Turn the shaft adjusting screw so that no backlash will be felt while the worm is turned between approximately 45 degrees either side of the centerline. Clearance should be at a minimum at the degree positions without binding. Do not adjust the cross shaft roller and worm too tightly. Hold the adjusting screw in the adjusted position and tighten the lock nut to a torque of 20-25 lb. ft.

Spur Gear Adjustment— With worm gear and piston arm centered, turn the tube coupling slot in a vertical position and proceed as follows: Install adjusting plate on adjusting pin. Rotate adjusting pin and plate until no backlash is felt at steering tube shaft coupling. Hold locking plate in adjusted position. Install and tighten cap screw to 12 lb. ft. torque.

Lubrication

The oil level in the reservoir is ½" above the filter element. If reservoir is tilted the oil level shoud be ½" above the highest point of the filter element. An oil level mark is stamped on the inside of the reservoir.

Replenish the oil as necessary with SAE 10W engine oil. When temperatures are consistently below—10 degrees, drain the hydraulic system and refill with SAE 5W engine oil.

When temperature is below—10 degrees, run the engine for at least three minutes before putting the car in motion or turning the steering wheel.

Saginaw Offset Type

THE unit consists of a conventional manually operated steering gear to which hydraulic power mechanism has been added. The hydraulic mechanism furnishes additional power to *assist* the manual operation so that the turning effort required at the steering wheel is greatly reduced.

The engine drives the oil pump which furnishes hydraulic pressure. When the engine is not running, or when any part of the power mechanism is inoperative, steering is entirely manual and requires approximately the same effort at the steering wheel as the conventional manual gear.

Power Steering Units

The hydraulic power mechanism added to the steering gear includes a power cylinder and rack connected to a separate gear sector on the steering gear pitman shaft, a hydraulic valve mounted concentric with the steering worm shaft and operated by the shaft, a high pressure oil pump driven by a belt from the engine, an oil reservoir, and connecting pipes and hoses.

Power Steering Gear Assembly

As shown in S1, the upper end of the pitman shaft is extended and provided with a separate gear sector which meshes with a power rack mounted in the gear housing. The power rack is pinned to the piston rod of the power cylinder, mounted on the rear side of the gear housing, and is held in proper mesh with the pitman shaft sector by a guide attached to a shim-adjusted housing cover (not shown).

The power cylinder is a double acting type since oil pressure may be applied to either side of the piston through external tubes connected to the hydraulic valve.

An adapter closes the inner end of the cylinder and provides a bearing for the piston rod. The two outer grooves in the circumference of the adapter contain "O" ring rubber seals, and the bore is fitted with a spring loaded rubber seal to prevent escape of oil at the piston rod.

Normal seepage of oil through the bearing is held back to the hydraulic valve through passages in the adapter and cylinder connected to an external tube.

The housing has one central annular groove connected to the oil pump and two outer annular grooves connected to the reservoir.

A valve spool, having a very close sliding fit in the valve housing, is mounted concentric with the worm shaft and between the worm thrust bearings so that it moves with these parts. The spool contains two annular grooves which control the flow of oil between the grooves and oil passages in the housing.

The housing contains five equally spaced *pairs* of centering plungers which

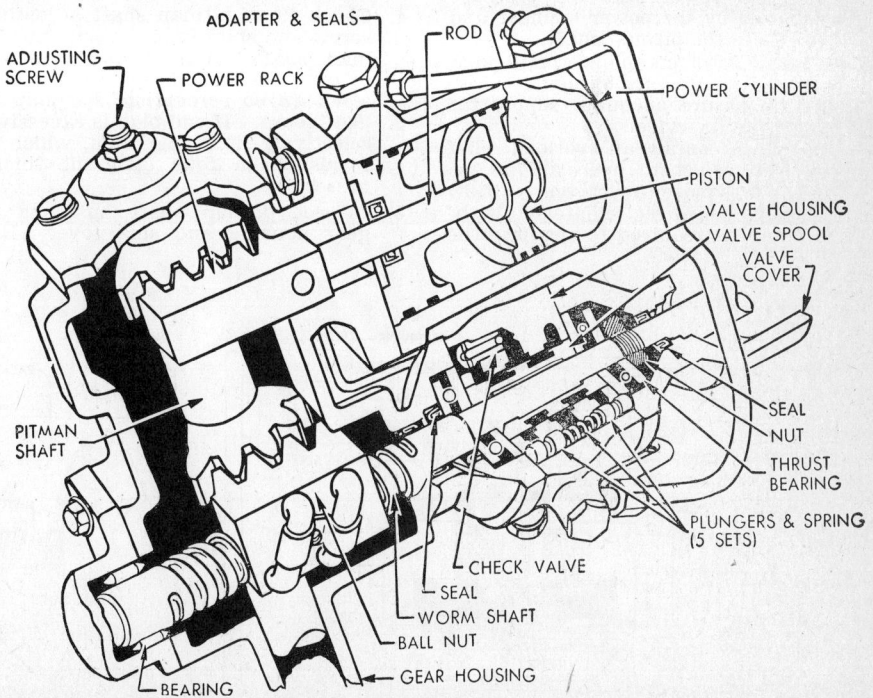

ADJUSTING SCREW — ADAPTER & SEALS — POWER RACK — ROD — POWER CYLINDER — PISTON — VALVE HOUSING — VALVE SPOOL — VALVE COVER — SEAL — NUT — THRUST BEARING — PLUNGERS & SPRING (5 SETS) — SEAL — CHECK VALVE — WORM SHAFT — BALL NUT — GEAR HOUSING — BEARING — PITMAN SHAFT

Fig. S1 Saginaw offset type steering gear assembly

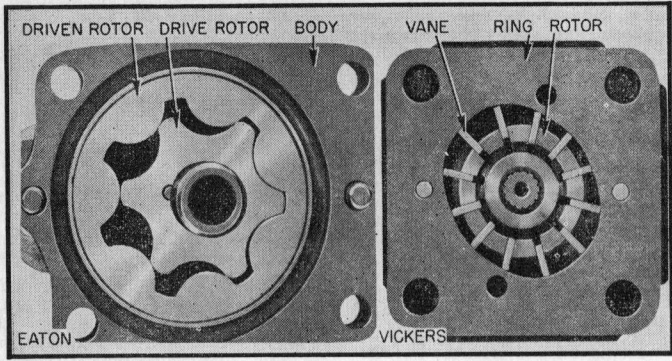

Fig. S2   Eaton and Vickers pumping elements

are forced outward against the gear housing and the valve cover by a heavy coil spring located between the plungers. The worm thrust bearings contact the plungers so that axial movement of the worm shaft is opposed by the plungers and springs.

The worm shaft and thrust bearings will move the spool endwise in the valve housing, permitting oil flow to the power cylinder, whenever the thrust load on the worm shaft is sufficient to overcome the preload of the centering springs.

A check valve mounted in the valve housing permits the oil displaced by the power cylinder piston to by-pass the oil pump during manual operation whenever the oil pump is not operating. It also prevents oil from overflowing through the reservoir vent under the same conditions (see Figs. S3 and S4).

Oil Pump

The oil pump, which is mounted on the engine in position to be driven by a belt from the crankshaft pulley, converts some engine power into oil pressure which is used by the power cylinder and rack to rotate the pitman shaft.

The Eaton rotor pump and the Vickers balanced vane pump are optionally used, Fig. S2, to assure adequate supply for production and service.

Both pumps contain an overload relief valve which is set to open at 750 psi (pounds per square inch) and a flow control valve which recirculates oil within the pump as required to regulate the output volume to approximately 1½ gallons per minute at all operating speeds.

Power Steering Repairs

When it becomes necessary to disassemble the steering gear for repairs, refer to the illustrations and, when disassembled, inspect the parts for damage or wear as outlined below.

The special tools illustrated may be obtained from the Kent-Moore Organization, Inc., Warren, Michigan.

1. Wash all parts in clean kerosene or other solvent and wipe dry with clean, lint-free cloth.

2. Inspect steering shaft for wear or brinnelling in ball and needle bearing races, which would require replacement of shaft. Check shaft to make sure it is straight.

3. Inspect teeth of ball nut and all sector teeth of pitman shaft. If teeth are excessively worn or scored, replace the part. Replace pitman shaft if serrated end is twisted.

4. Check fit of pitman shaft adjusting screw and shim in slot in end of pitman shaft. *With shim in place, screw head must be free to turn in slot with no perceptible end play to .002" loose.* If end play is excessive, selectively fit a new shim, which is furnished in four different thicknesses.

5. Inspect pitman shaft bushings in gear housing and side cover. Re-

place bushings in housing and cover assembly if bushings are worn excessively.

6. Remove worm seal from gear housing with a punch and use the tool shown in Fig. S11, to install *a new seal with spring side outward.*

7. If worm bearing in housing requires replacement, drive it out with a punch and use the tool shown in Fig. S11, to install the new bearing.

8. If the worm bearing in the housing end cover requires replacement, insert the tool shown in Fig. S12 into the bearing and turn the screw, which will expand two plates under the bearing and will then force the tool and bearing out. Install new bearing with the tool shown in Fig. S13, which has a shoulder to locate the bearing at proper depth in cover.

9. Replace pitman shaft seal, installing new seal with feather edge toward inside of gear housing.

10. Inspect oil shedder and control shaft bearing in valve cover. If bearing is at all doubtful replace it.

11. Inspect piston rod, teeth and guide surface of power rack, and rack guide for excessive wear or scoring. If necessary to replace piston rod or rack, drive out coupling pin and use new pin to connect new parts. Stake rack at three places on each side to retain the pin, and file down burrs raised by staking.

12. Inspect power cylinder bore for scores or other damage. Inspect piston rings for scores or breaks. Inspect seal in power cylinder adapter. If seal is worn or damaged, replace adapter assembly (the seal is not furnished separately for service).

13. Inspect valve housing, spool, and centering plunger for scores, nicks or burred edges. Replace damaged parts and make sure that spool and plungers slide freely in housing.

14. Test the check valve by blowing through both ends. Ball should seat when blowing through small end, and allow passage of air when blowing through slotted end of valve body.

15. Remove seal from valve cover with a punch, and use the tool shown in Fig. S14 to install a new seal *with the spring side of seal outward* toward shoulder of tool.

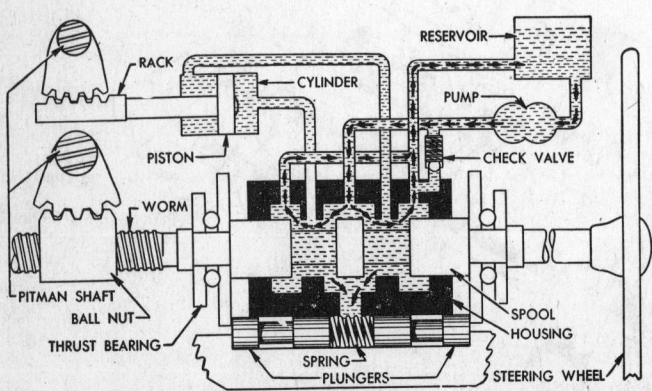

Fig. S3   Oil circulation without power application

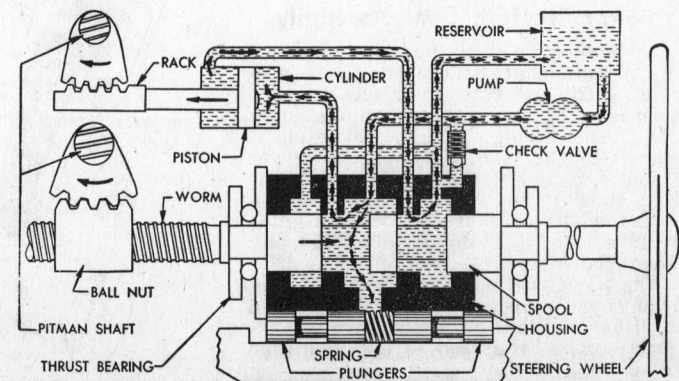

Fig. S4   Oil circulation during power application on a left turn

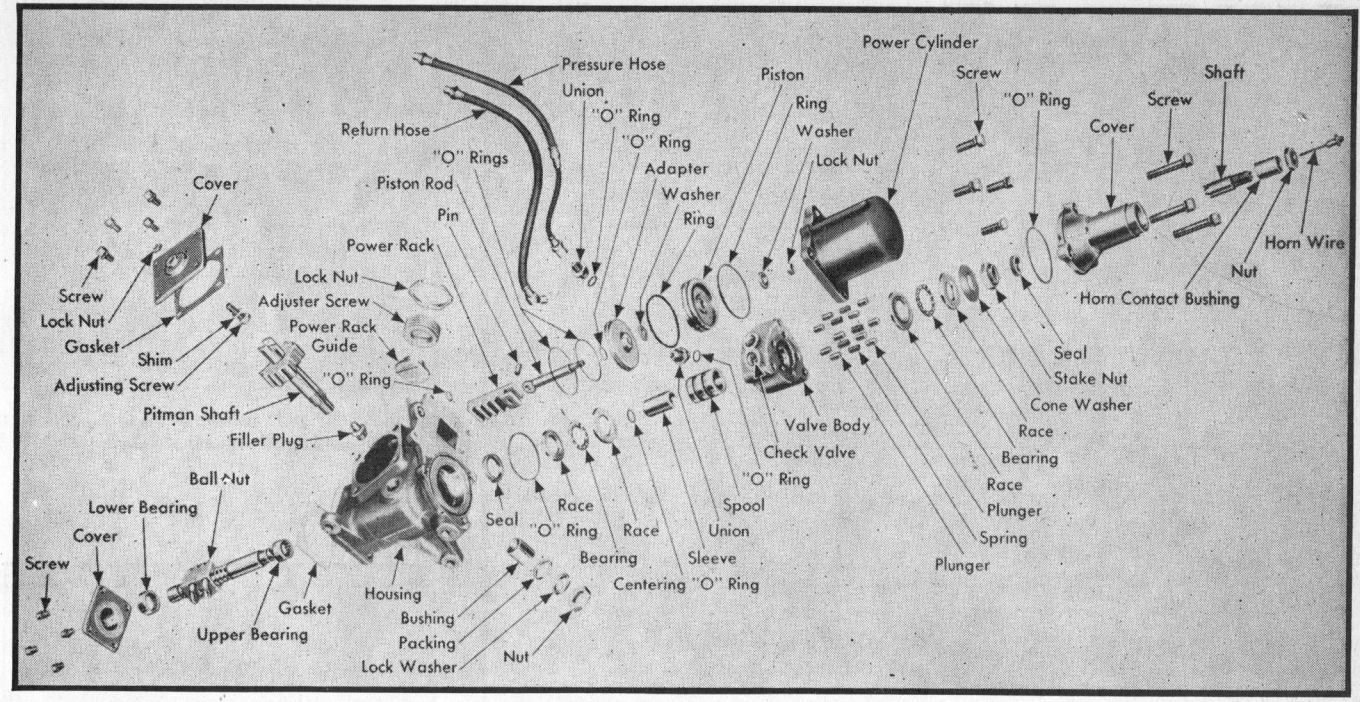

Fig. S5 Saginaw Offset type power steering

16. Inspect steering column jacket for distortion. A rippled or wavy feeling of jacket surface, particularly at lower end, will usually indicate a sprung jacket. Replace jacket if sprung or otherwise damaged.

Service Operations On Car

LUBRICARE (1000 MILES) — Thoroughly clean surrounding area before removing filler plugs to avoid entrance of dirt. Remove reservoir filler plug, wipe off the attached gauge rod, insert rod in reservoir *with plug seated on edge of filler opening.* Remove plug and check oil level, which should be at mark on rod. Add Automatic Transmission Oil, Type A, as required to bring oil level to mark on rod.

Remove gear housing filler plug with attached vent and add lubricant up to filler opening, using gear lubricant specified for synchromesh transmissions. *Do not fill with pressure because lubricant may be forced through worm and piston rod seals into the hydraulic system.*

Pump Drive Belt Adjustment

The pump drive belt has proper tension when one side can be depressed about ⅜" on In-Line engines and ⅞" on V-8 engines, with thumb pressure applied midway between pulleys.

To adjust belt, loosen pump mounting bolts and move pump horizontally as permitted by the slotted bolt holes in mounting bracket. Then tighten bolts securely.

Bleeding Hydraulic System

1. After connecting all hoses and filling reservoir to proper level, let the job set for five minutes with engine shut off. If a Vickers pump is installed, remove pipe plug from top of pump manifold and when oil starts to flow out of opening, install plug just tight enough to prevent oil from flowing out. Then wait five minutes. (Eaton pumps do not have pipe plug.)

2. Start engine and run it at approximately 1000 rpm for two or three minutes. Then turn steering wheel from one extreme to the other until all air is worked out, as evidenced by operation of the oil pump at a normal noise level.

3. In some cases it may be necessary to repeat the setting, engine running, and steering operations to eliminate all air. Tighten the plug in the Vickers pump manifold when bleeding operations are completed.

Pitman Shaft & Power Rack Adjustments

1. Disconnect pitman arm from steering tie rod and check tightness of

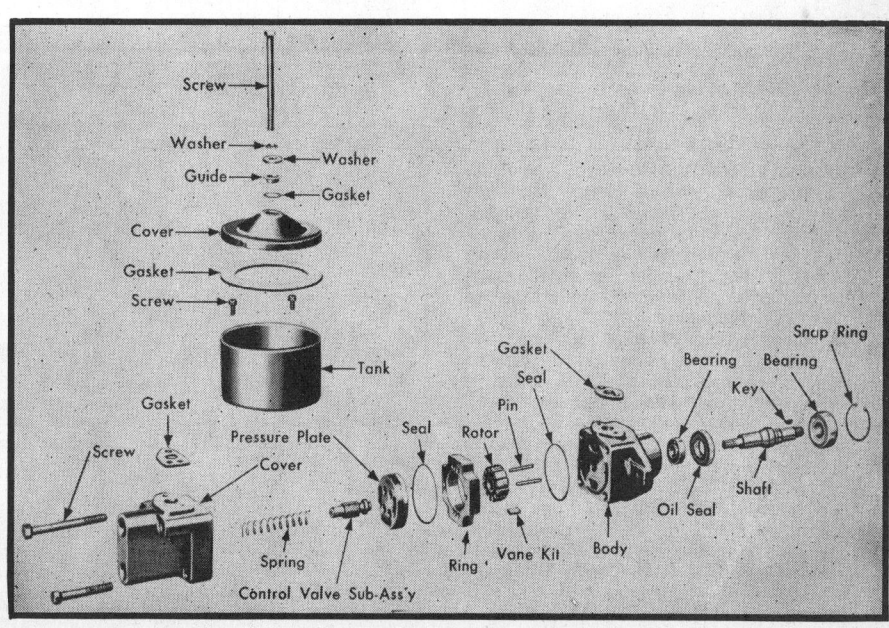

Fig. S6 Vickers type oil pump

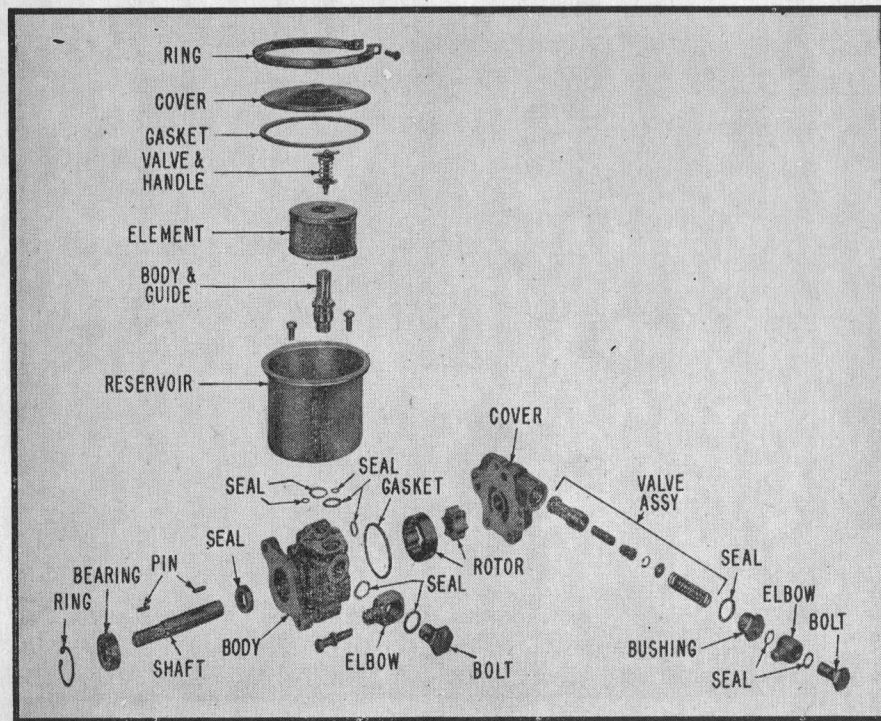

Fig. S7   Eaton type oil pump

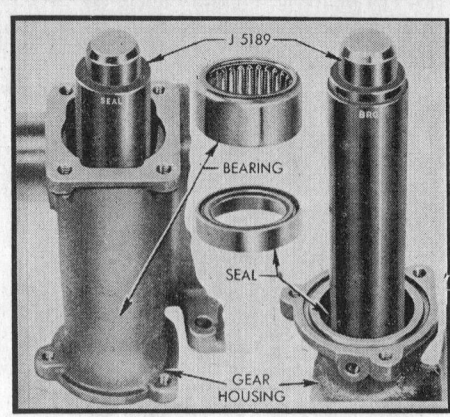

Fig. S11   Installing bearing
and seal in valve housing

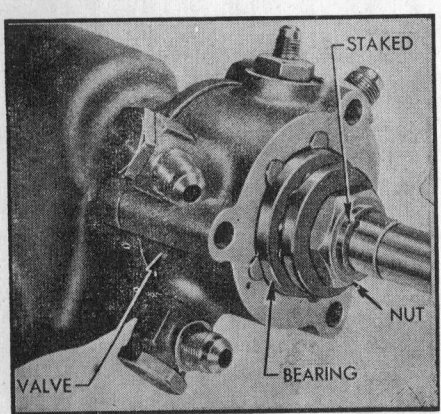

Fig. S8   Detail of thrust bearing and nut

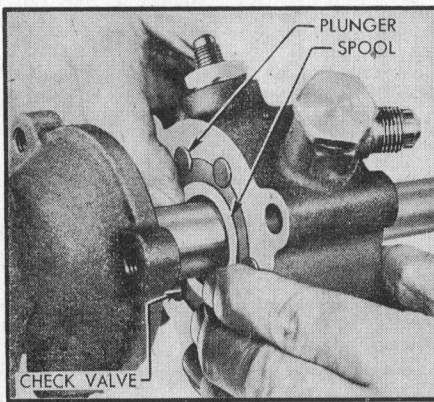

Fig. S9   Removing valve assembly

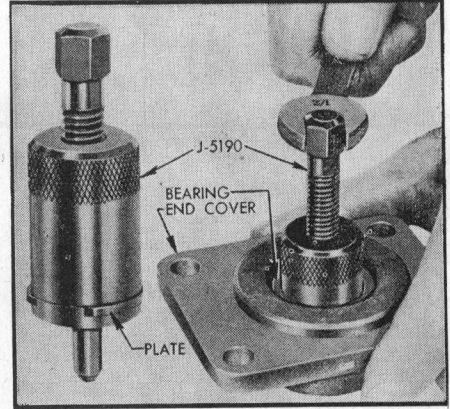

Fig. S12   Removing bearing from end cover

pitman arm nut with an 18" wrench.
2. Turn steering wheel slowly through its full travel to check for binding, which would indicate misalignment of steering gear in mountings. Any binding due to misalignment must be corrected before adjustments can be properly made.
3. Remove filler plug with vent attached and use a clean oil gun to draw out approximately ¾ pint of lubricant from gear housing.
4. Loosen four corner bolts of power rack guide cover just enough to assure lash between power rack and pitman shaft. If bolts are loosened too much, rack will bind on sector teeth.
5. Remove steering gear housing cover and adjusting screw. Check for proper fit of adjusting screw ball in pitman shaft slot as outlined in Step 4 under "Power Steering Repairs".

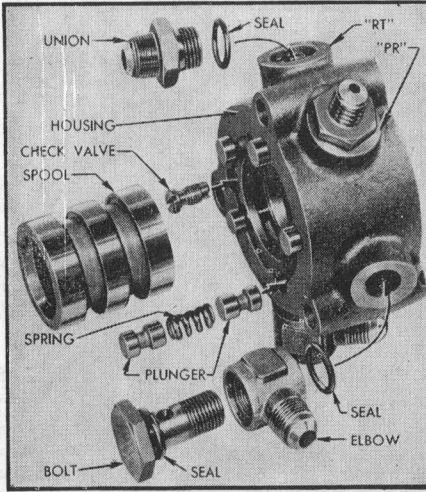

Fig. S10   Layout of hydraulic valve parts

Fig. S13   Installing bearing in end cover

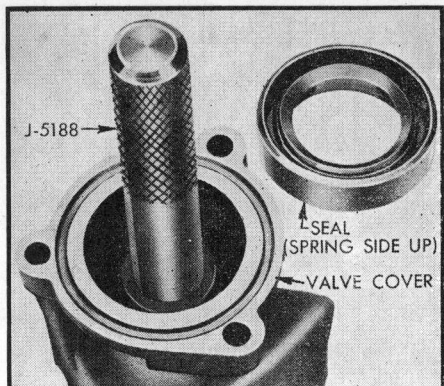

Fig. S14   Installing valve cover seal

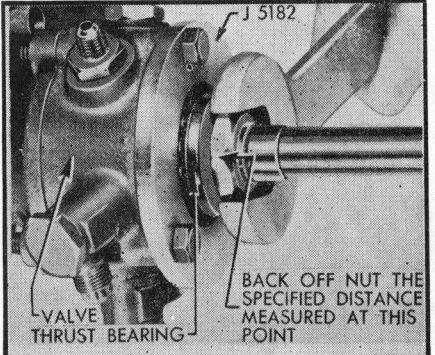

Fig. S15   Adjusting worm thrust bearings (Back off 1/16" to 3/32")

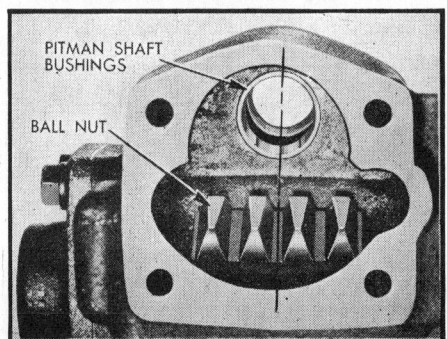

Fig. S16   Position of ball nut for installation of pitman shaft

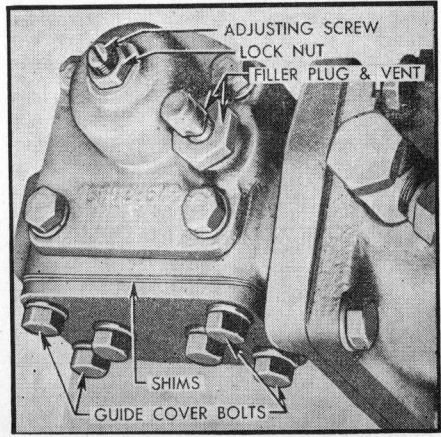

Fig. S17   Lash adjusting screw

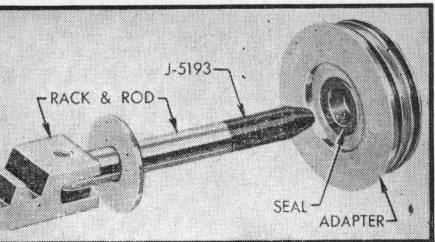

Fig. S18 Application of special rod inserter

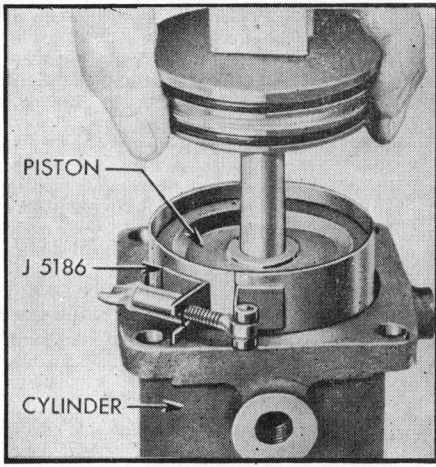

Fig. S19   Installing piston with ring compressor

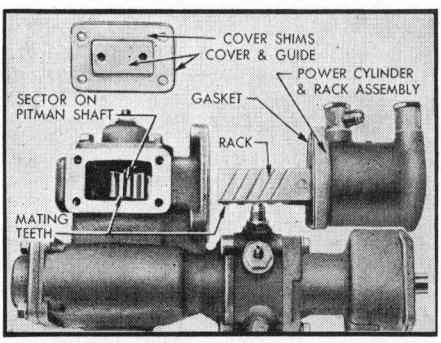

Fig. S20   Position of rack and sector for installation of power cylinder

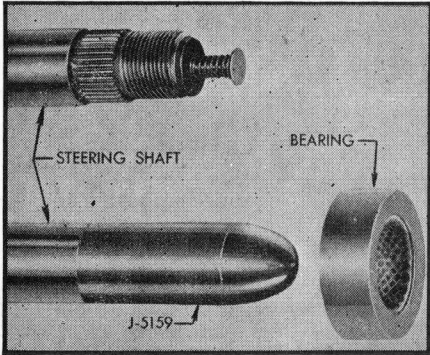

Fig. S21   Use of steering shaft bearing protector J-5159

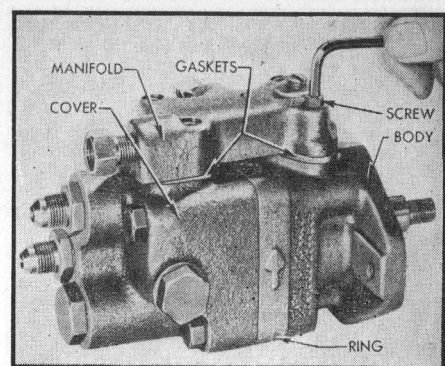

Fig. S22 Removing manifold from Vickers pump

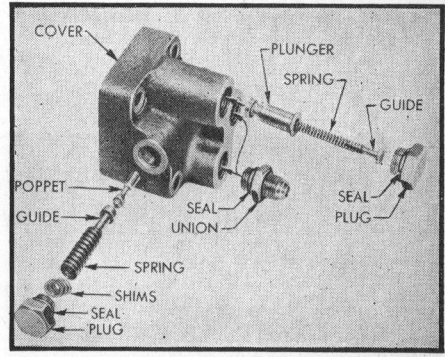

Fig. S23   Relief and flow control valve parts of Vickers pump

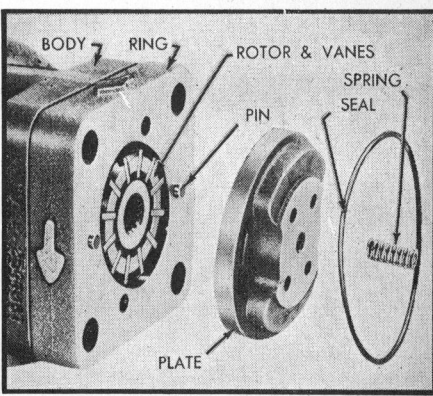

Fig. S24   Pressure plate, ring, rotor and vanes of Vickers pump

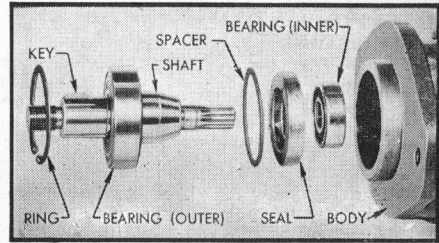

Fig. S25   Drive shaft, bearings and seal of Vickers pump

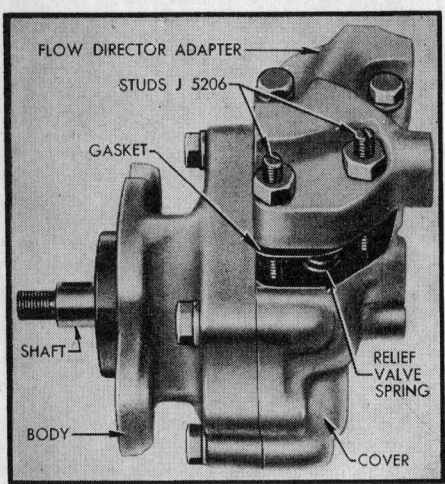

Fig. S26 Removing adapter with special studs from Eaton pump

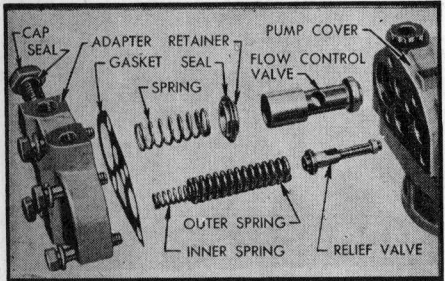

Fig. S27 Layout of relief and flow control valves of Eaton pump

Fig. S28 Checking clearance between rotors of Eaton pump

Replace adjusting screw and cover. Before tightening cover bolts, be sure that the adjusting screw is backed out far enough to allow the cover to seat properly.

6. Place steering wheel in straight-ahead position and tighten adjusting screw until a drag of 1 to 1½ lb. is needed to move the steering wheel through a 3″ arc. Tighten adjusting screw lock nut, being careful not to change the adjustment.

7. Tighten four bolts of power steering rack cover and measure steering wheel drag.

8. If the amount of pull necessary to move the steering wheel through a 3″ arc is unchanged, remove shims from under the power rack cover, one at a time, replacing and tightening the power rack cover after each shim is removed, until an increase in steering wheel drag is observed.

9. If the amount of pull necessary to move the steering wheel increases, add the amount of shims necessary to restore the 1 to 1½ lb. drag at the steering wheel.

10. Fill the gear housing to filler opening with proper lubricant and connect steering tie rod to pitman arm. Run up the tie rod plug solid and back off two turns before inserting cotter pin.

Servicing Oil Pump

1. When removing the pump, use plugs and caps to cover the hose connectors and unions on pump, and plug open ends of pressure and return line hose to avoid entrance of dirt.

2. When installing the pump, connect the pressure hose line marked "PR" on pump end to the union installed in pump port marked "PR". On the Eaton pump this union is the one nearest engine but on the Vickers pump it is the one farthest from engine.

3. Connect the return line hose marked "RT" on pump end to the other union on pump. This pump port is marked "RT".

4. Connect the two reservoir line hoses to pump. Then fill reservoir to proper level and bleed the hydraulic system as previously described.

NOTE — The small reservoir-to-pump pipe and hose assembly, the drive belt, and the pump pulley used with the Eaton pump are different from the corresponding parts used with the Vickers pump. If it becomes necessary to replace an Eaton pump with a Vickers, or vice versa, the three parts listed must also be changed.

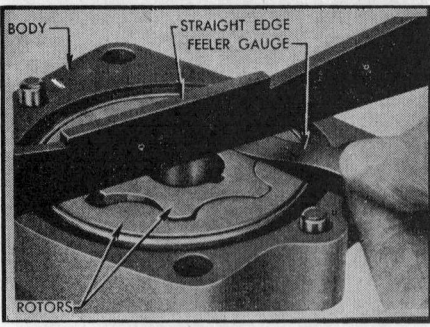

Fig. S29 Checking side clearance of rotors in body of Eaton pump

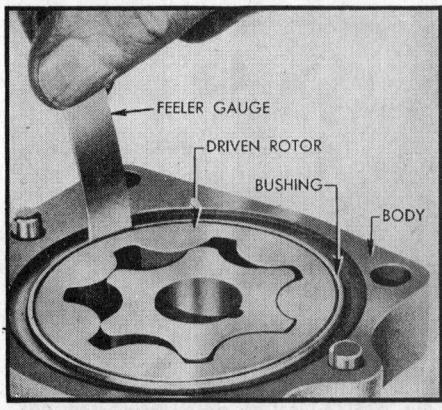

Fig. S30 Checking clearance between rotor and bushing of Eaton pump

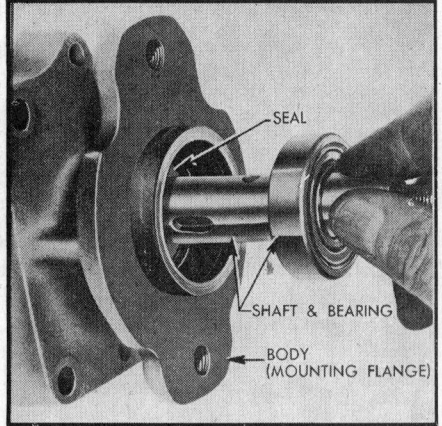

Fig. S31 Installing bearing and shaft in Eaton pump

Saginaw In-Line Type

This power steering mechanism, Fig. S32, is designed with the steering shaft, worm and ball nut, power piston and rack and the power cylinder all in line. With the hydraulic valve mounted on the top side of the gear housing, it makes possible internal oil passages between the valve and cylinder, thus eliminating all external lines and hoses except the pressure and return hoses between the pump and valve.

The power cylinder is an integral part of the gear housing. The piston is the double acting type in that oil pressure may be applied to either side of the piston. The piston, which includes the power rack, is meshed to the sector gear on the pitman shaft.

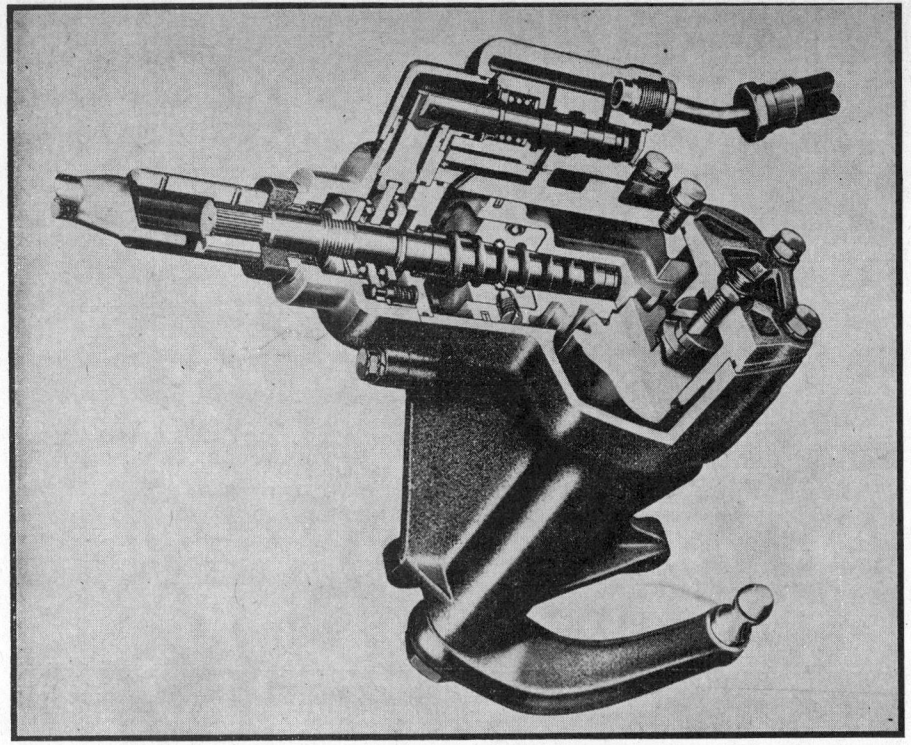

Fig. S32 Saginaw In-Line power steering

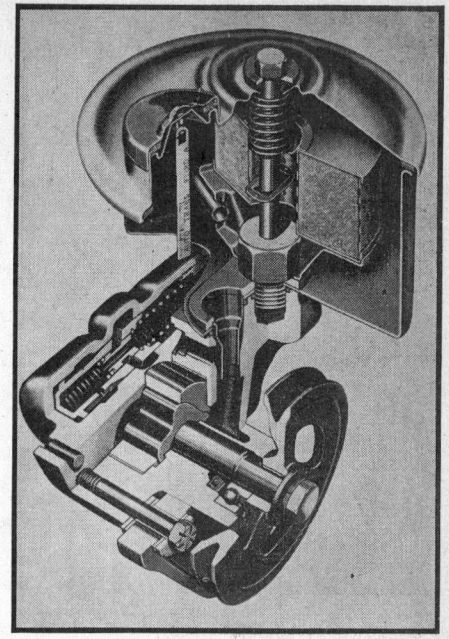

Fig. S33 Cutaway of rotor type power steering pump. Other pumps in use are the vane type and sleeve type

Fig. S33 illustrates the rotor type pump used in some applications. Also used is the vane type, similar to that which is used with the Saginaw Offset type of power steering. Another design is the spool type pump.

Power Steering Repairs

Before disassembling the unit, remove the shaft and coupling to make the unit easier to handle. The copuling must be supported when driving the pin out to prevent damaging the bearing in the end cover.

After removing the shaft and coupling, thoroughly clean the exterior of the unit with a suitable solvent and drain as much of the hydraulic fluid as possible. To assist in draining, place the unit with the control valve down and turn the worm through its entire range two or three times.

When disassembling the unit, refer to Figs. S36, S37 and S38. As each component is disassembled, thoroughly clean and inspect each part for evidence of wear or damage.

Hydraulic Control Valve, Fig. S37

1. When reassembling the control valve, lubricate the internal parts with Automatic Transmission fluid.
2. Clamp lower end of control spool in vise and install reaction control spring and spool.
3. Place spring thrust washer (lip up) on spool.

4. Place valve centering spring on washer.
5. Install new inner and outer O-rings on stop spacer, lubricate and assemble on spool with narrow inner land of spacer toward spring.
6. Hold spacer down on spool, compress spring and install actuating link.
7. Remove spool assembly for vise.
8. Carefully insert spool into valve body, rotating it while installing to facilitate installation.
9. Install spacer retaining washer and ring in valve body, being sure ring is properly seated.
10. Install new O-ring on end plug, lubricate and install plug and retaining ring in control valve.

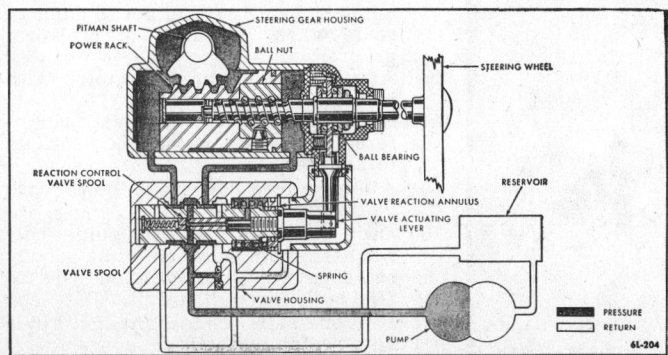

Fig. S34 Oil flow circuit with control valve in neutral. Saginaw In-Line

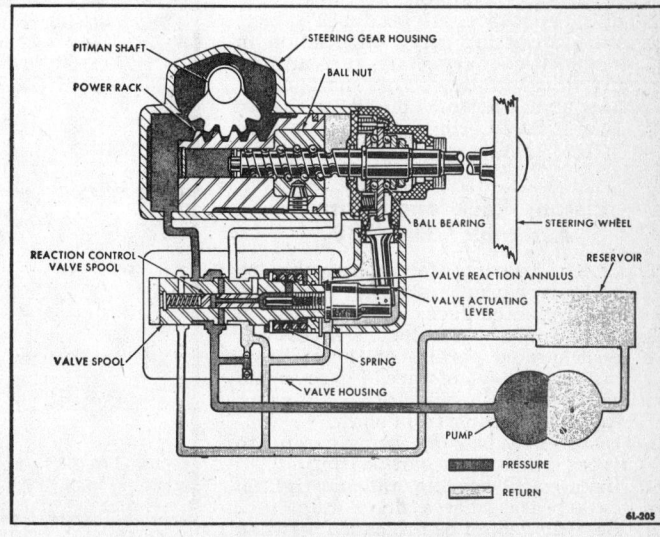

Fig. S35 Oil flow circuit with control valve in right turn position. Saginaw In-Line

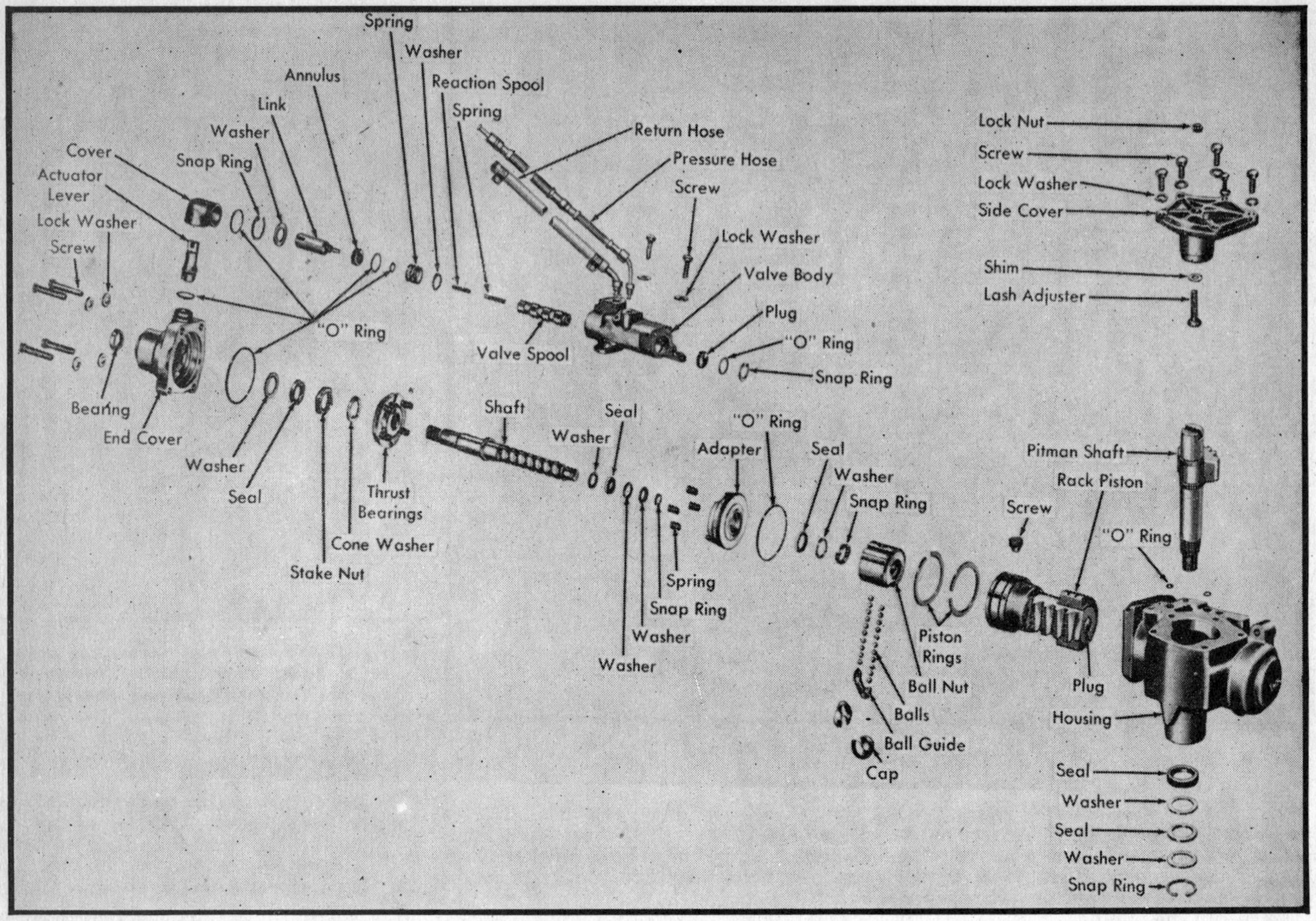

Cover
Actuator Lever
Lock Washer
Screw
Snap Ring
Washer
Link
Annulus
Spring
Washer
Reaction Spool
Spring
Return Hose
Pressure Hose
Screw
Lock Washer
Valve Body
Plug
"O" Ring
Snap Ring
"O" Ring
Valve Spool
Bearing
End Cover
Washer
Seal
Thrust Bearings
Cone Washer
Stake Nut
Shaft
Washer
Seal
Adapter
"O" Ring
Seal
Washer
Snap Ring
Spring
Snap Ring
Washer
Washer
Lock Nut
Screw
Lock Washer
Side Cover
Shim
Lash Adjuster
Pitman Shaft
Rack Piston
Screw
"O" Ring
Piston Rings
Ball Nut
Balls
Ball Guide
Cap
Plug
Housing
Seal
Washer
Seal
Washer
Snap Ring

Fig. S36 Saginaw In-Line power steering

Sector Shaft, Assemble

1. Check end play of adjusting screw in slot of pitman shaft by inserting feeler gauge between head of screw and bottom of slot in shaft. If end play exceeds .002", select the proper shim to give the desired end play. Shims are available in thicknesses of .063", .065", .067" and .069".
2. With adjusting screw in position in slot of secondary shaft, turn adjusting screw into sector shaft cover until cover bottoms on sector shafts.
3. Install new O-ring in groove in face of side cover.

Piston, Rack and Worm, Assemble, Fig. S38

1. Check bearing for roughness by holding worm stationary and rotating center race.
2. If bearing replacement is necessary, push staked portion of thrust bearing nut up out of thread groove and remove nut.
3. Remove bearing from shaft.
4. Install new bearing, being careful to press on inner race of bearing.
5. Install new bearing nut and tighten until bearing has a slight drag.
6. Bearing should be preloaded between ¾ and 3 lbs. measured as follows:
7. Clamp splined end of worm in vise.

Fasten a cord to one of the rivets and wind it around the center race several times. Attach the other end of cord to a spring scale. Then slowly pull on the scale and check the reading. If the preload is not

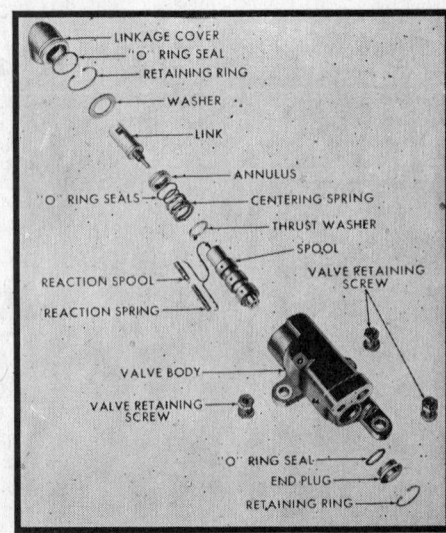

LINKAGE COVER
"O" RING SEAL
RETAINING RING
WASHER
LINK
ANNULUS
"O" RING SEALS
CENTERING SPRING
THRUST WASHER
SPOOL
REACTION SPOOL
VALVE RETAINING SCREW
REACTION SPRING
VALVE BODY
VALVE RETAINING SCREW
"O" RING SEAL
END PLUG
RETAINING RING

Fig. S37 Control valve assembly. Saginaw In-Line

within limits, push the staked portion of the thrust bearing nut up out of the thread groove and tighten or loosen the nut to bring the preload within specified limits. After nut is restaked, recheck bearing for roughness.

8. Lubricate internal parts with Automatic Transmission fluid.
9. Install new seal in cover adapter.
10. Install seal retaining washer and ring.
11. Place centering springs in shallow holes of cover adapter.
12. Hold adapter with springs facing up and insert worm through seal in adapter, being careful not to damage seal when passing over worm grooves.
13. Align locating pin on adapter with hole in bearing.
14. Slide ball nut over worm with chamfered edge over worm shoulder, up to adapter.
15. Align ball return guide holes with worm groove.
16. Drop balls into return guide hole farthest from adapter while slowly rotating worm counterclockwise to feed balls through circuit.
17. Fill one-half of ball return guide with remaining balls.
18. Place other half of guide over balls and plug each end with heavy grease to prevent balls from falling out

when installing guide into ball nut.

19. Push guide into guide holes of ball nut.
20. If guide does not push all the way down easily, tap it lightly with soft mallet to seat it.
21. Wrap a strip of tape around ball nut and guide to prevent guide from falling out.
22. The worm groove is ground with a high point in the center. When ball nut passes over high point a preload of 1 to 6 lbs. should be obtained.
23. To measure preload, clamp splined end of worm in vise. Fasten a cord to the ball nut and wind it around ball nut two or three times. With spring scale attached to other end of cord, slowly pull on spring scale, unwinding cord and rotating ball nut over high point of worm. If preload is less than 1 lb., install next larger size balls and recheck preload (ball size is stamped on end of ball nut). If preload is more than 6 lbs., install next smaller size ball and recheck preload.
24. Install worm seal rear washer, worm seal, worm seal front washer and retaining ring on worm.
25. Lubricate worm seal.
26. Remove tape from ball nut and install ball and worm assembly in piston-rack.
27. Line up retaining screw hole in ball nut with screw hole in piston.
28. Install ball nut retaining screw and tighten to a torque of 20-25 lb. ft. and stake screw securely.
29. Install O-ring on adapter.
30. Install two piston rings on piston-rack.

End Cover, Assemble

1. Install needle bearings in end cover.
2. Place seal back up washer, with chamfer side in first, against inner face of needle bearing and install new seal.
3. Install new linkage cover-to-end cover O-ring on end cover.

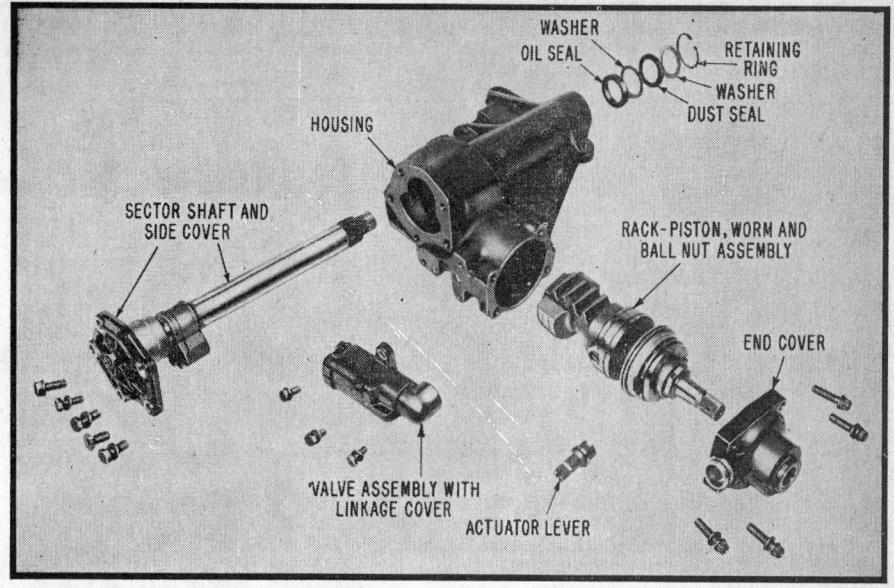

Fig. S39 Layout of Saginaw In-Line power steering components

Steering Gear, Assemble, Fig. S39

1. Install pitman shaft oil seal.
2. Install seal back up washer, leather dust seal and another seal back up washer.
3. Install sector seal retaining ring.
4. Install a suitable ring compressor over piston ring and tighten to compress rings.
5. Place piston-rack and worm in housing and tap piston-rack into housing until piston rings are into cylinder bore.
6. Remove ring compressor, turning worm counterclockwise if more clearance is needed.
7. Push piston-rack into housing until adapter is seated in housing counterbore.
8. Align actuator lever relief in adapter with valve mounting face.

9. Lubricate needle bearing with a special "lifetime" grease.
10. Assemble end cover over worm bearing and cover adapter, making certain that adapter pin enters proper hole in end cover.
11. Align end cover holes with housing holes and tighten screws to 25-30 lb. ft. torque.
12. Turn worm shaft as necessary to align center groove of piston-rack with center of pitman shaft bushing.
13. Install sector shaft so that center tooth in sector meshes with center groove of rack-piston. Make sure side cover O-ring is in place before pushing cover down on gear housing.
14. Install and tighten side cover screws to a torque of 25-30 lb. ft. Tighten flat head screw first.
15. Install actuator lever in end cover, making certain that it is seated over thrust bearing center race.
16. Position valve link so that slot is perpendicular with bottom of valve.
17. Install new O-ring in linkage cover. Lubricate seal and insert end of cover into control valve.
18. Place new O-rings on oil passages of steering housing.
19. Position control valve including linkage cover on gear housing.
20. Start actuator lever into actuating link slot and push linkage cover down into end cover until valve is seated.
21. Install and tighten control valve cap screws to a torque of 15-20 lb. ft. Tighten screw on lower end of control valve first.
22. Install steering shaft and insulator on steering gear coupling and retain with roll pin.

Sector Shaft, Adjust

1. Install steering wheel.
2. Locate "on center" of steering gear by turning wheel from one extreme to the other, counting number of turns. Then turn wheel back exactly

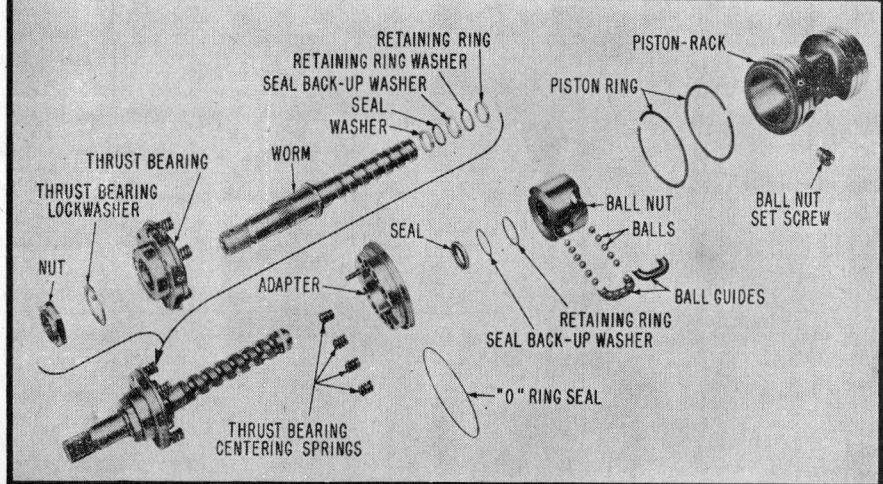

Fig. S38 Piston-rack, worm and ball nut assembly. Saginaw In-Line

one-half total number of turns, which is "on center" position.
3. Hook a spring scale to the steering wheel rim and measure pull it takes to turn wheel through a three-inch arc at the steering wheel rim.
4. Adjust pitman shaft adjusting screw so that a preload of 1½ to 1 lb. in excess of worm bearing and ball nut preloads. Total load must be 1¼ to 1¾ lbs.

Saginaw Rotary Valve Type

This type power steering gear operates entirely on displacing oil to provide hydraulic oil pressure assists only when turning, Figs. S40 and S41. As the entire gear assembly is always full of oil, all internal components of the gear are immersed in oil, making periodic lubrication unnecessary. In addition this oil acts as a cushion to absorb road shocks that may be transmitted to the driver.

The steering shaft, hydraulic valve, worm and the rack-piston nut are all in line, making a compact and space saving gear. All oil passages are internal except the pressure and return hoses between the gear and pump.

The rotary valve feature provides a smooth transmission through the driving range of steering wheel effort. A torsion bar transmits the "road feel" to the driver. Response of the steering gear gives the driver greater control and minimizes over-steering.

ADJUSTMENT ON CAR

1. Disconnect steering gear connecting rod from pitman arm.

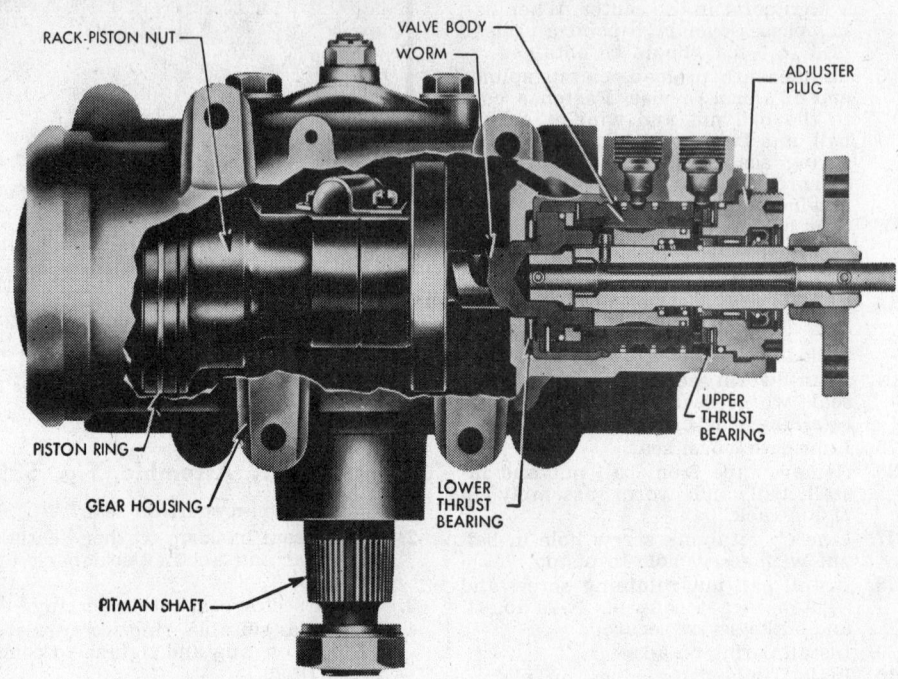

Fig. S40   Saginaw rotary valve type power steering gear

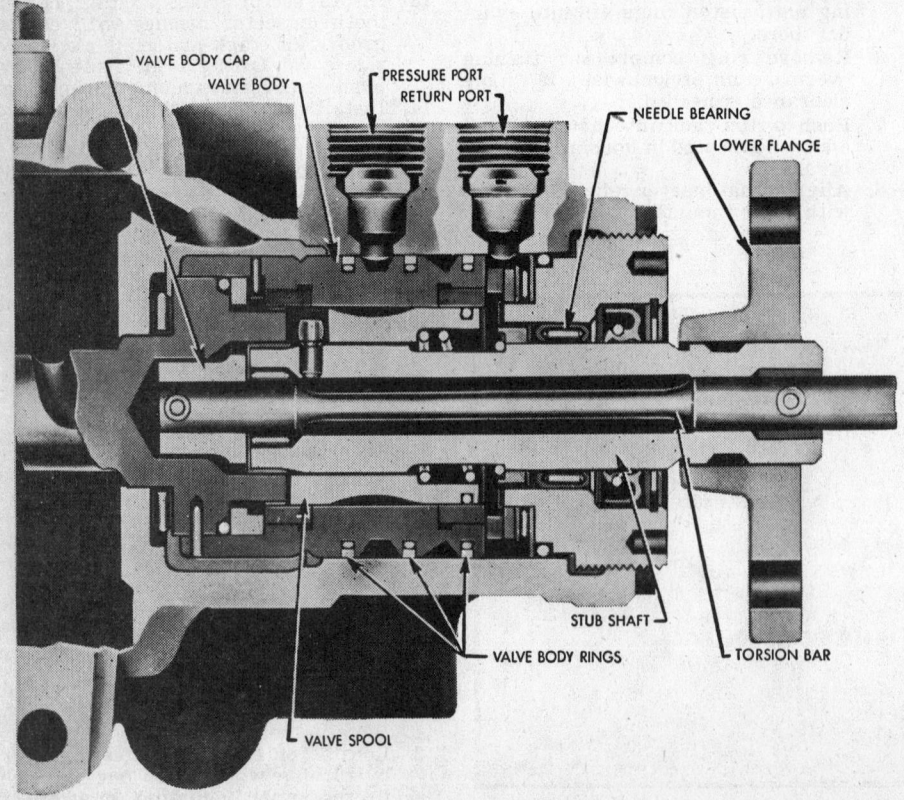

Fig. S41   Rotary valve assembly

2. Remove steering wheel.
3. With an inch pound torque wrench attached to a suitable socket on the steering shaft nut, measure and record readings taken from the following steering gear positions. *Do not use a torque wrench having a maximum reading of more than 100 inch pounds.* When taking the following torque readings, take a reading pulling the torque wrench to the right and a reading pulling the wrench to the left. Total both readings and take ½ of this total as the average torque.
4. *One full turn off center high point:* This reading represents adjuster plug preload plus resistance offered by seals and bearings and should not exceed 10 inch pounds torque. If the reading is below 3 inch pounds, it may indicate some lash in the thrust bearing.
5. *One-half turn off center high point:* This reading represents resistance offered in Step 4 and also worm preload as determined by the size of the balls used in the rack-piston nut. This reading should be 0.5 to 5.0 inch pounds torque higher than the reading in Step 4.
6. If readings obtained in Steps 4 and 5 are not within specifications, remove steering gear assembly for complete

adjustment. If the reading for Step 4 is not within specifications, correct adjuster plug bearing preload. If after obtaining proper adjuster plug preload in Step 4 the torque reading in Step 5 is not within specifications, then *do not* re-fit rack-piston balls unless a complaint of loose steering is received. Upon such a complaint, a thrust adjustment (Step 4) and over center adjustment (Step 7) should correct the problem if it lies in the steering gear.

7. *Through center high point:* This reading represents resistance offered in Step 5 and also pitman shaft lash. This reading should be 4.0 to 8.0 inch pounds torque higher than the reading obtained in Step 5.

8. If the reading in Step 7 is not within specifications, loosen pitman shaft gear lash adjuster nut and adjust lash with a suitable allen wrench. Tighten lock nut to 25-35 ft. lbs. torque. *Final adjustment should always be made in a clockwise direction.*

9. Install steering wheel and pitman arm. Screw steering connecting rod end plug in until tight; then back off to align cotter pin hole and insert cotter pin.

PITMAN SHAFT SEALS

Replace With Gear In Car

Removal of these seals can be accomplished with the steering gear in the car using hydraulic pressure from the gear assembly to force the seals out of the pitman shaft bore.

1. Remove pitman arm.
2. Remove pitman shaft outer seal retaining ring.
3. Remove outer dust seal using screwdriver and place a cloth around housing and pitman shaft to absorb oil leakage from seal bore.
4. Hold a clean pan under gear housing and with engine running, momentarily turn gear to extreme left position for not more than two seconds. This will build up pressure on upper side of piston and in pitman shaft chamber, forcing seals and inner back-up washer out of bore. *If pressure of oil does not remove the seals, turn off engine, remove pitman shaft and remove seals in normal manner, being careful not to score the seal bore in housing.*

Fig. S43 Position of pitman shaft gear for removal

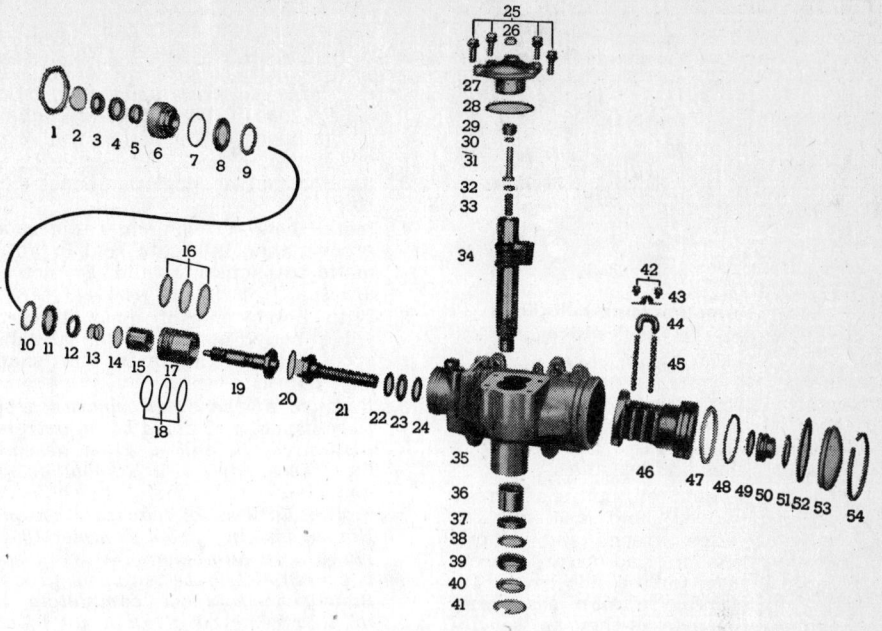

Fig. S42 Saginaw rotary valve type power steering gear

1. Lock nut	28. "O" ring seal
2. Ring	29. Retainer
3. Dust seal	30. Thrust washer
4. Plug seal	31. Lash adjuster
5. Bearing	32. Thrust washer
6. Adjuster plug	33. Spring
7. "O" ring seal	34. Pitman shaft
8. Bearing race	35. Gear housing
9. Thrust bearing	36. Needle bearing
10. Bearing race	37. Single lip oil seal
11. Spacer	38. Back-up washer
12. Retainer	39. Double lip oil seal
13. Spring	40. Dust seal
14. "O" ring	41. Retaining ring
15. Valve spool	42. Screws
16. Teflon seals	43. Retainer
17. Rotary valve	44. Ball return guide
18. "O" ring seals	45. Balls
19. Torsion bar and stub shaft	46. Rack-piston nut
20. "O" ring	47. Ring
21. Worm shaft	48. Seal
22. Bearing race	49. "O" ring seal
23. Thrust bearing	50. Plug
24. Bearing race	51. Retaining ring
25. Cover screws	52. "O" ring seal
26. Lock nut	53. End plug
27. Side cover	54. Retainer

STEERING GEAR, DISASSEMBLE

1. Referring to Fig. S42, remove retaining ring from housing lower end plug. Rotate gear (stub shaft) flange to left and force end plug out of housing.
2. Remove rack-piston nut end plug retaining ring and end plug.
3. To remove pitman shaft gear and side cover, remove screws from cover and rotate cover as necessary to see when pitman shaft is centered in gear housing opening while rotating gear flange, Fig. S43. Remove pitman shaft.
4. To remove rack-piston nut, hold a suitable arbor against end of steering worm and rotate stub shaft to left until rack-piston is free from worm, Fig. S44. With arbor in rack-piston, remove rack-piston nut from housing bore (arbor prevents balls from falling out of rack-piston nut).
5. To remove adjuster plug, remove locking bolt and remove flange. Remove adjuster plug lock nut using punch or suitable spanner wrench. Then remove adjuster plug, Fig. S45.
6. To remove rotary valve with worm shaft and pin, push on end of worm shaft with a hammer handle while pulling on stub shaft with a slight rotary motion. Remove rotary valve and worm shaft as a unit. Separate worm shaft and valve by pulling

Fig. S44 Arbor prevents balls from falling out of rack-piston nut

apart. Remove and discard torsion bar cap to worm "O" ring seal in rotary valve, Fig. S46. Remove spacer, races and bearings.

7. To disassemble pitman shaft gear and side cover, hold lash adjuster with an allen wrench and remove lash adjuster nut and discard. Screw lash adjuster out of side cover. Do not disassemble pitman shaft and component parts as they are serviced as an assembly, Fig. S47.

8. To disassemble rack-piston nut, place nut on a clean cloth. Remove arbor tool (see Fig. S44), ball return guide and balls, making sure all balls are caught on the cloth (22 balls). Remove and discard Teflon ring and back-up seal from rack-piston nut.

9. To disassemble adjuster plug, remove and discard adjuster plug retainer and remove bearing, races and spacer. Mount adjuster plug in a vise with soft jaws. Remove retaining ring and stub shaft dust seal. Remove and discard stub shaft seal. Inspect needle bearings in adjuster plug; if rollers are broken or pitted, remove needle bearing and discard.

Replacing Valve Spool Dampener "O" Ring (Only If Gear Squawks)

The rotary valve assembly includes the valve body, valve spool and stub shaft assembly. All these parts are precision units and are hydraulically balanced at the factory. Under no circumstances are parts in this unit to be replaced or interchanged with other parts or units. If unit parts are scored or damaged the entire rotary valve assembly is to be replaced.

1. To replace the valve spool dampener "O" ring, work spool spring into bearing diameter of stub shaft and

remove spool spring.

2. Tap end of stub shaft gently against workbench to remove valve spool. *The diametrical clearance between the valve body and spool may be as low as .0004". The slightest cocking of the spool may jam it in the valve body.*

3. Remove valve spool dampener "O" ring.

4. Install new "O" ring in valve spool groove, then lubricate seal in automatic transmission fluid. Do not allow seal to twist in groove.

5. With notch end of spool towards valve body, install spool, aligning spool notch with pin in stub shaft, Fig. S49.

6. *Because of the small clearance between spool and valve body, extreme care must be taken when assembling these parts. Push spool evenly and slowly with a slight oscillating motion until spool reaches drive pin. Before pushing spool completely in, make sure dampener "O" ring seal is evenly distributed in spool groove. Slowly push spool completely in, with extreme care taken not to cut or pinch "O" ring seal.*

7. Slide spool spring over stub shaft and work spring into position.

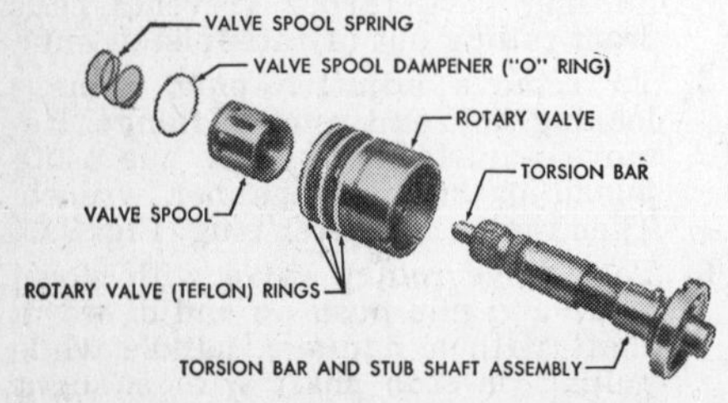

Disassemble Rotary Valve

1. Work spool spring onto bearing diameter of stub shaft and remove spool spring.

2. Tap end of stub shaft gently against workbench to remove valve spool. *Because of the slight clearance between valve body and spool, the slightest cocking of spool may jam it in valve body. If slight cocking occurs, make a gentle attempt to reverse removal procedure. If this does not free spool, it has become cocked in valve body bore and may be removed later.*

3. Remove and discard valve spool dampener "O" ring.

4. Remove stub shaft, torsion bar (small diameter bar extending through stub shaft) and valve cap by tapping end of torsion bar lightly with a plastic hammer. This will dislodge cap from valve body cap pin, Fig. S49. Do not disassemble stub shaft as these parts are pinned together and serviced only as an assembly.

5. If valve spool has become cocked as mentioned above, first inspect parts to determine in which direction the spool is cocked. A few very light

Fig. S45 Removing adjuster plug

taps with a plastic hammer should align and free the spool in the bore. Remove and discard "O" ring dampener seal from spool.

6. Carefully remove valve body Teflon rings and ring back-up "O" ring seals.

Disassemble Housing

1. Remove pitmen shaft outer dust seal retaining ring.

2. Remove outer dust seal.

3. Remove seal (double lip) by inserting offset screwdriver between seal and back-up washer and prying out of housing.

4. Remove back-up washer.

5. Remove seal (single lip) by cutting and collapsing seal.

6. Remove pitmen shaft needle bearings (if necessary) with a suitable driver.

7. If connectors are to be removed, tap threads in holes of connectors using 5/16-18 NF tap. Remove connectors by using threaded bolt into tapped holes with washer and nut as extractor.

ASSEMBLE SUB-ASSEMBLIES

Refer to Fig. S42 and lubricate all parts as they are assembled.

1. Screw lash adjuster through side cover until cover bottoms on pitman shaft gear. Install lash adjuster lock nut while holding lash adjuster with 7/32" allen wrench.

2. Mount adjuster plug in vise with soft jaws.

3. If it has been removed, assemble needle bearing by pressing towards thrust bearing end of adjuster plug against identification end of bearing. End of bearing to be flush with

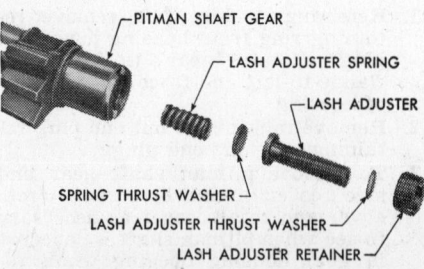

Fig. S46 Location of torsion bar cap to worm "O" ring seal

VALVE SPOOL SPRING
VALVE SPOOL DAMPENER ("O" RING)
ROTARY VALVE
TORSION BAR
VALVE SPOOL
ROTARY VALVE (TEFLON) RINGS
TORSION BAR AND STUB SHAFT ASSEMBLY

Fig. S47 Parts in end of pitman shaft gear (do not disassemble)

PITMAN SHAFT GEAR
LASH ADJUSTER SPRING
LASH ADJUSTER
SPRING THRUST WASHER
LASH ADJUSTER THRUST WASHER
LASH ADJUSTER RETAINER

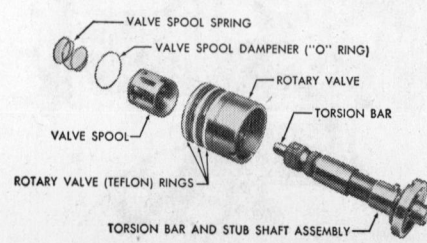

Fig. S49 Rotary valve parts

VALVE SPOOL SPRING
VALVE SPOOL DAMPENER ("O" RING)
ROTARY VALVE
TORSION BAR
VALVE SPOOL
ROTARY VALVE (TEFLON) RINGS
TORSION BAR AND STUB SHAFT ASSEMBLY

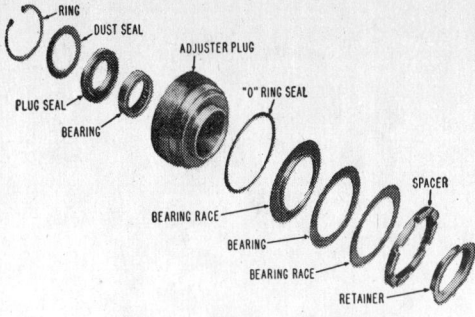

Fig. S50 Adjuster plug parts

bottom surface of stub shaft seal bore.

4. Install stub shaft far enough to provide clearance for dust seal and retaning ring. Install new dust seal with rubber surface outward. Install new retaining ring.

5. Assemble large thrust bearing race, thrust bearing, small race and spacer (with grooves up) on adjuster plug, Fig. S50, and secure with retainer.

Assembly Rotary Valve

1. Assemble one valve body Teflon ring back-up "O" ring seal in each groove in valve body, being sure seals do not become twisted.

2. Assemble valve Teflon rings in ring grooves over "O" ring seals by carefully slipping rings over valve body. The rings may appear loose or twisted in the grooves but the heat of the oil during subsequent operation will cause them to straighten.

3. Install valve spool dampener "O" ring seal in valve spool groove, being sure it is not twisted.

4. Assemble stub shaft in valve body, aligning groove in valve cap with pin in valve body, Fig. S49. Press on cap until it is against shoulder in valve body with body pin in cap groove. Hold these parts together during rest of assembly.

5. With notch end of spool towards valve body, install spool, aligning spool notch with pin in stub shaft.

6. Slide spool spring over stub shaft and work spring into position.

7. Lubricate cap-to-worm "O" ring and install in valve body. *During assembly of the valve, if the stub shaft and cap is allowed to slip out of engagement with the valve body pin, the spool will be permitted to enter the valve body too far. The dampener "O" ring seal may expand into valve body oil grooves, preventing removal of spool. If this happens, remove spool spring and disassemble rotary valve. Press on spool until "O" ring seal is cut and can be removed. Install new "O" ring and reassemble.*

Assemble Housing

1. With stamped end of needle bearing facing outward, drive bearing into bore from outside of housing until flush to $\frac{1}{32}''$ below shoulder. Make sure bearings rotate freely.

2. Lubricate cavity between lips of pitman shaft (double lip) seal with high melting point, water resistant wheel bearing lubricant.

3. Lubricate and install pitman shaft seals as shown in Fig. S51. Make sure seal lips are properly positioned, retaining ring is seated, and that approximately $\frac{1}{16}''$ clearance is maintained between the inner (single lip) seal and bearing.

4. If connectors were removed, install new ones by driving them into place.

Assemble Rack-Piston and Worm

1. Lubricate and install new ring back-up seal and Teflon piston ring on rack-piston nut, being careful ring and seal do not twist during installation.

2. Insert worm into rack-piston nut to bearing shoulder, Fig. S52.

3. Align ball return guide holes with worm groove. Load 16 balls into guide hole nearest the Teflon piston ring while slowly rotating worm to left to feed balls through circuit. If balls are installed properly the worm should turn out of rack-piston nut.

4. Fill one-half of ball return guide with remaining six balls. Place other guide over balls and plug each end with heavy grease to prevent balls from falling out when installing guides into rack-piston nut.

5. Insert guides into guide holes of rack-piston nut. Guides should fit loosely.

Check Worm Preload

The worm groove is ground with a high point in the center. When the rack-piston nut passes over this high point, a preload of a ½ to 5 inch pounds torque should be obtained.

1. With worm pointing up, clamp rack-piston nut in a vise with soft jaws (do not hold rack-piston nut in area of Teflon ring).

2. Place valve on worm, engaging worm drive pin.

3. Rotate worm until it extends 1¼" from rack-piston nut to thrust bearing face, Fig. S53. This is the center position.

4. Attach an inch pound torque wrench with socket on stub shaft, Fig. S53. Oscillate wrench through a total arc of approximately 60° in both directions several times and take a reading. The highest reading obtained

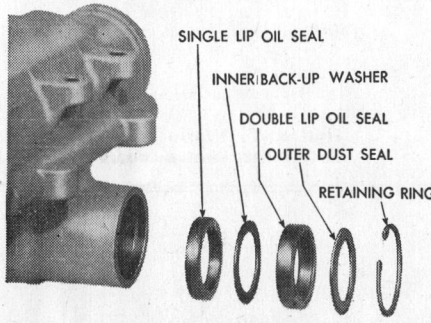

Fig. S51 pitman shaft seals and washers

SINGLE LIP OIL SEAL
INNER BACK-UP WASHER
DOUBLE LIP OIL SEAL
OUTER DUST SEAL
RETAINING RING

Fig. S52 Loading rack-piston nut

with worm rotating should be between ½ and 5 inch pounds. Take a torque reading pulling the torque wrench to the right and a reading pulling the wrench to the left. Total both readings and take one-half of this total as the average torque. *Do not use a torque wrench having maximum torque reading of more than 100 inch pounds.*

Refitting Rack-Piston Balls

Do not refit balls unless the steering is loose. If such is the case, a thrust adjustment and over-center adjustment should correct the problem if it lies in the steering gear. If balls are pitted or rough, then select the proper ball size for proper adjustment.

If the torque reading obtained above is too high or too low (on new balls only), disassemble and reassemble, using the next size smaller (or larger) balls and recheck worm preload.

A rack-piston nut with a ball size of 7 does not have a number stamped on the flat surface. For ball sizes other than 7, the ball size is stamped on the flat surface of the rack-piston nut. Ball sizes are numbered from 6 to 11, with 6 being the smallest and 11 the largest. Ball sizes are graduated in increments of .00008″ from .28117″ to .28157″.

STEERING GEAR, ASSEMBLE

Install Rack-Piston Worm and Valve

1. Install valve and worm in housing as a unit, Fig. S54.

2. Install new "O" rings on adjuster plug.

3. Install adjuster plug on stub shaft in gear housing finger tight.

4. Slip stub shaft flange on end of stub shaft.

5. Holding a suitable Teflon ring compressor sleeve tightly against shoulder of gear housing, insert rack-piston nut and arbor into housing, holding arbor until it contacts worm end.

6. Holding arbor tight against worm, turn stub shaft flange and worm to draw ball nut onto worm and into housing until arbor is free. Be certain that no balls drop out.

7. Remove arbor and sleeve.

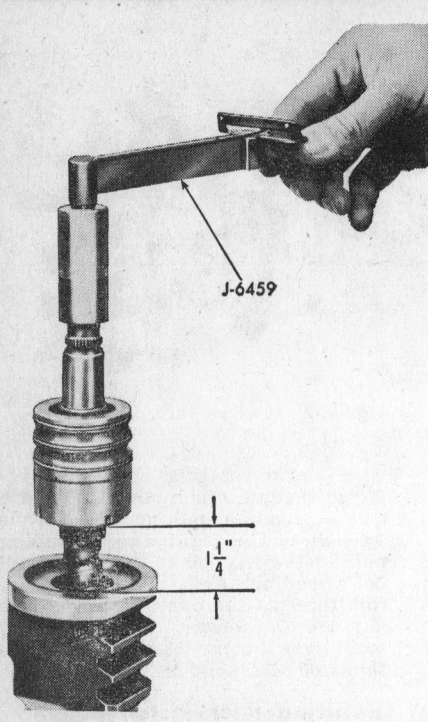

Fig. S53 Checking worm preload

Install Rack-Piston Nut End Plug

1. Install new "O" ring seal on end plug, being careful not to allow seal to twist in groove.
2. Install end plug in rack-piston nut by pressing into place.
3. Install end plug retaining ring, being sure ring is bottomed in its groove.

Install Housing Lower End Plug

1. Install new housing end plug "O" ring seal.
2. Insert end plug into gear housing and seat against "O" ring. Slight pressure may be necessary to seat end plug properly.
3. Install end plug retainer ring so end of ring extends over and at least ½" beyond ring removal assist hole.

Thrust Bearing Preload, Adjust

1. Position rack-piston nut in housing to end of travel, back off ¼ turn and remove stub shaft flange.
2. Tighten adjuster plug snug and back it off ⅛ turn.
3. Center the worm and adjust thrust bearing so that *preload is 3 to 4 inch pounds in excess of worm and rack-piston nut preload, when holding rack-piston from turning and swinging torque wrench back and forth through a 60° arc.*
4. Install adjuster plug lock nut and tighten to 50 ft. lb. torque.

5. Recheck thrust bearing preload. Total thrust bearing adjustment plus seal drag not to exceed 10 inch pounds torque.

Install Pitman Shaft Gear and Side Cover

1. Install stub shaft flange and turn steering worm until center groove of rack-piston is aligned with center of pitman shaft needle bearings.
2. Install new side cover "O" ring.
3. Install pitman shaft gear so that center tooth of gear meshes with center groove of rack-piston. Make sure side cover "O" ring is in place before pushing cover against housing.
4. Install and torque side cover screws to 25-30 ft. lbs. torque.

Adjust Pitman Shaft Preload Through Center High Point

After steering gear is assembled. find center or straight-ahead position of worm by rotating worm through full travel, counting the number of turns and reversing one-half the number of turns counted.

Using a suitable socket and inch pound torque wrench as shown in Fig. S55, adjust lash adjuster so torque is between 4 and 8 inch pounds in excess of total preload (after recording of adjuster nut preload) when swinging torque wrench back and forth through a 20° arc.

Total over center preload must not exceed 18 inch pounds through center high point when rotating worm shaft through an arc of 20°. Tighten lash adjuster nut to a torque of 25-30 ft lbs. Recheck preload after nut has been tightened.

Install Stub Shaft Flange

Rotate stub shaft slightly over two complete turns from either extreme right or left turn. This will place gear in center position, which will place torsion bar pin through stub shaft in a straight up and down position.

Rotate flange so the bolt with the large head is in top position. Visually align the block tooth in the serrations

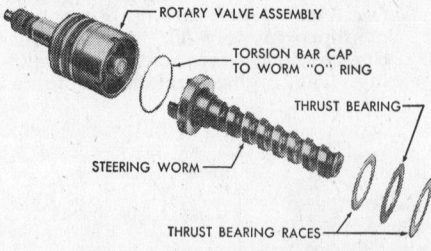

Fig. S54 Worm shaft and rotary valve parts

Labels in figure: ROTARY VALVE ASSEMBLY; TORSION BAR CAP TO WORM "O" RING; THRUST BEARING; STEERING WORM; THRUST BEARING RACES

Fig. S55 Adjusting pinion shaft preload

J-5205   J-6459

of the flange with the torsion bar pin and install flange on stub shaft. Tighten flange clamping bolt to a torque of 25-30 ft. lbs.

Assembly Notes

1. Make sure all parts are absolutely clean. Lubricate seals and moving parts with automatic transmission oil during assembly.
2. If shaft seal was removed, use a suitable tool to drive the new seal into the housing with the spring side of the seal toward the housing.
3. Install flow control plunger with its hex head going into housing first.
4. Install pump ring with small holes in ring on dowel pins and with arrow to rear of housing. Arrow must be pointing in a counterclockwise direction when viewed from rear of housing. *Arrow on outer edge of pump ring points in direction of pump rotation.*
3. Install rotor on pump shaft with alignment sleeve toward front of housing. Rotor must be free on shaft splines.
5. Install 10 vanes in rotor slots with flat edge toward center of rotor.
6. Lubricate outside diameter and chamfer on pressure plate with vaseline and install on dowel pins with ported face toward pump ring. Dowel pins fit in slots in plate that are nearest outside diameter of plate.
7. Use soft plastic or wood rod and lightly tap around outside diameter of pressure plate to seat it. Pressure plate will travel about 1/16" to seat. *Never press or hammer on center of pressure plate as this will cause permanent distortion and result in pump failure.*
8. When installing new end plate O-ring seal, be sure *not* to install it in end plate retaining ring groove which is the first groove from rear of housing.

AIR CONDITIONING

FUNDAMENTALS OF REFRIGERATION

In order to understand how an air conditioning system works, we must have a knowledge of the fundamentals of refrigeration. And since refrigeration is the process of removing heat from things, an air conditioner removes heat from the surrounding air. In both cases, the process is simplified by one of Nature's laws—heat always moves from a warm object to a cold object.

When we put milk or vegetables into an ice box, they are warmer than the ice. Since heat always travels from warmer to cooler objects, the heat in the milk and vegetables naturally travels to the cold ice. Then, of course, as heat is removed from these articles, they begin to grow cooler—they have less heat than before.

Therefore, if refrigeration is the removal of heat, then anything can be made cooler by finding a method of absorbing heat from it.

In order to maintain cold temperatures, we have to have continuous refrigeration. This is accomplished in modern refrigerators and cooling systems (1) by using a refrigerant that will readily absorb heat and (2) by using the same refrigerant over and over.

Ice can refrigerate effectively *only when it is changing from a solid to a liquid. A liquid can refrigerate only when it is changing from a liquid to a vapor.* A vapor cannot refrigerate since the absorption of heat will not change it to any other state. The only thing to do with a vapor is to change it back to a liquid- by removing heat from it.

In other words, if the ice didn't melt, it could absorb a little heat from the objects and the air around it but not enough to do an effective job of cooling. But when it begins to change to a liquid (water), then the ice is absorbing heat rapidly and effectively.

The same applies to a liquid refrigerant. No matter how cold the liquid is, it won't actually "refrigerate" until it is absorbing heat fast enough to change its form into a vapor.

Liquid Refrigerants

Whenever we think of anything boiling, we instinctively think of it being hot. However, that is not true in every case. Just because water boils at 212 degrees above zero Fahrenheit does not mean that all other substances will boil at the same temperature. Some would have to be put in a blast furnace to make them boil and give off vapor, such as iron, aluminum, etc. On the other hand, others will boil violently while setting on a cake of ice, such as ammonia, sulphurdioxide, freon, etc.

And so, each substance has its own peculiar boiling point temperature. But regardless of whether it is high or low, they all absorb unusually large quantities of heat *without getting any warmer*

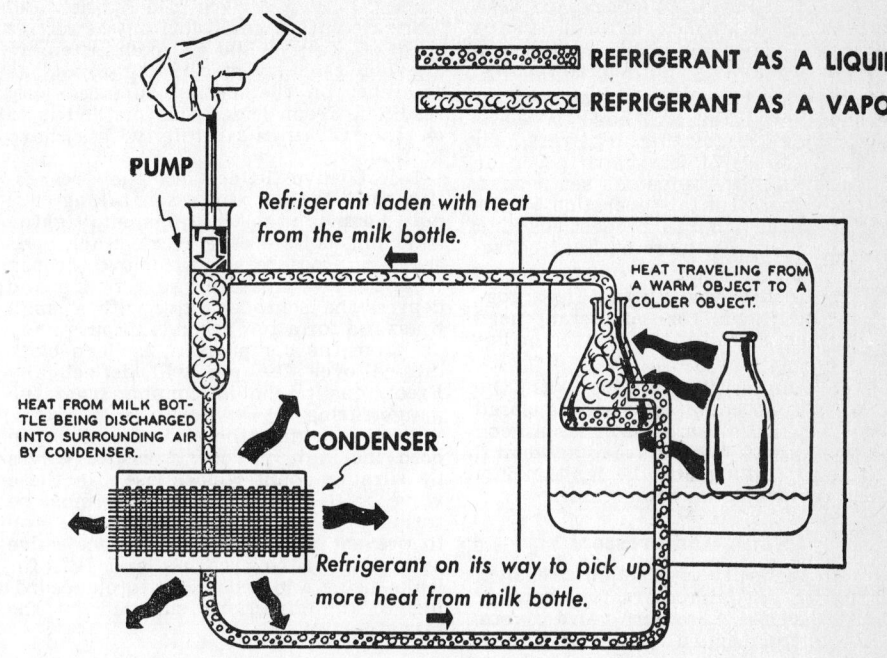

PUMP

REFRIGERANT AS A LIQUID

REFRIGERANT AS A VAPOR

Refrigerant laden with heat from the milk bottle.

HEAT TRAVELING FROM A WARM OBJECT TO A COLDER OBJECT.

HEAT FROM MILK BOTTLE BEING DISCHARGED INTO SURROUNDING AIR BY CONDENSER.

CONDENSER

Refrigerant on its way to pick up more heat from milk bottle.

Fig. 1   Diagram showing refrigerant cycle

when they change from a liquid into a vapor.

Consequently, any liquid, such as ammonia or Freon, that will boil at a temperature below the freezing point of water, will make ice cubes and keep vegetables cool in a mechanical refrigerator. Years ago, ammonia actually was one of the first and most popular refrigerants used. Today though, it is supplanted by better and safer Freon refrigerants.

Nearly everyone is familiar with ammonia. But actually the so-called ammonia we know is so highly diluted that it is practically all water. However, if it were in its pure form. it would boil at *28 degrees below zero.* No one would dare pick up a flask of pure ammonia with bare hands because, even though boiling, it would be so cold and it would be drawing heat away from nearby objects so fast the human flesh would freeze in a very short time. The same is true of Freon.

If we were to put a flask of ammonia or Freon inside a refrigerator cabinet it would boil and draw heat away from everything surrounding it as the transfer of temperature is always from a warm to a cooler object. So long as any liquid remains in the flask it would keep on soaking up heat until the temperature got down to well below zero.

In the ice box, water from melting ice literally carried away heat out of the cabinet. Now, rising vapors do the same job. Of course, water was so cheap that we could afford to throw it away. But ammonia—or Freon, which is the mod-

ern refrigerant—is too expensive just to let it float away into the atmosphere. So we recover the refrigerant by applying pressure to it to make the vapor condense back into a liquid so it can be used again. How this is done is shown in Fig. 1.

Operating Cycle of Car Air Conditioning System

1. The compressor compresses heat-laden, low-pressure vaporous refrigerant and discharges it into the condenser.
2. In the condenser, the vapor changes into a liquid as the heat is dissipated into the surrounding air.
3. From the condenser, the liquid is forced into the reservoir or receiver, which is simply a storage container the function of which is to ensure a supply of *liquid* Freon to the expansion valve. (The expansion valve functions in much the same manner as a hose nozzle).
4. From the reservoir, the liquid Freon passes through a combination strainer-drier, then through the expansion valve into the evaporator.
5. Being connected to the suction line of the compressor, the evaporator is a low-pressure region in which the refrigerant boils and reverts to a vapor, absorbing heat in the process and thereby cooling the evaporator coil and the air passing over it.
6. Upon leaving the evaporator, the vaporous refrigerant returns to the compressor inlet and completes the refrigeration cycle.

ENGINE WORK ON AIR CONDITIONED CARS

An entirely new set of service problems has arisen with the use of car air conditioning systems. Even shops which do not plan to diagnose and repair these systems will sometimes find it necessary to remove the cooling system compressor in order to make certain engine repairs.

Because the compressor is mounted on the engine, the unit will have to be removed when performing repairs which require removal of the valve cover or cylinder head. A competent serviceman can easily perform this operation by observing a few simple precautions and following the procedures outlined below.

One precaution which should always be taken is the wearing of safety goggles, since Freon, the refrigerant used is extremely harmful to the eyes in liquid form.

Since running the engine with the cooling system compressor valves closed may damage the compressor, it's a good idea to eliminate the chance of accidental starting by taking out the ignition key before removing the compressor.

Rotary Compressors

When engine repairs require removal of rotary type compressors, first take off the high and low pressure valve covers, holding the mating fitting with a wrench to avoid loosening it. Then, using a square socket, close both valves tightly by turning clockwise, thereby shutting off the refrigerant lines to the compressor.

The lines can now be removed by unscrewing the two bolts at each valve fitting about seven turns and tapping the fitting so that it moves out quickly and firmly against the bolt heads. This permits the automatic shut-off valve built into each compressor port to close quickly, preventing loss of Freon from the compressor. A slight amount of vapor is normally released when the fitting leaves the compressor. If vapor continues to escape, the spring-loaded automatic valve is not seating properly and should be repaired.

After removing bolts and valve fittings from the compressor, cover the openings in both compressor and fittings with masking tape to keep out dirt, thereby protecting the valves and working parts. After removing the drive belts, the compressor can be lifted out of place after removing mounting bolts and nuts.

When engine repairs have been completed, reinstall the compressor on its mounting brackets, assemble belts and adjust belt tension. Before attaching the high and low pressure valve fittings, replace "O" ring seals in the fittings and lubricate with a small amount of refrigerant oil. Care should be taken in removing old seals from their grooves, as scratches on the mating surfaces may result in Freon leaks. One method is to cut the "O" rings carefully with a sharp knife.

Insert valve fittings into their respective ports in the compressor, taking care not to damage the "O" rings, and tighten attaching bolts evenly. Next, crack open the high pressure valve, remove the cap from the low pressure gauge fitting and depress the Schrader valve with a small brass rod for a few seconds to purge any air from the compressor. A clean cloth draped over the rod will deflect any Freon gas or liquid coming from the gauge fitting.

After purging the compressor, open both the high and low pressure valves by turning counter-clockwise. As these valves seat against a seal, they must be turned open all the way against the stop to prevent leaks. Finally, replace valve and gauge fitting covers and test for leaks, using a leak detector torch according to the directions supplied by the manufacturer.

Reciprocating Compressors

When removing these compressors, it is recommended that the engine be run at a low speed for a few minutes until the compressor is warm. Take out the ignition key, remove the discharge and suction valve caps and close each valve by turning the valve stem clockwise. As this compressor does not contain shut-off valves, bleed the compressor by loosening the discharge service port cap about a quarter turn until pressure within the compressor has been relieved, and then tighten the cap.

Clean and detach the discharge valve plate and suction valve plate and cover valve openings with masking tape. Do not twist or bend the lines in removal, since the vibration eliminators may be damaged by careless handling.

Remove the drive belt and remove the compressor from the engine. In handling the compressor, always keep it in an upright position to prevent loss of oil, and place it on a block of wood or the edge of a bench so that the weight of the compressor does not rest on the drive pulley.

When remounting the compressor on the engine, tighten the mounting screws and adjust the drive belt. Before installing the two valves, carefully clean the gasket surfaces on both the valves and compressor, and lubricate new refrigeration gaskets with compressor lubricant.

When the valves have been installed, open the discharge service port cap about a quarter turn and crack the suction valve. Allow about 10 seconds to purge air from the compressor, tighten the service port cap, and fully open the discharge and service valves by turning the valve stems counter-clockwise as far as they will go. Replace valve covers and test for leaks with a leak detector torch.

Finally, start the engine and run it at low speed until the compressor is warm. While the engine is running, check the Freon supply in the system by observing the sight glass located on the evaporator unit. Bubbles in the sight glass indicate additional Freon is required, and it should be added according to manufacturers' recommendations.

At the same time, check the oil level in the compressor. If oil splash cannot be seen in the compressor sight glass, add just enough refrigeration compressor oil to make the splash visible.

PRECAUTIONS REGARDING FREON

All car air conditioning systems use Freon as the refrigerating medium. Colorless and odorless, this refrigerant is under pressure, in a liquid or vapor form, in all the lines, whether the engine is running or not. As a result, if connections are carelessly loosened, Freon will rush out. *While not harmful as a vapor, it can cause serious injury if it reaches the eyes in liquid form, for rapid evaporation will tend to freeze the eyeball*

If Freon liquid should get into your eye, don't follow the natural tendency to rub it. Instead, immediately splash quantities of cold water on the eye to raise the temperature gradually above the freezing point, apply an antiseptic oil to reduce possibility of infection and immediately consult a doctor.

It is also wise to avoid welding or steam cleaning near the refrigeration lines or units. Abnormal heat on the lines will cause the Freon to boil, resulting in excessive pressure and possible damage to the system.

BORG-WARNER
AUTOMATIC DRIVE, 1953-56

For Linkage Adjustment See Studebaker Chapter

CONTENTS

Description of Transmission..............179
Trouble Shooting 29

Maintenance

Adding Fluid 179
Changing Fluid 179

"In Car" Repairs

Bands, Adjust 179
Oil Pressure Tests......................180
Extension Case 181
Governor 182
Rear Oil Pump..........................182
Valve Block 184

Repairs Requiring
Transmission Removal

Front pump 184
Mainshaft Assembly 185
Bands 189
Reverse Servo 190
Low and Forward Servos.................191

DESCRIPTION

This transmission, Fig. 1, consists of two major assemblies: 1) A torque converter which provides a smooth transfer of power, through use of fluid, supplies a range of torque multiplication, and in combination with the transmission permits the elimination of the clutch pedal.

2) An hydraulically controlled transmission which provides three forward ratios and a reverse ratio. One of these forward ratios is a direct drive ratio which is obtained automatically through the use of a direct drive clutch enclosed in the torque converter. An electrically-operated anti-creep system is employed in conjunction with the automatic transmission to eliminate creeping.

MAINTENANCE

Adding Fluid

1. With engine idling and running at normal operating temperature, set hand brake and place selector lever in L.
2. Clean area around inspection hole to prevent dirt from entering the transmission.
3. Remove dipstick. The space between "Full" and "Low" marks represent one pint.
4. Add Automatic Transmission Fluid as required to bring the level to the "Full" mark on dipstick.

Changing Fluid

Drain and refill the transmission every 15,000 miles or once a year as follows:
1. Set selector lever at L and raise transmission oil temperature by idling engine to normal operating temperature.
2. Stop engine and remove inspection hole cover to expose oil level gauge. Clean the area around the inspection hole and remove the gauge.
3. Remove the drain plug from the left side of the transmission oil pan near the front.
4. Remove the converter housing cover plate and rotate the converter until drain plug is in position for draining. Remove converter drain plug.
5. Remove converter pressure take-off plug from the left side of the transmission to facilitate draining.
6. After oil has drained, install and tighten drain plugs in the transmission oil pan and converter. Install converter housing cover plate. Install and tighten converter pressure take-off plug.
7. Pour six quarts of fluid into the transmission oil filler tube.
8. Start engine and idle for approximately one minute with the selector lever set in the L position to transfer the oil to the converter from the transmission case.
9. With engine still idling and selector lever in L position, add three more quarts of oil and then add additional oil as required to bring the level to the "Full" mark on the oil level gauge. Do not overfill.

BANDS, ADJUST

Bands should be adjusted with a gauge where possible but if because of interference of other parts of the car the gauge cannot be inserted, the adjustment can be made with a small wrench (about 5" long) by turning the adjusting screw in until snug and backing off four complete turns. Figs. 2 and 3 show the position of the three adjustment screws.

To check and adjust any of the three bands with the adjusting tool, Fig. 4, proceed as follows:
1. Remove the cap screw or plug from the adjusting screw hole.
2. Screw the adjusting tool into the hole.
3. If the band is in proper adjustment, the indicator plug will be flush with the end of the tool handle when the tool shoulder rests against the transmission case.
4. If the indicator plug becomes flush with the end of the tool handle before the tool shoulder is against the transmission case the adjustment is too tight.
5. If the adjustment is too tight, loosen the lock nut on the opposite side of the transmission and back off the adjusting screw two full turns before the tool is fully screwed into position.
6. If the indicator plug is not flush with the end of the tool when its shoulder is against the transmission case, the band is loose.

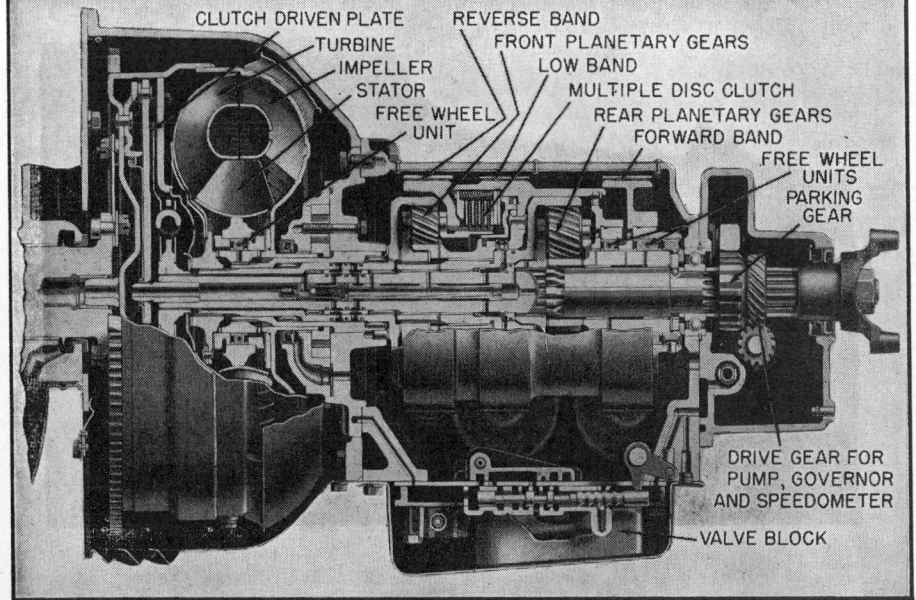

Fig. 1   Sectional view of Borg-Warner Automatic transmission used on 1954 Hudson and 1950-55 Studebaker and 1956 Studebaker Champion

CLUTCH DRIVEN PLATE
TURBINE
IMPELLER
STATOR
FREE WHEEL UNIT
REVERSE BAND
FRONT PLANETARY GEARS
LOW BAND
MULTIPLE DISC CLUTCH
REAR PLANETARY GEARS
FORWARD BAND
FREE WHEEL UNITS PARKING GEAR
DRIVE GEAR FOR PUMP, GOVERNOR AND SPEEDOMETER
VALVE BLOCK

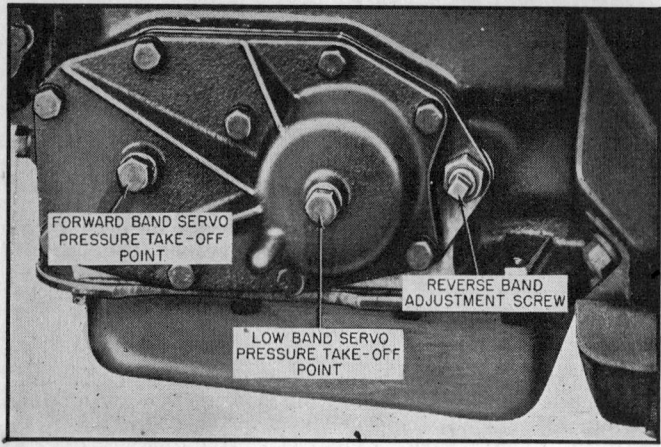

Fig. 2 Right side of transmission on Studebaker Champion and Commander. Hudson 1954 and Studebaker President units have double pistons on the forward and low servos.

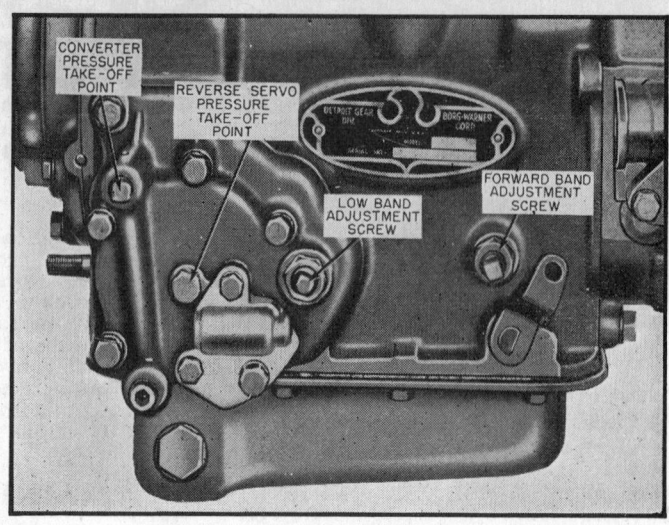

Fig. 3 Left side of transmission

7. To adjust, loosen the lock nut on the band adjustment screw and turn the screw in until the indicator plug is flush with the end of the handle.
8. Tighten the lock nut, being sure the screw does not turn during the process.

OIL PRESSURE TESTS

Before making any pressure tests be sure that the oil is at the proper level and at normal operating temperature. During the tests, do not run the engine at speeds above idle for more than 30 seconds with the selector lever in the D, L or R positions with rear wheels stationary, otherwise the transmission will overheat.

The equipment needed to make the following tests include an oil pressure gauge with suitable line and fittings, and an electric tachometer connected to the engine ignition system.

For convenience, place the oil pressure gauge on the floor of the driver's compartment and allow the pressure gauge line to go through the oil level inspection opening to the transmission pressure take-off point.

Front Pump Pressure

Remove the Allen head pipe plug at the front transmission oil pan flange, and connect the pressure fitting at this point.

With the selector lever in the P or N position, start the engine and bring its speed up to 1000 rpm, at which speed, the gauge should indicate a minimum of 60 pounds pressure.

Stop the engine, remove the gauge fitting and reinstall the pipe plug, tightening it to 15-18 lbs. ft. torque.

Forward Band Servo Pressure

Remove the capscrew from the forward hand servo mechanism cover plate and connect the gauge fitting at this point, Fig. 2. Apply the parking brake and foot brakes to prevent forward movement of the car.

Start the engine and move the selector lever to the D position. Gradually increase engine speed to 1000 rpm. At this speed the gauge should indicate a pressure of 60 pounds.

Stop the engine, remove the pressure fitting and reinstall the capscrew with a new copper washer and tighten it to 28-33 lbs. ft. torque.

Reverse Band Servo Pressure

Disconnect the hand control bellcrank-to-transmission selector valve lever rod at the bellcrank. Move the selector valve lever to the R position. Remove the capscrew from the reverse band servo cover and install the pressure gauge fitting at this point.

Apply the parking and service brakes. Start the engine and increase its speed to 1000 rpm. At this speed the gauge should show a minimum of 160 pounds pressure.

Stop the engine, remove the fitting and reinstall the capscrew, using a new copper gasket. Tighten the capscrew to 28-33 lbs. ft. torque.

Low Band Servo Pressure

Remove the capscrew from the low

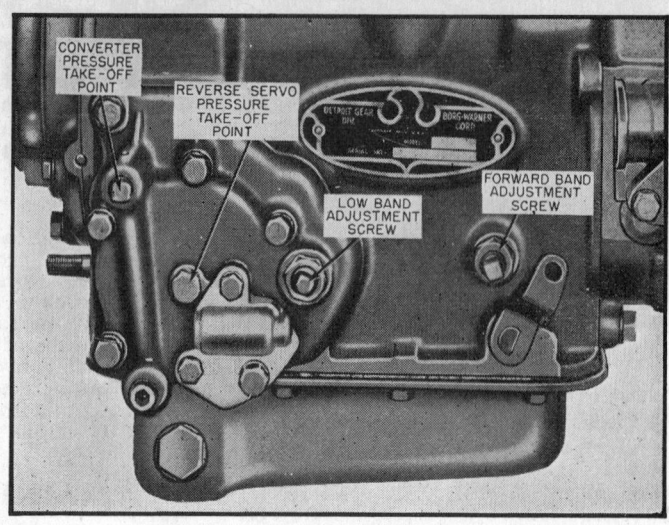

BAND ADJUSTING TOOL

Fig. 4 Band adjusting tool

band servo cover plate and install the pressure gauge fitting at this point, Fig. 2. Apply the parking and service brakes and start the engine. Move the selector lever to the L position and increase engine speed to 1000 rpm. At this speed the gauge should indicate a minimum of 60 pounds pressure at the low band servo.

Stop the engine and remove the pressure fitting. Reinstall the capscrew with a new gasket and tighten it to 28-33 lbs. ft. torque.

Multiple Disc Clutch Pressure

Remove the pipe plug from the rear transmission extension housing, and install the pressure gauge fitting at this point.

Apply the parking and service brakes and start the engine. Place the selector lever in the D position and increase engine speed to 1000 rpm. At this speed the gauge should show a minimum of 60 pounds pressure.

Stop the engine, remove the pressure fitting and reinstall the pipe plug, tightening it to 15-18 lbs. ft. torque.

Torque Converter Pressure

Remove the pipe plug from the torque converter pressure point, Fig. 3, and install the fitting. With the transmission selector valve lever in N (neutral) position, and engine running at approximately 1000 rpm, pressure reading should be 25-35 lbs.

With the rear wheels jacked up and free to rotate and selector lever in the D position and engine running at 1500 rpm, pressure should be 25-35 lbs.

Stop the engine, remove the pressure fitting and reinstall the pipe plug, tightening it to 6 or 7 lbs. ft. torque.

Direct Drive Clutch Pressure

Remove the Allen head pipe plug from the rear transmission oil pan flange and install the pressure gauge fitting at this point. With the rear wheels raised off the floor and free to rotate, and engine running at idle, place the selector lever in

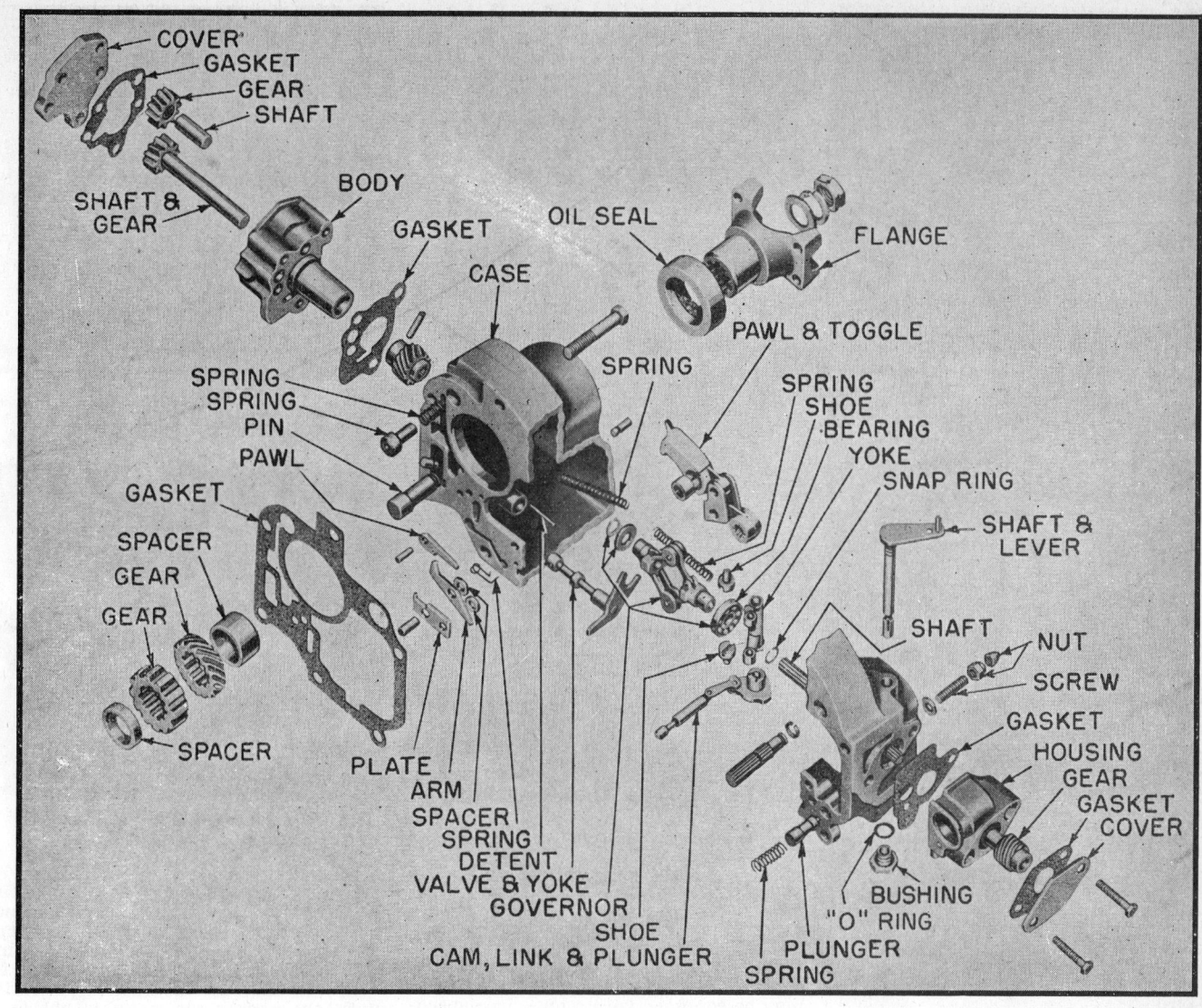

Fig. 5 Extension case, governor, rear oil pump and speedometer gear housing

the D position. Pressure gauge should show zero pressure at the direct drive clutch.

Increase engine speed to 1500 rpm. At approximately 1200 rpm, the transmission should shift to direct drive which will be indicated by a rapid pressure rise in the direct drive clutch. While in direct drive, the pressure gauge should show a minimum of 60 pounds pressure.

Check the direct drive clutch pressure during deceleration. When the speedometer indicates approximately 10-12 mph, the pressure should drop to zero.

Remove the gauge fitting and replace the pipe plug and tighten it to 15-18 lbs. ft. torque.

Rear Pump Pressure

Remove the anti-creep wiring harness from the anti-creep switch and remove the switch from the transmission case. Install the pressure gauge fitting in the rear pump.

With engine running and all brakes applied, the pressure gauge should indicate zero pressure.

With engine running at idle and rear wheels raised from the floor and free to rotate, place the selector lever in the D position. Rear pump pressure should build up as evidenced by a steady increase in pressure reading. At 20 mph on the speedometer, the rear pump pressure should be a minimum of 60 pounds.

Remove the test equipment and reinstall the anti-creep control switch and connect the wiring.

EXTENSION CASE

The extension case is mounted on the rear of the transmission and consists primarily of the governor, parking pawl-to-toggle assembly, rear oil pump, speedometer drive gear and, on early units, the direct drive control mechanism, Fig. 5.

Removal

Shifting the transmission into Park position will hold the mainshaft stationary while removing the universal joint

flange nut. After the nut is removed, punchmark one spline of the mainshaft and corresponding groove of the flange so that these parts can be assembled in the same position. After unfastening the extension case from the transmission case, use care not to allow the mainshaft to move backward which might cause dislocation of the thrust washers in the gear train.

Inspection

If the extension case is equipped with a ball jet check valve, Fig. 6, see that it is free and seating properly. Both ends of the governor must operate freely on the governor shaft.

On early units, the direct drive pawl should unlock the governor valve to allow the shift from direct drive to intermediate on deceleration. To check for proper operation, Fig. 7, position the pawl so it locks the governor. Then, using a spring scale, check the amount of pull required to release the governor valve. If more than 9 ounces pull is required,

Fig. 6 Ball check jet valve found in some extension cases. If present, be sure it is free and seating properly

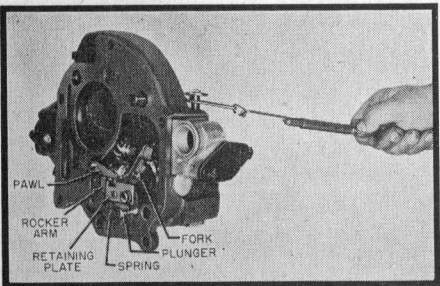

Fig. 7 Checking for proper operation of governor valve and direct drive pawl with spring scale (early units only)

Fig. 8 Checking end play of governor fork

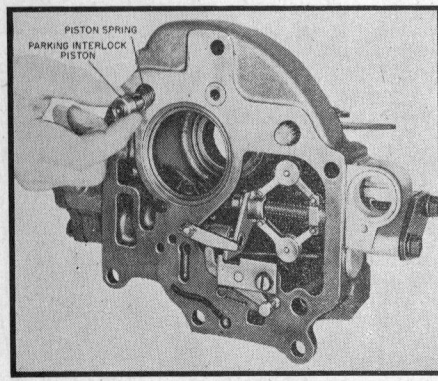

Fig. 9 Parking interlock piston and spring

examine all parts indicated in Fig. 7 for burrs or damage. Check to make sure the governor valve or governor control plunger is not sticking. If a bind exists, rough spots or burrs may be polished off.

Check the end play of the governor fork with a feeler gauge, Fig. 8. If end play is more than .030", replace the governor assembly.

Installation

If a new extension case is being installed, remove the parking interlock piston and spring, Fig. 9, from the old case and install it in the new case. Check the fit of the piston in the bore to make sure it moves freely. Remove the governor control detent and spring, Fig. 10, and install it in the new case with the tapered end first.

When installing the extension case on the mainshaft, engage the splines of the toggle arm shaft with the sleeve splines. It may be necessary to move the selector control shaft lever slightly to facilitate engagement. Push the case forward against the tramsmission case. Install the cap screws *finger tight* so the transmission companion flange, when installed, will center the oil seal and case.

When installing the companion flange, push the selector control shaft lever all the way forward to Park position. Align the punchmarks on the mainshaft and companion flange and install the flange. When installed, tighten the flange nut to a torque of 60-80 lb. ft. This amount of torque is necessary since the companion flange controls the end play in the rear half of the mainshaft.

GOVERNOR

Removal

The extension case must be removed to service the governor. The extension case may be equipped with a one-piece speedometer drive gear and governor shaft assembly or the parts may be separate with the gear splined to the shaft. If equipped with the one-piece assembly, it must be removed to permit removal of the speedometer gear housing. Pull the gear housing away from the extension case and withdraw the governor shaft and gear from the governor. Then remove the shaft and gear from the housing.

Inspection

Inspect the governor shaft and make sure it is free of burrs and that the splines are not scored. Burrs on the shaft can be caused by the governor spring not seating properly in the end brackets.

Make sure the governor valve operates freely in the valve bore, Fig. 11. Be certain the hydraulic detent piston, Fig. 11, is in place. If it is the stepped type, the stepped end should be inserted in the cylinder first, Fig. 12.

Installation

If a new governor is being installed, check the clearance between the end brackets, Fig. 13. The governor must be

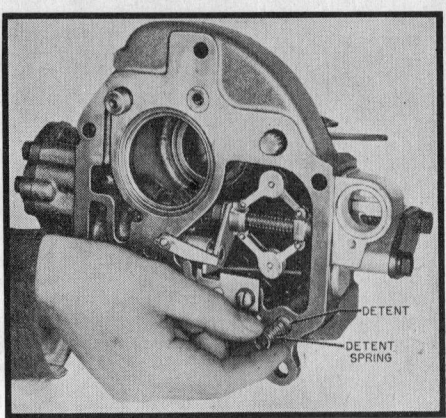

Fig. 10 Governor control detent and spring

Fig. 11 Governor valve and hydraulic detent piston

fully open and the control lever in its full forward position. If the clearance is not approximately .010", remove the acorn nut located on the rear of the transmission case, loosen the lock nut, Fig. 14, and turn the adjusting screw clockwise until the proper clearance is obtained. If a subsequent road test indicates that the kickdown upshift speed is too high, turn the screw clockwise a little at a time until proper speed is obtained. Turning the screw ¼ turn changes the shift speed about 2 mph.

REAR OIL PUMP

Removal

The pump may be removed without the extension case from the transmission if the extension case is equipped with a one-piece governor shaft and speedometer drive gear assembly. But if equipped with a two-piece assembly the extension case must be removed before the oil pump can be taken out. To distinguish between the one and two-piece assemblies, remove the speedometer gear housing cover and, if the position of the shaft is flush with the outer end of the gear when the gear is held in the operating position in the housing, it is a two-piece assembly.

Inspection

Make sure the anti-creep pressure

HYDRAULIC
DETENT
PISTON

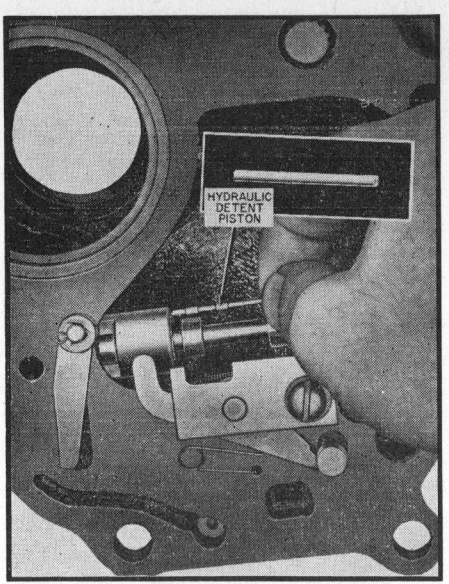

Fig. 12 Installing stepped type of hydraulic detent piston. Inset shows straight type piston

END
BRACKETS

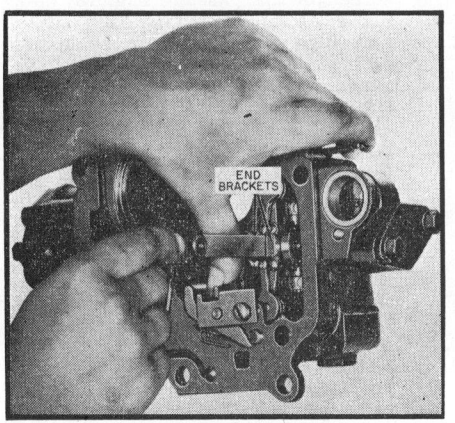

Fig. 13 Checking clearance between governor end brackets with feeler gauge

LOCK
NUT
ADJUSTING
SCREW

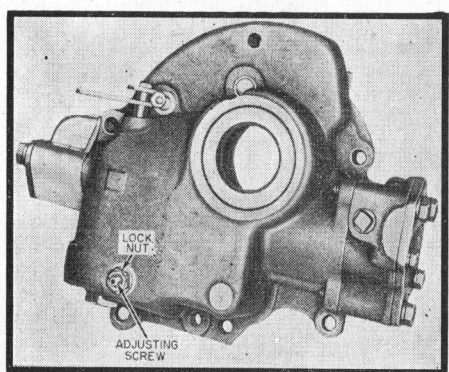

Fig. 14 Adjusting screw for obtaining proper clearance between governor end brackets

COVER
GASKET
BODY & VALVES
GASKET
GASKET
RETAINER
VALVE BLOCK ASS'Y
BASE PLATE
SPRING
BALL
BALL
GASKET
BALL
BALL
SPRING
RETAINER
PLATE & VALVE
GASKET
SCREEN
BASE PLATE
BODY
RETAINER
GASKET
SHROUD
OIL PAN
FILTER OR SCREEN
RETAINER
GASKET
GASKET
PLUG

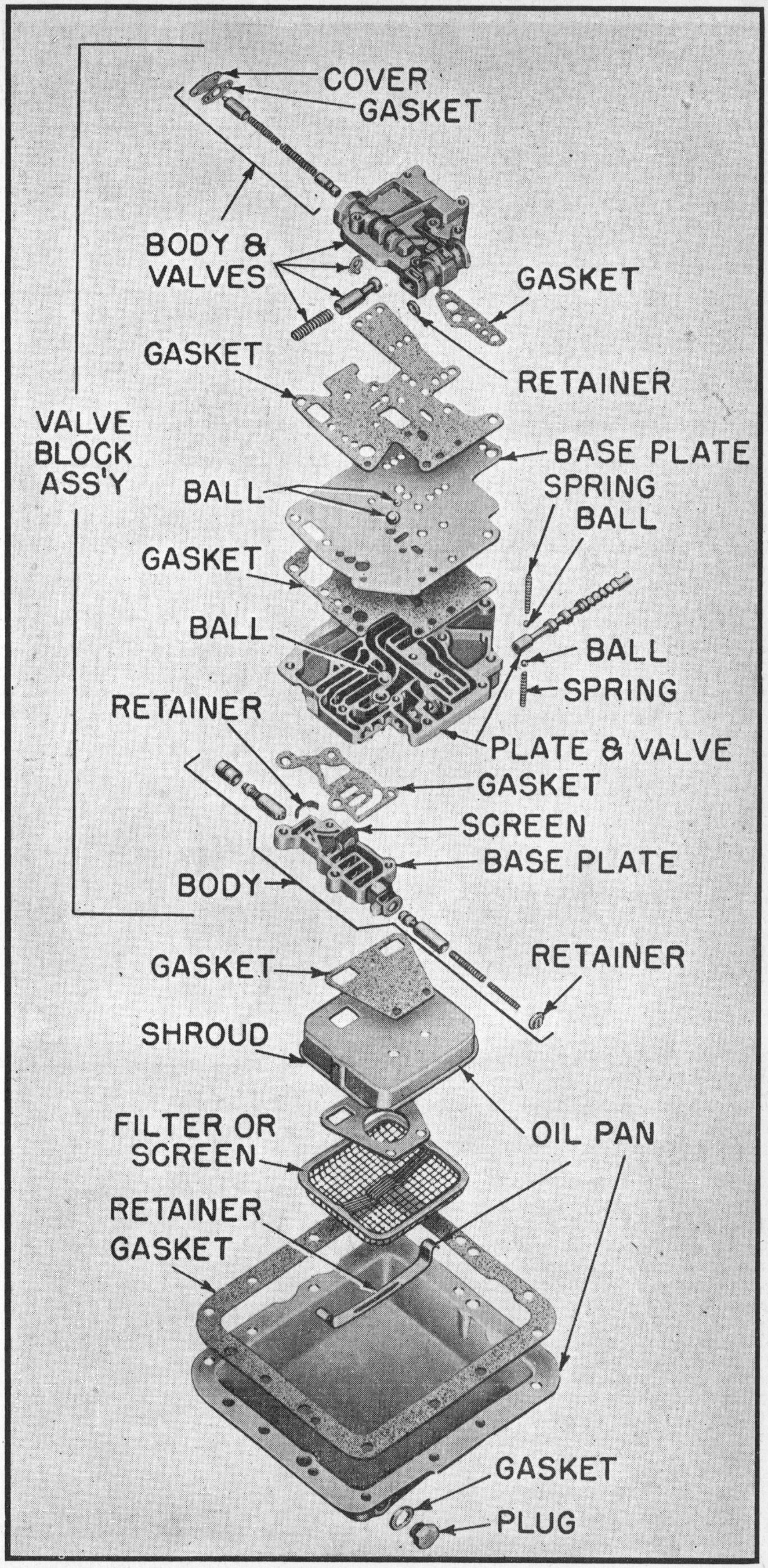

Fig. 15 Exploded view of valve block assembly

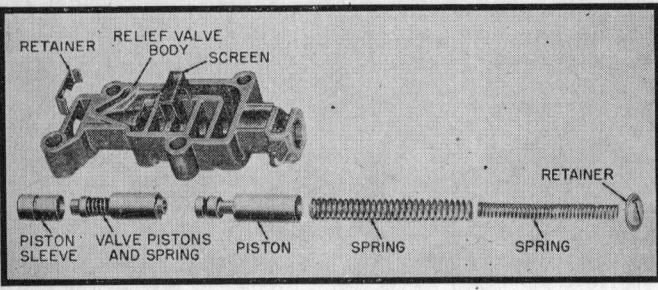

Fig. 16 Front and rear pump relief valve body

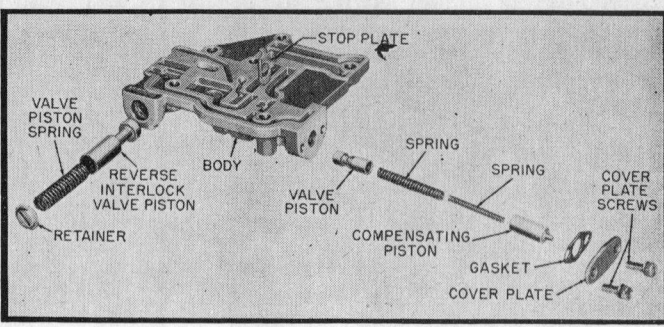

Fig. 19 Converter valve and reverse interlock parts (1950-55)

switch passage in the pump body is not obstructed. Check to make sure the governor valve drain hole is open. Check for worn or damaged gears, pump cover and pump body. If wear or damage is evident, install a new pump.

Installation

Make sure the pump-to-extension case gasket does not obstruct the governor drain hole. If equipped with the two-piece speedometer drive gear and shaft assembly, hold the shaft to prevent moving the governor and yoke out of position when installing the pump.

SERVICE NOTE—If a leak occurs between the pump body and cover, remove the two center cap screws, take off the pump cover and examine it for scoring or wear. The gaskets are available in five thicknesses and the same thickness gasket should be installed as the one removed.

VALVE BLOCK

The valve block assembly, Fig. 15, is mounted on the bottom of the transmission case and, through a series of valves and passages, controls and directs the flow of oil in the transmission.

Removal

Drain fluid from the transmission only. Remove the oil pan and then the valve block assembly.

Disassemble

Refer to Figs. 15 to 20.

Inspection

Inspect all valves and valve bores in their respective valve bodies for evidence of scratching or scoring and for free operation. Slight scratches may be polished out to provide free operation. If a valve or valve bore is badly scored or scratched, a new body assembly must be installed.

Make sure that the passages in the valve block manifold have no obstructions, and check for signs of porocity. Check the front pump ball check seat and rear pump ball check seat; they must be tight in the manifold and plate.

Assemble

Make sure all parts have been thoroughly cleaned. Every precaution must be taken to keep parts clean during assembly. Apply automatic transmission

fluid to the gaskets during the installation to keep them in place. During the assembly procedure, refer to Figs. 15 to 23, being sure to observe the following:
1. When installing the selector valve in the valve block manifold, the milled slot should be at the detent housing. Make sure the valve slot is away from the detent housing. Position the valve so its end clears the opening in the detent housing.
2. Install the spring and ball in the detent housing. Using a small screwdriver, force the ball down into the opening. Then carefully move the selector valve over the ball and, at the same time, push the screwdriver off the ball. Move the valve out until the ball locks up in the first groove in the valve. Turn the selector valve so the milled slot is toward the valve block manifold.

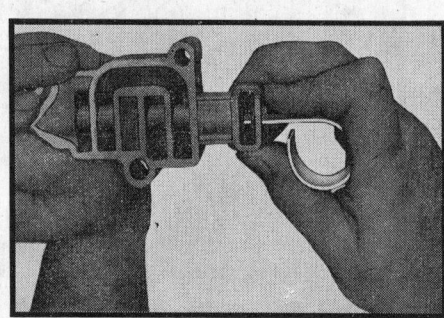

Fig. 17 Using special Valve Spring Unloader to compress rear pump relief valve spring

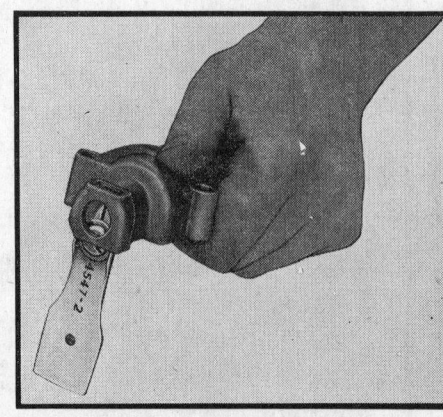

Fig. 18 Removing spring retainer with special tool

3. Place the converter ball check and rear pump ball check in the proper holes, Fig. 21. Then carefully place the converter control valve body over the ball checks and position the body on the base plate. Install the cap screw shown in Fig. 22. Do not tighten this cap screw as it may be necessary later to shift the converter valve body slightly to secure alignment when installing the other parts of the assembly.
4. Turn the assembly over and place the relief valve body gasket in position.
5. Insert the rear pump relief valve screen in the passage Fig. 16, making sure the screen is fully seated and flush with and below the surface of the body.
6. Place the relief valve body and align the mounting holes. Install the two remaining cap screws and shift the body as far as possible in the direction indicated by the arrows in Fig. 23 and tighten the cap screws *finger tight*.
7. Place the oil screen shroud gasket on the valve block manifold, making sure all openings are aligned. Install shroud and reinforcing plate and install the three 1¼" cap screws *finger tight*.
8. After making certain all parts are properly positioned by inserting the valve block-to-transmission case cap screws, tighten all cap screws from 6 to 8 lb. ft. torque.

Installation

When placing the valve block in position against the transmission case, guide the inner control shaft inner lever into the slot of the selector valve, making sure that the gaskets are properly aligned with the holes in the housing flange and valve block. Install the retaining cap screws *finger tight*.

Disconnect the bell crank-to-transmission rod from the selector valve lever and move the selector control shaft lever through its full travel to make sure that a bind does not exist between inner selector lever and selector valve. If there is a bind, loosen the valve block cap screws and reposition the assembly to relieve the bind. Then tighten the cap screws to a torque of 10 to 13 lb. ft.

FRONT PUMP

The front pump is mounted on the front of the transmission. It is the ex-

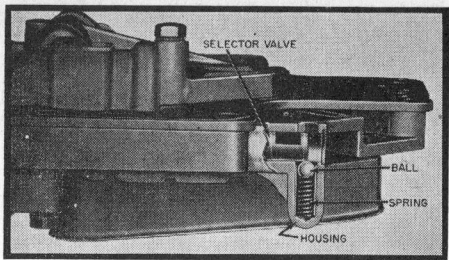

Fig. 20   Selector valve and related parts

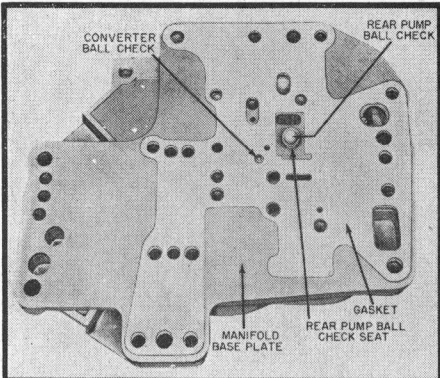

Fig. 21   Showing location of rear pump ball check and converter ball check

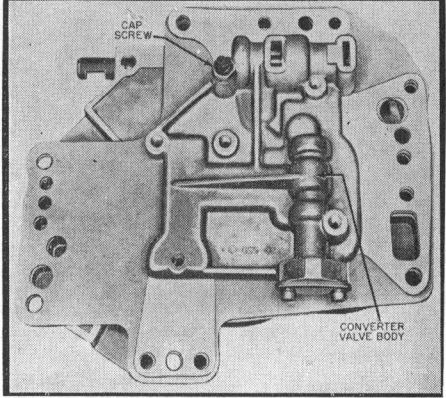

Fig. 22   Capscrew which is in-itially installed to hold con-verter valve body to manifold

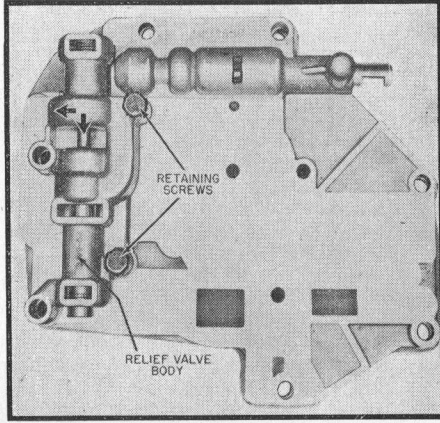

Fig. 23   Shift relief valve body as far as possible in direction indicated by arrows and tighten capscrews finger tight

ternal-internal gear type, Fig. 24, and is driven by the converter hub. The pump supplies oil pressure to the torque converter and the transmission during idling, low speed and reverse operation.

Removal

After removing the transmission, place the ring gear retaining clip on the mainshaft and secure it with a rubber band, Fig. 25. Remove the pump from the transmission case and take the thrust washer from the rear side of the pump.

Inspection

Make sure the oil passages are not obstructed. After disassembling the pump, check for evidence of wear or damage to the gears and casting. If any damage is found, install a new oil pump body and gears.

Assemble

Lubricate the gears with automatic transmission fluid and install in the body. The side of the gear having the drive lugs must be to the outside. After the pump is assembled to the collector ring, check the pump for free operation.

Installation

Before installing the pump, check the end play of the mainshaft assembly to determine the thickness of the front ring gear thrust washer that is required to obtain proper end play. Make certain that the extension case and companion flange are tight before checking end play.

Install the special gauge, Fig. 26, over the mainshaft and ring gear shaft and fit it to the transmission case. Use three of the pump attaching screws to hold the gauge securely in place.

Turn the hub of the gauge so the indicator is over the first step. Then rotate the hub counterclockwise while pushing the hub inward, keeping a steady pressure on the hub. The step over which the indicator is stopped by the next higher step represents the thickness of the thrust washer to be used. The code number of the thrust washer and the thickness is stamped on the face of the ring opposite the step.

Coat the hub of the collector ring with vaseline and stick the selected thrust washer on the rear face of the assembly, fully engaging the tongues of the washer in the slots. The steel face of the washer must be against the hub.

Check the three seal rings, Fig. 27, to make sure they are not broken or damaged. Coat the rings with vaseline and center them in the grooves. When installing the pump, hold it so the elongated inlet hole and the round outlet hole in the flange are at the bottom. Check to see that all oil passages are indexed with corresponding passages in the case. Then slip the assembly on the mainshaft.

MAINSHAFT & RELATED PARTS

The mainshaft assembly, Fig. 24, is supported at the rear by a ball bearing

and at the front by needle bearings in the front pump. The assembly consists primarily of the mainshaft, two planetary gear sets, three brake drums and the multiple disc clutch.

Removal

1. Remove front pump, extension case, oil pan and valve block.
2. Strip rear end of mainshaft.
3. Pull off rear bearing, Fig. 28.
4. Install spacer and sleeve of bearing installer tools, Fig. 29, on rear end of mainshaft and secure with companion flange nut.
5. Make sure ring gear retaining clip is securely in place on front end of mainshaft.
6. Pull mainshaft forward out of case, being careful not to disengage ends of bands from struts or dislodge bands from guide at top of transmission case. Any cocking of bands will hinder removal of assembly.

Installation

1. Support the mainshaft with one hand under the low drum, insert the assembly in the case, thread it through the brake bands and seat the bearing in the bore of the rear face of the case. Make sure the brake bands and anchor struts have not been moved out of position.
2. Remove the sleeve and spacer from the end of the mainshaft. Make sure the rear bearing spacer is in position on the mainshaft. Then install the rear bearing, using the equipment shown in Fig. 29. Do not remove the pusher at this time.
3. Install the rear bearing lock ring. Push against the rear face of the case and remove the pusher tools.
4. Install the extension case as outlined previously.
5. With a new mainshaft assembly, it will be necessary to check the end play of the assembly and determine the thickness of the front ring thrust washer required to obtain proper end play. The gauge shown in Fig. 26 is used for this purpose. Follow the procedure outlined under *Front Pump.*

Fig. 25   Ring Gear Retaining Clip installed on mainshaft to prevent movement of ring gear and dislocation of thrust washers in gear train

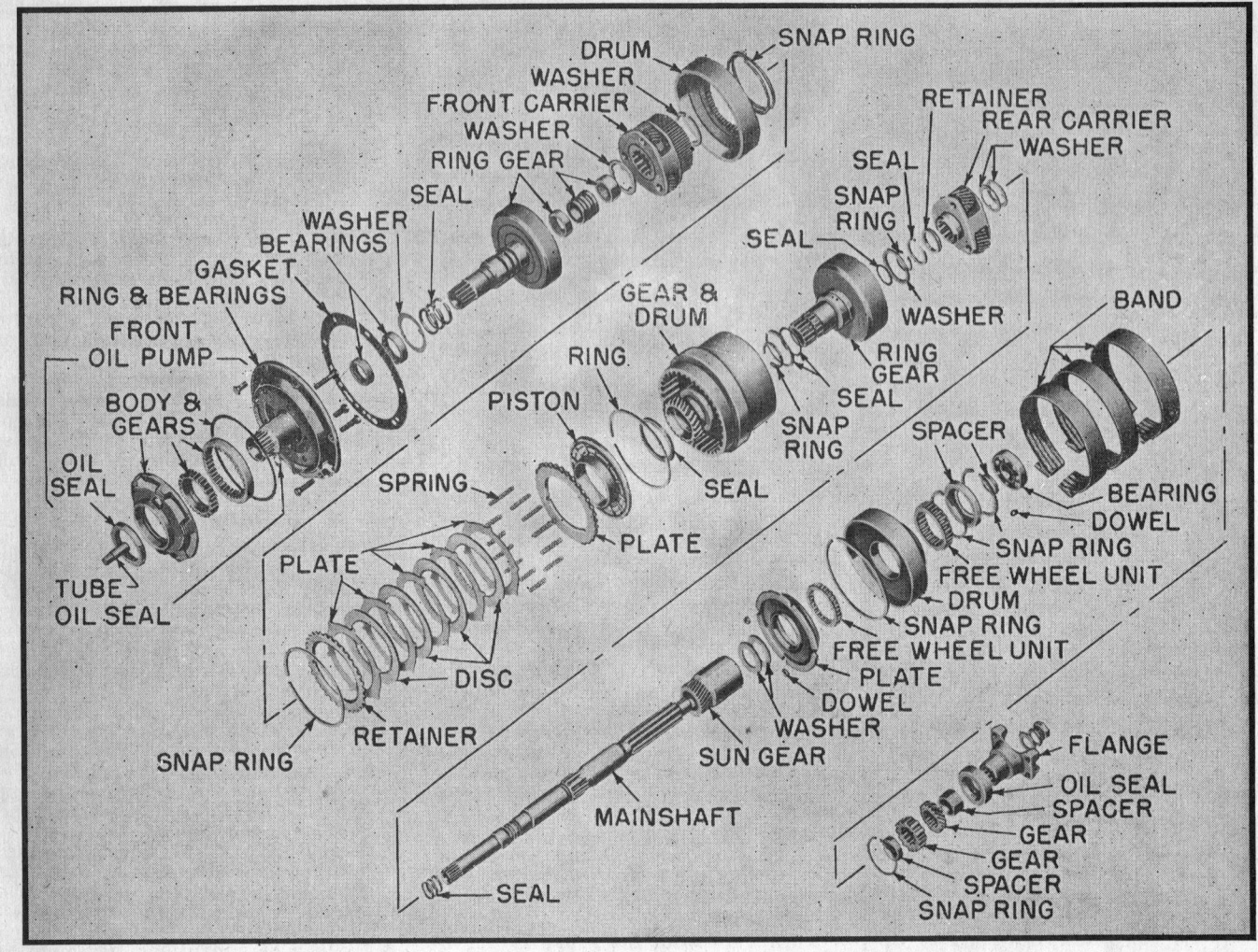

Fig. 24   Exploded view of front oil pump and collector ring, mainshaft, multiple disc clutch and drums

6. To make sure that the ring gear has not moved forward or that the ring gear thrust washer has not dropped out of position while handling the assembly, measure the distance from the end of the ring gear shaft to the end of the mainshaft. This should not be less than 1¾₆″, Fig. 30. If the measurement is less than 1¹³⁄₁₆″, slip the ring gear off the shaft and reposition the thrust washer over the gear teeth, applying petroleum jelly to the washer to hold it in place. Make sure that the steel face of the washer is toward the rear of the transmission. Then coat the seal rings, Fig. 31, with petroleum jelly and reinstall the ring gear.

7. Reinstall the front pump and valve block and install the transmission in the vehicle.

Mainshaft, Disassemble

To provide a means of holding the mainshaft during disassembly and reassembly, drill a 2½″ hole in a piece of wood 2″ x 4″ x 2″ and fasten it to the work bench with a large C clamp. The assembly can then be placed upright with the end of the mainshaft through the hole.

1. Remove front ring gear.

2. It is not necessary to remove the ring gear oil seal rings unless they are to be replaced. If only one of the rings is broken, all rings ahead of the broken ring must be replaced.

3. The needle bearings and bushing of the front ring gear are not serviced separately but are available only as part of the ring gear assembly.

4. Remove front ring gear thrust washer.

5. Slide reverse drum and front planetary carrier off mainshaft.

6. Remove front sun gear thrust washer.

7. The planetary carrier and pinions are serviced only as an assembly.

8. Remove rear bearing spacer.

9. Remove forward brake drum from mainshaft.

10. Remove forward free wheel unit spacer snap ring and remove spacer plate from drum.

11. Remove spacer dowel, free wheel unit snap ring and free wheel unit from drum.

12. Remove rear sun gear rear spacer washer retainer and thrust washer from mainshaft.

13. Remove low brake drum plate snap ring. Pick the two dowels out of the plate and remove the plate and rear

sun gear as a unit.

14. Slip rear sun gear out of reverse free wheel unit. Remove snap ring and lift free wheel unit out of plate.

15. Pull mainshaft rearward and remove from low brake drum.

16. Remove rear planet carrier front thrust washer.

17. Remove rear planetary carrier oil seal ring retainer snap ring. Place the assembly in an arbor press and press the shaft out of the seal retainer and carrier. Two types of rear planetary carriers are used: one counterbored at the thrust washer position, the other not counterbored. If the carrier is counterbored, a steel spacer must be used in addition to the thrust washer.

18. Slide the rear ring gear out of the low brake drum. Pick the inner O-ring seal out of the retainer and remove it from inside the bore of the rear ring gear.

19. Pick the outer O-ring seal out of the groove and slip it off the hub of the ring gear.

20. Mount low brake drum and clutch assembly in an arbor press with the special fixture shown in Fig. 32. Apply sufficient pressure to relieve pressure from the retractor spring

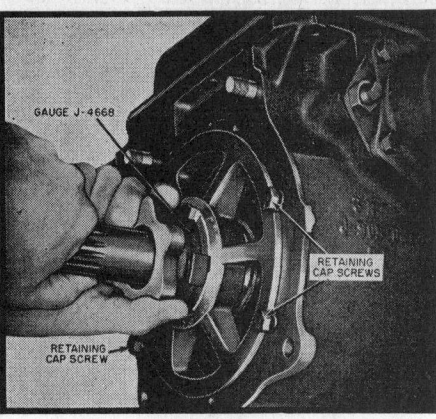

Fig. 26 Gauge in position to check end play of mainshaft

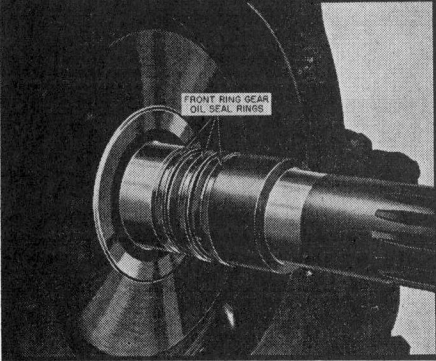

Fig. 27 Front ring gear oil seal rings

Fig. 28 Removing mainshaft rear bearing with puller

Fig. 29 Installing mainshaft rear bearing with special pusher

retainer. Then remove the retainer snap ring. Slowly release pressure and dismantle the clutch, Fig. 33.

21. To facilitate removal of clutch piston, insert Piston Installing Pins J-5487, Fig. 34, in grooves as shown The pins will permit the piston seal to slip past the circular grooves inside drum.

22. To prevent damage to the clutch piston inner cylinder bore during removal, place about two layers of masking tape over the teeth of the front sun gear.

23. To remove the piston inner seal, squeeze it to one side and pick it out of the groove and out of the drum.

24. On some models, the clutch piston has a rubber outer seal while a cast iron ring seal is used on other models. If a rubber seal is used and is to be replaced, the piston should be replaced with the piston and cast iron seal kit.

Mainshaft, Inspect

1. Inspect all carriers, pinion ring gear and sun gear teeth for wear or damage.

2. Inspect all bushings and mating surfaces for wear or scoring. Bushings are not furnished separately. They are available only as part of the unit in which they are contained.

3. Inspect oil seal rings for wear or damage.

4. Inspect thrust washers for wear or scoring.

5. Inspect free wheel unit sprags for damage or wear.

6. If the reverse free wheel unit is damaged, the low drum plate and rear sun gear should be replaced. If the forward brake drum free wheel unit is damaged, the drum and rear sun gear should be replaced.

7. Inspect linings of clutch friction discs.

8. Check the clutch disc plates for dishing by placing the plate on a flat surface and, using a feeler gauge, check the clearance at the inner diameter of the plate. If the dish is more than .010″, the plate must be replaced.

9. Inspect brake drums for scoring.

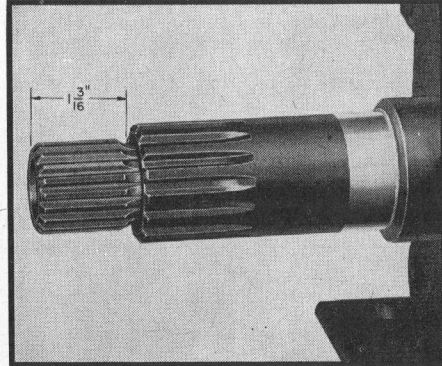

Fig. 30 If the dimension shown is not correct, it indicates that the ring gear thrust washer has probably dropped out of position

Fig. 31 Proper location of thrust washer which controls mainshaft end play

Fig. 32 Special fixture used to apply pressure to clutch in order to remove snap ring

10. Make sure check valve in clutch cylinder is free.

11. Make sure lubrication valve in end of mainshaft is tight and in proper position.

Mainshaft, Assemble

1. Apply Automatic Transmission Fluid to a new clutch piston inner seal, Fig. 33. Hold the seal so that its lip is toward the drum. Stretch the seal just enough to slip it over the sun gear and place it in the groove.

2. Apply Automatic Transmission Fluid to the inside of the low brake drum and clutch piston seal. If a steel piston seal is used, install the seal in the ring groove of the clutch piston. Place the Installing Pins, Fig. 34, in the grooves of the drum. Compress the clutch piston ring and slip the piston into the cylinder.

3. If a rubber piston seal is used, the Installing Pins cannot be used. Instead, use a piece of .002″ steel shim stock 3″ wide and 18″ long. All edges of the shim stock should be honed

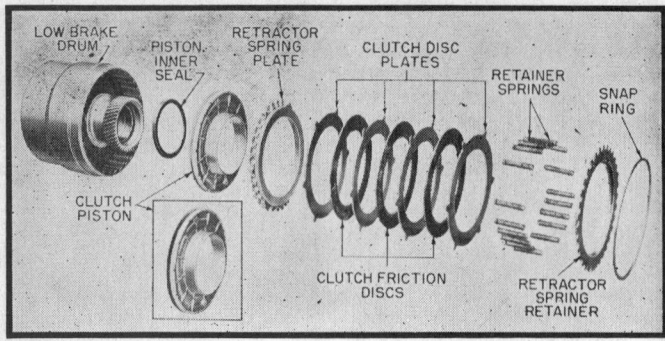

Fig. 33   Layout of multiple disc clutch, piston and low brake drum

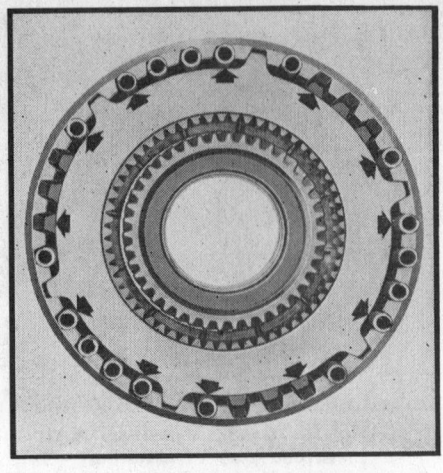

Fig. 35   Arrows point to the correct location of retractor springs on clutches having only 12 springs

smooth to prevent cutting the rubber seal. Coat the shim stock with Automatic Transmission Fluid and then place the shim stock around the inside bore of the clutch cylinder. Slip the piston and seal into the sleeve formed by the shim stock and push the piston down into position. Be sure the piston is at the bottom of the cylinder and then remove the shim stock.

4. Slip the clutch retractor spring plate into the drum with the spring recesses up.

5. Apply Automatic Transmission Fluid to the clutch discs and plates.

6. Starting with a disc, place the plates and discs alternately in the drum. Since the lugs are not evenly spaced, make sure that the lugs of the disc plates are in the same grooves with the master lugs of the retractor spring plate. The disc plates are dished and may be installed with the dish either to the front or rear, but all plates must have the dish in the same direction.

7. Center the friction discs around the sun gear and align the teeth of the friction discs.

8. If the low brake drum is equipped with a centrifugal check valve in the clutch cylinder, only 12 clutch retractor springs are used. If the valve is not used, then 18 retractor springs

must be installed. If 12 springs are used, position them as indicated by the arrows in Fig. 35.

9. Place retractor spring retainer over the springs, Fig. 32. Then, using an arbor press, Fig. 32, compress the springs in the drum. Install the snap ring, making sure it is fully seated in the groove, and remove the assembly from the press.

10. Apply Automatic Transmission Fluid to the ring gear inner and outer O-ring seals and install the seals.

11. If the ring gear oil seal ring and front planetary carrier snap ring have been removed, install the parts on the ring gear shaft.

12. Install the rear ring gear in the low brake drum.

13. Place the rear planetary sun gear front thrust washer on the mainshaft with the steel face of the washer to the front of the shaft and engage the washer with the splines of the shaft.

14. If the carrier is counterbored, install the carrier spacer washer in the same manner. Slip the rear planetary carrier on the front end of the mainshaft, engage the splines, and seat the carrier against the shoulder on the mainshaft.

15. Install the planetary carrier oil seal ring in the retainer and slip the retainer on the mainshaft.

16. Place the assembly in an arbor press and press the shaft into the seal retainer just enough to install the snap ring. Make sure the ring is free in the groove.

17. Install the retainer snap ring. If there is clearance between the retainer and snap ring, press the retainer back against the snap ring.

18. Place the rear planetary carrier front thrust washer over the shaft and on the rear planetary carrier with the steel face of the washer against the carrier. Apply a light coating of petroleum jelly to the washer to hold it in place.

19. Install the mainshaft-and-rear carrier assembly in the rear ring gear and low brake drum.

20. Install the reverse free wheel unit in the low brake drum plate, making sure the side of the unit which has the arrows is up. Then install the snap ring in the groove.

21. Lubricate the rear sun gear bushings and the outside of the rear sun gear with Automatic Transmission Fluid and install the sun gear on the shaft.

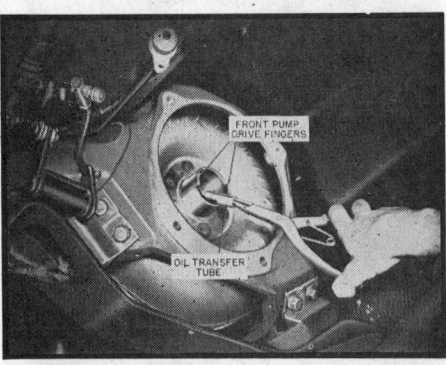

Fig. 36   Removing mainshaft oil transfer tube from torque converter in cases when it fails to come out with mainshaft

22. Place the low brake drum plate over the end of the sun gear with the flat side of the plate toward the drum.

23. Tilt the assembly slightly and slip the free wheel sprags down over the edge of the sun gear on one side. Then, with a screwdriver, move each sprag outward, slipping it over the edge of the gear and, at the same time, holding the free wheel unit against the sun gear.

24. After all the sprags are outside the edge of the gear, rotate the unit counterclockwise and slide the assembly down on the sun gear.

25. Seat the low brake drum plate in the drum. Align the slots of the plate and drum and place the dowels in position in the openings. Install the snap ring, making sure it is seated in the groove.

26. Place the forward free wheel unit in the forward brake drum, making sure the side which has the arrows is down. Then install the snap ring in the groove.

27. Place the forward brake drum over the rear sun gear, and install the free wheel sprags in the same manner as for the low brake drum. However, after all the sprags are outside the edge of the gear, rotate the

Fig. 34   Showing special Piston Installing Pins which permits piston seal to slip past circular grooves in drum

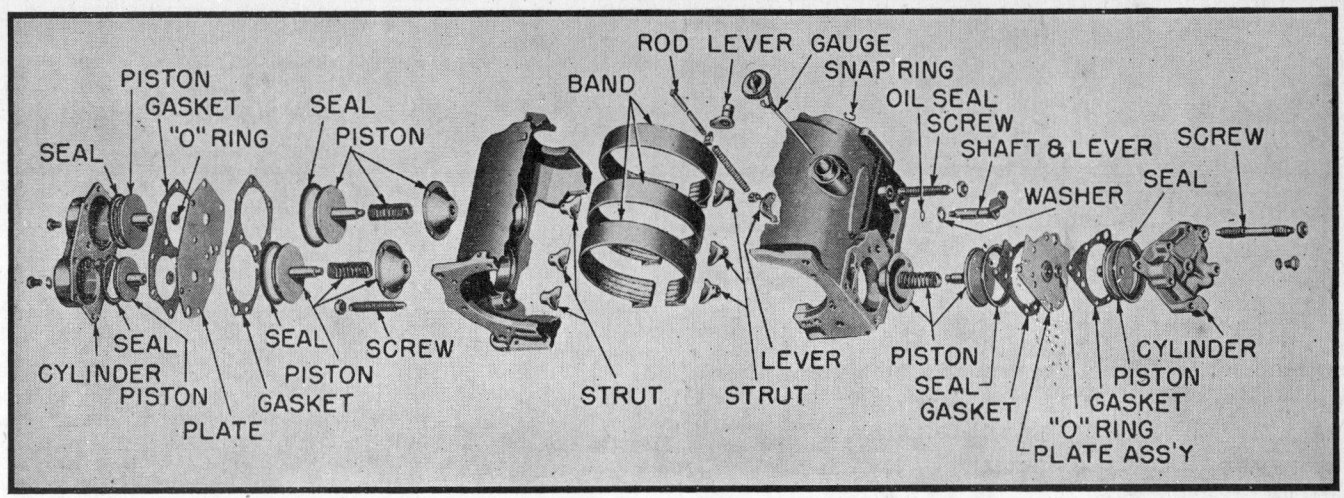

Fig. 37 Exploded view of transmission case, servos, brake bands and selector lever

unit *clockwise* and slide the assembly down on the sun gear.

28. Slip the rear sun gear rear thrust washer on the shaft with the bronze face of the washer toward the sun gear and place it on the rear face of the gear.

29. On early 1951 and prior models, install the spacer washer by engaging the lug of the washer with the slot in the spacer and the slot at the inner edge of the spacer with the retainer ball in the mainshaft.

30. On late 1951 transmissions, the thrust washer and retainer are of different designs and the retainer ball is not used in the mainshaft. Only the later type thrust washer and spacer are available for service, and it will be necessary to remove the ball from the mainshaft if it is necessary to replace either the front thrust washer or spacer on an early model shaft.

31. Insert the free wheel unit spacer dowel in the hub of the forward brake drum and position the spacer within the drum. Then install the spacer snap ring securely in the groove of the hub.

32. Install the spacer and sleeve of the tools shown in Fig. 29 on the mainshaft, after the rear bearing spacer has been installed. Hold these parts in place by installing the companion flange, flat washer and nut.

33. Align the splines of the front planetary carrier and reverse brake drum and, using an arbor press, press the carrier into the drum. Install the snap ring.

34. Coat the front sun gear thrust washer with petroleum jelly and install the washer within the front planetary carrier hub with the tangs in the slots and with the steel face against the hub.

35. Install the reverse drum-and-front planetary carrier assembly. After engaging the carrier splines with the rear ring gear splines, it may be necessary to turn the assembly to engage the clutch disc teeth. Do not force the assembly into position as this may cause damage to the disc teeth.

36. Apply petroleum jelly to the front planetary carrier thrust washer and place it in position on the ring gear shaft splines with the steel face of the washer against the front planetary carrier.

37. If the front ring gear or mainshaft oil seal rings have been removed, install new rings.

38. Coat the mainshaft oil seal rings with petroleum jelly and install the front ring gear.

39. Install Retaining Clip, Fig. 25, on the front end of the mainshaft to hold the assembly in position.

40. Install the mainshaft assembly in the case as outlined previously.

Mainshaft Oil Transfer Tube

With the transmission removed from the vehicle, slip the oil transfer tube out of the end of the mainshaft. If the tube does not come out with the transmission, use long nose pliers or snap ring pliers to remove it from the torque converter assembly, Fig. 36.

The oil transfer tube is installed in the end of the transmission mainshaft with the tapered end toward the front.

BANDS

The bands are located in the transmission case, Fig. 37, and encircle the mainshaft assembly. The bands are used to hold their respective drums in order to obtain the required speed ratios. In reverse, the reverse band is applied. In intermediate and direct drive the forward band is applied, while in the low range, both the low and forward bands are applied.

The low and forward bands are lighter than the reverse band and are interchangeable. Do not under any circumstances interchange the reverse band with the low or forward brake band.

Inspection

1. Make certain that the interior of the transmission case is clean.
2. Inspect the band linings for wear and the bands and shoes for damage.
3. Inspect the band guide strap and retaining rivets to make sure guide is tight in the case and all rivets are tight.

Removal

1. Remove the transmission and mainshaft assembly as outlined previously.
2. Remove the brake anchor side strut from the forward brake band by pulling the band shoe away from the

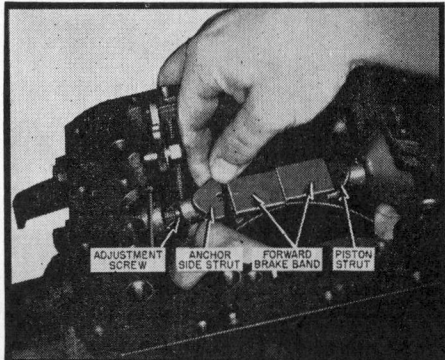

Fig. 38 Identification of brake band parts

Fig. 39 Removing band from transmission case

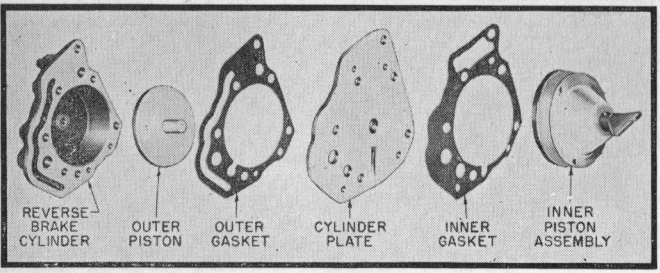

Fig. 40   Layout of reverse servo parts

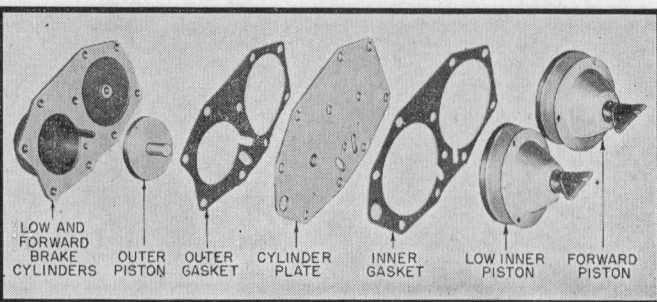

Fig. 43   Layout of low and forward servo unit parts

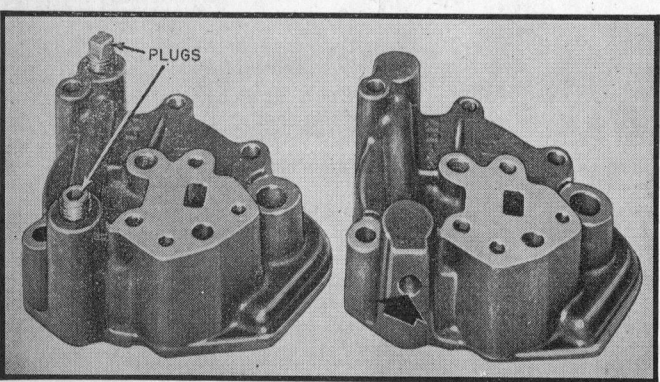

Fig. 41   Two types of reverse brake outer cylinders

adjustment screw. Disengage the pin from the notch in the strut and remove the strut.

3. Disengage the other end of the band from the piston strut, Fig. 38, lift the band out of the guide and move the band to the rear of the transmission case.
4. Disengage the low band in the same manner and move it to the rear of the case.
5. Disengage the reverse band shoe from the anchor side strut and remove the strut from the screw.
6. Disengage the reverse band shoe from the piston strut, turn the band 90 degrees, spread it slightly, and slip the end of the band out of the case over the flange, Fig. 39.
7. Remove the two other bands in the same manner.

Installation

1. Select one of the lighter bands and install it in the case in the reverse manner of its removal, Fig. 39.
2. With the band in the case, turn it so that the end of the band which has the offset pin is toward the low and forward piston side of the case. Then move the band to the rear of the case.
3. Install the other lighter band in the same manner and move it also to the rear of the case.
4. Install the reverse band in the same manner except that the band is turned so that the end of the band which has the offset pin is toward the reverse piston side of the case.
5. All three bands are positioned as follows: Set the band into the guide strap at the top of the case. Engage the band on the piston side with the piston strut, making sure the pin is

in the notch of the strut. Pull the shoes of the band together, without disengaging the strut, and slip the anchor side strut on the end of the adjustment screw. Then release the band and allow the shoe to engage the anchor side strut.
6. Make sure that the pins of all the shoes properly engage the notches of their respective struts and that the bands are properly positioned in the guide strap.
7. Install the mainshaft in the case. Then adjust the bands as outlined under *Maintenance* section of this chapter.

REVERSE SERVO

The reverse servo unit is located on the left side of the transmission case and consists primarily of two pistons, Fig. 40.

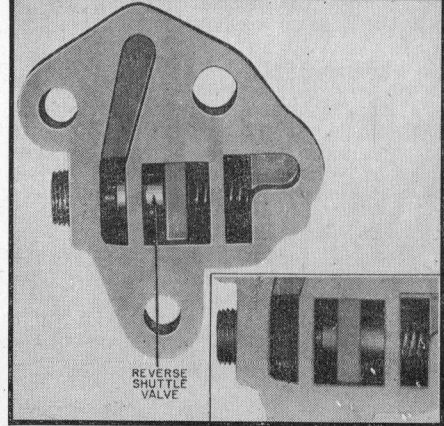

Fig. 42   Reverse shuttle valve

The pistons, actuated by oil pressure, control the operation of the reverse brake band. Two pistons are used to acquire smooth engagement of the band: the inner piston actuated by unrestricted oil pressure and the outer piston receiving oil pressure regulated by the reverse shuttle valve.

Two types of reverse brake outer cylinders are used, Fig. 41. No. 2 cylinder does not have the pipe plugs. Because of a change in production, the passages are not drilled completely through the casting. The two cylinders are interchangeable and the service procedure is the same for both. However, when checking the converter pressure of a transmission which has a No. 2 cylinder, the gauge is installed in the hole indicated by the arrow at the bottom of the cylinder. Also, when draining the converter, the top plug is removed from cylinder No. 1 and the bottom plug is removed from cylinder No. 2.

Removal

1. Disconnect the linkage from the left side of the transmission.
2. Remove the low band adjustment screw lock nut.
3. Place a pan under the cylinder to catch the oil as the unit is removed.
4. Unfasten and remove the reverse brake outer cylinder and plate as a unit.
5. Remove the cylinder inner gasket from the case. *Use care to prevent the inner brake piston from coming out of the inner cylinder in the case. Should this happen, it will be necessary to remove the oil pan and valve block.*

Disassembly

1. Separate the reverse brake cylinder plate from the cylinder, lift the plate off the piston rod, and remove it from the cylinder. Remove the gasket from the plate.
2. Grasp the outer piston rod and pull the piston out of the cylinder.
3. Pick the O-ring seal out of the plate.
4. Lift the piston seal out of the groove of the piston.

Inspection

Clean all parts thoroughly, and check the gasket surface of the cylinder for warpage. Make sure the cylinder plate is not warped. Check the cylinder bore for pits or scoring.

Reassembly

1. Lubricate a new piston seal with

Automatic Transmission Fluid and slip the edge of the seal into the piston groove at one point, making sure the lip of the seal is toward the outer face of the piston away from the piston rod. Then work the seal progressively into the groove all around.

2. Lubricate a new O-ring seal and install it in the groove in the cylinder plate.

3. Hold the piston at an angle and insert it in the cylinder, being careful not to damage the lip of the seal. After all of the piston is below the bottom edge of the cylinder, straighten the piston and push it into the cylinder.

4. Apply a thin coat of petroleum jelly to the machined surface of the cylinder and place a new outer gasket on the cylinder.

5. Slip the cylinder plate over the rod of the outer piston and position the plate on the cylinder.

Installation

1. Stick a new cylinder plate gasket in position on the case.

2. Slip the reverse brake outer cylinder over the low band adjusting screw and install the retaining capscrews. Tighten the 3" screws to 10-13 lbs. ft. torque and the other screws to 15-18 lbs. ft.

3. Install the low band adjustment screw lock nut.

4. Adjust the band if necessary as outlined under *Maintenance*.

5. Retorque the reverse cylinder retaining capscrews.

6. Connect the transmission linkage, make necessary adjustments as outlined under *Service Adjustments* in the car chapter and follow the recommended procedure in filling the transmission with fluid.

Reverse Shuttle Valve

Remove the three capscrews which fasten the reverse shuttle valve to the reverse brake cylinder. Using an Allen wrench, remove the valve cover plug and take out the valve and spring, Fig. 42. Inspect the shuttle valve for excessive wear or scoring. The inset of Fig. 55 shows the valve in the open position.

Install the valve and spring in the body, making sure the valve is free in the bore. Install the cover plug and tighten securely. Install a new gasket and install the shuttle valve assembly on the cylinder and installing the retaining capscrews. Tighten the $\frac{5}{16}$" screws to 10-13 lbs. ft. and the ¼" screws to 6-8 lbs. ft. torque.

Fill the transmission with fluid according to the recommended procedure.

LOW & FORWARD SERVO UNITS

The low and forward servo units are located on the right side of the transmission and control the operation of the low and forward bands, Fig. 43. The bands are actuated by pistons: one piston for each band except on the larger cars where the low band is applied by means of two pistons.

Service on these units is similar to that for the reverse servo.

Buick Flight-Pitch & Triple Turbine Transmissions

CONTENTS

Description 191
Trouble Shooting 18

Maintenance

Adding Fluid 191
Changing Fluid 191

Transmission Repairs

Testing Oil Pressures 192
Transmission, Overhaul 193

DESCRIPTION

This transmission, Fig. 1, available as standard equipment on Series 70 and 700, and as optional equipment on Series 40, 50 and 60, embodies three turbines in a new five-element torque converter. Two turbines are connected individually to the output shaft through elements of two planetary gear sets. The third turbine is connected directly to the output shaft. Thus, total torque output is the sum of the output of the two geared turbines plus that of the third turbine.

In conjunction with the three turbines, a multiple pitch stator is utilized. This is a further development of the Dynaflow variable pitch stator in that the blades of the multiple pitch stator have an infinite number of positions from "Low" to "High" angle. The blades are shifted to the most desirable angle for performance and "feel" by a control system which is actuated by throttle position.

With a maximum starting ratio of 4.5 to 1, the acceleration is comparable to that of a Variable Pitch Dynaflow when manually shifted from "Low" to "Drive" range. This performance, however, is obtained without shifting as required in the Variable Pitch Dynaflow. *The broad ratio coverage of the three turbines plus the multiple pitch stator eliminates any necessity for a "Low" range.*

Downhill Braking

Downhill braking, which in the Variable Pitch Dynaflow is achieved by the use of the "Low" range, is achieved in the Flight Pitch Dynaflow by shifting to the "Grade" (G) position on the quadrant. The design of the Flight Pitch Dynaflow in this range utilizes both the engine and transmission converter as the braking forces. The "Grade" retarder clutch may be engaged at any vehicle speed up to 45 mph to control car speed when descending grades.

Clutching Elements

All clutching elements of the Flight Pitch Dynaflow are of the friction plate type. There are four clutch assemblies which are Neutral, Drive, Reverse and Grade. *No band type control elements are used in this transmission, so service adjustments are unnecessary.*

Hydraulic Oil Pressure

Oil pressure to apply the clutches and circulate lubricating and cooling oil is modulated in response to throttle opening. With this arrangement, the power used to pump oil is reduced to a minimum when light loads are being transmitted. When the throttle is opened, linkage from the engine actuates a pressure control valve in the transmission to increase the hydraulic oil pressure, enabling the clutches to handle the increased loads.

MAINTENANCE

Adding Fluid

Check the oil level with the transmission oil warm, selector lever in Parking position and with engine idling. Remove the oil gauge rod, wipe dry and reinstall to its full depth. Remove gauge rod again and check oil level.

If the oil level is more than one inch below the "Full" mark on the gauge rod, add Automatic Transmission Fluid as required to bring the level up to (but not above) the "Full" mark.

Changing Fluid

1. Remove converter housing cover.
2. Turn flywheel until one converter

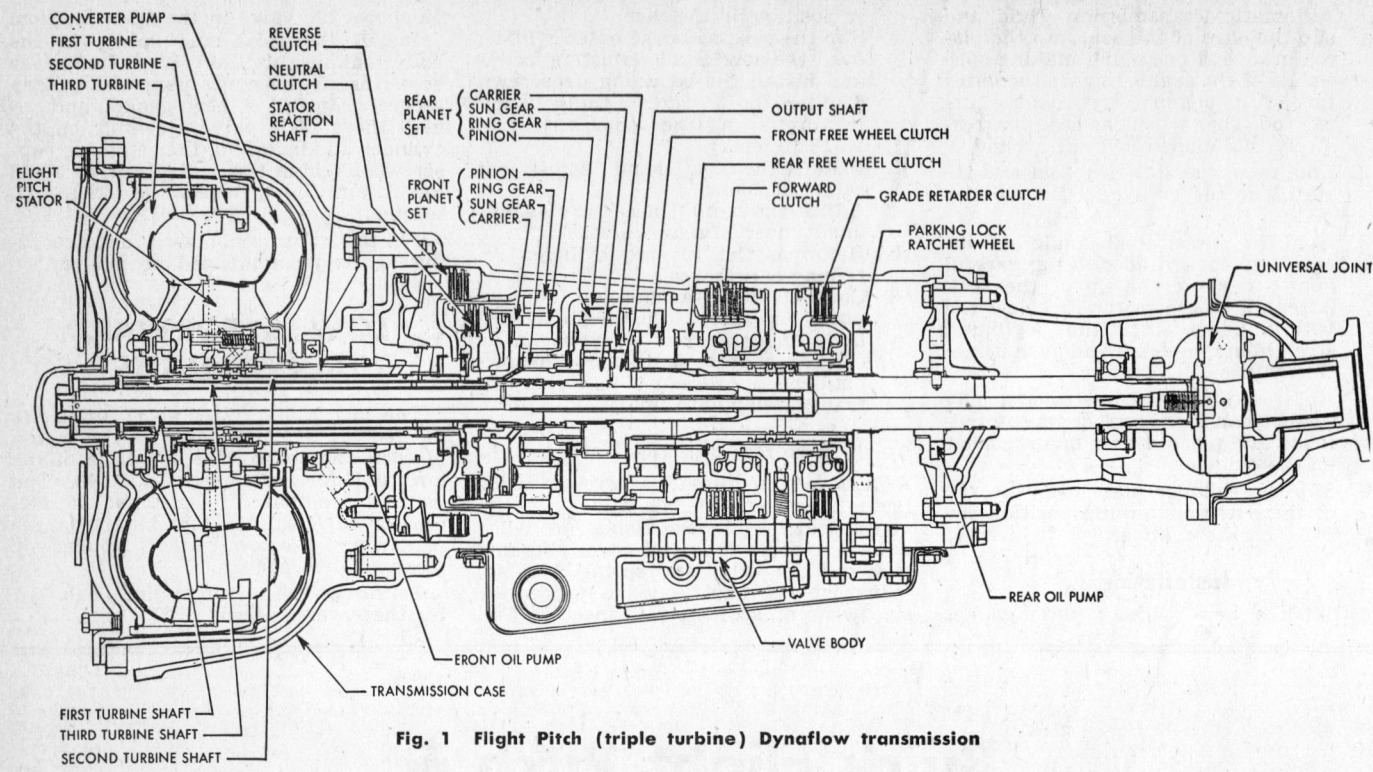

Fig. 1 Flight Pitch (triple turbine) Dynaflow transmission

drain plug can be loosened to provide an air vent. Then turn flywheel until opposite drain plug is down. Remove this plug and allow oil to drain from converter.

3. Remove filler pipe from oil pan and allow oil to drain from transmission.
4. Replace drain plugs and filler pipe.
5. Pour four quarts of fluid in transmission.
6. Raise rear wheels and with transmission in Drive range and engine idling, add eight more quarts of fluid.
7. Place selector lever in Neutral and lower rear wheels to floor.
8. Check oil level and add oil as necessary to bring level to "Full" mark on gauge rod.

TESTING OIL PRESSURES

Figs. 2 and 3 show the location of the oil pressure take-off points. When testing pressures, observe the following:

1. Warm up engine and transmission.
2. Support car in a safe manner with wheels clear of floor and brakes off.
3. Connect pressure gauge at point to be checked.
4. Disconnect stator lever linkage to allow stator lever position to be changed without moving throttle.
5. Connect tachometer to engine.
6. Start engine and take pressure reading at specified rpm.
7. Stop engine, remove gauge, replace plug and lower car.

NOTE—The following pressures should be attained with a correctly functioning Flight Pitch Dynaflow. Never drive car on a road test with stator linkage disconnected.

In Drive Range At 500 RPM, Stator In Low Angle

Unit	Pressure
Stator	0-10
Front pump	40-80
Rear pump	0
Forward clutch	40-80
Reverse clutch	0
Cooler return	5-30

In Drive Range At 1000 RPM, Stator In Low Angle

Stator	0-10
Front pump	67-80
Rear pump	67-80
Forward clutch	67-80
Reverse clutch	0
Cooler return	20-30

In Drive Range At 2000 RPM, Stator In High Angle

Stator	80-90
Front pump	0-180

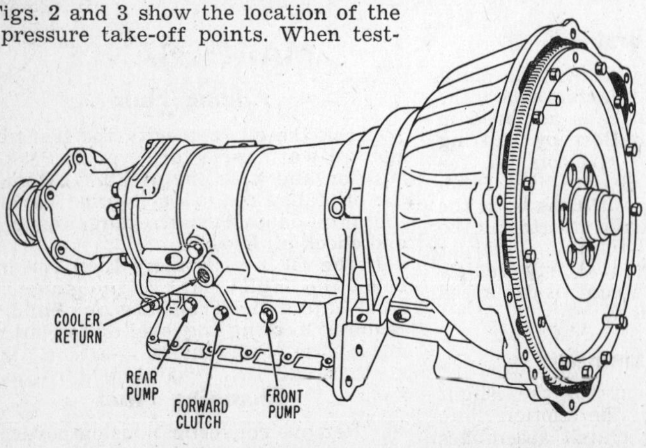

Fig. 3 Oil pressure check locations (right side)

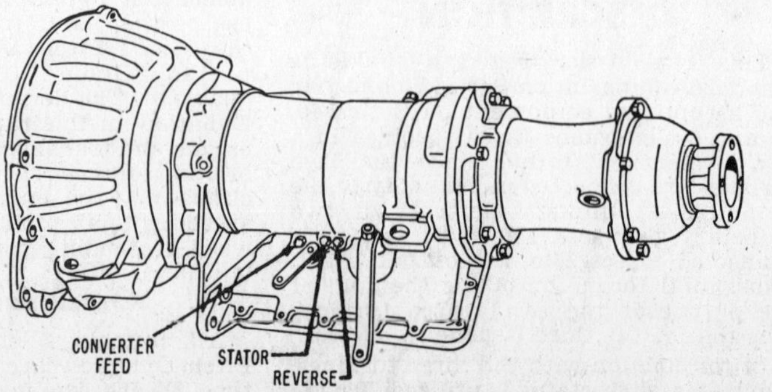

Fig. 2 Oil pressure check locations (left side)

		In Reverse Range At 1000 RPM, Stator In High Angle			
Rear pump	170-180			Rear pump	0
Forward clutch	170-180			Forward clutch	0
Reverse clutch	0	Stator	80-90	Reverse clutch	190-210
Cooler return	30-45	Front pump	190-210	Cooler return	5-45

Transmission Overhaul

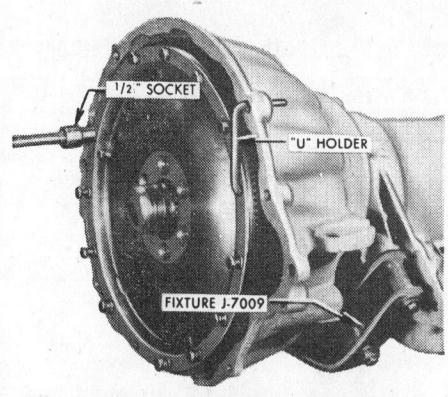

Fig. 4 Remove converter cover bolts. Pump and cover are balanced as a unit and should be assembled in same location. Pry off cover and discard "O" ring. If converter pump bushing is damaged, collapse bushing with chisel and remove. Install new bushing with suitable driver

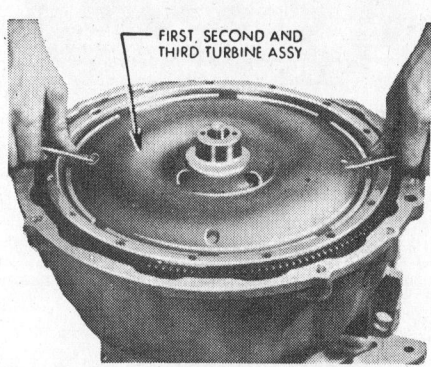

Fig. 6 Use two screwdrivers as shown to remove turbines. Set assembly on bench with shafts up

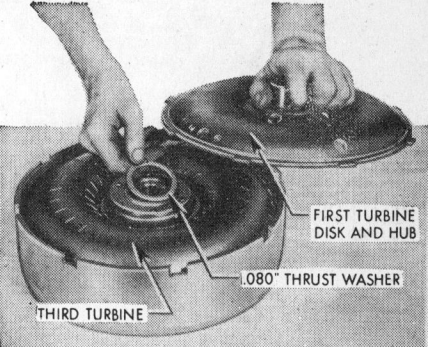

Fig. 9 Remove first turbine, disc, hub and thrust washer on third turbine hub

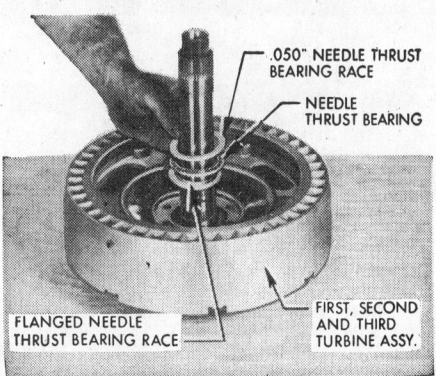

Fig. 7 Remove parts shown from second turbine hub

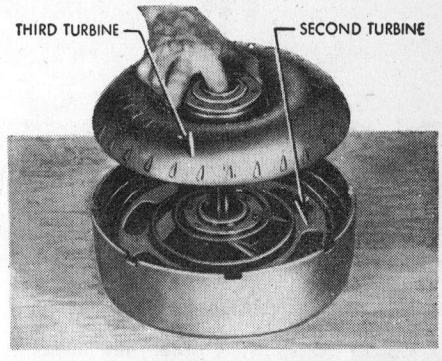

Fig. 10 Remove third turbine, flanged needle bearing race, needle bearing and plain needle bearing race. Examine third turbine bushing. If worn remove it with chisel and install new bushing with suitable driver. Also examine third turbine rear bushing and replace if necessary

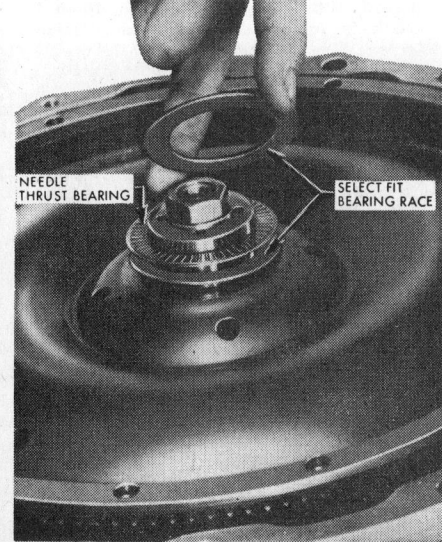

Fig. 5 Remove select fit bearing races and needle thrust bearing. Loosen first turbine shaft nut, using "U" holder, Fig. 4. Remove nut and special washer (discard washer)

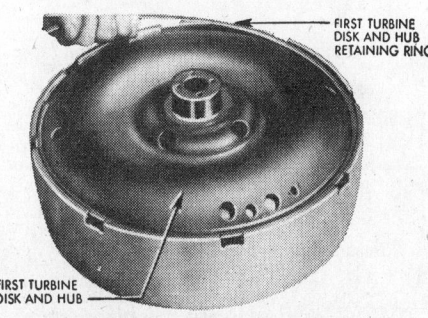

Fig. 8 Set assembly shafts down through hole in bench. Remove retaining ring with thin screwdriver

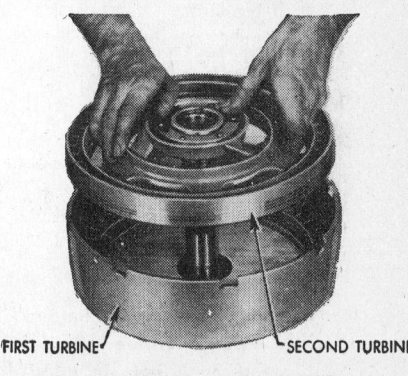

Fig. 11 Remove second turbine

Fig. 12 If necessary unhook, expand and remove second turbine shaft hooked oil rings. Examine second turbine shaft front and rear bushings. If necessary cut out with chisel and use suitable driver to install new bushings

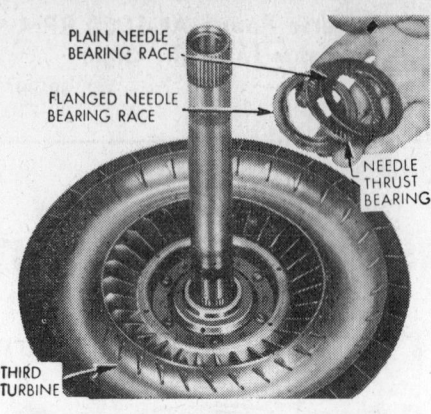

Fig. 15 Install parts shown on third turbine hub. Always measure needle bearings and races. Some are within .010" thickness and 1/16" diameter of each other and can easily be incorrectly assembled

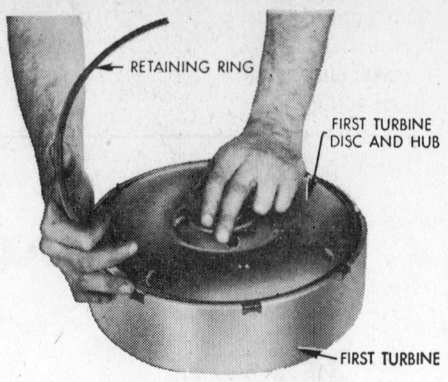

Fig. 18 Install retaining ring

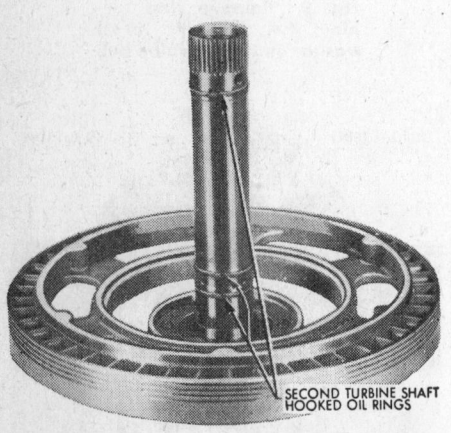

Fig. 13 Expand and install new hooked rings on second turbine shaft

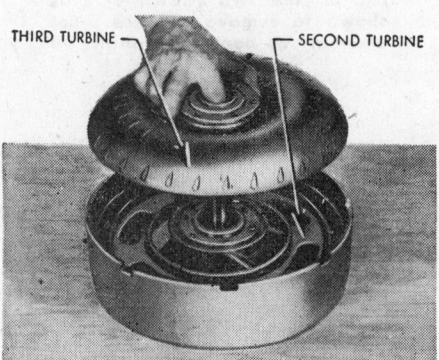

Fig. 16 With needle bearing and races held in place with heavy grease, insert third turbine shaft into second turbine shaft

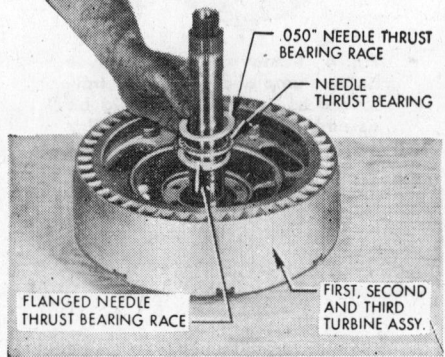

Fig. 19 Install parts as shown, being sure flanged needle thrust bearing race is installed with flange up. Set completed sub-assembly aside if further work is to be done on transmission

Fig. 14 With first turbine over hole in bench, insert second turbine with oil rings in place through hole in bench to rest on first turbine

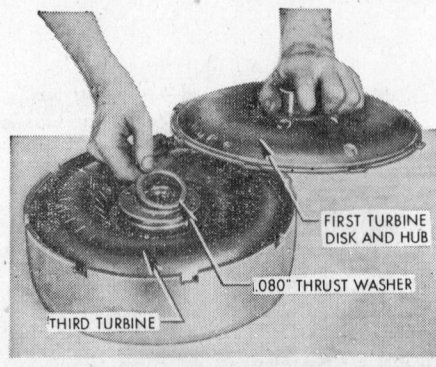

Fig. 17 If necessary, place new .080" lead-coated bronze thrust washer on hub of third turbine, and position first turbine disc and hub with tangs in slots of first turbine

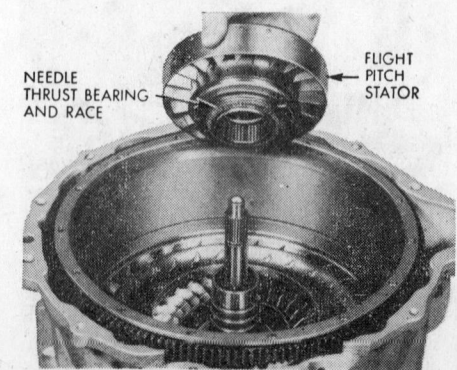

Fig. 20 Lift converter pump until stator race is clear of splines on reaction shaft. Lower pump and remove stator

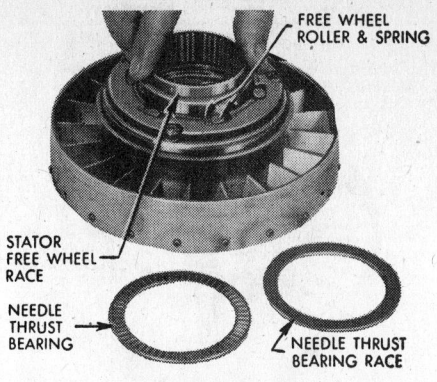

Fig. 21 Pull out stator free wheel race by rotating clockwise

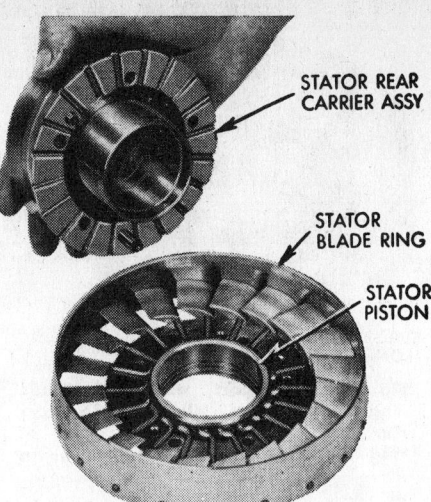

Fig. 24 Invert assembly and rotate all stator blades to extreme high angle and remove rear carrier. Remove blades and blade ring. Examine rear carrier bushing and replace if necessary

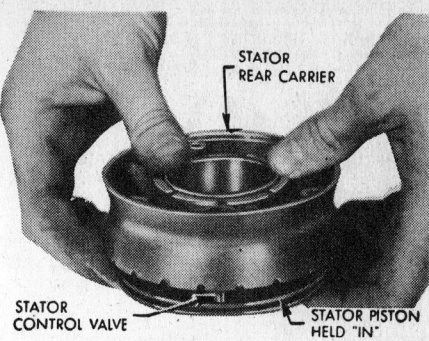

Fig. 27 For gauging purposes only assemble stator piston shoulder "up" to rear carrier and press together. Insert valve in bore of rear carrier

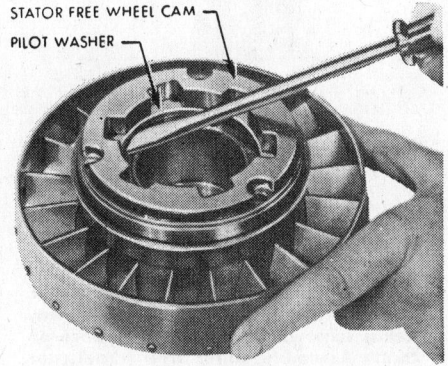

Fig. 22 Remove three screws from stator cam-to-stator carrier. Pry up free wheel cam and bronze washer with screwdriver and remove cam and washer

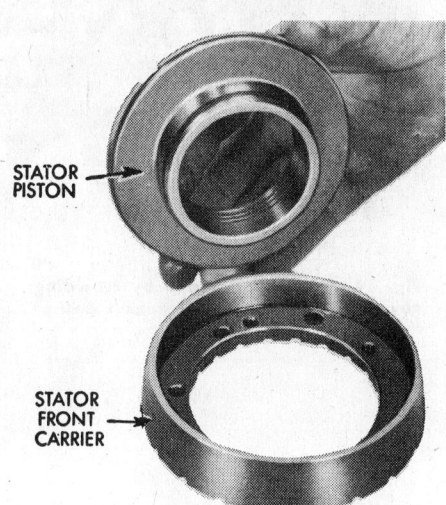

Fig. 25 Remove stator piston and ring from front carrier. Remove ring from piston with snap ring pliers

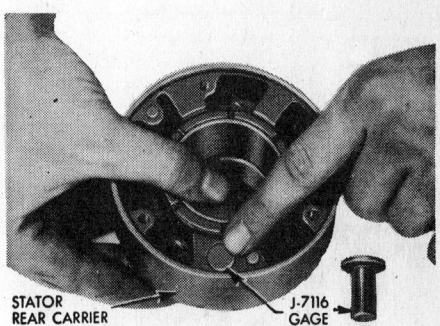

Fig. 28 Insert gauge shown in stator control valve. With piston held against carrier and tool in place, top of tool should be flush with boss of rear carrier

Fig. 23 Remove five front-to-rear carrier screws. Then invert assembly and remove stator piston retaining ring

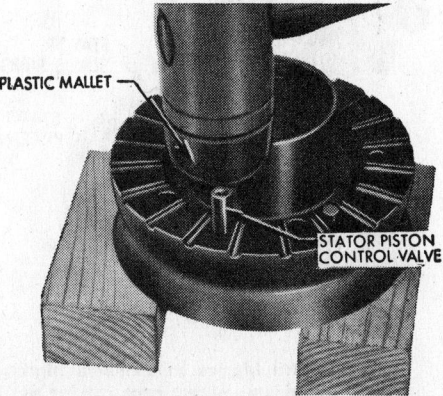

Fig. 26 If stator piston control valve is sticking or there is reason to believe spring is weak, remove valve

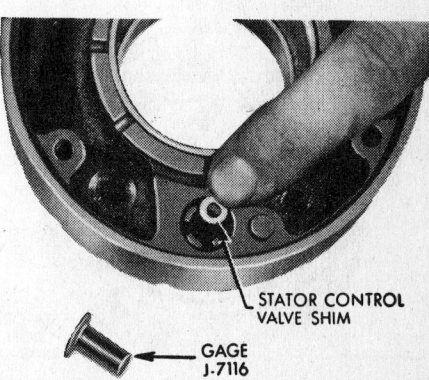

Fig. 29 If gauge is below surface of rear carrier, add shims to bring gauge as close to flush with surface as possible. Shims are available in thicknesses of .007" and .021". Total thickness of shims used should not exceed .042". If shims required exceed .042", rear carrier, piston or valve may require replacement

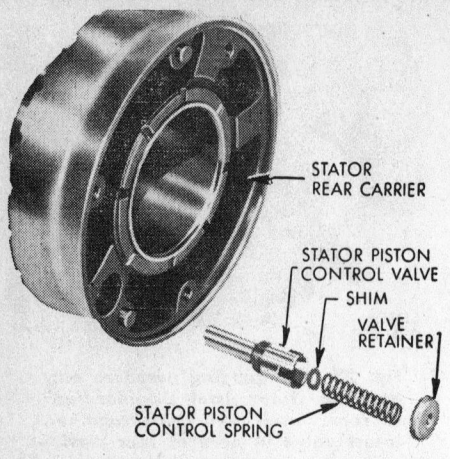

Fig. 30 After stator valve has been checked and shims added, assemble valve, new service spring and retainer to stator rear carrier. Be certain shims lay flat inside valve bore

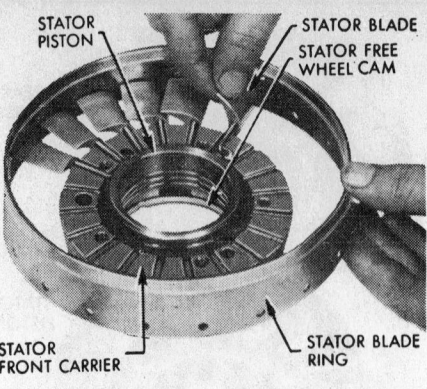

Fig. 33 Support edge of blade ring and insert blades into carrier and piston. Be sure edge of ring nearest holes is "down" as shown

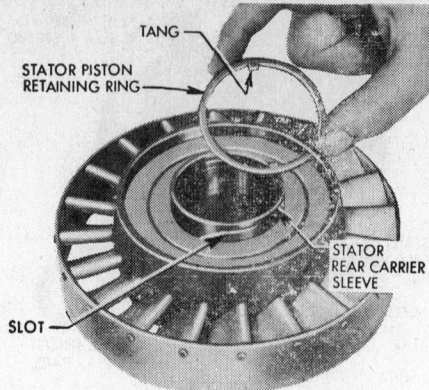

Fig. 36 Install piston retaining ring on rear carrier sleeve. Tangs on ring must enter slots in sleeve. Move blades from high to low angle several times to see that they operate freely

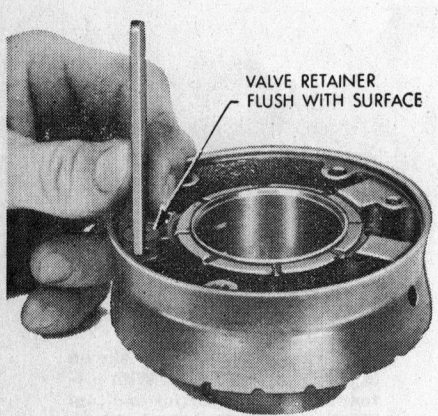

Fig. 31 Tap valve retainer in squarely and flush with carrier surface. Use flat tool to drive retainer to prevent cocking

Fig. 34 Install last blade by crowding several adjacent blade cranks together

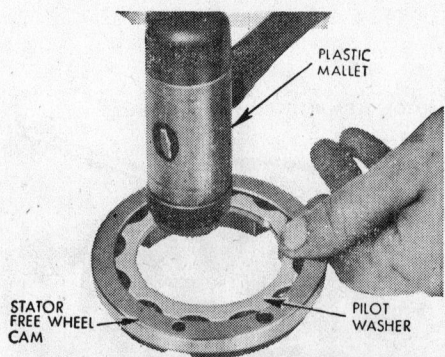

Fig. 37 If necessary, remove pilot washer. Install new washer as shown, being sure washer is seated in bore of cam. Assemble stator free wheel cam and pilot washer assembly to rear carrier with three screws and lockwashers. Torque screws to 10-12 lb. ft.

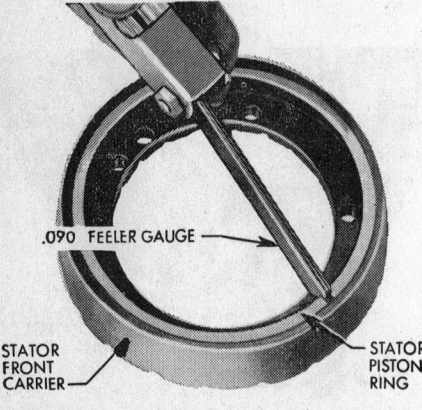

Fig. 32 Insert stator piston ring in bore of carrier. Ring gap should be .090" (plus or minus .010"). This gap serves as bleed hole for piston. Install piston ring on piston. Install piston and ring into front carrier by tilting and inserting gap side of ring first and then pressing in

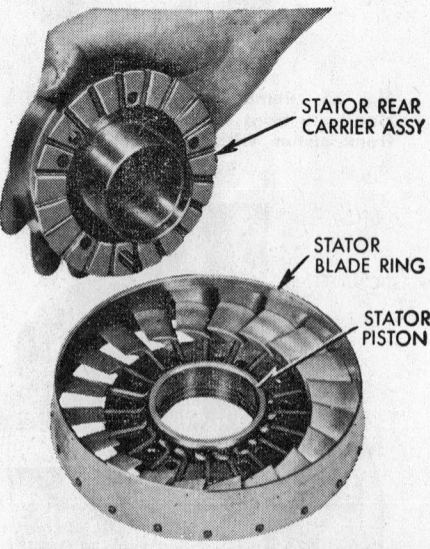

Fig. 35 With blades at extreme high angle position, assemble rear carrier to front carrier. Note position of dowels and dowel holes. Install five screws and lockwashers and torque to 10-12 lb. ft.

Fig. 38 Insert free wheel clutch inner race, small diameter end up, into pilot washer. Inner race should rotate freely in pilot washer. Install free wheel clutch rollers and springs with roller toward narrow end of cam opening and spring at wide end of opening. Inner race should rotate freely in clockwise direction and lock on counterclockwise rotation

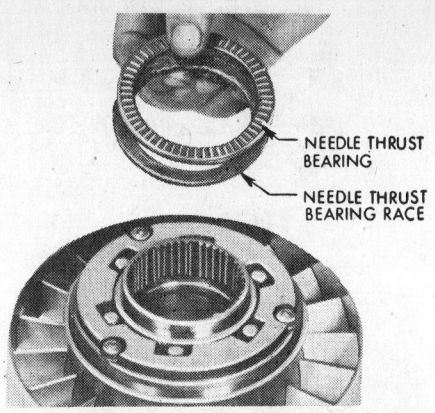

Fig. 39 Apply heavy grease and install bearing and race shown on free wheel race. Set assembly aside if further work is to be done on transmission. Always assemble needle bearing race with same face toward rollers as when disassembled

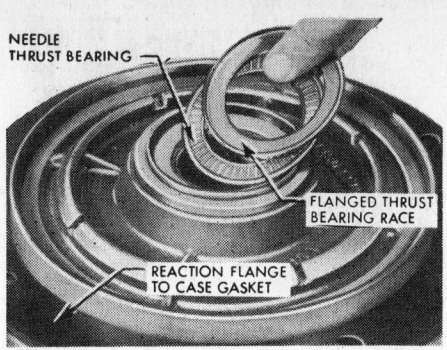

Fig. 42 Remove parts shown. Then lift out reverse clutch piston, using pliers to grip piston ribs if piston sticks in bore. Remove reverse piston seal from outer diameter of piston

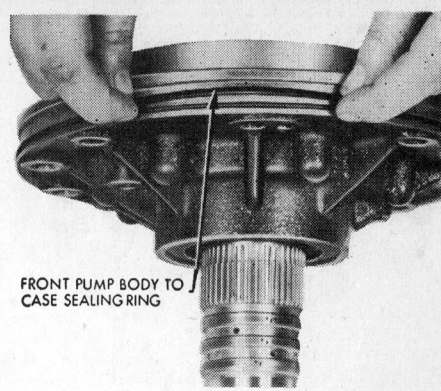

Fig. 45 Remove sealing ring (square section)

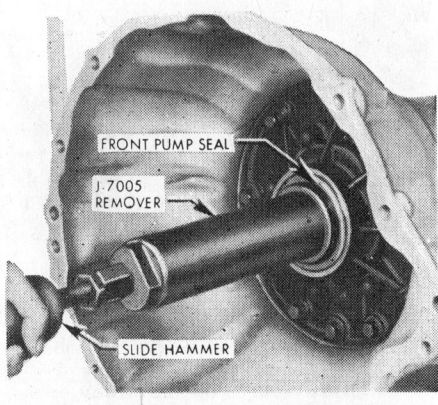

Fig. 40 Remove converter pump. Then remove front pump seal with tool shown. Thread tool into seal until threads are engaged with sheet metal portion of seal. Install a new seal with a suitable driver

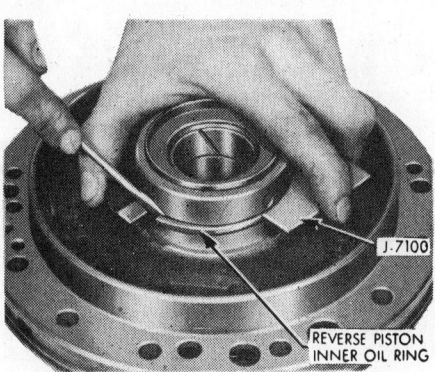

Fig. 43 If necessary, unhook reverse piston oil ring. Remove tool shown and remove piston oil ring with snap ring pliers

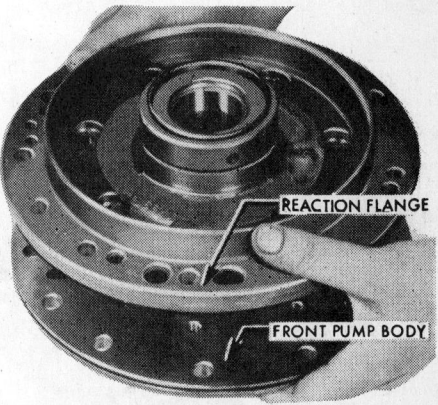

Fig. 46 Remove seven reaction flange - to - front pump body bolts. Separate pump body from reaction flange by tapping assembly on bench. If necessary remove three reaction shaft oil rings. Examine second turbine shaft - to - reaction shaft bushing. If worn or damaged, remove it with a chisel and install the new bushing with a suitable driver

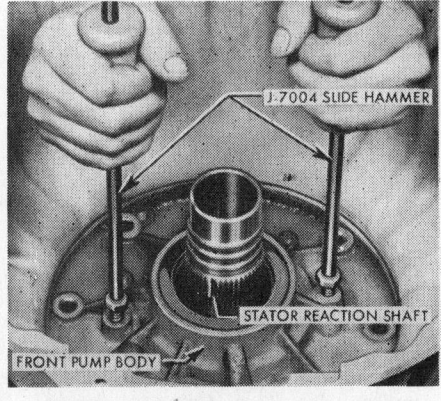

Fig. 41 Unfasten front pump from case and with slide hammers shown, remove front pump, stator reaction shaft and flange, and reverse clutch piston. Set assembly on bench and remove slide hammers

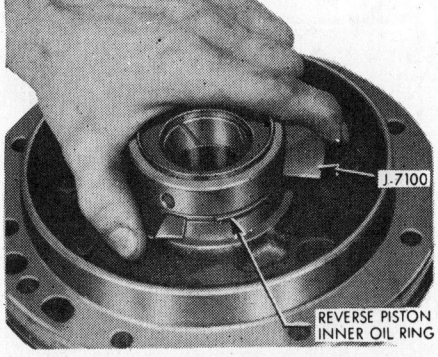

Fig. 44 Install new piston oil ring on reaction shaft. Assemble tool on ring so ring is forced solidly in groove and movable arm of tool contacts ring about 1/4" from end. Press in on tool arms to hook ends

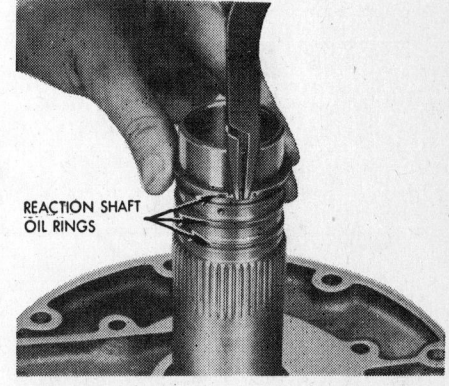

Fig. 47 Install three reaction shaft oil rings in groove. Rotate hooked ring in groove to check for burrs or dirt

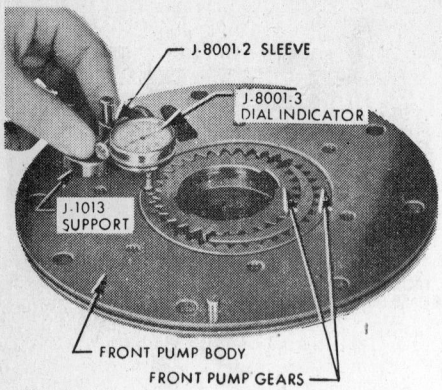

Fig 48 With equipment shown check front pump gear end clearance. Reading should be between .001" and .0025" below pump body

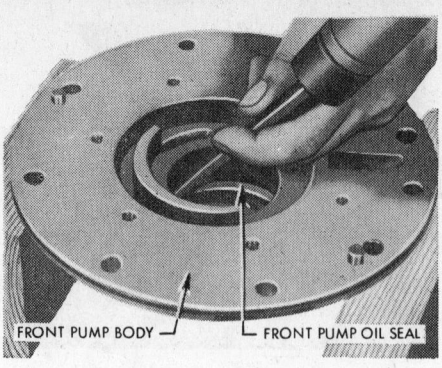

Fig. 51 Remove pump gears by lifting straight up. If pump seal is to be replaced at this time rather than with pump in transmission, support pump body and drive out seal with drift and hammer. If front pump bushing is badly worn or scored, complete front pump must be replaced

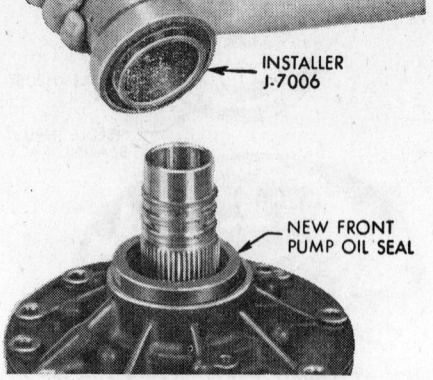

Fig. 54 Support assembly to protect needle bearings and drive in new pump seal

Fig. 49 Hold drive gear away from crescent and check gap between gear and crescent. A .009" feeler gauge should "go" and a .017" gauge should "not go". If clearance is not within these limits, replace pump

Fig. 52 Clean and oil pump gears and install in pump body. Drive gear is installed as shown and with counterbored side toward pump seal. If new front pump is being installed, check drive gear on converter hub for proper fit

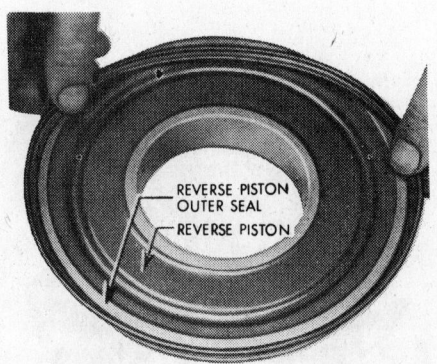

Fig. 55 Install new reverse piston seal with lip away from ribbed side of piston

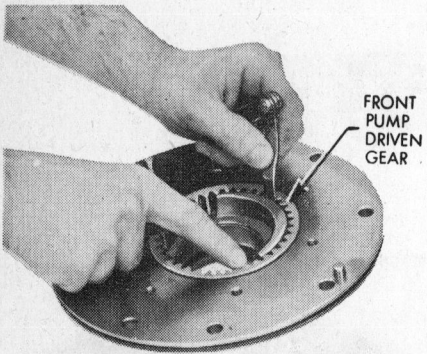

Fig. 50 Hold pump driven gear away from crescent and check gap between gear and crescent. A .004" feeler gauge should "go" and a .010" gauge should "not go". If clearance is not within these limits, replace pump

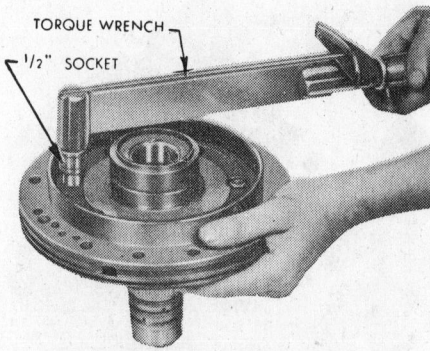

Fig. 53 Lubricate with automatic transmission oil and assemble front pump to reaction shaft flange, noting position of dowels and dowel holes. Install attaching screws and tighten alternately and evenly to a torque of 20-25 lb. ft.

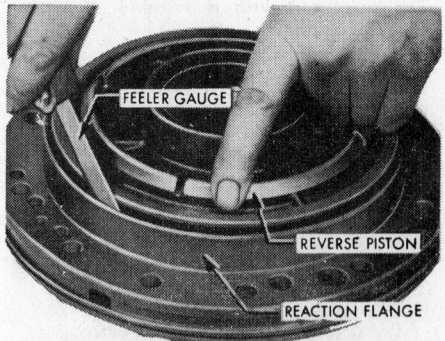

Fig. 56 Lubricate reverse piston seal and install piston in bore of reaction flange by running a smooth edged feeler gauge around piston to keep lip of seal down. Install new pump body-to-case sealing ring (see Fig. 45) squarely in groove of front pump body. If further work is to be done on transmission, set front pump aside, otherwise install it in case using a new gasket and guide pins

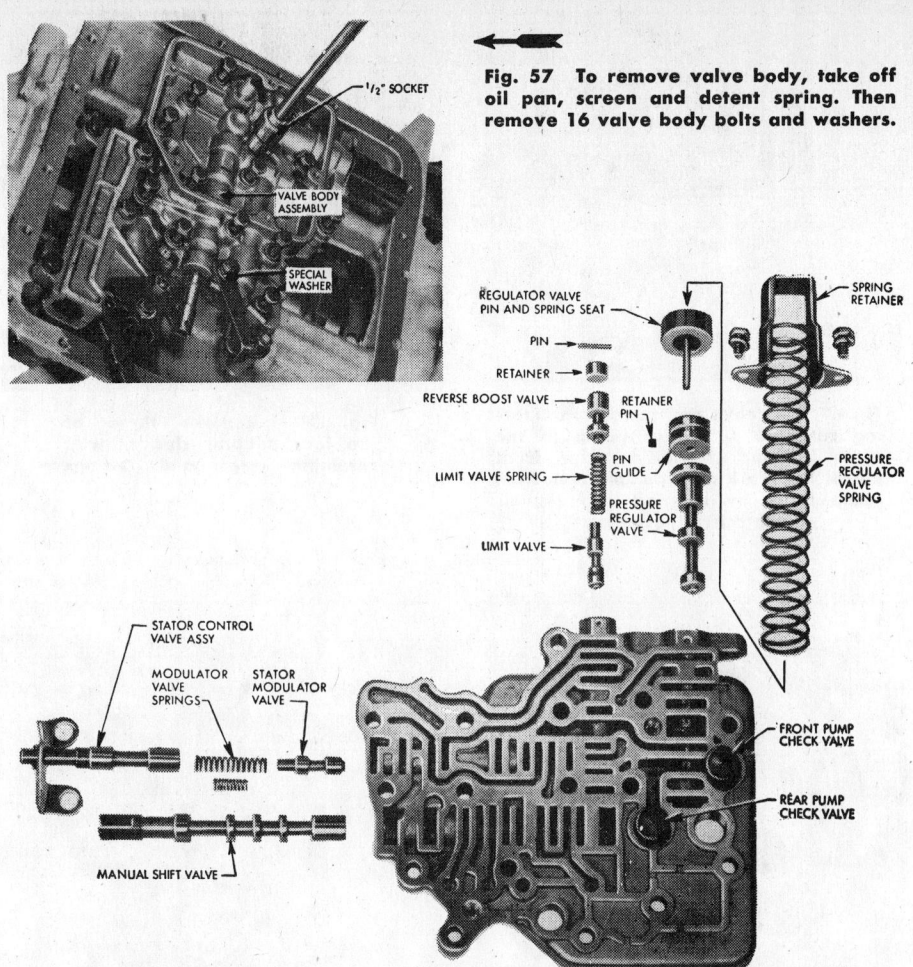

Fig. 57 To remove valve body, take off oil pan, screen and detent spring. Then remove 16 valve body bolts and washers.

Fig. 58 Use this illustration as a guide when disassembling and assembling valve body.

Fig. 61 Pour small quantity of solvent on each check valve. If valve leaks it is burred or worn and must be repaired or replaced. Set valve body aside if further work is to be done on transmission

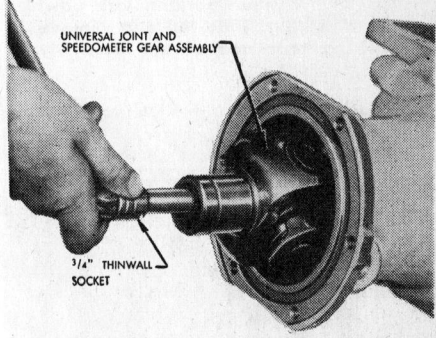

Fig. 62 To remove torque ball and universal joint, remove torque ball and sealing ring from outside of inner retainer. Engage parking lock pawl and remove U-joint bolt. Remove U-joint and speedometer gear

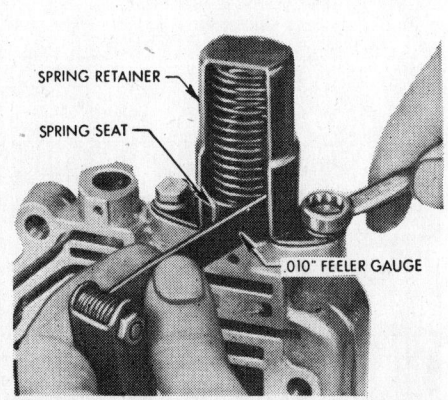

Fig. 59 Install pressure regulator valve spring and retainer. Before tightening retainer nuts, check clearance between spring seat and retainer with .010" feeler gauge. Spring seat must rotate and move in retainer without touching retainer

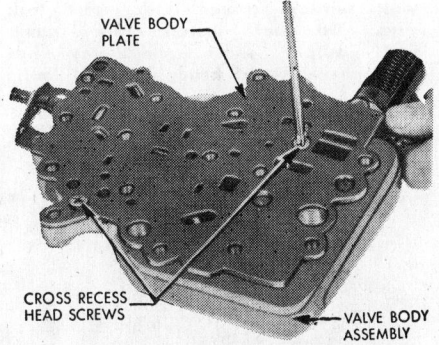

Fig. 60 Install check valves and springs with step sides of valves toward springs. Be certain that surface of valve body is free of dirt and has no burrs. Install new plate gasket. Be certain that pressure regulator valve pin guide retaining pin is in place. Install body plate with two cross recess head screws as shown. Be sure check valves are correctly positioned and operate freely during installation of body plate

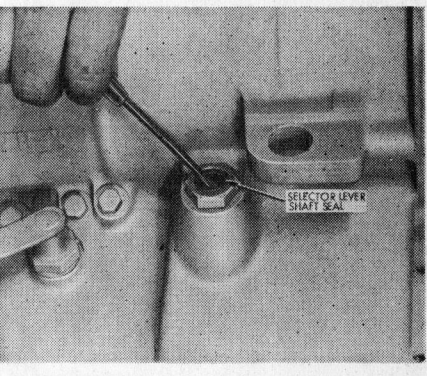

Fig. 63 Remove transmission selector lever and pry out lever shaft seal

See page 200

Fig. 66 Unfasten rear bearing retainer from case. Insert loading tool shown in end of output shaft to prevent spacer and shim from falling. Hold tool forward while sliding retainer and rear pump from case. Leave loading tool in retainer. If rear bearing or rear pump are not to be repaired, leave loading tool in place and set assembly aside

Fig. 64 Remove parking lock pawl return spring. Unfasten and remove parking lock and detent assembly

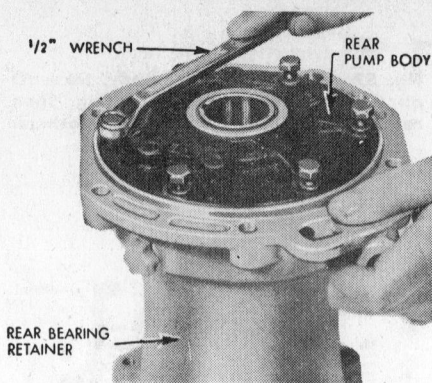

Fig. 67 Remove rear pump from bearing retainer. Service pump in the same manner as outlined for front pump. Separate rear pump cover from pump body by rapping two dowels with drift if necessary

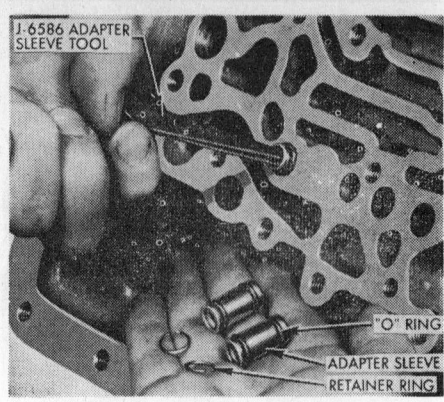

Fig. 70 Remove three of the four adapter sleeves with retaining rings and O-rings

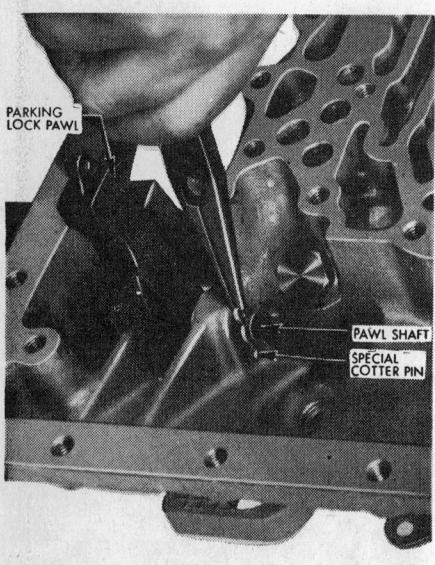

Fig. 65 If parking lock pawl or pawl shaft require replacement, follow instructions below; otherwise swing pawl out of the way. If necessary, remove spring pin from shaft, slide shaft rearward and remove pawl

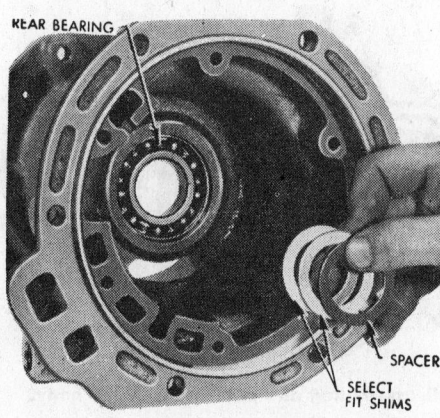

Fig. 68 Remove select fit shims and spacer from rear bearing retainer. If rear bearing requires replacement, pry out lock ring with screwdriver. Remove bearing by driving from front to rear. Install new bearing with suitable driver and insert lock ring. Do not install rear pump until output shaft end play has been checked and brought within limits

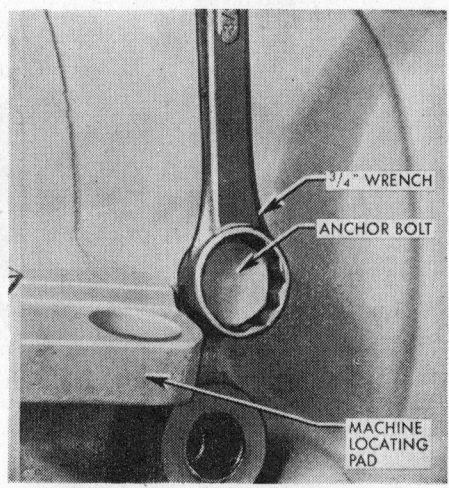

Fig. 71 Remove one of the two output shaft support anchor bolts forward to right rear machine locating pad (outside case)

Fig. 66 (see page 199)

Fig. 69 To remove output shaft, first remove rear oil pump drive pin

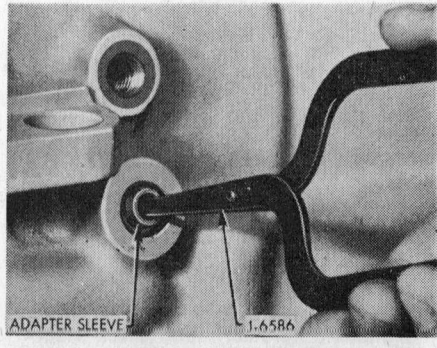

Fig. 72 Remove fourth adapter sleeve with O-rings at oil cooler return pipe location (no retaining ring)

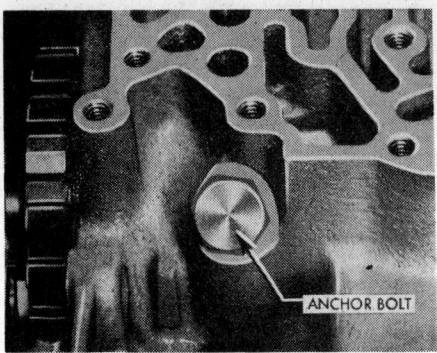

Fig. 73 Remove second output shaft support anchor bolt forward of ratchet wheel (inside case)

Fig. 76 Install suitable slide hammer in threaded end of output shaft and hammer sharply to dislodge internal parts. After assembly has been moved part way, remove slide hammer and lift assembly from case

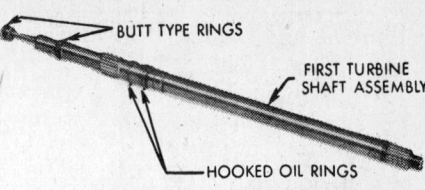

Fig. 80 If necessary install rings on first turbine shaft in positions shown

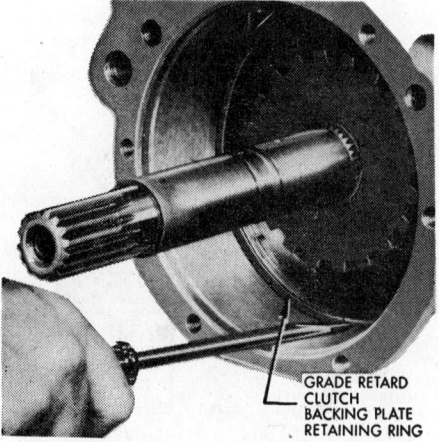

Fig. 74 Remove grade retard clutch backing plate retaining ring

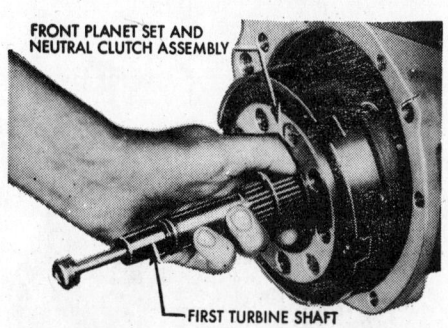

Fig. 77 Remove assembly shown. Remove needle thrust bearing and cupped race (these parts may have been removed with front pump). First turbine shaft may have been removed with output shaft

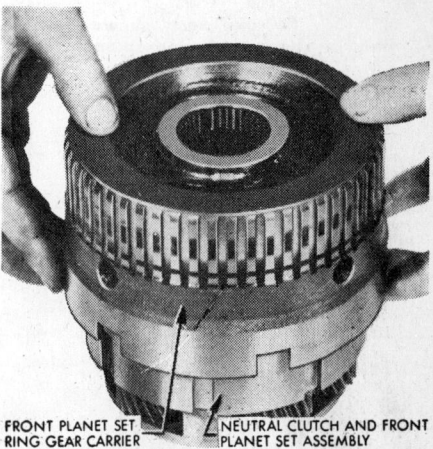

Fig. 81 Remove front planet set ring gear retaining ring, using a screwdriver to pry out of groove in carrier. Remove ring gear from carrier. Invert assembly and remove ring gear carrier

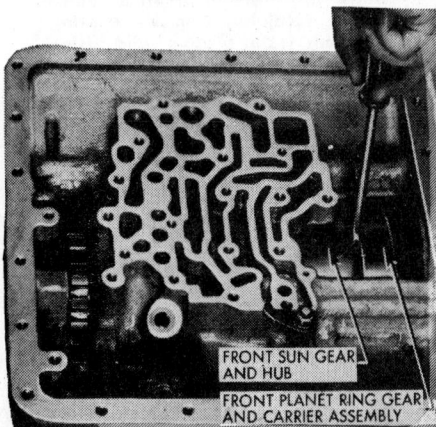

Fig. 75 To facilitate removal, carefully pry front sun gear and hub from front planetary ring gear and carrier

Fig. 79 Slide first turbine shaft rearward out of neutral clutch and front planet set if it was not removed with output shaft

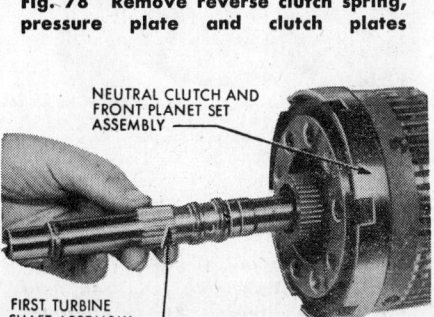

Fig. 78 Remove reverse clutch spring, pressure plate and clutch plates

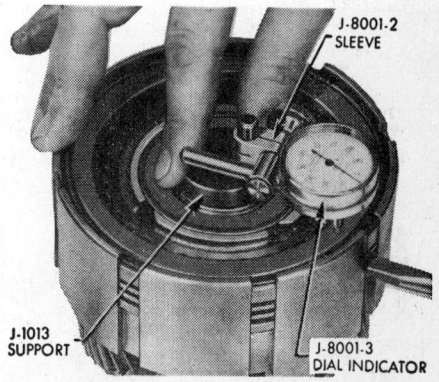

Fig. 82 Check clearance in neutral clutch pack with tools shown. Set dial indicator plunger on backing plate. Force plate pack down with fingers and note reading. Force plate pack up with screwdriver between neutral clutch spring snap ring and pressure plate and note clearance which should be .010" to .060"

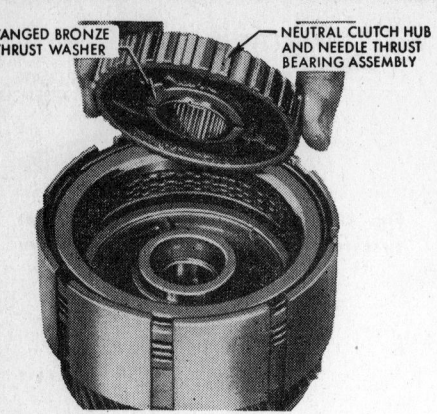

Fig. 83 Remove parts shown from neutral clutch and front planet set

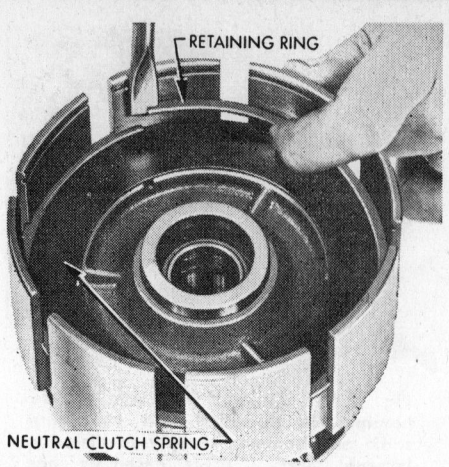

Fig. 86 Remove retaining ring and lift out neutral clutch spring

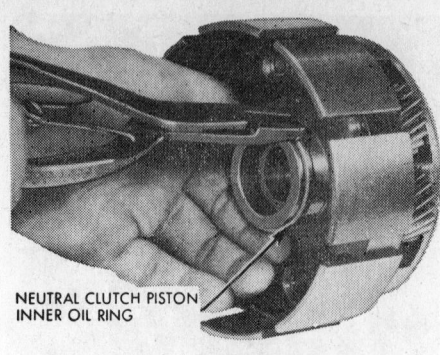

Fig. 89 If necessary to replace, remove old and install new piston inner oil ring. Install new piston sealing ring around outer diameter of piston with lip away from hub

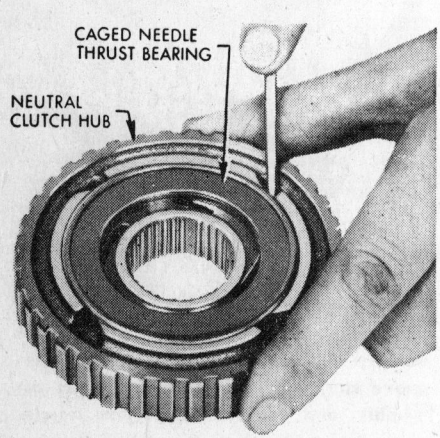

Fig. 84 If necessary to replace, pry out caged needle bearing. Install new bearing so that it is squarely in neutral clutch hub. Race must operate freely

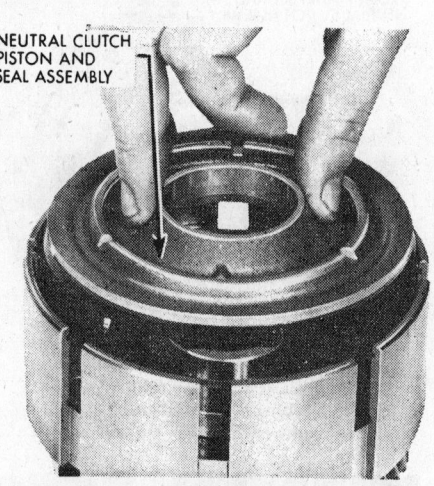

Fig. 87 Remove neutral clutch piston and seal. Remove rubber sealing ring from outer diameter of piston

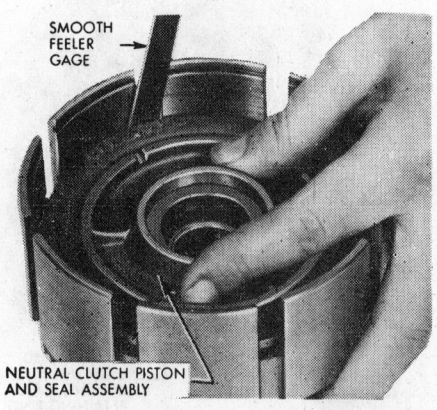

Fig. 90 Oil and install neutral clutch piston and seal in planet carrier, using a smooth feeler gauge to aid entry of seal lip. Install neutral clutch spring on top of piston with outer "high" edge up. Install neutral clutch spring retaining ring by starting one end into groove and using plastic hammer and drift to force remainder of ring in groove

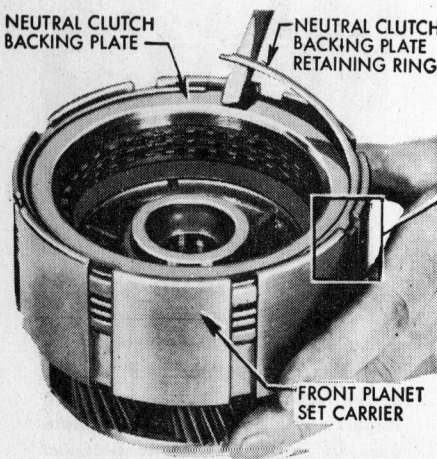

Fig. 85 Remove retaining ring and neutral clutch backing plate, clutch plates and pressure plate

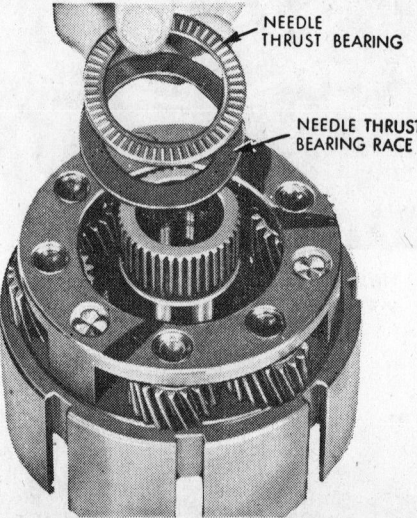

Fig. 88 Remove bearing and race shown. If stuck with oil, use two sharp awls inserted between planet pinion gears and under-edge of race

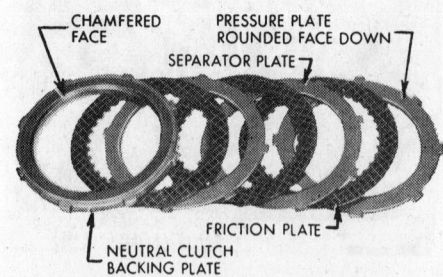

Fig. 91 Install clutch plate pack in sequence shown. Then, referring to Fig. 83, stick bronze thrust washer to hub and needle bearing assembly with heavy grease, line up grooves of friction plates and install hub in bore of carrier. Install neutral clutch retaining ring in groove of front planet carrier. Tap solidly into groove with drift. Assemble front planet set as shown in Fig. 81

FRONT PLANET SET RING GEAR RETAINING RING

Fig. 92 Mesh ring gear with planet gears and install in carrier with tangs up. Install ring gear retaining ring and tap into groove of ring gear carrier

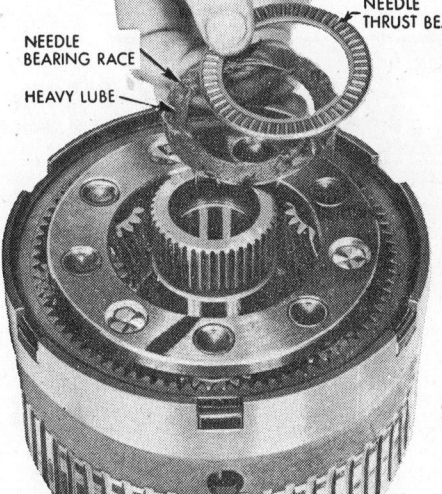

NEEDLE THRUST BEARING
NEEDLE BEARING RACE
HEAVY LUBE

Fig. 93 Apply heavy grease to needle bearing race and needle bearing. Insert race first, then bearing into bore of front planet set. Press down to seat. This bearing and race are smaller than bearings used in turbine build-up; see that they are not interchanged.

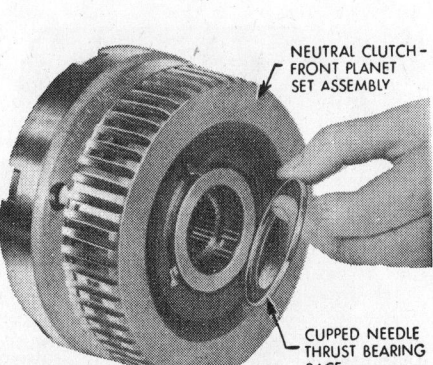

NEUTRAL CLUTCH – FRONT PLANET SET ASSEMBLY

CUPPED NEEDLE THRUST BEARING RACE

Fig. 94 Invert assembly and, after applying heavy grease to it, install cupped inner bearing race. Set this assembly aside

RETAINER
PARKING LOCK RACHET WHEEL

Fig. 95 Remove parking lock ratchet wheel retaining ring

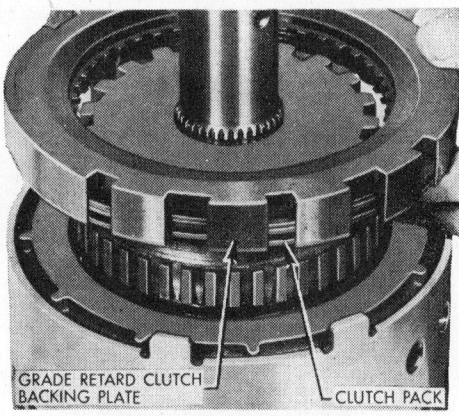

GRADE RETARD CLUTCH BACKING PLATE
CLUTCH PACK

Fig. 96 Slide grade retard clutch backing plate and clutch pack off clutch hub and output shaft

GRADE RETARD CLUTCH HUB
NEEDLE THRUST BEARING RACES
NEEDLE THRUST BEARING
PARKING LOCK RATCHET WHEEL

Fig. 97 Strip output shaft of parts shown

Fig. 101 Use same tools shown in Fig. 99 on side of support having four lugs and remove snap ring. Then remove parts shown. Remove old and install new rubber oil sealing ring from outer diameter tof grade retard piston

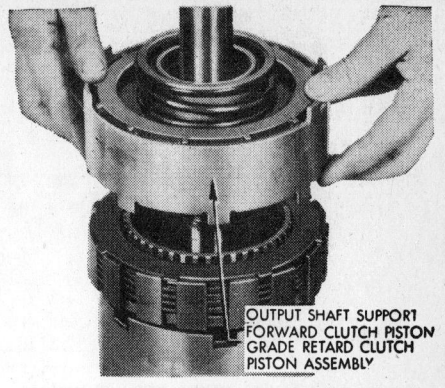

OUTPUT SHAFT SUPPORT
FORWARD CLUTCH PISTON
GRADE RETARD CLUTCH PISTON ASSEMBLY

Fig. 98 Slide assembly shown off output shaft

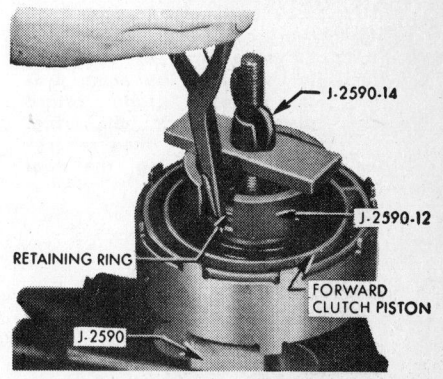

J-2590-14
J-2590-12
RETAINING RING
FORWARD CLUTCH PISTON
J-2590

Fig. 99 From side of output shaft support having eight lugs, remove forward clutch piston spring retainer ring

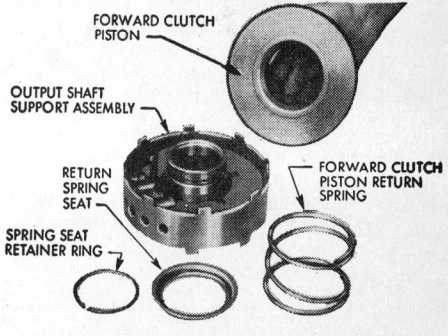

FORWARD CLUTCH PISTON
OUTPUT SHAFT SUPPORT ASSEMBLY
RETURN SPRING SEAT
SPRING SEAT RETAINER RING
FORWARD CLUTCH PISTON RETURN SPRING

Fig. 100 Remove tool and parts shown from support. Remove old and install a new rubber outer seal from piston

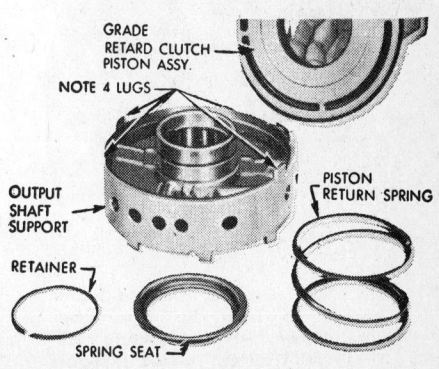

GRADE RETARD CLUTCH PISTON ASSY.
NOTE 4 LUGS
OUTPUT SHAFT SUPPORT
RETAINER
SPRING SEAT
PISTON RETURN SPRING

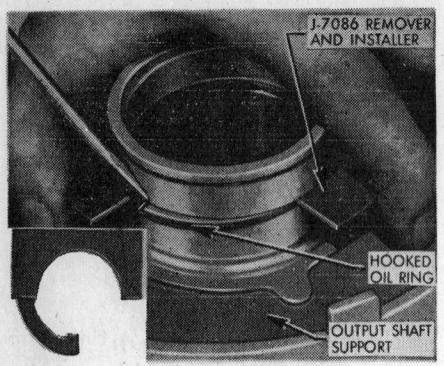

Fig. 102 If necessary, assemble tool shown so forward clutch inner oil ring is forced solidly into groove. Press down movable arm of tool and pry free end of hooked ring out with screwdriver. Release movable arm of tool and remove hooked ring. Use same procedure to remove grade retard clutch piston inner oil ring. Install the rings in the reverse order of removal, using the tool

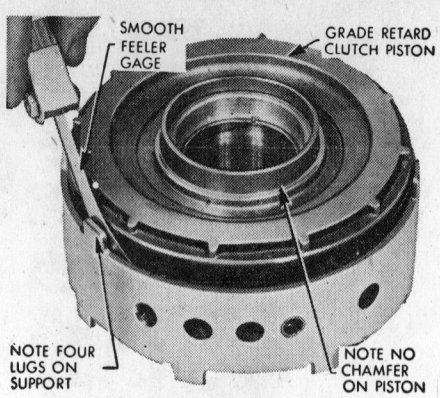

Fig. 105 Grease and use feeler gauge to hold lip of rubber ring down while inserting piston into output shaft support. Install forward clutch and grade retard piston inner snap rings with aid of tool shown in Fig. 99

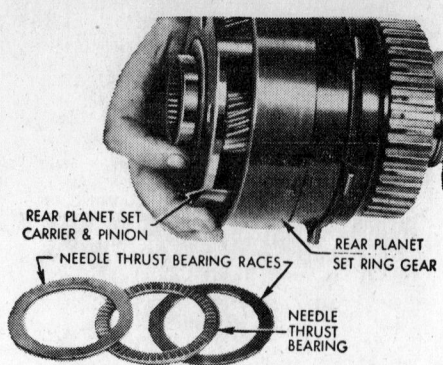

Fig. 108 Remove bearing and races from hub of carriers. Grasp and slide carrier and planet assembly out of rear planet set ring gear

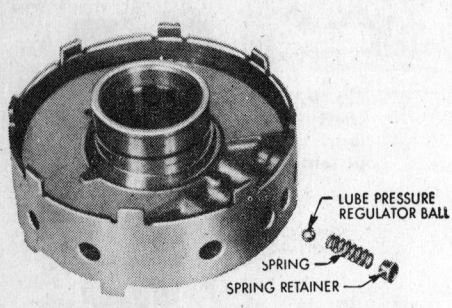

Fig. 103 Using hook made of stiff wire, pull out lube pressure regulator spring retainer, spring and ball. Using a plastic hammer, drive spring retainer in flush to .010" below surface of support

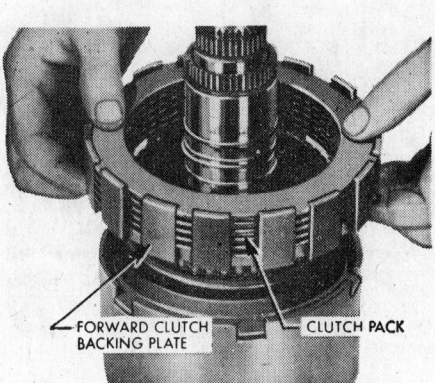

Fig. 106 Slide forward clutch backing plate and clutch pack off forward clutch hub and output shaft

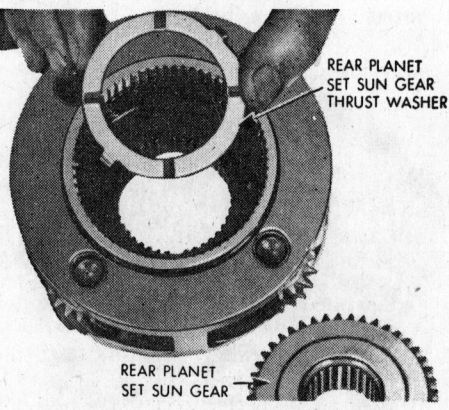

Fig. 109 Pry rear carrier thrust ring out of groove in carrier. Remove sun gear and thrust washer. Apply grease to thrust washer and position in carrier, tangs down, in holes in carrier. Install sun gear and rear planet carrier thrust ring

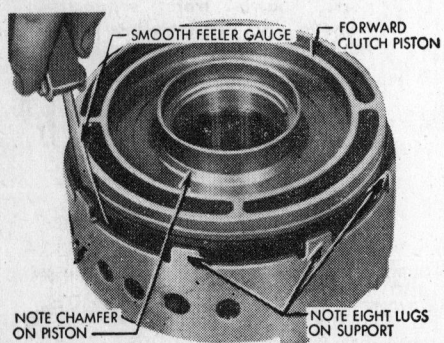

Fig. 104 Grease and use feeler gauge to hold lip or rubber ring down while inserting piston into output shaft support

Fig. 107 Separate front planet set sun gear and hub from tangs from front inner and outer free wheel race by prying with screwdriver. Remove sun gear and hub. If necessary, remove old and install new sun gear bushing

Fig. 110 Remove needle thrust bearing from front of output shaft (no separate bearing races used at this point)

Fig. 111 Slide output shaft forward through grade retard reaction shaft. Needle thrust bearing has no races. If necessary, remove old and install new output shaft bushing

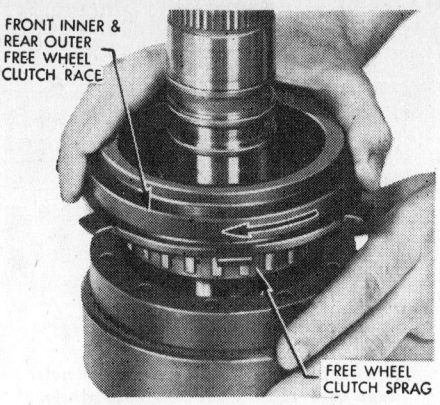

Fig. 114 Rotate clutch race clockwise and slide race and sprag out of rear planet ring gear. Remove and examine sprag. If necessary, remove old and install new clutch race bushing. Front free wheel sprag has an inner cage 1/32" longer than outer cage

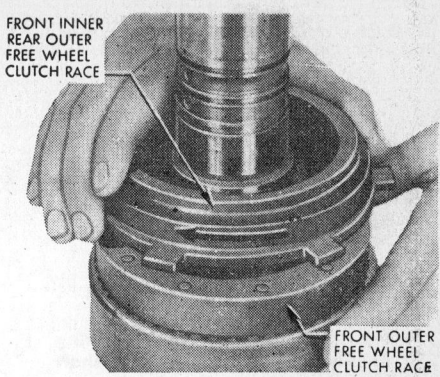

Fig. 117 Insert clutch race into sprag while rotating clockwise. Inner race must rotate freely on clockwise rotation and lock on counterclockwise rotation. When correctly installed, front inner free wheel race will be about 1/16" from front outer race. If this dimension is about 1/8", inner race is hanging up on bronze strip near bottom of sprag assembly. Insert rear free wheel clutch sprag into rear outer race with shoulder "up"

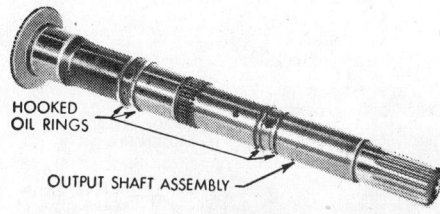

Fig. 112 If necessary, replace four hooked oil rings on shaft. Blow compressed air through rear end of output shaft to clean small oil bleed hole and screen. Apply heavy grease to needle bearing and place on output shaft

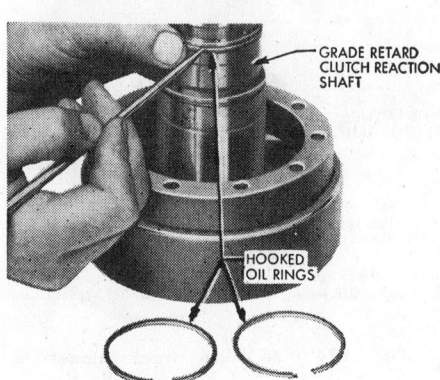

Fig. 115 If necessary, remove old and install three new oil rings on grade reaction shaft. If necessary, remove old and install new grade retard reaction shaft bushings

Fig. 118 Insert rear free wheel clutch inner race into sprag while rotating clockwise. Inner race must rotate freely on clockwise rotation and lock on counterclockwise rotation

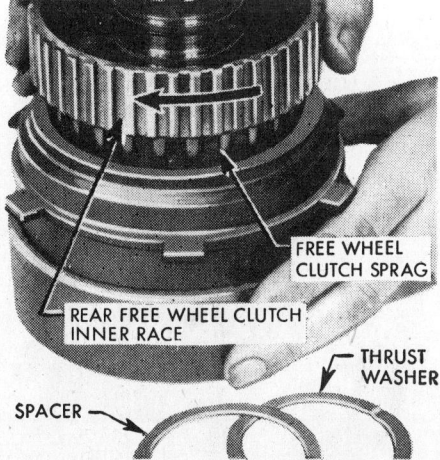

Fig. 113 Remove retaining ring and lift off rear free wheel clutch inner race thrust washer and spacer. Rotate race clockwise and slide sprag and race out of free wheel outer race. Remove and examine sprag. If necessary, remove old and install new free wheel inner race bushing

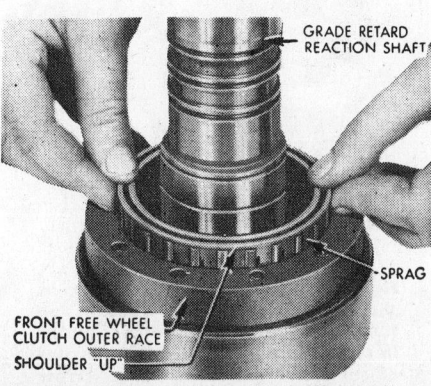

Fig. 116 Slip sprag into clutch race

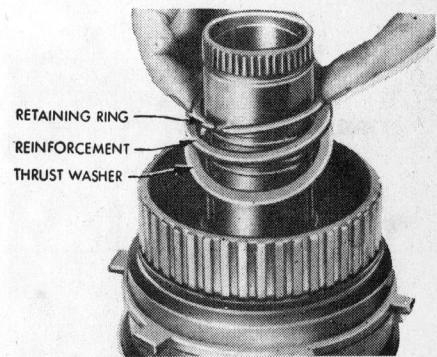

Fig. 119 Assemble new rear free wheel clutch inner race thrust washer first, then reinforcement and retaining ring on grade retard reaction shaft

Fig. 120 Install retaining ring solidly in groove in reaction shaft

Fig. 123 Install sun gear and hub over rear planet set and free wheel clutch. Do not lift assembly by end of output shaft as thrust washer, etc., may fall out of position. It is best to make this installation with assembly in horizontal position and it may be necessary to tap front sun gear and hub into position

Fig. 126 Grease and install support on output shaft, eight lugs down and four lugs toward end of output shaft. Engage eight lugs in wide slots of forward clutch backing plate

Fig. 121 Slide free wheel clutch assembly over output shaft with needle bearing thrust washer in place. Apply heavy grease to new output shaft-to-rear planet sun gear needle thrust bearing and set on forward end of output shaft (no races used here). Insert rear planet set and sun gear into rear planet ring gear

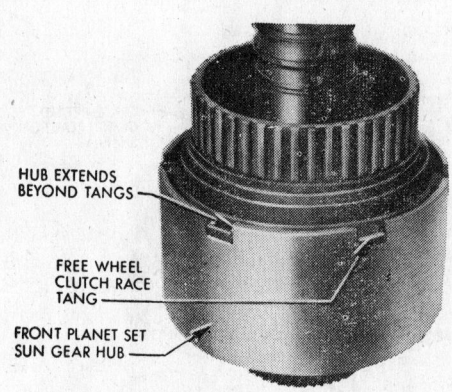

Fig. 124 Be sure front planet set sun gear and hub extends beyond tangs as shown. Tangs of front inner-rear outer race do not seat in bottom of slots of sun gear hub

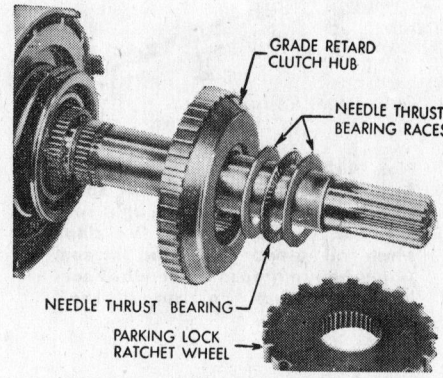

Fig. 127 Install needle bearing and races as shown

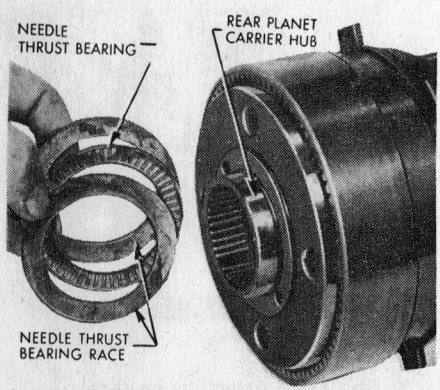

Fig. 122 Apply heavy grease to needle bearing and races and position on carrier hub

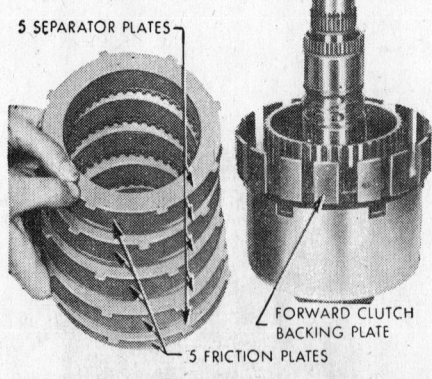

Fig. 125 Install backing plate as shown. Lubricate with transmission fluid and install clutch plates in sequence illustrated. Align notches of separator plates in same narrow slots of backing plate

Fig. 128 Slip on parking lock ratchet wheel and install retaining ring

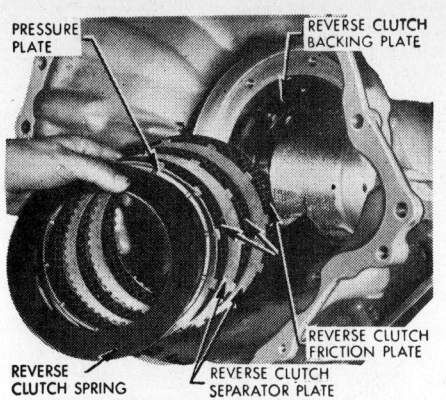

Fig. 129 With transmission front end up, lubricate and install reverse clutch plates as shown. Install pressure plate with rounded edge up, and install clutch spring with center high edge up. Separator plates must be dished same way

Fig. 131 With transmission upside down, apply heavy grease and install needle thrust bearing in cupped bearing race at rear of stator reaction shaft. Then install assembly shown into case, being sure cupped bearing race is in position on hub of front planet ring gear carrier

Fig. 134 Start input and output shaft into rear of transmission case (input shaft first). Guide first turbine shaft through neutral clutch. Push into case until assembly is in position shown. Check forward clutch backing plate to be certain that it is in contact with output shaft support. Be certain clutch plates are properly positioned in slots in backing plate and oil sleeve holes in support are up

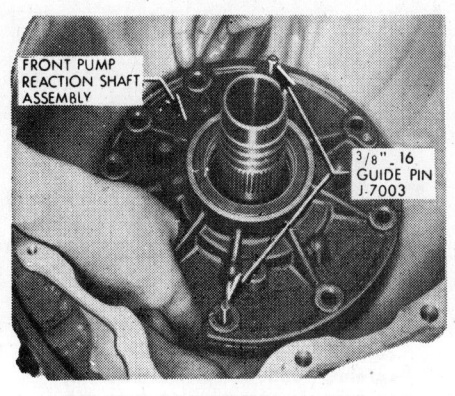

Fig. 130 Install front pump and reaction shaft as shown, tapping evenly and solidly into position before attempting to draw up attaching bolts. Install at least two front pump attaching bolts to check reverse clutch pack clearance. Check clearance between any two plates. Clearance should be .007" to .055". If more than .055", replace friction plates. Remove guide pins and install all front pump attaching bolts, tightening them to a torque of 30-35 lb. ft.

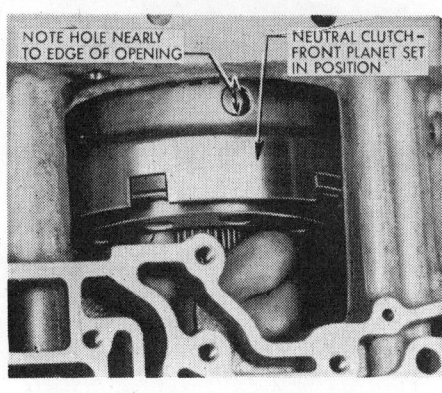

Fig. 132 , When installing neutral clutch into reverse clutch pack, rotate neutral clutch to line up splines and allow front planet ring gear carrier hub to seat against needle thrust bearing, which will be indicated when hole in front ring gear carrier will be nearly even with edge of opening in case

Fig. 135 Install grade retard clutch separator plate next to piston with center tang of three tangs between lugs of support, then friction plate, separator plate and so on, until three separator plates and three friction plates are installed. It makes no difference whether separator plates are installed with dish "in" or "out" but all must be installed the same way

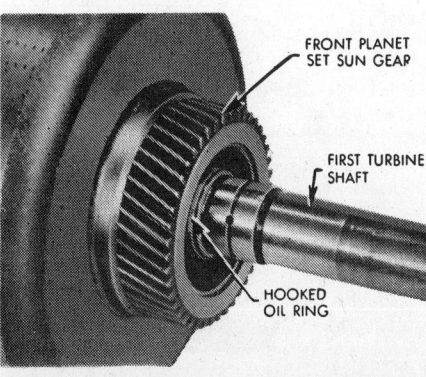

Fig. 133 If parking lock pawl and shaft were removed, install pawl, shaft and retaining pin. Insert first turbine shaft in output shaft until last oil ring is inside front planet sun gear

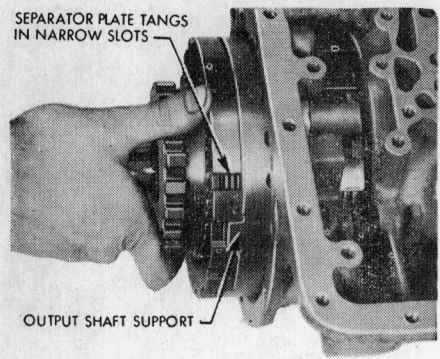

Fig. 136 Maintain hand pressure forward on grade retard clutch backing plate at all times until assembly is correctly positioned in case and backing plate retainer ring is installed. If backing plate is allowed to separate from support, clutch pack will fall out of position and complete assembly must be removed from case and reassembled. It may be necessary to rotate front planet ring gear or carrier with screwdriver to line up teeth on sun gear with pinions. Assembly is correctly positioned in case when grade retard backing plate retaining ring can be installed in groove in case

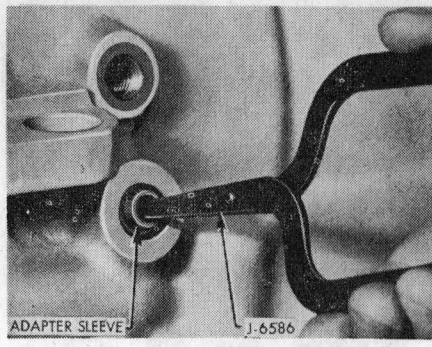

Fig. 138 Lube and install fourth adapter sleeve with new O-rings (no retainer ring used here). Install inner and outer anchor bolts and tighten to a torque of 35-40 lb. ft.

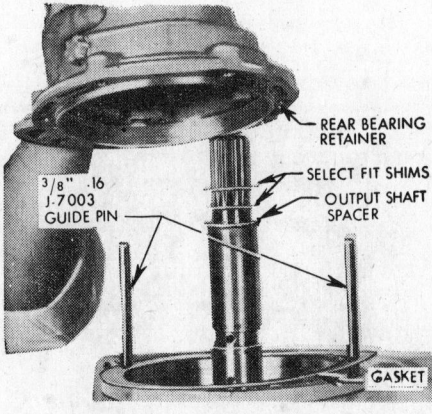

Fig. 139 Install rear pump drive pin in output shaft. If rear pump and loading tool were removed from rear bearing retainer, install .120" spacer on output shaft with shims removed from shaft when transmission was disassembled. Install two guide pins, gasket and rear bearing retainer without oil pump

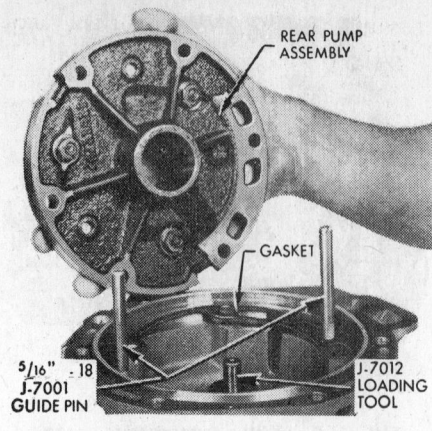

Fig. 141 When end play is within limits, remove rear bearing retainer and tools. Slip correct shims and spacers from output shaft onto loading tool with shim next to bearing. Install pump gasket in place. Install and tighten pump attaching bolts to a torque of 15-20 lb. ft.

Fig. 142 Assemble rear bearing retainer and oil pump assembly to case. If necessary to turn output shaft to line up with oil pump drive gear, turn parking lock ratchet wheel. Hold loading tool forward while sliding assembly onto output shaft to transfer spacer and shims onto shaft. Remove loading tool and torque alternately and evenly retainer bolts to 25-30 lb. ft.

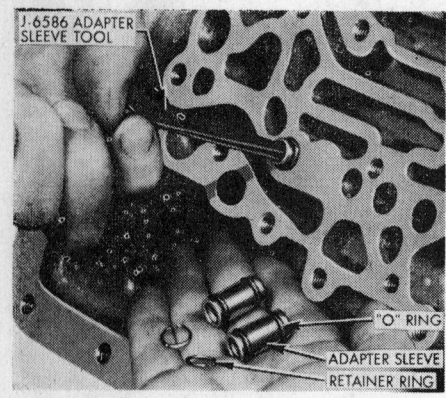

Fig. 137 Use punch inserted in anchor bolt hole to line up oil sleeve adapter holes in support with holes in case. Install three adapter sleeves into valve body portion of case. Push down firmly to seat sleeves in output shaft support. Install retainer rings above oil rings. Center sleeve does not enter case as far as other two

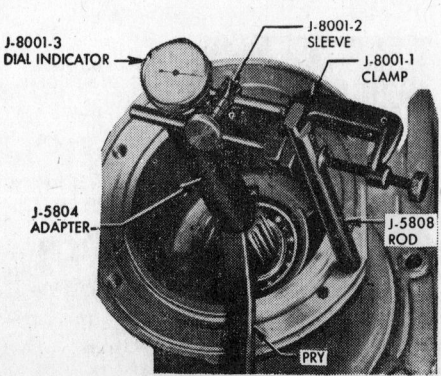

Fig. 140 Check output shaft end clearance with rear bearing retainer bolted to case with at least two bolts and transmission upside down. Tap output shaft several times to squeeze out grease used on thrust bearings during assembly. With tools mounted as shown, use pry bar under edge of adapter to move output shaft. If end clearance is less than .015" remove bearing retainer and install a thinner shim. If end clearance is more than .035", install a thicker shim

Fig. 143 Install parking lock mechanism and torque bolts to 15-20 lb. ft. Install parking lock pawl return spring

Fig. 146 Torque all valve body bolts to 15-20 lb. ft. in sequence shown except two bolts on stator stop. Check for free operation of shift control valve.

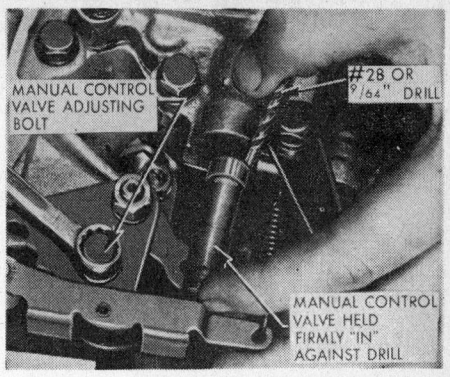

Fig. 148 With transmission in "Park" position (detent plate rotated rearward to last notch) loosen manual control valve adjusting bolt. Insert drill shown between inner edge of first land of manual valve and valve body. Hold valve "in" toward body with drill in position. At same time hold detent lever solidly in notch and tighten adjusting bolt in this position. With transmission in "Park" position, loosen parking lock adjusting screw. Insert .015" gauge between parking lock roller and slide cover. Turn eccentric screw to give .015" clearance between roller and slide cover. Hold screw in this position and tighten nut. This insures proper adjustment of parking lock pawl

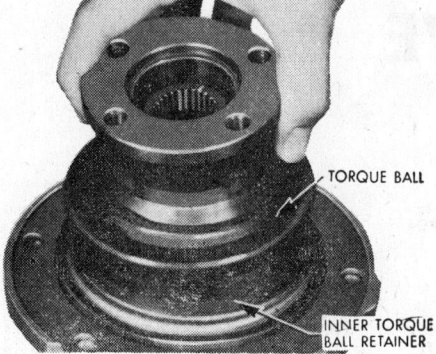

Fig. 144 Install universal joint, torque the bolt to 50-55 lb. ft. Install torque ball parts, positioning torque ball with drain slot down as transmission is installed in car

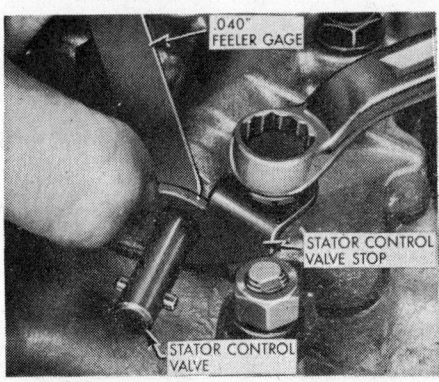

Fig. 147 Swing lever stop aside and slip .040" feeler gauge between valve body and stop. Press stator valve stop toward valve body and hold in this position by tightening forward bolt as shown. Position lever stop over stator control lever. Place .005" feeler gauge between end of stator valve and lever. Hold valve "out" and lever stop against lever. Tighten lever stop clamp bolt in this position. Install detent spring

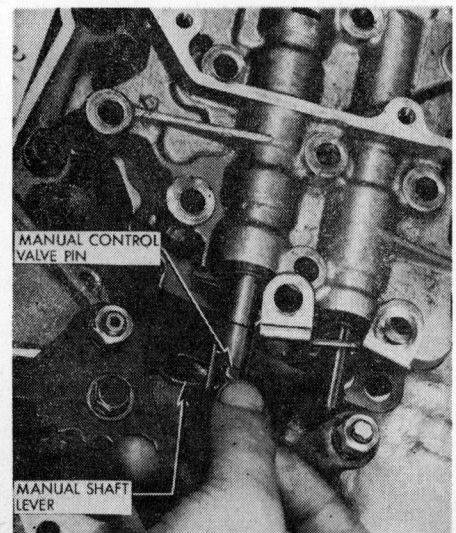

Fig. 145 Install valve body, being sure to engage slot in shift lever with slot and pin in manual control valve

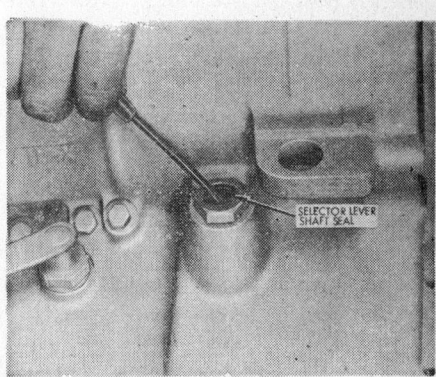

Fig. 149 Install oil screen and oil pan. Torque oil pan bolts to 10-12 lb. ft. Install selector shaft seal as shown, and selector lever

209

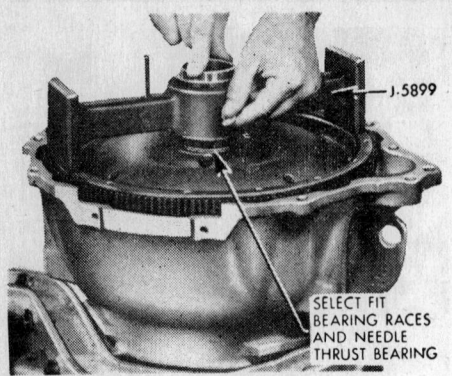

Fig. 150 Install converter components in reverse order of removal. Then set converter clearance gauge in place as shown with small diameter of sleeve up. Loosen set screw and push sleeve firmly down to seat and tighten set screw

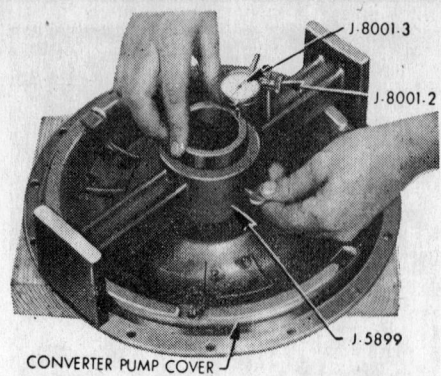

Fig. 151 Remove gauge from first turbine hub. Invert gauge and place on converter pump cover. Assemble dial indicator to post. Zero the gauge. Loosen set screw and push sleeve down. Reading on dial is total converter clearance. If clearance is less than .004" change select fit bearing races (Fig. 150) to a thinner size. If clearance is more than .017" change to thicker bearing races

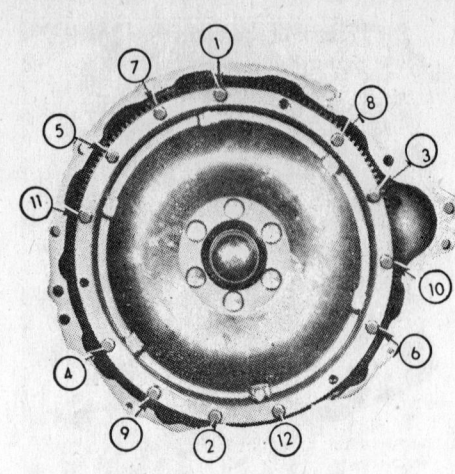

Fig. 152 Install new O-ring on outer diameter of converter pump cover. Install converter pump cover and torque the bolts in the sequence shown to 30-35 lb. ft.

DYNAFLOW DRIVE

Twin Turbine Types

For Linkage Adjustment See Buick Chapter

CONTENTS

Description 210
Trouble Shooting 16

Maintenance

Adding Fluid .211
Changing Fluid 211

"In Car" Repairs

Testing Oil Pressures 211
Bands, Adjust 212
Valve and Servos 212
Accumulators 214

Repairs Requiring Transmission Removal

Torque Converter 216
Front Oil Pump 222
Rear Oil Pump 227
Planetary Unit 226
Clutch 224
Rear Bearing Retainer 227
Assembling Transmission 228

DESCRIPTION

The complete transmission, Fig. 1, consists of a combination torque converter combined with an auxiliary gear box. The torque converter constitutes a complete automatic transmission within itself, the gear box being used solely for the purpose of providing a neutral position, a reverse gear, a parking brake and a rarely used emergency low gear. During all normal driving the gear box is inactive.

1953-54 Torque Converter

This torque converter, Fig. 2, has two turbines interconnected through a planetary gear set in place of the single turbine used formerly. Compared with the previous model, this twin turbine converter has one pump in place of the former primary and secondary pumps, one stator in place of the former primary and secondary stators, and consequently only one clutch (in stator) instead of the three used formerly.

1955 Torque Converter

The major feature of this torque converter is a stator with variable pitch blades, Fig. 3. The pump and second turbine are essentially the same as formerly except for the modifications necessary for the installation of the new stator. The new stator gives the equivalent of a passing gear with no gear change, and is accomplished by changing the angle (or pitch) of the stator blades.

1956-60 Torque Converter

The major change in this unit from the previous one is the incorporation of a second stator to improve the "take off" performance or acceleration at low car speeds. The oil channels have been modified so that low stator blade angle occurs in all ranges rather than drive range only.

Auxiliary Gear Box

The gear box consists primarily of a planetary gear set and multiple disc clutch. The clutch locks the planetary gears to give direct drive when the control lever is in Drive. In Neutral and Parking the free turning gears and disengaged clutch provide a condition in which the engine is disconnected from the propeller shaft.

Hydraulic Controls

Two oil pumps are used to provide oil circulation and pressure, and valves are used to regulate and control the oil

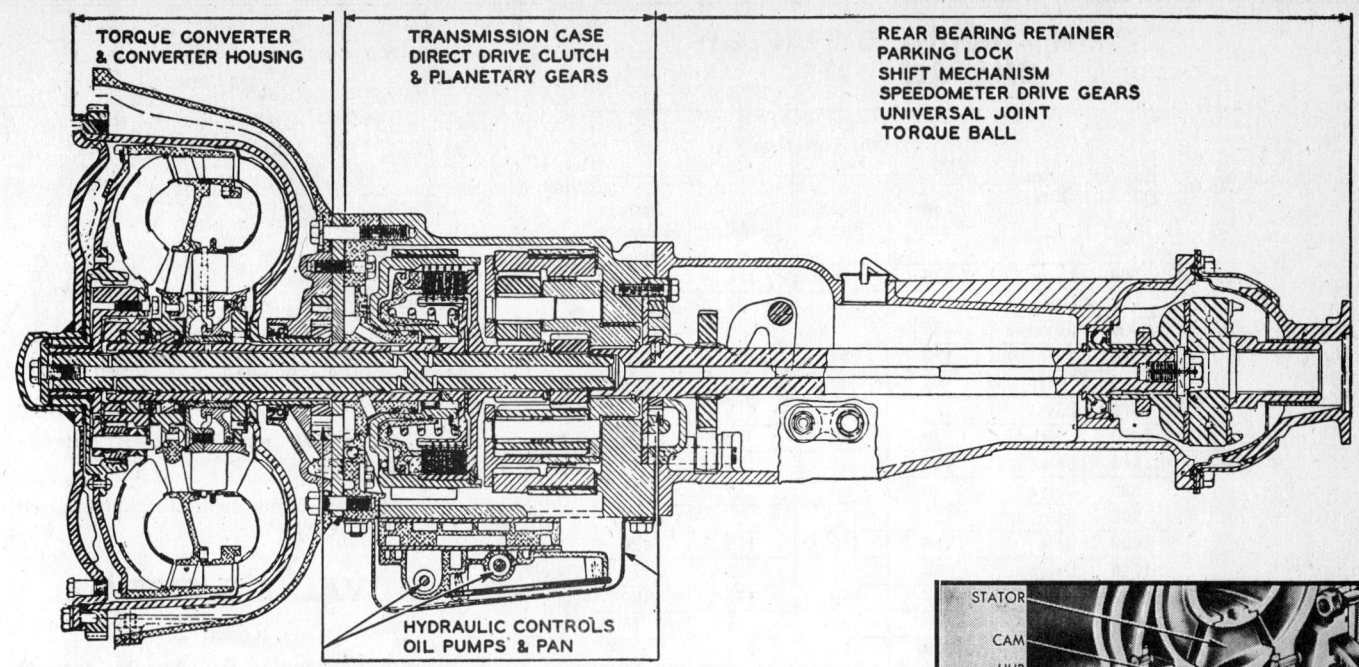

TORQUE CONVERTER & CONVERTER HOUSING

TRANSMISSION CASE
DIRECT DRIVE CLUTCH
& PLANETARY GEARS

REAR BEARING RETAINER
PARKING LOCK
SHIFT MECHANISM
SPEEDOMETER DRIVE GEARS
UNIVERSAL JOINT
TORQUE BALL

HYDRAULIC CONTROLS
OIL PUMPS & PAN

Fig. 1 Twin Turbine Dynaflow transmission, 1955-60

pressure. The hydraulic system performs the following functions: (1) Keeps torque converter filled with oil; (2) provides lubrication to all working parts; (3) applies clutch in direct drive; (4) applies low band in low range; (5) applies reverse band in reverse range.

For 1955-60 models, additional controls are used to change the angle of the stators when the transmission is in direct drive.

The transmission is provided with two accumulators. An accumulator is simply a surge chamber which cushions the application of hydraulic pressure (somewhat on the order of an hydraulic door check.) The high accumulator cushions the engagement of the multiple disc clutch for direct drive, whereas the low accumulator cushions the application of the low band.

MAINTENANCE

Adding Fluid

Check the oil level with the transmission oil warm, selector lever in Parking position and with engine idling. Remove the oil gauge rod, wipe dry and reinstall to its full depth. Remove gauge rod again and check oil level.

If the oil level is more than one inch below the "Full" mark on the gauge rod, add Automatic Transmission Fluid as required to bring the level up to (but not above) the "Full" mark. The distance between the "Full" mark and the "Add Oil" mark is one inch and represents approximately one pint.

Changing Fluid

1. Warm up transmission.
2. Remove bell housing cover.
3. Loosen one converter drain plug (through opening in flywheel.)
4. Turn flywheel until opposite drain plug is straight down.
5. Remove this plug and drain converter.
6. Remove drain plug from oil pan and drain transmission.
7. Put three quarts of oil in transmission.
8. With engine idling and transmission in Park position, complete the refilling to bring the oil level 1¾" below "Full" mark on gauge rod. When transmission oil is warmed up, the level should then be at the "Full" mark on the rod.

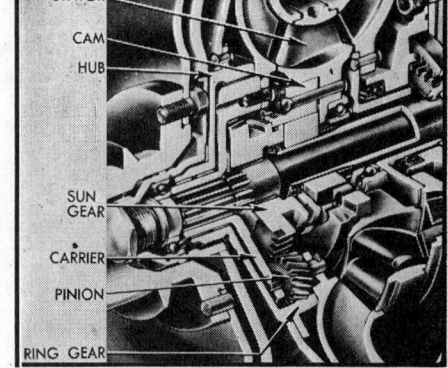

STATOR
CAM
HUB
SUN GEAR
CARRIER
PINION
RING GEAR

Fig. 2 Turbine planetary gears. 1953-54

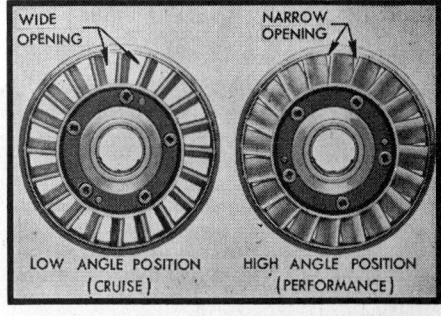

WIDE OPENING   NARROW OPENING

LOW ANGLE POSITION (CRUISE)   HIGH ANGLE POSITION (PERFORMANCE)

Fig. 3 Variable pitch stator. 1955-60

"In Car" Repairs

TESTING OIL PRESSURES

Before making any pressure tests oil level must be correct and the transmission warmed up to operating temperature.

With rear wheels raised from floor, run engine at 500 rpm and test pump and accumulator pressures in Low, Drive and Reverse, Fig. 4. Test front pump in all ranges and rear pump in all but Reverse. Test high accumulator only in Drive and low accumulator only in Low. Repeat tests at 1000 rpm in Low and Drive only. The pressures that should obtain are shown in the chart.

Low or erratic oil pressure indicates an air leak into the pump suction line, faulty pressure regulator valve operation, or excessive clearance in pump.

Low rear pump pressure also may be caused by a leak in the valve and servo body passages which connect the rear pump with the pressure regulator valve.

If pressure of one pump is low but pressure in other pump is satisfactory,

TWIN TURBINE DYNAFLOW OIL PRESSURES

Year	Engine R.P.M.	Trans. Range	Oil Pressures, Lbs.			
			Front Pump	Rear Pump	Accu-mulator	Stator Minimum
1953–55	500	Low	120	90	115	...
	500	Drive	90	90	80	70
	500	Reverse	120	...	...	...
	1000	Low	180	180	175	...
	1000	Drive	90	90	85	75
	1800	Low	180	180	175	...
	1800	Drive	90	90	85	75
1956	500	Low	120	90	115	10
	500	Drive	90	90	80	10
	500	Reverse	120	...	...	10
	1000	Low	180	180	175	20
	1000	Drive	90	90	85	70
	1800	Low	180	180	175	100
	1800	Drive	90	90	85	75
1957–59	500	Low	120	90	115	...
	500	Drive	90	90	80	10
	500	Reverse	120	...	...	...
	1000	Low	180	180	175	...
	1000	Drive	90	90	85	70
	1800	Low	180	180	175	...
	1800	Drive	90	90	85	75
1960–61	500	Low	120	...	115	...
	500	Drive	90	...	80	10
	500	Reverse	120	...	...	...
	1000	Low	180	...	175	...
	1000	Drive	90	...	85	70
	1800	Low	180	...	175	...
	1800	Drive	90	...	85	75

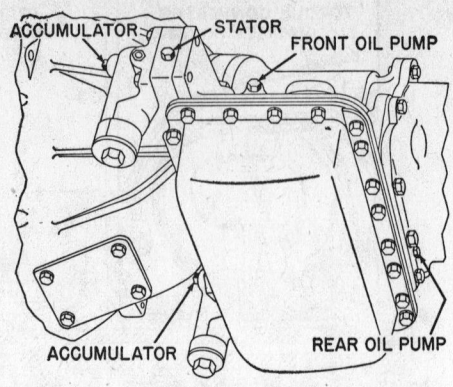

Fig. 4 Oil pressure take-off points

5. Install band adjusting covers with new gaskets.

VALVE & SERVOS

Removal

When removing the assembly from the transmission (after removing oil pan), slightly loosen all valve and servo body attaching screws but do not loosen the slotted safety nuts on the valve-to-servo body studs. Remove all screws, turning each a little at a time in succession until pressure of anchor pin spring is relieved.

Push shift control valve and lower operating lever inward to align lower lever with opening in transmission case. As the assembly is lifted from the case, reach under to hold the anchor piston to prevent it from falling out and getting damaged.

Remove reverse band operating strut by extending a finger through adjustment hole to prevent strut from falling into transmission case. Then release the strut by raising the operating lever.

air leaks into suction line and faulty pressure regulator valve are eliminated as possible causes since both pumps use a common suction line and the same valve regulates pressure of both pumps.

Very low accumulator pressure may be caused by external or internal leakage past the accumulator body gasket. A difference of more than 10 pounds pressure between front pump and an accumulator indicates an excessive leak between the accumulator and the clutch (if high accumulator pressure is low). The metering orifice in the accumulator may be restricted or plugged.

1955-61 Service Note

Because oil pressure for stator operation is taken from the clutch apply line at the high accumulator, front pump and high accumulator pressures should be checked before testing the stator pressure.

If when checking high accumulator pressure it is noticeably low, the cause may be in either the accumulator or stator circuits. To determine which is at fault, disconnect the stator operating rod at the high accumulator. Make certain the stator valve operating lever is properly positioned and tight on the stator valve operating crank, then raise the lever against the stop pin while noting the gauge reading. If gauge reading remains the same, the trouble is in the high accumulator and may be caused by external or internal leakage past the accumulator body gasket. A rise in accumulator pressure, with the lever against the stop pin, indicates a leak in the stator control circuit.

BANDS, ADJUST

The reverse band adjusting screw is located on the left side of the transmission and the low band on the right. To adjust, proceed as follows:

1. Loosen lock nut and turn adjusting screw clockwise until considerable resistance is felt, indicating that the band is in full contact with the low drum or reverse ring gear.
2. Back off the screw until just a trace of play can be felt by prying up on the lock nut with a screwdriver, Fig. 8.
3. Back off the screw 6 complete turns and tighten lock nut.
4. After noting position of adjusting screw slot, tighten lock nut 20-25 lb. ft. torque. Remove wrench and check to make sure adjusting screw did not turn during the tightening process.

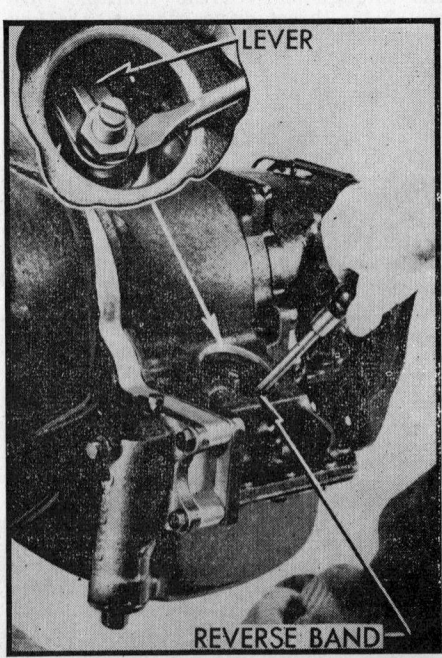

Fig. 8 Band adjustment

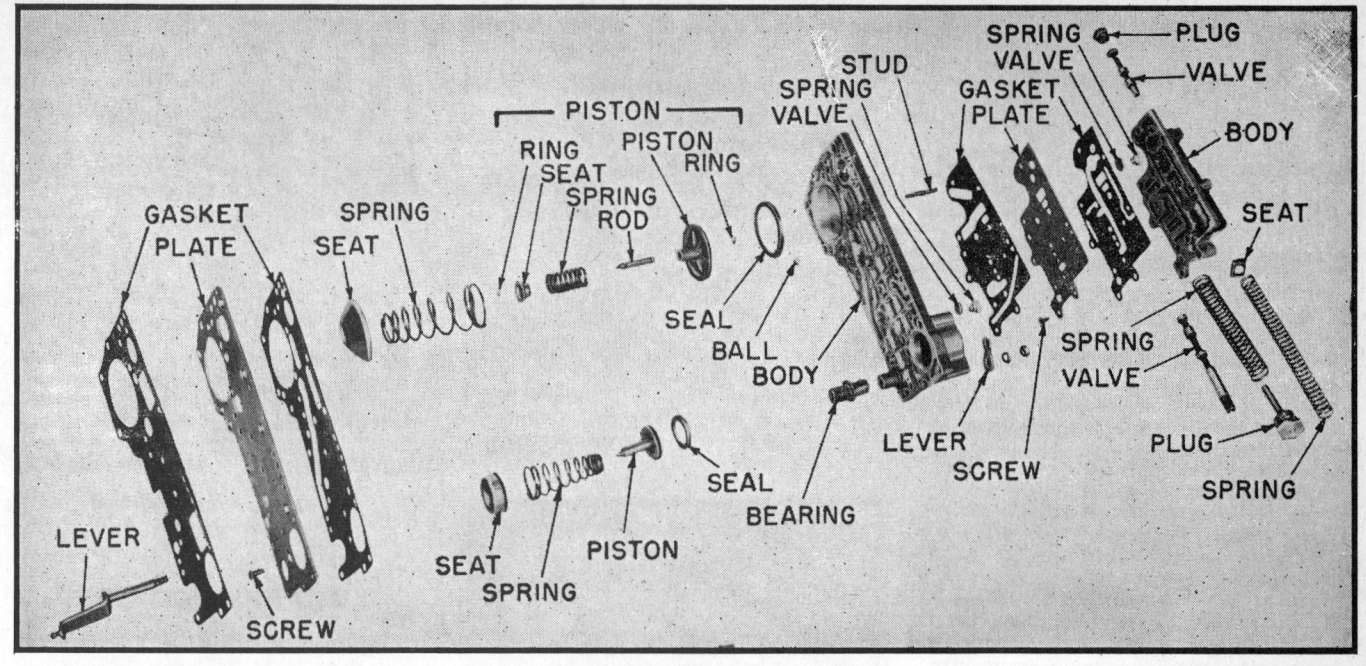

Fig. 10   Valve and servo body

Valve Body, Disassemble

1953-54, Fig. 10
1. Remove low band anchor piston, spring and shims from servo body.
2. Remove valve body from servo body.
3. Remove rear pump delivery check valve and spring from servo body.
4. Remove pressure regulator plug, two springs and spring seat.
5. Remove small valve plug and pressure regulator valve.
6. Remove valve body plate and gasket, front pump delivery check valve and spring.

1955-61, Fig. 11.
1. Remove safety nuts and washers from studs, then lift valve body and gasket from servo body. Remove shift control valve from valve body. Check gasket for evidence of oil leakage.
2. Remove rear pump delivery check valve and spring from servo body.
3. Remove large pressure regulator valve plug from valve body, using care because of the heavy spring pressure behind the plug. Remove the two springs and spring seat.
4. Remove the small valve plug and remove pressure regulator valve from body.
5. Remove valve body plate and gasket; then remove the front pump delivery check valve and spring. Check gasket for evidence of oil leakage.

Servo Body, Disassemble

Remove nut and washer which attaches the lower valve operating lever and linkage adjusting lever to lever shaft and remove levers.

When removing servo body spacer plate, use wood block as shown in Fig. 12. Hold block down firmly while removing spacer plate screws. Then carefully release pressure on block to allow servo springs to expand.

Inspect Valve & Servo Parts

1. Wash parts, dry and blow out all assages with air pressure.
2. Inspect bodies for cracks, damage to gasket surfaces, scores in piston and valve bores, or other damage which would render these parts unfit for use.
3. Inspect surfaces and shoulders of shift control valve, pressure regulator valve and anchor piston. Surfaces must be free of nicks, scores or deep scratches.
4. A valve or piston must be replaced if sharp edges are marred or rounded because such conditions will permit fine particles of foreign matter to work in between part and body and cause sticking.
5. Check valves on surface plate and replace if bent.
6. Worn or damaged piston seals should be replaced. When a new seal is installed on a piston, be sure the lip fits over the smaller diameter land, Fig. 13.

Servo Body, Assemble

1953-54, Fig. 10.
1. Oil and install low and reverse servo pistons in body. Start each piston at an angle and then straighten, being careful not to curl or damage edge of seal. Check pistons for freedom of movement in servo body.
2. Install anchor piston, spring and original shims in servo body.
3. Install smallest piston return spring with small end in groove in low servo piston. Install the two large return springs with large ends in grooves in reverse servo piston. Install spring

seats on upper ends of springs.
4. Install new spacer plate gasket and place spacer plate in position over spring seats. Install spacer plate screws with the aid of wooden block shown in Fig. 12. Tighten screws uniformly to avoid distorting spacer plate.
5. Check anchor piston to make sure that no interference exists between piston and spacer plate or gasket. If interference exists, slightly loosen all spacer plate screws and tap plate in required direction to provide clearance all around piston. Tighten spacer plate screws uniformly.
6. Using the "go" and "no go" ends of Anchor Piston Gauge J-2657, Fig. 14, and a narrow .010" feeler gauge, check distance from face of spacer plate and anchor piston as shown. Height of piston land is adjusted by installing or removing shims between spring and piston. If piston land is too high with all shims removed, grind off end of spring.
7. Insert valve operating lower lever shaft through bearing in servo body. With lower lever pointing to low servo body, install upper lever on shaft so that it points to reverse servo piston spring seat. Install lockwasher and nut and torque tighten 5-7 lbs. ft.

1955-61, Fig. 15.
1. Oil and install low and reverse piston assemblies in servo body. To avoid curling or damaging edge of piston seal, start each piston into cylinder at an angle then turn piston slightly as it is straightened and pushed into cylinder. Check pistons for free movement in cylinders.
2. Install small return spring with small end against low servo piston. Install large return spring with large end against reverse servo piston.

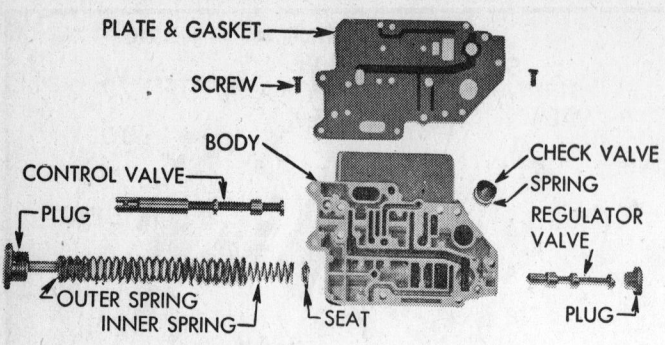

Fig. 11 Valve body disassembled. 1955-61

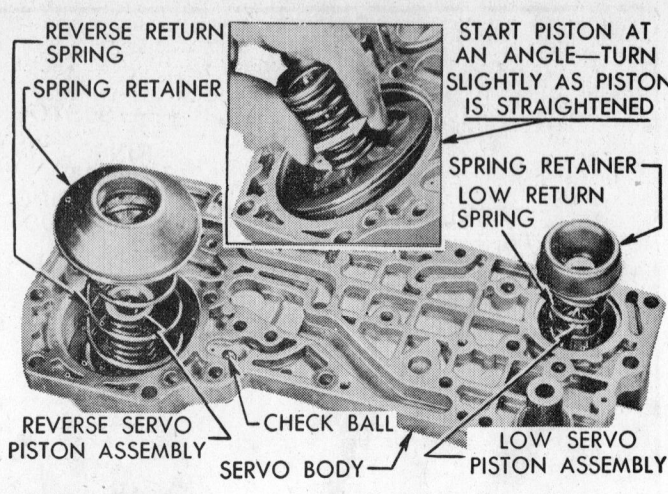

Fig. 15 Parts installed in servo body. 1955-61

Place spring seats on upper ends of both springs.
3. Place check ball in reverse servo feed channel.
4. Install spacer plate with the aid of the wood block shown in Fig. 12. Tighten screws uniformly to avoid distorting spacer plate.
5. Insert valve operating upper lever shaft through bearing in servo body. With upper lever pointing toward reverse servo, place lower lever with linkage adjusting lever on shaft so that forked end of lower lever points to the low servo; then install lock-washer and nut.

Valve Body, Assemble

1953-54, Fig. 10.

1. Place front pump delivery check valve spring in body with large end down and place check valve in spring with ridged side up.
2. Install valve body plate and a *new* gasket, making sure check valve is seated against plate and is not caught under gasket.
3. Place pressure regulator spring seat on inner spring, then install spring seat, inner and outer springs, and large plug in valve body. Torque tighten plug 20-25 lbs. ft.
4. See that oil orifice in pressure regulator valve end land is clear, then install valve with this land outward. Install plug and torque tighten 25-25 lbs. ft.
5. Install shift control valve with slotted end on same end of valve body as large pressure regulator plug.
6. Install rear pump delivery check valve in its seat in servo body, ridged face inward, and place valve spring on valve with large end up.
7. Install a *new* gasket and valve body

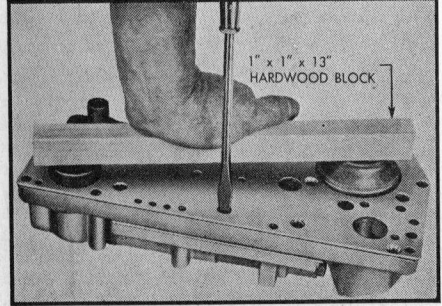

Fig. 12 Removing servo body spacer plate

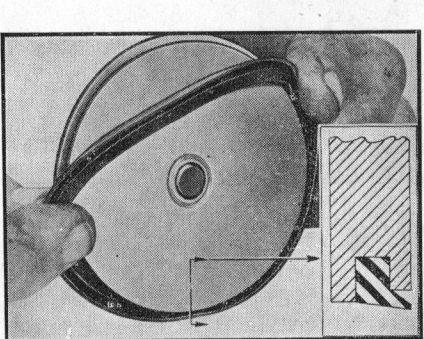

Fig. 13 Installation of servo piston seal

on servo body, using care to keep pump delivery check valve spring below the gasket. Then install plain washers and safety nuts on all studs. Torque tighten stud nuts 11-15 lbs. ft.

1955-61, Fig. 11.

1. Place front pump delivery check valve spring in body with large end down and place check valve on spring with ridged side up.
2. Install valve body plate and new gasket, making sure that check valve is seated against plate and is not caught under gasket.
3. Place pressure regulator spring seat on the inner spring; then install spring seat, inner and outer springs and large plug in valve body. Tighten plug to 20-25 lb. ft. torque.
4. See that oil orifice in pressure regulator valve end land is clear, then install valve with this land outward. Install plug and tighten to 20-25 lb. ft. torque.
5. Install shift control valve with slotted end on same end of valve body as the large pressure regulator plug.
6. Install rear pump delivery check valve in its seat in servo body, ridged face inward, and place valve spring on valve with large end up.
7. Install a new gasket and valve body on servo body, using care to keep pump delivery check valve spring below gasket; then install plain washers and safety nuts on two studs adjacent to control valve. Tighten stud nuts evenly to 11-15 lb. ft. torque.

ACCUMULATORS

1953-54

1. Remove cap, gasket, spring and piston from accumulator body, Fig. 16.
2. Remove pipe plug from top of accumulator body, depress dump valve with small screwdriver, Fig. 17, to relieve spring pressure on valve retaining pin and remove pin.
3. Wash accumulator parts in clean solvent, dry thoroughly and blow out all passages with air. Examine all parts for excessive wear, scoring or other damage.
4. Remove any nicks or burrs from pistons or valves with an Arkansas stone. *Do not round the sharp edges of lands on pistons and valves. If the sharp edges are marred or rounded, foreign particles may wedge between the part and body and cause sticking.*
5. With parts clean and dry, install pistons and valves and check for free sliding as body is tipped back and forth.
6. Check mounting surface of body with a straight edge. If surface is uneven it may be trued up by moving body in a circular motion over emery cloth placed on a surface

Fig. 14 Checking height of anchor piston land, 1953-54

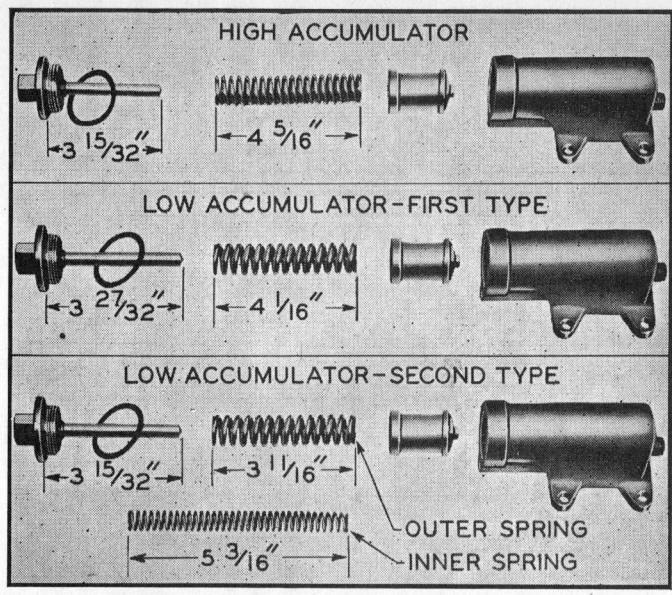

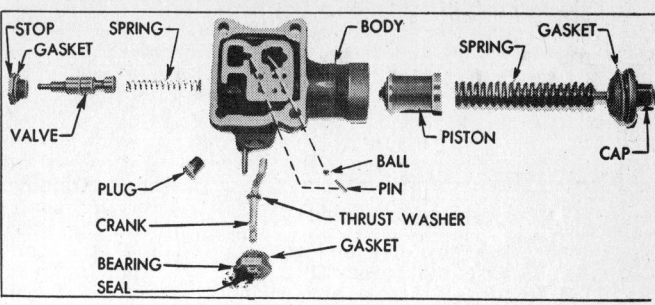

Fig. 18 High accumulator disassembled. 1955-61

Fig. 16 Accumulator caps, springs and pistons. 1953-54

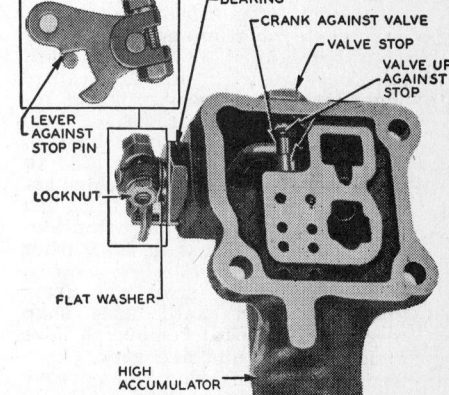

Fig. 19 Valve operating lever adjustment. 1955-61 high accumulator

plate. Remove all traces of emery.

7. If body, piston or valve is worn or damaged, or the parts do not slide freely after burrs are removed, it will be necessary to replace the accumulator assembly because pistons and valves are not furnished separately.

8. Assemble each accumulator, observing the following: (A) Lubricate dump valve and install with narrow land outward, Fig. 17. (B) Lubricate piston and start squarely into body with open end outward. *Do not tap or force piston into body.* (C) Install the correct spring and cap in each accumulator, checking dimensions shown in Fig. 16, and identification letter stamped on each cap. Use *new* cap gasket and tighten cap finger tight.

1955-61 Accumulators

1. Remove retaining pin and check valve from high accumulator body (no check ball on low accumulator).
2. Remove pipe plug, cap, gasket, spring (2 in low) and piston from accumulator body. Keep parts separated so same parts will be installed in same body, Fig. 18.
3. *On high accumulator only,* remove clamp bolt, lever, bearing with seal, gasket, thrust washer and conrol valve crank from body; then remove valve stop with gasket, control valve and spring.
4. Wash all parts, air dry and blow out all passages. Examine all parts for excessive wear, scoring or other damage.
5. With all parts clean and dry, install pistons and check for free sliding as body is tipped back and forth.
6. Check mounting surface of body with straightedge. If necessary, body may be trued up by moving body in a circular motion on emery cloth placed on a surface plate. Be sure to wash body to remove all traces of emery.
7. If body or piston is worn or damaged or piston does not slide freely in body after all burrs are removed, replace accumulator assembly.
8. Lubricate each piston and install it in body from which it was removed. Start piston squarely (do not tap or force) in body.
9. Install proper piston springs in each body. The high accumulator uses one heavy spring approximately 4 5/16" long. The low accumulator uses one shorter heavy spring and one inner spring. Install caps with new gaskets but tighten caps later.
10. On high accumulator only, install spring, control valve and stop; then install crank with thrust washer, bearing with new gasket and seal

(grooved side inward), operating lever and clamp bolt.

11. On 1957-61, adjust operating lever on crank so that lever contacts its stop and the crank contacts the valve with valve in extreme upper position, Fig. 19; then tighten clamp bolt. On 1955-56, adjust operating lever on crank so that lever contacts its stop and the crank contacts the valve without depressing the spring, Fig. 20; then tighten clamp bolt.
12. Install pipe plugs in both accumulator bodies and install check valve and retaining pin in high accumulator body.

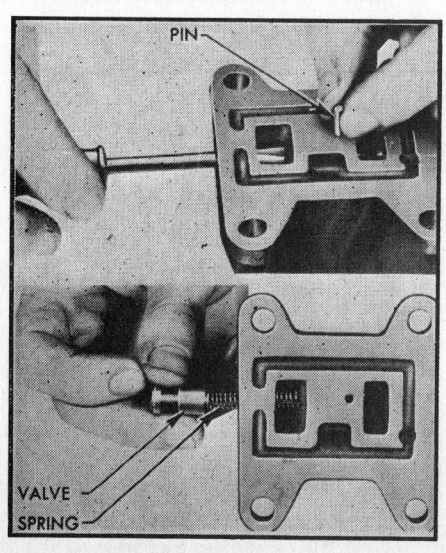

Fig. 17 Removing dump valve. 1953-54

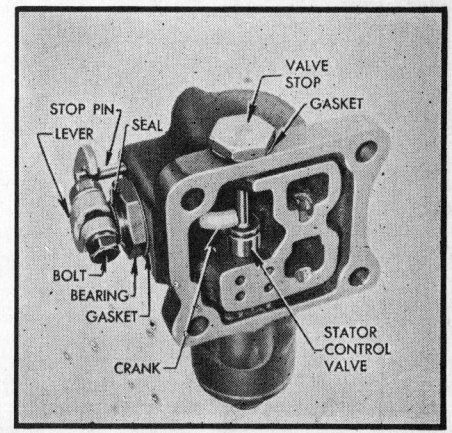

Fig. 20 High accumulator parts. 1955-56

Repairs Requiring Transmission Removal

1953-54 CONVERTER

Removal

1. Remove large hex plug and gasket from hub of pump cover. Then remove socket set screw and lockwasher located in hub.
2. Remove all nuts, plain washers and bolts attaching cover to pump. A punch inserted through bell housing hand hole into a drive bolt hole will hold pump from turning.
3. Remove cover from pump, tapping or prying against the edge to loosen it. Check the cover seal for damage or evidence of oil leakage before removing it from the cover.
4. Insert screwdriver into a hole in the first turbine disc, Fig. 23, to aid in removing the twin turbine assembly from the input shaft. Push inward on shaft to avoid withdrawing it. Remove bronze thrust washer from turbine hub.
5. Remove retaining snap ring from groove in input shaft, using snap ring pliers, then remove bronze thrust washer and sun gear.
6. Remove retaining ring from groove in reaction shaft and slide stator and free wheel roller race from reaction shaft. Remove stator bearing from reaction shaft if it did not come out with the stator.
7. Pull the converter pump forward from the reaction shaft and immediately check for evidence of oil leakage. Radial streaks of fresh oil on back of pump and fresh oil streaks on face of front oil pump body indicate leakage past the oil pump seal.

Disassembly of Converter

1. Pry disc retaining ring out of groove in first turbine, Fig. 24, insert screwdriver in a hole in the disc and lift the disc hub assembly out of the first turbine. Tap on center of second turbine to separate parts.
2. Lift second turbine and carrier assembly out of first turbine, Fig. 25.
3. Remove four turbine-to-carrier bolts and lockwashers. Then remove pinion pin lock plate.
4. With second turbine suitably supported, tap carrier free of counterbore in turbine, using hammer and a hardwood dowel or other soft punch, Fig. 26. *Do not drive against surface of thrust boss in carrier.*
5. Remove pins and planet pinions from turbine carrier, Fig. 27, then remove thrust washers and bearing rollers (22) from each pinion.
6. Remove ball bearing from rear side of converter stator, push free wheel roller race out of free wheel cam in front side of stator. Then remove all rollers, cups and springs from cam.
7. Pry pilot bearing retaining ring out of its groove in hub of pump cover. Then push pilot bearing and retainer out of hub.

Inspection of Converter Parts

1. Wash all parts in clean solvent and dry thoroughly.
2. Inspect all bearings, thrust washers, bushings and related bearing surfaces for excessive wear, scoring or other damage.
3. Inspect rear edge of first turbine hub (at ring gear) and the mating thrust surface on second turbine (around carrier) for wear, scoring or other damage.
4. Inspect all planetary gear teeth for wear or scoring.
5. Inspect converter pump hub for scores and for wear caused by the front oil pump seal and inspect the seal in oil pump for wear or damage.
6. Inspect free wheel roller springs for distortion and check rollers and race for nicks or burrs. Small nicks or burrs should be removed with an Arkansas stone and polished with crocus cloth.
7. Inspect vanes of converter pump, turbines and stator for damaged or cracked vanes.
8. Replace all worn or damaged parts.
9. If the stator is replaced, make certain that the new part is correct for the transmission.

Assembly of Converter

1. Place input shaft pilot bearing retainer in hub of converter pump

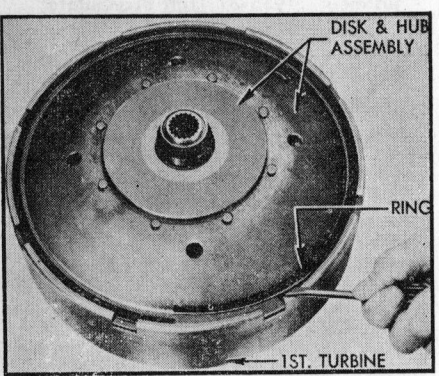

Fig. 24   Removing retaining ring. 1953-54

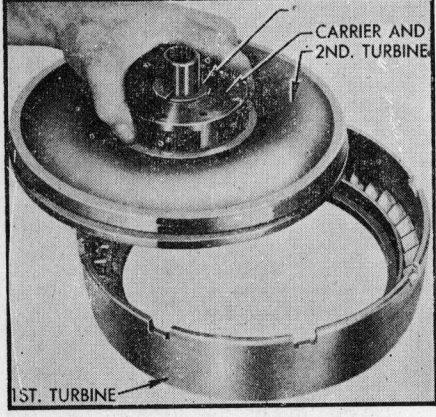

Fig. 25   Removing turbine and carrier assembly. 1953-54

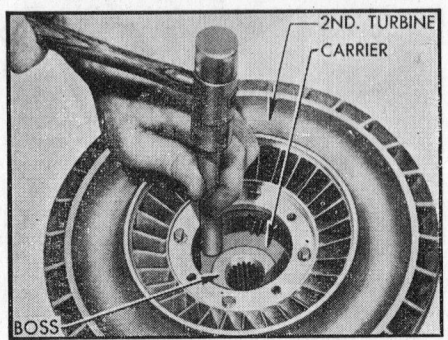

Fig. 26   Removing carrier from turbine. 1953-54

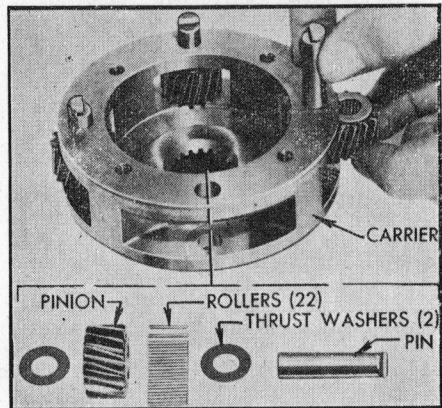

Fig. 27   Disassembling turbine carrier. 1953-54

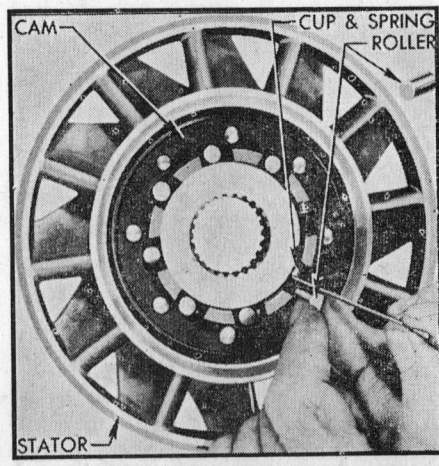

Fig. 28   Installing free wheel roller. 1953-54

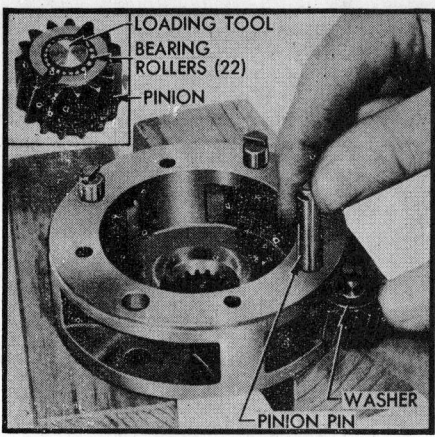

Fig. 29　Installing pinion in carrier.　1953-54

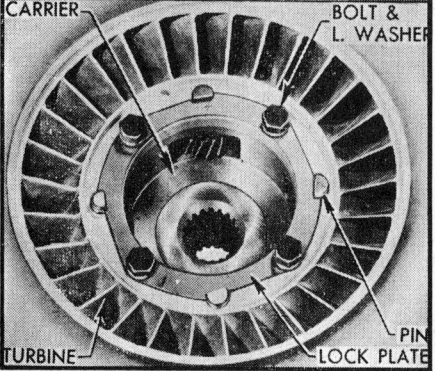

Fig. 30　Pinion pin lock plate installation.　1953-54

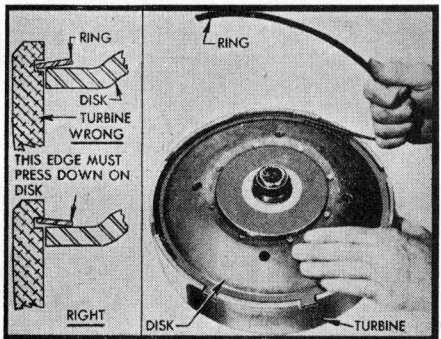

Fig. 31　Installing disc retaining ring.　1953-54

Fig. 32　Installing second turbine retaining ring.　1953-54

cover with shouldered side upward.

2. Push pilot bearing into hub of cover until its outer race bears against shoulder in hub.

3. Install retaining ring in groove in hub above bearing.

4. Install springs and cups and free wheel roller race in cam on front side of stator. Then use a suitable thin blade to depress the cup and spring while inserting each of the rollers, Fig. 28.

5. Install ball bearing in rear side of stator, using care to start it squarely into place. The bearing must be fully seated in the counterboard recess and the outer race must be free to turn.

6. Support turbine carrier on two wood blocks with hub side down. Then assemble and install four pinions as follows:

7. Place planet pinion on thrust washer, install 22 rollers in pinion and place a thrust washer on top of pinion Fig. 29. A loading tool can be made from a steel rod ⅜" in diameter by 1 1/16" long.

8. Place assembled pinion in carrier and install a pinion pin with notched end up. After loading tool is pushed out of carrier, slide a block under pinion pin to hold it in place. Turn all pins so that notches face center of carrier.

9. Make certain that counterbored recess in second turbine and mating surfaces of carrier are clean and free of burrs. Apply a film of oil to these surfaces and place the turbine in position so that carrier is squarely started into recess in turbine.

10. Use a hammer and hard wood dowel or other soft punch to tap turbine down over carrier. Avoid distortion of turbine by using light blows applied midway between holes and alternated from side to side to keep parts square with each other. If turbine cannot be assembled on carrier with moderate force, remove it and check for burrs in counterbored recess.

11. Install pinion pin lock plate, Fig. 30, so that it enters the notches of all pins. Then install the four turbine-to-carrier bolts with lockwashers.

12. Place second turbine and carrier assembly in first turbine. Then install the first turbine disc and hub assembly over second turbine.

13. Rotate disc until ring gear meshes with carrier pinions. Then align driving lugs on disc with notches in first turbine and push assembly all the way down into turbine.

14. Note that the turbine disc retaining ring, Fig. 31, is "dished". Place the ring in position with the "dish" upward so that the inner edge will bear firmly against the disc when the ring is engaged in the groove in first turbine.

15. Start one end of ring into groove in turbine. Then twist the ring upward as shown in Fig. 31 to lay the ring flat on the disc so that it can be progressively entered into the groove all the way around.

16. Make certain that the ring is fully

Fig. 33　Special tools used to set dial indicator at zero by means of indicator extension.　1953-54

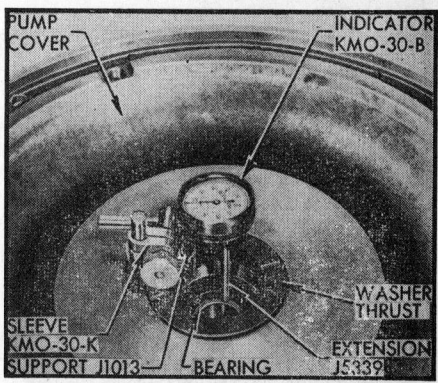

Fig. 34　With dial indicator zeroed as shown in Fig. 33, mount indicator on pump cover as shown to determine correct size thrust washer to use

entered in the groove and that inner edge bears against the turbine disc. Tap inner edge down against disc if it has raised up.

Installation of Converter Units

1. Install converter pump on reaction shaft, turning it until lugs on pump hub enter slots in front oil pump driving gear.

2. Make sure that ball bearing is properly seated in converter stator, then install this unit on reaction shaft. Push against roller race to keep it from sliding out of place.

3. Install stator retaining ring with tang pointing outward, making sure that ring is fully seated in groove in reaction shaft.

4. Install sun gear on input shaft and mesh it with free wheel cam in stator. Then install bronze thrust washer on shaft.

5. Use the tools shown in Fig. 32 to push the second turbine retaining ring over the expander and shaft until it seats in groove in shaft.

6. Support the twin turbine assembly so that all weight rests on a block placed under the center of the second turbine.

7. Mount the tools shown in Fig. 33 on the turbine and adjust the dial indicator extension to obtain zero reading on dial.

8. Then remove tools and indicator without disturbing extension. Support pump cover in horizontal position and lightly tap the input shaft

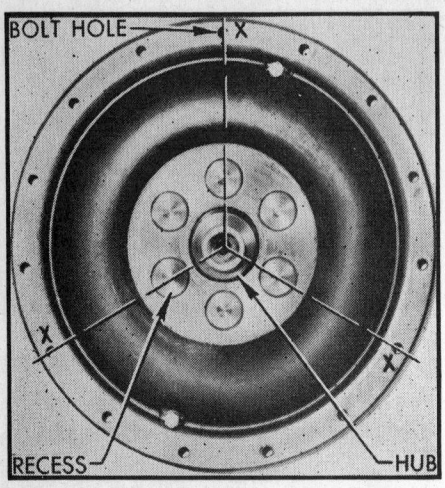

Fig. 35   X marks location of driving bolt holes on pump cover.   1953-54

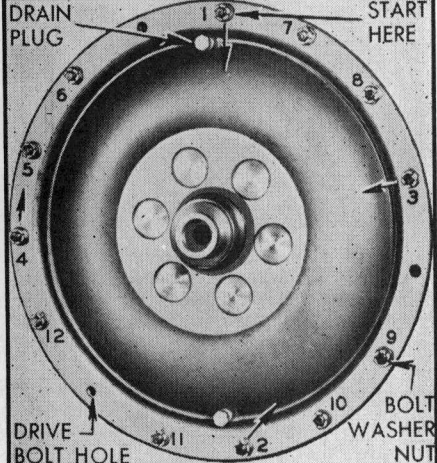

Fig. 36   Pump cover bolt tightening sequence. 1953-54

pilot bearing down against shoulder in hub of cover.

9. Place a bronze thrust washer in recess at center of pump cover. Then set the dial indicator support firmly on washer, Fig. 34, so that indicator plunger extension bears against inner race of pilot bearing. The reading should be .002″ to .010″ clockwise on dial or on minus side from zero reading set on turbine. If reading is not within these limits, select another washer of proper thickness to obtain the specified reading. Three thicknesses of washers are available, marked 5, 6 and 7 with 5 being the thinnest and 7 the thickest.

10. When correct thrust washer is selected, place the turbine assembly on the input shaft, turning it as required to mesh the planet pinions with the sun gear.

11. Looking at the front face of the pump cover, select the three bolt holes (X), Fig. 35, that are aligned with the center of the hub and one of the counterbored recesses adjacent to hub. Mark these holes for later installation of the flywheel-to-pump driving bolts.

12. Install a new O-ring seal on pump cover, making sure that surfaces are clean and that seal has even tension all around and is not twisted.

13. Grease the selected thrust washer so it will adhere and place it in recess in cover. Then install cover on pump so that the three marked driving bolt holes are *not aligned with any hole* at pump rim at which a balance weight is located.

14. Install bolts with plain washers and special nuts in all but the three driving bolt holes, but do not tighten.

15. Insert the shank of a $\frac{11}{32}$″ drill through one bolt hole to align all holes.   Then tighten bolts to approximately 5 lbs. ft. torque in numerical sequence shown in Fig. 36. Finally tighten bolts in same sequence to 25-30 lbs. ft. torque. When tightening bolts, insert a wide screwdriver blade between flat side of bolt head and pump to prevent a corner of bolt from digging into pump casting.

16. Screw socket set screw with lockwasher into the input shaft through opening in pump cover hub.

17. Remove reverse band adjustment cover and shift into "Parking". Pry up on reverse band operating lever, Fig. 37, to lock the input shaft while tightening the set screw to 25-30 lbs. ft. torque.

1955-61 CONVERTER

Removal of Converter

This operation is not required for removal of valve and servo body, universal joint or rear bearing retainer.

1. Remove both drain plugs from converter pump cover and drain any oil remaining in converter.

2. Detach cover from converter pump. A punch inserted through bell housing hand hole into a drive bolt hole will hold pump from turning. Check cover seal for damage or evidence of oil leak before removing it from cover.

3. Remove reverse band adjustment cover and shift transmission into "Parking". Pry up on reverse band operating lever with screw driver to lock input shaft, then remove bolt, washers and thrust washer from hub of turbine and input shaft.

4. Remove Twin Turbine assembly. A screw driver inserted into a hole in the first turbine disc will aid in removal.

5. Before removing sun gear on 1955 units, check to see if sun gear free wheels when rotated clockwise (facing converter) and locks on shaft when attempt is made to rotate it counterclockwise, then slide sun gear off shaft.

6. Pull stator slowly forward on reaction shaft. Then with stator installing tool J-5806 in position shown in Fig. 38, reach behind stator and hold thrust washer, spacer, rollers and springs in position while sliding stator forward off reaction shaft and on special tool.

7. Pull converter pump forward from

Fig. 37   Pry up reverse band operating lever to lock input shaft while tightening input shaft set screw.   1953-54

Fig. 38   Removing stator.   1955-59

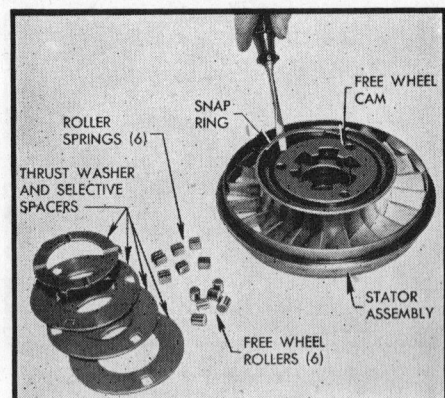

Fig. 39   Removing stator free wheel cam.   1955

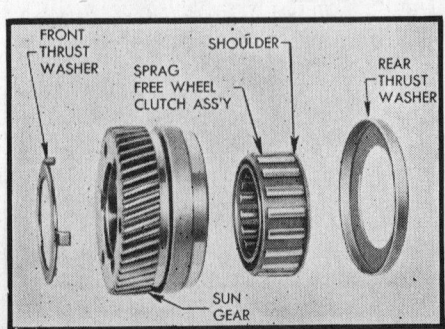

Fig. 40   Converter sun gear parts.   1955

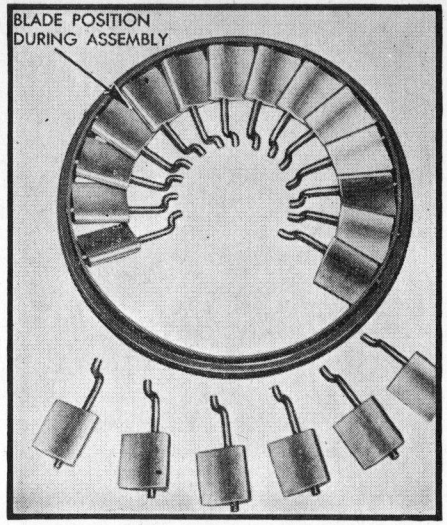

Fig. 41   Stator blade installation. 1955

reaction shaft and immediately check for evidence of oil leakage. Radial streaks of fresh oil on back of pump and fresh oil streaks on face of front oil pump body indicate leakage in the oil pump seal.

8. Before removing bell housing, check to see whether all attaching bolts are tight. Loose bolts may be the cause of leakage at this point.

9. Place bell housing over edge of bench and remove it. Examine rubber oil seal located around front oil pump to see whether it has been uniformly compressed by the bell housing. If not, check for any obstacle that may be around the oil pump or opening in bell housing that would prevent uniform compression of seal.

1955 Converter, Disassemble

Disassembly procedure is essentially the same as 1954 except for the new sun gear and variable pitch stator.

1955 Sun Gear, Disassemble

Remove the thrust washer (with tangs) from face of gear. Using a suitable puller, carefully pry flanged thrust washer from gear. Remove free wheeling clutch (sprag) from inside of sun gear.

1955 Stator, Disassemble

Remove steel thrust washer and selective spacers and take out free wheel rollers and springs. Pry cam retaining snap ring from groove in stator carrier and remove the free wheel cam with three driving keys, Fig. 39. Turn stator over and remove five special screws and lock washers and lift front stator carrier from assembly. *Do not use blade of any type to pry apart front and rear carriers.* Remove snap ring and thrust washer which retain stator crankpins in contact with stator piston and lift stator blade carrier ring and blades from rear carrier. Remove piston from rear carrier.

1955 Converter Parts, Inspect

In addition to the inspection procedures outlined for 1954 converter, inspect the following:

1. Condition of stator blades for distortion, excessive wear, cracks or other damage.
2. Condition of free wheel cam and rollers. Remove any nicks or burrs with an Arkansas Stone and polish with crocus cloth.
3. Check free wheel roller springs for

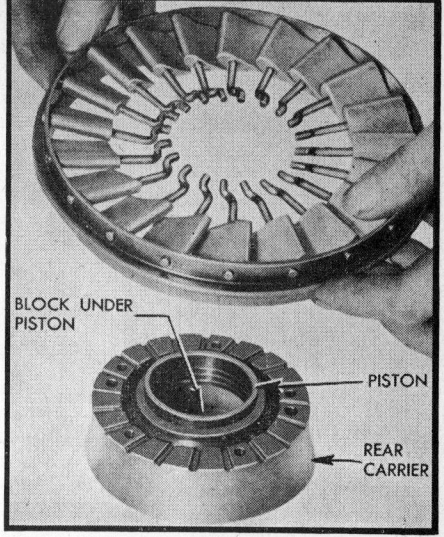

Fig. 42   Installing stator carrier ring and blades. 1955

loss of tension. Weak springs should be replaced.
4. Condition of piston oil seal ring and bore for excessive wear or scoring.

1955 Sun Gear, Assemble

Install free wheel clutch (sprag) in bore of sun gear with shoulder on clutch toward the outside, Fig. 40. Position flanged thrust washer over clutch and gear and carefully press washer squarely in place. If a plastic hammer is used to tap washer in place, use care to prevent damage to washer. Install front thrust washer with tangs entered in holes of gear.

1955 Stator, Assemble

1. Be certain oil sealing ring is in place on stator piston, then carefully install piston in carrier so that protruding end of piston, when seated, extends through the grooved end. *Slightly tilting the piston as it is installed will aid in the assembly.*
2. With protruding end of piston and grooved side of carrier up, place assembly on a suitable block so that the piston is held firmly seated.
3. Place stator blade carrier ring on bench with perforated edge in ring up, then insert the stator blades in the carrier ring with the cranks toward the center and the dished side up. When assembled, the blades should be nearly closed as shown in Fig. 41.
4. Carefully lift stator blade carrier ring with blades, lower it over carrier and piston so that stator blade crankpins are aligned with carrier grooves, using care to prevent blades from dropping out of ring, Fig. 42.
5. If necessary, shift carrier ring slightly to position stator blade crankpins in carrier grooves.
6. Install stator blade crank thrust washer and snap ring in groove in piston.

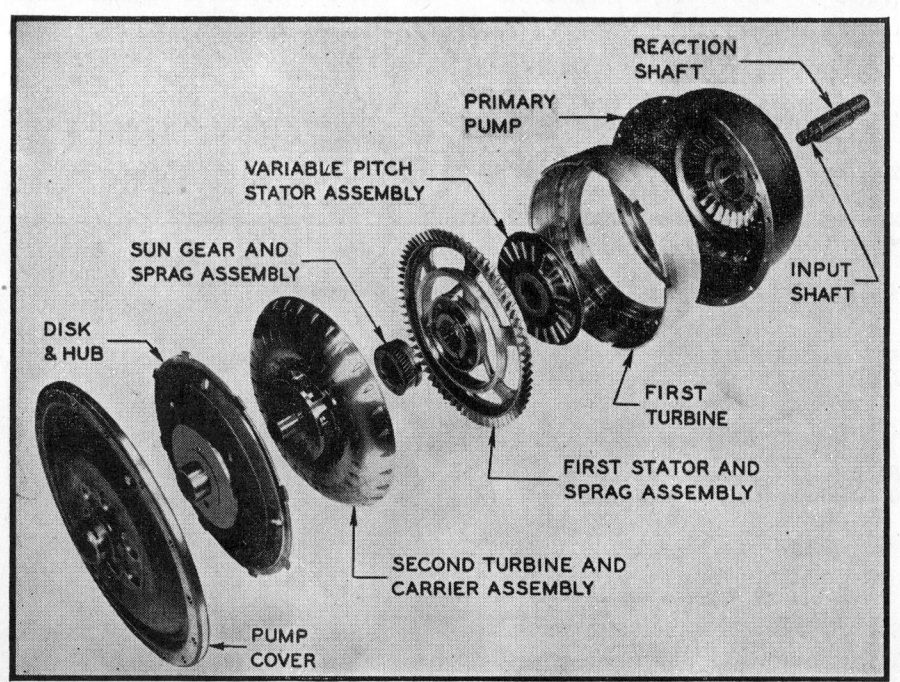

Fig. 43 Major components of 1956-61 torque converter

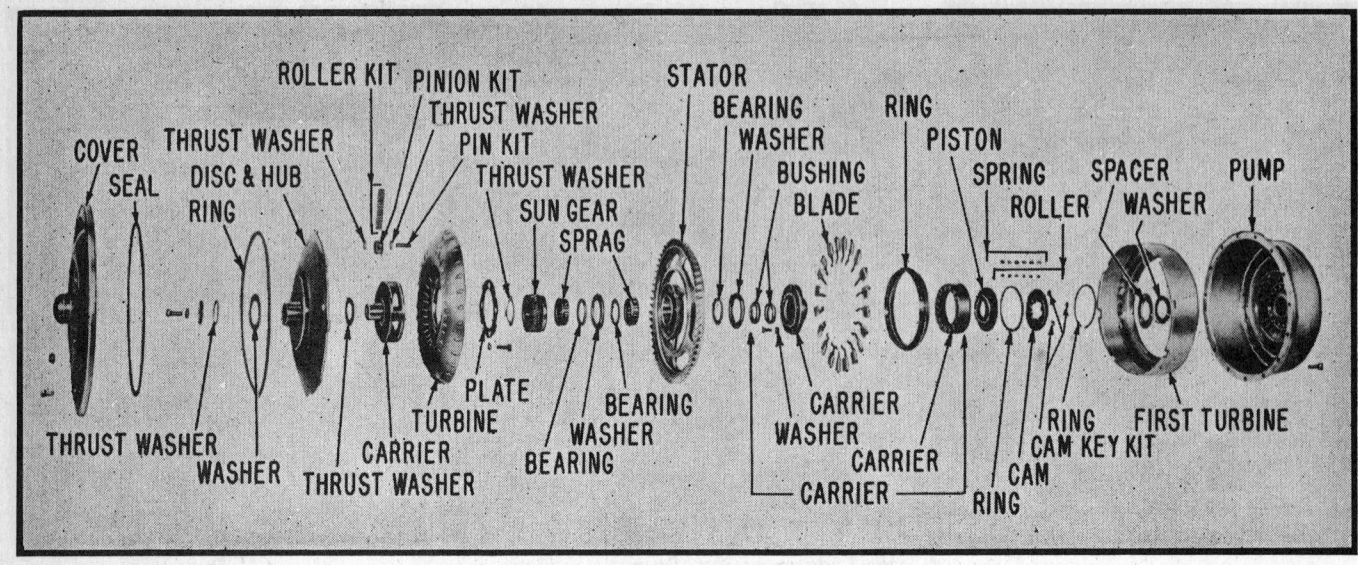

Fig. 44 Exploded view of 1956-61 torque converter

7. Position front half of carrier over rear half so that dowels and screw holes are lined up. Install star lock washers and screws, tightening screws 10-12 lb. ft. torque.
8. Check blades for smooth operation. They should reach both high and low angle positions without binding or locking. If they do not rotate freely within the full range of travel, look for misalignment of crankpins in stator grooves.
9. Turn assembly over and install free wheel cam, three driving keys and snap ring.
10. Check and, if necessary, alter free wheel springs to obtain uniform height, then install rollers and spring (position rollers at rounded end of cams).
11. Place Installer J-5806 in hub of stator so that flat end is flush with rollers to prevent rollers from dropping out. Slight rotation of tool will assist in installation.
12. Be certain spacers, thrust washer and cam surface is free of grease and dirt, then align holes in spacer with tangs on washer and install them with tangs entering cam holes.

Fig. 45 Removing disk and hub assembly

Fig. 46 Installing pinion in carrier

1956-61 Converter, Disassemble Figs. 43, 44

1. Pry retaining ring out of groove in first turbine, insert screwdriver in hole in disc and lift disc and hub assembly out of first turbine, Fig. 45.
2. Lift second turbine and carrier assembly out of first turbine.
3. Remove tanged thrust washer, which may remain in carrier or be found on top of sun gear.
4. Slide sun gear off first turbine, being careful to hold sun gear bearing in place.
5. Lift first stator out of first turbine.
6. Remove bronze bearing and sprag from sun gear.
7. Lay first turbine on bench with narrow edge of vanes up.
8. Pry off cupped thrust washer.
9. Remove first stator bearing and sprag.
10. Using brass drift, carefully tap first stator bearing to remove bearing and cupped thrust washer.

1956-61 Stator, Disassemble

1. Remove stator thrust bearing or washer and selective spacers from rear side of stator, and remove free wheel rollers and springs from cam.

2. Pry retaining ring from groove in stator blade rear carrier, and remove free wheel cam and three driving keys.
3. Remove front carrier screws and lift off front carrier.
4. Tilt three or four blades toward low angle position and slide crank pin ends clockwise around stator piston groove. The next blade and all succeeding blades will then have enough clearance to be removed.

Inspection of Converter Parts, 1956-61

1. Inspect converter pump hub for scores or for wear caused by front pump seal.
2. Look for cracked or damaged vanes in pump or turbines.
3. Inspect free wheel rollers and cam for damage. Nicks or burrs may be removed with an Arkansas stone and polished with crocus cloth. Discard any roller springs that are damaged or distorted.
4. Inspect stator blades for distortion, cracks, loose on cranks or other damage.
5. Inspect piston oil seal ring and bore of blade carrier for wear or scores. If bushings in carrier are worn, they should be replaced.

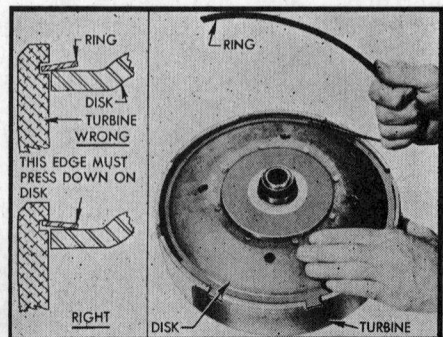

Fig. 47 Installing disk retaining ring

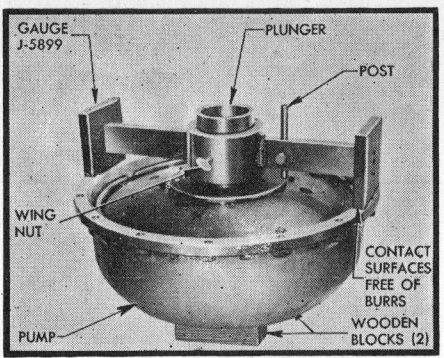

Fig. 48 Checking converter clearance in pump. 1955-61

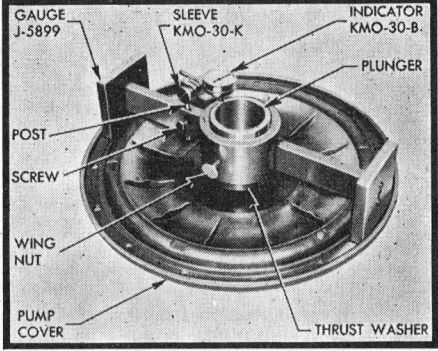

Fig. 49 Checking converter clearance in cover. 1955-61

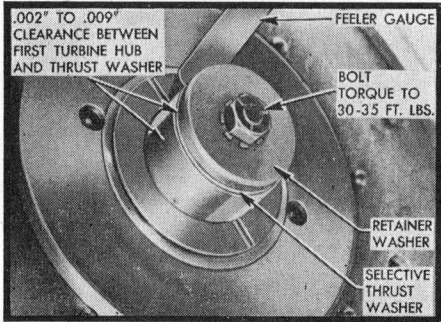

Fig. 50 Checking turbine clearance. 1955-61

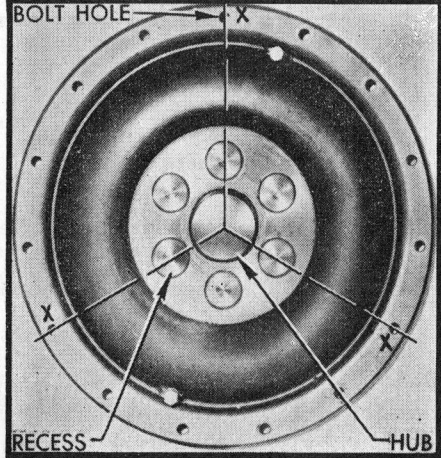

Fig. 51 Location of driving bolt holes. 1955-61

1956-61 Stator, Assemble

1. Insert stator piston and oil seal ring in rear carrier and push to extreme forward position.
2. Place rear carrier and piston on a suitable fixture to hold piston in position.
3. Install stator outer ring with crank pin holes up.
4. Holding a blade in the approximate "low pitch" position, insert crank pin in outer ring. Then rotate blade to bring crank throw into piston groove.
5. Hold piston, blades and outer ring together.
6. Install remainder of blades, working in a clockwise direction.
7. To insert last blade, it will be necessary to tilt the adjacent three blades.
8. Install front carrier and bolt in place. Be sure blades operate freely in carrier.

1956-61 Sun Gear & Twin Turbine, Assemble

1. Install sprag in bore of sun gear with shouldered end outward, and press bearing in place.
2. Check operation of sun gear sprag clutch by sliding sun gear on reaction shaft with gear end toward front of transmission. Sun gear must rotate freely clockwise and lock in a counterclockwise direction when viewed from front of transmission.
3. Lay first stator on bench with thin edges up. Place first stator sprag in hub of first stator with shoulder down. Install one bronze bearing with cupped thrust washer on each side of sprag. Check operation of sprag clutch.
4. Support carrier on suitable blocks and install several pinion pins to serve as pilots, then place turbine in position so that carrier is squarely started into recess in turbine.
5. Use a hammer and hardwood dowel or other soft punch to tap turbine down over carrier. *If turbine cannot be assembled on carrier with moderate force, remove it and check for burrs in counterbored recess.*
6. Assemble and install planet pins as shown in Fig. 46.
7. Install pinion lock plate so that it enters notches of all pins, and install carrier bolts and washers.
8. Place first stator in first turbine with thin edges of blades up.
9. Place sun gear on first stator with gear end up.
10. Place tanged thrust washer in planet carrier, using grease to hold washer in place.
11. Place second turbine and carrier in first turbine, being sure pinions mesh with sun gear.
12. Place thrust washer or bearing on carrier.
13. Install first turbine disk and hub over second turbine.
14. Rotate disk until ring gear meshes with carrier pinions, then align driving lugs on disk with notches in first turbine and push assembly down into turbine.
15. Note that turbine disk retaining ring

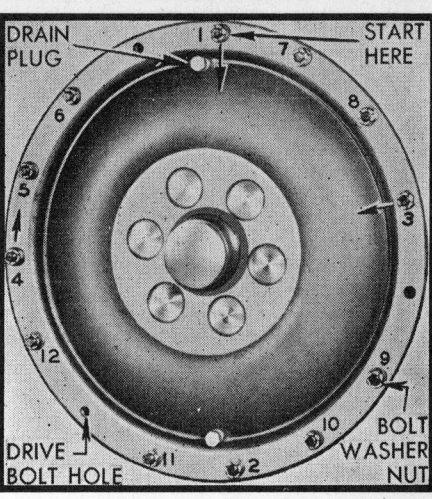

Fig. 52 Bolt tightening sequence. 1955-61

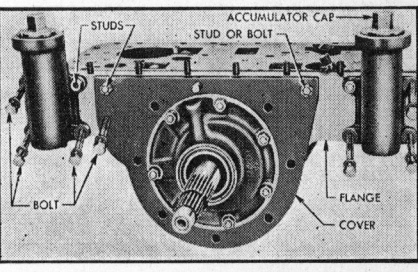

Fig. 53 Accumulator body and reaction shaft flange and front pump, 1953-54

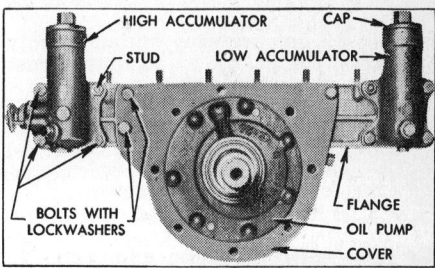

Fig. 54 Accumulator body, reaction shaft flange and front pump. 1955-61

is dished and should be installed as shown in Fig. 47.

1955-61 Converter Units, Install

1. Install front oil pump seal ring around pump body against pump cover.
2. Install bell housing, using lock washers on bolts and stud. *Sparingly coat threads of lower right side bolt with Permatex No. 3 because the bolt hole opens into transmission case.* Torque bolts and stud nut to 35-40 lb. ft.
3. Place converter pump on a suitable support with open end up. Carefully place stator in proper position, with original spacers and thrust washer between stator and pump. *Grease should not be used to hold thrust washer and spacers in place as this will affect clearance check described below.*

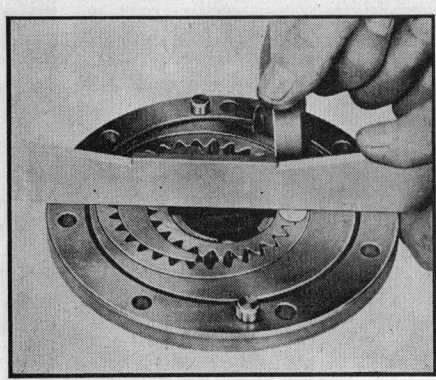

Fig. 55 Checking side clearance of gears in pump body

4. On 1955 units, place sun gear in position with tanged thrust washer up, then carefully lower Twin Turbine assembly in place, being certain that planet pinions mesh properly with sun gear.

5. Place converter clearance gauge J-5899 on pump as shown in Fig. 48. Loosen wing nut and firmly press plunger down against first turbine hub and tighten wing nut.

6. Support converter pump cover on bench with inside surface up and bronze thrust washer in place. Then remove clearance gauge, invert it and center it on the cover as shown in Fig. 49.

7. Attach dial indicator to sleeve, Fig. 49, and mount indicator on gauge post so that indicator button is contacting upper rim of gauge plunger. Set dial at zero.

8. Loosen plunger wing nut and firmly press plunger down against thrust washer, noting gauge reading.

9. The dial should read between .017" and .030" counterclockwise from zero, because the distance measured is existing clearance between converter units and pump cover.

10. If the indicator does not read within specified limits, change spacer thickness between stator and pump to obtain proper clearance. Increasing spacer thickness will decrease clearance and vice-versa. Spacers are available in thickness of .010-.013", .020-023" and .030-.033".

11. Install converter pump on reaction shaft, turning it until lugs on pump

hub enter slots in front pump driving gear.

12. With stator installer J-5806 in hub of stator (see Fig. 38) position assembly so that stator will slide off tool and on reaction shaft. Be certain that thrust washer and spacers remain in position until stator is seated against converter pump. Vaseline between spacers will assist in retaining them in position.

13. Install sun gear with tanged thrust washer toward front. If clutch is properly installed, sun gear may be rotated clockwise only.

14. Be certain snap ring is on input shaft. Then install Twin Turbine on input shaft, turning it as required to mesh the planet pinions with the sun gear.

15. Place second turbine retaining washer on input shaft bolt, then screw bolt into input shaft with selective thrust washer between retaining washer and first turbine hub. Tighten bolt to 30-35 lb. ft. torque.

16. Using a feeler gauge, check clearance between selective thrust washer and first turbine hub. Clearance should be .002 to .009", Fig. 50. If specified clearance does not exist, select a washer of proper thickness. Two such washers are available: One marked "6" is .060" to .063" thick: the other is marked "7" and is .067" to .070" thick.

17. Mark three bolt holes that are aligned with center of hub, Fig. 51, and one of the counterbored recesses adjacent to hub. These holes should be marked for later installation of flywheel-to-pump driving bolts.

18. Install new O-ring seal on pump cover, making sure that surfaces are clean and that the seal has even tension all around and is not twisted.

19. Grease bronze washer so it will stick in recess of pump cover, then install cover on pump so that the three marked driving bolt holes are *not aligned with any hole in pump rim at which a balance weight is located.*

20. Install bolts with plain washers and special nuts in all but the three driving bolt holes. Insert the shank of a $\frac{11}{32}$" drill through one hole to align all holes and tighten bolts to about 5 lb. ft. torque in the sequence shown in Fig. 52. Finally, tighten bolts in same sequence to 25-30 lb.

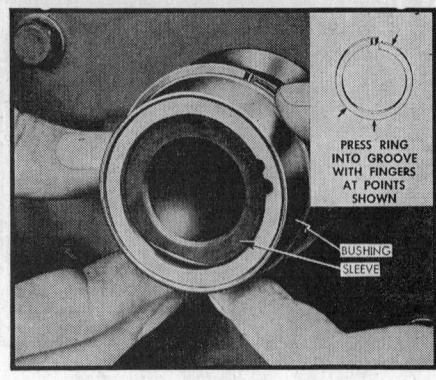

Fig. 57 Sealing rings, bushings and sleeve on reaction flange hub

ft. torque. When tightening bolts, insert a wide screw driver blade between flat side of bolt head and the pump to prevent a corner of bolt from digging into pump casting.

FRONT OIL PUMP

Removal

1. Loosen, but do not remove servo body caps.

2. Remove three bolts which attach each accumulator body but do not remove the stud nut, Figs. 53, 54.

3. Remove bolts extending through front oil pump cover but do not remove any stud nuts. First type transmissions had one screw and two stud nuts; later jobs have two screws and one stud nut.

4. Tap very lightly on rear of accumulator bodies with fiber mallet to loosen reaction shaft flange, then remove assembly and gasket. Leave input shaft in place in transmission.

5. Check reaction flange gasket for good imprint and freedom from damage which would cause an oil leak at this point.

1955-61 Service Note

Removal procedure remains unchanged except that the first step in reaction flange removal is the removal of the snap ring from the input shaft.

Following snap ring removal, proceed as outlined above.

Disassemble Front Pump

1. Remove high and low accumulators and gaskets from reaction flange. Check gaskets for indication of oil leakage.

2. Before removing front oil pump, check the nuts for tightness (loose nuts would be the cause of oil leakage around pump). Remove front pump, if necessary, tapping body lightly with mallet to free it.

3. Remove front pump cover and gasket from reaction flange, and check gasket for evidence of oil leakage.

4. If check ball which is located in clutch feed passage of reaction flange is free to drop out, remove ball to avoid loss in handling parts. Do not remove ball if it is securely retained by peened edge of hole.

Fig. 56 Checking clearance between crescent and gears

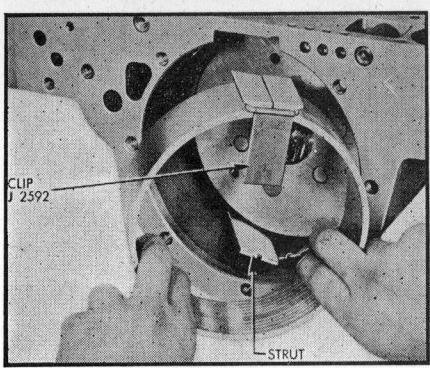

Fig. 58   Removing band with installing clip J-2592

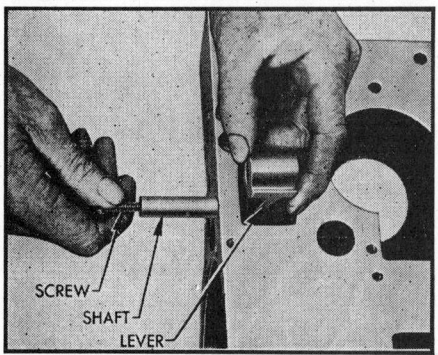

Fig. 59   Removing low band lever and shaft

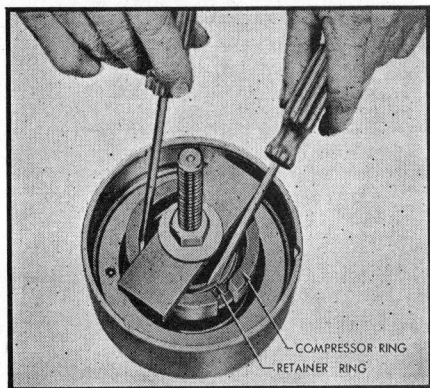

Fig. 60   Using clutch spring compressor J-2590

1955-61 Service Note

The front oil pump retaining bolts enter the pump from the clutch side of the reaction flange. Therefore, the flange must be removed prior to removing the front oil pump.

Pump Inspection

1. Wash pump parts in clean solvent and dry thoroughly.
2. Check mounting faces of pump bodies, gears, front pump cover and rear pump cover plate for excessive wear.
3. Inspect front oil pump bushing. If bushing is loose or excessively worn

replace pump assembly. If pump bushing is excessively worn or pump was noisy, always check for flywheel run-out, primary pump hub run-out, and misalignment of bell housing. Flywheel run-out should not exceed .005"; primary pump hub run-out should not exceed .007"; run-out of rear face of bell housing not over .005"; run-out of bell housing pilot hole not over .004".

4. Inspect front pump oil seal but replace it only if there is definite evidence of leakage or damage. Drive out defective seal with a punch. Lightly coat outside of new seal with No. 3 Permatex, start seal squarely into pump body with deep groove in seal retainer outward and tap into place with hard wood block and mallet. Wipe off excess Permatex.
5. Make following checks and replace worn parts if clearances exceed specified limits. (A) Using straight edge and feeler gauge as shown in Fig. 55, clearance should be .001" to .002". (B) Using feeler gauge as shown in Fig. 56, clearance between crescent and driving gear, should be .003" to .006". (C) Using feeler gauge between crescent and driving gear, clearance should be .006" to .009" on front pump, and .004" to .006" on rear pump.
6. Check front pump cover and rear pump cover plate for depth of wear caused by the gears. Replace part if depth wear exceeds .001" or surface is scored.

Inspect Reaction Shaft Flange

1. Wash flange in clean solvent, dry thoroughly and blow out all passages with air.
2. Place straight edge on case mounting surface of reaction flange and check any low spots with feeler gauge. If out of true more than .002", replace flange assembly.
3. Inspect flange mounting face on transmission case in same manner. If face of case cannot be trued up within .002", it should be replaced.
4. Inspect surfaces of reaction flange and transmission case for nicks or burrs and remove with mill file.
5. Inspect bronze bushing on rear hub of reaction shaft flange and the cast iron sealing sleeve pressed into the hub, Fig. 57. If these parts are worn excessively or scored, replace reaction shaft flange.
6. Inspect oil sealing rings on hub of reaction flange and replace if damaged in any way. To remove ring, apply pressure with index finger and thumbs at points indicated by arrows in Fig. 56 in order to unlock the ends by depressing one end and raising the other.
7. Check all studs for tightness and replace any with damaged threads. If stud threads are stripped in reaction flange, it will be necessary to tap out the hole for installation of step studs which are available.

Assemble Front Pump

1. Install check ball in clutch feed passage if ball was removed. Then in-

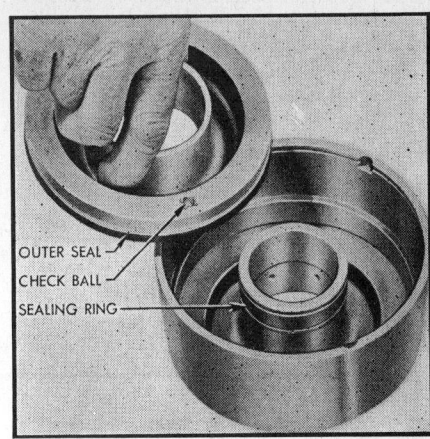

Fig. 61   Removing clutch piston

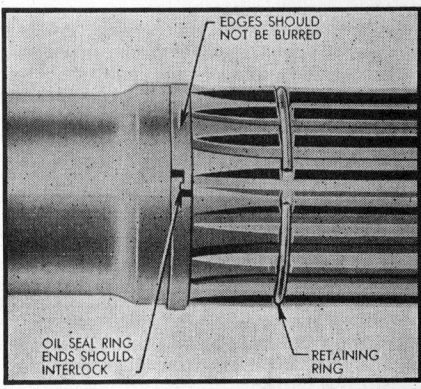

Fig. 62   Input shaft oil seal and retaining rings

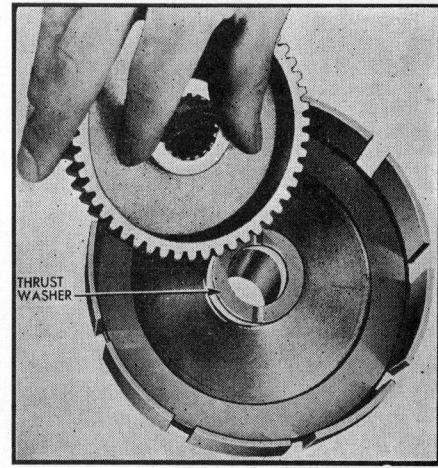

Fig. 63   Installing thrust washer and clutch hub in reaction gear

stall a new gasket and pump cover on reaction flange.

2. Lubricate and install gears in front pump body. Driving gear must be installed with beveled side outward so that this side will be against cover when pump is installed. *Reversing this gear in pump body will result in severe damage to transmission.*
3. Install oil pump on reaction shaft flange with lockwashers under nuts. On early jobs with steel pump cover the body must seat squarely in re-

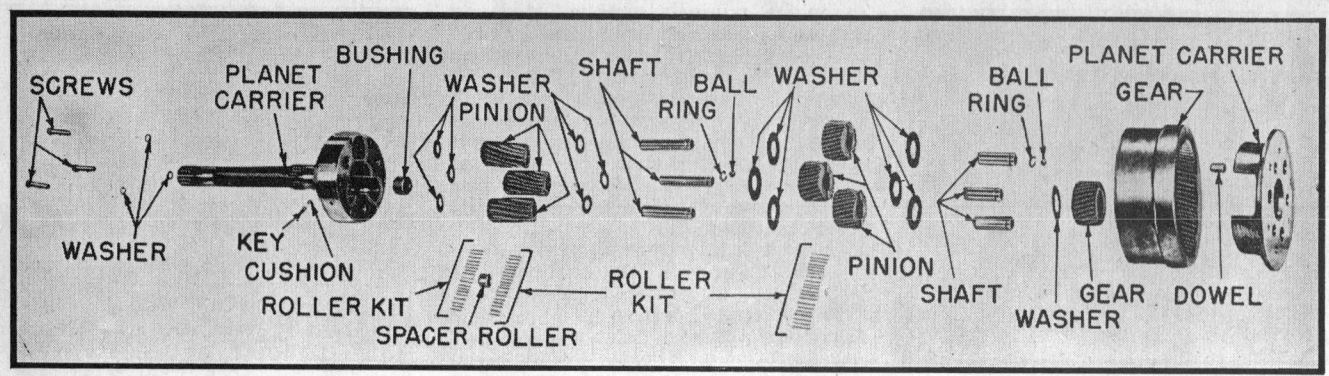

Fig. 65 Planetary gear set and carriers

cess in cover. On later jobs with cast iron cover, pump is located by two dowel pins.

4. Tighten pump bolt or stud nuts to approximately 5 lbs. ft. torque in an alternate side-to-side sequence and then tighten in same sequence to 25-30 lbs. ft. Torque tighten cover attaching stud nut 25-30 lbs. ft.

CLUTCH & INPUT SHAFT

Removal

The converter, bell housing, valve and servo body and reaction shaft flange must be removed.

1. Pull input shaft and clutch hub front thrust washer from clutch. Then remove clutch.
2. Block low band anchor lever down with screw driver and compress low band with operating lever while applying Band Installing Clip J-2595 across strut flanges of band, Fig. 58. Release levers and remove low band. Then remove struts which will drop into case.
3. Remove low band anchor and operating levers by threading ¼" capscrew into each lever shaft and pulling shaft out of case, Fig. 59.

Disassemble Clutch

1. Remove reaction gear flange retaining ring with screwdriver and remove three flange driving keys with pointed tool.
2. Remove low range reaction gear, thrust washer, clutch hub and 10 clutch plates, from drum.
3. Install Clutch Spring Compressor J-2590 in assembled drum, placing slot in compressor ring over ends of spring seat retaining ring. Compress clutch sufficiently to remove retaining ring, Fig. 60.
4. Release pressure on clutch spring, making sure that spring seat does not engage retaining ring groove in drum, then remove spring compressor, spring seat and spring.
5. Forcibly rap drum, open end down, on a block of wood to remove clutch piston. The steel check ball, Fig 61, may come out of its seat in this operation; if it does, snap it back into place.

Inspection

1. Wash all parts in clean solvent and

dry thoroughly. Use only gasoline or kerosene to clean clutch plates and bands; do not use any chemical degreaser or other commercial solvents.

2. Inspect all clutch plates and replace any that are scored, burned, warped or worn excessively. Check fit of any new internally splined plates on clutch hub to make certain that they slide freely on hub. Tight plates will prevent full disengagement of the clutch.
3. Inspect drum for cracks or scores. Inspect oil sealing ring on clutch hub and if damaged, replace it as shown in Fig. 56.
4. Inspect clutch piston outer seal and

Fig. 64 Installing drum over reaction gear flange

replace if it is hardened, broken or has turned edges. Install new seal with lip over smaller diameter land of piston.

5. Make sure that small bleed hole in piston is open and that check ball is in place and not stuck.
6. Inspect the low band. If band lining is worn smooth so that grooves are gone, replace band.
7. Inspect input shaft oil seal ring and if damaged or broken, replace it as shown in Fig. 56. Make sure that retaining ring is in place on shaft, Fig. 62.

Assemble Clutch

1. Apply light oil to piston outer seal and inside of drum. Then install piston carefully to avoid distorting or turning lip of seal. When piston is fully installed in drum, top of piston will be approximately flush with shoulder on inside of drum.
2. Place clutch spring in piston and place spring seat and seat retaining ring on spring. Install spring compressor J-2590, Fig. 60, and compress spring until retaining ring can be snapped into groove in hub of drum. Then remove spring compressor.
3. Place reaction gear on bench with flange upward, then install clutch hub thrust washer and clutch hub over hub of reaction gear, with open end of clutch hub facing up, Fig. 63.
4. Separate faced clutch plates from plain steel clutch plates. Faced plates are flat and may be installed in either direction. Plain steel plates are dished and all these plates must be installed with the dish in the same direction; however, the dish may be either up or down. Check each plate for dish with a straight edge and stack plates so that all are dished in same direction.
5. Install a faced plate over clutch hub, next to gear flange. Then install a plain steel plate. Alternately install the remaining plates. If installed correctly, the top plate will be plain steel.
6. Place drum and clutch piston assembly over reaction gear flange so that driving key recesses in drum and flange are approximately aligned, Fig. 64. Press drum evenly into place over reaction gear flange.
7. Complete alignment of driving key recesses by tapping reaction gear flange. Then install three driving

Fig. 66 Removing planetary gear set

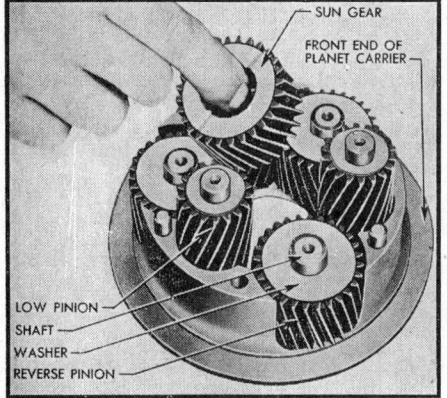

Fig. 68 Removing sun gear and planet pinions

keys and reaction gear flange retaining ring.

1955-61 Service Note

The reaction shaft flange has been redesigned to accommodate the installation of the new variable pitch stator, free wheeling sun gear assembly and a new needle bearing in the direct drive clutch.

The reaction shaft is larger in diameter and extends through the flange to provide an inner race for the needle bearing which supports the direct drive clutch. The shaft provides the bearing surface for the stator and sun gear. A babbitt bearing, retained inside the shaft by two snap rings, supports the front of the input shaft.

Oil passages in the reaction flange have been relocated to utilize direct drive clutch oil pressure from the high accumulator to control the angle of the new stator.

1955-61 Input Shaft Bearing

1. Temporarily mount front oil pump and cover on reaction flange to add support to flange while removing bearing.
2. Remove outer retaining snap ring from front of bearing.
3. Remove bearing with suitable puller
4. If inner snap ring did not come out with removing tool, it may be left in place. However, check to see that it is firmly seated in groove. If loose, replace it.
5. Install new bearing with suitable driver and install outer snap ring.

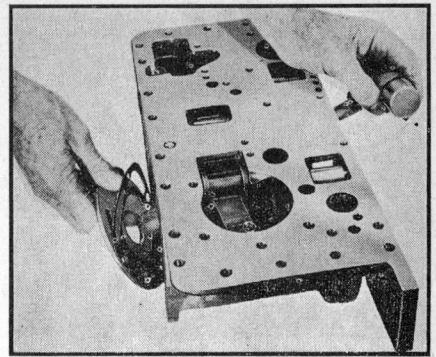

Fig. 67 Removing rear oil pump plate and gasket

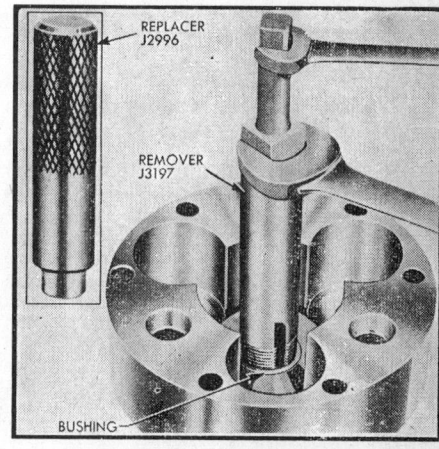

Fig. 69 Replacing planet carrier bushing

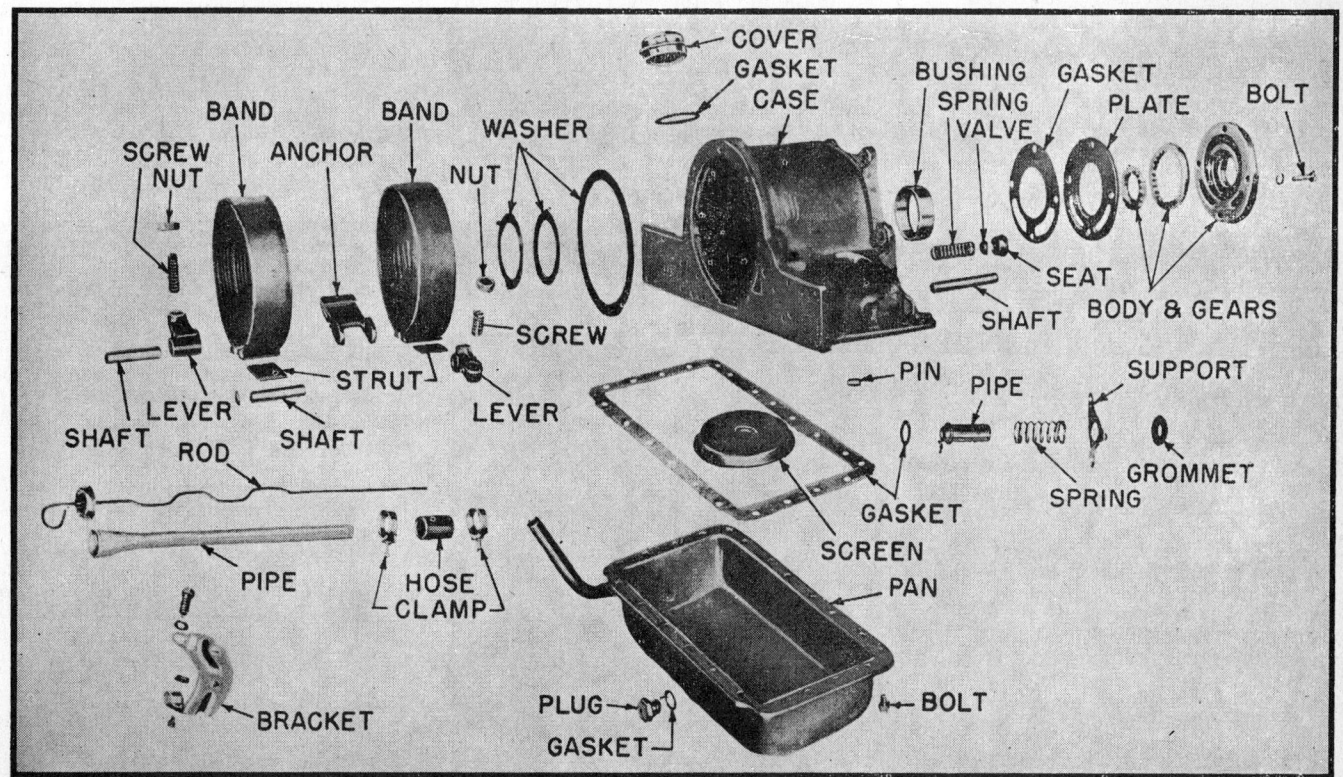

Fig. 70 Transmission case, rear oil pump and bands

Fig. 71 Transmission case bushing remover and replacer J-3175

1955-61 Clutch Needle Bearing

Disassembly and assembly of direct drive clutch remains the same as 1954 except for the removal and installation of the clutch needle bearing which is a new part.

With clutch plates removed, place drum flat on bench with open end down and drive bearing out through hub. Drive the new bearing into place with numbered side of bearing against driver. The edge of the bearing race should be flush with beveled shoulder in clutch drum.

PLANETARY GEAR SET

Removal, Fig. 65

1. Before the planetary gear set can be removed, it will be necessary to remove the torque converter, oil pan, valve and servo body, front oil pump, accumulators, input shaft, clutch, torque ball and universal joint, rear bearing retainer and parking lock mechanism, rear oil pump and regulator valve.
2. Remove gear set through front of case, Fig. 66.
3. Remove reverse ring gear and two planet carrier thrust washers if they did not come out with the planetary gear set.
4. If rear pump plates and gasket were not previously removed, tap them out with a hammer handle from front side of case, Fig. 67.
5. Thread a ¼" bolt into the reverse band anchor shaft and pull it from transmission case; then remove operating lever.
6. Rotate reverse band toward adjusting hole until anchor can be disengaged, then remove this part.
7. Compress ends of reverse band and apply Band Installing Clip J-2595 across strut flanges and remove band.
8. Remove reverse ring gear rear thrust washer from case.

Disassemble, Fig. 65

1. Remove reverse ring gear front thrust washer, if used. Units start-

ing with A-42,475 and B-1 do not have this washer.
2. Remove three planet carrier screws and special lockwashers, using a $\frac{7}{32}$" hexagon (Allen) wrench. A used universal joint front yoke may be placed on output shaft and held with a bar while loosening the screws.
3. Separate front and rear ends of planet carrier by carefully tapping around front flange while holding unit clear of bench.
4. Remove sun gear rear thrust washer, which may be either on sun gear or stuck in rear end of carrier. Remove reverse sun gear, Fig. 68.
5. Remove three low planet pinion assemblies, each consisting of a pinion, shaft and bearing rollers retained at each end of pinion by steel thrust washers. A retaining ring snapped into a groove in shaft will hold lower thrust washer in place as shaft is tapped out of carrier. Shaft is prevented from turning in carrier by a steel ball imbedded in end of shaft.
6. Remove three reverse planet pinion assemblies in the same manner as the low planet pinion assemblies.
7. Remove thrust washers and shafts from pinions, then remove bearing rollers. Note that the reverse planet pinions have a single set of rollers whereas the low planet pinions have two sets of rollers separated by a spacer.

Inspection

1. Wash all parts in clean solvent and dry thoroughly.
2. Carefully inspect shaft and rollers for excessive wear. Replace if worn.
3. Inspect reverse ring gear, sun gear and pinions for wear; remove any nicks or burrs with Arkansas stone.
4. Inspect bushing in rear end of planet carrier, and replace if worn or scored. Bushing may be removed with Bushing Remover J-3197 and new bushing may be installed, either end first, with Bushing Replacer J-2996, Fig. 69. Reaming bushing to size is not required.
5. Inspect reverse band anchor for cracks.
6. Inspect reverse band and replace if

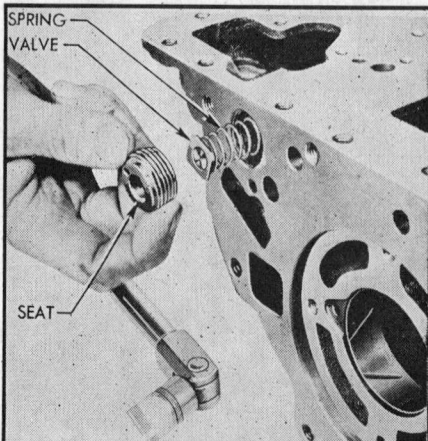

Fig. 72 Removing lubrication oil pressure regulator valve

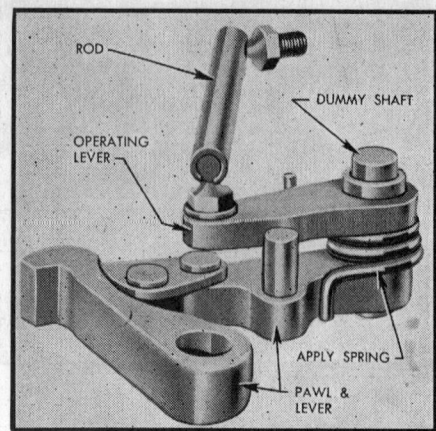

Fig. 73 Assembly of parking lock control parts and dummy shaft, 1953-54

it is cracked or if lining is worn so that grooves are gone.

Transmission Case, Fig. 70

1. Wash case thoroughly and blow out all passages.
2. Carefully inspect case for cracks, breaks and stripped threads in bolt holes.
3. Inspect all machined surfaces for nicks or burrs and smooth off with a mill file.
4. If oil gauge rod base (first type filler) is bent where it enters transmission case it should be replaced to avoid oil leakage. Coat outside of new base with Permatex No. 3 and press into case until distance from top of base to surface of case is $2\frac{11}{16}$".
5. Inspect bushing for wear and scoring. Insert planet carrier into bushing and check clearance with feeler gauge. If clearance is excessive due to wear of bushing, replace bushing.
6. To remove old bushing, place case over an opening with rear end down and drive bushing from case with Tool J-3175-1. To install new bushing, place Tool J-3175-2 in rear oil pump recess in case to serve as a pilot. Slip bushing over J-3175-1 and drive bushing into case from front side until bushing is flush with front surface of wall which supports bushing. Bushing must be installed with wide deep ends of oil grooves toward rear side of case, Fig. 71.

Assemble Planetary Gear Set

1. Reassemble planet pinions and shafts with bearing rollers and thrust washers. Bottom thrust washer goes between retaining ring on shaft and end of pinion. Each reverse planet pinion contains 24 rollers. Each low planet pinion contains 20 rollers at each end separated by a spacer. Place a thrust washer on upper end of each assembly to hold rollers in place.
2. Make sure that steel ball is imbedded in each shaft to prevent turning in carrier. Then install pinion assemblies in front end of planet carrier, using care to engage steel balls in notches in carrier, Fig. 68.

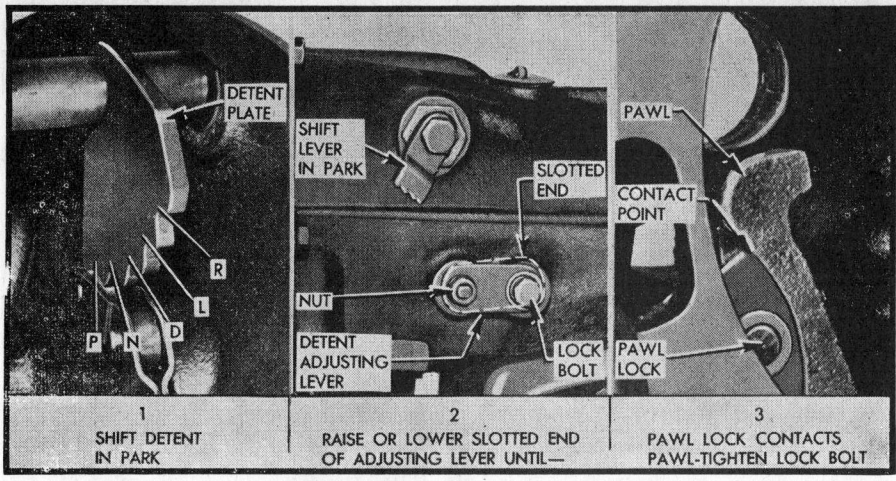

1	2	3
SHIFT DETENT IN PARK	RAISE OR LOWER SLOTTED END OF ADJUSTING LEVER UNTIL—	PAWL LOCK CONTACTS PAWL-TIGHTEN LOCK BOLT

Fig. 74 Shift detent adjustment. 1955-61

3. Install reverse sun gear and place bronze thrust washer on top of gear.
4. Install rear end of planet carrier on assembled front end, making sure that assembly marks on both parts are aligned. These marks are numbers which are placed over the dividing line during the production of the carrier.
5. Install the three Allen head screws and torque tighten 25-30 lbs. ft.
6. Install reverse ring gear thrust washer if one was removed and ring gear has not been replaced by later type.
7. Install reverse ring gear on planetary gear set.

REAR BEARING RETAINER

Torque Ball & Universal Joint, Remove

1. Remove torque ball rubber boot.
2. Remove attaching bolts and take off mounting thrust plate and gasket, torque ball, inner and outer retainers and all paper shims. These shims govern the adjustment of the torque ball.
3. Remove speedometer driven gear and sleeve.
4. Place transmission shift lever on across shaft and push lever forward while turning universal joint until locking pawl engages parking lock ratchet wheel.
5. Unfasten and pull universal joint

from output shaft, using Universal Joint Puller J-682-A on Series 40, 50, or J-859-A on Series 70 if joint cannot be removed by hand.
6. Remove transmission shift lever.

Removing Rear Bearing Retainer & Parking Lock Ratchet Wheel, Remove

Only the torque ball, universal joint and oil pan need be removed to perform this operation.
1. Disconnect valve operating rod from upper operating lever if not previously done.
2. Remove universal joint retaining ring from output shaft. Use care to avoid nicking output shaft as nicks will damage rear bearing retainer bushing during removal of retainer.
3. Remove retaining bolts and take off rear bearing retainer and gasket. Check gasket for evidences of oil leakage.
4. Using snap ring pliers, remove ratchet wheel outer retaining ring, slide wheel from output shaft and remove inner retaining ring.

Removing Rear Oil Pump & Regulator Valve

1. Remove retaining bolts and take off pump body, which contains pump gears. In transmissions below A-36,-000 the pump assembly consisted of a separate cover, gasket, and body and gear assembly. Check gaskets for indication of oil leakage.
2. Remove drive key and use pointed tool to remove rubber cushion which is located under drive key in output shaft.
3. Remove rear pump plate and gasket if they can be removed from case without prying. If plate is stuck, it can be tapped out after removal of planetary gear set. Check gasket for indication of oil leakage.
4. Remove oil pressure regulator valve seat, using a suitable drag link socket, Fig. 72.

Rear Bearing Retainer, Disassemble, 1953-54

1. Remove clevis pin which connects

valve operating rod clevis to valve operating cross shaft. Then remove rod and clevis through front end of bearing retainer.
2. Disconnect parking lock operating rod from cross shaft by unscrewing rod end from cross shaft lever.
3. Remove cross shaft bearing, using a box wrench. A socket which does not fully engage bearing, or an end wrench will distort the bearing. Remove cross shaft.
4. Screw a ¼" bolt into parking lock pawl shaft and pull shaft from rear bearing retainer, allowing end of pawl to swing free.
5. Tap parking lock operating lever toward front of rear bearing retainer, using a long punch, and remove operating lever shaft. The operating lever, lever and pawl assembly and apply spring can then be removed.
6. Remove special connector, torque converter pressure valve and spring from rear bearing retainer, using a socket or box wrench on connector; an end wrench would distort connector.

Inspection

1. Wash all parts in clean solvent and dry thoroughly.
2. Inspect converter pressure valve for scoring or other damage. Inspect valve spring for distortion or breakage, and the special connector for distortion or stripped threads.
3. Inspect parking brake lock pawl, pawl locking link, and ratchet wheel for cracks and for worn teeth that would prevent positive locking.
4. Inspect valve operating cross shaft and bearing for excessive wear. Remove and discard rubber seal from bearing.
5. Inspect rear bearing retainer bushing for scoring or excessive wear. Insert output shaft in bushing and check clearance, which should be .001" to .006". If necessary, replace bushing, using Bushing Remover and Replacer J-2997. Reaming to size is not required.

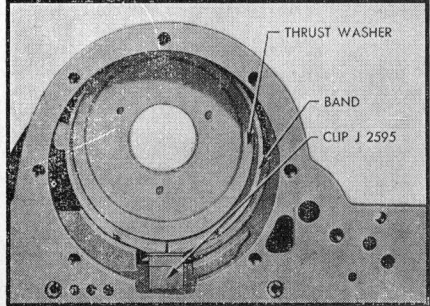

Fig. 75 Ring gear thrust washer and reverse band installed

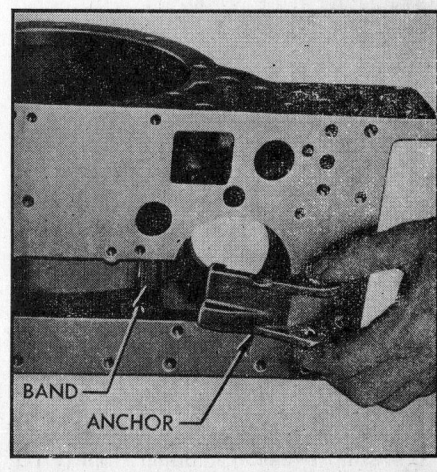

Fig. 76 Installing reverse band anchor

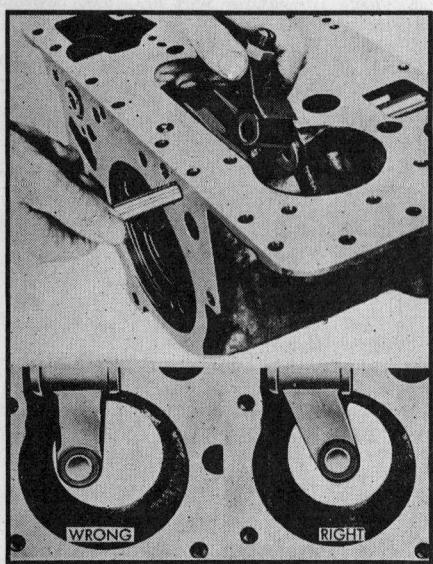

Fig. 77   Installing operating lever and shaft

Fig. 78   Installing rear oil pump plate and gasket

Fig. 79 Oil pump driving gear and key installed

Rear Bearing Retainer, Disassemble, 1955-60

1. Remove detent spring from inside of rear bearing retainer.
2. Remove detent adjusting lever attaching nut, washer and lock bolt on outside of case, then remove lever.
3. Using a plastic hammer, lightly tap the detent support shaft toward the inside of the case and remove the detent roller lever support assembly. Discard the oil seal.
4. Disconnect parking lock operating rod from the cross shaft by unscrewing the rod end from the cross shaft lever.
5. Disconnect valve operating rod from cross shaft, remove rod and retaining clip.
6. Screw a ¼"-20 bolt into parking lock operating lever shaft and lock pawl shaft and pull these parts from bearing retainer. Then remove lock pawl and lever assembly.
7. Remove cross shaft bearing and seal, using a box wrench, and remove cross shaft.

Universal Joint & Torque Ball Repairs

1. Inspect universal joint for wear and play between spider pins and bushings. Allowable play is .002" to .004".
2. Check fit of universal joint yokes on output and propeller shafts. Allowable backlash of rear yoke on propeller shaft splines is .0005" to .0045". Front yoke must be a tight fit, rotatively on output shaft to prevent "snap" when alternating car movement between forward and reverse.
3. Inspect rear yoke of universal joint for excessive wear at point of contact with oil seal in torque ball. Rear yoke and bushing in torque ball must be free of scores and not worn excessively; clearance between these parts should be .004" to .006".
4. Clean and inspect spherical surfaces of torque ball and both retainers. If scored or pitted, replace these parts.
5. Inspect oil seal in torque ball and replace if worn. When installing a new seal, place it in position with the feather edge pointing into torque ball. Then press seal squarely into place, using a flat piece of metal to avoid distorting on seal. Press new seal *flush* with boss on flange of torque ball.

Rear Bearing Retainer, Assemble, 1953-54

1. Install torque converter pressure valve spring valve with closed end outward, and the special connector in rear bearing retainer. Make sure all parts are clean.
2. Assemble locking pawl and lever assembly, apply spring, and parking lock operating lever with operating rod on dummy shaft as shown in Fig. 73. Note position of each end of apply spring.
3. Place assembled parts in position in rear bearing retainer. Then install operating lever shaft through retainer and lever.
4. Install parking lock pawl shaft through bearing retainer and lock pawl, making sure that tapped end is outward to permit future removal.
5. Install valve-operating cross shaft and bearing. Install a *new* seal in bearing with grooved side facing inward.
6. Connect parking lock operating rod to cross shaft lever, using a lock-

Fig. 80   Installing parking lock ratchet wheel

washer on threaded end of rod. Do not connect valve operating rod and clevis to cross shaft at this time.

Rear Bearing Retainer, Assemble, 1955-60

1. Install operating cross shaft and bearing. Install a new seal in bearing with grooved side facing inward.
2. Install parking lock pawl and lever in bearing retainer. Then install lock pawl shaft and operating lever shaft with tapped end outward.
3. Attach operating rod to cross shaft and snap retainer in place. Then connect parking lock operating rod to cross shaft lever, using a lock washer on threaded rod end.
4. Install detent lever and support with new seal, using care to prevent damage to oil seal.
5. Install adjusting lever on support shaft on outside of case with lock washer and nut. Install flat washer, lock washer and bolt at slotted end of linkage adjusting lever. *Do not tighten bolt at this time.*
6. *At this point shift detent adjustment must be made as follows:*
   Temporarily install shift lever on cross shaft, then shift parking pawl into park position as shown in Fig. 74.

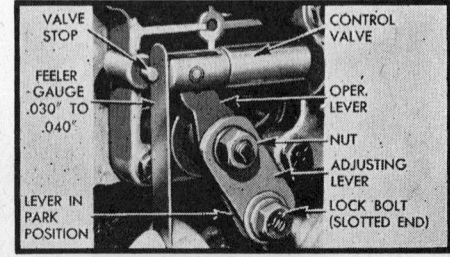

Fig. 81   Control valve linkage adjustment.   1955-60

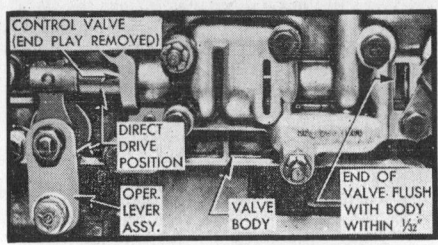

Fig. 82 Position of shift control valve in Drive Range. 1955-60

7. Raise or lower adjusting lever at slotted end until pawl lock contacts parking pawl, then tighten lock bolt on adjusting lever, being certain contact is made. In this position the roller should be in the deepest portion of the detent and the pawl lock should break contact at the same moment the detent roller begins to move toward the neutral position.

ASSEMBLING TRANSMISSION

General Precautions

1. Make certain that all parts are absolutely clean. Keep hands and tools clean to avoid getting dirt into assembly. If work is stopped before assembly is completed, cover all openings with clean cloth.
2. All moving parts should be given a light coating of 10-W oil before installation. Thrust washers should be held in place with vaseline or chassis lubricant, sparingly applied.
3. Use all new gaskets and seals to avoid oil leaks.
4. Use care to avoid making nicks or burrs on parts, particularly at bearing surfaces and surfaces where gaskets are used.
5. It is extremely important to tighten all parts evenly and in the proper sequence to avoid distortion of parts and leakage at gaskets and other joints. Use a reliable torque wrench to tighten all bolts and nuts to specified torque and in specified sequence.

Install Planetary Gear Set

1. Install reverse ring gear rear thrust washer in transmission case, Fig. 75.
2. Compress ends of reverse band with Band Installing Clip J-2595 and install in case, Fig. 75. Remove clip.
3. Rotate reverse band approximately 45 degrees toward servo opening, insert anchor through opening and engage with hooked end of band, Fig. 76. Then rotate band back to normal position.
4. Hold band operating lever (with offset end) in place with strut shoulder toward inside of case and insert anchor shaft through case, anchor and lever, Fig. 77. Tapped end of shaft must be outward. If adjustment screw is not centered in servo opening, low band operating lever has been installed by mistake.
5. Install planet carrier front (steel) thrust washer on carrier with three tangs engaged in holes in carrier.
6. Install planet carrier rear (bronze) thrust washer in case with three tangs engaged in holes in case. Then install assembled planetary gear set in case. If gear set is properly installed and thrust washers are in place, chamfer on output shaft journal will be flush with rear end of transmission case bushing.

Install Rear Oil Pump & Pressure Regulator Valve

1. Place rear oil pump gasket against transmission case, install plate and line up bolt holes. Do not use pump cover gasket, which has a smaller center hole, Fig. 78.
2. Install oil pump drive key cushion, Fig. 79, and drive key in output shaft. Then install driving gear to engage key. Install old gear in same position as before removal; install a new gear either way.
3. Lubricate both pump gears and pump body. Then install driven gear and body over driving gear (first series Buick 70 jobs, body had separate cover and gasket).
4. Install pump bolts with lockwashers, torque tighten evenly and alternately to 5 lbs. ft. Then tighten in same sequence to 25-30 lbs. ft.

Caution: If pump body and cover are separate, be certain that cover is centered on body, otherwise rear bearing retainer cannot be installed.

5. Turn output shaft to make sure pump operates freely.
6. Install lubrication oil pressure regulator valve spring, valve and valve seat in transmission case. Tighten valve seat with a suitable drag link socket.

Install Parking Lock Ratchet Wheel & Rear Bearing Retainer

1. Install a retaining ring in forward groove in output shaft and install ratchet wheel. Then install retaining ring in rearward groove in output shaft, Fig. 80.
2. Insert valve operating rod through square hole in front face of rear bearing retainer and connect clevis to cross shaft lever with snap fastener or clevis pin. Socket on forward end of operating rod must face bottom of bearing retainer.

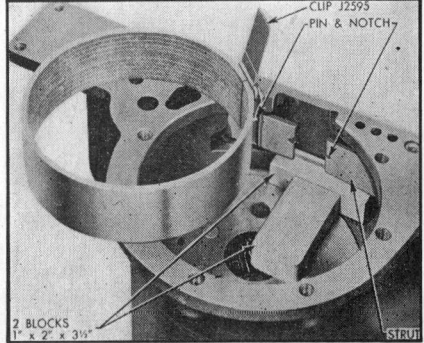

Fig. 83 Installation of low band and struts

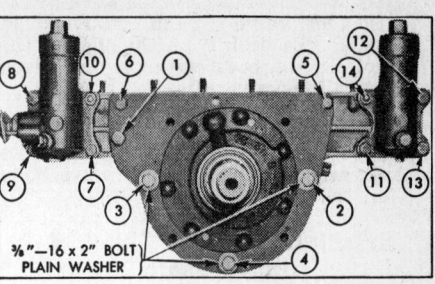

Fig. 84 Tightening sequence on accumulator and reaction flange bolts. 1955-60

Fig. 85 Reaction shaft flange and accumulator bolt tightening sequence, 1953-54

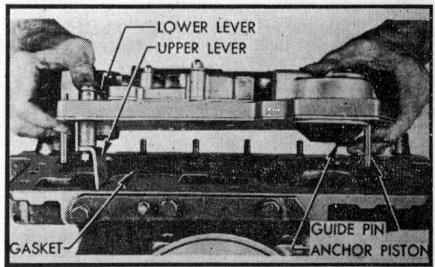

Fig. 86 Installing valve and servo body assembly

3. Install rear bearing retainer and gasket on transmission case. Use lockwashers on attaching bolts and torque tighten to 35-50 lbs. ft.
4. Install universal joint retaining ring in groove in output shaft.

1955-61 Service Note

After the rear bearing retainer is installed as outlined above, the control valve linkage must be adjusted as follows:

1. Move shift lever to park position, making certain output shaft is locked, then push control valve (in valve body) away from stop pin (on servo body) just enough to remove play from linkage. Then check clearance between stop pin and end of valve, using a feeler gauge as shown in Fig. 81. Clearance should be .030" to .040".
2. If clearance is not correct, loosen lock bolt on adjusting lever at valve lower operating lever and adjust to obtain proper clearance.
3. Tighten lock bolt on adjusting lever, making sure clearance does not change.
4. Move shift lever to drive position and note position of control valve.

End of valve should be 1/32" in either direction from the edge of the hole in the body with play removed from the valve, Fig. 82.

5. The valve body can be moved approximately 1/32" in either direction by loosening the valve body bolts slightly and shifting the valve body on the servo body.

Install Low Band, Clutch & Input Shaft

1. Install low band operating lever (with adjusting screw) and shaft on side of case having large servo opening, and install low band anchor lever and shaft on opposite side. Strut shoulders of levers must be toward inside of case and tapped ends of shafts must be outward.

2. With assembly standing on end of rear bearing retainer, install two wooden blocks as shown in Fig. 83. Set low band struts in position, with notched ends together and other ends engaged in strut shoulders of levers. Spread struts as far apart as possible.

3. Compress ends of low band with Band Installing Clip J-2595, Fig. 83. A used band must be reinstalled in original position (heaviest wear will be on anchor end); a new band can be installed either way.

4. Install band in case with ends between struts and rest band on wooden blocks. Apply operating lever and remove installing clip and blocks. **Caution:** Make certain that notches on struts straddle pins in ends of bands.

5. Place bronze reaction gear thrust washer centrally over sun gear.

6. Install clutch assembly. If drum binds against low band so that clutch does not go all the way down, use a hooked wire to lift band on side opposite struts.

7. Place bronze thrust washer on front face of clutch hub. Then use a flashlight to make sure that all four thrust washers are centrally located so that input shaft can be inserted.

8. Make sure that ends of input shaft oil seal ring are properly locked, and retaining ring is in its groove. Then install input shaft until retaining ring rests on clutch hub. It may be necessary to wiggle the shaft to get it through all four thrust washers.

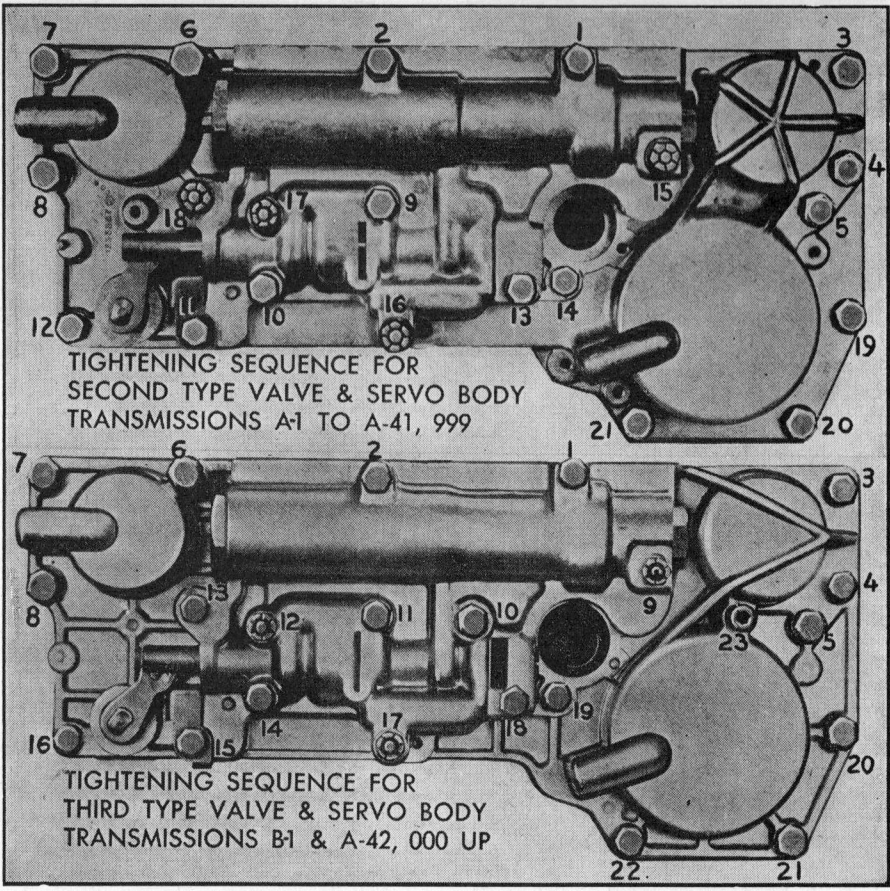

Fig. 87   Valve and servo body bolt tightening sequence, 1953-54

Install Reaction Flange, Front Oil Pump & Accumulators

1. Install a $\frac{5}{16}$" guide pin in accumulator bolt hole at each end of flange on transmission case.

2. Place reaction shaft flange gasket in position on case so that all holes in gasket and case are aligned.

3. Make certain that ends of oil seal rings on flange hub are properly locked. Then install flange on case, using care to avoid damaging oil seal rings.

4. Install low accumulator and gasket on same side as low band operating lever and adjustment screw. Install high accumulator and gasket on opposite side of flange. Make sure holes in gaskets match holes in flange. Coat accumulator bolt threads with No. 3 Permatex (nonhardening) and install bolts and nuts with lockwashers but do not tighten. Remove guide pins.

5. Install three special bolts (⅜" x 2") with *plain* washers in positions marked 2, 3, 4, in Figs. 84, 85. These bolts are for assembly purposes only. Install regular pump cover bolts, nuts and lockwashers at positions marked 1, 5, 6. Coat threads of No. 5 and 6 bolt with Permatex No. 3.

6. Tighten all bolts and nuts (1 through 14) to 5 lbs. ft. torque in the numerical sequence shown in Figs. 84, 85. Following the same sequence, torque tighten bolts 1 through 4 to 35-40 lbs. ft. and remaining bolts and nuts to 20-25 lbs. ft.

7. Remove three special bolts and tighten accumulator body caps to 40-50 lbs. ft. torque.

8. If edge of flange gasket projects beyond bottom surface of transmission case, use a sharp knife to trim it flush.

1955-61 Service Note

The installation procedure of the reaction shaft flange assembly is the same as previous models except for the following adjustment, and the installation of

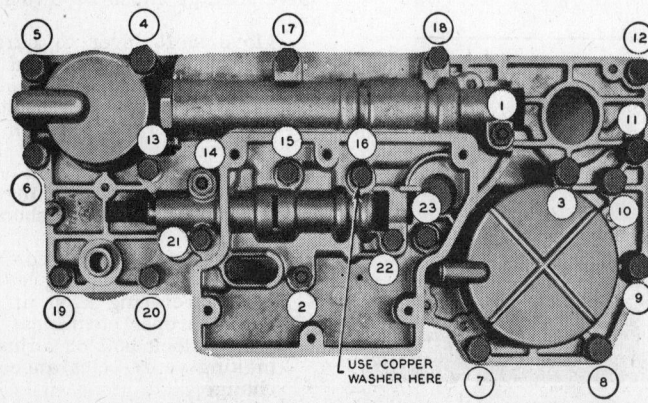

Fig. 88   Valve and servo body tightening sequence. 1955-61

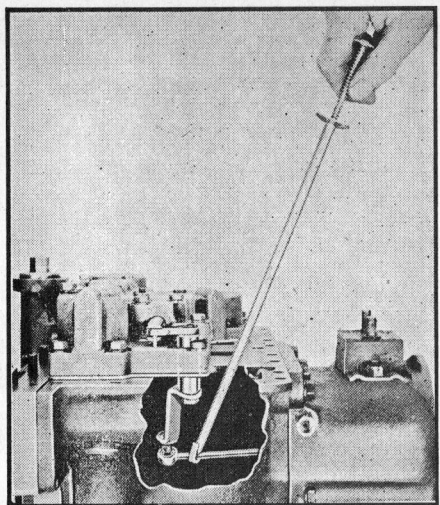

Fig. 89 Connecting valve operating rod to upper lever

the new input shaft snap ring which is the final assembly step.

Output Shaft End Play, Adjust 1955-61

This adjustment provides control of end play between the direct drive clutch planetary gear set and transmission case and tends to reduce the "clunk" when shifting from low to reverse and vice-versa.

A selective thrust washer has been installed between the reaction gear and reverse sun gear. The reaction gear has been recessed and the reverse sun gear has been reduced in thickness to allow a thicker washer to be used.

During assembly of transmission just prior to installation of reaction flange, a thrust washer of proper thickness should be selected. With clutch assembly in position and selective thrust washer installed with its grooved side toward sun gear, temporarily install reaction flange, using gasket and a few bolts.

With suitable tools, including an end play gauge and dial gauge, check end play in output shaft. End play should be between .020" and .034". If not within these limits, remove reaction flange and clutch and install a thrust washer of proper thickness, which are available in thicknesses of .100-.103", 114-117", 128-131" and 142-145".

If specified clearance cannot be obtained by using the selective thrust washers, recheck the other thrust washers and mating surfaces within the transmission case for defects.

When proper thrust washer has been selected, reassemble reaction flange to the case as outlined for previous models and install the input shaft snap ring.

Install Valve & Servo Body

1. With transmission laying bottom side up, raise reverse band operating lever and insert strut between shoulders on lever and end of band (rounded ends must be against lever and band). **Caution:** Do not lift lever during following steps because strut will fall into transmission case.
2. Install two ⁵⁄₁₆" guide pins in transmission case to guide each end of servo body, and install servo body spacer plate gasket over guide pins.
3. Push shift control valve and lower operating lever inward to align upper lever with opening in case. Hold anchor piston in place with finger and install valve and servo body on transmission case, Fig. 86.
4. Engage pin in control valve with slot in operating lever. Install various length bolts with lockwashers according to depth of holes through bodies. *On third type valve use copper washer on center bolt adjacent to suction pipe opening* Fig. 88 Install operating lever stop only if oil screen is first type; stop not required with second type screen. Remove guide pins.
5. If oil screen is second type, install cork gasket, suction pipe, retaining spring, and spring support which is attached by a valve body bolt and stud nut.
6. Tighten all bolts to 5 lbs. ft. torque in numerical sequence shown in Figs. 87, 88. Note that two different sequences are given; use the one which applies to the unit being serviced.
7. Repeating same sequence as above, tighten all ¼" bolts and nuts to 11-15 lbs. ft. torque and all ⁵⁄₁₆" bolts to 15-20 lbs. ft. While tightening bolts and nuts adjacent to shift control valve, operate valve to make certain that it is not binding; it may be necessary to adjust some bolts to the low torque limit to prevent valve binding.
8. Using Linkage Hook-Up Finger J-2591, Fig.89, position socket of valve operating rod under ball of valve upper operating lever and pull upward until ball snaps into socket.
9. Temporarily install shift lever on cross shaft and operate valve linkage to make sure it works freely. Move lever toward front of transmission to engage parking lock pawl in ratchet wheel. When pawl is fully engaged in wheel, pawl lock must be in full contact with pawl, Fig. 90.
10. Push shift control valve away from stop pin, *just enough to remove play from valve linkage.* Then check clearance between stop pin and end of valve, using feeler gauge. Clearance should be .030" to .040", Fig. 90.
11. When clearance is correct on 1949-54

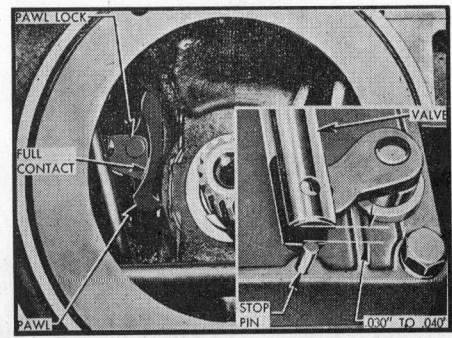

Fig. 90 Control valve linkage adjustment

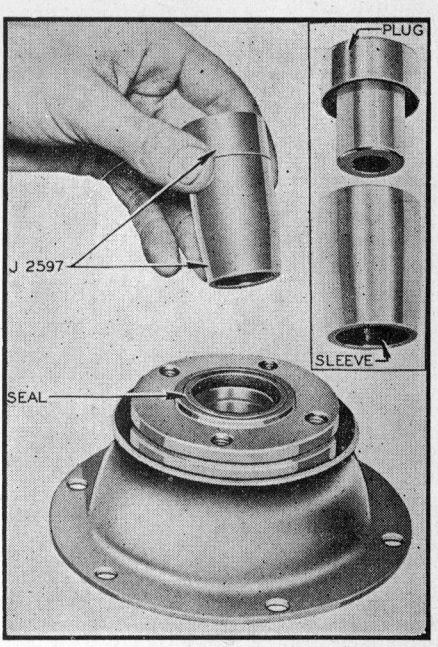

Fig. 91 Torque ball installing tool J-2597, 1953-54

models, spring travel at end of shift lever will be ⅛" to ³⁄₁₆". If clearance is not correct, adjust by turning clevis on valve operating rod.

12. If clearance is not correct on 1955-59 models, loosen lock bolt and shift adjusting lever on valve lower operating lever as required. Tighten bolt and nut on levers, making sure that adjustment does not change.

Install Oil Pan

1. Spread a thin coat of Permatex No. 3 on transmission case only in the area where case is cut away under oil pan gasket. This is adjacent to valve operating lever. Make sure new gasket is properly placed.
2. Install oil screen. Install oil pan with bolts and stud nuts provided with heavy duty internal tooth lockwashers. Evenly tighten all bolts and nuts to 15-18 lbs. ft. torque.

Torque Ball, Adjust, 1953-54

Correct adjustment of the torque ball is very important. If torque ball is loose and has end play, it will be noisy and will act as a pump to cause leakage of transmission lubricant. If torque ball is too tight, it will cause scoring of ball and retainers, and may cause breakage of bolts which attach torque ball to torque tube.

1. Install ⅜" headless guide pins in upper bolt holes in rear bearing retainer flange. Place one gasket or shim (having three notches in outer edge) and inner retainer on guide pins, with oil drain hole and notch in edge of retainer toward bottom of transmission.
2. Lubricate leather oil seal and bearing surfaces of torque ball and retainers with 10-W oil. Place torque ball in outer retainer so that "TOP" mark on ball and flat top edge of re-

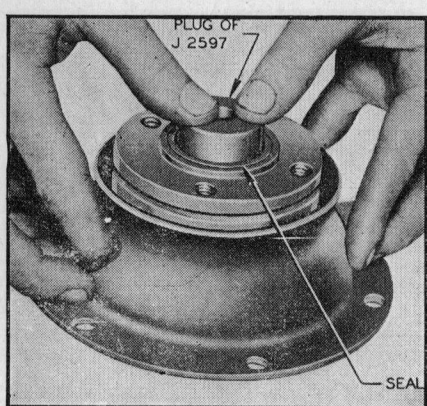

Fig. 92 Pushing installation tool into universal joint oil seal, 1953-54

tainer are together.

3. Assemble sleeve and plug of Installing Tool J-2597 together, Fig. 90. Then push tool through *rear* side of oil seal until leather edge is on plug, at which time the sleeve will drop off plug, Fig. 91.

4. Install torque ball and outer retainer with "TOP" sides toward top of transmission, using shims of sufficient thickness to fill space between flanges of inner and outer retainers. Hold plug of installing tool firmly against end of universal joint until oil seal has moved forward upon universal joint, then remove plug, Fig. 92.

5. Install thrust plate and all attaching bolts, removing guide pins and placing short bolts in these holes; *do not tighten bolts*. Thrust plate must be installed to prevent creeping or distortion of outer retainer.

6. Insert hardwood club, Fig. 93, in universal joint and, while moving torque ball up, down and sideways, tighten retainer bolts evenly to 35-40 lbs. ft. torque. **Caution:** It is absolutely necessary to continually move torque ball while tightening bolts in order to properly center the ball and retainers. If torque ball binds as bolts are tightened, tap outer retainer lightly at several points, using a soft mallet.

7. Attach spring scale to club at groove and test pull required to move torque ball when all bolts are tight, Fig. 94. If torque ball is too tight or too loose, loosen bolts and repeat centering and tightening operation. Then recheck drag with club and spring scale.

8. If torque ball is too tight after repeating the centering and tightening operation, remove the outer retainer and increase total thickness of shims; if ball is too loose, decrease

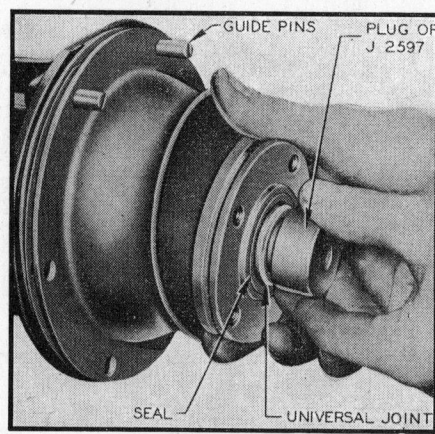

Fig. 93 Installing torque ball and retainer, 1953-54

Fig. 94 Checking torque ball drag, 1953-54

total thickness of shims. Shims are furnished in four thicknesses and are notched on outer edge for identification as follows:

Thickness	Notches
.000 - .006"	3
.009 - .011"	2
.011 - .013"	1
.013 - .015"	None

9. Always use Installing Tool J-2597 when installing torque ball to avoid damage to oil seal, Fig. 92.

10. Install torque ball boot. Turn large end back over small end, engage rib in small end in groove on flange of torque ball, then turn large end forward to engage rear end of outer retainer.

FLASHOMATIC

For Linkage Adjustment See Rambler Chapter

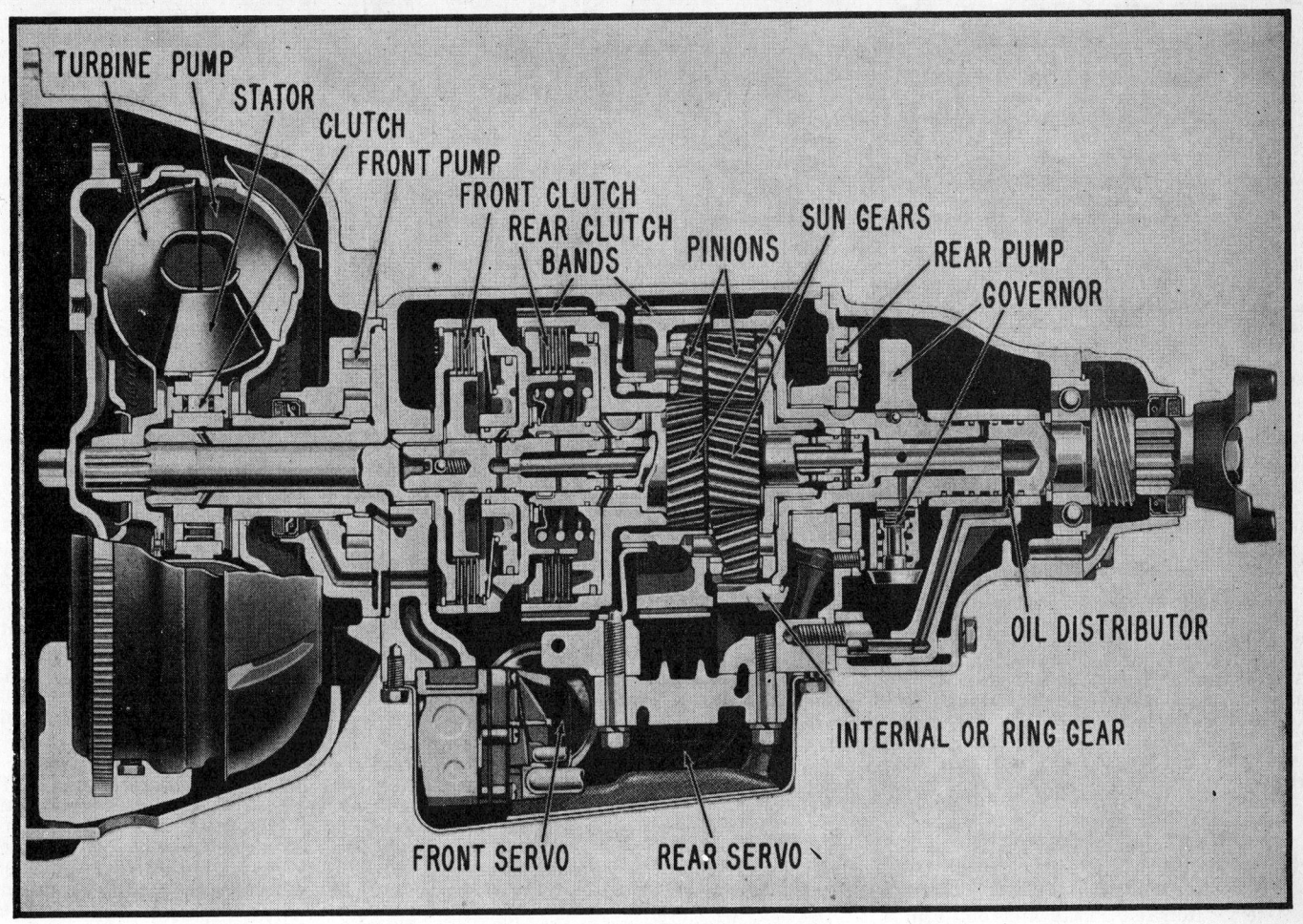

Fig. 1   Sectional view of transmission

CONTENTS

Description 233
Trouble Shooting 30

Maintenance

Adding Fluid 234
Changing Fluid 234

"In Car" Repairs

Bands, Adjust 234
Air Pressure Checks...................236
Vacuum and Solenoid Control...........235
Pressure Regulator Valve..............236
Control Valve 236
Servos 237
Governor 238

Repairs Requiring Transmission Removal

Transmission, Disassemble 238
Front Pump 238
Rear Pump 238
Output Shaft and Internal Gear........238
Pinion Carrier 238
Sprag Clutch 239
Center Support 239
Front Clutch 239
Rear Clutch and Primary Sun Gear......239
Transmission, Assemble 240

DESCRIPTION

The two major assemblies of the transmission, Fig. 1, are: (1) The torque converter which provides for a smooth transfer of power through the use of fluid, supplies a range of torque multiplication and, combined with the transmission assembly, permits elimination of the conventional clutch pedal; (2) a hydraulically controlled planetary transmission which provides three forward ratios and one reverse ratio. The transmission normally starts in 2nd gear regardless of throttle. When more power is required, the transmission may be "kicked-down" from 3rd to 2nd gear or from 2nd to 1st gear by depressing the accelerator pedal beyond the wide open throttle position.

Torque Converter

The torque converter consists of (1) a pump (driving member) connected to the engine crankshaft, (2) a turbine (driven member) splined to the transmission input shaft and (3) a stator (reaction member) connected to the transmission case through a freewheel (one-way clutch) unit.

These units are enclosed in a housing filled with a fluid. The starter ring gear

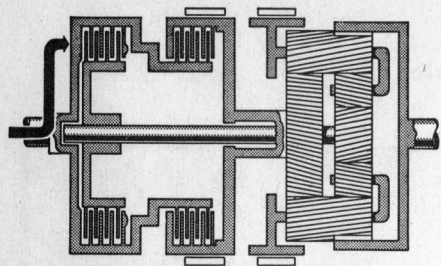

Fig. 2 Power flow in neutral. None of the gear train members are held or driving

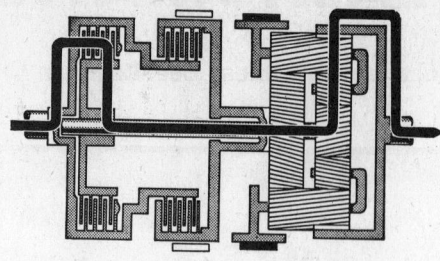

Fig. 3 Power flow in Low. Front clutch and rear band are applied

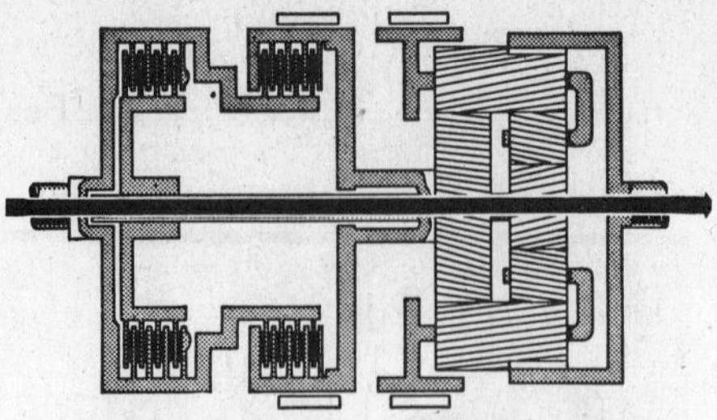

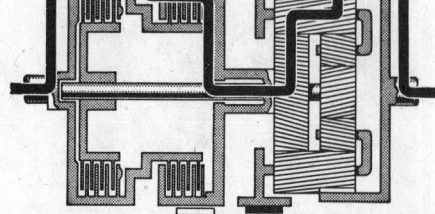

Fig. 5 Power flow in high. Front and rear clutches are applied

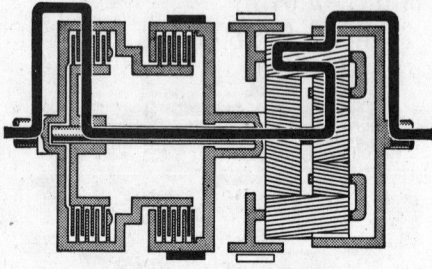

Fig. 4 Power flow in Intermediate. Front clutch and front band are applied

Fig. 6 Power flow in Reverse. Rear clutch and rear band are applied

is welded to the pump housing and is not serviced separately. The converter assembly is welded together in manufacture and cannot be disassembled for service.

Planetary Gear Train

A compound planetary gear train is used to provide for low, intermediate, high and reverse ratios as certain gears or combination of gears are held or driven. The selection of the proper driving range supplies the necessary gear ratio to provide smooth performance and to meet all driving conditions.

The gear train consists of a primary sun gear, a secondary sun gear, primary and secondary pinions held in a common pinion carrier, an internal gear that is attached to the transmission output shaft. The transfer of power through the transmission is dependent on the combination of gears held or driven. Figs. 2 to 6 show the power flow in the various ratios.

MAINTENANCE

Adding Fluid

Use Automatic Transmission Fluid only. Check fluid level every 1000 miles.

To check the level, place the gear selector button in the N position and set the hand brake. Start the engine and

operate it for approximately four minutes or until the engine and transmission have reached operating temperature.

Press the buttons D-2, D-1, L and R and then to the D-2 position. Remove the dipstick, wipe clean and re-insert. Then remove again and check the fluid level. The quantity of fluid required to raise the fluid level from the L mark to the F mark on the dipstick is approximately 1½ pints.

Changing Fluid

The transmission and converter should be drained and refilled with Automatic Transmission Fluid at 15,000 mile intervals. The fluid must be drained from the transmission and converter after operation before the fluid has a chance to cool.

Turn the converter until one of the drain plugs is visible through the round or square opening hole in the converter

housing. Remove this plug and quickly turn the converter 180 deg. and remove the second drain plug. Remove the transmission case oil filler tube at the right side of the oil pan.

After the oil has completely drained, replace the oil filler tube. Replace and tighten the two converter drain plugs and tighten to a torque of 7 to 10 lb. ft.

Pour five quarts of fluid (six in 80 series) in the transmission and set the parking brake. Start the engine and run it with selector button in N position. Add 3½ quarts of oil and press the selector buttons through all ranges. Check the level and, if necessary, add oil to bring the fluid to the F mark on the dipstick.

Do not overfill as this will cause foaming when the transmission is warm. If too much oil has been inserted, remove the excess with a suction gun.

"In Car" Repairs

BANDS, ADJUST

The front and rear band of the transmission should be adjusted at 15,000 mile intervals or as operation of the transmission indicates.

Front Band

The tool shown in Fig. 7 is especially made for this adjustment. However, by using a piece of ¼" wide metal block and an ordinary end or box wrench a satisfactory adjustment can be made. With transmission oil pan removed, back off the adjusting screw lock nut and screw far enough to permit the ¼" metal block to be inserted between the

Fig. 7 Adjusting front band with Tool J-5880

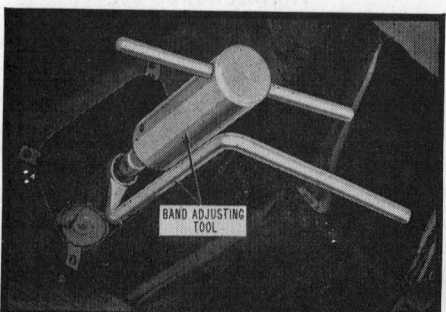

Fig. 8. Adjusting rear band with Tool J-5883

Fig. 9 Oil pressure test take-off point

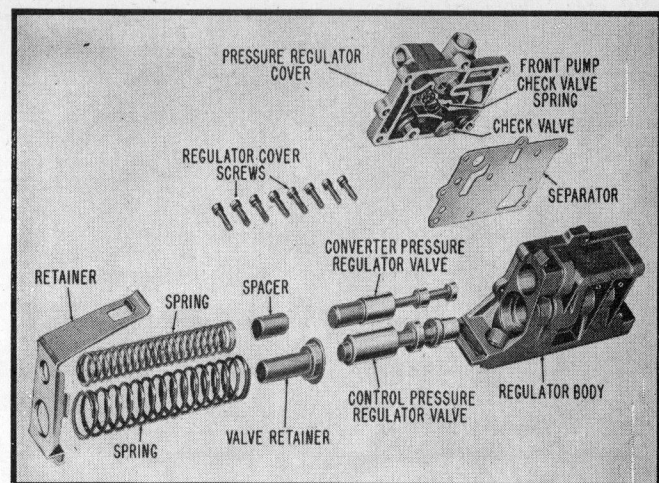

Fig. 11 Pressure regulator valve assembly

servo piston rod and adjusting screw. Turn screw until it contacts metal block. Then tighten adjusting screw a little more (equivalent to 10 inch lbs.) and back off one turn on 1957 and ½ turn on 1958-61. Use torque wrench to tighten lock nut to 20-25 lbs. ft.

Rear Band

The tool shown in Fig. 8 is especially made for this adjustment. However, a satisfactory adjustment may be made by using a conventional torque wrench. Loosen lock nut and tighten adjusting screw to a torque of 10 lb. ft. Then back off the screw 1½ turns and tighten lock nut to a torque of 35-40 lbs. ft.

VACUUM & SOLENOID CONTROL

Service Note

A new and improved method for adjusting vacuum and solenoid control pressure setting for proper shift pattern without stall testing supercedes any previous instructions. This new method requires the use of Vacuum and Solenoid Control Adjusting Tool Kit J-8773 and eliminates the possibility of damage to the transmission while stall testing, saves valuable time and provides a more positive means of properly setting the shift pattern.

1. Remove pressure test plug at left front side of transmission, Fig. 9, and install the ⅛″ pipe plug extension provided with the tool kit.
2. Connect an oil pressure gauge to this extension outlet.
3. Disconnect vacuum line at the vacuum and solenoid unit.
4. Connect Tool J-8773 to the vacuum line and vacuum and solenoid unit.
5. Attach vacuum gauge to "T" fitting on test line.
6. Start engine and warm up to operating temperature with transmission in neutral.
7. At engine idle speed of 475 rpm in neutral, turn needle valve on test line to lower vacuum reading on test gauge as follows:

Series	Vacuum, In.
01 (L-head eng.)	8.6

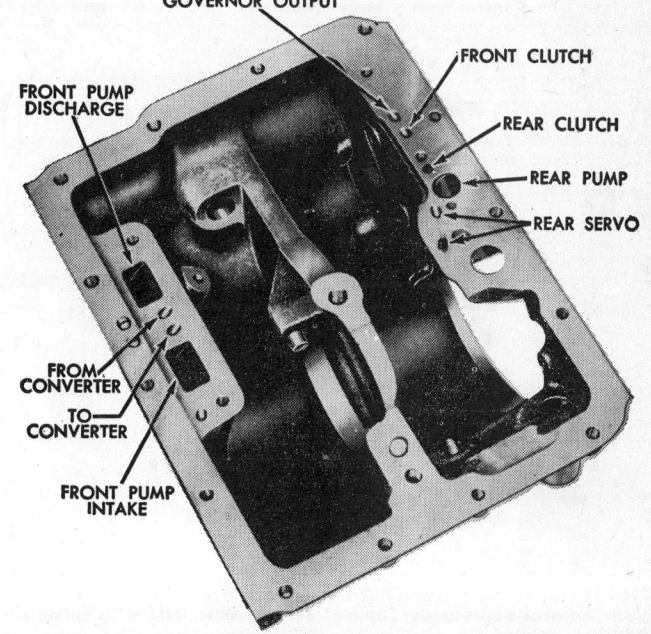

Fig. 10 Oil passages in transmission case

Series	Vacuum, In.
01 (O.H.V. eng.)	10.5
10	10.5
20	12.1
80	13.8

8. The oil pressure gauge should then read:

Series	P.S.I.*
01	85
5710, 5810	85
5820, 5920	85
5880, 5980	85
5910 Early	85
5910 Special	100
5910 Late	100
6010	100
6020	85
6080	85

*Plus or minus 3 psi.

9. In order to obtain the above oil pressure readings, loosen the vacuum and solenoid unit locknut and turn the unit in toward the case if pressure is too low; if pressure is too high, turn away from case.
10. If proper vacuum cannot be obtained or held after adjusting the needle valve on the vacuum test line, this would indicate a leaky diaphragm in the vacuum and solenoid unit or a possible leak in the test line connectors.
11. After making the correct adjustment, cover the bleed hole provided in the needle valve to stop atmospheric pressure from entering the test line. This will bring the vacuum reading on the test gauge to optimum engine vacuum and the oil pressure gauge should then read 55 to 65 psi.
12. With the rear wheels raised off the floor, place the transmission in D-2 position. Cover the bleed hole in the needle valve. Then accelerate the engine so the transmission shifts into direct drive. The pressure gauge should then read 25 to 35 psi. *Fluctuation of the oil pressure gauge at idle in neutral is a natural condition.*

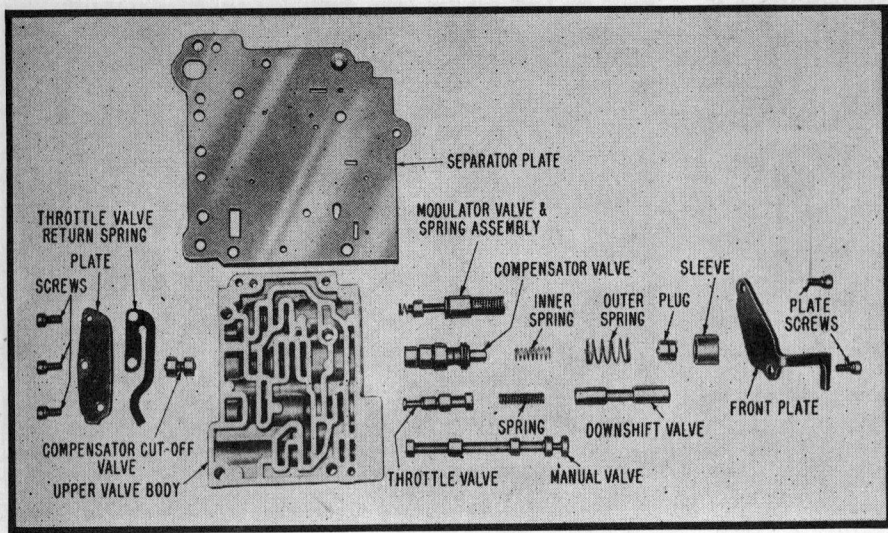

Fig. 12   Control valve body (upper).   Series 01 and 10

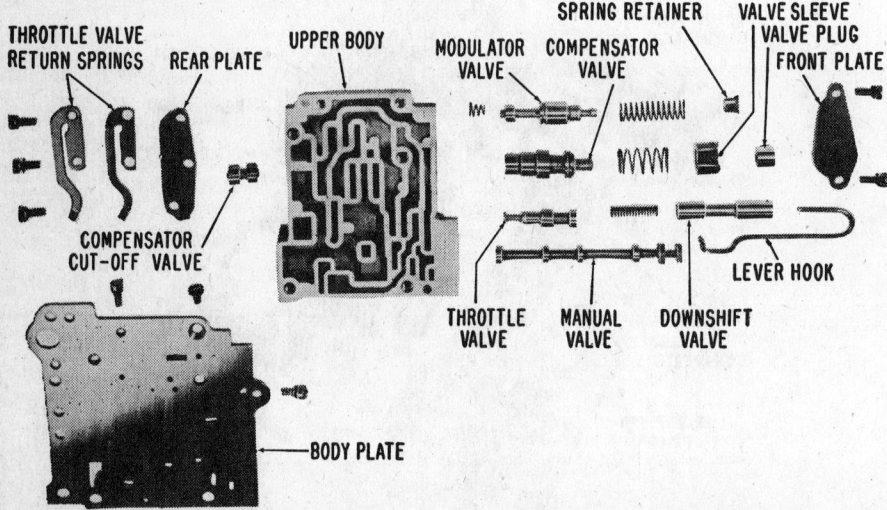

Fig. 13   Control valve body (upper) for transmissions with sprag clutch

AIR PRESSURE CHECKS

A series of air pressure tests can be made on the transmission with the unit in the car. These tests are helpful in determining if clutches, bands and servos are operating in a normal manner.

To make the tests, drain the fluid from the transmission. Remove the transmission oil pan, screen and control valve assembly. The front servo tubes should remain in the front servo and the attaching screw must be tight. *When making tests, hold a clean towel over the transmission opening to prevent excessive oil spray.* Refer to Fig. 10 for oil passage locations.

Front Clutch

Apply air pressure to the front clutch passage. Listen for a dull thud which indicates the clutch is operating. Keep air pressure in the passage for several seconds to check for leaks in this circuit.

Governor Valve

Remove the governor inspection hole cover and apply air pressure to the front clutch passage. Listen for a click and watch the valve snap inward.

Rear Clutch

Apply air pressure to the rear clutch passage. Listen for a dull thud which indicates the clutch is operating. Keep air pressure in the passage for several seconds to check for leaks in this circuit.

Front Band and Front Servo

Apply air pressure to the front servo apply tube and observe band application.

Rear Band and Rear Servo

Apply air pressure to the rear servo and observe band application.

Result of Tests

If servos, bands, clutches and governor operation is normal with air pressure, the condition of *no drive, erratic upshifts or downshifts* points to the control valve assembly and pressure regulator valve. These should be disassembled, cleaned and inspected.

PRESSURE REGULATOR VALVE

Remove oil pan and screen. Maintain constant pressure on spring retainer to prevent damage to springs and remove retainer from bosses on pressure regulator valve. Remove springs and pilots. Remove the three pipes. Unfasten and remove the pressure regulator valve from the case.

Disassemble the unit as shown in Fig. 11. After cleaning and inspecting parts, assemble the unit and tighten the regulator body screws to a torque of 17-22 inch lbs.

CONTROL VALVE

Remove the oil pan and screen. Remove

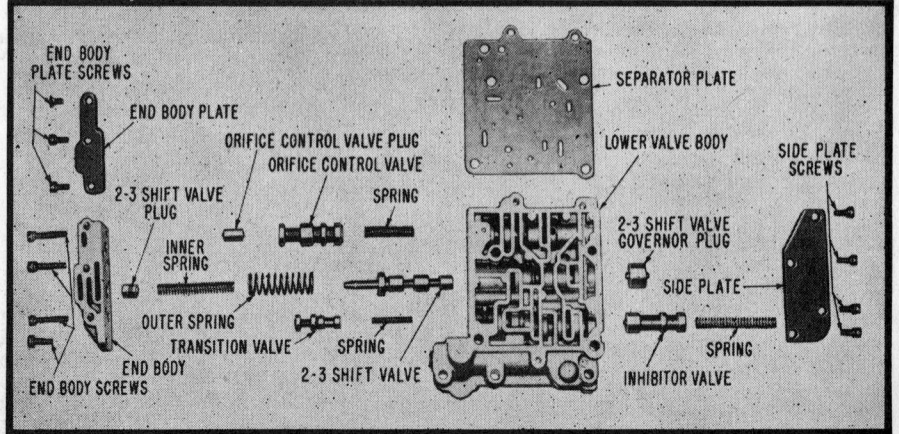

Fig. 14   Control valve body (lower).   Series 01 and 10

the large control pressure tube and small compensator pressure tube from the pressure regulator valve and control valve.

Loosen the front servo retaining screw and unfasten the control valve (3 screws) from the transmission case. Remove vacuum and solenoid unit from case and align throttle valve lever hook to permit removal of the control valve. Disengage the front servo pressure tubes from the control valve and lift the assembly from the transmission case.

When servicing the control valve it is recommended that each valve body of the assembly be disassembled, cleaned, inspected and reassembled one at a time. This will reduce the possibility of accidentally interchanging the springs in the unit. To aid in reassembly, it is also recommended that the parts of each body be placed on a clean bench in the order in which they are removed from the body.

Disassemble and assemble the unit as illustrated in Figs. 12 to 15.

When disassembled, clean all parts in each valve body thoroughly with clean solvent and blow dry with moisture-free compressed air. Inspect all valves and valve bores for scores and burns. Check all fluid passages for obstructions. Inspect all mating surfaces for burrs and distortion. Inspect all springs for distortion.

Crocus cloth may be used to polish valves and plugs. However, care must be taken to avoid rounding the sharp edges of valves and plugs. Check all valves and plugs for freedom of movement in their respective bores. Valves and plugs, when dry, should fall from their own weight in their respective bores.

Tighten attaching screws to a torque of 8-10 lbs. ft.

SERVOS

To remove the front servo, remove the cap screw which holds it to the case. Hold the actuating lever strut with one hand and lift the servo from the case. To remove the rear servo, take out the two attaching cap screws. Then hold the anchor strut and lift the servo from the case.

Front Servo Repairs

Disassemble the servo as shown in Fig. 16. When disassembled, inspect the servo body for cracks, burrs and obstructed fluid passages. Inspect piston bore and piston stem for scores. Inspect the actuating lever and shaft for wear and freeness in the servo body. Also inspect the

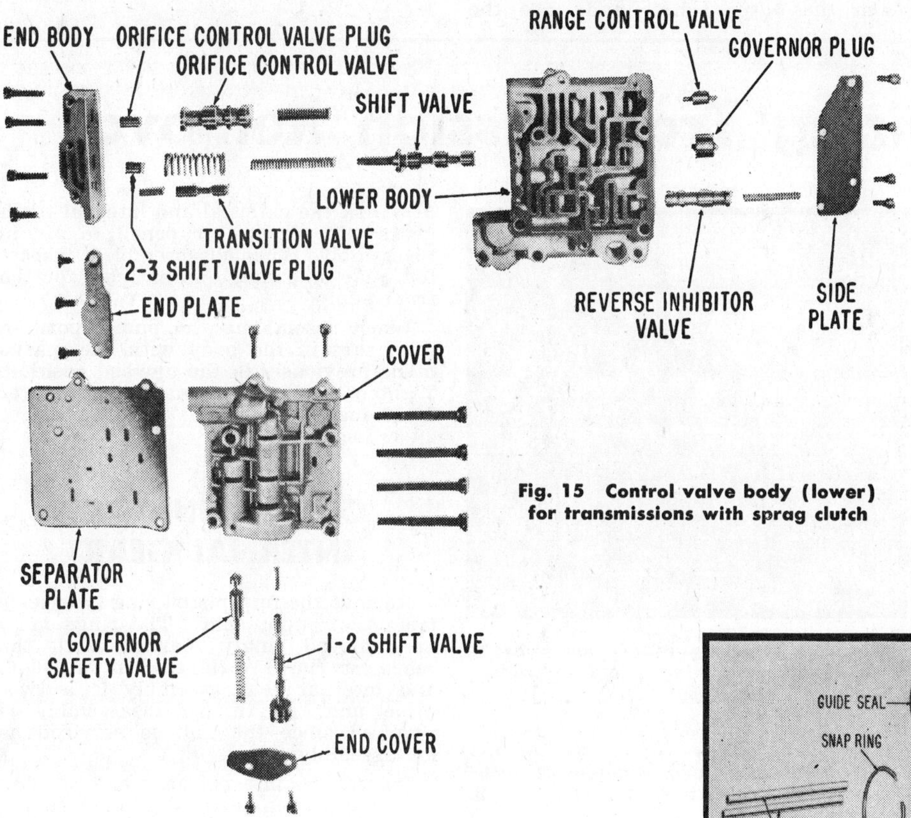

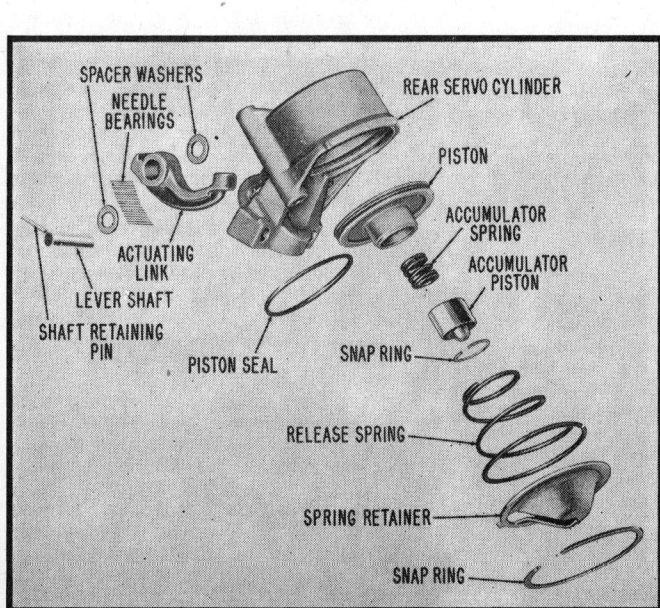

Fig. 15 Control valve body (lower) for transmissions with sprag clutch

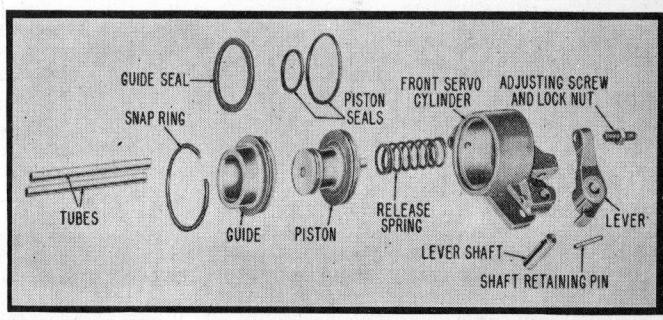

Fig. 16 Front servo assembly. Series 20 and 80 (typical of series 01 and 10)

Fig. 17 Rear servo assembly

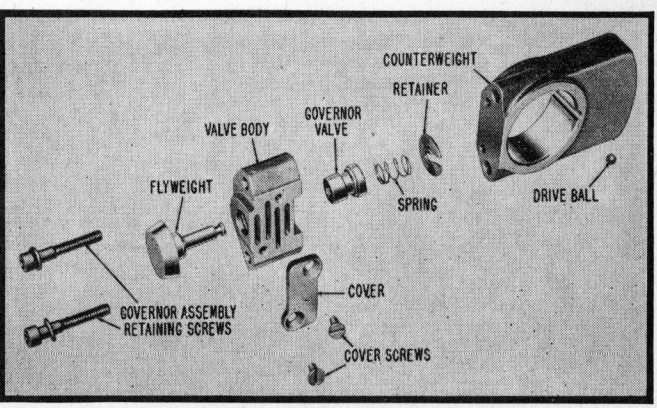

Fig. 18 Governor and counterweight assembly

adjusting screw threads and the threads in the actuating lever. Inspect the servo band for wear and bonding of the lining to the band. Replace the band if the grooves in the lining are worn even with the rest of the lining. Inspect the band ends for cracks and distortion. Install the piston and guide in the servo body and check for freedom of travel.

Minor burrs may be removed with crocus cloth. However, parts showing deep burrs, scores, cracks or excessive wear should be replaced.

Lubricate all parts with automatic transmission fluid before starting reassembly. Then assemble the unit as shown in Fig. 16.

Rear Servo Repairs

Disassemble the servo as shown in Fig. 17. Inspect the parts for the same conditions outlined for the front servo.

GOVERNOR

After removing the extension case and oil distributor, remove the snap ring from the output shaft and slide the governor toward the rear of the transmission. Remove the governor drive ball from the output shaft.

Disassemble the governor and counterweight assembly as shown in Fig. 18. When disassembled, inspect the mating surfaces of the governor valve and counterweight for burrs and distortion. These surfaces must be flat. Inspect all fluid passages for obstructions. Inspect the governor valve for freedom of movement in the valve body.

Assemble the parts as shown in Fig. 18.

Repairs Requiring Transmission Removal

TRANSMISSION, DISASSEMBLE

1. Remove pressure regulator valve, control valve assembly and both servos as previously outlined.
2. The next step is to check the mainshaft end play for future reference when reassembling the transmission. Remove one of the front oil pump retaining screws and mount a dial indicator so that the indicator button rests against the end of the input shaft. Use a large screwdriver to pry the front clutch to the rear and, while holding pressure against the screwdriver, zero the dial indicator. Insert the screwdriver between the parking gear and the transmission case and pry the units toward the front of the case. *If end play is not within the limits of .010" to .029", record the amount of end play present so that a suitable thrust washer may be installed to establish the correct end play when the transmission is reassembled.*
3. Unfasten the front pump from the transmission case and tap the screw bosses lightly with a plastic hammer and remove the pump and gasket.
4. Remove the extension housing, oil distributor and governor assembly as outlined previously.
5. Remove rear pump inlet tube. Using tool shown in Fig. 19, remove outlet tube. Slide pump off output shaft and remove gasket and rear pump drive key.
6. Hold the pinion carrier in position and slide the output shaft and internal gear toward rear of transmission. Remove thrust washer from pinion carrier. *This washer, supplied in various thicknesses, determines the end play of the mainshaft assembly.*
7. Hold pressure against the primary sun gear shaft and remove pinion carrier by sliding toward rear of case. Remove thrust washer from inside of pinion carrier. *Note position of cone on inner diameter of thrust washer.*
8. Remove the two remaining cap screws which attach center support to transmission case. *These screws*

Fig. 19 Removing rear pump outlet tube with snap ring pliers or with special tool J-5865

are located on the outside of the transmission case. Remove the center support through the rear of the case.
9. Remove front clutch, rear clutch and sun gears as a unit. Remove the thrust washer from in front of the front clutch. Separate front and rear clutches and remove thrust washer and contour thrust washer from between clutches.
10. Remove and tilt front band and remove through bottom of case.

FRONT PUMP

When disassembled, inspect the pump body for excessive wear and scores. Inspect the external and internal tooth gears for scores, scratches and excessive wear. Inspect the stator support face for scores, scratches and excessive wear.

Minor scratches and scores can be removed with crocus cloth. However, parts showing deep scratches, scores or excessive wear should be replaced.

Assemble the pump as shown in Fig. 20. Tighten the stator support attaching screws to a torque of 25-35 lb. ft.

REAR PUMP

Before disassembling the pump, Fig. 21, mark the external and internal tooth gears with crayon or pencil to aid in reassembly. When disassembled, inspect for wear or damage as outlined for the front pump.

When assembling the pump, position the gears in the body with the marks made previously in the upward position. Tighten the large screws to a torque of 50-60 inch lbs. and the small screw to 20-30 inch lbs.

OUTPUT SHAFT & INTERNAL GEAR

Remove the four piston ring type seals from the output shaft. The rings must be removed singly starting with the rearmost ring. While the output shaft and internal gear assembly is a two-piece unit, no further disassembly is required since the unit is serviced as an assembly.

Inspect the internal gear and parking gear for broken teeth and burrs on the thrust surfaces. Inspect the output shaft for burrs and scores on the bearing surfaces and ring grooves. Inspect the rear pump drive keyway and governor drive ball socket for wear.

Minor burrs and scratches may be removed with crocus cloth. However, parts having broken teeth, large burrs, scratches or scores, or showing excessive wear should be replaced.

Install the four seal rings on the output shaft, starting with the foremost ring and working toward the rear.

PINION CARRIER

The pinion carrier is serviced as an assembly; therefore, there is no disassembly or assembly procedure. To check its serviceability, however, inspect the band surface and the inner and outer bushings for scores. Rotate the pinions on their shafts to check for freedom of movement and inspect for worn or broken teeth. Use a feeler gauge to check pinion end play, which should be .010" to .020". Inspect pinion shaft for tightness to the pinion carrier.

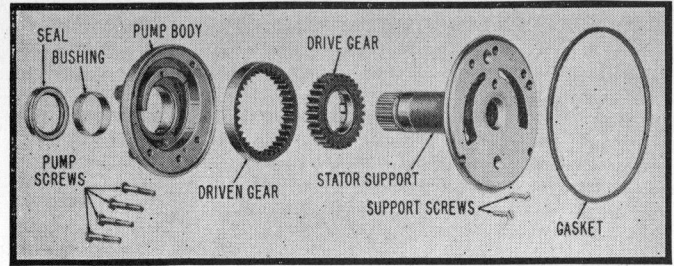
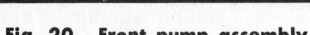

Fig. 20   Front pump assembly

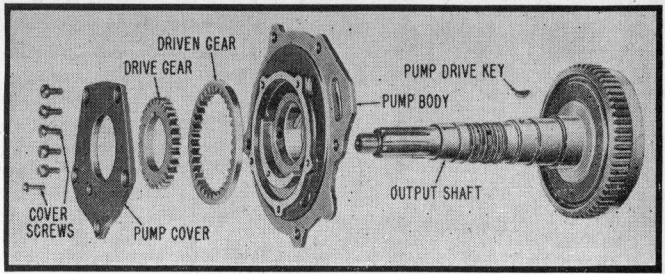

Fig. 21   Rear pump assembly

SPRAG CLUTCH

Series 20, 80

A sprag clutch, Fig. 21A, is incorporated in the pinion carrier on the above series cars. The outer race is fitted in the pinion carrier and is held in place by a snap ring. The inner sprag race is a machined surface on the center support.

The sprag clutch will perform the function of the rear band in low ratio while in D-1 range. When torque from the engine is delivered through the front clutch, the torque reaction on the one-way sprag clutch causes it to lock up and hold the drum stationary, thus giving low gear ratio. At the time of the 1-2 upshift, the front servo is engaged and as soon as the front band picks up the reaction torque, the one-way sprag clutch will start to free wheel and the transmission will be in second gear ratio.

The purpose of the sprag clutch is to aid in the timing of the 1-2 upshift and the 2-1 downshift.

CENTER SUPPORT

The center support is serviced only as an assembly. To check its serviceability, however, inspect for burrs or distortion, and the bearing surface for scores and scratches.

Minor burrs and scratches may be removed with crocus cloth. Any damage more serious than that requires the support to be replaced.

FRONT CLUTCH

Disassemble, Fig. 22

1. Remove clutch cover snap ring.
2. Remove turbine shaft and fiber thrust washer from clutch hub.

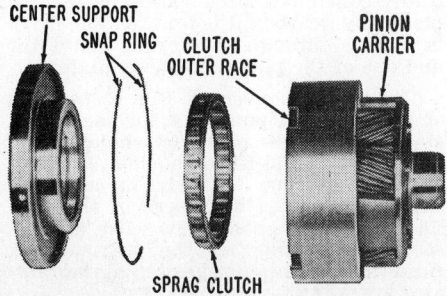

Fig. 21A   Center support, sprag clutch and pinion carrier

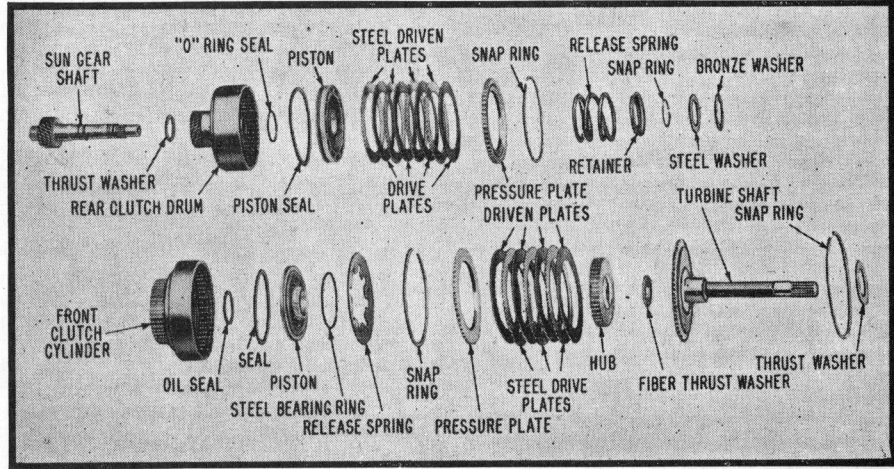

Fig. 22   Front and rear clutches and related parts

3. Remove plates and clutch hub from drum; also clutch pressure plate.
4. Using a suitable spring compressor (tool J-5875) on clutch release spring, exert sufficient pressure to compress spring and remove snap ring.
5. Remove tool and clutch spring.
6. Apply air pressure to clutch inlet hole to force clutch piston out of clutch drum bore.
7. Remove rubber outer piston seal from piston and remove piston metal wear ring from piston.
8. Remove O-ring seal from clutch drum.

Inspection

1. Inspect turbine shaft and clutch hub for burrs on thrust surfaces, splines and serrations.
2. Inspect clutch piston for burrs, scores or cracks.
3. Inspect clutch drum for burrs on thrust surfaces and splines, and clutch bore for scratches and scores.
4. Inspect clutch release spring for cracks or distortion and pressure plate for cracks and scratches.
5. Inspect steel plates for burrs on serration and for wear, and for flatness.
6. The lined plates should be replaced when grooves in lining are no longer visible, as if plates are warped.

Assemble

1. Lubricate all parts with transmission fluid before assembly.
2. Install new O-ring seal in clutch drum and a new seal on clutch piston and install piston in clutch drum bore.
3. Press piston down lightly until it bottoms in bore, being careful not to damage outer piston seal.
4. Install metal wear ring on piston.
5. Install clutch spring on piston with concave side upward.
6. Position compressor tool on spring and exert sufficient pressure to compress spring so that snap ring can be installed. Use the thicker snap ring.
7. Remove compressor and install pressure plate with smooth side upward.
8. Install hub in drum bore with thrust surface upward.
9. Install lined plates and steel plates alternately, starting with a lined plate.
10. Coat fiber thrust washer with heavy grease to hold it in place and position it on clutch hub.
11. Align serrations of clutch cover and turbine shaft with serrations in drum and install cover and snap ring.

REAR CLUTCH & PRIMARY SUN GEAR

Disassemble, Fig. 22

1. Remove two ring seals from primary sun gear shaft and remove rear clutch assembly.

FLASHOMATIC

2. Remove primary sun gear thrust washer and ring seals from sun gear shaft.
3. With a suitable spring compressor tool (J-5886), exert sufficient pressure on clutch spring to compress it so that snap ring can be removed.
4. Remove the balance of the clutch parts.

Inspection

1. Inspect primary sun gear and shaft for burrs, scratches, worn ring grooves and broken teeth.
2. Use an awl to check front clutch lubrication ball check valve in front end of sun gear shaft for freedom of movement.
3. Inspect the balance of the clutch parts as outlined for the front clutch. However, check each steel plate for proper coning. Each plate is coned to .010″ to .020″ clearance. If any plate requires replacement, the entire clutch plate pack should be installed.

Assemble

1. Lubricate all parts with transmission fluid before assembly.
2. Install new inner O-ring seal on drum hub and new clutch outer seal on piston.
3. Install piston in drum bore.
4. Press piston down until it bottoms, being careful not to damage outer seal.
5. Install clutch spring and retainer.
6. Compress spring and install snap ring.
7. Install bronze plates and steel plates alternately, starting with a steel plate. Steel plates are installed with concave side up.
8. Install pressure plate with smooth side down and install snap ring.
9. Install two ring seals on short end of primary sun gear shaft.
10. Install sun gear thrust washer.
11. Install two ring seals on sun gear shaft adjacent to sun gear.
12. Position clutch on sun gear shaft.
13. Install two remaining ring seals on primary sun gear shaft.

TRANSMISSION, ASSEMBLE

1. Place new front pump gasket in counterbore in transmission case. Install pump and tighten cap screws to a torque of 17-22 lb. ft.
2. Tilt front band and install through bottom of transmission case. Position band so that its anchor end is aligned with anchor in case.
3. Install sun gear steel thrust washer on rear clutch. Install secondary sun gear thrust washer (bronze) on top of steel washer. Position clutch on primary sun gear shaft and rotate front clutch to align serrations on bronze plates of rear clutch to permit engagement with rear clutch. Install turbine shaft thrust washer on turbine shaft. Then install entire assembly in case, being careful not to allow clutch assemblies to separate.
4. Place center support in case and install two cap screws and lockwashers; these washers must be installed with rolled edge toward case to assure a tight seal. Tighten cap screw 20-25 lb. ft.
5. Install rear band through rear of case and position it so that its anchor side (with depression) is toward adjusting screw.
6. Install primary sun gear thrust washer on sun gear shaft with cone of inner diameter of washer toward pinion carrier. Align ring seals on sun gear shaft to prevent breakage and install pinion carrier in case. Install output shaft front thrust washer on rear of pinion carrier.
7. *In the event mainshaft end play was not within specified limits when checked on disassembly, a thicker or thinner washer must be installed to bring end play within limits. Thrust washers are furnished in nominal thicknesses ranging from .061″ to .107″, six washers in all.*
8. Install output shaft and internal gear assembly so internal gear meshes with pinion carrier pinions.
9. Place rear pump drive key in keyway on output shaft. Use vaseline to hold a new pump gasket to transmission case. Align keyway of rear pump external gear with key on shaft and install rear pump.
10. Install governor, oil distributor, extension housing, rear servo, front servo, control valve assembly and pressure regulator as outlined previously.
11. Install transmission oil pan.

CRUISE-O-MATIC · EDSEL · FLIGHTOMATIC
FORD-O-MATIC★ · MERC-O-MATIC
MULTI-DRIVE · TURBO-DRIVE · TWIN TURBO-DRIVE

★ All 1953-58 and 1959-61 Three-Speed Units   For Linkage Adjustment See Car Chapter

CONTENTS

Description 240
Trouble Shooting 24

Maintenance

Adding Fluid 242
Changing Fluid 242

"In Car" Repairs

Bands, Adjust 243
Air Pressure Checks.....................243
Oil Pressure Tests......................245
Oil Pressure Regulator..................246
Control Valve...........................246
Front and Rear Servos...................246
Extension Housing Seal..................247
Oil Distributor 248
Governor 249

Repairs Requiring Transmission Removal

Transmission, Disassemble 249
Front Pump 250
Rear Pump 250
Output shaft and Internal Gear.........250
Pinion Carrier 250
Center Support 250
Front Clutch 250
Rear Clutch and Primary Sun Gear.......251
Transmission Case and Linkage..........252
Transmission, Assemble 252
Torque Converter 252

DESCRIPTION

These transmissions combine a three-element torque converter and a hydraulically-controlled three-speed and reverse planetary gearbox, Figs. 1, 1A. The drive is always through the torque converter and one of the planetary gear ranges.

The torque converter, Fig. 2, consists of an impeller (pump), a turbine and a stator. All these parts are enclosed and operate in a fluid-filled housing. When an aluminum torque converter is used the unit is air cooled by means of the fins. The steel torque converter, when used, is cooled by circulating the transmission fluid through a cooler located in the radiator lower tank.

The planetary gear train in all units transmit power from the torque con-

240

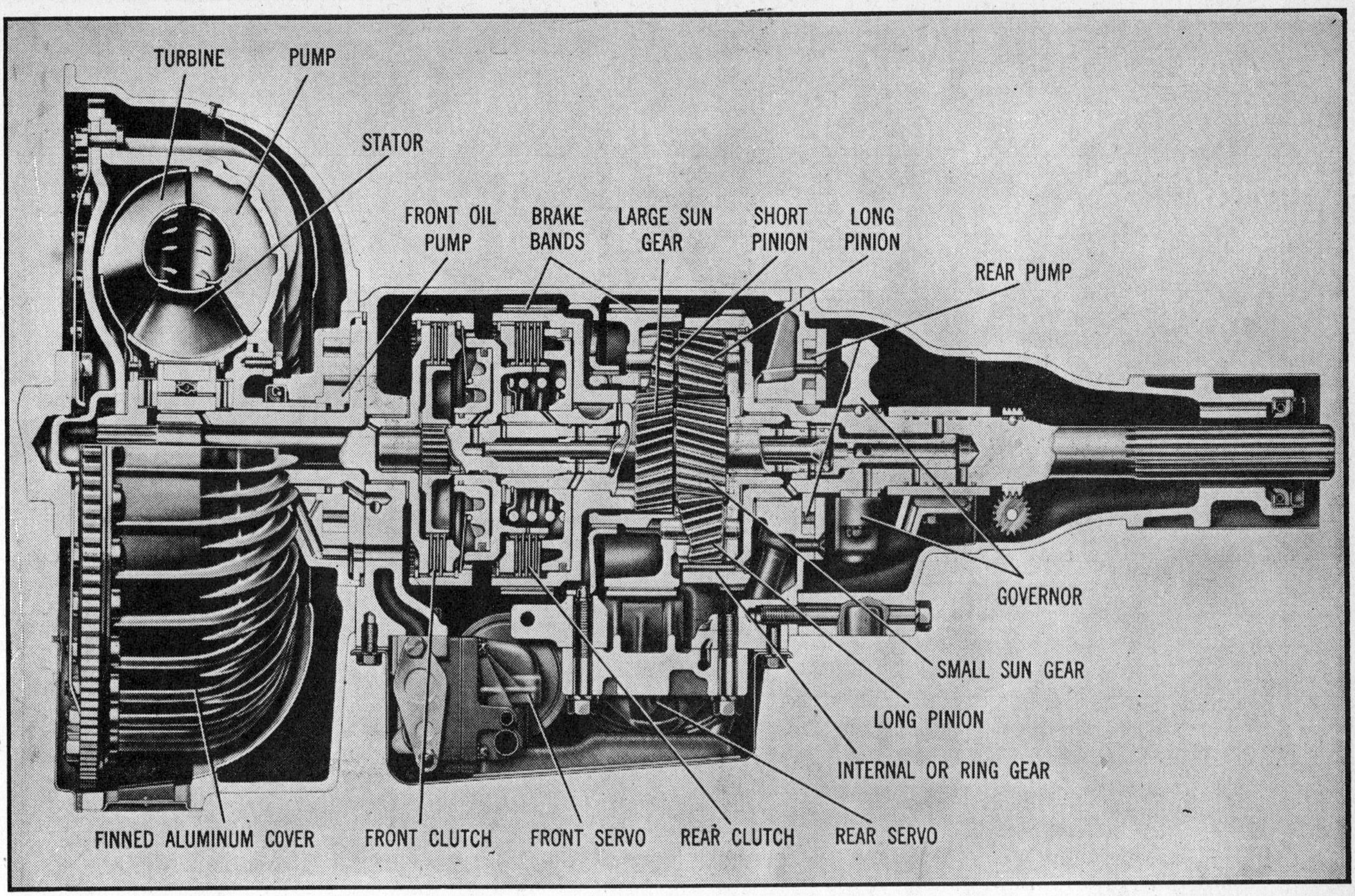

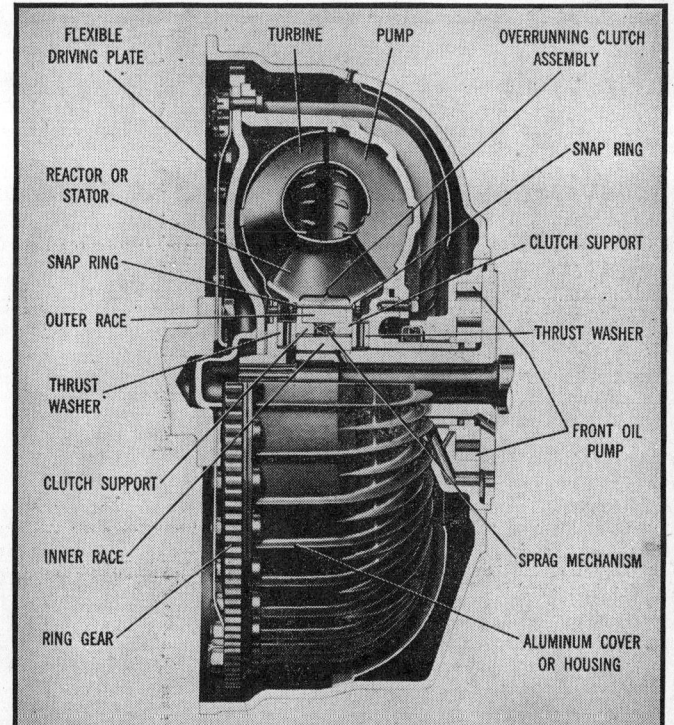

TURBINE PUMP

STATOR

FRONT OIL PUMP BRAKE BANDS LARGE SUN GEAR SHORT PINION LONG PINION

REAR PUMP

GOVERNOR

SMALL SUN GEAR

LONG PINION

INTERNAL OR RING GEAR

FINNED ALUMINUM COVER FRONT CLUTCH FRONT SERVO REAR CLUTCH REAR SERVO

Fig. 1 Sectional view of transmission with air-cooled torque converter

verter turbine shaft to the transmission output shaft. Hydraulic clutches and servo-operated bands drive or hold certain gears to provide the various transmission output ratios.

SPRAG CLUTCH

Edsel, Cruise-O-Matic, Multi-Drive, Twin Range Turbo-Drive, Flightomatic on 1961 Studebaker Six

The sprag clutch, Fig. 3, is incorporated in the pinion carrier on the above-mentioned transmissions only. The outer race is fitted in the pinion carrier and is held in place by a snap ring. The inner sprag race is a machined surface on the center support.

When the torque from the engine is delivered through the front clutch, the torque reaction of the one-way sprag clutch causes it to lock up and hold the drum stationary, thus giving low gear ratio. At the time of the 1-2 upshift, the front servo is engaged and as soon as the front band picks up the reaction torque, the sprag clutch will start to free wheel and the transmission will be in second gear ratio.

The purpose of the sprag clutch is to aid in the timing of the 1-2 upshift and 2-1 downshift.

FLEXIBLE DRIVING PLATE TURBINE PUMP OVERRUNNING CLUTCH ASSEMBLY

REACTOR OR STATOR

SNAP RING

SNAP RING

OUTER RACE

THRUST WASHER

CLUTCH SUPPORT

INNER RACE

RING GEAR

SNAP RING

CLUTCH SUPPORT

THRUST WASHER

FRONT OIL PUMP

SPRAG MECHANISM

ALUMINUM COVER OR HOUSING

Fig. 2 Sectional view of torque converter (air-cooled)

241

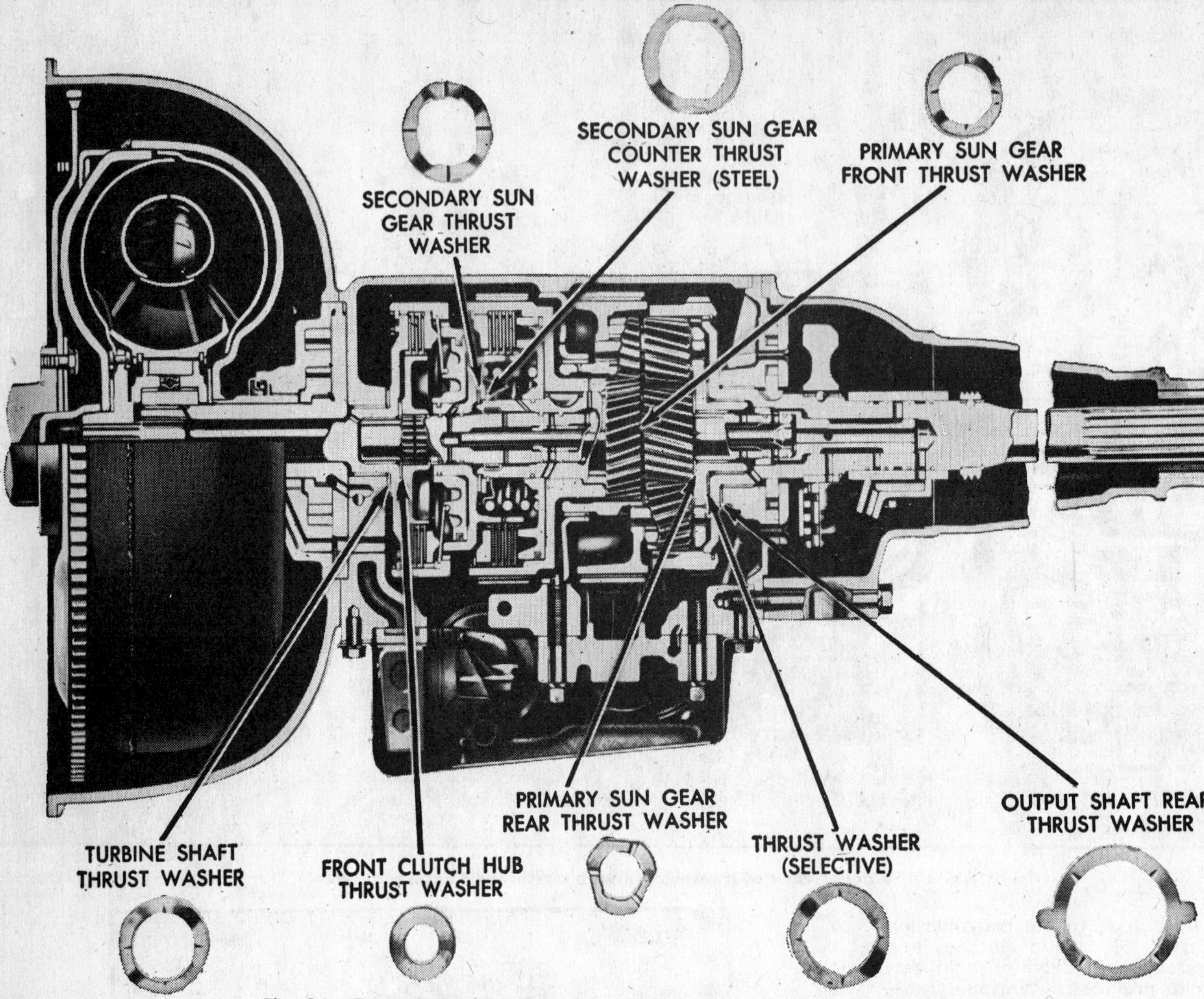

SECONDARY SUN GEAR
COUNTER THRUST
WASHER (STEEL)

SECONDARY SUN
GEAR THRUST
WASHER

PRIMARY SUN GEAR
FRONT THRUST WASHER

TURBINE SHAFT
THRUST WASHER

FRONT CLUTCH HUB
THRUST WASHER

PRIMARY SUN GEAR
REAR THRUST WASHER

THRUST WASHER
(SELECTIVE)

OUTPUT SHAFT REAR
THRUST WASHER

Fig. 1A Transmission thrust washer locations. Late 1959 and 1960 the primary sun gear has a radial thrust bearing which replaces the rear thrust washer shown

MAINTENANCE

Adding Fluid

The fluid level in the transmission should be checked at 1000-mile intervals. Make sure that the car is standing level, and firmly apply the parking brake.

Run the engine at normal idle speed. If the transmission fluid is cold, run the engine at fast idle speed until the fluid reaches normal operating temperature. When the fluid is warm, slow the engine down to normal idle speed, shift the transmission through all ranges and then place the lever or button at P.

Clean all dirt from the transmission fluid dipstick cap before removing the dipstick from the filler tube. Pull the dipstick out of the tube, wipe it clean and push it all the way back into the tube.

Pull the dipstick out again and check the fluid level. If necessary, add enough Automatic Transmission Fluid to the transmission to raise the fluid level to the F (full mark) on the dipstick.

Changing Fluid

The transmission fluid should be changed at 24,000-mile intervals. The procedure for changing fluid is as follows:

1. Remove cover from lower front side

of converter housing.

2. Remove one of the converter drain plugs. Then rotate the converter 180 deg. and remove the other plug. *Do not attempt to turn the converter with a wrench on the converter stud*

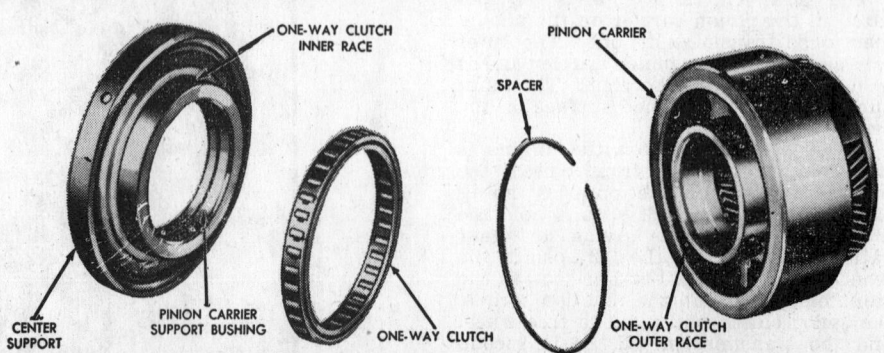

ONE-WAY CLUTCH
INNER RACE

PINION CARRIER

SPACER

CENTER
SUPPORT

PINION CARRIER
SUPPORT BUSHING

ONE-WAY CLUTCH

ONE-WAY CLUTCH
OUTER RACE

Fig. 3 One way (sprag) clutch used on dual range models and 1961 Studebaker Six Flightomatic. This device provides a means of starting in low "gear" while selector lever is in Drive position

nuts as there is danger of stripping threads as well as skinning your knuckles on the bell housing.

3. When all fluid has drained, remove and clean the oil pan and screen.

4. Using a new pan gasket, install screen and pan.

5. Connect filler tube to oil pan and tighten fitting securely.

6. Install both converter drain plugs and torque them to 15-25 lbs. ft.

7. Install converter housing cover.

8. Install 5 quarts of Automatic Transmission Fluid.

9. Run engine at idle speed for about 2 minutes; then add the additional quantity of oil required for the particular transmission being serviced.

10. Run engine at a fast idle until it reaches normal operating temperature.

11. Shift the transmission through all positions; then place it at P and check fluid level. If necessary, add enough fluid to bring the level to the F mark on the dipstick.

"In Car" Repairs

BAND ADJUSTMENTS

The front and rear band of the transmission should be adjusted at 15,000 mile intervals or as operation of the transmission indicates.

On 1961 Lincoln both bands are adjusted from outside of transmission case.

Front Band

The tool shown in Fig. 4 is especially made for this adjustment. However, by using a piece of ¼" wide metal block and an ordinary end or box wrench a satisfactory adjustment can be made.

With transmission oil pan removed, back off adjusting screw lock nut and screw far enough to permit the ¼" metal block to be inserted between servo piston rod and adjusting screw. Turn screw until it contacts metal block. Then tighten adjusting screw a little more (equivalent to 10 inch lbs.) and back off one turn. Use torque wrench to tighten lock nut 20-25 lb. ft.

Rear Band

The tool shown in Fig. 5 is especially made for this adjustment. However, a satisfactory adjustment may be made by using a conventional torque wrench. Loosen lock nut and tighten adjusting screw to a torque of 10 lb. ft. Then back off the screw 1½ turns and tighten lock nut to a torque of 35-40 lb. ft.

AIR PRESSURE CHECKS

A series of air pressure tests can be made on the transmission with the unit in the car. These tests are helpful in deter-

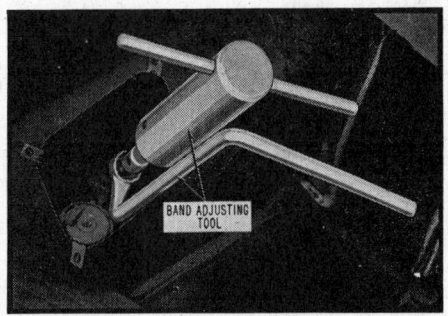

Fig. 5   Adjusting rear band

mining if clutches, bands and servos are operating in a normal manner.

To make the tests, drain the fluid from the transmission. Remove the transmission oil pan, screen and control valve assembly. The front servo tubes should remain in the front servo and the attaching screw must be tight. *When making tests, hold a clean towel over the transmission opening to prevent excessive oil spray.* Refer to Fig. 6 for oil passage locations.

Front Clutch

Apply air pressure to the front clutch passage. Listen for a dull thud which indicates the clutch is operating. Keep air pressure in the passage for several seconds to check for leaks in this circuit.

Governor Valve

Remove the governor inspection hole cover and apply air pressure to the front clutch passage. Listen for a click and watch the valve snap inward.

Rear Clutch

Apply air pressure to the rear clutch passage. Listen for a dull thud which indicates the clutch is operating. Keep air pressure in the passage for several seconds to check for leaks in this circuit.

Front Band and Front Servo

Apply air pressure to the front servo apply tube and observe band application.

Rear Band and Rear Servo

Apply air pressure to the rear servo and observe band application.

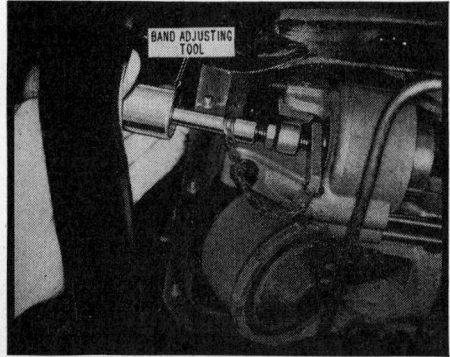

Fig. 4   Adjusting front band

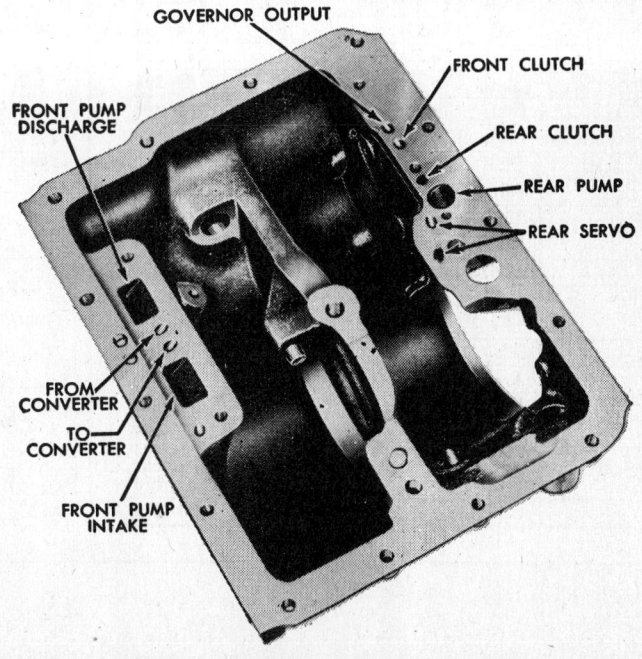

Fig. 6   Transmission case fluid passages

OIL PRESSURE CHART

Year	Model	Engine R.P.M.	Throttle Position	Trans. Range	Pressure P.S.I.
EDSEL					
1958-59	All	Idle	Closed	All	55-65
	All	Stall	To Detent	R	196-216
	All	Stall	To Detent	D, L	150-170
	All	Stall	Thru Detent	D	150-170
	All	1000	Thru Detent	D	80-95
1960	All	Idle	Closed	All	55-70
	All	1000	....	D1	80-85
	All	Stall	To Detent	R, L	195-215
	All	Stall	To Detent	D1, D2	150-170
FORD & THUNDERBIRD					
1953-57	Six	Idle	Closed	D	49-63
	V8-272, 292	Idle	Closed	D	51-69
	V8-312	Idle	Closed	D	55-70
	All	1000	....	D	80-85
	Six	Stall	To Detent	D	124-155
	V8-272, 292	Stall	To Detent	D	133-165
	V8-312	Stall	To Detent	D	147-180
	Six	Stall	To Detent	R	173-195
	V8-272, 292	Stall	To Detent	R	181-205
	V8-312	Stall	To Detent	R	194-216
1958	Six(1)	Idle	Closed	All	51-61
	V8-292(1)	Idle	Closed	All	52-67
	V8-332(1)	Idle	Closed	All	52-67
	V8-352(1)	Idle	Closed	All	55-65
	Cruiseomatic(2)	Idle	Closed	All	56-68
	All Engines	1000	....	D	80-85
	Six(1)	Stall	To Detent	D, L	129-148
	V8-292(1)	Stall	To Detent	D, L	137-157
	V8-332(1)	Stall	To Detent	D, L	137-157
	V8-352(1)	Stall	To Detent	D, L	150-170
	Six(1)	Stall	To Detent	R	174-195
	V8-292(1)	Stall	To Detent	R	184-204
	V8-332(1)	Stall	To Detent	R	184-204
	V8-352(1)	Stall	To Detent	R	196-216
	Cruiseomatic(2)	Stall	To Detent	R	196-216
	Cruiseomatic(2)	Stall	Thru Detent	L	196-216
1959	All	Idle	Closed	All	56-68
	All	1000	....	D1, D2	80-85
	All	Stall	To Detent	D1, D2	149-169
	All	Stall	To Detent	R	196-216
	All	Stall	Thru Detent	L	196-216
1960	All	Idle	Closed	All	56-72
	All	1000	....	D1, D2	80-85
	All	Stall	To Detent	D1, D2	150-170
	All	Stall	To Detent	L, R	196-216
1961	V8	Idle(6)	Closed	N, D1, D2	57-69
	V8	Idle(6)	Closed	P, R, L	57-213
	V8	Stall(7)	....	D1, D2	145-170
	V8	Stall(7)	....	R, L	201-213

Year	Model	Engine R.P.M.	Throttle Position	Trans. Range	Pressure P.S.I.
CONTINENTAL, LINCOLN & MERCURY					
1953-57	(4)	Idle	Closed	All	56-70
	(4)	1000	....	D	80-85
	(4)	Stall	To Detent	R	197-215
	(4)	Stall	To Detent	D, L	152-180
	(4)	Stall	Thru Detent	D	152-180
1957-58	(5)	Idle	Closed	All	52-67
	(5)	Stall	To Detent	R	184-204
	(5)	Stall	To Detent	D	137-157
	(5)	1000	....	D	80-85
1958-60	(3)	Idle	Closed	All	55-70
	(3)	1000	....	D1	80-85
	(3)	Stall	To Detent	R, L	195-215
	(3)	Stall	To Detent	D1, D2	150-170
1961	(4)	Idle	Closed	All	55-70
	(4)	1000	....	D	80-85
	(4)	Stall	To Detent	R, L	195-215
	(4)	Stall	To Detent	D	150-170
	(3)	Idle(6)	Closed	N, D1, D2	57-69
	(3)	Idle(6)	Closed	P, R, L	57-213
	(3)	Stall(7)	....	D1, D2	145-170
	(3)	Stall(7)	....	R, L	201-213
STUDEBAKER					
1956	All	Idle	Closed	All	50-80
	All	1000	....	D	80-85
	All	Stall	To Detent	D, L	130-175
	All	Stall	To Detent	R	170-190
1957-58	All	Idle	Closed	All	62-95
	All	1000	....	All	95-100
	All	Stall	To Detent	D, L	132-184
	All	Stall	To Detent	R	184-203
1959-60	All	Idle	Closed	D, L, R	50-80
	All	1000	....	D	80-85
	All	Stall	....	D, L	130-175
	All	Stall	....	R	170-190
1961	V8	(8)	(8)	(8)	(8)
1961	Six	Idle	Closed	D, L, R	50-60
	Six	1000	....	D	70-75
	Six	Stall	....	D, L	100-130
	Six	Stall	....	R	160 Min.

(1)—Fordomatic.
(2)—All engines.
(3)—Twin-Range Turbo-Drive and Multi-Drive.
(4)—Turbo-Drive and Mercomatic.
(5)—Mercury Medalist.
(6)—With 18" minimum vacuum.
(7)—With 1½" or less of vacuum.
(8)—Same as 1959-60 models.

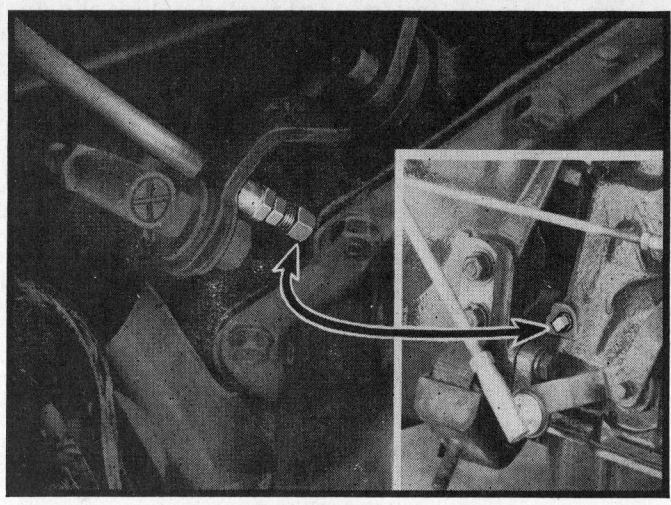

Fig. 7   Oil pressure test take-off point

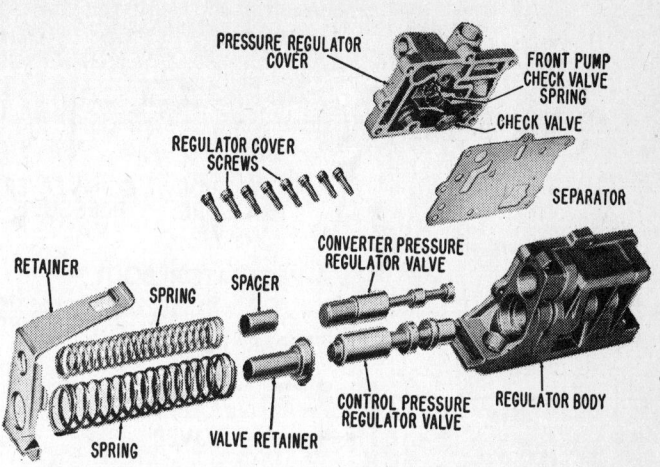

Fig. 8   Oil pressure regulator. 1955 and later Ford-omatic, Flightomatic, Mercomatic and Turbo-Drive

Results of Tests

If servos, bands, clutches and governor operation is normal with air pressure, the condition of *no drive, erratic upshifts or downshifts* points to the control valve assembly and pressure regulator valve. These should be disassembled, cleaned and inspected.

VACUUM THROTTLE CONTROL

1961 Dual Range Units

On Cruiseomatic, Multi-Drive and Twin-Range Turbo-Drive, a shift control vacuum cam assembly and transmission shift timing valve are built in the transmission to give precise, constant transmission shift control setting, eliminating the need for periodic adjustment. The only linkage adjustment required is the carburetor throttle control. The system is actuated by a vacuum diaphragm unit located at the back end of the transmission case which is connected by a tube running to the intake manifold of the engine.

OIL PRESSURE TESTS

The oil pressure tests should be performed to ascertain whether or not the pressure regulator system is functioning correctly and to determine if there is fluid leakage in the clutch circuits.

Remove the ⅛" pipe plug, Fig. 7, and install a pressure gauge. The gauge should be placed in the passenger compartment where it can be observed by the operator. Connect a tachometer to the engine where it also can be read by the operator. Then perform the following tests:

Idle Pressure Test

Start engine and operate until engine and transmission reaches normal operating temperature. With the engine at idle speed, move the selector lever to the D, L and R positions. The pressure obtained should be as given in the chart.

If the pressure is low in any one range, an oil leak in that range circuit is indicated and must be corrected. If the pressure is high the throttle linkage should be checked and adjusted as outlined in the *Car Chapter*.

Pressure Regulation Check

Move the selector lever to the D range and firmly set the hand and foot brakes. Run the engine at 1000 rpm and read the pressure gauge. If the reading is less than specified in the chart, it indicates the throttle valve linkage is too long and must be readjusted. If the pressure is greater than specified in the chart, it indicates the throttle valve linkage is too short and must be readjusted.

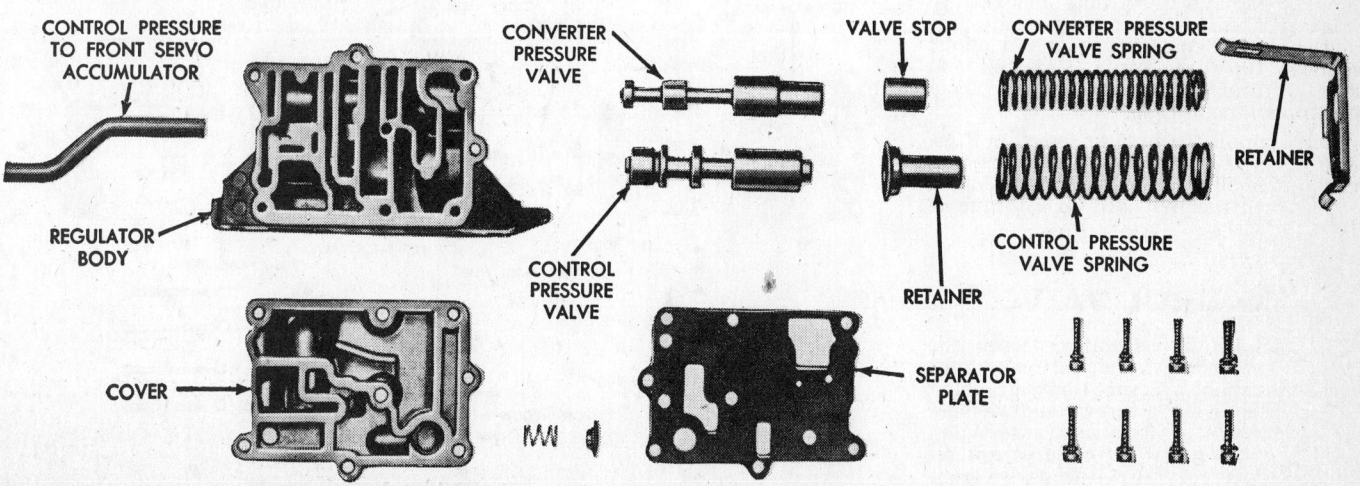

Fig. 9   Oil pressure regulator. Transmissions with sprag clutch

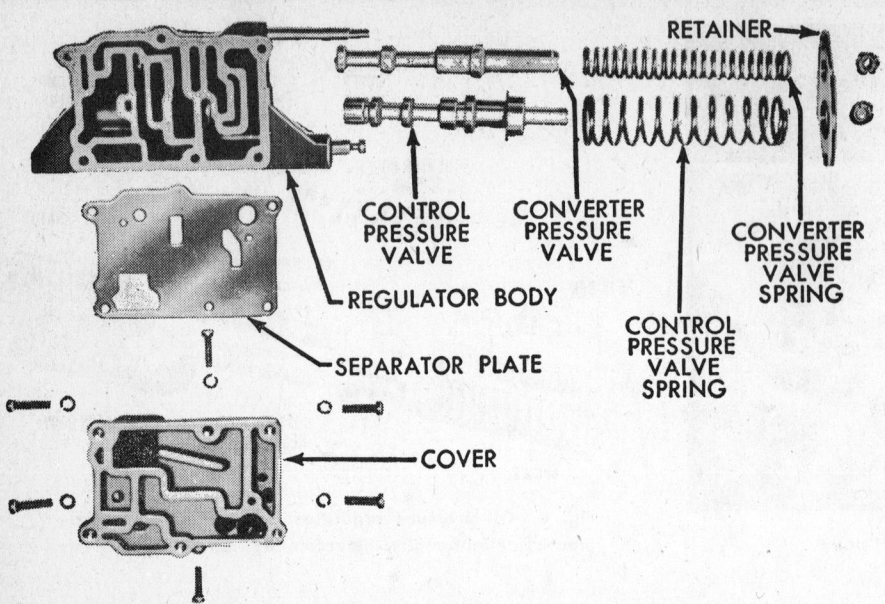

Fig. 10 Oil pressure regulator. 1954 and earlier units

inspected and reassembled one at a time. To aid in reassembly, it is also recommended that the parts of each body be placed on a clean bench in the order in which they are removed from the body.

Disassemble and assemble the unit as illustrated in Figs. 11 to 15.

When disassembled, clean all parts in each valve body thoroughly with solvent and blow dry with moisture-free compressed air. Inspect all valves and valve bores for scores and burrs. Check all fluid passages for obstructions. Inspect all mating surfaces for burrs or distortion. Inspect all springs for distortion.

Crocus cloth may be used to polish valves and plugs. However, care must be taken to avoid rounding the sharp edges of valves and plugs. Check all valves and plugs for freedom of movement in their respective bores. Valves and plugs, when dry, should fall from their own weight in their respective bores.

FRONT & REAR SERVOS

To remove the front servo, remove the cap screw which holds it to the case. Hold the actuating lever strut with one hand and lift the servo from the case.

To remove the rear servo, take out the attaching cap screws. Then hold the

Stall Pressure Tests

Firmly set the hand and foot brakes and operate the engine at full kickdown position. Move the selector lever to D, L and R ranges and read the pressure gauge.

If the pressure is not within specified limits, malfunctioning of the throttle valve, modulator valve, compensator valve, or pressure regulator assembly is indicated and it will be necessary to remove and clean the control valve assembly and pressure regulator valve assembly.

OIL PRESSURE REGULATOR

Remove oil pan and screen. Maintain constant pressure on spring retainer to prevent damage to springs and remove retainer from bosses on oil pressure regulator body. Remove springs and pilots. Remove the three pipes. Unfasten and remove the oil pressure regulator from the transmission case.

Disassemble the unit as shown in Figs. 8, 9, 10. After cleaning and inspecting parts, assemble the unit and tighten the regulator attaching bolts to a torque of 17-22 lb. ft.

CONTROL VALVE

To remove the assembly, loosen the adjustment on the front and rear bands 5 or 6 turns. Loosen front servo attaching screws. Remove cap screws and washers which attach control valve to case. Align throttle and manual levers to permit removal of control valve. Disengage front servo tubes from control valve and lift valve assembly from case.

When servicing the control valve, it is recommended that each valve body of the assembly be disassembled, cleaned,

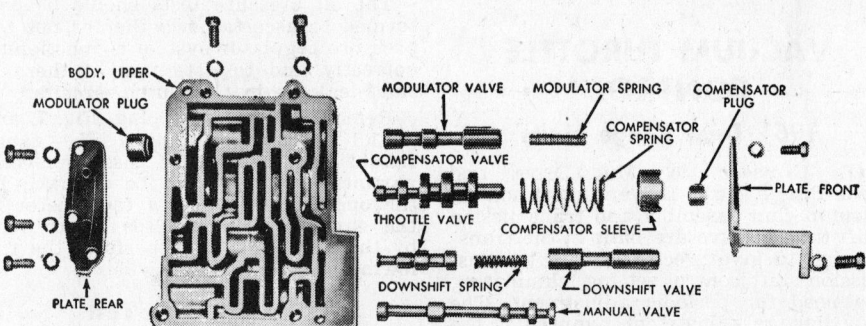

Fig. 11 Control valve body (upper). 1954 and earlier units

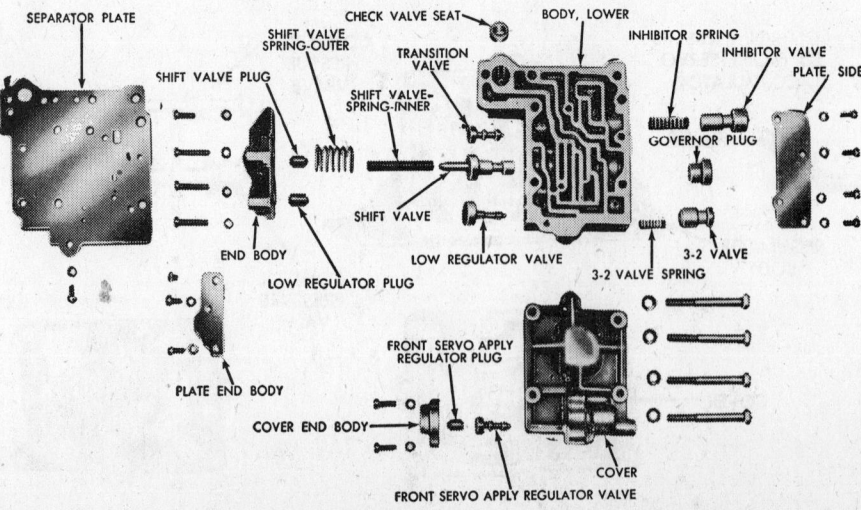

Fig. 12 Control valve body (lower). 1954 and earlier units

anchor strut and lift the servo from the case.

Front Servo Repairs

Disassemble the servo as shown in Figs. 16 to 18. When disassembled, inspect the servo body for cracks, burrs and obstructed fluid passages. Inspect the piston bore and piston stem for scores. Inspect the actuating lever and shaft for wear and freeness in the servo body. Also inspect the adjusting screw threads and the threads in the actuating lever. Inspect the servo band for wear and bonding of the lining to the band. Replace the band if the grooves in the lining are worn even with the rest of the lining. Inspect the band ends for cracks or distortion. Install the piston and guide in the servo body and check for freedom of travel.

Minor burrs may be removed with crocus cloth. However, parts showing deep burrs, scores, scratches or excessive wear should be replaced.

Lubricate all parts with automatic transmission fluid before starting reassembly. Then assemble the unit as shown in the illustrations.

Rear Servo Repairs

Disassemble the servo as shown in Figs. 19 and 20. Inspect the parts for the same conditions outlined for the front servo.

EXTENSION HOUSING SEAL

After removing the drive shaft and telescopic shield, the seal may be pulled out of the extension housing.

Before installing the new seal, inspect the sealing surface of the universal joint yoke for scores. If scores are evident, replace the yoke. Inspect the counterbore in the housing for burrs. Polish all burrs with crocus cloth.

To install the new seal, position it in the bore of the extension housing with the felt side of the seal to the rear. The seal may be driven into the housing with a special tool designed for the purpose.

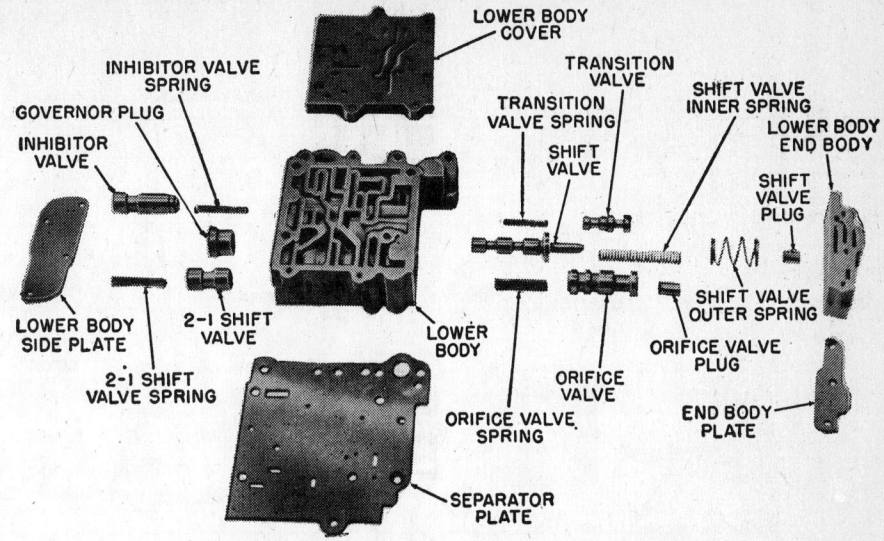

Fig. 13   Control valve body (lower). 1955 and later Fordomatic, Flightomatic, Mercomatic and Turbo-Drive

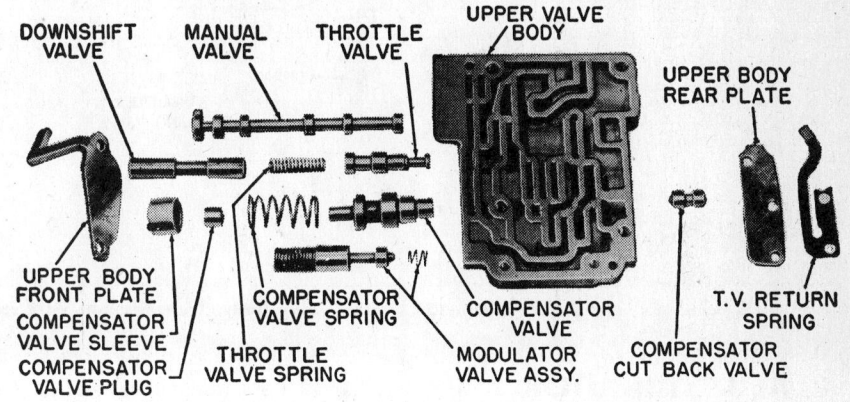

Fig. 14   Control valve body (upper). 1955 and later Fordomatic, Flightomatic, Mercomatic and Turbo-Drive

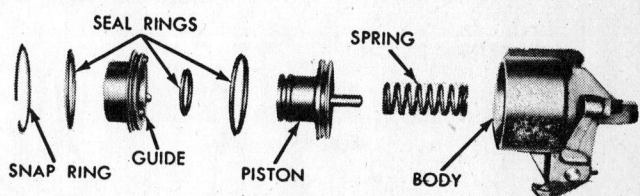

Fig. 16   Front servo. Ford 6-cylinder 1955 and later models

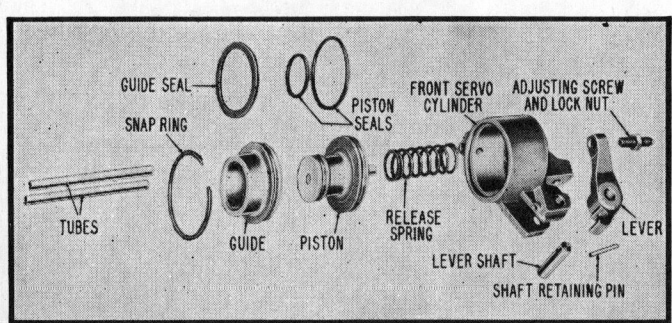

Fig. 18   Front servo. 1955 and later V8 Fordomatic, Flightomatic, Mercomatic and Turbo-Drive

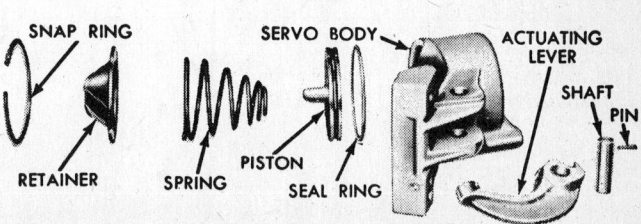

Fig. 19   Rear servo. 1954 and earlier units

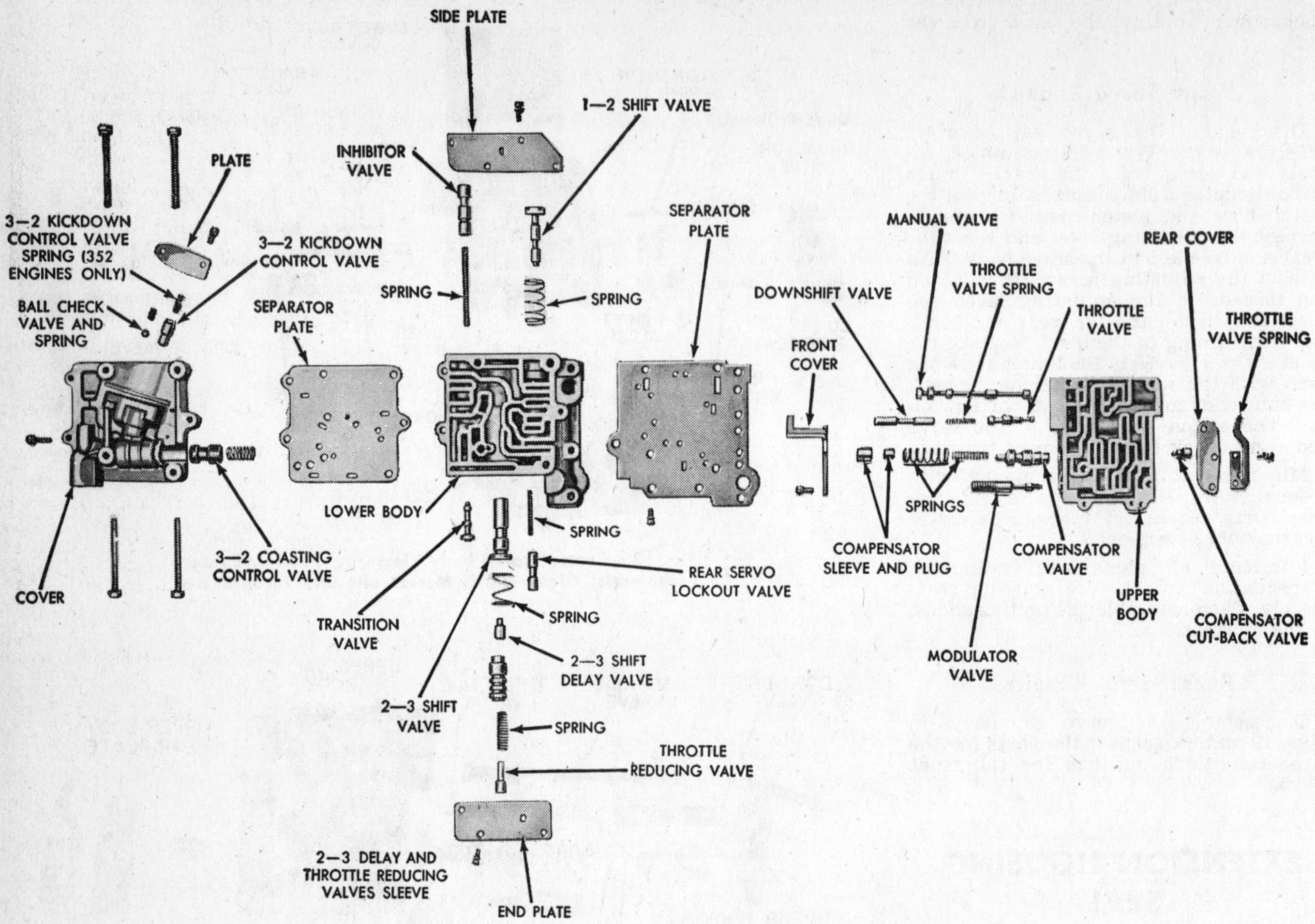

SIDE PLATE

1—2 SHIFT VALVE

INHIBITOR VALVE

SEPARATOR PLATE

PLATE

3—2 KICKDOWN CONTROL VALVE SPRING (352 ENGINES ONLY)

3—2 KICKDOWN CONTROL VALVE

BALL CHECK VALVE AND SPRING

SEPARATOR PLATE

SPRING

SPRING

MANUAL VALVE

DOWNSHIFT VALVE

THROTTLE VALVE SPRING

THROTTLE VALVE

REAR COVER

THROTTLE VALVE SPRING

FRONT COVER

COVER

LOWER BODY

3—2 COASTING CONTROL VALVE

TRANSITION VALVE

SPRING

REAR SERVO LOCKOUT VALVE

2—3 SHIFT VALVE

SPRING

2—3 SHIFT DELAY VALVE

SPRING

THROTTLE REDUCING VALVE

COMPENSATOR SLEEVE AND PLUG

SPRINGS

COMPENSATOR VALVE

MODULATOR VALVE

UPPER BODY

COMPENSATOR CUT-BACK VALVE

2—3 DELAY AND THROTTLE REDUCING VALVES SLEEVE

END PLATE

Fig. 15 Control valve body. Transmissions with sprag clutch

OIL DISTRIBUTOR

After removing the extension case remove the spacer from the transmission output shaft and slide the distributor toward the rear of the transmission. Note that the tube spacer is located in the center tube.

Remove the three tubes and spacer from the distributor. Remove the screws which attach the distributor to the sleeve and separate these parts.

Inspect the distributor and sleeve for burrs on the mating surfaces and obstructed fluid passages. Check the fit of the tubes in the distributor. Inspect the distributor sleeve for wear and scores in the sleeve bore.

To assemble, align the distributor and sleeve and install the cap screws. Install the tubes in the distributor with the spacer installed on the center tube.

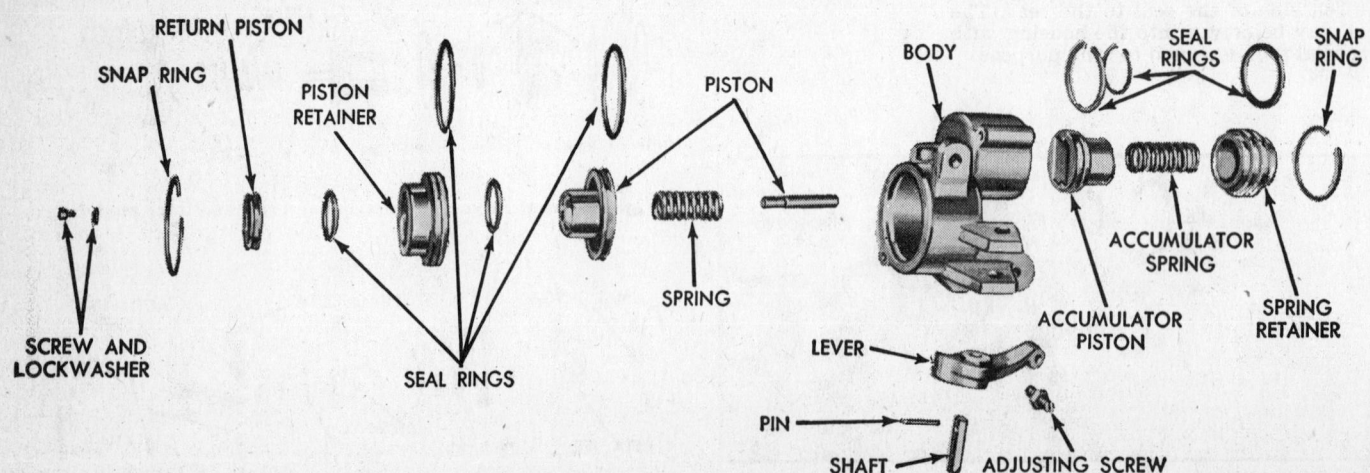

RETURN PISTON

SNAP RING

PISTON RETAINER

PISTON

BODY

SEAL RINGS

SNAP RING

ACCUMULATOR SPRING

SPRING

SCREW AND LOCKWASHER

SEAL RINGS

LEVER

ACCUMULATOR PISTON

SPRING RETAINER

PIN

SHAFT

ADJUSTING SCREW

Fig. 17 Front servo. Units with sprag clutch

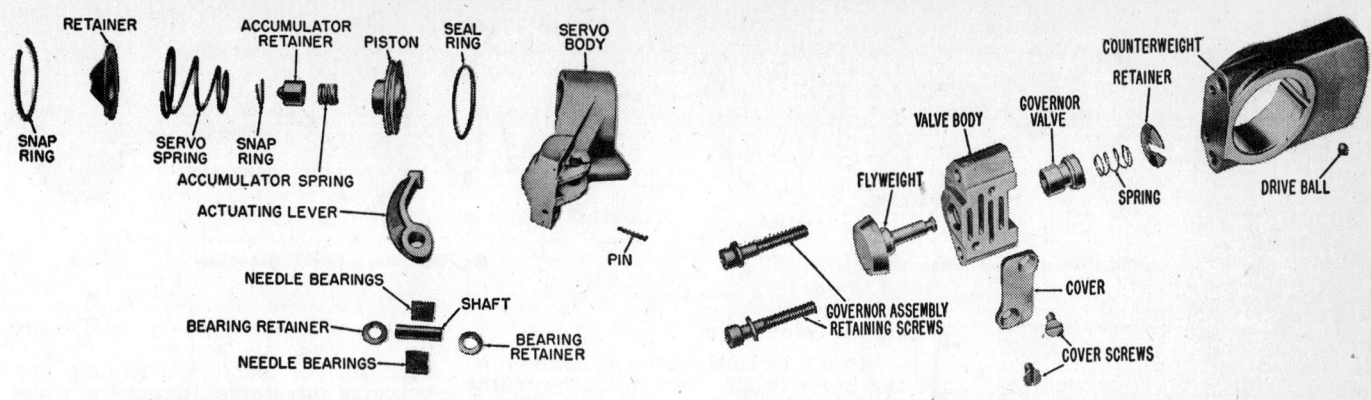

Fig 20   Rear servo. 1955 and later units

Fig. 21   Layout of governor parts

Tighten the screws to a torque of 8-10 lb. ft.

GOVERNOR

Remove the governor inspection cover from the extension housing. Rotate the drive shaft to bring the governor body in line with the inspection hole. Remove the two screws which attach the governor body to the counterweight, and remove the body.

Remove the valve from the new governor body. Lubricate the valve with automatic transmission fluid. Install the valve in the body, making sure the valve moves freely in the bore. Install the body in the counterweight with the side plate forward. Be sure the fluid passages in the counterweight and body are aligned. Fig. 21 illustrates the entire governor assembly.

Repairs Requiring Transmission Removal

TRANSMISSION, DISASSEMBLE

1. Remove pressure regulator valve, control valve assembly and both servos as outlined previously.
2. The next step is to check the mainshaft end play for future reference when reassembling the transmission. Remove one of the front pump retaining screws and mount a dial indicator so that the indicator button rests against the end of the input shaft. Use a large screwdriver to pry the front clutch to the rear and, while holding pressure against the screwdriver, zero the dial indicator. Insert the screwdriver between the parking gear and transmission case and pry the units toward the front of the case. *If end play is not within the limits of .010" to .029", record the amount of end play present so that a suitable thrust washer may be installed to establish the correct end play when the transmission is reassembled.*
3. Unfasten and remove the front pump from the transmission case.
4. Remove extension housing and oil distributor.
5. Remove the oil distributor sleeve from the output shaft. Slip the four seal rings from the shaft. Remove the governor snap ring and slide off the governor, being sure not to lose the governor drive ball.
6. Remove rear pump inlet tube. Using

Fig. 22   Removing rear pump discharge tube with snap ring pliers or with tool shown

tool shown in Fig. 22, remove outlet tube. Slide pump off output shaft and remove gasket and rear pump drive key, Fig. 23.

7. Hold the pinion carrier in position and slide the output shaft and internal gear toward rear of transmission. Remove thrust washer from pinion carrier. *This washer, supplied* in various thicknesses, determines the end play of the mainshaft assembly.

8. Hold pressure against the primary sun gear shaft and remove pinion carrier by sliding toward rear of case. Remove thrust washer from inside of pinion carrier. *Note position of cone on inner diameter of thrust washer.*

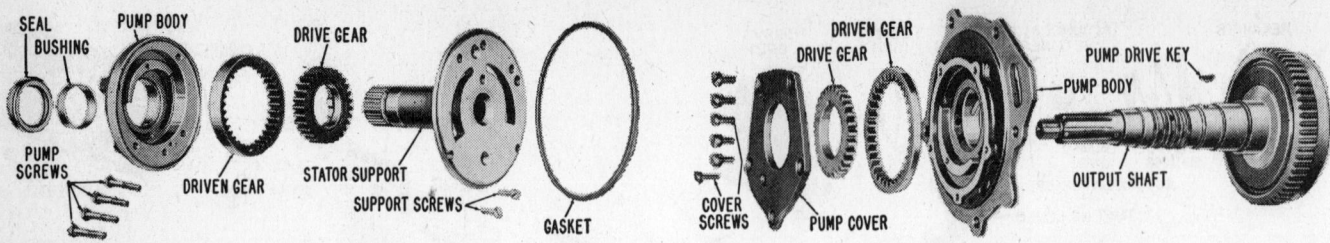

Fig. 24 Front pump assembly   **Fig. 25 Rear pump assembly**

Fig. 23 Location of rear pump drive key

9. Remove the two remaining cap screws which attach the center support to the transmission case. *These screws are located on the outside of the case.* Remove center support through rear of case.

10. Remove front clutch, rear clutch and sun gears as a unit. Remove the thrust washer from in front of the front clutch. Separate front and rear clutches and remove thrust washer and contour thrust washer from between clutches.

11. Remove and tilt front band and remove through bottom of case.

FRONT PUMP

When disassembled, inspect the pump body for excessive wear and scores. Inspect the internal and external tooth gears for scores, scratches and excessive wear. Inspect the stator support face for scores, scratches and excessive wear.

Minor scratches and scores can be removed with corcus cloth. However, parts showing deep scratches, scores or excessive wear should be replaced.

Assemble the pump as shown in Fig. 24. Tighten the stator support attaching screws to a torque of 25-35 lb. ft.

REAR PUMP

Before disassembling the pump, Fig. 25, mark the external and internal tooth gears with crayon or pencil to aid in reassembly. When disassembled, inspect all parts for wear or damage as outlined for the front pump.

When reassembling the pump, position the gears in the body with the marks made previously in the upward position.

OUTPUT SHAFT & INTERNAL GEAR

Remove the four piston ring type seals from the output shaft. The rings must be removed singly starting with the rearmost ring. While the output shaft and internal gear assembly is a two-piece unit, no further disassembly is required since the unit is serviced as an assembly.

Inspect the internal gear and parking gear for broken teeth and burrs on the thrust surfaces. Inspect the output shaft for burrs and scores on the bearing surfaces and ring grooves. Inspect the rear pump drive keyway and governor drive ball socket for wear.

Minor burrs and scratches may be removed with crocus cloth. However, parts having broken teeth, large burrs, scratches or scores, or showing evidence of wear should be replaced.

Install the four seal rings on the output shaft, starting with the foremost ring and working toward the rear.

PINION CARRIER

The pinion carrier is serviced as an assembly; therefore, there is no disas-sembly or assembly procedure. To check its serviceability, however, inspect the band surface and the inner and outer bushings for scores. Rotate the pinions on their shafts to check for freedom of movement and inspect for worn or broken teeth. Use a feeler gauge to check pinion end play, which should be .010" to .020". Inspect pinion shaft for tightness to the pinion carrier.

CENTER SUPPORT

The center support is serviced only as an assembly. To check its serviceability, however, inspect for burrs or distortion, and the bearing surface for scores and scratches.

Minor burrs and scratches may be removed with crocus cloth. Any damage more serious than that requires the support to be replaced.

FRONT CLUTCH

Disassemble, Fig. 26

1. Remove clutch cover snap ring.
2. Remove turbine shaft and fiber thrust washer from clutch hub.
3. Remove plates and clutch hub from drum; also clutch pressure plate.
4. Using a suitable spring compressor on clutch release spring, exert sufficient pressure to compress spring and remove snap ring.
5. Remove tool and clutch spring.
6. Apply air pressure to clutch inlet

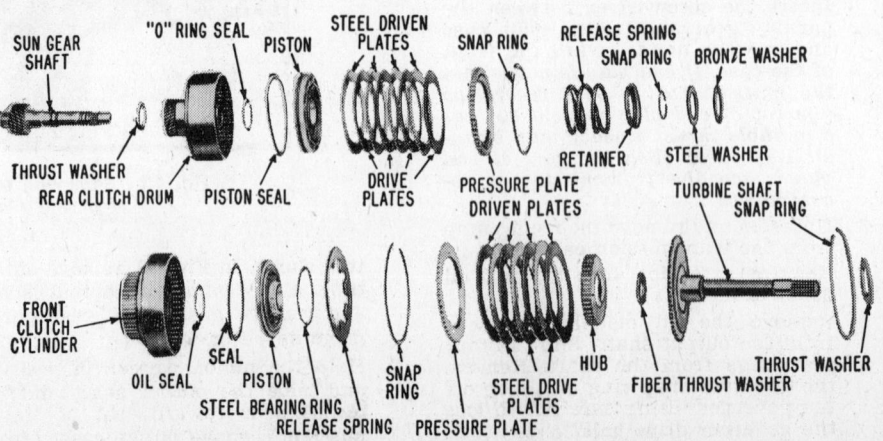

Fig. 26 Front and rear clutches and related parts

Fig. 27 Sprag clutch-to-center support installation

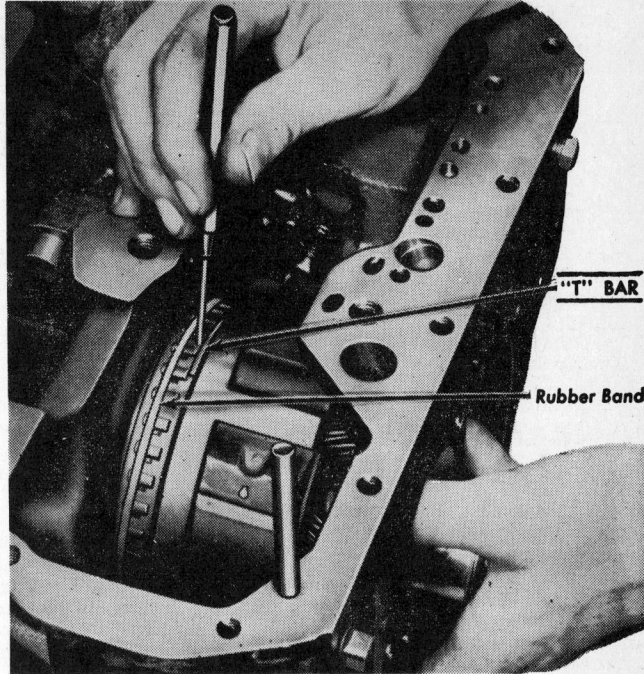

Fig. 28 Pinion carrier installation on units with sprag clutch

hole to force clutch piston out of clutch drum bore.

7. Remove rubber outer piston seal from piston and remove piston metal wear ring from piston.

8. Remove O-ring seal from clutch drum.

Inspection

1. Inspect turbine shaft and clutch hub for burrs on thrust surfaces, splines and serrations.

2. Inspect clutch piston for burrs, scores or cracks.

3. Inspect clutch drum for burrs on thrust surfaces and splines, and clutch bore for scratches and scores.

4. Inspect clutch release spring for cracks or distortion and pressure plate for cracks and scratches.

5. Inspect steel plates for burrs on serration and for wear, and for flatness.

6. The lined plates should be replaced when grooves in lining are no longer visible, as if plates are warped.

Assemble

1. Lubricate all parts with transmission fluid before assembly.

2. Install new O-ring seal in clutch drum and a new seal on clutch piston and install piston in clutch drum bore.

3. Press piston down lightly until it bottoms in bore, being careful not to damage outer piston seal.

4. Install metal wear ring on piston.

5. Install clutch spring on piston with concave side upward.

6. Position compressor tool on spring and exert sufficient pressure to compress spring so that snap ring can be installed. Use the thicker snap ring.

7. Remove compressor and install pressure plate with smooth side upward.

8. Install hub in drum bore with thrust surface upward.

9. Install lined plates and steel plates alternately, starting with a lined plate.

10. Coat fiber thrust washer with heavy grease to hold it in place and position it on clutch hub.

11. Align serrations of clutch cover and turbine shaft with serrations in drum and install cover and snap ring.

REAR CLUTCH & PRIMARY SUN GEAR

Disassemble, Fig. 26

1. Remove two ring seals from primary sun gear shaft and remove rear clutch assembly.

2. Remove primary sun gear thrust washer and ring seals from sun gear shaft.

3. With a suitable spring compressor tool, exert sufficient pressure on clutch spring to compress it so that snap ring can be removed.

4. Remove the balance of the clutch parts.

Inspection

1. Inspect primary sun gear and shaft for burrs, scratches, worn ring grooves and broken teeth.

2. Use an awl to check front clutch lubrication ball check valve in front end of sun gear shaft for freedom of movement.

3. Inspect the balance of the clutch parts as outlined for the front clutch. However, check each steel plate for proper coning. Each plate is coned to .010" to .020" clearance. If any plate requires replacement, the entire clutch plate pack should be installed.

Assemble

1. Lubricate all parts with transmission fluid before assembly.

2. Install new inner O-ring seal on drum hub and new clutch outer seal on piston.

3. Install piston in drum bore.

4. Press piston down until it bottoms, being careful not to damage outer seal.

5. Install clutch spring and retainer.

6. Compress spring and install snap ring.

7. Install bronze plates and steel plates alternately, starting with a steel plate. Coned steel plates must face same direction; either all concave or all convex side up.

8. Install pressure plate with smooth side down and install snap ring.

9. Install two ring seals on short end of primary sun gear shaft.

10. Install sun gear thrust washer.

11. Install two ring seals on sun gear

shaft adjacent to sun gear.

12. Position clutch on sun gear shaft.
13. Install two remaining ring seals on primary sun gear shaft.

TRANSMISSION CASE & LINKAGE

Remove linkage parts as required. Clean the transmission case thoroughly and blow out fluid passages with compressed air. Inspect the case for stripped threads, obstructed fluid passages, cracks, and mating surfaces for burrs. Inspect case bushings for scores, and linkage parts for wear or distortion.

TRANSMISSION, ASSEMBLE

When installing the sub-assemblies in the transmission case, do not use force to assemble mating parts. If the parts do not mesh freely, examine them for the cause of the difficulty. Always use new gaskets. Use only Automatic Transmission Fluid to lubricate parts.

Clutch Assemblies

1. Install front band in transmission case so that anchor end is aligned with anchor in case. Lift clutch assemblies out of holding block. *Do not allow clutches to separate.*
2. Install sub-assemblies in case from the rear while positioning servo band on drum. Hold units together while making installation.
3. Position center support in case, aligning hole in center support with hole in right-hand side of case.
4. Install right and left-hand center support outer bolts and external tooth lockwashers. *Lockwashers must be installed with rolled edge toward transmission case to insure a tight seal.*

Center Support, Sprag Clutch And Pinion Carrier

1. On the bench, install sprag clutch on center support with flange side of cage rings up, Fig. 27.
2. Carefully compress each drag spring as it is started on the inner race. After all drag springs are started on race, rotate clutch to tilt sprags; then push clutch all the way down on center suport. Place a strong rubber band around sprag outer ends, Fig. 28.
3. Install center support and clutch in case.
4. Position rear band in case. Install thrust washer on thrust face inside pinion carrier.
5. Install pinion carrier in case and start pinion carrier front pilot in center support bushing. Depress the "T" bar and work pinion carrier forward until sprags are started on clutch outer race, Fig. 28.
6. Remove rubber band.
7. Work pinion carrier forward to the point that the sprag clutch is visible.

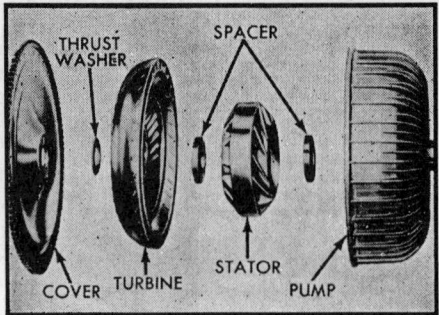

Fig. 29   Layout of torque converter

Rotate pinion carrier counterclockwise (from rear) and note whether clutch rotates with pinion carrier or remains stationary with center support.

8. The clutch is so designed that the "T" bar frictional grip on the clutch outer race is stronger than the drag spring frictional grip on the inner race; hence the clutch should rotate with the pinion carrier. If it does not, replace the sprag clutch.

Pinion Carrier (Units Without Sprag Clutch)

1. Position rear servo band in case with strut ends up. Place anchor end with depression toward adjusting screw. Install a bronze thrust washer on thrust face inside pinion carrier.
2. To install pinion carrier, position rear band over drum while meshing planet pinions. Install the two seal rings on primary sun gear shaft and check rings for free movement in grooves.

Mainshaft End Play

If the end play was not within specifications when checked prior to disassembly, replace the washer with one of proper thickness. The following selective washers are available in the following thicknessses:

$$.061'' \text{ to } .063''$$
$$.067'' \text{ to } .069''$$
$$.074'' \text{ to } .076''$$
$$.081'' \text{ to } .083''$$

After installing the proper washer, install the output shaft, carefully meshing the internal gear with the pinions.

Rear Pump

1. Put drive key in keyway on output shaft.
2. Place new front and rear gaskets on pump body.
3. Install thrust washer on pump body with bronze side up. Align thrust washer tangs with bosses on pump body and install rear pump.

Governor

Place governor drive ball in pocket in output shaft. Install governor, aligning groove with ball in output shaft. Install governor snap ring.

Install governor with governor body plate toward front of transmission.

Oil Distributor

1. Place four seal rings in oil distributor sleeve and check ring gaps to see that they are spaced equally around the sleeve. Check fit of seal rings in grooves in output shaft; rings should rotate freely. Install rings in grooves in output shaft.
2. Install three tubes in distributor sleeve. Install distributor sleeve on output shaft with chamfer forward. Slide sleeve forward over four rings and at the same time start tubes into case. The distributor sleeve is located between governor snap ring and speedometer drive gear.
3. Install new seal on rear pump outlet tube and install tube in transmission case and rear pump body.

Extension Housing

1. Position speedometer drive gear ball in pocket in output shaft. Install speedometer drive gear and retain gear in place with snap ring.
2. Insert extension housing oil seal replacer and pilot in housing; then install extension housing on transmission case. Install attaching bolts with external tooth lockwashers with rolled edge of washers toward transmission case to insure a tight seal.
3. Torque extension housing bolts to 23-38 lbs. ft.
4. Install governor inspection cover and a new gasket on housing.

Front Pump

Position new gasket in counterbore in front of transmission case. Install front pump, aligning pump bolt holes with holes in case. Install three of front pump attaching bolts and torque them to 17-22 lbs. ft.

Recheck transmission end play, which should be .010" to .029". Then install remaining pump bolt.

Final Assembly

Install progressively the front servo, rear servo, pressure regulator body and control valve body as previously outlined. Then adjust front and rear servo bands. Finally, install oil screen and oil pan, using new gasket.

TORQUE CONVERTER

Removal

To remove the converter from the transmission, grasp the converter cover with both hands and pull straight out. To prevent damage to the front seal, do not rock the assembly from side to side. After removing the attaching bolts, the converter housing may be taken off the transmission.

Disassembly

Note—Torque converter on 1958-61 cars

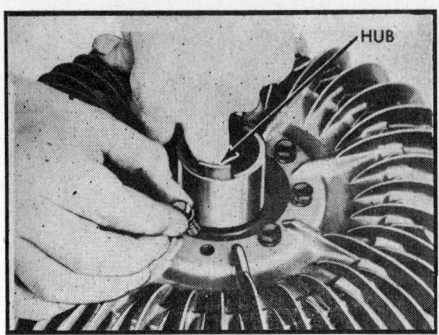

Fig. 30   Removing pump hub

Inspection

•Inspect the turbine and pump blades for looseness. Inspect all thrust surfaces for scores. Check the turbine splines for burrs and wear. Inspect the seal surface and front pump driving lugs for wear. Inspect the hub to pump mating surfaces for scores. Inspect the stator thrust surfaces for scores and the stator splines for wear. Check the sprag assembly for worn or broken sprags and a broken or distorted spring. Inspect the stator inner and outer races for scores, Fig. 31.

Reassembly

Install the stator inner hub and snap ring. Turn the assembly over and install the outer race in the stator. Then install the sprag into the outer race, Fig. 32. Make sure the sprags are pointed in the correct direction.

Install the outer hub and snap ring. Insert the inner race replacer (tapered side first) into the sprag assembly while rotating the tool counterclockwise to position the sprags as shown in Fig. 32.

Install the inner race with the spline section up. Guide the tool with the hand

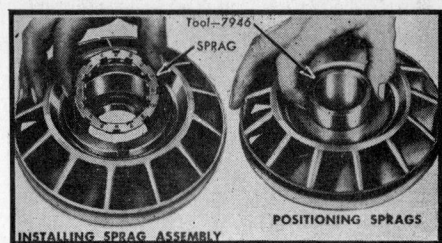

**Fig. 32   Correct position
of sprag in race**

while pushing the inner race into position. Check the stator for clockwise rotation while holding the inner race.

To assemble the pump, install a new seal on the pump hub and place the hub in the pump. Install the thrust washer into the hub of the converter pump.

To assemble the converter, install the stator with "Front" up. Install the thrust washer in the hub of the turbine. Retain the washer in place with transmission fluid. Install the turbine. Place the bronze thrust washer on the turbine hub. Install the converter cover, using a new gasket. Note position of cover and pump aligning marks. Install the cover to pump body attaching bolts and tighten them to 25-28 lbs. ft. torque.

Install On Transmission

Attach the converter housing to the transmission, tightening the bolts to 40-50 lbs. ft. torque. Install the converter into the housing, being sure not to rock the assembly as it is being installed otherwise the seal may be damaged.

---

is a sealed assembly and is serviced only as a unit.

Place the converter in a holding fixture. Note the location of the pump and cover aligning marks, then remove the cover attaching bolts, Fig. 29.

Remove the cover and gasket. Slip the bronze thrust washer from the pump housing. Lift out the stator, noting its position in the housing. Take the thrust washer from the pump hub.

To disassemble the stator, remove the one way clutch inner race. Release the snap ring which retains the outer hub to the stator. Remove outer hub, sprag assembly and outer race. Remove the snap ring retaining the inner hub to the stator and take out the inner hub.

To disassemble the pump, remove the bolts which attach the pump hub to the pump, Fig. 30. Take out the hub and remove the seal from the groove in the hub.

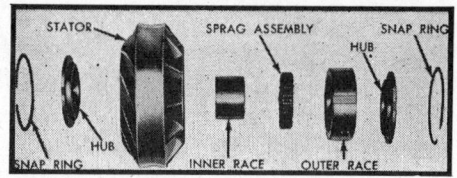

Fig. 31   Layout of stator parts

TWO-SPEED FORD-O-MATIC •
COMET DRIVE • EDSEL MILE-O-MATIC • FALCON

See car chapter for linkage adjustments

CONTENTS

Trouble Shooting 25
Adding Oil 253
Changing Oil 254
Low Band, Adjust 254
Reverse Band, Adjust 254
Control Pressure Checks........... 255
Air Pressure Checks............... 256
Sub-Assemblies, Remove 256
Sub-Assemblies, Overhaul 257
Transmission, Assemble 261
Valve Body Service................ 260

DESCRIPTION

This transmission, Fig. 1, is different in design and construction from any previously used Fordomatic. It is a two-speed unit, with a low and high gear in the forward range, and a reverse. Automatic shifts are provided from low to high and from high to low.

The transmission can be force downshifted (kickdown) from high to low at speeds below about 50 mph. On a coastdown, the transmission will automatically shift from high to low at about 9 mph.

Four models of this transmission are available to match the torque, horsepower and crankshaft speed range of the various engines. Therefore, when replacement parts are necessary, be sure to specify the engine with which the transmission operates.

MAINTENANCE

Adding Oil

1. Every 1000 miles, check oil level. Make sure car is standing level. Apply parking brake.
2. Run engine at normal idle speed. If transmission oil is cold, run engine at fast idle until oil reaches its normal operating temperature. When oil is warm, slow engine to normal idle speed.
3. Shift selector lever to all positions; then place lever at P.
4. Clean all dirt from transmission dipstick cap before removing stick from filler tube.
5. Wipe dipstick clean and push it all the way back in the tube.

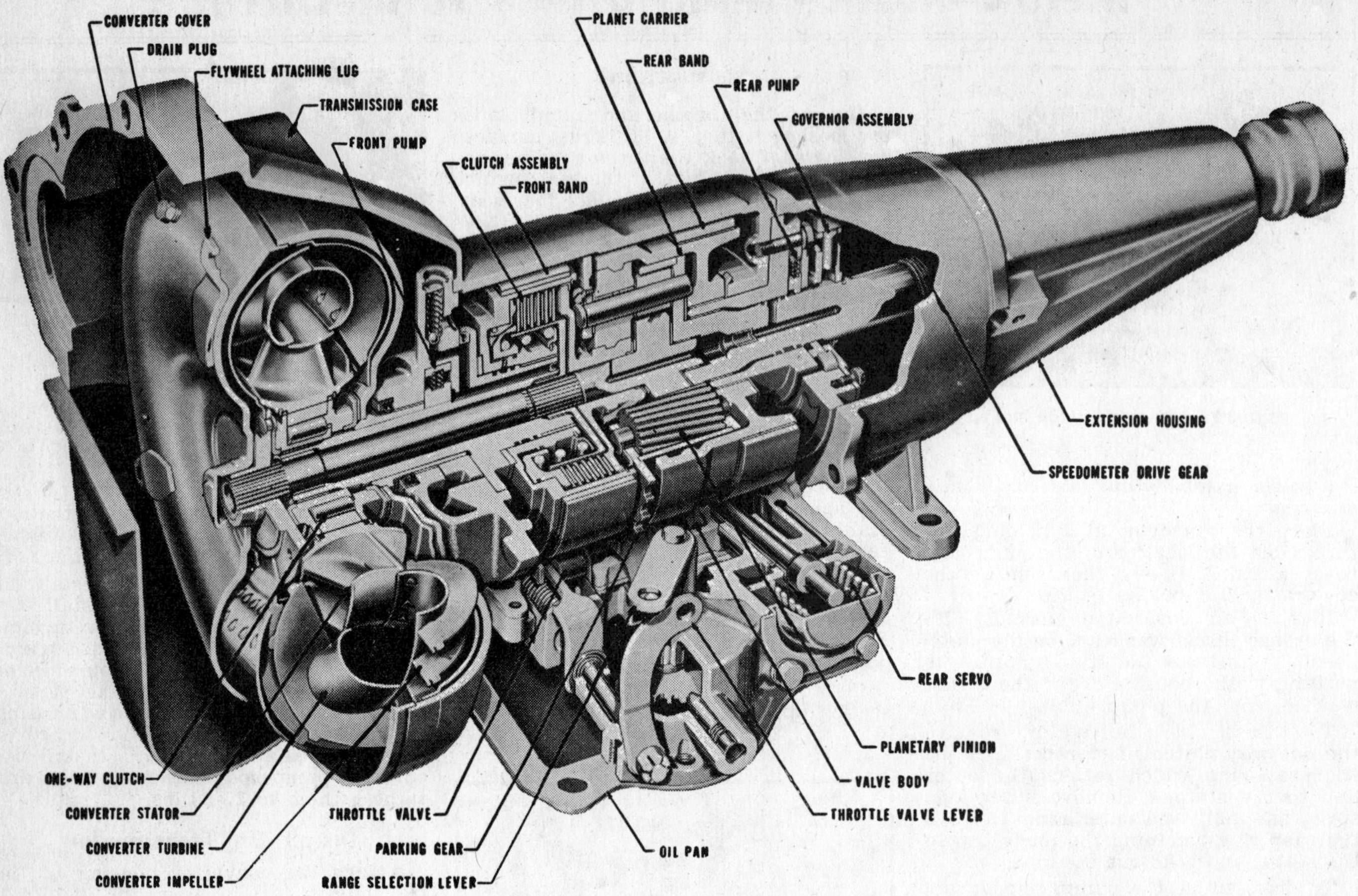

Fig. 1 Cutaway view of transmission

6. Remove stick and check level. Add automatic transmission oil to bring the level up to the "Full" mark on dipstick.

Changing Oil

1. Every 24,000 miles, remove cover from lower front side of converter housing.
2. Remove one of converter drain plugs.
3. Rotate converter 180 deg. and remove other drain plug.
4. Remove drain plug from transmission oil pan.
5. Remove, clean and replace transmission oil pan and screen, using new pan gasket.
6. Install converter drain plugs and tighten to 15-25 lbs. ft.
7. Install converter housing cover.
8. Pour 4 quarts of fluid in transmission.
9. Run engine at idle speed for about 2 minutes; then pour 5 more quarts (2 qts. on Comet and Falcon) of oil in transmission. Then run engine at a fast idle until it reaches normal operating temperature.
10. Shift selector lever through all positions. Place lever at P. Then add fluid as necessary to bring level to "Full" mark on dipstick.

LOW BAND, ADJUST

The low band adjusting screw is threaded through the front left side of the case. When making the adjustment, it is recommended that the special tool shown in Fig. 2 be used. This is a pre-set torque wrench that clicks or overruns when the torque on the screw reaches 10 lbs. ft.

To make the adjustment, loosen the lock nut several turns. Tighten the adjusting screw until the wrench clicks and back it off exactly two turns. Hold the adjusting screw in this position and tighten the lock nut to a torque of 35-40 lbs. ft.

If the special wrench is not available, an emergency adjustment may be made by turning the adjusting screw in until a resistance is felt, which indicates that the band is snug against the drum. Then back it off two full turns.

REVERSE BAND, ADJUST

Fig. 3 illustrates the special tools required to make this adjustment. With the oil pan removed, place the tool on the rear servo piston rod so that the two forks straddle the band apply lever. The inner fork must engage the flat on the

Fig. 2 Low band adjustment

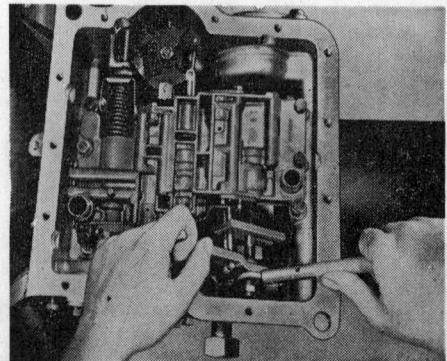

Fig. 3 Reverse band adjustment

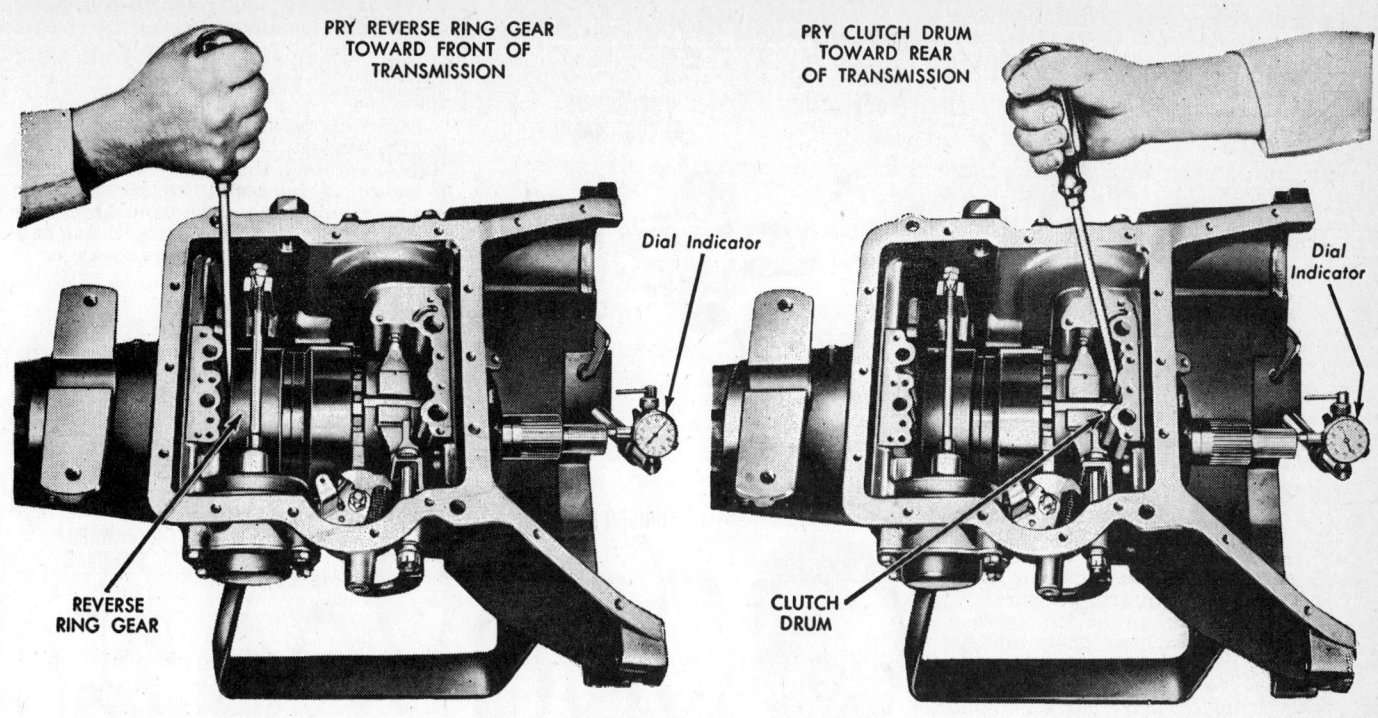

PRY REVERSE RING GEAR TOWARD FRONT OF TRANSMISSION

PRY CLUTCH DRUM TOWARD REAR OF TRANSMISSION

Dial Indicator

Dial Indicator

REVERSE RING GEAR

CLUTCH DRUM

Fig. 5 Transmission end play check

servo piston rod. The outer fork is a spacer and must be inserted between the piston rod seat and the adjusting nut.

Loosen the piston rod lock nut and adjusting nut. Tighten the adjusting nut until the tool is felt to ratchet and heard to click as it overruns. Then back off adjusting nut exactly two turns and tighten locknut to 15-18 ft. lbs. while holding the adjusting nut against rotation.

CONTROL PRESSURE CHECKS

When transmission troubles occur and their causes are not obvious, control pressure should be checked at engine idle and at stall. For this purpose a ⅛" pipe plug is installed on the left side of the case forward and above the low band

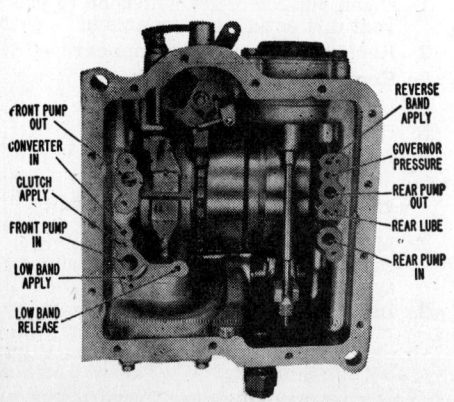

FRONT PUMP OUT

CONVERTER IN

CLUTCH APPLY

FRONT PUMP IN

LOW BAND APPLY

LOW BAND RELEASE

REVERSE BAND APPLY

GOVERNOR PRESSURE

REAR PUMP OUT

REAR LUBE

REAR PUMP IN

Fig. 4 Air pressure check points

OIL PRESSURE CHART

Year	Model	Engine R. P. M.	Trans. Range	Pressure P. S. I.
COMET				
1960	All	Idle	All	40–48
	All	1200	D	55–60
	All	Stall	D, L, R	135–155
1961	PBZ①	Idle	All	40–48
	PBZ①	1200	D	53–57
	PBZ①	Stall	D, L, R	135–155
	PCF①	Idle	All	46–56
	PCF①	1200	D	77–84
	PCF①	Stall	D, L, R	170–192
FALCON				
1960	All	Idle	All	46–56
	All	1200	D	78–82
	All	Stall	D, L, R	170–192
FORD & EDSEL				
1959–61	All	Idle	All	46–56
	All	1000	D	77–84
	All	Stall	D, L, R	170–192
MERCURY				
1961	Six Cyl.	Idle	All	46–56
	Six Cyl.	1000	D	77–84
	Six Cyl.	Stall	D, L, R	170–192

①—Transmission model located on transmission case.

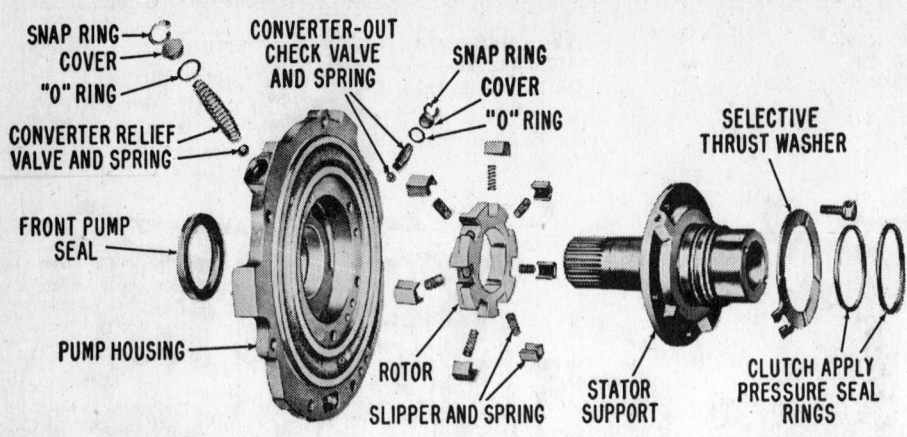

Fig. 6 Exploded view of front pump

adjusting screw. A pressure gauge installed here will read the pressure between the front pump and front pump check valve. This pressure is regulated by the control pressure regulator valve and is transmission control pressure.

1. Apply parking brake to prevent operation of the rear pump and for safety.
2. Remove valve cap from pressure tube fitting at left rear of engine.
3. Install pressure gauge.
4. Position gauge so it can be read from driver's seat, and connect tachometer to engine.
5. Apply service brakes and start engine.
6. Shift selector lever to D.
7. Increase engine speed to 1200 rpm and note gauge reading (engine must be at normal operating temperature). If pressure reading is below the minimum specified in chart, the throttle control rod clevis must be rotated to shorten the rod. If pressure reading is more than the maximum specified in chart, the rod must be lengthened. If control pressure cannot be brought within specifications by adjusting the throttle control rod, transmission trouble is indicated.
8. Check control rod at idle and stall speeds. Refer to chart for pressures which should be obtained.

AIR PRESSURE CHECKS

A "no drive" condition can exist because of inoperative bands or clutch even though the control pressures in the trans-

mission are normal. The inoperative units can be located through a series of checks by substituting air pressure for oil pressure. It is recommended that a special hose nozzle, having a rubber tip, be used for making air checks.

When the selector lever is in D or L, a "no drive" condition may be caused by an inoperative low band. Failure of the transmission to shift into high may be due to an inoperative clutch. Failure to drive in the reverse range may be caused by an inoperative reverse band.

To make air pressure checks, remove the transmission oil pan and control

valve assembly, and refer to Fig. 4 for check point locations.

Front Servo

Direct air pressure into the front servo apply passage. The low band should tighten around the drum. The moment pressure is released, the servo return spring should release the band. Direct air pressure into the front servo release passage and listen for excessive leakage.

Rear Servo

With air pressure applied to the reverse servo, the reverse band should tighten around the drum. When the air pressure is released, the piston return spring should release the band.

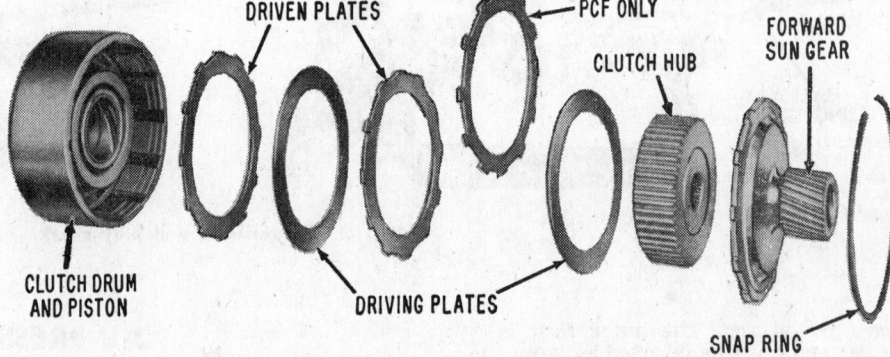

Fig. 8 Clutch and related parts. See plate on transmission case to identify transmission model

Clutch

With air pressure applied to the clutch apply passage a dull thud will be heard when the clutch piston is applied. If no noise is heard, place finger tips on the drum. Movement of the piston can be felt when air pressure is applied. If the bands or clutch fail to respond to air pressure, disassemble and repair the transmission.

SUB-ASSEMBLIES, REMOVE

Oil Pan and Control Valve

1. Clean outside of transmission to prevent dirt entering mechanism.
2. Remove transmission from car.
3. Remove torque converter.
4. Remove oil pan and gasket.
5. Remove oil screen.
6. Remove control valve body (6 bolts).

Transmission End Play Check

1. Mount dial indicator on transmission case so that contact rests on primary sun gear shaft.
2. Install extension housing seal replacer or a front universal joint yoke on the output shaft spline to align output shaft.
3. Pry reverse ring gear forward with a

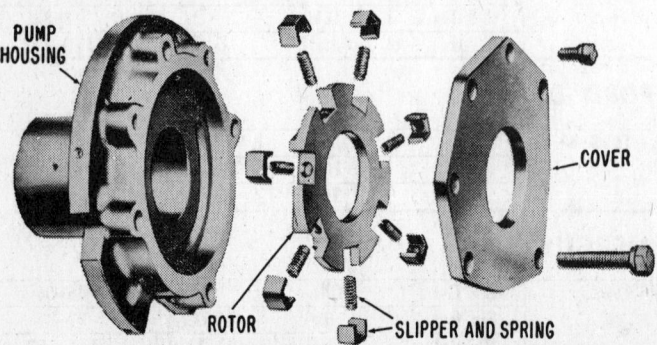

Fig. 7 Exploded view of rear pump

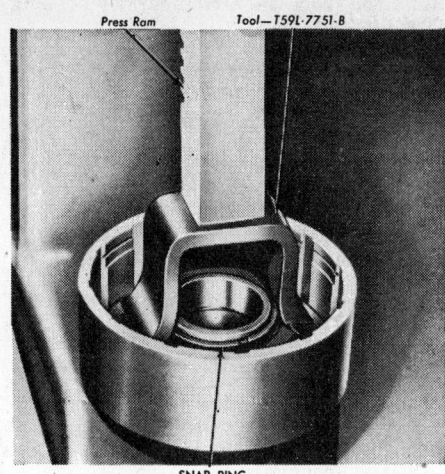

Fig. 9 Clutch spring snap ring removal

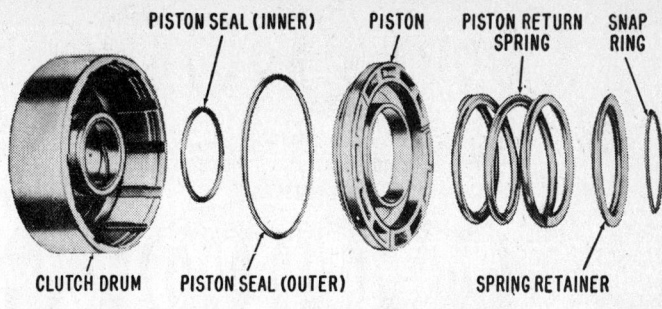

Fig. 11 Clutch drum and piston

large screwdriver. Set dial indicator at zero while maintaining a slight pressure on screwdriver, Fig. 5.

4. Now pry clutch drum to the rear. Record the indicator reading for use during transmission assembly. End play should be between .024" and .039"

5. Remove dial indicator and seal replacer or yoke.

Transmission, Disassemble

1. Remove extension housing (5 bolts.)
2. Remove governor and drive ball.
3. Remove front pump and stator support (7 bolts.)
4. Loosen low band adjusting screw and remove low band struts. Compress band ends and slide band out of front of case. If band cannot be removed from case, remove seal ring from primary sun gear shaft and then remove clutch drum. Now remove low band.
5. Pull on primary sun gear shaft and remove clutch and integral pinion carrier and output shaft. Rotate assembly so that reverse ring gear can separate from short pinions and stay in case.
6. Remove seal ring from primary sun gear shaft; then remove clutch drum.
7. Remove governor pressure seal rings from output shaft.
8. Place output shaft and pinion carrier in bench fixture. Then remove reverse ring gear and thrust washer from case.
9. Remove rear pump (4 bolts).
10. Remove reverse band.

SUB-ASSEMBLIES, OVERHAUL

During repair of sub-assemblies, handle all parts carefully to avoid nicking or burring bearing or mating surfaces. Lubricate all internal parts before assembly with automatic transmission fluid. Gaskets and thrust washers may be coated with vaseline to facilitate assembly. Always use new gaskets. Tighten all bolts and screws to the recommended torque.

The only bushing available for replacement is the extension housing bushing. If excessive bushing wear is encountered, the part containing the worn bushing must be replaced.

Front Pump and Stator Support

1. Detach stator support from pump housing (5 bolts). Remove stator support shaft from pump housing, Fig. 6.
2. Inspect clutch drum journal for wear and roughness.
3. Check side clearance between clutch apply pressure seal rings and their grooves in stator support. These clearances should be .0035" and .0045".
4. Remove rings and install them in their normal running position in clutch drum. Then check ring gaps which should be .002" to .009".
5. Inspect clutch drum front (selective) thrust washer for wear. Inspect primary sun gear shaft bushing in stator support shaft.
6. Lift rotor and slippers and slipper springs from front pump housing. Check pump housing and slippers for excessive wear.
7. The converter pressure relief valve and converter-out check valve may be removed from pump housing.
8. Inspect converter pump drive hub bushing in pump housing. Inspect drive hub seal and replace if necessary.
9. To assemble front pump, place rotor in housing with flat side up.
10. As slippers and springs are installed between rotor and housing, make sure each spring bottoms in spring holes in slipper and rotor.
11. Place stator support in housing, install 5 bolts and torque them to 12-15 lbs. ft.

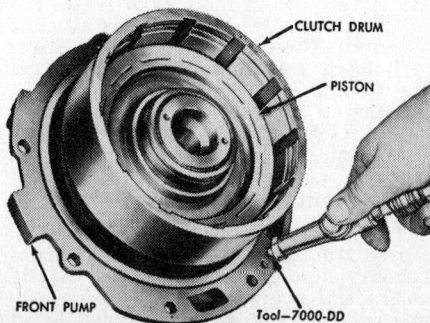

Fig. 10 Applying air pressure to hole indicated to force out clutch piston

12. Check pump for rotation by placing it on converter pump drive hub in normal running position and turning pump housing.

Rear Pump

1. Remove rear pump cover plate, Fig. 7.
2. Remove rotor slippers and springs.
3. Inspect output shaft support bronze bushing in pump housing for wear. Inspect rear area of housing I.D. for governor pressure seal ring wear.
4. Install governor pressure seal rings in pump housing and check ring gap which should be .001" to .006".
5. Check governor pressure orifice for obstruction.
6. Inspect slippers and pump housing for wear. Pump housing and rotor must be replaced as a matched assembly. Slippers may be replaced as a set in the old housing and rotor.
7. To assemble rear pump, place rotor in housing with flat side up. Turn rotor so that flat surface on I.D. is toward bottom of pump housing. Install slippers and springs between rotor and housing *with marked side of each slipper up.*
8. Place cover on pump housing and torque screws to 50-60 inch lbs.
9. Install pump on output shaft in its normal running position. Check pump for free rotation by turning pump housing.
10. Before removing pump from output shaft, make sure that flat surface on pump rotor I.D. is toward bottom of pump housing.

Governor

1. Detach governor end plate from housing (2 screws).
2. Remove valve from housing.
3. Inspect valve and housing for wear. *Crocus cloth may be used to polish valve if care is taken to avoid rounding sharp edges of valve.*
4. Install governor valve in valve body and check valve for free movement. Valve should fall of its own weight when dry.
5. Install end cover and torque screws to 20-30 inch lbs.

High Clutch

1. Remove snap ring and lift forward sun gear and flange from clutch drum, Fig. 8.
2. Remove clutch plates and clutch hub.
3. Place tool shown in Fig. 9 or equivalent on clutch piston return spring

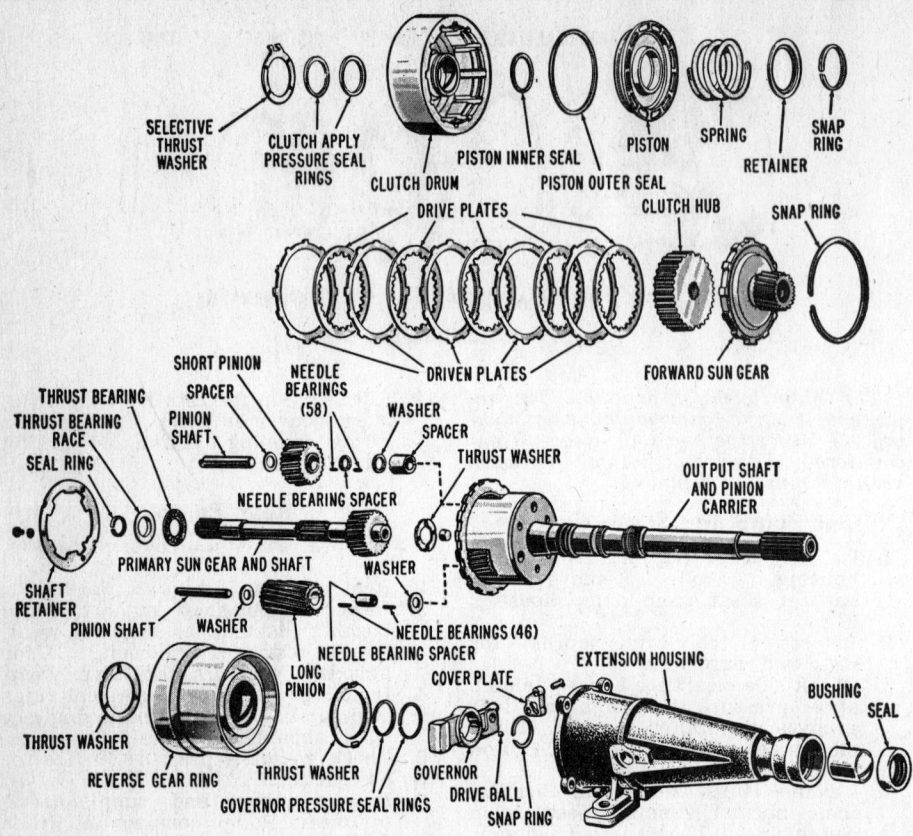

SELECTIVE THRUST WASHER · CLUTCH APPLY PRESSURE SEAL RINGS · CLUTCH DRUM · PISTON INNER SEAL · PISTON OUTER SEAL · PISTON · SPRING · RETAINER · SNAP RING

DRIVE PLATES · DRIVEN PLATES · CLUTCH HUB · FORWARD SUN GEAR · SNAP RING

THRUST BEARING · THRUST BEARING RACE · SEAL RING · SHAFT RETAINER · PINION SHAFT · SHORT PINION · SPACER · PINION SHAFT · NEEDLE BEARINGS (58) · WASHER · SPACER · THRUST WASHER · OUTPUT SHAFT AND PINION CARRIER

NEEDLE BEARING SPACER · PRIMARY SUN GEAR AND SHAFT · WASHER · WASHER · NEEDLE BEARINGS (46) · NEEDLE BEARING SPACER · LONG PINION · EXTENSION HOUSING · BUSHING · SEAL

THRUST WASHER · REVERSE GEAR RING · THRUST WASHER · GOVERNOR PRESSURE SEAL RINGS · GOVERNOR · DRIVE BALL · SNAP RING · COVER PLATE

Fig. 12 Exploded view of transmission

retainer; then place clutch drum under a press. Compress spring and remove snap ring. Guide spring retainer as press ram rises so that retainer does not slide into snap ring groove.

4. Place clutch drum on completely assembled stator support shaft and front pump housing. Apply air pressure to hole in pump housing flange to force piston out of clutch drum, Fig. 10.

5. Remove piston outer seal from piston and piston inner seal from drum, Fig. 11.

6. Inspect drive plates for damage. Plates must be flat.

7. Inspect steel driven clutch plates. These plates should also be flat. If there is any perceptible dish in drive or driven plates, they should be replaced.

8. Inspect bronze bushing in clutch drum for wear.

9. Install new piston seal in clutch drum. Install new outer seal in clutch piston. Lubricate seals with transmission fluid and install piston in clutch drum.

10. Place return spring and retainer on piston. Place clutch drum under press and install snap ring.

11. Install drive and driven plates alternately in clutch drum, starting with a steel plate next to piston. Number of plates vary with transmission model. The last plate in clutch pack (top of pack) should be a non-metallic drive plate.

12. After correct number of plates have been installed in drum, install clutch hub. There is no washer between clutch hub and forward sun gear flange.

13. Install forward sun gear and flange in clutch drum. Then install snap ring.

Planetary Gear System

The primary sun gear must be removed from the pinon carrier to inspect primary sun gear front thrust bearing and race, primary sun gear thrust washer and primary sun gear pilot bushing. To remove the primary sun gear from the pinion carrier, the short pinions must be

removed from the pinion carrier housing, Fig. 12.

Disassembly

1. Mark pinion shafts so they can be reassembled in same locations.

2. Remove screws attaching pinion shaft retainer ring to pinion carrier. Turn retainer counterclockwise until shafts are unlocked.

3. With a suitable tool, Fig. 13, push a short pinion shaft up from the bottom until the tool clears the top of the gear spacer. Now, slide the short pinion and its upper and lower needle bearing thrust washers out of pinion carrier window. Retain needle bearings and spacer in short pinion by pushing tool out with the removed shaft.

4. Remove two remaining short pinions and spacers.

5. Remove primary sun gear and shaft.

6. With a suitable tool, Fig, 14, push a long pinion shaft up until the tool just clears the pinion carrier bottom plate. Remove the long pinion with its top and bottom needle bearing thrust washers out the center of the pinion carrier. With the pinion shaft, push the tool out of the gear. The shaft will hold the needle bearings, spacer and thrust washers in position.

7. Remove two remaining long pinions.

Inspection

1. Inspect pilot journal on primary sun gear shaft and pilot bushing in output shaft.

2. Inspect primary sun gear rear bronze thrust washer, primary sun gear front thrust bearing and bearing race.

3. Inspect converter-out pressure seal ring groove, which is machined in the primary sun gear shaft at the clutch hub spline. *Excessive leakage at this ring will permit converter-out fluid to by-pass the cooling system and return to the sump through the clutch and planetary gears.*

4. Inspect thrust washers which contain needle bearing end thrust for wear or roughness.

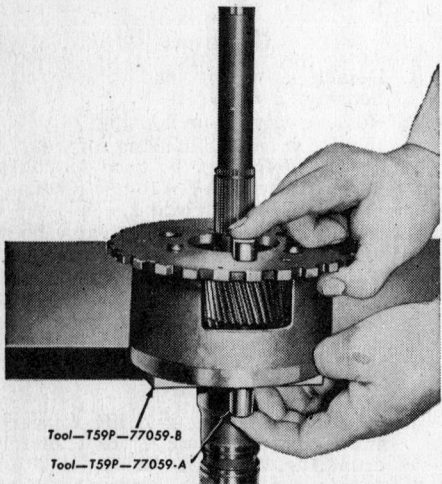

Tool—T59P—77059-B
Tool—T59P—77059-A

Fig. 13 Short pinion removal and installation

Tool—T59L-77059-A

Fig. 14 Long pinion removal and installation

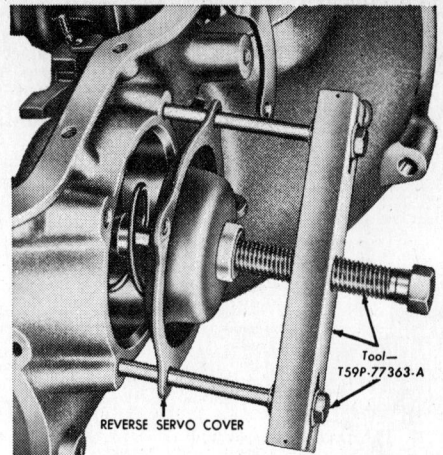

Fig. 15 Reverse servo cover removal or installation

5. Inspect planet carrier for excessive wear at thrust washer locations.
6. Inspect pinion shafts for wear and roughness.
7. Inspect all gear teeth for nicks, cracks or burrs.
8. Inspect pinion carrier teeth that are engaged by the parking pawl.
9. Inspect governor pressure seal ring grooves in output shaft.

Assembly

1. Referring to Fig. 9, place spacer in long pinion and insert dummy shaft through long pinion and needle bearing spacer, Fig. 14.
2. At each end of gear add a row of 23 needle bearings.
3. Place a thrust washer on each end of gear. Retain washer to gear with vaseline.
4. While holding the long pinion as-

sembly together, place it in position in pinion carrier. Use the marked shaft for this location to push dummy tool rod out of bottom.
5. Install remaining long pinions in same manner.
6. Place primary sun gear front thrust bearing and race on primary sun gear shaft. Place bronze thrust washer on pilot at rear of primary sun gear. Hold washer in place with vaseline. *Make sure concave side of this dished washer is toward rear of transmission.*
7. Place primary sun gear shaft in pinion carrier.
8. Place spacer in short pinion and insert dummy shaft through gear and needle bearing spacer, Fig. 13. Install a row of 29 needle bearings and a thrust washer at each end of gear. Retain washers in place with vaseline.
9. Place a short pinion spacer in pinion carrier. Insert pinion shaft through bottom of pinion carrier and into spacer. Hold shaft so that it is flush with top of spacer. Use marked shaft for this location to push dummy shaft out of bottom.
10. Install two remaining short pinions in same manner.
11. Install pinion shaft retainer, install screws and torque them to 20-30 inch lbs.

Reverse Servo

1. Remove lock nut, adjusting nut and the rod seat (half-ball) from reverse servo rod.
2. Remove strut between apply lever and band. Turn band to unhook it from its anchor and remove band.
3. Remove two reverse servo cover-to-case bolts. Install tool shown in Fig. 15 or equivalent, and remove remaining bolts.
4. With tool, relieve spring tension and remove cover and seal. Then remove

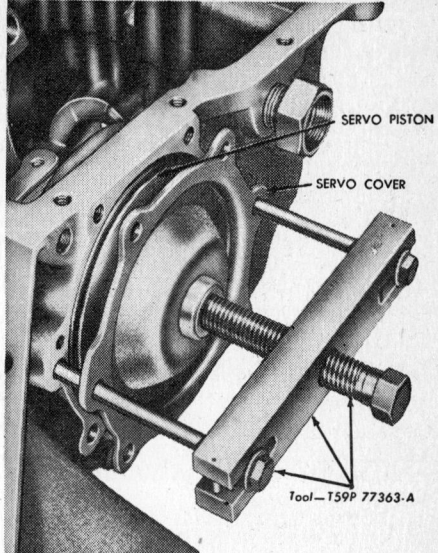

Fig. 16 Low servo cover removal or installation

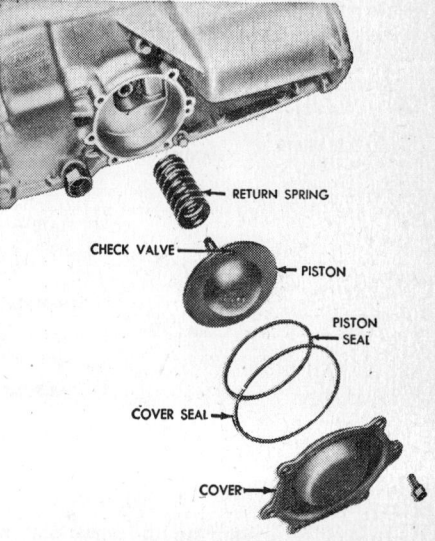

Fig. 17 Low servo assembly

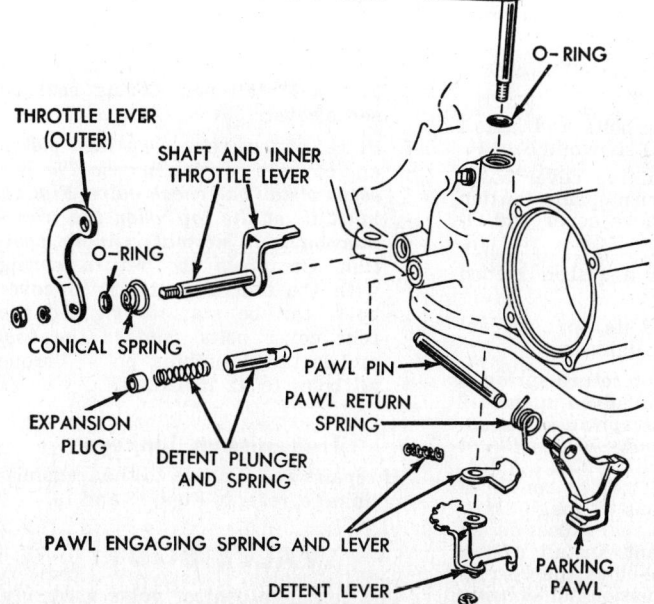

Fig. 18 Throttle and manual linkage

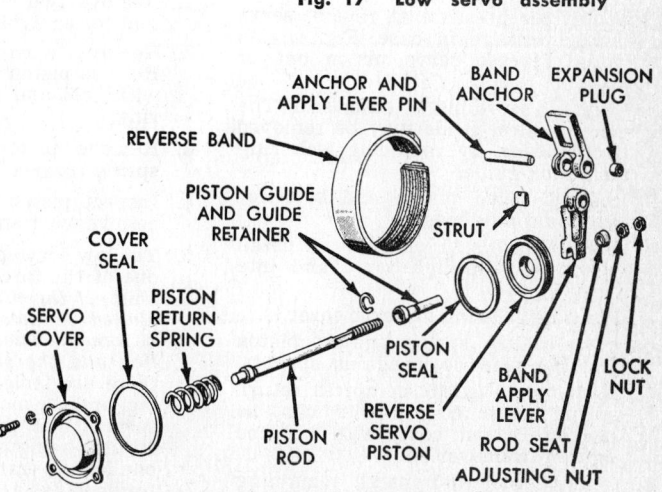

Fig. 19 Reverse servo piston and band apply linkage

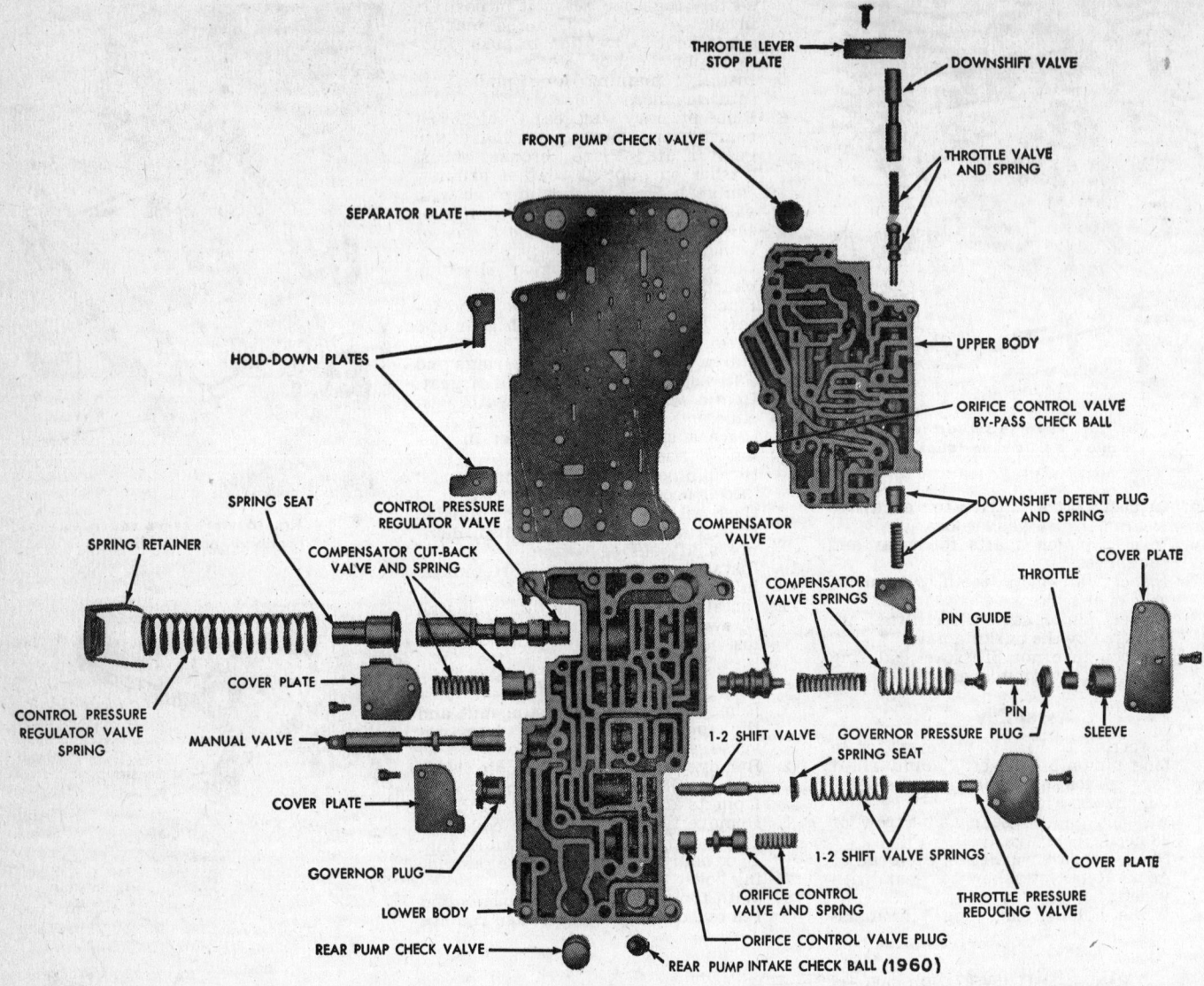

Fig. 20 Disassembled view of control valve

piston return spring and servo piston rod.

5. Apply air pressure at reverse servo apply passage in case, Fig. 4, and force reverse servo piston out of case.

6. Remove servo piston outer seal. The servo piston guide may be removed from piston by removing lock ring on piston guide.

7. Inspect servo piston and bore for wear and roughness.

8. Install new seal on piston. Install piston rod through servo and into case.

9. Place new O-ring on servo cover.

10. Place return spring against piston and then place cover against spring.

11. With tool, Fig. 15, compress return spring until cover bolts can be started. Bottom cover with tool and tighten two cover bolts.

12. Remove tool and install remaining two bolts. Then torque all cover bolts to 12-15 lbs. ft.

Low Servo

1. Remove two cover bolts and install tool (or equivalent) shown in Fig. 16.

2. Remove two remaining cover bolts. Release piston return spring tension with tool and remove cover and O-ring.

3. Remove piston and piston return spring from case.

4. Inspect piston and its bore for excessive wear and roughness.

5. The low servo piston return spring is one of the forces involved in the 1-2 shift. *If the proper spring is not installed, the low band release will not be synchronized with clutch application and the shift will be rough.* If there are indications of rough shifting, and the more usual causes do not seem to be present, install a new spring, being sure it is the correct one for the transmission model being serviced.

6. Install a new seal on low servo piston. Install new O-ring seal on servo cover.

7. Place piston return spring, piston and cover in position in case. *The low servo piston ball check valve, Fig. 17, must be at the top when the transmission is in normal running position.* Compress the return spring with the tool, Fig. 16, until cover bolts can be started. Tighten the four cover bolts, remove the tool and install remaining bolts. Torque all bolts to 12-15 lbs. ft.

Transmission Linkage

If repairs are required to the transmission linkage, refer to Figs. 18 and 19.

VALVE BODY

The complete control valve assembly, Fig. 20, consists of an upper body, a lower body, and a separator plate. These

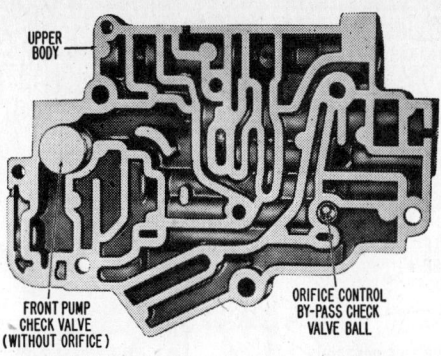

Fig. 21 Orifice control by-pass check valve and front pump check valve are placed in upper body

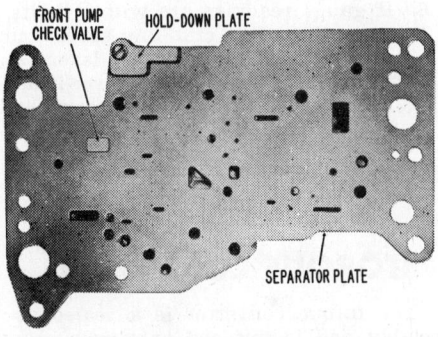

Fig. 22 Separator plate is fitted to upper body and retained in position by installing hold-down plate and screw

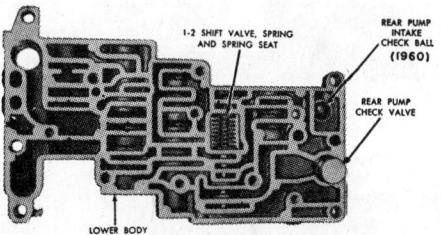

Fig. 23 The 1-2 shift valve with its spring and seat, together with rear pump check valve, is installed in lower body

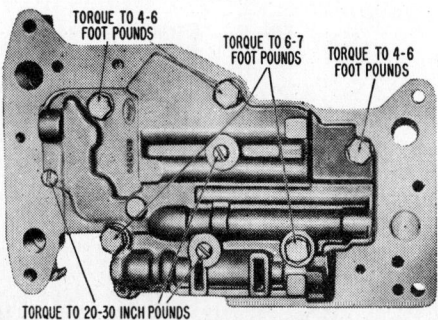

Fig. 24 Torque requirements for retaining bolts

three elements are bolted together and contain the various valves, springs and plugs that are required for the transmission hydraulic control system.

In servicing the valve body assembly, refer to Figs. 20 to 28. *All valves and plugs must fall into their respective bores by their own weight. They must not be forced.* Crocus cloth may be used to polish valves and plugs but care must be taken to avoid rounding the sharp edges of the lands. These sharp edges must be maintained to assure satisfactory operation of the valves and plugs.

TRANSMISSION ASSEMBLE

Transmission Case

1. Install rear pump in case. *Install but do not tighten the four attaching bolts.*
2. Place reverse band in case. Band end having guide pin for the strut goes toward apply lever strut. Make sure anchor end of band engages band anchor. Compress band and install strut between band apply lever and band.
3. Position reverse servo apply rod in band apply lever. Start rod seat (half ball), adjusting nut and lock nut on apply rod.
4. Place reverse ring gear thrust washer on rear pump extension at rear of case.
5. Install reverse ring gear on rear pump extension.

Gear Train

1. Place reverse ring gear front thrust washer on output shaft and against flange at pinion carrier.
2. Install governor pressure seal rings on output shaft. Ring gaps should be at the top as output shaft is installed, one of the flat surfaces which drives the rear pump should be up.
3. Install clutch on primary sun gear. Mesh forward sun gear with short pinion and then bottom forward sun gear on primary sun gear front thrust bearing and race.
4. Install converter-out pressure seal ring on primary sun gear shaft. This ring groove is in the clutch hub spline.
5. Install the assembly in the case. Some difficulty may be experienced

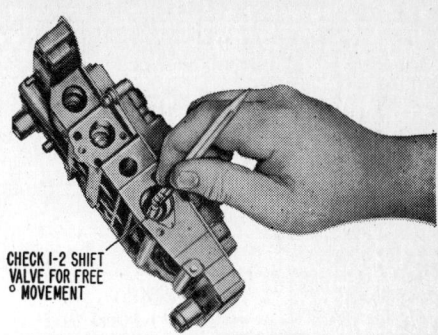

Fig. 25 At this point is is important that the 1-2 shift valve be checked for free movement, and adjusted as required.

in starting the output shaft flat surface which drives the rear pump into the rear pump rotor. One of the flats on the output shaft and the flat in the rotor should be up (actually toward the bottom of the transmission). The slipper springs will position the rotor in the center. Its normal running position is off-center and toward the bottom of the transmission. When the flat on the output shaft comes in contact with the rotor, lift upward on the rotor with a screwdriver, Fig. 29, while keeping steady pressure on the output shaft, and when the flats align, the output shaft will slip into position. If the rotor and output shaft will not align, remove the pump cover plate, rotor and slippers. Slide the output shaft into normal running position. Assemble the rotor on the output shaft and in the pump housing. Install slippers and springs, cover plate and attaching screws. As the bolts are tightened, check pump for free rotation. Torque bolts to 12-15 lbs. ft. and screws to 50-60 inch lbs.

6. Install low band, inserting it through front of transmission case. *The end of the band having the guide pin for the strut goes to the adjusting screw side.* Install band struts.
7. Using the end play reading which was taken prior to disassembly of transmission, use the proper selective thrust washer to be installed on the stator support shaft. These washers are available in thicknesses of .067-.069", .074.-.076", .083-.085" and .092-.094".

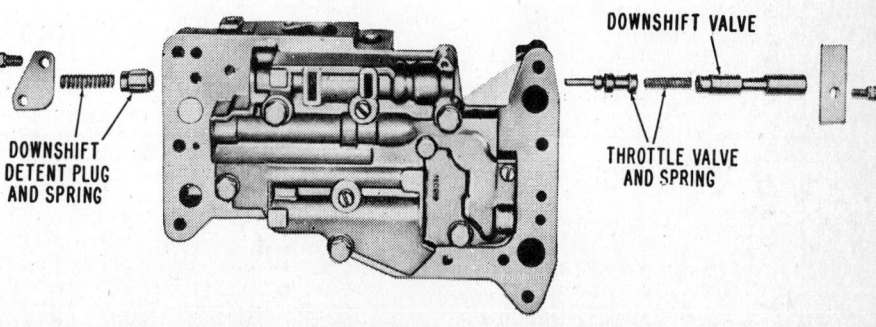

Fig. 26 Installation of parts in upper body

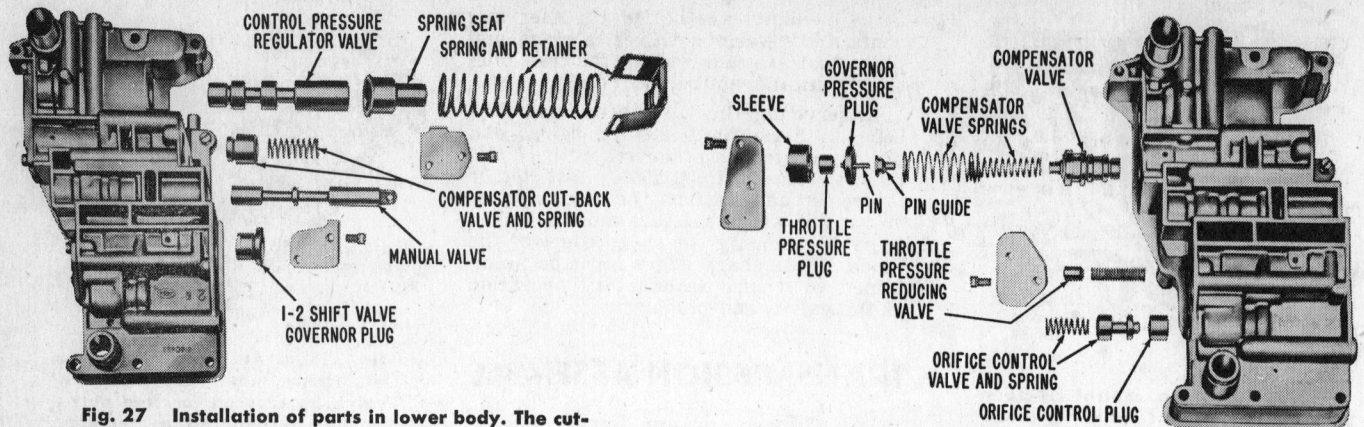

Fig. 27 Installation of parts in lower body. The cut-back valve cover screws are torqued to 20-30 lbs. ft.

Fig. 28 Further installation of parts in lower body. Torque cover plate screws to 30-40 lbs. ft.

8. Install clutch apply pressure seal rings on stator support shaft.
9. Place new gasket on pump housing. Install pump in case. Torque bolts to 12-15 lbs. ft.
10. Install governor on output shaft.
11. Place new gasket on case and install extension housing. Torque housing-to-case bolts to 28-38 lbs. ft.
12. Install extension housing seal replacer tool in extension housing to align output shaft. Check gear end play, using procedure given before disassembly. If end play is not within .024-.039", change selective washer to bring it within these limits.

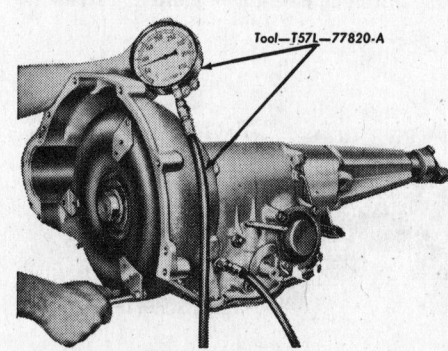

Fig. 29 Rear pump rotor alignment with output shaft

13. Adjust bands as outlined at the beginning of this chapter.
14. Install control valve body and oil pan. Torque valve body bolts to 8-10 lbs. ft. and oil pan bolts to 10-13 lbs. ft.

HYDRAULIC BENCH TESTS

After the transmission has been assembled and ready for installation in the vehicle, the hydraulic system should be checked to make sure it is operating properly.

1. Referring to Fig. 30, install plug in filler tube fitting in case. Tilt transmission and pour four quarts of transmission fluid into case through speedometer gear opening.
2. Install converter on transmission and in its normal running position.
3. Remove ⅛" pipe plug from left-hand side of case. Turn converter in clockwise direction at 75-100 rpm until a regular flow of transmission fluid leaves the hole in transmission case. This operation bleeds the air from the pump.
4. Install pressure gauge as shown, Fig. 30.
5. Turn front pump at 75-100 rpm and note gauge readings. Gauge reading at selector lever positions N, D and L should be 48-75 psi; with selector lever in R, 150-220.

6. If gauge readings are within limits, maintain a fast cranking speed and slowly advance throttle lever at transmission. As throttle lever is advanced, a minimum pressure rise of 50% should be obtained in all positions except reverse. In reverse, pressure may be maximum at closed throttle.

TORQUE CONVERTER

The torque converter is a sealed assembly and is serviced only as a unit.

Tool—T57L—77820-A

Fig. 30 Hydraulic system bench tests

HYDRA-MATIC
Two Coupling Type

Called "Flashaway" by American Motors Corp., "Jetaway" by Oldsmobile, and "Strato-Flight" by Pontiac. For Linkage Adjustment See Car Chapter

CONTENTS

Description 263
Trouble Shooting 28

Maintenance

Adding Fluid 265
Changing Fluid 265

"In Car" Repairs

Checking Oil Pressure 265
Seals Against Leakage 265
Correction of Leaks 266
Extension Housing Oil Seal 267
Servo and Accumulator 267
Control Valve Assembly 268
Parking Brake 269
Governor 270
Rear Pump 271
Reverse Unit 274
Pressure Regulator 274

Repairs Requiring Transmission Removal

Transmission, Disassemble 275
Front Pump 277
Center Bearing Support 277
Front Unit Coupling 278
Torus Check Valve 278
Rear Unit Clutch Cover 278
Rear Unit 280
Neutral Clutch Drum 280
Overrun Band 280
Transmission Case 280
Torus Cover 280
Transmission, Assemble 280

DESCRIPTION

1956-59

This transmission, Fig. 1, differs from the 1955 and earlier single coupling type in that many of the frictional elements of the earlier version has been eliminated in the later version. The following paragraphs outline the changes made.

Clutches & Bands Eliminated

The multiple disc type front clutch has been eliminated and has been replaced by a simple fluid coupling (fluid clutch). This change has resulted in a smoothness which is an inherent characteristic of a fluid coupling.

The front band has been eliminated and replaced by a simple one way clutch called a sprag clutch.

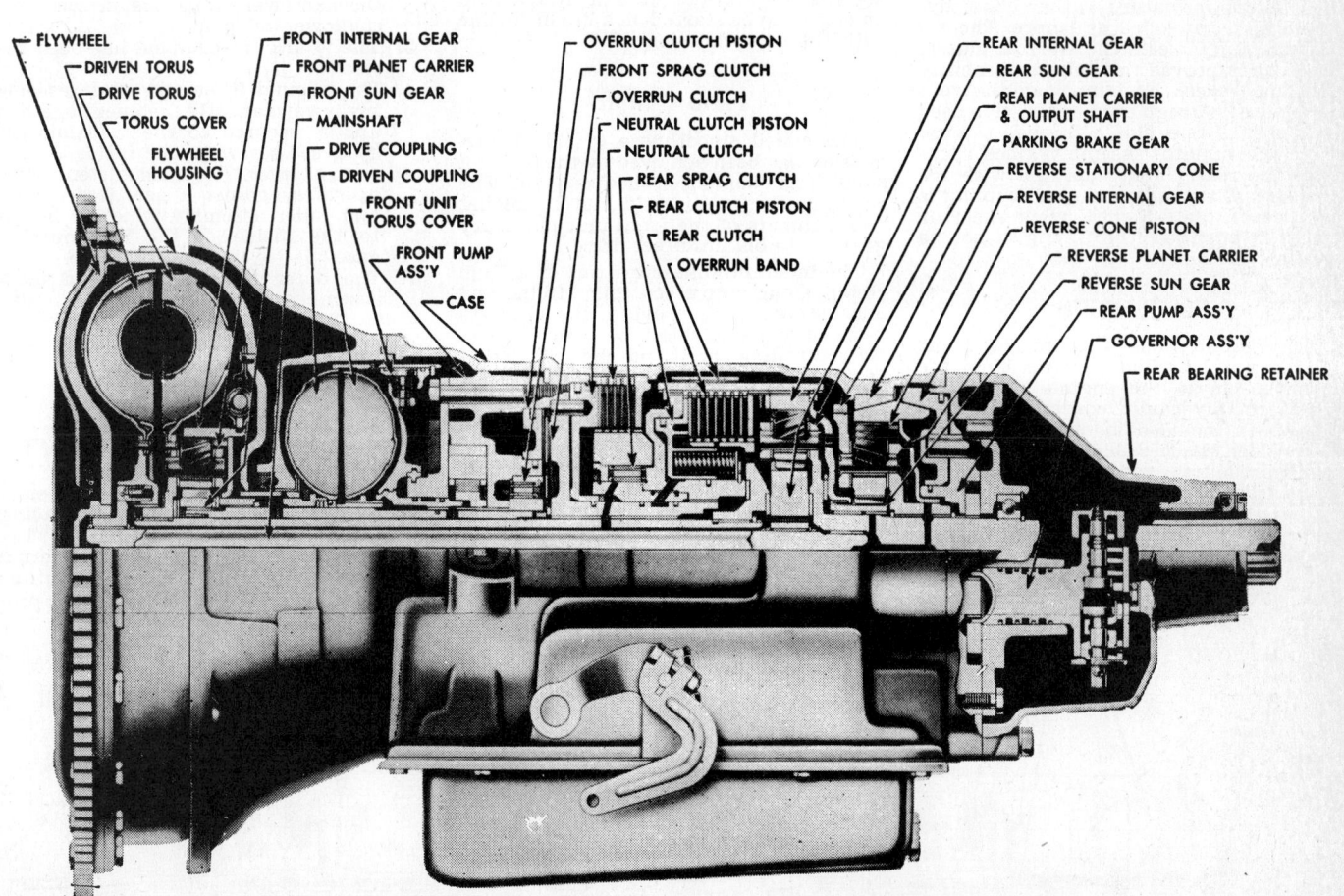

Fig. 1 Cutaway view of two coupling Hydra-Matic featuring sprag (one way) clutches and a small fluid coupling in place of the multiple disc clutches and servo applied bands used formerly. Rear pump is no longer used on 1959-61 units

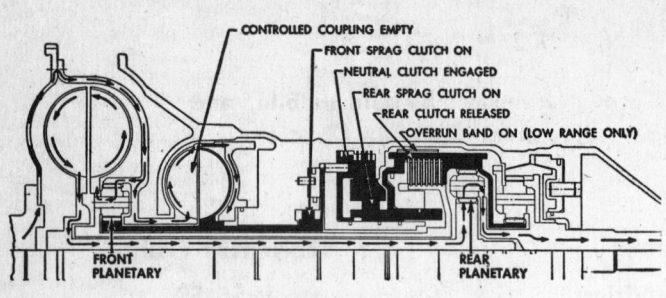

Fig. 2 FIRST SPEED—Front and rear planetaries in reduction

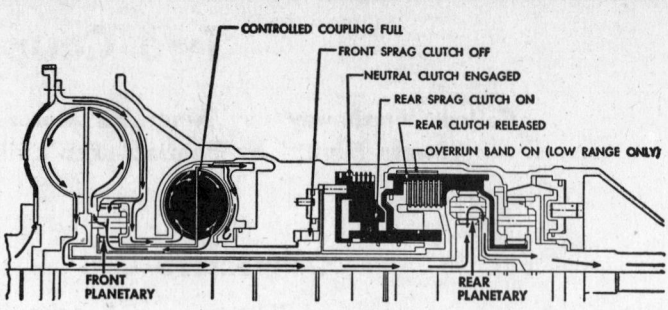

Fig. 3 SECOND SPEED—Front planetary in direct, rear planetary in reduction

The rear band has been eliminated and replaced by a sprag clutch which is similar to the one which replaces the front band.

It can be seen that the durability of the transmission will be greatly improved by the reduction of the wear factor on non-friction elements.

Timing Devices Eliminated

Many timing devices have been eliminated internally except those required for the 2-3 shift and rate of front unit coupling fill and exhaust. Because of the absence of all but one friction element, the gear ratio changes of the front and rear units will be more automatic and mechanical in nature rather than hydraulically controlled as before. The remaining friction element, the rear clutch, has been improved to increase durability and smoothness by increasing the rear clutch area. A regulated apply oil is used to apply the rear clutch through the use of an accumulator assembly which regulates the rear clutch apply oil with TV pressure. Since the front unit coupling is emptied on the 2-3 shift, while the rear clutch is engaged, the timing is not as critical.

Serviceability

Serviceability has been improved due to the new method of attaching the transmission to the engine. Practically all of the hydraulic controlling valves have been included in one major valve body which is accessible by removing the transmission oil pan. The new control valve assembly, in turn, has been divided into four separate assemblies, any one of which can be serviced separately if replacement becomes necessary.

Periodic band adjustments have been eliminated by the removal of the front and rear bands as holding devices for the front and rear planetary gear sets. However, one band, which is only used in the Lo range, has been added to the rear unit. It resists very little torque and is not subject to wear or adjustment.

Selector Lever Quadrant

The selector lever has one additional quadrant position, "Park", in addition to Neutral, Dr-4, Dr-3, Lo and Reverse. The "Park" position provides a definite lock for parking and can also be used for engine starting. This feature enables the car to be parked on a hill or an incline with the engine running without engaging the hand brake. It will also enable an engine to be started on a hill or incline with the drive line locked.

Fluid Clutch

The added smoothness of this transmission has been achieved by the use of a small fluid coupling in the front unit. The coupling acts as a fluid clutch holding two members of the front unit planetary gear set to obtain direct drive.

The inherent characteristics of a fluid clutch, along with a controlled filling and exhausting of oil, provides the ultimate in smoothness in this type transmission. By controlling the filling and exhausting of the front unit coupling, the change from reduction to direct drive is smoother than is possible with the use of friction elements.

The front unit planetary gear set is located behind the main fluid coupling torus members and thus is submerged in oil.

Figs. 2, 3, 4 and 5 illustrate the operation of the transmission in all forward speeds.

1960-61 Hydra-Matic

This transmission has been designed to reduce the overall size. Operationally, however, the transmission is unchanged. The following features are unique to the 1960 transmission and affect service procedures.

1. The transmission case is narrower and more compact.
2. The case center support locating bolt is no longer used.
3. The oil pan is smaller to accomodate the narrower transmission case and to provide additional ground clearance.
4. A new compact servo and accumulator assembly is used to accomodate the narrower transmission case and shallower oil pan.
5. The "Park" mechanism has been revised.
6. The manual lever and shaft assembly is permanently fastened together and is secured to the transmission by a set screw in the inside detent control lever. The inside detent lever operates against a new leaf spring and roller assembly which is bolted to the inside of the transmission case.
7. The outer throttle lever and shaft assembly has been revised similar to the manual lever and is secured to the transmission by means of clamping the inside throttle control lever to the TV shaft.
8. The control valve assembly has been modified for compactness. The reverse blocker is now a part of the manual body assembly.
9. A paper element type oil strainer is used in the intake system, replacing the screen used formerly. The strainer is provided with an internal by-pass for cold weather operation.
10. Additional cooling oil has been pro-

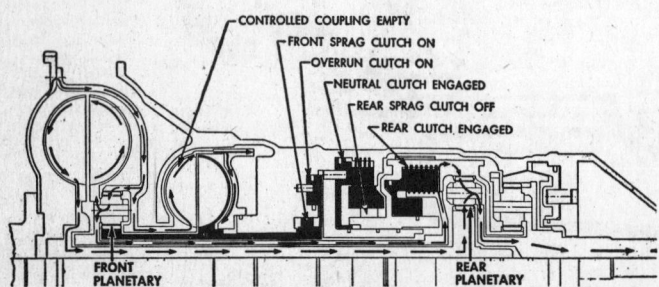

Fig. 4 THIRD SPEED—Front planetary in reduction, rear planetary in direct

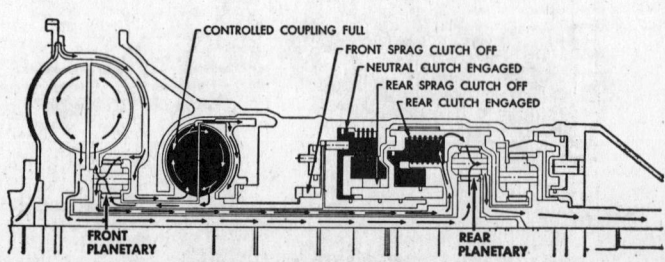

Fig. 5 FOURTH SPEED—Front and rear planetaries in direct

vided through a change in the torus feed valve.

11. The four flywheel - to - flex - plate spacer washers are no longer used.

MAINTENANCE

Adding Fluid, 1960-61

Due to the smaller size of this transmission, it is extremely important that the proper fluid level be maintained. A one pint tolerance is marked on the level indicator. Checking or changing the fluid should never be attempted when the transmission is extremely hot or cold because of fluid expansion and contraction.

The fluid level should be checked at every chassis lubrication. Add fluid, if necessary, until the proper level is indicated on the dipstick. Check the level after the engine has been running to make certain the fluid coupling is full. Run the engine with the selector lever in "N" or "P" at a fast idle (800 rpm) for 1½ minutes.

Reduce engine speed to slow idle. Remove and wipe dipstick and check fluid level. With engine still running, add fluid to bring it to the proper level. At normal operating temperature, from low mark (bottom dimple) to "F" requires one pint of fluid.

Adding Fluid, 1956-59

The fluid level should be checked every 1000 miles along with regular lubrication.

To check the fluid level, place the selector lever in N or P, run the engine at a high idle speed for approximately 1½ minutes. *Always check the oil level after the engine has been running to be sure the fluid coupling is filled and thus obtain an accurate reading.*

With engine still running, add fluid to bring the level to ¼" below the FULL mark on the dipstick.

Do not fill above the FULL mark as this will cause foaming when the transmission oil is hot. The level should be ¼" below the FULL mark when cold and at the FULL mark when hot.

Changing Fluid, 1960-61

Transmission fluid should be changed at 12,000-mile or one-year intervals. *Cadillac Note*—Before fluid can be changed, the starter motor will have to be removed; also the transmission linkage shield, on cars so equipped.

1. Remove lower flywheel housing cover plate.

2. Remove drain plugs from transmission oil pan and front face of flywheel.

3. When fluid has drained, reinstall drain plugs.

4. Pour 7 quarts of fluid into filler tube.

5. Run engine at a fast idle speed (800 rpm) for 1½ minutes with selector lever in "N".

6. Reduce engine speed to slow idle and add 1½ to 2 quarts to bring level to the "F" mark on dipstick provided transmission is at normal operating temperature (160-200°).

Adding Fluid, 1956-59

Cadillac Note—Before the fluid can be changed the starter motor will have to be removed.

1. Remove drain plug from transmission oil pan and from flywheel, which is accessible when the flywheel front cover is removed.

2. Drain fluid and install plugs.

3. Add 8 quarts of Automatic Transmission Fluid into filler tube.

4. Run engine at high idle speed for 1½ minutes with selector lever in N.

5. Reduce engine speed to slow idle and add fluid as required to bring level ¼" below FULL mark on dipstick.

"In Car" Repairs

CHECKING OIL PRESSURE

The pump pressure can be checked with the transmission in the car, using Checking Gauge No. J-2540-A.

Clean the dirt from the bottom of the rear pump body and remove pipe plug from pump body. Screw the pressure gauge line fitting into the hole in the pump case and place the gauge in the car so it can be seen from the driver's seat. Drive the car until the transmission oil has reached normal driving temperature (approximately 200°).

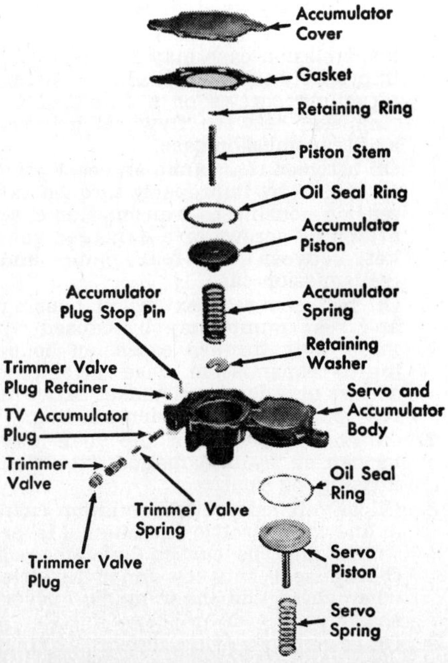

Drive Range Check

The following tests may be made by road test or with car on jack stands.

1. Zero throttle pressure above 20 mph in 4th speed with zero throttle, oil line pressure should be 60-70 psi.

2. Full throttle pressure (road test). Full throttle in any drive range should be at least 20 psi higher than zero throttle pressure reading (car on jacks).

3. To check the operation of the rear pump alone, drive the car at 40-45 mph in 4th speed. Then shift to neutral and turn off the ignition. Pressure should be at least 60 psi. Low rear pump pressure should be corrected by replacement of the pump gears or by checking for leakage in other units.

Reverse Pressure Check

1. Place selector lever in "Rev" position and note pressure with engine running at 400 rpm. This reading should be as high or higher than pressure checks in drive range.

2. With selector lever in "Rev", apply the foot brake and increase engine speed to half throttle. Pressure should increase to 160 psi minimum. The pressure range at the above conditions is from 160 to 200 psi. If pressure readings are below the specified amount for any of the above tests, a malfunctioning pressure regulator or a leak in the system is indicated.

SEALS AGAINST LEAKAGE

1. Use new gaskets and O-ring seals whenever there is a disassembly.

2. Use a very small amount of petrolatum to hold gaskets and thrust washers in place during assembly or to seal gaskets. *Never use gasket paste or shellac.*

3. Make sure that composition, cork or paper gaskets are not wrinkled or creased when installed. Make sure

Accumulator Cover

Gasket

Retaining Ring

Piston Stem

Oil Seal Ring

Accumulator Piston

Accumulator Plug Stop Pin

Accumulator Spring

Trimmer Valve Plug Retainer

Retaining Washer

TV Accumulator Plug

Servo and Accumulator Body

Trimmer Valve

Oil Seal Ring

Trimmer Valve Spring

Servo Piston

Trimmer Valve Plug

Servo Spring

Fig. 6 Servo and accumulator. 1960-61

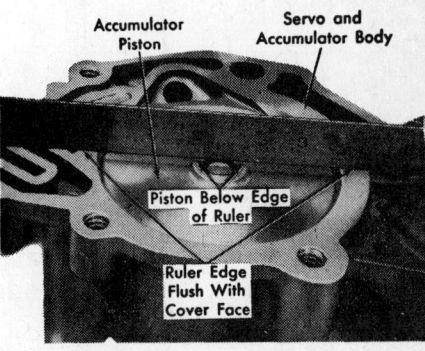

Fig. 7 Accumulator piston installed. 1960-61

Accumulator Piston   Servo and Accumulator Body

Piston Below Edge of Ruler

Ruler Edge Flush With Cover Face

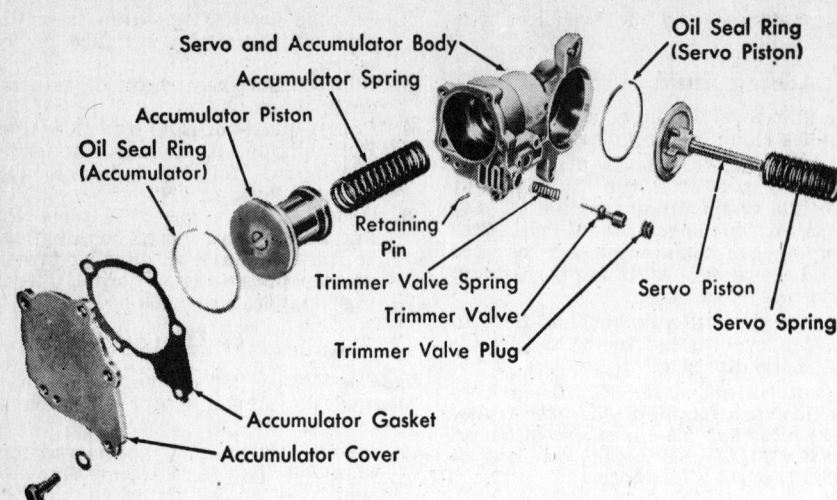

Servo and Accumulator Body
Accumulator Spring
Accumulator Piston
Oil Seal Ring (Accumulator)
Oil Seal Ring (Servo Piston)
Retaining Pin
Trimmer Valve Spring
Trimmer Valve
Trimmer Valve Plug
Servo Piston
Servo Spring
Accumulator Gasket
Accumulator Cover

Fig. 8   Servo and accumulator, 1956

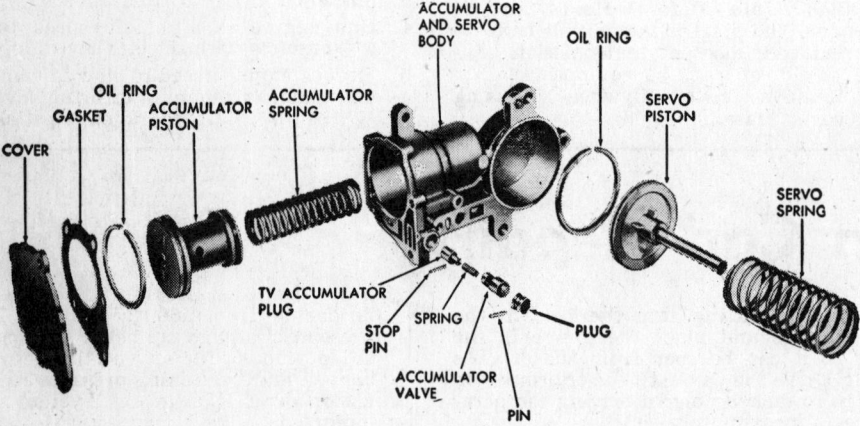

COVER
GASKET
OIL RING
ACCUMULATOR PISTON
ACCUMULATOR SPRING
ACCUMULATOR AND SERVO BODY
OIL RING
SERVO PISTON
SERVO SPRING
TV ACCUMULATOR PLUG
STOP PIN
SPRING
ACCUMULATOR VALVE
PIN
PLUG

Fig. 9   Servo and accumulator, 1957

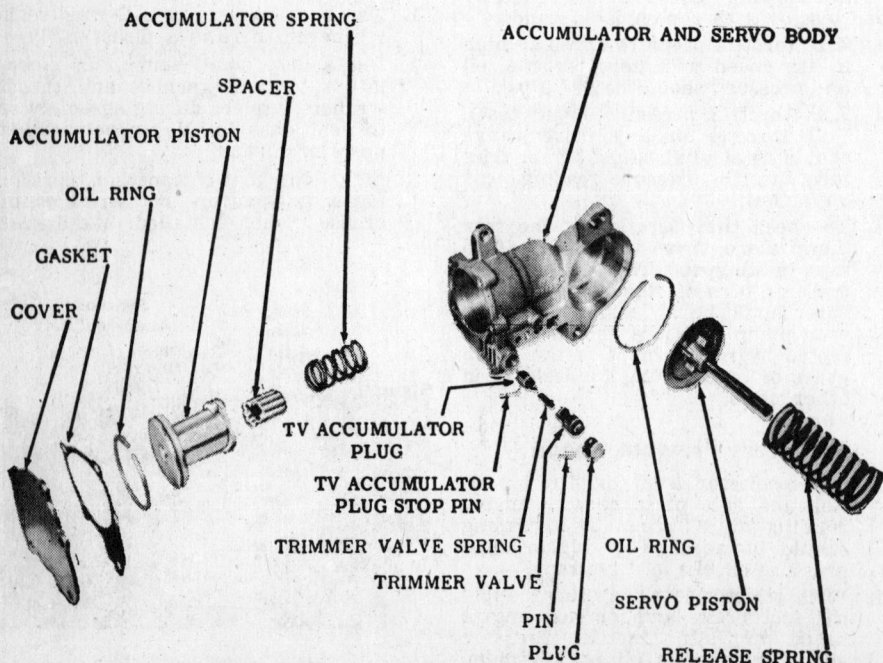

ACCUMULATOR SPRING
SPACER
ACCUMULATOR PISTON
OIL RING
GASKET
COVER
ACCUMULATOR AND SERVO BODY
TV ACCUMULATOR PLUG
TV ACCUMULATOR PLUG STOP PIN
TRIMMER VALVE SPRING
TRIMMER VALVE
PIN
PLUG
OIL RING
SERVO PISTON
RELEASE SPRING

Fig. 10   Servo and accumulator, 1958-59

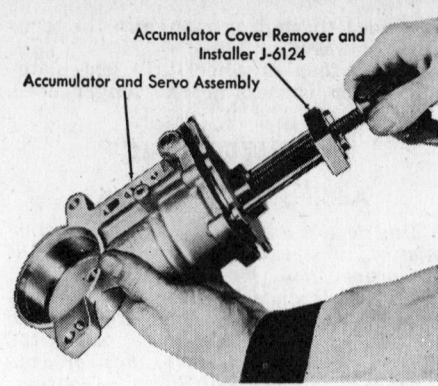

Accumulator Cover Remover and Installer J-6124
Accumulator and Servo Assembly

Fig. 11   Removing accumulator cover

that gaskets have not stretched or shrunk during storage.

4. Make sure that the square type O-ring seals are installed squarely and not twisted during assembly.

CORRECTION OF LEAKS

If the fluid level is found to be low during periodic lubrication inspections, check for fluid leaks. To determine leakage points in the fluid coupling, the flywheel housing front cover must be removed. Leakage points to check are as follows:

1. Oil around inside of flywheel housing and in line with drain plug may be caused by stripped threads on the drain plug in the flywheel or that it was not properly torqued.

2. Oil on transmission side of flywheel and inside of flywheel housing in line with torus cover-to-flywheel housing O-ring seal may be caused by torus cover-to-flywheel nuts not being properly torqued or that the O-ring seal is damaged.

3. Oil on torus cover and inside of flywheel housing may be caused by a defective flywheel housing oil seal.

4. Oil between flywheel housing and transmission case may be caused by improperly torqued flywheel housing attaching screws or a damaged O-ring seal between flywheel housing and transmission case.

5. Oil between rear pump and case may be caused by improperly torqued extension housing-to-transmission case attaching screws or a damaged gasket between the rear pump and transmission case.

6. Oil between rear extension housing and rear pump may be caused by improperly torqued extension housing-to-transmission case attaching screws or a damaged gasket between rear pump and extension housing.

7. Oil at universal joint slip yoke may be caused by a damaged extension housing oil seal.

8. Oil on left side of transmission case in line with throttle and manual lever shafts may be caused by damaged O-ring seal between inner throttle lever shaft and inner manual lever shaft.

9. Oil at center bearing support locking screw may be caused by improperly torqued screw.

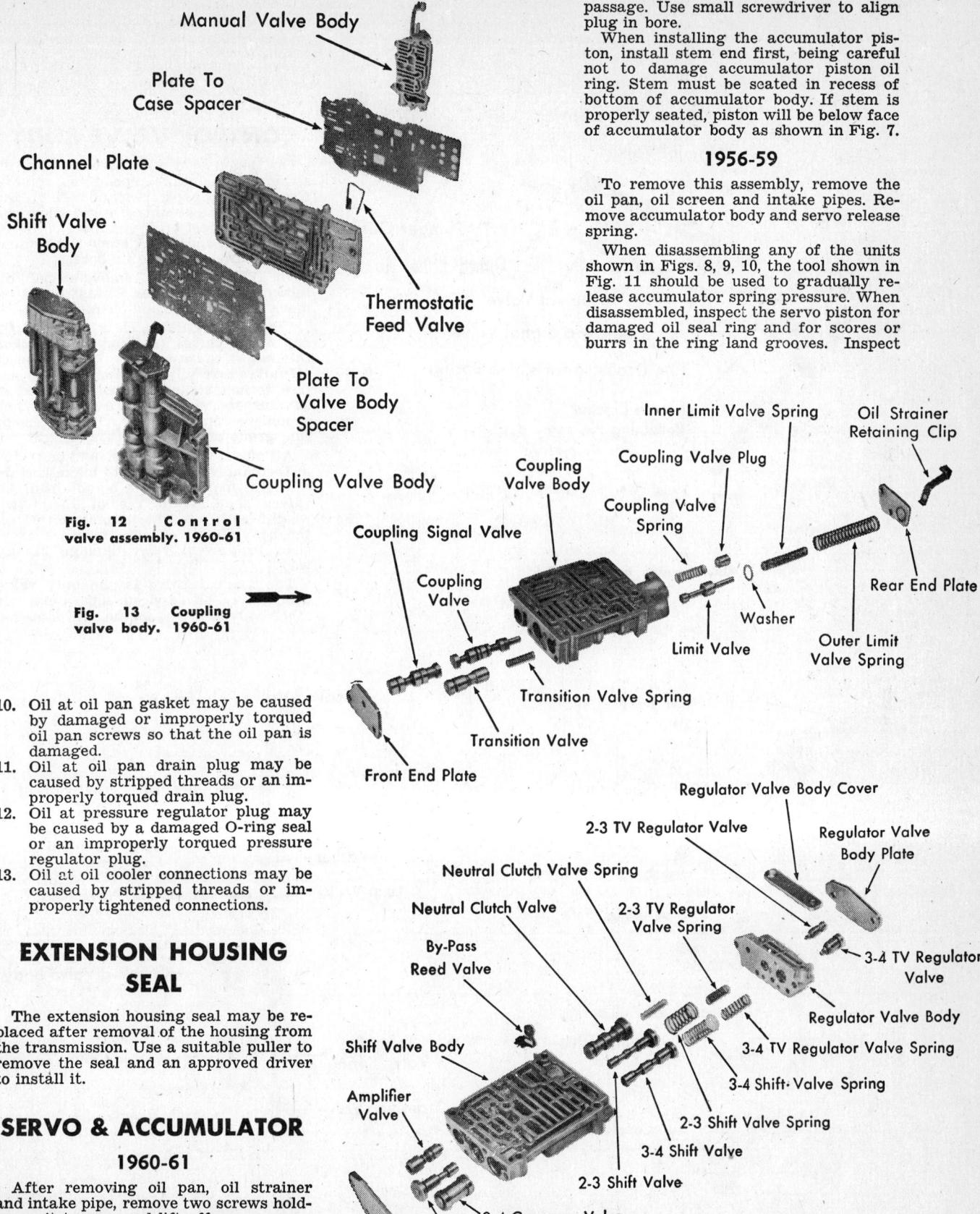

Fig. 12 Control valve assembly. 1960-61

Manual Valve Body

Plate To Case Spacer

Channel Plate

Shift Valve Body

Thermostatic Feed Valve

Plate To Valve Body Spacer

Coupling Valve Body

Fig. 13 Coupling valve body. 1960-61

passage. Use small screwdriver to align plug in bore.

When installing the accumulator piston, install stem end first, being careful not to damage accumulator piston oil ring. Stem must be seated in recess of bottom of accumulator body. If stem is properly seated, piston will be below face of accumulator body as shown in Fig. 7.

1956-59

To remove this assembly, remove the oil pan, oil screen and intake pipes. Remove accumulator body and servo release spring.

When disassembling any of the units shown in Figs. 8, 9, 10, the tool shown in Fig. 11 should be used to gradually release accumulator spring pressure. When disassembled, inspect the servo piston for damaged oil seal ring and for scores or burrs in the ring land grooves. Inspect

Inner Limit Valve Spring

Coupling Valve Plug

Coupling Valve Body

Coupling Valve Spring

Oil Strainer Retaining Clip

Coupling Signal Valve

Coupling Valve

Rear End Plate

Washer

Limit Valve

Outer Limit Valve Spring

Transition Valve Spring

Transition Valve

Front End Plate

10. Oil at oil pan gasket may be caused by damaged or improperly torqued oil pan screws so that the oil pan is damaged.
11. Oil at oil pan drain plug may be caused by stripped threads or an improperly torqued drain plug.
12. Oil at pressure regulator plug may be caused by a damaged O-ring seal or an improperly torqued pressure regulator plug.
13. Oil at oil cooler connections may be caused by stripped threads or improperly tightened connections.

EXTENSION HOUSING SEAL

The extension housing seal may be replaced after removal of the housing from the transmission. Use a suitable puller to remove the seal and an approved driver to install it.

SERVO & ACCUMULATOR

1960-61

After removing oil pan, oil strainer and intake pipe, remove two screws holding unit to case and lift off.

Disassemble the unit as indicated in Fig. 6. When installing the TV accumulator plug have the slotted end out and align the slot in the plug with the vent

Regulator Valve Body Cover

2-3 TV Regulator Valve

Regulator Valve Body Plate

Neutral Clutch Valve Spring

2-3 TV Regulator Valve Spring

Neutral Clutch Valve

3-4 TV Regulator Valve

By-Pass Reed Valve

Regulator Valve Body

Shift Valve Body

3-4 TV Regulator Valve Spring

Amplifier Valve

3-4 Shift Valve Spring

2-3 Shift Valve Spring

3-4 Shift Valve

2-3 Shift Valve

3-4 Governor Valve

2-3 Governor Valve

Shift Valve Body Plate

Fig 14 Shift valve body. 1960-61

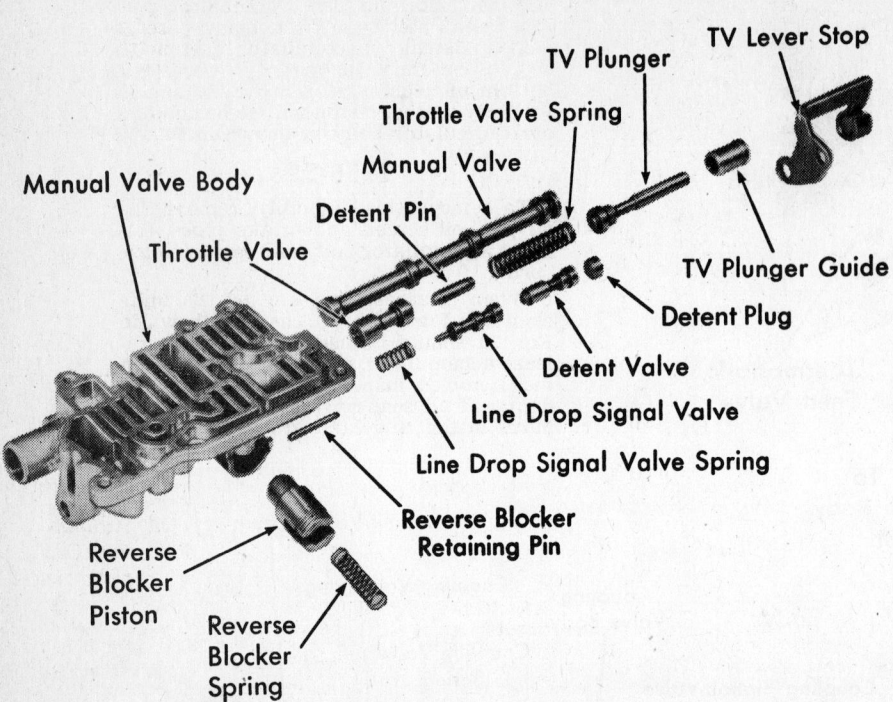

Fig. 15 Manual valve body. 1960-61

the accumulator spring for collapsed or distorted coils. Inspect accumulator body for restricted passages, scores or burrs. Inspect servo piston assembly for distorted pin, damaged oil seal ring lands, or broken oil seal ring.

CONTROL VALVE BODY

On 1960-61 units, remove oil pan, oil strainer and intake pipe. Then remove five attaching capscrews and take off the control valve assembly. Do not allow the assembly to rest on the channel plate-to-case spacer, and do not allow the manual valve to drop out from its bore.

On 1956-59 models, remove oil pan, oil screen and intake pipes. Unfasten and remove control valve and channel plate.

When disassembled, clean all parts. *Do not allow valves to bump together as this might cause nicks or burrs.* Inspect all valves carefully to make sure they are free from dirt and are not damaged in any respect. If burrs are present, they should be removed with a fine stone or fine grade of crocus cloth and light oil.

All plugs, valves, etc., should be tested in their individual bores to make certain that free movement can be obtained. All valves should fall free of their own weight with a slight tapping action on the body. However, care must be exercised to prevent valve damage in any way.

The manual valve is the only valve which may be serviced separately. If other valves are defective or damaged

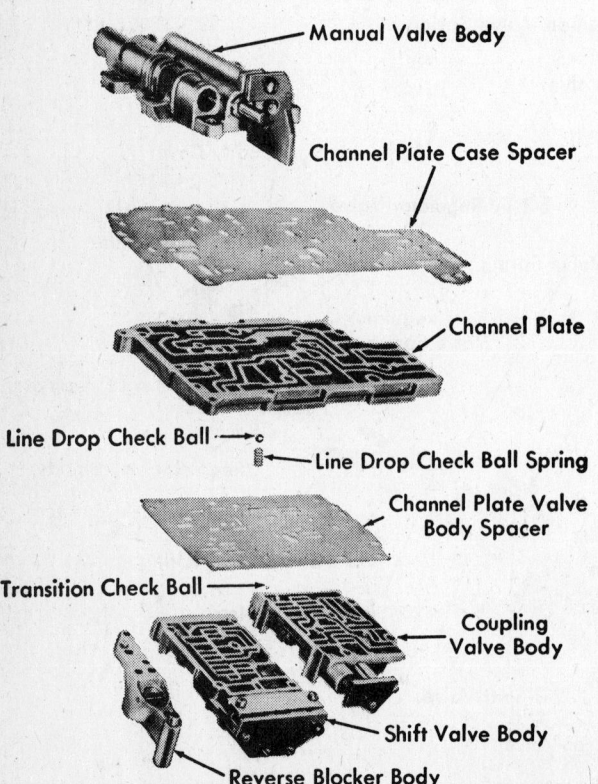

Fig. 16 Main oil control valve bodies, 1956-57

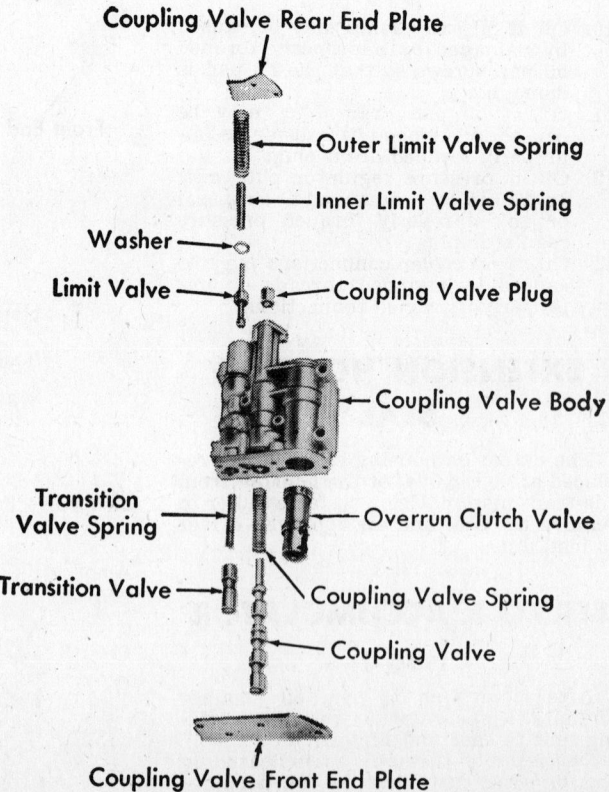

Fig. 18 Front clutch (or coupling) valve body, 1956-57

beyond repair, an individual assembly should be installed.

Before reassembly, be sure springs can be correctly identified for correct assembly. When disassembling and reassembling the various components of the control valve, refer to Figs. 12 to 30.

CONTROL LEVERS & PARKING BRAKE

1960-61

These units, Fig. 31, can be removed with the transmission in the car and involves the removal of the oil pan, oil strainer, intake pipe, control valve and servo-accumulator assemblies.

1. After above units have been removed, loosen inner TV lever-to-TV shaft clamp screw. Withdraw outer TV lever and shaft from case. Discard O-ring seal.
2. Remove inner TV lever.
3. Loosen inside detent control set screw.
4. Withdraw manual lever and shaft from case. Remove steel washer and discard seal ring, Fig. 32.

Installation

1. Referring to Figs. 31 and 32, install steel washer and O-ring seal on manual lever shaft.
2. Position detent lever in place against detent spring and roller with dowel pin on parking brake bracket outside detent lever.

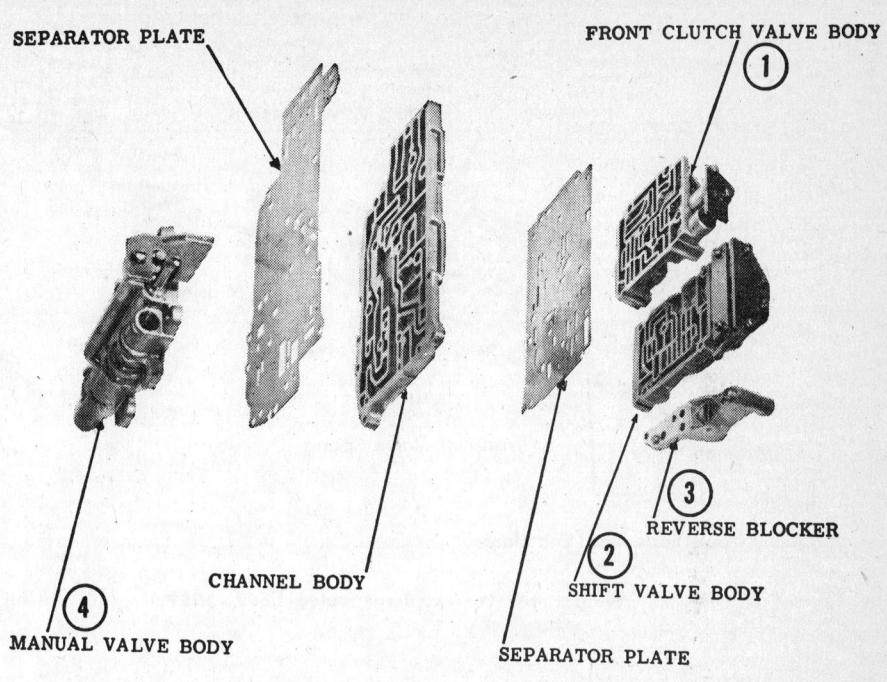

Fig. 17   Main oil control valve bodies, 1958-59

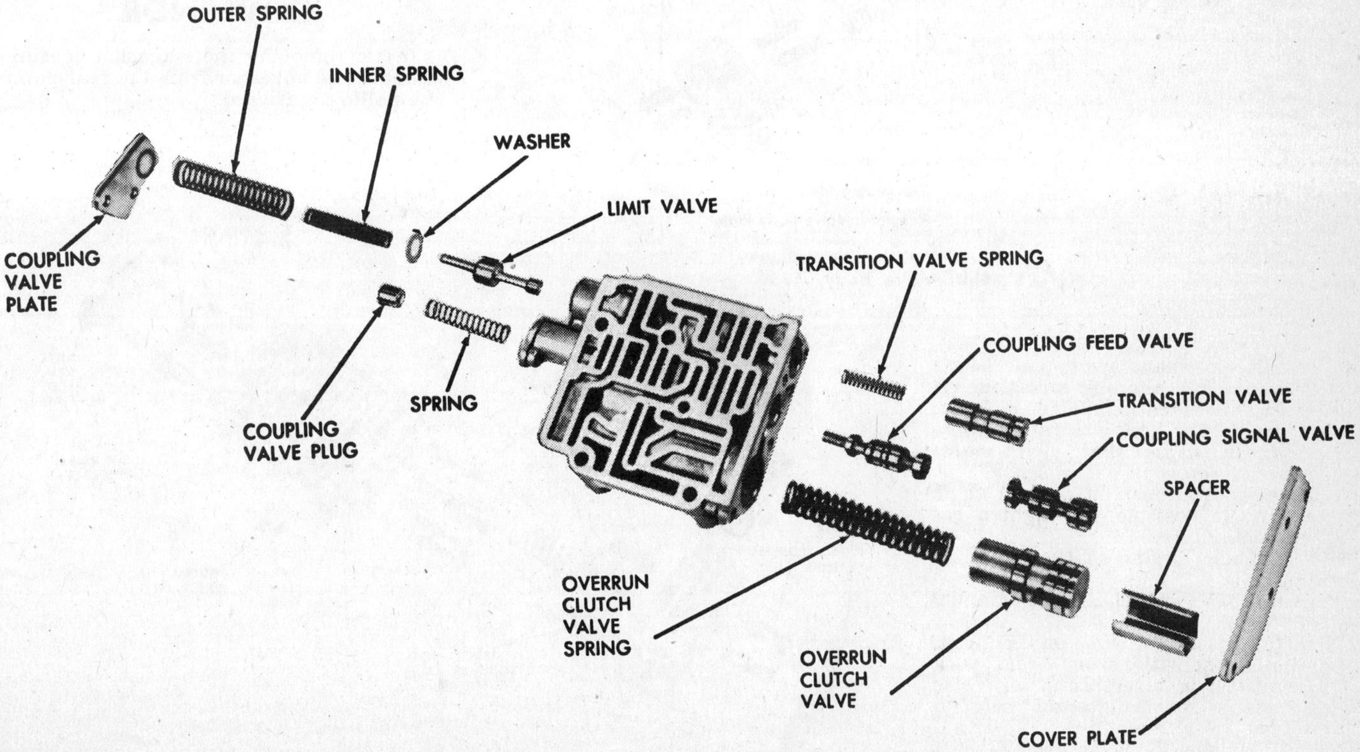

Fig. 19   Front clutch (or coupling) valve body, 1958

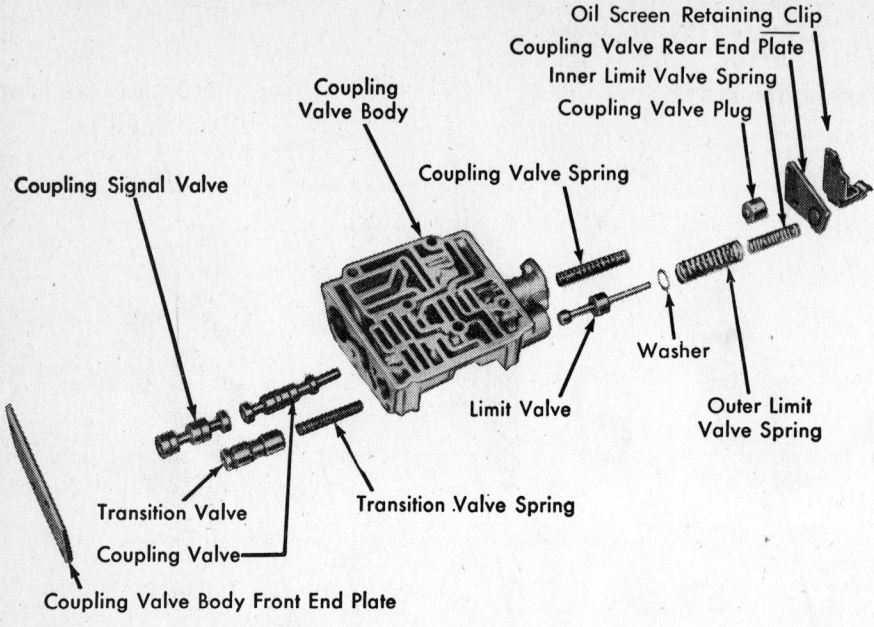

Fig. 20 Front clutch (or coupling) valve body, 1959

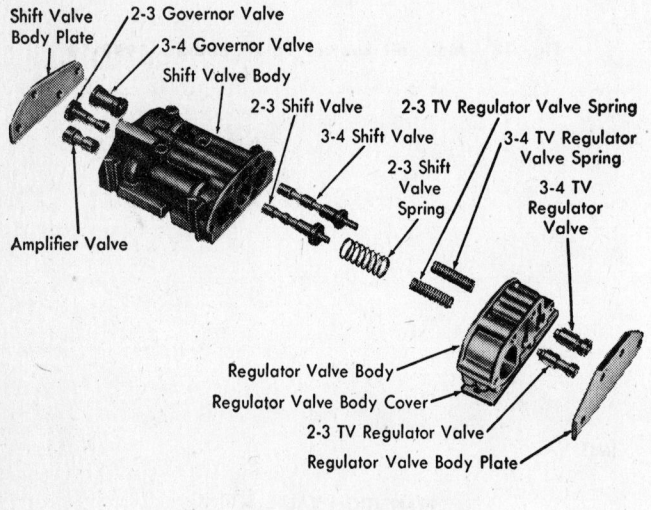

Fig. 21 Shift valve body, 1956

clearance between inside TV lever and inside detent lever. Tighten clamp screw.

9. Pull on outside TV lever to be sure inside TV lever is secure on shaft. Recheck clearance and adjust if necessary.

1956-59

The parking brake bracket and inside control levers, Fig. 33, can be removed with the transmission in the car. Requires removal of outside throttle control and manual lever arms as well as oil pan, oil screen and intake pipe. To remove control levers and parking brake, remove inside detent control and inside throttle control lever assembly as follows:

1. Remove snap ring retaining detent control lever to case.
2. Remove lever assembly, outer and inner washers and O-ring seal from case counterbore.
3. To remove parking brake, disconnect parking brake lever spring and remove retaining clip, bracket and spring. Install ⅜" bolt into parking brake pawl pin and remove pin and spacer. Remove lever and pawl as an assembly.

Installation

1. Install spacer, lever and pawl as an assembly.
2. Install bracket and spring.
3. Install parking pawl pivot pin and connect parking brake lever spring.
4. Install O-ring seal to case counterbore and install lever assembly with outer and inner washers.
5. Install ring retaining detent control lever to case.

GOVERNOR

After removing the extension housing, remove the governor from the rear pump by pulling rearward.

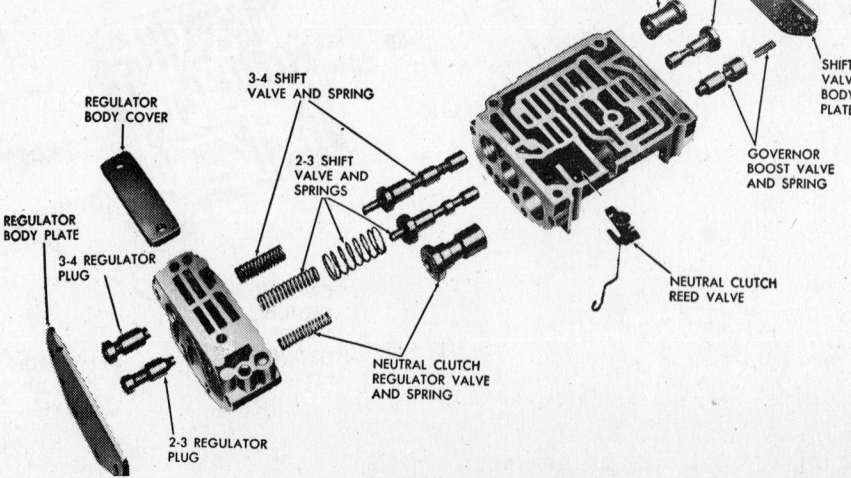

3. Install manual lever and shaft through case, aligning serrations on shaft with serrations in detent lever. *As an aid in aligning serrations, note recess in manual shaft which mates with set screw in detent lever.*
4. Press detent lever on manual shaft as far as possible and tighten set screw securely.
5. Install new O-ring seal on TV lever shaft.
6. Install TV shaft through manual shaft.
7. Install inside TV lever on TV shaft, aligning serrations on shaft with serrations in lever. *Tang on inside TV lever points toward side of transmission case.*
8. Press inside TV lever on TV shaft as far as possible and then back off slightly to provide .005" to .010"

Fig. 22 Shift valve body, 1957

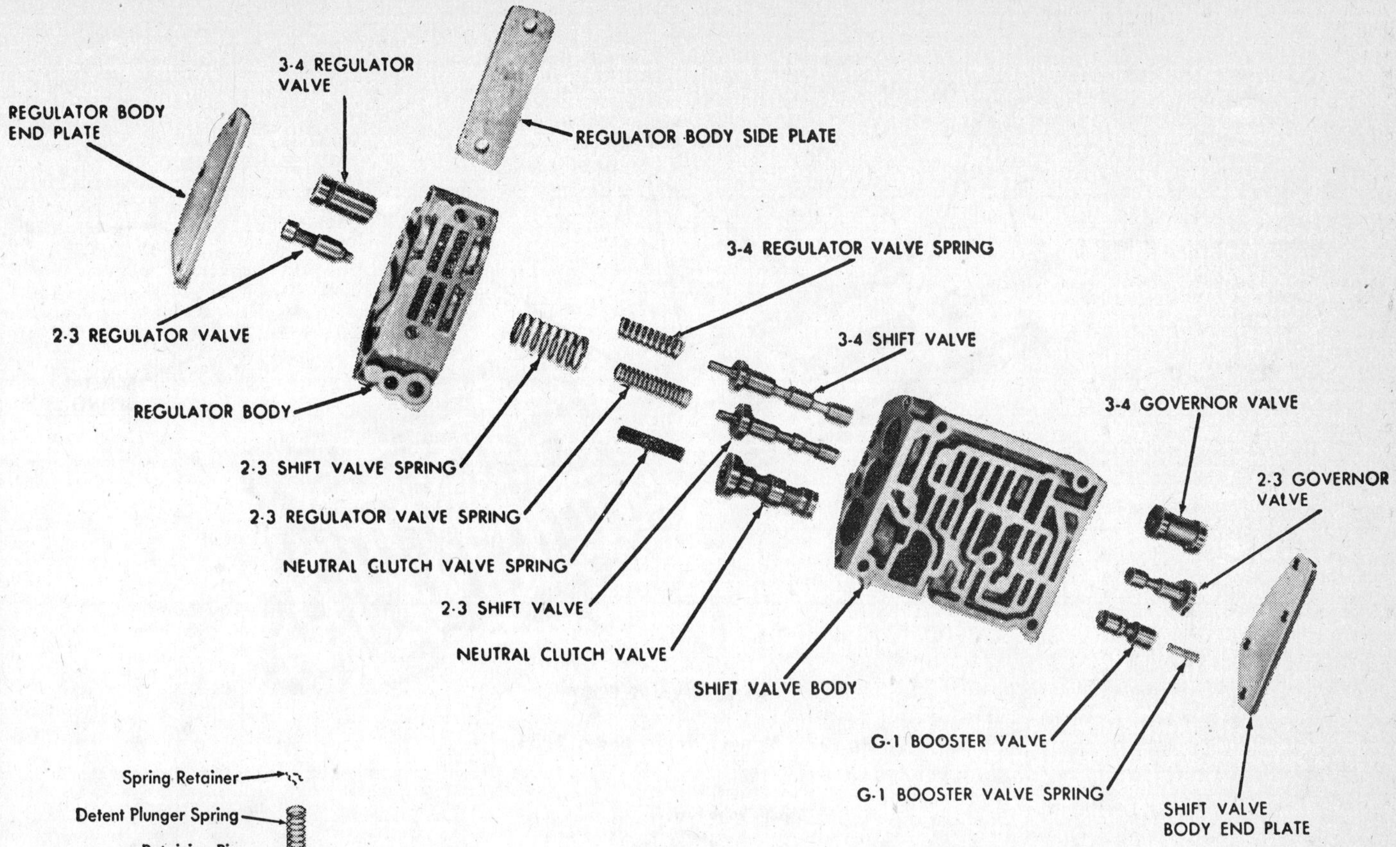

REGULATOR BODY END PLATE

3-4 REGULATOR VALVE

REGULATOR BODY SIDE PLATE

2-3 REGULATOR VALVE

3-4 REGULATOR VALVE SPRING

3-4 SHIFT VALVE

REGULATOR BODY

3-4 GOVERNOR VALVE

2-3 SHIFT VALVE SPRING

2-3 REGULATOR VALVE SPRING

2-3 GOVERNOR VALVE

NEUTRAL CLUTCH VALVE SPRING

2-3 SHIFT VALVE

NEUTRAL CLUTCH VALVE

SHIFT VALVE BODY

G-1 BOOSTER VALVE

G-1 BOOSTER VALVE SPRING

SHIFT VALVE BODY END PLATE

Fig. 23   Shift valve body, 1958

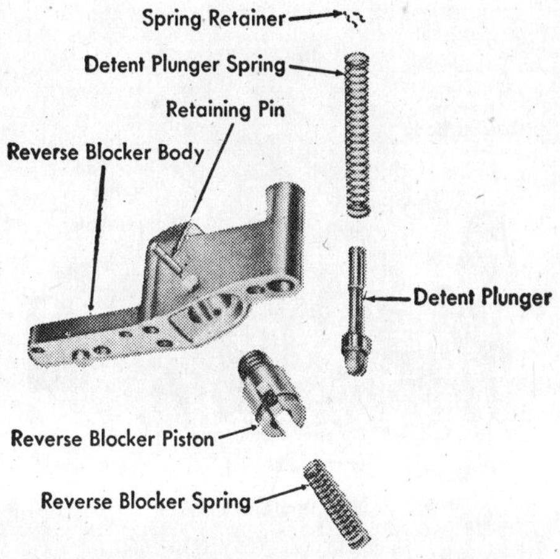

Spring Retainer

Detent Plunger Spring

Retaining Pin

Reverse Blocker Body

Detent Plunger

Reverse Blocker Piston

Reverse Blocker Spring

Fig. 25   Reverse blocker body, 1956-59

When disassembling, refer to Figs. 34, 35. When disassembled, see that all parts are free of dirt. Inspect valves and bushings for burrs or other damage; remove burrs with fine crocus cloth and light oil. Test valves and bushing in their respective bores for free movement. If valves stick, replace governor assembly. Inspect ring lands and rings for freedom in grooves. If lands are damaged or worn, replace governor assembly.

REAR PUMP

1956-58 Only

After removing the extension case and governor, remove the pump breather pipe. Remove rear bearing snap ring from output shaft. Unfasten the pump from the transmission and remove it from the output shaft.

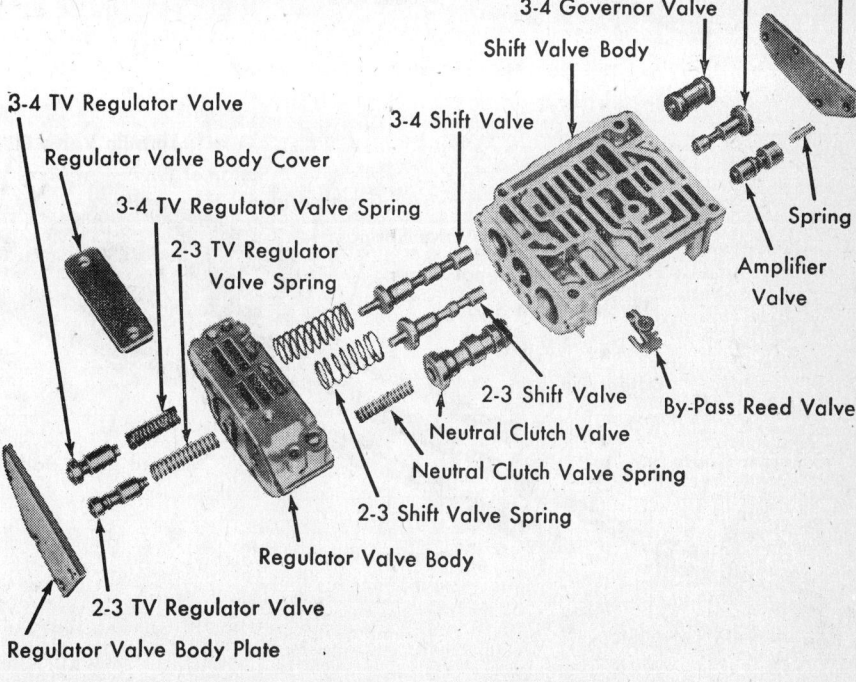

Shift Valve Body Plate

2-3 Governor Valve

3-4 Governor Valve

Shift Valve Body

3-4 TV Regulator Valve

Regulator Valve Body Cover

3-4 TV Regulator Valve Spring

2-3 TV Regulator Valve Spring

3-4 Shift Valve

Spring

Amplifier Valve

2-3 Shift Valve

Neutral Clutch Valve

Neutral Clutch Valve Spring

By-Pass Reed Valve

2-3 Shift Valve Spring

Regulator Valve Body

2-3 TV Regulator Valve

Regulator Valve Body Plate

Fig. 24   Shift valve body, 1959 (Amplifier valve spring not used in some units)

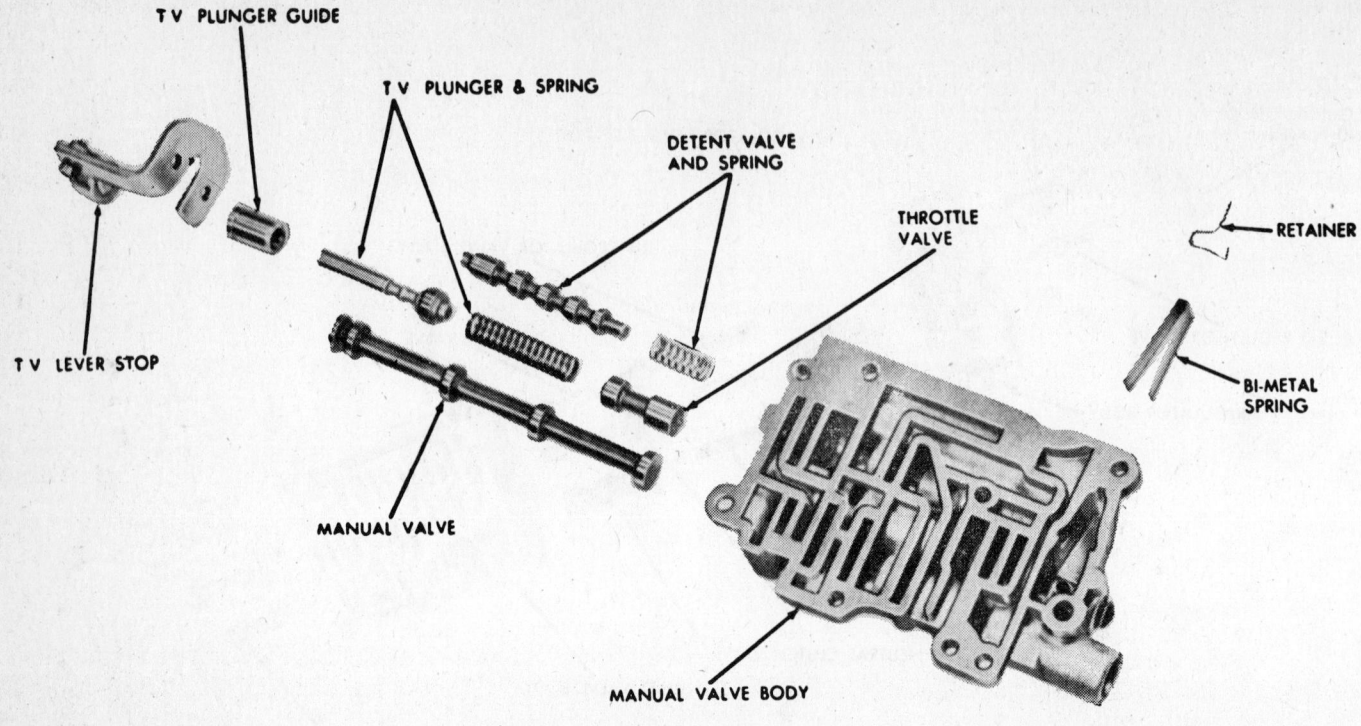

Fig. 27 Manual valve body, 1958

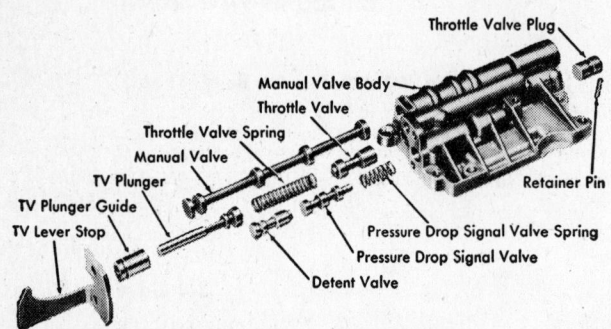

Fig. 26 Manual valve body, 1956-57

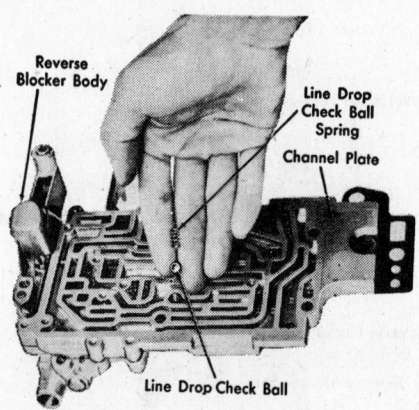

Fig. 29 Installing ball check and spring in channel body (not used after 1957)

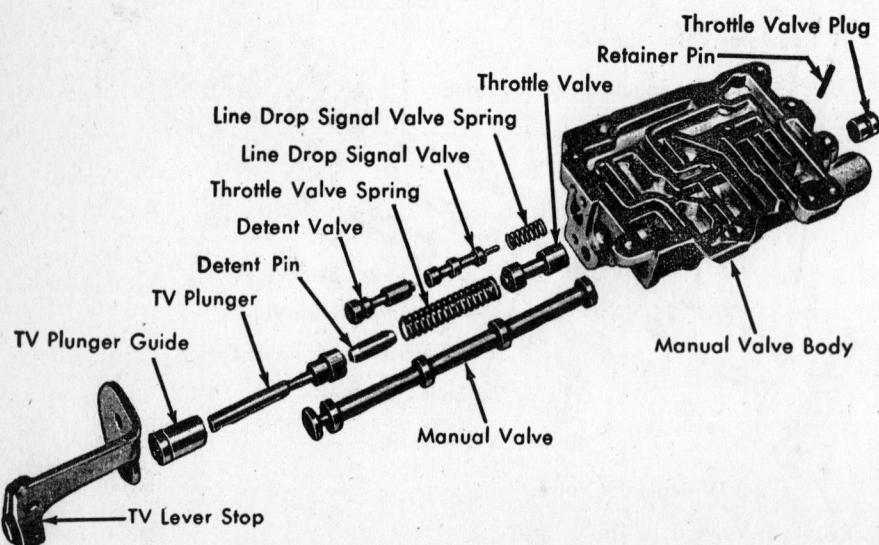

Fig. 28 Manual valve body, 1959

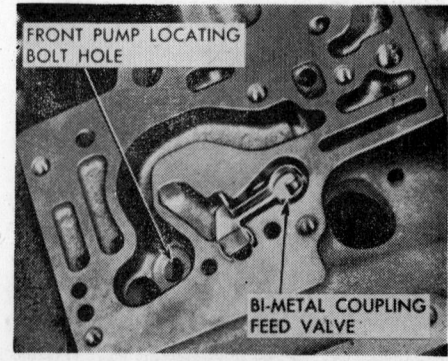

Fig. 30 Coupling feed valve, 1958-59

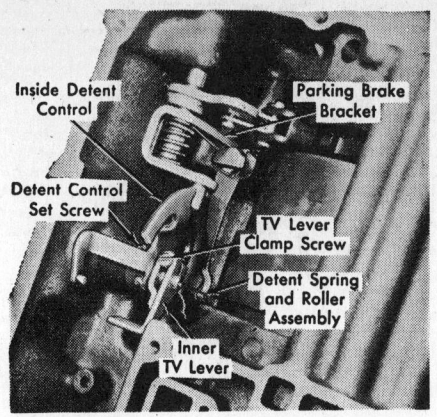

Fig. 31 Inside control levers. 1960-61

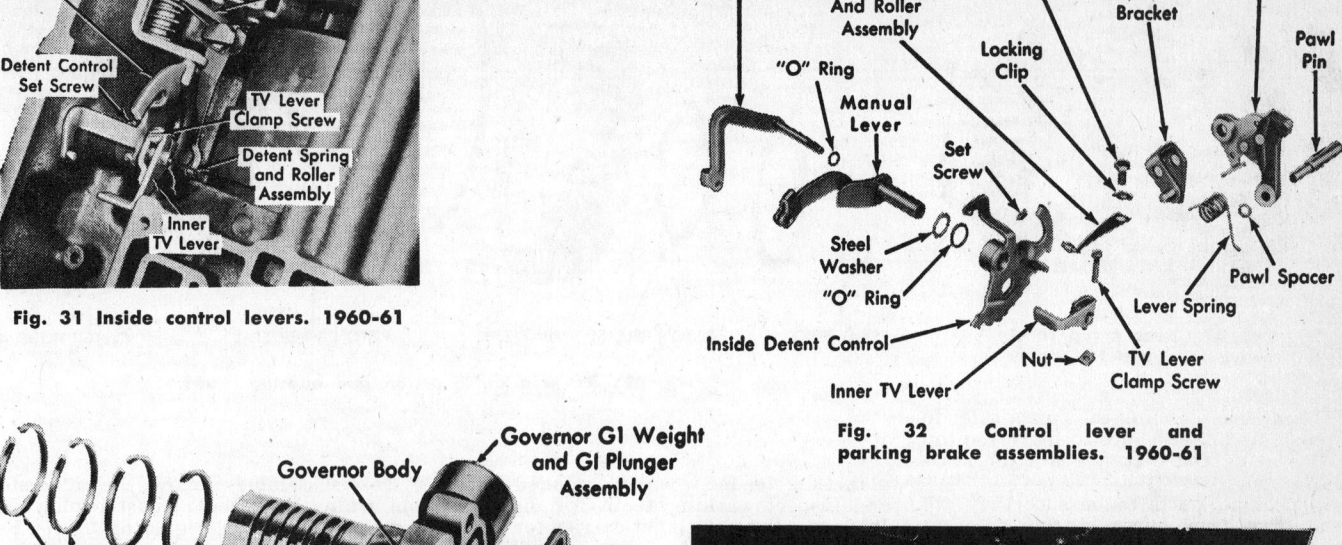

Fig. 32 Control lever and parking brake assemblies. 1960-61

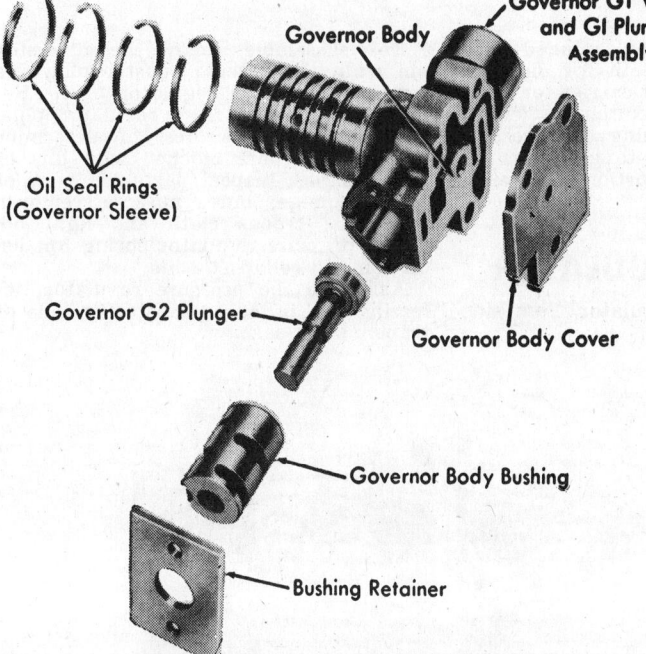

Fig. 34 Governor assembly, 1956-58

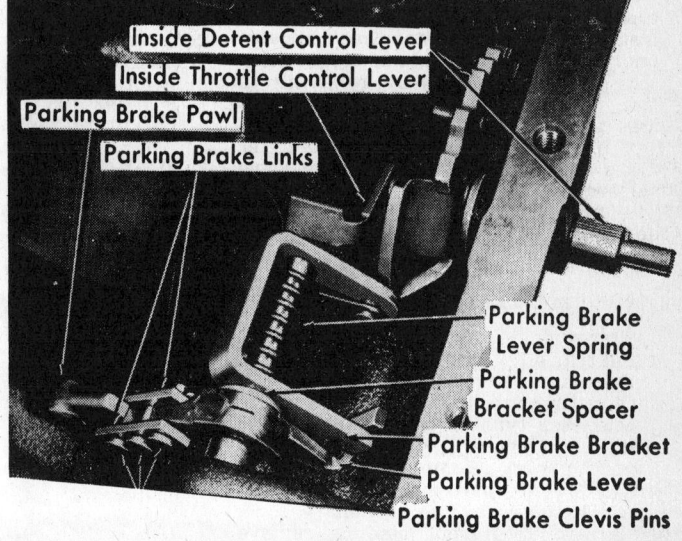

Fig. 33 Inside control levers and parking brake bracket (typical)

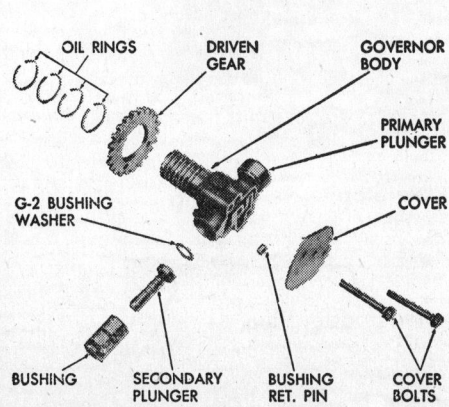

Fig. 35 Governor assembly, 1959-61

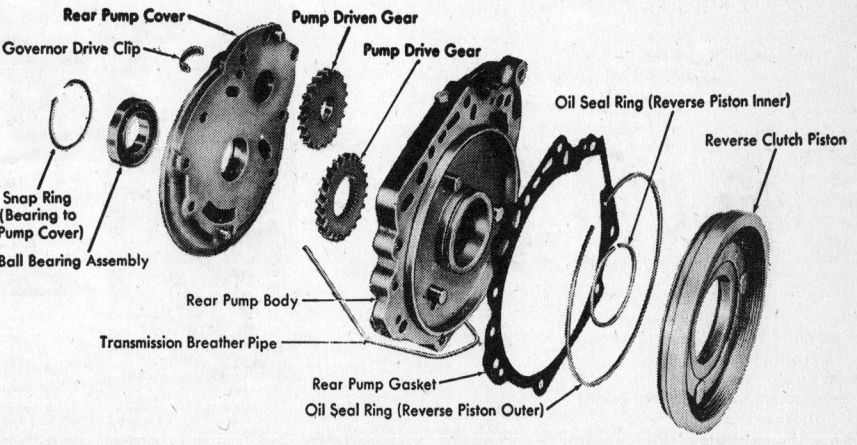

Fig. 36 Rear pump assembly, 1956-58

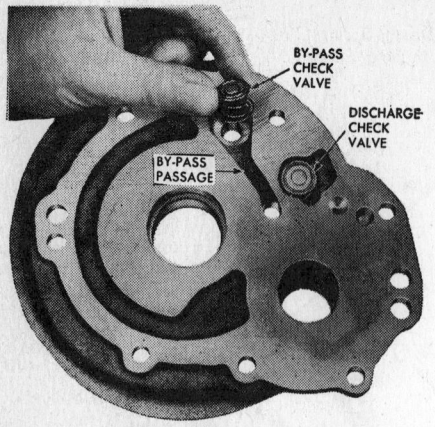

Fig. 37 Rear pump check valves, 1956-58 only

Fig. 39 Reverse clutch piston and housing, 1959

When disassembling the pump, refer to Figs. 36 and 37. Be sure to mark the top of the drive and driven gears for reassembly purposes.

Inspect all parts to be sure they are clean, free from burrs, scoring or other damage. Inspect oil seal ring grooves to be sure they are clean. See that vent pipe is not damaged and is free of restrictions.

Assemble the pump by referring to Figs. 36 and 37. When installing the large oil seal ring, compress it on the piston with fingers on one end of gap. After end is seated in cavity, gradually work seal around and at the same time apply light pressure, forcing the piston into the cavity.

REVERSE UNIT

After removing extension case, governor and rear oil pump, remove large wave-type reverse piston release spring. Remove reverse internal gear, thrust washer, and tang-type reverse clutch release spring (tangs point outward toward rear of transmission). Remove reverse planet carrier outer snap ring from output shaft. Remove reverse stationary cone, using care to prevent binding, remove stationary cone key from case and remove reverse planet carrier assembly while lifting up on output shaft.

When disassembled, Fig. 38, inspect internal gear for damaged teeth and scored or damaged outside cone surface. Inspect

planet carrier for worn or damaged teeth and inspect parking teeth for damage. Inspect splines of planet carrier for damage. Inspect reverse clutch stationary cone for signs of burning or excessive wear. Inspect wave and tang springs for signs of damage or distortion. Also refer to Fig. 39.

PRESSURE REGULATOR

Remove pressure regulator from side of transmission, Fig. 40.

To disassemble, remove the valve stop pin from the reverse booster plug and remove plug from regulator plug. Remove O-ring seal from regulator plug.

Inspect all passages to determine whether they are blocked with dirt or metal chips. Inspect parts for burrs or other damage; burrs may be removed with fine crocus cloth and light oil. Check pressure regulator spring for distortion and collapsed coils.

Assemble the pressure regulator, referring to Fig. 40 and install in side of transmission case.

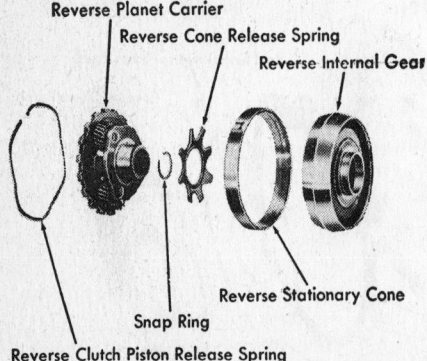

Fig. 38 Reverse unit assembly, 1956-58

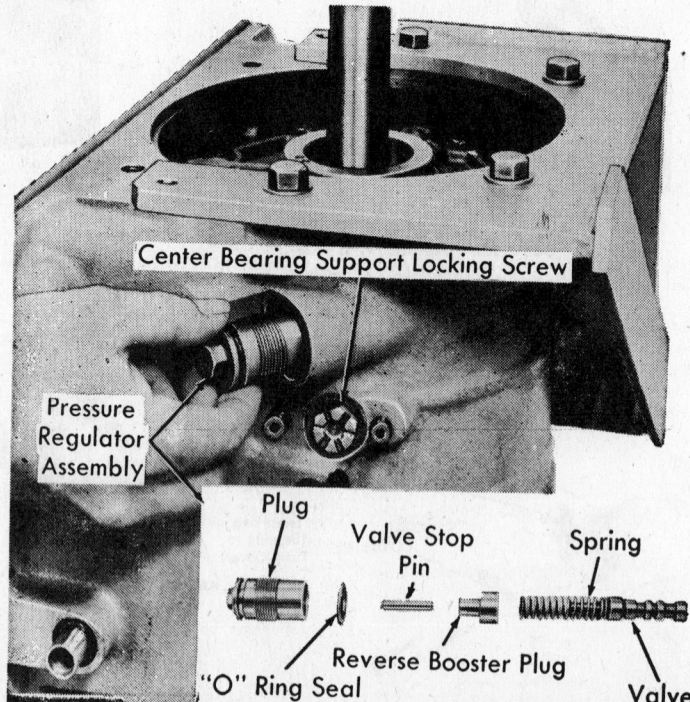

Fig. 40 Pressure regulator assembly. Center bearing support lock screw not used on 1960-61 units

Repairs Requiring Transmission Removal

TRANSMISSION, DISASSEMBLE

1. Remove the torus members and related parts piecemeal as shown in Figs. 41, 42. Do not attempt to remove the torus cover and driving torus member together. Remove torus cover by working it back through oil seal and pull cover out with a quick jerk.

2. Remove selective spacer from front unit coupling driven torus hub.

3. Disconnect oil cooler pipes from side of transmission and remove oil cooler. Remove cooler adapter and related parts, Fig. 43.

4. Remove flywheel housing, protecting front oil seal and bushing with a

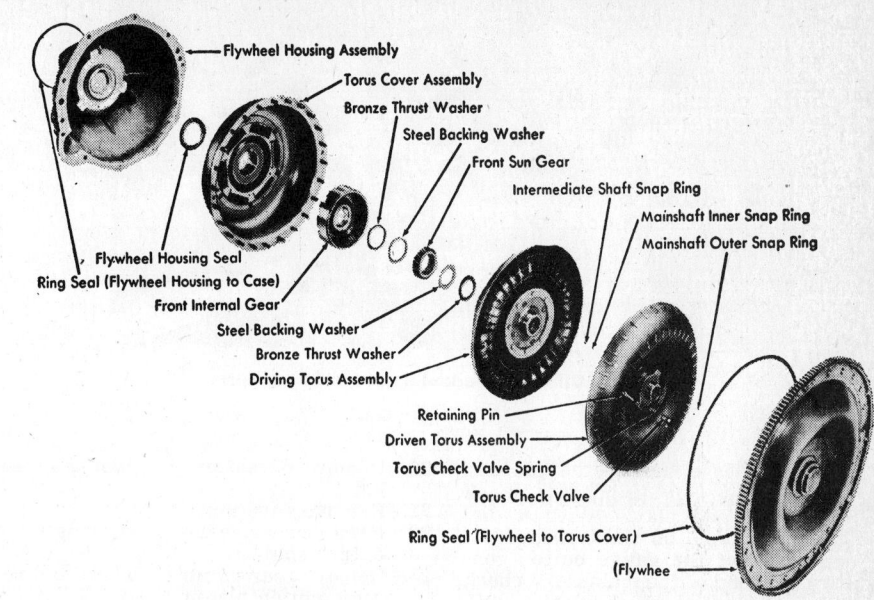

Fig. 41 Torus assembly, 1956-57

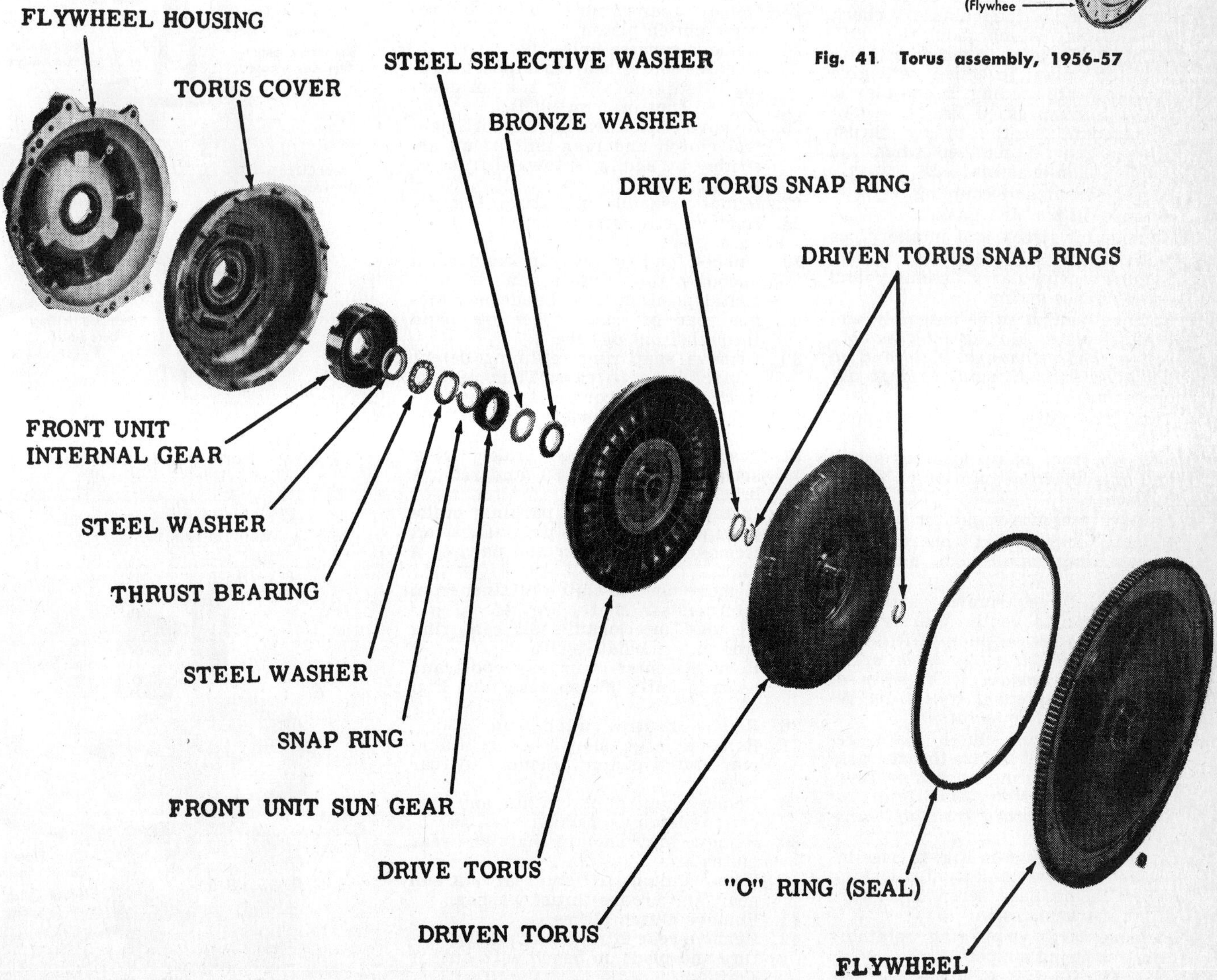

FLYWHEEL HOUSING

TORUS COVER

STEEL SELECTIVE WASHER

BRONZE WASHER

DRIVE TORUS SNAP RING

DRIVEN TORUS SNAP RINGS

FRONT UNIT INTERNAL GEAR

STEEL WASHER

THRUST BEARING

STEEL WASHER

SNAP RING

FRONT UNIT SUN GEAR

DRIVE TORUS

DRIVEN TORUS

"O" RING (SEAL)

FLYWHEEL

Fig. 42 Torus assembly, 1958-61

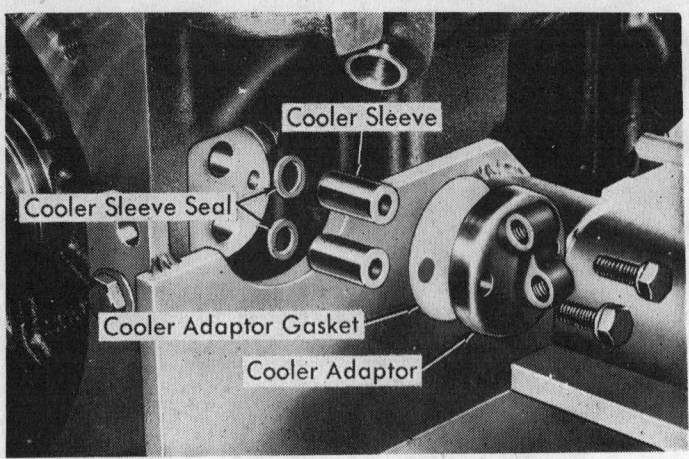

Fig. 43 Oil cooler adapter and related parts

Fig. 44 Removing front pump assembly

suitable sleeve during the process.

5. At this time it is essential to check mainshaft end play. With a dial gauge mounted on the transmission case so that the gauge button contacts the end of the mainshaft, check the end play which should be .004" to .018". Be sure to get free mainshaft end play; forcing it will give an inaccurate reading. If end play is not within specified limits, record the amount so the proper thrust washer can be installed when the transmission is assembled.

6. Remove front unit coupling.

7. Remove oil pan and gasket.

8. Remove oil screen and intake pipes as a unit.

9. Remove accumulator assembly and servo release spring.

10. Remove control valve assembly and channel plate. *Do not let assembly rest on end of channel plate and do not allow manual valve to drop out of its bore.*

11. Turn transmission to vertical position with extension housing down.

12. Remove front pump locating screw and washer from interior of transmission.

13. Remove pressure regulator plug.

14. Remove two front pump cover screws and install slide hammers, Fig. 44.

15. Remove three screws attaching front pump to center bearing support and remove pump with slide hammers. *Front pump inner sprag race should remain with pump at this time to prevent race from becoming nicked or scratched.*

16. Remove overrun clutch plate, release spring and bronze thrust washer which is resting on center bearing support. *Note that tangs of washer face toward front of transmission.*

17. Install tool shown in Fig. 45 over intermediate shaft and tighten locking screw, being sure screw is toward front of transmission.

18. Remove large snap ring retaining center bearing support.

19. Position transmission bottom side up.

20. Remove extension housing and gasket.

21. Remove governor.

22. Remove rear bearing snap ring from output shaft.

23. Remove rear pump (if used) and reverse clutch piston.

24. Remove reverse unit.

25. Remove center bearing support locking screw from side of transmission, Fig. 40 (not used on 1960).

26. Remove center bearing support, neutral clutch and rear unit as an assembly by sliding it toward front of transmission.

27. Mount assembly in fixture, Fig. 45.

28. Remove stationary stop key from case.

29. Unhook end of overrun band from anchor plate. Rotate band to horizontal position with band ends facing rear of case. Remove band through front of case.

30. Remove snap ring retaining detent control lever to case. Then remove inside throttle control lever and inner and outer washers. Remove O-ring seal from case counterbore.

31. Disconnect parking brake lever spring, Fig. 31 and 33, and remove bracket and spring.

32. Install ⅜" bolt in parking brake pawl pin and remove pin and spacer. Remove spacer, lever and pawl as a unit.

33. Remove neutral clutch retainer from intermediate shaft, Fig. 45.

34. Remove interlocking oil seal ring from intermediate shaft.

35. Remove center bearing support and neutral clutch piston assembly, Fig. 46.

36. Remove neutral clutch drum.

37. Remove large snap ring retaining rear clutch piston assembly to rear drum.

38. Remove neutral clutch hub and rear clutch piston as a unit.

39. Remove intermediate shaft and rear clutch hub.

40. Remove mainshaft and rear unit sun gear, and bronze thrust washer.

41. Remove clutch plates.

42. Remove rear drum from holding fixture and place on bench with output shaft up.

43. Remove reverse planet carrier inner

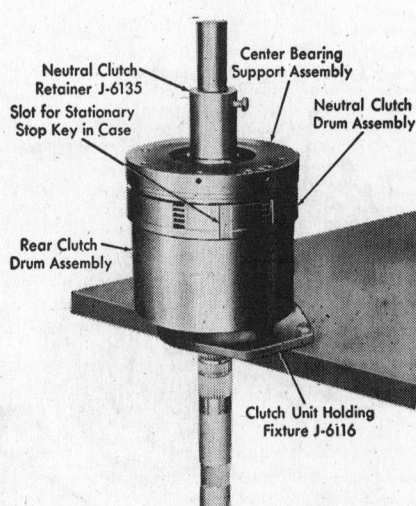

Fig. 45 Center bearing support, neutral clutch and rear unit

Fig. 46 Removing center bearing support

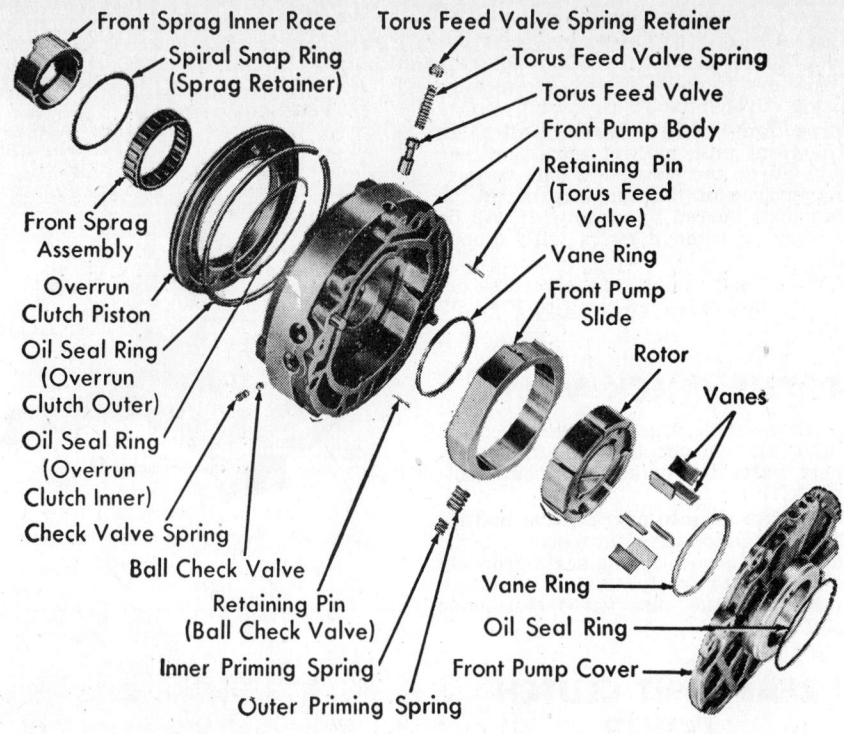

Fig. 47 Front pump assembly

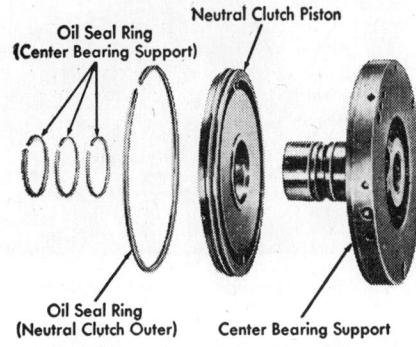

Fig. 48 Center bearing support 1959-60. Only two oil seal rings are used in 1961 units

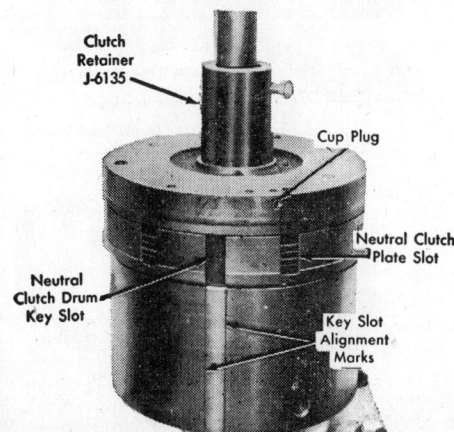

Fig. 49 Alignment of center bearing support and neutral clutch drum. 1960-61

locating snap ring from output shaft.

44. Remove large snap ring retaining reverse drive flange to rear drum and remove flange and output shaft.
45. Remove flange from output shaft.
46. Remove bronze thrust washer.
47. Mark rear unit internal gear to indicate proper side for reassembly and remove gear from rear drum.
48. Remove clutch backing plate from rear drum.

FRONT PUMP

Refer to Fig. 47 when disassembling and assembling the pump.

If the sprag outer race is damaged, the pump assembly must be replaced. Inspect all passages for dirt or restrictions with tag wire. The slide should move freely in pump body; slide should also be examined for excessive wear or scoring. Pump vanes will show a tendency to show a polished surface on the side bearing against the front pump slide; if not excessive, this is a normal condition. Check freeness of vanes in rotor slots.

Check torus slide valve priming springs for free movement in bore. Check bushing in pump for scores or flaking; a normal wear on the surface can be observed which is a normal condition if not excessive. Examine pump body and cover slide surface contacts for smoothness. Clean and dry all parts before reassembly.

When reassembling the pump, check location marks on pump body and overrun clutch piston. Align and install piston into pump cavity. Insert one side of oil seal ring and position in cavity by

working around ring, compressing and seating in pump cavity. *Do not force clutch piston into cavity; if sticking occurs dowels and holes are not correctly aligned.*

When installing the sprag into rear of body have the rim of the sprag facing up. Check rotation of sprag by inserting inner race; then remove inner race and install snap ring to retain sprag to pump body.

When installing the vanes in the rotor slots, make certain they fit between bottom of vane ring and slide. *Check edges of vanes for wear pattern; one edge will be polished full length—this edge should face slide.* When installed, check for free rotation of rotor and see that parts are positioned correctly.

CENTER BEARING SUPPORT

To disassemble, Fig. 48, remove the 3 (2 on 1961) oil seal rings and neutral clutch piston.

Inspect neutral clutch for scores or burrs. Be sure oil seal ring groove is thoroughly clean. Inspect oil seal rings on support and be sure all grooves are clean. Inspect support for burrs.

When assembling, install neutral clutch piston into support, indexing dowel holes in support with dowel pin holes in piston. Install three oil seal rings.

1960-61 Service Note

The elimination of the center bearing support bolt requires a new procedure for installing the center bearing support, neutral clutch and rear unit assembly so that the units are properly aligned in relation to the oil pump.

1. With assembly in holding fixture, Fig. 49, rotate case center support so that right hand edge of cup plug in edge of center bearing support is aligned with left edge of first neutral clutch plate slot to right of neutral clutch drum key slot, as shown in Fig. 49.
2. Install clutch retainer, Fig. 49, over intermediate shaft by compressing center bearing support into neutral clutch drum and tightening lock

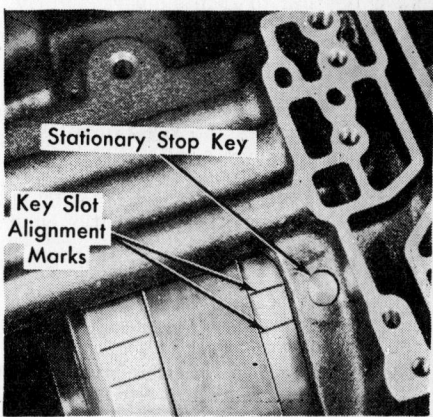

Fig. 50 Aligning center bearing support key slot. 1960-61

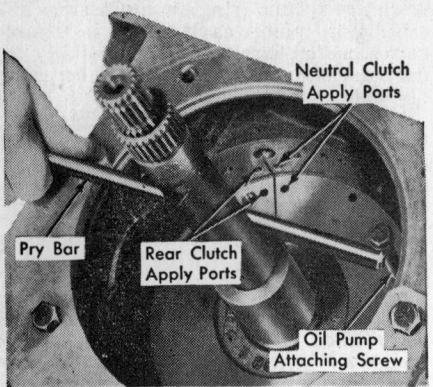

Fig. 51 Checking center bearing support alignment. 1960-61

screw on clutch retainer. *Lock screw on clutch retainer should be farthest away from center bearing support and screw must be withdrawn far enough so as not to score intermediate shaft during installation.*

3. Mark rear drum to indicate alignment of neutral clutch drum key slot, Fig. 49. This will help guide units into place during installation into transmission case.

4. Remove assembly from holding fixture and install in transmission case by inserting output shaft through front of transmission case. Use guide lines on rear unit drum to align neutral clutch drum locating slot with stationary stop key in transmission case, Fig. 50.

5. If unit does not go in far enough so that snap ring groove in transmission case is visible ahead of center bearing support, slight pressure may be necessary to force unit into place.

6. Install snap ring retaining center bearing support in position. *Install snap ring with opening in ring at top of transmission case.*

7. Rear clutch apply and neutral clutch apply ports in case and center bearing support should be in alignment, Fig. 51. If not properly aligned, center bearing support can be turned by temporarily installing one oil pump attaching screw and using a pry bar to turn support slightly.

FRONT UNIT COUPLING

1. To disassemble, install in holding fixture, Fig. 52, and install Coupling Cover Remover.
2. Remove large snap ring.
3. Install Valve Retainers, Fig. 52, to hold exhaust valves in position when removing cover.
4. Mark cover and driving torus member for reassembly purposes.
5. Remove coupling cover.
6. Remove two exhaust valves and springs, Fig. 53.
7. Remove driven torus member, steel and bronze washers and one intermediate locking oil seal ring from torus shaft.
8. Remove interlocking oil seal ring

from driven torus member.
9. Remove driving torus member from holding fixture.
10. Remove two oil seal rings from coupling cover hub.

Inspection should be made of all parts of the front unit, making sure they are free of burrs and scratches. This is particularly true of the coupling cover. If the cover is burred by removal it will be necessary to remove burrs with crocus cloth.

Reassemble the unit in the reverse order of disassembly, referring to Figs. 52 to 56.

TORUS CHECK VALVE

To disassemble, Fig. 57, remove cotter pin and take out check valve and spring. Inspect parts for nicks, burrs and collapsed spring.

Install spring into check valve and install spring and valve into driven torus member. Make sure spring seats properly and valve fits freely. After installing cotter pin, make sure valve can move freely.

REAR UNIT CLUTCH COVER

1. To disassemble, refer to Fig. 58 and remove spiral snap ring retaining neutral clutch hub to rear clutch cover.
2. Remove clutch hub by rotating counterclockwise around inner race.
3. Remove sprag clutch retainer and sprag.
4. Using tool shown in Fig. 58A, compress clutch release springs until snap ring can be removed. Then remove tool and take out remaining parts.

Inspection

1. Inspect sprag retainer for scored or damaged surfaces.
2. Inspect sprag for damaged land, broken spring or scored sprags. If defective, entire assembly must be replaced.
3. Inspect clutch hub for damaged splines.
4. Inspect clutch cover for scoring, burrs, damaged lugs and oil seal grooves.
5. Inspect clutch piston for scoring, burrs or damaged oil seal grooves.
6. Inspect clutch release springs for collapsed or distorted coils.
7. Inspect clutch spring retainer for cracks or damage.

Assemble

1. Install oil seal on clutch piston and oil seal on clutch cover hub.
2. Install piston into clutch cover.
3. Insert release springs into piston.
4. Position spring retainer (tangs up) and snap ring on release springs.
5. Using spring compressor, Fig. 58A, compress springs until snap ring can be inserted in its groove.
6 Install sprag in neutral clutch hub with rim edge of sprag facing up.

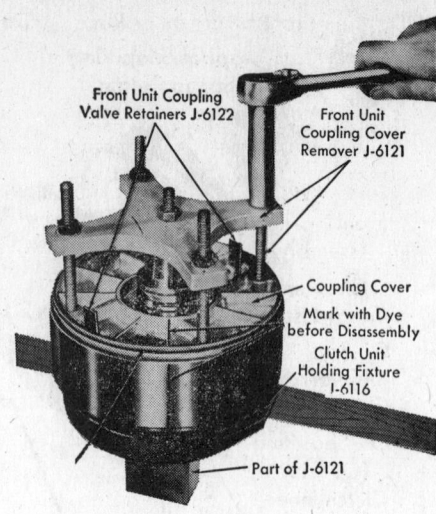

Fig. 52 Removing coupling cover

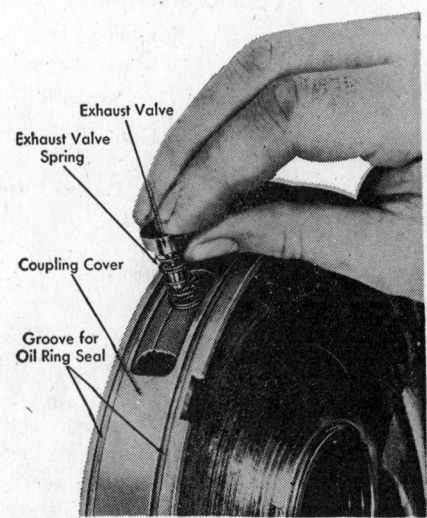

Fig. 53 Removing exhaust plungers

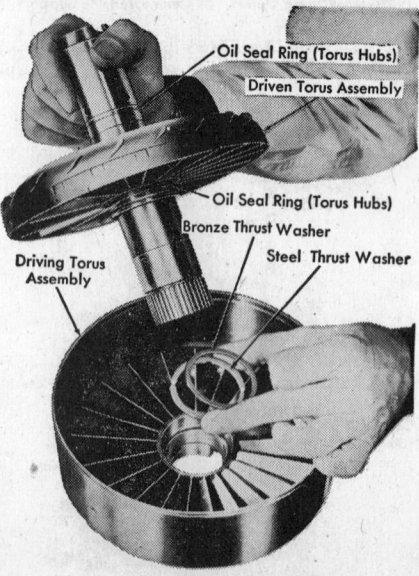

Fig. 54 Installing coupling driven torus member

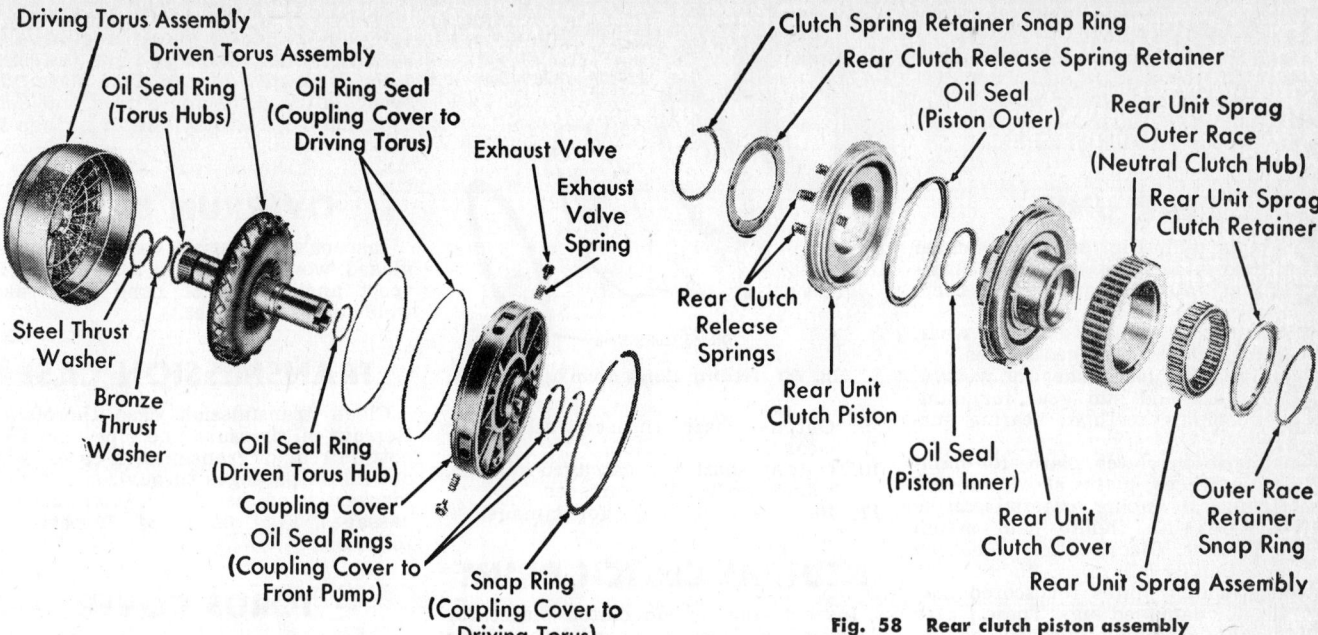

Driving Torus Assembly
Driven Torus Assembly
Oil Seal Ring (Torus Hubs)
Oil Ring Seal (Coupling Cover to Driving Torus)
Exhaust Valve
Exhaust Valve Spring
Steel Thrust Washer
Bronze Thrust Washer
Oil Seal Ring (Driven Torus Hub)
Coupling Cover
Oil Seal Rings (Coupling Cover to Front Pump)
Snap Ring (Coupling Cover to Driving Torus)

Fig. 55 Front unit coupling

Clutch Spring Retainer Snap Ring
Rear Clutch Release Spring Retainer
Oil Seal (Piston Outer)
Rear Unit Sprag Outer Race (Neutral Clutch Hub)
Rear Unit Sprag Clutch Retainer
Rear Clutch Release Springs
Rear Unit Clutch Piston
Oil Seal (Piston Inner)
Rear Unit Clutch Cover
Rear Unit Sprag Assembly
Outer Race Retainer Snap Ring

Fig. 58 Rear clutch piston assembly

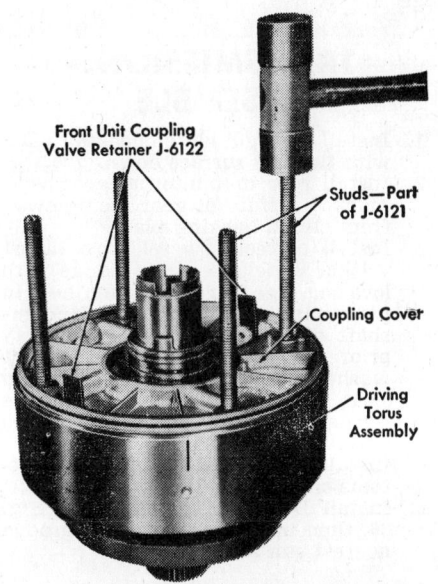

Front Unit Coupling Valve Retainer J-6122
Studs—Part of J-6121
Coupling Cover
Driving Torus Assembly

Fig. 56 Installing coupling cover

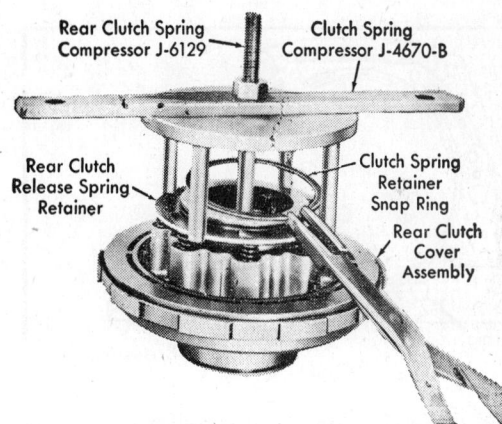

Rear Clutch Spring Compressor J-6129
Clutch Spring Compressor J-4670-B
Rear Clutch Release Spring Retainer
Clutch Spring Retainer Snap Ring
Rear Clutch Cover Assembly

Fig. 58A Removing snap ring retaining clutch release springs

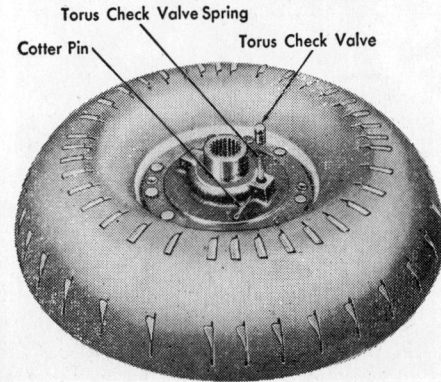

Torus Check Valve Spring
Cotter Pin
Torus Check Valve

Fig. 57 Torus check valve parts

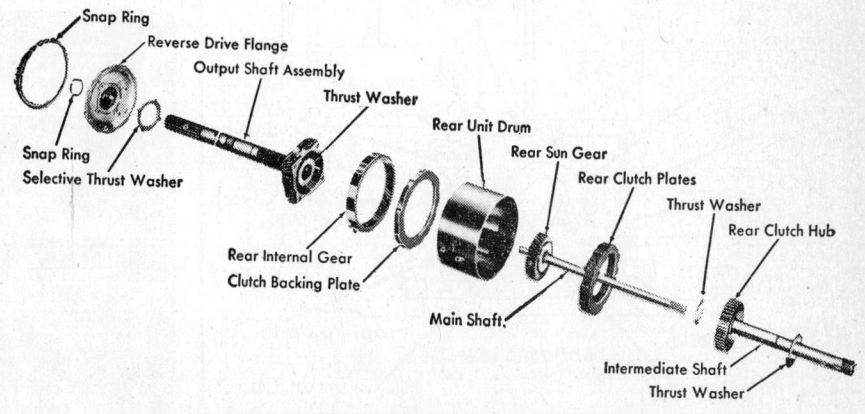

Snap Ring
Reverse Drive Flange
Output Shaft Assembly
Thrust Washer
Rear Unit Drum
Rear Sun Gear
Rear Clutch Plates
Thrust Washer
Rear Clutch Hub
Snap Ring
Selective Thrust Washer
Rear Internal Gear
Clutch Backing Plate
Main Shaft
Intermediate Shaft
Thrust Washer

Fig. 59 Rear unit assembly, 1956-57. For 1958-61 a needle thrust bearing is used instead of a thrust washer

7. Install rear sprag clutch retainer in neutral clutch hub.
8. Install neutral clutch hub on hub of rear clutch cover, rotating counter-clockwise around inner race.
9. Install spiral snap ring and check for proper rotation of sprag.

REAR UNIT

With this unit, Fig. 59, disassembled as outlined under *Transmission,* disassemble, wash all parts and inspect them as follows:

1. Clutch cover thrust washer for wear.
2. Clutch hub for damaged splines.
3. Sun gear thrust washer for wear.
4. Mainshaft and sun gear for damaged splines, teeth or bearing surfaces.
5. Composition clutch plates for damaged surfaces; *plates should be flat.* If flakes or facing material can be removed with thumb nail, install new plates. Discoloration is not an indication of failure.
6. Steel clutch plates for scored surfaces or damaged lugs. These plates must have six equally spaced waves, the waves to be .008" to .012" high when measured on a surface plate.
7. Rear drum for scores or cracks.
8. Internal gear for tooth damage.

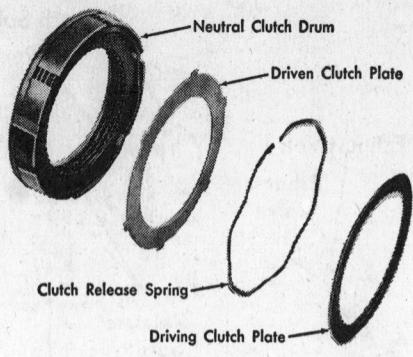

Fig. 60 Neutral clutch drum assembly

9. Output shaft thrust washer for wear.
10. Output shaft for damaged pinions, splines or bearing surfaces.
11. Reverse drive flange for damage.

NEUTRAL CLUTCH DRUM

Inspect composition clutch plates for damaged surfaces or worn teeth; plates should be flat, Fig. 60. If flakes can be scratched off with thumb nail, install new plates. Discoloration is not an indication of failure.

Inspect steel plates for scored surfaces and damage. These plates must have six equally spaced waves .008" to .012" high when measured on a surface plate. Inspect clutch drum for scored and damaged surfaces. Inspect wave springs for distortion.

OVERRUN BAND

Inspect the overrun band for burned, glazed, worn, cracked or loose lining. Inspect anchor end of band for broken welds or worn socket.

TRANSMISSION CASE

Clean transmission case thoroughly. Remove oil pressure line pipe plug from bottom rear of transmission case. Blow out all oil passages through case. Check for restricted, leaky or interconnected passages, Figs. 61 to 64. Inspect case for cracks.

TORUS COVER

Inspect inner and outer diameter of torus cover oil seal hub for score marks. Inspect splines of hub for wear and damage.

TRANSMISSION, ASSEMBLE

1. Install rear unit clutch backing plate with finished surface down.
2. Install rear unit internal gear with marked surface of gear facing away from clutch backing plate.
3. Install correct size selective thrust washer in reverse drive flange with locating lugs in retainer and hold in place with vaseline, Fig. 65. If mainshaft did no have correct end play prior to disassembly, select proper washer to bring end play within .004" to .018". These washers are furnished in nine sizes in graduated thicknesses of .005".
4. Install output shaft until carrier bottoms on selective thrust washer.
5. Install Drive Flange Retainer, Fig. 66, then install snap ring in groove nearest sun gear.

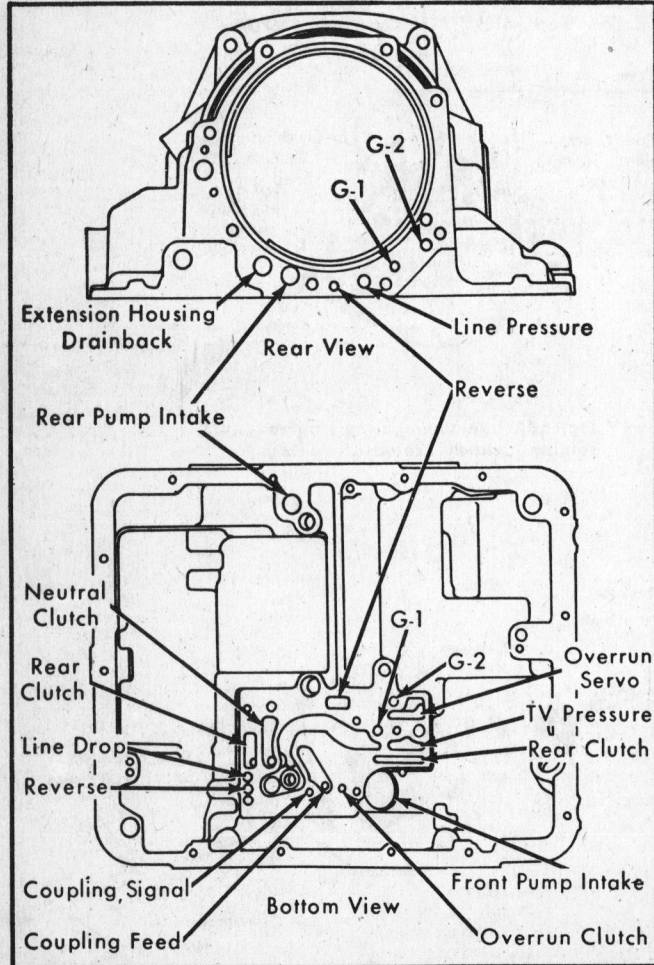

Fig. 61 Oil passage identification, 1956-57

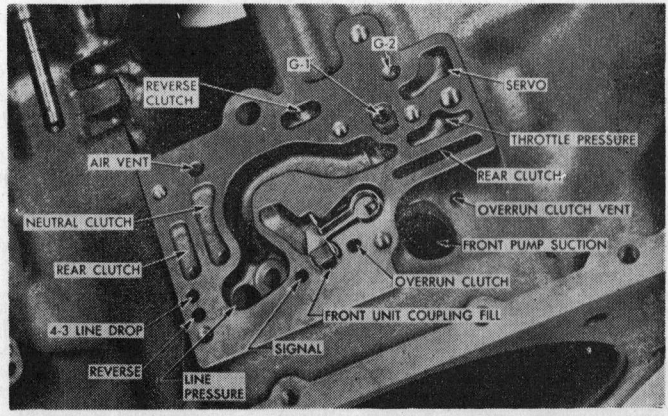

Fig. 62 Oil passage identification (bottom of case), 1958

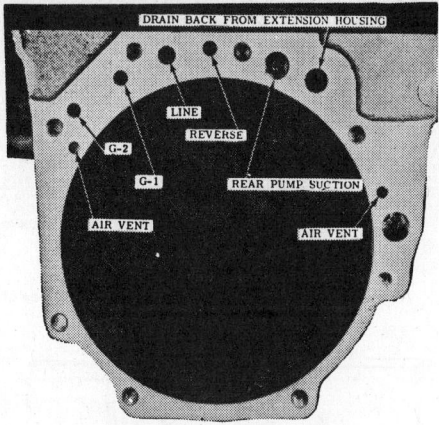

Fig. 63 Oil passage identification (rear of case), 1956-58

6. Install output shaft in rear drum and secure with large snap ring.
7. Install drum and output shaft in holding fixture (output shaft down) removing Drive Flange Retainer as assembly is placed in fixture.
8. Install bronze thrust washer in counterbore of output shaft and retain with petrolatum.
9. Apply transmission fluid to faces of clutch plates and alternately install them in rear unit drum, starting with a composition plate and ending with a steel plate. When installing steel plates, notches on outside diameter of plates should line up with one another.
10. Install mainshaft and sun gear assembly into output shaft, meshing sun gear with rear planet pinions.
11. Install bronze thrust washer on rear end of rear clutch hub and retain with petrolatum.
12. Install intermediate shaft and rear clutch hub assembly, rotating clutch hub to align splines with composition clutch plates.
13. Install bronze thrust washer on front of rear clutch hub and retain with petrolatum.
14. Install rear clutch piston and neutral clutch hub assembly into rear unit drum.
15. Install large snap ring retaining rear

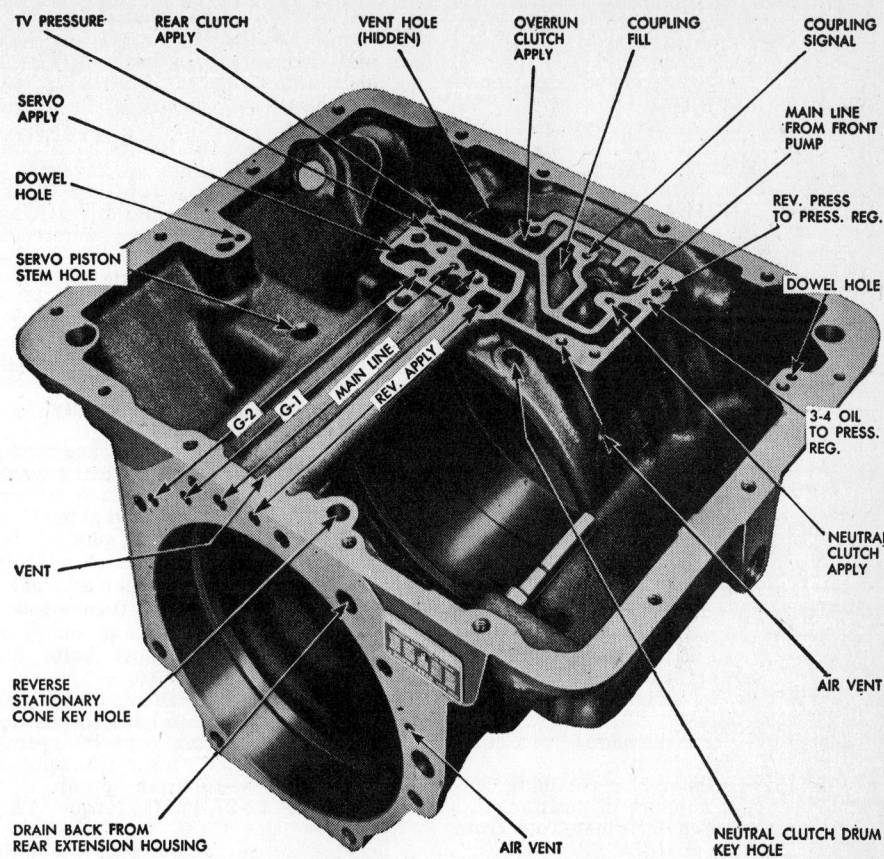

Fig. 64 Oil passage identification, 1959-61

clutch piston to rear unit drum.
16. Install neutral clutch drum on rear unit with driven clutch plate lugs up.
17. Apply transmission fluid to neutral clutch plates and install them, starting with and ending with a composition plate. Also install one wave type clutch release spring with each composition plate.
18. Install center bearing support in neutral clutch drum.
19. Install interlocking oil seal ring in intermediate shaft.
20. *The 1960 transmission does not have a center bearing support locating bolt. Therefore, for this phase of the assembly procedure, refer to the text which accompanies Figs. 49, 50 and 51.* For 1956-59 units, install Clutch Retainer Tool over intermediate shaft by compressing center bearing support into neutral clutch drum and tightening lock screw on Clutch Retainer. Lock screw should be furthest away from center bearing support.
21. Slide overrun band into case in horizontal position with band ends to rear of case. When band is halfway in case, rotate and attach band end on stationary anchor in case.
22. Install parking brake spacer, lever and pawl as an assembly. Install bracket and spring. Install spacer, pawl pivot pin and connect brake lever spring.
23. Install neutral clutch drum stationary stop key in interior of case and retain with petrolatum, Fig. 67.
24. Install inside detent control and in-

side throttle control lever assembly as follows: Install O-ring seal to case counterbore and install lever assembly with outer and inner washers. Install ring retaining detent control lever to case.
25. Remove assemblies from holding fixture and install in transmission case by entering output shaft through front of case. Care must be taken to align slot in neutral clutch drum to stationary stop key in case and at the same time aligning hole for cen-

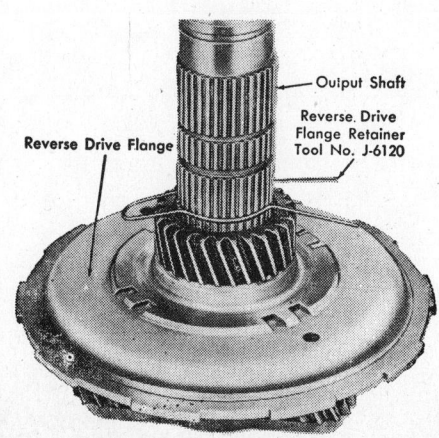

Fig. 66 Installing drive flange retainer

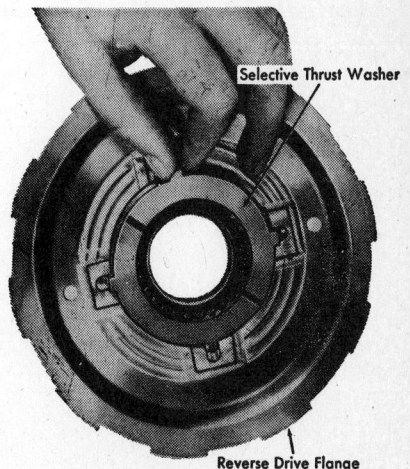

Fig. 65 Installing selective thrust washer which controls mainshaft end play

Fig. 67 Installing stationary stop key

ter bearing support locking screw. If unit does not go in far enough so that the snap ring groove is not visible ahead of the center bearing support, slight pressure may become necessary to drive unit into place.

26. Install center bearing support locking screw in side of transmission (1956-59 only).
27. Position transmission vertically (output shaft down).
28. Install large snap ring retaining center bearing support in position.
29. Remove Clutch Retainer Tool from intermediate shaft.
30. Position transmission vertically (output shaft up).
31. Install reverse planet carrier on output shaft, lining up hole in carrier hub with oil hole in output shaft.
32. Install snap ring retaining reverse planet carrier to output shaft.
33. Install reverse stationary cone, exercising care to prevent binding. Align slot in cone with key before installing.
34. Install tang type reverse carrier to rear internal gear release spring, with tangs pointing toward rear of transmission.
35. Install reverse internal gear on reverse planet carrier.
36. Install large wave type reverse piston to case outer release spring.
37. Using new gasket, install rear pump and reverse clutch piston assembly as a unit to case. Install snap ring retaining rear bearing to output shaft.
38. Install governor. Be sure to compress oil seal rings as governor is installed. Test by rotating output shaft. Governor should turn. Rings on governor should be compressed before insertion.
39. Install extension housing with new gasket.
40. Recheck mainshaft end play. If not within .004" to .018", a selective washer of the required thickness should be installed.
41. Turn transmission vertically with extension housing down.
42. Install overrun clutch release spring, clutch plate and bronze thrust washer. Tangs of washer face toward front of transmission and should line up with tangs of clutch plate.
43. Install front sprag inner race, aligning with tangs of washer and plate.
44. Install front pump in transmission.
45. Tighten the three front pump-to-center bearing support bolts and then back off ¼ turn.
46. Apply air in the neutral clutch hole of the transmission case to position the center bearing support against the snap ring. With air still applied, tighten case-to-front pump lock screw to 22-27 lb. ft. torque. Then tighten the three front pump-to-center support screws to 25-30 lb. ft. torque.
47. Install front pump locating screw in interior of transmission case.
48. Install pressure regulator valve in side of case.
49. Position transmission with bottom side facing up.
50. Install control valve and channel body.
51. Install servo release spring, servo and accumulator body.
52. Install O-ring seal in front pump body.
53. Install O-ring seal on rear pump (if used) intake pipe and install intake pipes and oil screen as an assembly. Install clamp to front intake pipe.

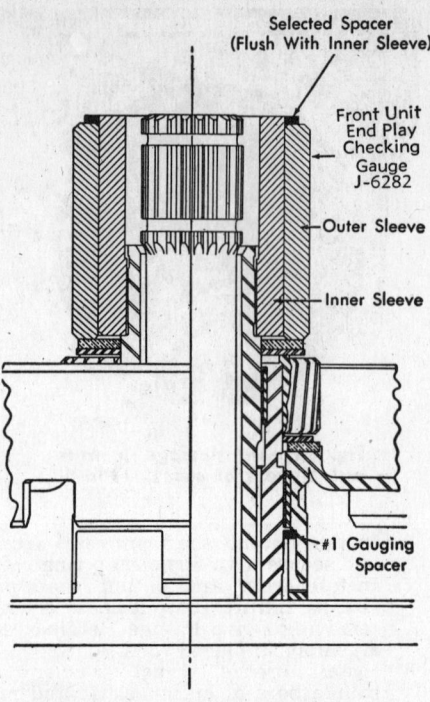

Fig. 68 Checking front unit end play

54. Install oil pan with new gasket.
55. Install front unit coupling into case, making sure that unit engages both front sprag and front pump rotor.
56. Check front unit end play as follows: With extension housing facing down, install #1 selective spacer to front unit coupling driven torus shaft, Fig. 68. Install internal gear with bronze thrust washer. Install steel backing washer and bronze thrust washer. Install front unit checking gauge, Fig. 68 and check end play. To obtain result shown, selective spacers of 14 sizes are available in sizes ranging from .0695" to .175".
57. Remove tools and place transmission on transmission hoist.
58. Install flywheel housing, torus cover, torus members and flywheel in the reverse order of removal.

HYDRA-MATIC
Single Coupling Type, 1953-56
For Linkage Adjustment See Car Chapter

CONTENTS

Description 283
Trouble Shooting 25

Maintenance

Adding Fluid 283
Changing Fluid 283

"In Car" Repairs

Air Pressure Tests 284
Band Adjustment (External) 284
Band Adjustment (Internal) 285
Throttle Lever, Adjust 286
Pressure Regulator 287
Control Valve 287
Parking Brake Bracket 288
Governor 288
Rear Oil Pump 288
Front Servo 288
Rear Servo 288
Reverse Unit 290

Repairs Requiring Transmission Removal

Transmission, Disassemble 291
Front Pump 292
Oil Delivery Sleeve 293
Band Inspection 293
Front Planetary Unit 293
Rear Planetary Unit 294
Transmission Case 294
Transmission, Assemble 295

IN this transmission, two planetary units are used to give four forward speeds, Fig. 1. In each unit a hydraulically operated clutch is used to lock two planetary members together for direct drive. Reduction (power multiplication)

is obtained in both units by means of a band which can be used to hold one of the planetary units stationary. The bands are operated by means of hydraulically controlled servos.

Oil for hydraulic operation is supplied by two oil pumps. The front pump is driven by the engine and the rear pump by the output shaft of the transmission.

Although both planetary units are similar, the rear unit differs in two ways from the front unit: It is longer, has more clutch plates and greater gear reduction; the rear servo is normally applied by spring pressure and released by oil pressure.

Clutch and Band Application

Fig. 2 shows the band and clutch application for all speeds. Bear in mind that in either planetary unit of the transmission (a) when the band is applied the clutch is disengaged and the unit is in reduction, (b) when the clutch is applied the band is disengaged and the unit is acting as a coupling for direct drive.

MAINTENANCE

Adding Fluid

1. Set hand brake and place selector in neutral.
2. Start engine and allow it to idle continuously for a minimum of two minutes to warm up the oil.
3. Remove and wipe dipstick and reinsert.
4. Add fluid as required to bring the level *exactly* to the FULL mark. Do not overfill the transmission as this will cause foaming which may result in improper operation. If the level is above the FULL mark, the excess should be drained.

Changing Fluid

Some models do not have a drain plug in the transmission oil pan; others do. In draining fluid from those transmissions having an oil pan drain plug remove the flywheel inspection plate, the ⅛" pipe plug from the torus cover and the drain plug from the back of the oil pan.

On transmissions not having an oil pan drain plug, proceed as follows:

1. Remove flywheel inspection plate.
2. Remove 7/16" "hex head" pipe plug from the torus cover and drain the fluid from the torus cover.
3. Center a drain pan directly below and as close as possible to the point where the external filler tube attaches to the transmission oil pan.
4. Hold the external filler tube with a rag if the transmission oil is hot and carefully loosen nut attaching tube to oil pan.
5. As soon as nut is completely loosened, quickly rotate filler tube

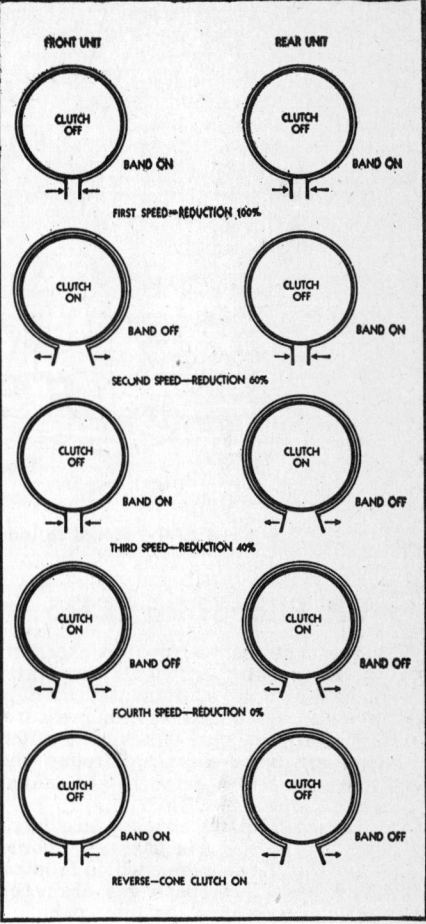

Fig. 2 Band and clutch application

away from transmission so that it will not interfere with fluid flow.
6. After draining install and tighten drain plugs.
7. Replace flywheel housing bottom cover.
8. Pour 9½ quarts of Automatic Transmission Fluid into transmission.
9. With selector lever in neutral, run engine at a fast idle for about 1½ minutes to fill the coupling.
10. Reduce engine speed to slow idle and check level. Then add fluid as required to bring level *exactly* to the FULL mark.

Caution

It is recommended that the oil pan and screen be removed and cleaned whenever the oil is changed. This is particularly important where the oil is drained by means of the filler tube since the opening is well above the bottom of the pan, thus allowing a considerable quantity of old oil and contaminants to remain in the pan.

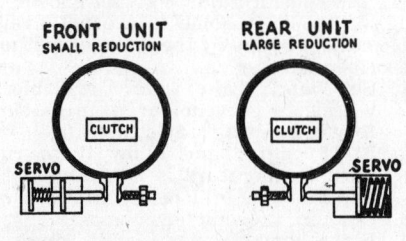

FRONT UNIT SMALL REDUCTION   **REAR UNIT** LARGE REDUCTION

CLUTCH   CLUTCH

SERVO   SERVO

NEUTRAL – Both bands and clutches released.
1st SPEED – Front & rear units-in reduction.
2nd SPEED – Front unit in direct drive-rear in reduction.
3rd SPEED – Front unit in reduction···rear in direct drive.
4th SPEED – Front and rear units–in direct drive.

Fig. 1 Band and clutch positions in different gears

"In Car" Repairs

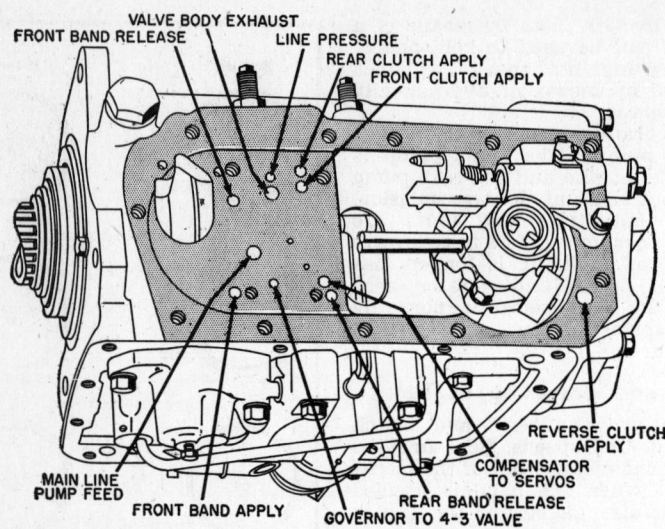

Fig. 4   Identification of oil passages (typical)

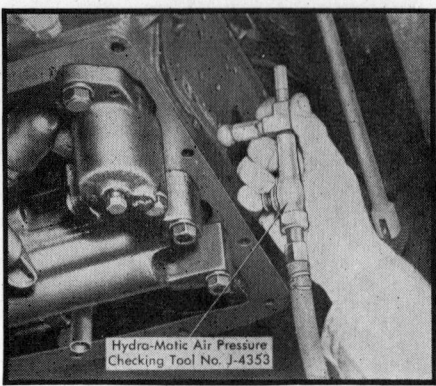

Fig. 3   Checking passage in transmission with blow gun

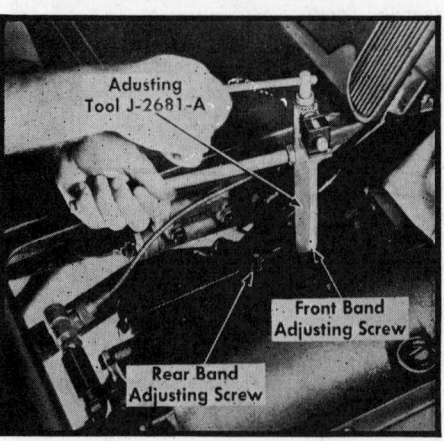

Fig. 5   Adjusting front band by external method

AIR PRESSURE TESTS

Air pressure tests afford an excellent means of tracking down Hydra-Matic troubles. The only equipment needed is air delivered at about 80 lb. of pressure, and a special blow gun attachment which prevents air from escaping around the nozzle when it is applied to the transmission oil passages, Fig. 3.

Oil passages to be checked are identified in Fig. 4, and the passages should be checked in the sequence which follows. To gain access to the passages, drain the transmission, remove bottom pan, oil screen, side cover and control valve assembly.

Front Clutch Apply

Air pressure applied intermittently should move clutch piston audibly and actuate the front clutch. Fog of oil accompanied by rush of air from inside front unit drum indicates faulty front clutch seal. Leakage from other passages in side of case mean "short circuit" due to faulty transmission case or oil delivery tube.

Front Band Apply—Air pressure should actuate front servo and apply band without appreciable escape of air around flat surface of servo body. Small amount of blow-by is permissible from front band release passage.

Front Band Release—Air pressure will not actuate servo. Check for unusual escape of air between servo body and transmission case, and around band release cylinder.

Governor to 4-3 Valve—Slight click will be heard when overrun control valve is actuated. No leakage is permissible except for slight amount from front servo body and front band apply passage.

Rear Band Release—Air pressure should release rear servo and band. Small amount of air will escape past servo piston ring. Slight leakage is also permissible from compensator passage.

Rear Clutch Apply—Air pressure applied intermittently should move clutch piston audibly and actuate rear clutch. Other conditions described under Front Clutch Apply also apply here except check is made at rear unit drum.

Compensator to Servos—Air pressure should actuate rear servo to tighten rear band, and front servo to apply front band. Except for normal escape past piston ring gaps, no air leakage is permissible.

Main Line Pump Feed—Large amounts of air and oil will blow out from front side of front drum assembly. Any other leakage of air and oil indicates interconnected passages due to faulty transmission case.

Line Pressure—No leakage is permissible at any point when plug is sealed in place between band adjusting screws.

Valve Body Exhaust—Complete blow-by to interior of transmission case should result. Partial obstruction of passage can cause erratic shifting.

Reverse Clutch Apply—Intermittent application of air pressure should audibly actuate the reverse cone clutch piston. Unusual escape of air around the piston indicates leakage of oil seals in the reverse cone assembly.

The foregoing applies to 1951 and later models. Prior to 1951, reverse operation is provided mechanically by means of a reverse anchor which engages the external teeth of the internal gear.

EXTERNAL BAND ADJUSTMENT

If the special adjusting tool shown in Fig. 5, and a tachometer are not available, adjust bands by the internal method described further on.

1. Set hand brake firmly and block wheels to prevent car from moving forward during adjustment.
2. Start engine and allow it to run until temperature is normal (choke and fast idle off) before proceeding.
3. Connect tachometer to engine.
4. Place control lever in DR range.
5. Adjust carburetor idle screw to give 700 rpm.

Front Band

1. Using band adjusting gauge, Fig. 5, loosen front band adjusting screw lock nut.
2. Loosen band adjusting screw until engine speed increases to 900-1000 rpm (front drum now spinning freely).
3. Tighten band adjusting screw until

Fig. 6 Adjusting front band by internal method

Fig. 7 Adjusting rear band by internal method

engine returns to 700 rpm (front drum stopped).

4. Again loosen adjusting screw until engine speed increases and retighten slowly until engine speed returns to 700 rpm. The object of loosening and tightening the screw is to locate the exact point at which the band stops the drum from spinning.
5. At this point wait 30 seconds.
6. If engine speed increases, tighten screw 1/10 of a turn.
7. Wait 30 seconds and if engine speed again increases, tighten screw 1/10 of a turn more.
8. Repeat this procedure until engine speed remains at 700 rpm for at least 30 seconds.
9. Set counter on tool to "00".
10. While holding lock nut stationary with long handle of tool, tighten adjusting screw 7.7 turns for 1952-56 models. *Oldsmobile 1954-56 and Pontiac 1955-56 have no provision for making the external adjustment; it must be done internally.*
11. Hold adjusting screw stationary and tighten lock nut securely.

Rear Band

Repeat Steps 1 to 9 under Front Band;

then proceed as follows:
1. Position selector lever in N.
2. While holding lock nut tighten adjusting screw exactly 2 turns.
3. Position selector lever in DR.
4. Hold adjusting screw stationary and tighten lock nut.
5. Reset engine to recommended speed.

INTERNAL BAND ADJUSTMENT

Before adjusting the bands, make sure the anchor of each band is seated on the adjusting screw and that the band is centered on the drum. Turn the output shaft and mainshaft by hand until band moves into operating position on drum.

Front Band

1. Remove pipe plug from top of front servo. Loosen hex adjusting screw of front servo gauge, Fig. 6, until approximately 1/8" of threads are exposed above gauge body. Install gauge in bore of servo body from which pipe plug was removed and *tighten gauge by hand only.*
2. Tighten hex adjusting screw of

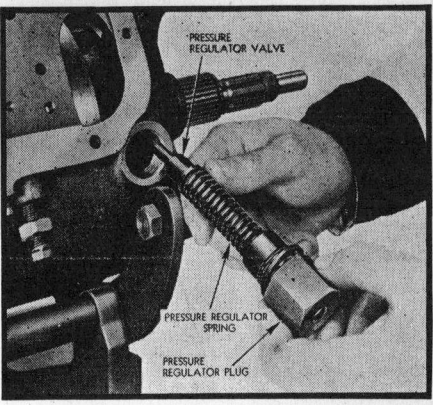

Fig. 9 Removing pressure regulator

gauge with fingers until stem of gauge is felt to *just touch* piston in front servo. Do not over-tighten.
3. Tighten hex adjusting screw of gauge five complete turns.
4. Tighten front band adjusting screw until knurled washer on top of adjusting gauge is *just free* to turn.
5. Hold front band adjusting screw and tighten lock nut securely to 40-50 lb. ft. torque.

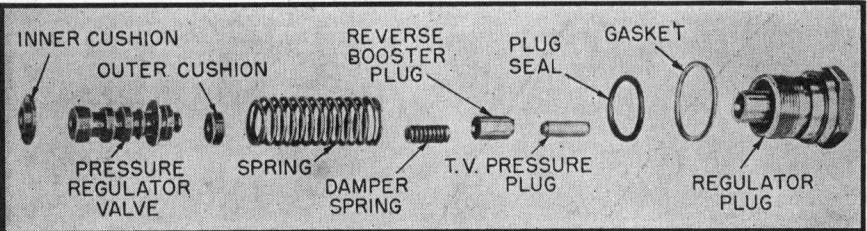

Fig. 10 Component parts of pressure regulator vary in different models. The assembly shown is one of the latest designs

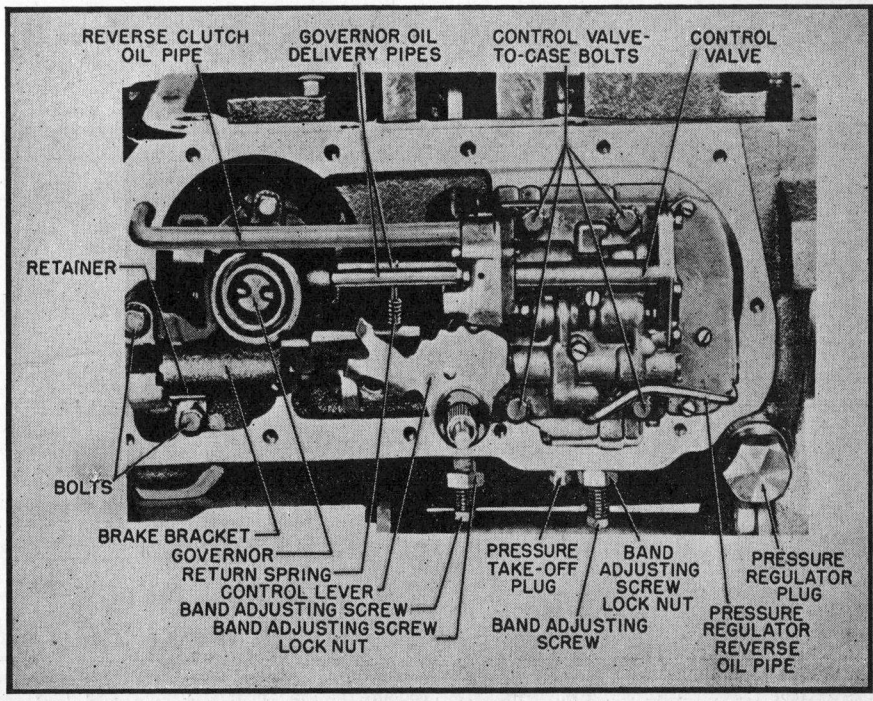

Fig. 11 Transmission with side cover removed

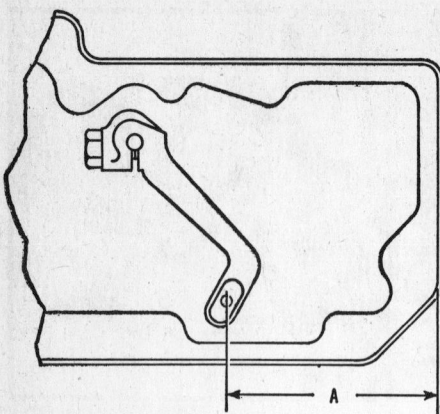

Fig. 11A Throttle lever position. Dimension "A" is measured in inches with lever back against its stop. Adjust by bending lever as required to obtain the dimension given below:

Cadillac 1946-48 .... 6½
 1949 .... 4 1/16
 1950-51 .... 4¼
 1952-53 .... 4 5/16
 1954 .... 4 9/16
 1955 4

Hudson 1950-56 .... 6½

Kaiser 1951-55 .... 4¾

Lincoln 1949-50 .... 4 7/16
 1951-54 .... 6 9/16

Nash Amb. 1949-51 .... 3 9/16
 Amb. 1952-56 .... 7¼
 Statesman 1950-55 .... 3 9/16
 Statesman 1956 .... 6½

Oldsmobile 1946-53 .... 6½
 1954-55 .... 6¾
 1956 S88 .... 6¾
 1956 88 .... 6 3/16

Pontiac 1948-54 .... 3 9/16

Rambler 1953-55 .... 7¼
 1956 .... 6½

Willys 1953 .... 3 9/16
 1954-55 .... 4¾

---

6. Loosen adjusting screw of gauge at least five full turns and remove the gauge from the servo.

7. Install pipe plug in front servo body.

Rear Band

1. With band centered on drum, make sure rear servo actuating lever is not under tension. Position gauge shown in Fig. 7 on rear servo, with short leg hooked over end of accumulator body and long leg resting on servo piston stem.

2. Tighten rear band adjusting screw until rear servo actuating lever just contacts face of gauge. *If adjusting screw is turned beyond adjustment point, back screw out 2 or 3 turns and repeat the adjustment.*

3. When correct adjustment is obtained, hold adjusting screw stationary and tighten lock nut to 40-50 lb. ft. torque.

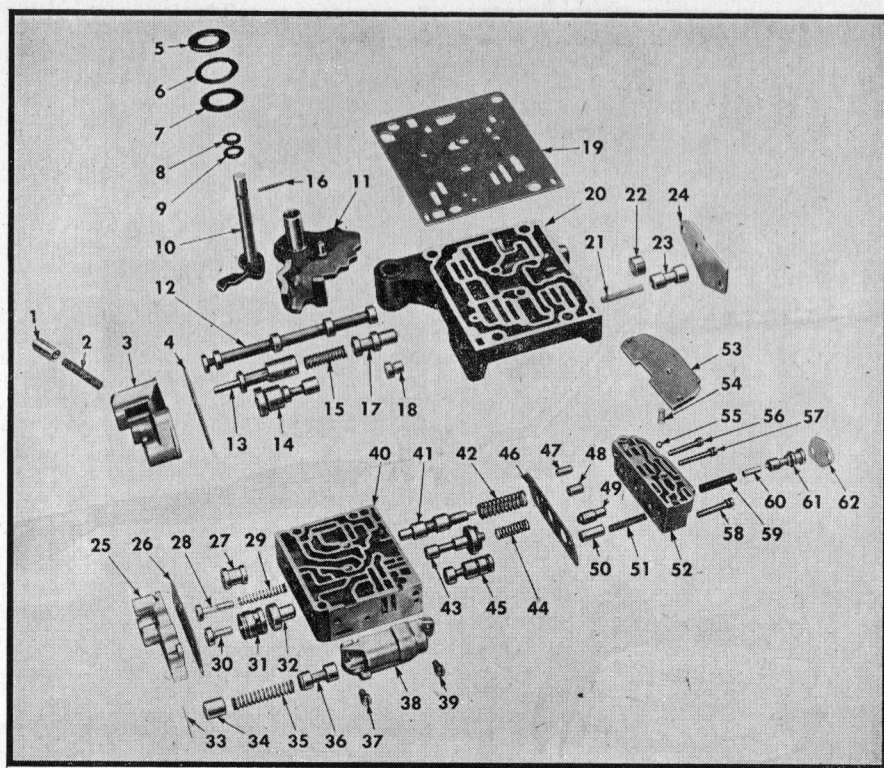

Fig. 12 Exploded view of a typical late model control valve. Use for identification of parts only inasmuch as units vary from year to year

1. Detent Plunger
2. Detent Plunger Spring
3. Detent Plunger Retainer
4. Detent Plunger Retainer Spacer
5. Manual Shaft Seal
6. Manual Shaft Outer Washer
7. Manual Shaft Inner Washer
8. Throttle Valve Operating Shaft Washer
9. Operating Shaft Seal
10. Inside Throttle Valve Lever
11. Inside Detent Control Lever
12. Manual Control Valve
13. T-Valve
14. Double Transition Valve
15. Throttle Valve Spring
16. Throttle Valve Operating Shaft Pin
17. Throttle Valve
18. Compensator Auxiliary Plug
19. Valve Body Spacer Plate
20. Outer Valve Body
21. Compensator Valve Spring
22. Detent Plug
23. Compensator Valve
24. Outer Valve Body Front Plate
25. Inner Valve Body Rear Cover
26. Valve Body Rear Cover Spacer
27. 3-4 Governor Plug
28. 2-1 Detent Plug
29. 2-1 Detent Plug Spring (½ Ton only)
30. 2-3 Governor Plug
31. 2-3 Governor Plug Sleeve
32. 2-3 Auxiliary Valve
33. 3-2 Timing Valve Plug Retainer Pin
34. 3-2 Timing Valve Plug
35. 3-2 Timing Valve Spring
36. 3-2 Timing Valve
37. 3-2 Timing Valve Body Screw
38. 3-2 Timing Valve Body
39. 3-2 Timing Valve Body Screw
40. Inner Valve Body
41. 3-4 Shift Valve
42. 3-4 Shift Valve Spring
43. 1-2 Shift Valve
44. 1-2 Regulator Plug Spring
45. 2-3 Shift Valve
46. Front Valve Body Spacer
47. 3-4 Regulator Plug
48. 4-3 Shuttle Valve
49. 1-2 Regulator Plug
50. T-V Regulator Valve
51. T-V Regulator Valve Spring
52. Front Valve Body
53. Front Valve Body Plate
54. "T" Oil Ball Check Valve Spring
55. "T" Oil Ball Check Valve
56. Front Body to Inner Body Screw
57. Front Body to Inner Body Screw
58. Front Body to Inner Body Screw
59. 2-3 Shifter Valve Spring
60. 2-3 Spring Guide Pin
61. 3-2 Detent Plug
62. Detent Plug Plate

THROTTLE LEVER, ADJUST

Whenever a transmission is overhauled or shifts are erratic, check the position of the throttle lever on the side of the transmission to see if it has become bent. This is a very important adjustment in that when the transmission throttle lever is all the way back against its stop the throttle valve in the carburetor must be fully closed. Gauges are available to measure the position of the

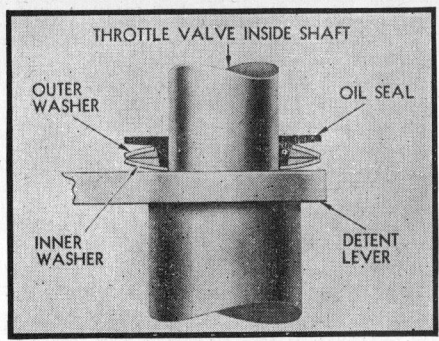

Fig. 13 Manual shaft seal

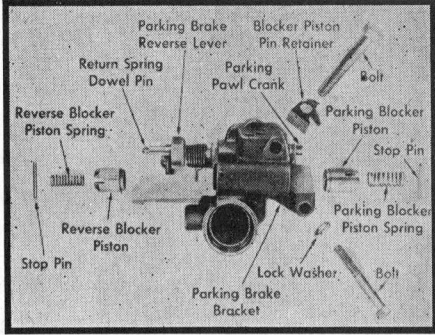

Fig. 14 Layout of parking brake bracket parts

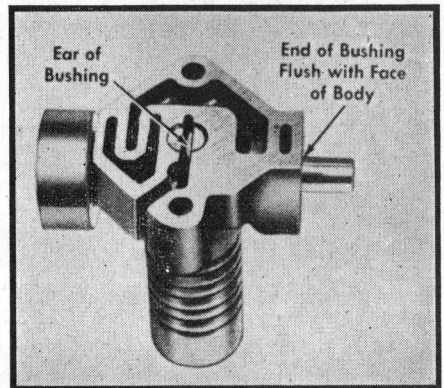

Fig. 16 Installation of G-2 plunger and bushing

throttle lever but if not available, use the data supplied in the caption under Fig. 11A.

After the lever has been bent to obtain the proper dimension, adjust the carburetor linkage as outlined in the car chapters.

PRESSURE REGULATOR

While removing the pressure regulator from the side of the transmission, Fig. 9, unscrew the plug while holding hand against spring tension to avoid losing parts.

In disassembling the regulator, Fig. 10, do not remove the valve inner and outer cushions unless inspection shows necessity for replacement.

Inspect springs for weakness, collapsed coils and distortion. Inspect plugs for nicks and scores. Blow out all passages

in regulator plug. Inspect regulator valve for nicks and scores, and make sure valve is clean. Clean all parts and wipe dry. Then reassemble the regulator.

CONTROL VALVE

To remove the control valve, take off the oil pan and side pan. Disconnect the speedometer cable. Unfasten and remove the control valve by working toward front of case.

Extreme care must be used when handling the control valve assembly. Do not grip valve bodies in a vise. Never use force when removing or installing valves or plugs.

The control valve should be laid flat on clean paper for disassembling. Keep component parts covered except parts on which work is being performed. Keep screws with correct part as valve body is disassembled.

Before inspection of valve bodies and plugs, make sure they are thoroughly cleaned and wiped dry. Then, referring to Fig. 12 as a guide, inspect the parts as follows:

1. Examine all valves and plugs to see that they are free of burrs, scores or other damage. Burrs may be removed with fine crocus cloth and light oil. Valves and plugs have sharp corners which prevent dirt from wedging between valves and plugs and valve bodies. *When removing burrs, do not round off sharp edges.*

2. With valves, plugs and valve bodies clean and dry, check each shifter valve, governor plug and regulator plug for free movement in their respective bores and operating positions. *It can be assumed that valves and plugs are free in their operating positions if they will fall of their own weight in their respective bores when valve body is shaken slightly.*

3. Check fit of throttle valve inside lever for looseness on throttle valve operating shaft.

4. Check inside detent control lever for looseness on manual shaft.

5. Make sure inside detent control lever pick-up pin is tight in place and not excessively worn.

6. Check for worn or damaged splines on manual shaft and throttle valve operating shaft.

7. Check action of throttle valve oper-

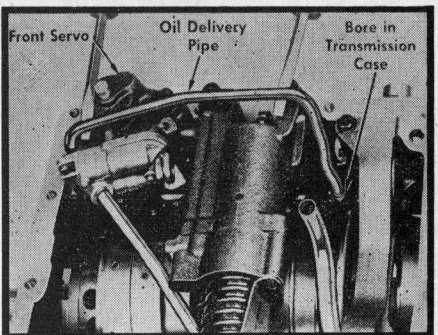

Fig. 17 Removing governor oil delivery pipe

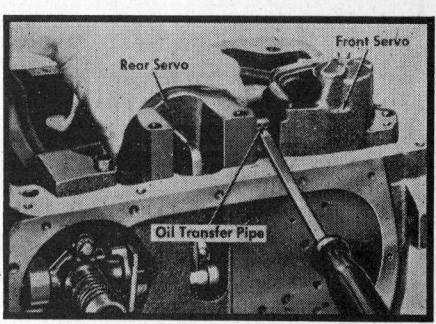

Fig. 18 Separating rear servo and oil transfer pipe

ating shaft in manual control shaft, and manual control shaft in hub of outer body.

8. If inspection shows levers and shafts bind, or loose and excessively worn, proceed as follows:

9. Support outer valve body and control shaft assembly so that throttle valve operating shaft, manual shaft and outer valve body will not be damaged during operating shaft pin removal.

10. Using a small punch and hammer, drive out pin.

11. Remove inside throttle valve lever, detent control lever, shaft seal and washer from outer valve body.

12. Replace damaged parts and reassemble to outer valve body.

13. While properly supporting outer valve body and control shaft, drive in new operating shaft pin. Check

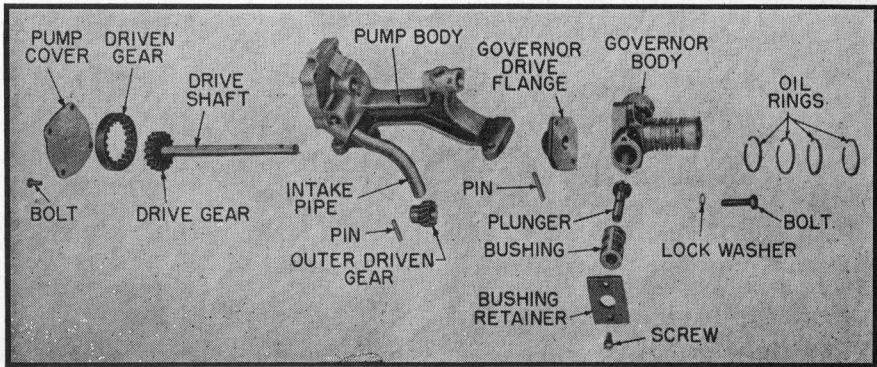

Fig. 15 Layout of rear pump and governor parts

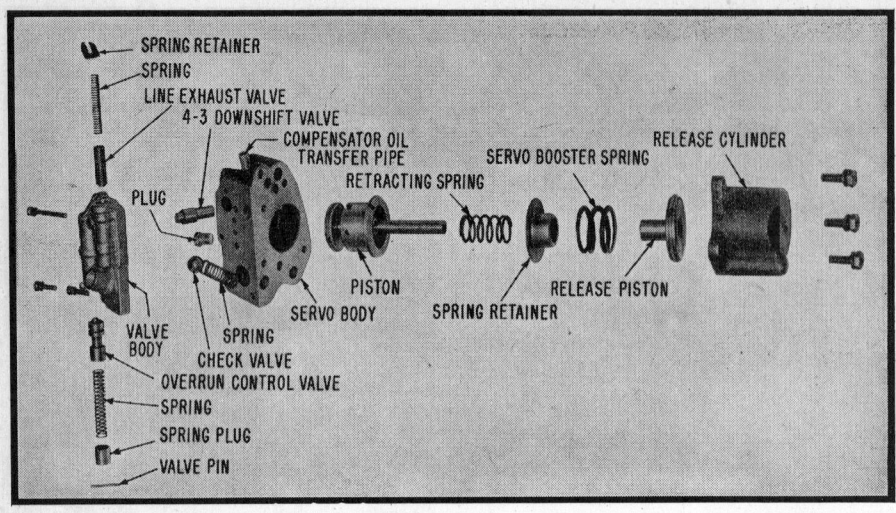

Fig. 19 Exploded view of front servo

shafts for freedom of movement.

14. Check all springs for weakness and distortion.
15. Check all valve body, plate and cover contact surfaces for cracks or scores. Clean all passages. Check threads for crossed condition. Examine valve bodies for warpage by placing a straight edge across mating surfaces. If either valve body requires replacement, the complete control valve assembly must be replaced.
16. Inspect "T" oil ball check valve for damage or rough surface.

Reassembly

Lubricate each moving part with clean transmission fluid before part is installed. Refer to Fig. 12 for identification and location of parts. Assemble the parts in the outer valve body first, then the inner valve body.

When installing manual control valve in outer valve body make sure pick-up pin on inside detent control lever engages manual control valve correctly.

When installing the manual shaft seal washers they should be as in Fig. 13.

PARKING BRAKE BRACKET

After removing the control valve as outlined previously, remove the parking brake bracket by carefully sliding from governor to avoid damage to oil rings. If shims are present between case and parking brake bracket, the same shims must be reinstalled as long as the original transmission case is used.

Disassembly

1. While holding finger over parking blocker piston spring, use needle nose pliers to remove piston stop pin.
2. Remove blocker piston spring and use snap ring pliers to remove piston.
3. Clip off head of stop pin. Then while holding finger over reverse blocker piston spring, pull pin from brake bracket with needle nose pliers.

4. Remove reverse blocker piston spring and then pull piston out with snap ring pliers.

Inspection

1. Referring to Fig. 14, check springs for evidence of weakness, distortion and collapsed coils.
2. Check pistons and their bores for scores or burrs. Check freeness of pistons in their bores.
3. Make sure three ¼" plugs are securely staked in place in brake bracket.
4. Make sure all oil passages are clean.
5. Check four governor oil seal rings in bore of bracket. Ring gap should be .001" to .006".
6. Inspect bracket sleeve for scores or signs of extreme wear.
7. Inspect bracket for cracks or other damage.
8. See that crank operates freely in bracket without binding, yet shows no signs of unusual wear.
9. Check reverse shifter crank roller for wear. Check crank pin for cracks at point where pin joins crank.
10. Make sure lever return dowel pin is secure in brake lever.
11. Inspect pawl for wear or damage.
12. Clean all parts and wipe dry.

Reassembly

1. Lubricate each moving part with transmission fluid before part is installed.

2. Install reverse blocker piston (with slotted end exposed) and spring in bore of bracket. Compress spring with blunt screwdriver and install new stop pin. Peen ends of pin to hold in place.
3. Install parking blocker piston and spring in same manner and secure with stop pin.

GOVERNOR

After removing the control valve and parking brake bracket as outlined previously, use a file to mark the edge of governor and drive flange so they may be reassembled in the same relative position. Then unfasten the governor from the flange and withdraw it from case.

Disassembly and repair procedures are the same for all governors. Refer to Fig. 15 when repairing the governor and inspect the parts as follows:

1. Inspect governor ring lands for wear; if lands are damaged or worn thin replace complete governor.
2. Inspect governor oil seal rings and for freedom in grooves of governor tower.
3. Inspect governor body for damage.
4. Inspect governor plungers for free movement. If G-1 plunger sticks, replace complete governor. If G-2 plunger sticks, replace this plunger and bushing.

When assembling the governor, insert the G-2 plunger with ear of bushing toward flat side of governor body. Body has slot on inside to accomodate ear of bushing. When properly assembled, end of bushing will be flush with bushing retainer of governor body, Fig. 16. When attaching governor to drive flange, be sure to match the marks made on disassembly. When installed, be sure the governor does not bind; check by turning the output shaft while checking the governor in various positions.

REAR OIL PUMP & SERVOS

To remove the rear pump, take off the control valve and parking brake bracket, then proceed as follows:

1. Back off band adjusting screws at least five turns.
2. Remove governor oil delivery pipe by prying gently with a screwdriver, Fig. 17.
3. Remove rear pump and both servo attaching screws.

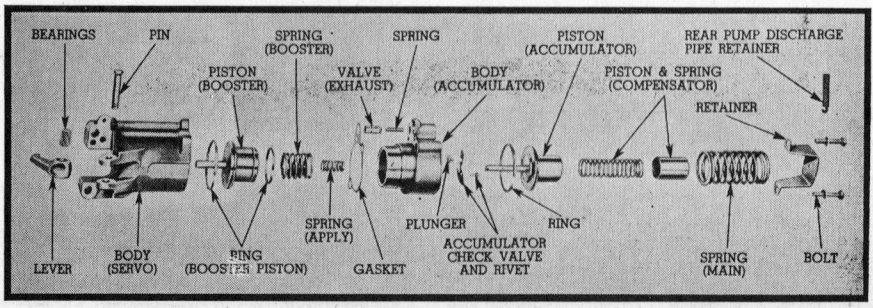

Fig. 22 Rear servo

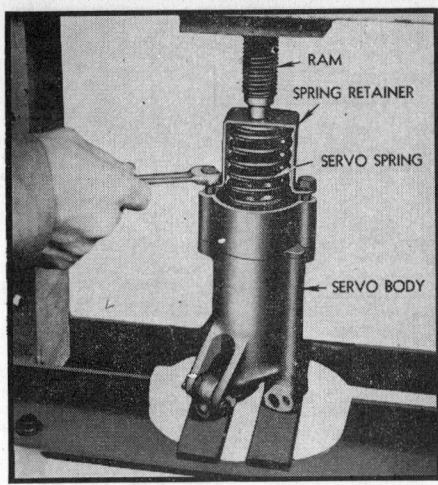

Fig. 23 Compressing rear servo spring so unit can be taken apart

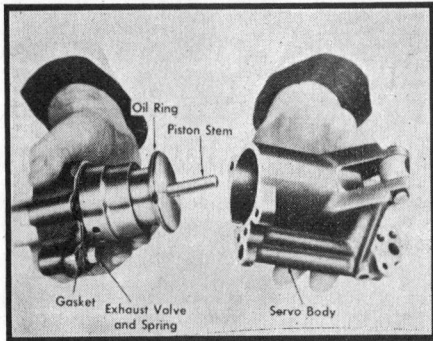

Fig. 24 Removing accumulator body and piston from servo body

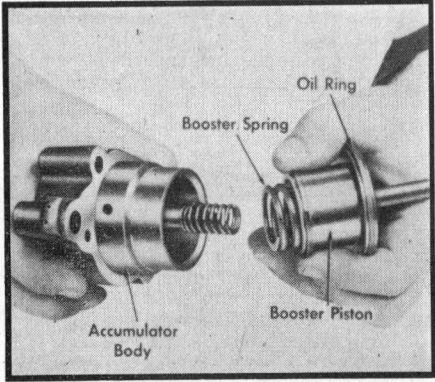

Fig. 25 Disassembly of booster piston and spring and accumulator body

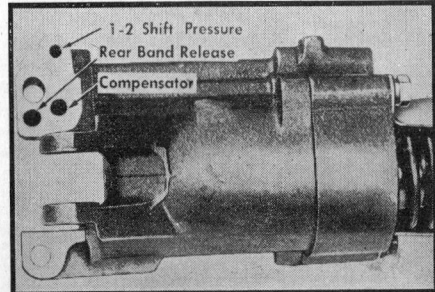

Fig. 26 Rear servo oil passages

4. Separate front and rear servos at oil transfer pipe by moving rear servo toward rear of transmission, Fig. 18.
5. Remove rear servo.
6. Remove rear pump delivery pipe.
7. Remove front servo and front pump delivery pipe.
8. Position governor so large round counterweight is toward front of transmission.
9. Position one reverse drive flange attaching bolt so that no interference will be encountered when removing the rear pump and governor assembly from case. (If removing this assembly with transmission in car, position the reverse bolt straight down; if transmission is out of car and inverted, attaching screw must be straight up.)

Rear Pump Repairs

Separate the pump cover from the body. Mark the outside of the pump driven gear with pencil or prussian blue so reassembly may be made in the original position.

Referring to Fig. 15, inspect the pump gears for worn or damaged teeth. Inspect pump body for damage. Check mating surfaces of pump body for nicks and scores. Examine pump gear pocket for wear and scores. Check cover for scores or nicks, and check for warpage. Make sure rear oil pump intake pipe is not loose in pump body, and that the passageway in the pipe is not obstructed. Check for worn shaft and bushings by attempting to move shaft sideways in pump body.

Mount dial indicator on pump body to check drive flange runout. If runout, measured inside tapped holes, exceeds .002", the drive flange or complete pump must be replaced.

When assembling the pump, lubricate each part with automatic transmission fluid. Install pump driven gear in gear pocket with side previously marked facing out. Attach cover to pump body.

Front Servo Repairs

When disassembled, inspect body for roughness, scoring, and for blocked or interconnected passages. Inspect release cylinder for scores. Inspect release piston and apply piston for scores, broken rings, freedom of rings in grooves, and see that oil passage is clear. Inspect springs for distortion. Refer to Fig. 19.

Rear Servo Repairs

Disassemble the rear servo as shown in Figs. 23, 24 and 25. Then refer to Fig. 22 for identification and location of parts.

Inspection

1. Referring to Fig. 22, inspect exhaust valve and its bore in accumulator body for scores. Check freedom of valve in bore.
2. Inspect servo body for scores, cracks or nicks. Using air pressure, check for interconnected or restricted passages, Fig. 26. Make sure two ¼" plugs are tight in servo body.

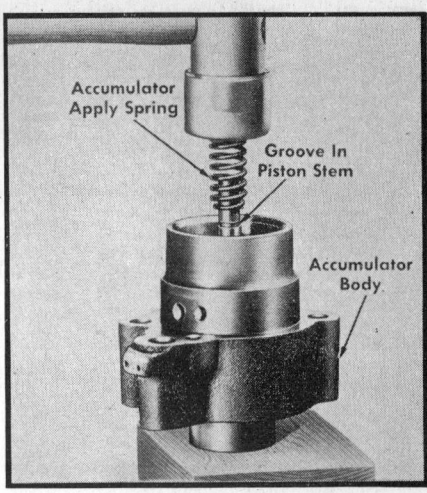

Fig. 27 Installing accumulator apply spring

Fig. 28 Position of screwdriver for removal of reverse unit

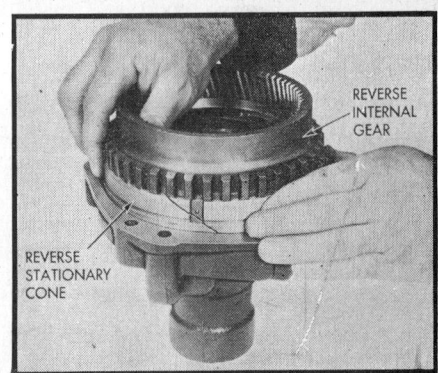

Fig. 29 Removing reverse clutch internal gear and stationary cone

3. Check rear band actuating lever for free operation, worn socket, or excessive wear at actuating pin.
4. Make sure oil rings are not broken. Check ring gap and freedom of rings in piston grooves.
5. Check booster spring for scores. Make sure ring grooves of piston are clean. Check booster piston stem for looseness.
6. Inspect accumulator piston for

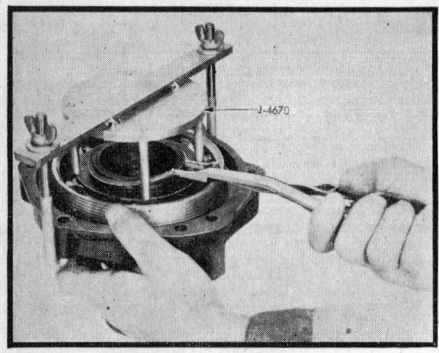

Fig. 30 Removing reverse piston-to-rear bearing retainer snap ring

scores. Check piston stem for looseness and obstructed passage. Make sure ring groove is clean.

7. Check all springs for weakness, collapsed coils or distortion.

8. Inspect accumulator body for scores or obstructed passages. Make sure check valve is not broken or rivet loose. Be certain check valve plunger is free. See that hole in check valve is open and that valve seats flat on accumulator body.

9. Clean parts and wipe dry.

Reassembly

1. Parts should be lubricated with transmission fluid unless otherwise specified.

2. Position servo actuating lever flat on bench. All parts used in this step must be dry. Install pin and 18 needle bearings in lever. Carefully withdraw pin. While pressing downward with thumb on needle bearings, rotate thumb and lever in opposite directions. Needle bearings will lock in place.

3. Position rear band actuating lever in bracket of servo body and install clevis pin. Secure clevis pin with cotter pin.

4. Install oil rings in grooves of pistons.

5. Compress oil ring and install accumulator piston in its body.

6. With accumulator piston seated on soft block of wood, position tapered end of accumulator apply spring over stem of piston. Tap spring into groove of stem with plastic hammer, Fig. 27.

7. Install spring in booster piston, being sure spring fits against bottom of piston.

8. Install booster piston and spring in accumulator body.

9. Install exhaust valve and spring in accumulator body.

10. Position new gasket on accumulator body.

11. Compress booster piston oil ring, then install servo body over accumulator and piston assembly, lining up bosses of both bodies. Guide stem of booster piston through small hole in servo body.

12. Place assembly in spring compressor, Fig. 23. After assembly, tighten spring retainer bolts to 10-13 lb. ft.

13. Test operation of servo by applying air pressure in rear band release passage, Fig. 26.

REVERSE UNIT

Before the reverse unit can be removed, it is necessary to remove the oil pan, side cover, control valve, parking brake bracket, governor, front and rear servos and rear pump. How these units are removed has been outlined previously.

Remove the six reverse drive flange attaching cap screws; the drive flange can be held from turning by using a hammer handle as a lever on the rear band strut.

Insert a screwdriver or a suitable spacer, Fig. 28, between the center bearing cap and rear clutch drum to prevent the drum from moving forward. This will prevent the forward clutch plate from dropping off the front end of the rear clutch hub. Should this happen the transmission will have to be removed to replace it.

Unfasten the rear bearing retainer from the transmission and withdraw the retainer and reverse unit from the mainshaft. Take out the reverse clutch stationary cone key to prevent its loss, Fig. 28.

Disassembly

1. Remove speedometer driven gear and sleeve from rear bearing retainer.

2. Remove snap ring from output shaft. Remove output shaft.

3. Compress reverse stationary cone with hands and lift off internal gear and clutch cone, Fig. 29.

4. Remove snap ring and bearing from bearing retainer.

5. Mount bearing retainer in compressor tool shown in Fig. 30, and remove the large snap ring.

6. Remove the tool and take out the release spring retainer washer and six piston release springs.

7. Remove clutch piston from bearing retainer by lifting straight out. *It may be necessary to apply air pressure behind piston to aid in removal. If so, apply the pressure to small hole "A", Fig. 31.*

8. Remove piston outer oil seal from

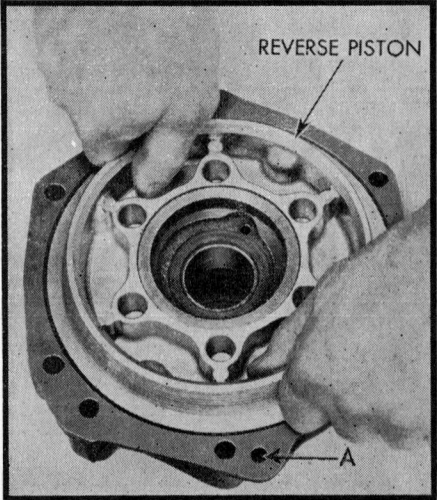

Fig. 31 Removing reverse clutch piston

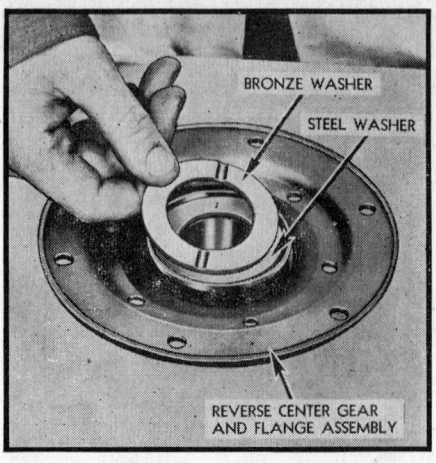

Fig. 32 Installation of thrust washers

Fig. 33 Installation of reverse internal gear and stationary cone

piston and inner oil seal from hub of rear bearing retainer.

9. Remove large bronze thrust washer from internal gear or bearing retainer.

10. Use snap ring pliers to expand clutch stationary cone and remove cone from internal gear.

11. Remove clutch release spring retainer and release (wave) spring from internal gear by rotating to the left to release retaining lugs.

12. Remove planet carrier snap ring.

13. Lift planet carrier from output shaft.

14. Remove planet carrier locating snap ring from output shaft.

15. Lift center gear and flange from output shaft.

16. Remove center gear steel and bronze thrust washers from shaft.

Inspection

1. Inspect all parts for nicks, burrs, scores, excessive wear or other damage. Check springs for weakness or distortion.

2. See that rear oil pump drive gear is tight on carrier and that pump drive gear ball is in place. If gap in snap ring is not over ball, move snap ring around to where ball can be seen.

3. Inspect reverse center gear and flange for damaged teeth or worn bushing. Gear is not furnished separately; if necessary, replace gear and flange. Position flange on rear

planetary unit internal gear and check for distortion.

4. Check fit of key in cone slot.
5. Make sure oil passages in rear bearing retainer are open.
6. Clean all parts and wipe dry.

Reassembly

1. Install thrust washers in drive flange recess as shown in Fig. 32.
2. Insert output shaft through drive flange and center gear until planet carrier bottoms on the two thrust washers.
3. Keep thrust washers from moving and set output shaft on bench with carrier end down.
4. Install planet carrier-to-output shaft snap ring.
5. Install planet carrier over output shaft with rear oil pump drive gear down, meshing pinions with center gear. Be sure assembly is bottomed against planet carrier snap ring.
6. Install snap ring in groove above planet carrier on output shaft.
7. Install clutch stationary cone on internal gear cone, using snap ring

pliers to spread stationary cone for installation.

8. Position bronze internal gear thrust washer over collar of internal gear, retaining with grease.
9. Install clutch release (wave) spring and spring retainer on internal gear side of reverse internal gear. Open ends of spring must be down against internal gear and midway between two of three locating holes. Depress retainer and twist clockwise to engage lugs.
10. Install clutch piston inner seal with lip down in seal groove of rear bearing retainer hub.
11. Position piston inner seal by inserting clutch piston into bore of bearing retainer. Then remove piston.
12. Install piston outer seal in groove of reverse piston with lip of seal toward flat side of piston.
13. Install reverse piston in rear bearing retainer. Because of interference between ledge inside rear bearing retainer and piston outer seal a suitable sleeve or Tool J-4752 must be used to install the piston. After in-

stallation, run a .010″ feeler around the piston to make sure the outer seal is properly positioned.

14. Insert six clutch piston release springs in their bores of piston.
15. Position release spring retainer on release springs and lay snap ring in position. Then compress springs with tool shown in Fig. 30.
16. Remove compressor tool and install internal gear and stationary cone in rear bearing retainer as follows: While compressing clutch stationary cone with the hands as shown in Fig. 29, install gear and cone in bearing retainer. Position keyway of cone so it will line up with keyway in transmission case, Fig. 33.
17. Install output shaft to rear bearing retainer, meshing teeth of planet carrier with teeth of internal gear.
18. Install output shaft bearing and snap rings in rear bearing retainer.
19. Install speedometer driven gear.
20. Stick a new gasket on rear bearing retainer with grease.
21. Place key in keyway of stationary cone, retaining with grease.

Repairs Requiring Transmission Removal

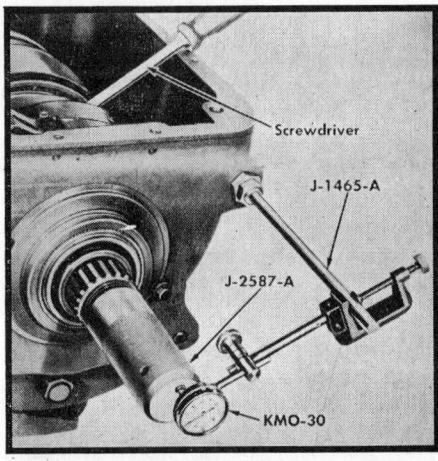

Fig. 35   Checking mainshaft end play

Fig. 36   Removing front pump locating washer

TRANSMISSION, DISASSEMBLE

1. Strip the fluid coupling parts from the mainshaft. Remove the torus cover by working neck of cover gently over oil seal; then pull cover out with a quick jerk.
2. With torus members removed, remove driven torus snap ring from mainshaft, Fig. 34.
3. Remove control valve, parking brake bracket, front and rear servos, rear oil pump, governor, and pressure regulator as outlined previously.
4. At this time the mainshaft end play should be checked to determine the correct size selective thickness thrust washer to be used when reassembling the transmission. Mount a dial indicator as shown in Fig. 35 and move the mainshaft back and forth while holding the mainshaft end play guide with a screwdriver as shown. Correct end play should be .004″ to .015″. Do not force mainshaft as this will produce an inaccurate reading. *If end play is not within specified limits, record the amount of end play so the proper thickness washer can be installed when the transmission is reassembled.*
5. Remove intermediate shaft snap ring and steel and bronze thrust washers from planet carrier shaft.
6. Remove front pump locating washer, Fig. 36.
7. Unfasten and remove front pump, Fig. 37.
8. Remove front drive gear rear thrust washer (bronze) from front planet carrier shaft.

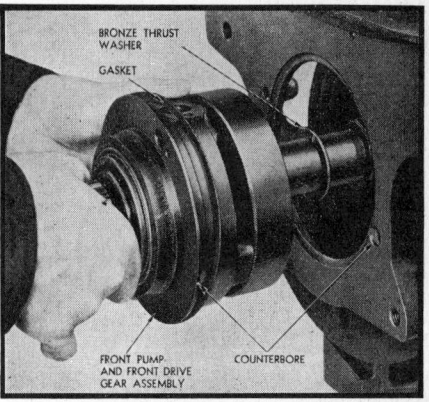

Fig. 37   Removing front pump and drive gear

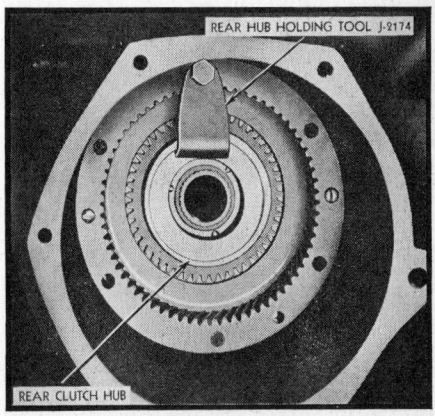

Fig. 38   Rear hub retainer tool bolted in position

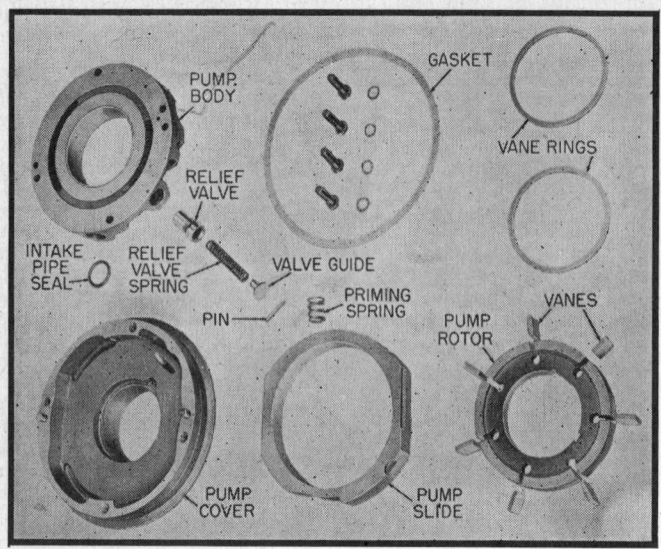

Fig. 42 Layout of front pump parts

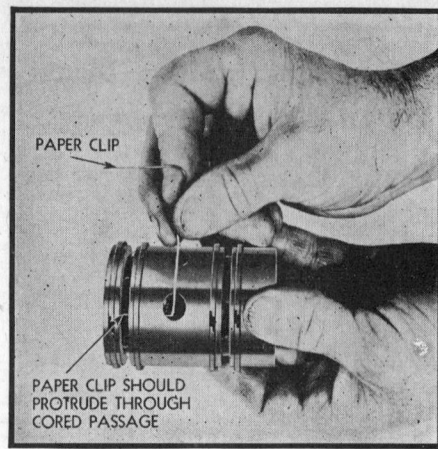

Fig. 43 Checking passages in oil delivery sleeve

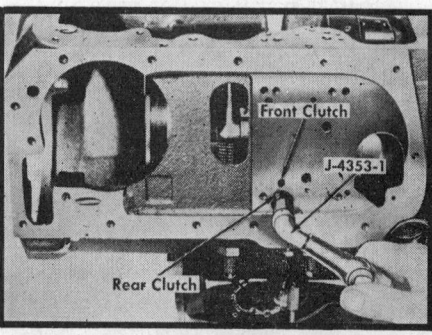

Fig. 44 Clutch oil passage identification

9. Remove reverse unit as outlined previously.
10. Install rear hub retainer tool, Fig. 38, on rear unit drum.
11. Remove two center bearing cap bolts and lock plate. Then lift the front and rear planetary units from the case.
12. Remove rear clutch hub rear snap ring.
13. Lift rear unit from shaft.
14. Remove center bearing cap from oil delivery sleeve.
15. Remove rear clutch hub washer and snap ring.
16. Slide oil delivery sleeve off shaft.
17. While holding snap ring pliers in one hand and using the other hand to guide snap ring, remove ring from shaft, Fig. 39.

FRONT PUMP

Disassembly, Fig. 42

1. Remove pump from drive gear.
2. Separate cover from body.
3. Lift body from cover.

Fig. 39 Removing front unit rear snap ring

4. Press valve guide with blunt screwdriver and slip retaining pin from body.
5. Remove pump relief valve and related parts.
6. Remove intake pipe oil seal.
7. Mark outer face of rotor with pencil or prussian blue so it will be installed in same relative position.
8. Remove remaining parts from body and cover.
9. With a chisel, remove oil seal from cover and discard seal.

Inspection

1. Referring to Fig. 42, check pump slide bleed holes for dirt or restrictions. A piece of tag wire should be pushed through holes to make sure they are open.
2. Make sure slide is free in pump cover. Examine slide for nicks, scores or excessive wear.
3. Examine vanes for scores, burrs or nicks. Vanes will have a distinct polished wear pattern on side bearing against slide. Check vanes in slot of rotor for freeness.
4. Check pressure regulator valve in its bore for freeness.
5. Check freedom of pump relief valve in its bore. Check relief valve for nicks or burrs.
6. Check oil seal ring in groove of pump cover for freeness. Make sure ring is not broken. Check ring gap.
7. Inspect pump bushing for scores or flaking. Slight wear is permissible.
8. Check keyway in rotor for burrs or wear. Inspect all rotor contact surfaces for wear, burrs or nicks.
9. Make sure all passageways are free of restrictions.
10. Inspect pump body and cover for cracks or damage. Make sure the two dowel pins in cover are not loose. Check mating surfaces of body and cover for nicks or scores.
11. Examine body and cover slide contact surfaces for nicks or burrs.

Fig. 45 Removing clutch drum snap ring

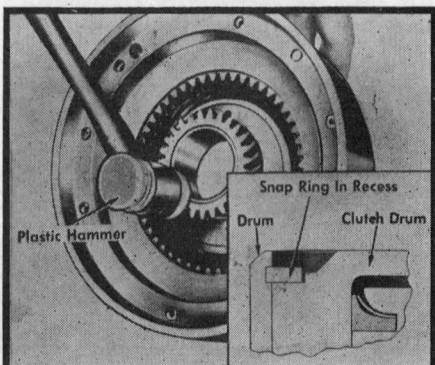

Fig. 46 Seating front clutch drum against snap ring

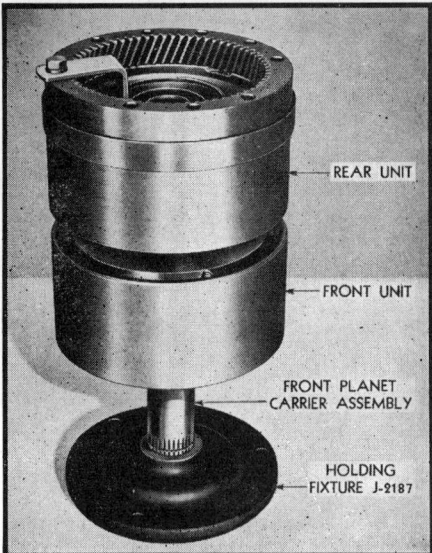

Fig. 45A Front and rear units in holding fixture

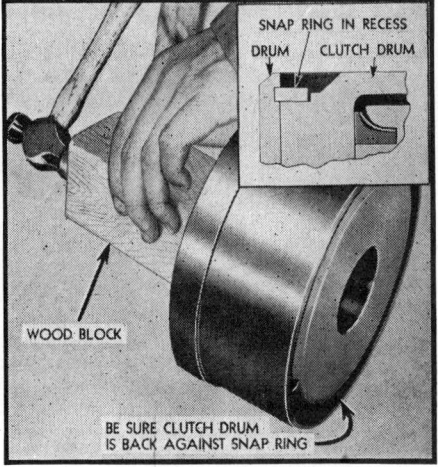

Fig. 47 Seating rear clutch drum against snap ring

Fig. 48 Assembling front planet carrier, front drum and plates by rotating parts as shown by arrows

12. Check all springs for weakness or distortion.
13. Inspect front drive gear for damaged teeth, worn bushings, or scored contact surfaces.
14. Inspect drive gear key and keyway in gear for wear or burrs.
15. Clean all parts and wipe dry.

Reassembly

1. Lubricate each moving part with transmission fluid before part is installed.
2. Install relief valve parts.
3. Insert new intake pipe oil seal in body.
4. Install priming springs and slide in cover.
5. Install one vane ring. Then install rotor in cover with previously marked face of rotor up.
6. Install seven pump vanes in slots of rotor. Be sure vanes fit between vane ring and slide. *Inspect vanes for wear pattern. One edge of vane will be polished for its entire length; this edge should face slide. The opposite edge will be polished only where it contacts vane rings.*
7. Center rotor in slide and install second vane ring.
8. Check with feeler gauge between vane and slide. With vanes contacting slide on one side, clearance should not exceed .003″ on opposite side. If clearance is excessive, replace pump.
9. Assemble body to cover and tighten attaching bolts to 12-15 lb. ft. torque.
10. Move rotor by hand to make sure rotor, vanes and slide move freely. After compressing priming spring, make sure it will return slide after spring is released.
11. Install new oil seal ring in groove of cover. Then install new front cover oil seal (step side up) in cover. Lubricate rubber and felt portions of oil seal before installing.
12. Apply sealing compound (Permatex No. 3) around edge of oil seal and cover.
13. Assemble pump on drive gear, being sure they assemble freely.

OIL DELIVERY SLEEVE

1. Examine oil delivery sleeve for scored bearing surface.
2. Inspect oil seal ring grooves to see that they are clean and not damaged. Check for freedom of rings in sleeve grooves.
3. Insert paper clip, Fig. 43, through both oil holes to see that passages are open. End of paper clip must protrude through passage as illustrated.
4. Test oil delivery sleeve for leaks as follows: Position sleeve in case with dowel hole toward case. Install center bearing cap with dowel in one of the two oil holes. Install and tighten center bearing cap bolts. Make sure sleeve is tight and cannot be rocked. *If sleeve can be rocked, a new sleeve must be installed. If the new sleeve can be rocked, transmission case must be*

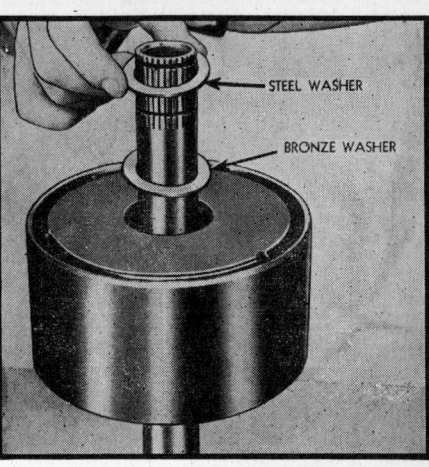

Fig. 49 Installing thrust washers on intermediate shaft

replaced since center bearing cap is sold only with matched transmission case.
5. Apply transmission fluid on each side of center bearing cap. Using a blow gun (J-4353-1) connected to a source of air pressure, apply pressure to each of clutch holes, Fig. 44, in side of transmission case.
6. If leakage is indicated, attempt correction by installing new oil delivery sleeve. If the new sleeve leaks, dress the center bearing cap down with fine emery cloth on a surface plate. Repeat test and if sleeve still leaks, replace transmission case.
7. Remove sleeve from case.

BAND INSPECTION

1. Do not pry either band open or distort in any way. Bands are surface ground at the factory for drum fit.
2. Inspect both bands for burned or worn linings or loose rivets. If face of linings are worn down to bottom of grooves, replace band and lining assemblies.
3. Inspect steel bands for cracks or distortion.
4. Check strut on rear band for alignment and free pivoting.
5. Inspect anchor ends of front band for broken welds or worn sockets.
6. Inspect rear band release spring for weakness, distortion or collapsed coils.

FRONT PLANETARY UNIT

Disassembly

1. Remove clutch drum snap ring, Fig. 45.
2. Remove clutch drum with piston from front unit drum by tapping sun gear.
3. Remove inner and outer clutch release springs from front unit drum.
4. Remove clutch plates as a unit.
5. Hold clutch drum in hand and tap sun gear around its face to remove clutch piston.
6. With blunt screwdriver, remove

Fig. 50 Installation of oil delivery sleeve

large clutch piston seal and expander from piston and small seal with expander from clutch drum. Discard seals and expanders.

Inspection

1. Inspect clutch drive pins for scoring, looseness or distortion. Replace drum assembly if any of these conditions are found. Pins are not furnished separately.
2. Inspect drum for deep grooves, scores or cracks at band or clutch plate surfaces.
3. Inspect clutch springs for weakness, collapsed coils or distortion. *Slight wear (bright) spots on side of outer springs, indicating slight contact with drum is permissible.*
4. Removing one clutch plate at a time, inspect steel plates for scored surfaces. Inspect composition plates for roughness or damage. If flakes of facing can be removed by scratching by thumb nail, plate must be replaced. Discoloration, however, is not an indication of failure.
5. Inspect clutch piston for scores, cracks or distortion. Make sure oil seal groove is clean.
6. Examine front clutch drum for scores in piston bore and oil delivery sleeve bore. Be sure oil seal groove is clean. Inspect gear teeth and thrust faces. Inspect clutch drum bushings for wear.
7. Inspect planet carrier pinion gears for damaged teeth and excessive roller bearing wear. Inspect bearing surface of planet carrier (intermediate) shaft, which contacts torus check valve, for roughness or nicks. Smooth off with a stone if this condition exists.
8. Check thrust washers for wear or scores.
9. Clean all parts and wipe dry.

Reassembly

1. Position planet carrier in fixture Fig. 45A, with clutch hub up.
2. Apply transmission fluid to both sides of clutch plates. Starting with a composition plate, install composition and steel plates alternately. Install steel plates with square notches over clutch drive pins.
3. Position front unit drum with drive pins up over hub of carrier and resting on pinion gears.
4. Install six outer clutch release springs through plates into spring holes of drum. Install six inner springs in outer springs.
5. Position new inner rubber seal on clutch drum above seal groove. Install new brass expander into seal groove with expanding lips down.
6. While holding brass expander in position with fingers, work new inner piston rubber seal into groove with lip down over brass expander. *Work expander well back under seal so brass edges are not exposed.*
7. Install clutch piston in drum to insure proper positioning of inner seal and expander. Then remove piston from drum.
8. Apply a small amount of transmission fluid to new large rubber piston seal.
9. Insert new large brass expander in groove in piston, with expanding lips toward flat surface of piston. Hold expander in place with thumb over ends of expander.
10. While holding piston and expander, insert new large rubber seal in piston groove with lip toward flat side of piston. Start seal into groove a short distance from point where thumb is holding expander ends. Work seal into groove toward thumb until seal is over expander ends. Then gradually work remainder of seal into groove.
11. Install piston in clutch drum. Apply hand pressure to face of piston and start seal into drum, using a smooth screwdriver in a wiping action. Rotate piston until it bottoms in drum and square notches in piston are aligned with holes in drum.
12. With sun gear down, install clutch drum and piston over planet carrier and into front drum, engaging release springs in pockets of clutch piston.
13. Lift unit from carrier and position in arbor press, and apply only enough pressure to install snap ring. Position snap ring gap halfway between two of the drive pins.
14. Remove unit from press and tap sun

Fig. 51 Installing front and rear units

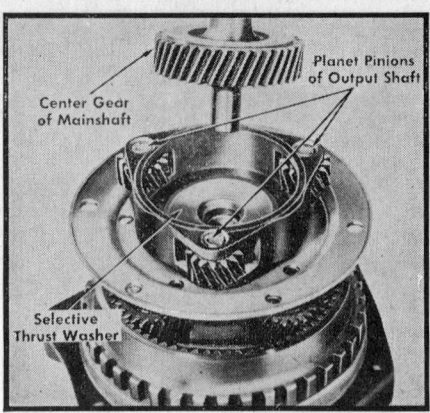

Fig. 52 Installing mainshaft in output shaft

gear to seat drum against snap ring, Fig. 46.

REAR PLANETARY UNIT

1. Remove clutch hub retainer bracket (Tool J-2174) from rear unit drum.
2. Remove clutch hub and thrust washer.
3. With rear unit in press as for front unit, remove snap ring.
4. Separate clutch drum from rear unit drum by tapping lightly on clutch drum rear thrust face.
5. Remove clutch release springs and guide pins from rear unit drum.
6. Remove clutch plates as a unit.
7. Hold clutch drum in hand and tap against inner hub of drum to remove clutch piston.

Inspection & Reassembly

Inspect this assembly in the same manner outlined for the front unit. Reassemble the unit in the reverse order of disassembly, following the same procedure for installing clutch piston seals as outlined for the front unit clutch.

Seat the rear clutch drum against the snap ring as illustrated in Fig. 47. After the clutch hub and thrust washer is installed into the clutch drive plates, rotate the hub and drum in opposite directions to mesh splines of hub with teeth of plates. When properly installed, clutch hub should be flush or slightly below counterbore in drum.

Install rear clutch hub retainer bracket (tool J-2174) on rear unit to hold clutch hub in place (see Fig. 38).

TRANSMISSION CASE INSPECTION

After cleaning transmission case, inspect for cracks, stripped threads, nicks and burrs. Poke a piece of ⅛" welding rod through all passages to remove any restrictions. Apply air pressure to all passages.

If band adjusting screw threads are stripped, transmission case must be replaced. Never tap oversize threads and insert oversize adjusting screws as it will be impossible to make proper external band adjustments.

TRANSMISSION, ASSEMBLE

1. Mount transmission case upside down in holding fixture.
2. Install front and rear band adjusting screws and lock nuts.
3. Install pressure take-off pipe plug in hole located between band adjusting screws. Tighten plug to 15-18 lb. ft. torque.

Assemble Planetary Units to Front Planet Carrier

1. Insert front carrier into front unit drum and clutch drive plates. Rotate carrier while working into position in front drum, Fig. 48.
2. Position carrier in holding fixture.
3. Install thrust washers as shown in Fig. 49. Locating lug of steel thrust washer must fit over flat of intermediate shaft.
4. Position new locating snap ring on bench with tapered points up. With snap ring pliers held vertically, engage points of ring. While guiding ring with one hand, slide ring downward over intermediate shaft and into groove of shaft above steel thrust washer.
5. Position oil delivery sleeve on intermediate shaft of front planet carrier. Oil rings nearest end of sleeve must be down into front planetary unit.
6. Compress lower set of oil rings with compressor tool, Fig. 50. Tap sleeve until it bottoms in bore of front unit drum.
7. Install rear clutch hub snap ring in groove of planet carrier intermediate shaft. Then install snap ring spacer.
8. With compressor tool, compress exposed oil delivery sleeve rings. Latch handles of compressor securely.
9. Place rear planetary unit over intermediate shaft until it bottoms on compressor tool. Keeping rings compressed with tool, release handle latch and, while slightly releasing pressure on tool, push rear unit downward on oil delivery sleeve.
10. Remove compressor tool and install rear clutch hub rear snap ring.
11. Make sure both drums rotate with slight force. If either drum binds, disassemble the unit to correct cause of trouble.

Fig. 53 Checking governor tower runout

Install Front & Rear Planetary Units

1. Position center bearing cap on oil delivery sleeve with dowel registered in dowel hole. *Cast taper on bearing cap should be toward front unit.*
2. Position front band over drum so short anchor end will fit over band adjusting screw when units are placed in case. Install suitable wire or spring to hold band on drum.
3. Guide planetary units in case as shown in Fig. 51.
4. Remove spring or wire from band and position anchor end of front band on adjusting screw.
5. Install rear band on drum so anchor end of band rests on adjusting screw.
6. Install new center bearing cap lock plate and attaching bolts, tightening bolts only finger tight.
7. Apply air pressure through each of the clutch passage holes in case. Listen for sound of clutch application.
8. Install large screwdriver between center bearing cap and rear clutch drum to prevent rear drum from moving forward.
9. Remove clutch hub retainer bracket (J-2174) from rear unit drum.
10. Coat rear clutch hub rear thrust washer with grease and stick it in the counterbore of rear clutch hub.

Install Reverse Unit & Mainshaft

1. If shaft did not have correct end play prior to disassembly, select proper size selective washer to obtain .004″ to .015″ end play. Eight sizes of thrust washers are available for this purpose.
2. Stick the correct size thrust washer in counterbore of output shaft with grease.
3. Insert mainshaft into output shaft, meshing center gear of mainshaft with planet pinions of output shaft, Fig. 52.
4. Insert mainshaft, output shaft and reverse unit through rear of case, guiding mainshaft through intermediate shaft of front planet carrier. Align stationary cone lock key with keyway in case and rear bearing retainer bolt holes with holes in case. *Rear bearing retainer will not fit tightly against case at this point.*
5. Just start five rear bearing retainer attaching bolts and parking brake pawl support bolt and lock.
6. Rotate mainshaft to align holes in reverse drive flange and rear unit drum, then install six attaching bolts and washers. After two of the bolts are centered finger tight, remove the wedging screwdriver. While holding drum with tool J-1459, tighten bolts to 10-13 lb. ft. torque. *Do not torque parking brake pawl support bolt at this time.*
7. Test for freeness by turning mainshaft, output shaft and both drums.

Install Front Oil Pump

1. Position thrust washer over intermediate shaft against shoulder of front planet carrier.
2. Install new "O" ring seal over front

Fig. 54 Checking governor drive flange runout

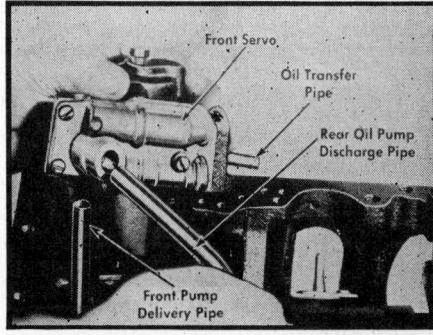

Fig. 55 Installing front servo

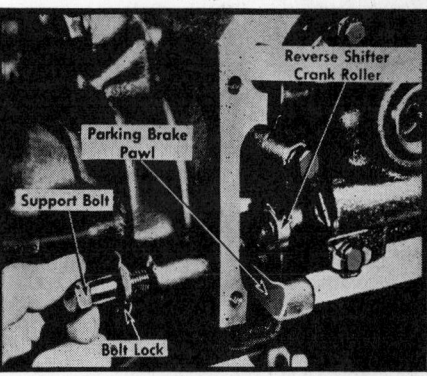

Fig. 56 Installing parking brake pawl support bolt and lock

Fig. 57 Installation of reverse oil pipe

pump body and against pump cover.

3. Position front oil pump and drive gear over intermediate shaft, aligning locating washer counterbore in pump cover with counterbore in transmission case.

4. Install washer in counterbore of pump cover and case.

5. Install pump cover attaching bolts and tighten to 10-13 lb. ft. torque.

6. Install bronze and then steel thrust washers over intermediate shaft and against front end of front drive gear.

7. Install snap ring in groove of intermediate shaft, immediately forward of the two thrust washers just installed.

8. Tighten center bearing cap bolts evenly to 40-50 lb. ft. torque. Using large pliers, bend lock plate edges up against flats at bolt heads.

Mainshaft End Play

Mainshaft end play should be checked at this time before proceeding with the assembly of the transmission. Check end play as previously described when transmission was disassembled.

Install driven torus snap ring in groove of mainshaft.

Install Rear Oil Pump & Governor

1. Position large round governor weight toward front of case and locate one of reverse drive flange attaching bolts up. This will provide clearance for pump and governor to be installed.

2. Install pump and governor, rotating governor to mesh driven gear with bronze drive gear. Attach pump to case and tighten bolts to 15-18 lb. ft. torque.

3. Install rear pump discharge pipe into passage of pump.

Checking Governor & Drive Flange Runout

1. Mount dial indicator as shown in Fig. 53 and check runout of governor tower. Rotate output shaft several revolutions and note reading. If runout exceeds .005", remove governor from drive flange and reinstall it 180° from original position and recheck runout.

2. If runout still exceeds .005", remove governor from drive flange and mount dial indicator as shown in Fig. 54.

3. Rotate output shaft several revolutions and if drive flange runout is less than .002", install a new governor. If runout exceeds .002", correct the condition by installing one or all of the following parts: Governor drive flange, gear set, or complete rear oil pump assembly.

Install Front & Rear Servos

1. Loosen but do not remove two front oil pump attaching bolts.

2. Insert front pump delivery pipe in front pump.

3. Position front servo with piston stem in slot on end of front band

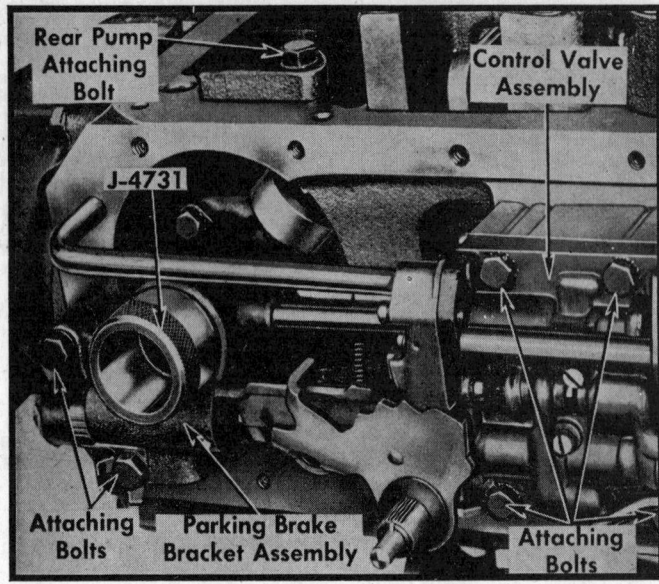

Fig. 58   Aligning governor

and front oil pump delivery pipe aligned with passage in servo body.

4. While holding front servo, align rear oil pump discharge pipe with passage in front servo valve body, Fig. 55.

5. Move front servo toward position on case while guiding front pump delivery pipe and rear pump discharge pipe into proper passages in front servo.

6. Just start (2 or 3 threads) two front servo attaching bolts and washers.

7. Rotate rear band until ends of band are exposed. Install rear band release spring in recess in end of band and over guide pin on rear band strut. Turn band until its end is against band adjusting screw.

8. Place rear servo in position, engaging rear band strut with actuating lever of servo and, while raising front servo slightly, enter oil transfer pipe from front servo into rear servo. Then push both servos into position on transmission case.

9. Enter two rear servo attaching bolts and washers. Then tighten front and rear servo attaching bolts to 23-28 lb. ft. torque.

10. Retighten the two previously loosened front oil pump attaching bolts to 10-13 lb. ft. torque.

Install Oil Pressure Regulator

Install pressure regulator in transmission case and tighten regulator valve plug to 40-50 lb. ft. torque.

Install Parking Brake & Control Valve

1. Remove parking brake pawl support bolt from rear bearing retainer.

2. Position brake pawl in case as far down as it will go.

3. Position gaps in oil rings on governor tower up to facilitate installation. Place chamfered side of brake bracket oil delivery sleeve over end of governor tower. Press bracket

gently into position, guiding oil rings on governor tower into oil delivery sleeve of brake bracket.

4. Install reverse shifter crank roller on brake pawl crank. Raise pawl to position and install pawl support bolt and bolt lock to transmission case, Fig. 56. Tighten bolt to 23-28 lb. ft. torque.

5. Bend one lip of lock against bolt and two lips against rear bearing retainer.

6. Install parking brake bracket attaching bolts, blocker piston stop pin retainer and lock washer. Do not tighten bolts. Leave brake bracket 1/8" away from transmission case. *Be sure to install blocker piston stop pin retainer on bottom bolt. This retainer keeps parking blocker stop pin in place, seals against oil pressure leaking through bolt hole and locks bracket-to-case bolt in place.*

7. Install reverse clutch oil pipe with "L" end in transmission case.

8. Install two oil delivery pipes in parking brake bracket.

9. Position pawl return spring over inside governor oil delivery pipe, then hook other end of spring over brake lever pin.

10. Install control valve and start four attaching bolts. Press control valve and brake bracket against case and tighten valve attaching bolts to 6-8 lb. ft. torque.

11. Insert short end of pressure regulator reverse oil pipe into bore of control valve and long end of pipe into case, Fig. 57.

12. Loosen two rear oil pump attaching bolts. Position governor aligning tool, Fig. 58.

13. Tighten rear oil pump bolts and brake bracket to 15-18 lb. ft. torque.

14. Rotate tool. Turn mainshaft to rotate governor, which should turn freely. Turn mainshaft to turn governor 1/4 turn. Recheck governor and tool for freeness. If governor or tool bind at any point, loosen park-

ing brake bracket and/or rear oil pump and reposition to give freedom to governor. Recheck governor each ¼ turn for a complete revolution.
15. Remove governor aligning tool.
16. Install governor oil delivery pipe.

17. Turn mainshaft to rotate governor one full turn. Make sure governor weights do not strike oil delivery pipe. Pipe should have correct bend to provide clearance for governor weights in their outward positions.

Final Assembly

Adjust bands as outlined elsewhere in this section. Then install side cover, oil pan and screen. Move transmission outer shift lever to neutral position. Install oil breather and indicator in case.

POWERFLITE

For Linkage Adjustment See Car Chapter

CONTENTS

Description 297
Trouble Shooting 21

Maintenance

Adding Oil 301
Changing Oil 301

"In Car" Repairs

Bands, Adjust 301
Oil Pressure Tests 301
Throttle Pressure Tests 302

Oil Pan 302
Valve Body and Transfer Plate,
   Remove and Install.............302
Valve Body Repairs.................315
Manual Control Valve Lever Shaft Oil Seal 303
Kickdown Piston 303
Reverse Servo 304
Transmission Ourput Shaft Rear Bearing
   Oil Seal 304
Regulator Valve and Converter Control
   Valve 304
Oil Cooler 304

Repairs Requiring Transmission Removal

Transmission, Disassemble 304
Transmission, Reassemble 310

DESCRIPTION

This transmission, Fig. 1, combines a torque converter and an automatic two-speed planetary gearbox. The driver need only select the desired driving range and depress the accelerator to start. If additional acceleration is desired while driving in direct drive, the transmission may

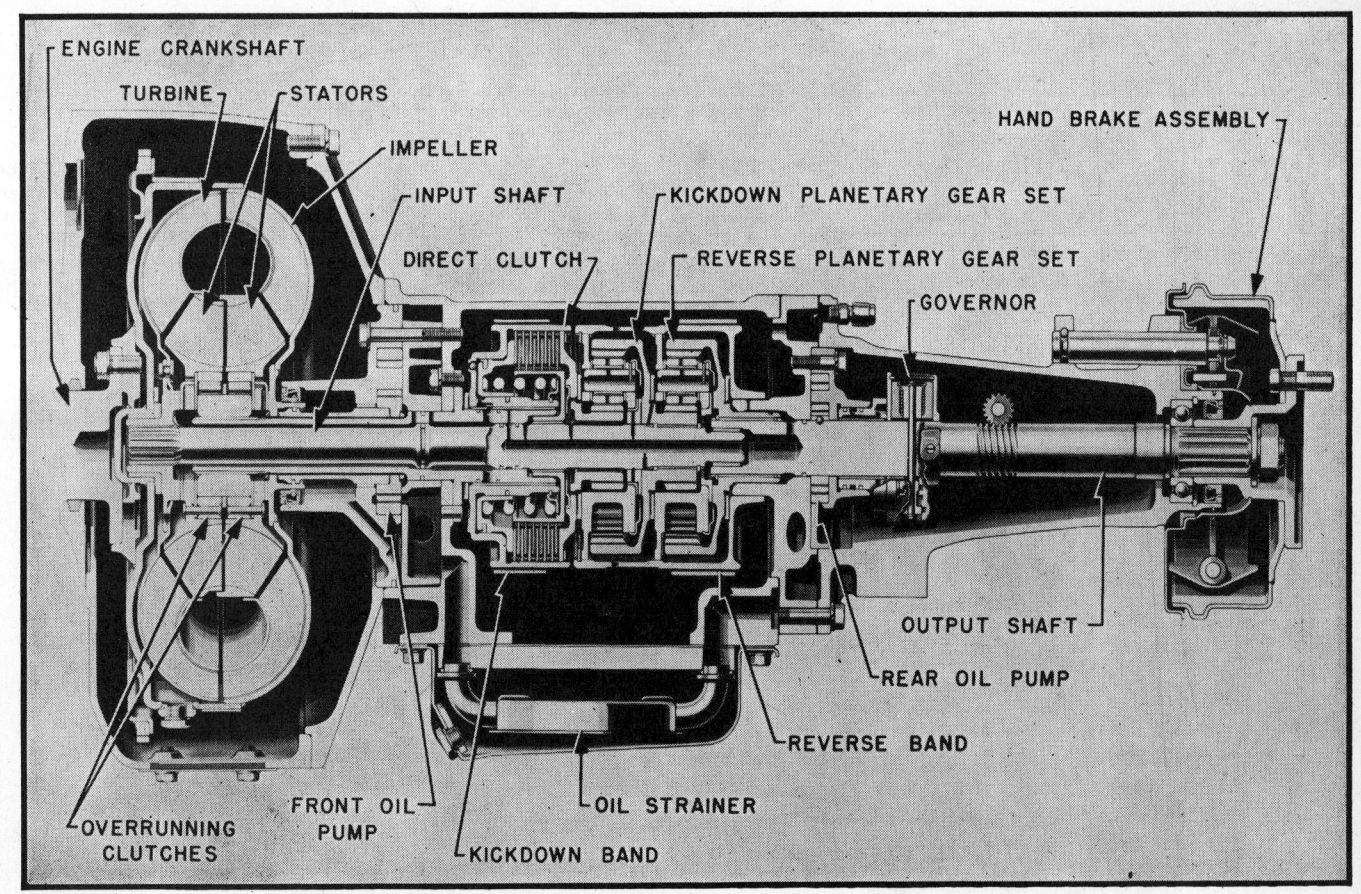

Fig. 1 PowerFlite transmission showing torque converter (left), direct clutch and planetary gear sets that provide two automatically selected forward speeds and reverse. Starting in late 1954 a single stator instead of the two stators shown is used. Likewise, a single overrunning clutch is used instead of two

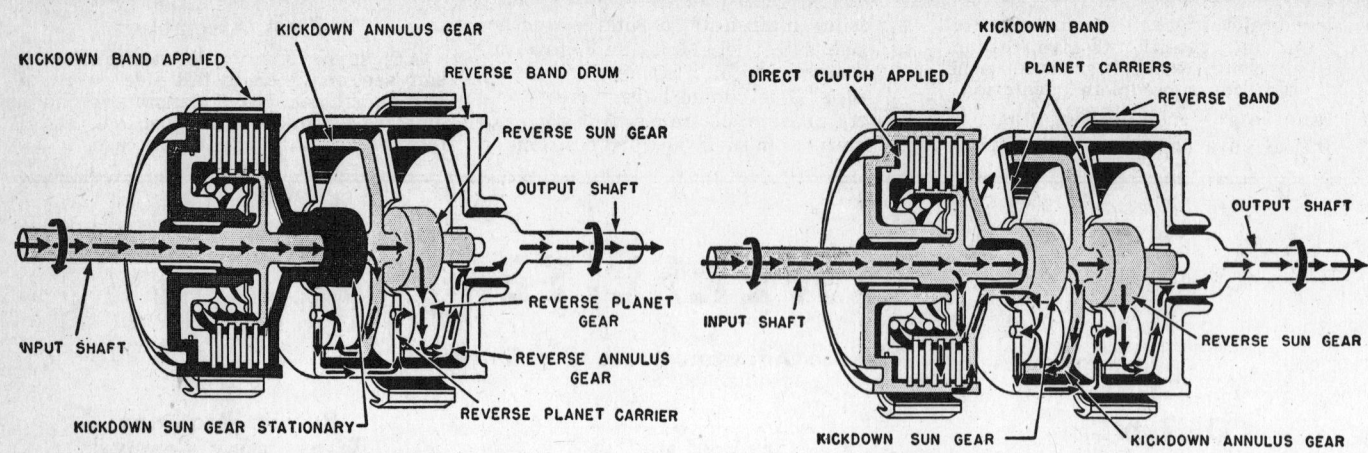

Fig. 2   Power flow in breakaway, kickdown or low

Fig. 3   Power flow in direct drive

be downshifted into low gear by merely pressing the accelerator pedal to the floor. This kickdown feature insures rapid acceleration when needed.

Gearbox

For low range operation, starting in drive or during kickdown operation, the kickdown band is applied and the direct clutch is disengaged, Fig. 2. For direct drive the kickdown band is automatically released and the direct clutch engaged,

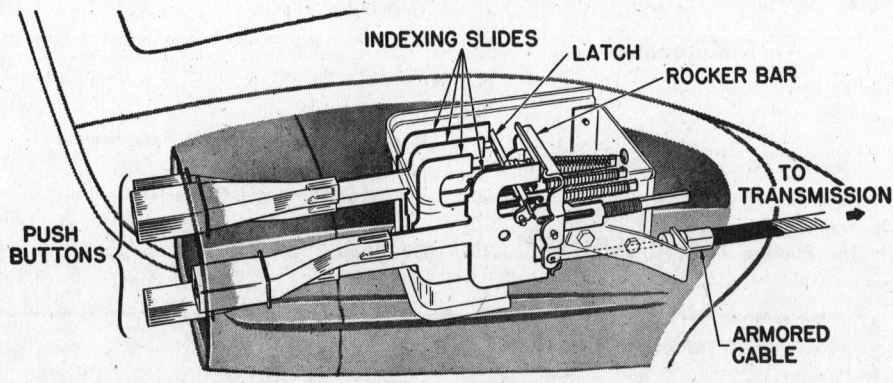

Fig. 7   Cutaway view of push button control unit.   1956-57

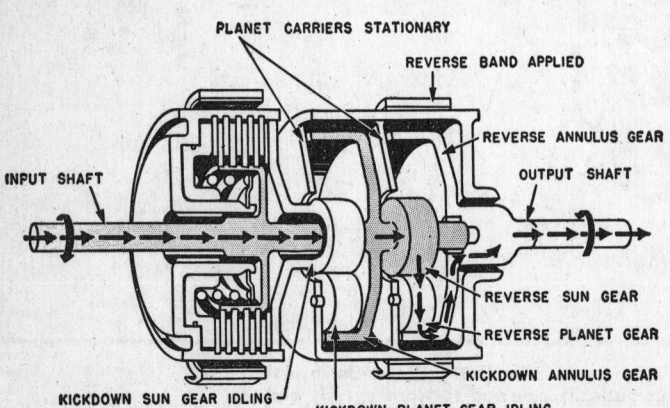

Fig. 6 Torque converter overrunning   c l u t c h

locking the kickdown ring gear and sun gears together, Fig. 3. Reverse is engaged by applying the reverse band, thereby locking the planet pinion carriers so they cannot move, Fig. 4. When in neutral, all friction elements in the transmission—front and rear bands and direct clutch—are released.

Both the front and rear bands and direct clutch are actuated by hydraulic means. The clutch is released by the action of the direct clutch spring when the oil pressure is removed. The front and rear bands are engaged and disengaged by the action of the kickdown and reverse servos, respectively. The kickdown servo applies the front band and the reverse servo applies the reverse band.

Fig. 4   Power flow in reverse

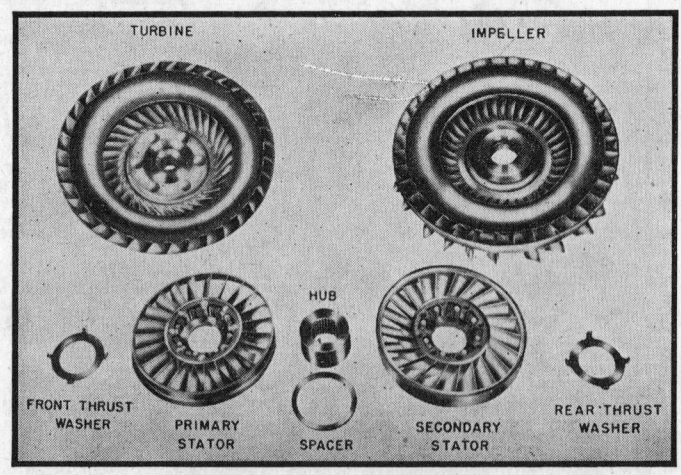

Fig. 5   Layout of 1953 and early 1954 torque converter parts. Starting in late 1954 a single stator and overrunning clutch is used. Since the two halves of the torque converter shell are welded together, helping preserve leak-proof performance, the unit is serviced as a complete assembly only

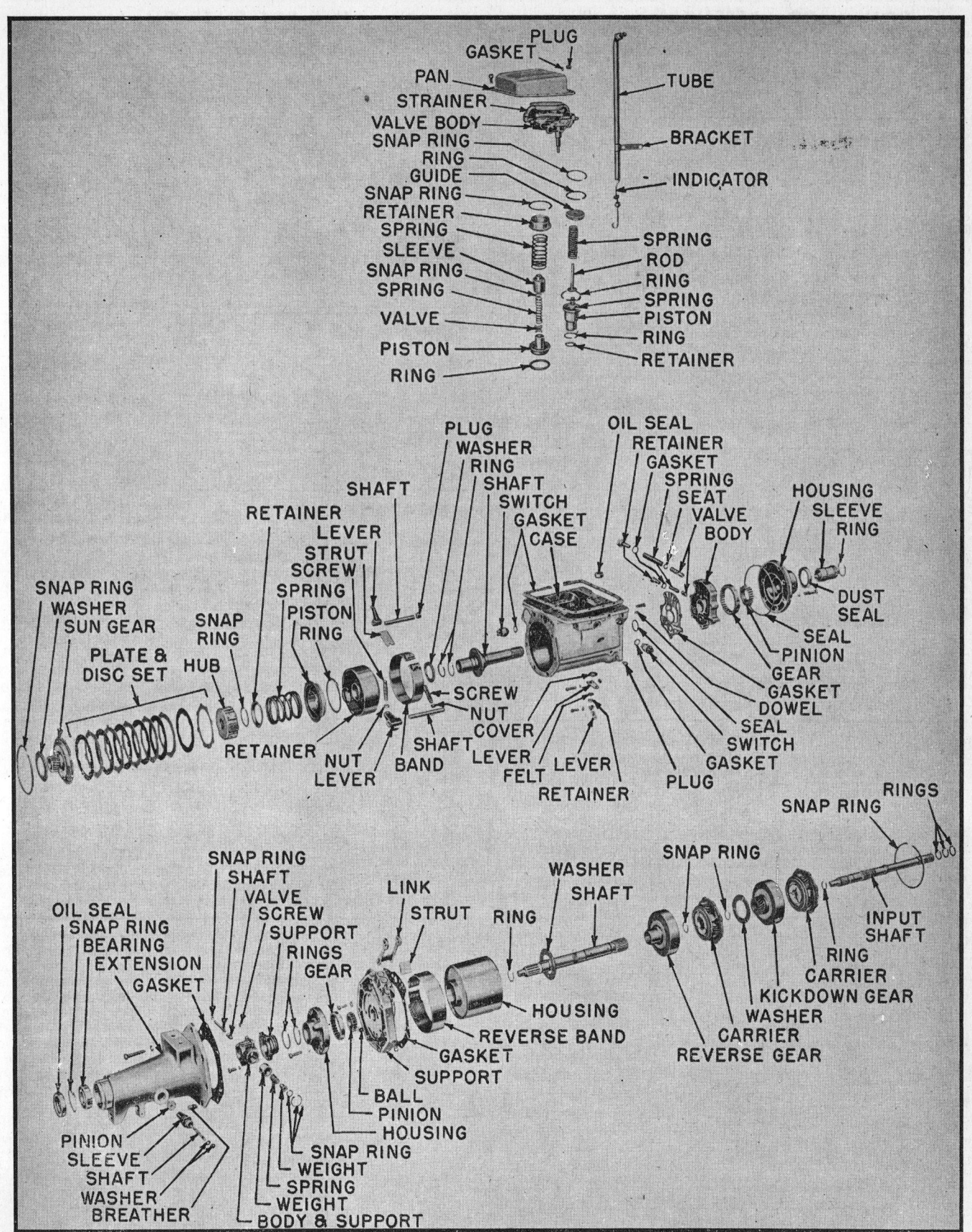

Fig. 8   Exploded view of Powerflite transmission

POWERFLITE

GOVERNOR PRESSURE CHART

Year	Selector Position	Rear Wheels	Car Speed	Governor Pressure
CHRYSLER & IMPERIAL				
1954	D	Free	14–17	15
	D	Free	24–27	45
	D	Free	58–65	60
1955, C67	D	Free	13–15	15
	D	Free	23–32	45
	D	Free	51–61	60
1955 Others	D	Free	14–16	15
	D	Free	25–34	45
	D	Free	55–65	60
1956, C71	D	Free	13–15	15
	D	Free	23–31	45
	D	Free	51–58	60
1956 Others	D	Free	14–16	15
	D	Free	25–33	45
	D	Free	56–64	60
DE SOTO				
1954–55	D	Free	14–17	15
	D	Free	24–27	45
	D	Free	58–65	60
1956, S23	D	Free	12–14	15
	D	Free	22–29	45
	D	Free	48–55	60
1956, S24	D	Free	13–15	15
	D	Free	23–31	45
	D	Free	51–58	60
1957	D	Free	13–16	15
	D	Free	23–26	45
	D	Free	55–62	60
DODGE				
1954–57	D	Free	13–16	15
	D	Free	23–26	45
	D	Free	55–62	60
1958–59	D	Free	12–14	15
	D	Free	21–29	45
	D	Free	48–55①	60
1960	D	Free	12–16②	15
	D	Free	23–34②	45
	D	Free	54–65②	60
1961	D	Free	12–16	15
	D	Free	23–34	45
	D	Free	54–65	60
PLYMOUTH				
1954–59	D	Free	12–14③	15
	D	Free	19–23④	45
	D	Free	41–48⑤	60
1960	D	Free	13–15	15
	D	Free	24–32	45
	D	Free	51–60	60
1961	D	Free	12–16	15
	D	Free	23–34	45
	D	Free	54–65	60

①—For 6-cylinder, 40–43 M.P.H.
②—For standard rear axle ratio.
③—For V8, 13–16 M.P.H.
④—For V8, 23–26 M.P.H.
⑤—For V8, 55–62 M.P.H.

LINE PRESSURE CHART

Year	Selector Position	Rear Wheels	Engine R.P.M.	Line Pressure
CHRYSLER, DE SOTO & IMPERIAL				
1954–56	R①	Free	1600	225–275
	N	....	800	85–95
	D①	Locked	800	85–95
	L①	Locked	800	85–95
1957	R①	Free	1400	225–275
	N	....	800	85–95
	D①	Locked	800	85–95
	L①	Locked	800	85–95
DODGE				
1954–59	R①	Free	1400	225–275
	N	....	800	85–95
	D①	Locked	800	85–95
	L①	Locked	800	85–95
1960–61	R①	Free	1400	225–275
	N	....	800	85–95
	D①	Locked	800	85–95
PLYMOUTH				
1954–59	R①	Free	1600	225–275
	N	....	800	85–95
	D①	Locked	800	85–95
	L①	Locked	800	85–95
1960–61	R①	Free	1400	225–275
	N	....	800	85–95
	D①	Locked	800	85–95

①—Engine must be at operating temperature.

Torque Converter

The torque converter used in 1953 and early 1954, Fig. 5, consists of four basic elements: and impeller, a turbine and two stators. Starting in late 1954, a single stator is used. The assembly is rigidly attached and supported by the crankshaft flange. *Since the two halves of the torque converter are welded together the unit is furnished for service only as a complete assembly.*

Each stator is mounted on an over-running clutch which consists of eight spring-loaded rollers mounted within an internal cam and around a hub, Fig. 6. The hub is held stationary by the stator reaction shaft which is bolted to the transmission case. As a result each over-running clutch prevents its stator from moving in a direction opposite to the turbine and impeller rotation but allows the stator to rotate freely with the turbine and impeller.

Push Button Control

The Powerflite push button control, Fig. 7, consists of a single cable running between the push buttons and the transmission. As buttons are depressed, the cable moves a pre-determined distance to actuate the manual control valve lever in the transmission.

THROTTLE PRESSURE CHART

Year	Selector Position	Rear Wheels	Throttle Position	Engine R.P.M.	Throttle Pressure
CHRYSLER & IMPERIAL					
1954-55	D	Locked	Closed①	Idle	13-15
	D	Locked	Wide Open	1300-1500	80-90
1956	D	Locked	Closed①	Idle	13-15
	D	Locked	Wide Open	1580-1685	80-90
DE SOTO					
1954-55	D	Locked	Closed①	Idle	13-15
	D	Locked	Wide Open	1300-1500	80-90
1956-57	D	Locked	Closed①	Idle	13-15
	D	Locked	Wide Open	1400-1500	80-90
DODGE					
1954-57	D	Locked	Closed①	Idle	13-15
	D	Locked	Wide Open	1400-1500	80-90
1958-59	D	Locked	Closed①	Idle	15-17
	D	Locked	Wide Open	1400-1500	80-90
1960-61	D	Locked	Closed①	Idle	13-15
	D	Locked	Wide Open	1400-1500	80-90
PLYMOUTH					
1954-59	D	Locked	Closed①	450	14
	D	Locked	Wide Open	1500	90
1960-61	D	Locked	Closed①	450	13-15
	D	Locked	Wide Open	1400-1500	80-90

①—Do not hold throttle wide open for more than a few seconds.

POWERFLITE BAND ADJUSTMENTS

Year	Model	Adjusting Screw Back-Off Number of Turns	
		Kickdown	Reverse
CHRYSLER & IMPERIAL			
1954-55	All	3	10
1956	All	2¾	10
DE SOTO			
1954-55	All	3	10
1956-57	All	2¾	10
1958-60	All	2¾	12
DODGE			
1954-56	All	3	10
1957	All	2¾	10
1958-61	All	2¾	12
PLYMOUTH			
1954-58	All	3	10
1959-61	All	2¾	12

When the operator pushes another button to select a different range, the following events take place: During initial movement of the operating slide, the edge of the detent on the slide strikes the lock pawl, thereby releasing the first button from the restraint of the lock pawl. The first button is now free to return (under spring pressure) to its original position.

MAINTENANCE

Adding Oil

The oil level should be checked at regular lubrication periods. If checked with the engine cold the oil should be up to the "L" (low) mark on the dipstick. After the engine reaches normal operating temperature, oil expansion in the torque converter will raise the level to the "F" (full) mark.

Add oil to bring the level to the full mark only after normal operating temperature has been reached, usually after 10 miles of driving.

Changing Oil

Drain and refill the transmission every 20,000 miles as follows:

1. Remove transmission oil pan drain plug (to 1956) or filler tube (from 1957).
2. Remove the plate from the bottom of the torque converter housing and rotate the torque converter until the converter drain plug is accessible.
3. After draining, install filler tube and drain plug(s), and torque converter plate.
4. Pour 5 quarts of transmission fluid through oil pan filler tube.
5. With engine idling in neutral, add enough fluid to bring fluid level to "L" mark on indicator (approximately three quarts).
6. Shift transmission through all ranges and recheck.

"In Car" Repairs

BANDS, ADJUST

Kickdown (Front) Band

Working from beneath the car, use a box wrench to loosen locknut and back off at least four turns. Using an inch-pound torque wrench, Fig. 9, adjust screw and tighten to 72 inch pounds. With chalk, mark a reference point on the adjusting screw and transmission case, then back off adjusting screw exactly 2¾ turns (3 turns on 1958 and earlier). Hold screw stationary and tighten locknut.

Reverse (Rear) Band

Drain transmission and remove oil pan. Remove band adjusting screw locknut and, with an inch-pound torque wrench, tighten adjusting screw to 25 inch pounds, Fig. 10. Mark a reference point on adjusting screw and case and back off adjusting screw 12 turns (10 turns on 1958 and earlier). Hold adjusting screw, replace locknut and tighten to 30-35 foot pounds. Replace oil pan and refill tranmission.

OIL PRESSURE TESTS

When checking pressures the engine must be at operating temperature. Refer to Figs. 11 to 14 for location of pressure take-off points.

Line Pressure

Remove ⅛" pipe plug from the line

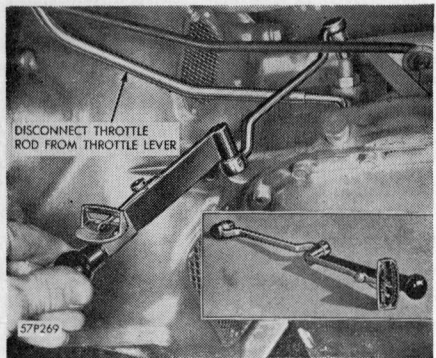

Fig. 9 Adjusting kickdown (front) band

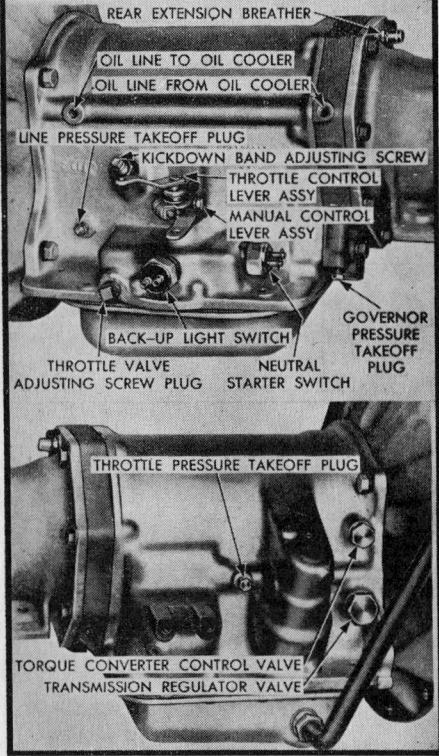

Fig. 11 Exterior views of transmission, 1953-54

pressure take-off hole. Install a 300-lb. pressure gauge at this point. With tachometer attached to engine the pressures given in the chart should be obtained.

THROTTLE PRESSURE

To prevent overheating of transmission and torque converter, do not hold throttle wide open for more than a few seconds when making throttle pressure check.

Install pressure gauge in throttle pressure take-off hole. With tachometer attached to engine, the pressures given in the chart should be obtained.

Direct Clutch Pressure

Before checking direct clutch pressure, check line pressure since any deviation in line pressure directly affects clutch pressure. Then remove direct clutch pressure take-off plug and connect pressure gauge in the hole.

With rear wheels free to turn, accelerate engine slowly until upshift occurs. During the upshift, the pressure should rise rapidly from 0 to 90 psi in 1½ to 2 seconds.

With an engine speed of not less than 650 rpm and transmission upshifted, the direct clutch pressure should read within 10 psi of line pressure.

Governor Pressure

With selector lever in "D" position and rear wheels free to turn and pressure gauge connected to governor pressure take-off hole the pressures given in the chart should be obtained.

OIL PAN

To remove the pan, drain transmission, reinstall drain plug and tighten. Remove filler tube. Unfasten pan from transmission and remove with gasket.

Using a new gasket, install pan on transmission and torque tighten attaching screws 12-17 lbs. ft. Install filler tube and tighten nut 35-40 lbs. ft. torque.

VALVE BODY & TRANSFER PLATE

Removal—After removing the oil pan:
1. Disconnect throttle and manual con-

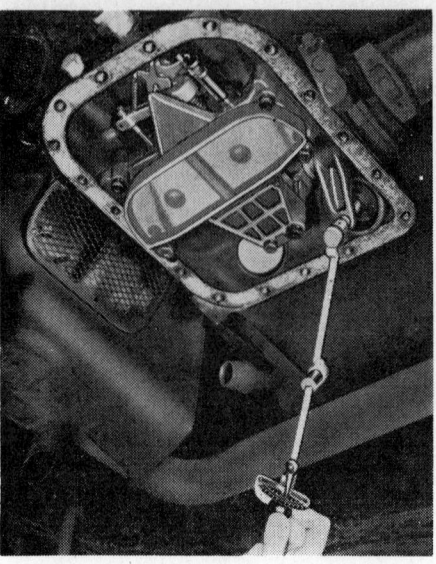

Fig. 10 Adjusting reverse band

trol lever linkage from levers.
2. Loosen throttle and manual control lever locking screws.
3. Slide throttle valve operating lever off shaft and remove throttle valve camshaft felt retainer and felt.
4. Slide manual valve lever off shaft and remove shaft seal cover.
5. Remove oil strainer from valve body and transfer plate.
6. Remove five transfer plate screws and lockwashers and take off the valve body and transfer plate assembly, Fig. 15.

Installation—After servicing the unit as described in the major repair section of this chapter, clean the mating surfaces and check for burrs on both the transmission case and valve body transfer plate. Place the assembly into position and install the transfer plate screws and lockwashers. *Two screws are 1⅝" long; these go through the transfer plate cover on the valve body.* Draw screws down evenly and torque tighten them to 12-17 lbs. ft.

Complete the installation in the reverse order of removal. Adjust throttle and gearshift linkage as previously described.

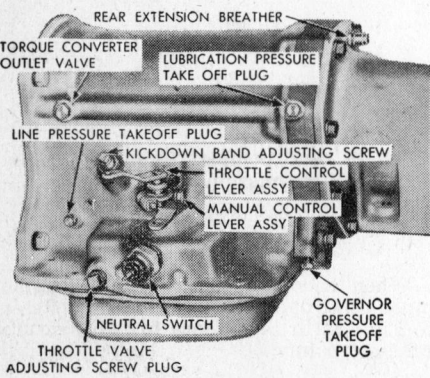

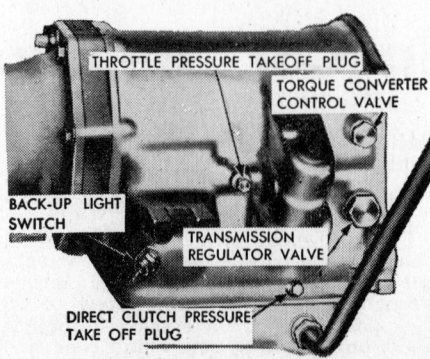

Fig. 12 Left side of transmission. 1955-60

Fig. 13 Right side of transmission. 1955

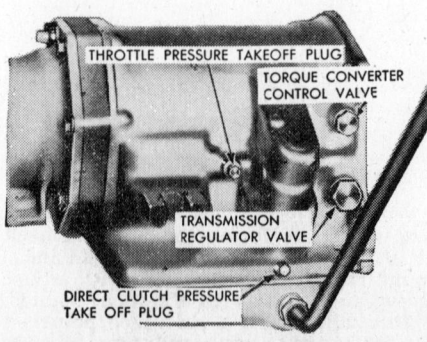

Fig. 14 Right side of transmission. 1956-60

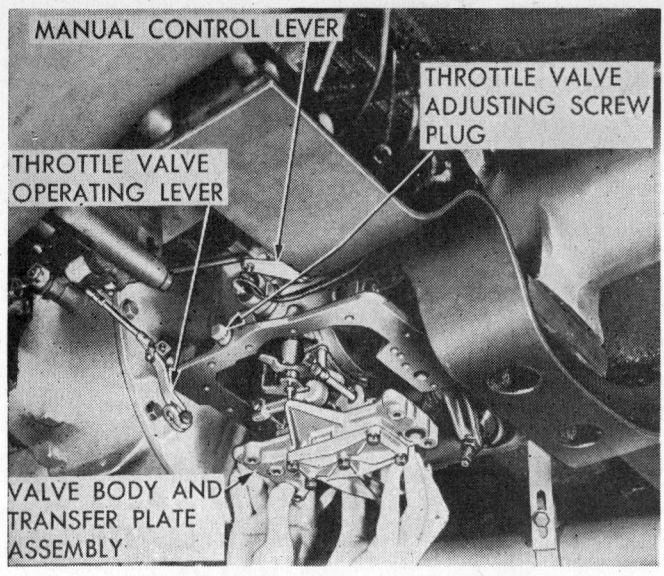

Fig. 15 Removing and installing valve body and transfer plate assembly

Fig. 16 Installing manual control valve lever shaft oil seal

MANUAL CONTROL VALVE LEVER SHAFT OIL SEAL

To remove the seal, take off the oil pan and valve body and transfer plate. Then, using a suitable brass drift, drive the seal out of the case from below.

To install, use the tool shown in Fig. 16 and start the oil seal squarely. Tighten until the tool is flush with the case, which positions the seal correctly.

KICKDOWN PISTON

Removal—After removing oil pan, valve body and transfer plate:

1. Loosen kickdown band adjusting screw lock nut and back out adjusting screw enough to permit kickdown band strut to be removed by compressing both ends.

2. With kickdown band lever hanging down, install tool shown in Fig. 17 on the case. Apply sufficient pressure on the kickdown rod guide to permit easy removal of the snap ring.

3. Loosen the compressing portion of the tool and remove the piston rod guide, piston spring and kickdown piston rod. The kickdown piston cushion spring will fall out of the piston when the piston rod is removed.

4. Using snap ring pliers inside of kickdown piston, remove piston from case. For disassembly and in-

spection, refer to the major repair section of this chapter.

Installation—

1. Make sure the two interlocking seals are locked in position and all seals are coated with Lubriplate. Then place kickdown piston in transmission case. With one hand, apply slight pressure to piston and at the same time *carefully compress bottom seal* and push piston into case. *After bottom seal has entered, piston will seem to hang at two different locations while being pushed into case. This is due to seals entering cylinder. Do not use extreme force. If any of the rings should be broken when piston assembly is being installed, transmission will not operate properly.*

Fig. 17 Removing and installing kickdown piston rod guide snap ring

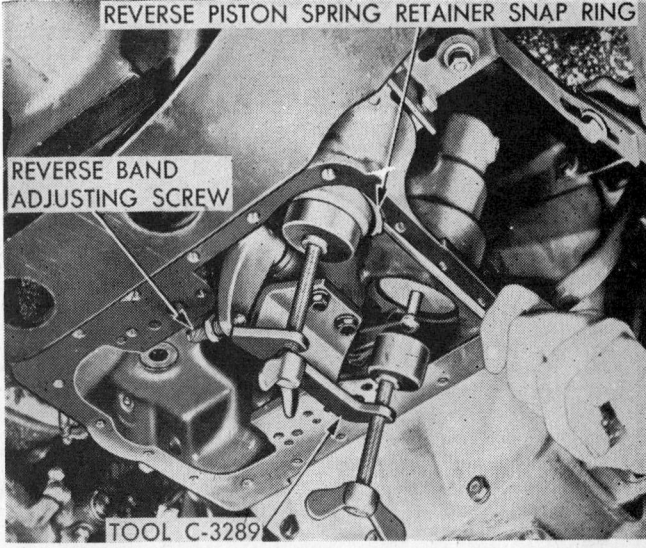

Fig. 18 Removing and installing reverse piston spring retainer snap ring

2. Slide piston spring over piston rod and balance the piston cushion spring on rod and install in piston.
3. Holding it in this position, install piston rod guide and piston rod.
4. Using the tool shown in Fig. 17, compress the piston spring to the point that piston guide seal slightly binds on transmission case. Work seal into position and gradually compress spring until seal enters case and snap ring can be installed.
5. Install piston rod guide snap ring, making sure it is properly seated.
6. Loosen compressing portion of tool and remove tool from transmission.
7. With one end of band fitted over adjusting screw, compress other end enough to install band strut between band and lever. *Make sure band strut slot engages with strut pin in band end.*
8. Install valve body, transfer plate and oil pan. Then adjust kickdown band as described previously.

REVERSE SERVO

Removal—After removing oil pan, valve body and transfer plate:

1. Loosen servo adjusting screw lock nut and back out adjusting screw far enough to permit band strut to be removed by compressing band ends.
2. Remove servo piston sleeve.
3. Mount the tool shown in Fig. 18 on the transmission case and compress the piston spring retainer.
4. Using a screwdriver, remove the servo piston and valve spring retainer snap ring. Loosen compressing part of tool.
5. Remove spring retainer, spring, piston and valve from case.
6. Remove piston valve spring snap ring and take spring and valve from piston.
7. For disassembly and inspection, re-

fer to the major repair section of this chapter.

Installation—
1. Place valve and spring in servo piston with shaft on valve protruding through hole in bottom of piston.
2. Install piston valve spring snap ring, being sure it is seated properly.
3. Coat neoprene piston ring with Lubriplate. Insert piston and valve into case in a cocked position. Then, by rotating piston, ring will enter case without damage.
4. Place piston spring over piston and position retainer over spring. Using the tool shown in Fig. 18, compress spring and install snap ring.
5. Remove tool and install piston sleeve. Make sure sleeve slides freely on piston by working it up and down.
6. Hook one end of reverse band in reverse link and compress other end enough to install reverse band strut in slots of band and lever.
7. Adjust reverse band as outlined previously.
8. Install valve body, transfer plate and oil pan.

TRANSMISSION OUTPUT SHAFT REAR BEARING OIL SEAL

Removal—
1. Disconnect front propeller shaft universal joint and secure shaft to frame out of the way.
2. Apply hand brake and remove propeller shaft flange nut, shakeproof washer and washer.
3. Release hand brake and with a suitable puller remove propeller shaft flange and brake drum.
4. Remove transmission support grease shield spring (small one).
5. Remove brake support grease shield from extension housing. If a screw-

driver or similar instrument is used in performing this operation, care must be exercised not to damage the neoprene sealing surface at bottom of shield.
6. With a suitable puller, remove the output shaft bearing oil seal.

Installation—Reverse the procedure to install, using a suitable driver for the seal. The indent on the brake support grease shield must match the groove in the housing for correct positioning. Also, shield must be located on housing far enough to permit installation of the spring. Opening in spring must be toward adjusting sleeve.

After installing propeller shaft flange, apply hand brake and torque tighten flange nut 140-160 lbs. ft.

REGULATOR VALVE & CONVERTER CONTROL VALVE

Remove the valve spring retainer, gasket and spring, Figs. 11 to 14, of the valve to be removed. Using a mechanical retriever or a piece of welding rod inserted in end of valve, remove valve. Install the valve and related parts and tighten. The regulator valve should be torqued to 40-45 lbs. ft.

OIL COOLER

Removal—Drain water from radiator and remove battery and battery pan. Remove water hose connected to cooler and detach the inlet and outlet oil tubes. Unfasten cooler from water pump flange.

To install, clean mating surfaces and install a new flange gasket. Install cooler and tighten attaching bolts. Install oil tubes, water hose, battery and pan, and refill radiator. Start engine and check for water and oil leaks.

Repairs Requiring Transmission Removal

TRANSMISSION, DISASSEMBLE

1. Remove oil pan, throttle and manual control lever lock screw and slide throttle valve operating lever off shaft. Take off felt retainer and felt. Slide manual valve lever off shaft and remove shaft seal cover.
2. Remove oil strainer and inspect seal rings at both outlet sides of strainer.
3. Remove valve body and transfer plate assembly from case.
4. Remove neutral starter and back-up light switches and gasket (see Figs. 11 to 14).
5. Check transmission end play with

either a dial indicator or feeler gauge and write it down for future reference when reassembling. To make this check, first measure the distance between the direct clutch and carrier housing when clutch is in rearward position. Next, pry the clutch forward by carefully inserting screwdriver between direct clutch and carrier housing. Remove screwdriver and measure again. Limits are from .043 to .069".

Hand Brake, Remove

1. Remove transmission flange nut and washers.
2. Use a suitable puller to remove the brake drum.

3. Remove transmission brake support grease shield spring.
4. Place a rubber band around brake shoes to hold them in position and remove brake shoe return spring.
5. Remove brake anchor shoe washer and brake shoe guide.
6. Remove both brake shoe assemblies, adjusting sleeve, nut, screw and brake shoe operating lever link. The link is marked for installation purposes. Make sure adjusting screw nut turns freely on screw.
7. Remove other brake shoe guide from anchor pin.
8. Remove brake support grease shield from extension housing. Note the indent on grease shield for correct

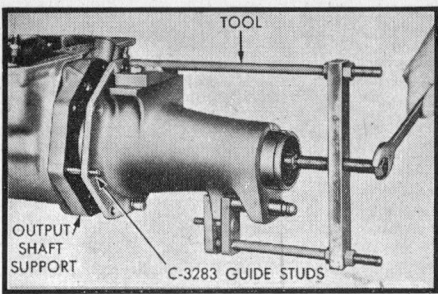

Fig. 19 Removing transmission extension housing

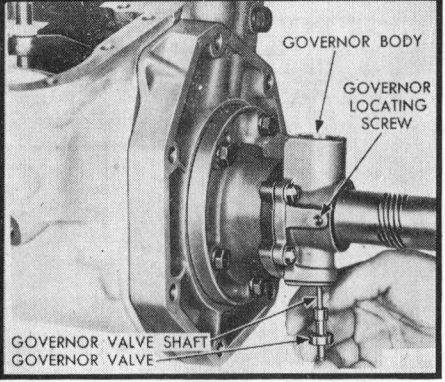

Fig. 20 Removing and installing governor valve and shaft

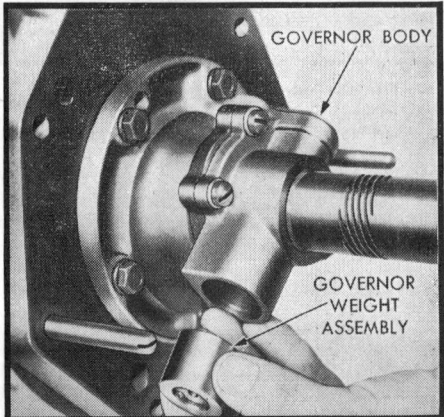

Fig. 21 Removing and installing governor weight assembly

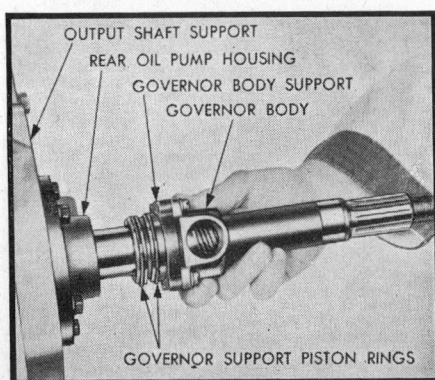

Fig. 22 Removing and installing governor body and support assembly

positioning on extension housing.

9. Slide the brake support assembly from rear extension housing and anchor. Inspect neoprene spacer on back of support plate for deterioration and note the steel sleeve used between neoprene spacer and extention housing.

Transmission Extension, Remove

1. Remove speedometer drive pinion.
2. With a suitable puller, remove output shaft rear bearing oil seal. Remove any burrs from counterbore of extension housing.
3. Remove seven extension case attaching screws.
4. Install a couple of guide studs and, with a suitable puller, pull extension housing from output shaft support and remove gasket, Fig. 19. *Use care in removing extension housing to prevent damaging governor housing which is made of aluminum.* Inspect extension housing for cracks in casting and remove burrs from gasket surface.
5. With long nose pliers, remove output shaft rear bearing snap ring. Note snap ring has beveled edge. Inspect ring for being distorted.
6. Drive output shaft rear bearing out of rear of extension housing.
7. Remove vent in top of extension housing and make sure it is open and free of dirt, undercoating, etc. This vent is used to prevent vacuum from forming in transmission case when it is drained. The vent also takes care of fumes and expansion of oil caused by heat.

Governor, Remove

1. Using a sharp instrument, such as an ice pick, remove either of the governor valve shaft snap rings.
2. Remove governor valve shaft and valve from governor valve body, Fig. 20.
3. Remove governor weight large snap ring and take weights from body, Fig. 21.
4. Remove secondary weight snap ring. *Keep thumb pressure against secondary weight when removing snap ring as it is spring loaded.*
5. Remove secondary weight and spring.
6. Inspect all parts for burrs and wear. Check secondary weight for free movement in primary weight by placing secondary weight in primary weight without the spring. Primary weight should fall freely when both parts are clean and dry. Inspect weight spring for distortion.
7. Remove locating screw from governor body and output shaft. *Screwdriver must fit slot perfectly, otherwise damage will occur to governor body.*
8. Slide governor body and support from output shaft, Fig. 22.
9. Remove two governor support piston rings and inspect. *Inspect oil passages and make sure they are free of dirt or foreign matter. Governor support has pressed-in*

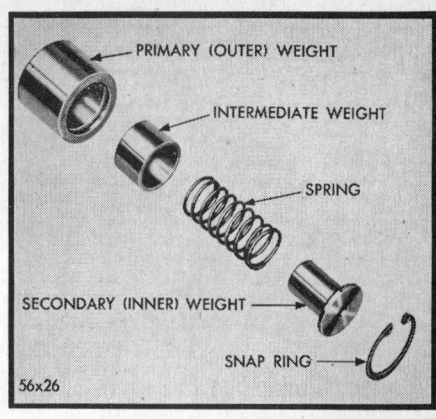

Fig. 23 Governor for 1956-61

steel sleeve which routes oil through the support. Make sure these passages are open. Do not attempt to replace sleeve if it is damaged—replace support. Clean passages with compressed air. Inspect valve and governor body for slight scores.

10. Remove four governor body-to-support screws and separate parts.

1956-61 Governor

The three-stage governor, Fig. 23, is designed to provide closer tolerances at the kickdown limit and wide-open throttle upshift. The new governor can be used as a replacement in older Power-Flite transmissions if the governor is replaced in its entirety. Transmissions having the new governor assembly can be identified by the letter "H" after the part number.

Rear Oil Pump, Remove

1. Remove five rear oil pump housing-to-output shaft screws and lockwashers. Remove housing and oil pump gear. *Use prussian blue to mark front side of gear in housing. Do not use a scribe.* Inspect machined surfaces for nicks and burrs, oil pump housing for being scored or pitted, and pump housing plug for leaks.
2. Remove pump pinion from output shaft and *mark front side with prus-*

Fig. 24 Removing and installing rear oil pump pinion

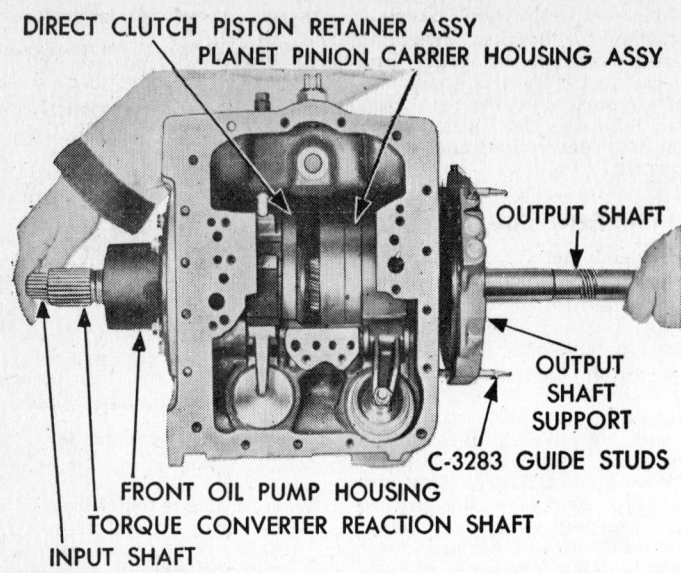

Fig. 25 Removal of output shaft, rear support, carrier housing and input shaft assembly

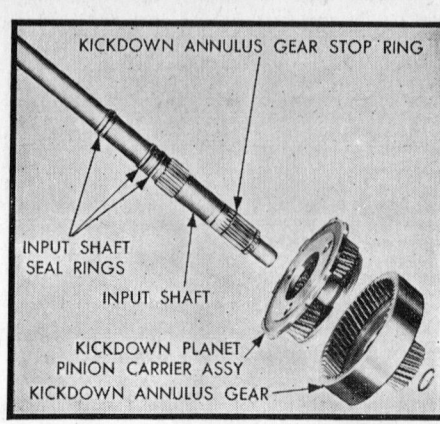

Fig. 28 Disassembled view of input shaft, kickdown planet pinion carrier and annulus gear. (Input shaft seal rings not used since early 1955)

sian blue, Fig. 24. The pinion is keyed to the output shaft by a small ball. Do not lose ball. Inspect keyway in pinion and ball pocket in output shaft for wear, also gear for being pitted or scored.

3. Using a straightedge and feeler gauge, check clearance between pump housing face and face of gears. Clearance limits are from .001-.003".

Output Shaft Support, Planet Pinion Carriers and Direct Clutch, Remove

1. Remove output shaft support-to-transmission case screw.
2. With one hand, work output shaft up and down and at the same time apply pressure with the other hand to the input shaft. Slide the output shaft rear support assembly, planet carrier housing and gasket from rear of case, Fig. 25. If rear support is stuck to case, install one of the oil pan screws into the case and, with the aid of a pry bar, pry

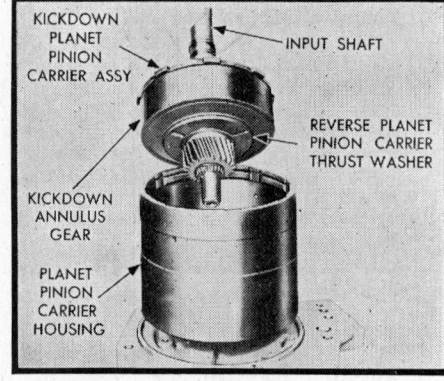

Fig. 27 Removing and installing input shaft and kickdown planet pinion carrier assembly

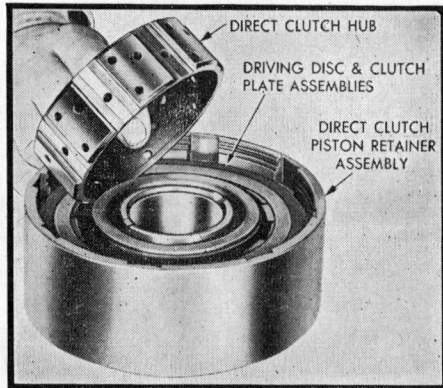

Fig. 29 Removal of direct clutch hub

against the support to separate it from the case.

3. Remove direct clutch piston retainer from torque converter reaction shaft.
4. Remove thrust washer from shaft. This washer is a select fit and controls end clearance between direct clutch and carrier housing. Inspect washer for cracks, burrs and wear; then identify for reassembly purposes.
5. Remove kickdown planet pinion carrier thrust washer from clutch retainer and inspect for cracks, burrs or wear.

Removing Planet Pinion Carriers from Housing

1. With unit in upright position, check clearance between kickdown planet pinion carrier housing snap ring and kickdown planet pinion carrier. This clearance should be .012-.038". If within these limits, identify each thrust washer as it is removed for reassembly purposes.

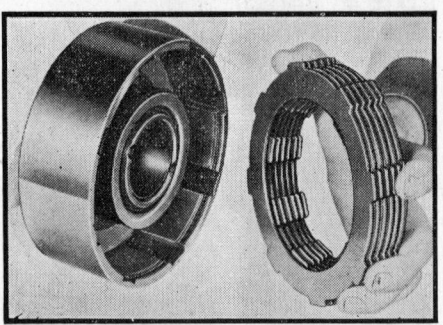

Fig. 30 Removing clutch plates and driving discs

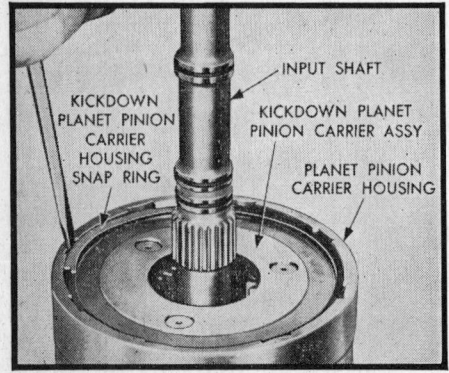

Fig. 26 Removing and installing kickdown planet pinion carrier housing snap ring

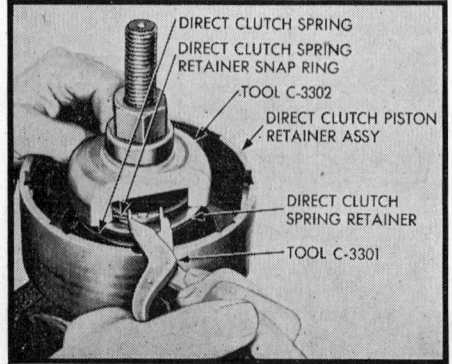

Fig. 31 Removing and installing direct clutch spring retainer snap ring

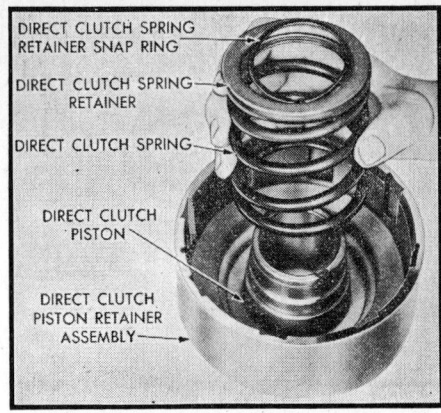

Fig. 32 Removing and installing direct clutch spring, retainer and snap ring

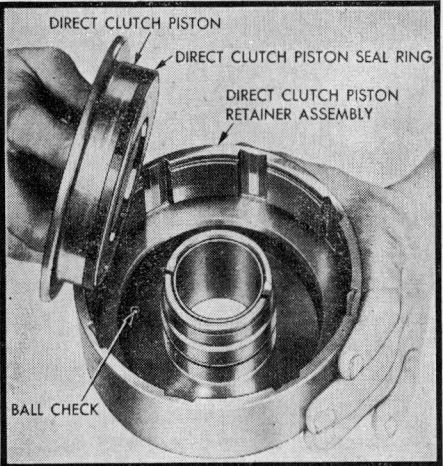

Fig. 33 Removing and installing direct clutch piston assembly

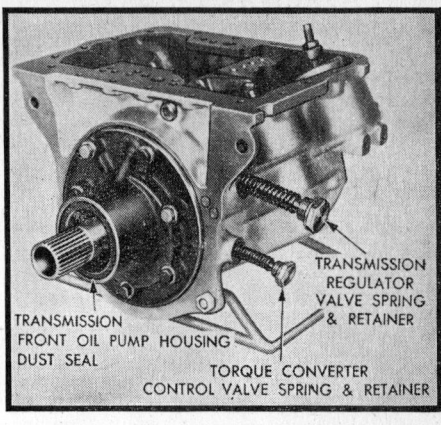

Fig. 36 Transmission regulator and torque converter control valve spring retainers (partially removed)

2. Using a screwdriver, remove snap ring, Fig. 26. Identify snap ring to aid in assembly (not a selective fit).

3. Remove input shaft, kickdown planet pinion carrier and kickdown annulus gear from carrier housing, Fig. 27.

4. Remove reverse planet pinion carrier thrust washer and inspect for cracks, burrs and wear.

5. Remove kickdown annulus gear snap ring. Then remove annulus gear from input shaft and inspect for worn, cracked or broken gear teeth.

6. Remove kickdown planet pinion assembly from input shaft and refer to Fig. 28. Inspect stop ring on end of shaft which controls position of annulus gear on input shaft. Check all oil passages in both gear and shaft for obstructions.

7. Inspect splines and bearing surfaces on input shaft for burrs and wear. Inspect rings for broken ends. Make sure they are free to rotate and move radially in grooves. Also, check surfaces adjacent to ring grooves for indications of rubbing.

8. Inspect planet pinion carrier for scores on thrust surfaces, broken or worn teeth. Using a feeler gauge, check end clearance on individual pinion gears, which should be .006-.017".

9. Inspect pinion shafts for tight fit in carrier and make sure pinions are free to rotate on shafts.

10. Check oil holes in gears and shafts for obstructions. Inspect oil holes in thrust washer of kickdown carrier to make certain they are open. *Do not replace carrier unless above inspections reveal it is necessary as the pinion carrier assembly is serviced only as a unit.*

11. Remove reverse planet pinion carrier housing and inspect in the same manner as for the kickdown carrier. This unit is also serviced as a complete assembly.

12. Remove output shaft and reverse annulus gear from carrier housing and output shaft support.

13. Remove reverse annulus gear snap ring and take gear from shaft. Inspect thrust surfaces, journals, and

Fig. 34 Removing and installing direct clutch piston retainer seal ring

inner bushings for scores, and annulus gear for worn or broken teeth. Inspect ring groove for burrs and ring for broken ends. Inspect splines on both shaft and gear for burrs and wear.

14. Inspect speedometer pinion gear and gear on output shaft for burrs. Inspect output shaft bushing for wear, scores or burrs. Output shaft is serviced only as an assembly.

15. Remove planet pinion carrier hous-

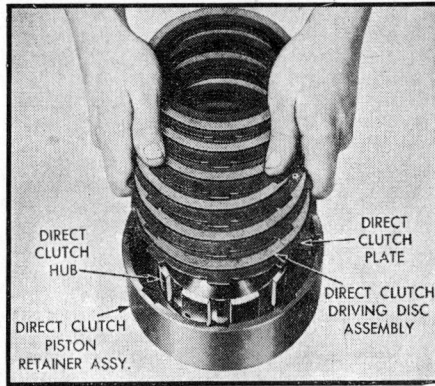

Fig. 35 Installation of clutch plates and driving discs

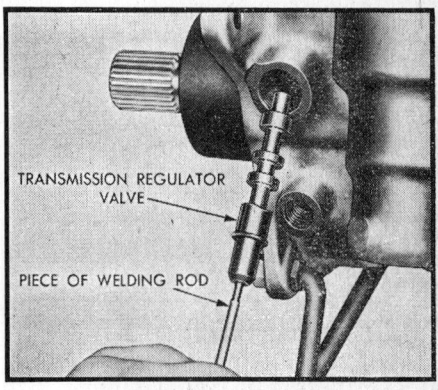

Fig. 37 Removing transmission regulator valve

ing thrust washer and inspect for cracks or wear.

16. Remove planet pinion carrier housing from output shaft and inspect driving lug slots inside of housing for wear. Inspect bearing and thrust surfaces for scores and burrs. Closely inspect band contacting surface for burned spots and scoring, especially if lining has become worn excessively.

17. Inspect all oil passages in output shaft support for any obstructions. Check rear oil pump mating surface for burrs and score marks. Check for stripped threads in support. Inspect gasket surfaces for burrs and dirt. Inspect both inside and outside bearing surfaces for wear and scoring.

Direct Clutch Piston Retainer, Disassemble

1. Remove kickdown sun gear snap ring, which is a selective fit and should be identified to aid in assembly.

2. Lift out kickdown sun gear assembly, noting oil slinger on reverse side. Oil passages in front are to lubricate direct clutch kickdown carrier thrust washer. Inspect for clutch material obstructing oil pass-

Fig. 38 Removing front oil pump housing assembly

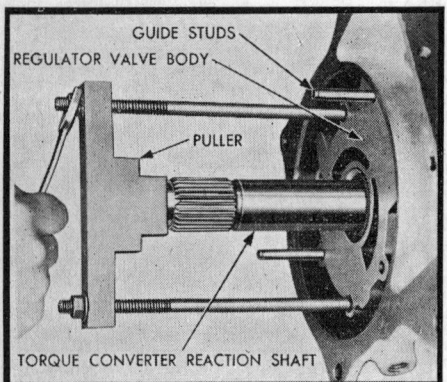

Fig. 39 Removing regulator valve body

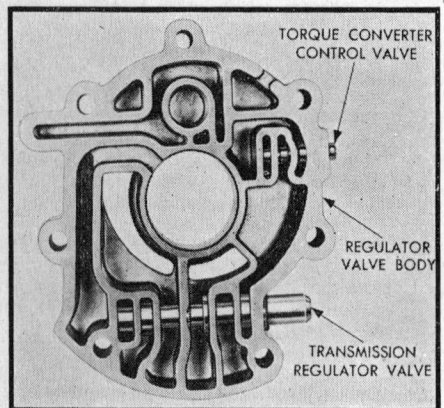

Fig. 40 Valves in valve body

Fig. 41 Removing torque converter reaction shaft

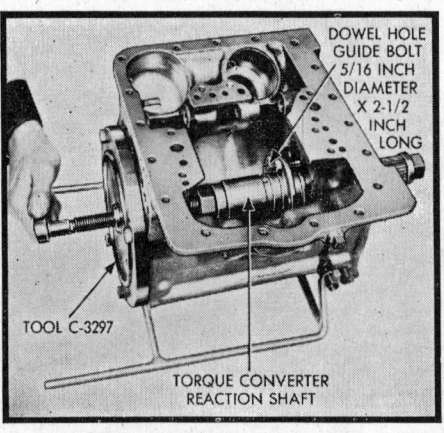

Fig. 42 Installing torque converter reaction shaft

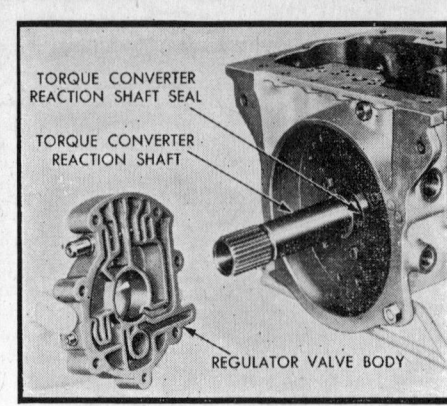

Fig. 43 Installing valve body assembly

Fig. 44 Installing front oil pump

ages and slinger. Remove any metal pickup which may have accumulated on front side. Inspect sun gear for cracked or broken teeth.

3. Lift out direct clutch hub from center of direct clutch piston retainer, Fig. 29. Oil passages in hub are to lubricate the clutch plates when clutch is released. Inspect clutch hub driving lugs for wear and remove any metal pickup which may have accumulated on either side of the hub. Inspect splines in center of hub for burrs and wear.

4. Invert direct clutch piston retainer and remove the steel clutch plates and driving discs, Fig. 30. Note position in which these were assembled. If assembly was started with the cork portion on outer top, the same sequence was followed all through the assembly, or vice versa. Assembling in this manner assures a more even contact.

5. Check discs by scratching facings with finger nail. If material collects under nail, replace all driving discs. Also replace driving discs if splines have become damaged. Inspect steel plates for evidence of burning, scoring and damaged splines.

6. Using the tool shown in Fig. 31, compress direct clutch spring so as to unseat the snap ring.

7. Release the tool and the parts, Fig. 32. The piston spring retainer may require guiding past snap ring grooves. Inspect spring, retainer and snap ring for distortion.

8. Using a twisting motion, remove clutch piston from retainer, Fig. 33. Air pressure may be used to blow piston out if it is tight. Note the ball check in clutch retainer housing. Its purpose is to relieve centrifugal oil pressure when transmission is in neutral and engine speeds are increased, otherwise clutch may en-

gage. Make sure ball operates freely.

9. The piston retainer bushing (steel backed bronze) is not replaceable. If the torque converter reaction shaft seal rings have worn or grooved the bushing so that bronze is no longer visible at that point, replace the clutch piston retainer.

10. Inspect the band contacting surface for deep scores and burns, especially if the band lining is worn to the point where the steel band has been contacting the clutch piston retainer. *Do not turn the retainer in a lathe to remove score marks.*

11. Inspect steel clutch plate contacting surfaces for deep scores and burrs and replace as needed.

12. Make sure clutch driving lugs will slide freely into retainer. Remove any metal pickup on hub of retainer.

13. Inspect inside bore of piston for score marks; if light remove with crocus cloth; if heavy replace piston.

14. Unlock clutch piston retainer seal ring and remove from retainer, Fig. 34. Inspect for wear and broken ends.

15. Remove seal ring from piston and inspect for deterioration, wear and hardness.

Direct Clutch Piston Retainer, Assemble

1. Coat seal ring with Lubriplate and install on piston with lip of ring facing away from flange.

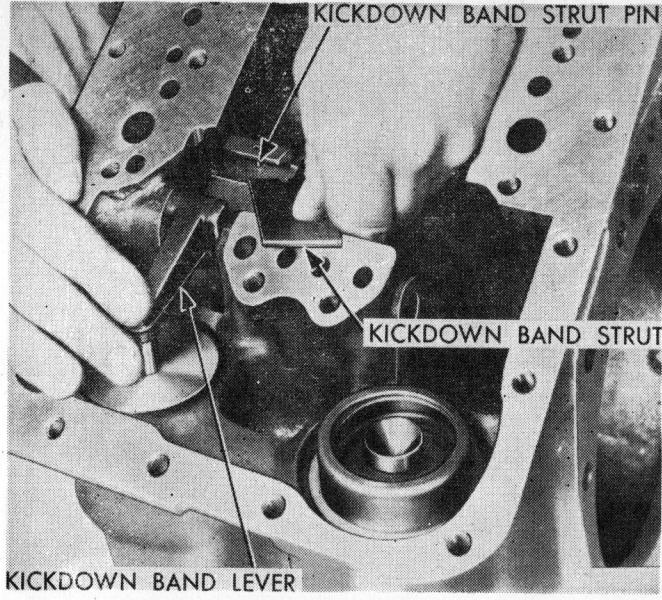

Fig. 45   Installing kickdown band strut

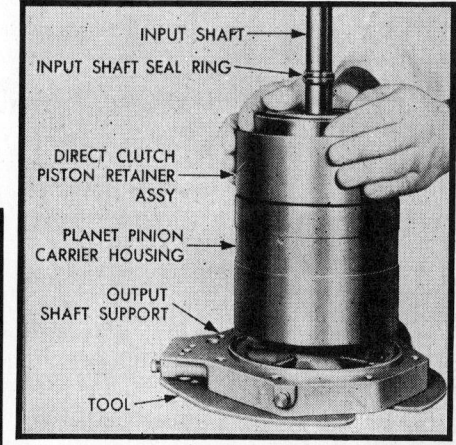

Fig. 48   Installing power train in transmission

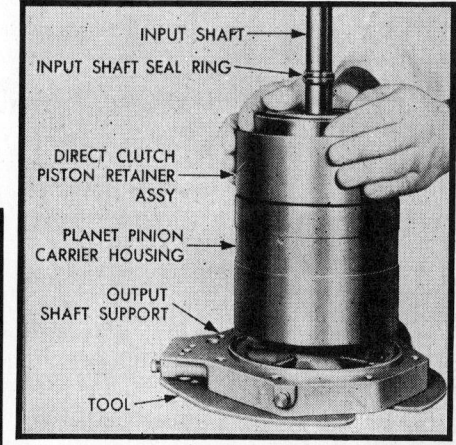

Fig. 47   Installing direct clutch piston retainer on input shaft

2. Coat piston retainer seal ring with Lubriplate and install on retainer hub. Using the tool shown in Fig. 34, lock seal ring into position and make sure it is free to rotate in the lands.
3. Place piston in retainer and, with a twisting motion, seat piston in bottom of retainer. *Use care not to damage lip of seal.*
4. Seat clutch spring in retainer and position spring retainer and snap ring on spring, Fig. 33.
5. Using tool shown in Fig. 32, compress clutch spring and install snap ring, being sure it is properly seated.
6. Place clutch hub in center of clutch piston retainer.
7. Lubricate all clutch plates and driving discs with automatic transmission fluid and assemble by placing one of the clutch plates in the piston retainer, followed by a driving disc.
8. Install all plates and discs in the same order as they were removed, referring to Fig. 35.
9. Place kickdown sun gear in piston retainer and install snap ring, which is a select fit.
10. Using a feeler gauge, check clearance under kickdown sun gear snap ring. Clearance limits are as close to zero as possible. Snap rings are available in three thicknesses to obtain the desired result.

Reverse and Kickdown Bands, Remove

1. Mark reverse band for installation purposes. Then compress ends of bands enough to remove reverse band strut.
2. Unhook reverse band from link and remove by rotating band ends through rear opening in transmission case.
3. Compress kickdown band ends enough to remove its strut. Note

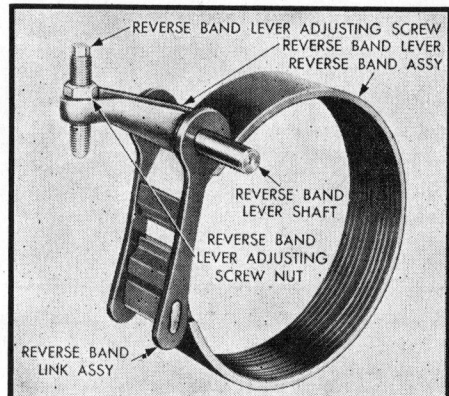

Fig. 46   Reverse band linkage

that this strut is grooved to act as a guide to the kickdown band strut pin on the band end.
4. Remove kickdown band by rotating band ends through rear opening in transmission case.
5. If linings are worn to the point that grooves are no longer visible, bands must be replaced. Inspect bands for distortion and cracked ends.

Reverse and Kickdown Band Levers, Remove

1. Inspect reverse band link for wear and riveting of assemblies. Inspect levers for being cracked and worn, making sure they have side clearance and are free to turn on shafts. *Do not remove these parts unless inspection reveals it is necessary to do so.*
2. Insert finger in back of reverse band and link lever shaft and, holding lever and link with other hand, push shaft out of rear opening in case.
3. Remove kickdown band lever shaft plug in front of transmission case.

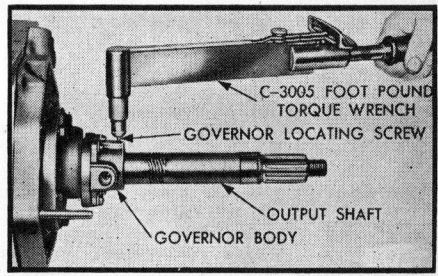

Fig. 49   Tightening governor locating screw

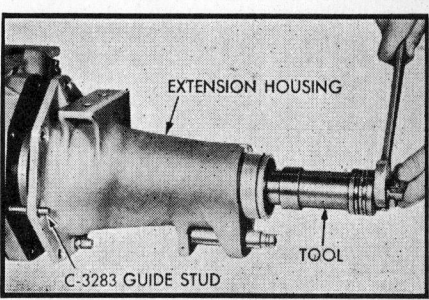

Fig. 50   Installing transmission extension housing

309

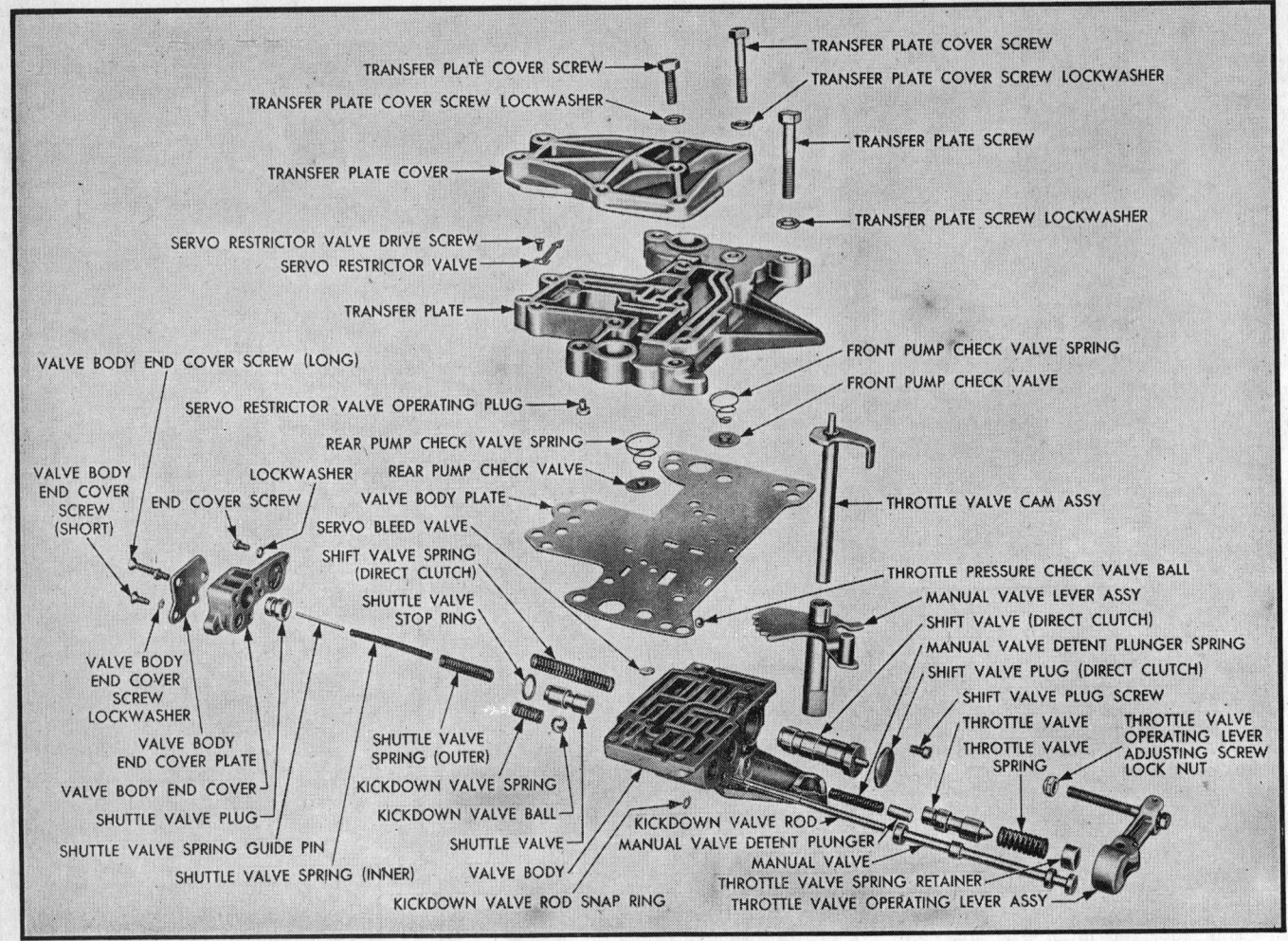

Fig. 51 Exploded view of valve body and transfer plate assembly. 1953-55

4. Rotate kickdown band lever by inserting finger in back of kickdown lever shaft and, holding band lever with other hand, push shaft out through front of transmission case.

Front Oil Pump, Remove

1. Remove regulator valve and torque converter control valve, Figs. 36, 37.
2. Unfasten pump housing from case. Sealing washers used under bolts are aluminum or copper; discard and use new ones for assembly.
3. Using the two threaded holes provided in the oil pump housing, Fig. 38, install the guide studs shown and pull pump housing and gears from case. *Use prussian blue to mark front side of gears. Do not use scribe marks.*
4. Remove pump gear from housing.
5. Remove large neoprene seal from housing and inspect for deterioration and hardness.
6. Using a brass drift, drive pump housing dust seal out through front of housing.
7. Inspect housing bushings for scores (bushing not replaceable). Slight scores may be removed with crocus cloth. Inspect housing and gears for scores.

Regulator Valve Body, Remove

Using the tools shown in Fig. 39, pull regulator valve body off of torque converter reaction shaft.

Regulator valve body is made of aluminum and requires care in handling to avoid damage. Place body and both valves in pan containing clean solvent, wash thoroughly and dry with compressed air.

Inspect both valves for free movement in valve body. They should fall in and out of their bores when valves and body are dry. Crocus cloth may be used to polish valves provided care is exercised not to round the sharp edge portion of the valves. Check all fluid passages for obstructions and inspect all mating surfaces for burrs and distortion.

If regulator valve body should have a slight nick or raised portion on the mating surfaces, it may be removed by using a surface plate and crocus cloth.

Check regulator valve spring seat (snap ring). Leave valves in body, Fig. 40, and protect against dirt or damage until ready for installation.

Torque Converter Reaction Shaft, Remove

1. Remove shaft neoprene seal.

2. Using a suitable brass drift, remove dowel pin from shaft flange and transmission case.
3. Remove three transmission-to-reaction shaft screws and washers.
4. Using the tool shown in Fig. 41, press shaft out of transmission case.
5. Remove two shaft interlocking seal rings.

TRANSMISSION, REASSEMBLE

Torque Converter Reaction Shaft, Install

1. The front of the transmission case should be heated to about 170-190 degrees. Chrysler recommends the use of sun lamps for this purpose.
2. Coat portion of reaction shaft that presses into case with Lubriplate. Position shaft into front of case so that holes in shaft align with screw holes in case.
3. Press reaction shaft into position, using the tools shown in Fig. 42. Do not remove the guide bolt from the dowel pin holes at this point.
4. Start and tighten the three attaching screws and washers but do not torque at this time.

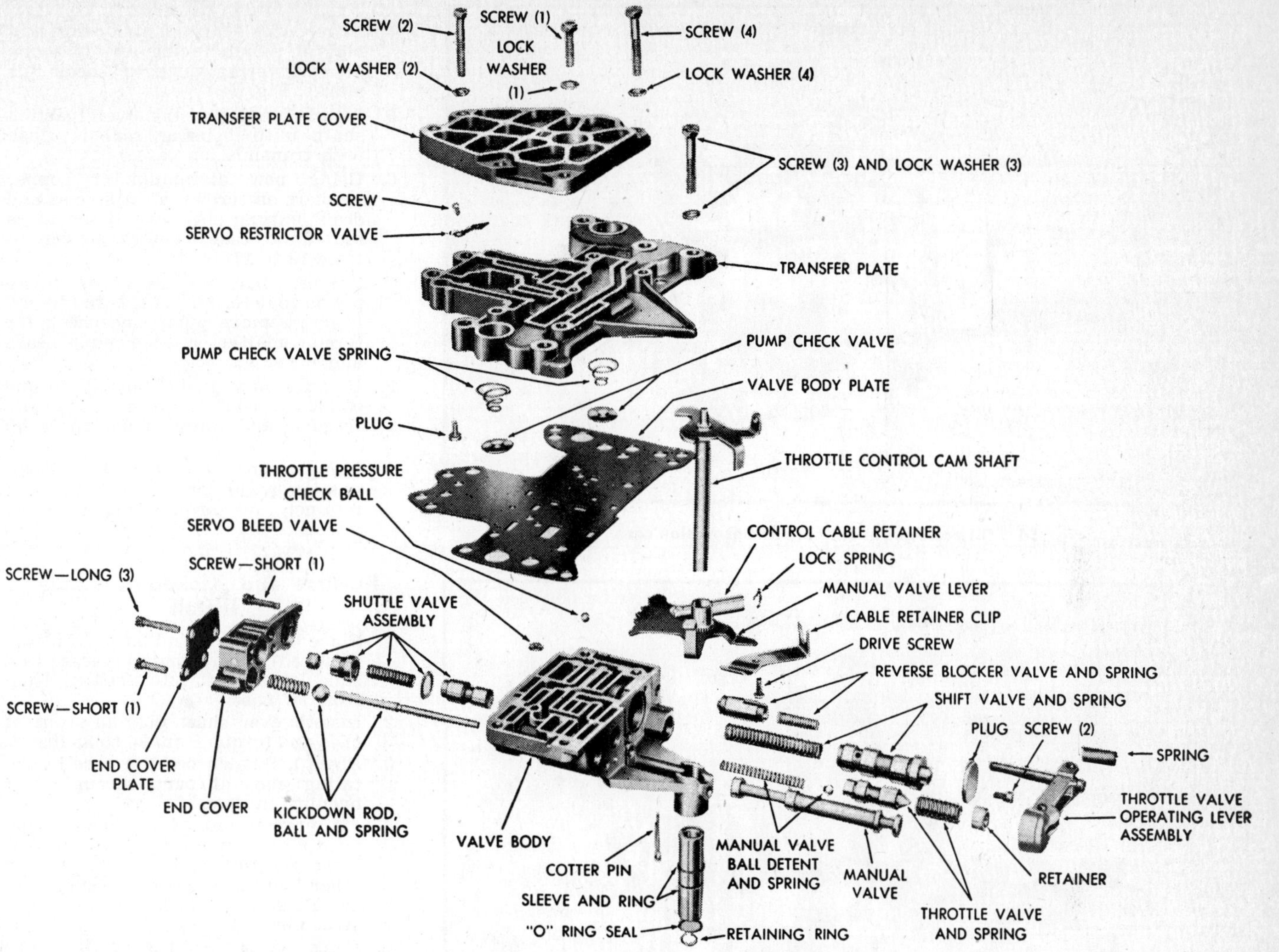

SCREW (2) SCREW (1) SCREW (4)

LOCK WASHER (2) LOCK WASHER (1) LOCK WASHER (4)

TRANSFER PLATE COVER

SCREW (3) AND LOCK WASHER (3)

SCREW

SERVO RESTRICTOR VALVE

TRANSFER PLATE

PUMP CHECK VALVE SPRING

PUMP CHECK VALVE

VALVE BODY PLATE

PLUG

THROTTLE CONTROL CAM SHAFT

THROTTLE PRESSURE CHECK BALL

SERVO BLEED VALVE

CONTROL CABLE RETAINER

LOCK SPRING

SCREW—LONG (3) SCREW—SHORT (1)

SHUTTLE VALVE ASSEMBLY

MANUAL VALVE LEVER

CABLE RETAINER CLIP

DRIVE SCREW

REVERSE BLOCKER VALVE AND SPRING

SHIFT VALVE AND SPRING

PLUG SCREW (2)

SPRING

SCREW—SHORT (1)

END COVER PLATE

END COVER

KICKDOWN ROD, BALL AND SPRING

VALVE BODY

COTTER PIN

SLEEVE AND RING

"O" RING SEAL

MANUAL VALVE BALL DETENT AND SPRING

MANUAL VALVE

RETAINING RING

THROTTLE VALVE AND SPRING

RETAINER

THROTTLE VALVE OPERATING LEVER ASSEMBLY

Fig. 52 Exposed view of valve body assembly. 1956-61

5. Remove the guide bolt from the dowel pin hole and install the shaft dowel from inside the transmission case.
6. Torque the attaching screws from 10 to 15 lbs. ft.
7. Coat neoprene seal with Lubriplate and install on shaft.

Kickdown and Servo Pistons, Install

This procedure has already been given in the "In Car Repairs" section of this chapter.

Regulator Valve Body, Install

1. Inspect valve body and valves to make sure that no damage has occurred since first inspection and cleaning. Blow out passages with compressed air, Fig. 40.
2. Place regulator valve and torque converter control valve in valve body.
3. Install guide studs in front of transmission case. Then place valve body, with oil passages to rear, over reaction shaft and onto guide studs and seat firmly to front of transmission case, Fig. 43.

1956-61 Service Note

Due to the change in the regulator valve body, and the torque converter control valve and spring, the torque converter outlet valve has been eliminated. The regulator valve body is changed so that the torque converter control valve now regulates the pressure in the converter as it returns to the sump instead of regulating it before it enters the converter as done previously. The new design maintains working pressure in the converter, thus eliminating loss of fluid out of the filler tube under extreme operating conditions.

The new torque converter regulator valve can be installed on early transmissions but the small torque converter outlet valve assembly in the line has to be removed and the valve body (located behind front pump) must be replaced as an assembly.

Always install converter control valve with small hole in end to outside of valve body. If this is not done it will be impossible to remove the valve without first removing the regulator valve body from the transmission.

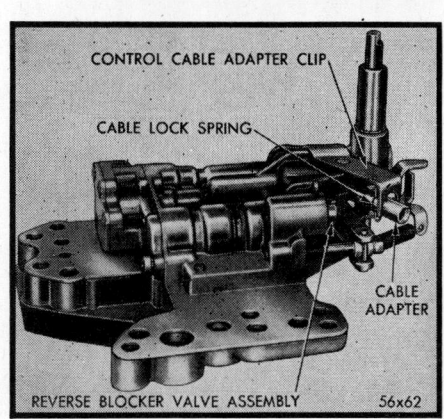

CONTROL CABLE ADAPTER CLIP

CABLE LOCK SPRING

CABLE ADAPTER

REVERSE BLOCKER VALVE ASSEMBLY   56x62

Fig. 53 Hydraulic control value assembly. 1956-61

Front Oil Pump, Assemble and Install

1. Position pump housing dust seal in front of pump housing with metal portion of seal down.
2. With a suitable driver, bottom seal in housing.
3. Coat housing seal with Lubriplate

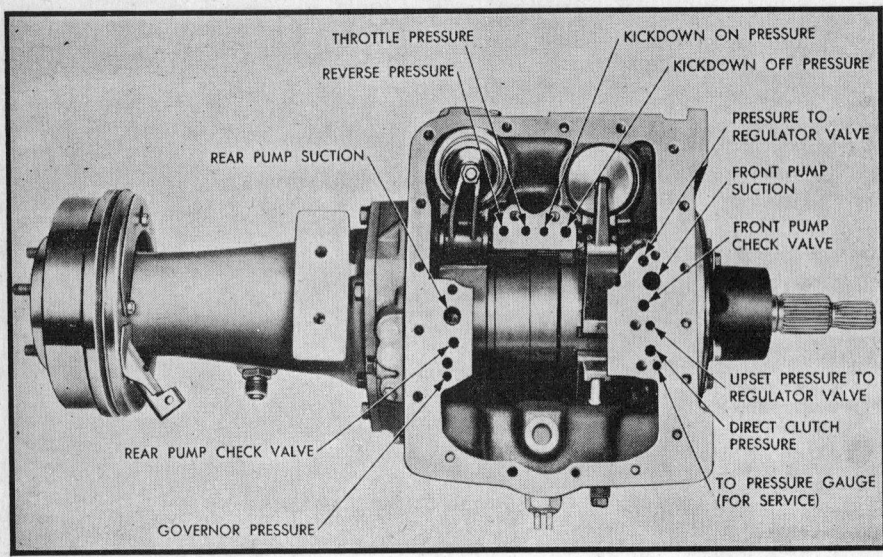

Fig. 54   Oil passages in bottom of transmission case

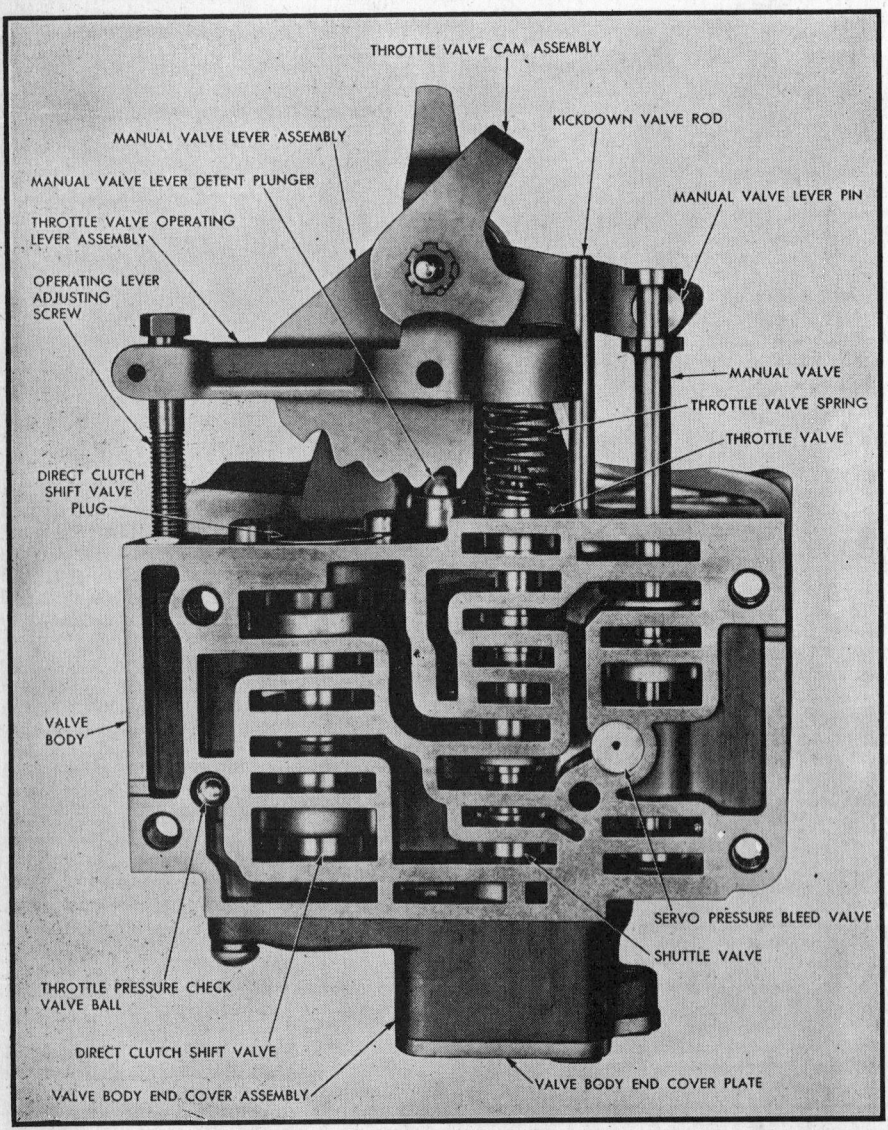

Fig. 55   Valve body assembly.   1953-55

and install on housing.

4. Place pump gear and pinion (driving lugs of pinion facing up) in pump housing, being sure to check the marks, Fig. 44.

5. Install pump housing over reaction shaft until housing seal is flush with transmission case.

6. Using new aluminum or copper washers on screws, start screws and draw housing down evenly until it is seated into case. Then torque screws from 12 to 17 lbs. ft.

7. Engage driving lugs of oil pump pinion to determine if it turns freely. If not, remove pump and check for foreign matter between pump gears and housing.

8. Using a new gasket, install torque converter control valve spring and retainer and torque from 35 to 40 lbs. ft.

9. Using a new gasket, install transmission regulator valve spring and retainer and torque from 45 to 50 lbs. ft.

Reverse and Kickdown Bands, Install

1. Place kickdown band lever (if it was removed) in transmission case and slide lever shaft into position from front of case.

2. Install lever shaft plug in front of case and torque from 30 to 35 lbs. ft.

3. Place kickdown band in case by rotating ends of band through rear opening in case.

4. Fit proper end of kickdown band over adjusting screw and compress band enough to install strut between other band end and band lever, Fig. 45. Be sure strut slot engages with strut pin in band end.

5. Place reverse band lever (if it was removed) in link and position in case, aligning holes in lever and link to holes in case.

6. Slide lever shaft in from rear of case, Fig. 46. If a new band is being installed, loosen lock nut and back adjustment out until about one inch of screw is above lever on lock nut side.

7. Install reverse band in case by rotating ends of band through rear opening in case.

8. Hook proper end of band in link. Compress band and install strut in slots of reverse band and lever.

1956-61 Service Note

The internal diameter of the kickdown band has been increased. Either end of the band can now be installed to the anchor pin. The strut is narrower and shorter, and the operating lever is narrower.

Installing Pinion Carriers In Housing

1. Place output shaft support in a suitable holding fixture with bearing surface up.

2. Lubricate bearing surface of planet pinion housing. Then place bearing

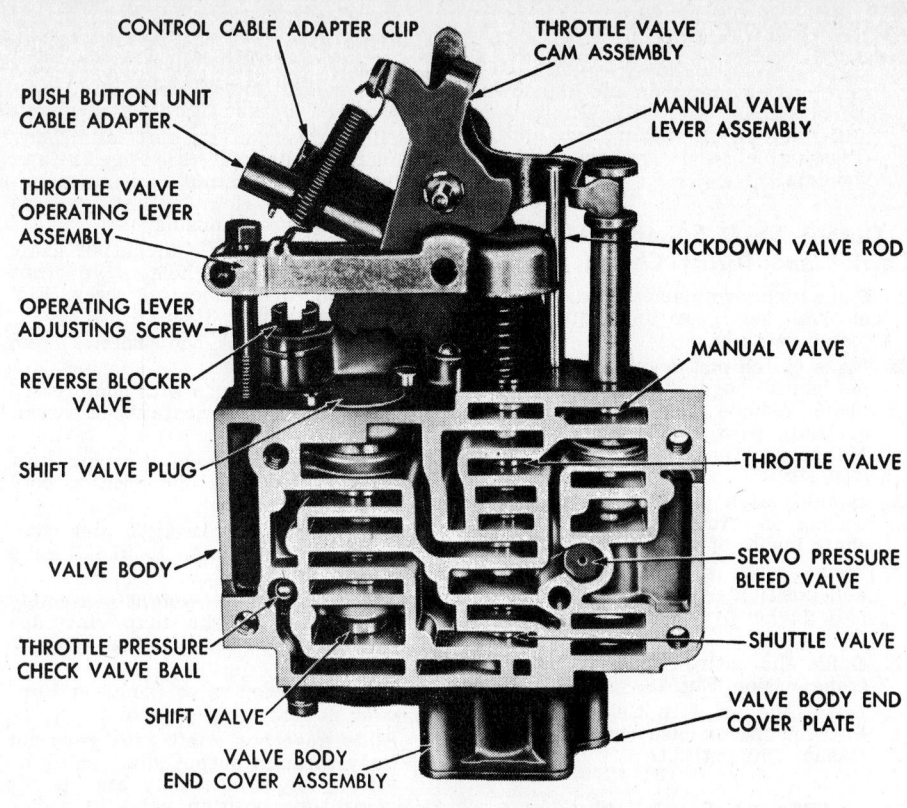

CONTROL CABLE ADAPTER CLIP

THROTTLE VALVE CAM ASSEMBLY

PUSH BUTTON UNIT CABLE ADAPTER

MANUAL VALVE LEVER ASSEMBLY

THROTTLE VALVE OPERATING LEVER ASSEMBLY

KICKDOWN VALVE ROD

OPERATING LEVER ADJUSTING SCREW

MANUAL VALVE

REVERSE BLOCKER VALVE

SHIFT VALVE PLUG

THROTTLE VALVE

VALVE BODY

SERVO PRESSURE BLEED VALVE

THROTTLE PRESSURE CHECK VALVE BALL

SHUTTLE VALVE

SHIFT VALVE

VALVE BODY END COVER PLATE

VALVE BODY END COVER ASSEMBLY

Fig. 56 Valve body assembly. 1956-61

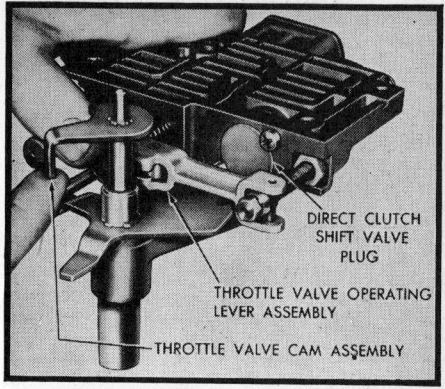

DIRECT CLUTCH SHIFT VALVE PLUG

THROTTLE VALVE OPERATING LEVER ASSEMBLY

THROTTLE VALVE CAM ASSEMBLY

Fig. 57 Removing and installing throttle valve cam. 1953-55

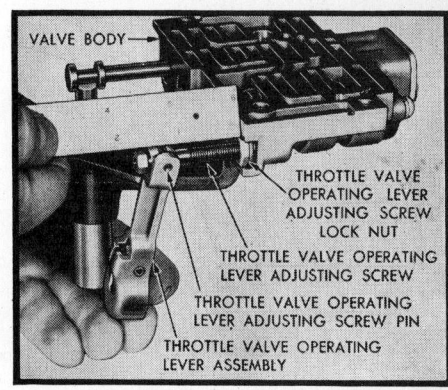

VALVE BODY

THROTTLE VALVE OPERATING LEVER ADJUSTING SCREW LOCK NUT

THROTTLE VALVE OPERATING LEVER ADJUSTING SCREW

THROTTLE VALVE OPERATING LEVER ADJUSTING SCREW PIN

THROTTLE VALVE OPERATING LEVER ASSEMBLY

Fig. 59 Adjusting throttle valve operating lever

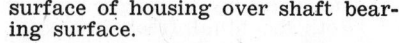

surface of housing over shaft bearing surface.

3. Place reverse annulus gear on output shaft and install snap ring. Annulus gear must fit tightly on output shaft. End clearance is controlled by snap rings which are available in three thicknesses.

4. Coat output shaft seal ring with Lubriplate and install on shaft. Lock in position and make sure ring rotates freely in lands.

5. Coat carrier housing thrust washer with Lubriplate, slide it over output shaft and on reverse annulus gear.

6. Install shaft and reverse annulus gear in carrier housing and through output shaft support, being careful not to damage shaft seal ring as it enters support. Make sure thrust washer seats properly between reverse annulus gear and carrier housing. Coat output shaft splines with Lubriplate.

7. Lubricate thrust surfaces and gear teeth of reverse planet pinion gear and carrier. Place carrier in reverse annulus gear.

8. On early 1955 units, coat the three input shaft seal rings with Lubriplate and lock in position on shaft. Make sure rings rotate freely in lands. Inspect stop ring for proper position in input shaft groove.

9. Slide kickdown planet pinion gear and carrier (oil collector ring up) down on input shaft and over stop ring.

10. Slide kickdown annulus gear on input shaft down to stop ring.

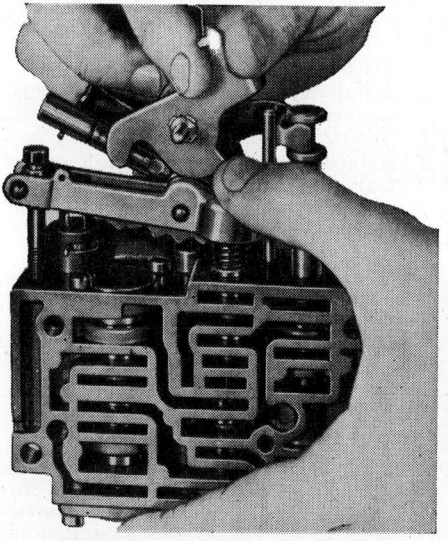

Fig. 58 Removing and installing throttle valve cam. 1956-61

11. Install kickdown annulus gear snap ring.

12. Slide pinion gear and carrier into position in kickdown annulus gear.

13. Install reverse planet carrier thrust washer on kickdown annulus gear.

14. Install kickdown planet carrier, annulus gear and input shaft in carrier housing (see Fig. 27). Make sure thrust washer remains on annulus.

15. Install planet pinion carrier housing

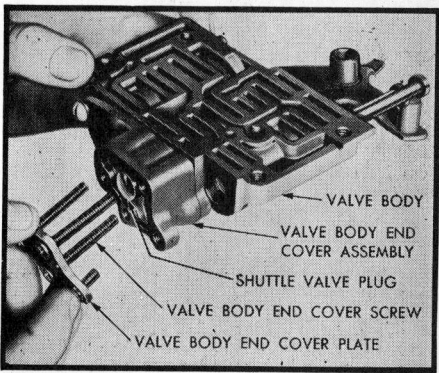

VALVE BODY

VALVE BODY END COVER ASSEMBLY

SHUTTLE VALVE PLUG

VALVE BODY END COVER SCREW

VALVE BODY END COVER PLATE

Fig. 60 Removing and installing valve body end cover plate

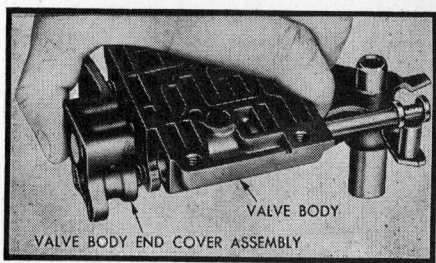

VALVE BODY

VALVE BODY END COVER ASSEMBLY

Fig. 61 Removing and installing valve body end cover assembly

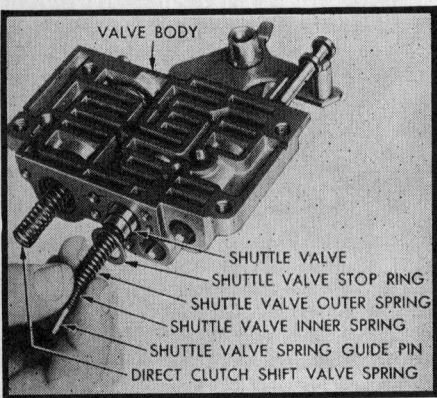

VALVE BODY

SHUTTLE VALVE
SHUTTLE VALVE STOP RING
SHUTTLE VALVE OUTER SPRING
SHUTTLE VALVE INNER SPRING
SHUTTLE VALVE SPRING GUIDE PIN
DIRECT CLUTCH SHIFT VALVE SPRING

Fig. 62 Removing and installing shuttle valve. 1953-56

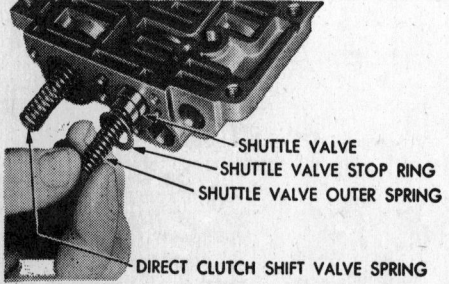

SHUTTLE VALVE
SHUTTLE VALVE STOP RING
SHUTTLE VALVE OUTER SPRING

DIRECT CLUTCH SHIFT VALVE SPRING

Fig. 63 Removing and installing shuttle valve. 1957-61

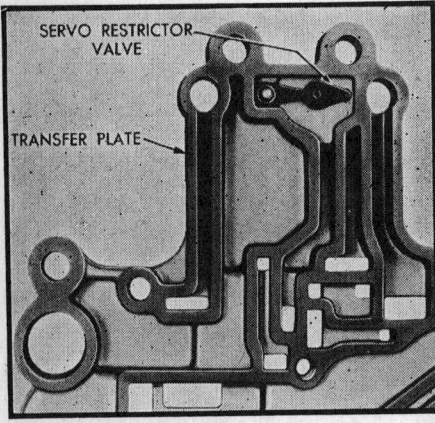

SERVO RESTRICTOR VALVE

TRANSFER PLATE

Fig. 64 Servo restrictor valve

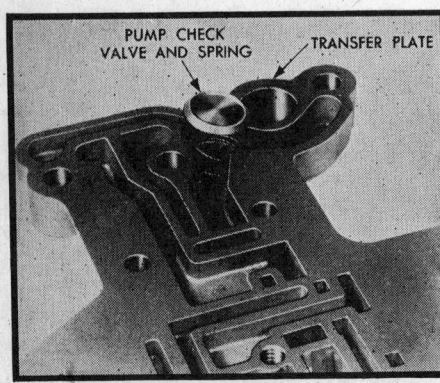

PUMP CHECK VALVE AND SPRING

TRANSFER PLATE

Fig. 65 Pump check valve and spring

snap ring (see Fig. 26).

16. Using a feeler gauge, check clearance between kickdown planet carrier housing snap ring and kickdown planet carrier assembly. Limits are .012-.038". If not within these limits, disassemble and recheck thrust washers.

Output Shaft Support, Planet Carrier and Direct Clutch, Install

1. Place kickdown carrier thrust washer over sun gear and onto clutch piston retainer.
2. Place clutch piston retainer over input shaft, engaging sun gear with planet pinions and engaging splines of shaft with clutch hub, Fig. 47. Make sure thrust washer remained in position.
3. Install clutch piston retainer thrust washer on torque converter reaction shaft inside of transmission case.
4. Install guide studs in rear of case and position new output shaft support gasket over guide studs and on to case.
5. Guide the entire assembly into the transmission, Fig. 48.
6. Install the one output shaft support-to-transmission case screw and lock-washer finger tight.

1956-61 Service Note

Because of the increase in size of the direct clutch retainer, it will be necessary to follow the steps in the order given below when assembling the power train in the transmission case:

1. Install kickdown band.
2. Install clutch retainer and thrust washer, sun gear and sun gear thrust washer to reaction shaft.
3. Rotate reverse band through end of transmission case and into linkage and assemble remainder of gear train into transmission case.

Rear Oil Pump, Assemble and Install

1. Insert rear oil pump pinion ball in pocket in output shaft (see Fig. 24).
2. Place pump drive pinion over shaft and slide into position, aligning keyway in pinion with ball in shaft.
3. Position rear oil pump gear into pump housing. *Be sure gear and pinion are installed according to marks made on them during disassembly.*
4. Slide rear oil pump housing over output shaft and against output shaft support. *There are two extra holes in housing which are used for vents. Make sure no screws are installed in these holes.*
5. Install attaching screws and torque them from 15 to 20 lbs. ft. After screws have been tightened, turn output shaft to make sure pump gears are free to rotate. If not, disassemble pump to determine cause.

Governor, Install

1. Install two governor support piston rings on support. Stagger rings and make sure they are free to rotate.
2. Position governor body on support and install four screws and lock-washers. Do not tighten screws yet.
3. Slide governor support and body over output shaft (see Fig. 22) and into rear oil pump housing. Compress piston rings with fingers as support enters housing.
4. Align locating hole in output shaft to locating screw hole in governor body and install locating screw, Fig. 49. Torque from 3½ to 4 lbs. ft.
5. Torque governor body screws from 5 to 10 lbs. ft.
6. Dry governor parts with compressed air but do not lubricate when assembling.
7. Place governor weight spring over secondary weight and position both in primary weight.
8. Guide secondary weight and compress spring enough to install snap ring.
9. Place governor weight assembly (secondary weight snap ring up) into governor body and install snap ring.
10. Slide governor valve (small end up) over governor valve shaft.
11. Slide governor valve shaft into governor body through output shaft and governor weight assembly and at the same time position valve in body.
12. Install governor valve shaft snap ring.
13. Check operation of governor weights and valve by turning output shaft. Both should fall freely in body.

Transmission Extension, Install

1. Install output shaft rear bearing (if it was removed) in extension housing, being sure bearing is seated and lubricated with automatic transmission fluid.
2. Install bearing snap ring with *beveled side up.*
3. Install extension breather (vent) and torque from 10 to 12 lbs. ft.
4. Install new gasket (without sealing material) and, using care to avoid damaging governor housing, place extension housing over output shaft.
5. Using the tools shown in Fig. 50, press housing into position.
6. Install extension housing screws, draw down evenly and torque from 25 to 30 lbs. ft.
7. Tighten output shaft support-to-case screw from 25 to 30 lbs. ft. After tightening, turn output shaft to make sure it turns freely.
8. Coat nylon gear and threads on speedometer pinion with Lubriplate and install in extension housing. Torque from 40 to 45 lbs. ft.

Checking Transmission End Play

Using a dial indicator or a feeler gauge, measure the distance between direct clutch assembly and carrier housing when clutch is in rearward position. Then, using a screwdriver inserted between direct clutch and carrier housing, carefully pry direct clutch forward. Remove screwdriver and measure again. The difference in the measurements is the end clearance and must be .043-.069". If it does not fall within these limits, the transmission will have to be partially disassembled to allow a direct clutch piston retainer thrust washer of the proper thickness to be installed.

To make the installation, remove the extension housing, output shaft, support and planet carrier housing as one assembly. Slide the direct clutch piston retainer from the torque converter reaction shaft and remove the thrust washer. Using a micrometer, measure the thickness of the washer and then select one which will provide the proper clearance. Washers are available in five thicknesses in steps of .010", the thinnest one measuring from .125 to .135".

Reassemble the parts removed and recheck end play. If correct, install the output shaft rear bearing oil seal.

Final Installations

Install the hand brake, adjust the bands and install the valve body and transfer plate as given in the "In Car Repairs" section of this chapter.

VALVE BODY REPAIRS

Fig. 51 is an exploded view of the hydraulic control valve assembly for 1953-55. For 1956-61, Fig. 52, the manual control valve lever assembly has been redesigned to accommodate the cable-actuated gear-shift control mechanism. The addition of a projection on the detent plate serves as a stop for the reverse blocker valve. The detent plate also serves to anchor the cable adapter assembly.

The reverse blocker valve, Fig. 53, located in the governor pressure line, moves outward when the vehicle is traveling forward in excess of 10 mph. In its outward position it serves as a stop to prevent the detent plate (by engaging a projection on the plate) from positioning the manual valve in the reverse position.

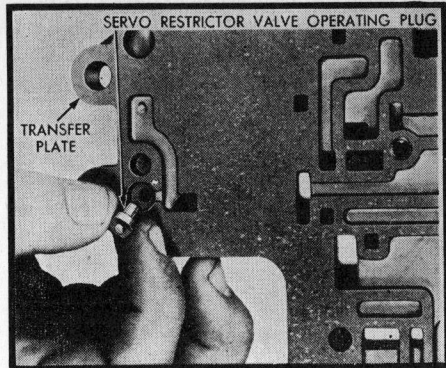

Fig. 66 Installing servo restrictor valve operating plug

Fig. 54 identifies the oil passages in the bottom of the transmission case. For 1956-60, a new hole has been machined in the case to receive the control cable assembly. An O-ring seal prevents leakage of transmission fluid past the cable housing.

When disassembling and assembling the valve body and transfer plate assembly, refer to Figs. 51 to 66. When disassembled, inspect the parts for the following:

Inspection

1. After each part has been cleaned and inspected, place on clean paper until ready for reassembly.
2. Place all parts in clean solvent, wash thoroughly and dry with compressed air. Make certain all passages are free of obstructions. Also check for porous castings.
3. Inspect all mating surfaces for burrs, nicks or grooves. Small ones may be removed with crocus cloth. Large ones require replacement.
4. Check all mating surfaces for distortion.
5. Using a light, inspect bores in valve body for score marks, pits and irregularities.
6. Inspect all springs for distortion and collapsed coils.
7. Inspect all valves and plugs for burrs, nicks and scores. Small ones may be removed with crocus cloth provided extreme care is used not to round off the sharp edge portion of the valve. The sharp edge portion helps to prevent dirt and foreign matter from getting between valves and body, thus reducing possibility of sticking.
8. Check valves and plugs for free operation in bores. When clean and dry they must fall freely in bores.
9. Inspect detent portion on manual valve lever for wear. Inspect detent plunger for wear and make sure it slides freely in valve body.
10. Inspect riveting and wear on manual valve lever pin.
11. Inspect staking of manual lever and throttle cam to their shafts.
12. Inspect throttle valve operating lever roller to make sure it rolls freely.
13. Inspect throttle valve operating lever adjusting screw and pin for wear. Make sure adjusting screw rotates freely in throttle valve operating lever.
14. Check nib in throttle valve operating lever which contacts throttle valve spring retainer for wear.
15. Inspect kickdown valve rod for wear; also inspect for wear at entering point in valve body.
16. Inspect kickdown valve ball seat in valve body for faulty casting.
17. Inspect servo restrictor valve in transfer plate to make sure valve is seating properly, Fig. 64. If valve is distorted, carefully remove the drive screw. Install new valve and screw. Make sure transfer plate is not distorted during this operation.
18. Make careful inspection of valve body plate for burrs, and make certain that five small holes are open.
19. Visually inspect pump check valve springs in transfer plate, Fig. 65.

POWERGLIDE

For Linkage Adjustment See Chevrolet Chapter

CONTENTS

Description 316
Trouble Shooting 19

Maintenance

Adding Oil 316
Changing Oil 316

"In Car" Repairs

Oil Pressure Tests 316
Bands, Adjust 317

Repairs Requiring Transmission Removal

Transmission Disassemble 318
Converter Repairs 319
Converter Assemble 328
Clutch 320
Modulator 321
Servo Cover 322
Front Pump 323

Rear Pump 324
Valve Body 324
Low and Drive Valve Body 325
Throttle Valve Inner Lever, Adjust ... 326
Governor 326
Reverse and Low Servo Pistons 327
Planet Unit and Input Shaft 327
Transmission Case, Assemble 327
Transmission to Converter Housing, Assemble 330

DESCRIPTION

A three-element torque converter is used and the overrun coupling used in 1952 models is eliminated. The new torque converter provides improved cruising economy and retains the braking low speed, push starting characteristics of the previous five-element design. In short, this transmission, with the addition of the new automatic shift mechanism, provides Drive with a Low and Cruising range. The flexibility of operation in Drive is extended to supply faster, more positive pick-up from starts, higher acceleration at traffic speeds and increased power for heavy going in mud, sand or snow. The gearbox uses the same basic components as the previous design.

MAINTENANCE

Adding Oil

Check the oil level with the engine idling, parking brake set, transmission warm and control lever in Neutral. Add only automatic transmission fluid when the level reaches the "Add 1 qt" mark on the dipstick. Do not allow dirt to enter the filler tube.

Changing Oil

For refilling the transmission, remove the drain plug from the transmission oil pan. When pan is drained, reinstall drain plug. Remove dipstick from oil filler tube and refill transmission with 3½ quarts of automatic transmission fluid.

Run the engine at idle speed with the transmission in neutral until the engine warms up, then add oil as required to raise the fluid level to the full mark on the dipstick.

If the transmission was removed for repairs but the converter was not drained, about 3½ quarts will be required for refilling. If the converter was drained, about 10½ quarts will be required. Do not overfill.

"In Car" Repairs

OIL PRESSURES, 1955-61

All pressures given in the tables below may vary approximately 5% (higher or lower) from the mean pressures shown. Location of the pressure take-off points are shown in Figs. 1, 2 and 3.

Front Pump Pressure

Idle 425 rpm	50-60
Above idle	85-95
Reverse—425 rpm	50-60
Reverse—Above idle (1955-57)	165-195
Reverse—at 1000 rpm—	
1958-61	240-275
1958-61 6 cyl.	167-191

Transmission In Low Range

Pressure Takeoff Location	Light Throttle 10 MPH	Thru Detent 45 MPH
Low Apply	85-95	85-95
Clutch Apply	0	0
Governor	Fig. 4	Fig. 4
Throttle Valve	*	*

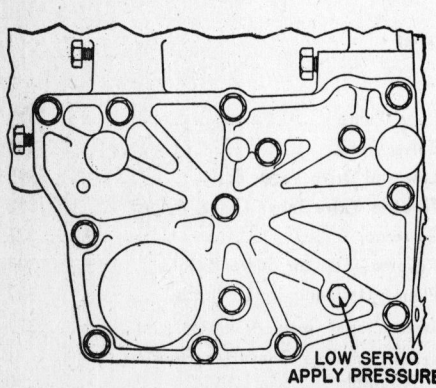

Fig. 1   Oil pressure check point

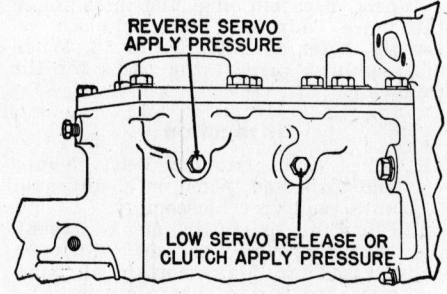

Fig. 2   Oil pressure check points

Transmission In High Range

Low Apply	85-95	85-95
Clutch Apply	85-95	85-95
Governor	Fig. 4	Fig. 4
Throttle Valve	*	*

* Throttle valve pressure will vary from 0 to 62 psi dependent on throttle position. At wide open throttle (thru detent) pressure should read 61 to 63 psi on acceleration.

OIL PRESSURES, 1953-54

Pressure tests will reveal the cause of slippage as well as several other causes of improper operation. Pressure gauge is connected to the following test points: Low servo apply; high clutch (release side of low servo); reverse servo; rear pump.

Drive Range

1. Adjust hot engine idle speed to 430-450 rpm.
2. Place selector lever in "D", and check idling pressure which should be 40-45 psi.
3. Increase speed to about 30 mph and note pressure; then load engine several times by partially applying the brakes while maintaining 30 mph. If vacuum modulator is operating properly, pressure will rise each time. If vacuum modulator is not operating correctly, check vacuum lines for leaks. If no vacuum leaks are found, the trouble is in the vacuum modulator.
4. Apply brakes and accelerate engine to normal stall speed (1560-1610 rpm). Pressure should be 75-100 psi.

Low Range

1. With selector in "L" and engine idling, pressure should be 125-150 psi.
2. Apply brakes and accelerate engine to 1560-1610 rpm. Pressure should be 160-200 psi.

Reverse Range

1. With selector lever in "R" and engine idling pressure should be 125-150 psi.
2. Apply brakes and accelerate engine to 1560-1610 rpm. Pressure should be 160-200 psi.

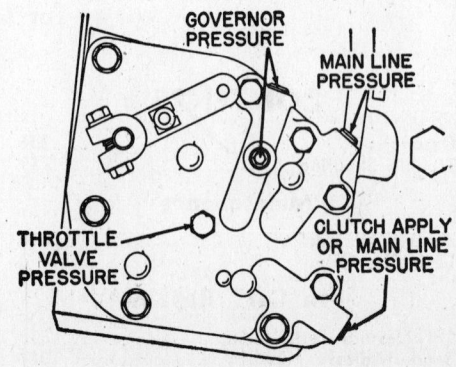

Fig. 3   Oil pressure check points

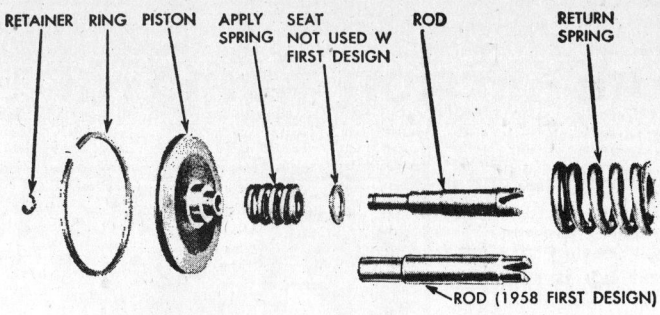

Fig. 5 Low servo piston. Apply spring design is used on all 1953-57 and late production 1958-61

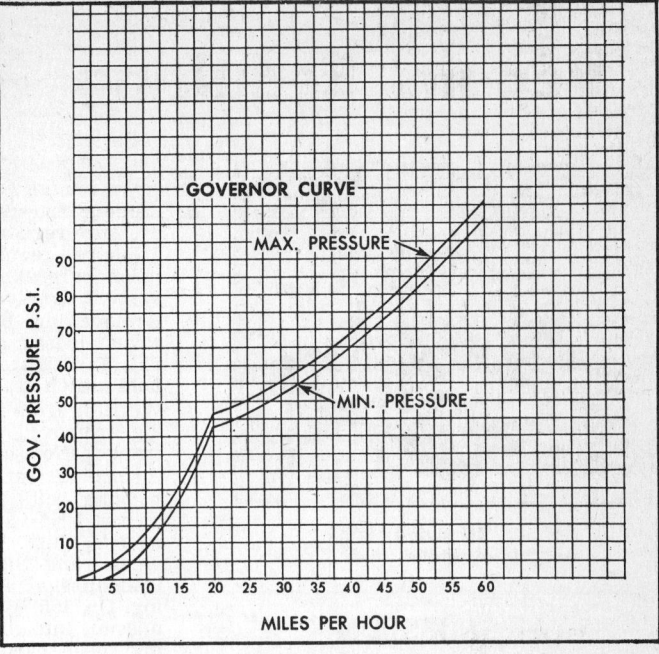

Fig. 4 Governor curve graph. 1955-61

Rear Pump

1. With selector lever in "D" range and parking brake released, accelerate engine until speedometer reads 30 mph. Pressure should be 50-75 psi.
2. Move selector to "L" and check pressure which should be 140-180 psi.

BANDS ADJUST

Low Band

It is essential that the low servo piston design used in a specific transmission be identified as the low servo piston construction dictates the low band adjustment required. Fig. 5 shows the difference in design between the two types. With the servo cover removed, positive identification of the "apply spring" design can be made as the pin retaining the piston head will be visible. After determining the type piston used, the low band may then be adjusted as follows (see Fig. 6).

1. Torque low servo adjusting screw 5 to 7 lb. ft.
2. Back off adjusting screw *three* complete turns if piston has no apply spring, or *four* complete turns on piston with apply spring. *The a-*

mount of back-off must be exactly as specified—not approximately.

Reverse Band, 1955-61

As a means of obtaining a more precise adjustment of the reverse band, it is recommended that a predetermined measurement of required reverse band piston travel be used to calculate the necessary reverse band adjustment. The procedure is as follows:

Rotate reverse brake drum to center it in the reverse band. Then tighten the adjusting screw until all end play between the linkage and the band is removed without compressing the band, Fig. 7. This adjustment should provide a reverse piston travel of $\frac{5}{32}$" to $\frac{7}{32}$" ($\frac{3}{32}$" to $\frac{5}{32}$" on 1959-61 models) from the retracted to the applied positions. To check the adjustment:

1. Measure distance from face of reverse piston outward to side of case with piston in its retracted (inboard) position with a scale rule. Record this dimension.
2. Pull reverse piston outward its full travel by grasping its hub with a pair of pliers. Again measure the distance from the face of the piston to the outboard side of the case. Record this dimension.
3. Subtract one dimension from the other; the difference will be the piston travel, which should be $\frac{5}{32}$" to $\frac{7}{32}$" ($\frac{3}{32}$" to $\frac{5}{32}$" on 1959-61 models).
4. If the travel is too great, tighten adjusting screw and recheck. If travel is too little, back off adjusting

screw and recheck.
5. When correct adjustment is obtained, tighten adjusting screw lock nut 20-25 lb. ft.

Reverse Band, 1953-54

Using one hand to turn down the adjusting screw, Fig. 7, check end play in linkage by grasping reverse servo return spring with the other hand. Continue turning down adjusting screw slowly until end play, as felt by push-pull on piston assembly, is taken up. Then back off adjusting screw $\frac{1}{8}$ to $\frac{1}{4}$ turn and tighten lock nut securely.

This is a sensitive adjustment and must be done carefully. When end play movement of the piston is just taken up, and before backing off the adjusting screw, the band must be free on the drum so that the drum can easily be rotated by hand.

Fig. 6 Adjusting low servo

Fig. 7 Adjusting reverse servo

Repairs Requiring Transmission Removal

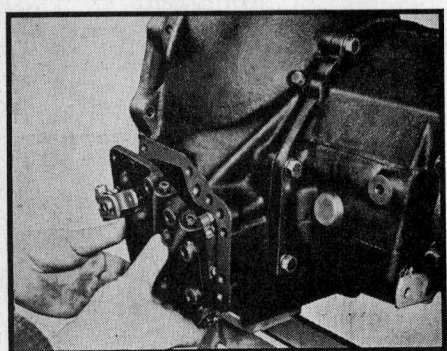

Fig. 8 Removing low and drive valve body

TRANSMISSION, DISASSEMBLE

1. Remove converter assembly.
2. Remove right side cover and gasket, and oil pump suction screen.
3. Remove transmission Low and Drive valve body assembly, Fig. 8, and gasket. *The throttle valve control outer lever assembly should not be removed at this time as it retains the throttle valve inner lever assembly to cover.*
4. Remove modulator assembly and gasket. *When removing the modulator housing be careful modulator pistons do not fall out and become damaged.*
5. Remove servo cover and gasket. *Reverse servo spring, pressure regulator valve springs and low servo piston return spring exert pressure against this cover; therefore, care should be taken when this cover is removed to maintain a pressure*

against it to eliminate possibility of cover breakage.

6. Remove reverse servo spring and pressure regulator valve springs and pressure regulator valve. *Handle valve carefully and lay it aside to prevent damage.*
7. Remove low band adjusting screw cover, loosen adjusting screw lock nut, and tighten adjusting screw to hold clutch assembly in place.
8. Working from inside converter housing, remove converter housing to transmission case self-locking bolt.
9. Remove transmission-to-converter housing bolts and install two guide pins (3/8"-16 x 3 3/4"). On 1953-57 models, shift transmission into "Reverse" and then carefully separate transmission from converter housing. On 1958-61 models, shift transmission into "Low" before separating these parts. On all models, remove transmission case-to-valve body gasket.
10. Remove manual valve from valve body and manual lever from converter housing. On 1953-57 models, remove bronze thrust washer from valve body oil delivery sleeve. On 1958-60 models, remove bronze thrust washer from clutch hub on valve body.
11. Remove valve body from converter housing. On 1958-61 models, remove oil baffle and pickup pipe suction screen.
12. Remove front pump from converter housing.
13. Back off low servo adjusting screw and remove transmission input shaft, clutch assembly and low sun gear thrust washer from transmission as an assembly. On 1958-61 models, remove input shaft snap ring from behind low sun gear thrust washer and remove thrust washer.

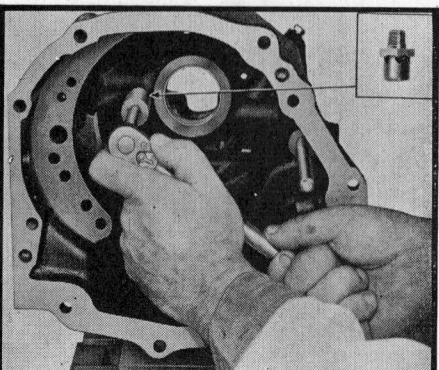

Fig. 9 Removing lubrication pressure relief valve

14. Remove low servo band, strut, low servo piston and its return spring.
15. Remove speedometer driven gear.
16. Remove governor cover and gasket from transmission case.
17. Remove governor, allowing it to turn in a clockwise direction when removing it from the bore.
18. Engage parking lock pawl spring and unhook from case. Remove spring and parking lock pawl.
19. Disconnect short manual shift rod from parking lock lever and remove parking lock lever. Then remove parking lock lever shaft and oil seal from case
20. Remove transmission extension oil seal if seal is leaking and replacement is required.
21. Remove transmission extension and O-ring seal.
22. With a suitable puller tool, remove speedometer drive gear from transmission output shaft. *Do not attempt to remove planet carrier assembly until transmission rear bearing lo-*

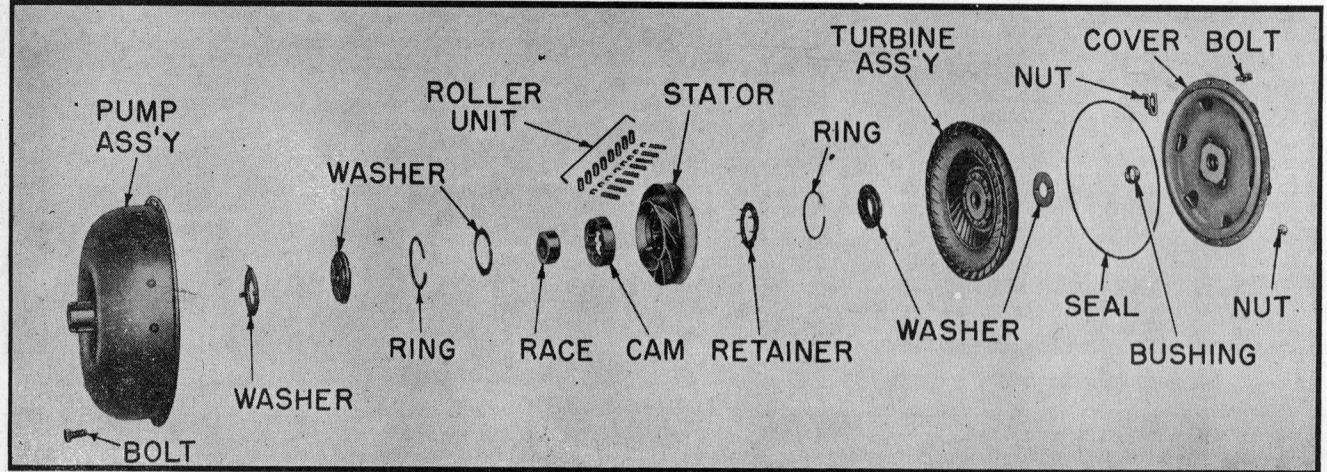

Fig. 10   Exploded view of torque converter. For 1960 a welded converter is used in partial production and is serviced only as a unit

Fig. 11 Removing converter cover bushing

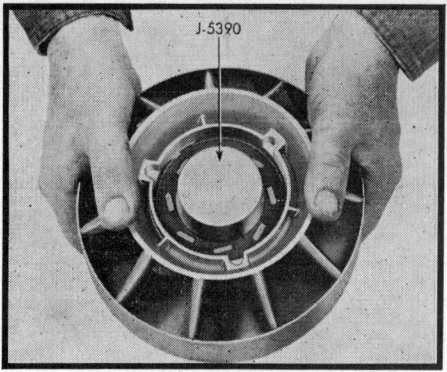

Fig. 13 Use of loading tool to assemble stator

Fig. 14 Checking end play of clutch flange

cating snap rings, retainer and bearing are removed.

23. Remove rear bearing retainer.
24. Remove rear bearing locating snap ring from transmission output shaft.
25. With a suitable puller, remove transmission rear bearing.
26. Remove rear bearing locating front snap ring from output shaft.
27. Working from rear of transmission, position "arrow" or "O" stamped on the face of output shaft at top center. This aligns the drive pin in the output shaft with the eyebrow opening in the rear oil pump cover. The planet carrier assembly can now be removed through the front of the case. *Do not drive on the end of the output shaft as damage may result to the oil pump drive pin or to the pump itself. Be careful not to lose the drive pin in the output shaft as it is a loose fit.*
28. Remove reverse drum and thrust washer.
29. Loosen reverse servo adjusting screw lock nut, back off adjusting screw and remove reverse brake band and servo piston.
30. Remove rear pump assembly.
31. Remove lubrication pressure relief valve from transmission case, Fig. 9.

CONVERTER REPAIRS

Disassemble, Fig. 10

1. Remove converter cover bolts and, with a small punch, drive two split dowel pins out of converter cover.
2. Remove cover, turbine, stator, stator thrust washers and converter pump thrust washer.
3. Remove thrust washer from turbine hub.
4. Remove "O" ring seal from converter cover.
5. Remove stator race from stator.
6. Remove snap ring and over-run cam retaining thrust washer. *Exercise care when separating the parts so that the cam rollers, springs and guides do not become lost.*
7. Remove snap ring and the over-run cam roller and spring retainer. *Exercise care that the cam does not become disengaged from the stator hub and become damaged.*

Inspection

1. Wash all parts in cleaning solvent. *Do not use rags to dry parts; use air.*
2. Inspect converter pump hub inner and outer surfaces for galling or scoring.
3. Inspect converter pump thrust washer for galling or scoring.
4. Check converter pump vanes for looseness or damage.
5. Inspect turbine hub and thrust washer for galling or scoring.

6. Check turbine vanes for looseness or damage.
7. Inspect converter cover bushing for galling, scoring or excessive wear.
8. Inspect stator race and cam rollers for galling or scoring.
9. Inspect cam springs for distortion and spring guides for excessive wear or damage.
10. Inspect over-run cam thrust washer and cam roller and spring retainer for excessive wear or damage.
11. Inspect stator thrust washers for galling, scoring or excessive wear.
12. Inspect stator vanes for looseness or damage.

Converter Cover Bushing, Replace—A precision type converter cover bushing, part number 3702078, should be used for field service replacement. This bushing will not require reaming after installation.

Should the converter cover bushing, during an overhaul inspection show evidence of being galled, scored or excessively worn, it may be replaced easily and accurately using the following procedure:

Insert the cover bushing remover, tool J-5381, in bore of bushing and turn puller screw clockwise, Fig. 11. Place the new bushing on pilot end of the bushing replacer, tool J-5382, and press bushing into position.

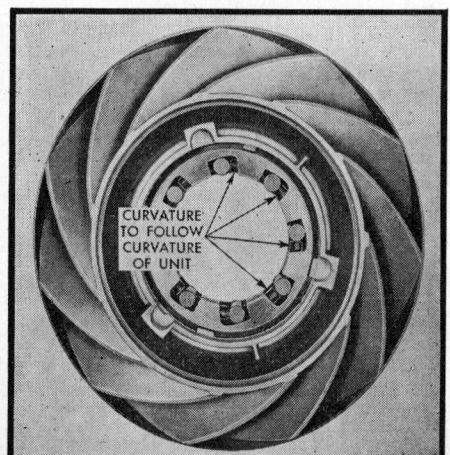

Fig. 12 Curvature of spring retainers

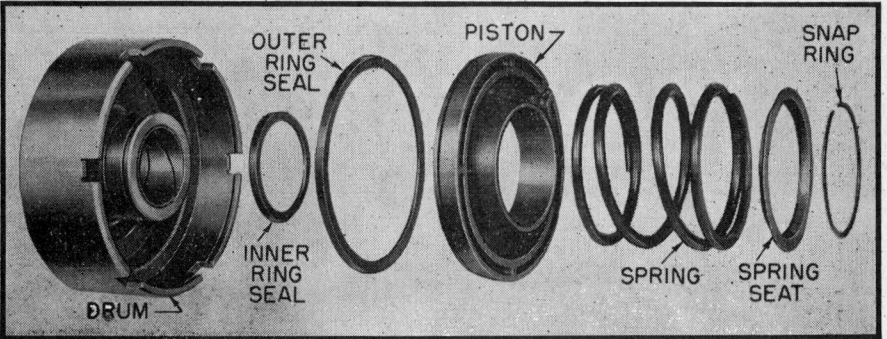

Fig. 15 Layout of clutch drum

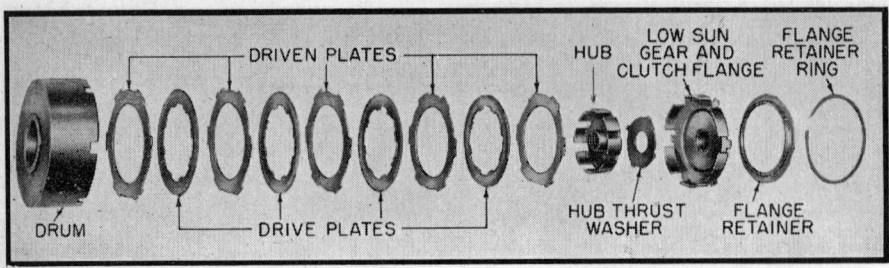

Fig. 16   Layout of clutch assembly.   1953-57

Fig. 18   Checking seating of clutch piston outer seal

Assemble

1. Assemble over-run cam roller and spring retainer to stator so that the prongs of the retainer are pointed toward the rear of the stator. Install retaining snap ring, making sure it is properly seated in groove. *The front of the stator can be identified by the vanes, which are thicker at the front than they are at the rear. The word "Front" are also cast in the stator.*

2. Assemble cam rollers, springs and guides in cam pockets. *Spring guides are curved and this curvature should fit curvature of unit, Fig. 12.*

3. Install over-run cam thrust washer and retaining snap ring. Be sure snap ring is properly seated in its groove.

4. Coat stator race and loading tool, J-5930, with a light film of oil. Then place stator race on pilot end of loading tool and carefully rotate stator over tapered end of loading tool and stator race, Fig. 13. *Carefully rotate stator in free wheel direction (clockwise) to eliminate* possibility of dislocating cam rollers.

5. Check operation of stator. It should free wheel in clockwise direction when viewed from the front.

6. Place converter pump on bench.

7. Install thrust washer to converter pump hub, being sure tabs are engaged in notches of the hub flange.

8. Assemble both thrust washers to stator and install to converter pump as an assembly. *Be sure that the cut-outs in the over-run cam roller and spring retainer are facing upward, toward the turbine.*

9. Install thrust washer on turbine hub and assemble turbine to converter pump.

10. Install new "O" ring seal on converter cover.

11. Align dowel pin holes in converter cover and dowel pins in pump and install converter cover.

12. Install pump-to-cover attaching bolts and lock nuts, tightening them to 12-15 lbs. ft. torque.

CLUTCH

Disassembly, Figs. 15, 16, 17

1. Remove clutch flange retainer ring and retainer.

2. Remove low sun gear and clutch flange from clutch drum.

3. Remove clutch hub thrust washer, hub and clutch plates from clutch drum.

4. Place clutch drum in bench press and install piston ring compression tool, J-5133, to compress clutch release spring.

5. Remove clutch spring snap ring. Release pressure slowly and remove clutch spring seat and spring.

6. Forcibly rap the clutch drum; face down, on a wood surface to remove clutch piston.

7. Remove outer ring seal from piston.

8. Remove piston inner ring seal from hub of clutch drum.

Inspection

1. Wash all parts in cleaning solvent and *air dry*.

2. Inspect drum brake band surface for excessive scoring or burning.

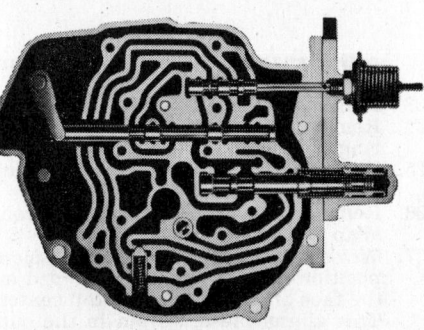

Fig. 19   Vacuum modulator installed.   1958-61

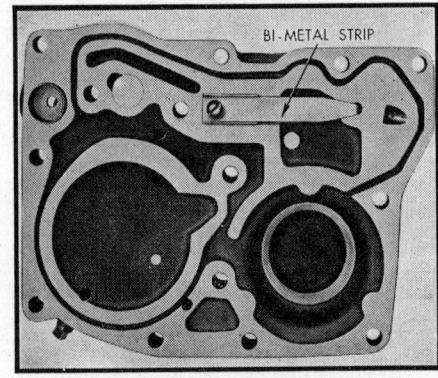

Fig. 20   Lubrication thermostatic valve.   1953-54

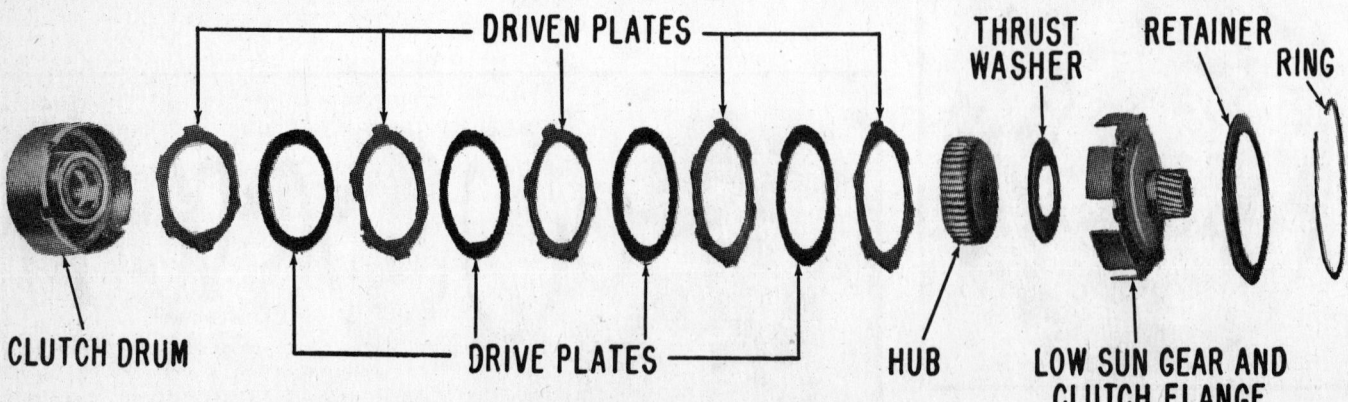

Fig 17   Layout of clutch parts. 1958-61

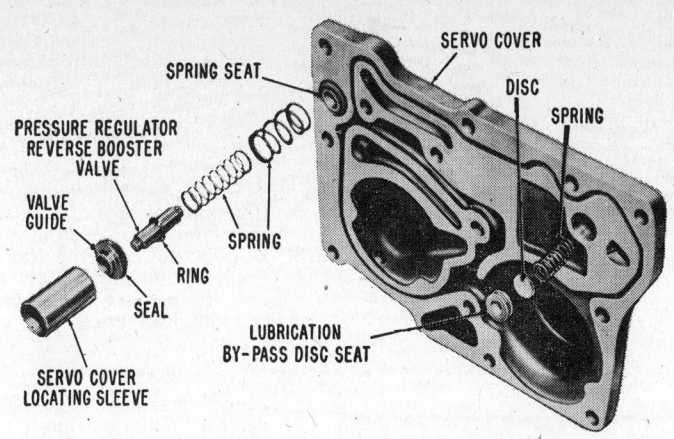

Fig. 21   Layout of servo cover.   1955-57

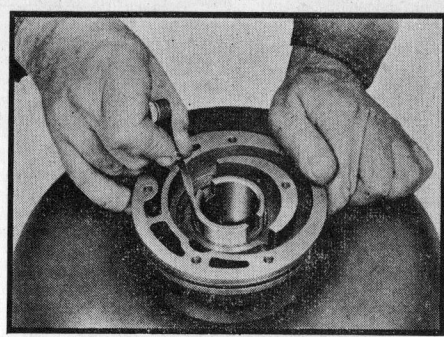

Fig. 24   Measuring clearance between pump body bushing and converter pump hub

Also, check drum bushing for scoring.

3. Check steel ball in clutch piston that acts as a relief valve. Be sure that it is free to move in the hole and that the orifice leading to the rear of the piston is open.

4. Check fit of clutch flange in drum slots. There should be no appreciable radial play between these two parts. Also check low sun gear for nicks or burrs.

5. Check clutch plates for burning or metal pick up. Also check to see that composition plates are a free fit over clutch hub and that steel plates are a free fit in clutch flange. *The steel plates are waved and are not interchangeable with past models.*

Clutch Relief Valve, Replace

Place the steel ball in the retaining hole and carefully stake around edge of the hole to make sure that it will not come out. *Be sure that the ball is free to move after staking.*

Assembly

1. Install new piston outer ring seal on clutch piston, being careful not to stretch seal. Lip of seal should be installed so that it is toward oil pressure side of piston.

2. Install new piston inner ring seal on inner hub of clutch drum with lip of seal toward bottom of piston pocket.

3. Place small amount of transmission oil on inner diameter of clutch drum and onto seals. Then carefully install piston into clutch drum, using a piece of feeler stock to insure seating of outer ring seal in clutch drum, Fig. 18.

4. Install clutch spring and spring seat. Place unit in press and using tool J-5133, compress spring and install snap ring. *When compressing spring be careful spring seat does not hang up in snap ring groove which will cause damage to spring seat and groove.*

5. Place the four equally spaced tabs on clutch hub thrust washer into slots in clutch hub. Then place clutch hub with thrust washer on clutch flange with open side of clutch hub up and install five steel and four composition plates alternately. *When installing plates start with a steel plate. The steel plates are waved instead of dished; therefore, they may be installed with either side toward the low sun gear and clutch flange assembly.*

6. Assemble clutch drum over clutch flange. Invert it and install clutch flange retainer and retainer ring.

7. Check end play with feeler gauge between clutch flange drive lug and drive slot in drum. Maximum allowable end play is .013". *Retainer rings are available in three thicknesses, .055", .064" and .073" to control end play of sun gear and clutch flange in clutch drum.*

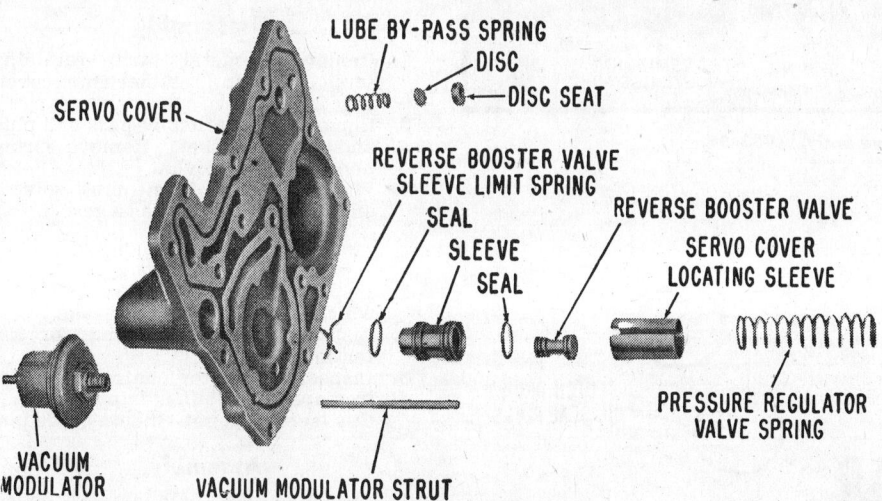

Fig. 22   Layout of servo cover.   1958-61

MODULATOR, 1953-54

Disassembly

1. Remove hydraulic pistons and carefully lay aside to prevent damage.

2. Remove outer cover screws, holding cover down against diaphragm spring pressure.

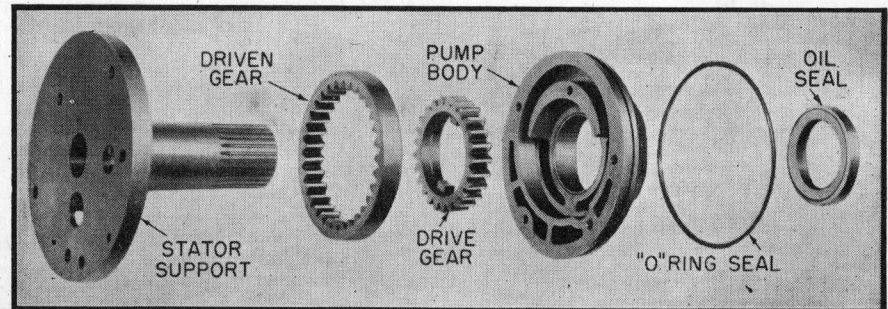

Fig. 23   Layout of front pump

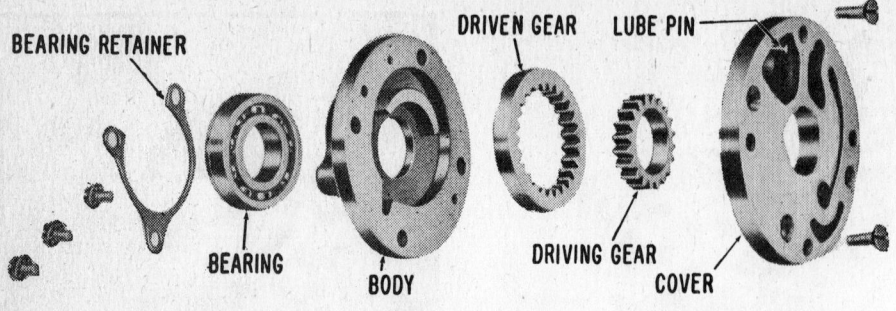

Fig. 25   Layout of rear pump

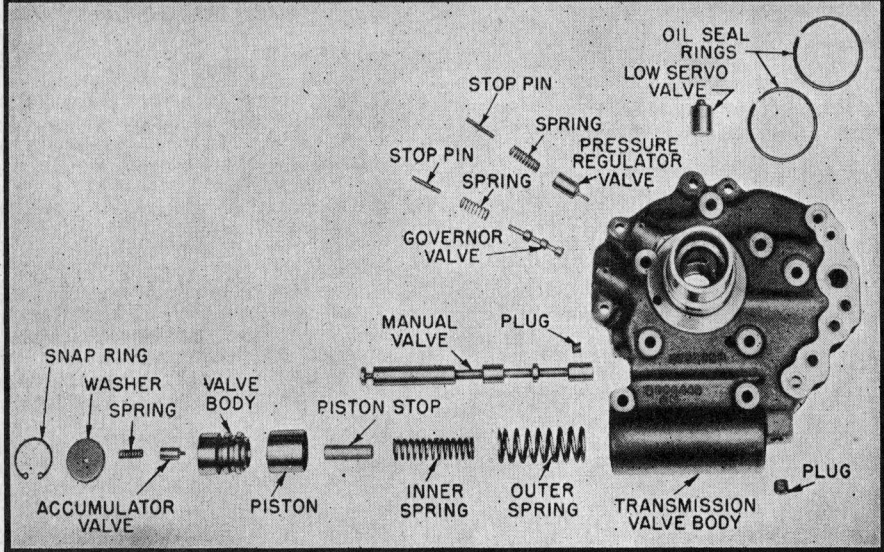

Fig. 26   Layout of valve body. 1953-54

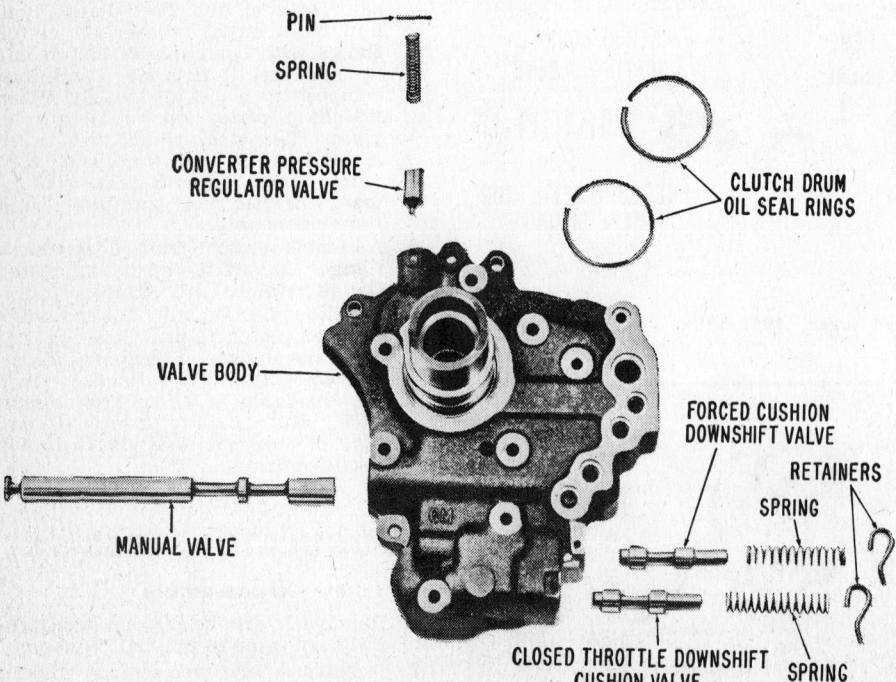

Fig. 27   Layout of main valve body.   1955-57

3. Remove diaphragm and spring.
4. Wash all parts in cleaning solvent and blow out all oil passages. Blow dry with air.

Inspection

1. Check diaphragm spring for distortion or loss of tension.
2. Check diaphragm for wear or cracks that would cause leaks.
3. Inspect outer cover for cracks.
4. Inspect hydraulic pistons for nicks and make sure they operate freely in modulator bore.

Assembly

1. Place assembly tool, J-5389, in hydraulic bore of modulator. Place diaphragm in position and place spring on diaphragm.
2. Install two 10-24x3″ guide pins (part of Pilot Stud Set J-3387) and install modulator cover. Install screws and tighten securely.
3. Install hydraulic pistons with crown toward modulator lever and diaphragm.

MODULATOR, 1958-61

The vacuum modulator is installed in the servo cover, Fig. 19. See *Servo Cover* for modulator strut alignment procedure.

SERVO COVER, 1953-54

Disassembly

1. Remove bi-metal strip retaining screw, strip and retainer from cover, Fig. 20.
2. Remove lubrication by-pass ball plug and copper gasket. Remove spring and ball from cover.
3. Wash all parts in cleaning solvent and blow out all oil passages.

Inspection

1. Inspect cover for nicks or cracks which would result in oil leaks.
2. Inspect by-pass ball spring for distortion.
3. Inspect modulator control lever for free operation. It is important that this lever does not bind on guide pin.

Assembly

1. Install by-pass ball in servo cover.
2. Install by-pass ball spring.
3. Using new plug gasket, install plug and tighten securely.
4. Install bi-metal strip retainer, strip and retaining screw and tighten securely.

1955-57

To disassemble, remove the booster valve parts by pulling on the protruding end of the booster valve. Wash all parts in cleaning solvent and blow out all passages.

Using a small punch, and working through opening in the by-pass disc seat, exert pressure on the disc to make sure the disc and spring are free to operate in their cavity, Fig. 21. Do not remove the disc seat unless there is evidence of damage.

When assembling, do not press the booster valve guide down too far as this would place heavy spring pressure on the guide and provide for the possibility of its release under pressure.

1958-61

To disassemble, Fig. 22, remove the pressure regulator reverse booster valve only. Wash all parts and clean out all passages. Do not remove the disc seat unless there is evidence of damage.

To prevent excessively high oil pressures, the reverse booster valve *must* be assembled into the servo cover and the cover installed on the case as follows:

1. Place new limit spring in servo cover bore with wide tabs seating on bottom of bore.
2. Install O-ring seals on booster valve sleeve and push into bore *so that end of sleeve is $\frac{13}{32}$" below face of servo cover ($\frac{19}{32}$" on models having pressure regulator damper)*.
3. Install reverse booster valve.
4. Install servo cover locating sleeve in bore of cover until it just conctacts booster valve sleeve, *using care not to exert any downward force on reverse booster valve sleeve*.
5. Install pressure regulator valve, damper valve and spring. Install reverse servo spring.
6. Using guide pins, assemble servo cover to transmission case, making certain the locating sleeve is in alignment with pressure regulator valve bore.

When installing the servo cover, before tightening the cover bolts, the vacuum modulator hole in the servo cover and modulator strut hole in the transmission case must be carefully aligned, Fig 19. Failure to install the servo cover with these holes concentric to each other causes the vacuum modulator strut to bind, resulting in improper pressures, harsh shifts and possible clutch failure. Due to the degree of accuracy required, the following alignment procedure is recommended:

1. Cut the hex-head threaded fitting from the end of a discarded vacuum modulator and screw the fitting into the modulator hole in the servo cover.

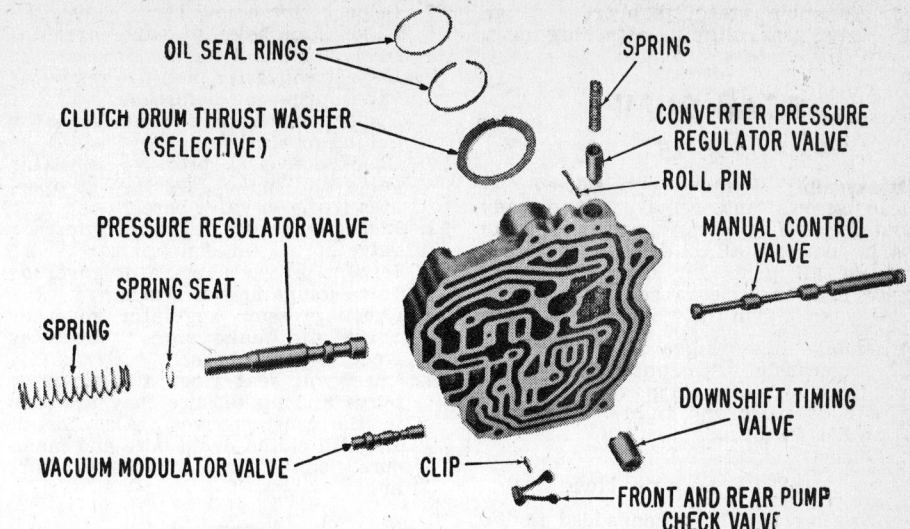

Fig. 28 Layout of main valve body. 1958-61

2. Slide the shank of a $\frac{15}{64}$" drill through both the hole in the fitting and the strut hole in the transmission case. The rod should slide freely through the two holes if alignment is correct. If not correct, shift by tapping the edges of the servo cover with a soft hammer.
3. When alignment is correct, tighten all servo cover bolts to a torque of 15-18 lb. ft., then remove the threaded fitting and drill, and install the strut and vacuum modulator.

FRONT PUMP

Disassembly, Fig. 23

1. Remove stator support from pump body.
2. Remove pump gears from body. *Care must be taken when removing and handling gears not to drop or nick them as they are not heat treated.*
3. Remove "O" ring from pump body.

Inspection

1. Wash all parts and air dry.

2. Inspect pump gears for nicks or damage.
3. Inspect stator support pump face for nicks or scores.
4. Inspect pump body for nicks or scores.
5. Inspect pump body oil seal for excessive wear or evidence of leakage. If necessary, pry out oil seal and install a new one.
6. Inspect pump body bushing for galling or scoring. Check clearance between bushing and converter pump hub, Fig. 24. Maximum clearance .007".
7. With parts clean and dry install pump gears and check: (a) Clearance between outside diameter of gear and body should be .0025-.0055". (b) Clearance between internal gear and crescent should be .003-.009". (c) With scale and feeler gauge check gear end clearance which should be .0005-.0015".

Assembly

1. Install new "O" ring seal in body.
2. Remove gears from body, oil generously with automatic transmission oil and install in body.

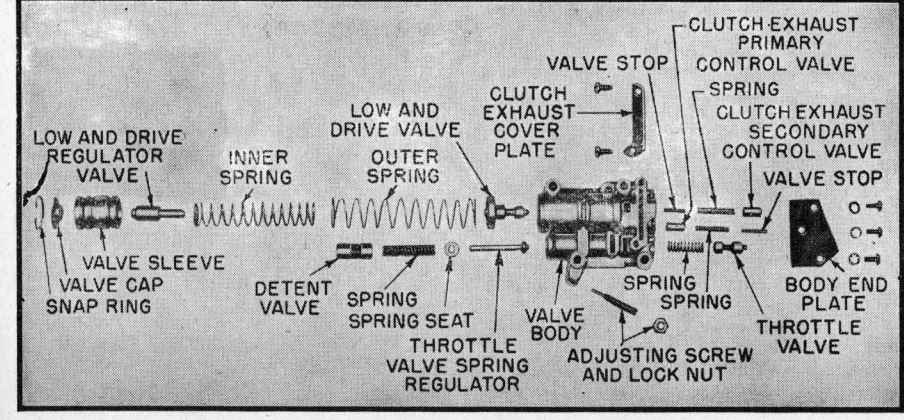

Fig. 29   Layout of low and drive valve body

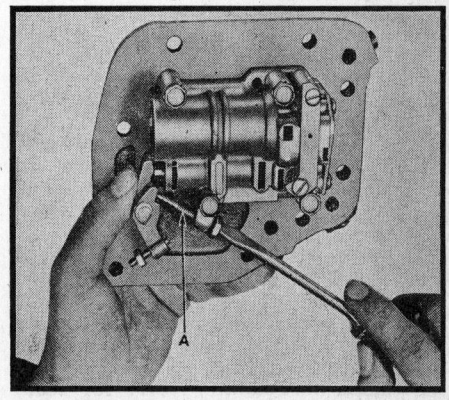

Fig. 30   Setting (A) of throttle valve inner lever adjustment

3. Assemble stator support through drive gear, aligning attaching holes.

REAR PUMP

Fig. 25

Disassembly—Remove two slotted flat head screws and remove pump body plate. Remove pump gears, wash all parts, blow out all oil delivery holes and inspect all parts for damage. Install gears and check clearances, which should be the same as in the front pump.

Assembly—Remove gears from body and oil generously with automatic transmission oil. Assemble gears to body, install body plate and tighten screws to 3½-5 lbs. ft. torque.

1958-61 Service Note

A hollow bolt has been added to the 1958 transmission. This bolt is installed in the top rear pump-to-case hole. This bolt is used for venting purposes to facilitate the addition of oil. The dipstick markings of "add" and "full" are one quart apart, and some transmissions without the hollow bolt were taking only one pint to change the oil level from "add" to "full". Subsequent running, of course, brought the level down to midway between the marks on the dipstick.

VALVE BODY, 1953-54

Disassembly, Fig. 26

1. Using pliers J-4245, remove accumulator special snap ring.
2. Remove accumulator valve spring washer, spring and valve.
3. Remove valve body and piston.
4. Remove inner and outer springs and piston stop from bore.
5. Remove clutch low servo valve from body.
6. Place valve body face down on two wood blocks of equal thickness and, with a small pin punch, drive the pressure regulator governor valve retaining pin from valve body.
7. Remove pressure regulator governor valve spring and valve.
8. Using a small pin punch, drive the converter pressure regulator valve retaining pin from valve body and remove spring and valve.
9. Remove two clutch drum oil seal rings.

Inspection

1. Wash all parts, air dry and blow out all oil passages.
2. Inspect accumulator valve body for scoring and make sure small fibre valve operates freely.
3. Check accumulator body in valve body bore to see that it operates freely.
4. Check accumulator piston for scoring and see that it operates freely in valve body bore.
5. Check accumulator valve for scoring and see that it operates freely in accumulator body bore.
6. Check springs for distortion.

7. Inspect clutch low servo valve and make sure bakelite valve operates freely.
8. Inspect converter pressure regulator valve spring for distortion.
9. Inspect converter regulator valve for galling or scoring.
10. Check converter pressure regulator valve and make sure that it operates freely in valve bore.
11. Inspect pressure regulator governor valve spring for distortion.
12. Inspect pressure regulator governor valve for galling or scoring.
13. Check pressure regulator governor valve and make sure it operates freely in valve bore.
14. Check oil seal rings for nicks or burrs and make sure they are free in the ring grooves. Also install rings in clutch drum bore and make sure hooked ring ends have clearance.

Assembly

1. Install accumulator piston inner and outer springs, and piston stop in accumulator piston. Then install piston in valve body.
2. Install accumulator valve and spring in valve body.
3. Install accumulator valve body in valve body bore.
4. Install accumulator valve spring washer, compress and install special snap ring, making sure it is properly seated in groove.
5. Install clutch low servo valve.
6. Place valve body face down on wood blocks.
7. Assemble spring to converter pressure regulator valve and install assembly. Install retaining pin. *Do not confuse the converter pressure regulator valve spring with the pressure regulator governor valve spring. The converter spring is longer and heavier.*
8. Assemble spring to pressure regulator governor valve and install assembly in valve bore. Install retaining pin.
9. Install two clutch drum oil seal rings.

1955-57

Disassembly, Fig. 27

1. Use needle nose pliers to remove the forced downshift cushion valve re-

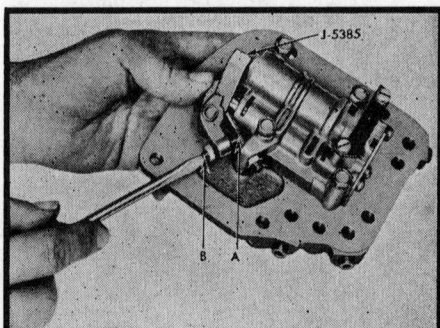

Fig. 31 Setting (2) of throttle valve inner lever adjustment

tainer from valve body.
2. Remove forced downshift cushion valve spring and valve from bore.
3. Using needle nose pliers, remove the closed throttle downshift cushion valve retainer from valve body and remove spring and valve from bore.
4. Place valve body face down on two wood blocks of equal thickness and with a small punch drive out the converter pressure regulator valve retaining pin and remove spring and valve from bore.
5. Remove two clutch drum oil seal rings from oil delivery sleeve.
6. Remove front and rear pump check valve.

Inspection

Wash all parts and air dry. Check all springs for distortion or damage. Check all valves for nicks, burrs, scoring or galling. Also for free operation in bores.

Check oil seal rings for nicks or burrs and make sure that they are free in the ring grooves. Also install rings in clutch drum bore and make sure hooked ring ends have clearance.

Assemble

Reassemble the parts in the reverse order of their removal. Do not confuse the forced downshift cushion valve spring with the closed throttle downshift cushion valve spring. The forced downshift spring is the longer of the two and is of heavier gauge wire.

The interlocking type cast iron rings in this transmission are easily removed from, or installed in, their grooves by applying pressure to the ring with the index finger and thumb at the proper points.

1958-61

Disassemble, Fig. 28

1. Remove hairpin from vacuum modulator valve and remove valve.
2. Place valve body face down on two blocks of wood and with a punch drive out the converter pressure regulator valve retaining pin; remove spring and valve.
3. Remove two clutch drum oil seal rings from oil delivery sleeve.
4. Remove front and rear pump check valve.
5. Remove pressure regulator valve and spring.
6. Remove manual control valve.

Inspection

Wash all parts and air dry. Check all springs for distortion or damage. Check all valves for nicks, burrs, scoring or galling. Also see that they are free in their respective bores. Check oil seal rings for damage and make sure they are free in the ring grooves.

Install rings in clutch drum bore and make sure hooked ring ends have clearance.

Service Note

The downshift timing valve must not be removed unless replacement is necessary as indicated by poor coast down-

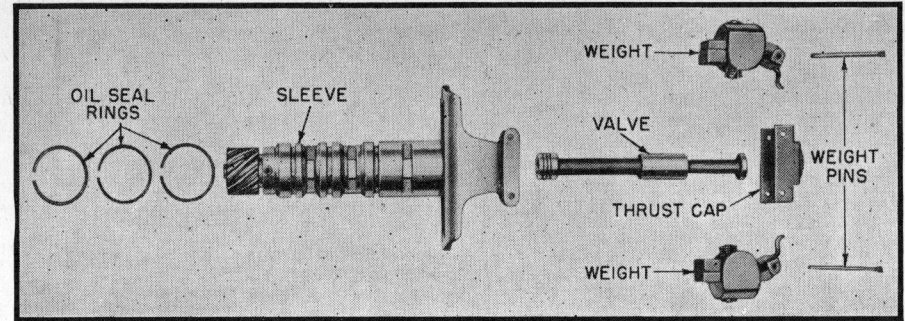

Fig. 32   Layout of governor assembly

shift. However, all linkage adjustments should be checked before it can be determined that the downshift timing valve is faulty.

If necessary to replace the downshift timing valve, pry the old valve out with a small pin punch, using care not to damage its bore. To install, use an arbor press and a $\frac{7}{16}''$ socket and press the new valve in the bore until the tip on the check ball end of the valve is flush to .015'' below the surface of the valve body.

Assemble

Replace the parts in the reverse order of their removal. Be sure to install the vacuum modulator valve clip, and the service check valve.

LOW & DRIVE VALVE BODY

Fig. 29—Should this assembly fail to function properly and it is necessary to disassemble it to locate the trouble, *do not disturb or tamper with the throttle valve adjustment, which has two settings.* The adjustment is pre-set at the factory to 62 psi and should not be disturbed unless new parts that would affect the adjustment are needed. It may be that foreign matter is responsible for the trouble and that a thorough cleaning would restore it to normal operation.

Disassembly, Fig. 29

1. Remove valve body attaching bolts.
2. Hold valve body in one hand and, with a soft faced hammer, tap on inner side of side cover until it is free of locating pins. *Exert pressure on detent valve when separating valve body from cover to prevent loss or damage to parts from falling. A clip can easily be made to retain the detent valve in its bore during disassembly and assembly.*
3. Remove detent valve, spring, spring seat and throttle valve spring regulator.
4. Remove throttle valve and spring.
5. Remove low and drive regulator valve cap retainer. Then remove cap, sleeve and valve as a unit, inner and outer springs and valve.
6. Remove clutch exhaust cover plate.
7. Remove low and drive body end plate. *Exert pressure on end plate while removing attaching screws to*

prevent loss of parts.
8. Remove clutch exhaust secondary control valve, spring and stop.
9. Remove clutch exhaust primary control valve, spring and stop.
10. Remove throttle valve control outer lever, shield, and inner lever and seal.

Inspection

1. Wash all parts, air dry and blow out all oil passages.
2. Inspect detent valve, spring seat, throttle valve spring regulator and throttle valve for nicks, burrs, scoring or galling.
3. Check detent and throttle valves for free operation in their respective bores.
4. Check throttle valve spring regulator for free operation in opening of detent valve.
5. Inspect detent valve spring and throttle valve spring for distortion.
6. Inspect low and drive regulator valve sleeve and valve for nicks, burrs, scoring or galling.
7. Check low and drive regulator valve for free operation in valve sleeve.
8. Check low and drive regulator valve

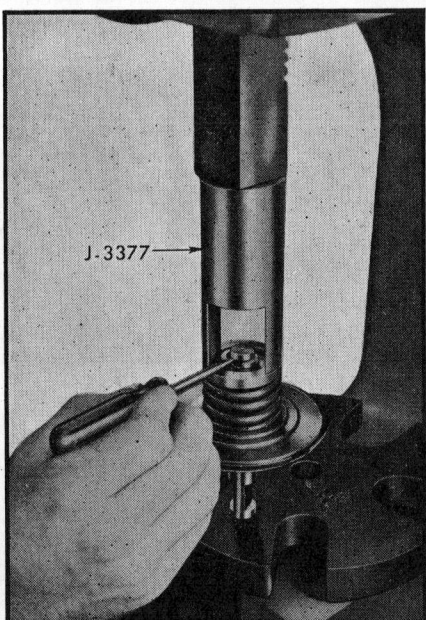

Fig. 33   Removing reverse servo piston keeper

sleeve and valve for free operation in their respective bores.
9. Inspect low and drive valve inner and outer springs for distortion.
10. Inspect clutch exhaust primary and secondary control valves for nicks, burrs, scoring or galling.
11. Check clutch exhaust primary and secondary control valves for free operation in their respective bores.
12. Inspect clutch primary and secondary control valve springs for distortion.
13. Inspect throttle valve inner lever shaft for scoring or galling and the lever for being tight on the shaft.
14. Check throttle valve inner lever shaft for free operation in its bore in the side cover.
15. Inspect detent valve stop in side cover for distortion or damage. Replace with new stop if necessary.
16. Inspect locating pins in valve body and side cover for distortion or damage. Replace with new pins if necessary.
17. Inspect mating surfaces of valve body and side cover. Be sure they are free from nicks or burrs.

Assembly

1. Install low and drive valve in valve body bore. *The valve must be guided into its bore to prevent damage to the bore. This can be accomplished with a piece of brake tubing. Insert it into the valve shank bore, in the rear of the valve body, engaging the tit on the end of the shank in the opening of the tubing. Then slowly move the valve into its proper position.*
2. Install low and drive regulator inner and outer springs in valve body bore.
3. Assemble low and drive regulator valve and cap to the valve sleeve. Then install as an assembly in the valve body. Be sure inner spring is properly seated on sleeve.
4. Compress low and drive regulator valve assembly into valve body and install retainer with snap ring pliers. Be sure retainer is properly seated in its groove in valve body.
5. Install clutch exhaust primary control valve. Then install the spring and stop in clutch exhaust primary control valve. *Do not confuse the primary control valve stop and spring with the secondary control valve stop and spring. The primary stop is longer and the primary spring is shorter.*
6. Assemble clutch exhaust secondary control valve spring and stop to piston. Then install this assembly in the valve body.
7. Install throttle valve spring and valve in valve body.
8. Place low and drive body end plate in position and install attaching screws and lockwashers, tightening screws to 1½-2½ lbs. ft. torque. *Exert pressure on end plate while installing to hold parts in position.*
9. Install clutch exhaust cover plate and tighten attaching screws to 2½-3½ lbs. ft. torque.
10. Install throttle valve spring regu-

Fig. 34   Checking servo piston ring gap

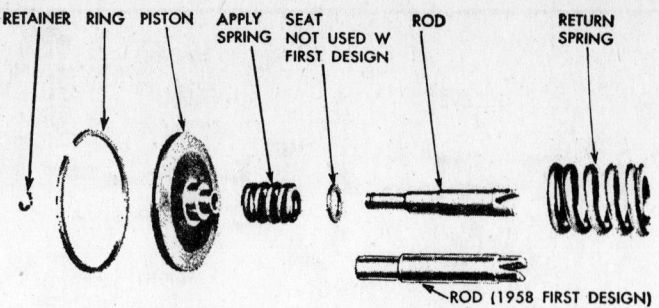

RETAINER RING   PISTON   APPLY SPRING   SEAT NOT USED W FIRST DESIGN   ROD   RETURN SPRING

ROD (1958 FIRST DESIGN)

Fig. 35   Low servo piston. Apply spring design is used on all 1953-57 and late production 1958-61

lator, being sure it is seated on the throttle valve spring.

11. Install detent valve spring seat in the valve body, threading the pin of the throttle valve spring regulator through the opening in the detent valve spring seat.

12. Install detent valve spring and valve, threading the pin of the throttle valve spring regulator through the opening in the detent valve.

13. Place the side cover in a vise face up. Align the locating pin hole in valve body and locating pin in side cover. Exert pressure on the valve body to keep the locating pin in the hole and at the same time compress the detent valve into the valve body. Rotate the valve counter-clockwise until the locating pin in the valve body enters the locating hole in the side cover. *Be sure that the face of the detent valve is resting against*

the detent valve stop pin in side cover.

14. Install low and drive body attaching bolts and lockwashers, tightening bolts to 3½-5 lbs. ft. torque.

15. Install throttle valve inner lever to side cover. Install new seal over shaft and into counterbore in cover. Then install shield.

16. Install throttle valve control outer lever on inner lever shaft.

17. From the underside, install outer lever attaching bolt, washer and nut and tighten securely.

THROTTLE VALVE INNER LEVER, ADJUST

If new throttle valve parts have been installed, the throttle valve should be readjusted. It has two settings and the procedure is as follows:

1. Rotate the throttle valve inner lever until it just contacts the face of the

detent valve. Hold the lever in this position and turn adjusting screw "A", Fig. 30, until it just contacts the flat surface of the step in the lever. Back off one complete turn and lock in this position by tightening the lock nut securely.

2. Place throttle valve inner lever positioning gauge, J-5385, Fig. 31, between the face of the detent valve and throttle valve inner lever. Hold in this position and turn adjusting screw "B" until it contacts threaded body of adjusting screw "A". Tighten lock nut securely.

GOVERNOR

All the components of the governor assembly, Fig. 32, with the exception of the oil seal rings on the governor sleeve, are of a select fit and each assembly is calibrated. Therefore, the only parts serviced for replacement are the governor assembly and oil seal rings.

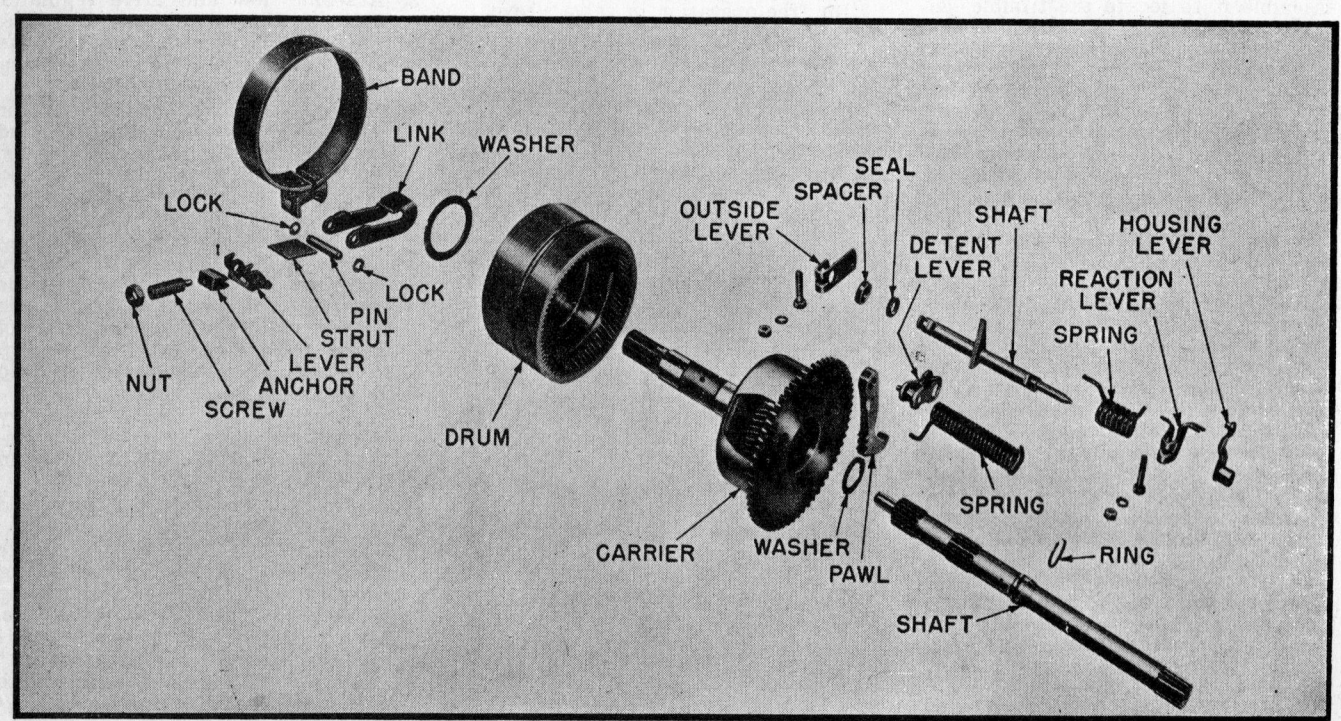

BAND — LINK — WASHER — LOCK — SEAL — SPACER — OUTSIDE LEVER — SHAFT — HOUSING LEVER — DETENT LEVER — REACTION LEVER — SPRING — LOCK — PIN STRUT LEVER ANCHOR — NUT — SCREW — DRUM — SPRING — CARRIER — WASHER — PAWL — SPRING — RING — SHAFT

Fig. 36   Exploded view of planet unit and related parts

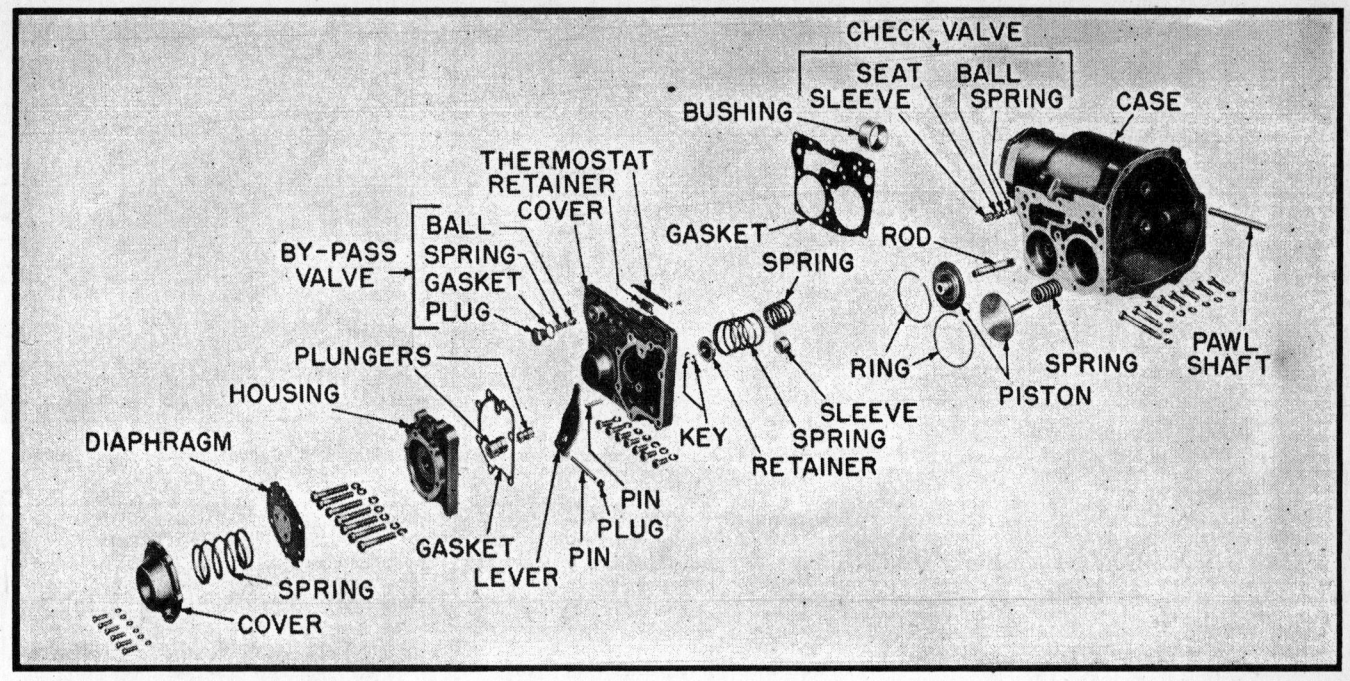

Fig. 38   Transmission case section

Disassembly

1. Cut off one end of each of the governor weight pins and remove pins, thrust cap, weights, and valve from sleeve. *The diameter of the pins should be measured with a micrometer upon their removal as the same gauge piano wire should be used when reassembling, otherwise the calibration of the assembly will be upset.*
2. Remove oil seal rings from sleeve.

Inspection

1. Wash all parts, air dry and blow out all passages.
2. Inspect sleeve for nicks, burrs, scoring or galling.
3. Check sleeve for free operation in transmission case bore.

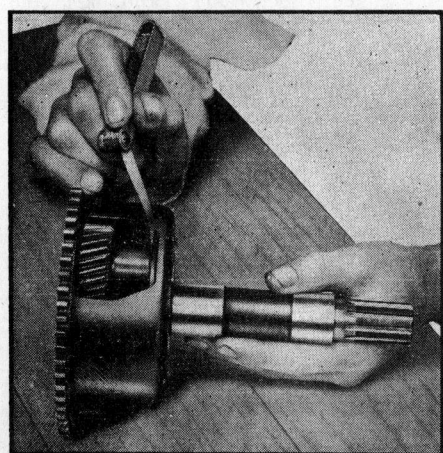

Fig. 37   Checking planet gear end clearance

4. Inspect valve for nicks, burrs, scoring or galling.
5. Check valve for free operation in bore of sleeve.
6. Inspect driven gear for nicks, burrs or damage.
7. Check driven gear for looseness on sleeve.
8. Inspect weight springs for distortion or damage. Do not disassemble weights.
9. Check weights for free operation in their retainers.
10. Inspect sleeve oil seal rings for damage. Then insert rings in governor bore in transmission case and check to see that the hooked ends have clearance.

Assembly

1. Install oil seal rings on sleeve, being sure ends of rings are hooked together and that rings are free in grooves.
2. Install valve in sleeve bore.
3. Align pin holes in thrust cap, weights and sleeve and install new pins. Crimp both ends of both pins to hold them in position.
4. Check weights for free operation on pins.

SERVO PISTONS

Fig. 35

1. Remove reverse servo piston ring from piston and install in reverse piston bore. Check ring gap which should be .005-.010″, Fig. 34.
2. Assemble piston ring on piston.
3. Remove low piston ring from piston and install in low piston bore. Check ring gap which should be .005-.010″.
4. Assemble ring on piston. Insert feeler gauge between side of ring

and one wall of ring groove. Ring clearance should be .0005″-.005″.

PLANET UNIT & INPUT SHAFT

Inspection

1. Wash in cleaning solvent, blow out all oil passages and air dry.
2. Inspect reverse brake drum outside diameter for scoring or burning. Also check internal gear for tooth damage and drum hub bushing for scoring or damage.
3. Inspect planet pinions for nicks or other tooth damage.
4. Check end clearance of planet gears, which should be .006-.030″, Fig. 37.
5. Check reverse sun gear for tooth damage, and sun gear rear thrust washer for damage.
6. Inspect output shaft bearing surface for nicks or scoring and inspect input pilot bushing.
7. Inspect input shaft splines for nicks or damage and check fit in clutch hub and reverse sun gear. Inspect fit of spline in turbine hub.
8. Check oil seal ring for clearance; ring must be free in shaft groove. Remove ring and insert in valve body bore and check to see that hooked ring ends have clearance. Replace ring on shaft.

TRANSMISSION CASE

Inspection, Fig. 38

1. Wash case thoroughly in solvent, air dry and blow out all oil passages.
2. Inspect case for cracks which may contribute to leakage.
3. Inspect case rear bushing for damage or excessive wear.

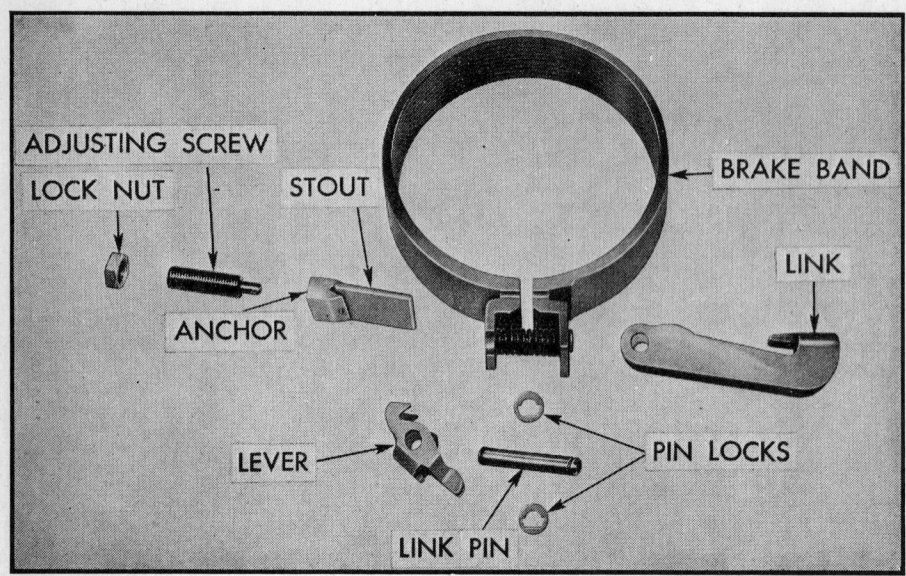

Fig. 39   Reverse brake band

Fig. 41   Guide pins in front pump

Fig. 42   Installing reverse servo piston

BRAKE BANDS

Brake bands have bonded lining which, due to the transmission characteristics and band usage should require very little attention. However, whenever the transmission is disassembled, the bands should be cleaned in solvent, air dried and inspected, Figs. 39 and 40.

1. Check linings for evidence of scoring or burning.
2. Check bands and linings for cracks.
3. Check all band linkage for excessive wear.

ASSEMBLING CONVERTER

1. After cleaning suction screen, install it in the oil sump, making sure sealing ring is in position.
2. Install two guide pins (¼-20x3½") in valve body attaching holes in converter housing.
3. Install new valve body gasket to converter housing.
4. Install valve body over guide pins, install attaching bolts and tighten them to 7½-10 lbs. ft. torque. *Lower left bolt over accumulator bore is self-locking. Therefore, be sure this bolt is installed in this position. Tighten all bolts in a criss-cross manner. Check to make sure manual and pressure regulator valves operate freely.*
5. Align holes in stator support with holes in front oil pump body and install two of the afore-mentioned guide pins in the front pump. Install pump to converter housing, using pump driver J-4263-5. *When installing pump, line up suction and delivery holes on left side of pump.*
6. Install five self-locking bolts through valve body and into pump. Tighten bolts to 7½-10 lbs. ft. torque. *After tightening across pressure regulator valve bore, check valve to make sure it operates freely.*
7. Check and make sure front pump operates freely.

8. Install two pilot studs (⁵⁄₁₆-18x3") in converter housing as guides for low and drive valve body and install new gasket.
9. Install low and drive valve body over guide pins. Install attaching bolts and tighten to 12½-15 lbs. ft. torque.

TRANSMISSION CASE ASSEMBLY
1953-54

1. Install two ⁵⁄₁₆"-18x3" guide pins in rear pump attaching holes. Install new gasket and pump, aligning suction and delivery holes. Install bolts and tighten to 12½-15 ft. lbs.
2. Install reverse servo piston, using ring compressor, Fig. 42. Notch on shaft should be positioned toward front of transmission case.
3. Install reverse band and strut assembly with thin end of band away from piston. Thread adjusting screw in until it indexes with hole in anchor.
4. Install bronze thrust washer on hub of reverse drum and install drum into case and brake band.
5. Rotate rear pump drive gear lug to top of pump. Then install planet carrier in drum, aligning slot on

carrier shaft with lug on pump drive gear. Carrier shaft should protrude a minimum of ⅞" and indicates proper seating of pump drive gear lug in shaft slot, Fig. 43.
6. Use a suitable pusher tool (or Tool J-938) into threaded end of planet carrier output shaft and bolt yoke of tool to rear face of transmission case. Turn tool handle counterclockwise until output shaft is seated in rear bearing. Remove tool.
7. Install universal joint front yoke, washer, lockwasher and bolt and tighten to 25-30 ft. lbs.
8. Hold reverse servo return spring in one hand and with the other slowly tighten the adjusting screw until end play, as felt by push-pull on piston,

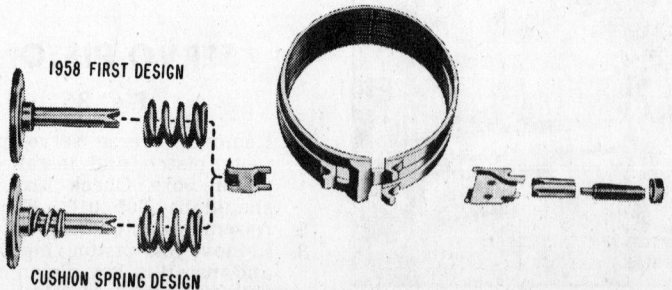

Fig. 40 Low brake band and related parts. 1953-57 and late production 1959-61 uses the cushion spring design

Fig. 43 Checking seating of output shaft. 1953-54

Fig. 44 Measuring sun gear depth

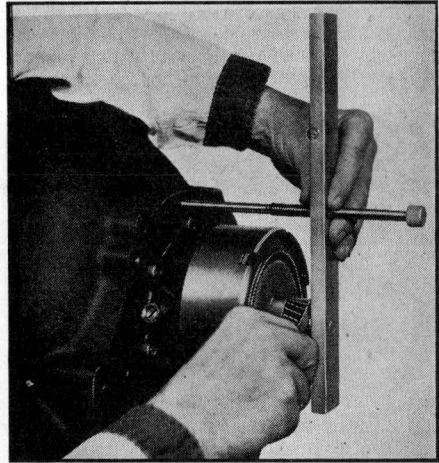

Fig. 45 Checking for proper low to reverse sun gear clearance

is just taken up. Then back off adjusting screw ⅛ to ¼ turn and tighten nut securely. When end play movement is just taken up, and before backing off the adjusting screw, the band must be free on the drum so that the drum can easily be rotated by hand.

9. To determine the thickness of the low sun gear-to-reverse sun gear thrust washer, proceed as follows:
   a. Install bronze thrust washer and clutch assembly on oil delivery sleeve.
   b. To measure distance from case flange to reverse sun gear, loosen set screw of Tool J-4260 and place bar of tool against case flange with stem of tool against face of reverse sun gear. While holding tool in this position, tighten thumb screw, Fig. 44.
   c. There are three hardened and ground steel washers furnished with this tool which are .095″, .120″ and .145″ thick. These washers are the same thickness as the bronze thrust washers available for service use in transmission.
   d. Select the .120″ steel washer furnished with the tool and place it over the pilot of the tool. Insert pilot in bore of low sun gear and, while holding tool securely, check clearance between end of low sun gear and steel washer with feeler gauge, Fig. 45. This clearance should be .007″ to .035″.
   e. If clearance is not within above limits, remove tool and then recheck, using either of the other two steel washers furnished with the tool until proper clearance is obtained.
   f. When proper clearance is obtained, install a bronze thrust washer which is the same thickness as the steel washer.
10. After above checks are completed, remove clutch assembly and thrust washer from oil delivery sleeve.
11. Install parking lock lever shaft and apply spring in case. Install small lip seal over end of parking lock lever shaft and into counterbore of case with lip of seal toward inside of case.
12. Install flat washer and parking lock lever on end of shaft, pushing lever onto shaft to obtain .000″ to .010″ clearance between lever and washer. Then tighten clamp screw to 8-12 ft. lbs.
13. Install parking lock pawl over pawl support rod and install pawl spring.
14. Wind up pawl spring, using Tool J-3383 so that spring catches on inside of case.
15. Install input shaft to clutch unit. Install thrust washer previously selected on reverse sun gear splines of input shaft. *It is important that the flat side of thrust washer be installed toward sun gear*, Fig. 46.
16. Install unit assembly into case, indexing input shaft pilot with pilot in output shaft and low sun gear with short pinions in planet carrier, Fig. 47.
17. Install low servo release spring on servo piston shaft and install piston and spring into case, using ring compressor J-3365.
18. Install low band over clutch drum with thin end of band toward piston.
19. Place strut guide spring over piston and anchor strut in piston slot with other end of strut engaging band.

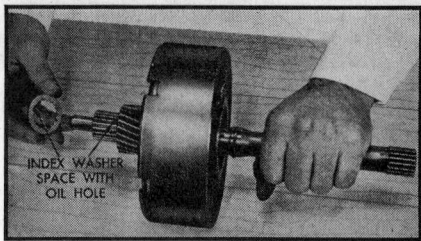

Fig. 46 Alignment of thrust washer oil slot with shaft oil hole

Fig. 47 Installing clutch and shaft into case

Fig. 48 Installing parking pawl spring

Fig. 49 Setting manual valve in reverse position

20. Place band strut in band groove, then engage slotted end of anchor over strut and locate over adjusting screw.
21. Install speedometer driven gear and tighten to 45-50 ft. lbs.

1955-61

1. Install two $\frac{5}{16}$"-18x3" guide pins in rear pump attaching holes. On 1958-61, install lube metering valve and governor filter screen.
2. Install new gasket and pump, aligning suction and delivery holes. Then install bolts and tighten to 12½-15 ft. lbs.
3. Install lubrication pressure relief valve in rear of transmission case and tighten securely.
4. Install reverse servo piston, using a suitable ring compressor, Fig. 42. Notch on shaft should be positioned toward front of case.
5. Install reverse band and lever and link. Then install anchor and strut. Thread adjusting screw in until it indexes with hole in anchor.
6. Install thrust washer on hub of reverse drum and install drum into case and reverse band.
7. Rotate rear pump drive slot to top of pump. Fill drive pin hole in output shaft of planet carrier with cup grease and install drive pin.
8. On 1957-61 models, install planet carrier including steel thrust washer on shaft in drum. Position "O" stamped on face of output shaft at top center. This aligns drive pin in output shaft with drive slot in internal gear of rear pump.

    On 1955-56 models, install planet carrier in drum, positioning arrow on face of external gear of planet carrier at top center. This aligns drive pin in output shaft with drive slot in internal gear of rear pump.
9. Install rear bearing locating front snap ring in its groove in output shaft.
10. Install rear bearing. *Groove in outer diameter of bearing should be to rear of transmission.*
11. Install rear bearing retainer in groove in outer diameter of rear bearing and attach to rear pump with screws and lockwashers. Tighten to 9-11 ft. lbs.
12. Install rear bearing rear locating snap ring in its groove in output shaft.
13. Install speedometer drive gear on output shaft. Center on raised ground surface of shaft so that it will mesh properly with speedometer driven gear.
14. Install new O-ring seal on speedometer driven gear fitting. Assemble driven gear in fitting and then install as an assembly in bore of extension. Install retainer, capscrew and lockwasher and tighten screw to 3½-5 ft. lbs.
15. Position new O-ring seal on transmission extension .Then carefully install extension on transmission case. Tighten attaching capscrews to 15-18½ ft. lbs.
16. Install extension oil seal.
17. On 1957-61 models, rotate reverse

Fig. 50 Converter assembly holding tool

drum to center it in reverse band. Tighten adjusting screw until all end play between linkage and band is removed without compressing band. This adjustment should provide a reverse piston travel of $\frac{5}{32}$" to $\frac{7}{32}$" from the retracted to applied positions.

On 1955-56 models, tighten adjusting screw until all end play is removed between linkage and band without compressing band. If reverse drum is not free to rotate after this adjustment has been made, back off the adjustment ¼ turn at a time until the drum is free to rotate.

18. To determine the correct thickness of the selective thrust washer (in front of clutch drum) proceed as follows:
   a. To measure distance from case flange to input sun gear, loosen set screw of tool J-4260, Fig. 44, and place bar of tool against case flange with stem of tool against face of input sun gear. While holding tool in this position, tighten thumb screw. *Washer behind input sun gear must be in proper location before check is started or a false reading will be obtained.*
   b. Select a thrust washer and install same with clutch assembly on valve body. Insert pilot of tool into bore of low sun gear. While holding tool securely, check clearance between end of low sun gear and bar of tool, Fig. 45.
   c. On 1958-61 models, to obtain a clearance of .025" to .050", washers of .061", .078" and .106" thicknesses are available. For 1957 models, washers of .078", .106" and .134" thicknesses are available to obtain a clearance of .025" to .050". On 1955-56 models, clearance should be .007" to .035" and washers of .095", .120" and .145" are available.
   d. After obtaining the correct clearance, remove clutch assembly and thrust washer from oil delivery sleeve.
19. Install parking lock lever shaft and apply spring in case. Install small lip seal over end of parking lock lever shaft and into counter-

bore of case with lip of seal toward inside of case.
20. Install flat washer and parking lock lever on end of lock lever shaft, pushing lever onto shaft to obtain .000" to .010" clearance between lever and washer. Connect short manual shift rod to parking lock lever and tighten clamp screw to 5-7 ft. lbs.
21. Install parking lock pawl over pawl support rod and install pawl spring.
22. Wind up pawl spring so that spring catches on inside of case.
23. On 1955-58 models, install input shaft to clutch unit. Install thrust washer and locating snap ring on input shaft. Install unit assembly into case, indexing input shaft pilot with pilot in output shaft and low sun gear with short pinions in planet carrier.

    On 1959-61 models, install input shaft to clutch unit. Install low sun gear bushing on input shaft spline, bottoming bushing against shoulder on shaft. (Wire type snap ring, used on input shaft with early type splined thrust washer is not used with this later design.) Assemble low sun gear thrust washer into planet carrier by tilting washer slightly to permit flange to enter behind short planet pinions. Vaseline can be used to hold washer in place.
24. Install low servo piston release spring on servo piston rod and install piston and spring into case, using piston ring compressor J-3365.
25. Install low band over drum.
26. Place the apply strut in piston shaft slot with other end of apply strut engaging band.
27. Place band anchor strut in band groove, then engage slotted end of anchor over strut, locating other end of anchor over adjusting screw.
28. Install governor in bore in transmission case, allowing it to rotate in a counterclockwise direction, as the driven gear of the governor meshes with the drive gear of the output shaft.
29. Install two guide pins ($\frac{5}{16}$"-18x3") as guides for governor cover and install new gasket.
30. Install governor cover and tighten attaching bolts to 9-11 ft. lbs.

ASSEMBLING TRANSMISSION TO CONVERTER HOUSING

1. Install manual valve in valve body and manual valve inner lever in converter housing. Index lever pin with pick-up slot in valve.
2. On 1958-61 models, set manual valve so end of valve protrudes 1$\frac{1}{4}$" from face of valve body, which places valve in "Low" position.

    On 1953-57 models, set manual valve so end of valve protrudes 1½" from face of body which places valve in "reverse" position.
3. Install new valve body to case gasket.
4. Raise transmission manual valve

lever to top detent position which is "Low" on 1958-61 models and "Reverse" on prior models. This aligns reaction lever so that it will index with manual valve inner lever.

5. Place clutch drum thrust washer over oil delivery sleeve.

6. Install two guide pins (⅜"-16x3¾") in converter housing. Push case and converter housing together, checking to see that the reaction lever indexes properly with manual valve inner lever. Tighten case-to-housing bolts to 29-37½ ft. lbs.

6. From front of converter housing, install special self-locking bolt and tighten to 29-37½ ft. lbs.

7. Install two guide pins (5/16"-18x3) as guides for servo cover and install new servo cover gasket.

8. Install servo cover locating sleeve in bore of cover, being careful not to exert any downward pressure on reverse booster valve sleeve.

9. Install pressure regulator valve and spring, and reverse servo return spring.

10. On 1958-61 models, install servo cover on guide pins. Then apply pressure to cover to compress springs, at the same time making sure that the locating sleeve is in alignment with pressure regulator valve bore. Secure cover with bolts

but do not fully tighten. Use non-hardening sealer under head of bolt installed directly above vacuum modulator. Before tightening servo cover bolts, the vacuum modulator hole in cover and though hole in transmission case must be carefully aligned. Failure to achieve alignment of these holes causes vacuum modulator strut to bind, resulting in improper pressures, harsh shifts and possible clutch failure. The following procedure is recommended due to the accuracy required:

a. Use a discarded vacuum modulator cut in half at the diaphragm and screw the threaded half in the modulator hole in the servo cover.

b. Slide a 15/64" drill through both holes. The drill should slide freely through both holes if alignment is correct; otherwise shift by tapping on edges of servo cover as required. When alignment is correct, tighten all servo bolts to 15-18½ ft. lbs. Then remove the modulator half and drill, and install strut and vacuum modulator. Be sure springs seat properly in servo cover.

On 1953-57 models, install servo cover on guide pins. Then, applying pressure to cover to compress springs, make sure that the locating sleeve is in alignment with pressure regulator valve bore.

Secure cover and tighten bolts to 12½-15 ft. lbs. Be sure springs are properly seated in servo cover.

11. On 1958-61 models, tighten low servo adjusting screw to a torque of 5-7 ft. lbs. The input and output shaft must be rotated simultaneously to properly center low band on clutch drum. Then back off three complete turns if servo piston is first design (without cushion spring) or four turns if cushion spring is used (second design). Then tighten lock nut securely and install adjusting screw cover.

On 1953-57 models, tighten low servo adjusting screw to 5-7 ft. lbs. Then back off four complete turns and tighten lock nut securely. Install adjusting screw cap.

12. Install converter assembly in converter housing, aligning front pump drive gear lugs with drive slots in converter pump hub. *After converter is installed, check to insure engagement of converter pump hub drive slots in lugs of front pump drive gear. This dimension should be 1 9/16" or less.*

13. Install converter holding tool, Fig. 50, to converter housing to prevent converter moving forward prior to installation of transmission assembly in car, otherwise disengagement of slots with lugs of front pump drive gear may occur.

TORQUEFLITE 6 Transmission Section

DESCRIPTION

The transmission, Fig. 1, combines a torque converter with a fully automatic, three speed gear system. The torque converter housing and transmission case are an integral aluminum casting. The transmission consists of two multiple disc clutches, an overrunning clutch, two servos and bands, and two planetary gear sets to provide three forward ratios and a reverse ratio. The common sun gear of the planetary gear sets is connected to the front clutch by a driving shell which is splined to the sun gear and to the front clutch retainer. The hydraulic system consists of a front and rear pump, and a single valve body which contains all of the valves except the governor valve.

The torque converter is attached to the crankshaft through a flexible driving plate. Cooling of the converter is accomplished by circulating the transmission fluid through an oil-to-water type cooler, located in the radiator lower tank. The torque converter is a sealed unit which requires no servicing other than cleaning.

Operation

The transmission is operated by a gearshift control unit consisting of five push buttons. In the drive range, the transmission shifts through all three gear ratios automatically. Shift points are determined by throttle opening and

car speed. If additional acceleration is desired while in drive range, the transmission will downshift (depending on vehicle speed) to second gear automatically when the accelerator pedal is completely depressed.

The intermediate or second position range is used to operate the transmission in the first two gears only. This range is suitable for heavy city traffic where the driver may desire part throttle second gear operation for more precise control. It may also be used on long down grades where additional engine braking is needed. A low or first position range is also available to keep the transmission in first gear only. This position provides added handling ease in mountain driving and exceptional pulling qualities in sand and snow.

MAINTENANCE

Adding Oil

Fluid level should be checked every 2000 miles or 60 days, whichever occurs first. With engine not running, the oil level should be at the "Full" mark when cold. When checking a warm transmission, oil level should be between the "Full" mark and ⅝" above the "Full" mark.

To check the oil level, apply the parking brake and operate the engine at idle speed. Depress each push button momentarily, ending with the "N" button

pushed in. Then add oil as necessary to bring the oil to the prescribed level.

Changing Oil

Oil should be changed every 10,000 miles or one year, whichever occurs first. Police cars, taxicabs and cars that frequently tow trailers, operate in heavy traffic in hot weather or operate continously with abnormal loads should have more frequent periodic maintenance. Transmission should not be idled in gear for long periods.

1. Remove drain plug from transmission oil pan and allow oil to drain.

2. Remove flywheel access plate, remove torque converter drain plug and allow to drain. Replace drain plug.

3. Remove transmission oil pan, clean intake screen and pan, and reinstall.

4. Install five quarts of approved automatic transmission fluid through filler tube.

5. Start engine and add approximately one quart while engine is idling.

6. Allow engine to idle for about two minutes. Then with parking brake applied, depress each push button momentarily, ending with the "N" button pushed in.

7. With engine shut off, add oil as necessary to bring level to "Full" mark. With transmission warm and engine shut off, oil level should be between "Full" mark and ⅝" above "Full" mark.

HYDRAULIC PRESSURE CHART

Year	Line & Front Servo Release					Lubrication		Governor		Rear Servo Apply		
	Selector Position	Rear Wheels	Engine R.P.M.	Line Pressure	Servo Release Pressure	Engine R.P.M.	Lube Pressure	Engine R.P.M.	Pressure	Selector Position	Engine R.P.M.	Servo Apply Pressure
DODGE DART, LANCER, PLYMOUTH, VALIANT												
1960–61	D	Free	800	52–60	45 Min.	800	5–25	320	2–4	R	1600	230–280
	D	Free	3500	90–96	80 Min.			1000	28–32			
								1400	40–45			
								2800	73–83			

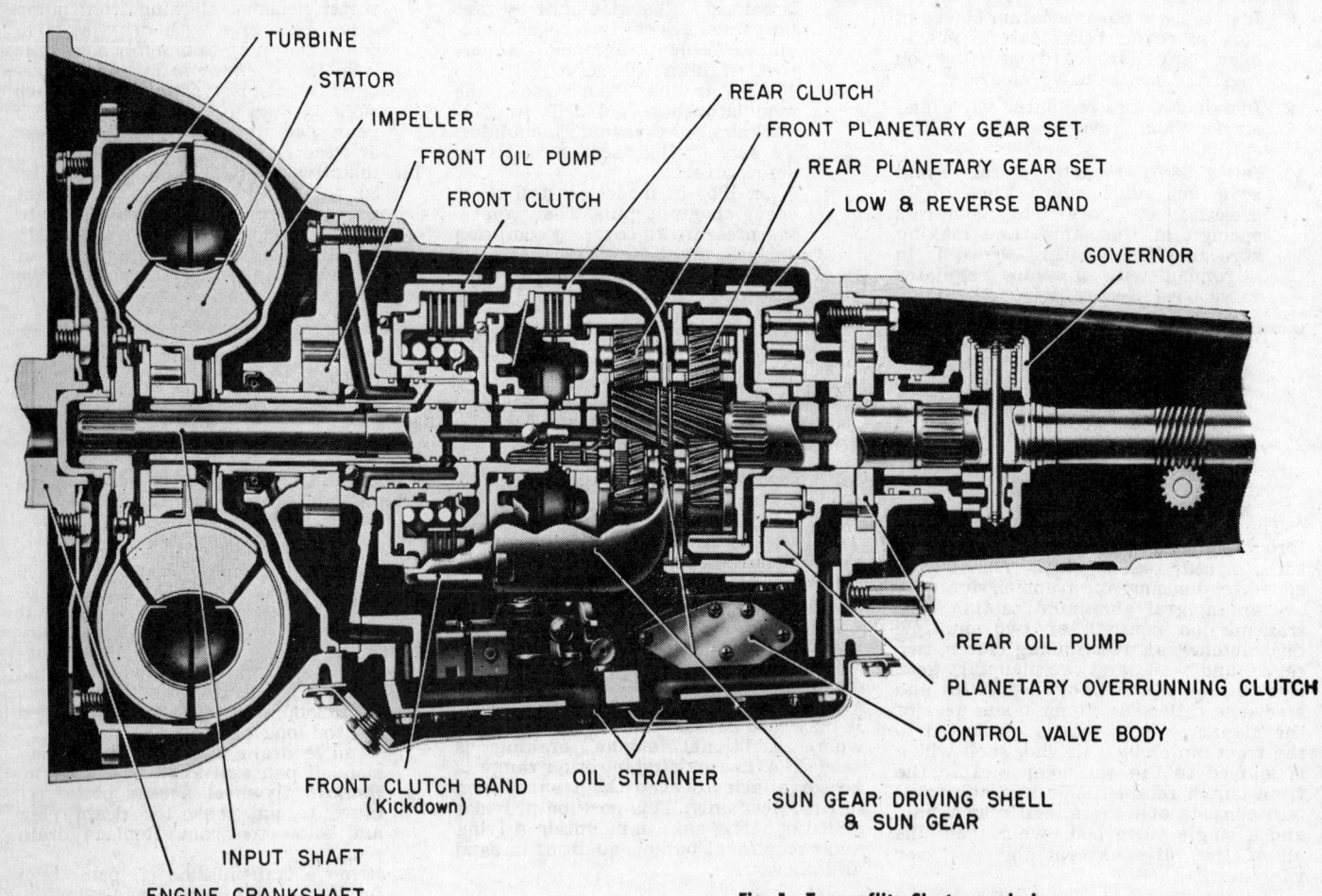

Fig. 1 Torqueflite Six transmission

"In Car" Repairs

BANDS, ADJUST

Kickdown Band

The kickdown band adjusting screw is located on the left side of the transmission case near the throttle lever shaft.
1. Loosen lock nut and back off approximately five turns. Check ad-

justing screw for free turning in transmission case.
2. Using an inch-pound torque wrench, tighten the band adjusting screw to a reading of 47-50 inch lbs.
3. Back off adjusting screw 2⅝ turns. Hold adjusting screw in this position and tighten lock nut to a torque of 20-25 ft. lbs.

Low and Reverse Band

1. Raise vehicle, drain transmission and remove oil pan.
2. Loosen adjusting screw lock nut and back off nut approximately five turns. Check adjusting screw for free turning in the lever.
3. Using an inch-pound torque wrench,

tighten band adjusting screw to a reading of 47-50 inch lbs.

4. Back off adjusting screw 5¼ turns. Hold adjusting screw in this position and tighten lock nut to 20-25 ft. lbs.

5. Install oil pan and torque bolts to 13-17 ft. lbs. Fill transmission with fluid.

CONTROL CABLE REPLACE

1. To remove the cable at the transmission end, drain approximately two quarts of fluid from transmission.

2. Depress the "L" push button.

3. Remove neutral starting switch.

4. Remove cable to transmission adjusting wheel lock screw.

5. Insert screwdriver through neutral starting switch opening. Push screwdriver gently against upper projecting portion of cable lock spring, and pull outward on cable to remove cable from adapter and case.

6. To install cable, have an assistant engage the "R" button and hold it firmly engaged until the cable attachment operation is completed.

7. Back the adjusting wheel off the cable housing (counterclockwise) until only two or three threads are showing behind the wheel on the guide.

8. Lubricate cable housing with transmission fluid, insert cable in case, push inward on cable, making sure lock spring engages cable. Then adjust cable as outlined below.

CONTROL CABLE ADJUST

1. Have an assistant hold the "R" button firmly depressed.

2. Remove cable adjustment wheel lock screw.

3. Back off adjusting wheel on cable guide (counterclockwise) until only two or three threads are showing behind wheel on guide. *Check wheel for free turning on guide; remove any burrs or dirt in threads of cable guide that may interfere. Lubricate threads with a few drops of transmission fluid.*

4. Hold cable guide centered in hole

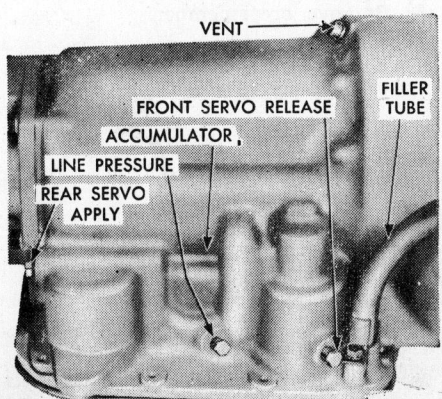

Fig. 3 Oil pressure test locations at right side of case

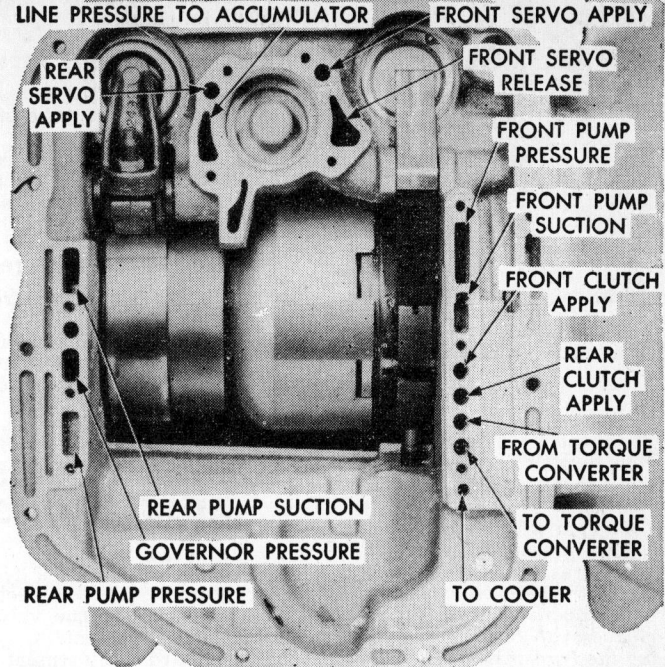

Fig. 2 Air pressure check points

of case and apply only enough inward force to bottom assembly at reverse detent. While holding cable bottomed, rotate adjustment wheel clockwise until it just contacts the case squarely.

5. Turn wheel clockwise just enough to make the next adjustment hole in the wheel line up with the screw hole in the case.

6. Counting this hole as number one, continue turning the wheel clockwise until the fifth hole lines up with the screw hole in the case.

7. Install lock screw and tighten to 30-50 inch lbs.

AIR PRESSURE CHECKS

The front clutch, rear clutch, kickdown servo, and low and reverse servo may be checked by applying air pressure to their respective passage after the valve body is removed, Fig. 2. To make the checks, proceed as follows, *being sure the compressed air is free of all dirt and moisture.*

Front and Rear Clutches

Apply air pressure to the clutch passages (one at a time) and listen for a dull "thud" which indicates that the clutch is operating. Hold the air pressure on for a few seconds and check system for excessive oil leaks.

If a dull "thud" cannot be heard in the clutches, place the finger tips on clutch housing and again apply air pressure. Movement of the piston can be felt as the clutch is applied.

Kickdown Servo

Direct air pressure into kickdown servo "apply" passage. Operation of

servo is indicated by a tightening of the front band. Spring tension on the servo should release the band.

Low and Reverse Servo

Direct air pressure into the low and reserve servo "apply" passage. Operation of the servo is indicated by a tightening of the rear band. Spring tension on servo piston should release band.

Service Note

If the clutches and servos operate properly but erratic shift or no upshift conditions are present it indicates that the malfunction exists in the control valve body.

Governor operating failures can generally be diagnosed by a road test or hydraulic pressure test.

HYDRAULIC PRESSURE TESTS

Line Pressure and Front Servo Release Pressure

These pressure checks must be made in "D" position with rear wheels free to turn. The transmission fluid must be at operating temperature (150-200°).

1. Install engine tachometer so it can be observed under the car.

2. Connect two 0-100 psi pressure gauges to pressure take-off points at accumulator and at front servo release, Fig. 3.

3. With "D" button depressed, speed up engine slightly until transmission shifts into drive. Reduce engine speed slowly to 800 rpm. Line pressure and front servo release pressure should be as given in chart.

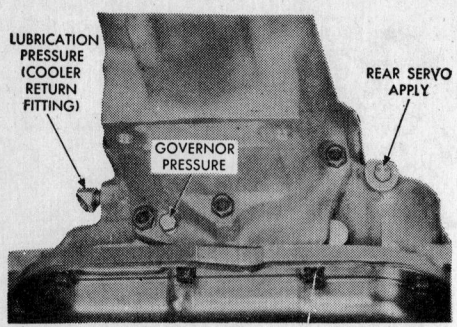

Fig. 4 Oil pressure test points at rear of case

4. Disconnect throttle linkage from transmission throttle lever *and hold transmission throttle lever at the detent position.* Increase engine speed to 3500 rpm with transmission in drive; line pressure and front servo release pressure should be as given in chart. *The transmission should not be operated with engine speeds in excess of 1500 rpm without opening the transmission throttle lever.*

5. If line pressure is not correct, adjust the pressure as outlined below. *Do not adjust line pressure to correct reading at 3500 rpm. If front servo release pressures are less than pressures specified and line pressures are within limits, there is excessive leakage in the front clutch and/or front servo circuits.*

Lubrication Pressure

The lubrication pressure check should be made at the same time that line pressure and front servo release pressure are checked.

1. Install a "tee" fitting between cooler return line fitting and fitting hole in transmission case at rear of left side of transmission, Fig. 4. Connect an 0-100 psi gauge to the "tee" fitting.
2. At 800 engine rpm with throttle closed and transmission in drive,

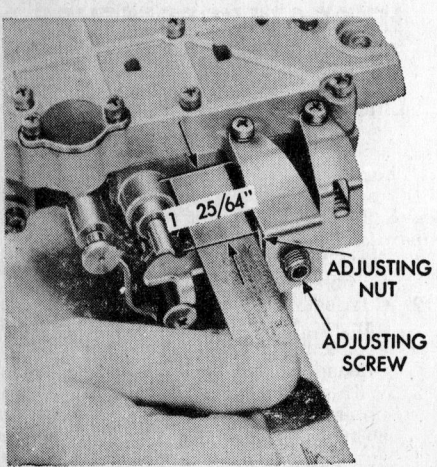

Fig. 5 Line pressure adjustment

lubrication pressure should be as given in chart.

Rear Servo Apply Pressure

1. Connect a 0-300 psi pressure gauge to apply pressure take-off point at rear servo, Fig. 3.
2. With transmission control in "R" position and engine speed set at 1600 rpm, reverse servo apply pressure should as given in chart.

Governor Pressure

Connect a 0-100 psi pressure gauge to the governor pressure take-off point, Fig. 4. Pressures should fall within limits given in the chart. If pressures are incorrect, governor valve and/or weights are probably sticking.

HYDRAULIC PRESSURE ADJUSTMENTS

Line Pressure

If line pressure is not correct, it will be necessary to remove the valve body to perform the adjustment.

The standard adjustment is $1\frac{25}{64}''$, measured from the valve body to the inner edge of the adjustment nut, Fig. 5. However, due to manufacturing tolerances, the adjustment can be varied to obtain the specified line pressure.

The adjusting screw may be turned with an Allen wrench. One complete turn of the adjusting screw changes closed throttle line pressure approximately $1\frac{2}{3}$ psi. Turning adjusting screw counterclockwise increases pressure, and clockwise decreases pressure.

Throttle Pressure

Throttle pressures cannot be checked; therefore, the adjustment should be checked and corrected, if necessary, whenever the valve body is serviced or conditions warrant.

1. Remove valve body from transmission.
2. Loosen throttle lever stop screw lock nut and back off screw approximately five turns, Fig. 6.
3. Insert gauge pin of Tool C-3763 between throttle lever cam and kickdown valve.
4. By pushing in on tool, compress kickdown valve against its spring so the throttle valve is completely bottomed inside the valve body.
5. As force is being exerted to com-

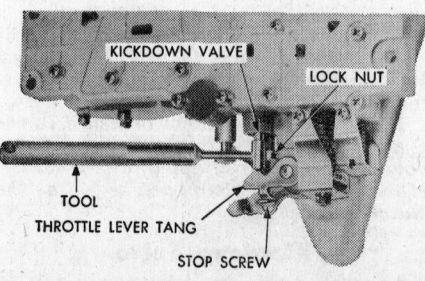

Fig. 6 Throttle pressure adjustment

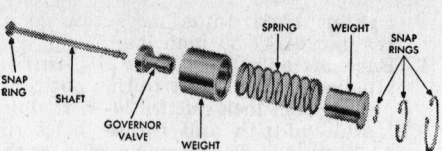

Fig. 7 Layout of governor parts

press the spring, tighten throttle lever stop screw finger tight against throttle lever tang with the throttle lever cam touching the tool and throttle valve bottomed. *Be sure the adjustment is made with the spring fully compressed and the valve bottomed.*

6. Remove tool and tighten stop screw lock nut securely.

OUTPUT SHAFT OIL SEAL

1. To remove seal, disconnect propeller shaft at transmission flange.
2. Remove transmission flange.
3. Removal seal (Tool C-3753 is available for this operation).
4. Install new seal with lip side facing in.
5. Install transmission flange and tighten nut to a torque of 175 ft. lbs.
6. Connect propeller shaft.

EXTENSION HOUSING

1. Remove speedometer drive pinion and sleeve assembly.
2. Remove transmission flange.
3. Drain about two quarts of fluid from transmission.
4. Loosen parking brake cable clamp bolt where cable enters the housing cover. Remove housing cover lower plug. Insert screwdriver through hole, then, while exerting pressure against projecting portion of cable lock spring, withdraw brake cable.
5. Remove nut securing extension housing insulator to crossmember.
6. With a suitable jack, raise transmission slightly to clear crossmember.
7. On Valiant cars, disconnect rear wheel brake control cable and housing at crossmember.
8. Remove crossmember.

Fig. 8 Aligning rear oil pump cover

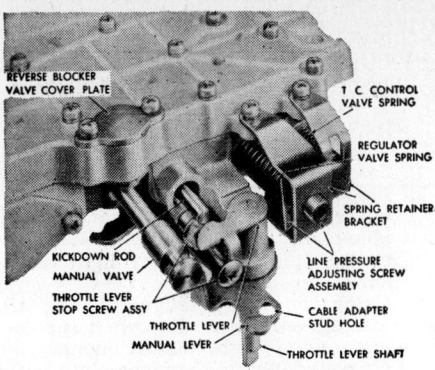

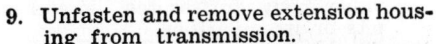

Fig. 9 Valve body external parts

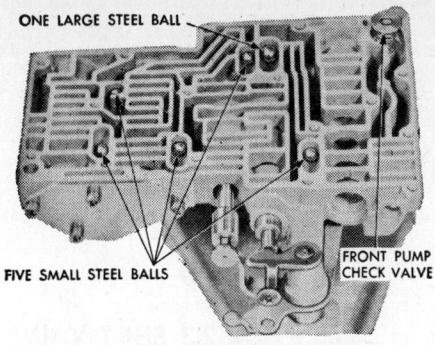

Fig. 10 Front pump check valve and steel ball locations

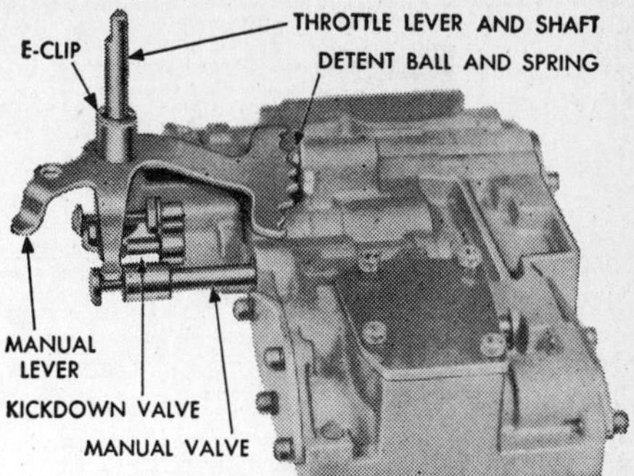

Fig. 11 Throttle lever and related parts

9. Unfasten and remove extension housing from transmission.
10. If necessary, the extension housing bushing may be replaced at this time. However, when installing the new bushing, make sure the oil hole in the bushing lines up with the slot in the housing.
11. Install the extension housing in the reverse order of its removal.

GOVERNOR

1. To remove the governor, take off the extension housing.
2. Using a screwdriver, carefully pry the snap ring from the weight end of the governor valve shaft, Fig. 7. Slide the valve and shaft out of governor housing.
3. Remove large snap ring from weight end of governor housing, and lift out weight assembly.
4. Remove snap ring from inside governor weight and remove inner weight and spring from outer weight.
5. Remove snap ring from behind governor housing, then slide governor housing and parking brake sprag assembly off input shaft. If necessary, separate governor housing from sprag (4 screws).
6. The primary cause of governor operating failure is due to a sticking governor valve or weights. Rough surfaces may be removed with crocus cloth. Thoroughly clean all parts and check for free movement before assembly.
7. Reverse above operations to assemble and install governor.

REAR OIL PUMP

1. To remove pump, remove extension housing, governor and parking sprag.
2. Remove oil pump cover.
3. Mark a line across the face of the inner and outer pump rotors with dye so they may be reinstalled in the same relation to each other.
4. *The oil pump inner rotor is keyed to output shaft by a small ball. Therefore, use care in sliding out inner rotor so as not to lose the ball.* Remove outer rotor from pump body.

Inspection

If rear oil pump body requires replacement, it will be necessary to disassemble the transmission as the pump body must be driven rearward out of the case with a wood block.
Inspect pump body and pump cover machined surfaces for nicks or burrs. Inspect rotors for scoring or pitting. With gears cleaned and installed in pump body, place a straightedge across face of rotors and pump body. Using a feeler gauge check clearance between straightedge and face of rotors. Clearance limits are from .001 to .0025".

Installation

Reverse removal procedure to install pump, being sure to align the rotors as marked at disassembly if same rotors are being used. When installing pump cover, thread retaining bolts in a few turns. Then slide aligning tool, Fig. 8, all the way in until it bottoms against rotors. Then tighten cover bolts to a torque of 14-16 ft. lbs.

VALVE BODY

1. To remove valve body and accumulator piston, drain transmission fluid and remove oil pan.

2. Loosen clamp bolt and lift throttle lever, washer and seal off transmission throttle lever shaft.
3. Shift manual control into "L" position to expose the nut securing the cable adapter to the manual lever. Remove nut and disengage cable adapter from lever.
4. Place drain pan under transmission; then remove ten hex-head valve body-to-transmission case bolts.
5. Lower valve body down out of transmission, being careful not to cock throttle lever shaft in case hole or lose the accumulator spring.
6. Withdraw accumulator piston from transmission case. Inspect piston for scoring, and check rings for wear or breakage.

Disassembly

Never clamp any portion of the valve body or transfer plate in a vise. Any slight distortion of the aluminum body or the transfer plate will result in sticking valves, excessive leakage or both. When removing or installing valves or plugs, slide them in or out carefully; do not use force.
1. Lift off screen (3 screws).
2. While holding spring retainer bracket firmly against spring force, remove three bracket retaining screws, Fig. 9.

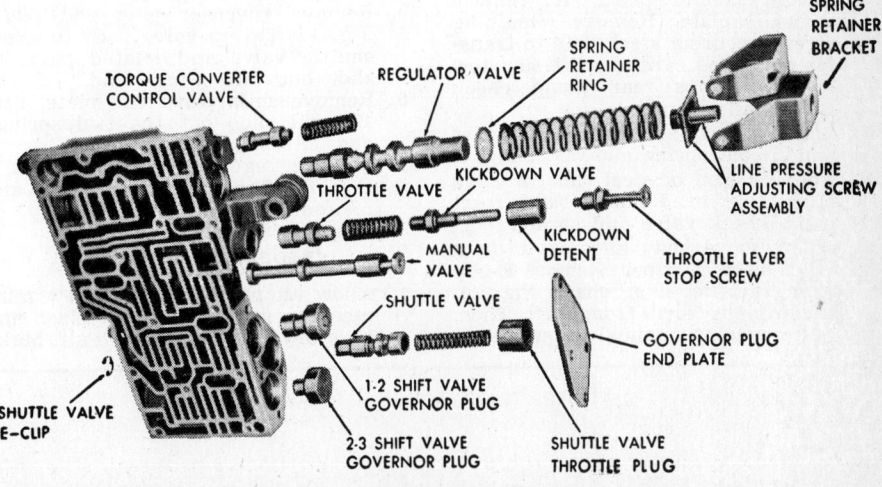

Fig. 12 Valve body (lever side)

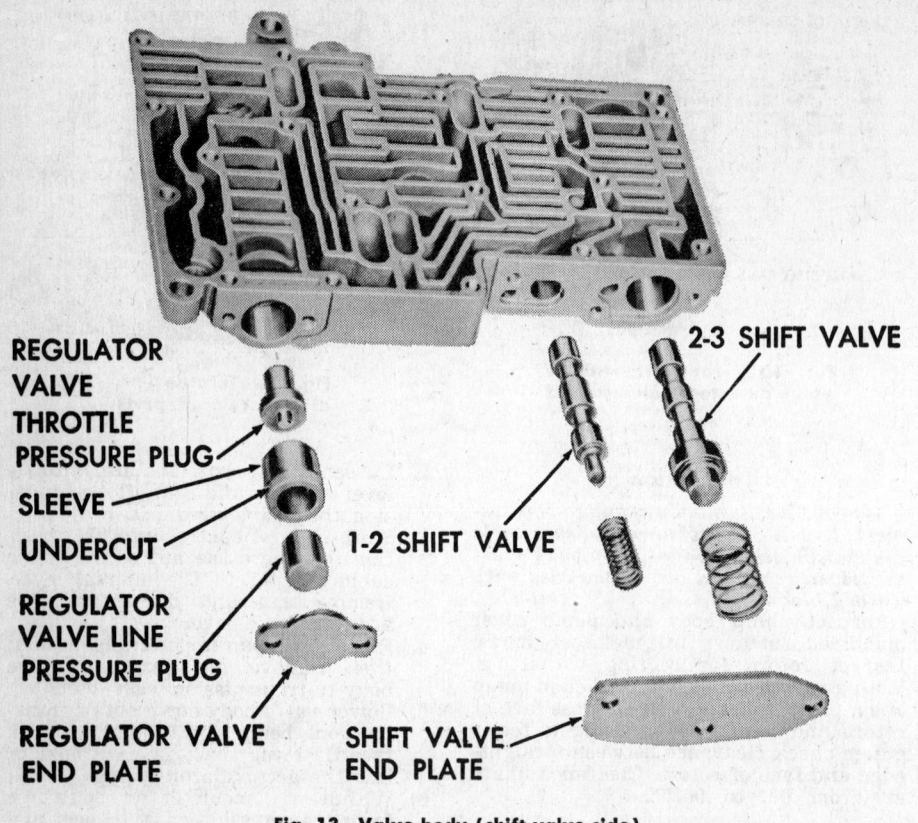

REGULATOR
VALVE
THROTTLE
PRESSURE PLUG
SLEEVE
UNDERCUT

REGULATOR
VALVE LINE
PRESSURE PLUG

REGULATOR VALVE
END PLATE

2-3 SHIFT VALVE

1-2 SHIFT VALVE

SHIFT VALVE
END PLATE

Fig. 13 Valve body (shift valve side)

3. Remove spring bracket, torque converter control valve spring, and the regulator valve spring with line pressure adjusting screw, Fig. 9. *Do not alter the setting of the line pressure adjusting screw and nut. The nut has an interference thread and does not turn easily on the screw.*

4. Slide regulator valve and spring retainer ring out of valve body. Slide torque converter control valve out of valve body.

5. Remove 14 transfer plate retaining screws. Carefully lift transfer plate and steel plate off valve body.

6. Invert transfer plate and remove stiffener plate. Remove remaining screws securing steel plate to transfer plate and carefully lift out steel plate. Remove rear pump check valve and spring.

7. Remove reverse blocker valve cover and lift out spring and valve, Fig. 9.

8. Note location of steel balls in valve body, Fig. 10. Remove balls, front pump check valve and spring.

9. Invert valve body and lay it on a clean piece of paper. Remove E-clip from throttle lever shaft, Fig. 11. Remove any burrs from shaft. Then, while holding manual lever detent

ball and spring in their bore with a suitable tool, slide manual lever off throttle shaft. Remove detent ball and spring.

10. Remove manual valve, carefully sliding it out of body with a rotating motion.

11. Remove throttle lever and shaft.

12. Remove shuttle valve cover plate. Remove E-clip from exposed end of shuttle valve, Fig. 12.

13. Remove throttle lever stop screw, Fig. 12, *being careful not to disturb the setting any more than necessary.*

14. Remove kickdown detent, kickdown valve, throttle valve spring and throttle valve, Fig. 12.

15. Remove governor plug end plate, Fig. 12. Tip up valve body to allow shuttle valve and related parts to slide out into your hand.

16. Remove shift valve end plate, Fig. 13, and slide out the two springs and valves.

17. Remove regulator valve end plate, Fig. 13. Slide regulator valve and related parts out of valve body.

Inspection of Parts

1. Allow all parts to soak a few minutes in a suitable solvent. Wash and blow dry with compressed air. Make

sure all oil passages are clean and free of obstructions.

2. Inspect manual and throttle valve operating levers for being bent, worn or loose. If a lever is loose on its shaft, it may be *silver-soldered only,* or the lever and shaft should be replaced.

3. Inspect all mating surfaces for burrs, nicks or scratches. Minor blemishes may be removed with crocus cloth, using very light pressure.

4. Using a straightedge, check all mating surfaces for warpage or distortion. Slight distortion may be corrected, using a surface plate with valve grinding compound.

5. Make sure all metering holes in steel plate are open.

6. Using a pen light, inspect bores in valve body for scores, scratches, pits or irregularities.

7. Check all valve springs for distortion and collapsed coils.

8. Inspect all valves and plugs for burrs, nicks and scores. Small nicks and scores may be removed with crocus cloth, providing extreme care is taken not to round off sharp edges. *The sharpness of these edges is vitally important because it prevents foreign matter from lodging between valve and valve body, thus reducing the possibility of sticking.*

9. Check all valves and plugs for freedom of operation in valve body bores.

10. The front and rear pump check valves are provided with a controlled leakage path to assure that the rear pump remains primed.

Assemble Valve Body

Assemble the valve body in the reverse order of disassembly, noting the following precautions: All screws should be tightened to 25 inch lbs.

1. When positioning the steel plate on the transfer plate, hold rear pump check valve in its bore with a thin steel scale and install the four retaining screws. After making sure bolts are properly aligned, tighten them evenly.

2. When installing regulator valve throttle pressure plug and sleeve, be sure undercut on sleeve is toward end plate.

3. When installing the kickdown detent on the kickdown valve, counterbore side of detent goes toward valve.

4. When positioning transfer plate on valve body, hold front pump check valve in place with a thin steel scale. Then install the 14 screws, tightening them by starting at the center and working outward.

5. After the valve body has been serviced and completely assembled, adjust the throttle and line pressures as outlined previously. However, *if line pressure was satisfactory before disassembly, do not alter this adjustment.*

Repairs Requiring Transmission Removal

FLUSHING CONVERTER

In the event that any part has failed in the transmission, the torque converter should be flushed to insure that fine metal particles are not later transfered back into the reconditioned transmission.

1. Reinstall converter and drain out fluid.
2. Insert screwdriver into converter and turn stator hub (large splined hub) counterclockwise so that one of the ⅛ x ⅜″ slots of this assembly is visible at the top. A second opening directly below provides an adequate opening for kerosene (if poured slowly).
3. Slowly pour two quarts of clean kerosene into converter, using a long spouted can. Close hub opening with masking tape.
4. Disconnect coil wire to prevent engine from starting. Then rotate conveter for about 10 seconds by cranking the engine.
5. Drain converter and repeat operation at least once, or as many times as required until drained kerosene is clear.
6. After flushing, rotate converter several revolutions with drain plugs removed. This will remove any residual solvent and trapped dirt.

TRANSMISSION, DISASSEMBLE

1. Remove oil pan.
2. Remove valve body as outlined previously.
3. Lift spring off accumulator piston and withdraw piston from case.
4. At this time, check the drive train end play before removing the extension housing. This will indicate the spacer required between input and output shafts to adjust end play during reassembly. Attach a dial indicator as shown in Fig. 14. Move the output shaft in and out to obtain end play reading. If necessary, tap shaft inward with a mallet, and

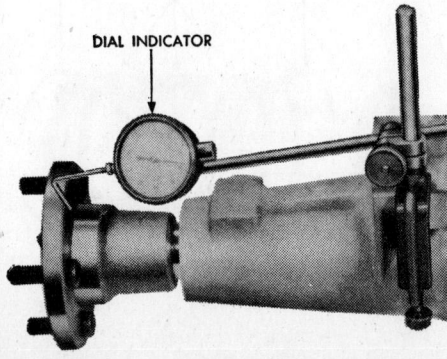

Fig. 14 Checking drive train end play

Fig. 15   Front oil pump and reaction shaft support

pry outward with a screwdriver to obtain the reading. Record the reading for reference when reassembling the transmission. End play should be .024″ to .062″.

5. Remove extension housing.
6. Remove governor and parking sprag as outlined previously.
7. Remove rear oil pump as outlined previously.
8. Remove front pump and reaction shaft support, using a suitable puller.
9. Loosen front band adjuster, remove band strut and slide band out of case.
10. Slide out front clutch.
11. Grasp input shaft and slide out shaft and rear clutch. *Be careful not to lose thrust washer located between rear end of input shaft and forward end of output shaft.*
12. While supporting output shaft and driving shell, slide assembly forward and out of case.
13. Loosen rear band adjuster, remove band strut and remove band.
14. Note position of overrunning clutch rollers and springs before disassembly to assist in reassembly. Then carefully slide out clutch hub and remove rollers and springs.
15. Remove low and reverse drum thrust washer from inside of overrunning clutch case.
16. Remove snap ring securing kickdown servo piston rod guide in case. Then remove rod guide, spring and piston rod from case. Withdraw piston from case, using Tool C-484 if available.
17. To remove low and reverse servo, depress piston spring retainer and remove snap ring. Then remove spring retainer, spring and servo piston and plug from case.

SUB-ASSEMBLIES, OVERHAUL

When it becomes necessary to recondition the transmission, and the vehicle has accumulated considerable mileage, install new seal rings on parts requiring their usage. Coat each part with automatic transmission fluid as it is being assembled.

FRONT PUMP & REACTION SHAFT SUPPORT

Service Note

A change was made with transmission serial number 118379 (1960) to incorporate a fiber thrust washer between the reaction shaft support and front clutch piston retainer. This improvement is designed to minimize the possibility of wear between these parts. The new thrust washer is approximately .060″ thick and the face of the front clutch retainer has been reduced the same amount. The overall end play remains the same.

Disassemble

1. Referring to Fig. 15, remove bolts from rear side of support and lift support off pump.
2. Mark face of inner and outer pump rotors with dye so they may be reinstalled in same relation to each other, then remove rotors.
3. Remove rubber seal ring from pump body flange.
4. Drive out seal with a blunt punch.

Inspection

1. Inspect interlocking seal rings on reaction shaft support for wear or broken locks. Make sure they turn freely in the grooves. Do not remove rings unless conditions warrant.
2. Inspect machined surfaces of oil pump body and reaction shaft support for nicks or burrs.
3. Inspect pump rotors for scoring or pitting.
4. With rotors cleaned and installed in pump body, place a straightedge across face of rotors and pump body. Using a feeler gauge, check clearance between straightedge and face of rotors. Clearance limits are from .001 to .0025″.

Assemble

1. Place reaction shaft support in assembling Tool C-3759 with hub of support resting on bench. Screw two pilot studs into threaded holes of support flange.
2. Assemble rotors with dye marks aligned and place in center of support. *The two driving lugs inside inner rotor must be next to face of reaction shaft support.*
3. Lower pump body over pilot studs. Insert Tool C-3756 through pump body and engage with pump inner rotor. Rotate rotors with tool to enter rotors in pump body; then with pump body firmly against reaction shaft support, tighten clamping tool securely.
4. Invert front pump and support assembly with clamping tool intact. Install support bolts and tighten to 14-16 ft. lbs. Remove clamping tool, pilot studs and rotor alignment tool.

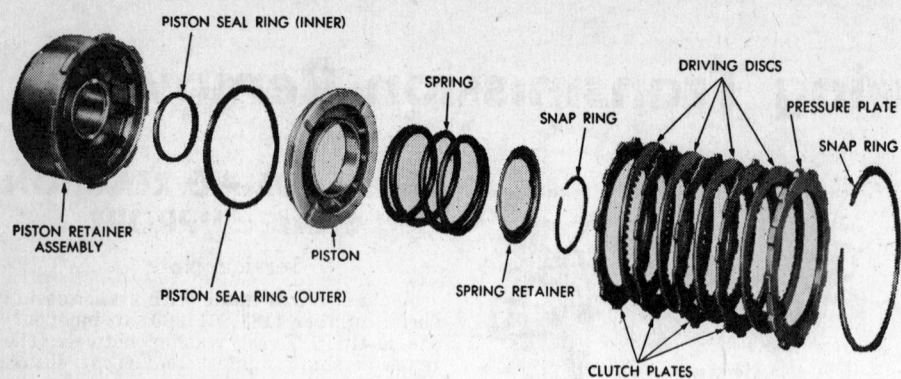

Fig. 16 Front clutch

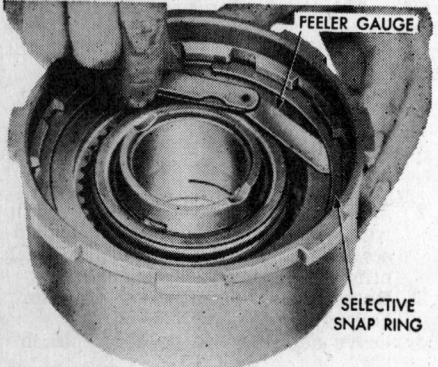

Fig. 17 Checking front clutch plate clearance

5. Place new oil seal in opening of pump housing, with lip of seal facing inward. Using seal driver (Tool C-3757) drive seal into housing until tool bottoms.

FRONT CLUTCH

Service Note

A change was made with transmission serial number 118379 (1960) to incorporate a fiber thrust washer between the reaction shaft support and front clutch piston retainer. This improvement is designed to minimize the possibility of wear between these parts. The new thrust washer is approximately .060" thick and the face of the front clutch retainer has been reduced the same amount. The overall end play remains the same.

Disassemble

1. Referring to Fig. 16, use a screwdriver to remove large snap ring that secures pressure plate in clutch piston retainer. Lift pressure plate and clutch plates out of retainer.
2. Install compressor (Tool C-3575) over piston spring retainer. Compress spring and remove snap ring; then slowly release tool until spring retainer is free of hub. Remove tool, retainer and spring.
3. Invert clutch retainer assembly and bump on a wood block to remove piston. Remove seal rings from piston and clutch retainer hub.

Inspection

1. Inspect driving discs for evidence of burning, glazing or flaking off of facing material. Scratch facings with finger nail; if material collects under nail, replace all driving discs. Check driving disc splines for wear or damage. Inspect steel plate and pressure plate surfaces for burning, scoring or damaged driving lugs.
2. Check steel plate lug grooves in clutch retainer for smooth surfaces. Plates must travel freely in grooves. Inspect band contacting surface on clutch retainer for scores. Note ball check in clutch retainer and make sure ball moves freely. Inspect seal ring surfaces in clutch retainer for nicks or deep scratches; light scratches will not interfere with sealing of neoprene rings.
3. Inspect inside bore of piston for score marks. If light, remove with crocus cloth. Check seal ring grooves for nicks or burrs. Inspect neoprene seal rings for damage, wear or hardness. Check piston spring, retainer and snap ring for distortion.

Assemble

1. Lubricate and install inner seal ring on hub of clutch retainer. Make sure lip of seal faces down and is properly seated in groove.
2. Lubricate and install outer seal ring on clutch piston, with lip of seal towards bottom of clutch re-

tainer. Place piston assembly in retainer and, with a twisting motion, seat piston in bottom of retainer.
3. Place spring on piston hub and position spring retainer and snap ring on spring. Compress spring with Tool C-3575 and seat snap ring in hub groove. Remove compressor tool.
4. Lubricate all clutch plates. Then install one steel plate followed by a lined plate and continue in this alternating fashion until all plates are installed. Install pressure plate and snap ring, making sure snap ring is properly seated.
5. With clutch completely assembled, insert feeler gauge between pressure plate and snap ring, Fig. 17. Clearance should be .056" to .104". If not, install a snap ring of proper thickness to obtain specified clearance. *Snap rings are the same as that used in the rear clutch and are available in thicknesses of .060-.062", .068-.070" and .076-.078".*

REAR CLUTCH

Disassemble

1. Referring to Fig. 18, remove large snap ring that secures pressure plate in clutch piston retainer. Lift pressure plate, clutch plates and inner pressure plate out of retainer.
2. Install compressor Tool C-3760 over piston spring. Compress spring just enough to clear snap ring and remove snap ring.
3. Remove compressor tool and piston spring. Invert clutch retainer and bump on a wood block to remove piston. Remove seal rings from piston.

Inspection

Inspect clutch parts as outlined for the front clutch. In addition, inspect interlocking seal rings on input shaft for wear or broken locks, and make sure they turn freely in the grooves. Do not remove rings unless conditions warrant.

Assemble

1. Lubricate and install inner and outer

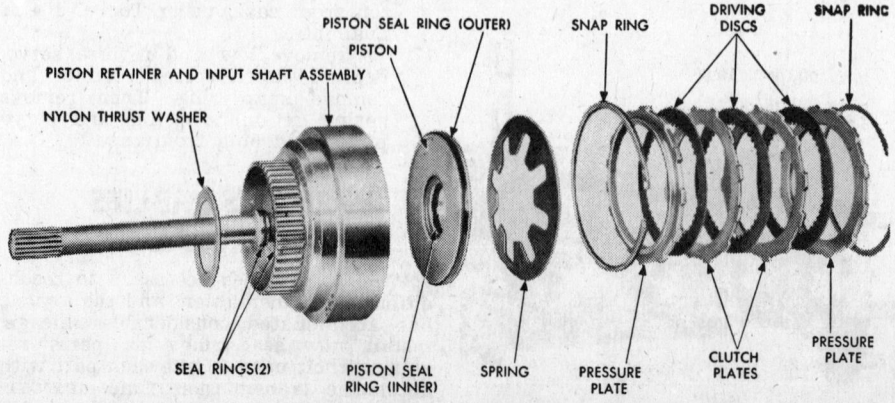

Fig. 18 Rear clutch

seal rings on clutch piston. Make sure lip of seals face toward head of clutch retainer, and are properly seated in piston grooves.

2. Place piston assembly in retainer and, with a twisting motion, seat piston in bottom of retainer.

3. Place spring over piston with outer edge of spring positioned below snap ring groove. Install compressor Tool C-3760 over spring and compress spring just enough to install snap ring. Remove tool.

4. Install inner pressure plate in clutch

and support off gear set. Remove thrust washer from rear side of planet gear set. If necessary, remove snap ring from front of annulus gear to separate support from annulus gear.

4. Slide sun gear, driving shell, rear planet unit with low and reverse drum off output shaft.

5. Lift sun gear and driving shell off rear planet unit. Remove snap ring and steel washer from sun gear (rear side of driving shell). Slide sun gear out of driving shell, and remove snap ring and steel washer from opposite end of sun gear if necessary.

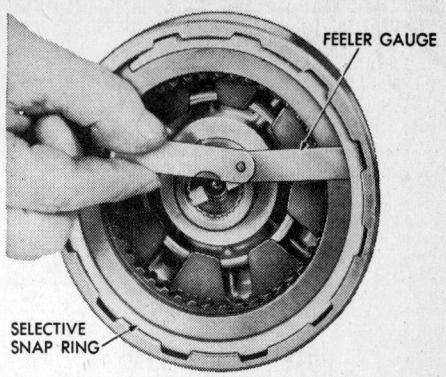

Fig. 19 Checking rear clutch plate clearance

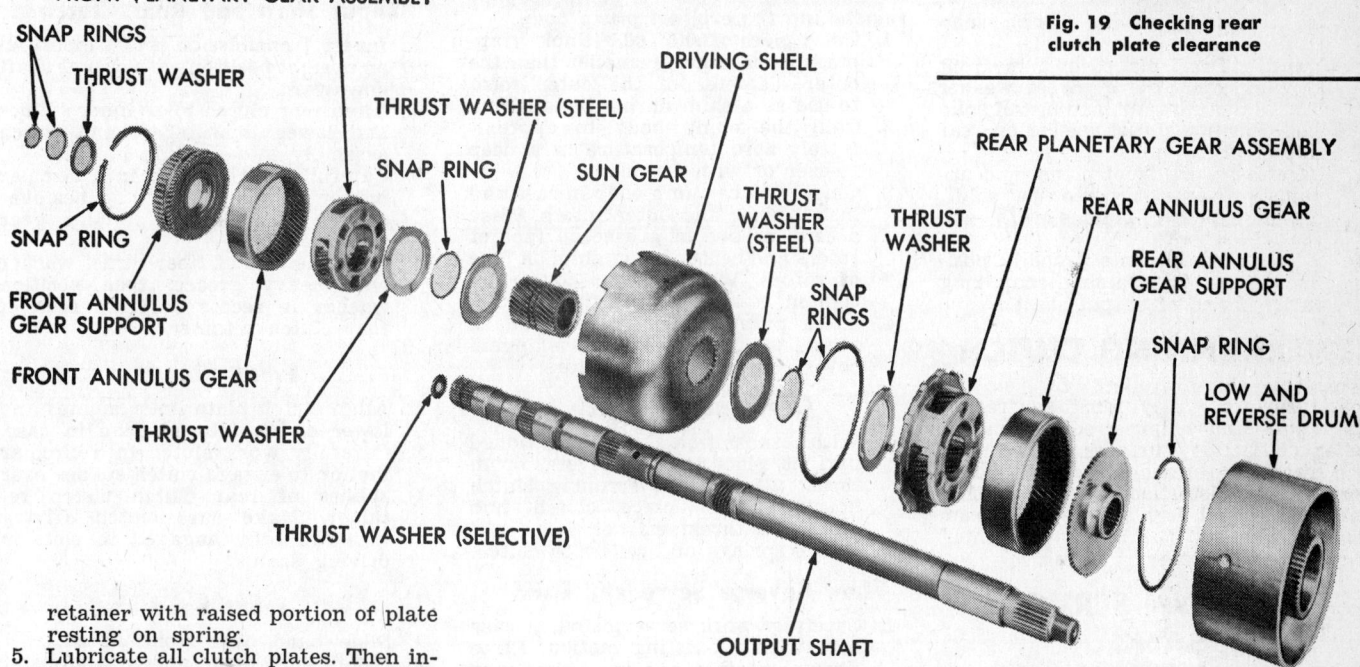

Fig. 20 Planet units, sun gear, driving shell, low-reverse drum and output shaft

retainer with raised portion of plate resting on spring.

5. Lubricate all clutch plates. Then install one lined plate followed by a steel plate and continue in this alternating fashion until all plates are installed. Install outer pressure plate and snap ring.

6. *Rear clutch plate clearance is very important in obtaining proper clutch operation.* The clearance can be adjusted by the use of various thickness outer snap rings. Snap rings are available in thicknesses of .060-.062", .068-.070" and .076-.078". With rear clutch completely assembled, insert feeler gauge between pressure plate and snap ring, Fig. 19. Clearance should be .018-.036". If not, install snap ring of proper thickness to obtain specified clearance.

PLANET GEARS, SUN GEAR, DRIVING SHELL, LOW & REVERSE DRUM

1. Referring to Fig. 20, remove thrust washer from forward end of output shaft.

2. Remove snap ring from forward end of output shaft, then slide front planet unit off shaft.

3. Remove snap ring and thrust washer from forward hub of front planet gear and slide front annulus gear

6. Remove thrust washer from forward side of rear planet unit. Remove snap ring from front side of low and reverse drum; then slide rear planet unit out of drum. If necessary, remove snap ring from rear of annulus gear to separate support from annulus gear.

Inspection

1. Inspect bearing surfaces on output shaft for nicks, burrs, scores or other damage. Light scratches, small nicks or burrs can be removed with crocus cloth or a fine stone. Check speedometer drive gear for nicks or burrs, and remove with a sharp-edged stone. Make sure all oil passages in shaft are open and clean.

2. Check bushings in sun gear for wear or scores, and replace sun gear assembly if bushings are damaged.

3. Inspect all thrust washers for wear or scores. Check all lock rings for distortion.

4. Inspect annulus gear and driving gear teeth for damage. Inspect planet gear carrier for cracks and

pinions for broken or worn gear teeth.

Assemble

1. Place rear annulus gear support in annulus gear and install snap ring.

2. Position rear planet unit in rear annulus gear, slide assembly into low and reverse drum, and secure with snap ring in edge of drum. Position thrust washer on front side of planet unit.

3. Insert output shaft in rear opening of drum. Carefully work shaft through annulus gear support and planet unit. Make sure shaft splines are fully engaged in splines of annulus gear support.

4. Install steel washer and snap ring on one end of sun gear. Insert sun gear through front side of driving shell, and install rear steel washer and snap ring.

5. Carefully slide driving shell and sun gear assembly on output shaft, engaging sun gear teeth with rear planet pinion teeth.

6. Place front annulus gear support

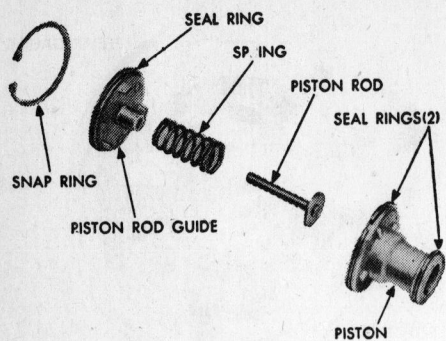

Fig. 21 Kickdown servo

in annulus gear and install snap ring.

7. Position front planet unit in front annulus gear. Place thrust washer over planet unit hub and install snap ring. Position thrust washer on rear side of planet unit.

8. Carefully work front planet and annulus gear assembly on output shaft, meshing planet pinions with sun gear teeth.

9. With all components properly positioned, install retaining snap ring on front end of output shaft.

OVERRUNNING CLUTCH

Inspect clutch rollers for smooth round surfaces; they must be free of flat spots and chipped edges. Inspect roller contacting surfaces in the cam and race for brinneling. Check roller springs for distortion, wear or other damage. Inspect low and reverse drum thrust washer (behind overrunning clutch hub) for wear or scores.

KICKDOWN SERVO & BAND

Referring to Fig. 21, inspect piston and guide seal rings for wear and make sure they turn freely in the grooves. It is not necessary to remove seal rings unless conditions warrant. Inspect piston for nicks, burrs, scores and wear. Check piston bore in case for scores or other damage. Check fit of guide on piston rod. Check piston spring for distortion.

Check band lining for wear and bond of lining to the band. If lining is worn so grooves are not visible at the ends or any portion of the band, replace the band. Inspect band for distortion or cracked ends.

LOW & REVERSE SERVO

Referring to Fig. 22, remove snap ring from piston and remove piston plug and spring.

Inspect neoprene seal ring for damage, wear or hardness. Check piston and plug for nicks, burrs, scratches or wear; piston plug must operate freely in piston. Check piston bore in case for scores or other damage. Check springs for distortion. Inspect band for damage in same manner described for kickdown band.

To assemble, lubricate and insert piston plug and spring in piston and secure with snap ring.

TRANSMISSION, ASSEMBLE

Do not use force in assembling mating parts. If parts do not assemble freely, investigate the cause and correct the trouble before proceeding further. Always use new gaskets during assembly operations. *Use only automatic transmission fluid to lubricate transmission parts during assembly.*

Rear Pump

To prevent pump distortion, the following procedure must be followed when installing a new rear oil pump body or reinstalling the original pump body.

1. Cut a piece of .002-.003" thick wrapping paper slightly smaller than the outer diameter of the outer rotor to use as a shim during installation.

2. Chill the pump body to approximately zero temperature in a deep freezer or with dry ice.

3. Quickly place pump body in case and install inner and outer rotors. Place a daub or two of grease on face of rotors and center paper shim on face of rotors. Install pump cover and tighten retaining bolts firmly.

4. After pump body has warmed to room temperature, remove pump cover, paper shim and rotors.

Overrunning Clutch

1. With transmission case positioned upright, place low and reverse drum thrust washer in overruning clutch housing; then place clutch hub (race) on thrust washer.

2. Install springs and rollers in clutch.

Low-Reverse Servo and Band

1. Carefully work servo piston in case bore with a twisting motion. Place spring, retainer and snap ring over piston.

2. Depress piston spring and install snap ring, Fig. 22.

3. Position rear band in case, install short strut, then connect long lever and strut to band.

4. Screw in band adjuster just enough to hold struts in place.

Kickdown Servo

Carefully push servo piston into case bore. Install piston rod, spring and guide, Fig. 21. Depress guide and install snap ring.

Planet Units, Sun Gear, Driving Shell and Low-Reverse Drum

1. While supporting assembly in case, insert output shaft through overrunning clutch hub. Carefully work assembly rearward, engaging drum splines with splines of overrunning clutch hub. *Be very careful not to damage ground surfaces on output shaft during installation.*

2. Apply a coat of grease to selective thrust washer, Fig. 20, and install washer on front end of output shaft.

3. If drive train end play was not within specifications (.024-.062") when checked as shown in Fig. 14

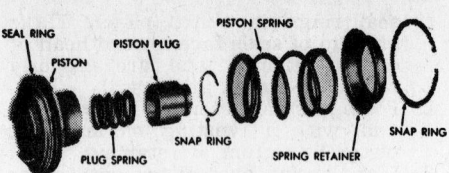

Fig. 22 Low-reverse servo

during disassembly procedure, replace thrust washer with one of proper thickness. Available washers are .052-.054" (natural), .068-.070" (red), and .083-.085" (black).

Input Shaft and Rear Clutch

1. Invert transmission and support in an upright position with output shaft downward.

2. Align rear clutch plate inner splines and lower input shaft and clutch assembly into position in case.

3. Carefully work clutch in a circular motion to engage clutch splines over splines of kickdown annulus gear support.

4. Coat one side of fiber thrust washer with heavy grease, then position washer in recess on front face of rear clutch retainer.

Front Clutch

1. Align clutch plate inner splines and lower clutch into position in case.

2. Carefully work clutch in a circular motion to engage clutch splines over splines of rear clutch piston retainer. Make sure clutch driving lugs are fully engaged in slots in driving shell.

Front Band

1. Slide band over front clutch.

2. Install band strut, screw in adjuster just enough to hold strut in place.

Front Pump and Reaction Shaft Support

1. Install two pilot studs in front pump opening in case.

2. Place a new rubber seal ring, Fig. 15, in groove on outer flange of pump. Make sure seal ring is not twisted.

3. Insert aligning Tool C-3756 through pump body and engage with inner rotor.

4. Install assembly in case, tapping lightly with a soft mallet if necessary. Install four bolts, remove pilot studs and install remaining bolts and pull down gently. Then torque bolts to 14-16 ft. lbs.

5. Rotate pump rotors (Tool C-3759) until two small holes in handle of tool are vertical. This will locate inner rotor so converter impeller shaft will engage inner rotor lugs during installation.

Final Assembly

Install rear oil pump, governor and parking sprag, and extension housing as outlined previously. Then recheck drive train end play as shown in Fig. 14.

V8 TORQUEFLITE

For Linkage Adjustment See Car Chapter

CONTENTS

Description 341
Trouble Shooting 23

Maintenance

Adding Oil 342
Changing Oil 342

"In Car" Repairs

Bands, Adjust 344
Oil Pressure Tests 344
Air Pressure Tests 344
Speedometer Pinion 345
Neutral Starter Switch 345
Regulator Valve 346
Torque Converter Control Valve 346
Oil Cooler 346
Oil Pan 346
Valve Bodies and Transfer Plate 346
Kickdown Piston 349
Accumulator Piston 350

Output Shaft Rear Bearing Oil Seal 351
Extension Case 351
Governor 353
Rear Oil Pump 354

Repairs Requiring Transmission Removal

Transmission Disassemble 356
Front Pump 356
Regulator Valve Body 357
Torque Converter Reaction Shaft 358
Unit No. 1 358
Unit No. 2 358
Unit No. 3 360
Checking Travel of Front Clutch Pressure
    Plate 361
Transmission Assemble 362

The transmission, Fig. 1, combines a torque converter and an automatic planetary gear box. The transmission consists of two multiple disc clutches, an overrunning clutch, two bands and two planetary gear sets to provide three forward ratios and a reverse ratio. With the front or forward clutch engaged and low gear reaction, transferred through the transmission overrunning clutch assembly, a low ratio is obtained. Engagement of the kickdown or second speed band will shift the transmission to second speed. Disengagement of the kickdown band and engagement of the rear or direct clutch locks the gear set so that direct drive is obtained. Since the overrunning clutch can transmit torque only on the drive side, it is necessary to apply the low and reverse band when using low for engine braking. Reverse ratio is obtained by application of the rear clutch and rear band.

In the drive range, the transmission shifts through all three gear ratios automatically. Shift points are determined by throttle opening and car speed. If additional acceleration is desired while in drive range, the transmission down-

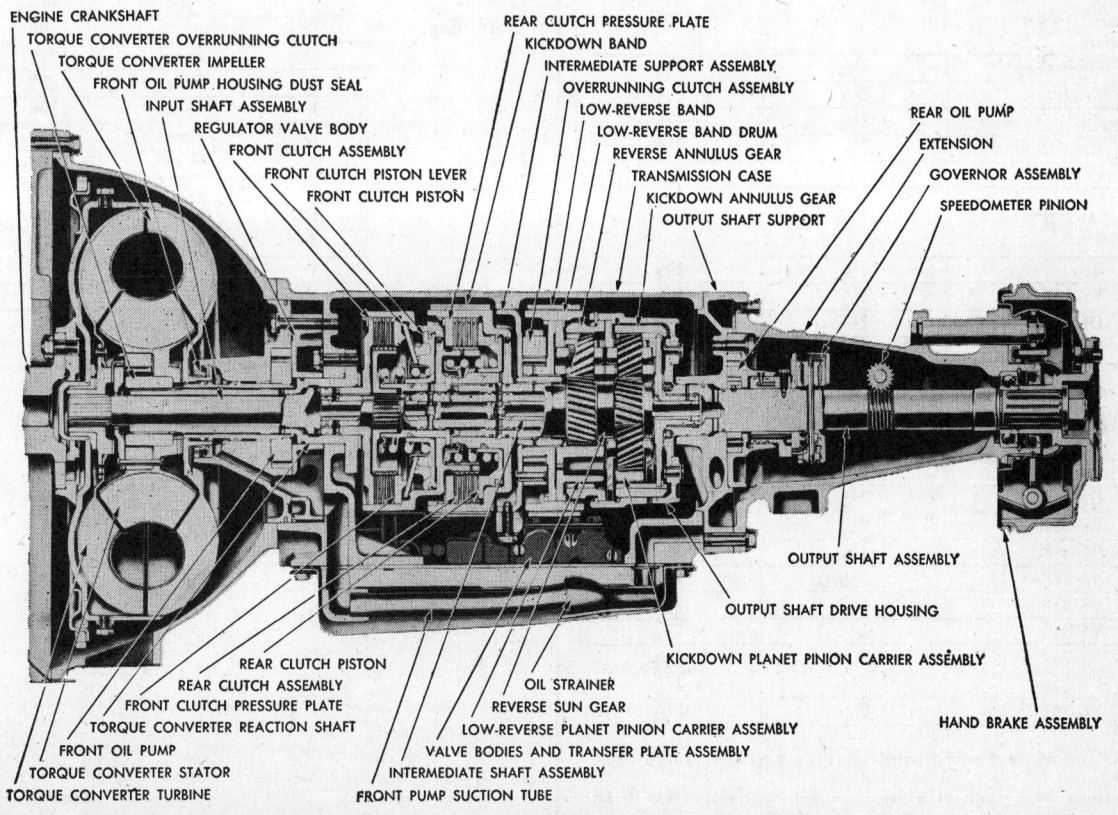

Fig. 1 Sectional view of Torqueflite transmission with torque converter

shifts (depending on vehicle speed) to second gear automatically when the accelerator pedal is fully depressed.

The intermediate or second position range is used to operate the transmission in the first two gears only. This range is suitable for heavy city traffic where the driver may desire part throttle second gear operation for more precise speed control. It may also be used on long down grades where additional engine braking is needed.

A low or first position range is also available to keep the transmission in first gear only. This position provides added handling ease in mountain driving and exceptional pulling qualities in sand and snow.

MAINTENANCE
Adding Oil

Allow engine to idle in N (neutral) while fluid is being checked. The "L" mark on the oil level indicator is the proper oil level for a cold (room temperature) transmission. After the transmission has been brought up to operating temperature, the oil level will have risen to the "F" mark on the oil level indicator. Oil level in a transmission that has been brought to operating temperature should not be allowed to go over the "F" mark on the oil level indicator. Add Automatic Transmission Fluid (Type A) if necessary to bring to the proper level.

Changing Oil

Drain and refill the transmission every 20,000 miles as follows:

1. Remove transmission oil pan drain plug (to 1956) or filler tube (from 1957).
2. Remove the plate from the bottom of the torque converter housing and rotate the torque converter until the converter drain plug is accessible.
3. After draining, replace drain filler tube and drain plug (s), and torque converter plate.
4. Pour 5 quarts of transmission fluid through oil pan filler tube.
5. With engine idling in neutral, add enough fluid to bring fluid level to "L" mark on indicator (approximately three quarts).
6. Shift transmission through all ranges and recheck.

TORQUEFLITE V8 BAND ADJUSTMENTS

Year	Model	Adjusting Screw Back-Off Number of Turns	
		Kickdown	Reverse

CHRYSLER & IMPERIAL

Year	Model	Kickdown	Reverse
1956	All	2	2
1957	All	3½	2⅝
1958–59	All	2¼	2⅝
1960–61	Ram Engine	2	2½
	Others	2½	2½

DE SOTO

Year	Model	Kickdown	Reverse
1957	Firesweep	3½	2⅝
	Others	2¼	2⅝
1958–59	All	2¼	2⅝
1960–61	Ram Engine	2	2½
	Others	2½	2½

DODGE & DART

Year	Model	Kickdown	Reverse
1957–58	All	3½	2⅝
1959	V8-325	3½	2⅝
	Others	2¼	2⅝
1960–61	V8-318	2½	2½
	V8-361	2	2½

PLYMOUTH

Year	Model	Kickdown	Reverse
1957–58	V8-350	2¼	2⅝
	Others	3½	2⅝
1959	V8-361	2¼	2⅝
	Others	3½	2⅝
1960	V8-318	2½ ①	2½
	V8-318	3 ②	2½
	V8-361	2½ ①	2½
	V8-361	2 ②	2½
1961	V8-318	2½	2½
	V8-361	2	2½

①—Transmissions without white paint mark on regulator valve boss.

②—Transmissions with daub of white paint on regulator valve boss.

LINE PRESSURE CHART

Year	Selector Position	Rear Wheels	Engine R. P. M.	Line Pressure
1956–57	R	Free	1600	200–250
	N	....	800	85–95
	D①	Free	800	89–91
	2	Free	800	85–95
	1	Free	800	85–95
1958–59	R	Free	1600	200–240
	N	....	1200	85–95
	D①	Free	1200	89–91
	2	Free	1200	85–95
	1	Free	1200	85–95
1960–61 Std. Eng.	R	Free	1600	200–240
	N	....	1200	85–95
	D①	Free	1200	89–91
	2	Free	1200	85–95
	1	Free	1200	85–95
	D	Free	3500	93–100
1960–61 Ram Eng.	R	Free	1600	235–275
	N	....	1200	100–110
	D①	Free	1200	104–106
	2	Free	1200	100–110
	1	Free	1200	100–110
	D	Free	3500	108–115

①—Shifted into direct drive.

GOVERNOR PRESSURE CHART★

★Rear wheels must be free to turn.

Year	Model	Selector Position	Car Speed	Pressure
CHRYSLER				
1956	All	D	8	2–3
		D	27	27–32
		D	38	44–47
		D	75	75–82
1957	Cars	D	17–19	15
		D	32–39	45
		D	66–71	75
1957	Wagons	D	16–18	15
		D	29–36	45
		D	63–67	75
1958–59	Cars	1	17–19	15
		2	32–39	45
		D	66–71	75
1958–59	Wagons	1	16–18	15
		2	29–36	45
		D	63–67	75
1960	Windsor	2	18–22	15
		D	41–50	50
		D	69–77	75
1960	Saratoga	2	18–22	15
		D	43–51	50
		D	72–80	75
1960	New Yorker	2	18–23	15
		D	43–51	50
		D	72–80	75
1960	Ram Engines	D	21–24	15
		D	36–43	50
		D	55–62	75
1961	Newport	2	18–22	15
		D	41–50	50
		D	69–77	75
1961	Windsor	2	18–22	15
		D	43–51	50
		D	72–80	75
1961	New Yorker	2	18–23	15
		D	43–51	50
		D	72–80	75
1961	Ram Engines	D	21–24	15
		D	36–43	50
		D	55–62	75
IMPERIAL				
1956	All	D	8	2–3
		D	27	27–32
		D	38	44–47
		D	75	75–82
1957	Cars	D	18–20	15
		D	33–40	45
		D	68–74	75
1957	Wagons	D	17–19	15
		D	31–37	45
		D	64–70	75

Year	Model	Selector Position	Car Speed	Pressure
IMPERIAL Continued				
1958–59	Cars	1	18–20	15
		2	33–40	45
		D	68–74	75
1958–59	Wagons	1	17–19	15
		2	31–37	45
		D	64–70	75
1960–61	All	2	19–24	15
		D	45–54	50
		D	75–83	75
DE SOTO				
1957	All	D	16–18	15
		D	29–35	45
		D	61–66	75
1958–59	Firesweep	D	0–3	2
		D	16–18	15
		D	29–35	45
		D	61–66	75
1958–59	Others	D	0–3	2
		D	16–18	15
		D	30–36	45
		D	62–67	75
1960	Std. Engines	2	15–20	15
		D	37–44	50
		D	61–68	75
1960–61	Ram Engines	D	20–24	15
		D	35–41	50
		D	53–60	75
DODGE & PLYMOUTH				
1957	All	D	16–18	15
		D	29–35	45
		D	61–66	75
1958	All	D	0–3	2
		D	16–19	15
		D	37–43	50
		D	61–68	75
1959	Std. Engines	D	1000①	25–31
		D	1600①	46–52
		D	2400①	63–71
1959	Hi Perf. Eng.	D	1000①	17–22
		D	1600①	39–45
		D	2400①	56–63
1960–61	Std. Engines	D	690–790①	15
		D	1250–1510①	45
		D	2650–2790①	75
1960–61	Hi Perf. Eng.	D	690–790①	15
		D	1680–1860①	45
		D	2850–3070①	75
1960–61	Ram Engine	D	860–970①	15
		D	1830–2100①	65
		D	2550–2800①	85

①—Engine R. P. M.

"In Car" Repairs

BANDS, ADJUST

Kickdown (Front) Band

The kickdown band adjusting screw is located on the left side of the transmission case, Fig. 7. Loosen the lock nut and back off the adjusting screw approximately five turns. Check the freeness of the adjusting screw in the transmission case.

Using an inch-pound torque wrench with a suitable extension (depending upon the accessibility due to the type of engine and exhaust equipment) tighten the adjusting screw to a reading of 47-50 *inch-pounds* torque. *This will be a true torque of 70-75 inch pounds, which should be used if the torque wrench is used without the extension as would be done if the adjustment is made with the transmission removed from the vehicle.*

Back off the adjusting screw according to the car model as given in the chart. Then, while holding the adjusting screw, tighten the locknut 30-35 foot pounds.

1960-61 Service Note

To prevent any misunderstanding of kickdown band adjustment, the proper back-off specifications are stamped on the transmission oil pan rail of the case. This became effective with transmission serial number 1442920. If the back-off specifications do not appear on the pan rail, back off the adjusting screw as indicated in the chart for the model being serviced.

Low-Reverse (Rear) Band

The low-reverse band adjusting screw is located on the right side of the transmission case, Fig. 8. Loosen the lock nut and back off nine turns. Check the freeness of the adjusting screw in the transmission case. If free, tighten the adjusting screw to 70-75 *inch pounds* torque. Using a reference mark of chalk or colored pencil on the corner of the adjusting screw square and the transmission case, back the adjusting screw out the number of turns listed in the chart. While holding the adjusting screw stationary, tighten the lock nut to 35-40 lb. ft. torque.

OIL PRESSURE TESTS

In making pressure checks, refer to Figs. 9 to 12. And be sure to have the engine and transmission at normal operating temperature.

Line Pressure

With a 300 psi gauge in the line pressure hole in the transmission case the line pressure should be as given in the chart.

If line pressure is not correct it may be adjusted by loosening the lock nut on the adjusting screw and turning screw clockwise to increase or counterclockwise to decrease pressure. All line pressure adjustments should fall within the limits specified in the above table.

Lubrication Pressure

Connect a pressure gauge in the lubrication pressure take-off hole. With engine running at 800 rpm in neutral, lubrication pressure should be 10 to 30 psi.

If the pressure is extremely high (above 50 psi) it is a good indication that there is a restriction due to dirt or foreign matter in the lubrication passages.

Governor Pressure

With a pressure gauge connected in the governor pressure take-off hole the governor pressures given in the chart should be obtained.

Throttle (Compensated) Pressure

With rear wheels free to turn, connect a pressure gauge at the throttle pressure take-off plug.   Disconnect the throttle linkage at the transmission. Start the engine and place the transmission in Drive position. While holding the transmission throttle lever toward the *closed throttle position* (against the internal stop) increase engine speed slowly to approximately 1500 rpm to obtain an upshift into direct ratio. After the shift takes place, compensated throttle pressure should be 26 to 32 psi. As the transmission throttle lever is advanced toward full throttle, compensated throttle pressure should begin to rise after 0 to 5 deg. movement. If compensated pressure rises immediately when the lever is moved, or if the pressure is incorrect or fails to rise after approximately 5 deg. movement, install a new valve body.

Before stopping the engine, advance the transmission throttle control lever slowly and then return to closed throttle.

Compensated throttle pressure should rise to approximately 80 to 90 psi and then fall smoothly without hesitation and should always return to a consistent reading at closed throttle. Failure to do this indicates faulty throttle compensator valve or throttle valve operation.

AIR PRESSURE TESTS

The front clutch, rear clutch, kickdown servo, and low-reverse servo may be checked by applying air pressure to the respective passage when the valve body assembly is removed. To make the complete air pressure check, proceed as follows, referring to Figs. 13, 14. Be sure compressed air supply is free of dirt and moisture.

Raise vehicle on hoist, drain transmission fluid and remove transmission oil pan and accumulator cover. Apply air pressure to the front clutch passage. Listen for a dull thud which indicates that the front clutch is operating. Hold the air pressure on for a few seconds and look for excessive oil leaks in the system.

Remove the valve body and apply air

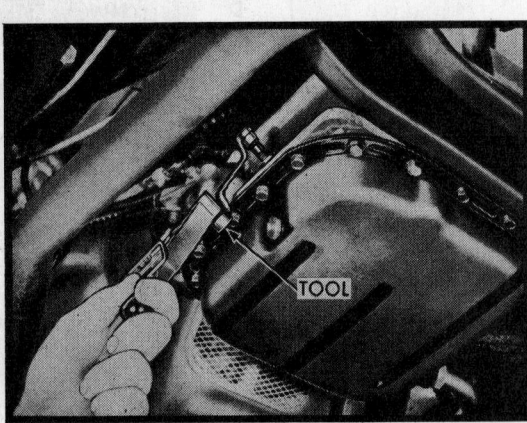

Fig. 7   Adjusting kickdown (front) band

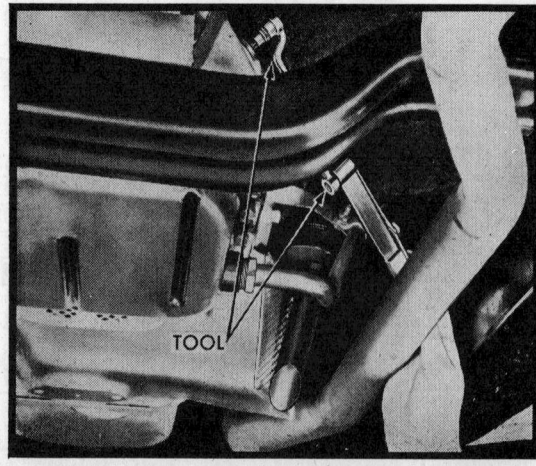

Fig. 8   Adjusting low-reverse (rear) band

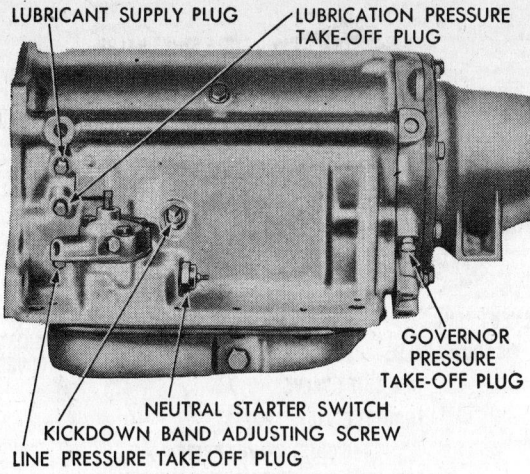

Fig. 9 Left side of transmission. 1956

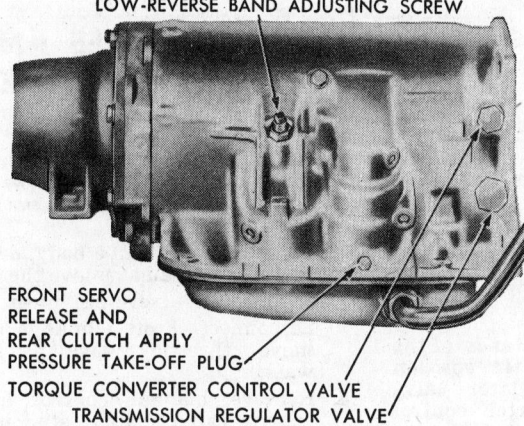

Fig. 11 Right side of transmission. 1956

A—GOVERNOR PRESSURE
B—LINE PRESSURE TO GOVERNOR
C—REAR PUMP INLET
D—REAR CLUTCH 'APPLY' (Line pressure)
E—LOW AND REVERSE SERVO 'APPLY' (Line pressure)
F—KICKDOWN SERVO 'APPLY' (Throttle compensated pressure)
G—LOW AND REVERSE SERVO (Location)
H—KICKDOWN SERVO (Location)
J—KICKDOWN SERVO 'APPLY' (Line pressure)
K—KICKDOWN SERVO 'RELEASE' (Line pressure)
L—ACCUMULATOR (Location)
M—FRONT CLUTCH AND ACCUMULATOR 'APPLY' (Line pressure)
N—LINE PRESSURE
O—FRONT PUMP INLET
P—REVERSE UPSET (Reverse blocker 'Apply') (Line pressure)
Q—LINE PRESSURE GAUGE

Fig. 13 Oil passages in transmission case. 1956

pressure to the rear clutch passage. A dull thud indicates that this clutch is operating. Also check for excessive oil leaks.

Apply air pressure to the kickdown "apply" (line) pressure passage and observe the action of the kickdown servo, lever and band.

Apply air pressure to the kickdown "apply" (compensated throttle) pressure passage and observe the operation of the kickdown servo.

Apply air pressure to the low and reverse servo passage and observe the operation of the servo, lever and band.

Apply air pressure to the "line pressure to governor" passage. Rotate the propeller shaft slightly to bring the governor flyweight down while applying the air pressure. Operation of the governor will be indicated by a "click" when air pressure is applied.

If the clutches, servos and governor operate properly, "no drive" conditions as well as erratic or no upshift conditions, indicates that the trouble exists in the control valve body assembly.

SPEEDOMETER PINION

Removal—Disconnect speedometer cable and housing from drive pinion and sleeve assembly in transmission. Remove pinion and sleeve assembly from transmission extension.

Installation—Install speedometer pinion and sleeve assembly in transmission extension and torque from 40 to 45 lb. ft. Connect speedometer cable and housing

to drive pinion and sleeve in transmission and tighten.

NEUTRAL STARTER SWITCH

Removal — Drain approximately two quarts of fluid from the transmission and reinstall drain plug. Remove wire at switch and remove switch and gasket, Figs. 9 and 10.

Installation—Install switch and gasket in transmission case and torque from 20

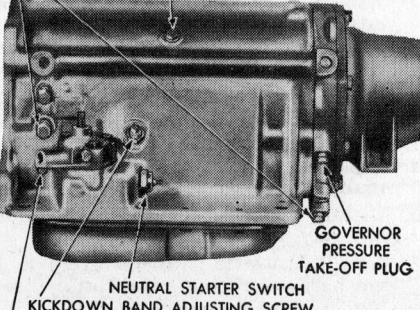

Fig. 10 Left side of transmission. 1957-61

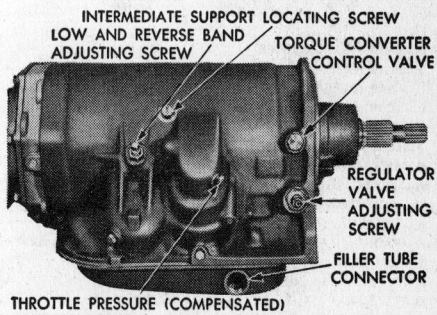

Fig. 12 Right side of transmission. 1957-61

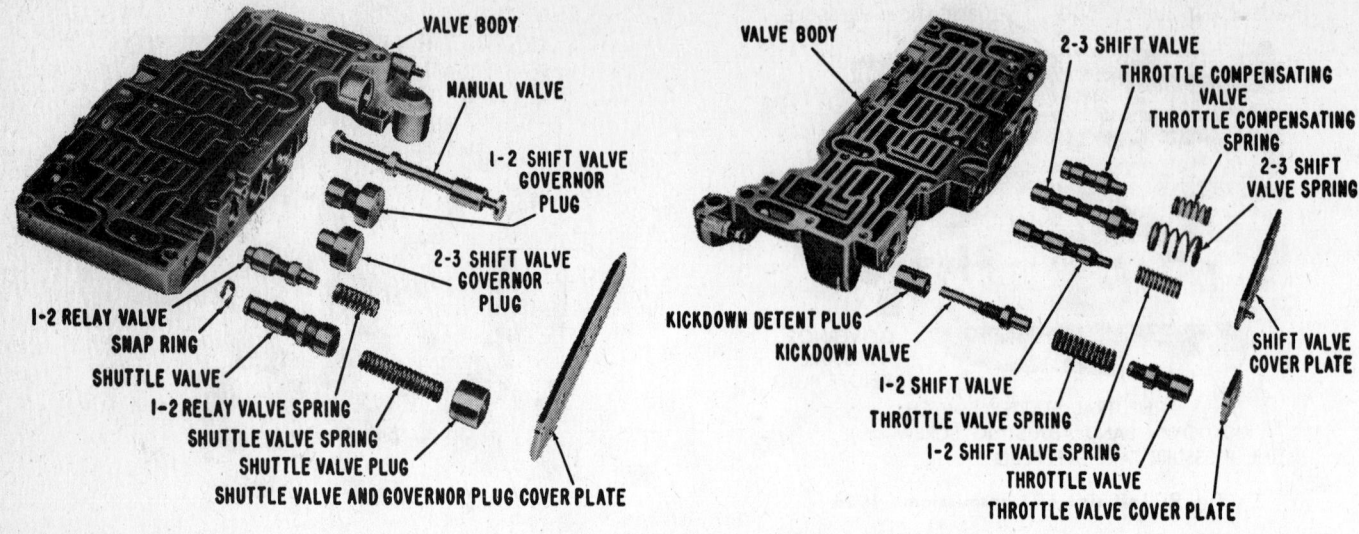

VALVE BODY
MANUAL VALVE
1-2 SHIFT VALVE
GOVERNOR PLUG
2-3 SHIFT VALVE GOVERNOR PLUG
1-2 RELAY VALVE
SNAP RING
SHUTTLE VALVE
1-2 RELAY VALVE SPRING
SHUTTLE VALVE SPRING
SHUTTLE VALVE PLUG
SHUTTLE VALVE AND GOVERNOR PLUG COVER PLATE

VALVE BODY
2-3 SHIFT VALVE
THROTTLE COMPENSATING VALVE
THROTTLE COMPENSATING SPRING
2-3 SHIFT VALVE SPRING
KICKDOWN DETENT PLUG
KICKDOWN VALVE
1-2 SHIFT VALVE
THROTTLE VALVE SPRING
1-2 SHIFT VALVE SPRING
THROTTLE VALVE
THROTTLE VALVE COVER PLATE
SHIFT VALVE COVER PLATE

Fig. 14A One piece valve body disassembled. 1959-61

to 25 lb. ft. Connect wire to switch. Refill transmission to proper level.

REGULATOR VALVE ASSEMBLY

Removal—Remove transmission regulator valve spring retainer, gasket and spring, Figs. 11 and 12. Using a mechanical retriever or a piece of $\frac{5}{32}$" welding rod inserted in end of valve, remove valve.

Installation—With the assistance of the retrieving tool, place valve in position and seat properly in regulator valve

A—GOVERNOR PRESSURE
B—REAR PUMP INLET
C—REAR CLUTCH 'APPLY' (Line pressure)
D—LOW AND REVERSE SERVO 'APPLY' (Line pressure)
E—KICKDOWN SERVO APPLY' (Throttle compensated pressure)
F—LOW AND REVERSE SERVO (Location)
G—KICKDOWN SERVO (Location)
H—KICKDOWN SERVO 'APPLY' (Line pressure)
J—KICKDOWN SERVO 'RELEASE' (Line pressure)
K—ACCUMULATOR (Location)
L—FRONT CLUTCH AND ACCUMULATOR APPLY' (Line pressure)
M—LINE PRESSURE
N—FRONT PUMP INLET
O—REVERSE UPSET (Reverse blocker Apply') (Line pressure)
P—LINE PRESSURE GAUGE

Fig. 14 Oil passages in transmission case. 1957-61

body. Install regulator valve spring, gasket and retainer. Torque from 45 to 50 lb. ft.

TORQUE CONVERTER CONTROL VALVE

Removal—Remove torque converter control valve spring retainer, gasket and spring, Figs. 11 and 12. Using a mechanical retriever or a piece of ¼" welding rod inserted in end of valve, remove valve.

Installation—With the assistance of the retrieving tool, place valve in position and seat properly in regulator valve body. Install torque converter control valve spring, gasket and retainer. Torque from 35 to 40 lb. ft.

OIL COOLER

Removal—If equipped with an oil cooler, drain water from radiator. Remove lower radiator-to-cooler water hose. Remove inlet and outlet oil tubes. Remove cooler-to-water pump flange bolts. Remove oil cooler and gasket.

Installation — Clean mating surfaces thoroughly. Install new flange gasket. Install cooler to water pump and tighten flange nuts. Install inlet and outlet oil tubes. Install water hose. Refill radiator. Start engine and check unit for water and oil leaks.

OIL PAN

Removal — Drain transmission, install drain plug and tighten. Remove oil pan filler tube from oil pan, and loosen support bracket screw. Remove oil pan screws and washers and remove oil pan and gasket from transmission case.

Installation—Using a new oil pan gasket, place pan in position on transmission case. Install oil pan screws and washers, drawing them down evenly and tighten from 12 to 17 lb. ft. torque. Install oil pan filler tube and tighten nut from 35 to 40 lb. ft. Tighten support bracket screw. Refill transmission.

VALVE BODIES AND TRANSFER PLATE

One Piece Type, 1959-61

It is not necessary to disconnect the control cable at the transmission to permit removal of the valve body with the transmission in the car.

1. To remove the valve body, drain the transmission and remove the oil pan.
2. Engage "R" (reverse) push button.
3. Disconnect throttle linkage and remove throttle valve lever and washer.
4. Remove manual control lever-to-control cable adapter stud nut.
5. Remove oil strainer and transfer plate bolts and lower valve body and transfer plate assembly.

Assemble and Install—Assemble the valve body as shown in Fig. 14A. Clean the mating surfaces and check for burrs on both transmission case and valve body transfer plate. Then install as follows:

1. Place manual lever in reverse position (all the way in).
2. Install accumulator piston spring into recess in top of transfer plate and carefully guide the spring up into the accumulator piston as the transfer plate and valve body are placed up against the transmission case. At the same time, index the cable adapter stud into the manual control lever.
3. Install the transfer plate bolts and washers (leave 4 holes vacant to attach the oil strainer), draw down evenly and torque to 14-16 lbs. ft.
4. Install oil strainer and torque remaining bolts to the same tightness.
5. Install cable adapter stud nut securely and tighten.
6. Install throttle valve lever and washer and reconnect throttle linkage.
7. Install oil pan and refill transmission to the proper level with automatic transmission fluid.

Multiple Piece Types

Removal—Place gearshift control in 1 (low) position. *It is necessary for control cable adapter to be in this position when removing cable from adapter housing on transmission.*

1. Remove oil pan.
2. Disconnect throttle linkage from throttle lever on transmission.
3. Remove dirt and foreign matter from around control cable housing.
4. Loosen throttle control lever screw and remove lever assembly.
5. Remove flat washer and felt seal from throttle lever shaft.
6. Remove control cable clip.
7. Remove control cable adapter housing plug, insert screwdriver through hole and release control cable spring lock, Fig. 15. While releasing spring lock, remove cable.
8. Using same screwdriver, insert through cable opening in adapter housing and push lever rearward to last detent.
9. Reinstall housing plug and tighten.
10. Remove control cable housing.
11. Loosen manual valve control lever screw and slide lever off shaft.
12. Remove oil strainer.
13. Loosen (to relieve spring load) and remove three accumulator cover screws.
14. Remove accumulator cover from transfer plate.
15. Remove valve bodies and transfer plate from transmission.

Overhaul—Never clamp any portion of this assembly in a vise or use force when removing or installing valves and plugs.

Separate the component parts of the assembly as shown in Figs. 16 to 27. Use extreme care to prevent the loss of the governor compensating valve retaining pin. Be sure to account for the servo pressure bleed valve to prevent its loss. Do not disturb the throttle valve stop screw setting when handling the front valve body.

After disassembly and when each part has been thoroughly cleaned and inspect-

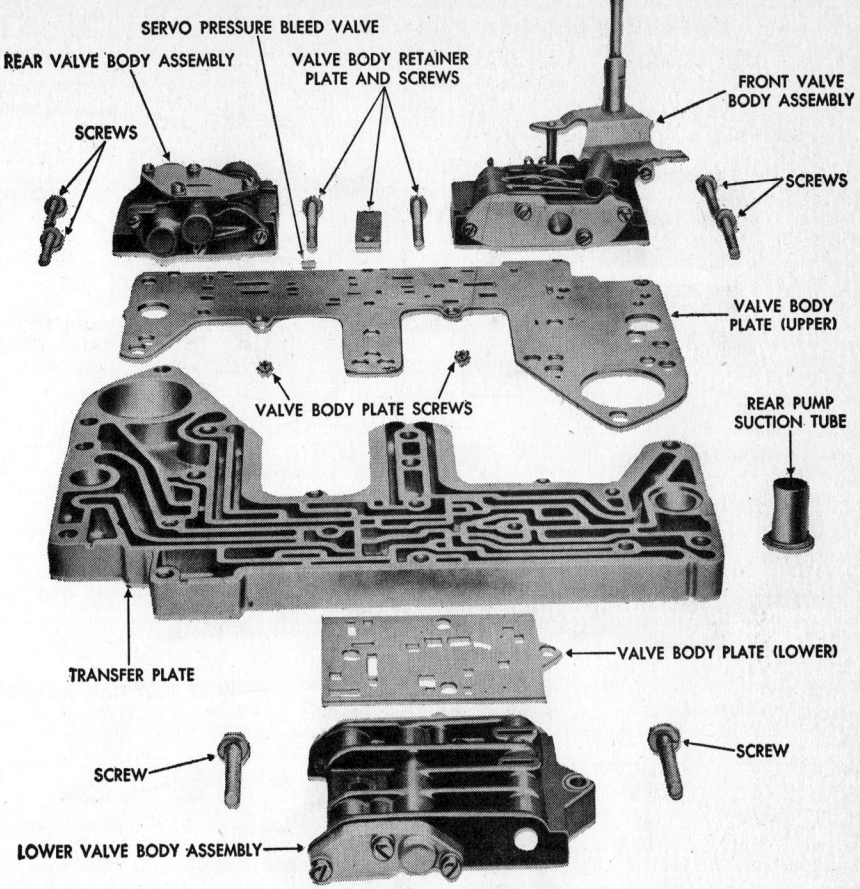

Fig. 16 Valve bodies and transfer plate. 1956

ed, place on clean paper (not rags) until ready for reassembly.

1. Place all parts in a clean solvent, wash thoroughly and dry with compressed air. Make sure all passages are free from obstructions. When inspecting, also check for the possibility of porous castings.
2. Inspect all mating surfaces for burrs, nicks and grooves. Small ones may be removed with crocus cloth; otherwise, damaged parts must be replaced.
3. Using a suitable straightedge, check all mating surfaces for distortion.
4. Using a lamp, inspect bores in valve body for score marks, pits or irregularities.
5. Inspect all springs for distortion and collapsed coils.
6. Inspect all valves and plugs for burrs, nicks or scores. Small ones may be removed with crocus cloth provided extreme care is used not to round off the sharp edge portion of the valve. *The sharp edge portion is very important to this type valve. It helps to prevent dirt and foreign matter from getting between tne valves and bodies, thus reducing the possibilities of sticking.*
7. Check valves and plugs for free operation in bores. They must fall freely in the bores when all parts are clean and dry.
8. Inspect valve body plates for nicks, scratches or burrs. Make sure metering holes are open.
9. Visually inspect transfer plate for porosity.
10. Inspect machined surface for nicks or burrs.
11. Inspect threaded holes for damaged threads.
12. In lower valve body, inspect ball

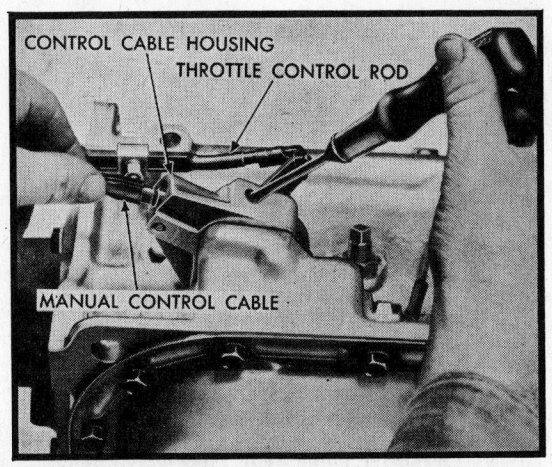

Fig. 15 Releasing manual control cable spring lock used with multiple piece valve body

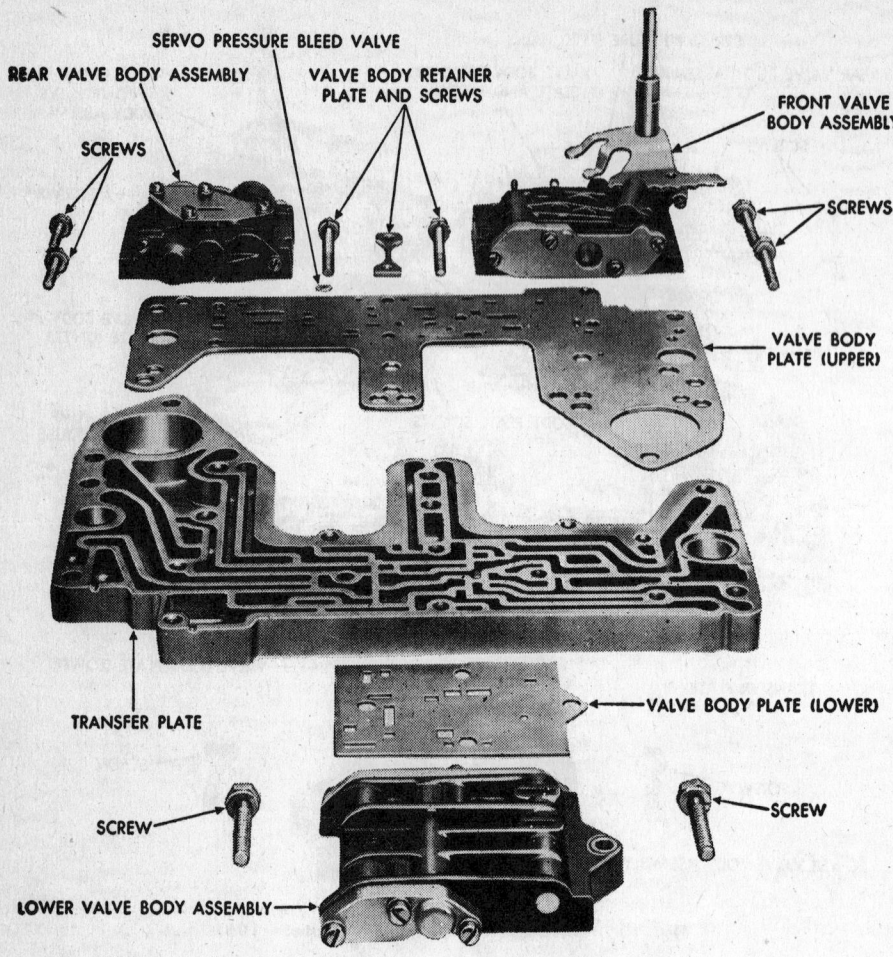

SERVO PRESSURE BLEED VALVE

REAR VALVE BODY ASSEMBLY

VALVE BODY RETAINER PLATE AND SCREWS

FRONT VALVE BODY ASSEMBLY

SCREWS

SCREWS

VALVE BODY PLATE (UPPER)

VALVE BODY PLATE (LOWER)

TRANSFER PLATE

SCREW

SCREW

LOWER VALVE BODY ASSEMBLY

Fig. 17 Valve bodies and transfer plate. 1957

to make sure it slides freely in valve. Inspect check valve ball seat in valve body for faulty casting. Inspect manual valve lever needle bearing in valve body; do not remove as body and bearing are serviced as an assembly.

Assemble—In assembling the valve bodies, refer to Figs. 16 to 27.

Installation—Clean mating surfaces and check for burrs on both the transmission case and transfer plate. Then proceed as follows:

1. Install valve bodies and transfer plate on transmission.
2. Install 5 transfer plate screws (short) with Belleville washers (2 at rear, 2 in center and 1 in front). Draw down evenly and tighten from 14 to 16 lb. ft.
3. Install accumulator spring through transfer plate and position in piston.
4. Install accumulator cover.
5. Place oil strainer in position over rear pump suction tube in transfer plate assembly.
6. Check position of front pump suction tube in elbow. *Opening in suction tube should be facing oil pan.*
7. Slide front pump suction tube into strainer and position elbow on transfer plate. Install two screws and Belleville washers. Draw down evenly and torque elbow and accumulator cover screws from 14 to 16 lb. ft.
8. Install oil pan.
9. Install manual control lever with locking screw to rear on lever shaft.
10. Position lever on shaft so there is $\frac{7}{32}''$ clearance (without gasket) between lever and transmission case, Fig. 28.
11. If control cable adapter has been removed from manual valve control lever, reinstall by positioning in lever (end of spring lock up) and installing pin.
12. Place manual valve control lever in reverse position (last detent to rear) and install gasket, control cable housing and screws with Belleville

contacting surface in valve seats and valve body for nicks or burrs. Inspect covers for flatness and porosity.

13. In the front valve body, inspect manual valve detent and make sure

it slides freely into valve body. Inspect riveting and wear on manual valve lever pin in lever. Inspect staking of manual lever and throttle cam to their respective shafts. Inspect kickdown valve detent plug

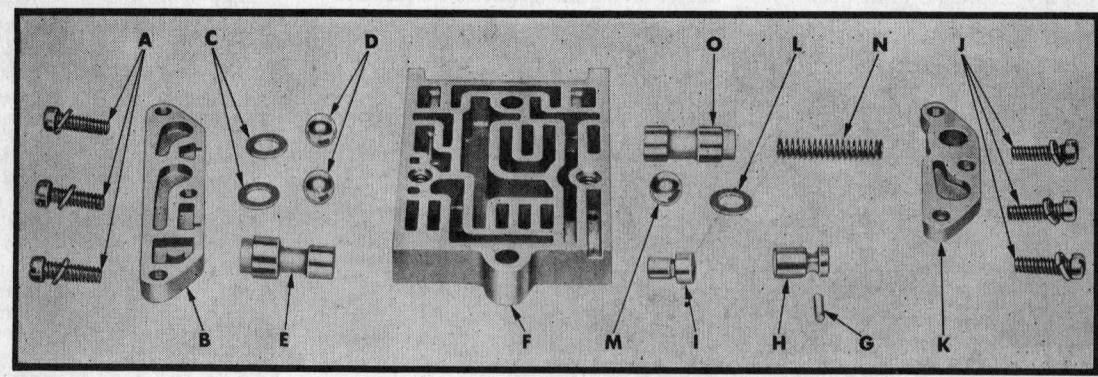

Fig. 19 Lower valve body. 1956

A. Screws
B. Governor compensator valve cover
C. Lower valve body check valve ball seats
D. Lower valve body check valve balls
E. Governor compensator valve
F. Lower valve body
G. Governor compensator valve plug retainer pin
H. Governor compensator valve plug retainer

I. Governor compensator valve plug
J. Screws
K. Throttle compensator valve cover
L. Lower valve body check valve ball seat
M. Lower valve body check valve ball
N. Throttle compensator valve spring
O. Throttle compensator valve

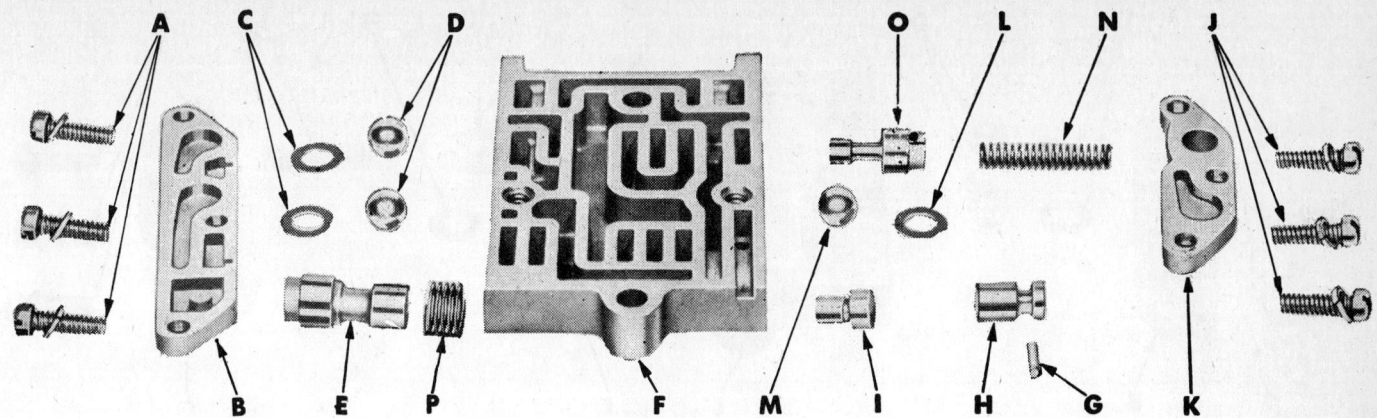

Fig. 20 Lower valve body. 1957

A. Cover screws
B. Compensator valve cover
C. Check valve ball seats
D. Check valve balls
E. Governor compensator valve

F. Lower valve body
G. Plug retainer pin
H. Compensator valve plug retainer
I. Compensator valve plug
J. Cover screws
K. Throttle compensator valve cover

L. Check valve ball seat
M. Check valve ball
N. Spring
O. Throttle compensator valve
P. Compensator valve spring

washers. Draw down evenly and torque from 14 to 16 lb. ft.

13. Install felt washer, flat washers and throttle lever control assembly and tighten clamping bolt.

14. Connect throttle linkage to transmission. Install control cable in housing and adapter, making sure spring lock engages cable.

15. Adjust manual control cable.
16. Refill transmission.
17. Adjust throttle linkage.

KICKDOWN PISTON

Removal — After removing the valve bodies and transfer plate, loosen the kickdown band adjusting screw out far enough to remove the anchor. Remove kickdown band strut. Install the tool shown in Fig. 29 and apply sufficient pressure on the kickdown piston rod guide and remove the snap ring. Loosen compressing portion of tool and remove piston rod guide, spring and rod. Using pliers, remove kickdown piston from case.

Inspection — Referring to Fig. 30, inspect riveting of kickdown piston rod. Inspect guide contacting surface for nicks or burrs. Inspect seal ring on guide for wear and make sure it turns freely in the groove. Check fit of guide on piston rod. Inspect the three rings (2 interlocking) on piston for wear or broken locks. Make sure they turn freely in groove. It is not necessary to remove rings unless condition warrants.

When replacing new rings, use extreme care to avoid damaging the interlocking portion of the ring. Inspect kickdown piston for light scores and wear. Inspect piston spring and rod guide snap ring for distortion.

Assemble — Lubricate piston seals and place kickdown piston into position. Compress outer ring and start assembly into case. With piston properly centered so as not to damage rings, tap lightly and bottom piston into case. Place piston rod in piston and slide spring over piston rod. Install the tool shown in Fig. 29 for kickdown piston installation. Place piston rod guide over spring and compress spring until piston rod enters the guide.

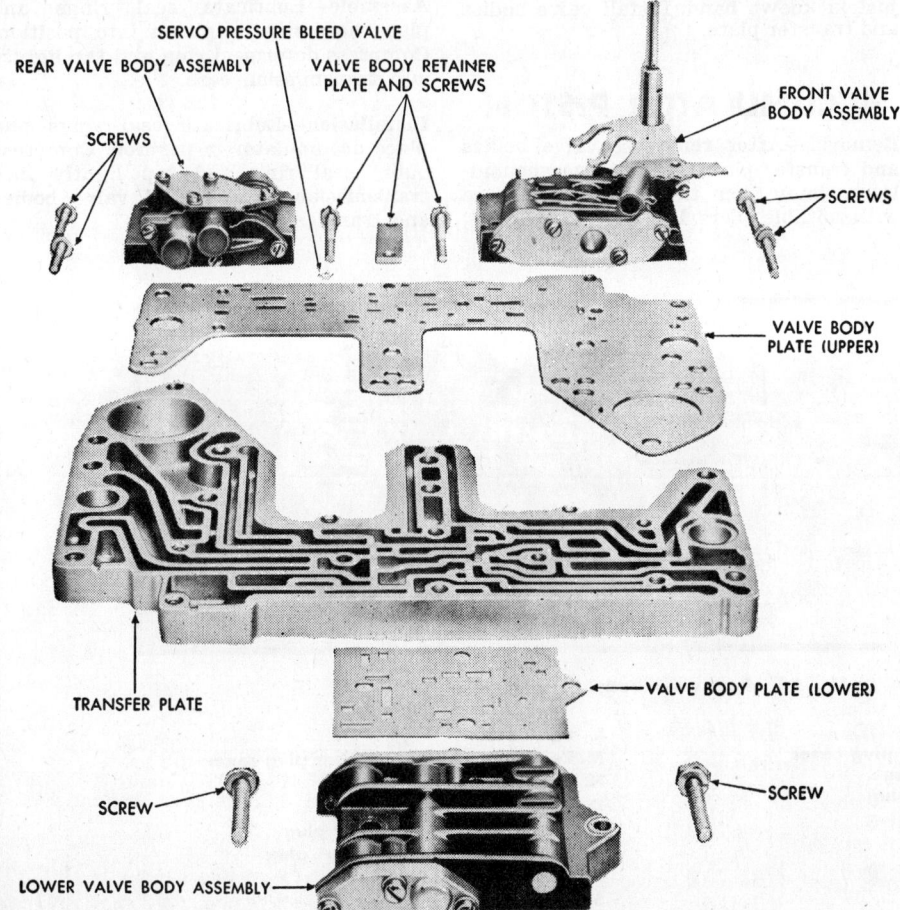

Fig. 18 Valve bodies and transfer plate. 1958-59 multiple piece type

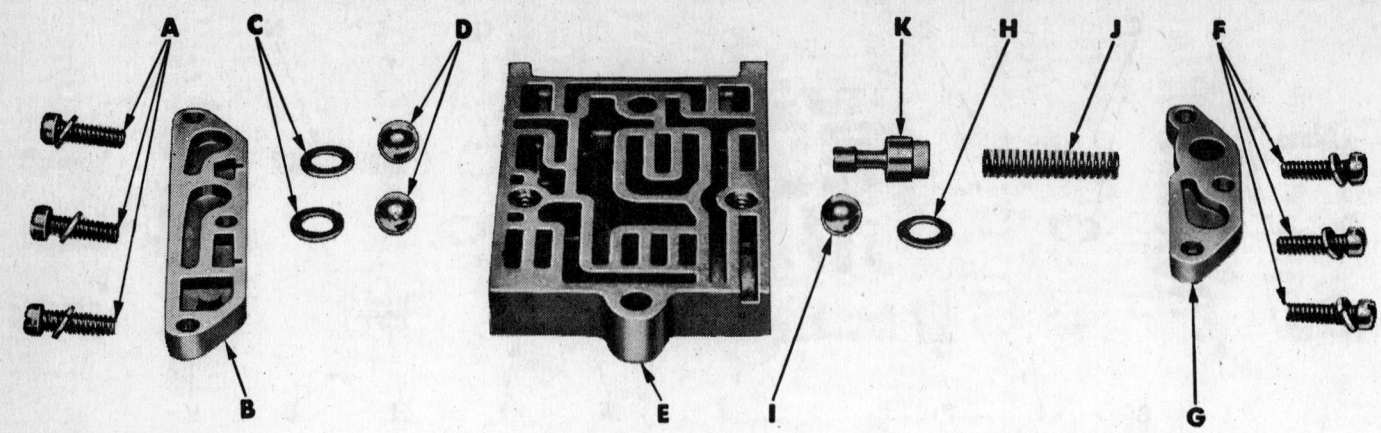

Fig. 21 Lower valve body. 1958-59 multiple piece type

A. Cover screws
B. Valve cover
C. Check valve ball seats
D. Check valve balls

E. Lower valve body
F. Cover screws
G. Compensator valve cover

H. Check valve ball seat
I. Check valve ball
J. Spring
K. Throttle compensator valve

Using extreme care, compress piston spring to the point that the rod guide seal ring slightly binds in case. Work seal ring into position by gradually compressing spring. Install snap ring. Loosen compressing portion of tool and remove.

Installation—Lubricate piston rings and place kickdown piston into position. Compress outer ring and start assembly into case. With piston properly centered, tap lightly and bottom piston into transmission case. Slide piston spring over kickdown piston rod and install in piston. While holding in this position, install kickdown piston rod guide on piston rod. Using the tool shown in Fig. 31, compress the piston spring to the point that the piston guide seal ring slightly binds

on the transmission case. Work the seal ring into position and gradually compress spring until seal ring enters case and snap ring can be installed. After installing snap ring, remove tool. Place band strut in position in band and lever and compress band end sufficiently to install anchor over adjusting screw. Adjust kickdown band. Install valve bodies and transfer plate.

ACCUMULATOR PISTON

Removal—After removing valve bodies and transfer plate, remove the accumulator piston from the transmission case with suitable pliers, Fig. 32.

Inspection—Referring to Fig. 30, inspect the 2 piston seal rings (1 interlocking) for wear or broken locks and make sure they turn freely in the grooves. Inspect piston for nicks, burrs or excessive wear. Inspect spring for distortion.

Assemble—Lubricate seal rings and place accumulator piston into position. Compress outer seal ring and tap lightly into transmission case.

Installation—Lubricate seal rings and place accumulator in position. Compress outer seal ring and tap lightly into transmission case. Install valve bodies and transfer plate.

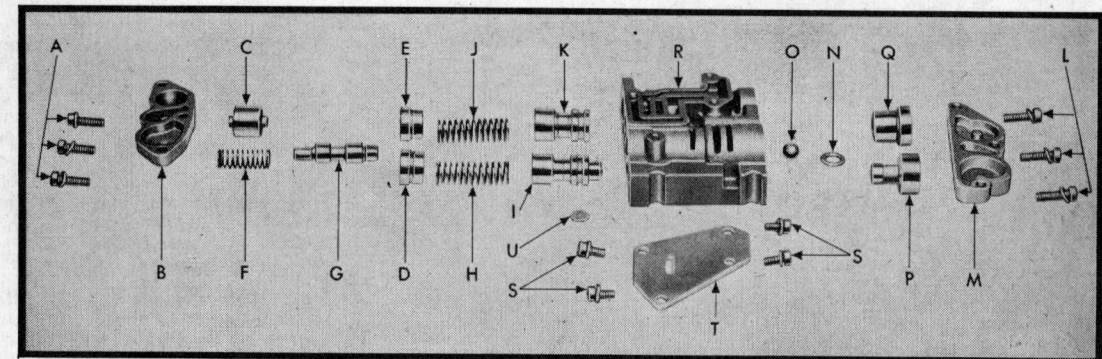

Fig. 22 Rear valve body. 1956

A. Screws
B. Rear valve body kickdown plug cover
C. 2-3 shift valve throttle plug
D. 1-2 shift valve kickdown plug
E. 2-3 shift valve kickdown plug
F. 3-1 relay valve spring
G. 3-1 relay valve
H. 1-2 shift valve spring
I. 1-2 shift valve
J. 2-3 shift valve spring
K. 2-3 shift valve

L. Screws
M. Rear valve body governor plug cover
N. Check valve ball seat
O. Check valve ball
P. 1-2 shift valve governor plug
Q. 2-3 shift valve governor plug
R. Rear valve body
S. Screws
T. Rear valve body plate
U. Servo pressure bleed valve

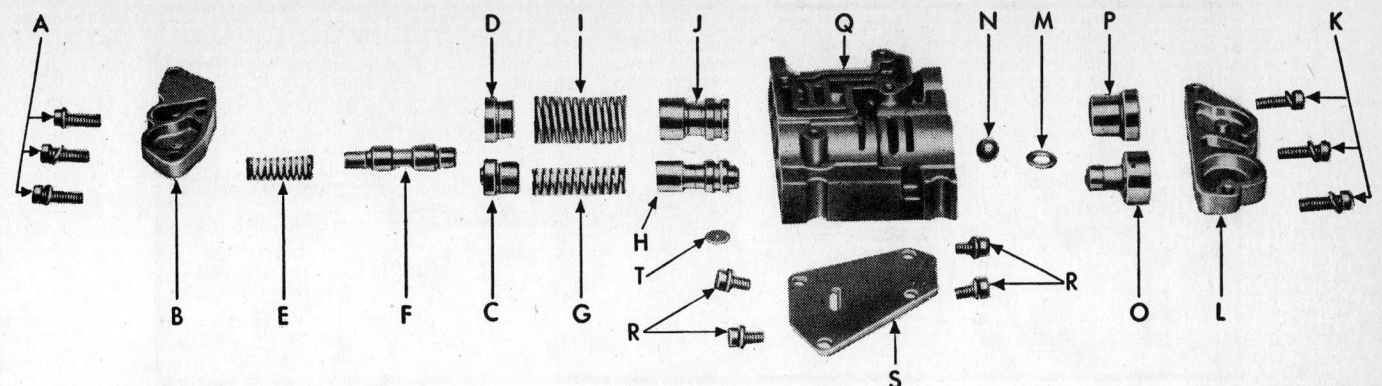

Fig. 23   Rear valve body. 1957

A. Cover screws
B. Kickdown plug cover
C. 1-2 shift valve kickdown plug
D. 2-3 shift valve kickdown plug
E. Spring
F. 3-1 relay valve
G. Spring

H. 1-2 shift valve
I. Spring
J. 2-3 shift valve
K. Cover screws
L. Governor plug cover
M. Ball seat

N. Check valve ball
O. 1-2 shift valve governor plug
P. 2-3 shift valve governor plug
Q. Rear valve body
R. Screws
S. Rear valve body plate
T. Servo pressure bleed valve

OUTPUT SHAFT REAR OIL SEAL

Removal—

1. Disconnect front universal joint.
2. Apply hand brake and remove propeller shaft flange nut and washer.
3. Release hand brake and remove flange and brake drum, using puller if necessary.
4. Remove transmission brake support grease shield spring (small one).
5. Remove brake support grease shield from extension.
6. Using a puller, remove rear bearing oil seal.

Installation—

1. With a suitable driver, install oil seal (metal portion of seal facing in) until driver bottoms on extension. *Indent on grease shield must match groove in extension for correct positioning. Also, shield must be located on extension far enough to permit installation of spring.*
2. Install grease shield spring with opening in spring toward adjusting sleeve. Make sure spring is properly seated in groove.
3. Install propeller shaft flange and brake drum.
4. Install flange, Belleville washer and nut. Apply hand brake and torque nut to 200 lb. ft.
5. Connect universal joint and tighten nuts from 33 to 40 lb. ft.
6. Refill transmission if necessary.

EXTENSION CASE

Removal—

1. Drain approximately 2 quarts of fluid from transmission.
2. Disconnect front universal joint.
3. Apply hand brake and remove propeller shaft nut. Release hand brake and pull off flange and brake drum.
4. Remove brake adjusting screw cover

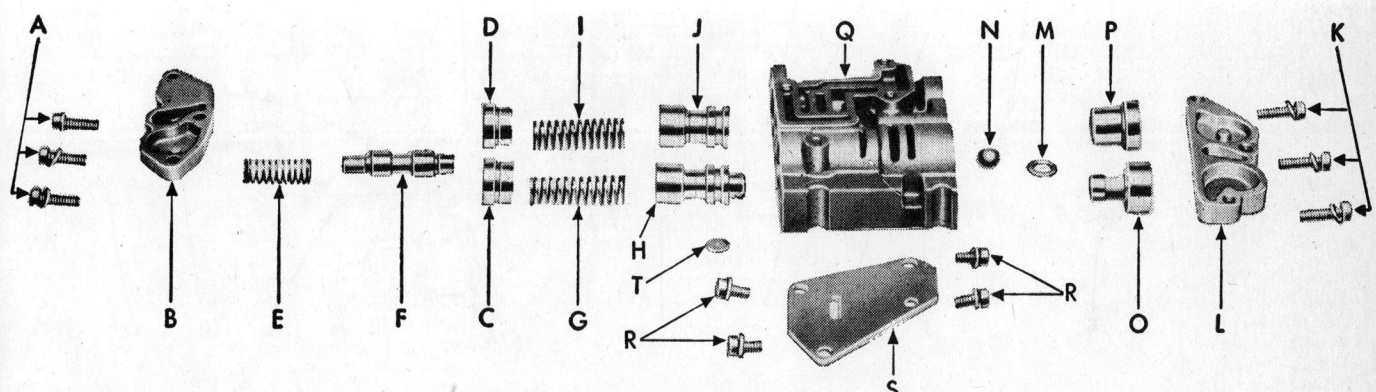

Fig. 24   Rear valve body. 1958-59 multiple piece type

A. Cover screws
B. Kickdown plug cover
C. 1-2 shift valve kickdown plug
D. 2-3 shift valve kickdown plug
E. Spring
F. 3-1 relay valve
G. Spring

H. 1-2 shift valve
I. Spring
J. 2-3 shift valve
K. Cover screws
L. Governor plug cover
M. Check ball seat

N. Check valve ball
O. 1-2 shift valve governor plug
P. 2-3 shift valve governor plug
Q. Rear valve body
R. Screws
S. Rear valve body plate
T. Servo pressure bleed valve

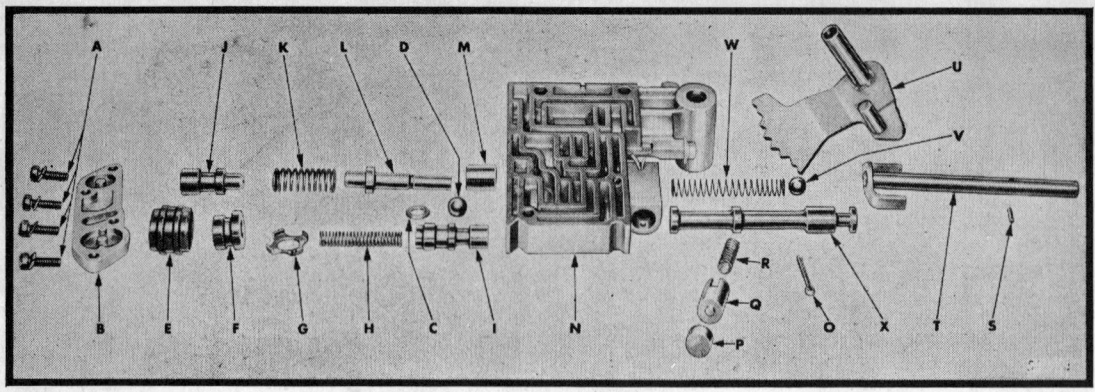

Fig. 25 Front valve body. 1956

A. Screws
B. Shuttle valve cover
C. Front check valve ball seat
D. Front check valve ball
E. Shuttle valve plug sleeve
F. Shuttle valve plug
G. Shuttle valve stop ring
H. Shuttle valve spring

I. Shuttle valve
J. Throttle valve
K. Throttle valve spring
L. Kickdown valve
M. Kickdown detent plug
N. Front valve body
O. Reverse blocker valve pin
P. Reverse blocker valve plug

Q. Reverse blocker valve
R. Reverse blocker valve spring
S. Throttle valve lever shaft pin
T. Throttle valve lever shaft
U. Manual valve lever assembly
V. Manual valve lever detent ball
W. Manual valve detent ball spring
X. Manual valve

plate and loosen cable clamp bolt on hand brake support.

5. Disengage ball end of cable from operating lever and remove cable from brake support.
6. Disconnect speedometer cable and housing from extension and remove speedometer pinion and sleeve.
7. Remove two nuts holding engine rear support insulator to crossmember, leaving insulator attached to extension.
8. Remove the 2 top transmission extension-to-case screws.
9. Using a suitable jack and extreme care to prevent damage to oil pan, raise transmission enough for insu-

lator on extension to clear crossmember.
10. Remove 4 of the remaining extension-to-case screws and install suitable guide studs, Fig. 33.
11. Due to interference of the insulator, it will be necessary to remove the bottom extension-to-case screw with the extension. *Do not remove the one output shaft-to-transmission case screw.*
12. Remove extension and hand brake as a unit, Fig. 33. *If care is used, it is not necessary to remove the hand brake support and shoe assemblies to replace output shaft rear bearing.*

Inspection—Inspect the extension for cracks in casting and remove burrs from

gasket surface. Inspect vent in top of extension to make sure it is open and free from dirt. The purpose of this vent is to prevent vacuum from forming in the transmission case when it is drained. The vent also takes care of fumes and expansion of oil caused by heat.

Do not remove bearing from extension unless inspection reveals it is necessary to do so.

Installation—
1. With guide studs installed, Fig. 33, install a new extension gasket over guide studs and into position against output shaft support. Do not use sealing compound on gasket.
2. Place extension and hand brake as-

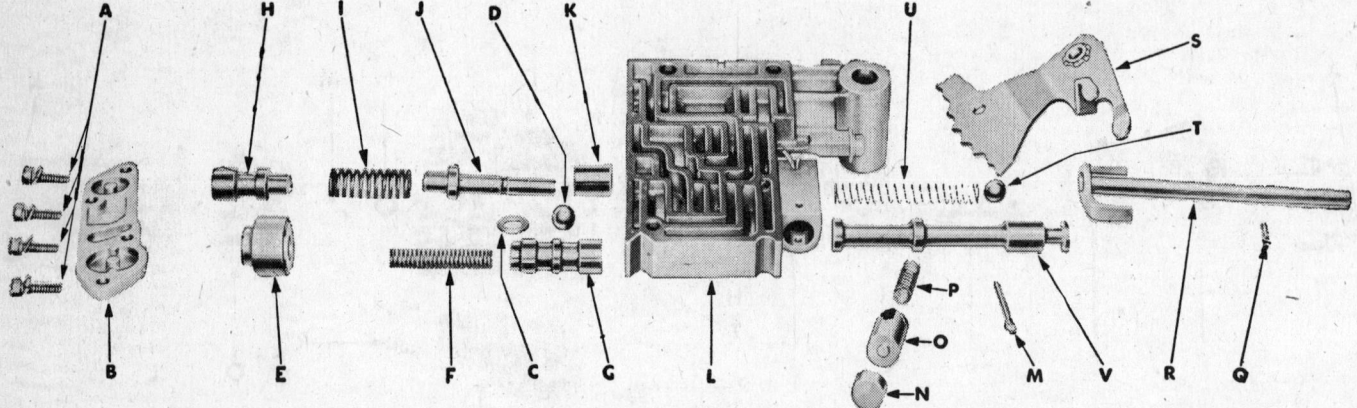

Fig. 26 Front valve body. 1957

A. Cover screws
B. Shuttle valve cover
C. Check ball seat
D. Check valve ball
E. Shuttle valve plug
F. Spring
G. Shuttle valve

H. Throttle valve
I. Spring
J. Kickdown valve
K. Kickdown detent plug
L. Front valve body
M. Blocker valve pin
N. Plug
O. Reverse blocker valve

P. Spring
Q. Pin
R. Throttle valve lever shaft
S. Manual valve lever
T. Detent ball
U. Spring
V. Manual valve

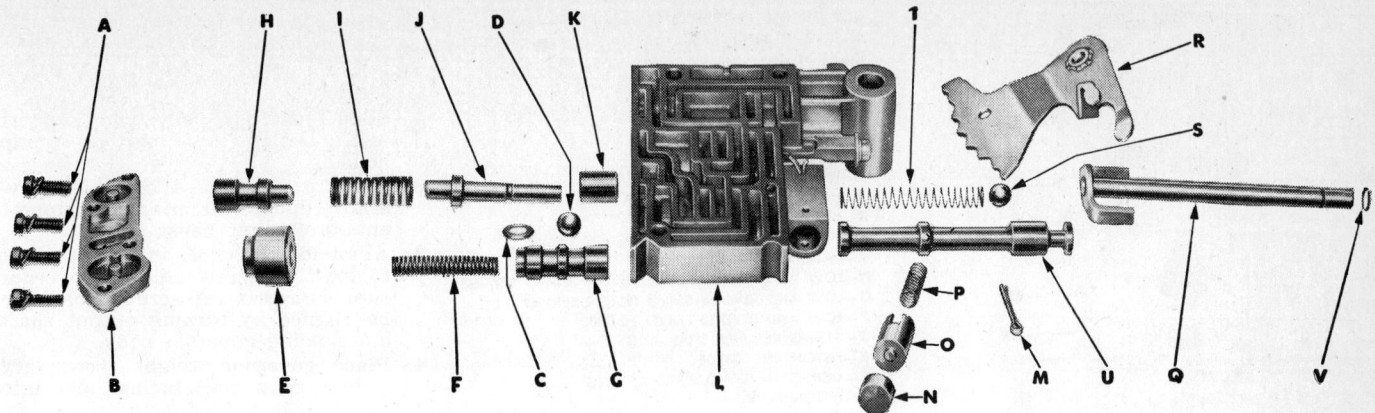

Fig. 27   Front valve body.   1958-59 multiple piece type

A. Cover screws
B. Shuttle valve cover
C. Check ball seat
D. Check valve ball
E. Shuttle valve plug
F. Spring
G. Shuttle valve

H. Throttle valve
I. Spring
J. Kickdown valve
K. Detent plug
L. Front valve body
M. Pin
N. Plug
O. Reverse blocker valve

P. Spring
Q. Throttle valve lever shaft
R. Manual valve lever
S. Detent ball
T. Spring
U. Manual valve
V. Snap ring

sembly over output shaft and on guides studs, Fig. 33. *Due to interference of the insulator, it will be necessary to start the bottom screw as the extension is pushed into position against support. Do not attempt to pull extension in with the aid of screws as damage may result. The propeller shaft flange and drum may be used to force bearing in extension on output shaft. Do not use hammer.*

3. Remove guide studs and install remaining screws. Draw down evenly and tighten from 25 to 30 lb. ft. Make sure output shaft turns freely.

4. Lower transmission and at the same time align mounting studs in insulator with holes in crossmember.

5. Install 2 nuts and lockwashers that hold rear engine support insulator and torque from 30 to 35 lb. ft.

6. Engage ball end of hand brake cable

in operating lever and tighten cable clamp bolt.

7. Install propeller shaft flange and drum assembly. Apply hand brake and tighten nut to 200 lb. ft.

8. Install adjusting screw cover plate on hand brake support.

9. Connect front universal joint and torque nuts from 33 to 37 lb. ft.

10. Install speedometer pinion and sleeve assembly. Torque from 40 to 45 lb. ft. and connect speedometer cable housing.

11. Refill transmission to proper level.

GOVERNOR

Removal—After removing the transmission extension, with a screwdriver remove the governor valve shaft snap ring *from the weight end.* Remove governor

valve shaft and valve, Fig. 34. Using pliers, remove governor weight snap ring (large) and remove weight assembly from governor body.

NOTE—The primary cause of governor operating failures is due to improper operation of governor valve which may be sticking in housing or travel restricted by chips or other foreign matter. If inspection reveals that it is necessary for further governor servicing, then remove the governor support locating screw and remove governor and support assembly from rear oil pump housing. Normal servicing does not require removal of the governor body from the support. If condition warrants, however, when reassembling, do not tighten governor body screws until governor body support is located on output shaft.

Overhaul—Referring to Fig. 35, keep

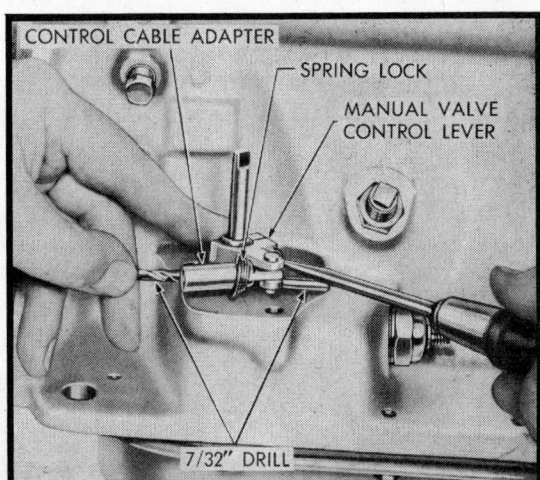

Fig. 28   Setting manual valve control lever clearance (multiple piece type valve)

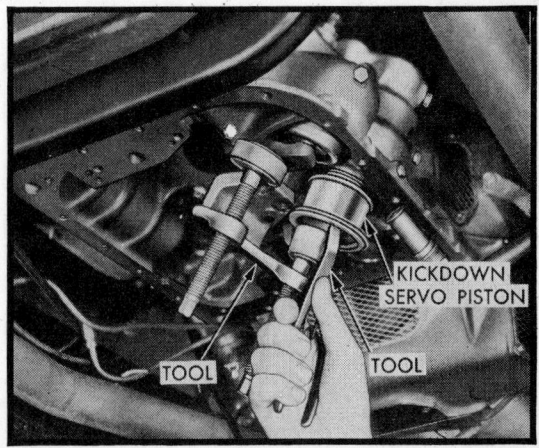

Fig. 29   Removal and installation of kickdown piston

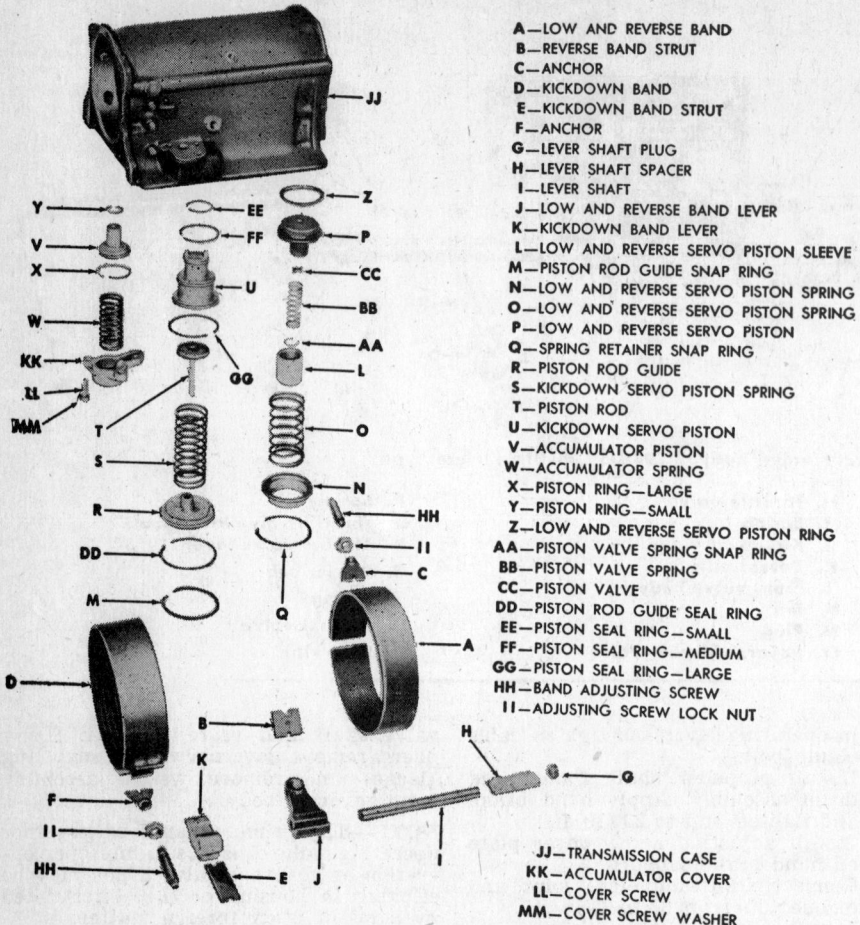

A—LOW AND REVERSE BAND
B—REVERSE BAND STRUT
C—ANCHOR
D—KICKDOWN BAND
E—KICKDOWN BAND STRUT
F—ANCHOR
G—LEVER SHAFT PLUG
H—LEVER SHAFT SPACER
I—LEVER SHAFT
J—LOW AND REVERSE BAND LEVER
K—KICKDOWN BAND LEVER
L—LOW AND REVERSE SERVO PISTON SLEEVE
M—PISTON ROD GUIDE SNAP RING
N—LOW AND REVERSE SERVO PISTON SPRING RETAINER
O—LOW AND REVERSE SERVO PISTON SPRING
P—LOW AND REVERSE SERVO PISTON
Q—SPRING RETAINER SNAP RING
R—PISTON ROD GUIDE
S—KICKDOWN SERVO PISTON SPRING
T—PISTON ROD
U—KICKDOWN SERVO PISTON
V—ACCUMULATOR PISTON
W—ACCUMULATOR SPRING
X—PISTON RING—LARGE
Y—PISTON RING—SMALL
Z—LOW AND REVERSE SERVO PISTON RING
AA—PISTON VALVE SPRING SNAP RING
BB—PISTON VALVE SPRING
CC—PISTON VALVE
DD—PISTON ROD GUIDE SEAL RING
EE—PISTON SEAL RING—SMALL
FF—PISTON SEAL RING—MEDIUM
GG—PISTON SEAL RING—LARGE
HH—BAND ADJUSTING SCREW
II—ADJUSTING SCREW LOCK NUT

JJ—TRANSMISSION CASE
KK—ACCUMULATOR COVER
LL—COVER SCREW
MM—COVER SCREW WASHER

Fig. 30 Servos and bands

thumb pressure against secondary weight when removing the snap ring as it is spring loaded. When disassembled, inspect all parts for burrs and wear. Check secondary weight for free movement in primary weight by placing secondary weight in primary weight without the spring. Primary weight should fall freely when both parts are clean and dry.

Mating surfaces are machined and can easily be damaged. Inspect oil passages and make sure they are free from dirt or foreign matter. Clean passages with compressed air. Inspect governor valve and body for slight scores. Valve should travel freely in governor body.

To assemble the governor, lubricate the two governor support seal rings with transmission fluid and install in governor support. Make sure they are free to rotate in grooves. Position governor body on support and install screws and washers, but *do not tighten at this time*.

Slide support and body in pump housing. Compress seal rings with fingers as support enters housing. Do not force.

Installation—
1. Slide governor body and support into position into rear oil pump housing.
2. Using extreme care, compress governor support seal rings as support enters oil pump housing.
3. Align locating hole in output shaft to locating screw hole in governor support and install screw. Holes can be aligned by turning output shaft and holding governor body.
4. Place governor weight (secondary weight snap ring facing out) into governor body, and install snap ring.
5. With governor valve (small end up) on governor valve shaft, slide shaft into governor body through output shaft and governor weight, Fig. 34. At the same time, position valve in body.
6. Install governor valve shaft snap ring. When installed, apply sufficient pressure to both ends of valve shaft to force snap rings to outer portion of snap ring grooves.
7. Check operation of governor weight assembly and valve by turning output shaft. Both should fall freely in body.
8. Install transmission extension.

REAR OIL PUMP

Removal—After removing transmission extension and governor weight assembly, remove the governor locating screw from governor support. Unfasten oil pump housing from output shaft support. Install guide studs and remove pump housing, gear and governor assembly from output shaft.

Use Prussian Blue and mark pump gears in relation to pump housing face. *Do not use a scribe. Oil pump pinion is keyed to output shaft pinion by a small ball. Use care when removing pinion not to lose ball.* Remove oil pump pinion from output shaft and mark in same manner. Remove governor from oil pump housing.

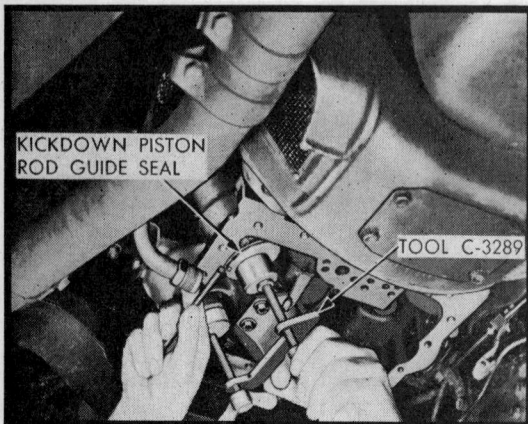

Fig. 31 Positioning kickdown piston rod guide seal

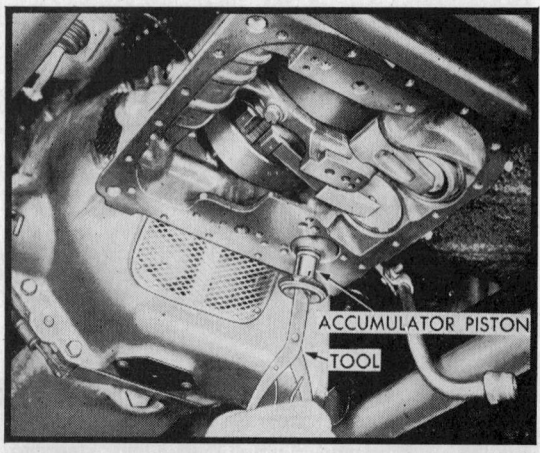

Fig. 32 Removal and installation of accumulator piston

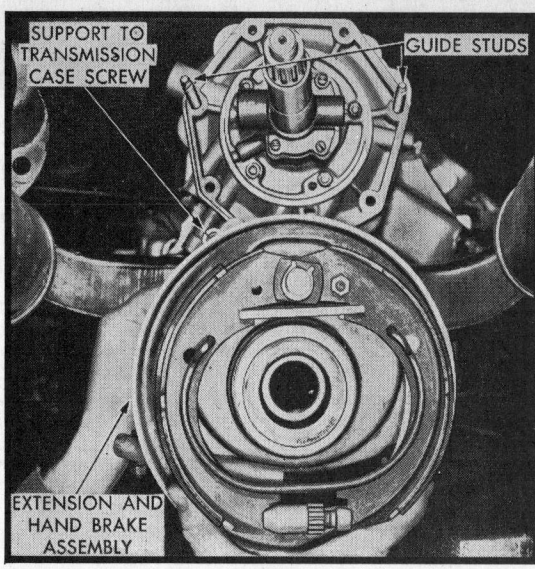

Fig. 33 Removal and installation of extension and hand brake

Fig. 34 Removal and installation of governor valve shaft and valve

Installation—

1. Slide governor support and body assembly into position in pump housing. *Compress governor support seal rings as support enters oil pump housing.*

2. Place ball in ball pocket in output shaft.

3. Place pump pinion (as marked when removed) over output shaft and into position, aligning keyway in pinion with ball in shaft.

4. With pump properly positioned in pump housing (check marking) slide pump and governor over output shaft and guide studs into position against support. *There are two extra holes in housing which are used for vents. Make sure you do not attempt to install screws in these holes.*

5. Remove guide studs and install 5 pump housing-to-output shaft support screws and Belleville washers. Draw down evenly and torque from 10 to 12 lb. ft. *After screws are tightened, turn output shaft to make sure pump gears are free to rotate. If not, remove pump to determine cause.*

6. Align locating hole in output shaft to locating screw hole in governor support, install locating screw and tighten from 5 to 7 lb. ft.

7. Install governor weight assembly and transmission extension.

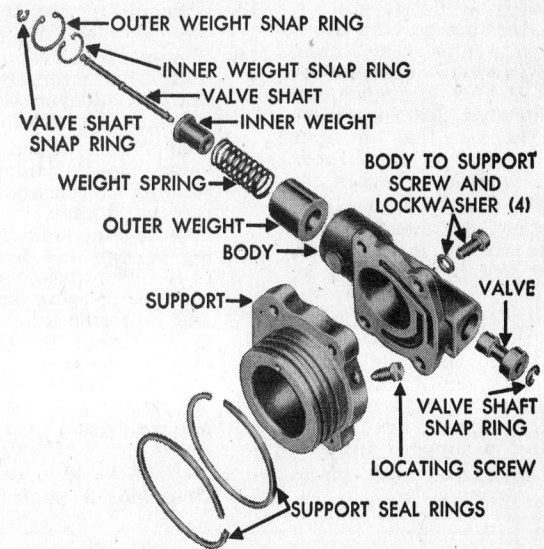

Fig. 35 Governor assembly

Continued on next page

Repairs Requiring Transmission Removal

TRANSMISSION DISASSEMBLE

1. With transmission removed and mounted on a repair stand, remove drive sleeve and oil pan, Figs. 36, 37.
2. Remove throttle control lever.
3. Move manual control lever to reverse position and remove control cable adapter housing.
4. Remove elbow and oil strainer.
5. Remove accumulator cover and spring.
6. Remove valve bodies and transfer plate.
7. Remove neutral starter switch.
8. Prior to removal of propeller shaft flange and hand brake drum, check end clearance of front clutch piston retainer, using a dial indicator as shown in Fig. 38. Pry the front clutch forward by inserting screwdriver between front and rear clutch. With dial indicator mounted as shown with indicator point contacting edge of front clutch retainer, set dial indicator to zero. Pry front clutch rearward against rear clutch, remove screwdriver and take indicator reading. If this clearance exceeds the limits of .020" to .050", note the clearance so that an input shaft thrust washer of the proper thickness can be installed when reassembling the transmission.
9. When removing the hand brake, note that the operating lever link is marked for installation purposes, Fig. 39.
10. When removing the extension case, first remove the speedometer drive pinion and sleeve. Use guide studs to guide the extension off the transmission. The housing may be separated from the support by using a pry bar against a support screw.
11. Remove governor and rear pump housing.

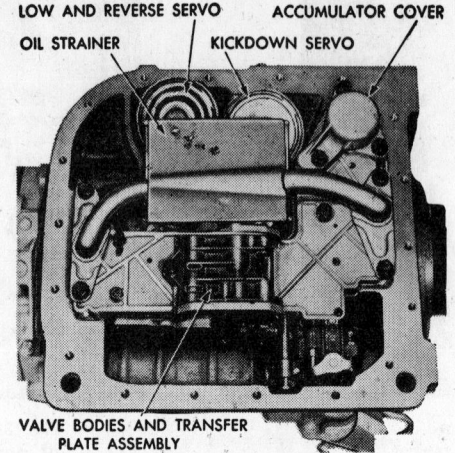

LOW AND REVERSE SERVO   ACCUMULATOR COVER
OIL STRAINER   KICKDOWN SERVO

VALVE BODIES AND TRANSFER PLATE ASSEMBLY

Fig. 37   Transmission with oil pan removed. 1957-61

12. Remove output shaft support.
13. Remove pressure take-off plugs and clean passages with compressed air.
14. Remove Unit No. 1 from transmission. This assembly includes output shaft, kickdown planet pinion carrier and intermediate shaft.
15. Unit No. 2 includes sun gear, reverse planet pinion carrier, over-running clutch and rear clutch. To remove, loosen lock nuts on low-reverse and kickdown band adjusting screws and back out screws 2 to 3 turns. Remove 3 intermediate support locating screws (2 outside and 1 inside of case). *When removing unit, identify locating hole in intermediate support to correspond to threaded locating hole inside of case for installation purposes.* Make sure sun gear and front clutch thrust washer remain in position in front of unit.
16. Unit No. 3 consists of the front clutch piston retainer and input shaft. Use extreme care when removing this unit from the transmission to prevent damage to seal rings on input shaft and sealing surface in reaction shaft.
17. Mark low-reverse band for installation purposes. Remove band through rear opening in transmission. Remove anchor from adjusting screw.
18. Compress kickdown band ends and remove strut, noting that strut is grooved to act as a guide. Remove anchor from adjusting screw and take out band by rotating its ends over center support in case.
19. Remove kickdown and reverse lever shaft stop plug at rear of transmission. With long-nosed pliers, remove shaft lever spacer (flat). Thread guide stud into shaft, Fig. 40, and remove shaft and levers from case.
20. With tool mounted as shown in Fig. 41, remove servo piston spring retainer snap ring. Loosen compression portion of tool and remove. Then remove low-reverse spring retainer, spring, piston and valve.
21. Install tool shown in Fig. 42 and apply sufficient pressure on kickdown piston rod guide and remove snap ring. Remove compression portion of tool and remove spring, guide and pickdown piston rod.
22. Remove accumulater piston.

FRONT PUMP

Removal—Remove regulator valve and torque converter control valve, using a piece of welding rod of suitable diameter inserted in end of valves. Unfasten and remove pump housing from case. Using prussian blue, mark pump gears in relation to pump housing for reassembly purposes.

If the pump dust seal requires replacement, use a brass drift and drive seal out front of housing. To install a new seal, use a suitable driver to drive the seal in place.

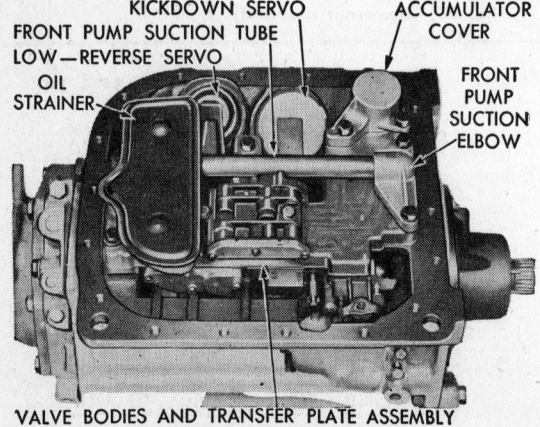

KICKDOWN SERVO
FRONT PUMP SUCTION TUBE   ACCUMULATOR COVER
LOW—REVERSE SERVO
OIL STRAINER   FRONT PUMP SUCTION ELBOW

VALVE BODIES AND TRANSFER PLATE ASSEMBLY

Fig. 36   Transmission with oil pan removed. 1956

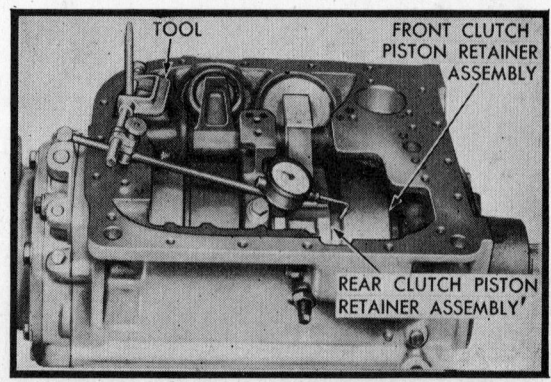

TOOL   FRONT CLUTCH PISTON RETAINER ASSEMBLY

REAR CLUTCH PISTON RETAINER ASSEMBLY

Fig. 38   Checking front clutch end clearance

Inspection—Inspect drive sleeve seal ring contacting surface in housing for wear and scratches. Inspect bushing in hub for scratches or scoring and excessive wear. Remove pump gears and inspect gear contacting surfaces for scratches, burrs or grooving. Inspect regulator body contacting surface on pump housing face for nicks or burrs. Inspect housing passages and make sure they are free from dirt and other foreign matter.

Assemble—Install pump gears in housing, being sure they are replaced as previously marked with counterbore in pinion gear facing down. Using a straightedge and feeler gauge, check clearance between pump housing face and face of gears. Clearance limits are .001″ to .0025″. Tip clearance between rotor lobes should be from .005″ to .008″; replace rotors if clearance exceeds .010″.

Measure clearance between outer rotor and pump housing bore; if clearance exceeds .010″, replace rotors or pump housing. Lubricate gears with automatic transmission fluid.

REGULATOR VALVE BODY

Using guide studs as shown in Fig. 43, pull regulator valve body off of torque

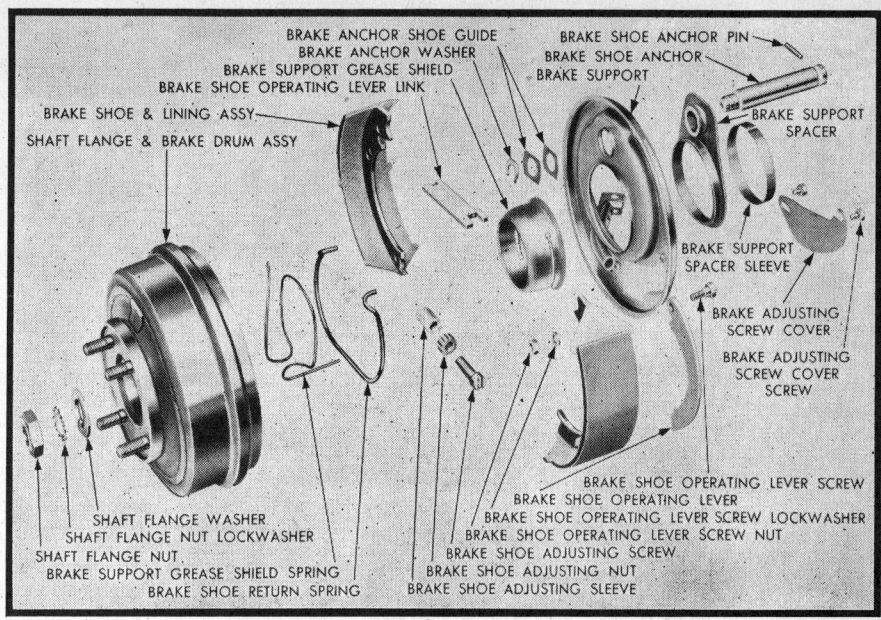

Fig. 39   Hand brake assembly (typical)

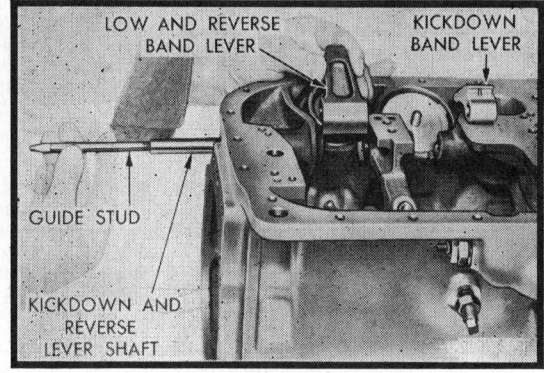

Fig. 40   Removal and installation of kickdown and reverse lever shaft

Fig. 42   Removal and installation of kickdown piston rod guide and spring

Fig. 41   Removal and installation of low-reverse servo piston spring retainer snap ring

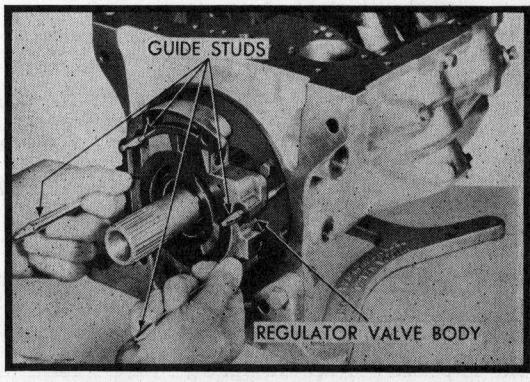

Fig. 43   Removal of regulator valve body

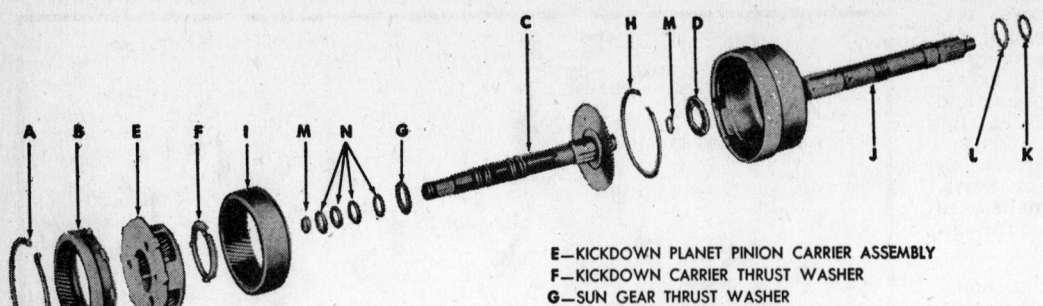

E—KICKDOWN PLANET PINION CARRIER ASSEMBLY
F—KICKDOWN CARRIER THRUST WASHER
G—SUN GEAR THRUST WASHER
H—KICKDOWN ANNULUS GEAR SNAP RING
I—KICKDOWN ANNULUS GEAR
J—OUTPUT SHAFT ASSEMBLY
K—OUTPUT SHAFT SEAL RING—SMALL
L—OUTPUT SHAFT SEAL RING—LARGE
M—INTERMEDIATE SHAFT SEAL RING—SMALL
N—INTERMEDIATE SHAFT SEAL RING—LARGE

A—OUTPUT SHAFT DRIVE HOUSING SNAP RING
B—REVERSE ANNULUS GEAR
C—INTERMEDIATE SHAFT
D—OUTPUT SHAFT THRUST WASHER

Fig. 46 Unit No. 1 disassembled

Fig. 45 Removal and installation of torque converter reaction shaft

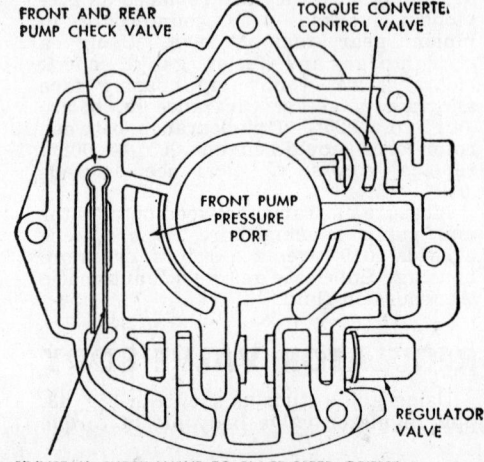

Fig. 44 Regulator valve body and valves. Bleed orifice in valve is omitted after transmission Ser. No. 547000

converter reaction shaft and remove gasket.

Place body and valves in pan containing a clean solvent, wash thoroughly and dry with compressed air. Inspect reaction shaft seal ring surface in bore for scratches, nicks or burrs. Inspect both valves, Fig. 44, for free movement in valve body. They should fall in and out of bores when both the valves and body are dry. Crocus cloth may be used to polish valves provided care is exercised not to round the sharp edge portion of the valves.

Check all fluid passages for obstruction and inspect all mating surfaces for burrs and distortion. If regulator valve body should have a slight nick or raised portion on mating surfaces, it may be removed by using a surface plate and crocus cloth.

Inspect front and rear pump check valve for proper seating on both surfaces. If necessary to remove valve, use long-nose pliers.

Service Note

It is recommended that the position of the front and rear pump check valve be reversed in the regulator body as shown in Fig. 44. *This only applies to transmissions built before serial number 547000. The orifice was omitted at the factory on all transmissions built after this number.*

By reversing this valve, the small bleed orifice will be positioned inward against the front pump pressure port, thereby improving low and idle speed line pressure for longer front clutch life.

TORQUE CONVERTER REACTION SHAFT

If inspection reveals that it is necessary to remove this shaft, remove the shaft seal ring (neoprene). Unfasten the reaction shaft from the transmission case and press the reaction shaft out of the case as shown in Fig. 45.

Inspect inside of shaft for burrs. Inspect splines on shaft for burrs or wear. Inspect seal ring for damage or hardness. Inspect thrust surface for wear and slight scores.

UNIT NO. 1

Fig. 46 is a layout of the parts that make up this assembly. The unit may be placed in the propeller shaft and brake drum assembly to aid in disassembly and assembly. After removing the output shaft drive housing snap ring the parts may be removed from the unit. Assemble the unit as follows:

1. Lubricate output shaft thrust washer with transmission fluid and place in housing.
2. Place kickdown annulus gear on intermediate shaft and install snap ring.
3. Using a feeler gauge, check clearance under annulus gear snap ring. Clearance limits are as close to zero as possible. To obtain this result two sizes of snap rings are available, one is .060″ to .062″ thick and the other is .064″ to .066.″ When checking clearance, support annulus gear on edge of bench so intermediate shaft will seat properly in gear.
4. Place intermediate shaft in output shaft housing.
5. Lubricate kickdown carrier thrust washer and place on kickdown planet carrier.
6. Place carrier in kickdown annulus gear, making sure thrust washer remains in position.
7. Place reverse annulus gear in housing and install output shaft drive housing snap ring.
8. Lubricate and install sun gear thrust washer (roller type) over intermediate shaft and into carrier.

UNIT NO. 2

Disassemble

Fig. 47 is a layout of the parts that make up this unit. With unit in upright position, remove sun gear and front clutch thrust washer. Using two screwdrivers between clutch and intermediate

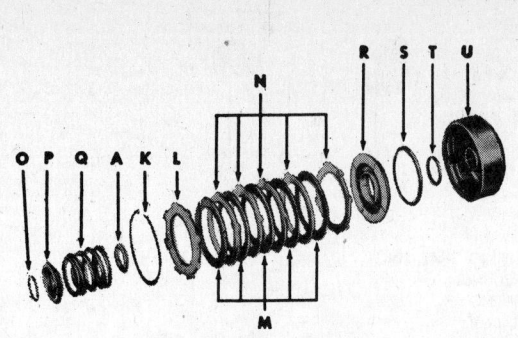

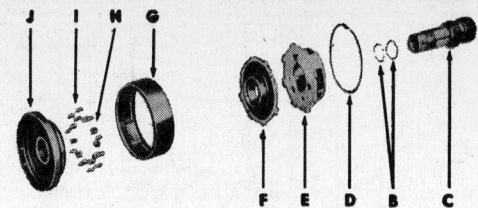

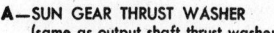

H—OVER-RUNNING CLUTCH CAM ROLLER SPRING
I—OVER-RUNNING CLUTCH CAM ROLLER
J—INTERMEDIATE SUPPORT AND CAM ASSEMBLY
K—REAR CLUTCH SNAP RING
L—PRESSURE PLATE
M—DRIVING DISC
N—CLUTCH PLATE
O—PISTON RETURN SPRING SNAP RING
P—RETURN SPRING RETAINER
Q—RETURN SPRING
R—PISTON
S—PISTON SEAL RING—OUTER
T—PISTON SEAL RING—INNER
U—PISTON RETAINER ASSEMBLY

A—SUN GEAR THRUST WASHER
(same as output shaft thrust washer)
B—SUN GEAR REAR CLUTCH SEAL RING
C—SUN GEAR ASSEMBLY
D—REVERSE BAND SNAP RING
E—REVERSE PLANET PINION CARRIER ASSEMBLY
F—OVER-RUNNING CLUTCH HUB ASSEMBLY
G—LOW AND REVERSE BAND DRUM

Fig. 47   Unit No. 2 disassembled

support, remove rear clutch retainer from sun gear. Remove seal rings from sun gear. Remove reverse sun gear from overrunning clutch and reverse planet pinion carrier assemblies.

Install the tool shown in Fig. 48 in intermediate support and cam assembly and from these parts from the overrunning clutch hub. Remove snap ring from low and reverse band drum. Remove overrunning clutch hub from reverse band drum. Remove the tool shown in Fig. 48 and take out the clutch cam rollers and springs (10 each).

Remove snap ring (large) from rear clutch piston retainer. Remove rear clutch pressure plate and retainer assembly. *The rear clutch plates (steel) are dished and identified by a notch in one of the driving lugs. When removing the steel plates from the clutch retainer, note that the dished side is facing down.*

Invert clutch piston retainer and remove clutch plates and driving discs (5 each). Using the tool shown in Fig. 49, compress the spring retainer and remove the snap ring. After taking out the spring and retainer, use a twisting motion to remove the clutch piston. Remove inner and outer seal rings.

Before assembling the rear clutch piston retainer, make sure the ball check operates freely in clutch retainer. Make sure clutch driving lugs on steel clutch plates travel freely into retainer.

1. To assemble, lubricate and install inner piston seal ring on hub of clutch retainer. Make sure that lip of seal is facing down and seated properly in groove.
2. Lubricate and install outer seal ring on clutch piston with lip of seal facing away from flange.
3. Place piston in clutch retainer and,

with a twisting motion, seat piston in bottom of retainer.
4. Install piston return spring in hub and position spring retainer and snap ring on spring.
5. Using tool shown in Fig. 49, compress clutch spring to seat snap ring. Then remove tool.
6. Lubricate all clutch plates and discs with transmission fluid.
7. Assemble by placing one of the steel plates with dished side facing out in retainer followed by a driving disc. Repeat this procedure until all discs and plates have been installed.
8. Install clutch pressure plate.
9. Select and install snap ring. Using feeler gauge, check clearance between snap ring and pressure plate. Clearance limits are as close to zero as possible. To obtain this result snap rings of two thicknesses are available, one is .060" to .062" thick and the other is .064" to .066".

Assemble

1. Install overrunning clutch hub (hub end first) into snap ring side of low and reverse drum.
2. Place low and reverse planet pinion carrier in drum.
3. With drum supported, select snap ring to minimum clearance. Snap

Fig. 48   Installation of Tool C-3527 in intermediate support and cam assembly

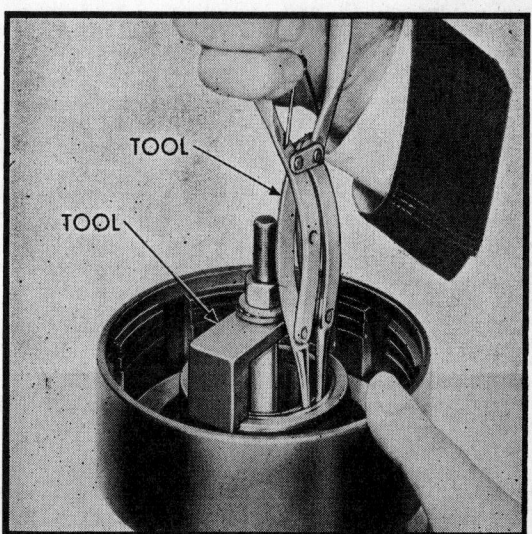

Fig. 49   Removal and installation of rear clutch spring retainer snap ring

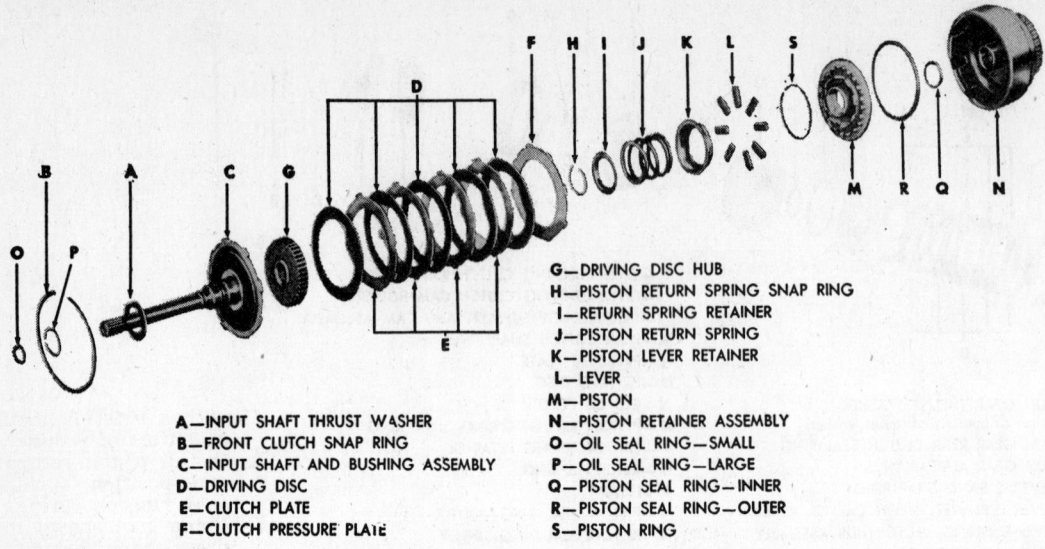

G—DRIVING DISC HUB
H—PISTON RETURN SPRING SNAP RING
I—RETURN SPRING RETAINER
J—PISTON RETURN SPRING
K—PISTON LEVER RETAINER
L—LEVER
M—PISTON
N—PISTON RETAINER ASSEMBLY
O—OIL SEAL RING—SMALL
P—OIL SEAL RING—LARGE
Q—PISTON SEAL RING—INNER
R—PISTON SEAL RING—OUTER
S—PISTON RING

A—INPUT SHAFT THRUST WASHER
B—FRONT CLUTCH SNAP RING
C—INPUT SHAFT AND BUSHING ASSEMBLY
D—DRIVING DISC
E—CLUTCH PLATE
F—CLUTCH PRESSURE PLATE

Fig. 51   Unit No. 3 disassembled.   1956-57

rings are available in thicknesses of .060" to .062", .064" to .066" and .068" to 070".

4. Place Tool C-3527 into position in intermediate support and cam assembly and install cam springs and rollers as shown in Fig. 50. *Make sure that cam springs and rollers are properly seated against cam, otherwise damage to springs will result when overrunning clutch hub is installed.*

5. With intermediate support and cam assembly resting on bench, lubricate bushing and install low and reverse band drum over hub.

6. While holding the two assemblies together, remove Tool C-3527.

7. Lubricate bearing surface on reverse sun gear and install in intermediate support and planet pinion carrier.

8. Lubricate the two sun gear rear clutch seal rings and install on reverse sun gear.

9. Install clutch piston retainer on reverse sun gear.

10. Install front clutch and sun gear

thrust washer, using Lubriplate to hold washer in place.

UNIT NO. 3
Disassemble

1. Referring to Figs. 51, 52, remove input shaft fiber thrust washer.
2. Remove front clutch snap ring.
3. Remove input shaft.
4. Identify top driving disc (select fit) for assembly purposes.
5. Invert clutch retainer and remove clutch plates, discs, pressure plate and clutch hub.
6. Compress piston return spring retainer and remove snap ring.
7. Remove piston return spring retainer and spring.
8. Remove lever retainer and levers.
9. Using twisting motion, remove piston from retainer.

Assemble

1. Lubricate and install inner seal ring

on hub of clutch retainer, being sure that lip of seal is facing down and properly seated in groove.

2. Lubricate and install outer seal ring on clutch piston with lip of seal facing away from flange.

3. With piston lever ring seated in piston, place piston in clutch retainer and with twisting motion, seat piston in bottom of retainer.

4. Place lever retainer in piston and install levers, being sure levers are free and properly seated in piston slots.

5. Install clutch return spring over hub of clutch retainer and position spring retainer and snap ring on spring.

6. Compress clutch return spring to seat snap ring.

7. Install pressure plate (smooth side up) in retainer.

8. Install discs and plates by starting with a driving disc followed by a steel plate, alternating in this manner until all five discs and four plates have been installed.

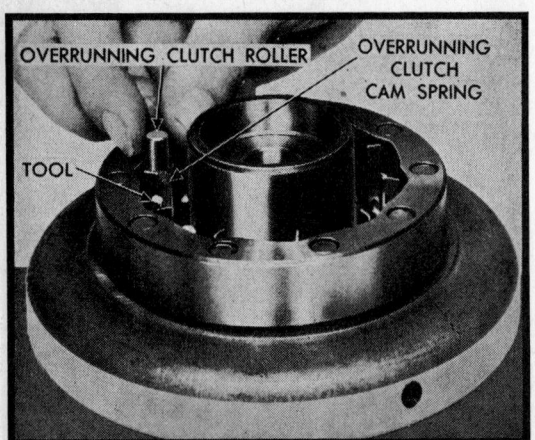

Fig. 50 Installing overrunning clutch rollers and springs

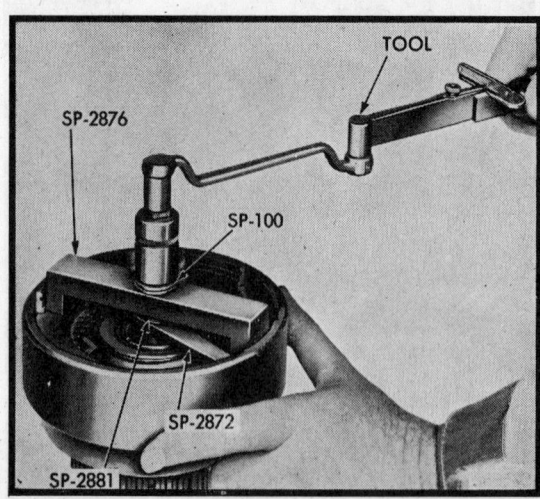

Fig. 53   Setting up front clutch with special tools preparatory to checking travel of clutch pressure plate

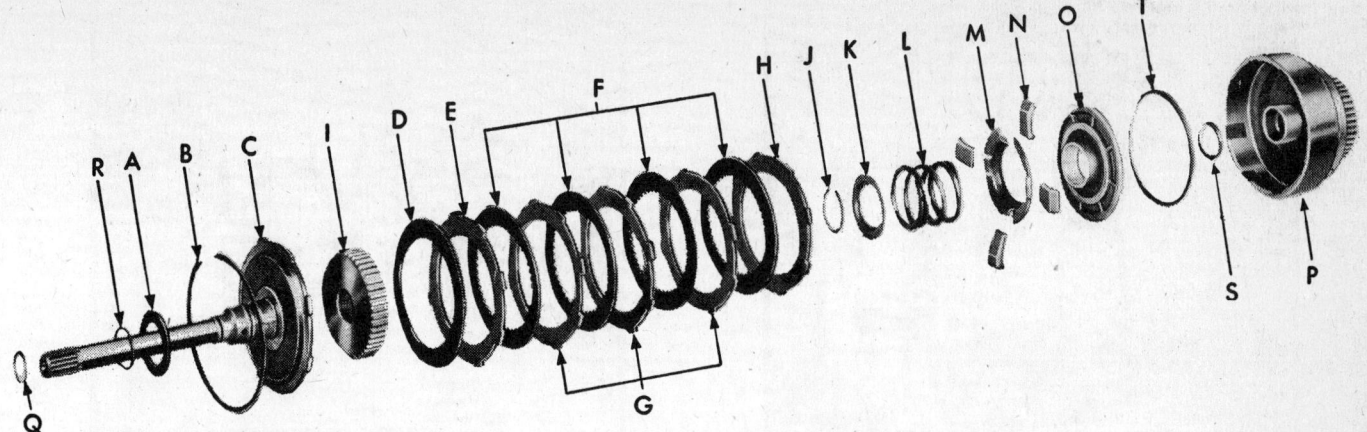

A—INPUT SHAFT THRUST WASHER
B—FRONT CLUTCH SNAP RING
C—INPUT SHAFT AND BUSHING ASSEMBLY
D—CUSHION SPRING
E—CUSHION SPRING RETAINING PLATE
F—DRIVING DISCS
G—CLUTCH PLATES

H—CLUTCH PRESSURE PLATE
I—DRIVING DISC HUB
J—PISTON RETURN SPRING
   RETAINER SNAP RING
K—RETURN SPRING RETAINER
L—PISTON RETURN SPRING
M—PISTON LEVER RETAINER

N—LEVER
O—PISTON
P—PISTON RETAINER ASSEMBLY
Q—OIL SEAL RING—SMALL
R—OIL SEAL RING—LARGE
S—PISTON SEAL RING—INNER
T—PISTON SEAL RING—OUTER

Fig. 52   Unit No. 3 disassembled.   1958.   The 1959-61 clutch has 8 levers instead of 4 as shown

CHECKING TRAVEL OF CLUTCH PRESSURE PLATE

It is important that the front clutch pressure plate has the proper travel where levers are used for applying additional pressure to clutch plates. Insufficient travel may cause clutch plates to drag. Excessive travel may allow slippage of clutch. To control the travel of the clutch pressure plate, the top driving disc is a selective fit and available in thicknesses of .060" to .063", .073" to .076" and .087" to .090". To select the proper top driving disc, proceed as follows:

1. Remove top driving disc.
2. Install the tools shown in Fig. 53. Torque nut to 10 *inch lbs.*
3. Using the checking gauge shown in Fig. 54, check distance between surface of top clutch plate (steel) and end of adapter SP-2872.
4. If first step of checking gauge will slide between top clutch plate and end of adaptor, use the standard disc, which is .060" to .063" thick. If second step of gauge will slide between plate and adaptor use disc which is .073" to .076" thick. And if third step of gauge will slide between plate and adaptor use disc which is .087" to .090" thick.

5. If there is excessive clearance between third step of gauge and end of adaptor due to worn disc facings, remove the gauge, top steel plate and second disc. Then install the disc which is .087" to .090" thick in second disc position. Reinstall top clutch plate and checking tool.
6. Recheck clearance as previously described. Then if the first step of the gauge will not slide in, disassemble the clutch to determine cause. Inspect for dirt, location of levers, distorted or improperly installed plates and tool installation. Reassemble and recheck.
7. Lubricate clutch disc and plate assemblies with transmission fluid and position clutch hub in plates and discs. To prevent damage to discs when installing input shaft, make

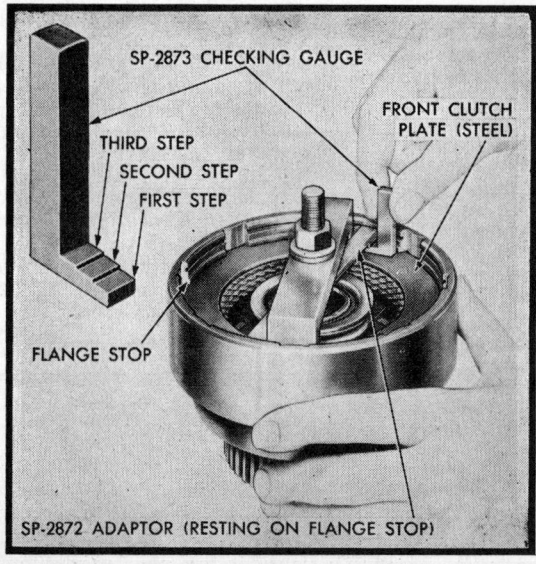

Fig. 54   Checking clutch pressure plate travel

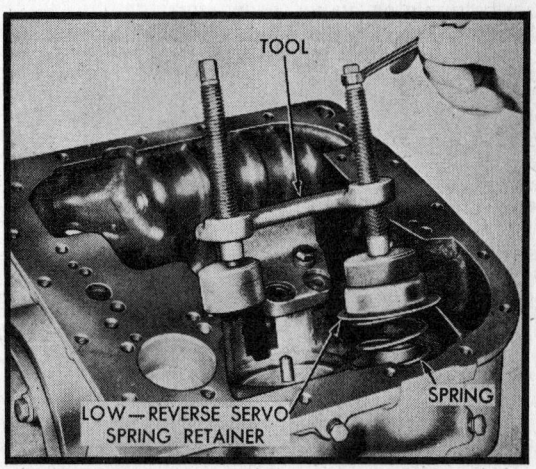

Fig. 55 Compressing low and reverse servo piston spring and retainer

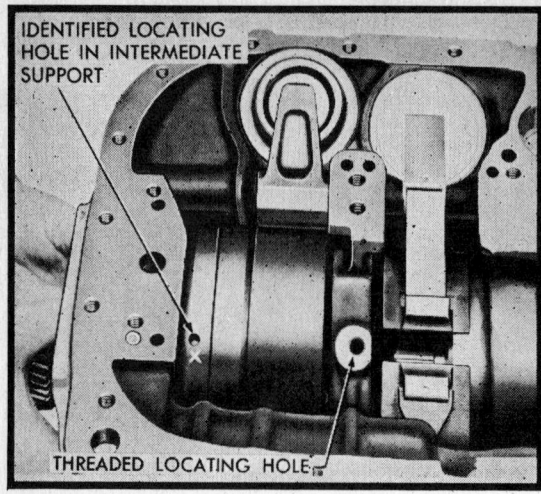

Fig. 56   Installation of Unit No. 2

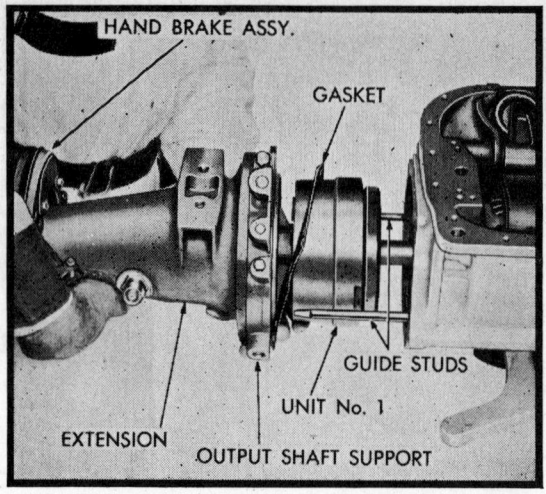

Fig. 57   Assembly to be removed so the proper thickness input shaft thrust washer can be installed to establish proper front clutch end clearance

sure hub engages splines in each disc.

8. Install input shaft in clutch retainer.

9. Select snap ring for minimum clearance. Available snap ring thicknesses are .060" to .062" and .064" to .066".

TRANSMISSION ASSEMBLE

1. When installing the torque converter reaction shaft, Chrysler recommends the use of two sun lamps to heat the front of the transmission case to about 180 degrees to expand the case before pressing in the reaction shaft.

2. Install guide studs in front face of reaction shaft flange. Lubricate the portion of the shaft that presses into the case. With tool shown in Fig. 45, press shaft into case. Install attaching screws evenly and torque from 10 to 15 lb. ft. Coat neoprene seal with transmission fluid and install on shaft.

3. Install guide studs as shown in Fig. 43. Install gasket over guide studs. Install regulator valve body and valves over guide studs. Hold valves in place to prevent damage while installing valve body.

4. With front pump gears in position in pump housing, place housing over studs and install in position. Start five of the screws (with aluminum washers) and draw housing down evenly until seated in case. Remove guide studs and install two remaining screws and washers, torqueing all screws from 14 to 16 lb. ft. *Im-*

proper tightening of these screws may cause pump gears to bind.

5. Lubricate and install front pump drive sleeve (bearing surface first) and engage driving lugs of oil pinion to determine if front pump gears turn freely; if not, remove and check for foreign matter between gears and housing.

6. Install torque converter control valve.

7. Install accumulator piston.

8. Install kickdown piston.

9. Install reverse servo piston, using tool shown in Fig. 55.

10. Install kickdown and low-reverse bands.

11. Place band levers in case and slide shaft through levers from rear of case as shown in Fig. 40.

12. If, when transmission was disassembled, the end clearance was found to be incorrect, select the proper thickness input shaft thrust washer to obtain end clearance of .020" to .050". Then with proper thrust washer in position, install Unit No. 3 in transmission, keeping it centered while guiding it through bands and reaction shaft.

13. Start Unit No. 2 through rear of case. Align locating hole in intermediate support with threaded hole inside of transmission case, Fig. 56. By keeping unit centered as much as possible, guide it through bands until it contacts hub of front clutch. While pushing in on the unit, rock the sun gear to engage plates of rear clutch.

14. Install three intermediate support

screws and tighten from 25 to 30 lb. ft. Check input shaft and sun gear for freedom of operation.

15. Before installing Unit No. 1, be sure reverse sun gear thrust washer (roller type) is in position in planet pinion carrier. Install unit by placing intermediate shaft in sun gear. Keeping unit centered as much as possible, and slowly turning output shaft, slide into position. Large seal ring on output shaft should be flush with rear of case.

16. With guide studs in rear of transmission case, place output shaft support gasket on rear of case. Install support and insert one (short) attaching screw finger tight.

17. Place ball in output shaft pocket. Place pump drive pinion over shaft and slide in place, aligning keyway in pinion with ball in shaft. *Pinion was marked when removed; make sure it is installed correctly.*

18. Place oil pump gear in pump housing, being sure gear is installed according to marks made when disassembled.

19. Slide pump and governor over output shaft and against support. After tightening attaching screws, turn output shaft to be sure pump gears are free to rotate.

20. Install governor weight and valves, extension and hand brake as outlined under *"In Car"* Repairs section of this chapter.

21. Recheck front clutch end clearance to be sure it is correct, Fig. 57.

22. Adjust bands.

23. Install valve bodies and oil pan.

TURBOGLIDE

CONTENTS

Description 363
Trouble Shooting 20

Maintenance

Adding Oil 363
Changing Oil 363

"In Car" Repairs

Air Pressure Checks 363
Oil Pressure Tests....................364
Valve Body 366

Repairs Requiring Transmission Removal

Transmission, Disassemble 367
Torque Converter 369
Rear Planet Carrier....................370
Front Planet Carrier...................371
Front Pump and Reverse Piston...........371
Rear Pump 371
Front Sun Gear Freewheel Assembly.....372
Neutral Clutch and Ring Gear..........372
Forward and Brake Piston and Support....373
Transmission, Assemble 374

DESCRIPTION

The Turboglide automatic transmission consists of a five-element torque converter and two planetary gearsets providing two reduction ratios, direct drive and reverse. Although three forward ratios are provided, there is no shifting of gears. Starting from rest with a maximum torque ratio of 4.3 to 1, there is a gradual transition to direct drive as speed increases.

Each of the three turbines can drive the transmission output shaft. As the car starts, the pump, driven by the engine, directs most of the oil in the converter against the vanes of the first turbine, which drives the sun gear of the rear planetary. A one-way roller clutch holds the ring gear, causing the rear planet carrier and output shaft to be driven at increased torque and reduced speed.

As car speed increases, a greater portion of the oil strikes the vanes of the second turbine. The first turbine gradually fades out of the picture, and the second turbine takes over, driving the output shaft through the front ring gear and planet pinions, which walk around the sun gear, held stationary by its one-way clutch. Reduction in this range is less than in the starting range because the front planetary has a lower gear ratio than the rear.

As the car approaches cruising speed, oil flow is concentrated against the third turbine, which drives the output shaft directly, with no gear reduction. From this point on, action is similar to a conventional converter. When a speed is reached when the unit can no longer provide torque multiplication, the stator free wheels and the converter becomes a simple fluid coupling. The stator is provided with variable pitch vanes. When the accelerator is floored past the detent, the pitch is increased, giving greater torque multiplication and allowing the engine to turn at a speed where it can develop more power.

The five positions on the quadrant are: Park, Reverse, Neutral, Drive and Hill Retarder. A separate low range is unnecessary because maximum torque multiplication is available in Drive. When the car is descending a steep grade, the selector can be placed in the Hill Retarder position to obtain more effective braking through the engine and transmission. Under this condition, a disc clutch holds the rear ring gear, permitting the rear wheels to drive the first turbine at 2.67 times the speed of the output shaft. This high turbine speed creates turbulance in the converter, changing the kenetic energy of the descending car into heat. Engine speed is also increased, providing further braking effect.

MAINTENANCE
Adding Oil

In order to check oil level accurately, the engine should be running at idle speed with the transmission oil hot and the control lever in Drive position.

It is important that the oil level be maintained no higher than the "FULL" mark on the oil level dipstick. *Do not overfill,* for when the oil level is at the full mark on the dipstick, it is just slightly below the planetary gear unit. If the level is above the full mark, the planetary unit will run in the oil, causing the oil to foam and aerate. This aerated oil may cause malfunction of the transmission, resulting in cavitation noise in the converter and improper action of pistons or spewing from the filler pipe or breather.

Changing Oil

Every 25,000 miles the transmission should be drained and refilled. The transmission should be warmed up before it is drained.

1. Remove transmission oil pan plug.
2. After draining, install drain plug.
3. Pour in 3½ quarts of automatic transmission fluid. (3½ quarts will not be adequate if transmission has been setting for a long period without operating due to partial draining of converter.)
4. Start and allow engine to idle for a few minutes in Neutral until oil is hot or at operating temperature. Then, with selector lever in Drive, check to see that the oil level is at the full mark on the dipstick. Add oil as required but do not overfill.

"In Car" Repairs

AIR PRESSURE CHECKS

Five air checks can be made on this transmission which are of value in determining the cause of a complaint prior to overhaul or as a means of checking clutch applications and seals during transmission overhaul. In order to perform the checks an air source of 100 lbs. pressure is required as well as an adapter (Tool 4353-1) to apply the air pressure.

To make the following checks with the transmission in the car, drain the oil, then remove the converter cover pan, transmission oil pan and the main valve body. The oil pressure tubes shown in the Forward Clutch and Grade Retarder apply ports, Figs. 1 and 2, must be installed to make the checks.

Caution—If the checks are being performed during transmission overhaul, rebuild to the stage shown in Figs. 1 and 2 and install Converter Holding Tool (No. 5384) to prevent the possibility of the converter being blown out of the transmission.

Apply air to the reverse clutch port and check that the reverse piston applies and listen for air leaks. If the reverse piston does not apply, determine whether the front pump-to-transmission case gasket is incorrectly positioned and blocking oil passages or if the reverse piston is bound. If air leaks are heard, check for a damaged front pump-to-transmission case gasket or for damaged seals in the reverse piston.

Stator Piston

Apply air to stator piston port and listen for air leaks. If air leaks are detected, check for a mispositioned front pump-to-transmission case gasket, broken or warped seal rings on second turbine shaft or defective stator piston seal.

Neutral Clutch

With air applied to the neutral clutch port, listen for application of the clutch and air leaks.

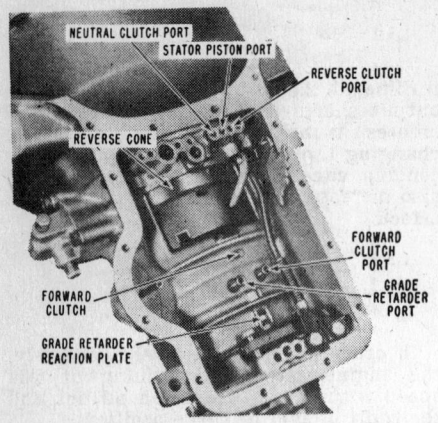

Fig. 1 Air pressure check points. 1957-58

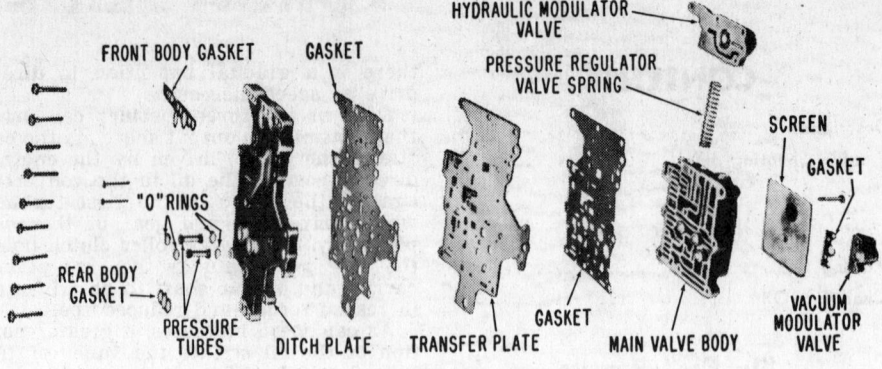

Fig. 4 Valve body components. 1957

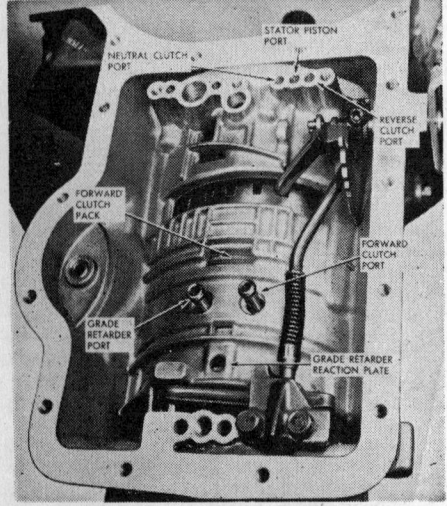

Fig. 2 Air pressure check points. 1959-61

If no clutch application is heard, determine if the front pump-to-transmission case gasket is incorrectly positioned and blocking oil passages; otherwise disassemble the neutral clutch and determine cause.

Forward Clutch

With oil pressure tubes installed as shown in Figs. 1 and 2, apply air and observe that the forward clutch applies and listen for air leaks. The first place to check if air leaks are found is the O-ring seals on the oil pressure tube in the forward clutch port; otherwise check for forward piston-to-support seals.

Grade Retarder (Brake) Piston

Apply air to the Grade Retarder port with the oil pressure tube installed. Check the Grade Retarder application by watching for movement of the Grade Retarder reaction plate which will occur as the brake plates are forced against it by piston moving rearward.

If brake piston does not move, check for cocked O-ring seals in the brake piston or check for blocked pressure passage in piston support.

Leakage can occur only at the oil pressure tube O-ring seal or brake piston O-ring seals.

OIL PRESSURE TESTS

Road Test

1957

1. Disconnect stator control from throttle.
2. Connect pressure gauge to test point on left side of transmission, Fig. 3. If available, connect vacuum gauge to engine.
3. With selector lever in "D" range, pressure gauge should read 46-60 psi.
4. With selector lever in "D" range and at a car speed of about 30 mph, push accelerator to wide open throttle, pressure will rise to 135-145 psi at 0 inches of vacuum. At any car speed with foot off accelerator, stator pressure should read 50-65 psi with engine vacuum of 16-25 inches.
5. To check stator operation on road test, reconnect stator control rod to the throttle, place selector lever in "D" range and drive car at 20 mph, open throttle quickly (going thru detent). Pressure will drop to 0 psi and engine speed will rise when stator is working correctly. *At wide open throttle, stator pressure should always read 0 at any car speed.*
6. With selector lever in "D" range, travelling at 40 mph and foot off

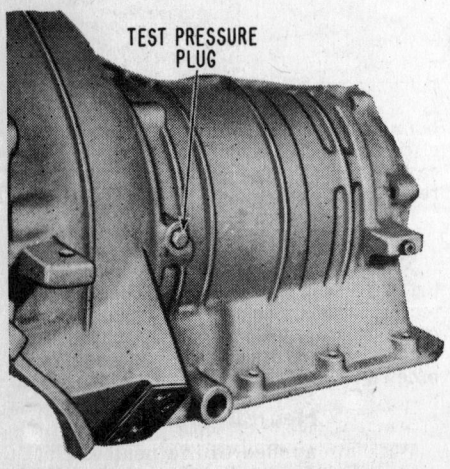

Fig. 3 Oil pressure test plug

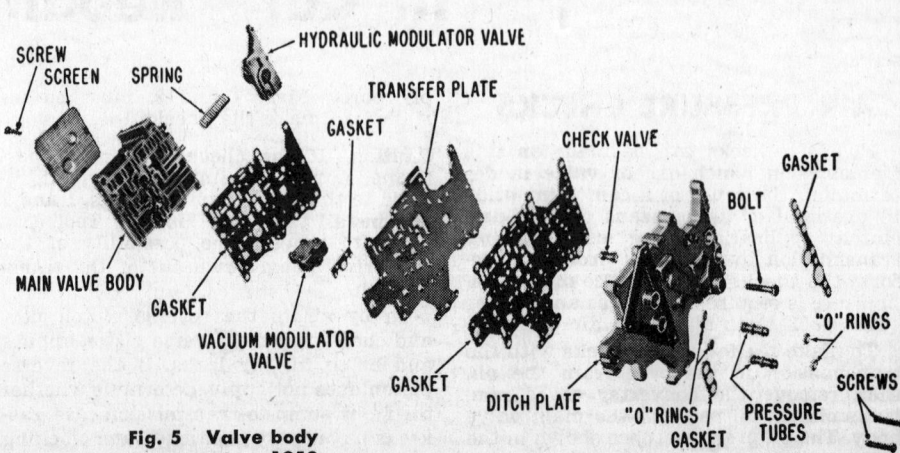

Fig. 5 Valve body components. 1958

accelerator stator pressure should read 50-65 psi. With selector lever in "HR" position at 40 mph and foot off accelerator, stator pressure should rise to 85-95 psi. *If tachometer is being used the engine speed will drop during the manual shift from "D" range to "HR" range and then when the Hill Retarder pressure reaches 85-95 psi the clutch will set down and the engine speed will increase.*

1958

1. Connect pressure gauge to test point on left side of transmission, Fig. 3, and vacuum gauge and tachometer to engine.
2. Warm up engine and transmission and check transmission fluid level.
3. With selector lever in "D" range and then in "R" range, pressure gauge should read 50-60 psi at 18" engine vacuum.
4. With selector lever in "D" range and at a car speed of about 30 mph, push on accelerator to wide open throttle condition. Engine speed should increase 400-700 rpm if stator is functioning properly and the pressure should raise to 195-210 psi at 2" manifold vacuum. At any car speed, with foot off throttle, pressure gauge should read 50-60 psi with 18-25 inches engine vacuum.
5. With selector lever in "D" range and a road speed of 45 mph, and foot off throttle, pressure gauge should read 50-60 psi. Place selector lever in "GR" range at 45 mph and pressure should drop to 0 psi. *The engine speed will drop momentarily during the manual shift from "D" to "GR" and then the Grade Retarder clutch will set down and the engine speed will increase.*

1959-61

1. Connect pressure gauge to test point on left side of transmission, Fig. 3.
2. Connect vacuum gauge and tachometer to engine.
3. Warm up engine and transmission and check transmission fluid level.
4. With selector lever in "D" range at

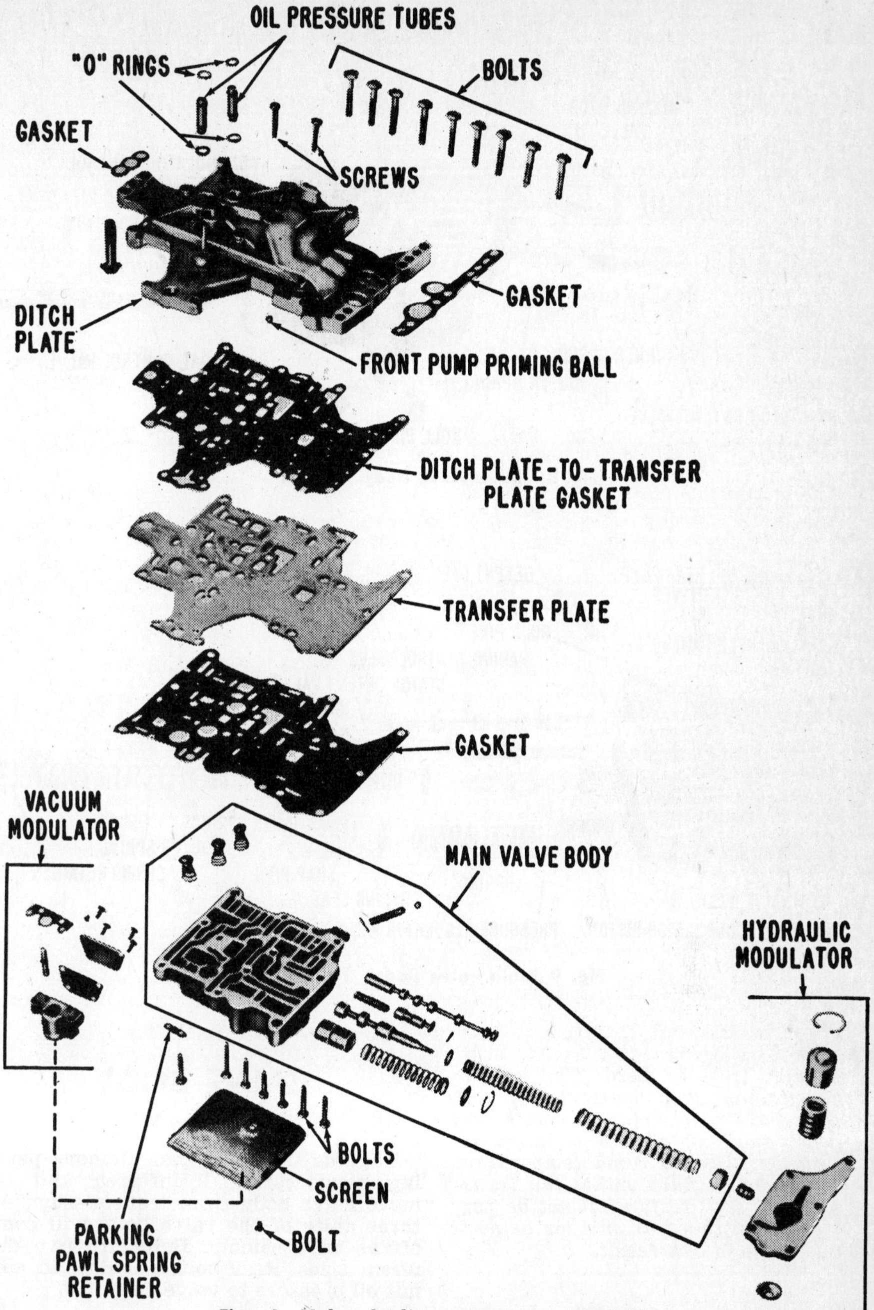

Fig. 6 Valve body components. 1959-61

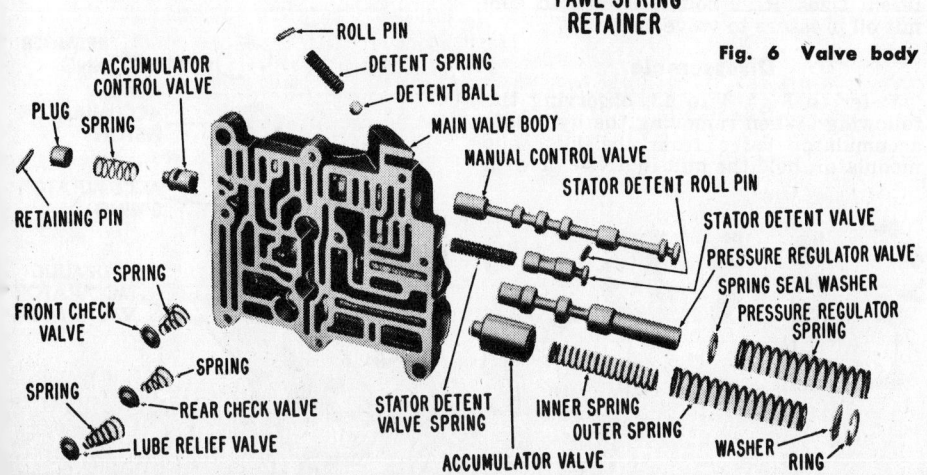

Fig. 7 Main valve body. 1957

car speed of about 30 mph, push accelerator to wide open throttle condition. Engine speed should increase 700-900 rpm if stator is functioning and the pressure should raise to 190-210 psi at 3" manifold vacuum. At any car speed, with foot off the throttle, pressure gauge should read 80-90 psi with 18-25" of vacuum. *Pressures in "Reverse" should be the same as in "Drive".*

5. With selector lever in "D" range, a road speed of 45 mph, and foot off throttle, pressure gauge should read 80-90 psi. Place selector lever in "GR" range at 45 mph and pressure

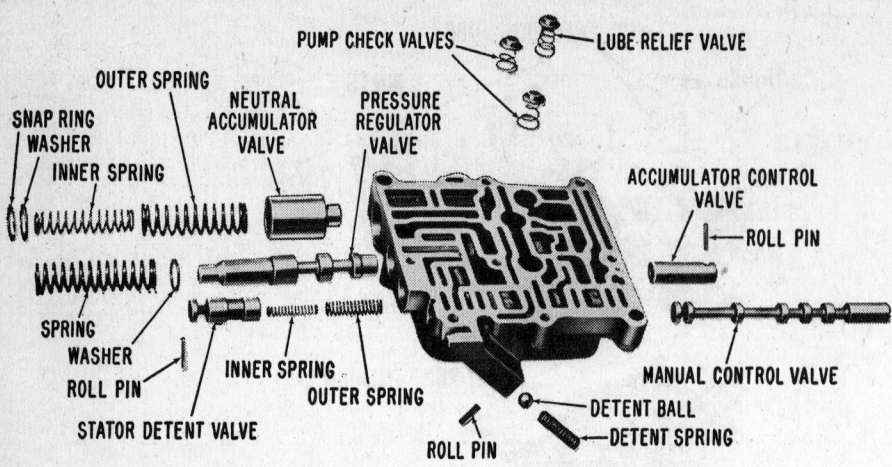

Fig. 8   Main valve body. 1958

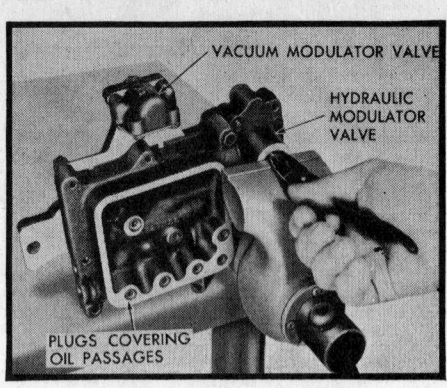

Fig. 9A Removing accumulator valve retaining ring

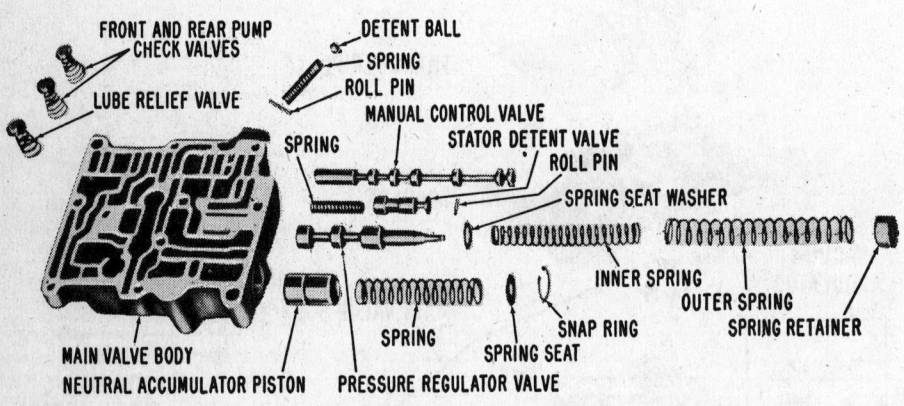

Fig. 9 Main valve body. 1959-61

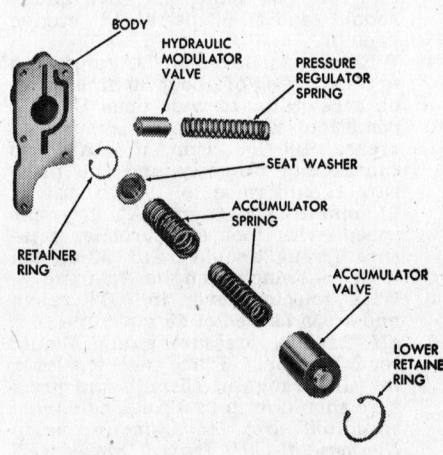

Fig. 10   Hydraulic modulator, 1957. For 1958, three grooves are machined around circumference of modulator valve

should drop to zero. *The engine speed may drop momentarily and then the Grade Retarder clutch will apply and engine speed will increase. Caution: Due to rapid temperature rises of the fluid within the transmission, stall tests must not be performed on this transmission as serious damage can result.*

VALVE BODY

Removal

Take down the oil pan. Remove parking pawl spring. Unfasten and remove valve body from transmission. All three units of the valve body will come off as an assembly. Bolts are two different sizes. Rear bolt is hollow to permit oil pressure to valve body.

Disassemble

Refer to Figs. 4 to 13, observing the following: When removing the hydraulic accumulator valve from the hydraulic modulator, hold the unit in a vise or with

a "C" clamp as the accumulator springs are under 90 lbs. pressure. Then remove snap ring and take out seat, springs and piston.

Inspection

Wash all parts in cleaning solvent, air dry and blow out all passages. Then in-

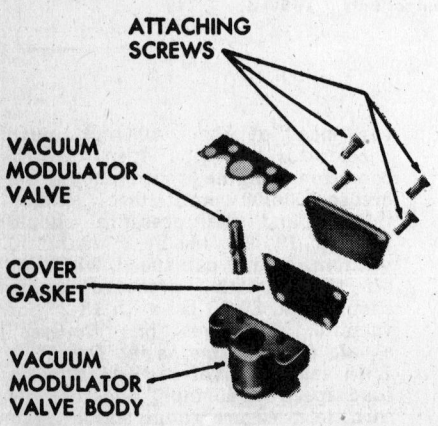

Fig. 13 Vacuum modulator. 1959-61

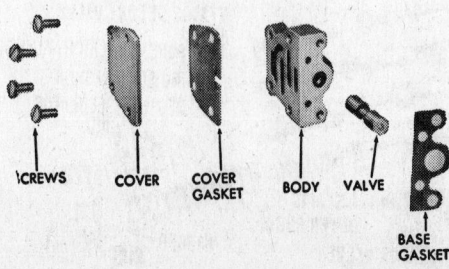

Fig. 12 Vacuum modulator. 1957-58

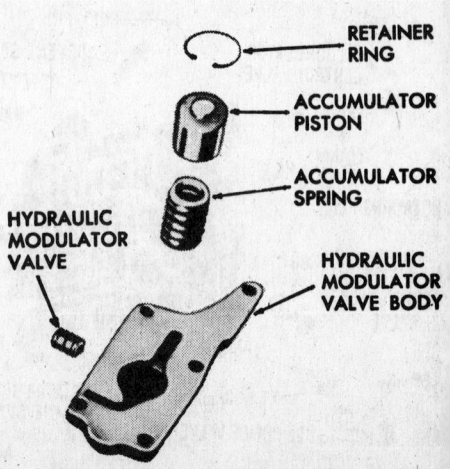

Fig. 11 Hydraulic modulator. 1959-61

spect as follows:
1. Check detent valve spring for distortion or damage.
2. Inspect detent valve for nicks, burrs, scoring or galling. Also check valve for freedom of operation in its bore.
3. Inspect lands of manual valve for wear or scratches.
4. Inspect modulator valve housing for galling or scoring. Check retaining ring grooves.
5. Inspect modulator valve and housing.

6. Inspect all pistons for freedom of operation in their respective bores.
7. Inspect springs for distortion or damage.
8. Clean sump screen thoroughly. Inspect rubber by-pass valve.

Assemble

Refer to Figs. 4 to 13, observing the following: Do not confuse the pressure regulator spring with the accumulator outer spring. The pressure regulator is

the heavier with a free length of 3¼".
Install stator detent valve spring in valve body, then install detent valve with hollow end indexing over spring. Hold valve in and press roll pin to engage in groove in end of valve. Do not install pin too deep; end of pin should not touch bottom of groove. Check freedom of assembly by stroking valve.

The accumulator spring is the lightest spring of the valve body and the check valve has a hole in the center.

Repairs Requiring Transmission Removal

TRANSMISSION DISASSEMBLE

1957-58

1. Place transmission in holding fixture.
2. Remove converter assembly.
3. Remove oil pan.
4. Unfasten speedometer gear housing from transmission extension.
5. Remove transmission extension.
6. Remove speedometer drive gear.
7. Remove rear pump body, seal ring and driven gear.
8. Remove rear pump drive gear.
9. Remove rear pump drive pin from output shaft, Fig. 14. Also wear plate on 1958.
10. Remove parking pawl spring, Fig. 15.
11. Remove valve body from case, Fig. 15.
12. Remove two oil pressure tubes, Fig. 16.
13. Remove front pump, stator support and reverse piston assembly. Note two threaded holes to mount puller, Fig. 17.
14. Remove reverse cone and cone spring.
15. Remove neutral clutch and reverse ring gear assembly, which includes

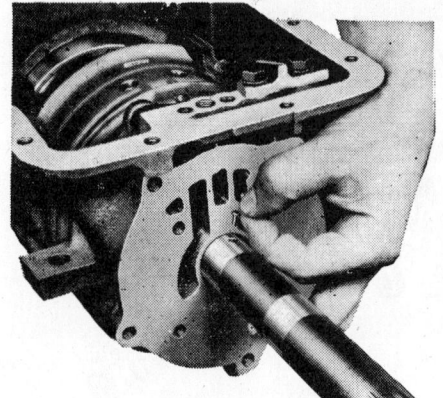
Fig. 14 Removing oil pump drive pin

turbine shaft, neutral shaft and neutral clutch piston.
16. Remove reverse cone ring.
17. Remove front planet carrier.
18. Remove front sun gear and free wheel assembly.
19. Remove forward cone retaining ring, Fig. 18.
20. Remove forward cone ring and cone.

Fig. 17 Removing front pump with pullers

By exerting slight pressure on output shaft both ring and cone can readily be removed.
21. Remove forward and brake piston and support as an assembly.
22. Remove rear unit ring gear and output shaft and rear planet carrier as an assembly. Also remove both brake clutch plates, aluminum separator and grade retarder components.
23. Disassemble ring gear from rear planet carrier by removing retainer ring and remove two races and needle bearing from output shaft.

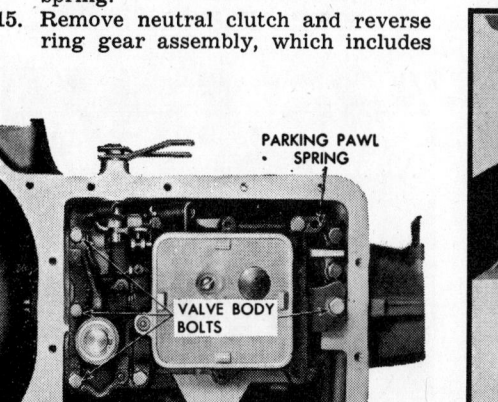
Fig. 15 Bottom view of transmission with oil pump removed

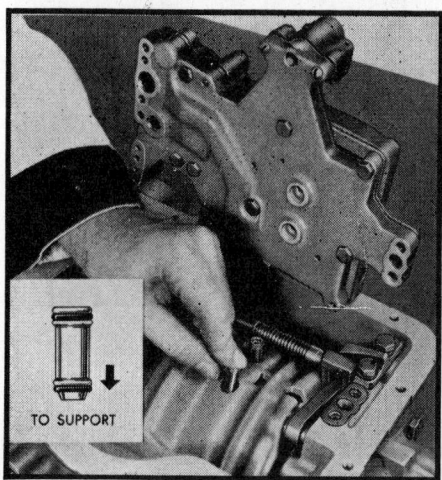
Fig. 16 Valve body and oil pressure tubes

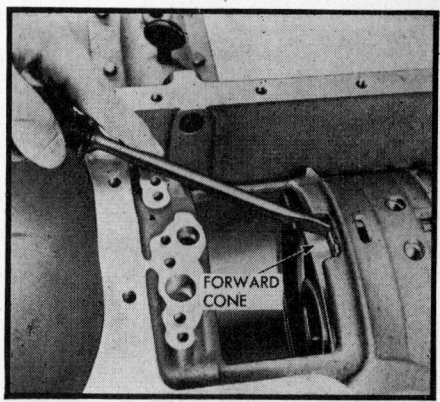
Fig. 18 Removing forward cone retaining ring

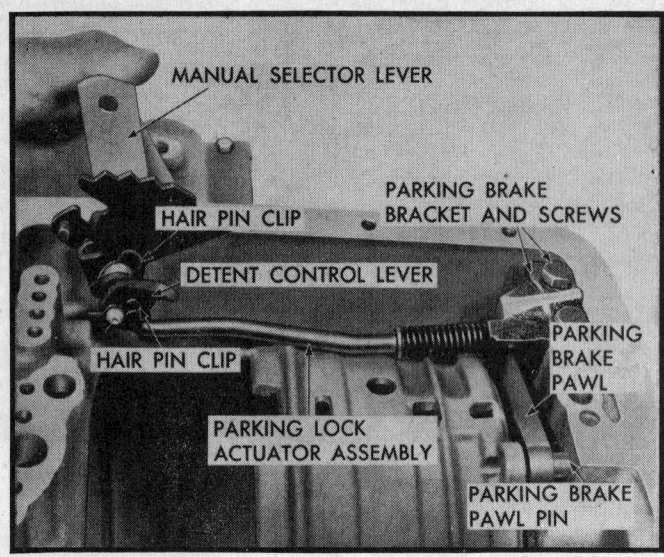

Fig. 19   Valve body controls.   1957

24. Remove detent control lever, Fig. 19.
25. Loosen screw and remove manual selector lever and parking lock actuator lever.
26. Remove parking brake bracket.
27. Remove parking brake pawl, pin and O-ring seal. Pin must be removed by driving on front of pin.
28. Remove thermal by-pass valve, Figs. 20 and 21.
29. Remove vacuum diaphragm (modulator) by holding body and removing retainer nut from inside of transmission case, Figs. 20 and 22. Lift out valve strut.

1959-61

1. Place transmission in fixture.
2. Remove oil pan.

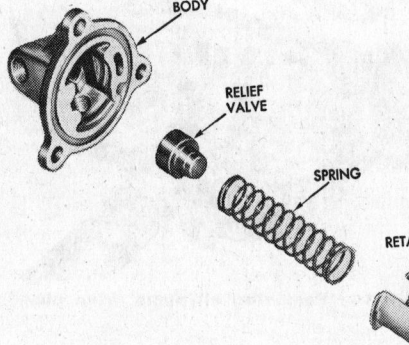

Fig. 21   By-pass valve.   1958

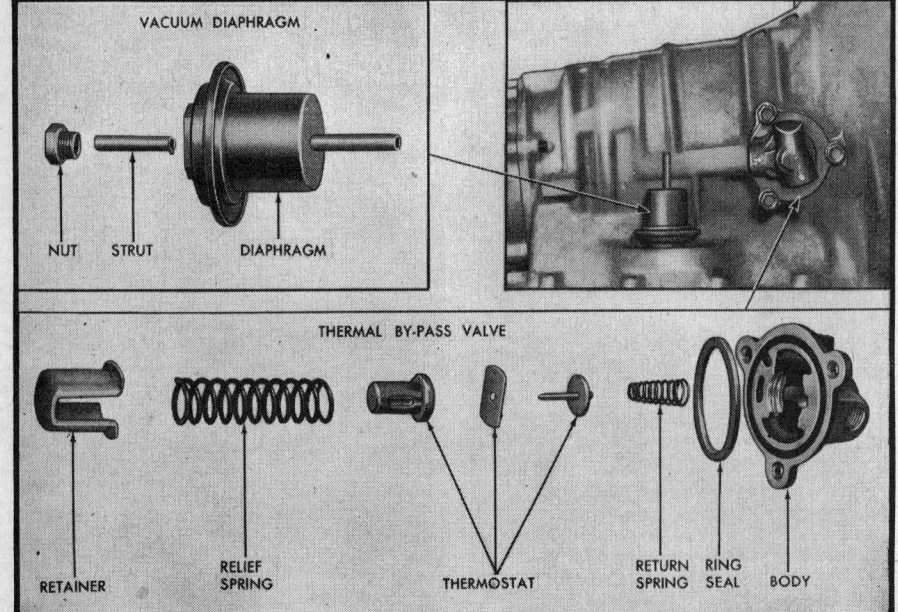

Fig. 20   Thermal by-pass valve and vacuum diaphragm.   1957

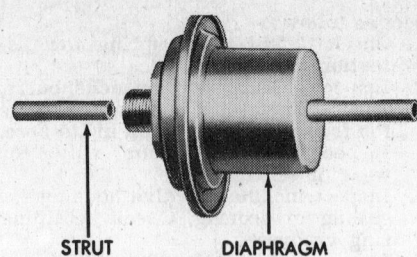

Fig. 22   Vacuum modulator.   1958

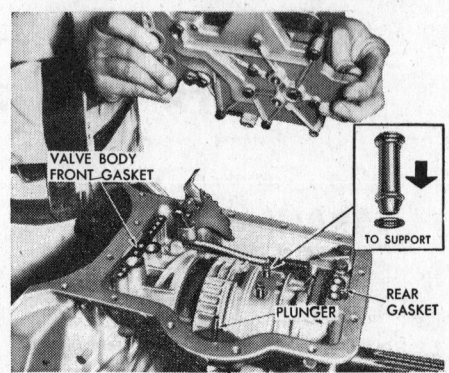

Fig. 23   Valve body oil pressure tubes and vacuum modulator plunger.   1959-61

Fig. 24   Removing front ring gear hub, neutral clutch and reverse clutch pack.   1959-61

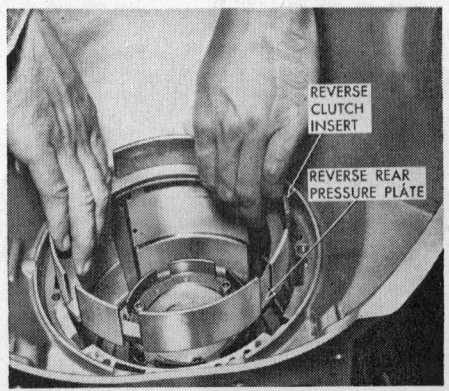

Fig. 25   Removing reverse clutch insert and reverse rear reaction plate.   1959-61

Fig. 26 Removing front planetary gear set. 1959-61

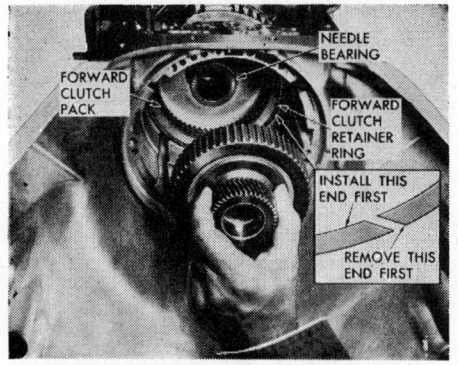

Fig. 27 Removing front sun gear and freewheeling unit. 1959-61

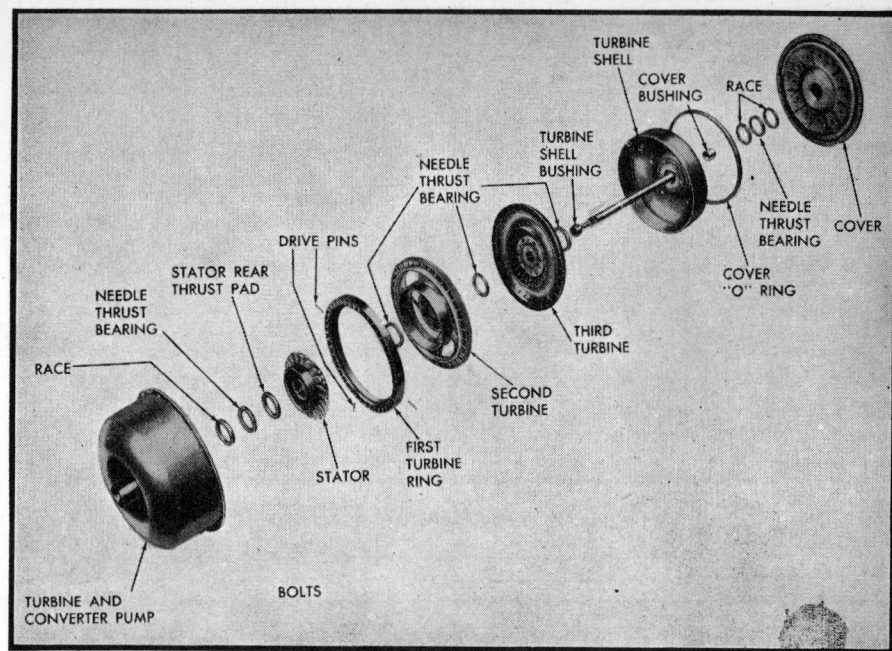

Fig. 31 Exploded view of torque converter. For 1960-61, thrust washer replaces needle bearing between converter cover and first turbine hub

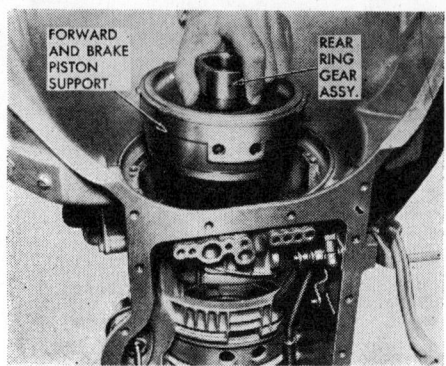

Fig. 28 Removing forward and brake piston and support, and rear ring gear. 1959-61

Fig. 29 Removing rear planetary gear set. 1959-61

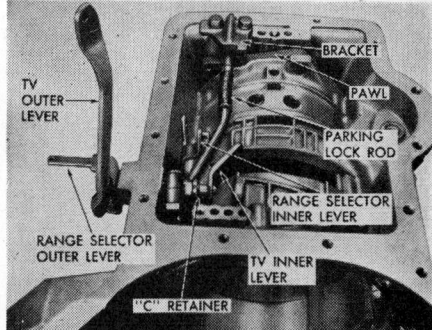

Fig. 30 Transmission manual controls. 1959-61

3. If replacement is necessary, remove speedometer driven gear.
4. Remove transmission extension.
5. Remove speedometer gear oil deflector by removing two pump bolts.
6. Remove speedometer drive gear.
7. Remove two remaining rear pump bolts and remove pump, seal ring and driven gear.
8. Remove rear pump drive gear, drive pin and wear plate.
9. Remove parking pawl spring.
10. Remove valve body.
11. Remove converter.
12. Remove two oil pressure tubes and vacuum modulator plunger, Fig. 23.
13. Remove front pump, Fig. 17.
14. Remove assembly shown in Fig. 24.
15. Remove reverse rear pressure plate and reverse clutch reaction insert, Fig. 25.
16. Remove front planet carrier thrust washer, front planet carrier and neutral clutch hub assembly, Fig. 26. Remove race, needle bearing and thrust ring from carrier extension.
17. Remove front sun gear freewheel assembly (overrunning clutch sprag unit) and thrust bearing, Fig. 27.
18. Remove forward clutch retainer ring from transmission case by prying out at case slots with screwdriver, noting inset in Fig. 27.
19. Remove forward clutch pack.
20. Remove retainer ring securing forward and brake piston and support by prying out at case slots with screwdriver.

21. Remove rear ring gear assembly, Fig. 28, and forward and brake piston and support as a unit. Separate the two units.
22. Remove rear planet carrier, Fig. 29, and race, needle bearing and race on hub of carrier. Also remove caged needle bearing from rear of carrier or case.
23. Remove brake retarder components.
24. If necessary, remove transmission manual controls, Fig. 30, and bypass valve and vacuum modulator.

TORQUE CONVERTER

Refer to Figs. 31 and 32 when disassembling and assembling the converter. Before disassembling, mark the cover and housing for alignment and balance upon reassembly. When disassembling the turbine assembly, note that the first turbine inner ring and turbine shell are marked to assure correct relationship of parts for balance on reassembly.

When disassembled, wash and air-dry all parts. Then inspect the following parts for scoring or galling: Converter hub outer surfaces, converter hub thrust washers, turbine hubs and thrust

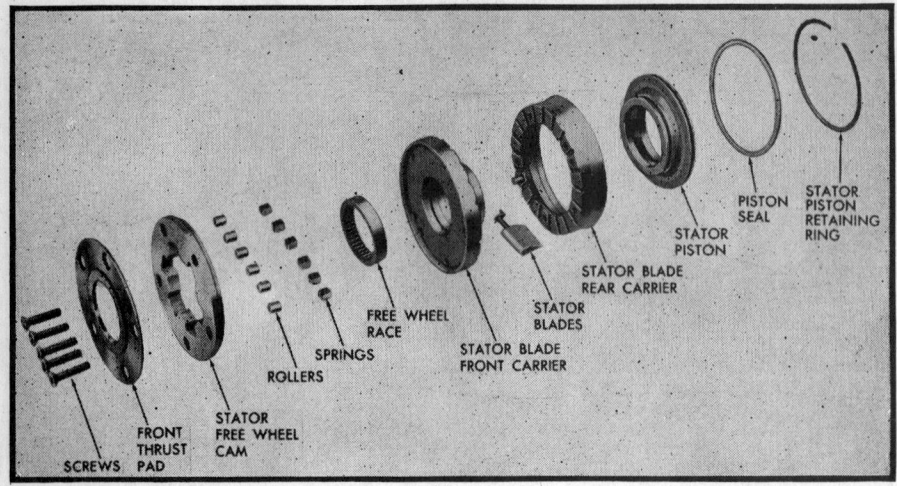

Fig. 32   Exploded view of stator

Fig. 35   Installing rear carrier to output shaft

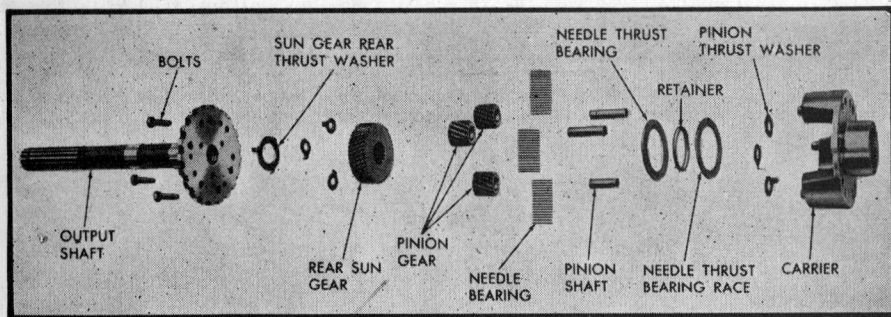

Fig. 33   Rear planetary carrier and output shaft.   1957

washers, converter cover bushing, stator race and cam rollers. Check converter pump vanes and turbine vanes for looseness or damage. Inspect cam springs for distortion. Check stator blades for excessive wear or damage.

When reassembling, refer to Figs. 31 and 32. When installing the stator blades, the trailing or sharp edges of the blades should point downward after installation in stator. Neck of stator piston must be pushed fully through rear carrier to install stator blades. When installing the turbines, align the balance marks. Then install first turbine inner ring with inner flat surface facing up in turbine shell.

REAR PLANET CARRIER

1. Wash planet carrier and gears, blow out all oil passages and air-dry.
2. Inspect planet pinions for nicks or other tooth damage. Check pinion shafts for pitting or irregular bearing surface, Figs. 33 and 34.
3. Check end clearance of planet gears, measuring between gears and output shaft flange thrust washers. This clearance should be .006" to .030". Check thrust washer for looseness and wear on rear plant carrier.
4. Check sun gear for tooth damage. Also check planet needle thrust bearing for damage.

5. Inspect output shaft bearing surface for nicks or scoring and output shaft bushing.
6. Inspect output shaft splines for nicks and damage and check fit to transmission case. Also check fit of rear carrier to front carrier output shaft.
7. Inspect bearing surface of speedometer gear on output shaft. Speedometer drive gear is pressed on shaft and looseness will result in driven gear failure.

When disassembling, mark the carrier and output shaft for correct relationship on reassembly. The separation of the carrier from the output shaft will enable all parts of the rear carrier assembly to be removed. The carrier pinion shafts will remain in either the carrier or the output shaft, depending on which piece has the closer fit. Do not attempt removal of pinion shafts by breaking four way stake. Pinion shafts must be removed by disassembling the planetary carrier only. Damaging the stake marks will ruin the retaining qualities of the carrier or output shaft and necessitate replacement of the carrier and output shaft assembly. The output shaft bushing is precision bored in place during assembly; this bushing is not replaceable.

Metal sometimes is shaved from carrier pinion shafts during reassembly when shafts are entering holes in hardened carrier. If shavings are not removed, false clearance readings can be obtained, Fig. 35. Pinion end clearance should be checked between washer and pinion as shown. Checking clearance between washer and carrier (location of shavings) will give false clearance readings.

Align alignment marks on carrier to marks on output shaft and insert dowels of carrier into respective holes in output shaft. While installing carrier to output shaft, align tangs of thrust washers to lock holes in carrier. To accomplish mating of the carrier and output shaft,

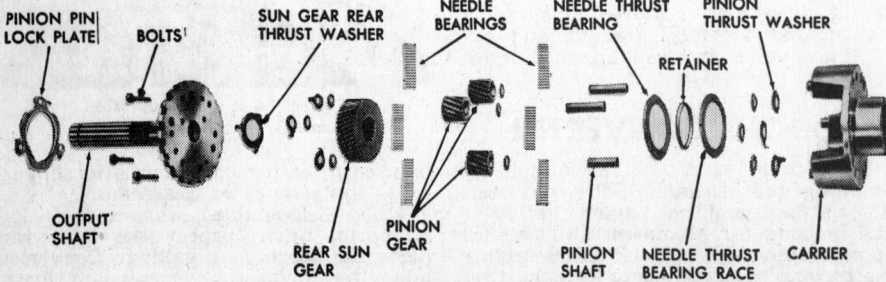

Fig. 34 Rear planet gearset. 1958-61

install the assembly in an arbor press, Fig. 35.

FRONT PLANET CARRIER

1957-58

Due to the similarity between the front planet carrier, Figs. 36 and 37, and the rear planet carrier, inspection and service procedures are almost identical. The front planet carrier is different inasmuch as it is minus the sun gear and sun gear thrust washers. All gear clearances for the rear planet carrier apply to the front planet carrier. The carrier bushing is precision bored in place in the carrier during assembly and is not replaceable.

1959-61

Component parts of the new six-pinion front planet carrier and neutral clutch hub assembly *are not available for service*. Whenever worn or damaged parts of this unit are encountered, it will be necessary to replace the entire carrier unit as an assembly. Inspection of the unit should be made in the same manner as described for the rear planet carrier. End clearance of the planet gears should be checked in the same manner as for the rear planet carrier. End clearance should be .006″ to .030″. If excessive end clearance is noted and components are fully seated, thrust washers are probably worn or components may not be fully pressed together.

FRONT PUMP & REVERSE PISTON

When disassembling and reassembling, refer to 38 and 39. When disassembled, wash all parts, blow out all oil passages and air-dry parts. Then inspect as follows:

1. Pump gears for nicks or damage.
2. Stator support pump face for nicks or being scored.
3. Pump body for nicks or scores.
4. If pump body oil seal shows excessive wear, hardness, damage or evidence of leakage, pry it out and press in a new seal.
5. Splines of stator shaft for wear.
6. Both ends of stator shaft inner diameter for wear.
7. If square seal ring (rubber) is damaged, install a new one.
8. Facing material on reverse piston and ring for cracks or flaking; questionable clutch facings should be replaced.
9. If reverse cone shows evidence of excessive heat, replace it.
10. Inspect pump bushing for scoring or galling. Check clearance between bushing and converter pump hub; clearance should be .005″ maximum.
11. Install pump gears and check: Clearance between outside diameter of driven gear and body should be .0025″ to .0055″. Clearance between internal gear and crescent should be .003 to .009″. With scale and feeler gauge check gear end clearance, which should be .0005″ to .0015″.

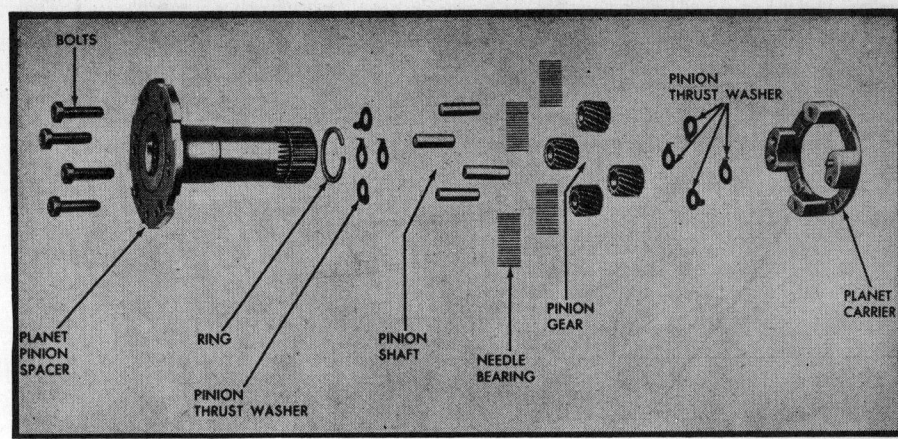

Fig. 36   Front planet carrier assembly.   1957

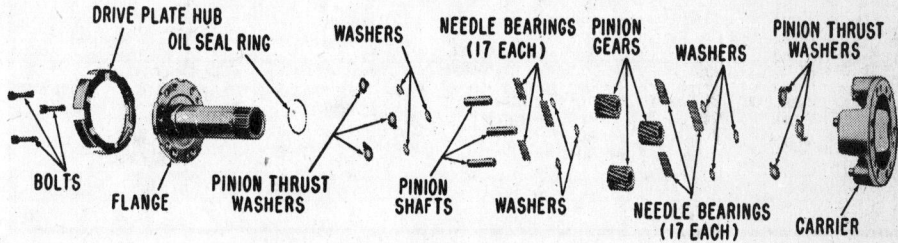

Fig. 37   Front planet gearset.   1958

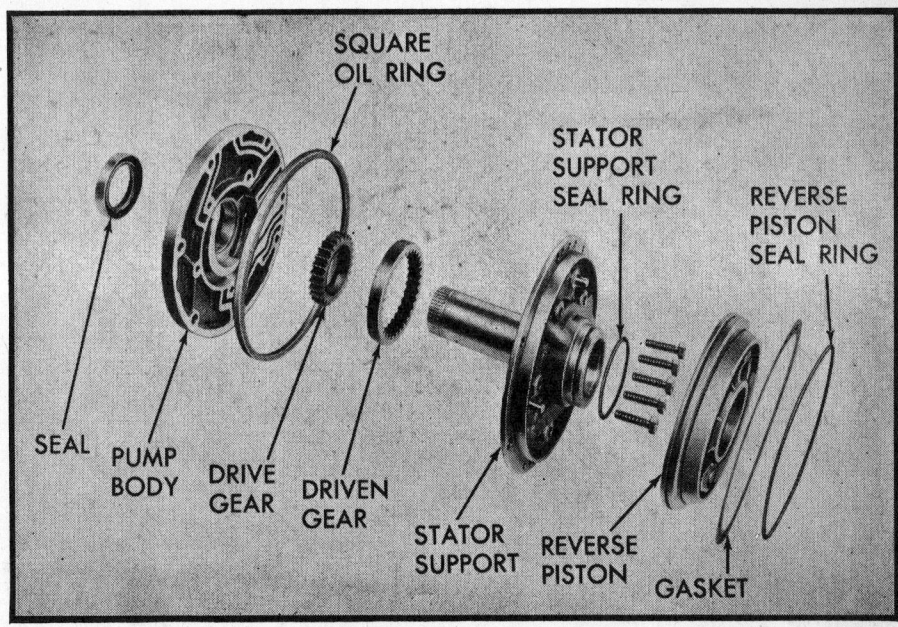

Fig. 38   Front pump and reverse piston assembly.   1957-58

Assemble

Remove gears from pump body, oil generously and replace in pump body. The drive gear is installed in the pump body with the lug toward the body. The lug mates with the slot in the converter housing. If drive gear is installed improperly the pump will not operate.

REAR PUMP

Remove pump gears, wash all parts, blow out all oil delivery holes and inspect all parts for visible damage.

Install gears and check all clearances, which are the same as comparable parts of the front pump. Then remove gears and oil generously with transmission fluid and assemble.

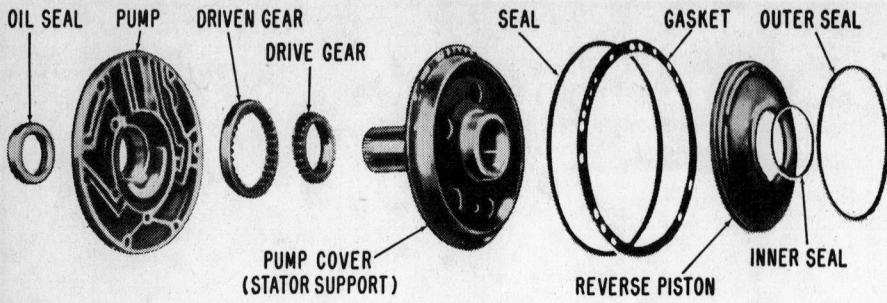

OIL SEAL PUMP DRIVEN GEAR DRIVE GEAR SEAL GASKET OUTER SEAL

PUMP COVER (STATOR SUPPORT) REVERSE PISTON INNER SEAL

Fig. 39 Front pump and reverse piston assembly. 1959-61

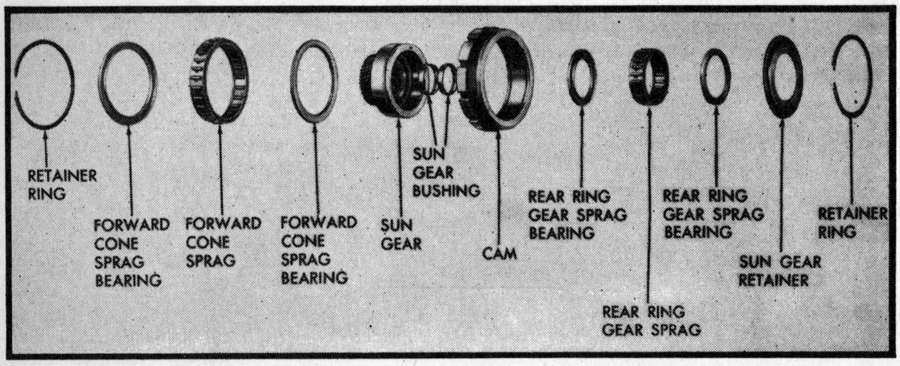

RETAINER RING — FORWARD CONE SPRAG BEARING — FORWARD CONE SPRAG — FORWARD CONE SPRAG BEARING — SUN GEAR — SUN GEAR BUSHING — CAM — REAR RING GEAR SPRAG BEARING — REAR RING GEAR SPRAG — REAR RING GEAR SPRAG BEARING — SUN GEAR RETAINER — RETAINER RING

Fig. 40 Front sun gear freewheeling assembly

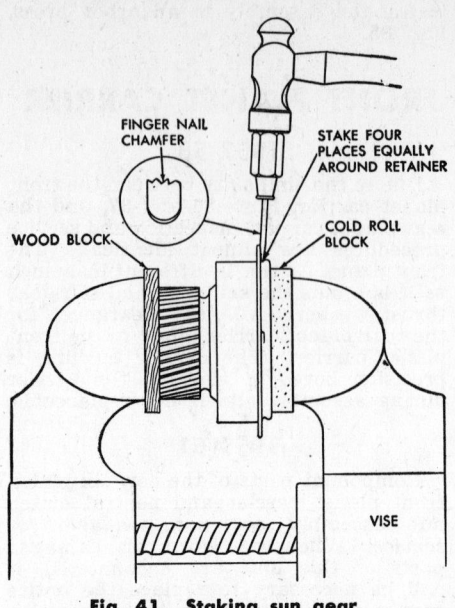

FINGER NAIL CHAMFER — STAKE FOUR PLACES EQUALLY AROUND RETAINER — WOOD BLOCK — COLD ROLL BLOCK — VISE

Fig. 41 Staking sun gear retainer to sun gear

Chevrolet-like parts numbered diagram

Fig. 42 Neutral clutch and ring gear. 1957

1. Converter oil seal ring
2. Turbine shaft oil seal rings
3. Gear thrust washer
4. Front ring gear hub
5. Ring gear hub bushing
6. Race
7. Needle bearing
8. Race
9. Oil rings
10. Clutch hub
11. Inner seal
12. Neutral clutch piston
13. Outer seal
14. Piston spring
15. Clutch cone
16. Cone ring
17. Cone ring retainer
18. Ring gear
19. Ring gear retaining ring

FRONT SUN GEAR FREE WHEEL ASSEMBLY

When disassembling and reassembling, refer to Fig. 40. The sprag assembly should not be disassembled. An arrow stamped on the outer cage of the sprag assembly designates front of transmission.

When disassembled, wash all parts, air-dry and inspect for damage as follows:

1. Inspect inner race of cam for excessive scoring or burning. Also check lugs on outer perimeter of cam for nicks or burrs.
2. Check bushings in sun gear for looseness or bushing scoring. Bushings must be replaced in pairs and while sun gear is removed from freewheel unit. Before installing bushings, note position of oil grooves in bushings. Grooves must point outward to maintain oil reservoir in sun gear.
3. Inspect sun gear teeth for nicks and burrs. Check sun gear for fit into front planetary unit.
4. Inspect internal and external races of sun gear for excessive scoring or burning.
5. Inspect sprag bearing for excessive wear.
6. If sprag wear is indicated, replace sprag assembly.

When reassembling, the sprag is installed with the stamped arrow on its outer cage toward front of transmission. Sprags are assembled correctly if they will slip while holding outer cam stationary and turning sun gear clockwise as viewed from the front.

When installing the sun gear retainer, index the tang of the new retainer into the hole in the rear of the sun gear and clamp in a vise, using the fixture shown in Fig. 41. Use care when staking not to bend the retainer due to the close tolerance between the retainer and sprag bearings.

Index the sun gear in the forward cone sprag, twisting counterclockwise to enable cams to twist, allowing sun gear race to seat under sprags while twisting.

NEUTRAL CLUTCH & RING GEAR

When disassembling and assembling, refer to Figs. 42 and 43. The gear thrust washer (3) is available in different thicknesses to give proper clearance within the transmission. To aid in removing the neutral clutch piston, apply air pressure into the ball check hole in the hub. The piston is doweled to the hub and therefore will not rotate independent of the hub. The ball check in the hub is not removable. Wash all parts and air-dry. Then inspect for the following conditions:

1. Splines in hub for nicks and burrs. Check hub for fit in third turbine.
2. Ball check in hub for looseness. If leakage is suspected, hub may be checked by filling cavity with oil and observing check ball.
3. Inspect inner race of hub for excessive scoring or burning. Surface on which piston moves must be micro smooth to eliminate possibility of oil ring breakage.
4. Check all ring lands for nicks or burrs which may hamper freedom of ring movement.

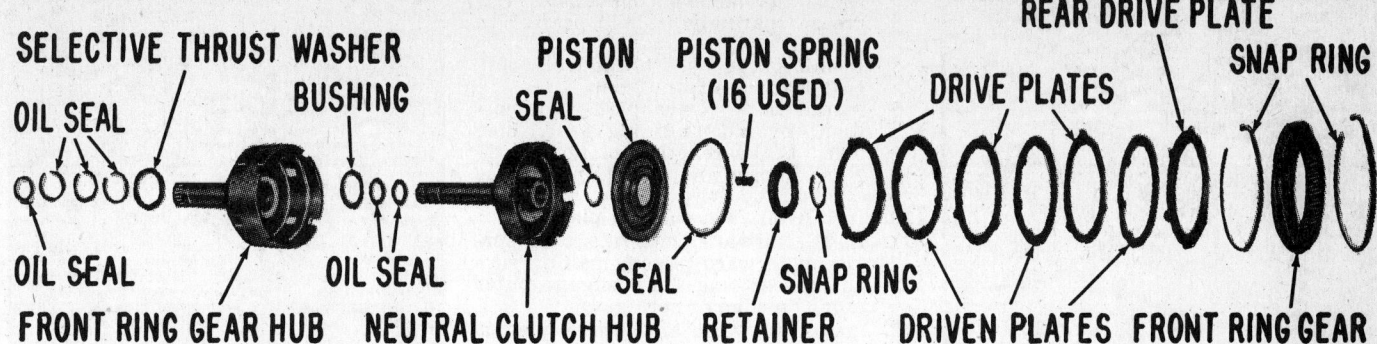

Fig. 43   Neutral clutch and front ring gear. 1958-61

5. Check bushing in center of hub. If bushing is scored or loose, or hub inner race is damaged, replace hub and shaft assembly.

6. Check neutral clutch piston for burred or nicked groove for piston outer seal or inner race being scored or pitted. Any surface roughness in contact with rubber seals will cause seal failure.

7. Inspect neutral clutch inner and outer facings for cracks or flaking. Questionable clutch facing damages should be repaired by replacement.

8. Check all tangs and keyways for proper engagement. The smallest burr will hamper assembly and possibly accelerate wear.

9. If neutral cone surface (1957) indicates excessive heat, replace.

10. Inspect driven plate facings (1958) for cracks or flaking. Questionable clutch facings should be replaced.

11. Inspect front ring gear teeth for wear and chips.

Before assembling any part to or with an "O" type round or square seal, lubricate all contacting parts with automatic transmission fluid. Assemble all parts except items 1, 2 and 3, Figs. 42, 43. These parts are not installed at this time due to their being removed during selective washer checking operation.

FORWARD & BRAKE PISTON & SUPPORT

1957-58

Refer to Fig. 44 when servicing this unit. When disassembled, inspect for the following conditions:

1. Inspect splines of hub for nicks or burrs. Check hub of brake piston for fit into hub or forward piston.

2. Inspect all surfaces contacting "O" rings or square seal rings for scoring or burning. All surfaces must be micro smooth to prevent seal failures.

3. Inspect piston and cone ring facing material for cracks or flaking. Replace facings if at all questionable.

4. If forward cone surface shows signs of excessive heat, replace cone.

5. Inspect Hill Retarder composition plates. If facings are at all questionable, replace them.

When assembling, lightly lubricate all "O" ring seals and square seals to insure proper mating of parts to seals to prevent damage of seal during assembly.

1959-61

Refer to Fig. 45 when servicing this unit. When disassembled, inspect for the following conditions:

1. Inspect forward piston, brake piston and support for evidence of excessive heat or damage.

2. Inspect all contacting seal rings for scoring or burning. Surfaces must be smooth to prevent seal failures.

3. Check fits of forward and brake piston into support.

4. Inspect I.D. of forward piston which mates with rear ring gear for nicks or burrs.

5. Inspect forward clutch facings for wear or damage. Also check forward clutch reaction and pressure plates

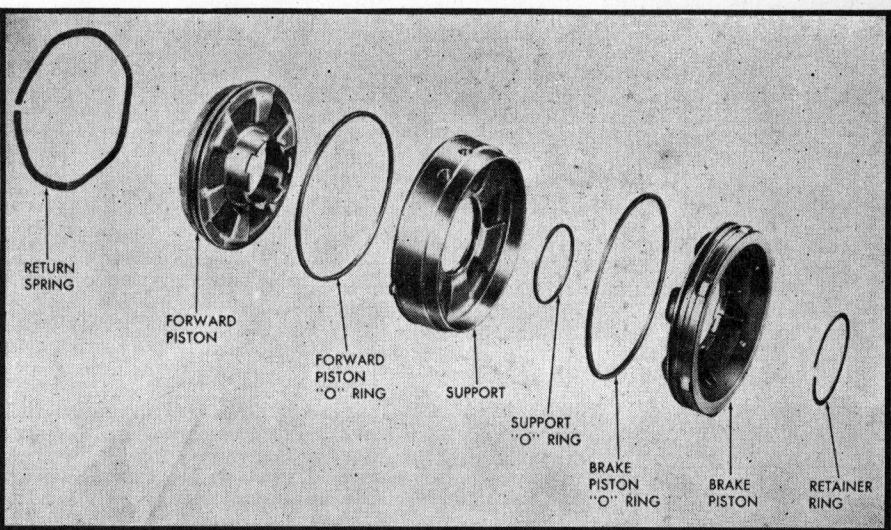

Fig. 44   Forward and brake piston and support.   1957-58

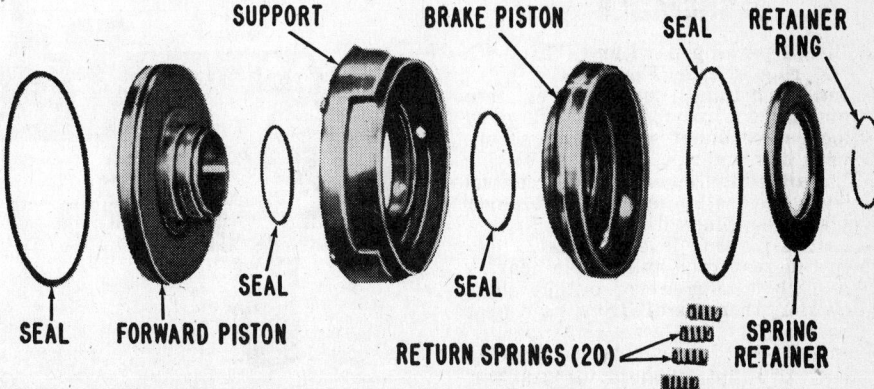

Fig. 45   Forward and brake piston and support.   1959-61

Fig. 46 Installing stator control lever

for evidence of excessive heat, wear or damage. Replace all questionable parts.

6. Inspect brake (grade retarder) drive and reaction plates for evidence of excessive heat, wear or damage and replace all questionable parts.

7. Inspect for distorted or damaged return springs and return spring seat and replace if necessary.

Assemble

1. Assemble new seals to O.D. of forward piston. Also assemble new seals to O.D. and I.D. of brake piston. Lubricate seals.

2. Carefully install forward piston in support, using extreme care to avoid damage to seals as they enter support. Fully seat forward piston in support.

3. Use a suitable sleeve on support hub to protect seal on I.D. of brake piston, then carefully guide brake piston into support over seal protector, using extreme care not to damage large seal on brake piston as it enters support at slightly chamfered edge.

4. Set unit in a press, forward piston end down, and assemble 20 springs to brake piston. Place spring seat over springs. Compress seat and springs and install retaining ring.

1957 TRANSMISSION, ASSEMBLE

1. Install parking pawl and shaft with "O" ring in case, Fig. 46.

2. Index manual control lever into manual control rod and park pawl lock rod (bullet type) and secure with bolt and nut (see Fig. 19).

3. Install stator lever through control lever and install detent control lever plate, securing with hairpin clip.

4. Install parking lever bracket.

5. Install rear race and needle bearing assembly on front of output shaft carrier, then install front race over shaft.

6. Install caged needle thrust bearing on rear of output shaft, using grease sparingly to hold bearings in place.

7. Install rear ring gear onto rear planet carrier and output shaft. Use grease sparingly to hold bearing in place.

8. Install output shaft and rear ring gear into case from front.

9. Install brake drive plate (composition) by indexing ring gear. Then index brake reaction plate (aluminum) to case and follow up with the other brake drive plate.

10. Install forward cone on piston.

11. Install forward cone ring over spring on forward piston, making sure notches of ring fully engage outer tangs on edge of spring.

12. Install forward and brake pistons and support in case. Index outer support and forward cone ring to case and the six lugs on brake piston to case, being careful not to remove cone ring from over spring. *Keep taper section of forward piston to front of transmission.*

13. Install forward cone ring retainer to secure unit to case. Outer forward cone ring may have to be tapped gently to compress spring in piston to provide enough space to install retainer. *Be sure retainer is firmly seated in its groove.*

14. Install needle thrust bearing race over extension of front planet carrier and install needle bearing over race.

15. Install tanged washer onto front end of front planetary, using a small amount of grease to keep washer located.

16. Holding neutral clutch assembly with one hand with shaft pointing up, lift front planetary with tanged washer installed and index keyways on front planetary housing to cone lugs in neutral clutch assembly.

17. After planetary is installed, rest shaft of neutral clutch on bench and install freewheeling sprag over rear extension of planetary. Twist sprag to mate sun gear to planetary gears.

18. Install needle thrust bearing over extension of front planetary gear extending through freewheel unit.

19. Install unit in case, twisting shaft to engage lugs of freewheeling outer cam to forward cone in forward clutch mounted in case. Forward cone is loose and may be turned to align with lugs of freewheeling cam.

Fig. 47 Dial gauge mounted on rear of front pump

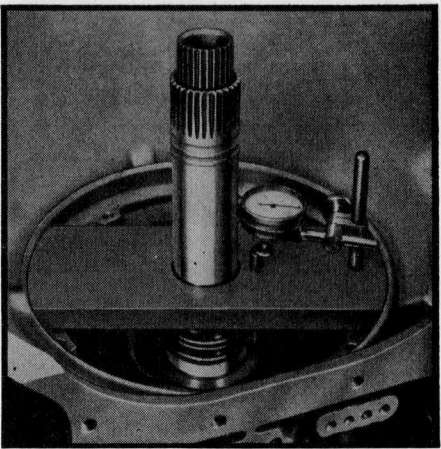

Fig. 48 Dial gauge installed in transmission case

20. Turn transmission so input shaft is facing up.

21. Install reverse cone ring in case with tapered portion forward. Tang fits in case and drain back notch should be at bottom of case.

22. At this time the end play of the transmission should be checked, using equipment shown in Figs. 47 and 48. With gauge mounted as shown in Fig. 47, note highest reading as indicated at several points on pump mounting. Then install gauge as shown in Fig. 48 and note the highest reading. Subtract the read-in obtained with Fig. 47 with that of Fig. 48. This difference will give the thickness of the thrust washer to install. Allowable clearance is .008" to .028". Install the thrust washer which will give the proper clearance. Washers are available in thicknesses of .068", .085" and .103".

23. Install four oil seal rings to extension on front ring gear hub.

24. Install reverse cone into case, meshing tangs with slots in neutral clutch and front ring gear.

25. Install reverse cone spring into case.

26. Install two guide studs in case to guide pump to avoid damage to oil seal rings on front ring gear hub shaft.

27. Install stator support gasket.

28. Install square seal ring on outer lip of stator support. Align tang of oil pump drive gear to bottom of pump housing. *It is important that transmission be in vertical position with front end facing up. The installation of pump over oil seal rings on second turbine shaft is accomplished by sliding pump down easily and centering pump over guide studs. Also, this will enable converter to be installed without damaging oil seal rings.* Pump housing may have to be tapped to fully seat in case.

29. Remove guide studs and install pump attaching screws.

30. Install converter driving lug of pump to mate with keyway of front pump drive gear. Converter may be rotated to complete mating of splines. *A minimum measurement of*

¾" from front of case to front of converter must be present, assuring that all parts are properly engaged.

31. Install converter holding tool, Fig. 49.
32. Place transmission parallel to floor.
33. Turn output shaft to locate drive pin hole to top of output shaft and install drive pin (see Fig. 14).
34. Position pump on output shaft, indexing drive gear to drive pin.
35. Install pump attaching bolts. Then install square ring seal over pump. *Converter must be assembled to transmission before oil pump can be tightened.*
36. Install by-pass valve.
37. Install vacuum diaphragm outside of case along with vacuum modulator strut and attaching nut.
38. Install oil pressure tubes.
39. Install valve body.
40. Install speedometer drive gear.
41. Install rear extension.
42. Install speedometer driven gear.
43. Install transmission oil pan.

1958 TRANSMISSION ASSEMBLE

1. Install parking pawl and shaft with "O" ring in case.
2. Index manual control lever into manual control rod and parking lock pawl rod and secure with bolt and nut.
3. Install stator lever through control lever, Fig. 46.
4. Install parking lever bracket and torque bolts to 15-18 lb. ft.
5. Install rear race, needle bearing and front race on front of output shaft carrier.
6. Install caged needle thrust bearing on rear of output shaft.
7. Install ring gear on rear planet carrier and output shaft.
8. Install output shaft and rear ring gear into case from front.
9. Install grade retarder members in following order:
   Thin reaction plate (steel)
   Brake plate (lined)
   Thick reaction plate (steel)
   Brake plate (lined)
   Thick reaction plate
   Brake plate
   Thin reaction plate

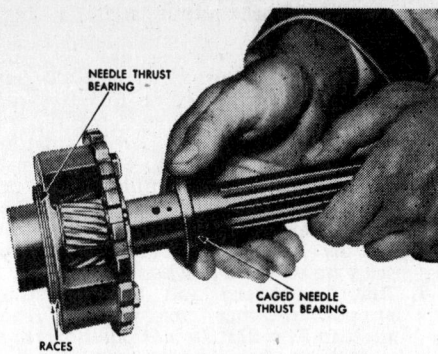

Fig. 50 Thrust bearings installed on rear planet carrier. 1959-60

10. Install forward and brake piston support in case with forward piston toward front. Check that this unit is fully seated in case by seeing that the oil transfer tube holes in case and piston support line up.
11. Install forward cone (steel) and forward cone ring.
12. Install forward cone ring retainer. Outer forward cone ring may have to be tapped gently to compress spring in forward piston to provide space to install retainer.
13. Install needle thrust bearing and race over extension of front planet carrier.
14. Install tanged washer onto front of front planetary.
15. Holding neutral clutch assembly with one hand with shaft pointing up, lift front planetary with tanged washer installed and index keyways on front planetary housing to driven plate lugs in neutral clutch.
16. After planetary unit is installed, rest shaft of neutral clutch on bench and install front sun gear freewheeling unit over rear extension of planetary. Twist sprag assembly to mate sun gear to planetary gears. Install needle thrust bearing over extension of front planetary gear extending through freewheel unit.
17. Install unit in case, twisting shaft to engage lugs of freewheeling unit outer cam to forward cone in clutch unit mounted in transmission case. Forward cone is loose and may be turned to align with lugs.
18. Turn transmission so input shaft is facing up.
19. Install reverse cone ring in case, tapered portion forward. Oil return grove should be at bottom of case.
20. Install reverse cone ring in case and reverse cone. Mesh tangs of cone with slots in neutral clutch and front ring gear.
21. Install reverse cone spring in case with rounded ends forward.
22. Install two guide studs in case to guide front pump to avoid damaging oil seal rings on front ring gear hub shaft.
23. Install stator support gasket to case.
24. Install square seal ring on outer lip of stator support. Align tangs of oil pump drive gear to top and bottom of pump housing.
25. It is important that transmission be

in vertical position with front end up. The installation of pump over seal rings is accomplished by sliding pump down easily and centering pump over guide studs. Also, this will enable converter to be installed without damaging oil seal rings.

26. At this time, check for correct thickness of selective thrust washer to be used as follows:
   a. Install four of front pump-to-case bolts.
   b. Rotate transmission so that transmission output shaft is down.
   c. Mount dial indicator so that plunger is resting on end of neutral clutch hub. Then zero indicator.
   d. Push upward on output shaft and observe total indicator movement.
   e. Indicator should read .008" to .028". If within limits front pump bolts should be coated with sealer and installed.
   f. If clearance is not within limits, the selective thrust washer must be changed to obtain the specified clearance.
27. Torque front pump bolts to 15-18 lb. ft. and remove the guide studs. Install converter assembly. Lift converter up and down while turning slightly to engage pump lugs. This engagement will be indicated when the converter drops an additional ½". *A minimum measurement of ¾" from front of case to front of converter must be made to insure all parts being properly engaged.*
28. Install converter holding tool, Fig. 49; then turn transmission parallel to floor.
29. Turn output shaft to locate drive pin hole to top of output shaft; then install wear plate and rear pump drive pin.
30. Position rear pump on output shaft, indexing drive gear to drive pin; then install bolts and torque to 7-9 lb. ft. Install square seal ring over pump.
31. Install thermal by-pass valve and torque to 7-9 lb. ft.
32. Screw vacuum diaphragm into case; then insert strut into vacuum modulator.
33. Install two "O" rings on each oil pressure tube and install tubes in support (tapered end into support) through case, making sure oil seal rings are seated.

Fig. 49 Installing converter holding tool

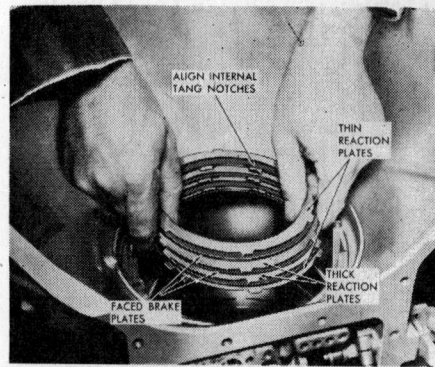

Fig. 51 Installing brake (grade retarder) plates. 1959-61

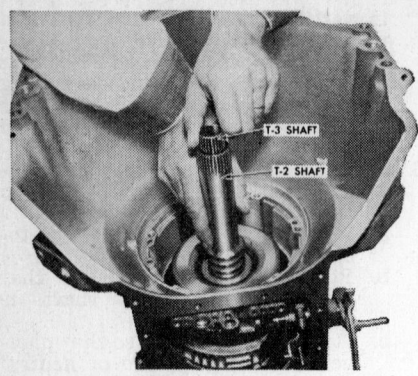

Fig. 52 Engaging neutral clutch plates with front planet carrier. 1959-61

34. Perform the air checks outlined at the beginning of this chapter before installing valve body to check assembly of the transmission up to this point.

35. Install valve body, guiding detent plate into groove, manual valve lever to manual valve detent valve, and carefully pick up manual valve, oil pressure tubes and vacuum modulator strut.

36. Install special drilled bolt at rear of valve body to rear case. Hole in bolt carries lube pressure to drilled passages in case to output shaft from valve body. Torque this hollow bolt to 18-21 lb. ft.

37. Install remaining bolts in valve body and torque to 8-10 lb. ft.

38. Index spring in parking lock pawl; then index into bracket on rear bolt of valve body.

39. Install speedometer gear on output shaft. When fully installed, distance from forward edge of gear to rearmost surface of rear pump should be ¼".

40. Install rear extension housing and torque to 23-26 lb. ft.

41. Install universal joint yoke and rotate freely. If yoke is tight, remove extension housing and tap rear pump body to center output shaft with extension bushing and seal.

42. Install speedometer driven gear.

43. Install transmission oil pan.

1959-61 TRANSMISSION ASSEMBLE

1. If removed, assemble transmission manual controls into case (Fig. 30).

2. Lubricate and install needle thrust bearing race, bearing and race on front hub of rear planet carrier, Fig. 50.

3. Dip caged needle bearing in transmission oil, assemble over output shaft of rear planet carrier and stick to carrier with vaseline. Lubricate all gears and friction surfaces before installing.

4. Lubricate and assemble rear ring gear unit to rear planet carrier with bearings installed. Hold up parking lock pawl and insert entire unit in

case. Support output shaft during installation.

5. Install grade retarder clutch pack as shown in Fig. 51. Align all internal notched tangs on faced brake plates.

6. Install forward and brake piston and support assembly. Seat assembly by tapping with mallet handle or brass drift. *Note: Pressure tube ports point toward valve body or bottom of transmission and align with holes in case when seated.*

7. Install forward and brake piston support retainer ring in case (see inset in Fig. 27). *Do not position ring gap at grooves in case.*

8. Lubricate and install needle thrust bearing into rear cavity of front sun gear free wheeling assembly (overrunning sprag clutch unit) and install assembly in case. *No races are used with this bearing.*

9. Lubricate and install forward clutch pack, alternating a steel plate with a faced plate, starting with a steel plate and ending with the thick steel pressure plate. Notched tangs on steel plates must align.

10. Install forward clutch retainer ring in case (see inset, Fig. 27). *Do not position ring gap at case grooves.*

11. Assemble new O-rings in top groove of each oil pressure tube and in the brake (grade retarder) and forward clutch orifices (see Fig. 2). Be sure seals are fully seated, then install tapered ends of pressure tubes into O-rings in orifices and air check forward and brake pistons for leakage and satisfactory operation as described under *Air Pressure Checks.*

12. Apply a small amount of vaseline and locate tanged thrust washer on front end of front planet carrier. Also lubricate and install needle bearing race and bearing over front planet carrier extension. Install thrust ring in groove on front planet extension.

13. Lubricate and install front planet carrier in case.

14. Install neutral clutch and front ring gear over front planet carrier. Hold front ring gear (T-2) shaft while turning the T-3 shaft to engage neutral clutch plates with front planet carrier, Fig. 52.

15. Lubricate and install reverse clutch reaction insert (see Fig. 25) and rear

Fig. 54 Checking end play for selective thrust washer on front ring gear hub. 1959-61

pressure plate in case. Alternately install faced plates and steel plates in insert, then complete assembly by installing the original selective reverse front pressure plate.

16. Install reverse piston spring with cone facing toward front of transmission.

17. Install new square seal ring on outer lip of stator support. Align tangs of oil pump drive gear to top and bottom of pump housing. *Note: It is important that transmission be in vertical position with front end facing upward to avoid damage to oil seal rings on second turbine shaft during front pump and converter installation. Align oil seal ring gaps for ease of installation.*

18. Install two guide studs in case to guide front pump to avoid damaging oil seal rings on front ring gear hub shaft.

19. Install front pump gasket to case.

20. Lubricate all four oil seal rings on second turbine shaft with vaseline. Center rings on shaft, then index pump on guide studs and carefully guide pump over oil seal rings. Pump housing may have to be tapped to seat in case.

21. Check second turbine shaft for free rotation. If shaft binds, remove assembly and check for broken seal rings. Install four of the front pump mounting bolts, tighten to 15-18 ft. lbs. and recheck second turbine.

22. Check for selective reverse front presure plate running clearance as follows:
    a. Position transmission in fixture so that output shaft is horizontal.
    b. Using feeler gauges, measure clearance between selective reverse pressure plate and adjacent faced plate, Fig. 53. Be careful to measure only the clearance. *Closely observe that clutch pack plates are not being compressed by insertion of feeler gauges.*
    c. If proper plate is installed, gauge measurement will be .025" to .050".
    d. If clearance is not within limits, it will be necessary to disassemble to the reverse clutch pack and install a thicker or thinner selective reverse plate, as required. Then rebuild and recheck running clearance. Three sizes of selective plates are available and are identifiable by the number of depressions on plate. The thinnest plate (.5971") has one depression; me-

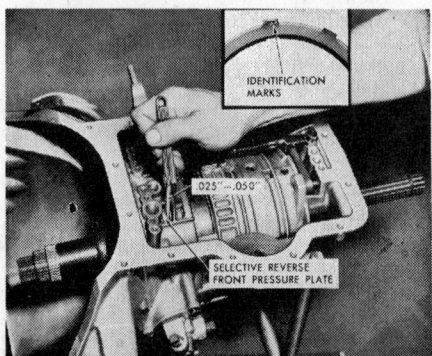

Fig. 53 Measuring reverse clutch running clearance. 1959-61

dium thickness plate (.5814″) has two depressions, and the thickest plate (.5657″) has three depressions. All three plates are subject to plus or minus .003″.

23. Check for correct thickness of selective thrust washer on front ring gear hub with dial gauge as shown in Fig. 54. With indicator zeroed, push upward on output shaft and observe total indicator movement. Reading should be .008″ to .028″. If not, change to the proper thickness washer, three of which are available in thicknesses of .068″, .085″ and 103″. When proper clearance is obtained, remove guide studs and coat all front pump bolts with non-hardening sealer and install. Tighten bolts to 15-18 ft. lbs.

24. Air check neutral and reverse clutches for leakage and satisfactory operation in a manner described under *Air Pressure Checks*.

25. Install converter. Two slots in converter pump hub should be toward top and bottom of transmission to engage lugs in front pump drive gear. Lift converter up and down while turning slightly to engage pump lugs. Converter will drop in approximately ½″ further when engagement with pump lugs is attained.

26. Measure from front of case to front of converter. If measurement of ¾″ minimum is obtained, all parts are properly engaged.

27. Install converter holding tool and place transmission parallel to floor, bottom side up.

28. Air check stator piston for air leaks.

29. Turn output shaft to locate drive pin hole at top of output shaft. Then install wear plate and pump drive pin (see Fig. 14).

30. Position rear pump on output shaft, indexing drive gear with drive pin, then install two lower pump bolts which are not used to secure oil deflector. Tighten bolts securely.

31. Install speedometer drive gear. Front face of drive gear should be ¼″ from rear pump.

32. Install oil deflector (two upper bolt positions) and tighten bolts snugly. Install seal ring around pump body and against rear face of case. *Converter must be in transmission before rear pump bolts are tightened.*

33. Install transmission extension.

34. Using a U-joint slip yoke, check for free rotation of output shaft. If there is binding, center rear oil pump by tapping on extension until shaft turns freely. When output shaft turns freely, carefully remove extension to avoid shifting oil pump. Tighten pump bolts to 7-9 ft. lbs. Install extension and tighten bolts to 23-26 ft. lbs. Install slip yoke and recheck for free rotation of output shaft.

35. Install speedometer driven gear, if removed. Position retainer and tighten capscrew to 3½-5 ft. lbs.

36. Install vacuum modulator plunger (see Fig. 23).

37. Install valve body, using new gaskets. Make sure inner selector lever engages with manual valve and detent ball and that pressure tubes and vacuum modulator plunger enter valve body. Install and tighten front bolts to 8-10 ft. lbs. and rear hollow bolt to 18-21 ft. lbs.

37. Install parking pawl spring.

38. Install oil pan and tighten bolts to 3-4 ft. lbs.

BUICK

INDEX OF SERVICE OPERATIONS

PAGE NO.

ACCESSORIES

Radio Removal 418
Speedometer Removal 417
Windshield Wiper 418
Windshield Wiper Troubles...........37

BODY

Air Conditioning 177
Automatic Seat Adjuster Troubles......36
Automatic Top Troubles..............36
Automatic Window Lift Troubles.......36

BRAKES (Mechanical)

Adjustments 112
Brake Cylinder Sizes................383
Hydraulic Brake System..............112
Master Cylinder, Replace............410
Trouble Shooting 31

BRAKES (Power)

Power Unit Repairs..................128
Power Unit, Replace.................411
Trouble Shooting 32

CLUTCH

Clutch, Install 399
Clutch, Overhaul 398
Clutch Pedal, Adjust...............397
Clutch, Remove 398
Trouble Shooting 13

COOLING SYSTEM

Cooling System Specs................382
Radiator, Replace 391
Trouble Shooting 4
Water Pump Repairs.................391
Water Pump, Replace................391

ELECTRIC SYSTEM

Dash Gauge Service.................85
Distributor, Replace................391
Distributor Service 46
Distributor Specifications 382
Generator & Regulator Service........62
Generator & Regulator Specifications..380
Horn Button or Ring, Replace........415
Ignition System Service.............46
Ignition Timing 392
Starter, Replace 392

Starter Switch Service..............83
Starter Motor Service...............77
Starting Motor Specifications........383
Trouble Shooting 10
Turn Signal Troubles................12

ENGINE

Camshaft & Bearings................388
Crankshaft & Bearing Specs..........381
Crankshaft Oil Seal, Replace.........390
Cylinder Head, Replace..............385
Engine, Replace 384
Main Bearings, Replace..............390
Piston Pins, Replace................389
Piston Rings, Replace...............389
Piston & Ring Specifications.........381
Pistons & Rods, Remove.............389
Piston & Rod, Assemble.............389
Pistons, Replace 389
Rocker Arms 385
Rod Bearings, Replace..............390
Timing Case Cover, Replace..........388
Timing Chain, Replace..............388
Trouble Shooting 4
Valve Arrangement 386
Valves, Grind 386
Valve Guides, Replace..............387
Valve Lifters 387
Valve Spring Installed Height........387
Valve Spring Testing...............387
Valve Timing Data.................388
Valve Specifications 381

ENGINE OILING

Oil Pan, Replace...................390
Oil Pump 390
Trouble Shooting 4

FRONT SUSPENSION

Camber & Caster...................411
Front End Repairs..................412
Toe-in, Adjust 412
Trouble Shooting 33
Wheel Alignment Specifications.......383
Wheel Bearings, Adjust.............412

FUEL & EXHAUST SYSTEM

Carburetors 392
Fuel Pumps 96
Mufflers and Pipes.................392
Trouble Shooting 4

REAR AXLE

Non-Slip Differentials...............109
Axle Shaft, Replace................410
General Service 102
Rear Axle Repairs..................408
Rear Axle, Replace.................406
Rear Axle Specifications............383
Trouble Shooting 31

SPECIFICATIONS

Brake Cylinder Sizes................383
Capacity Data 382
Carburetors 393
Cooling System 382
Crankshaft & Bearings..............381
Distributors 382
Generators & Regulators............380
Pistons, Pins & Rings...............381
Rear Axle 383
Starting Motors 383
Engine Tightening 381
Tune Up 380
Valve Timing 388
Valves 381
Wheel Alignment

STEERING GEARS (Mechanical)

Horn Button or Ring, Replace........415
Steering Gear, Repairs..............416
Steering Gear, Replace.............415
Steering Wheel, Replace............415
Trouble Shooting 33

STEERING GEARS (Power)

Steering Gear, Repairs..............145
Steering Gear, Replace.............417
Trouble Shooting 34

TRANSMISSIONS, Manual Shift

Gearshift Linkage 403
Transmission Repairs 401
Transmission, Replace 400
Trouble Shooting 14

TRANSMISSIONS, Automatic

Twin Turbine Types
  Remove & Replace.................404
  Repairs 210
  Linkage, Adjust................405
  Trouble Shooting 16
Triple Turbine Types
  Remove & Replace.................403
  Repairs 191
  Linkage, Adjust................403
  Trouble Shooting 18

TUNE UP 38

GENERAL SPECIFICATIONS

Year	Model Designation	Wheelbase, Inches	Valve Location	Bore and Stroke	Piston Displacement, Cubic Inches	Compression Ratio (Standard)	Maximum Brake H.P. @ R.P.M.	Maximum Torque Lbs. Ft. @ R.P.M.	Normal Oil Pressure Pounds
1953	Special 8..........Series 40	121½	In Head	3.187 x 4.125	263.3	7.0	125 @ 3800	224 @ 2200	35
	Super V8.........Series 50	121½①	In Head	4.000 x 3.200	322.0	8.0	164 @ 4000	286 @ 2200	35
	Roadmaster V8....Series 70	121½②	In Head	4.000 x 3.200	322.0	8.5	188 @ 4000	300 @ 2400	35
1954	Special V8 ④......Series 40	122	In Head	3.625 x 3.200	264	7.2	143 @ 4200	228 @ 2400	35
	Special V8 ⑤.......Series 40	122	In Head	3.625 x 3.200	264	8.1	150 @ 4200	240 @ 2400	35
	Super V8 ④........Series 50	127	In Head	4.000 x 3.200	322	8.0	177 @ 4100	295 @ 2000	35
	Super V8 ⑤........Series 50	127	In Head	4.000 x 3.200	322	8.5	182 @ 4100	300 @ 2000	35
	Century V8 ④......Series 60	122	In Head	4.000 x 3.200	322	8.0	195 @ 4100	302 @ 2400	35
	Century V8 ⑤......Series 60	122	In Head	4.000 x 3.200	322	8.5	200 @ 4100	309 @ 2400	35
	Roadmaster V8.....Series 70	127	In Head	4.000 x 3.200	322	8.5	200 @ 4100	309 @ 2400	35
1955	Special V8.......Series 40	122	In Head	3.625 x 3.200	264	8.4	188 @ 4800	256 @ 2400	35
	Super V8 ④........Series 50	127	In Head	4.000 x 3.200	322	8.4	188 @ 4800	256 @ 2400	35
	Super V8 ⑤........Series 50	127	In Head	4.000 x 3.200	322	9.0	236 @ 4600	330 @ 3000	35
	Century V8 ④......Series 60	122	In Head	4.000 x 3.200	322	8.4	188 @ 4800	250 @ 2400	35
	Century V8 ⑤......Series 60	122	In Head	4.000 x 3.200	322	9.0	236 @ 4600	330 @ 3000	35
	Roadmaster V8.....Series 70	127	In Head	4.000 x 3.200	322	9.0	236 @ 4600	330 @ 3000	35
1956	Special V8 ....Series 40	122	In Head	4.000 x 3.200	322	8.9	220 @ 4400	319 @ 2400	35
	Super V8.........Series 50	127	In Head	4.000 x 3.200	322	9.5	255 @ 4400	341 @ 3200	35
	Century V8.......Series 60	122	In Head	4.000 x 3.200	322	9.5	255 @ 4400	341 @ 3200	35
	Roadmaster V8......Series 70	127	In Head	4.000 x 3.200	322	9.5	255 @ 4400	341 @ 3200	35
1957	Special V8 ⑤......Series 40	122	In Head	4.125 x 3.400	364	9.5	250 @ 4400	380 @ 2400	40
	Super V8.........Series 50	127½	In Head	4.125 x 3.400	364	10.0	300 @ 4600	400 @ 3200	40
	Century V8.......Series 60	122	In Head	4.125 x 3.400	364	10.0	300 @ 4600	400 @ 3200	40
	Roadmaster V8.....Series 70	127½	In Head	4.125 x 3.400	364	10.0	300 @ 4600	400 @ 3200	40
1958	Special V8.......Series 40	122	In Head	4.125 x 3.400	364	9.5	250 @ 4400	380 @ 2400	40
	Super V8........Series 50	127.5	In Head	4.125 x 3.400	364	10.0	300 @ 4600	400 @ 3200	40
	Century V8.......Series 60	122	In Head	4.125 x 3.400	364	10.0	300 @ 4600	400 @ 3200	40
	Roadmaster V8....Series 70	127.5	In Head	4.125 x 3.400	364	10.0	300 @ 4600	400 @ 3200	40
	Limited V8.......Series 700	127.5	In Head	4.125 x 3.400	364	10.0	300 @ 4600	400 @ 3200	40
1959	Le Sabre V8.............4400	123	In Head	4.125 x 3.400	364	10.5⑧	250 @ 4400	384 @ 2400	40
	Invicta V8.............4600	123	In Head	4.1875 x 3.640	401	10.5	325 @ 4400	445 @ 2800	40
	Electra V8.............4700	126.3	In Head	4.1875 x 3.640	401	10.5	325 @ 4400	445 @ 2800	40
	Electra V8.............4800	126.3	In Head	4.1875 x 3.640	401	10.5	325 @ 4400	445 @ 2800	40
1960	Le Sabre V8④.........4400	123	In Head	4.1250 x 3.40	364	8.5	210 @ 4000	340 @ 2400	40
	Le Sabre V8⑥.........4400	123	In Head	4.1250 x 3.40	364	10.25	250 @ 4400	384 @ 2400	40
	Le Sabre V8⑦.........4400	123	In Head	4.1250 x 3.40	364	9.0	235 @ 4400	362 @ 2400	40
	Le Sabre V8⑧.........4400	123	In Head	4.1250 x 3.40	364	10.25	300 @ 4400	405 @ 2800	40
	Invicta V8............4600	123	In Head	4.1875 x 3.64	401	10.25	325 @ 4400	445 @ 2800	40
	Electra V8.............4700	126.3	In Head	4.1875 x 3.64	401	10.25	325 @ 4400	445 @ 2800	40
	Electra V8 ("225")......4800	126.3	In Head	4.1875 x 3.64	401	10.25	325 @ 4400	445 @ 2800	40
1961	Le Sabre V8⑥.........4400	123	In Head	4.1250 x 3.40	364	10.25	250 @ 4400	384 @ 2400	40
	Le Sabre V8⑦.........4400	123	In Head	4.1250 x 3.40	364	9.0	235 @ 4400	375 @ 2400	40
	Invicta V8.............4600	123	In Head	4.1875 x 3.64	401	10.25	325 @ 4400	445 @ 2800	40
	Electra V8.............4700	126	In Head	4.1875 x 3.64	401	10.25	325 @ 4400	445 @ 2800	40

①—125½" wheelbase on model 52.
②—125½'' wheelbase on model 72R.
③—8.5 to 1 with manual shift trans.
④—Synchromesh transmission.

⑤—Dynaflow.
⑥—Standard engine.
⑦—Regular gasoline option.
⑧—Performance option.

TUNE UP SPECIFICATIONS

★When setting timing, adjust idle speed to 400 RPM so that vacuum and centrifugal advance mechanisms are not in operation.

Year	Model	Ground Polarity and Voltage	Spark Plug Type	Spark Plug Gap Inch	Distributor Point Gap Inch	Distributor Cam Angle Degrees	Firing Order ①	Ignition Timing★ Mark	Ignition Timing★ Location	Idle Speed RPM In Neutral	Compression Pressure @ Cranking Speed Minimum
1953	40	N-6	AC 46X	.025	.016	26–33	16258374	ADV	Flywheel	450	114
	50, 70	N-12	AC 44-5	.032	.016	26–33	12784563	②	Flywheel	450	160
1954	40	N-12	AC 44-5	.032	.016	26–33	12784563	③	Pulley	450	130
	50, 60, 70	N-12	AC 44-5	.032	.016	26–33	12784563	③	Damper	450	150
1955	40	N-12	AC 44-5	.032	.016	26–33	12784563	③	Pulley	450	140
	50, 60, 70	N-12	AC 44-5	.032	.016	26–33	12784563	③	Damper	450	155
1956	All	N-12	AC 44	.032	.016	26–33	12784563	③	Damper	450	170
1957	All	N-12	AC 44	.032	⑤	30	12784563	③	Damper	485⑦	⑥
1958	All	N-12	AC-44	.032	⑤	30	12784563	⑧	Damper	485⑦	⑥
1959–60	All	N-12	AC 44S	.032	⑤	30	12784563	12°BTDC④	Damper	485⑦	⑥
1961	All	N-12	AC-44S	.032	⑤	30	12784563	12°BTC	Damper	500	180

①—V8 cylinder numbering (front to rear): Right bank 1–3–5–7, left bank 2–4–6–8.

②—Flywheel tooth painted yellow and stamped "5".

③—Yellow timing mark aligned with "5" on timing indicator.

④—With synchromesh trans. 5° BTDC.

⑤—Turn adjusting screw in (clockwise) until engine misfires. Then turn screw ½ turn in opposite direction.

⑥—Automatic trans. 180, synchromesh 150.

⑦—With air conditioning 550 RPM.

⑧—For distributor 1110870 5°BTC; distributor 1110934 12°BTC.

GENERATOR AND REGULATOR SPECIFICATIONS

★To polarize generator, reconnect the leads to the regulator; then momentarily connect a jumper wire from the "Gen" to the "Bat" terminals of the regulator.

Year	Generator Number	Rotation and Ground Polarity ①	Rated Cap. Amps.	Gen. Field Ground Location★	Brush Spring Tension, Ounces	Field Current Amperes	Regulator Number	Cutout Relay Voltage to Close Points	Cutout Relay Armature Air Gap, Inch	Voltage Regulator Setting Volts	Current Regulator Setting Amperes	Current and Voltage Armature Air Gap, Inch
1953 6-Vt	1102798	C-N	45	External	28	1.87–2.0②	1118729	6.3	.020	7.1	44	.075
1953 12-Vt	1102003	C-N	30	External	28	1.48–1.62③	1118825	12.6	.020	14.3	30	.075
1954–55	1102008	C-N	30	External	28	1.48–1.62③	1118825	12.6	.020	14.3	30	.075
1956	1102008	C-N	30	External	28	1.48–1.62③	1119003	12.6	.020	14.3	30	.075
	1102053	C-N	35	External	28	1.62–1.82③	1119162	12.6	.020	14.3	34	.075
	1102051	C-N	35	External	28	1.62–1.82③	1119162	12.6	.020	14.3	34	.075
1957	1102066	C-N	35	External	28	1.62–1.82③	1119168	12.4	.020	14.2	35	.075
1958	1102101	C-N	45	External	28	2.66–2.86③	1119600	12.4	.020	14.2④	41	.075⑤
1959	1102147	C-N	35	External	28	1.69–1.79③	1119242	12.3	.020	14.3	35	.075
	1102138	C-N	45	External	28	2.66–2.86③	1119617	12.4	.020	14.2④	45	.075⑤
1960–61	1102181	C-N	35	External	28	1.69–1.79③	1119242	12.3	.020	14.3	35	.075
	1102215	C-N	45	External	28	2.66–2.86③	1119617	12.4	.020	14.2④	45	.075⑤

①—C-Clockwise. N-Negative.   ②—At 6 volts.   ③—At 12 volts.

④—Lower contact setting .1 to .3 volt lower.

⑤—Voltage regulator contact opening: upper .016", lower .067".

VALVE SPECIFICATIONS

Year	Model	Valve Lash		Valve Angles		Valve Spring Installed Height	Valve Spring Pressure Lbs. @ In.	Valve Lift		Stem Clearance		Stem Diameter	
		Int.	Exh.	Seat	Face			Int.	Exh.	Intake	Exhaust	Int.	Exh.
1953	40①	.015H	.015H	45	45	1¹⁵⁄₁₆②	77 @ 1¹⁹⁄₃₂②	.348	.342	.0015-.0035	.002-.004	.3720	.3715
	40③	Zero	Zero	45	45	1¹⁵⁄₁₆②	100 @ 1¹⁹⁄₃₂②	.348	.342	.0015-.0035	.002-.004	.3720	.3715
	50, 70	Zero	Zero	45	45	1½②	88 @ 1⅛②	.378	.350	.0015-.0035	.002-.004	.3720	.3715
1954	40	Zero	Zero	45	45	1½②	88 @ 1⅛②	.358	.350	.0015-.0035	.002-.004	.3720	.3715
	60, 70	Zero	Zero	45	45	1½②	88 @ 1⅛②	.378	.350	.0015-.0035	.002-.004	.3720	.3715
1955	40	Zero	Zero	45	45	1½②	88 @ 1⅛②	.358	.350	.0015-.0035	.002-.004	.3720	.3715
	60, 70	Zero	Zero	45	45	1½②	88 @ 1⅛②	.378	.350	.0015-.0035	.002-.004	.3720	.3715
1956	All	Zero	Zero	45	45	1½②	94 @ 1⅛②	.378	.378	.002-.003	.003-.004	.3720	.3715
1957	All	Zero	Zero	45	45	1½②	96 @ 1⅛②	.423	.423	.002-.003	.003-.004	.3720	.3715
1958	Auto. Tr.	Zero	Zero	45	45	1½②	96 @ 1⅛②	.423	.423	.0015-.0035	.003-.005	.3720	.3715
	Std. Tr.	Zero	Zero	45	45	1½②	96 @ 1⅛②	.378	.378	.0015-.0035	.003-.005	.3720	.3715
1959	4400	Zero	Zero	45	45	1¹¹⁄₁₆②	96 @ 1⁵⁄₃₂②	.403	.403	.0015-.0035	.003-.005	.3725	.3710
	Others	Zero	Zero	45	45	1¹¹⁄₁₆②	96 @ 1⁵⁄₃₂②	.438	.441	.0015-.0035	.003-.005	.3725	.3710
1960-61	4400	Zero	Zero	45	45	1¹⁹⁄₃₂②	96 @ 1⁵⁄₃₂②	.443④	.439④	⑤	⑥	⑦	⑧
	Others	Zero	Zero	45	45	1¹⁹⁄₃₂②	96 @ 1⁵⁄₃₂②	.439	.441	⑤	⑥	⑦	⑧

①—Mechanical valve lifters.
②—Outer spring.
③—Hydraulic valve lifters.
④—Manual shift transmission .403″.

⑤—Top .001-.003″, bottom .0025-.0045″.
⑥—Top .002-.004″, bottom .0035-.0055″.
⑦—Top .373″, bottom .3715″.
⑧—Top .372″, bottom .3705″.

PISTONS, PINS, RINGS, CRANKSHAFT & BEARINGS

Year	Model	Fitting Pistons		Ring End Gap ①		Wrist-pin Diameter	Rod Bearings		Main Bearings		Thrust on Bear. No.	Shaft End Play
		Shim To Use	Pounds Pull On Scale	Comp.	Oil		Shaft Diameter	Bearing Clearance	Shaft Diameter	Bearing Clearance		
1953	40	②	②	.010	.010③	.8126	2.125-2.126	.0005-.002	2.5625-2.5635	.0005-.002	3	.004-.008
	50, 70	.003	7-13	.010	.010③	.940	2.249-2.250	.0002-.002	2.498-2.499	.0005-.003	3	.004-.008
1954	All	.003	7-13	.010	.015③	.940	2.249-2.250	.0002-.002	2.498-2.499	.0005-.003	5	.004-.008
1955	All	.003	7-13	.010	.015	.940	2.249-2.250	.0002-.002	2.498-2.499	.0005-.003	5	.004-.008
1956	All	.003	7-13	.010	.015	.940	2.249-2.250	.0002-.002	2.498-2.499	.0005-.0025	5	.004-.008
1957	All	.003	7-13	.010	.015	.9995	2.249-2.250	.0002-.002	2.498-2.499	.0005-.0025	5	.004-.008
1958	All	.003	7-13	.015	.015	.9995	2.249-2.250	.0002-.0023	2.498-2.499	.0005-.0025	5	.004-.008
1959-61	Le Sabre	.003	7-13	.015	.015	.9995	2.249-2.250	.0002-.0023	2.498-2.499	.0005-.0021	5	.004-.008
	Others	.003	7-13	.015	.015	.9995	2.249-2.250	.0002-.0023	2.498-2.499	.0005-.0021	3	.004-.008

①—Fit rings in tapered bores for clearance given in tightest portion of ring travel.
②—Piston should fall of its own weight on a .0015″ feeler and hold on a .002″ feeler.
③—No checking or fitting is required on Flex-Fit oil rings.

ENGINE TIGHTENING SPECIFICATIONS★

★Torque specifications are for clean and lightly lubricated threads only. Dry or dirty threads produce increased friction which prevents accurate measurement of tightness.

Year	Spark Plugs Ft. Lbs.	Cylinder Head Bolts Ft. Lbs.	Intake Manifold Ft. Lbs.	Exhaust Manifold Ft. Lbs.	Rocker Arm Shaft Bracket Ft. Lbs.	Rocker Arm Cover Ft. Lbs.	Connecting Rod Cap Bolts Ft. Lbs.	Main Bearing Cap Bolts Ft. Lbs.	Flywheel to Crankshaft Ft. Lbs.	Vibration Damper or Pulley Ft. Lbs.
1953-55	22-28	65-75	25-30	10-15	30-35	4-6	40-45	100-110	50-55	100-110
1956	22-28	65-75	25-30	10-15	30-35	4-5	40-45	100-110	50-55	55-65
1957-58	22-28	65-75	25-30	10-15	30-35	4-6	40-45	100-110	50-60	100-110
1959-61	25-30	65-75	25-30	10-15	30-35	4-6	40-45	100-110	50-60	200-220

COOLING SYSTEM & CAPACITY DATA

| Year and Model | Cooling System Data | | | | | Fuel Tank Gals. | Engine Oil | | | Transmissions | | | Rear Axle Pints |
	Quarts No Heater	Quarts With Heater	Rad. Cap Relief Pressure	Thermostat Opening Temp. ①	②		Refill Qts.③	Summer Grade	Winter Grade	Std. Pints	With Over-drive Pints	Auto-matic Qts.	
1953 40	12④	13½⑨	7	180	160	19	5½	20W	10W	1⅜	None	10	4
1953 50	16½⑤	18⑩	7	180	160	19	6	20W	10W	2½	None	10	4
1953 70	18	19½	7	180	160	19	6	20W	10W	None	None	10	4
1954-55, 40	16½⑦	18½⑧	7	180	160	19	6	20W	10W	1¾	None	10	4½
1954-55 50, 60	16½⑦	18½⑧	7	180	160	19	6	20W	10W	2½	None	10	4½
1954-55 70	18½	20	7	180	160	19	6	20W	10W	None	None	10	4½
1956 All	17½	19	7⑥	180	160	19	6	20W	10W	2½	None	10½	6
1957 All	16½	18	13	180	160	20	5	20W	10W	2½	None	11	6
1958 All	16½	19	15	180	160	20	5	20W	10W	2½	None	11⑪	6
1959 Le Sabre	16.5	19	15	180	170	20	4	20W	10W	2½	None	12	6½
1959 Exc. LeSabre	16.5	19	15	180	170	20	4	20W	10W	None	None	12	6½
1960 LeSabre	16.5	18.5	15	180	170	20	4	20W	10W	2½	None	12	6½
1960 Exc. LeSabre	16.5	18.5	15	180	170	20	4	20W	10W	None	None	12	6½
1961 All	17	18½	15	170	—	20	4	20W	10W	None	None	14	6½

①—For permanent type anti-freeze.
②—For alcohol type anti-freeze.
③—Add one quart with filter change.
④—Dynaflow 13½ qts.
⑤—Dynaflow 18 qts.
⑥—13 lbs. with Air Conditioning.
⑦—Dynaflow 18½ qts.
⑧—Dynaflow 20 qts.
⑨—Dynaflow 15 qts.
⑩—Dynaflow 19½ qts.
⑪—Flight Pitch Dynaflow 12½ qts.

DISTRIBUTOR SPECIFICATIONS

| Car and Model | Part No. ① | Rota-tion ② | Cam Angle, Degrees | Breaker Point Opening, Inch | Con-denser Capac-ity, Mfds.③ | Breaker Arm Spring Tension, Ounces | Centrifugal Advance Data Degrees @ R.P.M. of Dist. | | Vacuum Advance Data | | |
							Advance Starts	Full Advance	Inches of Vacuum to Start Plunger Movement	Inches of Vacuum for Full Plunger Travel	Maximum Vacuum Advance, Dist. Degrees
1953, 40	1110838	CC	26-33④	.016	.18-.23	19-23	1 @ 350	12 @ 2000	5-7	13	10
1953 V8	1110827	C	26-33④	.016	.18-.23	19-23	1 @ 350	14 @ 2000	5-7	11-14	11-12½
1954-55	1110849	C	26-33④	.016	.18-.23	19-23	1 @ 375	12 @ 1750	6.5-8.5	12-14	9-10½
1956	1110861	C	26-33④	.016	.18-.23	19-23	1 @ 375	12 @ 1750	6.5-8.5	12-14	9-10½
1957-58	1110870	C	30	⑤	.18-.23	19-23	1 @ 475	13 @ 1875	6.5-8.5	12-14	9-10½
1958	1110934	C	30	⑤	.18-.23	19-23	1 @ 850	10 @ 1925	6.5-8.5	12-14	9-10½
1959	1110936	C	30	⑤	.18-.23	19-23	1 @ 850	10 @ 1925	6.5-8.5	12-14	9-10½
	1110949	C	30	⑤	.18-.23	19-23	1 @ 475	13 @ 1875	6.5-8.5	12-14	9-10½
1960-61	1110961	C	30	⑤	.18-.23	19-23	1 @ 450	10 @ 1900	8-10	16-18	7-9
	1110962	C	30	⑤	.18-.23	19-23	1 @ 450	10 @ 1900	6.5-8.5	12-14	9-10½
	1110963	C	30	⑤	.18-.23	19-23	1 @ 475	13 @ 1875	6.5-8.5	12-14	9-10½

①—Distributor number stamped on plate riveted to side of housing.
②—As viewed from the top. C—Clockwise. CC—Counter-clockwise.
③—Microfarads—as indicated on a condenser tester.
④—Buick does not recommend use of dwell meter for setting point opening.
⑤—Turn adjusting screw in (clockwise) until engine misfires. Then turn screw ½ turn in opposite direction.

STARTING MOTOR SPECIFICATIONS

Year	Model	Part No.	Rotation ①	Brush Spring Tension, Ounces	No Load Test			Torque Test		
					Amperes	Volts	R.P.M.	Amperes	Volts	Torque, Lbs. Ft.
1953 6 Vt.	40	1107110	C	24 Min.	70	5.65	5500	550	3.25	11
1953 12 Vt.	50, 70	1107601	C	24 Min.	75	10.3	6500	520	4.9	11
1954–55	All	1107621	C	35 Min.	95	10.1	3500	470	5.4	10.5
1956	All	1107646	C	35 Min.	95	10.1	3500	470	5.4	10.5
1957-58	All	1107667	C	35 Min.	100	10.6	5100	330	3.5	②
1959	364 Eng.	1107724	C	35 Min.	65–100	10.6	3600–5100	300–360	3.5	②
	401 Eng.	1107739	C	35 Min.	80–120	10.6	4700–5400	290–370	2.0	②
1960	364 Eng.	1107783	C	35 Min.	65–100	10.6	3600–5100	300–600	3.5	②
	401 Eng.	1107773	C	35 Min.	80–120	10.6	3900–5400	290–370	2.0	②
	401 Eng.	1107784	C	35 Min.	80–120	10.6	3900–5400	290–370	2.0	②
1961	364 Eng.	1107800	C	35 Min.	100	10.6	3600	300–360	3.5	②
	401 Eng.	1107876	C	35 Min.	120	10.6	4700	290–370	2.0	②

C—Clockwise. ①—As viewed from drive end. ②—Armature locked.

REAR AXLE AND BRAKE CYLINDER SPECIFICATIONS

Year	Model	Ring Gear & Pinion Backlash, Inch	Drive Pinion Adjustment	Drive Pinion Bearing Preload, Inch Lbs.	Drive Pinion Bearing Adjustment	Axle Shaft End Play, Inch	Hydraulic Cylinder Bore Sizes, Inch		
							Wheel Cylinder		Master Cylinder
							Front	Rear	
1953–55	All	.008–.012	Shims	④	None	.000–.008	1⅛	1	1
1956	All	.007–.009	Shims	10–30	Spacers	①	1⅛	1	②
1957–58	All	.007–.009	Shims	10–30	Spacers	①	1⅛	1	③
1959–61	All	.007–.009	Shim	10–30	Shim	①	1⅛	1	1

①—Wheel bearing retainer positioning, .005–.020″ crush on bearing outer race, obtained by use of shims.
②—Standard 1 17/32″, power brake 21/32″.
③—Standard 1″, power brake 21/32″.
④—Tighten adjuster 2–3 notches from the "free position".

WHEEL ALIGNMENT SPECIFICATIONS

Year	Model	Caster, Degrees		Camber, Degrees		Toe-In, Inch	Toe-Out On Turns, Degrees		Kingpin Angle, Degrees② Theoretical
		Limits	Desired	Limits	Desired		Outer Wheel	Inner Wheel①	
1953	All	− ½ to + ¾	0	− ⅝ to + ⅞	+ ⅜	1/16 to ⅛	20	20¾ to 22½	4¼ @ ⅜ Camber
1954–55	All	− ¾ to + ½	− ⅛	− ⅝ to + ⅞	+ ⅜	0 to 1/16	20	21¾ to 23¼	0 @ ⅞ Camber
1956	All	− 1½ to + ½	− ½	− ⅝ to + ⅞	+ ⅜	1/16 to ⅛	20	21¾ to 23¼	7 @ ⅞ Camber
1957	Manual Steering	− ¼ to − 2¾	− 1¾	− ½ to + 1	+ ½	1/16 to ⅛	20	23	8 @ 0 Camber
	Power Steering	− ¼ to − 2¾	− 1¾	− ½ to + 1	+ ½	1/16 to ⅛	20	21¾	8 @ 0 Camber
1958	Manual Steering	− 1¾ to + ¾	− ½	− ½ to + 1	+ ½	1/16 to ⅛	20	22° 55′	7° @ 50′ Camber
	Power Steering	− 1¾ to + ¾	− ½	− ½ to + 1	+ ½	1/16 to ⅛	20	22° 50′	7° @ 50′ Camber
1959	Manual Steering	− ½ to − 2½	− 1½	− ½ to + 1	+ ½	1/16 to 5/32	20	23	7° @ 50′ Camber
	Power Steering	− ½ to − 2½	− 1½	− ½ to + 1	+ ½	1/16 to 5/32	20	22	7° @ 50′ Camber
1960	Manual Steering	− 1¼ to − 2¾	− 2	− ½ to + 1	+ ½	1/16 to 5/32	20	23	7° @ ¾° Camber
	Power Steering	− 1¼ to − 2¾	− 2	− ½ to + 1	+ ½	1/16 to 5/32	20	22	7° @ ¾° Camber
1961	Manual Steering	− ½ to − 1½	− 1	0 to + ¾	+ ⅜	3/16 to ¼	20	22½	10° @ ⅚° Camber
	Power Steering	− ½ to − 1½	− 1	0 to + ¾	+ ⅜	3/16 to ¼	20	22½	10° @ ⅚° Camber

①—Incorrect toe-out, when other adjustments are correct, generally indicates bent steering arms.
②—Incorrect kingpin angle with correct camber indicates bent suspension arms or steering knuckle support.

SERIAL NUMBER LOCATION
Plate On Left Front Door Pillar

ENGINE NUMBER LOCATION
1953 Ser. 40: Right Side Of Engine
1953 Ser. 50, 70: Left Bank Cylinder Block
1954-56: Left Bank Cylinder Block
1957-61: Extension On Left Cylinder Block
Forward Of Valve Lifter Cover

1957

1953

1958

1954

1959

1955

1960

1956

1961

Engine Section

ENGINE, REPLACE

1. Drain cooling system and remove radiator.
2. Disconnect linkage at transmission and clutch (if equipped).
3. Remove transmission.
4. Remove hood and battery.
5. Disconnect exhaust pipes from manifolds.
6. Disconnect usual items under hood such as fuel lines, radiator hoses, wires, etc.
7. If equipped with an oil cooler, disconnect cooler lines.
8. If engine lifting fixture is used, remove carburetor after disconnecting automatic choke tube and fuel lines as mentioned above.
9. Attach engine lifting fixture to carburetor flange studs on intake manifold.
10. Remove engine mounting bolts and lift engine from chassis.
11. To install, reverse foregoing procedure.

CYLINDER HEADS

1. Drain cooling system.
2. Remove air cleaner and disconnect all pipes from carburetor and intake manifold.
3. Disconnect wires from accelerator vacuum switch and remove throttle return spring.
4. Remove resistance unit (1954-57), ignition coil and equalizer shaft bracket from engine.
5. Take off intake manifold and carburetor as an assembly.
6. When removing *right* cylinder head, remove generator mounting bracket, and air conditioning compressor (if equipped), exercising precautions outlined in the *Air Conditioning* chapter.
7. When removing *left* cylinder head, disconnect temperature gauge tube, remove power steering gear pump with mounting bracket (if equipped) and move it out of the way with hoses attached.
8. Remove spark plug cover and disconnect wires from plugs.
9. Disconnect water manifold from both cylinder heads and disconnect exhaust manifold from head to be removed.
10. With air hose and cloths, clean dirt off cylinder head and adjacent area to avoid getting dirt into engine, and *particularly into the hydraulic valve lifters.*
11. Remove rocker arm cover and rocker arm and shaft assembly.
12. Lift out push rods. *On 1957-61 models, due to close tolerance in the engine compartment it is necessary to leave some of the bolts and push rods in the head during removal. The push rods should be pulled up and taped in position while cylinder is being removed. The same parts must be in the head during installation.*
13. Remove cylinder head attaching bolts and lift off head.
14. Installation is made in the reverse order of removal. Tighten head bolts in the sequence shown in Fig. 1 and to the torque given in the *Tune Up Specifications* chart.

ROCKER ARMS

1. To disassemble, remove cotter pin, flat washer and spring washer from each end of the rocker arm shaft and remove bolts from brackets. Remove rocker arms, springs and brackets from shaft.
2. Clean and inspect all parts and re-place those that are excessively worn.
3. Assemble springs, rocker arms and brackets on shaft, Fig. 2. Note that the long spring is at the middle of the shaft, the valve ends of all rock-

Cross section of V8 engine

Fig. 1 Cylinder head bolt tightening sequence

V8 Engine lubrication

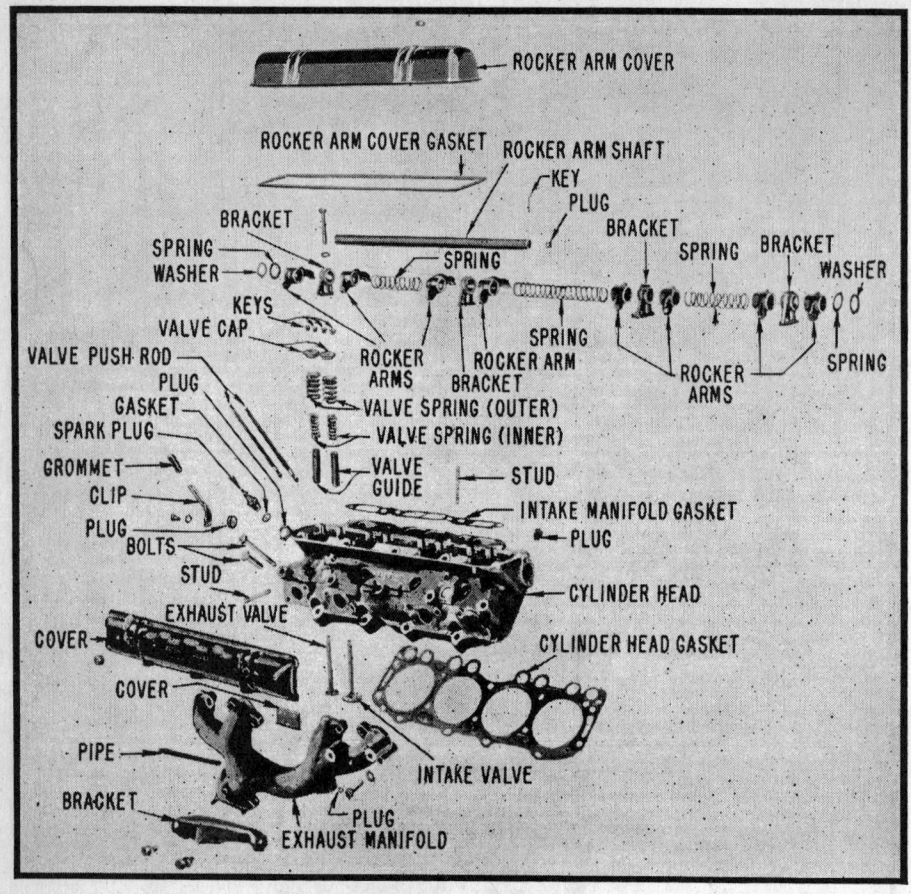

Layout of cylinder head and related parts

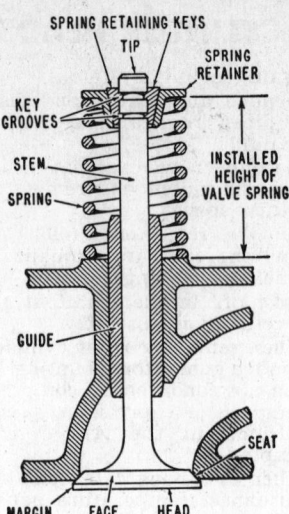

Fig. 2A Checking installed height of valve spring

er arms slant toward middle of shaft, and a bracket is located between each pair of rocker arms.

4. Install spring washer, flat washer and cotter pin on each end of the shaft in the order named.

5. Install bolts with plain washers through brackets and shaft so that the notch on one end of the shaft is *upward* in line with bolt heads. This places the oil holes on lower side of shaft in proper relationship to rocker arms.

VALVE ARRANGEMENT
Front to Rear

V8's .... E-I-E-I-I-E-I-E

VALVES, GRIND

After removing valves and springs from cylinder head, scrape all carbon from combustion chambers and valves. If wire brushes are used for cleaning carbon, use care to avoid scratching valve seats and valve faces. Clean all carbon and gum deposits from valve guides.

In refacing valves, take off only the minimum of metal required to clean up the valve faces. If the outer edge of the valve becomes too thin or sharp due to excessive grinding the valve must be replaced. In other words the valve head margin must be at least $\frac{3}{64}$", otherwise the valve must be replaced. This margin is the area above the contact surface of the valve face, Fig. 2A.

Inspect the valve seats in the head for cracks, burns, pitting, ridges or improper angle. During any general engine overhaul it is advisable to reface the valve seats regardless of their condition. If new valve guides are required, they must be installed and reamed before refacing the seats if the equipment used for refacing them has a valve guide pilot.

Reface valves and true up seats to 45 degrees. Cutting a valve seat results in

Fig. 3 Special equipment for removing and installing valve guides

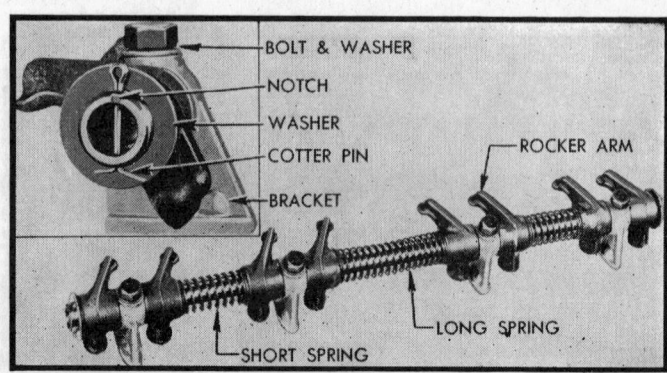

Fig. 2 Rocker arm and shaft assembly

lowering the valve spring pressure and increases the width of the seat. The nominal width of a valve seat is $\frac{3}{64}''$ to $\frac{5}{64}''$ ($\frac{1}{16}''$ average). If valve seat is over $\frac{5}{64}''$ after truing up, it should be narrowed to specified width by using the proper 20 and 70 degree cutters.

Improper hydraulic valve lifter operation may result if valve and seat have been refinished enough to allow the end of the valve stem to raise approximately .050" above normal position. In this case it will be necessary to grind off the end of the valve stem or replace parts.

Test valves for concentricity with seats and for tight seating. Valves can be tested by lightly coating the valve face with prussian blue and turning the valve against its seat. This indicates whether the seat is concentric with the valve guide *but does not prove that the valve face is concentric with the valve stem, or that the valve is seating all around.* After making this test, wash all blue from the surfaces, lightly coat the *valve seat* with blue and repeat the test to see whether a full mark is obtained on the valve. *Both tests are necessary to prove that a proper seat is being obtained.*

VALVE SPRING INSTALLED HEIGHT

When valves and seats are reground the position of the valve in the head is changed so as to lessen the valve spring tension. Without proper valve spring tension the valve does not seat long enough or it may not seat completely. Since the valve is cooled by transferring heat from the valve head to the seat and thence to the coolant, improper valve spring tension will cause worn, pitted and distorted valves which result in loss of compression and power as well as poor gasoline mileage.

When valves, springs, retainers and locks are installed, measure the assembled height of the valve springs from the surface of the cylinder head spring pad to the underside of the spring retainer as shown in Fig 2A. If the assembled height is greater than the dimension given in the *Valve Specification Chart,* install a spacer or shim of proper thickness between cylinder head spring pad and spring to bring the assembled height to specifications.

Do not install spacers unless necessary. Excessive use of spacers will result in overstressing valve springs and overloading camshaft lobes which could lead to spring breakage and worn camshaft lobes.

VALVE SPRING TESTING

Wash all valve springs with a suitable solvent. Examine the springs for damage or corrosion due to acid etching, which will develop into surface cracks and cause spring failure.

Check the valve spring tension on a spring testing fixture if one is available. If a fixture is not available, at least check the free length of each spring by standing it alongside a new spring. Any spring that does not conform to

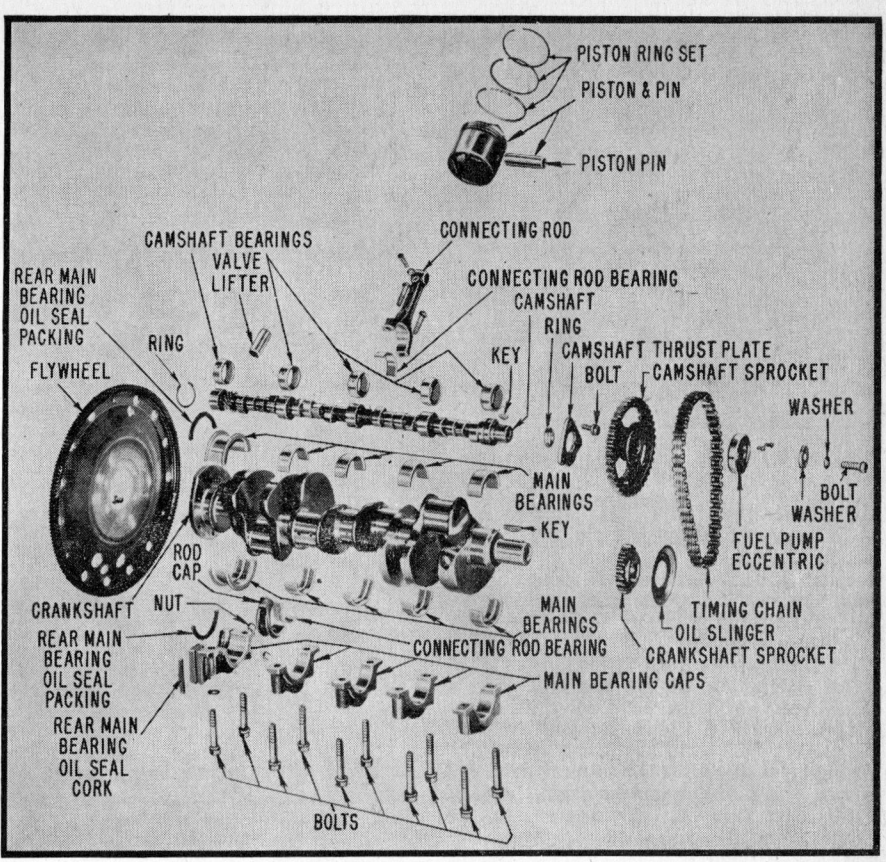

Layout of internal engine parts

the pressure specifications in the *Valve Specifications* table within 10 per cent should be replaced. Likewise any spring that stands shorter than the new spring used for comparison should be discarded.

VALVE GUIDES

Clean the valve guides with a wire guide brush and check the clearance between valve stems and guides carefully. The standard clearances are given in the *Valve Specifications* table.

Excessive clearance between valve stems and guides will cause improper seating and burned valves. When there is too much clearance between intake valve stems and guides, there is a tendency to draw oil vapor through the guide on the suction stroke, causing excessive oil consumption, fouled spark plugs and poor low speed performance.

To check valve stem-to-guide clearance, take a new valve and place it in each valve guide and feel the clearance by moving the valve stem from side to side. If this check shows excessive clearance, it will be necessary to replace the valve guide.

If the clearance is not excessive when checking with a new valve but is excessive when checked with the old valve, the old valve stem is worn and a new valve must be installed.

If it is necessary to replace valve guides, use a suitable driver to drive them out of the cylinder head. Fig. 3 shows the equipment designed for re-

moving and installing V8 valve guides. If suitable tools are not available, guides can be pulled out by using a piece of pipe together with a long bolt and washers.

Before removing guides, carefully measure the portion of the guide that protrudes from the cylinder head and install the new guides accordingly.

After the new guides have been installed, they should be reamed to provide the clearance given in the *Valve Specifications* table.

HYDRAULIC VALVE LIFTERS

Failure of an hydraulic valve lifter, Figs. 4 and 5, is generally caused by an inadequate oil supply or dirt. An air leak at the intake side of the oil pump or too much oil in the engine will cause air bubbles in the oil supply to the lifters, causing them to collapse. This is a probable cause of trouble if several lifters fail to function, but air in the oil is an unlikely cause of failure of a single unit.

The valve lifters may be lifted out of their bores after removing the rocker arms and push rods. Adjustable pliers with taped jaws may be used to remove lifters that are stuck due to varnish, carbon, etc.

To disassemble, press down on the center of the push rod cup. Using a pointed tool, remove lock wire from the groove while holding cup down. Invert lifter and slide out push rod cup, plunger, ball retainer and spring.

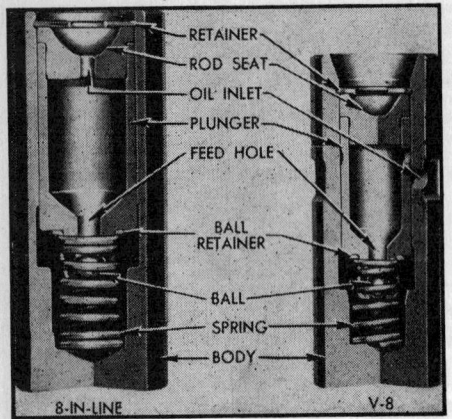

Fig. 4 Hydraulic valve lifters. 1953-55

To assemble, place the ball on its seat in the lower end of the plunger while holding the plunger upside down. Position the ball retainer and spring over ball and end of plunger. Lower the body over the plunger. Turn the assembly right side up and fill the plunger with clean engine oil. Jiggle the ball with a small piece of wire until oil drains out of plunger into the body and trapped air is released from the body. Refill the plunger with oil, place the push rod cup on the plunger and position the lock wire over the cup, locking it in its groove, Fig. 6.

TIMING CHAIN & COVER

1. To remove the timing chain, drain cooling system, then remove radiator, shroud, fan belt, fan and pulley, and vibration damper.
2. Remove all bolts that attach timing chain cover and water manifold to engine. *Do not remove five small bolts attaching water pump to chain cover.* Remove cover and manifold, using care to avoid damaging oil pan gasket.
3. Remove oil slinger from crankshaft and remove bolt, lockwasher and plain washer that attaches fuel pump operating eccentric and camshaft sprocket to camshaft.
4. If there has been doubt about the valve timing, turn the crankshaft until the camshaft sprocket keyway is straight down toward the crankshaft and the timing marks on both sprockets are as shown in Figs. 7 and 8.
5. Using two large screwdrivers, alternately work the sprockets outward until the camshaft sprocket is free of the camshaft. Remove this sprocket and chain, then remove the other sprocket from the crankshaft.
6. Thoroughly clean all sludge from cover and front face of crankcase. Inspect crankshaft oil seal in chain cover and replace if worn, Fig. 9.
7. When ready to install the chain, turn crankshaft until Nos. 1 and 4 pistons are on top dead center. Turn camshaft so that sprocket key points straight down toward crankshaft.
8. Place timing chain over sprockets so that timing marks are located as shown in Figs. 7 and 8. Install sprockets with chain on the two shafts.
9. Install fuel pump eccentric and oil slinger. Then complete the installation in the reverse order of parts removal.

VALVE TIMING DATA

Year	Model	Intake Opens①	Intake Closes②	Exhaust Opens③	Exhaust Closes④
1953	40⑤	13	68	55	22
	40⑥	14	71	56	25
	50, 70	25	77	70	42
1954	40	25	67	70	42
	Others	25	77	70	42
1955	40	25	67	70	42
	50, 60	25	77	70	42
	70	28	79	75	42
1956	40⑦	25	77	75	42
	40⑧	30	82	78	44
	Others	30	82	78	44
1957	40	25	77	65	37
	Others	34	83	76	41
1958	40⑦	25	77	65	37
	40⑧	34	83	76	41
	Others	34	83	76	41
1959	4400⑦	25	77	65	37
	4400⑧	35	73	73	37
	Others	33	77	75	44
1960	4400⑦	25	77	65	37
	4400⑧	35	73	73	37
	Others	33	77	75	44
1961	4400	31	77	69	41
	Others	33	77	75	44

① — Degrees before top dead center.
② — Degrees after bottom dead center.
③ — Degrees before bottom dead center.
④ — Degrees after top dead center.
⑤ — With mechanical valve lifters.
⑥ — With hydraulic valve lifters.
⑦ — With manual shift transmission.
⑧ — With automatic transmission.

CAMSHAFT & BEARINGS

The camshaft is supported in five steel-backed babbitt-lined bearings which are pressed into the block. The bearings must be line-reamed to size after being pressed into place. Since this operation requires special reaming equipment the original bearings should be retained unless severely damaged.

Slightly scored camshaft bearings will be satisfactory if the surface of the camshaft journals are polished and bearings are cleaned up to remove burrs, and the fit of the bearings is free.

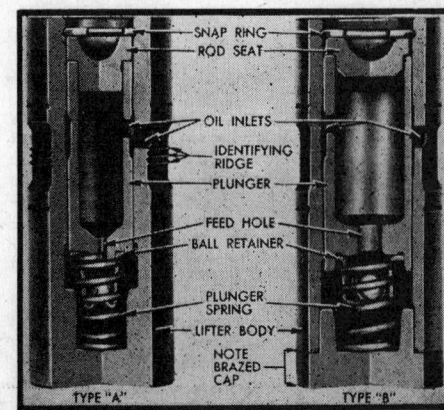

Fig. 5 Hydraulic valve lifters. 1956-61

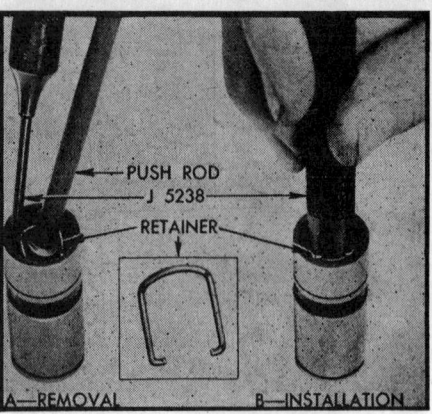

Fig. 6 Servicing V8 hydraulic valve lifters

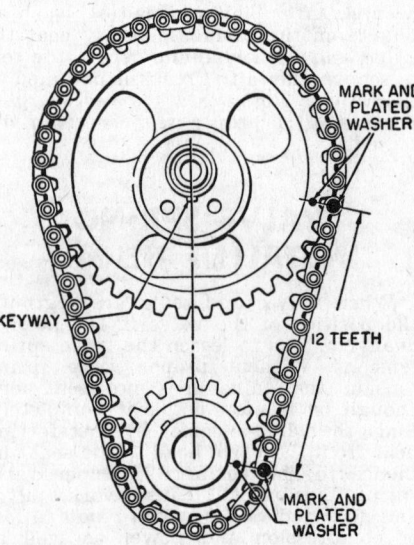

Fig. 7 Valve timing. 1953-56 V8

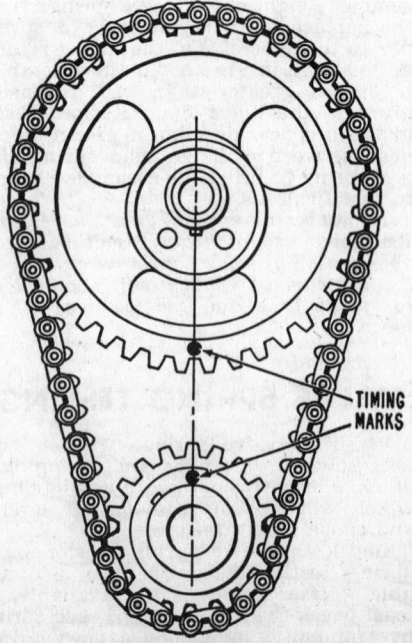

Fig. 8 Valve timing. 1957-61

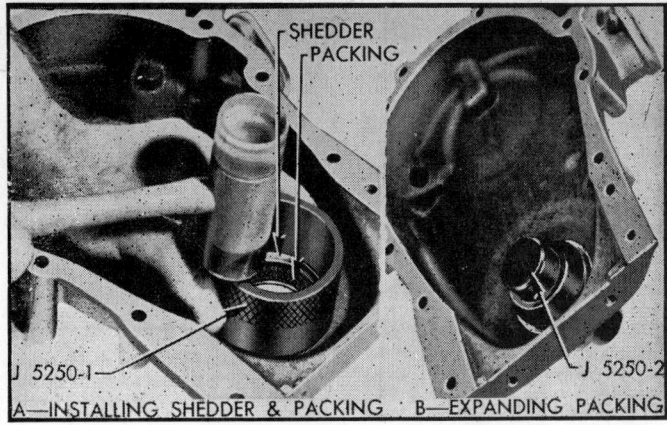

Fig. 9   Installing timing chain cover oil seal

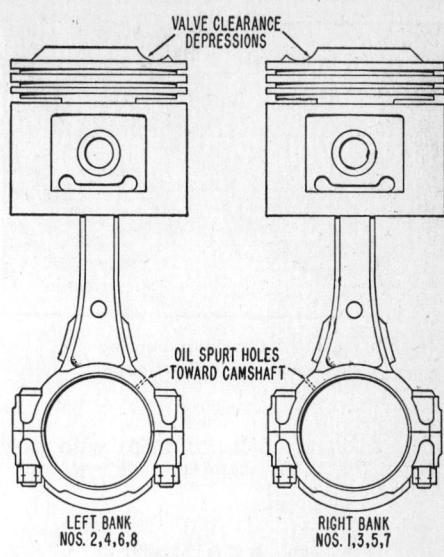

Fig. 11   Piston and rod assembly. 1956-61

PISTONS & RODS, REMOVE

After removing the cylinder head, examine the cylinder bores above the ring travel area. If bores are worn so that a shoulder or ridge exists at this point, remove the ridge with a ridge reamer to avoid damaging rings or cracking ring lands of pistons during removal.

Remove connecting rod caps and push pistons and rods out of cylinders, using care to prevent rod bolts from contacting and nicking crankshaft journals.

Make sure the rods and pistons are properly numbered so that they can be reinstalled in original locations. It is advisable to install caps on rods to avoid mixing parts.

PISTONS & RODS, ASSEMBLE

Rods and pistons should be assembled and installed as shown in Figs. 10 and 11.

PISTONS

Standard size Buick service pistons are high limit or maximum diameter; therefore, they can usually be used with a slight amount of honing to correct slight scoring or excessive clearances in engines having relatively low mileage. Service pistons are also furnished in .001, .005, .010, .020 and .030 inch oversizes.

If the pistons are to be reused with new rings, remove the carbon from the ring grooves. A special tool is available for this work but a satisfactory job can be done by breaking an old piston ring, filing the broken end to a sharp, square edge and using it to scrape out the carbon. Soak the piston in cleaning solvent to loosen any carbon residue. Clean out the loosened carbon, being careful not to cut away any piston material.

Clean out the oil return holes with a drill just large enough to fill the holes. Hold the drill in a tap wrench and make sure the drill does not remove any metal from the piston.

Rinse the piston in solvent and wipe off the carbon on the sides of the piston. *Never use a wire brush to clean a piston*

as the brush will round off the edges of the ring lands. Pistons showing scuffed or scored skirts should be scrapped. Examine the ring lands carefully for cracks. If the piston is in the least bit doubtful, it should be discarded.

PISTON RINGS

When new piston rings are installed without reboring cylinders, the glazed cylinder walls should be slightly dulled, but without increasing the bore diameter. This is done with a "Glazebuster" or with a hone equipped with the finest grade of stones.

New piston rings must be checked for clearance in piston grooves and for gap in cylinder bores. Cylinder bores and piston grooves must be clean, dry and free of carbon and burrs.

Check the clearance of each ring in its piston groove by installing the ring and then inserting feeler gauges *under* the ring. Any wear that occurs in the piston groove forms a step or ridge at the inner portion of the lower land. If gauges are inserted above the ring, the

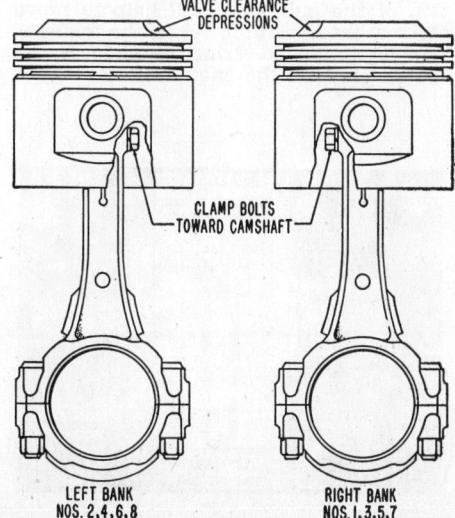

Fig. 10   Piston and rod assembly. 1953-55

ring may rest on the step instead of on the worn portion of the lower land, and a false measurement of clearance will result.

If the piston grooves have worn to the extent that relatively high steps or ridges exist on the lower lands, the piston should be replaced because the steps will interfere with the operation of new rings and the ring clearances will be excessive. Piston rings are not furnished in oversize widths to compensate for ring groove wear.

See the *Piston and Ring Data* chart for end gap clearances.

To check the end gaps of rings, place the ring in the cylinder in which it will be used. Square it in the body by tapping with the lower end of the piston, then measure the gap with feeler gauges. If necessary to increase the gap, file the ends of rings carefully with a smooth file.

PISTON PINS

Piston pins are fitted with a clearance of from .0003" to .0004" at approximately 70 degrees F., which is equivalent to an easy finger push at that temperature.

All service pistons are diamond bored at the pin holes and are fitted with pins. When piston fits are found to be too tight or too loose, new piston and pin assemblies will have to be installed. Slight tightness on new pistons will correct itself as mileage builds up.

Note — Sometimes pins will be found tight due to varnish or other accumulation from lubricants. Removing this accumulation will usually correct the fit. Pistons which have been scored, even though the score is slight, may have tight pins due to the two piston pin bosses being pulled out of alignment with each other.

Caution—To prevent the possibility of wristpin distortion, with a consequent binding in the piston, do not tighten the

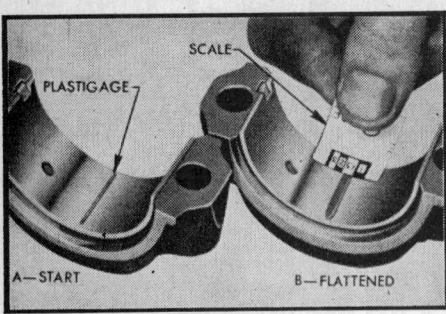

Fig. 12 Checking bearing clearance with Plastigage

wristpin clamp bolt (to 1955) with extreme force. A standard 5½" wrench should be used.

ROD BEARINGS

Connecting rod bearings are of the precision insert type and if worn can be replaced without removing the rod assembly by removing the cap and replacing the upper and lower halves. The clearance between the rod bearing and the crankshaft can be measured by the use of Plastigage as follows:

1. Remove bearing cap and wipe oil from crankshaft journal and bearing insert.
2. With crankpin at approximately bottom dead center, place a piece of Plastigage in the center of the cap.
3. Reinstall cap and tighten the bolts to the torque value listed in the *Engine Tightening Data* table.
4. Remove bearing cap and determine bearing clearance by comparing the width of the flattened Plastigage at its widest point with the graduation on the Plastigage envelope. The number within the graduation on the envelope indicates the clearance in thousandths of an inch, Fig. 12.

MAIN BEARINGS

Caution—Main bearing clearance can be checked with Plastigage in the same manner described for rod bearings. If bearings are measured with the engine in the chassis, the crankshaft must be supported in order to take up clearance between the upper bearing insert and crankshaft journal. This can be done by tightening bearing caps of adjacent bearing with .005" to .015" cardboard, (such as a calling card) between lower bearing shell and journal. Use extreme care when this is done to avoid unnecessary strain on the crankshaft or bearings or a false reading may be obtained. Do not rotate crankshaft while Plastigage is installed. *Be sure to remove cardboard.* To install new bearings, proceed as follows:

1. Remove bearing cap and worn lower shell.
2. Rotate crankshaft in normal direction to turn upper bearing shell out of crankcase. Use a cotter pin with a flattened head or the special tool made for the purpose in the crankshaft oil hole to contact the bearing and force it out, Fig. 13.

3. Place a new upper shell on the crankshaft journal with the locating notch in the correct position and rotate the shaft to turn the bearing in place.
4. Install the lower bearing shell in the cap.
5. Tighten all cap nuts to the torque value given in the *Engine Tightening Data* table.

CRANKSHAFT OIL SEAL

A braided oil seal is pressed into the upper and lower grooves behind the rear main bearing. Directly in front of this seal is an oil slinger which deflects the oil back into the oil pan. Should the braided seal require replacement, the installation of the lower half is accomplished as follows:

With the bearing cap and lower bearing half removed, install a new seal so that both ends protrude above the cap. Tap the seal down into position or roll it snugly in its groove with a smooth rounded tool. Then cut off the protruding ends of the seal with a sharp knife or razor blade, Fig. 14.

Installing Upper Seal

Although the usual practice is to remove the crankshaft when the upper half of the seal is to be replaced it is possible to do the job without removing the crankshaft as follows:

To remove the seal, use needle-nose pliers to grasp the end of the seal which is most accessible. Pull the seal downward while rotating the crankshaft slowly in the direction that the seal is being removed.

To install the new seal, fasten a length of wire or strong string such as fishing line securely to one end of the new seal. See that the point of fastening is not bulky and that it is not over ⅜" from the end of the seal. Coat the seal with Lubriplate. Pass the free end of the wire or string up over the crankshaft at the point where the seal is to be installed. Then exert a firm, steady pull on the wire or string and at the same time rotate the crankshaft slowly in the direction of the pull. This will help to move the seal into position. When the installation is completed, trim the ends of the seal flush with the engine block.

Fig. 13 Tool for removing upper main bearing shells

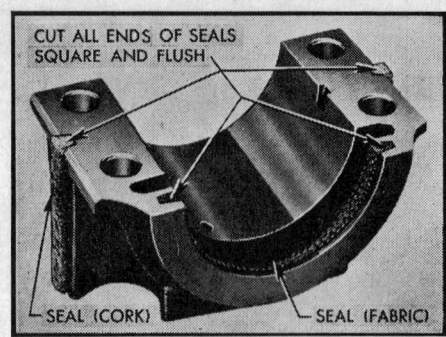

Fig. 14 Rear main bearing oil seals. All Models

OIL PAN

1953 V8

The oil pan can be removed by simply removing the attaching bolts and lowering the pan.

1954-61

On single exhaust models the exhaust crossover pipe must be removed. On some models, it may be necessary to remove the flywheel housing lower cover and starter splash shield. It may also be necessary to disconnect the steering idler arm bracket from the right frame side rail and lower the steering linkage for clearance. *The idler arm bracket should be fastened in its relative position to the idler arm while disconnected from the frame. This will prevent turning and possible changing of toe-in adjustment.*

OIL PUMP

1953-56

The oil pump is readily removed after taking down the oil pan. After disassembling the pump, thoroughly wash the screen and pump parts in solvent and blow dry with an air hose.

Check the oil pressure valve to see if it is free in the pump body. Also check the hole in the body to see that it is not oversize and that the valve fits the hole throughout its length. Check the spring to see that it is not collapsed, worn on its side, or broken.

Inspect the pump gears, body and shaft for scoring and wear, and replace any parts that are damaged.

Install the gear and shaft assembly in the body and install the idler gear with the rounded end of its teeth placed inward or away from the pump cover.

Check for clearance between gears and cover by using a steel straight edge. The clearance between the straight edge and gears should be such that the gears turn freely and must not be more than .005".

Assemble the pump and, after the screws are tightened, turn the shaft by hand to make sure that it turns freely and has a slight amount of end play (.0005" to .005").

Before installing the pump, check the crankcase and pump body for dirt or burrs that might tilt the pump and cause binding.

Install the pump with a new gasket, tightening the attaching bolts alternately a little at a time with one hand while turning the pump shaft back and forth through gear lash with the other.

If the pump tends to bind when the bolts are evenly tightened, it may be freed up by rapping the pump body lightly with a rawhide mallet. The pump shaft must be free of bind when the bolts are tightened securely.

1957-58 Oil & Vacuum Pump

The vacuum pump, Fig. 15, which is used for windshield wiper operation, replaces the conventional fuel and vacuum pump used formerly.

The oil pump is serviced in the same manner as previous models. The vacuum pump is serviced only as a complete assembly. If severe damage to the vacuum pump is encountered, it is recommended that the oil pump idler gear and driving key be inspected before replacing the vacuum pump.

1959-61

Inasmuch as electric windshield wipers are used there is no longer a need for the vacuum pump as used for 1957-58 models. Therefore, the 1959-61 pump is similar to the 1956 pump and service procedures are the same as described for the 1956 pump.

RADIATOR

To remove the radiator, unfasten it from its attaching points and lift it out over the top of the engine. On In-Line-8 models, first take off the water pump.

WATER PUMP, REPLACE

Drain cooling system, being sure to drain into a clean container if antifreeze solution is to be saved. Remove the fan belt and disconnect all hoses from water pump. Remove water pump.

WATER PUMP REPAIRS

1953-57

The water pump shaft is incorporated in a double-row ball bearing which is sealed at both ends to exclude dirt and water and is lubricated during manufacture so that no further lubrication is required, Fig. 16. The pump is sealed against leakage by a packless non-adjustable seal mounted in the pump cover in position to bear against the hub of the impeller.

When assembling the pump, press the fan hub into position $1\frac{3}{64}''$ from the end of the shaft. Press the impeller on the inner end of the shaft until the rear face of the impeller is flush with the end of the shaft.

1958

The water pump cover is die-cast aluminum. Due to the comparative softness of this material, pressing the old shaft and bearing assembly out would enlarge the bore to the extent that a new bearing would not have a tight press fit.

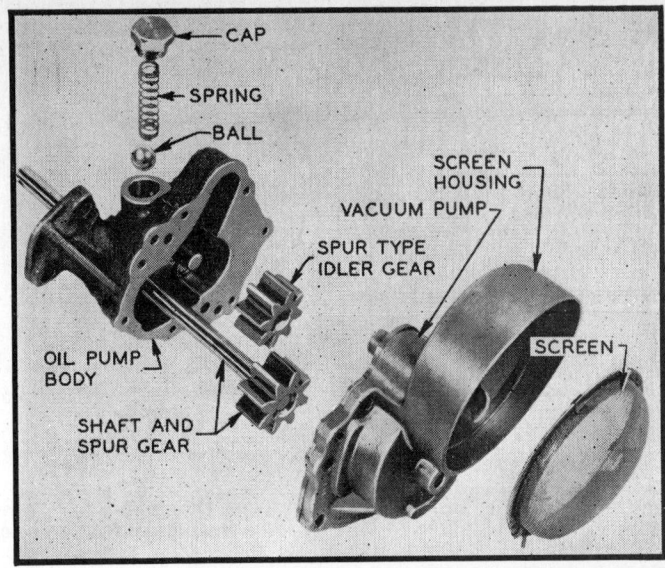

Fig. 15 Oil and vacuum pump. 1957-58

Because it is felt that a rebuilt aluminum water pump would not be safe, *a defective pump should be replaced with a new one.*

1959-61

The bearing arrangement in this water pump consists of two single row ball bearings. As the body is a shrink fit on the bearings, the bearings and shaft cannot be satisfactorily replaced in the field. Therefore, if bearings or shaft require replacement, a new pump assembly must be installed. The seal, however, may be replaced by pulling the impeller with a suitable puller, replacing the seal and pressing the impeller back on the shaft to the original position. *When pressing the impeller on the shaft, do not support the pump on the housing as the housing will be damaged. Support on forward end of shaft.*

DISTRIBUTOR, REPLACE

Removal

1. Disconnect primary wire from distributor and disconnect pipe from vacuum control unit.
2. Remove distributor cap.
3. Crank engine until distributor rotor is in position to fire No. 1 cylinder and the timing mark (see *Tune Up Chart*) is aligned with the timing indicator.
4. Remove distributor clamp and lift the distributor out of the crankcase.

Installation

Before installation of either a new or repaired distributor apply a few drops of engine oil to the drain hole near the lower end of the housing and apply oil to the oiler on the housing. Rotate the distributor shaft several times by hand to distribute the oil and to make sure that the shaft turns freely.

1. Check to make sure that the timing mark is aligned with the timing indicator with No. 1 piston on the compression stroke in position to fire.
2. Place a new seal on distributor housing.
3. Rotate distributor cam in direction of arrow on cam until rotor is in position to fire No. 1 cylinder, Figs. 17 and 18.
4. Rotate oil pump shaft with screwdriver to align slot in shaft with tongue on lower end of distributor shaft.
5. Install distributor in crankcase with vacuum control pointing to right side of engine, in position to connect to vacuum pipe.
6. Install distributor clamp and bolt with lockwasher, leaving bolt just loose enough to permit movement of distributor.
7. Rotate distributor housing until breaker points just start to open and tighten clamp bolt. This will permit starting engine for setting timing.
8. Connect pipe to vacuum control and primary wire to terminal stud.
9. Install distributor cap. If spark plug wires are disconnected from cap make certain that wires are connected in accordance with firing order.

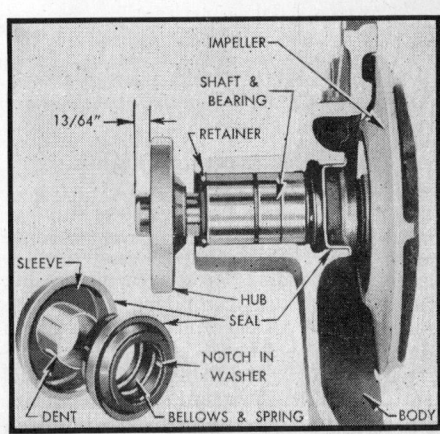

Fig. 16 Water pump parts

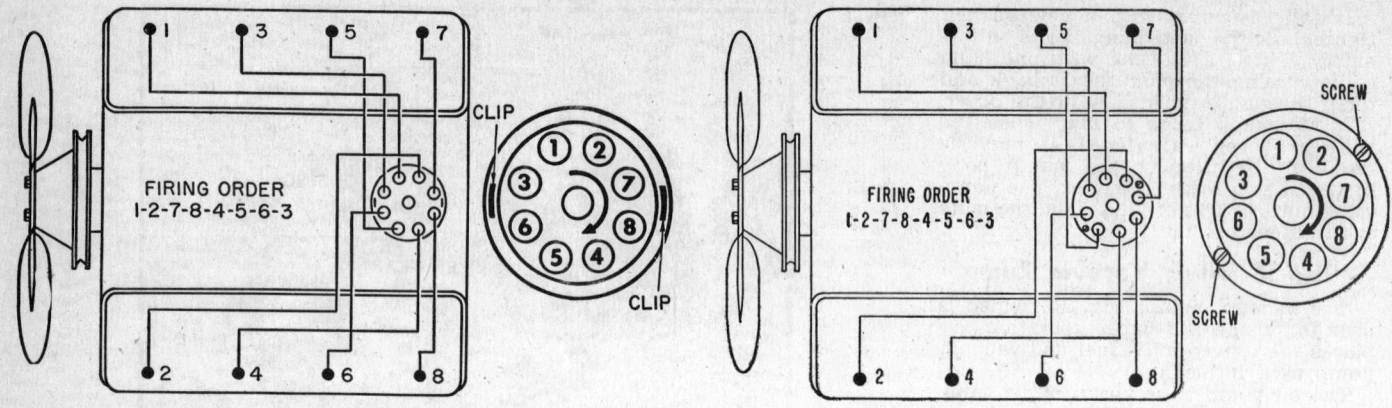

Fig. 17 Ignition details. 1953-56   Fig. 18 Ignition details. 1957-61

10. Check and set ignition timing as given below.

IGNITION TIMING

Ignition timing should be set with a synchroscope or power timing light because this shows the actual timing with the engine running. Breaker point opening must be within specified limits before setting ignition timing. See the *Tune Up Chart* for location of timing mark and proceed as follows:

1. Connect the timing light to No. 1 spark plug wire at the distributor cap, using a suitable adapter and following the instructions of the instrument manufacturer.
2. Start engine and set it to idle at a speed of 400 rpm so that the vacuum and centrifugal advance mechanisms are not in operation. *This is absolutely necessary to insure correct timing.*
3. Direct the beam of the timing light on the ignition timing mark.
4. If the beam does not fall on the timing mark, loosen the distributor clamp bolt and turn the distributor housing very slowly in the required direction so the light beam falls on the timing mark. Then tighten clamp bolt securely.

5. Reset the engine idle speed to specifications given in the *Tune Up Chart*.

STARTER, REPLACE

To remove the starter, disconnect battery cable from battery. Disconnect cable and solenoid lead wire from solenoid switch. Remove starter attaching bolts and take off starter.

MUFFLERS & PIPES

1953-56

Removing the mufflers and pipes on these models is an obvious operation. However, on 1956 Roadmaster Hardtop with single exhaust system, disconnect the stabilizer bar to provide clearance and remove pipe by sliding it to the rear between axle and stabilizer. With dual system, remove right pipe first in the same manner, then slide left pipe over differential housing to right side and remove.

1957-58

On dual exhaust models only, the pitman arm will strike the left exhaust pipe if it is not properly positioned. Position the exhaust pipe so it clears the pitman

arm approximately one inch when wheels are turned full left.

1959

Pipes connecting the front and rear mufflers are placed above the crossmember. This design permits easy removal of mufflers and pipes.

1960-61

The arrangement of both the single and dual exhaust systems is simple and no special problems will be encountered when service becomes necessary.

With the dual exhaust system, a single muffler, placed crosswise at the rear of the car, takes the place of the four mufflers used formerly. This new muffler has an inlet and outlet on each end, and the gases from each bank of cylinders, after passing through individual resonating chambers, enter into one common chamber. This blending makes the silencing action more complete. This system also eliminates the "cold side" muffler. This "cold side" has been the side of dual exhaust systems which incorporates the engine thermostatic heat control valve. During warm-up, and much of average cold weather driving, this valve is closed, forcing most all of the exhaust gas to travel through the other side of the system.

Carburetor Section

Performance Complaints

Flooding, stumble on acceleration or other performance complaints are in many instances caused by the presence of dirt, water or other foreign matter in the carburetor. To aid in diagnosing the cause of the complaint, the carburetor should be carefully removed from the engine without draining the fuel from the bowl. The contents of the fuel bowl may then be examined for contamination as the carburetor is disassembled.

Check the fuel in the bowl for contamination by dirt, water, gum or other foreign matter. A magnet moved through the fuel in the bowl will pick up and identify any iron oxide dust that may have caused intake needle and seat leakage.

Inspect gasketed surfaces between body and air horn. Small nicks or burrs should be smoothed down to eliminate air or fuel leakage. On carburetors having a vacuum piston, be especially particular when inspecting the top surface of the inner wall of the bowl around the vacuum piston passage. A poor seal

at this location may contribute to a "cutting-out" on turns complaint.

Fill the carburetor bowl with clean fuel before installing on manifold. This will help prevent dirt trapped in the fuel system from being dislodged by the free flow of fuel as the carburetor is primed. The operation of the floats and intake needle and seats may be checked under pressure if a fuel pump is used at the bench to fill the carburetor bowl. Operate the throttle several times and visually check the discharge from pump jets.

Poor Mileage and Engine Loading Complaints

Cases of poor mileage and engine loading may be due in many instances to sluggish choke valve opening during cold driveaway, caused by insufficient vacuum in choke housing, a plugged or restricted heat pipe or inlet in choke cover. To check for this condition, have engine warm and running at slow idle. Remove choke heat pipe and hold a finger over the heat inlet hole (hole is on choke housing on some carburetors). If there is little or no vacuum pull on the finger, check the choke housing for gasket leaks or plugged vacuum passages. If these are OK, check choke vacuum passages in carburetor between choke housing and manifold.

Dirty or Rusty Choke Housing

In cases where it is found that the interior of the choke housing is dirty, gummed or rusty while the carburetor itself is comparatively clean, look for a punctured or eroded manifold heat tube (if one is used).

Manifold Heat Control Valve

An engine equipped with a manifold heat control valve can operate with the valve stuck in either the open or closed position. Because of this, an inoperative valve is frequently overlooked at vehicle lubrication or tune-up.

A valve stuck in the "heat-off" position can result in slow warm up, deposits in combustion chamber, carburetor icing, flat spots during acceleration, low gas mileage and spark plug fouling.

A valve stuck in the "heat-on" position can result in power loss, engine knocking, sticking or burned valves and spark plug burning.

To prevent the possibility of a stuck valve, check and lubricate the valve each time the vehicle is lubricated or tuned-up. Check the operation of the valve manually. To lubricate the valve, place a few drops of penetrating oil on the valve shaft where it passes through the manifold. Then move the valve up and down a few times to work the oil in. *Do not use engine oil to lubricate the valve as it will leave a residue which hampers valve operation.*

Engine Stumble on Acceleration

1960 Two-Barrel Carburetors—This condition is caused by improper positioning of the air cleaner inlet tube. To prevent this, the inlet tube should be turned 44° to the left of the engine centerline, and the word "front" stamped on the cleaner cover should be used to locate the inlet tube correctly.

CARTER CARBURETOR ADJUSTMENTS

Year	Carburetor Model	Idle Adjustments				Float Level		Float Drop		Pump Travel Setting	Choke Unloader Setting	Choke Setting
		Mixture Screws Turns Open	Hot Idle Speed Neutral	Fast Idle Speed	Dashpot Plunger Clearance	Primary	Secondary	Primary	Secondary			
1961	AFB-	1½	500	625[13]	[2]							
1960	WGD-2979S, SA	¼-2	485	1500[1]	[2]	¼[3]	None	None	None	[5]	7/32[4]	Index
	WGD-2980S, SA	¼-2	485	1500[1]	[2]	¼[3]	None	None	None	[5]	7/32[4]	Index
	AFB-2981S	1½	485	1500[1]	[2]	7/32[6]	7/32[6]	¾[7]	¾[7]	½[8]	3/16[4]	1 Rich
	AFB-2982S	1½	485	1500[1]	[2]	7/32[6]	7/32[6]	¾[7]	¾[7]	½[8]	3/16[4]	1 Rich
1959	WGD-2837S	¾-2	485	1500[1]	[2]	¼[3]	None	None	None	[5]	3/16[4]	1 Lean
	WGD-2838S	¾-2	485	1500[1]	[2]	¼[3]	None	None	None	[5]	3/16[4]	1 Lean
	AFB-2877S	¼-1¾	485	1500[1]	[2]	7/32[6]	7/32[6]	23/32[7]	23/32[7]	33/64[8]	3/16[4]	1 Rich
	AFB-2840S	¼-1¾	485	1500[1]	[2]	7/32[6]	7/32[6]	23/32[7]	23/32[7]	33/64[8]	3/16[4]	1 Rich
1958	AFB-2800S	¼-1¾	485	1500[1]	[2]	7/32[6]	7/32[6]	23/32[7]	23/32[7]	33/64[8]	3/16[4]	1 Rich
	WGD-2674S	¾-2	485	1500[1]	[2]	¼[3]	None	None	None	[5]	3/16[4]	1 Lean
	WGD-2675S	¾-2	485	1500[1]	[2]	¼[3]	None	None	None	[5]	3/16[4]	Index
	WGD-2845S	¾-2	485	1500[1]	[2]	¼[3]	None	None	None	[5]	3/16[4]	Index
1957	WGD-2529S	½-1½	485	1500[1]	[2]	17/64[3]	None	None	None	[5]	9/64[4]	1 Lean
	WGD-2536S	½-1½	485	1500[1]	[2]	17/64[3]	None	None	None	[5]	11/64[4]	Index
	AFB-2507S	¾-1¾	485	1500[1]	[2]	7/32[6]	7/32[6]	23/32[7]	23/32[7]	33/64[8]	3/16[4]	Index
1956	WGD-2378S	¼-1¼	450	.028[9]	.030[10]	¼[3]	None	None	None	[5]	5/32[4]	Index
	WGD-2400S	½-1½	450	.028[9]	.030[10]	¼[3]	None	None	None	[5]	5/32[4]	Index
	WCFB-2347S	¾-1¾	450	.020[9]	.030[10]	3/16[11]	3/16[11]	11/16[12]	11/16[12]	[5]	5/32[4]	1 Lean
1955	WCFB-2197S	¾-1¾	450	.018[9]	.030[10]	3/32[11]	3/16[11]	19/32[12]	11/16[12]	[5]	11/64[4]	Index
	WCD-2179S	½-1½	450	.020[9]	.030[10]	3/8[11]	None	None	None	17/64[8]	3/16[4]	Index
1954	WCFB-2082S	½-1½	450	.012[9]	.030[10]	1/8[11]	3/16[11]	5/8[12]	11/16[12]	[5]	11/64[4]	Index
1953-54	WCD-2017S	½-1½	450	.015[9]	.030[10]	15/64[11]	None	None	None	17/64[8]	3/16[4]	Index
	WCD-2081S	½-1½	450	.028[9]	.030[10]	15/64[11]	None	None	None	17/64[8]	3/16[4]	Index
1953	WCFB-2053S	¾-1¾	450	.020[9]	.030[10]	3/32[11]	3/16[11]	5/8[12]	11/16[12]	9/32[8]	3/16[4]	Index

CARTER NOTES
METERING ROD

WCFB, WGD and WCD—This adjustment must be made after pump setting. Back out throttle set screw until throttle valves are fully closed and loosen metering rod arm clamp screw. With metering rods in place, press down on vacumeter link until metering rods bottom in casting. Holding rods down, revolve metering rod arm until finger on arm contacts lip of vacumeter link. Hold in place and tighten clamp screw.

AFB and WGD—With choke valve wide open and throttle valve fully closed, measure with scale between center of idle speed screw and top edge of throttle lever stop lug. With ignition on or test lamp connected, open throttle until switch makes contact, at which time distance from top edge of stop lug to center of idle speed screw should be 19/64″ to 9/16″ on AFB models, or 3/4″ to 1 1/8″ on WGD units. Adjust by adding or removing shims from switch guide block.

CAR STARTER SWITCH

WCFB and WCD—Check the travel by holding a scale against the choke unloader arm of throttle lever and mark carburetor body at the ½″ division of scale on WCFB models or at the 1″ division for WCD units. With ignition on or test lamp connected, open throttle until switch makes contact, at which time scale should read 1¼″ to 1 9/16″ at mark on WCFB models or 1 15/16″ to 2 5/16″ on WCD models. Adjust by adding or removing shims from switch guide block.

CARTER NOTES Continued

①—With engine running at normal operating temperature, turn fast idle screw against index mark on fast idle cam until specified rpm is obtained.

②—With fast idle screw on highest step on fast idle cam, adjust dashpot until plunger just touches throttle lever. Final adjustment is made with engine running at idle speed and transmission in drive range. Test dashpot action and readjust for best results.

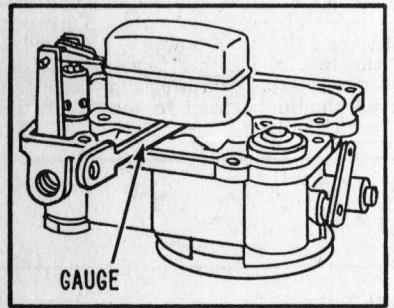

Fig. ③—WGD float level. To adjust, bend float lever.

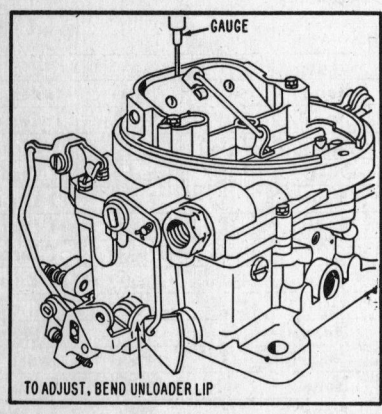

Fig. ④—With throttle valve wide open, clearance between upper edge of choke valve and inner wall of air horn should be as specified. Adjust by bending unloader lip on throttle shaft lever (AFB shown).

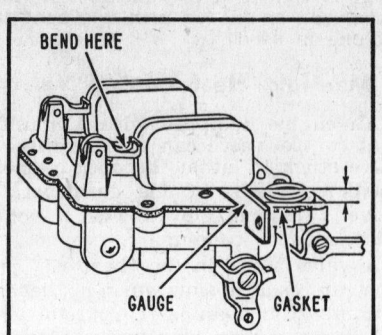

Fig. ⑥—AFB float level. Adjust by bending float lever.

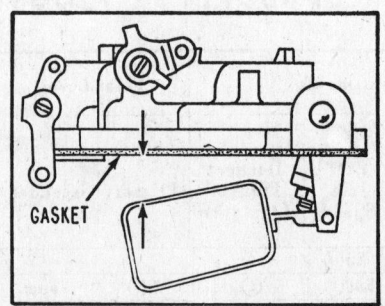

Fig. ⑦—AFB float drop. Adjust by bending stop tabs on float brackets.

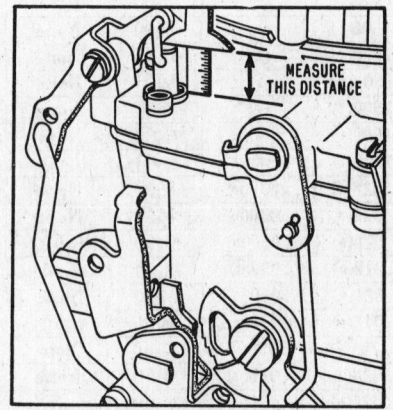

Fig. ⑧—Measure from top of float bowl to top of pump plunger shaft. Adjust by bending throttle connector rod (AFB shown).

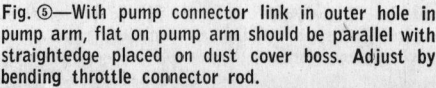

Fig. ⑤—With pump connector link in outer hole in pump arm, flat on pump arm should be parallel with straightedge placed on dust cover boss. Adjust by bending throttle connector rod.

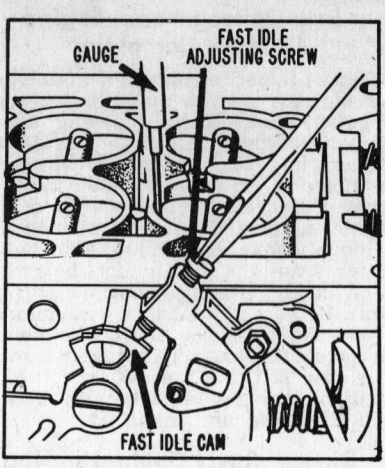

Fig. ⑨—With choke valve closed, tighten fast idle adjusting screw against high step of fast idle cam until clearance between throttle valve and carburetor bore is as specified (AFB shown).

⑩—Rotate fast idle cam to extreme cold idle position (choke closed). Hold throttle lever closed against a feeler gauge of the thickness specified between stop screw and highest step on fast idle cam. Adjust dashpot until it barely clears arm on throttle lever and tighten locknut. Test dashpot action with engine running at hot idle speed and transmission in drive range, and readjust as required for best results.

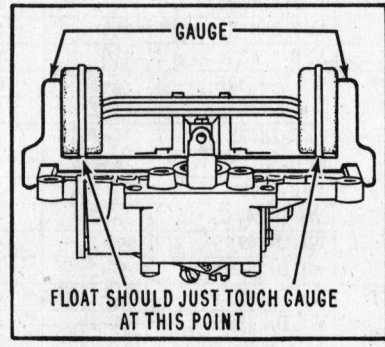

Fig. ⑪—WCFB and WCD float level. Adjust by bending float arms.

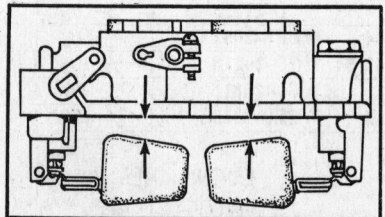

Fig. ⑫—WCFB float drop. Adjust by bending stop tabs on float brackets.

⑬—Rotate fast idle cam so that fast idle screw contacts low step on fast idle cam. Turn fast idle screw to obtain engine speed specified with engine at normal operating temperature.

ROCHESTER CARBURETOR ADJUSTMENTS

Year	Carburetor Model	Idle Adjustments				Float Level		Float Drop		Pump Rod Setting	Choke Unloader Setting	Choke Setting
		Mixture Screws Turns Open	Hot Idle Speed Neutral	Fast Idle Speed	Dashpot Plunger Clearance	Primary	Secondary	Primary	Secondary			
1961	4GC-	1½	500	625⑰								
	2GC-	1½	525	⑱								
1960	4GC-7015040	1½	485	1500①	②	9/64③	1⅜④	1⅜⑤	1 5/16⑥	1 1/64⑦	.128⑧	Index
1959	4GC-7013044⑨	1½	485	1500①	②	9/32⑪	1¾④	1½⑤	1 5/16⑥	1 1/64⑦	.128⑧	Index
	4GC-7013044⑩	1½	485	1500①	②	1⅜⑫	1⅜④	1 7/16⑤	1 5/16⑥	1 1/64⑦	.128⑧	Index
1958	4GC-7011600	1¼	485	1500①	②	1⅜⑫	1⅜④	1 5/16⑥	1 5/16⑥	1 1/64⑦	.128⑧	Index
	4GC-7013100	1¼	485	1500①	②	1 13/32⑫	1⅜④	1 11/32⑥	1 11/32⑥	1 1/64⑦	.128⑧	Index
1957	4GC-7010070	1¼	485	1500①	②	1⅜⑫	1⅜⑫	1 13/16⑬	1 13/16⑬	1 1/64⑦	.128⑧	Index
	4GC-7011570	1¼	485	1500①	②	1⅜⑫	1⅜⑫	1 13/16⑬	1 13/16⑬	1 1/64⑦	.128⑧	Index
1956	4GC-7009200	1¼	450	1700①	.028⑭	1 35/64⑮	1 35/64⑮	2¼⑯	2¼⑯	1 1/32⑦	.115⑧	Index
1955	4GC-7006200	1¼	450	1700①	.028⑭	1 35/64⑮	1 35/64⑮	2¼⑯	2¼⑯	1 3/32⑦	.115⑧	Index
	4GC-7009100	1¼	450	1700①	.028⑭	1 35/64⑮	1 35/64⑮	2¼⑯	2¼⑯	1 3/32⑦	.115⑧	Index

ROCHESTER CARBURETOR NOTES

CAR STARTER SWITCH

1957—Measure distance from diaphragm flange to edge of throttle valve with throttle valves closed. Then with ignition on or test lamp connected, open throttle until switch makes contact and again measure this distance. The difference between the two measurements should be ½" to ¾". Adjust by adding or removing shims from switch as required.

1955-56—Switch must make contact between 30° and 45° of throttle shaft rotation. If timing is too early reduce shim total; if too late increase shim total.

①—Tighten fast idle screw against highest step of fast idle cam until specified rpm is obtained.

②—With fast idle screw on highest step on fast idle cam, adjust dashpot until plunger just touches throttle lever. Final adjustment is made with engine running at idle speed and transmission in drive range. Test dashpot action and readjust for best results.

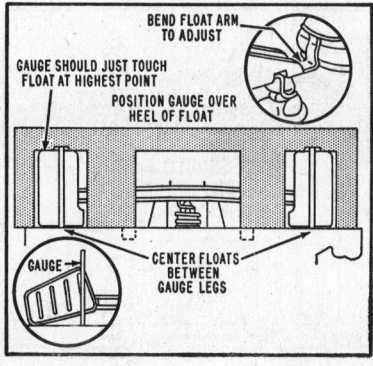

Fig. ④—4GC float level.

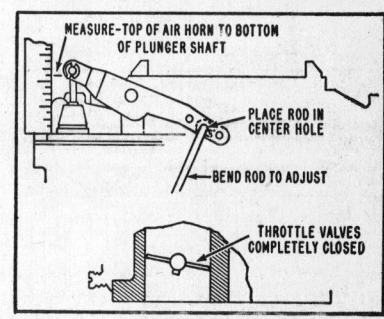

Fig. ⑦—4GC pump rod adjustment.

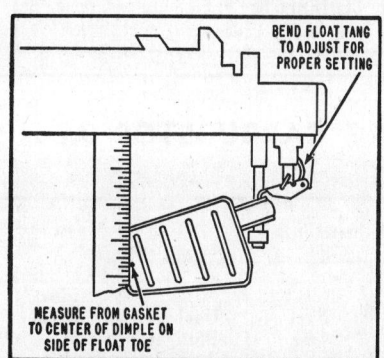

Fig. ⑤—4GC float drop.

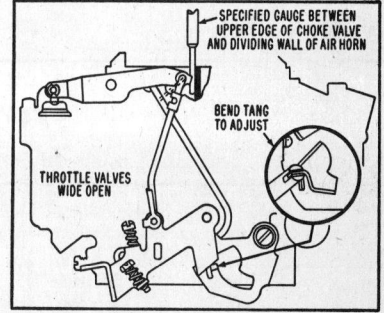

Fig. ⑧—Bend unloader tang on fast idle cam to obtain the clearance specified between edge of choke valve and dividing air horn wall with throttle valves wide open.

⑨—Early production identified by A or B or no letter following carburetor number on tag.

⑩—Late production identified by letters C or D following carburetor number on tag.

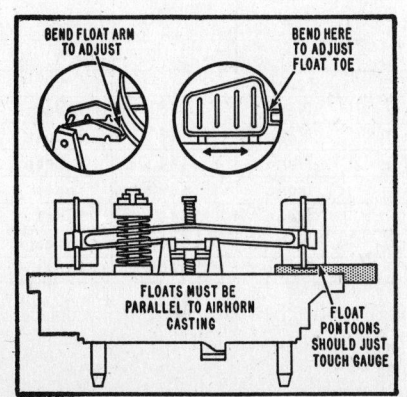

Fig. ⑥—4GC float level.

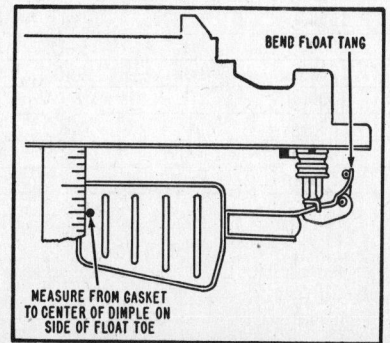

Fig. ⑥—4GC float drop.

ROCHESTER CARBURETOR NOTES continued

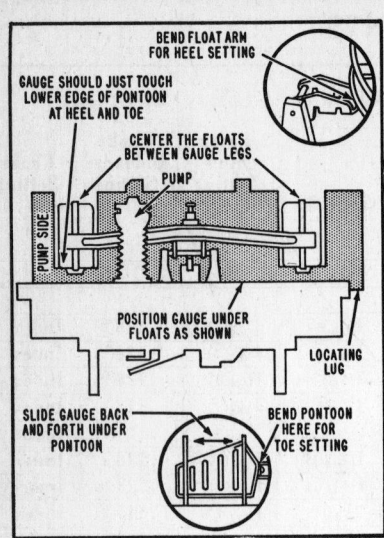

Fig. ⑪—4GC float level.

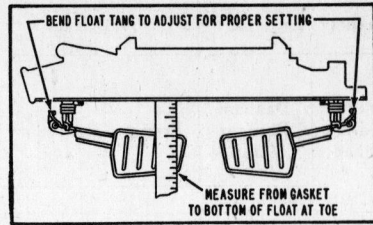

Fig. ⑬—4GC float drop.

⑭—Rotate fast idle cam to extreme cold idle position (choke closed). Hold throttle lever closed against a feeler gauge of the thickness specified between stop screw and highest step on fast idle cam. Adjust dashpot until it barely clears arm on throttle lever and tighten locknut. Test dashpot action with engine running at hot idle speed and transmission in drive range, and readjust as required for best results.

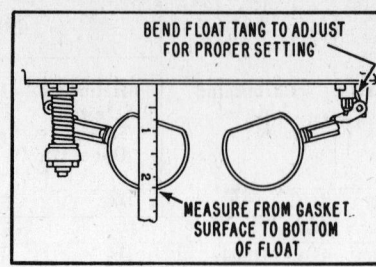

Fig. ⑯—4GC float drop.

⑰—Rotate fast idle cam so that fast idle screw contacts low step of cam. Turn fast idle screw to obtain specified engine speed with engine at normal operating temperature.

⑱—Fast idle speed adjustment is not required because it is controlled by the idle adjusting screw.

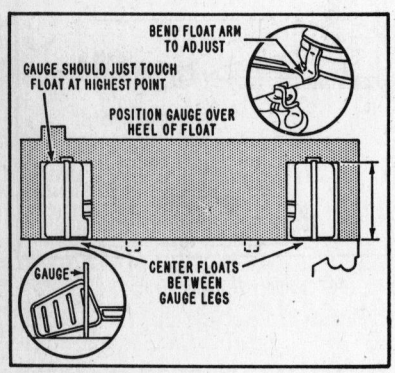

Fig. ⑫—4GC float level.

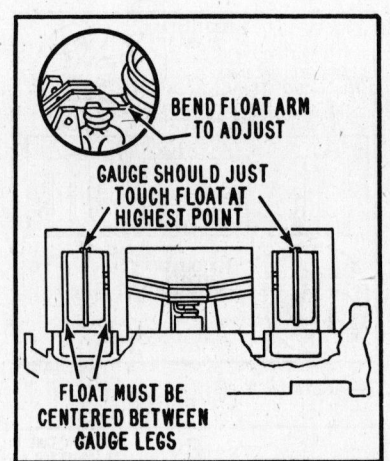

Fig. ⑮—4GC float level.

STROMBERG CARBURETOR ADJUSTMENTS

Year	Carburetor Model	Idle Adjustments				Float Level	Pump Travel	Bowl Vent Valve	Choke Unloader	Choke Setting
		Mixture Screws Turns Open	Hot Idle Speed Neutral	Fast Idle Speed	Dashpot Plunger Clearance					
1961	WW2-	1	500	625⑦				5/64⑧		
1960	WW7-113	1	485	1500⑥	①	5/32②	7/8③	None	.146⑤	Index
1959	WW7-112A	1	485	1500⑥	①	5/32②	7/8③	None	.146⑤	1 Lean
1958	WW7-109B	1	485	1500⑥	①	5/32②	7/8③	None	.144⑤	1 Lean
1957	WW7-106B	1	485	1500⑥	①	7/32②	7/8③	None	.144⑤	Index
1956	WW7-103	1	450	5 5/8④	①	3/16②	25/64③	None	.144⑤	Index
	WW7-105B	1	450	6 1/8④	①	3/16②	61/64③	None	.144⑤	Index
1955	WW7-104	1	450	5 5/8④	①	3/16②	7/8③	None	.144⑤	Index

STROMBERG NOTES

CAR STARTER SWITCH

Remove filler cap from rocker arm cover. With throttle valve fully closed, hold 6" scale against dashpot pad of throttle lever and mark rocker arm cover at end of scale. Then with ignition on, open throttle until switch makes contact and make a second mark on rocker arm cover even with end of scale. If switch is correctly timed, the distance between the two marks will be ¾" to 1⅛". Adjust by adding or removing shims as required.

CARBURETOR BALL CHECKS

Whenever it becomes necessary to dismantle a carburetor be sure to account for the ball checks that may be found under pump plungers and compensating or power valves.

①—With fast idle screw on highest step on fast idle cam, adjust dashpot until plunger just touches throttle lever. Final adjustment is made with engine running at idle speed and transmission in drive range. Test dashpot action and readjust for best results.

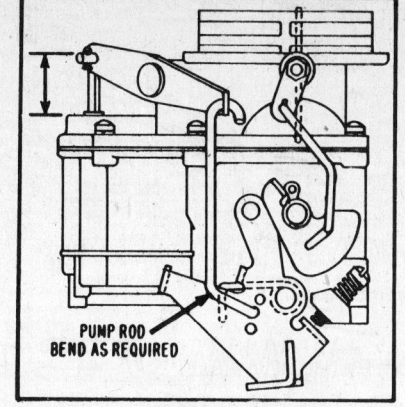

Fig. ③—With throttle valves fully closed, measure distance between top of pump plunger rod to top of air horn (pump rod in center hole). Adjust by bending pump connector rod.

④—With throttle valves closed, turn fast idle screw the number of turns listed from point of initial contact with high step of fast idle cam.

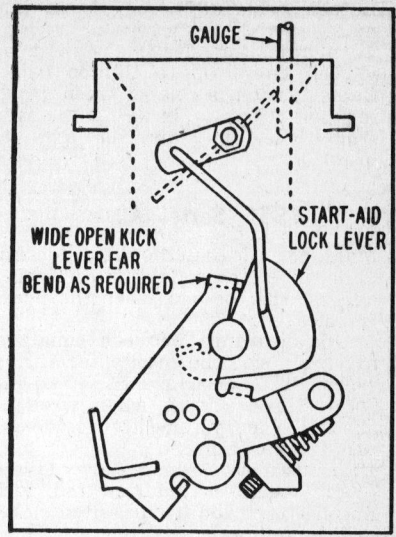

Fig. ⑤—With throttle valves wide open choke valve should be open the dimension specified between choke valve and air horn. Adjust by bending ear on throttle lever.

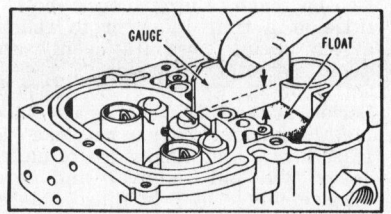

Fig. ②—WW float level. Adjust by bending float lever.

⑥—With engine running at normal operating temperature, turn fast idle screw against highest step of fast idle cam until specified rpm is obtained.

⑦—Rotate fast idle cam so that fast idle screw contacts low step of cam. Turn fast idle screw to obtain specified engine speed with engine at normal operating temperature.

⑧—This setting is made after pump travel setting. With throttle fully closed and choke valve wide open, test opening of bowl vent valve at center of hole with rubber valve hanging free. If not as specified, bend bowl vent lever as required.

Clutch and Transmission Section

CLUTCH PEDAL, ADJUST

1959-60

Only two adjustments are required. The pedal arm to idler lever rod determines the position of the equalizer shaft and therefore the overcenter spring position also. The clutch release rod adjustment is made to correct pedal lash and therefore clearance between the clutch release bearing and pressure plate release fingers.

Overcenter Spring Adjustment—

1. Remove clevis pin from clutch pedal rod clevis at pedal location. Fig. 1.
2. Loosen clevis lock nut and turn clevis in desired direction.
3. Attach rod and clevis to arm temporarily and check overcenter spring position. A clearance of ¼" should exist between extension and equalizer shaft. A ¼" drill may be used for checking clearance. Be certain pedal arm is against stop.
4. Tighten clevis lock nut and install cotter pin.

Pedal Lash Adjustment—

1. To adjust pedal lash, loosen adjusting nut lock nut on clutch release rod.
2. Turn adjusting nut in desired direction until a pedal lash of 1⅛" to 1¼" is obtained, measured at the pedal.
3. Tighten lock nut.

1957-58 Series 40

1. Make certain that return spring pulls clutch pedal firmly against pedal bumper when pedal is released. If pedal does not contact bumper, check pedal and linkage for binding or lack of lubrication.
2. Before making any linkage adjustments, clutch equalizer must be in correct position. Position equalizer by inserting a ¼" x 2½" bolt through gauging hole in equalizer from bottom as it lines up with two holes in equalizer bracket, Fig. 2. If cable is too loose, pull slack out of cable until holes align; if cable is too tight, tension must be loosened at cable adjusting sleeve until ¼" bolt will be held in gauging holes.
3. Remove return spring and release rod-to-yoke clevis pin.
4. Loosen release rod adjusting end jam nut and adjust end until clevis pin fits freely with yoke held to rear.
5. Lengthen release rod by rotating adjusting end four complete turns. This will provide proper clearance between clutch release bearing and release levers. Free pedal play should be 1⅛" to 1¼".
6. Attach release rod and secure.
7. To tighten cable to proper tension, first clamp locking pliers on both upper and lower cables just off threaded sections to keep cables from twisting.

8. Loosen cable adjusting sleeve jam nuts.
9. Turn adjusting sleeve clockwise as viewed from top to tighten cable. Cable tension is correct when gauging bolt drops or is easily removed from holes in equalizer and its bracket.

1956 Series 40

1. Make certain that the return spring pulls the clutch pedal bumper firmly against the toe-pan when the pedal is released.
2. Check clearance between equalizer assembly and the overcenter spring extension. A clearance of $\frac{1}{16}$" to $\frac{1}{8}$" (slip fit on a $\frac{3}{32}$" Allen wrench) should be maintained to provide for proper operation.
3. If adjustment is necessary, loosen clutch pedal-to-equalizer rod lock nut and turn rod until desired clearance is maintained.
4. Check free pedal movement or lash by pushing on the pedal pad until contact can be felt between release bearing and clutch springs.
5. Free movement or lash of clutch pedal should be $\frac{7}{8}$" measured at the pedal pad. If adjustment is necessary, loosen clutch release rod lock nut and turn adjusting nut as required to secure proper lash. Tighten nut securely.

1953-55

1. Make certain that the return spring pulls the clutch pedal firmly against the pedal bumper on the toe board when pedal is released. If pedal does not contact bumper, check pedal and linkage for binding or lack of lubrication.
2. Check condition of return spring, and on 1953-55 Series 50-60, check condition of actuating spring and

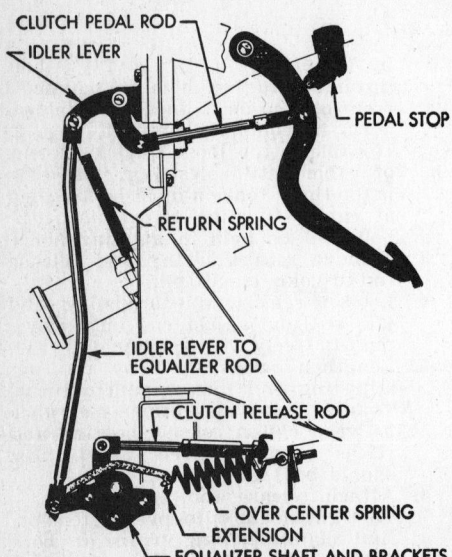

Fig. 1 Clutch linkage. 1959-60

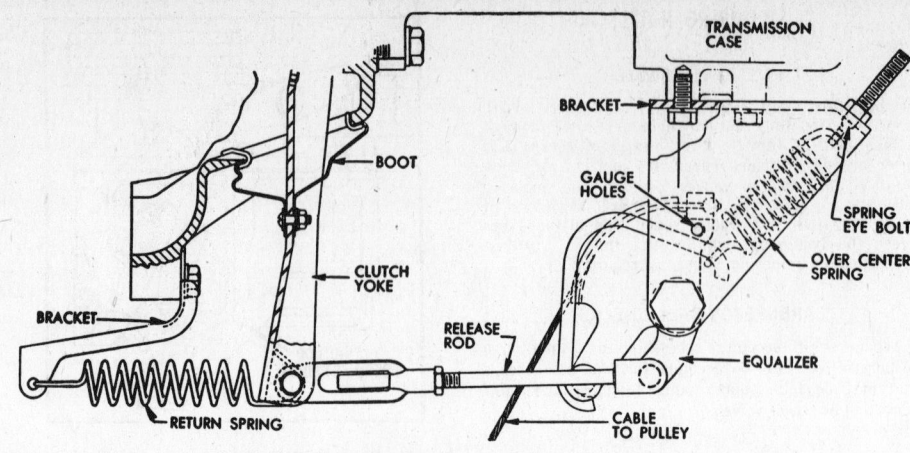

Fig. 2 Clutch equalizer bracket. 1957-58 Series 40

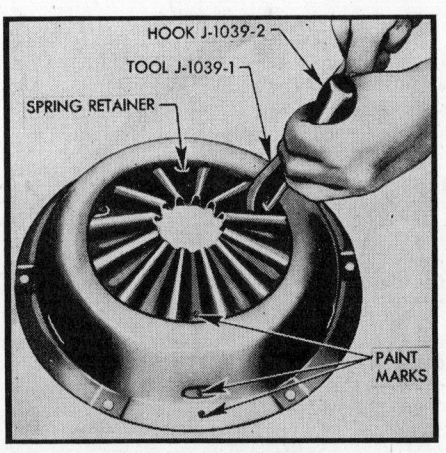

Fig. 3 Attaching spring retainer to cover

make sure that spring eye bolt is fully tightened.
3. Check pedal free movement or lash by pushing on pedal pad until release bearing contacts clutch spring. *Do not mistake tension of pedal return spring as an indication of lack of pedal lash.*
4. If pedal free movement is not $\frac{3}{4}$" to 1" loosen lock nut and turn adjusting nut on clutch release rod to secure proper lash and tighten lock nut securely.

CLUTCH, REMOVE

1. Remove rear axle and transmission as outlined under their respective headings.
2. Remove flywheel lower housing.
3. Disconnect release rod from release yoke and remove yoke boot and release rod lock nut which are bolted to yoke.
4. Remove spring washer which retains release bearing support in flywheel housing and remove support and gasket.
5. Pull outward on release yoke to free it from ball stud in flywheel housing and remove yoke and release bearing through bottom of housing.

6. Separate yoke from bearing.
7. *Mark clutch cover and flywheel* with a center punch so that the cover can be reinstalled in the same position on flywheel in order to preserve engine balance.
8. Loosen each clutch cover bolt a little at a time in order to relieve clutch spring pressure evenly and avoid distortion of cover.
9. On 1953-55 Series 50-60, 1956-58 Series 40 and 1959-60 Series 4400, metal spacers placed between release levers and inner edge of clutch cover will aid removal and later disassembly by holding clutch springs compressed.
10. Support pressure plate and cover assembly while removing last bolts, then remove clutch and driven plate.

CLUTCH, OVERHAUL

Corrugated Spring Type, 1953-55

1. Place pressure plate and cover assembly on flat work surface and *mark cover, pressure plate and clutch spring* with paint so that parts can be reassembled in the same relationship to each other in order to preserve engine balance.
2. Unhook spring retainers from ears on clutch cover.
3. Lift off clutch cover.
4. Unhook all spring retainers from corrugated spring.
5. Lift off corrugated spring and remove retainers from pressure plate.

Assemble

1. At points where clutch spring contacts clutch cover, pressure plate and ends of spring retainers, apply a light coating of Lubriplate.
2. Install spring retainers.
3. Place clutch spring on pressure plate *with marks made at disassembly in alignment,* then push spring retainers up over corrugated spring.
4. Place cover over spring and pressure plate *with marks made at disassembly* in alignment.

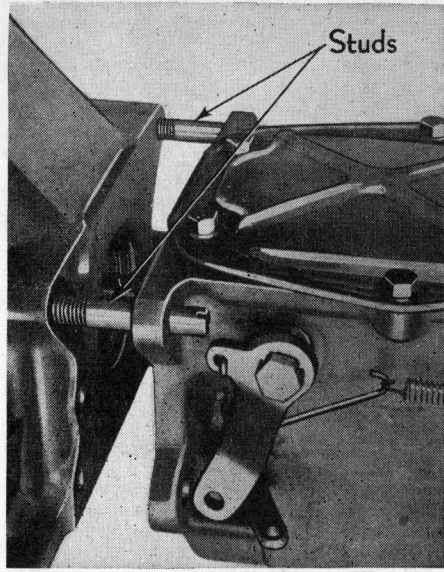

Fig. 4 Use of guide studs in transmission mounting holes when removing and installing synchromesh transmission

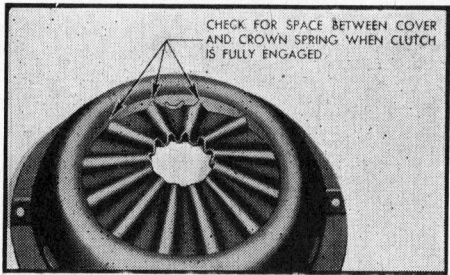

CHECK FOR SPACE BETWEEN COVER AND CROWN SPRING WHEN CLUTCH IS FULLY ENGAGED

Fig. 5 Points to check contact of clutch spring with cover

5. Hook loop of each spring retainer over ear on clutch cover, Fig. 3. If retainers appear weak or distorted they should be replaced in complete sets to insure even tension.

Coil Spring Type, 1956-60

Unless special clutch rebuilding equipment is available, it is recommended that the clutch assembly be exchanged for a rebuilt unit should the clutch require rebuilding. The driven disc, however, may be replaced without special equipment. If clutch rebuilding equipment is available, follow the equipment manufacturer's instructions.

CLUTCH, INSTALL

1. Very sparingly apply front wheel bearing lubricant to the main drive gear pilot bearing in crankshaft. If too much lubricant is used it will run out on face of flywheel when hot and ruin driven plate facings. Make sure that surface of flywheel is clean and dry.
2. Make sure that splines in driven plate hub are clean and apply a light coating of Lubriplate. Driven plate facings must be clean and dry.
3. Place driven plate on pressure plate with oil slinger toward pressure plate; then place clutch assembly in position on flywheel, *being sure to align marks made on flywheel and cover before removal.*
4. Install cover bolts with washers *but do not tighten.*
5. Insert a spare main drive gear through hub of driven plate and into pilot bearing.
6. Tighten each clutch cover bolt several turns at a time to draw cover evenly into pilot of flywheel and avoid distortion of cover.

7. While tightening cover bolts, move main drive gear from side to side to center driven plate with pilot bearing. If driven plate is not centered it will be difficult to slide transmission into place. Make sure all cover bolts are uniformly tightened.
8. On 1953-55 Series 50-60, 1956-58 Series 40 and 1959-60 Series 4400, remove spacers from between cover and release levers if they were placed there during removal.
9. Fill groove in release bearing sleeve with wheel bearing grease. Coat release yoke ball stud and ball recess in release yoke with Lubriplate.
10. Attach release bearing to release yoke and attach yoke to ball stud in flywheel housing.
11. Install release bearing support with new gasket, placing support in flywheel housing with tab on support aligned with molded recess in housing to permit positive drain back of oil to transmission.
12. Install spring washer with outer edge against bearing support.
13. Install transmission, being sure to use guide pins, Fig. 4, to avoid damage to clutch driven plate which would result if weight of transmission is allowed to rest on main drive gear in driven plate hub.
14. Install boot and release rod nut lock on yoke. Attach release rod to yoke and adjust pedal free movement as outlined previously.
15. On corrugated spring type clutches, have a helper hold the clutch fully disengaged and check with a feeler gauge for space between cover and clutch spring at point of contact, Fig. 5. Clutch will not fully disengage if any one of the clutch spring contact points fails to contact the cover solidly. This condition must be

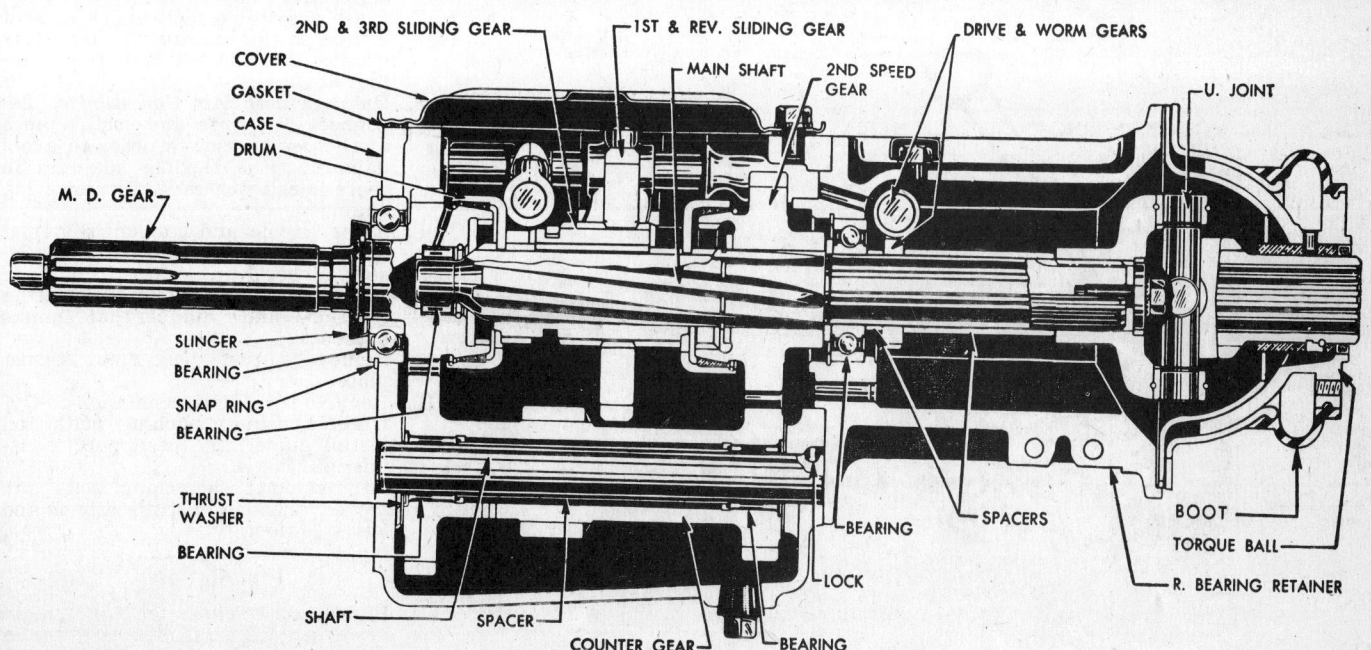

Fig. 6 1953-55 Series 40 synchromesh transmission

corrected by removing clutch and properly setting spring retainer ears on cover.

16. Install flywheel lower housing, making sure gasket is in condition to insure a tight seal.
17. Install rear axle assembly.

TRANSMISSION, REPLACE

1959-60

1. Remove rear axle assembly.
2. If transmission is to be disassembled, drain lubricant. Fill with kerosene and run transmission in neutral about 15 seconds. Drain kerosene.
3. Remove torque ball retainers and torque ball. It is not necessary to remove U-joint.
4. Disconnect speedometer cable, shift rod and selector rod from their levers at transmission and pull clutch release rod sideways to disengage it from release yoke clip.
5. Loosen exhaust pipes at exhaust manifolds.
6. Disconnect rubber thrust pad from thrust bracket, allowing thrust pad to remain bolted to transmission support. Disconnect rubber mounting pad from transmission support, allowing mounting pad to remain bolted to transmission.
7. Place suitable jacks under engine and transmission.
8. Raise engine and transmission enough to relieve load on transmission support. Then remove support, *noting number and location of shims present.*
9. Unfasten transmission from flywheel housing (4 bolts).
10. Move transmission rearward as far as possible. U-joint will center into large opening in frame crossmember.
11. Lower rear of engine and front of transmission until end of main drive

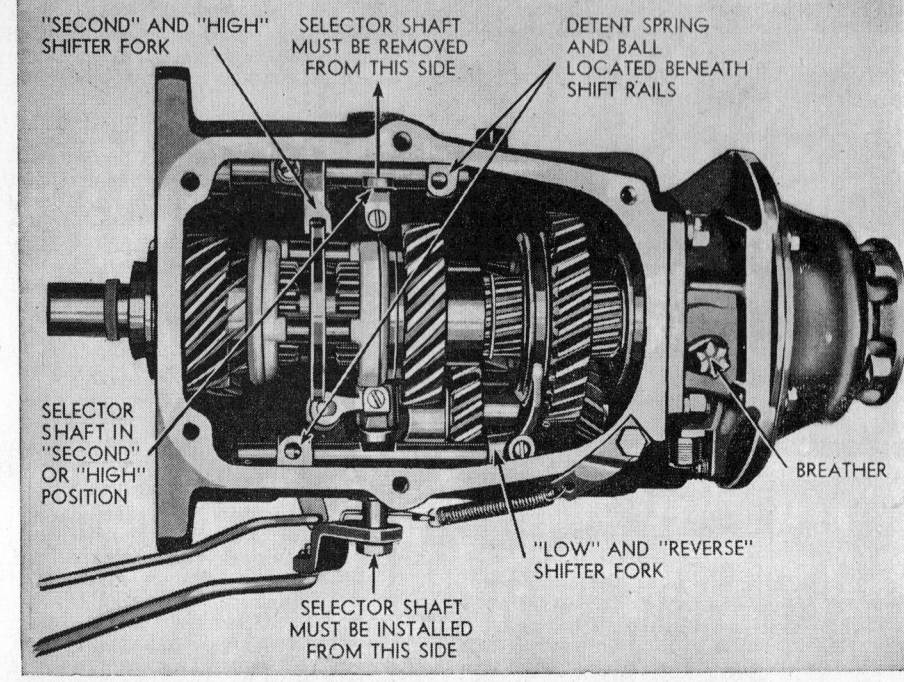

Fig. 8 Transmission. 1953 Series 50, 60. Typical of 1954-55 Series 50, 60, 1956-58 Series 40 and 1959-60 Series 4400

gear clears clutch release bearing.
12. Move transmission forward; then lower and remove.

1953-58

1. Remove rear axle assembly.
2. Drain transmission lubricant.
3. Disconnect speedometer cable, shift rod and selector rod from transmission.
4. On Series 40 prior to 1956, remove toggle spring and extension, shift lever and washer from selector shaft,

and outer selector lever, to provide clearance for removing transmission-to-flywheel housing bolts. *Hold shift lever in neutral while removing attaching bolt to avoid damaging shift lever on shaft inside transmission.*
5. On all models, disconnect rubber thrust pad from transmission support by removing three nuts and plate, then lift out shims located between support and thrust pad.
6. Remove two bolts and plate which attach transmission mounting pad to support.
7. Place a suitable jack under rear of engine so that engine will be safely supported while transmission is removed.
8. *On cars with Air Conditioner,* disconnect discharge and suction lines at the compressor in order to avoid damaging the flexible adapters in these lines when raising or lowering engine.
9. Raise engine and transmission just enough to relieve load on transmission support.
10. Remove support from frame, noting location and number of shims present.
11. Remove thrust pad from thrust plate.
12. Remove two top transmission-to-flywheel housing attaching bolts and install guide pins to support transmission, Fig. 4.
13. Remove lower attaching bolts and move transmission straight back and lower to floor.

Installation

1. Lightly coat splines on end of main drive gear with Lubriplate for a distance of not more than 1". Do not apply an excess that will push off at

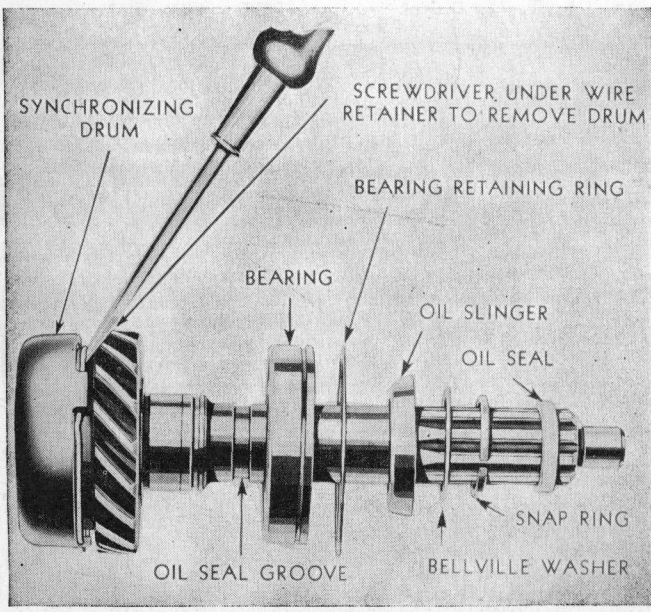

Fig. 7 Main drive gear parts. 1953-55 Series 40 synchromesh transmission

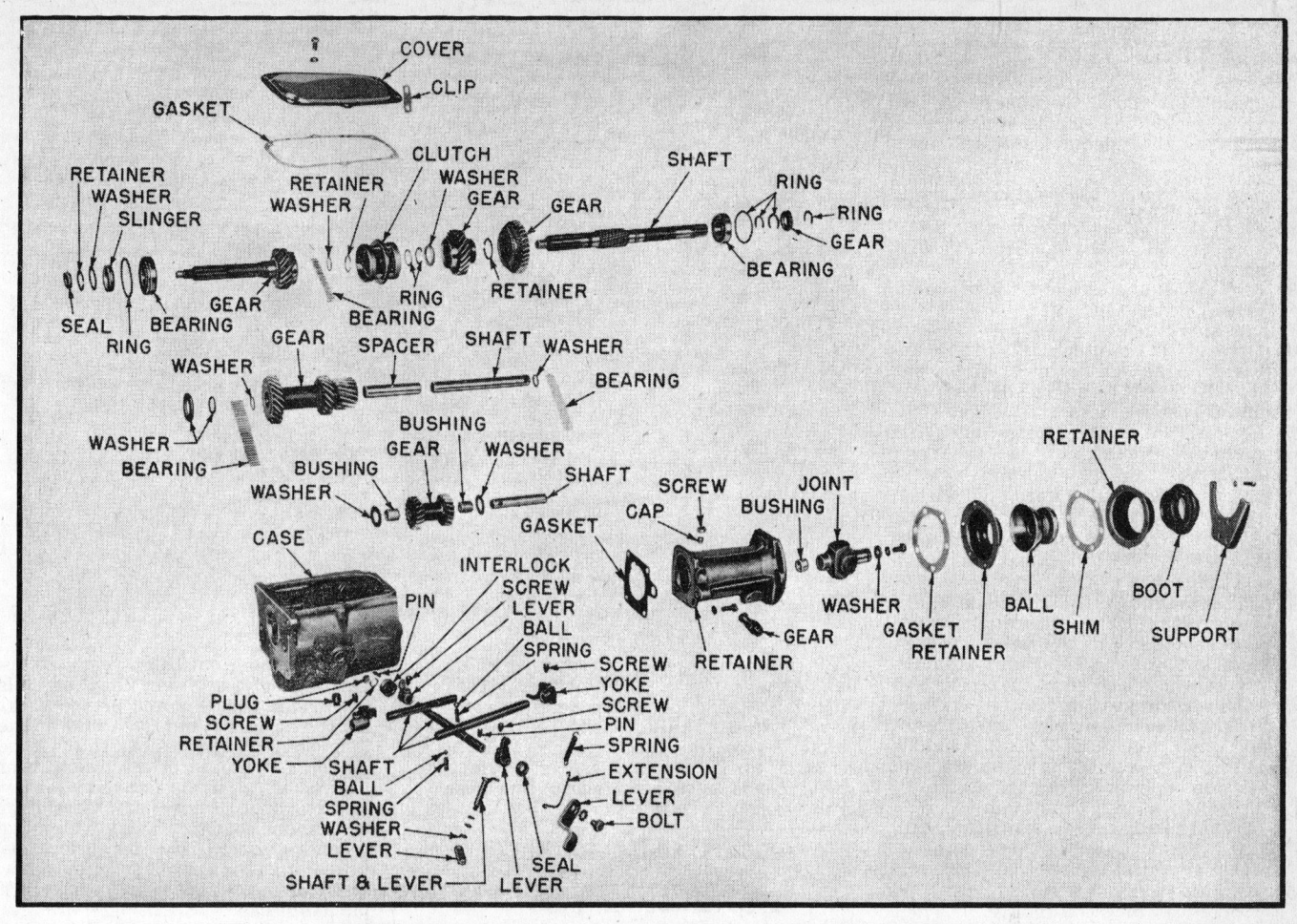

Fig. 9 Exploded view of synchromesh transmission. 1953-55 Series 50-60, 1956-58 Series 40, and 1959-60 Series 4400. The two steel washers and single bronze thrust washer used at rear of cluster gear have been replaced by a single steel washer and steel-backed bronze thrust washer for 1959-60 units. The steel washer is positioned against the gear with the bronze side of the combination washer against the steel washer

the driven plate hub and get on the clutch facings.

2. Make certain that front face of transmission case and face of fly-wheel housing are absolutely clean.

3. Install guide pins in upper holes, Fig. 4, and install a new transmission gasket.

4. Make certain that spring washer is in place behind clutch release bearing support in housing.

5. Lift transmission into place and fully support it until the main drive gear bearing enters flywheel housing.

6. Install lower transmission bolts, and then the upper bolts, tightening all bolts evenly and securely. *If a gap exists between transmission case and flywheel housing, do not tighten bolts as case may be broken. Remove transmission and check position of main drive gear bearing snap ring, which may have slipped out of place during installation.*

7. Install rubber thrust pad on thrust plate attached to bearing retainer.

8. Install transmission support with original shims, which should be of proper number and thickness to just fill space between support and frame.

9. Lower transmission to rest on support and attach mounting pad to support with bolt plate and self-locking nuts.

10. With engine and transmission resting freely and normally on mountings, install sufficient shims between thrust pad and support to fill existing space. Insert shims from above, then install bolt plate and three nuts which attach thrust pad to support.

11. Connect speedometer cable.

12. On Series 40 prior to 1956, install outer selector lever, shift lever, toggle spring and extension. *Hold shift lever in neutral* while installing and tightening attaching bolt and washer to avoid damaging shifter levers on selector shaft. Install toggle spring and extension so that extension passes underneath selector shaft.

13. Connect lower shift rod and selector rod to their levers and install clutch release rod end under clutch yoke clip.

14. Insert specified quantity of transmission lubricant in case. In addition, inject ½ pint of transmission lubricant through universal joint yoke.

15. Install rear axle assembly.

16. *On cars with Air Conditioner,* connect discharge and suction lines at compressor.

17. Road test car, checking for proper selection and shifting of transmission, correct synchronization and quiet operation. In neutral, the shift control lever should be slightly above the horizontal. It may be necessary to loosen the steering column jacket clamp and the column bracket cap and shift the jacket or clamp slightly to obtain proper position. A slight adjustment of the control rods may be required.

TRANSMISSION REPAIRS
1953-55 Series 40

Disassemble, Fig. 6—

1. Disconnect shift shaft lever from selector lever.

2. Take off transmission cover.

3. Lock transmission in high gear to prevent sliding sleeve and low speed gear from dropping into case.

4. Remove universal ball and retainers and take universal joint from mainshaft.

5. Unfasten rear bearing retainer and

take mainshaft and second speed gear out through rear of case.

6. Remove set screws from selector cams and shift forks. (If the low speed gear and sliding sleeve are not to be removed, it is not necessary to take out the selector shaft and shift rails.)

7. Tap selector shaft out through right side of case.

8. Slide shift rails out rearward, being sure to collect the poppet balls and springs.

9. Slip the sliding sleeve from the main drive gear and lift out the sleeve and low speed gear.

10. Drive the countershaft out rearward, using an arbor of the right length to hold the needle bearings and thrust washers in position.

11. Expand the snap ring and push the main drive gear into the case and lift it out.

12. Lift out the cluster gear and related parts.

13. Drive the reverse idler lock pin into the shaft. Then tap out the shaft and lift out the gear.

14. To disassemble the mainshaft, pry the synchronizer drum retainer over the shoulder on the second speed gear and remove the drum. Remove the second speed gear snap ring and take off the gear and thrust washer. Release the mainshaft rear bearing snap ring and bump the mainshaft on a wooden block to release it from the rear bearing retainer. Remove the snap ring from the rear of the bearing and take off the bearing, thrust washer, speedometer drive gear and spacer.

15. To disassemble the main drive gear, proceed as directed in Fig. 7. Then remove the snap ring and washer which retains the bearing and bump the shaft on a wooden block to remove the bearing.

Assembly of Transmission — Assemble the transmission by reversing the sequence given for disassembly.

Make certain that all parts are absolutely clean and that gears and synchronizing drums are free of nicks or burrs. Use all new gaskets and oil seals or packings to insure against leakage of lubricant. Use all new snap rings, and retainers of the snap ring type. Snap rings are frequently distorted during removal and are difficult to true up satisfactorily for further service.

To insure initial lubrication, coat all bearings with clean transmission lubricant at time of installation.

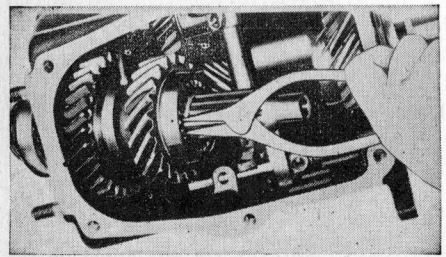

Fig. 10 Removing second speed gear. 1953-55 Series 50, 60, 1956-58 Series 40 and 1959-60 4400

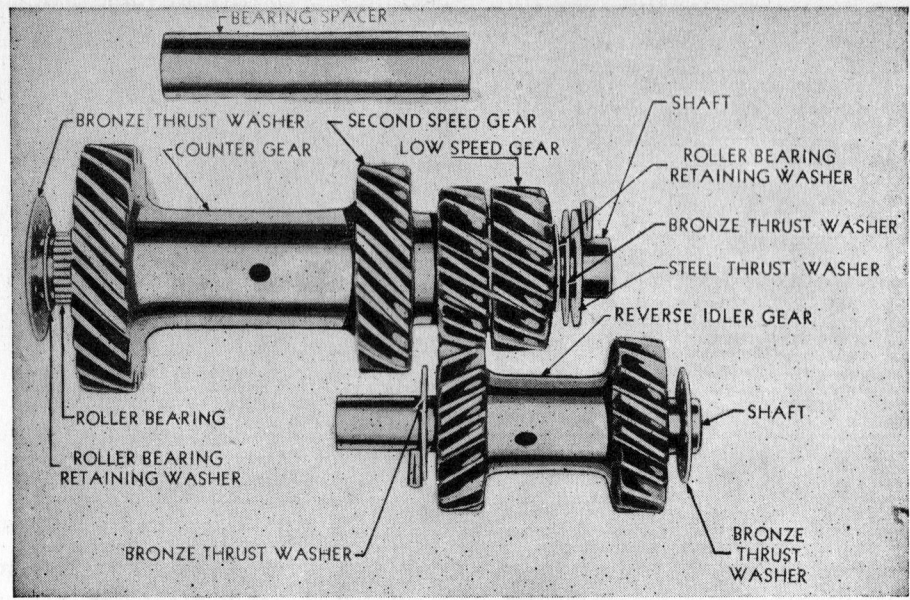

Fig. 11 Arrangement of cluster gear and reverse idler gear parts. 1953-55 Series 50, 60

When installing the reverse idler shaft lock, always use a new lock and coat with white lead or other sealing compound before installation to prevent oil leaks. Drive the lock into the hole in the shaft until the outer end of the lock is $\frac{3}{32}$ inch below the surface of the boss on the case.

1953-55 Series 50, 60;
1956-58 Series 40
1959-60 Series 4400

Disassemble, Figs. 8 and 9—

1. Thoroughly clean all dirt from exterior of transmission to avoid getting dirt into bearings when transmission is opened.

2. Remove transmission cover and gasket, toggle spring and spring extension.

3. Remove speedometer driven gear, thrust plate and gasket, torque ball, retainers and shims from rear bearing retainer. (Installation of guide pins will aid in removal of torque ball and retainers.)

4. Remove retaining bolt and washer, then pull universal joint from mainshaft.

5. Remove universal joint spacer from mainshaft, then remove rear bearing retainer and gasket from transmission case.

6. Move mainshaft back until rear bearing is clear of case. Remove snap ring from bearing and pull bearing, spacer, and speedometer drive gear from shaft.

7. Remove shifter yoke set screws and lift mainshaft and assembled parts out through top of transmission case.

8. Remove synchronizing clutch and second speed sliding gear from mainshaft. Remove snap ring, Fig. 10, thrust washer and second speed gear. Remove first and reverse gear retainer and then remove gear.

9. Remove shifter yokes and shafts, using care to prevent poppet balls from jumping out, then remove poppet balls and springs. Poppet balls are under the rear end of the short shaft and under the front end of the long shaft. Selector shaft must be moved so that interlock is clear of each shaft as it is removed.

10. Remove set screws from shifter levers on selector shaft. Remove second and third speed interlock retainer in right end of selector shaft. Remove first and reverse interlock pin from case.

11. Remove shift lever and lock washer from left end of selector shaft, then drive the shaft out through the right side of the transmission case, using a soft faced hammer. The welch plug in the right side of the case will be driven out by the shaft. Do not let the shifter levers and interlock drop into the case.

12. Remove selector lever and shaft, spring washer, flat washer and oil seal from transmission case.

13. Drive counter gear shaft lock pin into the shaft. Then drive the shaft out through the rear end of the transmission case, using an arbor of the right length to hold the needle bearings and thrust washers in place. Allow the cluster gear to rest on the bottom of the case.

14. Remove the snap ring from the main drive gear bearing and tap the drive gear and bearing assembly toward the transmission case to remove it.

15. Carefully raise the cluster gear out of the case so that the arbor and needle bearings will not fall out. Remove all thrust washers.

16. Drive the reverse idler gear shaft lock pin into the shaft and remove the shaft, idler gear and thrust washers. (Fig. 11 shows a layout of the counter gear and reverse idler gear and their related parts.)

17. Disassemble the main drive gear if any parts are to be replaced. Remove oil seal, retainer (snap ring), washer and oil slinger from drive gear. Then remove bearing by jar-

ring the shaft on a wooden block. Remove the mainshaft pilot roller bearing by removing its retaining snap ring and retainer washer.

Assembly of Transmission—Reverse the order of disassembly to assemble the transmission, being sure to follow closely the precautions outlined for assembling the Series 40 transmission.

STD. TRANS. SHIFT LINKAGE

1957-61

All adjustments are made with the transmission in neutral and in position for shifting into second or third gear.

1. With adapter assembly forced against flexible coupling flange, raise or lower jacket clamp until selector control lever pivot bushing clears control shaft lever by $\frac{7}{16}''$. Then tighten clamp securely.
2. Adjust shift rod trunnion so that control shaft lever is midway in jacket opening with transmission in neutral.
3. Adjust selector rod trunnion so that with selector lever (on transmission) and selector rod *both* held to the rear, trunnion pin will freely enter hole in selector lever. Then lengthen selector rod by rotating trunnion two turns for proper adjustment.
4. Shift transmission into each gear to check for proper shifting and to check control shaft lever clearance in mast jacket opening.

1953-56

All adjustments are made with the transmission in neutral and in position for shifting into second or third gear.

1. Raise or lower the jacket clamp assembly until selector control lever pivot clears control shaft lever by $\frac{5}{8}''$. Then tighten clamp securely.
2. Adjust shift rod trunnion so that lower control shaft lever is midway in mast jacket opening with transmission in neutral.
3. Adjust selector rod clevis so that with selector rod held to rear, the clevis pin will enter hole in selector control lever without moving lever.
4. Shift transmission into each gear to check for proper shifting and to check control shaft lever clearance in mast jacket opening.

FLIGHT PITCH DYNA-FLOW, 1958

Transmission Remove

1. On Air-Poise cars, raise car by operating manual over-ride valve.
2. On all models, raise car front and rear, solidly supporting front suspension and rear of frame. Support axle housing with floor jack.
3. On Air-Poise models, carefully and slowly loosen air lines from rear air springs to allow springs to bleed air

out. Remove plungers from air springs. Disconnect height control valve links at strut rods.
4. On all models, disconnect radius rod at axle end, and shock absorbers at lower ends.
5. Disconnect parking brake cable at rear cable sheave and at bracket at torque tube.
6. Disconnect brake hose from pipe at frame X member and remove yoke. Cover hoses and pipe to prevent entrance of dirt.
7. To prevent strain on parts, disconnect exhaust pipe (s) at manifold (s) and loosen exhaust pipe-to-muffler joint (s).
8. Install 3" guide pins in alternate bolt holes in torque ball. Remove remaining two torque tube flange bolts.
9. Lower axle assembly and push back to clear torque ball.
10. Remove converter housing cover.
11. Turn flywheel until one converter drain plug can be positioned to provide an air vent. Then turn flywheel until opposite drain plug is down. Remove this plug and allow oil to drain from converter.
12. Remove filler pipe from oil pan and allow oil to drain from transmission.
13. Remove converter-to-flywheel bolts.
14. Disconnect oil cooler pipes.
15. Disconnect speedometer cable, stator control rod at transmission lever, lower shift rod at transmission lever, and upper shift rod at idler lever. *Leave lower rod, idler lever and bracket attached to cross member.*
16. Support transmission securely and use jack to safely support frame.
17. Remove transmission mounting bolts.
18. Raise engine and transmission just enough to relieve strain on support.
19. Remove transmission support. *If shims are present, note number and location so they may be reinstalled in original position.*
20. Lower transmission enough to remove six transmission-to-engine bolts.
21. With engine separately supported, move transmission to rear to dis-

engage converter pump cover from crankshaft.
22. Lower transmission and remove from under car. *If transmission is to be placed on an oily surface, remove mounts to prevent deterioration of rubber. Do not tilt transmission forward as weight of converter may damage bushings in front planet carrier and oil rings on first turbine shaft.*

Installation

Installation of the transmission is accomplished by reversing the removal procedure. However, be sure to observe the following:

1. When installing transmission be certain drive lugs on converter pump do not disengage from front pump gear.
2. Tighten converter housing-to-crankcase bolts to 45-55 lb. ft. torque.
3. Tighten three flywheel-to-converter bolts to a torque of 25-30 lb. ft.
4. If transmission cannot be made to seat on support, the front engine mounts should be loosened and the engine raised (by means of a pry bar) and pulled forward to remove bind from front mounts. If bind is allowed to remain, engine may set up a vibration when running. Following installation of transmission, re-tighten engine mounts.
5. Following installation of oil cooler pipes, check to be sure that pipes are not contacting transmission support, frame, front spring cross member, body, etc.
6. On Air-Poise models, loosely connect radius rod and shock absorbers. Connect air lines to rear air spring domes. Insert plungers into air springs and carefully pull down on height control valve arm to partially inflate air spring and retain plunger. Connect height control valve links to strut rod brackets. Then tighten exhaust system, radius rod and shock absorbers.

Checking Shift Linkage

1. Move manual control lever until

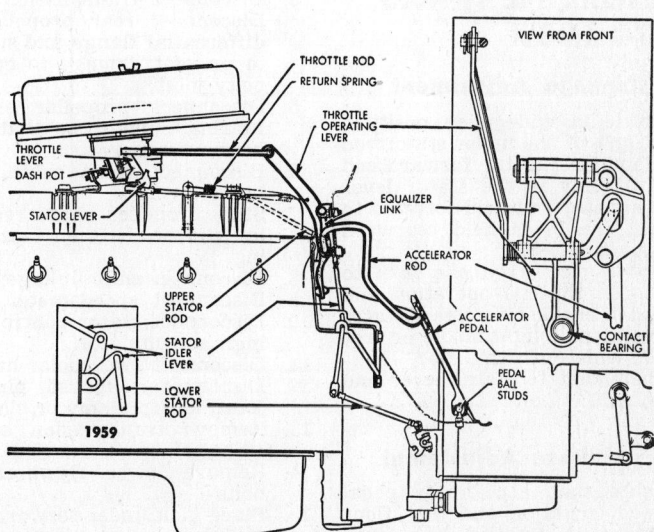

Fig. 11A   Throttle and stator control linkage.   1959-61 Twin Turbine transmission

transmission is shifted into its Drive "D" detent position.

2. Move manual control lever toward Grade Retard without lifting toward steering wheel. Note how far it moves before contacting stop.
3. Move manual control lever until transmission is in Neutral "N" detent position.
4. Move manual control lever toward Reverse and note how far it moves before contacting stop.
5. If movement from Drive detent is the same as from Neutral detent to stop, shift control linkage is properly adjusted.

Adjusting Shift Linkage

1. Loosen clevis lock nut, Fig. 12.
2. Remove clevis pin and washer.
3. Lengthen or shorten lower shift rod by turning clevis until distance from Drive detent to stop is the same as from Neutral detent to stop.
4. Check pointer on transmission dial; if pointer is not adjusted properly, pry off dial, loosen nut and adjust pointer in Drive range.
5. If external linkage has been checked and adjusted and transmission still does not shift properly, the transmission oil pan must be removed and internal linkage checked and adjusted as outlined in the *Flight Pitch Dynaflow* chapter.

Stator Linkage Adjustment

1. With throttle in *hot idle position*, adjust upper stator rod so that ball joint at forward end will just slip freely in stator lever with both stator lever and rod pushed rearward.
2. Shorten stator rod one full turn to provide clearance at stop inside transmission case.
3. Reconnect ball joint to stator lever and tighten nut.

TRIPLE TURBINE TRANS. 1959

Stator Linkage Adjustment

With throttle in wide open position, adjust the length of the upper stator rod so the ball joint stud at the forward end will just slip freely in the stator lever hole with the stator rod held forward to the stop and the lever held rearward against the pickup.

Lengthen the stator rod *one turn* to allow wide open throttle operation and provide an easy check for correct stator linkage adjustment (slight shake or free movement at wide open throttle).

Connect ball joint to stator lever and tighten lock nut.

Throttle Linkage Adjustment

1. Make sure that accelerator pedal is in good condition and that floor mat is properly installed. Make sure pedal ball studs are tight in floor pan.

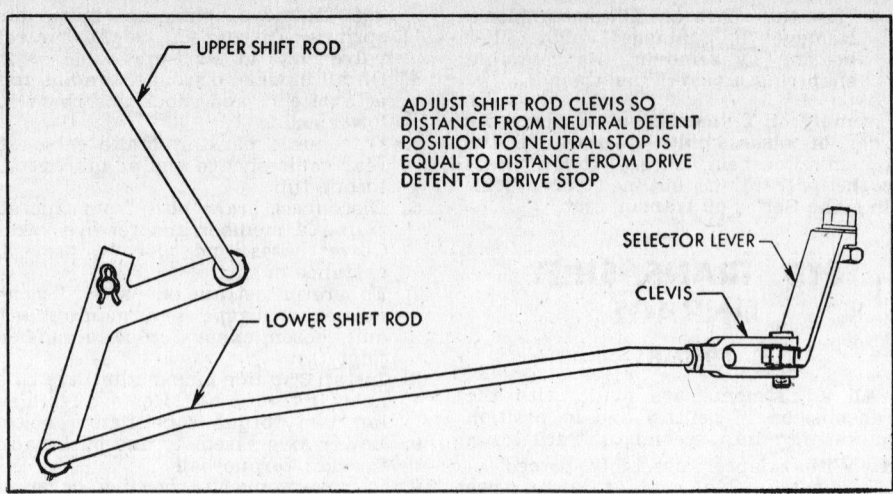

Fig. 12 Shift control linkage for 1958 Flight Pitch and 1957-58 Variable Pitch Dynaflow

2. Check throttle linkage for proper lubrication. Make sure that pedal rod does not bind going through floor, and see that pedal return spring fully closes the throttle.
3. Move throttle lever to wide open position and make sure stator linkage does not prevent throttle from opening completely. With throttle wide open, stator rod should still have a slight amount of free movement. If stator rod is not free, make stator linkage adjustment as outlined above before proceeding with throttle linkage adjustment.
4. *Adjust throttle linkage as directed for the Twin Turbine transmission.*

VARIABLE PITCH & TWIN TURBINE

Replace, 1961

1. Raise car front and rear.
2. Drain transmission.
3. Disconnect transmission filler tube.
4. Disconnect rear propeller shaft at differential flange and support shaft to prevent damage to constant velocity joint.
5. Disconnect propeller shaft center bearing support so that shaft may be moved rearward.
6. Disconnect front cable at parking brake lever.
7. Slide propeller shaft rearward and lay end of shaft on rear axle housing.
8. Disconnect shift linkage.
9. Disconnect speedometer cable.
10. Disconnect stator control linkage at high accumulator.
11. Disconnect two cooler lines.
12. Disconnect exhaust pipe at first joint; loosen clamp or clamps.
13. Remove transmission support pad (2 bolts).
14. Remove lower flywheel cover (6 bolts).
15. Place jack under forward portion of raised step on oil pan and raise engine to remove load from crossmember.

16. Carefully mark transmission support and frame at each end of support so support may be reinstalled in same fore and aft position. *This step is necessary to insure against any shear strain being imposed on engine mountings when support is reinstalled.*
17. Reverse removal procedure to install.

Replace, 1955-60

1. Hoist front and rear of car and rest it solidly on stands placed under frame. Frame side rails should be at least 20" above floor.

On 1959-60, disconnect rear shock absorbers at axle end, track bar at axle end, brake cable at equalizer and brake pipe at torque tube bracket. Remove rear exhaust pipes.

2. Disconnect torque tube from torque ball and move rear axle back to disengage propeller shaft from universal joint.
3. Remove converter housing cover.
4. Turn flywheel until one converter drain plug can be loosened sufficiently to provide an air vent, then turn flywheel until opposite drain plug is straight down. Remove this plug and allow oil to drain from converter.
5. Remove filler pipe from oil pan to drain oil from transmission.
6. Unfasten converter from flywheel.
7. Remove oil cooler pipes.
8. Disconnect speedometer cable, shift rod from shift lever, and stator operating control rod from lever on high accumulator.
9. Place transmission jack or hoist in position to securely support the transmission.
10. On 1955-58, disconnect exhaust pipes from exhaust manifolds and loosen front muffler joints.
11. Remove four bolts that attach the thrust plate to rear bearing retainer, then remove two nuts and plate that attach mounting pad to transmission support.
12. Raise engine and transmission just

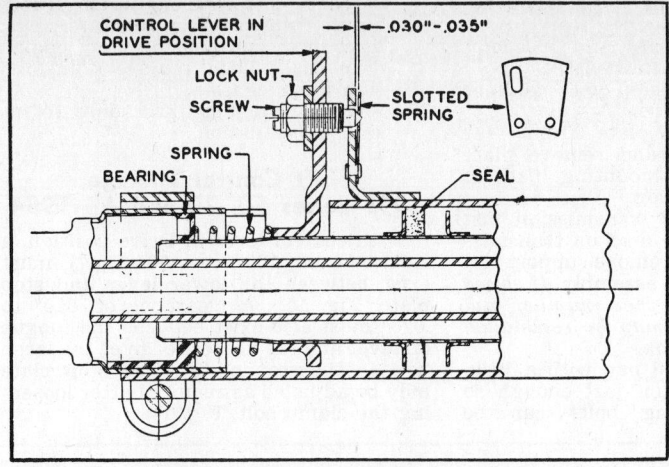

Fig. 13 Lower lever and stop plate. 1956 Dynaflow shift linkage

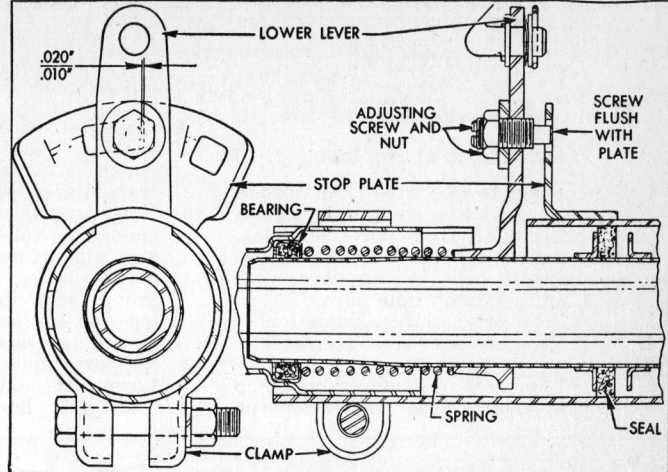

Fig. 14 Lower lever and stop plate. 1955 Dynaflow shift linkage

enough to relieve load on transmission support, then remove support and thrust plate as an assembly. *If shims are present, note their number and location so that they can be reinstalled in original position.*

13. Support rear of engine oil pan with a jack.
14. Lower transmission just enough so that converter housing bolts can be reached. With engine and transmission supported by separate jacks, unfasten converter housing from engine.
15. Move transmission rearward to disengage hub of converter pump cover from crankshaft, lower transmission and remove from car.
16. Reverse foregoing procedure to install the transmission.

Shift Control Linkage

When the transmission does not operate properly it is advisable to first check the shift control linkage adjustment, *after first checking to be sure transmission oil is at the proper level.*

1959-61 Throttle Linkage Adjust

1. Move throttle lever to wide open position and make sure stator linkage does not prevent throttle from opening completely. With throttle wide open, stator rod should still have a slight amount of free movement. If stator rod is not free, make stator linkage adjustment as outlined for the *Triple Turbine transmission.*
2. Disconnect throttle rod from throttle operating lever, Fig. 11A.
3. While a helper presses accelerator pedal firmly against floor mat, hold throttle in wide open position, and hold rear end of throttle rod at hole in throttle operating lever. Rod end must be approximately $\frac{1}{16}$″ short of entering hole in lever. Readjust throttle rod length as required to obtain this dimension.

1957-58

Check and adjust the shift control linkage as outlined for the Flight Pitch Dynaflow, referring to Fig. 12.

1956

1. With lower shift rod disconnected from idler lever and manual control lever in Drive position, adjust the stop screw into the slot of the spring until the spring is deflected .030″, Fig. 13.
2. Carefully move the lower shift rod forward and backward to determine when it is in the center of the slotted hole in the transmission shift lever (approximately .060″ movement is possible).
3. Adjust clevis until its pin enters hole in idler lever without moving rod in slotted hole in transmission shift lever.
4. Remove pin and assemble anti-rattle washers, clevis pin and cotter pin. Tighten lock nut.

1955

1. With shift control lever released, the stop screw in control shaft lower lever must be flush with upper surface of stop plate. Adjust as required, referring to Fig. 14.
2. With shift control lever in Drive position, .010″ to .020″ clearance must exist between the stop screw and the upper edge of the large opening in stop plate. Since this clearance cannot readily be checked because of location, it may be assured by carefully performing the following adjustment.
3. Disconnect lower shift rod clevis from idler lever and make sure that transmission shift lever is firmly held by detent in Drive position.
4. With shift control lever on steering column in Drive position, push upward on idler lever to hold stop screw in contact with stop plate, then adjust clevis in shift rod so that its pin will freely enter clevis and lever.
5. Shorten length of rod and clevis by turning clevis ½ turn up on rod, then install clevis pin with anti-rattle

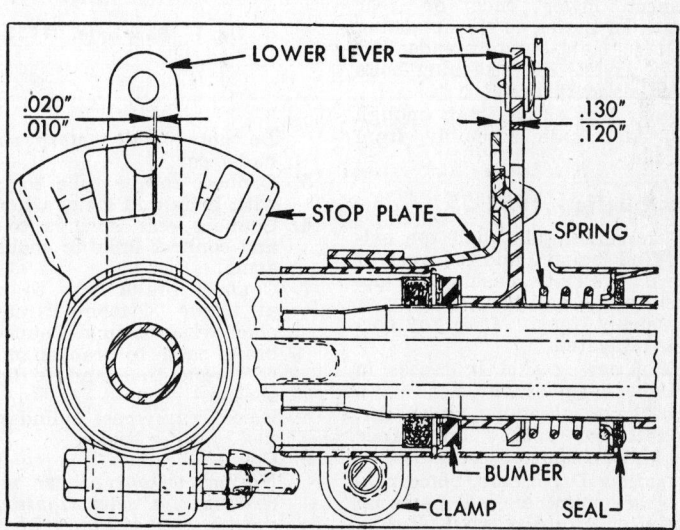

Fig. 15 Lower lever and stop plate. 1953 Series 50, 70 and all 1954 Dynaflow

washers and tighten clevis lock nut. The ½ turn of clevis provides the proper clearance at stop pin.

DYNAFLOW, 1953-54

Transmission, Replace

1. Disconnect torque tube from torque ball and move axle back to disengage propeller shaft from universal joint.
2. On V8 models, remove starter motor splash pan, bell housing cover and bell housing hand hole cover.
3. Drain converter and transmission.
4. Unfasten converter from flywheel.
5. Remove oil cooler.
6. On V8 models, disconnect oil filler pipe at rubber hose and disconnect exhaust pipe hanger at right accumulator.
7. Disconnect shift rod and speedometer cable at transmisison.
8. Support transmission with jack or hoist.
9. Unfasten thrust plate from rear bearing retainer and remove plate which attaches mounting pad to transmission support.
10. Raise engine and transmission just enough to relieve load on transmission support and remove support and thrust plate as an assembly. *If shims are present note their number and location so they may be reinstalled in original position.*
11. Support engine oil pan with a jack.
12. Lower transmission just enough so that bell housing bolts can be reached. Then with engine and transmission supported by separate jacks, disconnect bell housing from engine crankcase. Then remove transmission from chassis.
13. Reverse foregoing procedure to install transmission.

Shift Control Linkage
1953 Series 50, 70 and All 1954

With control lever in Drive position, a clearance of .120″ to .130″ (⅛″) must exist between the lower lever and stop plate, Fig. 15. A clearance of .010″ to .020″ must also exist between the tongue on lever and the nearest edge of the large hole in the stop plate. The stop plate may be adjusted as required after loosening the clamp bolt, Fig. 15.

Rear Axle and Brake Section

Refer To Hydraulic Brakes Chapter For Brake Adjustments

REAR AXLE, REPLACE

Removal, 1953-55

1. Place car stands solidly under frame so that rear end of car is high enough to permit working underneath.
2. Disconnect parking brake cable at rear brake cable sheave and at bracket on front end of torque tube. Disconnect brake hose from pipe at frame X member and remove retainer. Plug hose and brake pipe openings to prevent entrance of dirt.
3. Disconnect torque tube from torque ball by removing bolts at flange.
4. Disconnect links from shock absorber arms and disconnect radius rod at right end.
5. Disconnect lower ends of rear springs. On Series 40 the attaching studs have right-hand threads, but on other models the attaching bolts have left-hand threads.
6. Hoist rear end of car high enough to roll rear axle assembly from under car.

Installation 1953-55

1. Check universal joint ball for evidence of oil leakage and for wear of universal joint bushing. Note whether torque ball has end play or is excessively tight. Make any corrections indicated.
2. Cement a new gasket in recess in front end of torque tube.
3. Roll rear axle assembly under car. Then rest car solidly on stands placed under frame.
4. On Dynaflow Drive cars, place propeller shaft spline oil seal parts on front end of propeller shaft, Fig. 1. Install these parts just before connecting torque tube to torque ball.

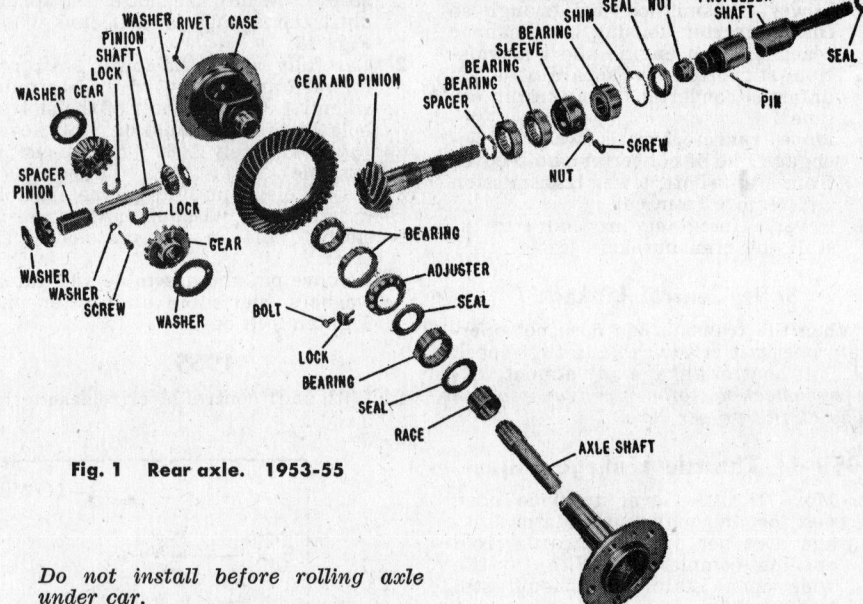

Fig. 1   Rear axle.   1953-55

Do not install before rolling axle under car.
5. Connect torque tube to torque ball with bolts and lockwashers.
6. Connect rear springs to rear axle and connect links to shock absorber arms.
7. Connect brake hose to brake pipe at frame X member and lock in place with retainer. Connect parking brake cable to bracket on front end of torque tube and to brake cable sheave.
8. Bleed rear wheel cylinders and adjust parking brake.
9. Connect radius rod to rear axle. *Normal weight of car must be on rear springs when tightening radius rod pin nuts so that rubber bushings in rod will be clamped in neutral position.*

Removal, 1956-60

1. Place car stands solidly under frame so rear end of car is high enough to permit working underneath, and place a floor jack under center of axle housing so it just supports weight of rear axle assembly.
2. Disconnect radius rod at axle end.
3. Disconnect lower ends of rear springs.
4. Disconnect lower ends of rear shock absorbers.
5. Disconnect parking brake cable at

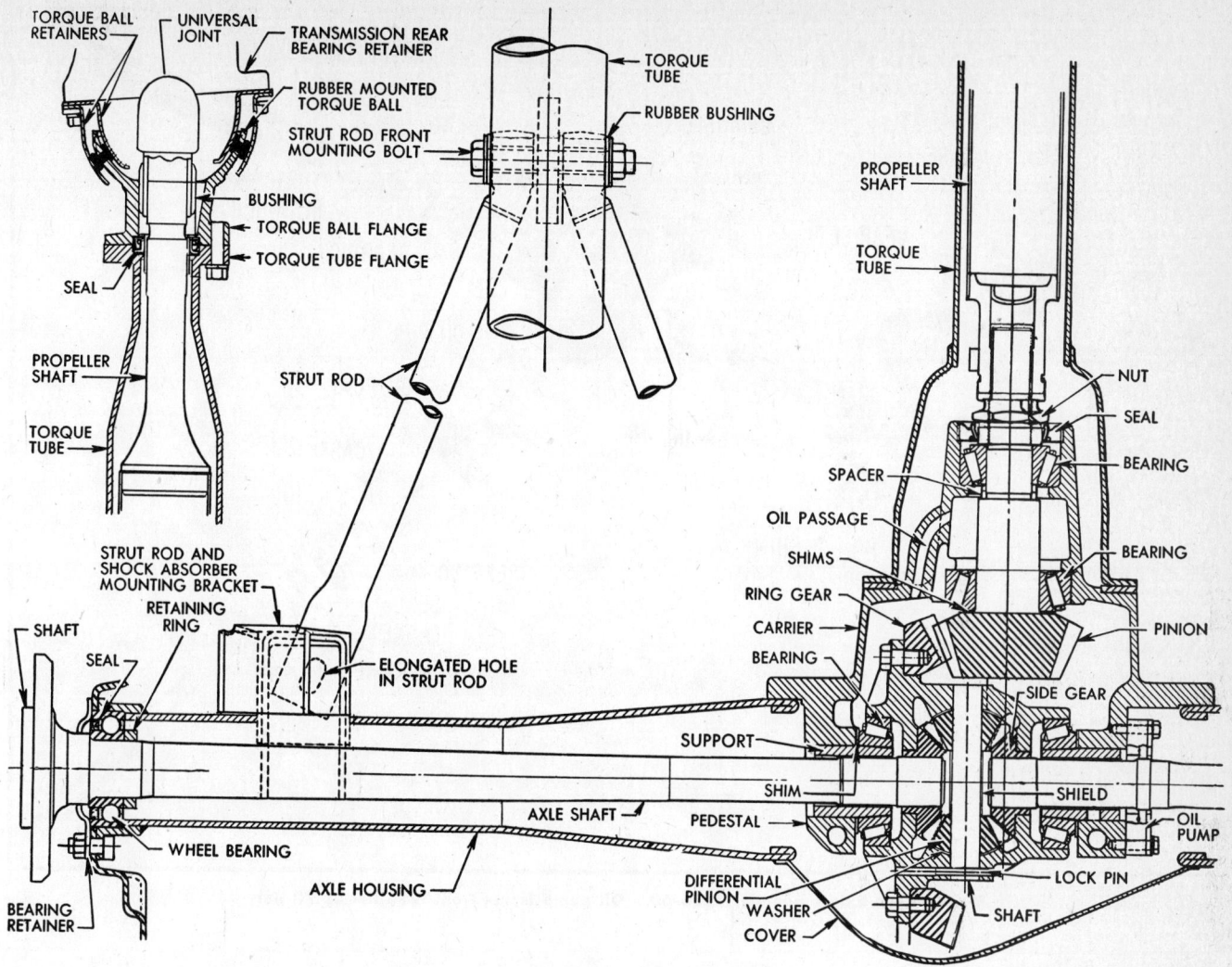

Fig. 3 Rear axle assembly, 1956-60. Oil pump shown at right-hand differential pedestal is used on 1956 Series 70 only

rear cable sheave and at bracket on torque tube.

6. Disconnect brake hose from pipe at frame X member and remove yoke.
7. Cover hose and brake pipe openings to prevent entrance of dirt.
8. Loosen torque ball retainer bolts so ball is free.
9. Remove two opposite torque tube flange bolts, replacing them with two 3" guide pins.
10. Remove other flange bolts.
11. Roll rear axle assembly out from under car.

Installation, 1956-60

1. Check torque ball for evidence of oil leaking and for wear of universal joint bushing.
2. Check propeller shaft seal for oil leaks or damage.
3. Roll rear axle assembly under car.
4. Guide propeller shaft and torque tube into proper alignment with torque ball, using two guide pins to avoid damage to propeller shaft seal. Rotate rear wheel to line up propeller shaft and universal joint splines.

5. Connect torque tube to torque ball, tightening bolts to 30-35 lb. ft. on 1956 and 50 lb. ft. on 1957-60. *Do not tighten torque ball retainer bolts at this time.*
6. Connect rear springs to rear axle assembly.
7. Connect shock absorber lower ends loosely.
8. Connect brake hose to brake pipe at frame X member and lock in place with yoke.
9. Connect parking brake cable through bracket on torque tube and to brake cable sheave.
10. Bleed rear wheel cylinders and adjust parking brake.
11. Connect radius rod loosely to rear axle.
12. Lower car on wheel stands. Then tighten torque ball retainer bolts, shock absorber lower ends and radius rod lower end. *Normal weight must be on rear wheels when tightening these parts so that rubber bushings will be clamped in neutral position.*
13. Lower car to floor and fill axle housing to filler plug hole, using approved gear lubricant.

1961

It is not necessary to remove the rear axle assembly from the car for removal of the differential carrier assembly.

1. Remove rear wheels, brake drums and axle shafts. *Note that studs are used on brake drums and left side has left-hand threads.*
2. Remove U-bolts from pinion flange to disconnect rear universal joint. Support propeller shaft to prevent damage to center bearing and constant velocity joint.
3. Loosen (do not remove) all carrier-to-axle housing nuts.
4. Place floor jack under carrier assembly and pry carrier loose. Raise jack until weight of carrier is resting on jack.
5. Remove nuts and take out carrier. *If necessary to pry carrier from axle housing use caution to avoid unnecessary damage to carrier and axle housing. After removal of carrier, check for burrs caused by prying and smooth as required.*

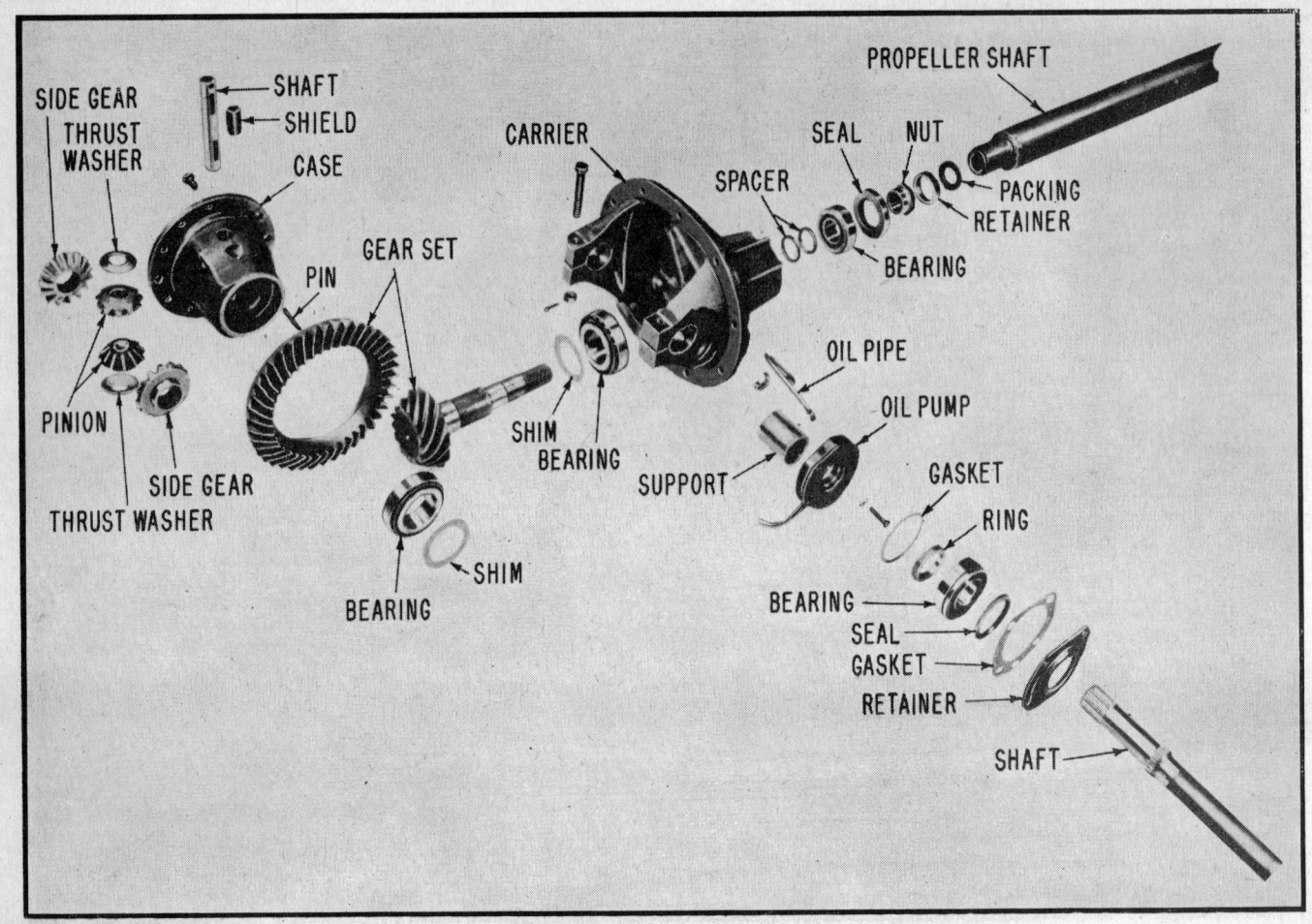

Fig. 4 Rear axle assembly, 1956-60. Oil pump is used on 1956 Series 70 only

REAR AXLE REPAIRS
1953-55

The drive pinion is splined and pressed in the propeller shaft, and end movement is prevented by a pin riveted through the shaft coupling and propeller shaft. The pinion is adjusted by shims between the outer race of the double-row ball bearing and the counterbore in the propeller shaft housing. This bearing is built with no looseness or end play, nor is it adjustable for end play. If there is any looseness between the race and cone, it is probably caused by abrasive matter in the lubricant.

The threaded nut type of differential bearing adjustment is used. The procedure for making this adjustment, as well as the assembly of the differential case, riveting on the ring gear, checking ring gear and pinion backlash and other differential case operations, is given in the *Rear Axle Service* chapter.

To replace the pinion and bearings, take out the rear axle assembly as already described, unbolt the differential carrier from the axle housing, remove the axle shafts and, after removing the differential bearing caps and adjusting nuts, lift the differential from the carrier.

Pinion & Bearings

After removing the axle shafts (described further on) and differential, remove the three tapered bearing retainer screws from the side of the carrier. Jar the carrier so that the splined end of the propeller shaft will strike on a wooden block or floor and the pinion shaft will slide out. Remove the bearing adjusting shims from the inside of the torque tube, noting their number and total thickness.

To disassemble the drive pinion from the propeller shaft, file off one head of the straight pin which fastens these parts together, and drive out the pin. Pull the pinion shaft from the propeller shaft with a suitable puller. Pounding or driving on the head of the pinion in an attempt to separate these parts will bend the propeller shaft.

To disassemble the pinion, pry up the staked section of the pinion bearing lock nut and unscrew the nut, gripping the pinion on its splines. Press the double-row ball bearing from the pinion shaft by using blocks under the outer race, then remove the spacer and single-row bearing. Thoroughly wash the bearings in unused cleaning solvent. Apply a small quantity of engine oil and check for smothness, looseness and other defects.

To assemble, install the spacer, single-

row bearing and lock sleeve. Then press on the double-row bearing, using a piece of tubing of the proper size to bear directly on the inner race. Draw up the pinion bearing lock nut tightly and stake it into the notch of the pinion shaft. Assemble the pinion shaft to the propeller shaft, then rivet these parts together with a new pin.

Every time the pinion and propeller shafts are pressed together, the assembly must be straightened to correct a tendency to "whip". Checking with a dial indicator, run-out should not exceed .015". To straighten the shaft, rotate the pinion to the high spot and force the end of the shaft down by hand to spring it into proper alignment.

Pinion & Propeller Shaft, Assemble

Install the same thickness of shims in the counterbore of the torque tube that were removed when the assembly was dismantled. Make sure the shims are flat in the counterbore and not cocked. Shims are available in several thicknesses so that a suitable combination may be selected to replace the original ones if they are damaged, or if another combination is needed to secure proper location of the pinion if a new gear set is installed.

Lubricate the bearings thoroughly and

coat the bearing surface of the lock sleeve with rear axle lubricant. Install the propeller shaft, driving it down until the bearings are seated in the housing. Tap the outer race of the single-row bearing until it seats against the collar which locks against the double-row bearing. This is important, otherwise the bearing rollers will bind the spacer between the single-row bearing and the pinion teeth.

Continue with the work by checking through the bearing lock screw holes in the side of the carrier to make sure the lock sleeve is in the correct position up against the back of the double-row bearing. Install the three tapered lock screws and draw them down evenly and tightly. Then tighten the lock nuts.

If a pinion setting gauge is available, check the pinion depth as outlined in the *Rear Axle Service* chapter.

If a correction is necessary, disassemble the parts and, if the pinion is to be moved toward the center of the axle add shims. If it is to be moved away from the center of the axle remove shims.

If no pinion setting gauge is available, assemble the differential unit and check the tooth contact by painting the ring gear teeth as described in the *Rear Axle Service* chapter.

When the adjustment is correct, set it securely with the lock screws and lock nuts as stated above.

REAR AXLE REPAIRS

1961

The rear axle and drive line have been redesigned to accomodate the new three-link type rear suspension. The torque tube drive has been supplanted by an open propeller shaft with drive and torque reaction forces being taken through rubber-mounted link connections to the frame at the rear of the car.

Internally, the rear axle is similar to that used in 1960. The drive pinion has been revised to accomodate the attachment of the pinion flange at the rear universal joint. The differential carrier has been redesigned to reduce weight and eliminate flanges formerly required for torque tube attachment.

1956-60

In this type rear axle, Figs. 3 and 4, the drive pinion is mounted on two tapered roller bearings which are pre-loaded by two selected spacers at assembly. The pinion is positioned by shims located between a shoulder on the drive pinion and rear bearing. The front bearing is held in place by a staked lock nut. The differential carrier casting has an oil feed passage to the pinion bearings and an oil return hole so that the oil will circulate and cool.

The differential is supported in the carrier by two tapered roller side bearings. These are pre-loaded by inserting shims between the bearings and the pedestals. The differential assembly is positioned for proper gear and pinion backlash by varying these shims. The bearings are centered on the cross axis

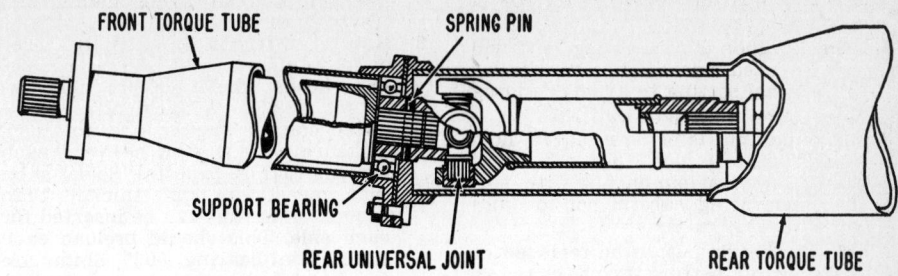

Fig. 4A   Rear universal joint and torque tube.   1957-60

by lock taper cones secured in the pedestal bores by clamp bolts. The ring gear is bolted to the case. The case houses two side gears in mesh with two pinions mounted on a pinion axle which is anchored in the case by a spring pin. The pinions are backed by bronze spherical thrust washers.

The oil pump shown at the right-hand differential pedestal, Fig. 3, is used on Series 70 cars only. The pump is the vane type and is used to provide a jet of oil at the point where the ring gear and pinion mesh. It is driven by a set of splines on the axle shaft.

Torque Tube & Propeller Shaft, Replace, 1956

1. Remove axle from car.
2. Disconnect torque tube brake line from tee fitting on axle housing.
3. Disconnect strut rods from torque tube bracket. Fasten strut rods to each other loosely, keeping all parts in their original position.
4. Unfasten torque tube from carrier and slide tube and propeller shaft from carrier.
5. Installation is made in the reverse order.

Torque Tube & Propeller Shaft, Replace, 1957-60

Since the overall car height has been lowered for 1957, the use of a depressed two-piece torque tube has replaced the straight one-piece torque tube used in 1956. And because of the depressed type torque tube, a two-piece propeller shaft is necessary. The front and rear shaft are connected by an additional universal joint that is supported in the torque tube by a bearing, Fig. 4A.

To remove the torque tube and propeller shaft, remove rear axle from car. Disconnect brake lines from axle housing and torque tube. Disconnect strut rods from torque tube. Separate front torque tube from rear one and remove front tube and propeller shaft.

To disassemble propeller shaft, support universal joint and drive out spring pin with punch, Fig. 4A.

The propeller shaft bearing is a permanently lubricated, sealed ball bearing. The bearing should not be removed except to replace it with a new one when worn or excessively loose.

Differential Carrier, Replace

1. Remove rear axle assembly.
2. Remove torque tube and propeller shaft.
3. Remove brake line from axle housing to avoid damaging it later.
4. Remove both axle shafts.
5. Locate axle housing so carrier is upward.
6. Unfasten carrier from housing and lift carrier from housing, using a suitable sling.
7. Installation is made in the reverse order.

Carrier, Disassemble

1. With carrier mounted in a suitable holding fixture, check existing gear lash with a dial indicator. This will show up gear or bearing wear or an error in backlash or preload setting. It will also enable used gears to be reinstalled at original lash setting to avoid changing gear tooth contact.
2. On Series 70 only, remove oil line and pump.
3. Remove differential bearing pedestal clamp bolts and open pedestals by tapping a wedge in each pedestal slot.
4. Pull differential bearing supports, using a suitable puller and slide hammer.
5. Use a suitable spreader to free differential case.
6. Lift case straight out until side bearings are half-way clear of pedestals. Then take hold at bearings with both hands to keep them from dropping and lift case assembly out.
7. Keep right and left bearings, shims and supports in sets so they may be reinstalled in their same position. Remove spreader tool.
8. Mark ring gear and case so they may be reassembled in same relative position.
9. Remove ring gear.
10. Drive differential pinion axle spring pin, pinion axle and shield from case. Mark pinions, side gears and washers so they may be reinstalled on the same side. Then remove these parts.
11. If differential bearing is to be replaced, use a suitable puller to pull bearing outer race from case.

Pinion & Bearings, Remove

1. Check pinion preload as outlined further on. This will show up ex-

cessive bearing wear or an error in preload setting.

2. Check pinion depth setting as it will enable used parts to be reinstalled at original setting to avoid changing gear tooth contact.

3. As pinion nut is being removed, hold hand under pinion to catch it. If necessary, tap pinion out with soft hammer, being careful not to damage bearing races.

4. If rear bearing is to be replaced or pinion depth setting is to be changed, remove rear bearing from pinion shaft with a press.

5. Pry oil seal from carrier.

6. If front pinion bearing is to be replaced, drive outer race from carrier.

7. If rear pinion bearing is to be replaced, drive outer race from carrier.

Pinion & Bearings, Install

1. Before installation, make certain that interior of carrier housing is absolutely clean and dry. Also make certain that parts to be assembled are clean and that pinion bearing shims are not burred. Bearings and oil seals should be lightly lubricated with rear axle lubricant just before assembly.

2. Drive front bearing outer race against shoulder in carrier.

3. Drive rear bearing outer race against shoulder in carrier.

4. Whenever a new carrier, a new pinion, or a new pinion bearing is to be used, a trial assembly must be made in order to determine correct pinion depth setting and correct pinion bearing preload. For a starting pinion depth setting, use a shim with a nominal thickness of .048". Place this shim against head of pinion and install rear pinion bearing.

5. For a starting pinion bearing preload adjustment, use a pair of spacers with a nominal thickness of .435". Place these spacers on pinion and hold pinion in position in carrier. Turn pinion counterclockwise into nut. Do not install pinion seal at this time. Torque pinion nut to 80 lb. ft.

6. Rotate pinion three or four times to seat bearings. Turn pinion slowly with an inch-pound torque wrench. Bearing preload should be 10-30 in. lb. If preload is under 10 in. lb., replace spacer with a thinner one; if over 30 in. lb., remove pinion nut and front bearing and replace preload spacer with a thicker one. These spacers are furnished to be used in pairs so that possible thicknesses range from .400" to .470". Service spacers are marked with their thickness in thousandths.

7. Assemble the differential unit and check the gear tooth contact as described in the *Rear Axle Chapter*.

Carrier, Assemble

1. Reassemble the differential and carrier assembly in the reverse order of disassembly.

2. When installing ring gear to case, first tighten bolts alternately on opposite sides of case to 25-30 lb. ft.,

then tighten in same manner to 65-75 lb. ft.

3. Rotate differential assembly three or four times to seat bearing rollers, then adjust the assembly sideways to get .008" gear backlash.

4. After correct backlash is obtained, measure with a shim between each bearing and its pedestal. Select shim that measures .002" thicker than largest shim that can be inserted for each side. This should preload each differential bearing .002". Shims are furnished to be used singly in thicknesses ranging from .040" to .082" in graduations of .002". To install shims it will be necessary to spread pedestals.

5. After shims are installed, drive each differential bearing support into its pedestal until seated solidly in bearing. Tighten pedestal clamp nuts to 30-40 lb. ft.

6. Recheck backlash, which must be .007"-.009" at point of minimum lash, with not more than .003" variation around gear.

7. On Series 70 axles, install oil pump and outlet line.

AXLE SHAFTS

1953-55

1. Raise car and take off wheel.
2. Remove brake drum.
3. Drain lubricant and remove differential cover.
4. Unscrew differential pinion shaft screw and pull pinion shaft and spacer block.
5. Rotate ring gear and lift out pinions.
6. Remove horseshoe washer from recess in end of axle shaft and use a suitable puller to remove axle shaft from housing.

If the bearing and oil seal are to be replaced, insert a bearing puller into housing and pull both parts out of housing as an assembly.

Replace the axle shaft in the reverse order of removal and check the end play. If the total side clearance of the spacer block exceeds .008", install an oversize spacer block. If the new spacer does not take up the excess clearance, new thrust washers should be installed behind the differential side gears.

1956-61

1. Raise rear wheels clear of floor and remove wheel and brake drum.
2. Remove nuts holding wheel bearing retainer plate to brake backing plate, leaving bolts in place to support backing plate.
3. Use slide hammer type puller to pull axle shaft out of housing.
4. Replace two opposite nuts finger tight to hold backing plate in position.

To replace bearing and oil seal, proceed as follows:

1. To replace the bearing, nick the retaining ring deep enough in three or four places to spread it. Ring will then slip off with light pressure.
2. Press off the bearing.
3. If seal only is defective, pry oil seal from bearing and install a new seal.

Push seal in carefully with fingers until lip is over bearing inner race. Drive seal in flush with flat wood block.

4. Press bearing and seal against shoulder on axle shaft. Bearing retainer plate must be on axle shaft before bearing is installed.
5. Press retaining ring against bearing with chamfer toward bearing.

To replace axle shaft, proceed as follows:

1. Rear axle shafts are not interchangeable between sides; right shaft is longer than left and has an extra set of splines for driving the oil pump.
2. Install new gasket at bearing shoulder in housing.
3. If wheel bearing or seal are only new parts used, replace old wheel bearing retainer gaskets with same number and thickness of new gaskets.
4. If new rear axle housing or new brake backing plate are used, install axle shaft and bearing assembly without retainer gaskets.
5. With backing plate pushed tight against housing flange, measure clearance between retainer and backing plate with feelers. Select number of new gaskets as required to give .005" to .020" less thickness than feeler measurement.
6. Remove axle shaft, install new gaskets as selected and replace shaft. *This adjustment must be made carefully to be sure that wheel bearing inner gasket is held tightly against its shoulder by the wheel bearing. A loose fit here will allow gear oil to leak around bearing outer race.*
7. Replace nuts holding retainer plate to brake backing plate and tighten to 65-75 lb. ft. Then check with a .001" feeler gauge under retainer plate between two lower bolts. Retainer must be tight against its gaskets to prevent any possible leak from draining into brake.
8. Install brake drum and wheel.

MASTER CYLINDER, REPLACE

1953-55

1. To remove master cylinder, disconnect push rod at pedal adjusting nut.
2. Disconnect brake pipe from cylinder and tape its end to prevent entrance of dirt.
3. Unfasten and remove master cylinder from frame.
4. To install, reverse foregoing procedure, adjust brake pedal for proper clearance and bleed brake system.

1956

1. To remove the cylinder, disconnect the brake pipe and tape its end to prevent the entrance of dirt.
2. Disconnect stop light wires from stop light switch.
3. Disconnect push rod from pedal and remove pedal.
4. Remove screws holding steering column jacket rubber seal retainer to

fire wall and push it up on column jacket.
5. Remove toe pan.
6. Unfasten master cylinder from toe pan.
7. To install, reverse foregoing procedure.

1957-58

1. To remove master cylinder, disconnect battery ground strap.
2. Remove pin from push rod clevis.
3. Lift brake pedal to pull linkage out of the way, then remove large nut holding master cylinder to cowl.
4. Disconnect stop light wire connector from switch.
5. Disconnect brake pipe from master cylinder and tape end of pipe to prevent entrance of dirt.
6. Unfasten cylinder from ventilation air duct and remove from car.
7. Reverse foregoing procedure to install. However, it will be necessary to loosen brake reinforcing bracket bolt and nut. After the large nut is tightened, tighten the reinforcing bracket bolt and nut.

1959-61

1. To remove standard brake master cylinder, remove clevis pin and spring washer from push rod clevis. On 1960-61, disconnect pedal from push rod by removing lock nut. Then remove shoulder bolt and spring washer.
2. Disconnect brake pipe from master cylinder and on 1960-61 remove connector from stop light switch.
3. Unfasten master cylinder (4 bolts) and remove.

POWER BRAKE UNIT
1953-54

1. Remove starting motor splash pan.
2. Disconnect return spring, remove clevis pin at front end and remove the brake pedal push rod with cylinder push rod attached.
3. Disconnect breather tube which is clamped to inlet tube on power cylinder air cleaner cover.
4. Disconnect and remove pipe and hose that connects vacuum check valve to power cylinder.
5. Disconnect reservoir - to - hydraulic cylinder pipe and allow reservoir and pipe to drain.
6. Disconnect distributor - to - cylinder pipe and allow to drain.
7. Discard old fluid and cover pipe ends with tape to exclude dirt.

8. Remove nuts and lockwashers attaching power cylinder to its support and remove cylinder from car.
9. Install power cylinder by reversing foregoing procedure except for the installation of the push rod and splash pan. Adjust brake pedal stop and push rod (see below) and bleed the hydraulic system to complete the installation.

1955

1. Remove starting motor splash pan.
2. Disconnect return spring, loosen lock nut on cylinder push rod, remove clevis pin at brake pedal and unscrew pedal push rod from cylinder push rod.
3. Disconnect air inlet hose at air filter on brake cylinder, and disconnect hoses from vacuum tee on opposite side of cylinder.
4. Disconnect reservoir-to-hydraulic cylinder pipe, and allow reservoir and pipe to drain. Discard old fluid and cover pipe ends with tape to exclude dirt.
5. Detach power cylinder from its support and remove cylinder from car.
6. Reverse foregoing procedure to install. Adjust push rod as described below before installing splash pan.
7. After installation is completed, bleed the system in the conventional manner as outlined in the *Brakes* chapter, and then fill the reservoir to the proper level.

1956

1. Disconnect brake pipe and tape its end to prevent entrance of dirt.
2. Disconnect vacuum lines from power unit.
3. Place a drip pan under reservoir and remove reservoir.
4. Disconnect stop light wires from switch.
5. Disconnect push rod from pedal and remove pedal.
6. Remove screws holding steering column jacket rubber seal retainer to fire wall and push it up on the jacket.
7. Remove toe pan and power unit.
8. Unfasten toe pan from power unit.
9. To install, reverse foregoing procedure.

1957-58

1. Disconnect battery ground strap.
2. Remove pin from push rod clevis.
3. Lift brake pedal to pull linkage out of the way, then remove large nut holding brake unit to cowl.
4. Disconnect stop light wire connector from switch.

5. Disconnect brake pipe from hydraulic cylinder and tape end of pipe to prevent entrance of dirt.
6. Disconnect vacuum hoses from vacuum tee.
7. Remove bolts holding unit to ventilation air duct and remove power brake unit from car.
8. To install, reverse above procedure.

1959

1. Disconnect brake pipe from master cylinder from below.
2. Remove clevis pin from push rod clevis and pedal.
3. Loosen and roll back front carpet.
4. Remove toe plate-to-power cylinder retaining bolts.
5. Unfasten toe plate from toe pan.
6. Remove toe plate.
7. Disconnect vacuum hoses from tee.
8. Remove power cylinder.

1960-61

1. Remove connector from stop light switch and disconnect brake pipe from master cylinder.
2. Remove retainer and special washer from brake pedal pin and disengage push rod eye.
3. Remove air silencer from power cylinder air intake.
4. Remove four nuts holding power cylinder to dash panel.
5. Disconnect vacuum hoses from tee.
6. Remove power cylinder.

Bleeding Brake System, 1955-61

The power brake hydraulic system must be filled with approved brake fluid and all air must be bled out after any work requiring disconnection of a hydraulic brake pipe. The conventional brake bleeding procedure (given in the *Brake Chapter*) should be used.

1953-54

First bleed the rear end bleeder screw on the hydraulic cylinder. Next bleed at the front bleeder screw at the cylinder flange, and finally bleed the four wheel cylinders in sequence of left front, right front, left rear, right rear.

When brake fluid runs free of air bubbles at all bleed points, start the engine and, while holding pressure on the brake pedal, bleed again at both hydraulic cylinder bleeder screws. *Be sure to close bleeder screws before brake pedal strikes floor mat.*

After bleeding is completed, make sure that the reservoir is filled to proper level and check the brake system for fluid leaks while applying heavy pressure to the brake pedal—with engine running.

Front End and Steering Section

CAMBER & CASTER
1957-61

Adjustments are performed by installing shims between the upper control arm and the mounting bracket on the frame. Installing or removing shims at either the front or rear bracket changes the *caster* setting. Installing or removing shims equally at both brackets changes the *camber*.

To adjust caster, remove shims at the front bracket or add shims at the rear bracket to increase caster. To decrease caster, add shims at the front bracket or remove shims at the rear bracket.

To adjust camber, remove shims at

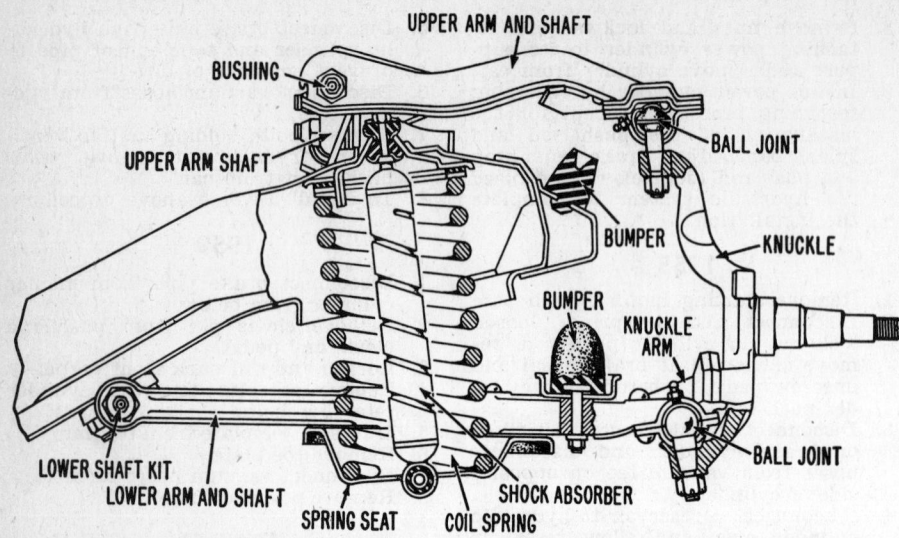

UPPER ARM AND SHAFT

BUSHING

UPPER ARM SHAFT

BALL JOINT

BUMPER

KNUCKLE

BUMPER

KNUCKLE ARM

BALL JOINT

LOWER SHAFT KIT
LOWER ARM AND SHAFT

SPRING SEAT

COIL SPRING

SHOCK ABSORBER

Fig. 5 Front suspension, 1959-60. The 1960 ball joint employs a steel coil preload spring in place of the 1959 rubber spring. Front end for 1958 is similar except that shock absorber is mounted outside of spring

both brackets to increase camber. To decrease camber, add shims at both brackets.

1953-56

One quarter turn of the pivot pin changes caster one quarter degree. The eccentric section of the pin allows a camber adjustment of $\frac{1}{3}$ degree either way from the neutral position of the eccentric. Turning the pivot pins will change both caster and camber. Therefore both angles must be checked together so that both will come within specified limits.

To adjust, jack up wheels and loosen clamp bolt at top of knuckle support. Remove grease fitting from threaded end of pin and insert wrench in hexagonal hole. Turn the pin in the desired direction to correct caster—which should be equal on both sides within $\frac{1}{2}$ degree. Camber should be equal on both sides within $\frac{3}{4}$ degree. In some cases, it will be necessary to average the settings in order to bring both within the specified limits.

TOE-IN, ADJUST

Adjust tie rod sleeves at outer ends. With front wheels in straight ahead position, the lower indented spoke of the steering wheel should be in center position. If not shorten one tie rod and lengthen the other. When this is done, recheck toe-in.

The intermediate rod is maintained in position by the pitman and idler arms. This requires proper location of the idler arm on its support so that the idler arm ball stud will be approximately level with the pitman arm ball stud to insure good steering action. The support must be threaded into the idler arm bushing until the distance from the center of the support lower bolt hole to the nearest face of the idler arm is $2\frac{21}{32}''$ to $2\frac{3}{4}''$ as shown. After any adjustment of the idler arm on its support, the front wheels

should be checked to insure proper toe-in.

If the idler arm support is dismounted from the frame for other work, such as when the oil pan is removed, wire the support to the idler arm so that it cannot turn from its existing position and possibly change the toe-in of the front wheels.

WHEEL BEARINGS, ADJUST

1. Tighten spindle nut to 30 ft. lbs. and rotate hub to seat bearings.
2. Back off spindle nut and re-torque to $12\frac{1}{2}$ ft. lbs.
3. If cotter pin does not line up, back off nut to nearest hole and insert cotter pin.
4. Before installing grease cap in hub, make sure that end of spindle and inside of cap are free of grease so radio static collector makes good contact. Be sure static collector is properly shaped to provide good contact.

1961 FRONT END

This suspension differs from that used in 1960 chiefly in that the lower control arms consist of two stamped steel plates welded together with the inner ends of the lower control arms bolted to the frame front crossmember through rubber bushings. In addition, to resist torsional roll characteristics and fore and aft movement of the lower control arm in relation to the frame, two solid steel rods are positioned between the lower control arms and front of the frame side rails. The forward ends of the rods are rubber mounted to hold securely to the frame bracket with nuts and cotter pins Torque is 60-80 ft. lbs. The rearward end of the brake reaction rod attaches to the lower control arm with two bolts torqued to 65-75 ft. lbs. A special hardened flat washer is used under the front bolt

to aid in maintaining required torque. *Brake reaction rod must be properly installed and secured prior to checking and adjusting caster and camber.*

1958-60 FRONT END

Upper Ball Joint, Replace

1. Raise car with jack under frame.
2. Remove wheel and tire.
3. Loosen but do not remove nut on ball joint tapered stud, Fig. 5, and rap steering knuckle in area of stud to separate stud from knuckle.
4. Support car weight under outer edge of spring seat and remove nut from ball joint stud.
5. Support car weight on frame and lower spring seat to lower knuckle, hub and drum slightly.
6. Raise upper control arm and remove rubber bumper under upper control arm.
7. Remove ball joint rivets.
8. Assemble new ball joint to upper control arm with $\frac{5}{16}''$ bolts inserted from bottom. Torque nuts to 15-20 ft. lbs.
9. Complete assembly by reversing disassembly procedure. Torque ball joint tapered stud nut to 30-40 ft. lbs.

Lower Ball Joint, Replace

1. Raise car and remove wheel.
2. Disconnect stabilizer link (if so equipped).
3. On 1958, disconnect shock absorber at lower end. On 1959-60, remove shock absorber.
4. Loosen but do not remove ball joint stud nut.
5. With car supported by frame, place roller jack under outer edge of spring seat. Wrap chain around upper control arm and under base of jack and fasten chain securely. Then raise jack to place tension on lower ball joint stud.
6. Rap steering knuckle in area of stud to separate stud from knuckle.
7. Raise jack and separate stud from knuckle. Lift knuckle, hub and drum and support in raised position by placing suitable prop between upper control arm and frame.
8. Lower jack carefully and remove chassis spring.
9. Remove ball joint rivets.
10. Install new ball joint, using $\frac{3}{8}''$ bolts head down. Torque nuts to 35-40 ft. lbs.
11. Tape rubber cushion to top of spring. On power steering jobs a $\frac{1}{8}''$ steel shim is used at top of left spring. On power steering and air conditioned jobs no shim is used.
12. Complete assembly in reverse order of disassembly procedure.

Upper Control Arm

A one-piece stamped steel upper control arm replaces the 1957 two-piece forged assembly. The upper ball joint is riveted to the outer end of the upper control arm. The inner end of the upper control arm is firmly anchored to the frame by the control shaft through heavier frame brackets.

Lower Control Arm

The lower ball joint is riveted to the outer end of the lower control arm. The inner end of the lower control arm is rigidly anchored to the frame by the lower control arm shaft.

1957 FRONT END REPAIRS, FIG. 6

Ball Joints & Steering Knuckle, Remove

1. Jack up car and support weight on front spring seat.
2. Remove front wheel with hub and drum, being careful not to damage wheel bearing inner seal.
3. Remove bolts through backing plate and steering knuckle.
4. Remove backing plate from knuckle. Do not remove brake hose.
5. Remove bolts through lower control arms and ball joint. Lower steering arm out of the way. Remove rubber bumper from ball joint if ball joint is to be replaced.
6. Remove bolts through upper control arms and ball joint. Then remove knuckle and ball joint assembly from upper and lower control arms.
7. Support knuckle in vise in a manner that will allow solid blows directly on end of ball joint stud, Fig. 7.
8. *If ball joints are to be replaced, remove nuts and drive on studs to remove. If knuckle is to be replaced and ball joints are to be reinstalled care must be taken to avoid damage to threads.*
9. Loosen nuts on tapered studs and install a short bolt half way into the nut and tighten. The upper ball joint stud has a $\frac{1}{2}$"-20 thread. The lower stud has a $\frac{9}{16}$"-18 thread.

Ball Joints & Steering Knuckle, Install

1. Lubricate lightly the tapered surfaces of ball joints and knuckle.
2. Install joints in knuckle and tap lightly with hammer. Install nuts and torque upper nut 30-40 lb. ft. and lower nut 40-50 lb. ft.
3. Position ball joint and knuckle in upper and lower control arms and install bolts. Bumper pad mounts to rear side of upper control arm. Torque bolts to 80-90 lb. ft.
4. Install rubber bumper in lower ball joint if it was removed.
5. Using a new dust seal, install steering arm and brake backing plate.
6. Install wheel and hub.

Front Spring, Replace

Removal and installation of front springs remains the same as 1956 models except that the lower ball joint should be disconnected from the lower control arm where the lower pivot pin was formerly removed. Torque bolts to 80-90 lb. ft.

Upper Control Arm, Replace

As upper control arms are not furnished separately, their replacement must be made as an assembly.

1. Jack up car, supporting weight on spring seat and remove wheel.
2. Remove upper control arm-to-ball joint bolts, supporting knuckle and brake drum to avoid damage to brake hose.
3. Remove shock absorber mounting bolt and force top of shock absorber down. *If work is being performed on right side it will be necessary to remove generator and its mounting bracket (disconnect battery ground strap).*
4. Remove shaft attaching bolts, care-

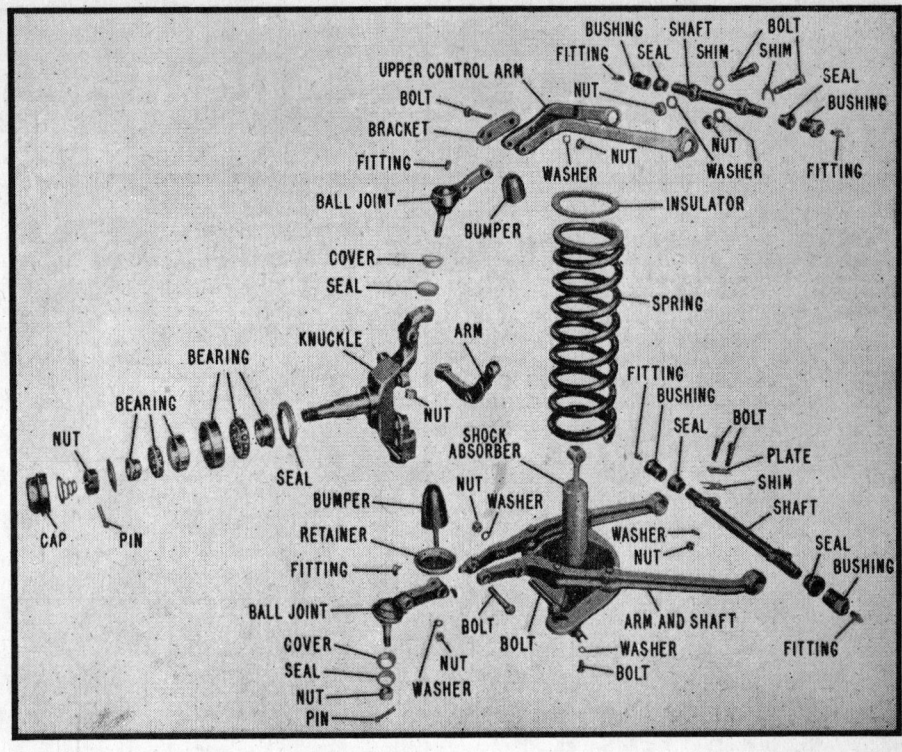

Fig. 6 1957 front suspension

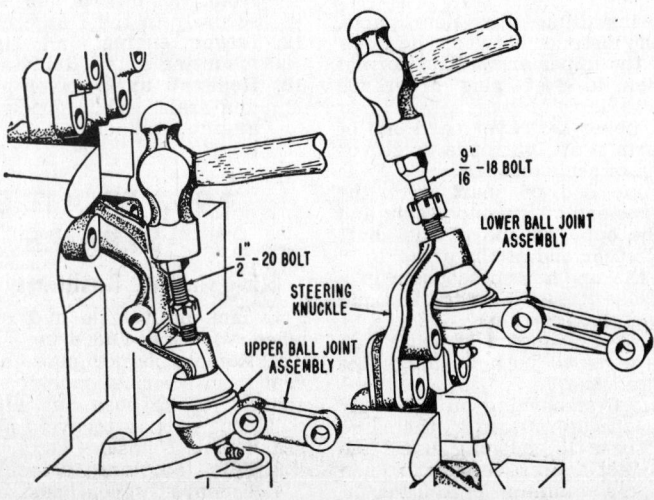

Fig. 7 Removing ball joints from steering knuckle. 1957

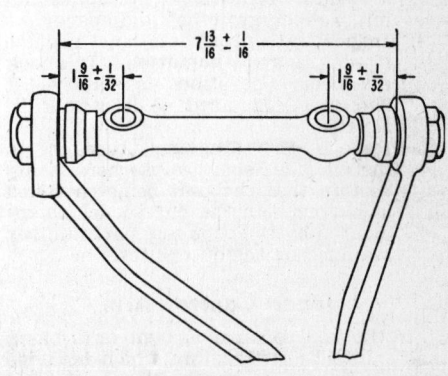

Fig. 8 Upper control arm shaft dimensions. 1957

fully noting position and number of adjusting shims. Remove arm and shaft from car.

5. If upper shaft and bushings only need replacement, clamp arms in vise and remove old shaft and bushings. Then apply a liberal amount of Lubriplate to new bushings and ends of shaft. Install bushings and tighten to 150 lb. ft. torque.

6. Install rubber dust seals on shaft and screw shaft into arm to the dimensions shown in Fig. 8.

7. Using care not to disturb dimensions shown in Fig. 7, install assembly on car by reversing removal procedure. Tighten upper ball joint bolts to 80-90 lb. ft. Tighten upper shaft-to-bracket bolts to 80-100 lb. ft. Check front wheel alignment and correct if necessary.

Lower Control Arm, Replace

Replacing lower control arms, shafts and bushings remain the same as 1956 models except that the lower ball joint should be disconnected from the lower control arm instead of removing the lower pivot pin.

1954-56 FRONT END REPAIRS, FIG. 9

NOTE—Except for the new type shock absorber, which necessitates the use of a new upper control arm, service on the front suspension is the same as for previous models. Therefore, follow the procedure given above for *Front Wheel Bearings* and *Kingpins and Bushings.* Service on the *Front Spring* and *Lower Control Arm* is also the same except that the shock absorber must be removed—the procedure for which is given below.

Shock Absorber, Replace

1. To remove a shock absorber, hold the shock absorber mounting stem with a ¼″ wrench while removing the pal-nut and retaining nut. Then remove retainer and rubber grommet, Fig. 9.

2. Remove bolts and lockwashers attaching lower mounting brackets to the spring seats on the lower control arm and pull the shock absorber and bracket down through the opening in the spring seat.

3. Clamp lower mounting bracket in a vise and remove the pivot bolt and nut, rubber grommet and spacer.

4. Inspect all grommets and replace if not in good condition. If shock absorber operation is faulty, it should be replaced as it cannot be repaired.

5. Reverse the foregoing procedure to install the shock absorber, being certain that the unit being installed is correct for the car model as indicated by the code and part number stamped on the outer tube.

Upper Control Arm

If the control arm is bent or broken, use a new arm assembly which includes the shaft, bushings and dirt seals. If only the shaft and bushings require re-

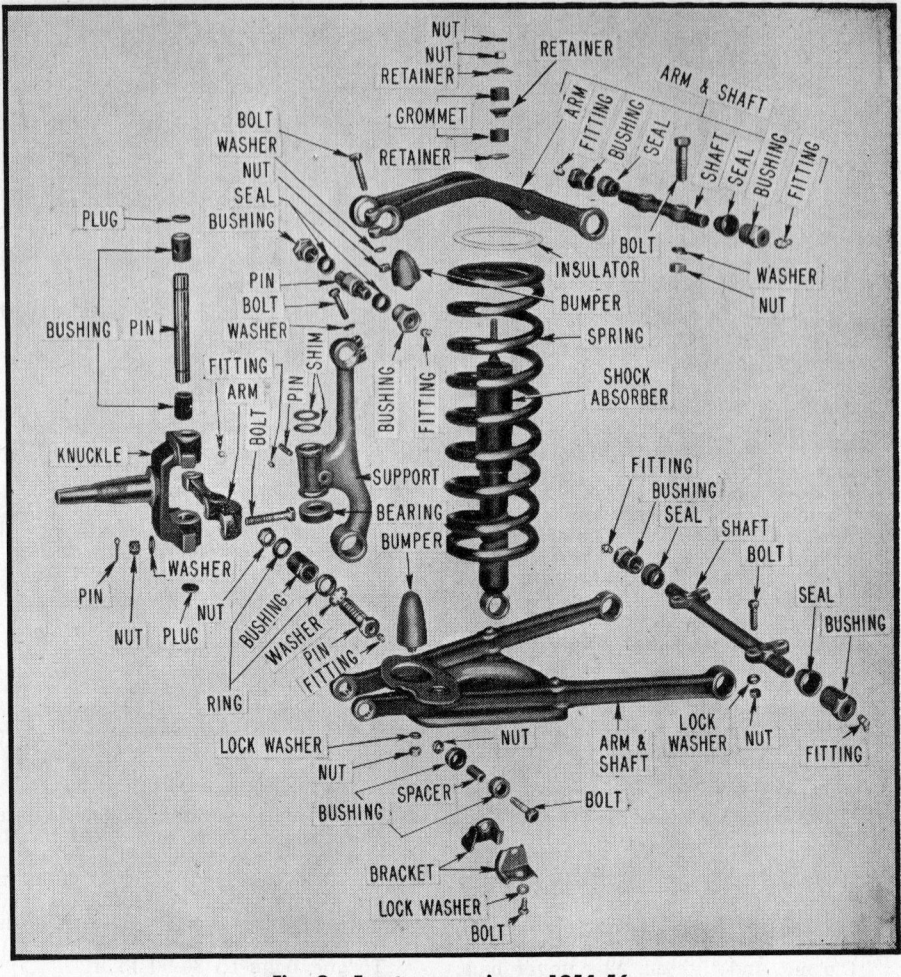

Fig. 9 Front suspension. 1954-56

placement, proceed as follows:

1. Remove generator and engine front mounting nuts and raise the engine just enough to allow removal of the upper arm shaft bolts.

2. Remove pivot pin and bushings and shaft attaching bolts and remove the arm assembly from the car.

3. Unscrew the shaft bushings and remove shaft and seals from upper arm.

4. Before installing any new parts, check the distance between the inner ends of the upper arm. The normal dimension is $6\frac{5}{16}″$ plus or minus .020″.

5. Install rubber seal over each end of upper arm shaft, with the large (or bell) end of seals outward.

6. Insert one end of shaft with the seal in one end of the upper arm and force the opposite end of the shaft into the other end of the arm.

7. Fasten the upper arm securely in a vise (close to one end to avoid springing or distortion).

8. Apply a liberal amount of white lead or Lubriplate to both bushings before installation.

9. Start the first bushing on the shaft and into the upper arm at the same time. Turn the bushing until the head is tight against the arm. Then tighten to a minimum of 100 lbs. ft. torque. On 1956 models, tighten to a

minimum of 150 lb. ft. torque.

10. Center the shaft between the ends of the arm and install the second bushing in the same manner, turning the shaft as required to thread into the bushing so that no binding exists.

11. Before installing the upper arm and shaft assembly, turn the shaft to locate the bolt holes equally distant from ends of arm and bolt the shaft securely to the frame crossmember.

12. Lower engine and tighten front mounting nuts. Reinstall generator.

13. Reinstall upper pivot pin, bushings and seals. Then check front wheel alignment.

1953 FRONT END REPAIRS

Kingpins & Bushings, Replace

1. Jack up vehicle and remove front wheel with hub and drum.

2. Remove brake plate and steering arm from steering knuckle. Do not disconnect brake hose but support brake plate out of way to avoid strain on hydraulic brake hose.

3. Drive out kingpin lock pin.

4. Remove upper dust plug from knuckle by piercing it with a sharp

punch and prying it out.

5. Drive kingpin down and out, which will drive lower dust plug from knuckle. Remove thrust bearing and shims.

6. Remove grease fittings and press old bushings from knuckle.

7. Press new bushings in place, being sure oil holes in bushings line up with hole for grease fittings.

8. Expand bushings tightly in place with a burnisher. Then line ream them to provide .0005 to .0025 in. clearance on the kingpin. Install grease fittings.

9. Install the steering knuckle by reversing removal procedure. Use shims as required between lower boss of knuckle and thrust bearing to provide .003 in. end play of knuckle support. Use new dust plugs at both ends of kingpin.

10. Lubricate and adjust front wheel bearings and check and adjust wheel alignment.

Upper Control Arm Pivot, Replace

1. Jack up under lower control arm and remove wheel.

2. Remove clamp bolt and unscrew the pivot pin bushings and remove rubber seals.

3. Loosen clamp bolt in knuckle support and remove pivot pin, using a ¼ in. hex Allen wrench.

4. Hold knuckle support in line with hole through control arm and screw new pivot pin into knuckle support with adjusting wrench hole in pin toward split side of control arm.

5. Turn pivot pin until large diameter section is centralized in knuckle support and tighten clamp bolt. Install rubber seals on both ends of pin.

6. Centralize knuckle support boss in upper control arm yoke and start externally threaded bushing on threads of pivot pin and into threads of control arm.

7. Start the plain (grooved) bushing on threads of pivot pin, then turn opposite bushing up tight. Turn plain bushing up until hex is just clear of control arm, then install and tighten clamp bolts.

8. Install grease fitting in bushing. Install wheel assembly, adjust front wheel bearings and wheel alignment.

Front Spring, Replace

1. Raise car with jack under lower control arm and take off wheel.

2. Support weight of car with another jack under frame side rail.

3. Disconnect stabilizer link from lower control arm and disconnect outer end of tie rod from steering arm if necessary.

4. Unfasten lower control arm inner shaft from frame crossmember.

5. Slowly lower jack under lower control arm until spring is loose and can be taken out.

6. To install, first make sure the rubberized fabric spring insulator is in place around the frame, and is in good condition.

7. Place small end coil of spring over center cup and, as lower control arm is raised, position lower end of spring so that the end coil seats in the recess provided in the spring seat.

8. Raise lower control arm and fasten

its inner shaft to the frame crossmember.

Lower Control Arm Service

If the lower control arm is bent or broken it should be replaced with a new assembly which includes shaft, bushings and dirt seals. The riveted parts of the assembly are not furnished separately.

1. Remove front spring as outlined previously.

2. Remove lower control arm from knuckle support.

3. To install new parts, first install a new rubber seal (if used) over each threaded end of the new control arm shaft, with the large or bell end of the seals outward toward end of shaft.

4. Insert one end of shaft in control arm end and force opposite end of shaft into other side of arm. A two-foot board can be used as a pry.

5. Fasten the control arm securely in a vise close to one end to prevent springing or distortion. Apply a liberal amount of white lead or Lubriplate to both bushings before installing them in the arm.

6. Start the first bushing on the shaft and into the control arm at the same time. Turn the bushing until its head is tight against the arm and tighten to a minimum of 100 lbs. ft. torque.

7. Center the shaft between the arms and install the second bushing as in step 6, turning the shaft as required to thread into the bushing so that no binding exists.

8. Install front spring, and check and adjust wheel alignment.

Front Shock Absorber, Replace

A front shock absorber can be replaced by removing the upper control arm pivot pin as outlined previously, and the shock absorber attaching bolts.

When the shock absorber is installed, wheel alignment must be checked and adjusted.

HORN BUTTON & RING

Flexible Spoke Wheels, 1960-61

The horn ring can be removed by prying emblem from center of steering wheel. Then remove wing-shaped shroud from steering wheel by removing two inner screws from front of wheel and two outer screws from back side of wheel. To remove either horn contact assembly, turn steering wheel shroud over and remove screw from back. Assemble parts in reverse order.

Flexible Spoke Wheels, 1955-59

The horn button used has a large operating ring mounted over the wheel hub and spokes. To remove ring, pry out the monogram which is held by the prongs of a retaining spring. Unscrew and remove the adjusting nut. Remove contact plate and spring with insulators. Remove steering wheel nut, operating ring with cushion and spacer.

Install operating ring by reversing the removal procedure. The steering wheel nut is self-locking and does not require a lockwasher. When the contact adjust-

ing nut is being installed, turn it down until contact is made and horns blow. Then back it off ½ turn to provide a proper clearance between contact plate and spacer.

Flexible Spoke Wheels, 1953-54

The horn button used with flexible spoke wheels includes an operating ring and a contact plate mounted in the steering wheel cap base. When the operating ring is pressed it touches the contact plate to close the circuit to ground, thus completing the relay circuit and causing the horns to operate.

The monogram and bezel assembly is held in the steering wheel cap base by three springs. The assembly may be removed by inserting a small screwdriver in a notch provided in the cap base and prying against the bezel. When the monogram and bezel are removed, the operating ring and wheel base assembly may be removed by taking out the three screws which attach the wheel base to the steering wheel hub.

Solid Spoke Wheels, 1953-61

The horn button used with the solid spoke wheels has a cap with a rubber retainer in its rim which snaps over the rim of a contact cup mounted in the wheel hub. The cap may be pried out with a thin bladed tool and the contact cup and other parts may then be removed on 1953-59 by taking out the three attaching screws and insulating spacer bushings and on 1960-61 by removing the steering wheel nut.

STEERING WHEEL

All Models—To remove the wheel, disconnect wire at horn cable connector on steering column to prevent horn from blowing. Remove horn button or operating ring. Reinstall steering wheel nut, leaving it backed off several turns. Set turn signal in "Off" position to avoid possible damage to switch operating mechanism. Apply a suitable puller and remove the wheel.

STEERING GEAR, REPLACE

1953 Manual Gear

1. Disconnect the pitman arm from the steering tie rod by unscrewing tie rod plug until bearing will release ball stud.

2. On series 70 only, remove air cleaner. Disconnect fuel and vacuum pipes from carburetor and carefully move them out of the way.

3. Disconnect clutch linkage anti-rattle spring from shift idler lever pin bracket and disconnect the upper shift rod from control shaft lower lever. On synchromesh transmission jobs, disconnect selector rod from selector control lever and unhook the anti-rattle spring.

4. Disconnect wires from horn cable connector, back up light switch, and neutral safety switch (Dynaflow cars only). Pull speedometer cable from clip and then remove horn cable connector from column jacket to avoid damage during removal of gear assembly.

5. Disconnect one end of brace at cut-

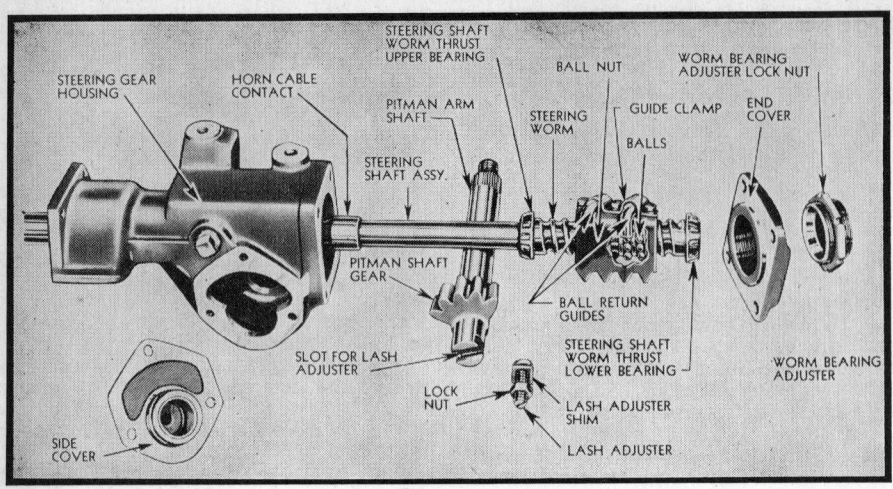

LABELS ON FIGURE:
STEERING GEAR HOUSING — HORN CABLE CONTACT — STEERING SHAFT WORM THRUST UPPER BEARING — PITMAN ARM SHAFT — BALL NUT — STEERING WORM — GUIDE CLAMP — WORM BEARING ADJUSTER LOCK NUT — END COVER — BALLS — STEERING SHAFT ASSY. — PITMAN SHAFT GEAR — BALL RETURN GUIDES — STEERING SHAFT WORM THRUST LOWER BEARING — WORM BEARING ADJUSTER — SLOT FOR LASH ADJUSTER — LOCK NUT — LASH ADJUSTER SHIM — LASH ADJUSTER — SIDE COVER

Fig. 10 Manual steering gear

out in cowl and swing brace to one side.

6. Remove front seat all the way back and cover the seat and back cushions.

7. Remove dash insulator retainer and steering column pad. Pull back the floor mat and remove pedal plate attached to toe panel.

8. Remove steering wheel and the upper bearing spring and spring seat. Remove shift control lever and signal switch control lever.

9. Disconnect direction signal switch wires from terminals on fuse block.

10. Remove steering column bracket and any spacers located between bracket and support on instrument panel.

11. Remove steering gear-to-frame bolts and clamps and carefully support the steering column to avoid damaging column jacket. Move gear assembly to the rear as far as possible, turn assembly over so that pitman arm is uppermost. Then lift forward end up between engine and fender and move forward to remove gear from car. It is advisable to have a helper guide the column jacket and signal switch housing through the cut-out in cowl panel to avoid damaging the finish of these parts.

1954-56 Manual Gear

1. Remove steering wheel.

2. Disconnect transmission shift rod from control shaft lower lever. On synchromesh cars, remove selector lever from jacket clamp by removing retainer and spring washer. Loosen bolt in clamp which secures column jacket to short tube in gear housing.

3. On 1955 Dynaflow cars, disconnect wires from neutral safety switch and remove speed ratio dial light bulb holder from support on steering column jacket.

4. On 1956 models, remove two screws holding the fuse block and lower the fuse block. On other models disconnect signal switch wires from fuse block and remove switch and transmission shift control levers.

5. On 1954-55 models, detach rubber insulator retainer from dash mat and pull it up about a foot on column jacket. Remove jute column pad.

6. Disconnect bracket from instrument panel and pull upward on column jacket to free it from steering gear.

7. Remove starter motor splash pan from frame.

8. Remove steering gear-to-frame lower bolts and clamps, then loosen upper bolts enough so that gear can be tilted sideways to provide room for pitman arm puller. Pull off pitman arm.

9. With a helper inside the car to guide the steering column and prevent damage to column jacket and front seat, carefully lift gear assembly up and forward out of engine compartment, leaving column jacket assembly in body. *On 1955-56 models, be careful not to damage or lose the control shaft return spring, which will be either on the end of control shaft or loose on steering shaft.*

10. Reverse the above procedure to install the gear.

Inspection of Parts

1. Clean and inspect all ball and roller bearings and races, including race in housing.

2. Inspect pitman shaft bushings or bearings in gear housing and end cover. Replace bushings or bearings in housing and replace end cover if bushings are worn excessively.

3. It is advisable to replace pitman shaft grease seal in housing to avoid possible leakage of lubricant. Seal must be installed with feather edge toward inside of housing.

4. Inspect steering shaft for wear or pits in bearing races, which would require replacement of shafts.

5. Check shaft for straightness.

6. Inspect teeth of ball nut and pitman shaft. If scored or excessively worn it is advisable to replace both parts to insure proper mating of teeth.

7. Check serrations of pitman shaft; if twisted, replace shaft.

8. Check fit of pitman shaft adjusting screw and shim in slot in end of pitman shaft. *With shim in place, screw head must be free to turn in slot with zero to .002" end play.* If end play is excessive, selectively fit

a new shim, which are furnished in four different thicknesses.

9. Inspect steering column jacket for distortion. A ripple or wavy feeling of jacket surface, particularly at lower end, will usually indicate a sprung jacket. Replace jacket if sprung or otherwise damaged.

10. Inspect control shaft bearing in tube of gear housing, and steering shaft upper bearing in control lever housing support. Replace worn or damaged parts.

1957-61 Manual Gear

The operation and construction of the 1957 steering gear is essentially the same as 1956 with the exception that the pitman shaft is shorter and the flexible coupling used on the 1956 power steering gear is also used on the manual steering gear.

The use of the flexible coupling makes it possible to remove the manual gear through the bottom of the engine compartment without removing the upper steering shaft and column jacket.

Before disconnecting the coupling, mark upper and lower steering shaft flanges for correct assembly.

MANUAL STEERING GEAR REPAIRS, 1953-61

Disassemble, Fig. 10

1. Loosen adjusting screw lock nut and remove housing side cover by unscrewing adjusting screw.

2. Loosen lock nut and back off worm bearing adjuster several turns, then remove housing end cover and gasket.

3. Remove lower thrust bearing, steering shaft and upper bearing from housing.

4. Remove ball return guide clamps and guides from ball nut, turn ball nut over to remove balls and remove ball nut from steering shaft worm.

Assemble

To assemble the steering gear, reverse the order of procedure given for disassembly. In addition, observe the following instructions.

1. Lubricate bearings and gears with steering gear lubricant.

2. Use all new gaskets to avoid oil leaks.

3. When assembling ball nut on worm, be sure to divide the balls evenly, placing half in each circuit.

4. When installing pitman shaft, avoid damaging or turning the feather edge of leather seal in gear housing.

5. Temporarily install steering wheel and adjust worm shaft thrust bearing for proper load and pitman shaft for proper gear lash as described below.

Adjustments

1. Disconnect steering linkage from pitman arm.

2. Turn steering wheel gently in one direction until it stops, then turn it

back one revolution. *Never turn steering gear hard against stopping point as damage to ball nut assembly may result.*

3. Check lash between ball nut and pitman shaft by working pitman arm. If a perceptible lash *does not* exist, loosen lock nut and turn pitman shaft adjusting screw counterclockwise until lash can be felt when working pitman arm.

4. Turn steering wheel slowly from one extreme to the other. Wheel should turn freely and smoothly through entire range. Roughness indicates faulty worm thrust bearings or pitted races. Hard pull or binding indicates misalignment of steering gear in its mountings, or an excessively tight adjustment of worm thrust bearings. Any misalignment must be corrected before steering gear can be properly adjusted.

5. Tighten housing and cover bolts.

6. Loosen worm thrust bearing adjuster lock nut and turn thrust bearing adjuster until a slight load is felt when turning steering wheel near extreme end positions, then tighten lock nut. (1956-57 gears have an external hex which replaces slot on bearing adjuster used formerly). *Do not back out adjuster far enough to* permit thrust bearings to get out of line with ends of worm.

7. After locking bearing adjuster, check load on thrust bearings with steering wheel turned to near one extreme position.

8. Attach a spring scale to rim of steering wheel. The pull required to keep steering wheel turning slowly should be between ⅞ and 1⅛ lbs. on 1952-56, ½ to ⅞ lb. on 1957-58, ⅜ to ¾ lb. on 1959 and ¼ to ¾ lb. on 1960-61. Readjust to obtain this load if necessary.

9. Turn steering wheel from one extreme to the other while counting the turns. Then turn wheel back exactly one-half the total number of turns and have the lower spoke pointing straight down. This places the steering gear on the "high point" at which no lash should exist between ball nut and pitman shaft teeth.

10. Tighten housing side cover bolts. Loosen lock nut and turn pitman shaft adjusting screw clockwise until lash is just removed.

11. After tightening adjusting screw lock nut, rotate wheel back and forth to check for tight spots. Also recheck pull at wheel rim as given above.

12. The pull required to keep the wheel moving through the "high point" should be between 2 and 2¼ lbs. on 1952-56, 1½ to 2 lbs. on 1957-58, 1¼ to 1¾ lbs. on 1959 and ⅞ to 1½ lb. on 1960-61. Readjust if necessary to remove tight spots.

POWER STEERING, REPLACE

1953-55 V8

To remove the power steering unit, proceed as follows:

1. Remove battery and battery heat deflector.
2. Remove selector control rod from arm on shift safety switch.
3. Remove bolts from metal strip located on rear end of fender skirt in wheel housing.
4. Remove pitman arm from steering gear shaft.
5. Remove two bolts of upper clamp which secures steering gear to frame bracket.
6. Loosen but do not remove the two bolts of the lower clamp which secure the steering gear to the frame bracket.
7. Have a suitable pan available and remove the two hydraulic oil lines at the pump. Drain all oil from these lines and plug them to prevent dirt from entering.
8. Cap the ports in the pump where oil lines were removed.
9. Remove horn contact button.
10. Remove the connection of the combination backup light switch and safety starting switch from the mast jacket.
11. Remove direction signal wires from fuse panel.
12. Remove screws that secure mast jacket rubber retainer and pull same up a foot or so on the jacket.
13. Remove metal section of floor board located just under brake pedal.
14. Remove steering wheel.
15. Loosen bolt from clamp which secures mast jacket to hydraulic valve cover.
16. Remove two bolts which secure mast jacket to instrument panel.
17. Cover threaded end of steering shaft with a cap or masking tape.
18. Remove mast jacket from steering shaft by lifting jacket up into car.
19. Remove power steering unit by lifting up and forward out to the engine compartment.

NOTE—If a block and tackle or a suitable hoist is available, considerable work can be saved by making up a sling and attaching it to the power piston rack cover by the two upper bolts.

Installation

Before actually installing the unit, check the lower clamp which secures the steering gear to the frame bracket. This should be in place but loose. Place the two upper clamp bolts in position, then install only the outer half of the upper clamp which secures the gear to the frame bracket. Place the gear in position and install the other half of the upper clamp. Hold in position by installing the nuts on the clamp bolts, but do not tighten at this time.

Install the remaining components of the gear in reverse of the removal procedure.

1956-61

1. To remove the assembly, disconnect pressure and return line hoses at steering gear and elevate ends of hoses higher than pump to prevent oil from draining out of pump.
2. Disconnect flexible coupling by removing two bolts which attach coupling to steering shaft or flanges. (For 1960-61, flexible coupling is installed on gear box spline and secured by one pinch bolt.)
3. Remove pitman arm.
4. Unfasten and remove steering gear from frame.
5. To install, reverse removal procedure.
6. Check toe-in after installation.
7. Bleed system by turning steering wheel throughout its range until all air bubbles cease to appear in power steering oil reservoir.

Speedometer, Windshield Wiper and Radio

SPEEDOMETER

1953-55

1. Disconnect battery.
2. Disconnect speedometer cable housing.
3. Remove bulb sockets and speedometer to dash panel attaching screws.
4. Remove speedometer from under the dash.

1956

1. Disconnect battery.
2. Remove dash top center panel.
3. Disconnect speedometer cable housing.
4. Disconnect gauges at either side of speedometer and remove bulb sockets.
5. Remove screws which fasten speedometer assembly to dash panel.
6. Lift speedometer out through top of dash.

1957-58

1. Disconnect battery.
2. Remove dash top center panel.
3. Disconnect speedometer cable housing.
4. Remove gauges from instrument cluster.
5. Remove speedometer assembly to dash attaching screws and lift assembly out through top of dash.

1959

1. Disconnect battery.
2. Remove dash top panel.
3. Disconnect speedometer cable housing.
4. Remove bulb sockets.
5. Remove speedometer to dash attaching screws and lift assembly out through top of dash.

RADIO REMOVAL

1953-56

Whenever the radio is being removed from a car with a rear seat speaker, it is advisable first to remove the speaker selector switch from its mounting bracket to avoid straining the wire connections at the switch. Remove the radio, then remove the back cover and disconnect switch wires from radio.

1957-59

To gain access to the radio, the upper instrument panel center section must first be removed.

1960

After removing the right lower control housing side panel, disconnect speaker wire, antenna lead-in wire and foot control wire. Remove control knobs, washers, etc., and remove radio from underneath.

1. Install radio from beneath, inserting threaded bushings through control holes in instrument panel. Install and tighten hex nuts on bushings.
2. Install and tighten tie bar to radio bracket slotted hole.
3. Install tone control escutcheon knob on shaft to left of dial. Install dummy escutcheon on shaft to right of dial. Install felt washers and control knobs, making sure spring clips

properly engage flats on control shafts.
4. Plug in speaker wire, antenna lead-in wire, wire harness wire (if equipped) and foot control wire.
5. Install right lower control housing side panel.

1961

The radio can easily be removed from the instrument panel by removing the control knobs, instrument panel console trim plate and the two bottom screws.

WINDSHIELD WIPER

1953-54 Series 40

The windshield wiper motor is mounted under the cowl and is connected to the right and left wiper transmission by steel links which are part of the transmission assemblies. Rubber inertia arresters are built into the drive lever on the motor and the driven levers on the transmissions for the purpose of absorbing the shock produced by reversal of direction at the end of each stroke.

1953-54 Series 50, 70

The wiper motor is mounted on an auxiliary drive which is attached to the front face of the cowl panel under the hood. The motor drives a short shaft in the auxiliary drive which extends through the cowl panel. A cross lever on the rear end of the auxiliary shaft actuates the wiper transmissions through cables attached to the lever and to pulleys in the transmissions. The cables run around pulleys on cable tensioners mounted under the cowl. *Each cable tensioner has a spring and ratchet which automatically take up slack and maintain proper tension on the cables. Wiper arms must not be rotated by hand for any reason as this places an undue strain on the cable fasteners.*

1955-58

The wiper transmission cables are tensioned by spring-loaded pulleys. When the end of the transmission shaft is pushed in the pulleys unlock and tension the cables. To obtain slack in the transmission cables, proceed as follows:

1. On wipers with Cam-O-Matic feature, remove the wiper arm by pulling upper section of arm upward to disengage cam follower from cam. Then pull arm from transmission shaft. Push in end of transmission shaft.
2. If wiper does not have the Cam-O-Matic feature, push in the base of the wiper arm where the arm fits over the transmission shaft to adjust tension in cables.
3. While the pulleys are unlocked, have a helper inside the car pull cable to obtain slack. When sufficient slack is obtained, release end of transmission shaft to lock cable in slack position.
4. To restore tenson to cables, push in on end of transmission shaft.
5. Repeat operation on opposite transmission.

To remove the wiper motor, remove the screws which attach the motor to the support and disengage the motor from the auxiliary drive assembly. Then disconnect the vacuum hoses and control cable from the motor. Unfasten and remove motor.

1959-60

To remove the wiper motor and/or transmission it will be necessary to remove the left side air intake grille. Remove the retaining screws, slide the grille out from under the reveal moulding. After removing the transmission retaining screws, slide the transmission and drive link toward the opposite side of the car. Then lift the transmission up at the opening and remove.

BUICK SPECIAL

INDEX OF SERVICE OPERATIONS

PAGE NO.

ACCESSORIES

Radio Removal 448
Instruments 448
Windshield Wiper 448
Windshield Wiper Troubles........... 37

BRAKES (Mechanical)

Adjustments 112
Brake Cylinder Sizes............... 422
Hydraulic Brake System.............. 112
Master Cylinder, Replace........... 444
Trouble Shooting 31

CLUTCH

Clutch Pedal, Adjust................. 429
Clutch Service 429
Trouble Shooting 13

COOLING SYSTEM

Radiator, Replace 426
Trouble Shooting 8
Water Pump Repairs................. 427
Water Pump, Replace................. 427

ELECTRIC SYSTEM

Dash Gauge Service................. 85
Distributor, Replace 427
Distributor Service 46
Distributor Specifications........... 421
Generator Regulator Service........... 62
Generator Regulator Specifications..... 421
Generator Service 62
Generator Specifications........... 421
Horn Ring, Replace................. 446
Ignition System Service............. 46
Ignition Timing 427
Starter, Replace 427
Starter Switch Service............. 83
Starting Motor Service............. 77
Starting Motor Specifications........ 421
Trouble Shooting 10
Turn Signal Troubles................ 12

PAGE NO.

ENGINE

Camshaft, Replace 425
Camshaft Bearings 425
Crankshaft Oil Seal, Replace....... 426
Cylinder Head, Replace............. 422
Crankshaft & Bearing Specs........ 420
Engine, Replace 422
Main Bearings, Replace............. 426
Piston Pins, Replace.............. 425
Piston Rings, Replace............. 425
Piston, Pin & Ring Specs.......... 420
Pistons & Rods, Remove........... 425
Piston & Rod, Assemble........... 425
Pistons, Replace 425
Rocker Arms 422
Rod Bearings, Replace............. 425
Timing Case Cover, Replace........ 424
Timing Chain, Replace............. 424
Trouble Shooting 4
Valve Arrangement 422
Valve Guides 424
Valve Spring Installed Height........ 423
Valve Spring Testing............... 424
Valve Timing Data............... 425
Valves, Grind 422
Valve Lifters 424
Valve Specifications 420

ENGINE OILING

Oil Pan, Replace................... 426
Oil Pump Repairs................. 426
Trouble Shooting 4

FRONT SUSPENSION

Camber, Adjust 445
Caster, Adjust 445
Front End Repairs................. 445
Toe-in, Adjust 445
Trouble Shooting 33
Wheel Alignment Specifications....... 422

FUEL & EXHAUST SYSTEM

Carburetors 427
Fuel Pumps 96
Mufflers and Pipes............... 427
Trouble Shooting 4

PAGE NO.

REAR AXLE

Axle Shaft, Replace............... 443
General Service 102
Non-Slip Differentials 109
Rear Axle Repairs................. 443
Rear Axle Specifications........... 422
Trouble Shooting 31

SPECIFICATIONS

Brake Cylinder Sizes............... 422
Capacity Data 421
Cooling System 421
Crankshaft & Bearings............. 420
Carburetors 428
Distributors 421
Engine Tightening 420
Generators & Regulators........... 421
Pistons, Pins & Rings............. 420
Rear Axle 422
Starting Motors 421
Tune Up 420
Valves 420
Valve Timing 425
Wheel Alignment 422

STEERING GEARS (Mechanical)

Horn Ring, Replace............... 446
Steering Gear, Adjust............. 446
Steering Gear Repairs............. 447
Steering Gear, Replace............. 447
Steering Wheel, Replace........... 446
Trouble Shooting 33

STEERING GEARS (Power)

Steering Gear, Replace............. 447
Steering Gear, Repairs............. 145
Trouble Shooting 34

TRANSMISSIONS (Manual Shift)

Gearshift, Adjust 429
Transmission Repairs 429
Transmission, Replace 429
Trouble Shooting 14

TRANSMISSIONS (Automatic)

Linkage, Adjust 432
Transmission, Replace 433
Transmission Repairs 433
Trouble Shooting 432

TUNE UP 38

GENERAL SPECIFICATIONS

Year	Model Designation	Wheelbase, Inches	Valve Location	Bore and Stroke	Piston Displacement, Cubic Inches	Compression Ratio (Standard)	Maximum Brake H.P. @ R.P.M.	Maximum Torque Lbs. Ft. @ R.P.M.	Normal Oil Pressure Pounds
1961	V8................4000	112	In Head	3.500 x 2.80	215	8.8	155 @ 4400	220 @ 2400	33

TUNE UP SPECIFICATIONS

★When using timing light, disconnect vacuum line to prevent advance mechanism from operating.

Year	Model	Ground Polarity and Voltage	Spark Plug Type	Spark Plug Gap Inch	Distributor Point Gap Inch	Distributor Cam Angle Degrees	Firing Order	★Ignition Timing Mark	★Ignition Timing Location	Idle Speed RPM In Neutral	Compression Pressure @ Cranking Speed Minimum
1961	4000	N-12	AC-45FFS	.035	.016	30	18436572①	②	②	525	150–160

①—Engine numbering (front to rear): Left bank 1-3-5-7, right bank 2-4-6-8.
②—Yellow mark on damper aligned with "5" on timing indicator.

VALVE SPECIFICATIONS

Year	Model	Valve Lash Int.	Valve Lash Exh.	Valve Angles Seat	Valve Angles Face	Valve Spring Installed Height	Valve Spring Pressure Lbs. @ In.	Valve Lift Int.	Valve Lift Exh.	Stem Clearance Intake	Stem Clearance Exhaust	Stem Diameter Int.	Stem Diameter Exh.
1961	4000	Zero	Zero	45	45	1⁴¹⁄₆₄	168 @ 1¹⁷⁄₆₄	.383	.383	①	②	③	④

①—Top .0005-.0025, bottom .001-.003.
②—Top .001-.003, bottom .0015-.0035.
③—Tapers from .3407 to .3412.
④—Tapers from .3402 to .3407.

PISTONS, PINS, RINGS, CRANKSHAFT & BEARINGS

Year	Model	Fitting Pistons Shim To Use	Fitting Pistons Pounds Pull On Scale	Ring End Gap① Comp.	Ring End Gap① Oil	Wristpin Diameter	Rod Bearings Shaft Diameter	Rod Bearings Bearing Clearance	Main Bearings Shaft Diameter	Main Bearings Bearing Clearance	Thrust on Bear. No.	Shaft End Play
1961	4000	.001	7–13	.010	.015	.8748	2.0000	.0002-.0022	2.2986	.0005-.0021	3	.004-.008

①—Fit rings in tapered bores for clearance given in tightest portion of ring travel.

ENGINE TIGHTENING SPECIFICATIONS★

★Torque specifications are for clean and lightly lubricated threads only. Dry or dirty threads produce increased friction which prevents accurate measurement of tightness.

Year	Spark Plugs Ft. Lbs.	Cylinder Head Bolts Ft. Lbs.	Intake Manifold Ft. Lbs.	Exhaust Manifold Ft. Lbs.	Rocker Arm Shaft Bracket Ft. Lbs.	Rocker Arm Cover Ft. Lbs.	Connecting Rod Cap Bolts Ft. Lbs.	Main Bearing Cap Bolts Ft. Lbs.	Flywheel to Crankshaft Ft. Lbs.	Vibration Damper or Pulley Ft. Lbs.
1961	20	50–55	25–30	10–15	25–30	3–5	30–35	50–55①	50–60	140–160

①—Rear bearing cap 70 ft. lbs.

DISTRIBUTOR SPECIFICATIONS

Year and Model	Part No. ①	Rotation ②	Cam Angle, Degrees	Breaker Point Opening, Inch	Condenser Capacity, Mfds.	Breaker Arm Spring Tension, Ounces	Centrifugal Advance Data Degrees @ R.P.M. of Dist.		Vacuum Advance Data		
							Advance Starts	Full Advance	Inches of Vacuum to Start Plunger Movement	Inches of Vacuum for Full Plunger Travel	Maximum Vacuum Advance, Dist. Degrees
1961	1110973	C	30	.016	.18–.23	19–23	1 @ 535	14 @ 1850	6–8	15	18

①—Number on plate attached to housing.
②—Viewed from top.

COOLING SYSTEM & CAPACITY DATA

Year and Model	Cooling System Data					Fuel Tank Gals.	Engine Oil			Transmissions			Rear Axle Pints
	Quarts No Heater	Quarts With Heater	Rad. Cap Relief Pressure	Thermostat Opening Temp.			Refill Qts. ③	Summer Grade	Winter Grade	Std. Pints	With Overdrive Pints	Auto-matic Qts.	
				①	②								
1961	12	13½	15	170	—	16	4	20W	10W	2¼	None	6	2½

①—For permanent type anti-freeze.   ②—For alcohol type anti-freeze.   ③—Add one quart with filter change.

GENERATOR AND REGULATOR SPECIFICATIONS

★ To polarize generator, reconnect the leads to the regulator; then momentarily connect a jumper wire from the "Gen" to the "Bat" terminals of the regulator.

Year	Generator						Regulator						
	Generator Number	Rotation and Ground Polarity	Rated Cap. Amps.	Gen. Field Ground Loca-tion★	Brush Spring Tension, Ounces	Field Current Amperes	Regulator Number	Cutout Relay		Voltage Regu-lator Setting Volts	Current Regu-lator Setting Amperes	Current and Voltage Arma-ture Air Gap, Inch
								Vol-tage to Close Points	Arma-ture Air Gap, Inch			
1961	1110389	C-N	35	External	26–32	1.69–1.79	1119242	12.3	.020	14.3	35	.075

STARTING MOTOR SPECIFICATIONS

Year	Model	Part No.	Rotation	Brush Spring Tension, Ounces	No Load Test			Torque Test		
					Amperes	Volts	R.P.M.	Amperes	Volts	Torque Lbs. Ft.
1961	4000	1108303	C	35 Min.	58–80	10.6	6750–8600	280–320	4	

①—Armature locked.

REAR AXLE AND BRAKE CYLINDER SPECIFICATIONS

Year	Model	Ring Gear & Pinion Backlash, Inch	Drive Pinion Adjustment	Drive Pinion Bearing Preload	Drive Pinion Bearing Adjustment	Axle Shaft End Play, Inch	Hydraulic Cylinder Bore Sizes, Inch		
							Wheel Cylinder		Master Cylinder
							Front	Rear	
1961	4000	.007–.009	Shim	①	Shim	None	1	⅞	1

①—New bearings 25–35 inch lbs., 15–25 inch lbs. with used bearings.

WHEEL ALIGNMENT SPECIFICATIONS

Year	Model	Caster, Degrees		Camber, Degrees		Toe-in, Inches	Toe-out on Turns, Degrees		Steering Axis Inclination, Deg.
		Limits	Desired	Limits	Desired		Outer Wheel	Inner Wheel	
1961	4000	— 1½ to — 2½	— 2	— ¼ to — 1	— ⅝	¹⁄₁₆ to ⅛	20	23⅔	7½ @ ¼ Camber

SERIAL NUMBER LOCATION
Stamped On Cowl-To-Frame Brace In Engine Compartment

ENGINE NUMBER LOCATION
On Crankcase Forward Of Right Cylinder Head

1961

Engine Section

ENGINE, REPLACE

1. Drain cooling system and remove radiator.
2. Disconnect linkage at transmission and clutch (if equipped).
3. Remove transmission.
4. Remove hood and battery.
5. Disconnect exhaust pipes from manifolds.
6. Disconnect usual items under hood such as fuel lines, radiator hoses, wires, etc.
7. If equipped with an oil cooler, disconnect cooler lines.
8. If engine lifting fixture is used, remove carburetor after disconnecting automatic choke tube and fuel lines as mentioned above.
9. Attach engine lifting fixture to carburetor flange studs on intake manifold.
10. Remove engine mounting bolts and lift engine from chassis.
11. To install, reverse foregoing procedure.

CYLINDER HEADS

1. To remove cylinder head, drain cooling system.
2. Remove intake manifold and carburetor as a unit.
3. Remove exhaust manifold.
4. Remove rocker arm assembly.
5. Remove push rods.
6. Unfasten and remove cylinder head.
7. When installing the head, refer to Fig. 1 for correct location of bolts and Fig. 2 for tightening sequence. Tighten bolts to the torque listed in the *Engine Tightening* chart.

ROCKER ARMS

1. To disassemble, remove cotter pin, plain washer and spring washer from each end of rocker arm shaft.
2. Remove bracket bolts and slide rocker arms and brackets off shaft.
3. Clean and inspect all parts, taking care to clean out all oil holes. Replace parts that are excessively worn.

4. Assemble springs, rocker arms and brackets. *Note that two different rocker arms are used and that the valve ends of rocker arms slant away from the brackets.*
5. Install spring washer, flat washer and cotter pin on each end of shaft in the order named.
6. Install bolts with plain washers through brackets and shaft so the notch on one end of the shaft is 'up' toward the shaft bracket bolt heads, Fig. 3. *With the notch up the oil holes in the shaft are correctly positioned to the rocker arms.*

VALVE ARRANGEMENT

Front to Rear . . . . E-I-E-I-E-I-E

VALVES, GRIND

After removing valves and springs from cylinder head, scrape all carbon from combustion chambers and valves. If wire brushes are used for cleaning

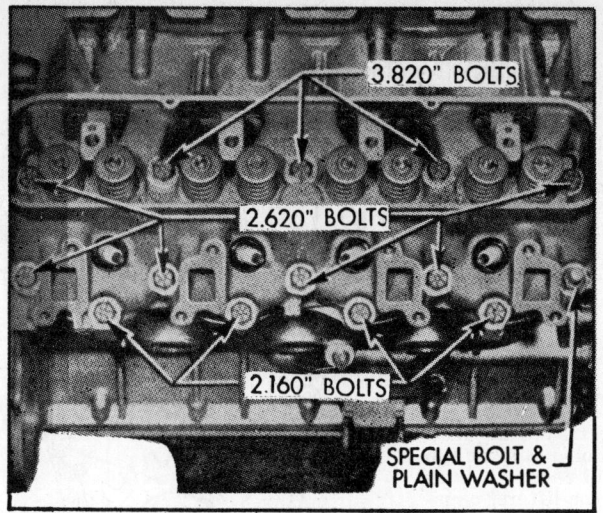

Fig. 1   Cylinder head bolt installation

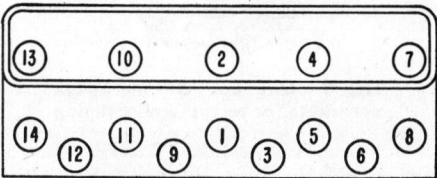

Fig. 2   Cylinder head tightening sequence

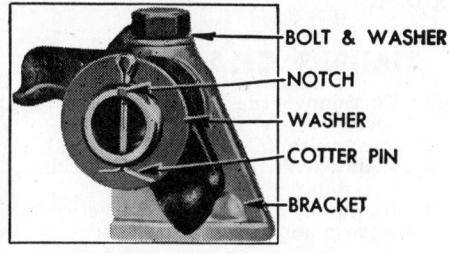

Fig. 3   Notch on end of rocker arm shaft should be "up" so oil holes in shaft are correctly positioned to rocker arms

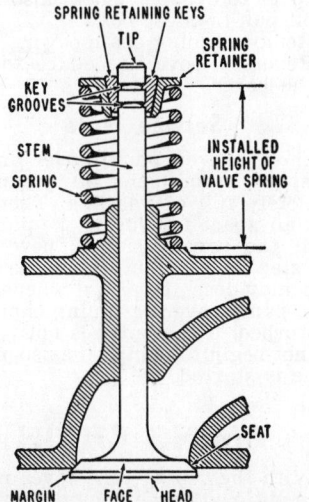

Fig. 4   Checking installed height of valve spring. Note that close wound coils of spring go toward cylinder head

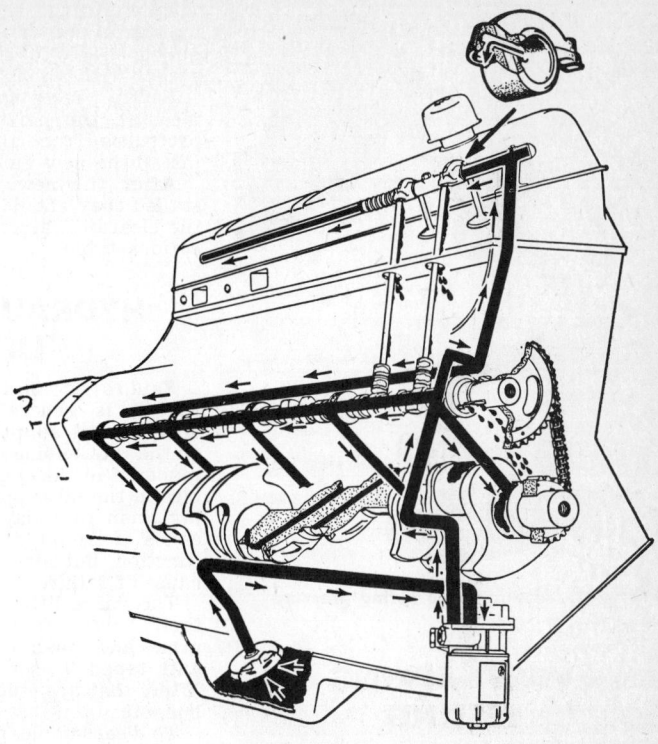

Engine lubrication diagram

carbon, use care to avoid scratching valve seats and valve faces. Clean all carbon and gum deposits from valve guides.

In refacing valves, take off only the minimum of metal required to clean up the valve faces. If the outer edge of the valve becomes too thin or sharp due to excessive grinding the valve must be replaced. In other words the valve head margin must be at least $\frac{3}{64}''$, otherwise the valve must be replaced. This margin is the area above the contact surface of the valve face, Fig. 4.

Inspect the valve seats in the head for cracks, burns, pitting, ridges or improper angle. During any general engine overhaul it is advisable to reface the valve seats regardless of their condition. If new valve guides are required, they must be installed and reamed before refacing the seats if the equipment used for refacing them has a valve guide pilot.

Reface valves and true up seats to 45 degrees. Cutting a valve seat results in lowering the valve spring pressure and increases the width of the seat. The nominal width of a valve seat is $\frac{1}{16}''$. If valve seat is over $\frac{5}{64}''$ after truing up, it should be narrowed to specified width by using the proper 20 and 70 degree cutters.

Improper hydraulic valve lifter operation may result if valve and seat have been refinished enough to allow the end of the valve stem to raise approximately .050" above normal position. In this case it will be necessary to grind off the end of the valve stem or replace parts.

Test valves for concentricity with seats and for tight seating. Valves can be tested by lightly coating the valve face with prussion blue and turning the valve against its seat. This indicates whether the seat is concentric with the valve guide *but does not prove that the valve*

face is concentric with the valve stem, or that the valve is seating all around. After making this test, wash all blue from the surfaces, lightly coat the valve seat with blue and repeat the test to see whether a full mark is obtained on the valve. Both tests are necessary to prove that a proper seat is being obtained.

VALVE SPRING INSTALLED HEIGHT

When valves and seats are reground the position of the valve in the head is changed so as to lessen the valve spring tension. Without proper valve spring tension the valve does not seat long enough or it may not seat completely. Since the valve is cooled by transferring heat from the valve head to the seat and thence to the coolant, improper valve spring tension will cause worn, pitted and distorted valves which result in loss of compression and power as well as poor gasoline mileage.

When valves, springs, retainers and locks are installed, measure the assembled height of the valve springs from the surface of the cylinder head spring pad to the underside of the spring retainer as shown in Fig. 4. If the assembled height is greater than the dimension given in the *Valve Specifications Chart,* install a spacer or shim of proper thickness between cylinder head spring pad and spring to bring the assembled height to specifications.

Do not install spacers unless necessary. Excessive use of spacers will result in overstressing valve springs and overloading camshaft lobes which could lead to spring breakage and worn camshaft lobes.

Fig. 5 Testing valve spring pressure

VALVE SPRING TESTING

Wash all valve springs with a suitable solvent. Examine the springs for damage or corrosion due to acid etching, which will develop into surface cracks and cause spring failure.

Check the valve spring tension on a spring testing fixture if one is available, Fig. 5. If a fixture is not available, at least check the free length of each spring by standing it alongside a new spring. Any spring that does not conform to the pressure specifications in the *Valve Specifications* table within 10 per cent should be replaced. Likewise any spring that stands shorter than the new spring used for comparison should be discarded.

VALVE GUIDES

Clean the valve guides with a wire guide brush and check the clearance between valve stems and guides carefully. The standard clearances are given in the *Valve Specifications* table.

Excessive clearance between valve stems and guides will cause improper seating and burned valves. When there is too much clearance between intake valve stems and guides, there is a tendency to draw oil vapor through the guide on the suction stroke, causing excessive oil consumption, fouled spark plugs and poor low speed performance.

To check valve stem-to-guide clearance, take a new valve and place it in each valve guide and feel the clearance by moving the valve stem from side to side. If this check shows excessive clearance, it will be necessary to replace the valve guide.

If the clearance is not excessive when checking with a new valve but is excessive when checked with the old valve, the old valve stem is worn and a new valve must be installed.

If it is necessary to replace valve guides, use a suitable driver to drive them out of the cylinder head. If suitable tools are not available, guides can be pulled out by using a piece of pipe together with a long bolt and washers.

Before removing guides, carefully measure the portion of the guide that protrudes from the cylinder head and install the new guides accordingly.

After the new guides have been installed they should be reamed to provide the clearance given in the *Valve Specifications* table.

HYDRAULIC VALVE LIFTERS

Failure of an hydraulic valve lifter, Fig. 6, is generally caused by an inadequate oil supply or dirt. An air leak at the intake side of the oil pump or too much oil in the engine will cause air bubbles in the oil supply to the lifters, causing them to collapse. This is a probable cause of trouble if several lifters fail to function, but air in the oil is an unlikely cause of failure of a single unit.

The valve lifters may be lifted out of their bores after removing the rocker arms and push rods. Adjustable pliers with taped jaws may be used to remove lifters that are stuck due to varnish, carbon, etc.

To disassemble, press down on the center of the push rod cup. Using a pointed tool, remove lock wire from the groove while holding cup down. Invert lifter and slide out push rod cup, plunger, ball retainer and spring.

To assemble, place the ball on its seat in the lower end of the plunger while holding the plunger upside down. Position the ball retainer and spring over ball and end of plunger. Lower the body over the plunger. Turn the assembly right side up and fill the plunger with clean engine oil. Jiggle the ball with a small piece of wire until oil drains out of plunger into the body and trapped

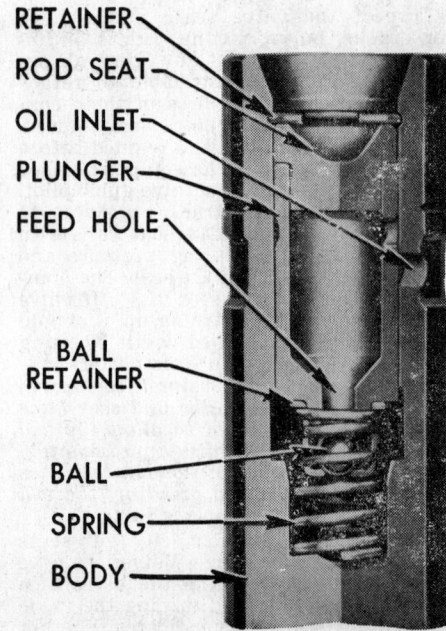

RETAINER
ROD SEAT
OIL INLET
PLUNGER
FEED HOLE
BALL RETAINER
BALL
SPRING
BODY

Fig. 6 Hydraulic valve lifter

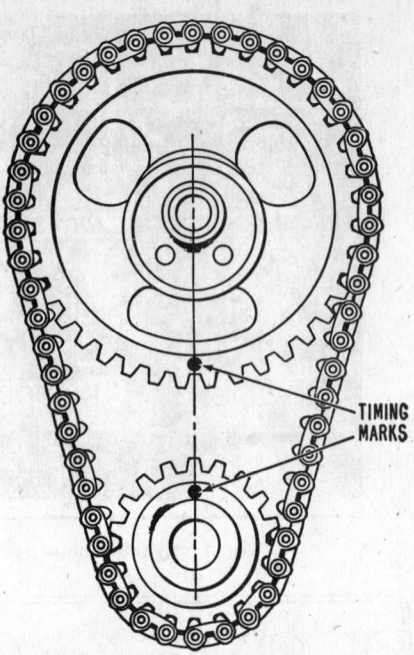

Fig. 7 Line up "O" marks on sprockets for correct valve timing

TIMING MARKS

air is released from the body. Refill the plunger with oil, place the push rod cup on the plunger and position the lock wire over the cup, locking it in its groove.

TIMING CHAIN COVER

1. To remove the cover, drain cooling system.
2. Remove radiator, fan pulley and belt.
3. Remove fan drive pulley and vibration damper.
4. If equipped with power steering, move pump out of the way.
5. Remove fuel pump and generator.
6. Remove distributor.
7. Loosen and slide front clamp on thermostat by-pass hose rearward.
8. Remove bolts attaching timing chain cover to cylinder block; also the two oil pan-to-cover bolts.
9. Remove timing chain cover.
10. Reverse above procedure to install the cover.

Service Note

Remove the oil pump cover and pack the space around the oil pump gears completely full of vaseline. There must be no air space left inside the pump. Reinstall the cover using a new gasket. This step is very important as the oil pump may lose its prime whenever the pump, pump cover or timing chain cover is disturbed. If the pump is not packed it may not begin to pump oil as soon as the engine is started.

TIMING CHAIN

1. With the timing case cover removed as outlined above, temporarily install the vibration damper bolt and washer in end of crankshaft.
2. Turn crankshaft so sprockets are

positioned as shown in Fig. 7. Use a sharp rap on a wrench handle to start the vibration damper bolt out without disturbing the position of the sprockets.

3. Remove front oil slinger.
4. Remove camshaft distributor drive gear and fuel pump eccentric.
5. Use two large screwdrivers to alternately pry the camshaft sprocket then the crankshaft sprocket forward until the camshaft sprocket is free. Then remove camshaft sprocket and chain, and crankshaft sprocket off crankshaft.
6. To install, assemble chain on sprockets and slide sprockets on their respective shafts with the "0" marks on the sprockets lined up as shown in Fig. 7.
7. Complete the installation in the reverse order of removal.

VALVE TIMING DATA

Year	Model	Intake Opens①	Intake Closes②	Exhaust Opens③	Exhaust Closes④
1961	4000	29	71	67	33

①—Degrees before top dead center.
②—Degrees after bottom dead center.
③—Degrees before bottom dead center.
④—Degrees after top dead center.

CAMSHAFT

1. To remove camshaft, remove rocker arm shaft assemblies, push rods and valve lifters.
2. Remove timing chain and sprockets.
3. Slide camshaft out of engine, using care not to mar the bearing surfaces.

CAMSHAFT BEARINGS

The camshaft is supported in five steel-backed babbitt-lined bearings that are pressed into the block. The bearings must be line-reamed to size after being pressed into place. Since this operation requires special reaming equipment the original bearings should be retained unless severely damaged.

Slightly scored camshaft bearings will

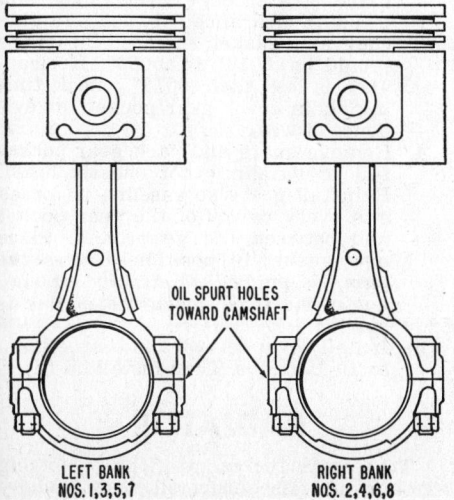

OIL SPURT HOLES TOWARD CAMSHAFT

LEFT BANK NOS. 1,3,5,7   RIGHT BANK NOS. 2,4,6,8

Fig. 8 Piston and rod assembly

be satisfactory if the surface of the camshaft journals are polished and bearings are cleaned up to remove burrs, and the fit of the bearings is free.

PISTONS & RODS, REMOVE

After removing the cylinder head, examine the cylinder bores above the ring travel area. If bores are worn so that a shoulder or ridge exists at this point, remove the ridge with a ridge reamer to avoid damaging rings or cracking ring lands of piston during removal.

Remove connecting rod caps and push pistons and rods out of cylinders, using care to prevent rod bolts from contacting and nicking crankshaft journals.

Make sure the rods and pistons are properly numbered so that they can be reinstalled in original locations. It is advisable to install caps on rods to avoid mixing parts.

PISTONS & RODS, ASSEMBLE

Rods and pistons should be assembled and installed as shown in Fig. 8.

PISTONS

Standard size Buick service pistons are high limit or maximum diameter; therefore, they can usually be used with a slight amount of honing to correct slight scoring or excessive clearances in engines having relatively low mileage. Service pistons are also furnished in .010" oversize.

If the pistons are to be reused with new rings, remove the carbon from the ring grooves. A special tool is available for this work but a satisfactory job can be done by breaking an old piston ring, filing the broken end to a sharp, square edge and using it to scrape out the carbon. Soak the piston in cleaning solvent to loosen any carbon residue. Clean out the loosened carbon, being careful not to cut away any piston material.

Clean out the oil return holes with a drill just large enough to fill the holes. Hold the drill in a tap wrench and make sure the drill does not remove any metal from the piston.

Rinse the piston in solvent and wipe off the carbon on the sides of the piston. *Never use a wire brush to clean a piston* as the brush will round off the edges of the ring lands. Pistons showing scuffed or scored skirts should be scrapped. Examine the ring lands carefully for cracks. If the piston is in the least bit doubtful, it should be discarded.

PISTON RINGS

When new piston rings are installed without reboring cylinders, the glazed cylinder walls should be slightly dulled, but without increasing the bore diameter. This is done with a "Glazebuster" or with a hone equipped with the finest grade of stones.

New piston rings must be checked for clearance in piston grooves and for gap in cylinder bores. Cylinder bores and

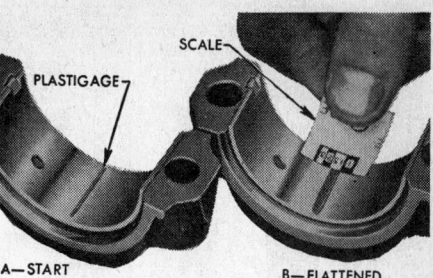

Fig. 9 Checking bearing clearance with Plastigage

piston grooves must be clean, dry and free of carbon and burrs.

Check the clearance of each ring in its piston groove by installing the ring and then inserting feeler gauges *under* the ring. Any wear that occurs in the piston groove forms a step or ridge at the inner portion of the lower land. If gauges are inserted above the ring, the ring may rest on the step instead of on the worn portion of the lower land, and a false measurement of clearance will result.

If the piston grooves have worn to the extent that relatively high steps or ridges exist on the lower lands, the piston should be replaced because the steps will interfere with the operation of new rings and the ring clearances will be excessive. Piston rings are not furnished in oversize widths to compensate for ring groove wear.

To check the end gaps of rings, place the ring in the cylinder in which it will be used. Square it in the body by tapping with the lower end of the piston, then measure the gap with feeler gauges. If necessary to increase the gap, file the ends of rings carefully with a smooth file.

PISTON PINS

Piston pins are a pressed fit in the upper end of the connecting rod and a slide fit in the piston bosses.

ROD BEARINGS

Connecting rod bearings are of the precision insert type and if worn can be replaced without removing the rod assembly by removing the cap and replacing the upper and lower halves. The clearance between the rod bearing and the crankshaft can be measured by the use of Plastigage as follows:

1. Remove bearing cap and wipe oil from crankshaft journal and bearing insert.
2. With crankpin at approximately bottom dead center, place a piece of Plastigage in the center of the cap.
3. Reinstall cap and tighten the bolts to the torque listed in the *Engine Tightening Data* table.
4. Remove bearing cap and determine bearing clearance by comparing the width of the flattened Plastigage at its widest point with the graduation on the Plastigage envelope. The number within the graduation on the envelope indicates the clearance in thousandths of an inch, Fig. 9.

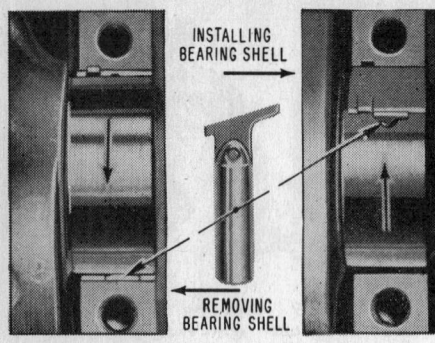

Fig. 10 Tool for removing upper main bearing shells

MAIN BEARINGS

Caution—Main bearing clearance can be checked with Plastigage in the same manner described for rod bearings. If bearings are measured with the engine in the chassis, the crankshaft must be supported in order to take up clearance between the upper bearing insert and crankshaft journal. This can be done by tightening bearing caps of adjacent bearing with .005" to .015" cardboard. (such as a calling card) between lower bearing shell and journal. Use extreme care when this is done to avoid unnecessary strain on the crankshaft or bearings or a false reading may be obtained. Do not rotate crankshaft while Plastigage is installed. *Be sure to remove cardboard.* To install new bearings, proceed as follows:

1. Remove bearing cap and worn lower shell.
2. Rotate crankshaft in normal direction to turn upper bearing shell out of crankcase. Use a cotter pin with a flattened head or the special tool made for the purpose in the crankshaft oil hole to contact the bearing and force it out, Fig. 10.
3. Place a new upper shell on the crankshaft journal with the locating notch in the correct position and rotate the shaft to turn the bearing in place.
4. Install the lower bearing shell in the cap.
5. Tighten all cap nuts to the torque value given in the *Engine Tightening Data* table.

CRANKSHAFT OIL SEAL

A braided oil seal is pressed into the upper and lower grooves behind the rear main bearing. Should the braided seal require replacement, the installation of the lower half is accomplished as follows:

With the bearing cap and lower bearing half removed, install a new seal so that both ends protrude above the cap. Tap the seal down into position or roll it snugly in its groove with a smooth rounded tool, Fig. 11. Then cut off the protruding ends of the seal with a sharp knife or razor blade.

Installing Upper Seal

Although the usual practice is to remove the crankshaft when the upper half of the seal is to be speraced it is possible to do the job without removing the crankshaft as follows:

To remove the seal, use needle-nose pliers to grasp the end of the seal which is most accessible. Pull the seal downward while rotating the crankshaft slowly in the direction that the seal is being removed.

To install the new seal, fasten a length of wire or strong string such as fishing line securely to one end of the new seal. See that the point of fastening is not bulky and that it is not over ⅜" from the end of the seal. Coat the seal with Lubriplate. Pass the free end of the wire or string up over the crankshaft at the point where the seal is to be installed. Then exert a firm, steady pull on the wire or string and at the same time rotate the crankshaft slowly in the direction of the pull. This will help to move the seal into position. When the installation is completed, trim the ends of the seal flush with the engine block.

OIL PAN

1. Raise car and drain oil.
2. Disconnect exhaust pipe at crossover.
3. If equipped with manual shift transmission, loosen clutch equalizer-to-frame bolts.
4. Remove steering idler arm bracket-to-suspension crossmember bolts.
5. Support engine either with a jack or with chains around the exhaust manifold.
6. Remove bolts and nuts attaching engine mounts to mount brackets.
7. Raise engine and insert bolts through bracket bolt holes, then lower engine so mounts rest on bolts.
8. Remove lower flywheel housing.
9. Remove oil pan bolts and lower pan enough to remove oil pump pipe and screen-to-cylinder block bolts.
10. Rotate crankshaft to provide maximum clearance at forward end of oil pan. Move front of pan to the right and lower pan through opening between crossmember and steering linkage intermediate shaft.

OIL PUMP

The oil pump is located in the timing chain cover where it is connected to a drilled passage in the crankcase to an oil screen housing and pipe assembly.

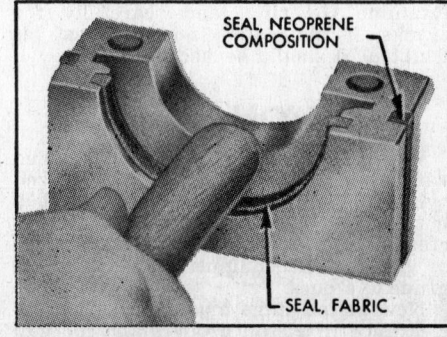

Fig. 11 Rear main bearing oil seals

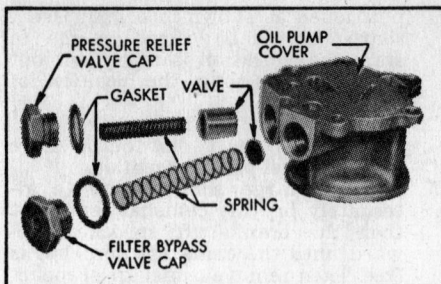

Fig. 12 Oil pump cover and related parts

1. To remove the oil pump cover and gears, first remove the oil filter.
2. Disconnect wire from oil pressure indicator switch in filter by-pass valve cap, Fig. 12.
3. Remove screws attaching oil pump cover assembly to timing chain cover.
4. Remove cover assembly and slide out oil pump gears.

Inspection

1. Wash all gears and replace any not found serviceable.
2. Disassemble oil pump cover.
3. Check relief valve for wear or scoring. Check the relief valve spring to see that it is not worn on its side or collapsed. Thoroughly clean the screen staked in the relief valve bore of the cover.
4. Check the valve in its bore in the cover. The valve should have no more clearance than an easy slip fit. If any perceptible side shake can be felt the valve and/or cover should be replaced.
5. Check filter by-pass valve for cracks, nicks or warping. The valve should be flat and free of nicks or scratches.

Assembly & Installation

1. Lubricate and install valve parts in cover, Fig. 12. Install caps and torque to 30-35 ft. lbs.
2. Install gears and shaft in oil pump body section of timing chain cover and check gear end clearance.
3. Place straightedge over gears and measure clearance between straightedge and gasket surface. Clearance should be .0018" to .0058". If clearance is less than .0018", check timing chain cover gear pocket for evidence of wear.
4. Remove gears and pack gear pocket full of vaseline (not chassis lube). Reinstall gears so vaseline is forced into every cavity of the gear pocket and between the gear teeth. Place new gasket in position. *Unless the pump is packed as directed, it may not prime itself when the engine is started.*
5. Install cover screws and torque them to 10-15 ft. lbs. Then install oil filter.

RADIATOR

To remove the radiator, drain cooling system and disconnect all hose. Remove attaching bolts and brackets and remove radiator.

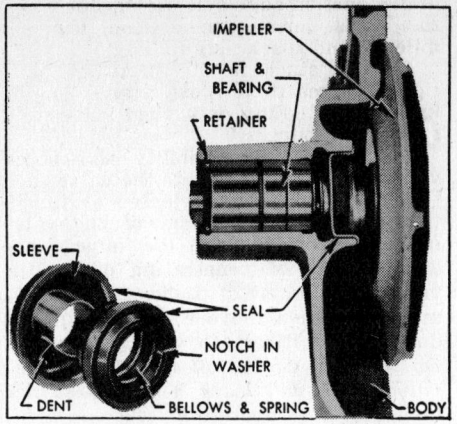

Fig. 13 Water pump

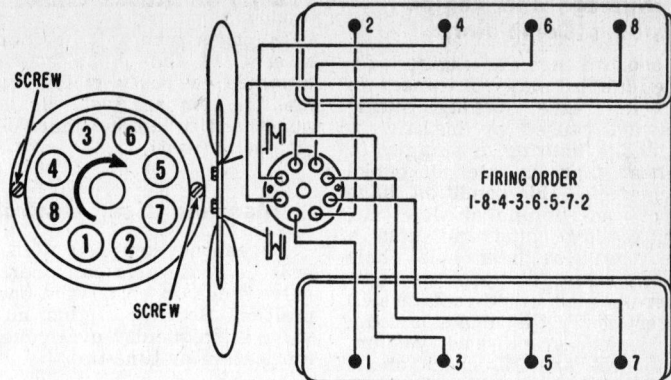

FIRING ORDER
1-8-4-3-6-5-7-2

Fig. 14 Ignition details

WATER PUMP, REPLACE

1. Drain cooling system.
2. Remove fan and pulley or pulleys from pump shaft.
3. Disconnect hose from pump.
4. Unfasten and remove pump from timing chain cover.

WATER PUMP REPAIRS

The water pump cover is die cast aluminum into which the water pump bearing outer race is shrunk fit. For this reason the cover, shaft bearing and hub are not replaceable. The shaft seal and impeller are the only replaceable parts of the pump, Fig. 13. To replace these parts, proceed as follows:

1. Pull impeller from shaft.
2. Remove carbon washer, pump bellows and spring from brass sleeve that is pressed into the pump housing. It is not necessary to remove the sleeve if it is in good condition. However, if it is necessary, drive the sleeve out with a punch inserted through the vent hole in pump body.
3. Clean pump cover to remove scale, etc. Do not use cleaning solvent as it may leak into bearings and destroy the lubricant.
4. If old brass seal sleeve was removed, carefully press new seal assembly into body using a thick walled tube of suitable diameter.
5. If old sleeve was not removed, separate new sleeve from bellows by soaking in hot water to soften cement used to hold seal parts together for ease of handling. Install carbon washer bellows and spring in old sleeve, being careful to engage notches of washer with driving dents of brass sleeve.
6. Coat face of carbon washer and impeller hub with rust preventative; then press impeller on shaft until rear face of impeller hub is flush with end of shaft. *Pump must be supported on forward end of shaft only while pressing on impeller.*

DISTRIBUTOR, REPLACE

1. Disconnect primary wire from coil and hose from vacuum unit.
2. Remove distributor cap by inserting a screwdriver in upper slotted end of cap latches; then press down and turn 90° counterclockwise.
3. Make a mark on distributor housing in line with the center of the rotor. Then carefully note the direction the vacuum unit points in relation to the engine so that the distributor can be replaced in the exact same position. *If engine is turned over while distributor is out, complete ignition tim-* *ing procedure must be followed.*
4. Remove distributor clamp and lift distributor out of timing chain cover.
5. Reverse removal procedure to install the distributor and leave the clamp bolt just loose enough to permit movement of the distributor for ignition timing, Fig. 14.

IGNITION TIMING

Correct ignition timing exists when the yellow timing mark on the vibration damper is aligned with the "5" mark on the timing indicator with engine running at slow idle and with No. 1 piston up on its compression stroke.

STARTER, REPLACE

To remove the starter, disconnect battery cable from battery. Disconnect cable and solenoid lead wire from solenoid switch. Remove starter attaching bolts and take off starter.

MUFFLER & PIPES

All connections except the muffler are of the ball joint type. These ball joints make for easy connection, disconnection and alignment of exhaust system parts. No gaskets are used in the entire exhaust system. Connections to the muffler are made with U-bolts and clamps.

Carburetor Section

Performance Complaints

Flooding, stumble on acceleration or other performance complaints are in many instances caused by the presence of dirt, water or other foreign matter in the carburetor. To aid in diagnosing the cause of the complaint, the carburetor should be carefully removed from the engine without draining the fuel from the bowl. The contents of the fuel bowl may then be examined for contamination as the carburetor is disassembled.

Check the fuel in the bowl for contamination by dirt, water, gum or other foreign matter. A magnet moved through the fuel in the bowl will pick up and identify any iron oxide dust that may have caused intake needle and seat leakage.

Inspect gasketed surfaces between body and air horn. Small nicks or burrs should be smoothed down to eliminate air or fuel leakage. On carburetors having a vacuum piston, be especially particular when inspecting the top surface of the inner wall of the bowl around the vacuum piston passage. A poor seal at this location may contribute to a "cutting-out" on turns complaint.

Fill the carburetor bowl with clean fuel before installing on manifold. This will help prevent dirt trapped in the fuel system from being dislodged by the free flow of fuel as the carburetor is primed. The operation of the floats and intake needle and seats may be checked under pressure if a fuel pump is used at the bench to fill the carburetor bowl. Operate the throttle several times and visually check the discharge from pump jets.

Poor Mileage and Engine Loading Complaints

Cases of poor mileage and engine loading may be due in many instances to sluggish choke valve opening during cold driveaway, caused by insufficient vacuum in choke housing, a plugged or restricted heat pipe or inlet in choke cover. To check for this condition, have engine warm and running at slow idle. Remove choke heat pipe and hold a finger over the heat inlet hole (hole is on choke housing on some carburetors). If there is little or no vacuum pull on the finger, check the choke housing for gasket leaks or plugged vacuum passages. If these are OK, check choke vacuum passages in carburetor between choke housing and manifold.

Dirty or Rusty Choke Housing

In cases where it is found that the interior of the choke housing is dirty, gummed or rusty while the carburetor itself is comparatively clean, look for a punctured or eroded manifold heat tube (if one is used).

Manifold Heat Control Valve

An engine equipped with a manifold heat control valve can operate with the valve stuck in either the open or closed position. Because of this, an inoperative valve is frequently overlooked at vehicle lubrication or tune-up.

A valve stuck in the "heat-off" position can result in slow warm up, deposits in combustion chamber, carburetor icing, flat spots during acceleration, low gas mileage and spark plug fouling.

A valve stuck in the "heat-on" position can result in power loss, engine knocking, sticking or burned valves and spark plug burning.

To prevent the possibility of a stuck valve, check and lubricate the valve each time the vehicle is lubricated or tuned-up. Check the operation of the valve manually. To lubricate the valve, place a few drops of penetrating oil on the valve shaft where it passes through the manifold. Then move the valve up and down a few times to work the oil in. *Do not use engine oil to lubricate the valve as it will leave a residue which hampers valve operation.*

ROCHESTER CARBURETOR ADJUSTMENTS

Year	Carburetor Model	Idle Adjustments				Float Level		Float Drop		Pump Rod Setting	Choke Unloader Setting	Choke Setting
		Mixture Screws Turns Open	Hot Idle Speed In Neutral	Fast Idle Speed	Dashpot Plunger Clearance	Primary	Secondary	Primary	Secondary			
1961	2GC-7019093	1½	525	.052⑤	⑥	1¹⁷⁄₆₄①	None	1²⁹⁄₃₂②	None	1³⁄₃₂⑧	.157④	Index
	2GC-7019090	1½	525	.052⑤	⑥	1¹⁷⁄₆₄①	None	1²⁹⁄₃₂②	None	1³⁄₃₂⑧	.157④	Index

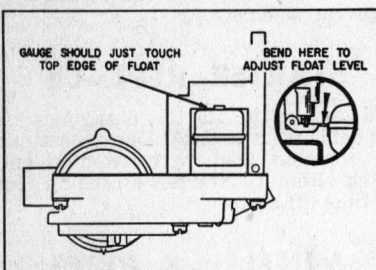

Fig. ①—2GC float level.

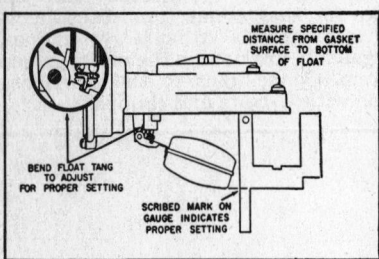

Fig. ②—2GC float drop.

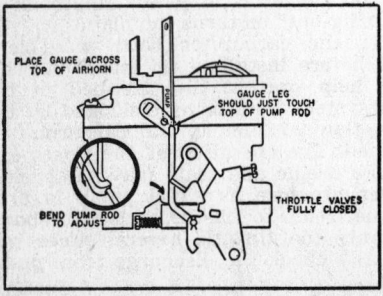

ROCHESTER NOTES

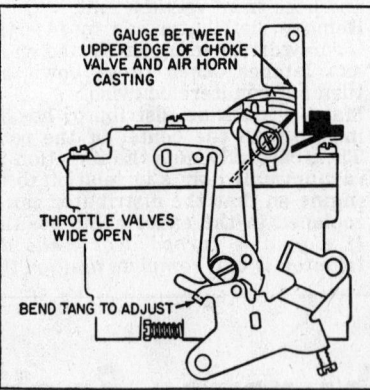

Fig. ④—Bend unloader tang on throttle lever to obtain clearance specified between upper edge of choke valve and inner wall of air horn with throttle valves wide open.

Fig. ③—With throttle valves fully closed, bend pump rod as necessary to obtain dimension specified from top of pump housing to top of pump rod.

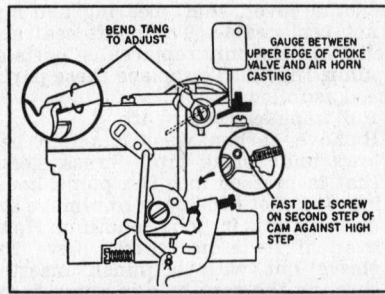

Fig. ⑤—Fast idle adjustment is not required if hot idle speed is correctly set and choke rod properly adjusted. To adjust choke rod, turn idle stop screw 1½ turns against fast idle cam with choke valve fully open. Place idle stop screw on second step on fast idle cam against shoulder of high step. There should be the clearance specified between upper edge of choke valve and wall of air horn. Bend tang to adjust.

⑥—With engine at normal operating temperature, open throttle to clear fast idle cam and rotate cam to extreme fast idle position; then allow throttle to close against fast idle cam. Adjust dashpot until it just touches throttle lever. With transmission in Drive and brakes applied, jab accelerator pedal and release rapidly. If engine stalls from too rapid closing of throttle, move dashpot toward throttle lever until its action prevents engine stalling. If excessive time is required for throttle to reach fully closed position, move dashpot away from throttle lever. If proper control cannot be obtained by adjustment, replace dashpot.

Clutch & Synchromesh Transmission Section

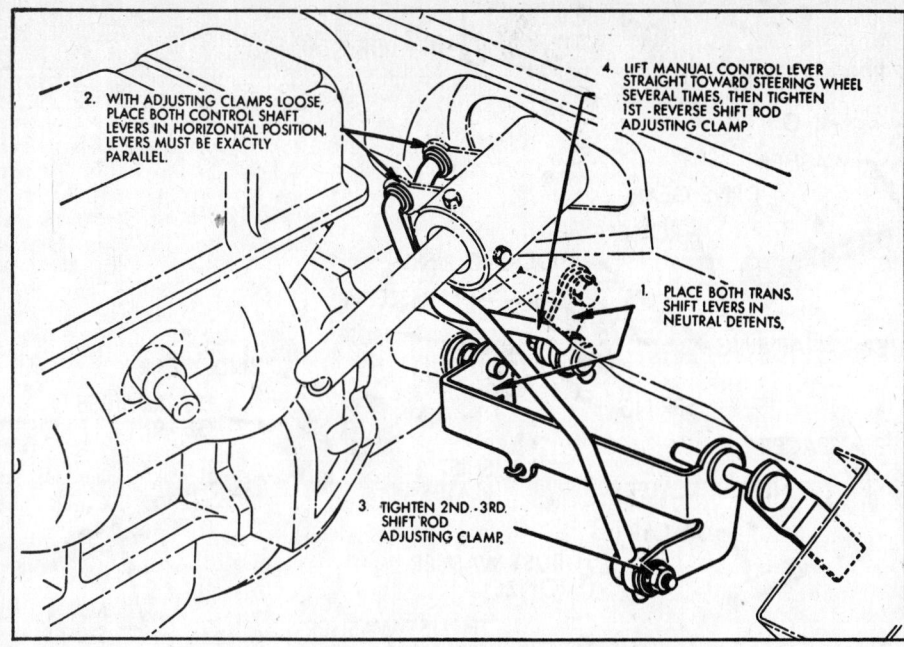

2. WITH ADJUSTING CLAMPS LOOSE, PLACE BOTH CONTROL SHAFT LEVERS IN HORIZONTAL POSITION. LEVERS MUST BE EXACTLY PARALLEL.

4. LIFT MANUAL CONTROL LEVER STRAIGHT TOWARD STEERING WHEEL SEVERAL TIMES, THEN TIGHTEN 1ST-REVERSE SHIFT ROD ADJUSTING CLAMP

1. PLACE BOTH TRANS. SHIFT LEVERS IN NEUTRAL DETENTS.

3. TIGHTEN 2ND.-3RD. SHIFT ROD ADJUSTING CLAMP.

Fig. 1   Synchromesh transmission shift controls

CLUTCH PEDAL, ADJUST

Free play of the clutch pedal should be ⅞" to 1" when the pedal is depressed by hand. Insufficient pedal free play will cause the clutch release bearing to ride against the clutch release levers all the time, resulting in abnormal wear of these parts. It may also cause clutch slippage and abnormal wear of the driven plate, flywheel and pressure plate if pressure on release levers is enough to prevent positive engagement of the clutch. To adjust the pedal free play, proceed as follows:

Pull outer end of clutch fork rearward until clutch release bearing contacts clutch release levers. Free movement at the outer end of the fork should be approximately 3/16".

If free movement of fork is not 3/16", remove clevis pin from rear end of clutch release rod and rotate rod as required to make free movement correct. Reinstall clevis pin and check to see that free pedal play is correct.

CLUTCH, REPLACE

1. Remove transmission as described further on.
2. Remove flywheel lower cover.
3. Remove clutch release bearing.
4. Disconnect release rod from fork.
5. Unhook fork boot from opening in flywheel housing.
6. Push inward on release fork to free it from ball stud in flywheel housing and remove fork through bottom of housing.
7. Mark clutch cover and flywheel with a center punch so that cover can be reinstalled in same position on flywheel in order to preserve engine balance.
8. Loosen each clutch cover bolt a turn at a time in order to relieve clutch spring pressure evenly and thereby avoid distortion of cover. Metal spacers (such as ¼" nuts) placed between release levers and inner edge of cover will aid removal and later reinstallation by holding clutch springs partially compressed.
9. Support pressure plate and clutch cover assembly while removing last bolts, then remove clutch cover and driven plate.
10. Reverse removal procedure to install the clutch and adjust free pedal play as outlined previously.

Clutch, Overhaul

Unless special clutch rebuilding equipment is available, it is recommended that the clutch assembly be exchanged for a rebuilt unit should the clutch require rebuilding. The driven disc, however, may be replaced without special equipment.

SHIFT CONTROLS, ADJUST

Need for shift control adjustment is indicated if either the lower control shaft lever contacts the edge of the steering column jacket opening, or if the manual control lever does not move smoothly from the 2nd-3rd range to the 1st-reverse range when the lever is lifted straight toward the steering wheel. If an adjustment is indicated, refer to Fig. 1.

TRANSMISSION, REPLACE

1. If transmission is to be disassembled, drain the lubricant. Fill with kerosene and run transmission in neutral for 15 seconds; then drain.
2. Mark front universal joint and front companion flange so that these parts can be reassembled in the same relative position.
3. Remove two U-bolts attaching U-joint to companion flange and slide propeller shaft rearward as far as possible for working clearance.
4. Disconnect shift linkage from transmission.
5. Disconnect speedometer cable.
6. Loosen all three exhaust pipe ball joints so that transmission and rear end of engine can be lowered.
7. Remove two bolts attaching transmission mounting pad to support. Leave mounting pad bolted to transmission.
8. Place a flat wood block on jack and jack under engine pan until transmission mounting pad clears transmission support.
9. Remove transmission support (4 bolts).
10. Lower jack so that transmission will clear underbody during removal.
11. Remove upper left and lower right transmission mounting bolts and install guide pins in these bolt holes.
12. Remove other two bolts and slide transmission straight back until drive gear shaft is free of clutch housing; then lower transmission.
13. Reverse removal procedure to install transmission.

TRANSMISSION REPAIRS

Disassembly

1. Referring to Fig. 2, remove top cover.
2. Remove front bearing retainer.
3. Remove retainer holding speedometer sleeve in rear bearing retainer, and remove driven gear and sleeve.
4. Remove companion flange from rear of transmission.
5. Remove rear bearing retainer.
6. Remove speedometer drive gear.
7. Drive countershaft-idler shaft lock plate from ends of shafts.
8. Drive countershaft rearward with a brass drift until shaft is just free in front shaft bore of case.
9. Using a suitable dummy shaft to hold bearings and thrust washers intact, allow countershaft to drop to bottom of case.
10. Remove main drive gear and bearing, and 14 pilot rollers from rear end of shaft.
11. Remove front bronze blocking ring from synchronizer. Remove snap ring from front of mainshaft.
12. Move mainshaft rearward until rear bearing is free of case. Then move

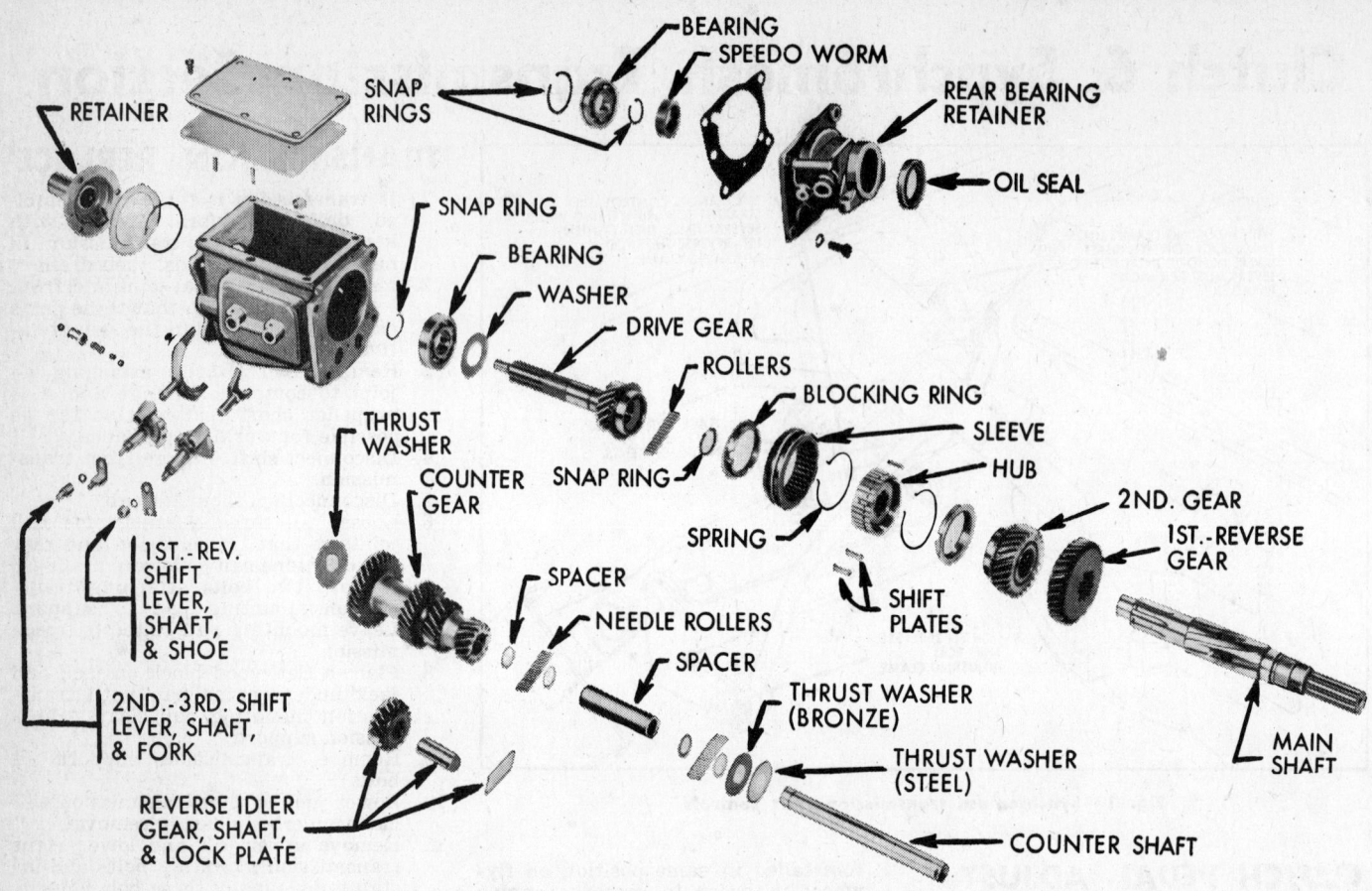

Fig. 2 Synchromesh transmission exploded

mainshaft to extreme right of case, which will permit the 2nd-3rd shift fork to be removed.

13. Remove mainshaft by sliding shaft rearward through rear of case, at the same time stripping mainshaft as shaft is being withdrawn.

14. Remove 1st-reverse shift shoe from shift shaft. Drive reverse idler shaft out of case using a brass drift. Lift out reverse idler gear.

15. Lift cluster gear assembly from case.

Reassembly

During reassembly, apply a thin film of transmission lube to all parts. Always use new seals and gaskets. Refer to Fig. 2 and assemble the transmission in the following sequence:

Countershaft Assembly

1. Install dummy shaft or Loading Tool J-8965 in cluster gear.
2. Insert tubular spacer.
3. Hold cluster gear in vertical position and while supporting loading tool from below, insert inner bearing spacer (washer) and place 22 rollers around loading tool, using heavy grease to hold them in place. Insert outer bearing spacer. Then insert rollers on opposite end.
4. Install inner rear bronze thrust washer so that lugs engage notches in cluster gear. Install outer rear

steel thrust washer. Large front thrust washer should not be installed at this time.

Synchronizer Assembly

1. Install springs solidly in recesses on both ends of synchronizer hub. One end of both springs should be located in same shift plate slot so that springs will extend in opposite directions from each other. Install shift plate directly over these ends.
2. While holding shift plates in their grooves, slide synchronizer sleeve over hub until detent is felt. The extended tapered portion of the sleeve faces the same direction (front) as the long extended portion at the center of the hub.
3. Place rear blocking ring in position at rear end of hub and rotate until shifting plates match notches in blocking ring. Blocking ring remains free until assembly of transmission.

Shift Levers & Interlock

Insert new seals and apply transmission lube in seals and shaft holes. Then install shift levers, interlock and related parts as indicated in Fig. 2.

When assembled, shift 2nd-3rd shift lever into 2nd speed position. With one end of interlock sleeve against 1st-reverse cam, the clearance between sleeve and 2nd-3rd cam should be .001-.007". If clearance is greater than specified, and

if it seems possible that the transmission can be forced into two gears at once, the old interlock sleeve should be measured with a micrometer and replaced with a new, longer sleeve. Sleeves are available in five lengths: 1.287", 1.291", 1.295", 1.299" and 1.303".

Mainshaft & Main Drive Gear

1. Locate slinger washer on drive gear shaft with raised center portion toward front. Press bearing on shaft with outer snap ring groove toward front. Install bearing outer snap ring and thickest shaft snap ring that will properly seat in snap ring groove (three thicknesses are available).
2. Press bearing on rear of mainshaft with outer snap ring groove toward rear. Install bearing outer snap ring and shaft snap ring.
3. With bearing loading tool in place, and with cluster gear parts in place except front thrust washer, lower cluster gear assembly vertically through top of case with rear section of gear down. Then position cluster gear in horizontal position to allow front of cluster gear to pass projections in transmission case.
4. Locate cluster gear in normal position with lug on outer rear thrust washer up, and move loading tool rearward about ¼" to pass into bore of case. Insert large front thrust washer with lug to front so as to en-

gage slot in case. Align hole in washer with bore in cluster gear and move loading tool forward allowing cluster gear to drop to bottom of case.

5. End play of cluster gear should be .005" to .017" measured between two rear thrust washers. If clearance is excessive, replace thrust washers.

6. Locate reverse idler gear with hub section and chamfered side of teeth forward. Drive reverse idler shaft in through rear of case with lock plate slot toward countershaft bore. Leave shaft projecting about $\frac{1}{16}$" from fully installed position.

7. Insert 1st-reverse shift shoe in its shift shaft and install mainshaft and bearing through rear of case. As shaft is being installed, slide 1st-reverse gear on shaft with groove on gear toward front. Slide 2nd speed gear on shaft with extended portion toward front. With rear blocking ring in position, slide synchronizer on shaft with extended portion of sleeve toward front. Install mainshaft snap ring. Insert 2nd-3rd shift

fork in its shaft and engage fork in grove in synchronizer sleeve. With 1st-reverse shoe offset toward front, engage shift shoe in groove on its gear. Move complete mainshaft assembly forward until rear bearing is fully installed in case bore.

8. With synchronizer hub and 2nd speed gear pressed forward against snap ring, there should be .003" to .016" end clearance between 2nd gear and front facing of 1st-reverse gear splines. Replace worn parts if clearance is excessive.

9. Place front blocking ring at front end of synchronizer hub and rotate until shift plates match notches in blocking ring.

10. Insert 14 pilot rollers in drive gear pocket, holding them in place with heavy grease.

11. Install drive gear and bearing through front of case, sliding bearing rollers in rear end of drive gear over front end of mainshaft.

12. Check clearance between front blocking ring teeth and drive gear teeth by lightly seating blocking ring on

contacting surface of gear. Minimum clearance should be .045". If less replace blocking ring.

13. Turn transmission upside down to allow cluster gear assembly to drop to normal position. Align holes in case with cluster gear and drive out loading tool by installing countershaft. Leave countershaft projecting about 1/16" from fully installed position.

14. Install lock plate in slots of countershaft and reverse idler shaft. Then drive both shafts forward until lock plate is tight against the case.

15. Install front bearing retainer and gasket, being sure oil return hole in retainer and gasket match oil hole in case.

16. Complete the assembly by installing rear bearing retainer seal, speedometer drive gear, companion flange, speedometer driven gear and sleeve with new O-ring, and driven gear retainer.

17. Install top cover with new gasket and check transmission in all shift positions.

Automatic Transmission Section

DESCRIPTION

This transmission, Fig. 1, provides five different control or operating ranges which may be manually selected by the driver through movement of the control lever. Letters on the stationary dial on the control panel identify each range as follows: P for parking; N for neutral; D for drive; L for low, and R for reverse.

The transmssion case is bolted to the engine crankcase through the converter

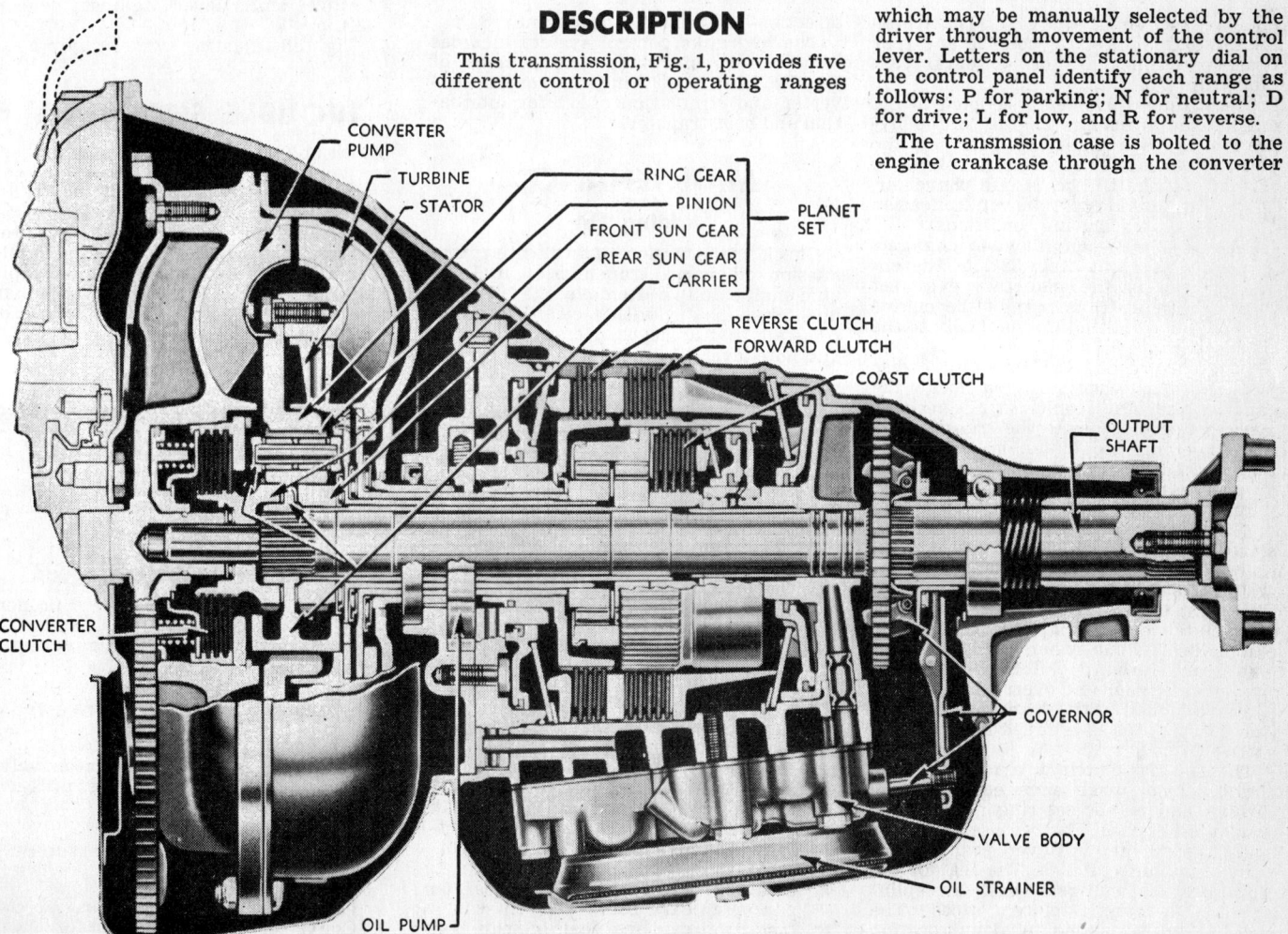

Fig. 1 Sectional view of automatic transmission

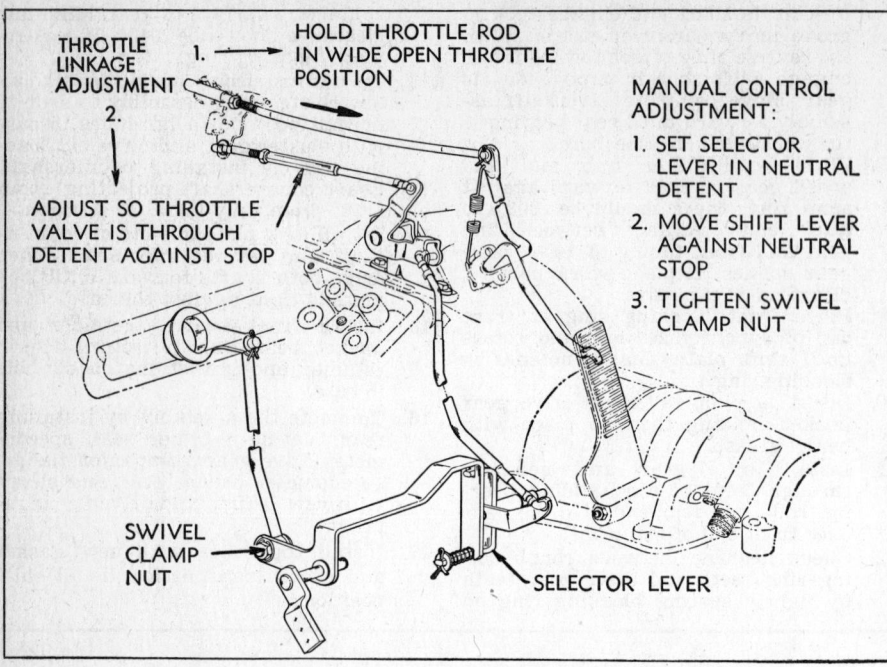

Fig. 2 Manual control and throttle linkage adjustments

Within the figure:

THROTTLE LINKAGE ADJUSTMENT

1. HOLD THROTTLE ROD IN WIDE OPEN THROTTLE POSITION

2. ADJUST SO THROTTLE VALVE IS THROUGH DETENT AGAINST STOP

MANUAL CONTROL ADJUSTMENT:
1. SET SELECTOR LEVER IN NEUTRAL DETENT
2. MOVE SHIFT LEVER AGAINST NEUTRAL STOP
3. TIGHTEN SWIVEL CLAMP NUT

SWIVEL CLAMP NUT

SELECTOR LEVER

---

housing section of the case. The transmission case, converter housing and rear bearing retainer are one integral cast aluminum part.

The torque converter is coupled to the engine and transmits engine torque hydraulically to a planetary gear set, the planet gear carrier of which is splined to the output shaft. The torque converter, of course, provides torque multiplication to meet varying driving conditions.

The converter clutch, when engaged, transmits approximately 36% of the engine torque to the planetary gear set front sun gear. Thus part of the engine torque is transmitted mechanically to the output shaft.

The forward clutch is a multiple disc clutch which, when engaged, locks the cam of the stator and rear sun gear overrunning clutches to the transmission case. The forward clutch is engaged in Low and Drive Ranges to allow the stator and rear sun gear to turn in one direction only (with the engine).

The coast clutch is a multiple disc clutch which, when engaged, locks the rear sun gear to the cam of the stator and rear sun gear overrunning clutches. The coast clutch also locks the overrunning clutch cam to part of the forward clutch discs. Thus, when both the coast clutch and forward clutch are engaged, the rear sun gear and overrunning clutch cam are locked to the transmission case. The coast clutch is engaged in all ranges except Drive.

The reverse clutch is a multiple disc clutch which, when engaged, locks the turbine and planet set ring gear to the transmission case. The reverse clutch, of course, is engaged in Reverse range.

Overrunning clutches. The rear of the stator and rear sun gear shafts are splined to overrunning clutch races. The clutches are arranged to allow rotation with respect to the clutch cam in one

direction only (with the engine).

The hydraulic control system includes devices for controlling engagement of the disc clutches, filling the torque converter and circulation of oil for lubrication and heat transfer.

MAINTENANCE

Adding Oil

Check transmission oil level with transmission oil warm, transmission in Park and engine idling. Remove the oil level dipstick, wipe dry with a clean cloth and reinstall to full depth. Remove dipstick and note level.

If oil level is below "ADD" mark on dipstick, add automatic transmission oil as required but do not fill above the "FULL" mark. The distance between the "FULL" and "ADD" marks represents approximately one pint.

Changing Oil

At 25,000 mile intervals, the transmission oil pan should be removed and cleaned. The oil strainer should be replaced and fresh oil added to the transmission. *This operation should not be attempted unless accurate foot pound and inch pound torque wrenches are available and the operator is fully qualified in their use.*

1. Remove bolt and seal attaching oil pan to transmission.
2. Remove oil pan and case seal.
3. Remove oil strainer and 0-ring seal.
4. Install new strainer and 0-ring seal. Torque strainer strap bolts to exactly 100 inch pounds. Do not overtighten.
5. Clean oil pan. Install new seal on pan using care not to stretch seal.
6. Install oil pan and seal, oil pan bolt and bolt seal. Torque oil pan bolt to

15-20 ft. lbs. Do not overtighten.

7. Add two quarts of oil to transmission. Start engine and allow to idle in Park range. Then add oil to bring level to the "FULL" mark on dipstick with transmission warmed up.

LINKAGE, ADJUST

Throttle Linkage

1. Referring to Fig. 2, hold throttle rod in wide open position (against stop on carburetor.)
2. Hold idler lever in full throttle valve position (through detent to stop). *Do not confuse detent position of throttle valve with stop position. Increased resistance will be felt as the throttle valve reaches detent position. The idler lever should be pushed through detent to stop.*
3. Adjust turnbuckle so no lost motion exists in slide link (wide open throttle and throttle valve stop reached simultaneously).
4. Tighten lock nut on turnbuckle.

Manual Linkage

1. Referring to Fig. 2, loosen adjusting swivel clamp bolt.
2. Set transmission selector lever in neutral detent.
3. Move shift lever against neutral stop.
4. Tighten adjusting swivel clamp nut.

TROUBLE SHOOTING

With linkage properly adjusted and engine warmed up, make a road test and observe general performance of transmission and check for abnormal noises. Accelerate from a stop with accelerator depressed just to detent. Upshift should occur smoothly between 40 and 45 mph. If upshift occurs at speeds other than those specified, refer to text below for possible causes.

Uphift At Too Low Speed

1. Governor valve not adjusted properly or sticking.
2. Shift valve or shift valve regulator sticking.
3. Throttle valve pressure too low—worn or broken spring or valve sticking.

Upshift At Too High Speed

1. Governor valve not adjusted properly or sticking.
2. Shift valve and shift valve regulator sticking.

Slow Engagement of Converter Clutch

1. Converter pressure regulator valve sticking, lowering converter pressure too slow.

Fast Engagement Of Converter Clutch

1. Converter charging pressure too low.
2. Converter pressure regulator valve sticking.

TRANSMISSION, REPLACE

1. Raise car and support front and rear.
2. Remove exhaust crossover pipe.
3. Remove front U-joint bolts and slide propeller shaft rearward to separate U-joint at transmission. Support propeller shaft to avoid weight of shaft damaging center U-joint.
4. Place suitable jack under transmission and fasten jack to transmission.
5. Remove transmission crossmember.
6. Disconnect speedometer cable.
7. Loosen shift linkage swivel clamp nut (see Fig. 2). Remove cotter pin, spring and washer attaching equalizer to range selector outer lever and remove equalizer.
8. Remove oil filler pipe.
9. Support engine at oil pan.
10. Remove transmission cover pan.
11. Mark flywheel and converter pump for reassembly in same position and remove three converter-to-flywheel bolts.
12. Remove transmission-to-engine bolts.
13. Move transmission rearward to provide clearance between converter pump and crankshaft.
14. Lower transmission out of car. *Wire converter to transmission case or otherwise suitably retain it. If not retained, converter will fall out if transmission is tilted forward even slightly.*
15. Reverse removal procedure to install the transmission.

TRANSMISSION REPAIRS

Converter & Gear Set

DISASSEMBLY

1. Remove converter-to-housing bolts.
2. Provide a pail to catch oil as it drains from converter.
3. Pry converter pump away from housing using screwdriver in slots provided.
4. Remove converter pump and clutch.
5. Remove front sun gear, thrust bearing and two select fit thrust bearing races.
6. Slide planet carrier out of ring gear.
7. Separate front and rear tanged thrust washers from front planet unit.
8. Remove rear sun gear and thrust bearing.
9. Lift out stator and turbine.
10. Remove converter pump housing.
11. Remove rear sun gear and thrust bearing.
12. Lift ring gear from turbine shaft after removing three bolts.
13. Lift stator and thrust bearing from turbine.
14. Lift turbine and thrust bearing from pump cover.

INSPECTION OF PARTS

1. Examine tanged thrust washers for scoring or wear.
2. Check all gears for scoring, imbedded metal or looseness on shafts. Worn or loose pinions require replacement of carrier assembly. Pick out imbedded metal with small screwdriver.

3. Check babbitted surfaces of rear sun gear, turbine and stator shafts. If babbitt is chipped or flaked off, effected part must be replaced.
4. Check needle thrust bearings for looseness or wear.
5. Check stator and turbine for chipped, cracked or broken vanes.
6. Examine converter pump housing for scoring, burrs or roughness that might damage pump seal or pump bushing when re-installed.

REASSEMBLY—Follow the step-by-step procedure shown in Figs. 3 through 12.

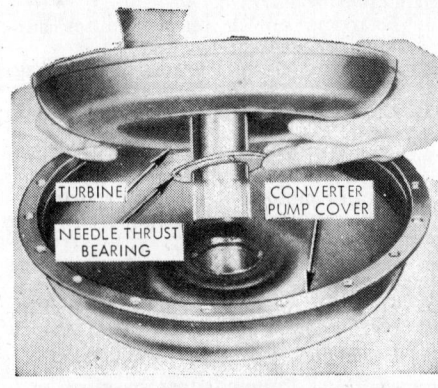

Fig. 3 Place turbine and needle thrust bearing in pump housing

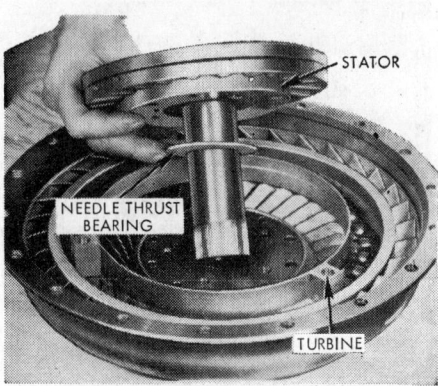

Fig. 4 Set stator and needle thrust bearing in turbine

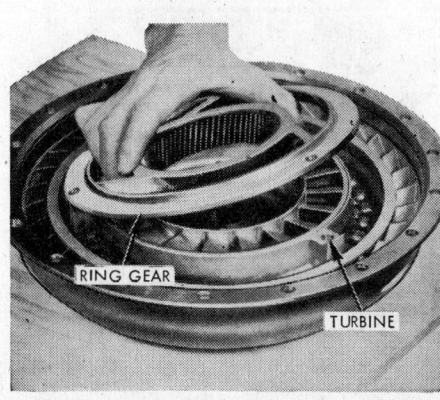

Fig. 5 Set ring gear in turbine. Bolt holes are unevenly spaced so ring gear may be installed in only one position. Torque ring gear bolts to 15-20 ft. lbs.

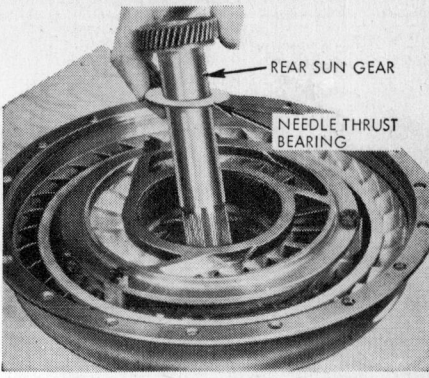

Fig. 6 Set sun gear and needle thrust bearing in place

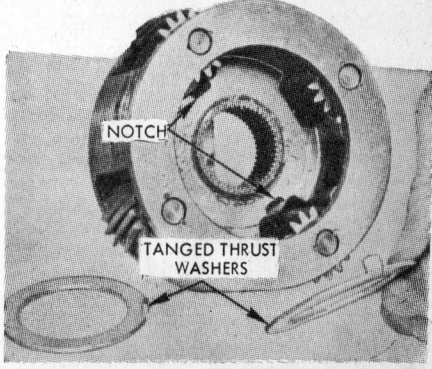

Fig. 7 Install tanged thrust washers in front and rear of planet carrier. Tangs on washers must engage notches in carrier

Fig. 8 Set carrier with tanged washers in place on rear sun gear. Deep side of carrier toward rear sun gear

Fig. 9 Set front sun gear in place on planet carrier

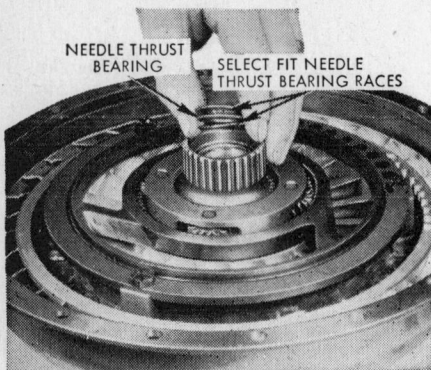

NEEDLE THRUST BEARING
SELECT FIT NEEDLE THRUST BEARING RACES

Fig. 10 Set needle thrust bearing and two select fit bearing races on top of front sun gear

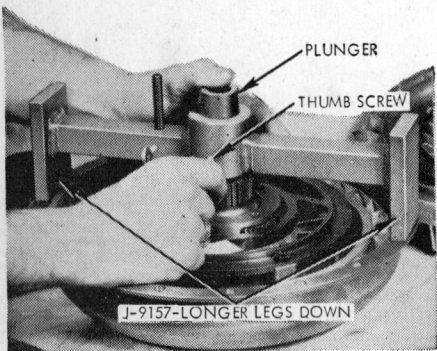

PLUNGER
THUMB SCREW
J-9157—LONGER LEGS DOWN

Fig. 11 Place converter clearance gauge in place as shown. Loosen thumb screw and push plunger down to bear on needle thrust bearing and races. Tighten thumb screw

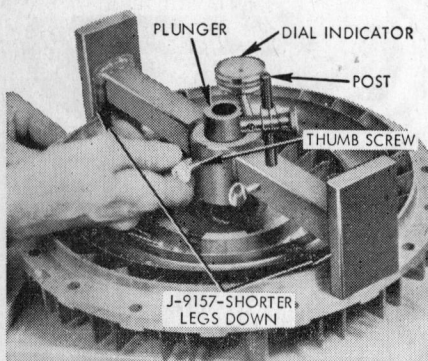

PLUNGER
DIAL INDICATOR
POST
THUMB SCREW
J-9157—SHORTER LEGS DOWN

Fig. 12 Turn gauge over and set on converter pump. Assemble dial indicator with indicator bearing on plunger. Zero indicator. Loosen thumb screw and observe indicator reading. If, when gauge is set in place, plunger holds gauge up so legs do not rest on pump rim, indicator reading when thumb screw is released will be in compression, not clearance. If plunger drops when thumb screw is released, indicator reading will be in clearance, not compression. Select needle thrust bearing races to provide .010" clearance to .005" compression

Converter Clutch & Converter Pump

Disassembly

1. Pry converter clutch housing retainer ring out of groove in converter pump.
2. Lift converter clutch housing out of pump.
3. Remove converter clutch pack.
4. Remove converter clutch piston and apply plate using pliers.
5. Unhook, expand and remove converter clutch piston inner ring.
6. Remove converter clutch outer piston ring.

Inspection of Parts

1. Examine clutch plate contact surface for wear or scoring.
2. Examine clutch plates for scoring, warping or excessive wear.
3. Examine apply plate for excessive wear.
4. Check piston bore in converter pump for scoring or pitting. Check inner bore of piston for wear or scoring.
5. Check clutch piston inner ring for wear or scoring.
6. Examine clutch outer piston ring for excessive wear.
7. Examine converter pump for chipped, cracked or broken vanes. Check for damaged or loose pump ring.

Reassembly—Follow step by step procedure shown in Fig. 13 through 20.

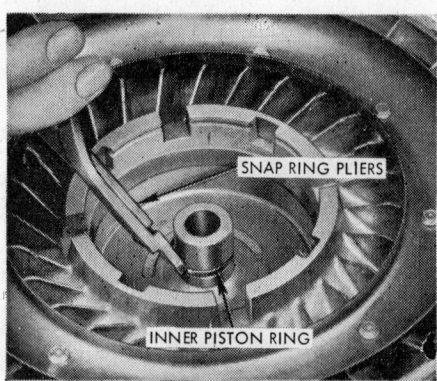

SNAP RING PLIERS
INNER PISTON RING

Fig. 13 Expand and install clutch inner piston ring and hook ends

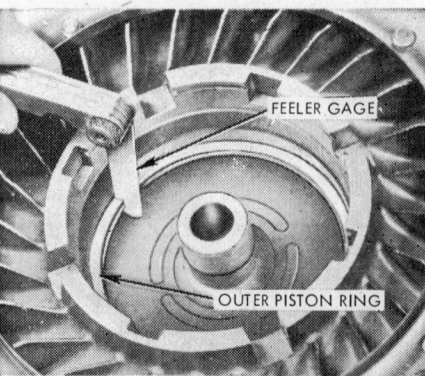

FEELER GAGE
OUTER PISTON RING

Fig. 14 Place clutch outer piston ring squarely in lower part of bore (about ¼" from bottom). Ring gap must be .002-.007". If less than .002" file end of ring; if more than .010" replace ring

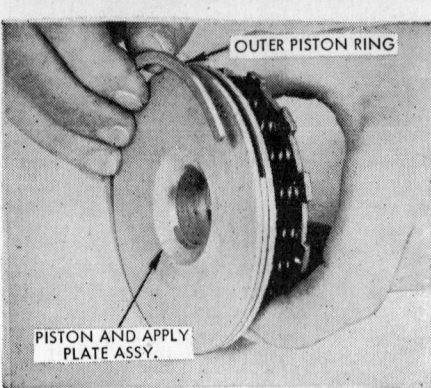

OUTER PISTON RING
PISTON AND APPLY PLATE ASSY.

Fig. 15 Install outer piston ring on clutch piston and apply plate

PISTON AND APPLY PLATE ASSY.

Fig. 16 Lubricate liberally and push piston and apply plate into bore of converter pump. A chamfer in bore serves to compress outer piston ring; however, if difficulty is encountered, a thin feeler gauge may be used to start ring ends over chamfer

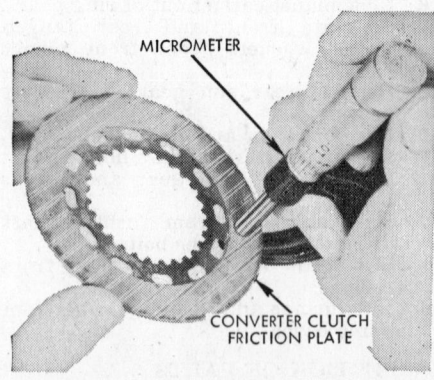

MICROMETER
CONVERTER CLUTCH FRICTION PLATE

Fig. 17 When new, clutch friction plates are .079-.084" thick. Plates worn thinner than .074" should be replaced. All separator plates must be installed with "dish" same way. Starting with a friction plate, then a separator plate, continue alternating plates, being sure to lubricate each friction plate as plates are installed

Fig. 18 Rotate piston apply plate so tangs of apply plate are centered in openings

Fig. 19 Lower clutch housing and clutch pack into converter pump. Retain clutch plates with fingers until assembly is properly aligned. Long tangs of housing must engage openings in converter pump

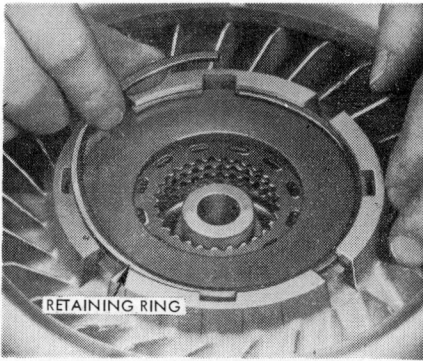

Fig. 20 Install housing retaining ring over clutch housing in groove of converter pump. Tap ring solidly into groove with drift

Front Pump

Disassembly

1. Remove pump bolts and grasp pump body with pliers and hand and lift pump clear of case.

2. Lift pump out of case. Reverse clutch hub will usually be removed with pump. A tanged thrust washer may remain on top of stator overrunning clutch race. It should be placed in rear of reverse clutch hub.
3. Use air pressure applied to reverse clutch piston apply hole to remove reverse clutch piston from clutch housing. Cover assembly with cloth to protect against oil spatter.
4. Examine clutch piston outer seal for damage; if necessary to replace, remove seal.
5. Upon inspection, if necessary to replace clutch piston inner seal, remove seal.
6. Remove and discard oil pump body-to-case seal.
7. Remove reverse clutch piston housing-to-pump body bolts.
8. Lift clutch piston housing off pump, lifting straight up to avoid damage to dowel pin holes. Slipper sealing pins may stick to reverse clutch piston housing and be removed with housing.

Inspection of Parts

1. Mount a dial indicator and zero indicator on pump body.
2. Move indicator plunger to bear on pump slippers one at a time. Slippers should be .001" to .0028" below surface of pump body.
3. Move indicator plunger to rest on rotor. Check rotor in several places. Rotor should be .001" to .0028" below pump body.
4. Examine bushing; if worn or scored, remove rotor, slippers, springs and pins and drive out bushing and seal with a suitable driver. Install new bushing. Apply Permatex to outer diameter of new seal and install seal.
5. Examine rotor, slippers, springs and pins for wear, scoring or pitting.

Reassembly

1. Install rotors with driving tangs "up", Fig. 21. Install slippers and springs.
2. Install sealing pins, Fig. 22. Lubricate assembly liberally with automatic transmission oil.
3. Set reverse clutch piston housing squarely in place on pump body. Dowel pins are unevenly spaced so assembly is possible in only one position.
4. Install reverse clutch piston housing-to-pump body bolts and torque alternately and evenly to 15-20 ft. lbs.
5. Install new oil pump body-to-transmission case sealing ring.
6. Install reverse clutch piston inner seal with lip toward front of piston.
7. Install reverse clutch piston outer seal with lip toward front of piston.
8. Lubricate seals and install piston in piston housing, using a loop of smooth wire to start lips of seals into bore, Fig. 23. Inner seal lip should be started first. A satisfactory tool can be made by crimping a loop of .020" music wire in a short length of copper tube.

Transmission Clutches

Disassemble Reverse Clutch

1. Remove lever assembly ring and

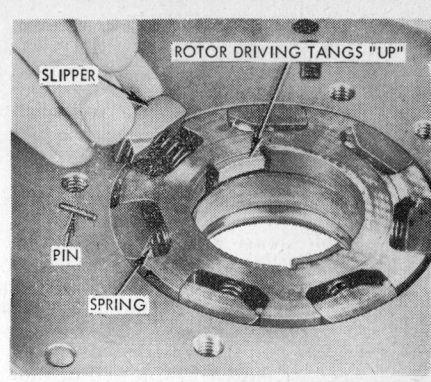

Fig. 21 Install rotor, slippers and springs

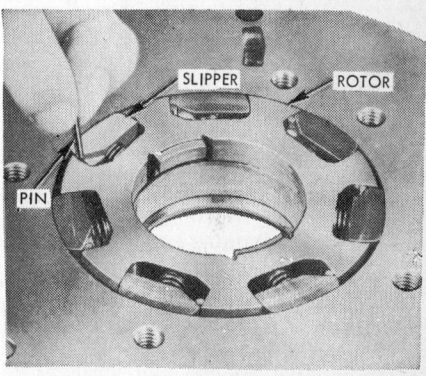

Fig. 22 Install sealing pins

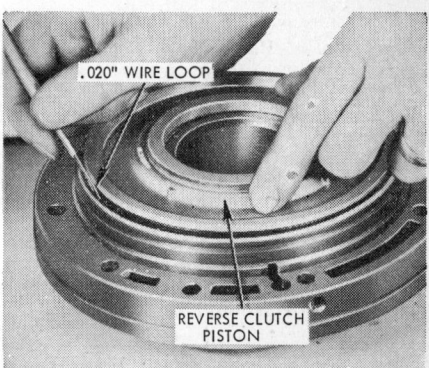

Fig. 23 Installing reverse clutch piston

apply levers.
2. Lift out reverse clutch hub, thrust washer on front side and tanged washer on rear.
3. Remove reverse clutch hub oil ring and thrust washer.
4. Remove bellville release spring.
5. Remove pressure plate.
6. Remove reverse clutch pack.

Remove Coast, Overrunning & Forward Clutches

1. Remove forward and reverse clutch anchor.
2. Rotate forward and reverse clutch backing plate to disengage lugs from slots in case. Remove backing plate.
3. Grasp overrunning clutch cam and roller retainer and lift out complete set of clutches.

4. Lift forward clutch pack off coast clutch housing.
5. Remove forward clutch pressure plate.
6. Pry forward clutch release spring retaining ring out of groove in case.
7. Remove bellville forward clutch release spring.
8. Remove forward clutch apply levers.

Disassemble Coast & Overrunning Clutches

1. Use a suitable compressing tool to bear against coast clutch cylinder and pry ring out of groove in housing.
2. Lift coast clutch piston and cylinder out of housing.
3. Use pliers to remove piston from cylinder.
4. Remove piston outer seal if damaged.
5. Remove piston inner seal if damaged.
6. Remove coast clutch hub-to-support thrust washer.
7. Remove coast clutch apply levers.
8. Remove coast clutch release spring.
9. Remove coast clutch pressure plate.
10. Tip coast clutch housing to remove clutch pack and hub.
11. Pry cam retaining ring out of groove in backing plate.
12. Tilt coast clutch housing to remove backing plate and overrunning clutch.
13. Pull rear sun gear race out of cam assembly. Rollers and springs will fall out.
14. Remove roller thrust washer.
15. Pull stator race out of cam. Rollers and springs will fall out.

Inspection of Parts

1. Check apply levers for wear or bending.
2. Examine clutch hub oil rings for wear.
3. Examine thrust washers and tanged washers for wear.
4. Check bellville springs for cracks or wear.
5. Examine pressure plates for wear.
6. When new, friction plates are .079" to .084" thick. Plates worn thinner than .074" should be replaced.

Fig. 24 Place stator race inside cam and assemble rollers and springs. Stator race has larger splined I.D. than rear sun gear race

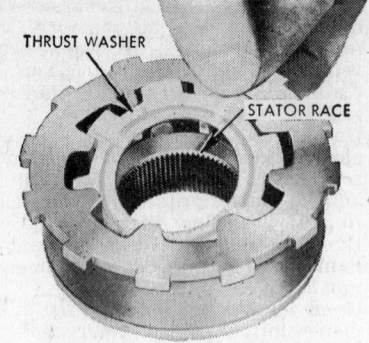

Fig. 25 Lubricate and install thrust washer on stator race

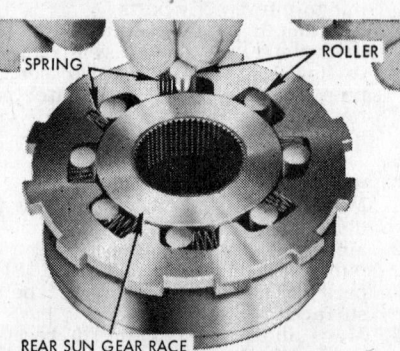

Fig. 26 Set rear sun gear cam in place on thrust washer and assemble rollers and springs

Fig. 27 Install cam and race in coast clutch housing. Rotate cam so lugs on cam engage notches in coast clutch housing

Fig. 28 Set assembly on blocks or otherwise support lower edge of coast clutch housing. Then install coast clutch backing plate on cam and race

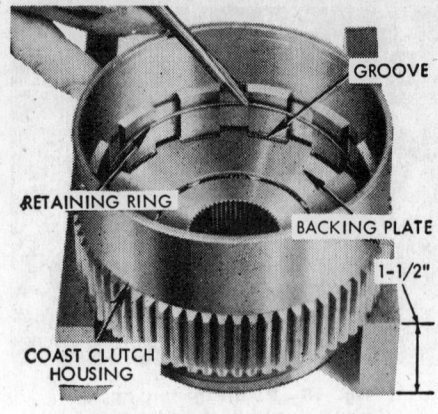

Fig. 29 Install retaining ring solidly in groove of coast clutch housing above backing plate

Fig. 30 Install coast clutch hub on rear sun gear race

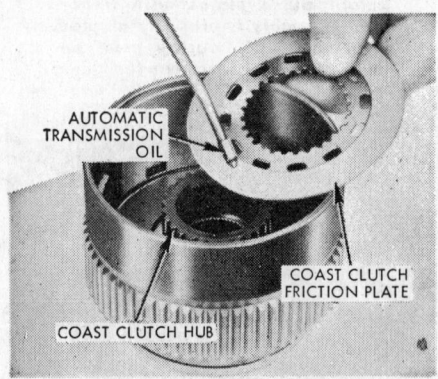

Fig. 31 Lubricate coast clutch friction plate and install on backing plate with splines engaged with coast clutch hub splines

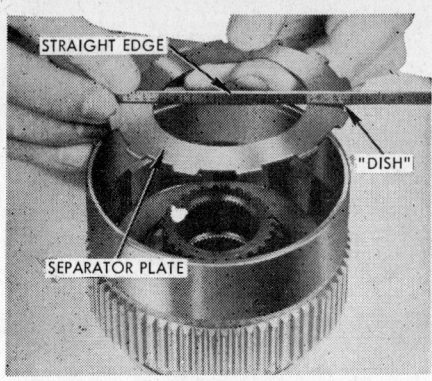

Fig. 32 All separator plates must be installed with "dish" same way. Alternately install friction plate, then separator plate and so on until all plates are installed, being sure all friction plates have been oiled

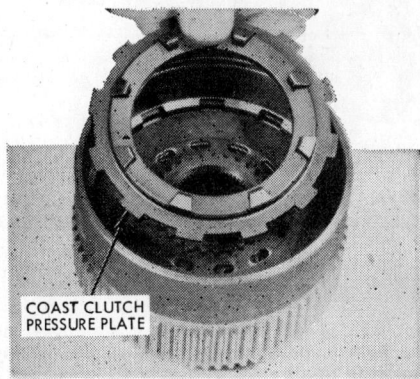

Fig. 33 Install pressure plate on top of last lubed friction plate. Engage lugs in notches of coast clutch housing

Assemble Coast & Overrunning Clutches

1. Follow procedure given in Figs. 24 through 33, then complete the assembly as follows:
2. Install bellville clutch release spring on pressure plate with inner edge of spring "up".
3. Install apply levers with concave edge "in" between lugs of pressure plate and flat on release spring. Apply a daub of chassis lube on each lever to hold in place.
4. Set thrust washer in place on top of coast clutch hub.
5. Install piston inner seal with lip toward rear of piston.
6. Install piston outer seal with lip toward rear of piston.
7. Lubricate seals and install piston in bore of coast clutch cylinder by using a loop of smooth wire to start lips of seals in bore. Start inner seal first.
8. Make sure thrust washer and all apply levers are properly in place. Then install cylinder and piston assembly squarely in bore of coast clutch housing.
9. Apply pressure to coast clutch cylinder so that the retaining ring can be installed in groove of coast clutch housing.

10. Insert rear sun gear in sun gear race. Turn sun gear clockwise to check for drag on coast clutch. Excessive drag will indicate clutch separator plates all not dished same way, or foreign material is present. Sun gear overrunning clutch should not permit rotation in the counterclockwise direction.

Assemble Reverse Clutch—This procedure is included with the installation of the front oil pump further on.

Valve Body

Removal
1. Remove oil pan.
2. Remove oil strainer strap bolts. Remove strap, strainer and O-ring seal.
3. Use needle nose pliers to remove parking lock pawl disengaging spring.
4. Remove remaining valve body bolts and valve body. Take care when removing valve body as some of the valves can fall out.

Disassemble—Use Fig. 34 as a guide when disassembling valve body. When disassembled, test each valve in its bore. All valves must move freely of their own weight.

Reassemble
1. Referring to Fig. 34, begin the assembly by installing the converter pressure regulator, shift and main line pressure regulator valves, sleeves and springs. Use new valve retaining plate-to-valve body gasket; install plate and oil gauge guide. Install and tighten screws.
2. Install throttle pressure regulator valve. Tilt valve body so valve slides to bottom of bore.
3. Being sure throttle pressure regulator valve is in bottom of bore, install throttle pressure valve stop; be sure it is in the correct opening.
4. Install second stage governor valve.
5. Install second stage governor valve spring, sleeve and retainer. Press in

on sleeve against spring pressure and install retainer through valve body in wide slot of sleeve.
6. Install check ball.
7. Install detent poppet and spring.
8. Use new gaskets, one on each side of valve body plate and position plate and gaskets on valve body. *It will be necessary to depress detent poppet to allow plate attaching screws to be started.*
9. Make sure detent poppet is properly in place and install screws (do not overtighten).
10. Install throttle detent valve and throttle pressure regulator valve spring.
11. Install range selector valve, governor valve and pin. *It may be necessary to shake valve body to start governor valve pin through hole in second stage governor valve.*

Coast Clutch Support & Forward Clutch Piston

Removal
1. Remove companion flange and pull three adapter sleeves and retainer out of transmission case and coast clutch support.
2. Pull output shaft forward to remove shaft, coast clutch support, parking lock ratchet wheel and governor as an assembly.
3. Slide governor lever actuating sleeve, needle thrust bearing, bearing race and parking lock ratchet wheel spacer off rear of output shaft.
4. Slide governor weight and retainer assembly off rear of output shaft.
5. Slide coast clutch support and forward clutch piston off forward end of output shaft.

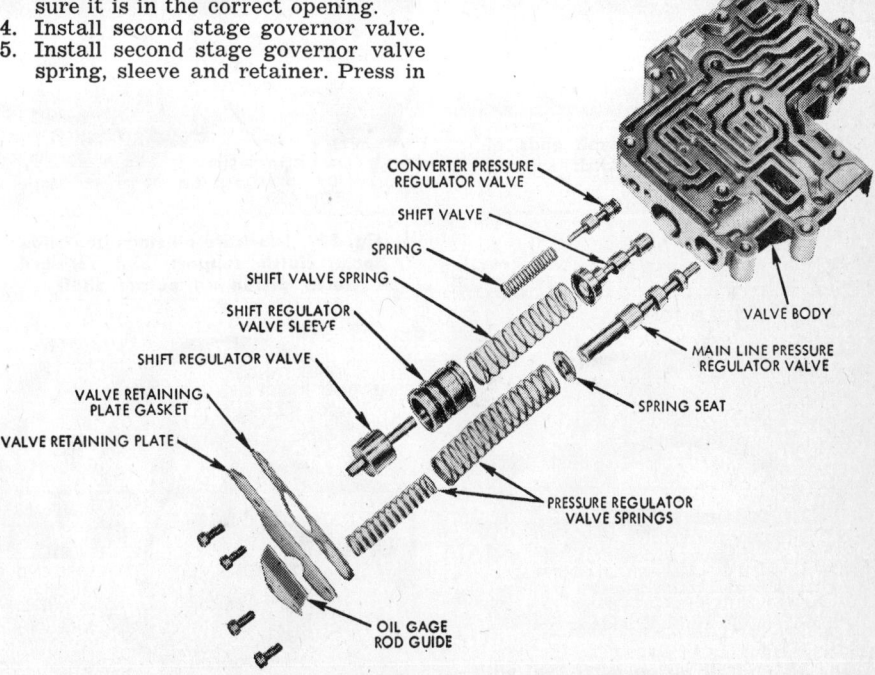

Fig. 34 Exploded view of valve body

Inspection

1. Discard any questionable O-ring seals.
2. Examine needle thrust bearing, race and sleeve for wear or scoring.
3. Check roll pins for looseness in governor weights.
4. If the two hooked oil rings on output shaft are worn or scored, unhook, expand and remove the rings.
5. If parking lock ratchet wheel is worn or broken, expand and remove retaining ring on output shaft forward of wheel. Slide wheel off shaft and examine output shaft for damaged splines, scored bearing surfaces, broken ring lands, etc.

Disassembly

1. Cover assembly with clean cloth as a protection against oil spatter and apply compressed air into center oil transfer sleeve hole to remove forward clutch piston from coast clutch support.
2. Examine hooked oil rings, forward clutch piston outer and inner seals and remove these parts if damage is evident.

Reassembly—Follow procedure shown in Figs. 35 through 41. Fig. 42 illustrates the removal and installation of governor lever and pin.

Fig. 35 Install and hook ends of oil rings on coast clutch support

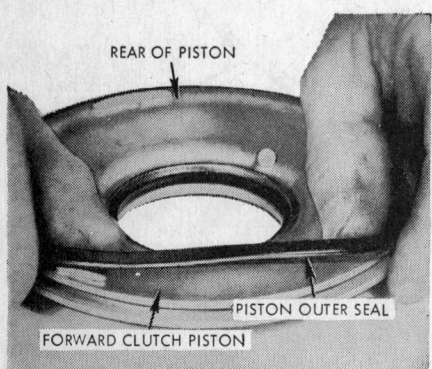

Fig. 36 Install piston outer seal with lip of seal toward rear of piston

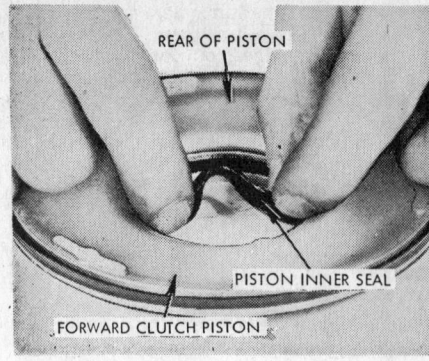

Fig. 37 Install piston inner seal with lip of seal toward rear of piston

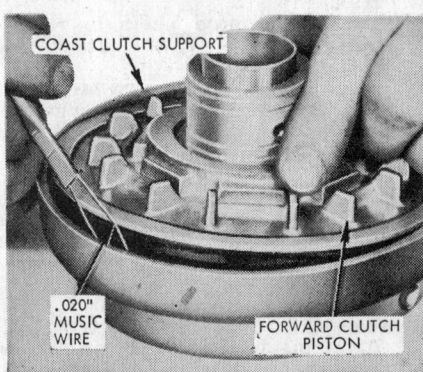

Fig. 38 Lubricate seals and install forward clutch piston. A loop of .020" music wire may be used as an aid in starting seal lip into piston bore. Start inner seal lip first

Fig. 39 Lubricate oil rings and slide coast clutch support and forward clutch piston on output shaft

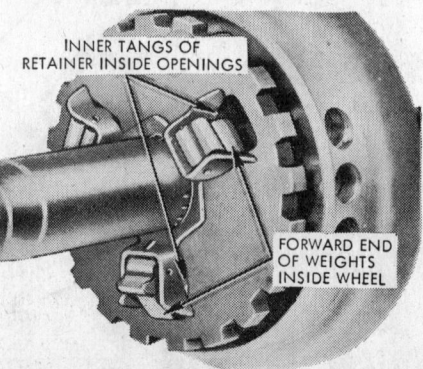

Fig. 40 Slide governor weight retainer and weight assembly on rear of output shaft. Inner tangs of retainer must be inside openings of parking lock ratchet wheel. Forward end of weights must also be inside openings of wheel

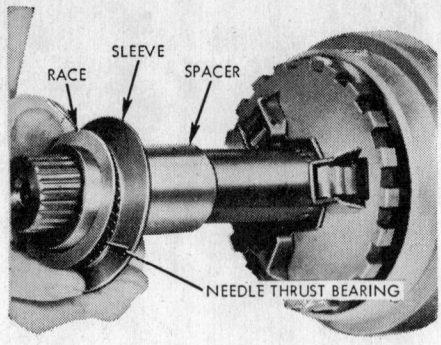

Fig. 41 Lubricate needle thrust bearing and slide spacer, sleeve, needle thrust bearing and race on rear of output shaft. Position against governor weights

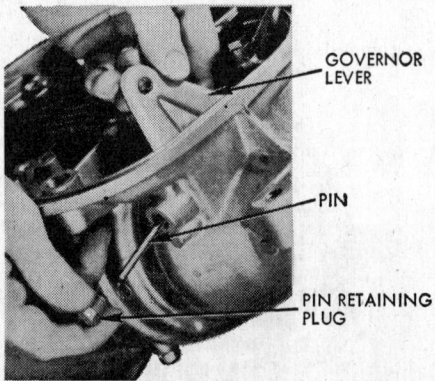

Fig. 42 If governor lever is damaged or pin hole is badly worn, remove pin retaining plug in side of transmission case. Slide pin out of case and lever. Install pin through lever and case and install plug

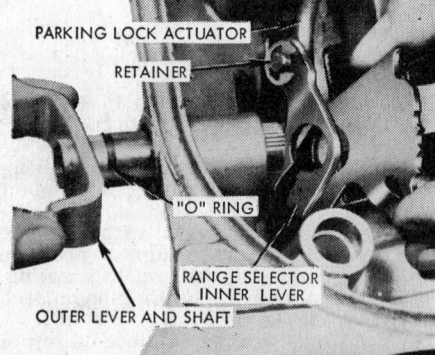

Fig. 43 Install and lube O-ring seal. Slide shaft through case and carefully align splines on shaft with splines in inner lever. Hold outer lever and shaft "in" against case and push inner lever completely on shaft

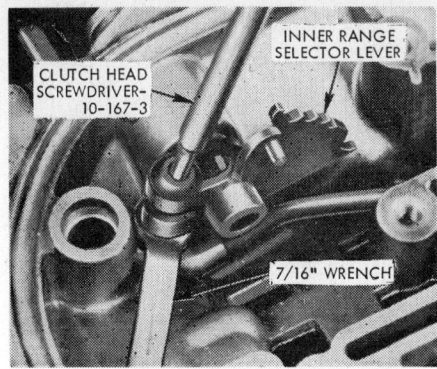

Fig. 44 Install and tighten screw and nut

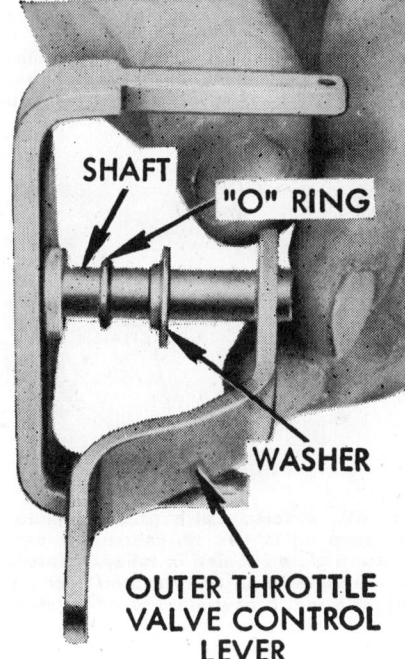

Fig. 45 Assemble special washer and O-ring on throttle control lever shaft. Lube O-ring and slide shaft onto range selector shaft

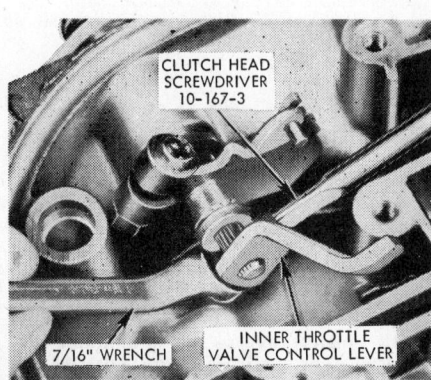

Fig. 46 Carefully engage splines on shaft with splines in inner lever. Press lever on shaft completely. Install and tighten clutch head screw and nut

Range Selector Levers & Shaft

If these parts are removed, make the installation as shown in Fig. 43 to 46.

Transmission, Assemble

Follow the procedure shown in the illustrations starting with Fig. 47 to 84.

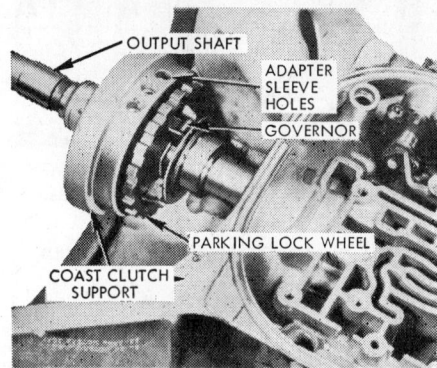

Fig. 47 Lube coast clutch support O.D. and position support so oil transfer holes are "up". Hold governor in place against parking lock wheel and start rear of shaft through bearing. Ease assembly into position. If parking lock pawl is installed, hold it "up" out of the way to allow assembly to move fully into case. If necessary to rotate support to line up oil transfer holes, insert a smooth punch through oil transfer holes in case to rotate support

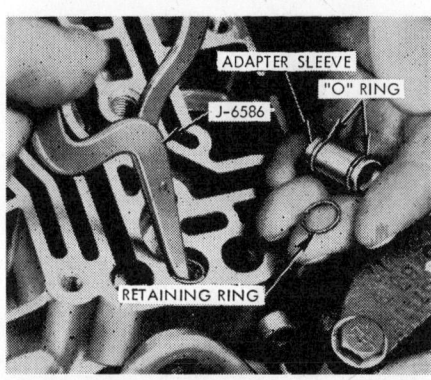

Fig. 48 Lube and install oil transfer sleeves, O-rings and retainers. Retainers should be positioned flat against sleeves. Lube liberally with chassis lube to avoid damage to seal and install speedometer drive gear on output shaft. Install companion flange

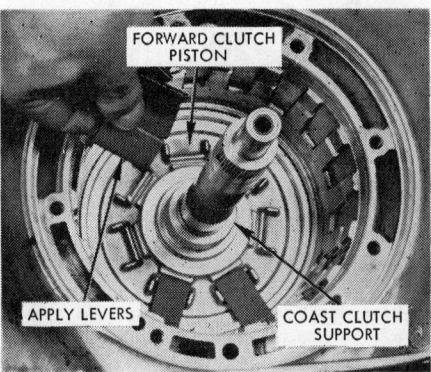

Fig. 50 Install forward clutch release spring flat on levers (inner edge of spring down)

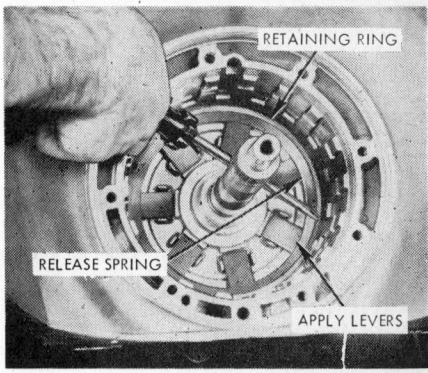

Fig. 51 Install release spring retainer solidly in groove of case. Center spring as necessary to install ring fully into groove. Be very certain that ring is in groove all the way around

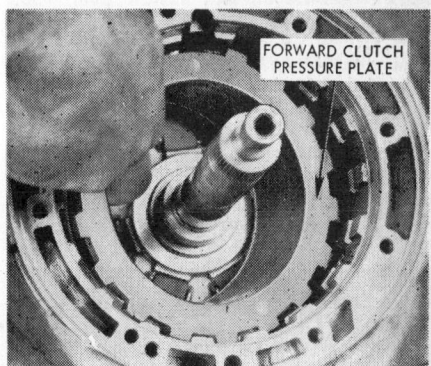

Fig. 52 Set forward clutch pressure plate on apply levers. Be sure to position wide space between lugs toward top of case for installation of anchor later

Fig. 49 Install forward clutch apply levers

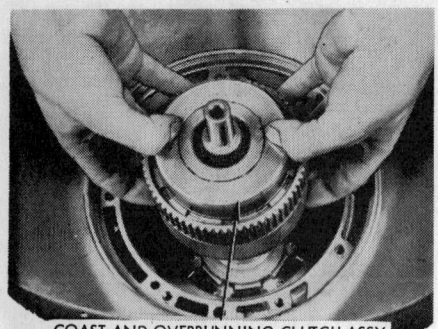

COAST AND OVERRUNNING CLUTCH ASSY

Fig. 53 Set coast and overrunning clutch assembly on coast clutch support

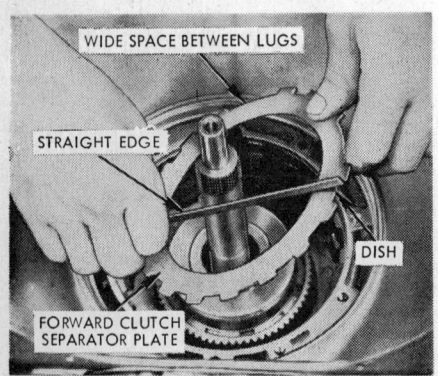

WIDE SPACE BETWEEN LUGS

STRAIGHT EDGE

DISH

FORWARD CLUTCH SEPARATOR PLATE

Fig. 54 Check forward clutch separator plate (no notches on lugs) for "dish". Note direction of dish and install it on forward clutch pressure plate. Be sure to position wide space between lugs toward top of case for installation of anchor later. Lube a forward clutch friction plate with automatic transmission oil. Install over coast clutch housing by engaging splines of plate with splines on coast clutch housing. Continue alternately installing a separator plate and a lubed friction plate until five separator plates (all dished same way) and five friction plates have been installed. All separator plates must be installed with wide space between lugs toward top of case for installation of anchor later

BACKING PLATE LUGS ENGAGE LUGS ON CASE

FORWARD AND REVERSE CLUTCH BACKING PLATE

Fig. 55 Install forward and reverse clutch backing plate on top of forward clutch pack. Rotate backing plate so its lugs engage lugs in case. Correct installation of forward clutch pack will provide sufficient clearance and require no force to install backing plate

FORWARD AND REVERSE CLUTCH ANCHOR

Fig. 56 Install forward and reverse clutch anchor in slot at top of case

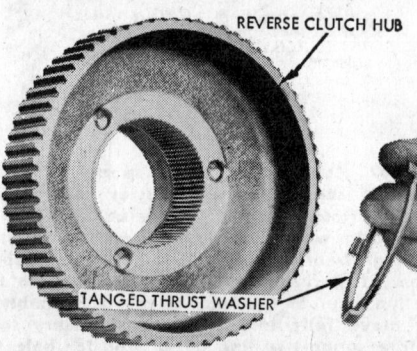

REVERSE CLUTCH HUB

TANGED THRUST WASHER

Fig. 57 Be sure tanged thrust washer is in place at rear of reverse clutch hub

REVERSE CLUTCH HUB

Fig. 58 Set reverse clutch hub in place on overrunning clutch

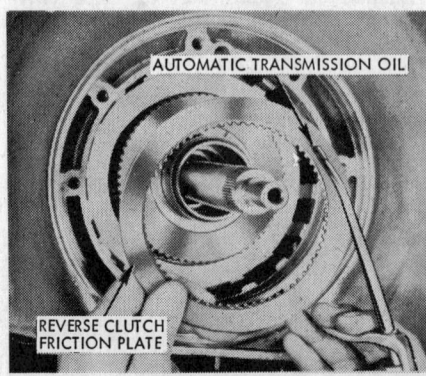

AUTOMATIC TRANSMISSION OIL

REVERSE CLUTCH FRICTION PLATE

Fig. 59 Lubricate and install reverse clutch friction plate on forward and reverse clutch backing plate by engaging splines on hub with splines on plate

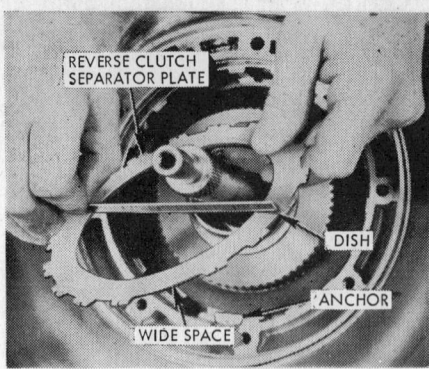

REVERSE CLUTCH SEPARATOR PLATE

DISH

ANCHOR

WIDE SPACE

Fig. 60 Check reverse clutch separator plate (notch in tangs) for "dish". Note direction of dish and install separator plate above friction plate. Install plate with wide space between lugs toward top of transmission to clear anchor. Continue the build-up of clutch by alternately installing a lubed friction plate and a separator plate until four friction plates and three separator plates have been installed. All separator plates must be installed with dish same way

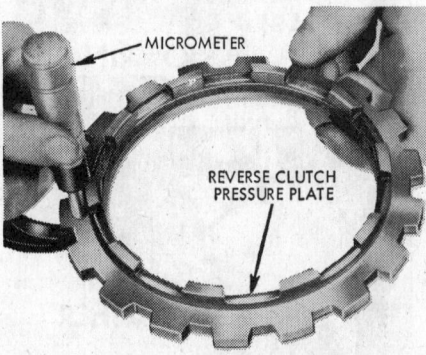

MICROMETER

REVERSE CLUTCH PRESSURE PLATE

Fig. 61 Reverse clutch pressure plates are supplied in two thicknesses. If new pressure plate is being installed, measure an old plate in an unworn area near the end of a lug. A new plate to be installed must be the same thickness or reverse clutch pack clearance will be adversely affected. Install pressure plate over top friction plate with wide space between lugs toward top of transmission to clear anchor

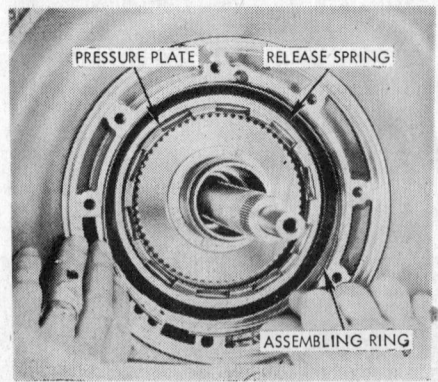

PRESSURE PLATE

RELEASE SPRING

ASSEMBLING RING

Fig. 62 Install reverse spring and assembling ring over pressure plate with center edge of release spring "up". Do not install apply levers until hub clearance has been checked and thrust washer between reverse clutch hub and reverse clutch piston housing has been selected

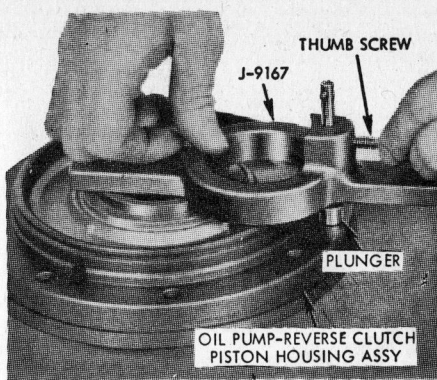

Fig. 63 Set gauge shown on oil pump-reverse piston housing with gauge bearing firmly on center hub of reverse clutch piston housing. Loosen thumb screw and allow plunger to bear on gasket surface of oil pump. Tighten thumb screw

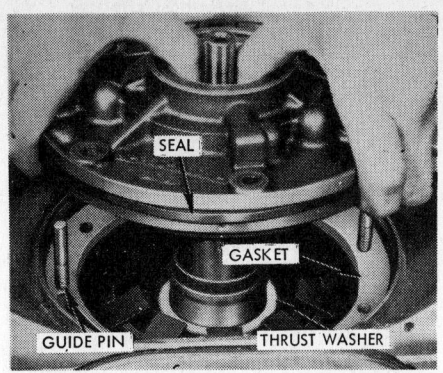

Fig. 66 Liberally lube thrust washer and oil pump body-to-case seal. Carefully line up bolt holes with guide pins and lower pump into place. Install and tighten at least three oil pump-to-case bolts

Fig. 68 Set valve body in place on case and engage pin of range selector inner lever with groove of selector valve. Install parking lock pawl disengaging spring. Install bolts as shown

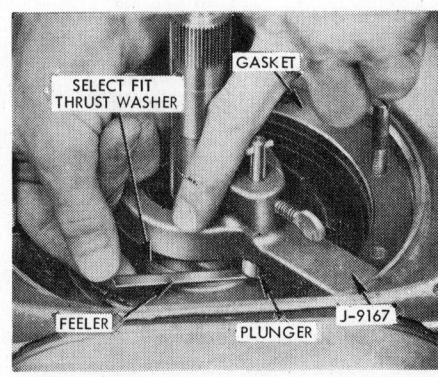

Fig. 64 Install new pump gasket over 5/16" guide pins in case. Place a select fit thrust washer on hub. Set gauge over reverse clutch hub with ends of gauge resting squarely on gasket. Check clearance between end of plunger and select fit thrust washer with .006" and .035" feeler gauges. If .006" gauge will not fit, select one size thinner washer. If the .035" feeler will fit, select one size thicker washer

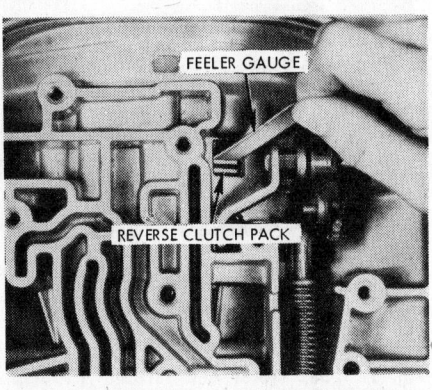

Fig. 67 Insert a .029" feeler gauge through case between reverse clutch friction plate and a separator plate. A .029" feeler should "go" and a .051" feeler should "not go". If pack clearance is less than .030", it may be due to an incorrect pressure plate, separator plates not dished same way or apply levers incorrectly installed and binding on piston. If pack clearance is more than .050", it may be due to incorrect pressure plate or excessively worn friction or separator plates. If reverse clutch pack is satisfactory, remove guide pins, install remaining special bolts and captive sealing lock washers. Torque alternately and evenly to 20-24 ft. lbs.

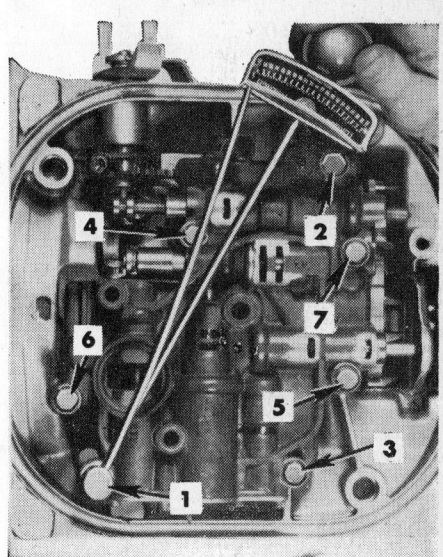

Fig. 69 Torque bolts in sequence shown to 100 inch pounds

← Fig. 65 Install reverse clutch apply levers in notches of pressure plate, flat on release spring and with lever ends under assembling ring. Push assembling ring down on levers to hold them in place. Chassis lube daubed on levers will help keep them in place. It is not necessary to remove guide pins and gasket for this operation

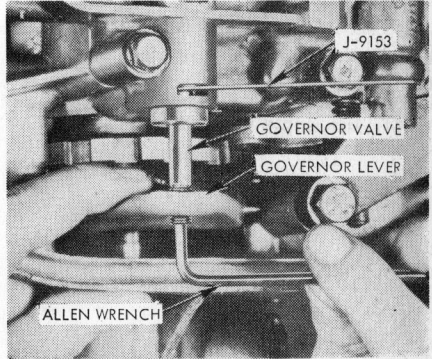

Fig. 70 Insert a .025" feeler between forward edge of rear land of governor valve and sleeve. Hold governor lever rearward and valve forward against feeler. Adjust screw so it just touches end of valve with valve held in against feeler. Remove feeler

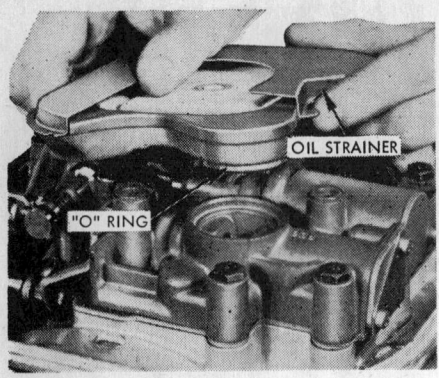

Fig. 71 Install new O-ring on oil strainer and set strainer in place on valve body

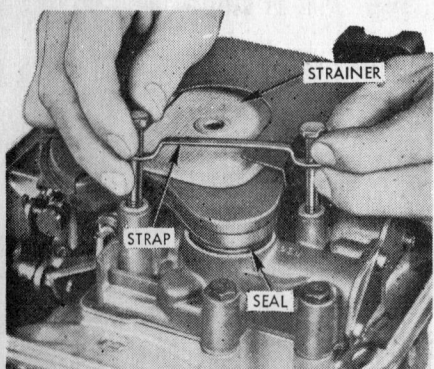

Fig. 72 Install strainer strap

Fig. 73 Torque bolts indicated to 100 inch pounds in sequence shown. If removed, install parking lock pawl. Install oil pan and torque the single pan bolt to 15-20 ft. lbs.

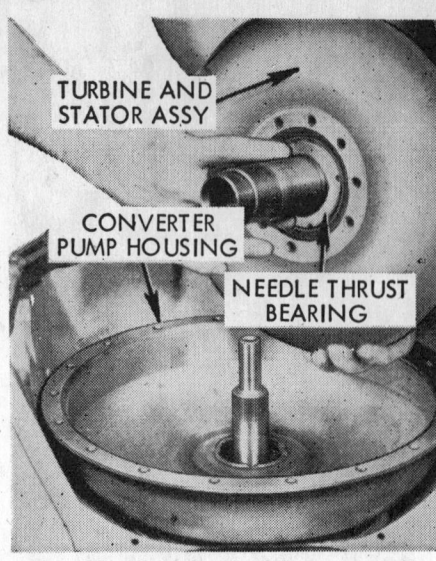

Fig. 75 Use chassis lube to retain caged needle thrust bearing to rear of turbine as shown. Oil exit holes to rear

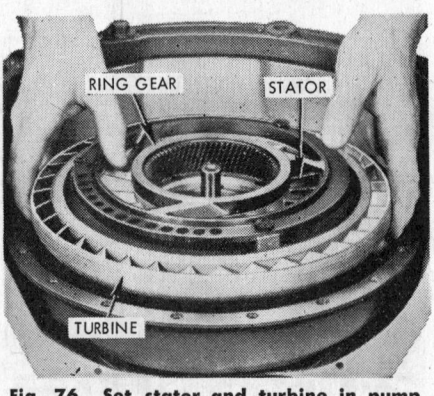

Fig. 76 Set stator and turbine in pump housing. Rotate turbine and stator to engage splines. Assembly will drop into place when splines are lined up

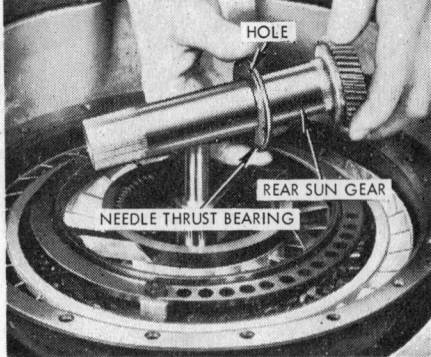

Fig. 77 Assemble caged needle thrust bearing to rear of rear sun gear. Oil exit holes to rear

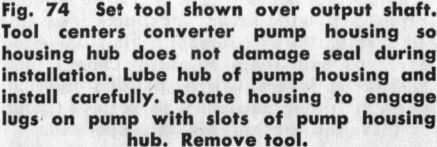

Fig. 74 Set tool shown over output shaft. Tool centers converter pump housing so housing hub does not damage seal during installation. Lube hub of pump housing and install carefully. Rotate housing to engage lugs on pump with slots of pump housing hub. Remove tool.

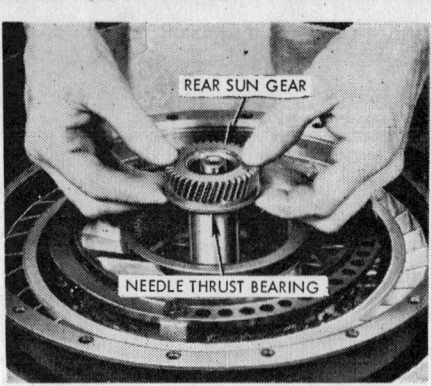

Fig. 78 Lube sun gear shaft inside and out. Slide sun gear and needle thrust bearing into place. Rotate gear to engage splines. Two sets of splines must be engaged (sun gear race and coast clutch hub). Do not force gear as damage to splines will result

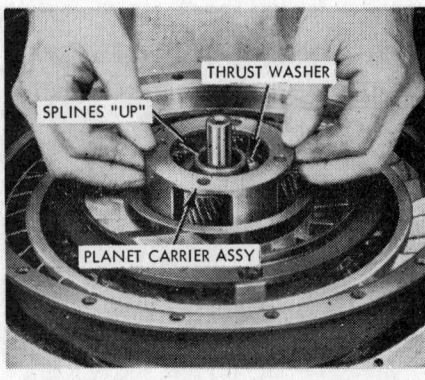

Fig. 79 Set planet carrier over rear sun gear with tanged thrust washers in place front and rear. Deeper pocket of carrier "down" toward rear sun gear and splined portion "up"

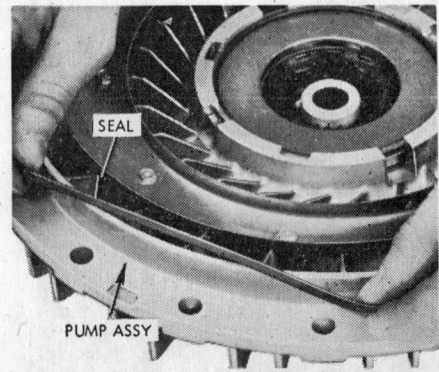

Fig. 80 Assemble new converter pump oil seal to pump. Seal is square section and must not be twisted

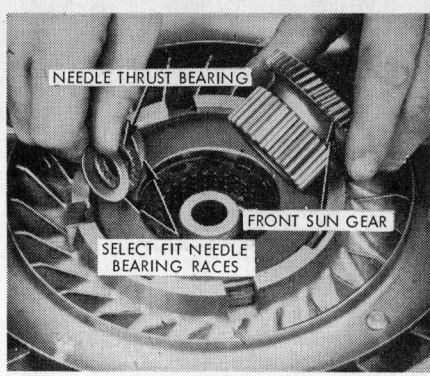

Fig. 81 Lube and assemble needle thrust bearing and two select fit bearing races into front sun gear. Retain with chassis lube

Fig. 83 Hold front sun gear in place with long screwdriver while positioning converter pump against pump housing. Rotate assembly very slightly to mesh front sun gear with planet pinions. When gears are in mesh, push converter pump into converter pump housing and pull housing toward pump

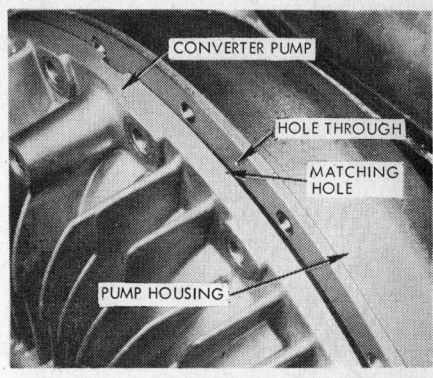

Fig. 84 Before installing attaching bolts, check locating hole through housing and matching hole part way through converter pump flange. These holes must line up to preserve balance of assembly. Set transmission vertical. Install and tighten special nuts and bolts alternately and evenly. Torque to 15-20 ft. lbs. Wire or otherwise retain converter to case prior to installation in car

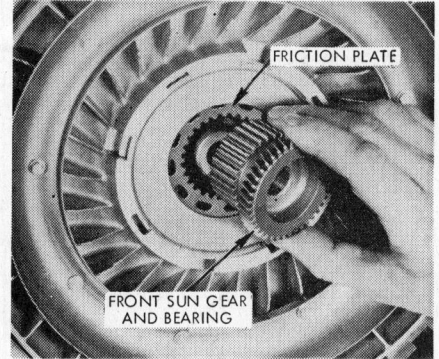

Fig. 82 Engage splines on sun gear hub with splines of converter clutch friction plates. Rotate gear while pressing down very lightly until all splines are engaged

Rear Axle & Brake Section

Refer To Hydraulic Brakes Chapter For Brake Adjustments

AXLE SHAFT

1. To remove the axle shafts, Fig. 1, take off the wheels. *Note that the left side wheel bolts have left hand threads and the nuts are marked "LH".*
2. Remove brake drums.
3. Remove nuts holding retainer plates to brake backing plates. Pull retainers clear of bolts and reinstall two lower nuts finger tight to hold brake backing plate in position.
4. Pull out axle shafts using a puller and adapter with a slide hammer. *While pulling axle shaft out through oil seal, support shaft carefully in center of seal to avoid cutting seal lip.*
5. Reverse removal procedure to install axle shafts. Note that the left shaft is shorter than the right shaft. Apply wheel bearing grease in the bearing recesses of the housing. Install new outer retainer gaskets. Insert axle shaft carefully until shaft splines engage in differential to avoid damage to seals. Torque retainer stud nuts to 60 ft. lbs.

Axle Shaft Bearing

1. With axle shaft removed, nick bearing retainer in three or four places with a chisel deep enough to spread ring. Retainer will then slip off.
2. Press bearing off shaft. An arbor press may be used.
3. Press new axle shaft bearing against shoulder on axle shaft. *Retainer plate which retains bearing in housing must be on axle shaft before bearing is installed; retainer gasket can be installed after bearing.*
4. Press new retainer ring against bearing.

Axle Shaft Seal

1. Insert axle shaft so that splined end is just through seal.
2. Using axle shaft as a lever, push down on shaft until seal is pried from housing.
3. Apply sealer to O.D. of new seal.
4. Position seal over a suitable installer and drive seal straight into axle housing until fully seated.

REAR AXLE

As shown in Fig. 1, the drive pinion is mounted on two tapered roller bearings that are preloaded by two selected spacers. The drive pinion is positioned by shims located between a shoulder on the pinion and the rear bearing. The front bearing is held in place by a large nut.

The differential is supported in the carrier by two tapered roller side bearings. These are preloaded by inserting shims between the bearings and the pedestals. The differential assembly is positioned for ring gear and pinion backlash by varying these shims.

Rear Axle Repairs

Disassembly and assembly of the differential case, replacing the ring gear, checking ring gear and pinion backlash and other differential case operations are given in the *Rear Axles Chapter*. The following operations are significant for this type rear axle.

Side Bearing Preload

After the differential case has been

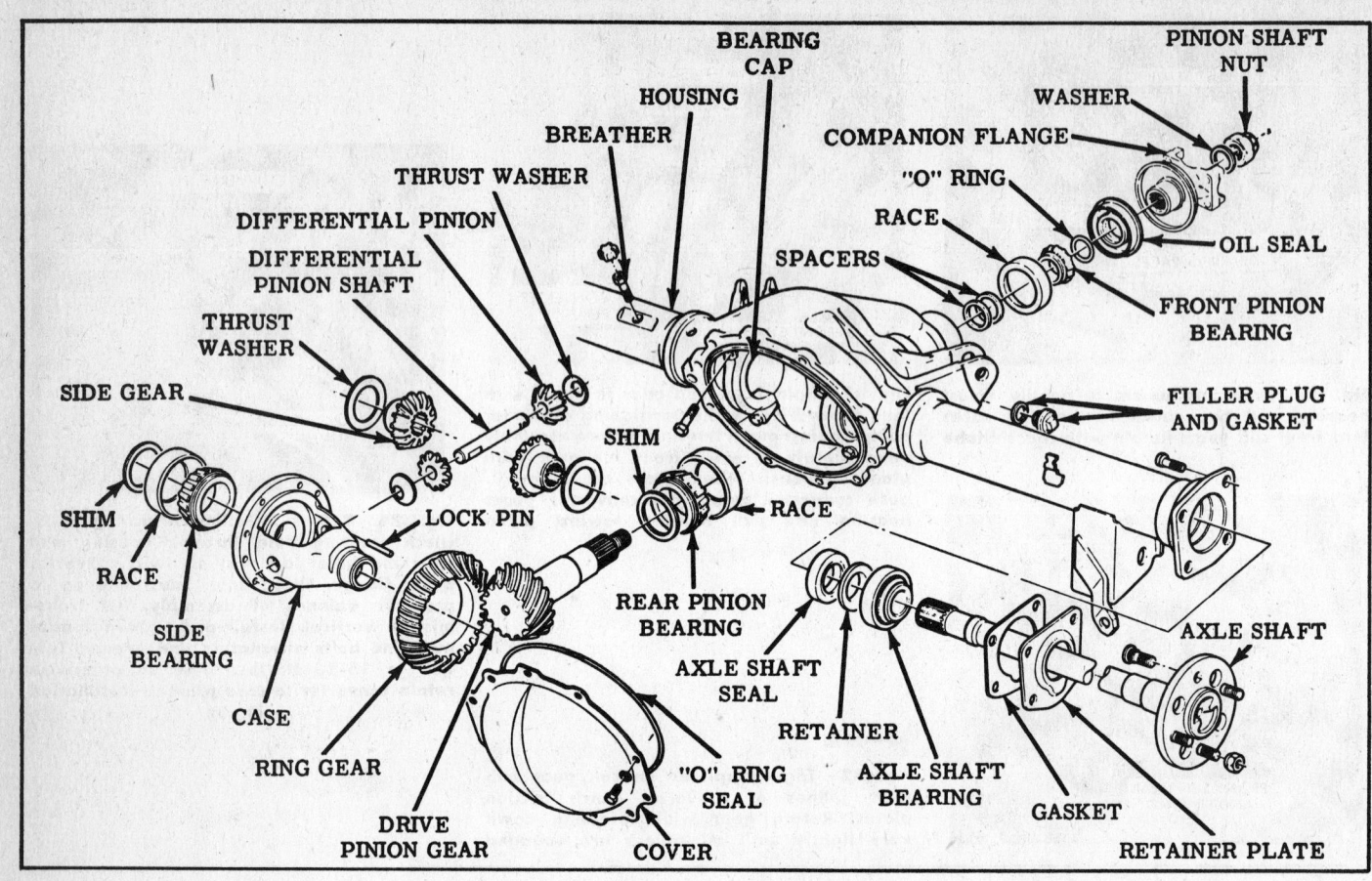

Fig. 1 Rear axle assembly

assembled, differential side bearing pre-load is adjusted by changing the thickness of both the right and left shim by an equal amount. By changing the thickness of both shims equally, the original back-lash will be maintained. Differential adjustment shims are available in thicknesses ranging from .040″ to .082″ in .002″ increments.

In order to adjust side bearing preload accurately, adjustment should be made before the pinion is installed. This allows the ring gear and case assembly to be rotated freely.

Place differential case and bearing assembly in carrier. If new side bearings are installed, use original adjusting shims; if same bearings are to be reused, select new right and left adjusting shims each .002″ thicker than the original shim. Slip right shim in position at right bearing, then drive left shim carefully into position using a soft hammer.

Rotate differential case several complete turns to seat bearings. Check bearing preload with an inch-pound torque wrench applied to a ring gear attaching bolt. With torque wrench projecting approximately straight out, bearing preload should read 20-30 inch lbs. with new bearings and 10-20 inch lbs. with reused

bearings. If preload is not within these limits, increase shim thickness .002″ on each side for each added 10 inch lbs. preload desired, or decrease shim thickness .002″ on each side for each 10 inch lbs. preload to be subtracted.

When adjustment is satisfactory, remove differential, keeping bearing caps and shims together so that they may be reinstalled properly after the drive pinion has been installed.

Drive Pinion Preload

If new pinion bearings are installed, use the original pinion preload spacers. If the same bearings are being reused, select a pair of pinion preload spacers having a total thickness of .002″ less than the original spacers. Install spacers on pinion and position pinion in carrier. Pinion preload spacers are furnished to be used in pairs so that the possible combined thickness ranges from .400″ to .470″.

Install pinion and bearings and new oil seal. Install flange and nut, torquing nut to 200 ft. lbs. Rotate pinion several times to seat bearings.

Check bearing preload using an inch pound torque wrench applied to the pin-

ion nut. The preload reading including drag of new seal should be 25-35 inch pounds with new bearings or 15 to 25 inch pounds for reused bearings. If preload torque is not within these specifications, reduce the total pinion spacer thickness .001″ for each 10 inch pounds preload desired, or decrease total pinion spacer thickness .001″ for each 10 inch pounds preload to be subtracted.

MASTER CYLINDER, REPLACE

1. Remove connector from stop light switch.
2. Disconnect brake pipe from master cylinder and tape end of pipe to prevent entrance of dirt.
3. Disconnect brake pedal from master cylinder push rod.
4. Unfasten master cylinder (4 nuts) from dash panel and remove cylinder.
5. Reverse removal procedure to install. Then bleed hydraulic system as outlined in the *Hydraulic Brakes Chapter.*

Front End & Steering Section

WHEEL ALIGNMENT

Caster & Camber

Caster and camber are adjusted by shimming at the upper control arm shaft attaching points. These shims are available in thicknesses of .030", .060" and .120".

Adding shims at the front locations will change caster toward negative with practically no change in camber. Adding shims at the rear locations will change caster toward positive and camber toward negative. Adding equal shims at both front and rear locations will not change caster but will change camber toward negative.

To adjust, loosen both front and rear bolts to free shims for removal or addition. After installing or removing shims (limit to .380" in any one stack) tighten and torque shaft bolts to 60-85 ft. lbs.

Toe-In, Adjust

Car must be at curb weight and running height; bounce front end and allow it to settle at running height. Steering gear and front wheel bearings must be properly adjusted with no looseness at tie rod ends. The car should be moved forward one complete revolution of the wheels before the toe-in check and adjustment is started and the car should never be moved backward while making the check and adjustment.

With front wheels in the straight ahead position, toe-in is adjusted by turning the tie rod adjusting sleeves as required. Left and right adjusting sleeves must be turned exactly the same amount but in opposite directions in order to maintain front wheels in straight ahead position when steering wheel is in straight ahead position.

The steering knuckle and steering arm "rock" or tilt as front wheel rises and falls. Therefore, it is vitally important to position the bottom face of the tie rod end parallel with the machined surface at the outer end of the steering arm when tie rod length is adjusted. Severe damage and possible failure can result unless this precaution is taken. The tie rod sleeve clamps must be straight down to 45° forward to provide clearance.

WHEEL BEARINGS, ADJUST

1. Tighten spindle nut to 17 ft. lbs. torque and rotate hub to seat bearings.
2. Back off spindle nut ½ turn and retorque to one ft. lb.
3. Back off 1/12 turn minimum to ¼ turn maximum to allow installation of cotter pin.
4. Before installation of grease cap in hub, make sure end of spindle and inside of cap are free of grease so that radio static collector makes good contact. Make sure that static

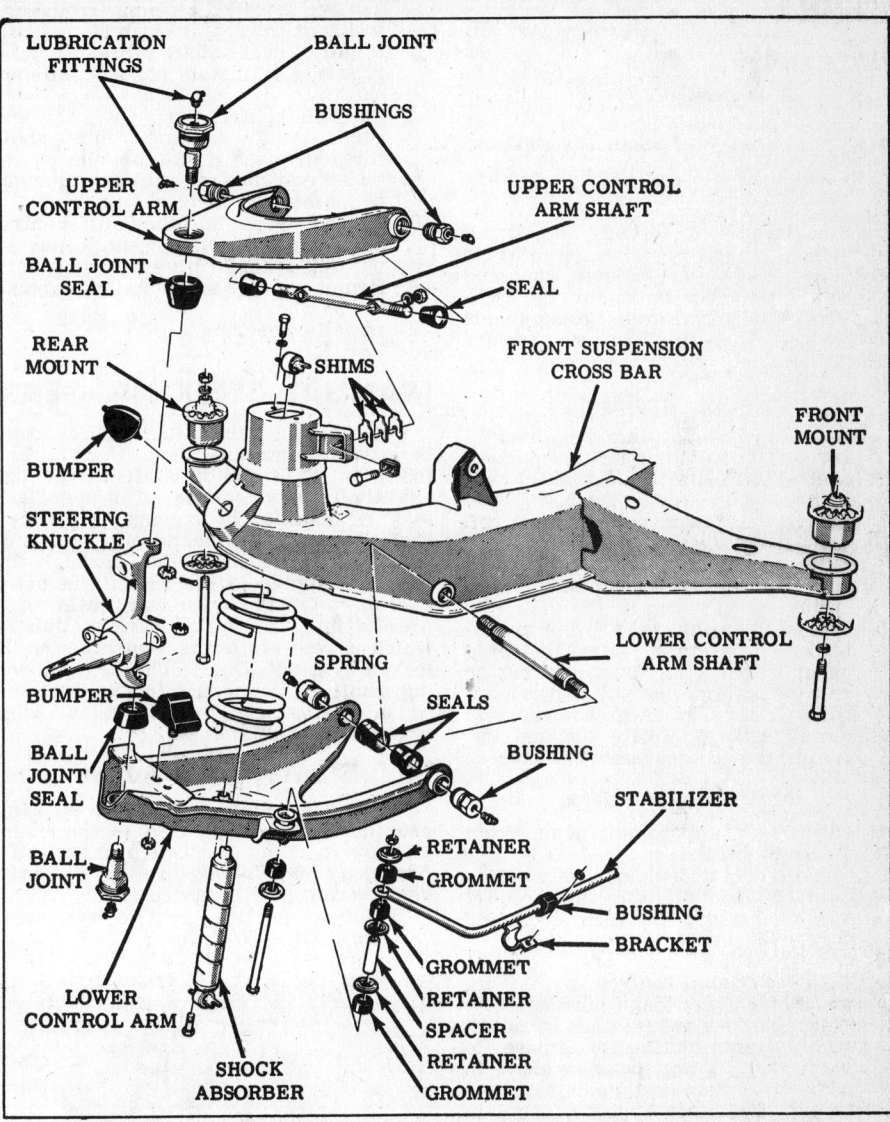

Fig. 1   Front suspension

collector is properly shaped to provide good contact between end of spindle and grease cap.

FRONT END REPAIRS

Ball Joints, Replace

Upper and lower ball joints are similar in appearance but are not interchangeable. Upper ball joints are spring-loaded to prevent looseness while the force of the chassis spring keeps the lower ball loaded, Fig. 1.

If the upper stud has any perceptible shake, or if it can be twisted in its socket with the fingers, it should be replaced.

1. Loosen (do not remove) stud nut.
2. Rap knuckle sharply in area of stud to disengage stud from knuckle.

3. Support lower control arm with jack and remove (loosened) nut from stud. Raise upper control arm to remove stud from knuckle.
4. Tie brake backing plate and steering knuckle out of the way.
5. Remove ball joint from control arm.
6. Install new ball joint into control arm and tighten until hex section of ball joint seats firmly into arms.
7. Turn tapered stud until cotter pin hole is fore and aft and assemble rubber dust shield over stud.
8. Assemble knuckle and backing plate and torque castellated nut to 35-60 ft. lbs.

Shock Absorber, Replace

Unfasten shock absorber top and bot-

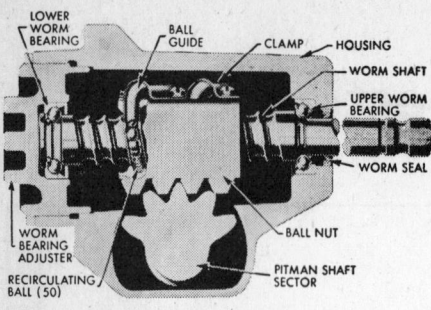

Fig. 2 Steering gear worm and ball nut

tom and remove it through the spring seat. Check shock absorber for obvious physical damage or oil leakage. Push and pull shock absorber in an upright position. If smooth hydraulic resistance is not present in both directions, replace shock absorber.

Spring, Replace

1. Remove wheel with hub and drum.
2. Disconnect stabilizer link from lower control arm and remove shock absorber.
3. Disconnect lower control arm ball joint from steering knuckle.
4. Lower floor jack under spring until spring is fully extended and remove spring.
5. To install spring, tape spring insulator to top of spring (identified by a ground flat coil). Rotate spring so end of bottom coil will index with edge of hole in lower control arm spring seat. Complete the installation in the reverse order of removal.

Upper Control Arm

1. Disconnect upper ball joint from steering knuckle.
2. Remove control arm, carefully noting number, location and thickness of adjusting shims between shaft and frame bracket.
3. If shaft and bushings only are to be replaced, clamp control arm in vise and remove shaft and bushings.
4. Assemble new grease seals on shaft. Apply light coating of grease to shaft threads and position shaft in arm. Start new bushing in arm and thread shaft into bushing to aid in alignment. Tighten bushing into arm until hex section of bushing seats firmly into arm.
5. Start second bushing into threads of arm with shaft threaded into opposite bushing.
6. After bushing has been threaded part way into arm, rotate shaft to engage threads of second bushing as an aid in piloting second bushing squarely into position.
7. Tighten bushing into arm until hex section of bushing seats firmly into arm. Shaft should be free enough to turn by hand. Install grease fittings and lubricate bushings.
8. Rotate shaft to make distance between shaft bolt holes and arm equal on both sides as nearly as possible.
9. Assemble upper control arm assembly, making certain the wheel alignment shims spare correct. Torque

shaft-to-bracket bolts to 60-85 ft. lbs.
10. Assemble ball joint.
11. Check and adjust wheel alignment if necessary.

Lower Control Arm

1. Remove coil spring.
2. Remove threaded bushings from control arm and remove arm from shaft.
3. Lightly coat shaft threads with grease and install rubber seals on shaft.
4. Position control arm on shaft and start front bushing onto shaft threads. Place a suitable spacer between control arm and crossmember to maintain control arm spread.
5. Thread front bushing into control arm. Tighten bushing until hex of bushing seats firmly into arm.
6. Remove spacer and install rear bushing as above.
7. Install coil spring.

MANUAL STEERING GEAR

The steering gear is the recirculating ball worm and nut type, Fig. 2. The teeth on the pitman shaft sector are slightly tapered so that a proper lash may be obtained by moving the pitman shaft endways by means of a lash adjuster screw which extends through the gear housing side cover, Fig. 3. The outer race or cup of the lower worm bearing is pressed into the worm bearing adjuster which screws into the housing and is locked by a nut, Fig. 2. The upper steering shaft is connected to the steering worm shaft through a universal joint type coupling, Fig. 4.

Steering Gear, Adjust

Never attempt to adjust the steering gear while it is connected to the intermediate rod. The steering gear must be free of all outside load to properly make any steering gear adjustments.

1. Torque steering gear-to-crossmember bolts to 55 ft. lbs.

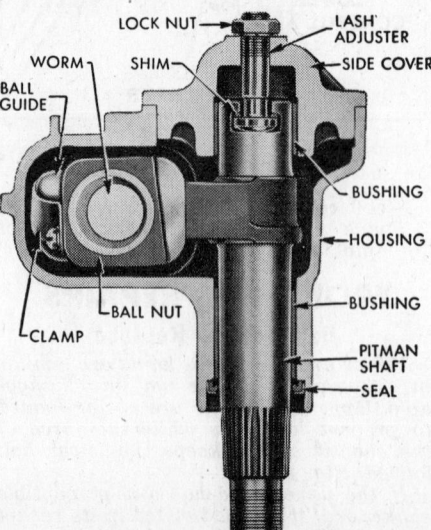

Fig. 3 Steering gear pitman shaft and ball nut

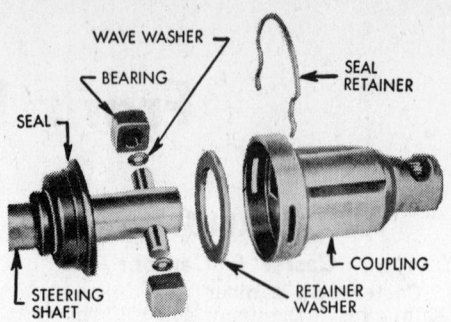

Fig. 4 Steering shaft coupling

2. Disconnect intermediate rod from pitman arm.
3. Turn steering wheel slowly from one extreme to the other. *Never turn wheel hard against end stops as damage to ball nut may result. If gear is hard pulling or binding it indicates an excessively tight adjustment of worm bearings or excessive misalignment of steering shaft. Roughness of gear indicates faulty internal parts. These conditions must be corrected before steering gear can be properly adjusted.*
4.
5. Remove emblem or cap from steering wheel hub.
6. Turn steering wheel gently in one direction until it stops.
7. Attach an inch-pound torque wrench to steering wheel nut and check torque required to turn wheel steadily in the range where lash exists between ball nut and pitman shaft sector. Torque required to keep wheel turning should be 2 to 7 inch pounds. If not within these limits, adjust worm bearing preload as follows:
8. Loosen worm bearing adjuster lock nut, Fig. 5. Turn bearing adjuster as required to bring wheel pull between 2 and 7 inch pounds. Tighten lock nut and recheck adjustment. Torque side cover bolts to 30 ft. lbs.
9. To check pitman shaft overcenter preload, turn steering wheel from one extreme to the other while counting the total turns; then turn wheel back ½ the number of turns. This positions gear on the high point where a preload should exist between ball nut and pitman shaft teeth.
10. A torque of 4 to 8 inch pounds *higher than the worm bearing preload* should be required to turn the wheel through the high point. Loosen the lock nut and turn the pitman shaft lash adjuster, Fig. 5, as required to obtain a total overcenter pull of not more than 13 inch pounds.
11. After tightening lock nut, rotate steering wheel back and forth through the high point and through the entire range to check for tight spots. *If lash cannot be removed at high point or if gear load varies greatly and feels rough, the gear should be removed for inspection of internal parts.*

Steering Wheel & Horn Button, Replace

1. Unplug horn ground wire connector

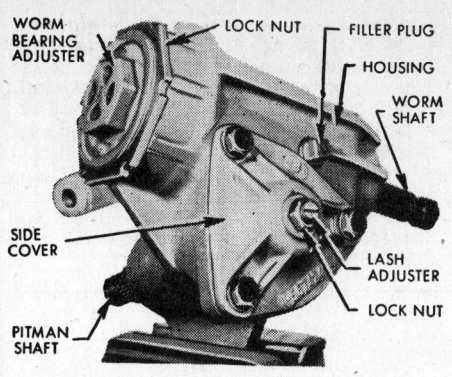

Fig. 5 Steering gear adjusters

at mast jacket to prevent horn from blowing.

2. Remove emblem from steering wheel hub. On standard wheels, remove cap by inserting screwdriver through hole in cap and loosening retaining screw. Unplug horn connector brush wire from cap.
3. Loosen steering wheel retaining nut several turns (do not remove).
4. Attach a suitable puller to wheel hub and pull wheel up to nut.
5. Remove puller, nut and steering wheel.
6. When installing the wheel, note that location marks of wheel on shaft are provided to insure straight ahead position of wheel when front wheels are pointing straight ahead.

Steering Gear, Replace

1. *Due to lack of clearance it is necessary to remove gear from car to remove pitman arm and nut from pitman shaft.*
2. Remove lower coupling clamp bolt.
3. Loosen clamp that retains mast jacket to toe pan cover and U-bolt that retains jacket to instrument panel. Pull mast jacket up to expose lower coupling.
4. Remove lower coupling.
5. Disconnect pitman arm from intermediate rod.
6. Unfasten steering gear from front suspension crossmember (4 bolts) and remove gear from car. *Do not remove pitman arm from gear unless pitman shaft or seal are to be removed.*
7. Reverse removal procedure to install steering gear (see Fig. 6). Torque pitman arm nut to 95 ft. lbs. Torque steering gear attaching bolts to 55 ft. lbs.

Steering Gear Repairs

Using Fig. 7 as a guide, disassemble the steering gear, observing the following:

1. The lower worm bearing cup is not replaced separately but is serviced with the worm bearing adjuster.
2. If the side cover bushing is worn, the side cover must be replaced as the bushing is not furnished separately.
4. Inspect teeth of ball nut and pitman shaft for pitting or scoring which would require replacement of nut or pitman shaft.

---

5. Check pitman shaft surface for wear or scoring, then check fit of lash adjuster and shim in the slot in end of pitman shaft by inserting a feeler gauge between head of screw and bottom of slot. Adjuster must be free to turn and end play should not exceed .002". If end play exceeds .002", install proper shim. Shims are available in thicknesses of .063", .065", .067", and .069".
6. Lubricate all seals, bushings, bearings and gears with multi-purpose gear lube just before assembling.

Steering Gear, Assemble

1. Position ball nut over worm shaft so that deep side of teeth will be toward side cover when installed in gear housing.
2. Install 19 balls in each circuit. Rock worm shaft slightly to aid in installing balls.
3. Place 6 balls in each return guide, using grease to hold balls in place.
4. Install return guides, clamp and screws.
5. Rotate worm through its complete travel several times to insure balls are installed correctly and rotate freely.
6. Place upper bearing on worm shaft into housing.
7. Place lower bearing in worm bearing adjuster and install bearing retainer.
8. Install adjuster with lock nut in housing. Tighten adjuster only enough to hold worm bearings in place.
9. Turn worm shaft until center groove in ball nut lines up with center of pitman shaft bushing. Install pitman shaft and lash adjuster with shim so that center tooth meshes with center groove in ball nut.
10. Install side cover with new gasket on lash adjuster by turning adjuster counterclockwise. Install and torque side cover bolts to 30 ft. lbs.
11. Turn lash adjuster so that teeth on shaft and ball nut engage but do not bind. Install lash adjuster lock nut loosely.
12. To protect pitman shaft seal from damage, cover shaft splines with masking tape. Slide new seal into

---

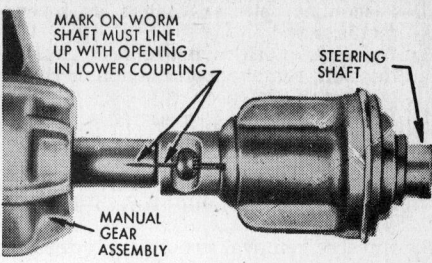

Fig. 6 Correct worm to lower coupling attachment

place and seat against shoulder in housing.

13. Install new worm shaft seal flush with surface of housing.
14. Fill gear with multi-purpose lubricant, install on car and adjust as previously described.

POWER STEERING

Service procedures on the power steering gear is given in the *Power Steering Chapter.* To remove the gear from the car, proceed as follows:

1. Disconnect hydraulic hoses from gear.
2. Remove two nuts that retain lower coupling to steering shaft flange.
3. Loosen clamp that retains mast jacket to toe pan cover and U-bolt that retains jacket to instrument panel.
4. Pull mast jacket up far enough to disengage steering shaft flange with flexible coupling.

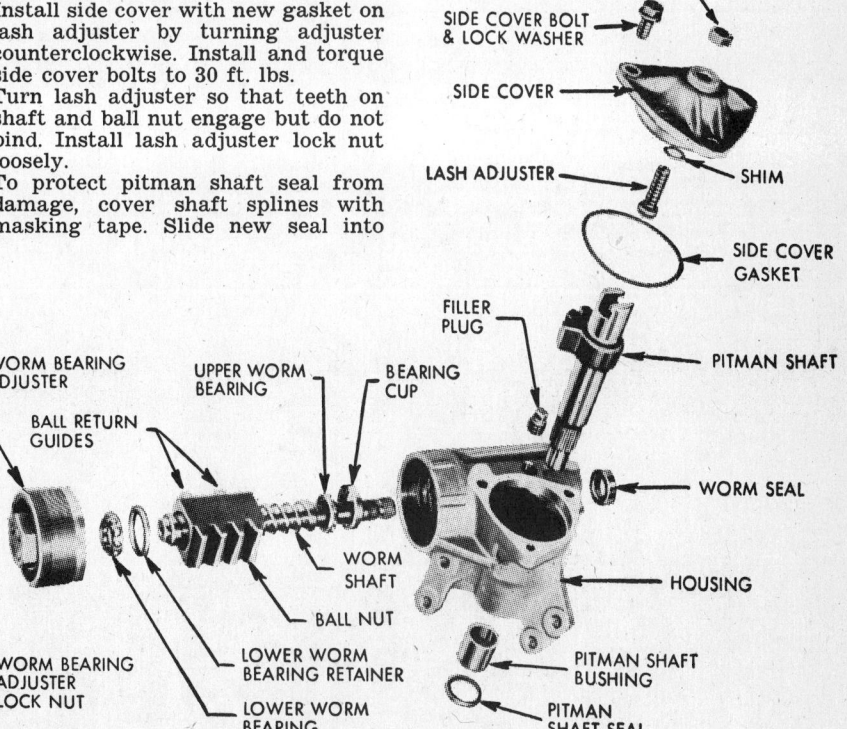

Fig. 7 Exploded view of manual steering gear

5. Disconnect pitman arm from intermediate rod.
6. On cars with synchromesh transmission, remove lower coupling from gear stub shaft.
7. Remove steering gear from front suspension crossmember (4 bolts). *Do not remove pitman arm from housing unless pitman shaft or seals or rack piston nut are to be removed.*
8. Reverse removal procedure to install

the gear. Tighten pitman arm nut to a torque of 95 ft. lbs. Torque gear attaching bolts to 55 ft. lbs.

9. On synchromesh cars, there must be at least $\frac{1}{16}''$ clearance between lower coupling and adjuster plug.
10. When installing the mast jacket, see that flange on steering shaft is properly positioned on flexible coupling. *Make sure coupling rivet heads are positioned in center of correct slots in flange. Small rivet goes in small*

slot and large rivet in large slot.
11. After hoses are connected to steering gear, fill pump reservoir to correct level with automatic transmission oil. Start engine and maintain oil level in reservoir while allowing engine to idle at least three minutes before turning steering wheel. Then rotate steering wheel throughout its entire range slowly a few times to bleed system of air. Recheck oil level and for leaks.

Instruments, Radio & Windshield Wiper

INSTRUMENT CLUSTER

1. Remove cluster hood. Then from under instrument panel, remove two nuts from studs that retain cluster at each side.
2. Remove two screws that retain lower edge of cluster to instrument panel tie bar.
3. Disconnect wiring harness connectors from headlight switch, windshield wiper switch, ignition switch and cigar lighter.
4. Disconnect speedometer cable and printed circuit plug.
5. Remove cluster by pulling rearward and lifting up.
6. Remove speedometer and other instruments or switches from cluster

7. When installing the cluster, *the projection on the disconnect plug must be lined up with the keyway in the printed circuit when assembling plug on connector pins.*

RADIO, REPLACE

1. On air conditioned cars it is necessary to lower evaporator assembly.
2. Disconnect antenna lead-in wire, speaker wire and battery wire from radio.
3. Remove knobs, escutcheons and retaining nuts from radio control shafts.
4. Remove support bracket-to-radio cap

screw located at right side of radio and lower radio from under instrument panel.
5. Installation is made in the reverse order of removal.

WINDSHIELD WIPER

The windshield wiper and washer switch is contained in the instrument cluster. To remove the switch it is necessary to remove the instrument cluster, the procedure for which is outlined above.

The wiper motor is held to the upper cowl by means of three bolts which fasten through three rubber bushings on the motor mounting plates and then into three weld nuts located in the cowl.

CADILLAC

INDEX OF SERVICE OPERATIONS

PAGE NO.

ACCESSORIES
Radio Removal 477
Instruments 476
Windshield Wiper 476
Windshield Wiper Troubles 37

BODY
Air Conditioning 177
Automatic Seat Adjuster Troubles 36
Automatic Top Troubles 36
Automatic Window Lift Troubles 36

BRAKES (Mechanical)
Adjustments 112
Brake Cylinder Sizes 454
Hydraulic Brake System 112
Master Cylinder, Replace 469
Trouble Shooting 31

BRAKES (Power)
Power Brake System, Bleed 469
Power Unit, Replace 469
Power Unit Repairs 128
Trouble Shooting 32

COOLING SYSTEM
Radiator, Replace 461
Trouble Shooting 8
Water Pump Repairs 462
Water Pump, Replace 461

ELECTRIC SYSTEM
Dash Gauge Service 85
Distributor, Replace 462
Distributor Service 46
Distributor Specifications 452
Generator Regulator Service 62
Generator Regulator Specifications 452
Generator Service 62
Generator Specifications 452
Horn Button or Ring, Replace 474
Ignition System Service 46
Ignition Timing 462
Starter, Replace 462
Starter Switch Service 83
Starting Motor Service 77
Starting Motor Specifications 451
Trouble Shooting 10
Turn Signal Troubles 12

PAGE NO.

ENGINE
Camshaft & Bearings 458
Crankshaft Oil Seal, Replace 460
Cylinder Head, Replace 455
Engine Bearing Specifications 451
Engine, Replace 455
Main Bearings, Replace 459
Piston Pins, Replace 459
Piston Rings, Replace 459
Piston & Ring Specifications 451
Pistons & Rods, Remove 458
Pistons & Rods, Assemble 458
Pistons, Replace 458
Rocker Arms 456
Rod Bearings, Replace 459
Timing Chain & Cover 458
Trouble Shooting 4
Valve Arrangement 455
Valves, Grind 457
Valve Guides 456
Valve Lifters 457
Valves, Remove 456
Valve Specifications 451
Valve Spring Testing 457
Valve Spring Installed Height 457
Valve Timing Data 458

ENGINE OILING
Oil Pan, Replace 460
Oil Pump Repairs 460
Trouble Shooting 4
Vacuum Pump 460

FRONT SUSPENSION
Camber, Adjust 470
Caster, Adjust 470
Front End Repairs 472
Toe-in, Adjust 470
Trouble Shooting 33
Wheel Alignment Specifications 453
Wheel Bearings, Adjust 471

FUEL & EXHAUST SYSTEM
Carburetors 463
Fuel Pumps 96
Mufflers and Pipes 463
Trouble Shooting 4

PAGE NO.

REAR AXLE
Axle Shaft, Replace 469
General Service 102
Non-Slip Differentials 109
Rear Axle Assembly, Replace 469
Rear Axle Specifications 454
Trouble Shooting 31

SPECIFICATIONS
Brake Cylinder Sizes 454
Capacity Data 453
Carburetors 463
Cooling System 453
Crankshaft & Bearings 451
Distributors 452
Engine Tightening 451
Generator & Regulators 452
Pistons & Rings 451
Rear Axle 454
Starting Motors 451
Tune Up 450
Valves 451
Wheel Alignment 453

STEERING GEARS (Mechanical)
Horn Button or Ring, Replace 474
Steering Gear Repairs 474
Steering Gear, Replace 474
Steering Wheel, Replace 474
Trouble Shooting 33

STEERING GEARS (Power)
Steering Gear Repairs 145
Steering Gear, Replace 475
Trouble Shooting 34

TRANSMISSIONS (Automatic)
Hydra-Matic Linkage, Adjust 467
Hydra-Matic, Replace 468
Hydra-Matic Repairs (Single Coupling) .283
Hydra-Matic Repairs (Two Coupling) ...263
Hydra-Matic Trouble Shooting
    Single Coupling Type 25
    Two Coupling Type 28

TUNE UP 38

Year	Model Designation	Wheel-base, Inches	Valve Location	Bore and Stroke	Piston Displace-ment, Cubic Inches	Compres-sion Ratio (Stand-ard)	Maximum Brake H.P. @ R.P.M.	Maximum Torque Lbs. Ft. @ R.P.M.	Normal Oil Pressure Pounds
1953	V8................Series 60S	130	In Head	3.8125 x 3.625	331.0	8.25	210 @ 4150	330 @ 2700	35
	V8................Series 62	126	In Head	3.8125 x 3.625	331.0	8.25	210 @ 4150	330 @ 2700	35
	V8................Series 75	146¾	In Head	3.8125 x 3.625	331.0	8.25	210 @ 4150	330 @ 2700	35
1954	V8................Series 60	133	In Head	3.8125 x 3.625	331.0	8.25	230 @ 4400	330 @ 2700	35
	V8................Series 62	129	In Head	3.8125 x 3.625	331.0	8.25	230 @ 4400	330 @ 2700	35
	V8................Series 75	149¾	In Head	3.8125 x 3.625	331.0	8.25	230 @ 4400	330 @ 2700	35
1955	V8................Series 60	133	In Head	3.8125 x 3.625	331	9.1	250 @ 4600	345 @ 2800	35
	V8................Series 62	129	In Head	3.8125 x 3.625	331	9.1	250 @ 4600	345 @ 2800	35
	Eldorado........Series 62	129	In Head	3.8125 x 3.625	331	9.1	270 @ 4800	345 @ 3200	35
	V8................Series 75	149¾	In Head	3.8125 x 3.625	331	9.1	250 @ 4600	345 @ 2800	35
1956	V8................Series 60	133	Tune Head	4.000 x 3.625	365	9.75	285 @ 4600	400 @ 2800	30–35
	V8................Series 62	129	In Head	4.000 x 3.625	365	9.75	285 @ 4600	400 @ 2800	30–35
	Eldorado........Series 62	129	In Head	4.000 x 3.625	365	9.75	305 @ 4700	400 @ 3200	30–35
	V8................Series 75	149¾	In Head	4.000 x 3.625	365	9.75	285 @ 4600	400 @ 2800	30–35
1957	V8................Series 60	133	In Head	4.000 x 3.625	365	10.0	300 @ 4800	400 @ 2800	30–35
	V8................Series 62	129½	In Head	4.000 x 3.625	365	10.0	300 @ 4800	400 @ 2800	30–35
	Eldorado........Series 62	129½	In Head	4.000 x 3.625	365	10.0	325 @ 4800	400 @ 3200	30–35
	V8................Series 75	149¾	In Head	4.000 x 3.625	365	10.0	300 @ 4800	400 @ 2800	30–35
1958	V8................Series 60	133	In Head	4.000 x 3.625	365	10.25	310 @ 4800	405 @ 3100	30–35
	V8................Series 62	129½	In Head	4.000 x 3.625	365	10.25	310 @ 4800	405 @ 3100	30–35
	V8................Series 75	147⅞	In Head	4.000 x 3.625	365	10.25	310 @ 4800	405 @ 3100	30–35
	V8 With 3 Carbs.............	...	In Head	4.000 x 3.625	365	10.25	335 @ 4800	405 @ 3400	30–35
1959	V8................Series 62	130	In Head	4.000 x 3.875	390	10.5	325 @ 4800	430 @ 3100	30–35
	V8 Eldorado.....Series 62	130	In Head	4.000 x 3.875	390	10.5	345 @ 4800	435 @ 3400	30–35
	V8................Series 60	130	In Head	4.000 x 3.875	390	10.5	325 @ 4800	430 @ 3100	30–35
	V8................Series 75	149.8	In Head	4.000 x 3.875	390	10.5	325 @ 4800	430 @ 3100	30–35
1960	V8................Series 62	130	In Head	4.000 x 3.875	390	10.5	325 @ 4800	430 @ 3100	30–35
	V8 Eldorado.....Series 62	130	In Head	4.000 x 3.875	390	10.5	345 @ 4800	435 @ 3100	30–35
	V8................Series 60	130	In Head	4.000 x 3.875	390	10.5	325 @ 4800	430 @ 3100	30–35
	V8................Series 75	149.8	In Head	4.000 x 3.875	390	10.5	325 @ 4800	430 @ 3100	30–35
1961	V8................Series 62	129½	In Head	4.000 x 3.875	390	10.5	325 @ 4800	430 @ 3100	30–35
	V8................Special 60	129½	In Head	4.000 x 3.875	390	10.5	325 @ 4800	430 @ 3100	30–35
	V8................Series 75	150	In Head	4.000 x 3.875	390	10.5	325 @ 4800	430 @ 3100	30–35

TUNE UP SPECIFICATIONS

★When using a timing light, disconnect vacuum line to prevent vacuum advance mechanism from operating.

Year	Model	Ground Polarity and Voltage	Spark Plug Type	Spark Plug Gap Inch	Distributor Point Gap Inch	Distributor Cam Angle Degrees	Firing Order ①	Ignition Timing★ Mark	Ignition Timing★ Location	Idle Speed RPM In Drive	Compression Pressure @ Cranking Speed Minimum
1953	All	N-12	AC 46-5	.035	.016	26–33	18436572	②	Damper	400	150
1954	All	N-12	AC 46-5	.035	.016	26–33	18436572	②	Damper	400	150
1955	All	N-12	AC 44	.035	.016	26–33	18436572	"A"	Damper	400	165
1956	All	N-12	AC 44	.035	③	30	18436572	"A"	Damper	420④	165
1957	All	N-12	AC 44	.035	③	30	18436572	"A"	Damper	420④	155–175
1958–59	All	N-12	AC-44	.035	③	30	18436572	"5"	Damper	450	165–185
1960–61	All	N-12	AC-44	.035	③	30	18436572	"5"	Damper	480⑤	165–185

①—Cylinder numbering (front to rear): Left bank 1-3-5-7, right bank 2-4-6-8.

②—"A" mark for premium fuel, "C" mark for regular fuel.

③—Turn adjusting screw in (clockwise) until engine begins to misfire. Then turn screw ½ turn in opposite direction.

④—For models with two carburetors 500 RPM.

⑤—The vacuum released parking brake must be made inoperative by pulling vacuum hose off right hand connector of the vacuum switch on the neutral safety switch and covering the switch opening with tape to prevent any air leak.

VALVE SPECIFICATIONS

Year	Model	Valve Lash		Valve Angles		Valve Spring Installed Height	Valve Spring Pressure Lbs. @ In.	Valve Lift		Stem Clearance		Stem Diameter	
		Int.	Exh.	Seat	Face			Int.	Exh.	Intake	Exhaust	Int.	Exh.
1953	All	Zero	Zero	44	44	1¹¹⁄₁₆	140 @ 1²¹⁄₆₄	.365	.365	.001–.0025	.001–.0025	.3420	.3418
1954	All	Zero	Zero	44	44	1¹¹⁄₁₆	140 @ 1²¹⁄₆₄	.365	.365	.001–.0025	.001–.0025	.3420	.3418
1955	All	Zero	Zero	44	44	1⁵⁷⁄₆₄	157 @ 1⁹⁄₃₂	.411	.411	.001–.0025	.001–.0025	.3420	.3418
1956	All	Zero	Zero	44	44	1⁵⁷⁄₆₄	157 @ 1⁹⁄₃₂	.411	.411	.001–.0025	.001–.0025	.3420	.3418
1957	All	Zero	Zero	44	44	1⁵⁷⁄₆₄	157 @ 1⁹⁄₃₂	.451	.451	.001–.0025	.001–.0025	.3420	.3418
1958	All	Zero	Zero	44	44	1¹⁵⁄₁₆	160 @ 1½	.451	.451	.001–.0025	.001–.0025	.3420	.3418
1959	All	Zero	Zero	44	44	1¹⁵⁄₁₆	160 @ 1½	.450	.450	.0005–.0025	.001–.0025	.3420	.3418
1960–61	All	Zero	Zero	44	44	1¹⁵⁄₁₆	160 @ 1½	.450	.450	.0005–.0025	.001–.0025	.3420	.3418

PISTONS, PINS, RINGS, CRANKSHAFT & BEARINGS

Year	Model	Fitting Pistons		Ring End Gap ①		Wrist-pin Diameter	Rod Bearings		Main Bearings		Thrust on Bear. No.	Shaft End Play
		Shim To Use	Pounds Pull On Scale	Comp.	Oil		Shaft Diameter	Bearing Clearance	Shaft Diameter	Bearing Clearance		
1953–55	All	②	②	.010	.010	.9995	2.2488–2.2493	.0005–.002	2.499–2.4995	.0008–.0025	5	.001–.007
1956–59	All	②	②	.013	.013	.9995	2.2488–2.2493	.0005–.002	2.624–2.625	.0008–.0025	5	.001–.007
1960–61	All	②	②	.013	.013	.9995	2.2488–2.2493	.0005–.002	2.624–2.625	.0008–.0025	5	.001–.007

①—Fit rings in tapered bores for clearance given in tightest portion of ring travel.
②—See Piston Clearance Chart, Fig. 11.

ENGINE TIGHTENING SPECIFICATIONS★

★Torque specifications are for clean and lightly lubricated threads only. Dry or dirty threads produce increased friction which prevents accurate measurement of tightness.

Year	Spark Plugs Ft. Lbs.	Cylinder Head Bolts Ft. Lbs.	Intake Manifold Ft. Lbs.	Exhaust Manifold Ft. Lbs.	Rocker Arm Shaft Bracket Ft. Lbs.	Rocker Arm Cover Ft. Lbs.	Connecting Rod Cap Bolts Ft. Lbs.	Main Bearing Cap Bolts Ft. Lbs.	Flywheel to Crankshaft Ft. Lbs.	Vibration Damper or Pulley Ft. Lbs.
1953–55	20–25	65–70	25–30	25–30	65–70	①	40–45	90–100	80–85	60–65
1956–57	20–25	65–70	25–30	25–30	65–70	①	40–45	90–100	75–80	60–65
1958–61	20–25	65–70	25–30	25–30	65–70	②	40–45	90–100	75–80	65–70

①—20–25 inch lbs.   ②—35–40 inch lbs.

STARTING MOTOR SPECIFICATIONS

Car and Model	Part No.	Rotation ①	Brush Spring Tension, Ounces	No Load Test			Torque Test		
				Amperes	Volts	R.P.M.	Amperes	Volts	Torque, Lbs. Ft.
1953	1107602	C	24 Min.	75	10.3	6500	520	4.9	11
1954	1107622	C	35 Min.	95	10.1	3500	470	5.4	10½
1955	1107629	C	35 Min.	95	10.1	3500	470	5.4	10½
1956	1107642	C	35 Min.	91	10.6	3240	395	3.5	②
1957–60	1107657	C	35	65–100	10.6	3600–5100	300–360	3.5	②
1958	1107668	C	35	65–100	10.6	3600–5100	300–360	3.5	②
1961	1107799	C	35	65–100	10.6	3600–5100	300–360	3.5	②

①—As viewed from the drive end. C—Clockwise.   ②—Armature locked.

CADILLAC

DISTRIBUTOR SPECIFICATIONS

Year	Model	Part No. ①	Rotation ②	Cam Angle, Degrees	Breaker Point Opening, Inch	Condenser Capacity, Mfds.③	Breaker Arm Spring Tension, Ounces	Centrifugal Advance Data Degrees @ R.P.M. of Dist.		Vacuum Advance Data		
								Advance Starts	Full Advance	Inches of Vacuum to Start Plunger Movement	Inches of Vacuum for Full Plunger Travel	Maximum Vacuum Advance, Dist. Degrees
1953	All	1110835	CC	26–33	.016	.18–.23	19–23	1 @ 500	12 @ 1950	6½–9	16½	13–14½
1954	All	1110844	CC	26–33	.016	.18–.23	19–23	1 @ 500	12 @ 1950	6½–9	16½	13–14½
1955	All	1110852	CC	26–33	.016	.18–.23	19–23	1 @ 500	12 @ 2075	6–8½	15½	13–14½
1956	1 Carb.	1110858	CC	30	④	.18–.23	19–23	1 @ 575	10 @ 1950	5–7	16½	18
1956	2 Carbs.	1110859	CC	30	④	.18–.23	19–23	1 @ 575	10 @ 1950	5–7	16½	18
1957	1 Carb.	1110876	CC	30	④	.18–.23	19–23	1 @ 450	12 @ 2075	8–10	14½	12
1957	2 Carbs.	1110877	CC	30	④	.18–.23	19–23	1 @ 450	12 @ 2075	8–10	14½	12
1958	1 Carb.	1110909	CC	30	④	.18–.23	19–23	1 @ 400	8 @ 2000	8–10	14½	12
1958	3 Carbs.	1110926	CC	30	④	.18–.23	19–23	1 @ 400	8 @ 2000	8–10	14½	12
1959	1 Carb.	1110932	CC	30	④	.18–.23	19–23	1 @ 400	8 @ 2000	7½–9½	15¾–17¼	10½–12
1959	2 Carbs.	1110933	CC	30	④	.18–.23	19–23	1 @ 400	8 @ 2000	7½–9½	15¾–17¼	10½–12
1960–61	1 Carb.	1110932	CC	30	④	.18–.23	19–23	1 @ 400	8 @ 2000	9	13¼–15¼	11¼
1960	3 Carbs.	1110952	CC	30	④	.18–.23	19–23	1 @ 450	9 @ 1175	7	14–15	9

①—Distributor number stamped on plate riveted to side of housing.
②—As viewed from the top. CC—Counter-clockwise. C—Clockwise.
③—Microfarads—as indicated on a condenser tester.
④—Turn adjusting screw in (clockwise) until engine begins to misfire. Then turn screw ½ turn in opposite direction.

GENERATOR AND REGULATOR SPECIFICATIONS

★To polarize generator, reconnect the leads to the regulator; then momentarily connect a jumper wire from the "Gen" to the "Bat" terminals of the regulator.

Year	Generator						Regulator					
	Generator Number	Rotation & Ground Polarity ③	Rated Cap. Amps.	Gen. Field Ground Location★	Brush Spring Tension, Ounces	Field Current Amperes	Regulator Number	Cutout Relay		Voltage Regulator Setting Volts	Current Regulator Setting Amperes	Current and Voltage Armature Air Gap, Inch
								Voltage to Close Points	Armature Air Gap, Inch			
1953–55	1102002	C-N	30	External	28	1.48–1.62	1118825	12.6	.020	14.3	30	.075
1956	1102002	C-N	30	External	28	1.48–1.62	1119003	12.6	.020	14.3	30	.075
1956	1102011	C-N	30	External	28	1.48–1.62	1119003	12.6	.020	14.3	30	.075
1957	1102002	C-N	30	External	28	1.48–1.62	1119001	12.6	.020	14.3	30	.075
1957	1102069	C-N	35	External	28	1.62–1.82	1119002	12.6	.020	14.3	35	.075
1957	1102060	C-N	40	External	28	3.5–3.76	1119163	12.6	.020	14.3①	40	.080②
1957	1106989	C-N	55	External	28	2.14–2.29	1119175	12.6	.020	14.3①	55	.080②
1958	1102109	C-N	35	External	28	1.62–1.82	1119002	12.6	.020	14.3	35	.075
1958	1102103	C-N	45	External	28	2.66–2.86	1119601	12.4	.020	14.2④	45	.075⑤
1958	1106989	C-N	55	External	20	2.14–2.28	1119605	12.4	.020	14.2④	55	.075⑤
1959	1102140	C-N	35	External	28	1.69–1.79	1119002	12.6	.020	14.5	35	.075
1959	1102141	C-N	45	External	28	2.66–2.86	1119601	12.4	.020	14.2④	45	.075⑤
1960–61	1102170	C-N	35	External	28	1.69–1.79	1119002	12.6	.020	14.3	35	.075
1960–61⑥	1102141	C-N	45	External	28	2.66–2.86	1119601	11.9	.020	14.2④	45	.075⑤

①—Operation on upper contracts must be .3 to .5 volt less than on lower contacts.
②—Lower contact opening .016".
③—C-Clockwise. N-Negative.
④—Lower contact setting .1 to .3 volt lower.
⑤—Voltage regulator contact air gap: Upper .016", lower .067".
⑥—With air conditioning.

COOLING SYSTEM & CAPACITY DATA

Year	Model	Cooling System Data					Fuel Tank Gals.	Engine Oil			Transmissions			Rear Axle Pints
		Quarts No Heater	Quarts With Heater	Rad. Cap Relief Pressure	Thermostat Opening Temp.			Refill Qts.③	Summer Grade	Winter Grade	Std. Pints	With Over-drive Pints	Auto-matic Qts.	
					①	②								
1953	All	19¾	20¾	12–15	180	165	20	5	20W	10W	2½	None	12	5
1954	60, 62	19¾	22	12–15	180	165	20	5	20W	10W	None	None	12	5
	75	19¾	24½	12–15	180	165	20	5	20W	10W	None	None	12	5
1955	60, 62	18	20¼	12–15	180	165	20	5	20W	10W	None	None	11	5
	75	18	22¾	12–15	180	165	20	5	20W	10W	None	None	11	5
1956	60, 62	17¼	19¼	12–15	180	165	20	5	20W	10W	None	None	12	5
	75	17¼	21½	12–15	180	165	20	5	20W	10W	None	None	12	5
1957	60, 62	19	20	12–15	180	165	20	5	20W	10W	None	None	11½	5
	75	19	21	12–15	180	165	20	5	20W	10W	None	None	11½	5
1958	60, 62	19½	20½	12–15	180	165	20	5	20W	10W	None	None	11½	5
	75	19½	22½	12–15	180	165	20	5	20W	10W	None	None	11½	5
1959	60, 62	18½	19¼	12–15	175		21	5	20W	10W	None	None	11½	5
	75	18½	20¾	12–15	175		21	5	20W	10W	None	None	11½	5
1960	60, 62	18½	19¼	12–15	175		21	5	20W	10W	None	None	10	5
	75	18½	20¾	12–15	175		21	5	20W	10W	None	None	10	5
1961	60, 62	18½	19¼	13½–16½	175		21	5	20W	10W	None	None	10	5
	75	18½	20¾	13½–16½	175		21	5	20W	10W	None	None	10	5

①—For permanent type anti-freeze.

②—For alcohol type anti-freeze.

③—Add one quart with filter change.

WHEEL ALIGNMENT SPECIFICATIONS

Year	Model	Caster, Degrees③		Camber, Degrees④		Toe-In Inch	Toe-out on Turns, Degrees①		Kingpin or Steering Axis Inclination Degrees②
		Limits	Desired	Limits	Desired		Outer Wheel	Inner Wheel	
1953	60S, 62	— ½ to + ½	0	— ⅜ to + ⅜	0	1/16 to ⅛	20	24½ to 25½	5⅚ @ 0 Camber
	75	— ½ to + ½	0	— ⅜ to + ⅜	0	1/16 to ⅛	20	23½ to 24½	5⅚ @ 0 Camber
1954–55	All	0 to — 1	— ½	— ⅜ to + ⅜	0	3/16 to ¼	22° 40'	20	5⅚ @ 0 Camber
1956	All	0 to — 1	— ½	— ⅜ to + ⅜	0	5/32 to 7/32	22° 40'	20	5⅚ @ 0 Camber
1957–58	All	0 to — 1	— ½	— ⅜ to + ⅜	0	3/16 to ¼⑤	22° 40'	20	4 @ 0 Camber
1959–60	60, 62	0 to — 1	— ½	— ⅜ to + ⅜	0	3/16 to ¼⑤	22° 40'	20	4 @ 0 Camber
	75	— ¾ to — 1¾	— 1¼	— ⅜ to + ⅜	0	3/16 to ¼⑤	22° 40'	20	4 @ 0 Camber
1961	All	— 1½ to — ½	— ⅞	L. — ⅛ to + ⅜ R. — ⅜ to + ⅛	L. + ⅛ R. — ⅛	3/16 to ¼	20	22° 11'	6°

①—Incorrect toe-out, when other adjustments are correct, generally indicates bent steering arms.

②—Incorrect angle with correct camber indicates bent suspension arms or steering knuckle support.

③—Adjustment must be within ½° or less on both sides of car.

④—¼° to ½° more positive camber of left wheel will help correct crowned road pull.

⑤—Air suspension cars 1/16".

CADILLAC

REAR AXLE AND BRAKE CYLINDER SPECIFICATIONS

Year	Model	Ring Gear & Pinion Backlash, Inch	Drive Pinion Adjustment	Drive Pinion Bearing Preload, Inch Lbs.	Drive Pinion Bearing Adjustment	Axle Shaft End Play, Inch	Hydraulic Cylinder Bore Sizes, Inch		
							Wheel Cylinder		Master Cylinder
							Front	Rear	
1953–55	All	.003–.010	None	②	Spacer	None	1⅛	1	1
1956	All	.003–.010	None	②	Spacer	None	1⅛	1	1¹¹⁄₁₆
1957	All	.003–.010	None	②	Spacer	None	1⅛	1	1
1958	All	.003–.010	None	②	Spacer	None	1⅛	1	1¹¹⁄₁₆
1959	All	.003–.010	None	②	Spacer	None	1⅛	1	1
1960	All	.003–.010	None	②	Spacer	None	1⅛	1¹⁄₁₆	1
1961	All	.003–.010	None	②	Spacer	None	1⅛	1⁵⁄₁₆	1

①—Power Brakes are standard equipment.

②—Maximum torque on an assembly over 1000 miles is 15 inch lbs. (used seal) and 20 inch lbs. (new seal). Torque on a new assembly is 50 inch lbs.

SERIAL & ENGINE NUMBER LOCATION
1953-58: Front Face Of Right Cylinder Block
1959-61: Lower Left Side Of Block

1957

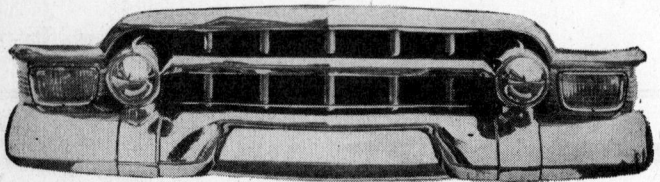

1953

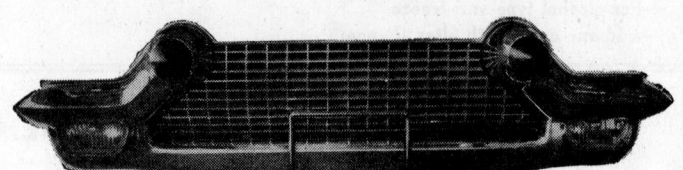

1957 Brougham

1954

1958

1955

1959

1956

1960

1961

Engine Section

ENGINE, REPLACE

1. Drain cooling system.
2. Remove hood and radiator.
3. Disconnect fuel, oil and vacuum lines, and wires connected to engine units.
4. Remove generator, starter and carburetor.
5. Remove fan and pulley.
6. Disconnect power steering hoses.
7. On cars so equipped, disconnect refrigerant lines, exercising precautions outlined in *Air Conditioning* chapter.
8. Remove propeller shaft.
9. Remove Hydra-Matic linkage slush deflector.
10. Disconnect speedometer cable.
11. Disconnect shift linkage at transmission.
12. Disconnect front engine mounts.
13. Disconnect exhaust pipes at manifolds.
14. Unfasten and lower steering idler arm and connecting link.
15. Attach engine lifting rig.
16. Remove rear engine support bracket from frame and extension housing.
17. Lift out engine and transmission.
18. To install, reverse above operations.

Fig. 2 Cylinder head tightening sequence. All models

CYLINDER HEAD, REPLACE

Drain radiator and cylinder block on side on which head is to be removed. If left head is to be removed, take off power steering pump, generator and disconnect water temperature wire. If right head is to be removed, disconnect windshield wiper pipe clamp, and the compressor on air conditioned cars. If both heads are to be taken off, proceed as follows:

1. Remove oil filter lines as necessary.
2. Remove two capscrews from water pump flange at cylinder head and loosen remaining capscrews about three turns.
3. Remove carburetor air cleaner.
4. Remove carburetor-to-fuel filter line.
5. Remove ground strap screws from rear of head at cowl.
6. Remove vacuum advance line from carburetor.
7. Disconnect intake manifold vacuum pipe hose.
8. Disconnect coil wires at distributor.
9. Disconnect carburetor linkage.
10. Remove choke heater pipe.
11. Remove rocker arm covers and distributor cap.
12. Remove intake manifold.
13. Remove exhaust pipe and heat valves.
14. Remove rocker arm assembly.
15. Remove push rods.
16. Remove cylinder heads, using lifting hooks in the first and third spark plug holes.
17. Reverse removal procedure to install the heads, tightening the capscrews in the sequence shown in Fig. 2.

VALVE ARRANGEMENT
Front to Rear

All Models . . . . E-I-I-E-E-I-I-E

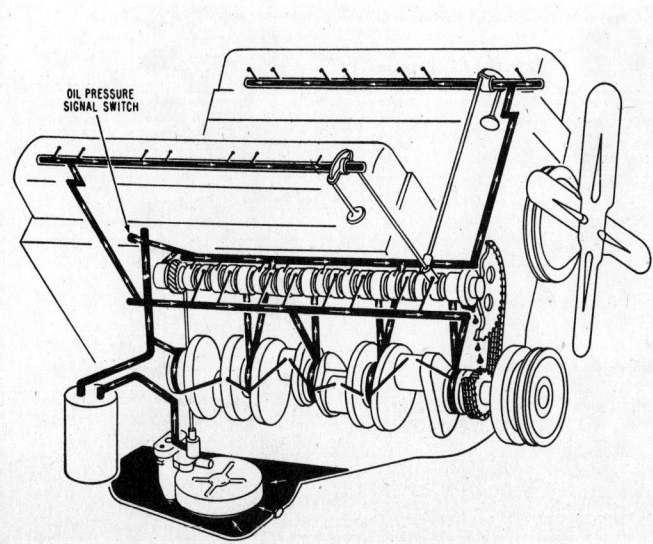

Engine lubrication. 1960-61

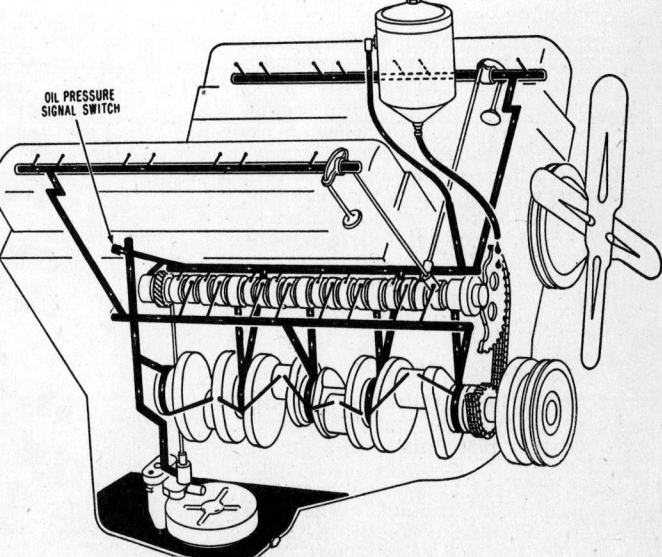

Engine lubrication. 1953-59

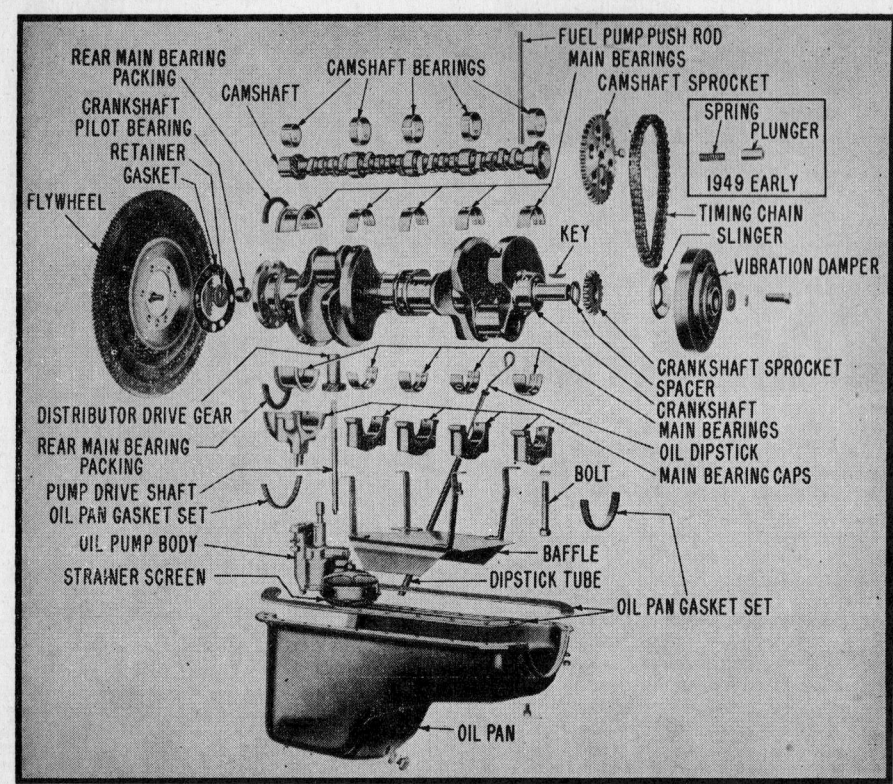

Internal parts of engine

Fig. 4 Tool used for removing and installing valves

ROCKER ARMS

Sludge and gum formation in the rocker arms and shafts, Fig. 3, will restrict the normal flow of oil to the rocker arms and valves. Therefore, each time the assemblies are removed, they should be disassembled and thoroughly cleaned.

Clean all gum and sludge formation from the inside and outside of the shafts and rocker arms. Check the fit of the rocker arms on the shafts and the valve end of the rocker arms for excessive wear. If the rocker arm radius is grooved on the valve end, do not attempt grinding; replace the part.

When the assemblies are installed, make sure the rocker arms are correctly positioned to actuate the valves.

Check each push rod for a bent condition. If bent more than .020″ when checked with a dial indicator, replace the push rod. Do not attempt to straighten a bent push rod. If a dial gauge is not available, at least check the rod for straightness by rolling it on a perfectly flat surface plate. *Push rods should be installed with the double grooved end up on 1952-54 engines and with single grooved end up on 1955-56 and early 1957.*

Service Note

An incorrectly installed rocker arm shaft permits oil to be sprayed directly on the valve stems. This causes an excessive amount of oil to be drawn past the guides into the combustion chamber, increasing oil consumption. When the rocker arm shaft is correctly installed, the notch on the end of the shaft faces down and toward the center of the engine, Fig. 3.

VALVES, REMOVE

With cylinder head removed as outlined previously, use a suitable valve spring compressor to compress the springs in order to take out the valve locks, Fig. 4. Then remove spring retainers, valve stem seals and valve springs. Remove burrs from valve stem lock grooves to prevent damage to valve guides, and slide valves from heads.

Place valves in a board with numbered holes to identify their location so that, if re-used, they can be returned to the original guide holes.

VALVE GUIDES

Check valve stem to guide clearance, using a $\frac{1}{16}$″ wide strip of .005″ brass shim stock on a "no-go" basis. Bend the end of the shim and hang it in the end of the valve guide. Shim should not extend more than $\frac{1}{4}$″ into the guide. If valve stem will enter guide, clearance is excessive and valve and guide should be replaced to prevent excessive oil consumption and improper seating of valves.

Unless the special tool shown in Fig. 5 is available, before removing a guide, measure the distance it sticks out of the valve port with a steel scale. Then drive out the old guide and install the new one to the measured depth.

VALVE SPRING INSTALLED HEIGHT

When valves and seats are reground the position of the valve in the head is changed so as to lessen the valve spring tension. Without proper valve spring tension the valve does not seat long enough or it may not seat completely. Since the valve is cooled by transferring heat from the valve head to the seat and thence to the coolant, improper valve

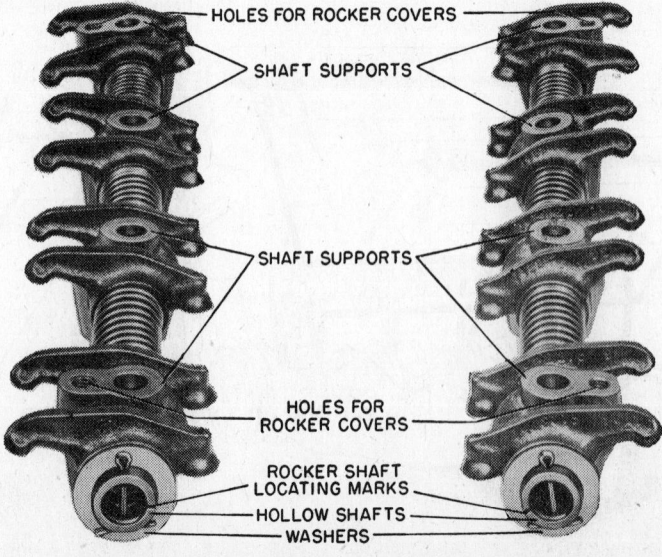

Fig. 3 Rocker arm details

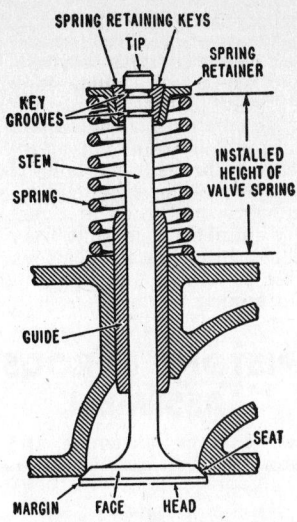

Fig. 5A   Checking valve spring installed height

spring tension will cause worn, pitted and distorted valves which result in loss of compression and power as well as poor gasoline mileage.

When valves, springs, retainers and locks are installed, measure the assembled height of the valve springs from the surface of the cylinder head spring pad to the underside of the spring retainer as shown in Fig. 5A. If the assembled height is greater than the dimension given in the *Valve Specifications Chart,* install a spacer or shim of proper thickness between cylinder head spring pad and spring to bring the assembled height to specifications.

Do not install spacers unless necessary. Excessive use of spacers will result in overstressing valve springs and overloading camshaft lobes which could lead to spring breakage and worn camshaft lobes.

VALVE SPRING TESTING

After taking out the valve springs, wash them with gasoline or other suitable solvent. Examine the springs for damage or corrosion due to acid etching, which will develop into surface cracks and cause spring failure.

Check the valve spring tension on a spring testing fixture, Fig. 6, if one is available, and according to the specifications given in the *Valve Specifications* table.

If a spring tester is not available, at least check the free length of each spring by standing it alongside a new spring. Any spring that does not conform to the pressure specifications within 10% should be replaced. Likewise, any spring that stands shorter than the new spring used for comparison should be discarded. Of course, cocked springs should also be scrapped.

VALVES, GRIND

New valve heads have a seat angle of 44 degrees to provide a hairline contact

between the head of the valve and the valve seat in the cylinder head which assures good seating of the valve and less chance of burning the valve head due to exhaust gas leakage. *Servicemen may, however, reface valves at a 45 degree angle.*

Valve seats should be cut so there is $\frac{1}{32}''$ from the outer edge of the seat to the edge of the flange on the valve head to allow heat to escape and to provide maximum life for newly ground valves.

Cars operated at moderate or slow speeds in city driving should have a valve seat width of $\frac{3}{64}''$ to $\frac{1}{16}''$. For cars driven a great deal at high speeds the seat width should be $\frac{1}{16}''$ to $\frac{3}{32}''$ to assure adequate cooling.

Test valves for concentricity with seats and for tight seating. Valves can be tested by lightly coating the valve face with prussian blue and turning the valve against its seat. This indicates whether the seat is concentric with the valve guide *but does not prove that the valve face is concentric with the valve stem, or that the valve is seating all around.* After making this test, wash all blue from the surfaces, lightly coat the *valve seat* with blue and repeat the test to see whether a full mark is obtained on the valve. Both tests are necessary to prove that a proper seat is being obtained.

HYDRAULIC VALVE LIFTERS
Fig. 7

Failure of a hydraulic valve lifter is generally caused by an inadequate oil supply or dirt. An air leak at the intake side of the oil pump or too much oil in the engine will cause air bubbles in the oil supply to the lifters, causing them to collapse. This is a probable cause of trouble if several lifters fail to function, but air in the oil is an unlikely cause of failure of a single unit.

Removing 1958-61 Lifters

The push rod holes in the engine block are large enough to permit the removal of the hydraulic lifters without removing the intake manifold. Therefore, when replacing hydraulic lifters in relatively new engines, or in those engines that have a minimum build-up of gum and varnish on the lifter body, do not remove the intake manifold. Instead, proceed as follows:

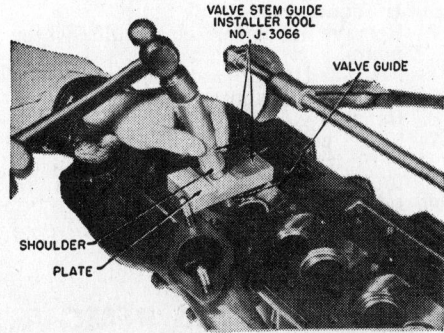

Fig. 5   Valve guides are correctly installed with tool shown

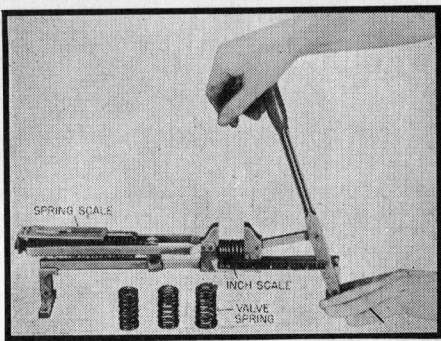

Fig. 6   Valve spring tester

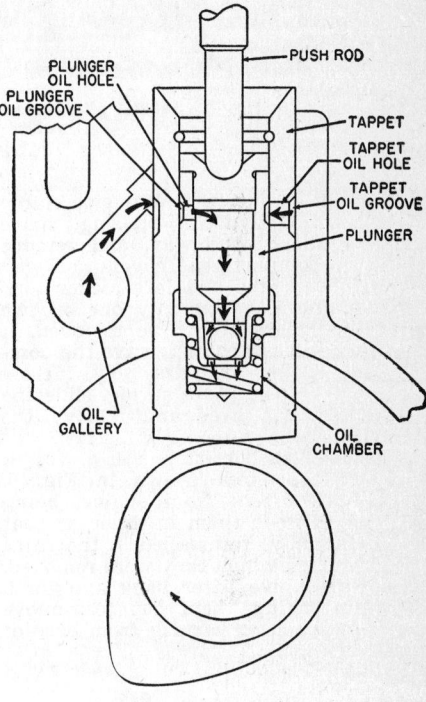

Fig. 7   Hydraulic valve lifter.   All models

1. Remove rocker arm cover.
2. Remove rocker arms. If rocker arm assemblies are to be disassembled, it is extremely important upon assembly that the large side of the rocker support bosses face the exhaust valve.
3. Remove push rods, keeping rods in order as they are removed.
4. With the aid of mechanical fingers or a magnet attached to a long rod, remove the lifters through the push rod openings.

Note: If, because of gum and varnish the lifters cannot be removed as outlined above, it will be necessary to follow the procedure outlined for earlier models.

Removing 1953-57 Lifters

1. Remove right and left rocker arm covers along with coil, high tension wiring, and bracket from cylinder heads and hang on cowl.
2. Remove intake manifold.
3. Remove three valve compartment cover screws.

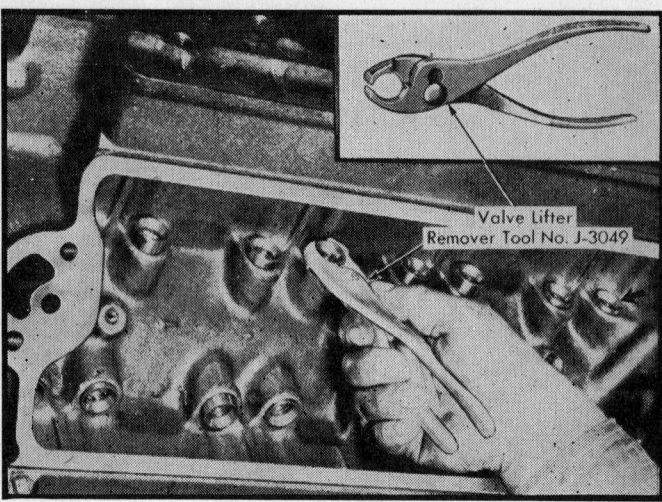

Fig. 8 Special pliers used to remove stuck valve lifters

4. Loosen engine ventilator pipe clamp screw at flywheel housing, move pipe out of the way, and remove valve compartment cover.
5. Remove right and left rocker arm assemblies. When only one or two valve lifters are to be removed, it is not necessary to remove the complete rocker arm assembly. Merely compress the valve spring, slide the rocker arm over and remove the push rod.
6. Remove push rods.
7. Using the tool shown in Fig. 8, remove lifters from engine, being sure to keep them in order so that they can be reinstalled in the same bore from which they were removed. Rotate valve lifter back and forth while lifting them out to remove any carbon or varnish from base of lifter.

Servicing Lifters

To disassemble, press down on the center of the push rod cup. Using a pointed tool, remove lock wire from the groove while holding cup down. Invert lifter and slide out push rod cup, plunger, ball retainer and spring.

To assemble, place the ball on its seat in the lower end of the plunger while holding the plunger upside down. Position the ball retainer and spring over ball and end of plunger. Lower the body over the plunger. Turn the assembly right side up and fill the plunger with clean engine oil. Jiggle the ball with a small piece of wire until oil drains out of plunger into the body and trapped air is released from the body. Refill the plunger with oil, place the push rod cup on the plunger and position the lock wire over the cup, locking it in its groove.

TIMING CHAIN & COVER

To remove the timing chain and sprockets, proceed as follows:
1. Turn engine over until distributor rotor is under the number six contact in the distributor cap.

2. Remove water pump and oil pan.
3. Remove crankshaft pulley.
4. Take off chain cover.
5. Remove two capscrews attaching sprocket to camshaft. Then remove chain together with camshaft sprocket.
6. Pull crankshaft sprocket.
7. To install the sprockets and chain, reverse the foregoing procedure, being sure to have the sprocket marks lined up as shown in Fig. 9 when the chain is installed.

VALVE TIMING DATA

Year	Model	Intake Opens①	Intake Closes②	Exhaust Opens③	Exhaust Closes④
1953	All	22	67	63	27
1954	All	22	67	63	27
1955	All	19	70	60	30
1956	All	22	67	63	27
1957	All	25	78	75	28
1958	All	27	75	73	29
1959	All	27	75	73	29
1960	All	27	75	73	29
1961	All	27	75	73	29

① —Degrees before top dead center.
② —Degrees after bottom dead center.
③ —Degrees before bottom dead center.
④ —Degrees after top dead center.

CAMSHAFT & BEARINGS

1. To remove the camshaft, remove hood lock plate support.
2. Remove Air Conditioning condenser (if equipped).
3. Remove radiator core and water pump.
4. Remove timing chain and sprockets.
5. Remove distributor.
6. Remove valve lifters.
7. Slide camshaft forward carefully until it is out of engine. Use care to avoid allowing cam lobes to scratch camshaft bushings.
8. Installation is made in the reverse order of removal.

PISTONS & RODS, REMOVE

After removing the cylinder head, examine the cylinder bores above the ring travel area. If bores are worn so that a shoulder or ridge exists at this point, remove the ridge with a ridge reamer to avoid damaging rings or cracking ring lands of pistons during removal.

Remove connecting rod caps and push the pistons and rods out of cylinders, using care to prevent rod bolts from contacting and nicking crankshaft journals.

Make sure that rods and pistons are properly numbered so that they can be reinstalled in original locations. It is advisable to install the caps on the rods to avoid mixing parts.

PISTONS & RODS, ASSEMBLE

On all engines, assemble and install the piston and rod assemblies as shown in Fig. 10.

PISTONS

Service replacement pistons are furnished by Cadillac in standard sizes and .010, .020 and .030 in. oversizes, with rings and pins fitted.

Before ordering pistons for replacement, it is extremely important to determine the size of the cylinder bores by actual measurement. Actual measurement at the time of replacement is the only certain way to avoid errors.

Where no micrometer or dial gauge is available to measure piston clearance, the use of a feeler gauge will serve satisfactorily as there is a definite relation between feeler gauge pull in pounds and micrometer clearance in thousandths of inches, as shown in Fig. 11, which is set up for .002, .0025 and .003 in. feeler gauge thickness.

In order to obtain the piston clearance at the upper end of the skirt, it is necessary to insert the piston into its upper extreme position, along with the

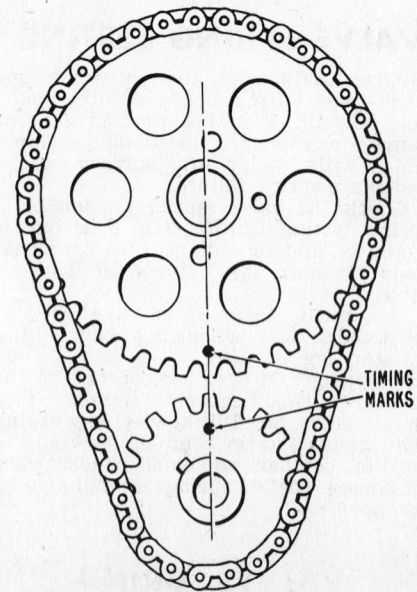

Fig. 9 Showing timing marks lined up for correct valve timing

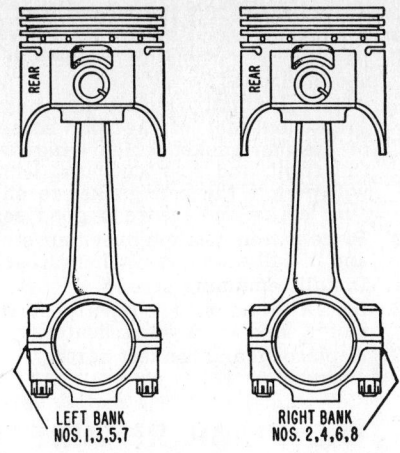

LEFT BANK
NOS. 1, 3, 5, 7

RIGHT BANK
NOS. 2, 4, 6, 8

Fig. 10 Connecting rods and pistons

feeler ribbon, which must be kept located over the vertical slot and not in excess of ½ in. below the upper end of the skirt. It is advisable to mark the feeler ribbon adjacent to the piston head so that its proper location on the piston can be maintained.   When the proper clearance is established, it should require the amount of pounds pull on the scale shown in Fig. 11 to withdraw the feeler, depending upon the thickness of the feeler ribbon being used.

Before a honing or boring operation is started, measure all new pistons with a micrometer at points exactly 90 degrees away from the piston pin (thrust side of piston). Then select the smallest piston for the first fitting. The slight variation usually found between pistons in a set may provide for correction in case the first piston is fitted too free.

It is important that refinished cylinder bores are trued up to have not over .0007 in. out-of-round or taper. Each bore must be final honed to remove all stone or cutter marks and provide a smooth surface. During final honing, each piston must be fitted individually to the bore in which it will be installed and should be marked to insure correct installation.

After final honing and before the piston is checked for fit, each bore must washed to remove all traces of abrasive and then dried thoroughly. The dry bore should be brushed clean with a power-driven fiber brush. If all traces of abrasive are not removed, rapid wear of new pistons and rings will result.

Both the piston and cylinder block must be at the same temperature (room temperature of 70 degrees) when the piston is checked for fit in the cylinder bore; therefore the cylinder should be allowed to cool after boring or honing and before the piston fit is checked. This is important because a difference of 10 degrees F. between parts is sufficient to produce a variation of .0005 in.

PISTON RINGS

When new piston rings are installed without reboring cylinders, the glazed cylinder walls should be slightly dulled, but without increasing the bores' diameter. This is done with a "Glazebuster"

or with a hone equipped with the finest grade of stones.

New piston rings must be checked for clearance in piston grooves and for gap in cylinder bores. Cylinder bores and piston grooves must be clean, dry and free of carbon and burrs.

Check the clearance of each ring in its piston groove by installing the ring and inserting feeler gauges *under* the ring. Any wear that occurs in the piston groove forms a step or ridge at the lower land. If gauges are inserted above the ring, the ring may rest on the step instead of on the worn portion of the lower land, and a false measurement of clearance will result.

If the piston grooves have worn to the extent that relatively high steps or ridges exist on the lower lands, the piston should be replaced because the steps will interfere with the operation of new rings and ring clearances will be excessive.. Piston rings are not furnished in oversize widths to compensate for ring groove wear.

See the *Piston and Ring Data* chart for end gap clearances.

To check the end gaps of piston rings, place the ring in the cylinder in which it will be used. Square it in the bore by tapping with the lower end of the piston, then measure the gap with feeler gauges. If necessary to increase the gap, file the ends of the ring carefully with a smooth file.

PISTON PINS

Piston pins are a matched fit with the piston and are not available separately. Piston pins are pressed in the connecting rods and will not become loose enough to cause a knock or tapping until after very high mileages. In such cases a new piston and pin assembly should be installed.

ROD BEARINGS

Connecting rod bearings are of the precision insert type, and if worn beyond .0045 in. can be replaced without removing the rod assembly by removing the cap and replacing the upper and lower halves. The clearance between the con-

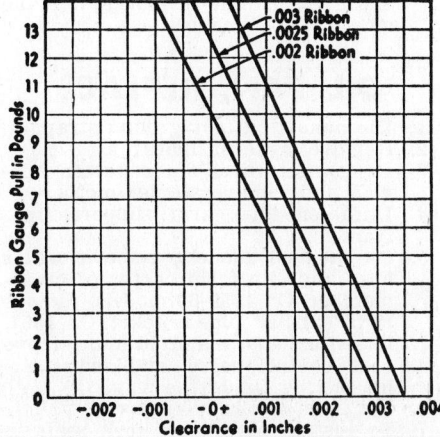

Fig. 11   Piston clearance chart

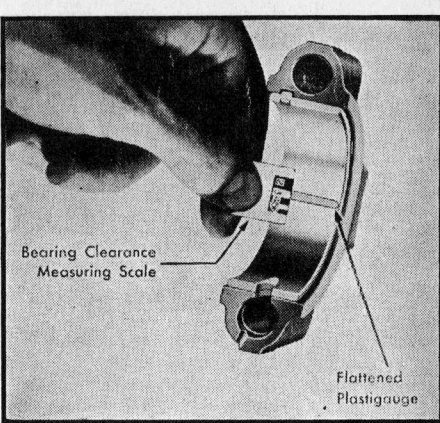

Bearing Clearance
Measuring Scale

Flattened
Plastigauge

**Fig. 12 Checking bearing clearance
with Plastigage**

necting rod bearing and the crankshaft can be measured by the use of Plastigage as follows:

1. Remove bearing cap and wipe oil from crankshaft journal and bearing insert.
2. With crankpin at approximately bottom dead center, place a piece of Plastigage in the center of the cap.
3. Reinstall cap and tighten to the torque value given in the *Engine Tightening Data* table.
4. Remove bearing cap and determine bearing clearance by comparing the width of the flattened Plastigage at its widest point with the graduation on the Plastigage envelope. The number within the graduation on the envelope indicates the clearance in thousandths of an inch, Fig. 12. If this clearance is greater than .0045 in., replace the bearing.

MAIN BEARINGS

Caution—Main bearing clearance can be checked with Plastigage in the same manner described for rod bearings. If bearings are measured with the engine in the chassis, the crankshaft must be supported in order to take up clearance between the upper bearing insert and crankshaft journal. This can be done by tightening bearing caps of adjacent bearings with .005″ to .015″ cardboard, (such as a calling card) between lower bearing shell and journal. Use extreme care when this is done to avoid unnecessary strain on the crankshaft or bearings or a false reading may be obtained. Do not rotate crankshaft while Plastigage is installed. *Be sure to remove cardboard.* To install new bearings, proceed as follows:

1. Remove bearing cap and worn lower shell.
2. Rotate crankshaft in normal direction to turn upper bearing shell out of crankcase. Use a cotter pin with a flattened head or the special tool made for the purpose in the crankshaft oil hole to contact the bearing and force it out.
3. Place a new upper shell on the crankshaft journal with the locating

notch in the correct position and rotate the shaft to turn the bearing in place.

4. Install the lower bearing shell in the cap.
5. Tighten all cap nuts to the torque value given in the *Engine Tightening Data* table.

CRANKSHAFT OIL SEAL

Braided Type, 1953-58

A braided oil seal is pressed into the upper and lower grooves behind the rear main bearing. Directly in front of this seal is an oil slinger which deflects the oil back into the oil pan. Should the braided seal require replacement, the installation of the lower half is accomplished as follows:

With the bearing cap and lower bearing half removed, install a new seal so that both ends protrude above the cap. Tap the seal down into position or roll it snugly in its groove with a smooth rounded tool. Then cut off the protruding ends of the seal with a sharp knife or razor blade, Fig. 13.

Installing Upper Seal

Although the usual practice is to remove the crankshaft when the upper half of the seal is to be replaced it is possible to do the job without removing the crankshaft as follows:

To remove the seal, use needle-nose pliers to grasp the end of the seal which is most accessible. Pull the seal downward while rotating the crankshaft slowly in the direction that the seal is being removed.

To install the new seal, fasten a length of wire or strong string such as fishing line securely to one end of the new seal. See that the point of fastening is not bulky and that it is not over ⅜" from the end of the seal. Coat the seal with Lubriplate. Pass the free end of the wire or string up over the crankshaft at the point where the seal is to be installed. Then exert a firm, steady pull on the wire or string and at the same time rotate the crankshaft slowly in the direction of the pull. This will help to move the seal into position. When the installation is completed, trim the ends of the seal flush with the engine block.

Lip Type Seal, 1958-61

After 1958 Engine No. 050909 a new lip type rear main bearing seal entered production. Due to differences in the groove in the main bearing cap and cylinder block, this new seal is *not* interchangeable with the earlier braided type. Replacement of the new lip type seal may be accomplished without removing the crankshaft, using the following procedure. The two seal halves are identical and can be used in either the upper or lower location.

1. Be sure grooves in bearing cap and block are clean, dry and free from burrs.
2. Start upper half of seal in block and rotate seal into position. Then press firmly on both ends of seal to be

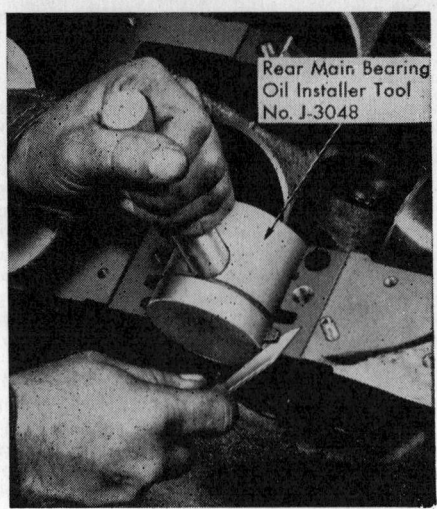

Fig. 13 Installing braided type rear main bearing oil seal. 1952-58

sure that it is protruding uniformly on each side.
3. Install lower half of seal into bearing cap with lip facing forward and with one end of seal over ridge and flush with split line. Hold one finger over this end to prevent it from slipping and push the seal into seated position by applying pressure to other end. Be sure seal is pressed down firmly and that it protrudes uniformly on each side. *Avoid pressing seal into position by applying pressure to the lip as damage to the sealing edge could result.*
4. Prior to assembly of main bearing cap on block, apply rubber cement to cap and block to act as a sealer, *being sure to keep the rubber cement off the seal lip and bearing surface to avoid damage to seal and engine.*
5. Lubricate lip of seal with thin film of engine oil.
6. Install bearing cap with screws finger tight. Then, using plastic hammer, drive crankshaft forward, then rearward, then forward again to assure proper alignment of bearing thrust faces.
7. Tighten bearing cap bolts to recommended torque. Then turn crankshaft at least one revolution to make sure it is not binding.

OIL PAN, REPLACE

1. Disconnect battery ground strap.
2. Remove oil level indicator.
3. Disconnect wires from starter solenoid and remove starter motor.
4. Unfasten idler arm support from frame.
5. On 1956-58 models, remove water hose and clip from center of crossmember. On 1959-60 models, remove right exhaust pipe bracket. On 1961, loosen exhaust manifold and remove heat control valve, and swing exhaust pipe out of the way.
6. Unfasten and remove pan.
7. To install, place new cork seals in rear main bearing cap and front cover, being sure ends of gaskets

are in recess provided for them.

8. Cement pan gaskets to both sides of pan, lining up holes in gaskets with those in pan.
9. Place a small amount of chassis grease on each of the four corners of the pan gasket which hang over the front and rear cut-outs, which will permit the pan gasket to slide over corks and insure a good seal.
10. Place pan in position over four studs and install nuts and washers loosely.
11. Install remaining screws.
12. Install idler arm support, starter motor, and oil level indicator.
13. Replace oil and connect battery.

OIL PUMP REPAIRS

1953 and 1959-61

To remove the pump, drain engine oil and remove oil pan. Unfasten pump from engine and disassemble as follows:

1. Remove oil pump float.
2. Remove oil pressure regulator valve and spring from pump body.
3. Remove pump bottom cover.
4. Slide idler gear out of pump body.
5. Remove pin from collar on end of drive shaft and press collar off of shaft.
6. Slide oil pump drive gear out of pump body.

Inspect strainer screen for dirt and float for leaks. Look for nicks or burrs on pressure regulator valve which might cause leaks or binding in pump body. Inspect pump gears for nicks and burrs. Inspect bottom cover for wear and dress down on a surface plate if necessary. Place bottom cover on pump and check drive shaft end play. If end play exceeds .006 in., replace drive and idler gears. Assemble and install oil pump in the reverse order of its removal and disassembly.

OIL & VACUUM PUMP REPAIRS

1954-58

The oil pump on these models is the same as past models except for the addition of a vacuum pump which is mounted on the bottom of the oil pump for windshield wiper operation. The Vacuum pump is the vane type and is driven by the oil pump through a hexagonal shaped drive key.

Vacuum Pump Test

Disconnect the vacuum pump hose leading from the crankcase at the check valve on the cowl. Connect a vacuum gauge to the vacuum pump hose and start the engine. If the vacuum pump is operating properly, the gauge will show a minimum of 20" mercury at sea level at 3600 rpm engine speed. If the gauge does not show this reading the pump is defective or there is a leak in the vacuum lines. If the vacuum does not increase after tightening the vacuum connections, replace the vacuum pump.

Vacuum Pump, Replace

Remove oil pan and baffle. Disconnect vacuum line at engine block. Unfasten the vacuum pump from the oil pump and remove the vacuum pump with the oil pump idler gear. Remove hexagonal drive shaft, and the vacuum line from the pump.

Installation is made in the reverse order.

RADIATOR, REPLACE

1953-54

Drain radiator and remove upper and lower hose. Remove capscrews holding radiator to support. Remove radiator anchor nut and spacers at frame bracket. Be sure to check the number of spacers removed and reinstall the same amount. Lift out radiator.

When radiator is installed, check space between radiator core and fan blade. This should be ½ to 1 inch and is important for efficient fan operation.

When replacing the radiator thermostat, be sure that the thermostatic spring strap is parallel to the centerline of the car (fore and aft). This will reduce the possibility of the right-hand bank running at a higher temperature than the left-hand bank.

Service Note

When it is necessary to remove both the radiator and water pump to perform other work on the engine, time will be saved if these parts are removed as a unit rather than as separate units, because of the difficulty of removing the upper and lower radiator hoses.

Drain cooling system and disconnect heater hose at water pump. Remove generator drive belt and all radiator and water pump attaching screws. Then lift the radiator and pump as an assembly.

On cars so equipped, it will also be necessary to remove the oil filter and/or power steering pumps from their brackets.

1955-57

To remove the radiator, drain cooling system and loosen upper and lower radiator hoses. On 1955-57 Air Conditioned equipped cars, remove condenser assembly. Remove six screws (also four spacers on Air Conditioned cars) which hold radiator to support. Lift out radiator with hoses.

When installed, the space between the radiator and the front edge of the fan blade assembly should be ½ to 1" for efficient fan operation.

1958-61 Standard Cars

1. Drain cooling system and disconnect hoses from radiator.
2. Disconnect two transmission fluid lines from radiator lower tank. Plug ends of lines to prevent loss of transmission fluid.
3. Unfasten and remove radiator from its cradle.

1958-60 Air Conditioned Cars

1. Drain cooling system and disconnect hoses from radiator.

2. Remove Freon hose retainer clip from right hand upper side of radiator cradle.
3. Unfasten condenser and dehydrator receiver from bracket on right and left sides of radiator. Access to lower screw on right side of radiator may be gained through grille.
4. Remove left tie bar between radiator cradle and hood lock plate.
5. On 1958, lift out condenser and dehydrator receiver assembly and swing to one side. Do not disconnect Freon lines, as flexible lines allow the condenser, with attachments, to be swung out over fender or out of the way. Remove six screws attaching radiator assembly and condenser brackets to radiator cradle and remove brackets.
6. On 1959 tilt condenser and dehydrator-receiver assembly forward, but do not disconnect Freon lines, as flexible line will allow the condenser, with attachments, to be moved out of the way.
7. Pull radiator forward until inlet and outlet necks clear radiator hoses and lift radiator up and out.
8. Reverse removal procedure to install the radiator. Then run engine long enough to pump coolant through entire system and check radiator and transmission fluid levels. On standard cars, it is important for efficient fan operation that radiator to fan clearance be ½" to 1".

1961 Air Conditioned Cars

1. Drain cooling system and disconnect radiator hose.
2. Disconnect two transmission cooler lines from the radiator lower tank, and plug ends of lines to prevent loss of transmission fluid.
3. Remove two top and two bottom cradle-to-shroud clamps, and push shroud away from radiator.
4. Remove radiator by lifting straight up.
5. Reverse removal procedure to install.

WATER PUMP, REPLACE

1961 Standard Cars

1. Drain cooling system and remove air cleaner.
2. Disconnect radiator and heater hoses.
3. Remove power steering and generator drive belts.
4. Disconnect throttle return spring and remove power steering pump bracket screws. Then move pump to one side without disconnecting hoses.
5. Remove attaching screws and pump from engine.
6. Reverse removal procedure to install pump.

1961 Air Conditioned Cars

1. Drain cooling system and remove air cleaner.
2. Disconnect radiator and heater hoses.
3. Remove Freon compressor, power steering pump and generator belts.
4. Remove fan and pulley.

5. Remove fan shroud.
6. Remove the two water pump-to-cylinder block screws that also retain the Freon compressor front mounting bracket to right upper and lower water pump flanges.
7. Remove Freon compressor front mounting bracket-to-cylinder head screw.
8. Remove remaining screws and lift off water pump.
9. Reverse removal procedure to install parts removed.

1958-60 Standard Cars

1. Drain cooling system.
2. Remove generator and power steering drive belts.
3. Disconnect throttle return spring, upper and lower hoses from radiator, and heater hoses from water pump.
4. Remove power steering pump and bracket and swing to one side (do not disconnect hoses).
5. Remove oil filter, disconnecting oil lines at filter.
6. Unfasten and remove water pump.

1958-60 Air Conditioned Cars

1. Drain cooling system.
2. Remove fan shroud (upper half on 1958).
3. Remove drive belts for Freon compressor, power steering pump and generator.
4. Disconnect upper and lower radiator hoses and heater hoses from water pump.
5. Remove power steering pump and bracket and swing to one side (do not disconnect hoses).
6. Disconnect throttle return spring and oil filter unit, disconnecting oil lines at filter.
7. Remove two water pump-to-cylinder block screws that also retain the Freon compressor front mounting bracket.
8. Remove Freon compressor front mounting bracket-to-cylinder block screw. Also on 1958, remove generator adjusting link-to-Freon compressor mounting bracket screw.
9. On 1958, loosen front Freon compressor adjusting link-to-mounting bracket screw, and swing lower portion of front mounting bracket toward right side of car.
10. Unfasten and remove fan and pulley.
11. Unfasten and remove water pump.

1958-60 Air Suspension Cars

Procedures for removing the water pump as outlined above may be followed as required. However, in order to move the power steering pump and air compressor out of the way, it will be necessary to disconnect the air lines from the air compressor.

1953-57

1. To remove the pump, drain cooling system.
2. Remove power steering pump drive belt (if equipped).
3. Remove drive belts.
4. Remove upper and lower radiator hoses and heater hoses from water pump.

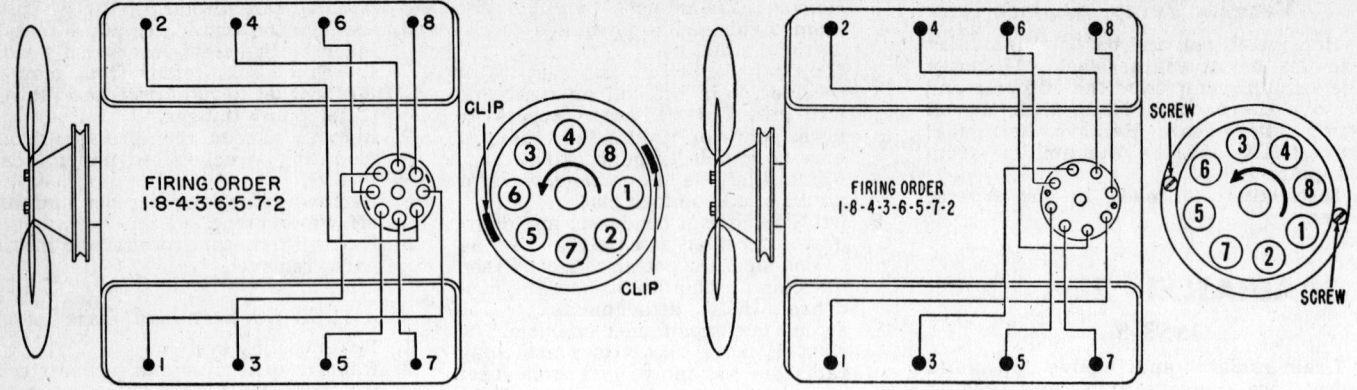

Fig. 14 Ignition details. 1953-55   **Fig. 15 Ignition details. 1956-61**

5. Remove power steering pump and bracket and place to one side (if equipped).
6. Unfasten and remove pump from engine.
7. On Air Conditioned cars, remove two screws which secure compressor mounting bracket to right upper and lower water pump flanges. Loosen compressor support-to-cylinder block screw and move support away from water pump. Then unfasten and remove water pump from engine.
8. Reverse the foregoing procedure to install the pump.

WATER PUMP REPAIRS

When disassembling the pump, note that the thermostat is installed with the element downward and that the jiggle valve on the thermostat hangs open, thus making it easier to fill the radiator.

To disassemble, remove the thermostat housing and lift the thermostat from the pump body. Remove the pulley, and take the bearing retainer ring from the pump body. Be careful not to compress the retainer too far as this will weaken it and possibly allow the ring to come out.

Take off the cover plate. Press the shaft, bearing, hub and slinger out of the impeller and pump body toward the fan pulley end. Remove the impeller from the body, and take out the wear washer, spring and seal from the body.

It should be noted that the wear washer contacts the pump body. It is extremely important that the face in the pump body that contacts this wear washer be free from nicks, burrs or ridges. A tool for refinishing this seat is available and must be used every time a new seal is installed.

Note, also, that a permanently sealed bearing is used at the front end of the pump body and is retained by a wire retaining ring. The bellows type seal that slides over the water pump shaft holds the wear washer against the pump body. This is held in position when the impeller is pressed on the rear end of the pump shaft.

To assemble the pump, press the shaft bearing hub and slinger assembly into the body, making sure it is pressed

against the end of the bearing bore in the body. Assemble the wear washer and seal over the driving lugs of the slinger from the rear side of the pump. It is important that the wear washer slides freely on the driving lug of the slinger, as any bind here will cause a leak.

Press the impeller on the shaft until the back of the impeller is .005 to .010" inside the cover face of the body but still does not touch the inner face. Be sure to support the opposite end of the shaft when pressing on the impeller to prevent damage to the housing and bearing.

DISTRIBUTOR, REPLACE

1. To remove the distributor, disconnect primary wire from coil.
2. Disconnect vacuum line from vacuum advance unit on distributor.
3. Crank engine until top dead center for No. 1 cylinder ("C" mark on vibration damper) is reached.
4. On 1956 remove distributor cap.
5. Remove distributor hold down nut and clamp.
6. Lift distributor from engine.

Service Note

The distributor rotor will turn slightly as the drive gear becomes disengaged from the teeth on the camshaft gear.

On cars prior to 1956, scribe a line on the edge of distributor cap, directly below the tip of the rotor. This will insure proper engagement of the drive gear teeth with the camshaft teeth to retain correct timing when reinstalling the distributor.

To retain correct timing on 1956, it is advisable to crank the engine until the copper contact on top of the rotor points directly to the rear of the engine before removing the distributor.

When the 1956 distributor is installed, fill the oiler tube with 10-W oil.

IGNITION TIMING

To set the timing, refer to Figs. 14 and 15 and proceed as follows:

1. Adjust distributor clamp nut to al-

low the distributor to be turned without excessive looseness.
2. Disconnect vacuum advance pipe to carburetor and place a piece of tape over end of pipe. *This is important as carburetor trouble can affect timing adjustments.*
3. Insert a rod or pin alongside No. 1 wire in distributor cap.
4. Connect a suitable timing light to the rod or pin.
5. Make certain that the timing marks and timing pointer are clean.
6. Start the engine and warm up to operating temperature, making sure the carburetor is on slow idle before proceeding.
7. Observe the timing light flashes on the timing marks in relation to the pointer. Rotate the distributor so that the light flashes as the pointer and chalk line are opposite each other. *In localities where gasoline of the required octane rating is not available, the ignition timing may be retarded toward the "C" line on the vibration damper to eliminate spark knock.*
8. Insert the rod or pin alongside No. 6 wire and note the chalk line with relation to the pointer when the light flashes. If the light flashes before or after the chalk line, set the distributor to divide the variance. If this variance is excessive, the distributor and its alignment should be checked.
9. Tighten the clamp nut to 15-18 lbs. ft. torque and recheck the timing to make sure it did not change.
10. Remove the tape from the carburetor pipe and connect the pipe. *Then if the timing advances with the engine idling, it is a fair indication that the throttle valves are open and the carburetor needs adjustment or repairs.*

STARTER, REPLACE

Remove battery cable at starter solenoid and starter button wire at solenoid terminals. Remove the two mounting bolts at flywheel housing and pull starter forward.

MUFFLER & PIPES, REPLACE

1952-58

To remove exhaust pipe raise front of car and disconnect steering connecting rod at pitman arm. On left side, remove slush deflector. To remove muffler, clear exhaust pipe in same manner and then disconnect rear muffler hanger from frame.

1959-61

Mufflers and pipes can be removed in the conventional manner.

Carburetor Section

Flooding, stumble on acceleration or other performance complaints are in many instances caused by the presence of dirt, water or other foreign matter in the carburetor. To aid in diagnosing the cause of the complaint, the carburetor should be carefully removed from the engine without draining the fuel from the bowl. The contents of the fuel bowl may then be examined for contamination as the carburetor is disassembled.

Check the fuel in the bowl for contamination by dirt, water, gum or other foreign matter. A magnet moved through the fuel in the bowl will pick up and identify any iron oxide dust that may have caused intake needle and seat leakage.

Inspect gasketed surfaces between body and air horn. Small nicks or burrs should be smoothed down to eliminate air or fuel leakage. On carburetors having a vacuum piston, be especially particular when inspecting the top surface of the inner wall of the bowl around the vacuum piston passage. A poor seal at this location may contribute to a "cutting-out" on turns complaint.

Fill the carburetor bowl with clean fuel before installing on manifold. This will help prevent dirt trapped in the fuel system from being dislodged by the free flow of fuel as the carburetor is primed.

The operation of the floats and intake needle and seats may be checked under pressure if a fuel pump is used at the bench to fill the carburetor bowl. Operate the throttle several times and visually check the discharge from pump jets.

Poor Mileage and Engine Loading Complaints

Cases of poor mileage and engine loading may be due in many instances to sluggish choke valve opening during cold driveaway, caused by insufficient vacuum in choke housing, a plugged or restricted heat pipe or inlet in choke cover. To check for this condition, have engine warm and running at slow idle. Remove choke heat pipe and hold a finger over the heat inlet hole (hole is on choke housing on some carburetors). If there is little or no vacuum pull on the finger, check the choke housing for gasket leaks or plugged vacuum passages. If these are OK, check choke vacuum passages in carburetor between choke housing and manifold.

Dirty or Rusty Choke Housing

In cases where it is found that the interior of the choke housing is dirty, gummed or rusty while the carburetor itself is comparatively clean, look for a punctured or eroded manifold heat tube (if one is used).

Manifold Heat Control Valve

An engine equipped with a manifold heat control valve can operate with the valve stuck in either the open or closed position. Because of this, an inoperative valve is frequently overlooked at vehicle lubrication or tune-up.

A valve stuck in the "heat-off" position can result in slow warm up, deposits in combustion chamber, carburetor icing, flat spots during acceleration, low gas mileage and spark plug fouling.

A valve stuck in the "heat-on" position can result in power loss, engine knocking, sticking or burned valves, and spark plug burning.

To prevent the possibility of a stuck valve, check and lubricate the valve each time the vehicle is lubricated or tuned-up. Check the operation of the valve manually. To lubricate the valve, place a few drops of penetrating oil on the valve shaft where it passes through the manifold. Then move the valve up and down a few times to work the oil in. *Do not use engine oil to lubricate the valve as it will leave a residue which hampers valve operation.*

CARTER NOTES

IDLE SPEED SETTING

1955-61—In making the idle adjustment on the engine, an air adjustment screw is used in a similar manner as the conventional throttle speed screw used on earlier models. The idle air screw is located in the throttle body and can be identified by it being larger than the idle mixture screws. Turning the air screw outward increases engine speeds but also leans the mixture. This must be compensated for by adjusting the idle mixture screws.

1960-61 With Cruise Control—Idle adjustment procedures are the same as outlined for earlier models. However, because of the vacuum-released parking brake, it is impossible to set the brake with the transmission selector in "Dr" position unless the vacuum release is disconnected. Therefore when adjusting idle speed (with selector lever in "Dr") it is necessary to disconnect temporarily the vacuum diaphragm at the neutral safety switch and tape the switch opening to prevent any air leak which would affect the idle adjustment.

AIR CONDITIONER FAST IDLE DEVICE

This adjustment must be made after the carburetor is installed, engine at normal operating temperature and slow idle adjustment is completed.

1953-61 (except 1958)—With shift lever in neutral and air conditioner turned on, engine should idle at 900 rpm (800 on 1953-54). To adjust, loosen lock nut on diaphragm shaft and adjust knurled nut as required.

1958—Place shift lever in drive range. Disconnect short wire from terminal at front of refrigeration compressor to stop compressor. Turn air conditioner on and turn temperature control switch toward cooler position. Loosen fast idle device lock nut on diaphragm shaft and turn knurled nut to idle engine at 525 rpm. Tighten lock nut and connect wire to compressor.

METERING ROD

WCFB—This adjustment must be made after the pump setting. Seat throttle valves in bores of carburetor and loosen metering rod arm clamp screw. With metering rods in place, press down on vacumeter link until metering rods bottom in casting. Holding rods down, revolve metering rod arm until finger on arm contacts lip of vacumeter link. Hold in place and tighten clamp screw.

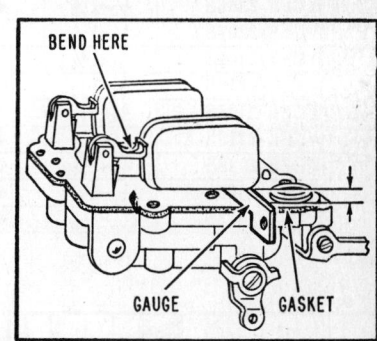

Fig. ①—AFB float level. Adjust by bending float lever.

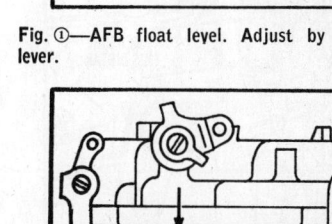

Fig. ②—AFB float drop. Adjust by bending stop tabs on float brackets.

CARTER CARBURETOR ADJUSTMENTS

Year	Carburetor Model	Idle Adjustments: Mixture Screws Turns Open	Idle Adjustments: Hot Idle Speed In Drive (11)	Idle Adjustments: Fast Idle Speed	Idle Adjustments: Dashpot Plunger Clearance	Float Level: Primary	Float Level: Secondary	Float Drop: Primary	Float Drop: Secondary	Pump Travel Setting	Choke Unloader Setting	Choke Setting
1961	AFB-	3/4–2 1/2	480(11)	1725(10)	(9)	3/8(1)	3/8(1)	13/16(2)	13/16(2)	15/32(3)	9/32(5)	Index
1960	AFB-2814S	1 1/4–2 3/4	480	1725(10)	(9)	5/16(1)	5/16(1)	23/32(2)	23/32(2)	15/32(3)	9/32(5)	Index
	AFB-2951S	1 1/4–2 3/4	480	1725(10)	(9)	5/16(1)	5/16(1)	23/32(2)	23/32(2)	15/32(3)	9/32(5)	Index
1959	AFB-2814S	1 1/4–2 3/4	450	1725(10)	(9)	5/16(1)	5/16(1)	23/32(2)	23/32(2)	15/32(3)	9/32(5)	Index
	AFB-2815S	1 1/4–2 3/4	450	1725(10)	(9)	5/16(1)	5/16(1)	23/32(2)	23/32(2)	15/32(3)	9/32(5)	Index
1958	AFB-2969S	3/4–2 1/4	450	1750(10)	(9)	5/16(1)	5/16(1)	23/32(2)	23/32(2)	15/32(3)	9/32(5)	Index
	AFB-2862S	3/4–2 1/4	450	1750(10)	(9)	5/16(1)	5/16(1)	23/32(2)	23/32(2)	15/32(3)	9/32(5)	Index
	AFB-2697S	3/4–2 1/4	450	1750(10)	(9)	5/16(1)	5/16(1)	23/32(2)	23/32(2)	15/32(3)	9/32(5)	Index
	AFB-2802S	3/4–2 1/4	450	1750(10)	(9)	5/16(1)	5/16(1)	23/32(2)	23/32(2)	15/32(3)	9/32(5)	Index
	AFB-2863S	3/4–2 1/4	450	1750(10)	(9)	5/16(1)	5/16(1)	23/32(2)	23/32(2)	15/32(3)	9/32(5)	Index
1957	AFB-2479S	3/4–2 1/4	420	1750(10)	(9)	5/16(1)	5/16(1)	23/32(2)	23/32(2)	15/32(3)	9/32(5)	Index
	AFB-2480S	3/4–2 1/4	420	1750(10)	(9)	5/16(1)	5/16(1)	23/32(2)	23/32(2)	15/32(3)	9/32(5)	Index
	WCFB-2690S	3/4–1 3/4	420	1750(10)	(9)	1/8(6)	1/4(6)	5/8(7)	3/4(7)	(8)	13/64(5)	Index
	WCFB-2691S	3/4–1 3/4	420	1750(10)	(9)	1/8(6)	1/4(6)	5/8(7)	3/4(7)	(8)	13/64(5)	Index
	WCFB-2692S	3/4–1 3/4	420	1750(10)	(9)	1/8(6)	1/4(6)	5/8(7)	3/4(7)	(8)	13/64(5)	Index
	WCFB-2582S	3/4–1 3/4	420	1750(10)	(9)	1/8(6)	1/4(6)	5/8(7)	3/4(7)	(8)	13/64(5)	Index
	WCFB-2583S	3/4–1 3/4	420	1750(10)	(9)	1/8(6)	1/4(6)	5/8(7)	3/4(7)	(8)	13/64(5)	Index
	WCFB-2584S	3/4–1 3/4	420	1750(10)	(9)	1/8(6)	1/4(6)	5/8(7)	3/4(7)	(8)	13/64(5)	Index
1956	WCFB-2543S	1–2	420	1700(10)	(9)	1/8(6)	3/16(6)	5/8(7)	11/16(7)	(4)	13/64(5)	1 Lean
	WCFB-2544S	1–2	420	1700(10)	(9)	1/8(6)	3/16(6)	5/8(7)	11/16(7)	(4)	13/64(5)	1 Lean
	WCFB-2545S	1–2	420	1700(10)	(9)	1/8(6)	3/16(6)	5/8(7)	11/16(7)	(4)	13/64(5)	1 Lean
	WCFB-2333S-A	1 3/4–2 3/4	420	1700(10)	(9)	1/8(6)	3/16(6)	5/8(7)	11/16(7)	(4)	13/64(5)	1 Lean
	WCFB-2334S-A	1 3/4–2 3/4	420	1700(10)	(9)	1/8(6)	3/16(6)	5/8(7)	11/16(7)	(4)	13/64(5)	1 Lean
	WCFB-2370S-A	1 3/4–2 3/4	420	1700(10)	(9)	1/8(6)	3/16(6)	5/8(7)	11/16(7)	(4)	13/64(5)	1 Lean
	WCFB-2371S	3/4–1 3/4	420	1700(10)	(9)	1/8(6)	3/16(6)	5/8(7)	11/16(7)	(4)	13/64(5)	Index
	WCFB-2372S	3/4–1 3/4	420	1700(10)	(9)	1/8(6)	3/16(6)	5/8(7)	11/16(7)	(4)	13/64(5)	Index
	WCFB-2373S	3/4–1 3/4	420	1700(10)	(9)	1/8(6)	3/16(6)	5/8(7)	11/16(7)	(4)	13/64(5)	Index
1955	WCFB-2185S	1/2–1 1/2	400	1700(10)	None	1/8(6)	3/16(6)	5/8(7)	11/16(7)	(4)	13/64(5)	1 Lean
	WCFB-2186S	1/2–1 1/2	400	1700(10)	None	1/8(6)	3/16(6)	5/8(7)	11/16(7)	(4)	13/64(5)	1 Lean
	WCFB-2255S	1/2–1 1/2	400	1700(10)	None	1/8(6)	3/16(6)	5/8(7)	11/16(7)	(4)	13/64(5)	1 Lean
	WCFB-2266S	1/2–1 1/2	400	1700(10)	None	1/8(6)	3/16(6)	5/8(7)	11/16(7)	(4)	13/64(5)	1 Lean
	WCFB-2267S	1/2–1 1/2	400	1700(10)	None	1/8(6)	3/16(6)	5/8(7)	11/16(7)	(4)	13/64(5)	1 Lean
1954	WCFB-2109S	3/4–1 3/4	400	1700(10)	None	1/8(6)	3/16(6)	5/8(7)	11/16(7)	(4)	3/16(5)	Index
	WCFB-2110S	3/4–1 3/4	400	1700(10)	None	1/8(6)	3/16(6)	5/8(7)	11/16(7)	(4)	3/16(5)	Index
1953–54	WCFB-2143S	3/4–1 3/4	400	1700(10)	(9)	1/8(6)	3/16(6)	5/8(7)	11/16(7)	(4)	3/16(5)	Index
1953	WCFB-2119S-A	3/4–1 3/4	400	1700(10)	(9)	1/8(6)	3/16(6)	5/8(7)	11/16(7)	(4)	3/16(5)	Index
	WCFB-2088S	3/4–1 3/4	400	1700(10)	(9)	1/8(6)	3/16(6)	5/8(7)	11/16(7)	(4)	3/16(5)	Index
	WCFB-2005S-A	1 1/4–2 1/4	400	1700(10)	None	1/8(6)	3/16(6)	5/8(7)	11/16(7)	(4)	3/16(5)	Index
	WCFB-2072S	1 1/4–2 1/4	400	1700(10)	None	1/8(6)	3/16(6)	5/8(7)	11/16(7)	(4)	3/16(5)	Index

CARTER NOTES Continued

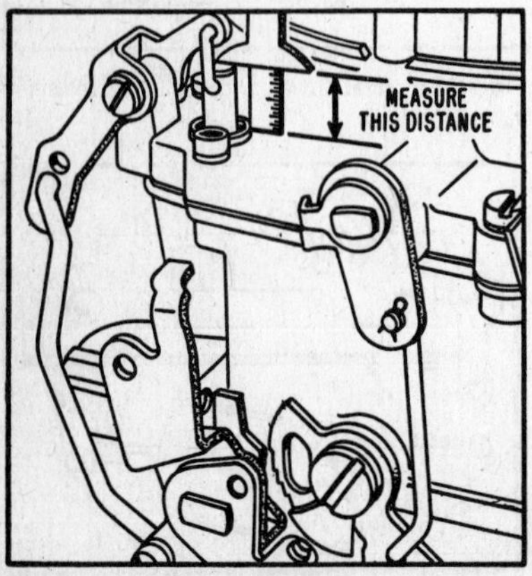

Fig. (3)—Measure from top of float bowl cover to top of plunger shaft with throttle connector rod in inner hole of pump arm. Adjust by bending throttle connector rod.

(4)—Same as (8) except pump connector link is placed in outer hole of pump arm.

Fig. (5)—With throttle valve wide open, clearance between upper edge of choke valve and inner wall of air horn should be as specified. Adjust by bending unloader lip on throttle shaft lever.

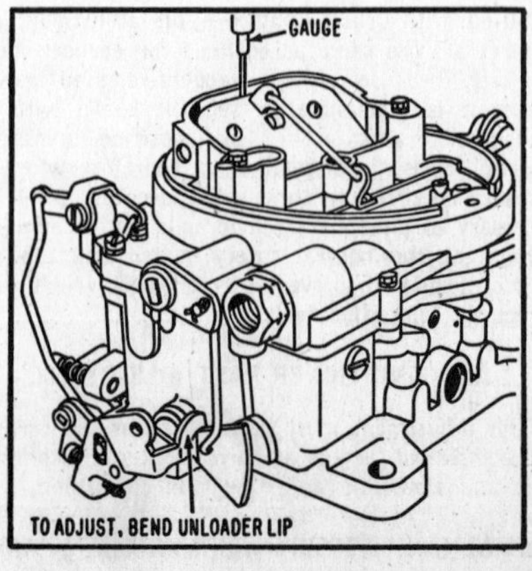

CARTER NOTES
Continued

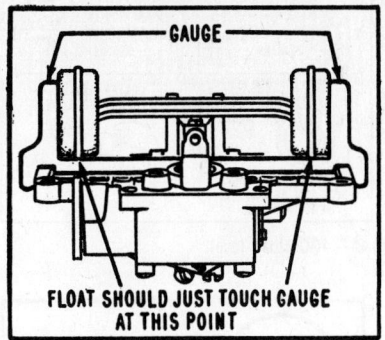

Fig. ⑥—WCFB float level. Adjust by bending float arms.

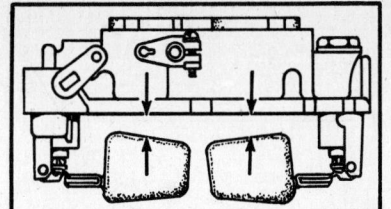

Fig. ⑦—WCFB float drop. Adjust by bending stop tabs on float bracket.

Fig. ⑧—With pump connector link in inner hole of pump arm, flat on pump arm should be parallel with a straightedge placed on dust cover boss. Adjust by bending throttle connector rod.

⑨—With engine running at hot idle speed, open throttle wide momentarily and allow plunger to come out. Let throttle snap shut. If engine races plunger is too long; if engine stalls plunger is too short. Adjust for best results.

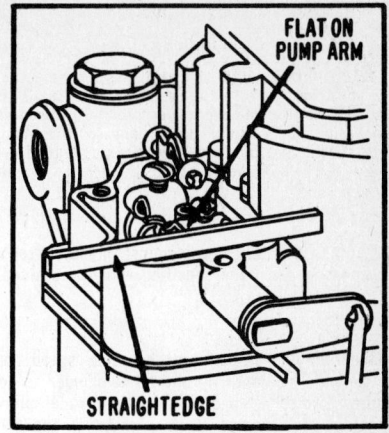

⑩—With engine running at normal operating temperature, turn fast idle screw against high step of fast idle cam or at index mark until specified rpm is obtained.

⑪—See special note regarding this adjustment.

ROCHESTER CARBURETOR ADJUSTMENTS

| Year | Carburetor Model | Idle Adjustments | | | | Float Level | | Float Drop | | Pump Rod Setting | Choke Unloader Setting | Choke Setting |
		Mixture Screws Turns Open	Hot Idle Speed In Drive ⑭	Fast Idle Speed	Dashpot Plunger Clearance	Primary	Secondary	Primary	Secondary			
1961	4GC-	1½-2½	480	1725①	②	9/32③	1⅜④	1½⑤	1 5/16⑥	29/32⑦	⅛⑧	1 Rich
1959-60	4GC-7013030	1½	480⑨	1700①	②	15/64③	1⅜④	1 13/16⑤	1 5/16⑥	27/32⑦	⅛⑧	1 Rich
1959-60	4GC-7013031	1½	480⑨	1700①	②	15/64③	1⅜④	1 13/16⑤	1 5/16⑥	27/32⑦	⅛⑧	1 Rich
1958	4GC-7012010	1½	450	1700①	②	.236⑩	1⅜⑩	1½⑤	1 5/16⑥	29/32⑦	⅛⑧	1 Rich
	4GC-7012011	1½	450	1700①	②	.236⑩	1⅜⑩	1½⑤	1 5/16⑥	29/32⑦	⅛⑧	1 Rich
	4GC-7012910	1½	450	1700①	②	.236⑩	1⅜⑩	1½⑤	1 5/16⑥	29/32⑦	⅛⑧	1 Rich
	4GC-7012811	1½	450	1700①	②	.236⑩	1⅜⑩	1½⑤	1 5/16⑥	29/32⑦	⅛⑧	1 Rich
1957	4GC-7010100	1½	420	1700①	②	1⅜④	1⅜④	1 13/16⑫	1 13/16⑫	15/16⑦	⅛⑧	Index
	4GC-7010101	1½	420	1700①	②	1⅜④	1⅜④	1 13/16⑫	1 13/16⑫	15/16⑦	⅛⑧	Index
	4GC-7012000	1½	420	1700①	②	1⅜④	1⅜④	1 13/16⑫	1 13/16⑫	15/16⑦	⅛⑧	Index
	4GC-7012001	1½	420	1700①	②	1⅜④	1⅜④	1 13/16⑫	1 13/16⑫	15/16⑦	⅛⑧	Index
1956	4GC-7008750	1½	420	1700①	②	1 19/32⑪	1 19/32⑪	2¼⑬	2¼⑬	1 1/16⑦	⅛⑧	Index
	4GC-7008751	1½	420	1700①	②	1 19/32⑪	1 19/32⑪	2¼⑬	2¼⑬	1 1/16⑦	⅛⑧	Index
	4GC-7009750	1½	420	1700①	②	1 19/32⑪	1 19/32⑪	2¼⑬	2¼⑬	1 1/16⑦	⅛⑧	Index
	4GC-7009751	1½	420	1700①	②	1 19/32⑪	1 19/32⑪	2¼⑬	2¼⑬	1 1/16⑦	⅛⑧	Index
1955	4GC-7007970	1½	400	1700①	None	1 19/32⑪	1 19/32⑪	2¼⑬	2¼⑬	63/64⑦	⅛⑧	Index
	4GC-7007971	1½	400	1700①	None	1 19/32⑪	1 19/32⑪	2¼⑬	2¼⑬	63/64⑦	⅛⑧	Index
	4GC-7009070	1½	400	1700①	None	1 19/32⑪	1 19/32⑪	2¼⑬	2¼⑬	63/64⑦	⅛⑧	Index
	4GC-7009071	1½	400	1700①	None	1 19/32⑪	1 19/32⑪	2¼⑬	2¼⑬	63/64⑦	⅛⑧	Index
1954	4GC-7006220	1½	400	1700①	None	1 19/32⑪	1 19/32⑪	2¼⑬	2¼⑬	15/16⑦	⅛⑧	Index
	4GC-7006221	1½	400	1700①	None	1 19/32⑪	1 19/32⑪	2¼⑬	2¼⑬	15/16⑦	⅛⑧	Index
	4GC-7006962	1½	400	1700①	None	1 19/32⑪	1 19/32⑪	2¼⑬	2¼⑬	15/16⑦	⅛⑧	Index
	4GC-7006963	1½	400	1700①	None	1 19/32⑪	1 19/32⑪	2¼⑬	2¼⑬	15/16⑦	⅛⑧	Index
1953	4GC-7005100	1½	400	1700①	None	1 9/16⑪	1 9/16⑪	2¼⑬	2¼⑬	15/16⑦	.067⑧	1 Rich
	4GC-7006215	1½	400	1700①	None	1 9/16⑪	1 9/16⑪	2¼⑬	2¼⑬	15/16⑦	.067⑧	1 Rich

ROCHESTER NOTES

IDLE SPEED SETTING

1955-61—In making the idle adjustment on the engine, an air adjustment screw is used in a similar manner as the conventional throttle speed screw used on earlier models. The idle air screw is located in the throttle body and can be identified by it being larger than the idle mixture screws. Turning the air screw outward increases engine speeds but also leans the mixture. This must be compensated for by adjusting the idle mixture screws. Idle adjustment must be made with the selector lever in "Dr".

1960-61 With Cruise Control—Adjustment procedures are the same as outlined above. However, because of the vacuum-released parking brake, it is impossible

ROCHESTER NOTES
Continued

to set the brake with the transmission selector in "Dr" position unless the vacuum release is disconnected. It is therefore necessary to disconnect temporarily the vacuum diaphragm at the neutral safety switch and tape the switch opening to prevent any air leak, which would affect the idle adjustment.

①—Turn fast idle screw against highest step on fast idle cam until the specified rpm is obtained.

②—With engine running at hot idle speed, open throttle wide momentarily and allow plunger to come out. Let throttle snap shut. If engine races plunger is too long; if engine stalls plunger is too short. Adjust for best results.

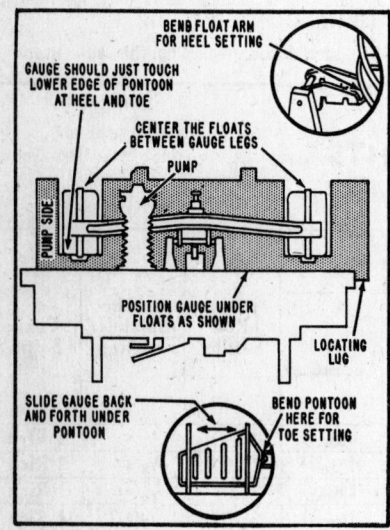

Fig. ③—4GC float level.

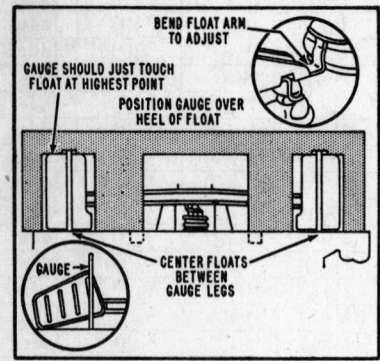

Fig. ④—4GC float level.

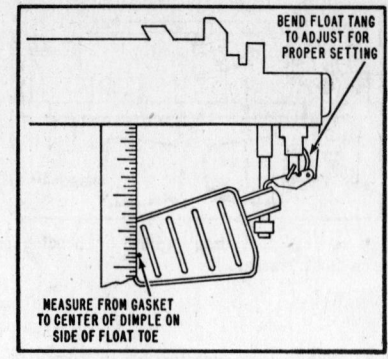

Fig. ⑤—4GC float drop.

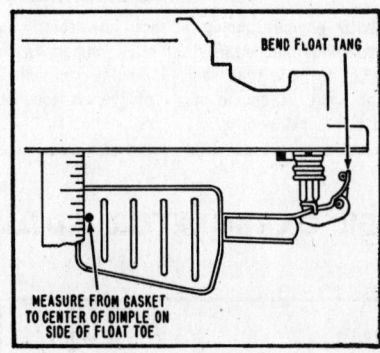

Fig. ⑥—4GC float drop.

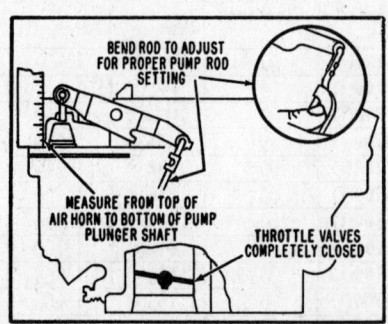

Fig. ⑦—With throttle valves closed, measure from top of air horn casting to bottom of pump plunger shaft. Adjust by bending pump rod.

⑧—Bend unloader tang on fast idle cam to obtain specified clearance between edge of choke valve and dividing air horn wall with throttle valves wide open.

⑨—450 rpm for 1959 models.

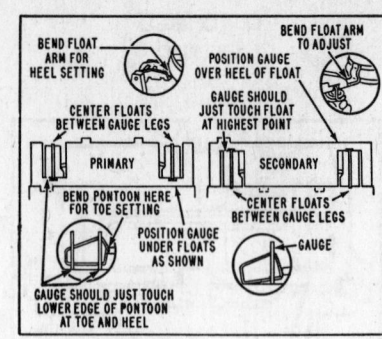

Fig. ⑩—4GC float level.

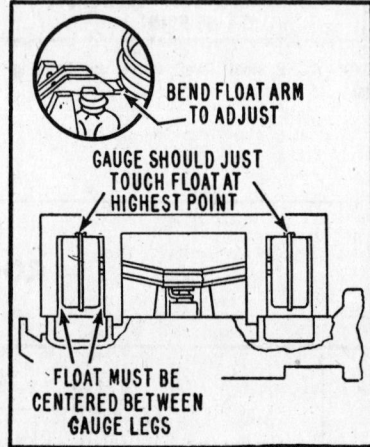

Fig. ⑪—4GC float level.

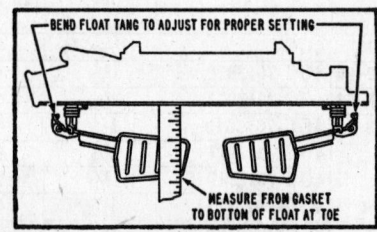

Fig. ⑫—4GC float drop.

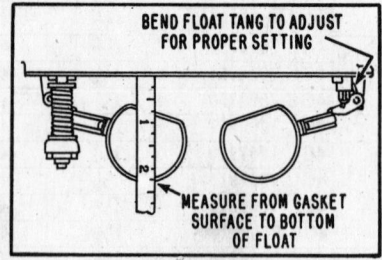

Fig. ⑬—4GC float drop.

⑭—See special note regarding this adjustment.

Hydra-Matic Transmission Section

HYDRA-MATIC DRIVE

Manual Linkage, 1953-55

Fig. 1. Disconnect manual control rod from control lever at transmission. Move the control lever at the transmission to its normal drive position. The drive position can be found by moving the manual lever at the transmission fully forward and upward and then moving it rearward until the first detent is felt. Move the lever to the "DR-4" (left hand arrow) position.

Adjust the clevis pin the lower end of the control rod until the clevis pin can be inserted freely through the clevis and manual control lever. Assemble clevis, pin and lever and install cotter pin.

Manual Linkage, 1956-60

1. Loosen adjusting nuts on transmission manual rod and back off about 1", Fig. 2.
2. Place manual lever on transmission fully forward to Park position.
3. Place selector lever on steering column in Park position.
4. Slide clevis on manual lever along manual rod in the direction of steering column until all slack in linkage is taken up. *If clevis contacts upper*

adjusting nut before all slack is taken up, the nut should be backed of still further.

5. Tighten lower adjusting nut with fingers against clevis to further remove slack. Bring upper adjusting nut down to contact clevis and tighten with wrench.
6. Check manual selector lever in car. It should be free to enter the Park position, and the Dr-4 stop in the steering column should correspond to the Dr-4 detent position in the transmission. Readjust if these conditions are not met.
7. Check to see that the indicator pointer indexes to the Dr-4 position when selector lever is at Dr-4 stop. Adjust if necessary.

Manual Linkage, 1961

1. Remove slush deflector.
2. Remove clevis from manual lever on transmission.
3. Loosen adjusting nuts on transmission manual rod.
4. Place manual lever on transmission in DR-4 position.
5. Place selector lever on steering column in DR-4 position.
6. Adjust length of manual rod until hole in manual lever lines up with

hole in clevis and then *increase length one more turn.*

7. Install clevis and tighten adjusting nuts.
8. Check manual selector lever; it should be free to enter "Park" position, and DR-4 stop in steering column should correspond to DR-4 detent position in transmission. Readjust if these conditions are not met.

Throttle Linkage, 1953-54

To adjust the throttle control linkage, Fig. 1, remove the transmission throttle lever clevis pin and check the lever position with Throttle Lever Checker Tool No. J-3065, by fitting the tool to the rear face of the transmission case and inserting the clevis pin through the lever and the hole in the tool while the lever is in its rearward position. If the throttle lever is misaligned, bring it into alignment by bending with Throttle Lever Bending Tool No. J-2029. Then adjust the throttle control as follows:

1. Assemble linkage to transmission throttle lever and install a new cotter.
2. Remove spring clip from carburetor-to-dash relay rod trunnion at relay and remove trunnion from dash relay lever.

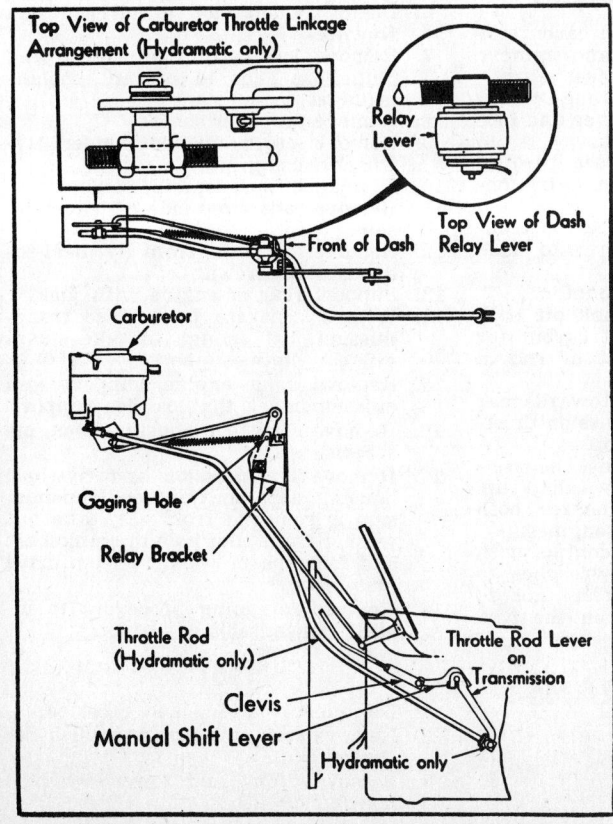

Fig. 1 1952-55 Hydra-Matic throttle linkage

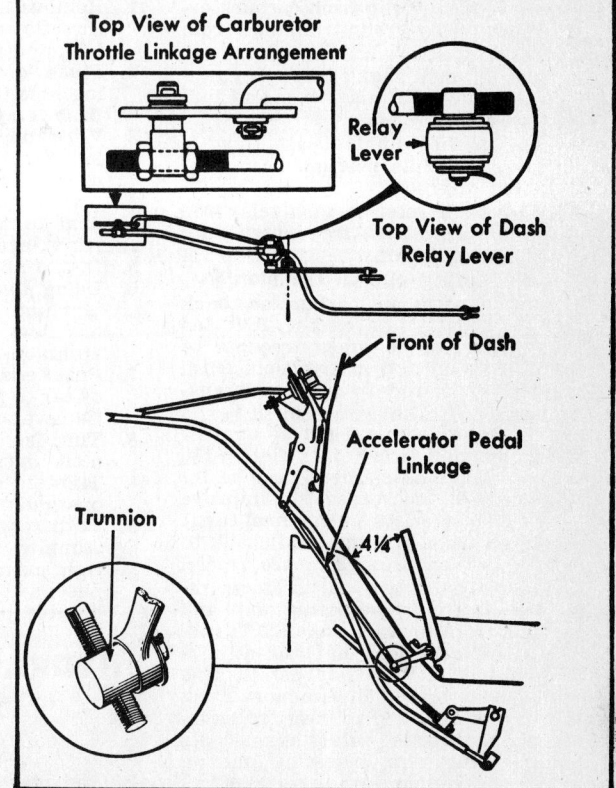

Fig. 2 Manual and throttle control linkage. 1956-61

3. Place ¼" drill shank through hole in dash relay lever and into dash relay bracket.
4. Set carburetor throttle in hot idle position.
5. Adjust carburetor-to-dash relay rod trunnion to allow it to enter freely into dash relay lever.
6. Install spring clip in trunnion.
7. Back off both jam nuts on throttle rod on carburetor to allow free movement of rod in trunnion.
8. Push on end of throttle rod to position transmission throttle valve against its stop.
9. Bring rear jam nut up against trunnion and back off two complete turns.
10. Tighten front jam nut, making certain linkage moves freely.
11. Remove ¼" drill shank from dash relay and check wide open throttle position of accelerator pedal. Pedal should just touch floor mat (allow ½" clearance if mat has been removed) when throttle is wide open.
12. Adjust accelerator pedal position at pedal end of dash relay-to-accelerator pedal rod.

Throttle Linkage, 1955

1. Using Fig. 1 as a guide, remove throttle control clevis pin and check lever position with Tool No. J-3065-C by fitting tool to rear face of transmission case and inserting clevis pin through lever and "49 E 50" hole in tool while lever is in rearward position. If throttle lever is misaligned, correct by bending with Tool J-3310.
2. Assemble linkage to transmission throttle lever and install cotter pin.
3. Remove spring clip from carburetor-to-dash relay rod trunnion from relay lever.
4. Place ¼" drill shank through gauging hole in dash relay lever and into dash relay bracket.
5. With engine running, set throttle lever in hot idle position (Air Conditioner off).
6. Adjust carburetor-to-dash relay rod trunnion to allow free entry into dash relay lever.
7. Install spring clip in trunnion.
8. On cars with one carburetor, back off both jam nuts on the T.V. rod at carburetor to allow freedom of movement of rod in trunnion. Push end of T.V. rod to position transmission throttle valve against its stop. Bring rear jam nut up against trunnion and back off 8 flats (1⅓ turn). (This adjustment may be increased or decreased to improve shift characteristics after road test.) Tighten front jam nut, and check to make certain linkage moves freely.
9. On cars with two carburetors, remove lock nut, adjusting nut and spring from forward end of T.V. rod. Back off rear lock nut and adjusting nut on T.V. rod to permit free movement of rod in trunnion. Push on end of T.V. rod to position transmission throttle valve against its stop. Bring rear adjusting nut up against trunnion and back off 3 complete turns. Tighten rear lock nut. Install spring and adjusting

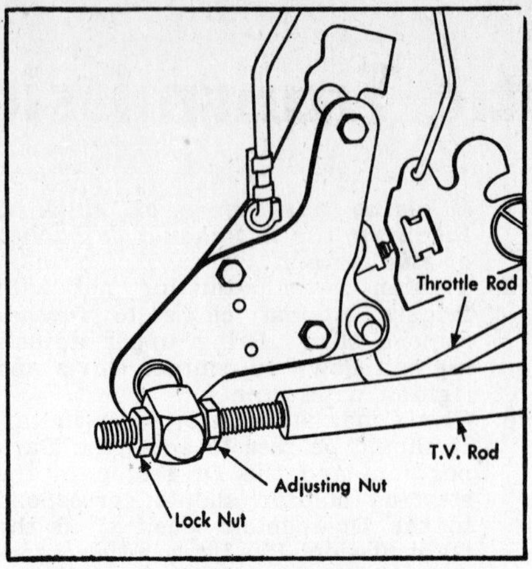

Fig. 3 T.V. rod adjustment. 1956. Typical of 1957-61

nut on front end of T.V. rod. Adjust nut until distance between front face of trunnion and rear face of adjusting nut is 1$\frac{1}{32}$". Install lock nut against front end of adjusting nut.
10. Continue on all cars by removing ¼" drill. Accelerator pedal should touch floor mat with slight pressure (allow ½" clearance if mat has been removed), when throttle is wide open.
11. Adjust accelerator pedal position at pedal end of dash relay-to-accelerator pedal rod.
12. Road test car to insure proper shifting characteristics.

Throttle Linkage, 1956-61

1. Remove spring clip from carburetor throttle rod trunnion and remove trunnion from relay bracket lever.
2. Place ¼" drill shank through gauging hole in dash relay lever and into dash relay bracket, Fig. 2.
3. With engine running, set throttle lever in hot idle position (Air Conditioner off).
4. Adjust carburetor throttle rod trunnion to allow free entry into dash relay lever.
5. Install spring clip in trunnion.
6. Using two wrenches, back off both jam nuts on T.V. rod at carburetor to allow free movement of rod in trunnion, Fig. 3.
7. Push end of T.V. rod toward rear of car to position transmission throttle lever against its stop.
8. Turn front jam nut against the trunnion until all slack is taken up. Tighten nut 3 full turns for both one and two-carburetor engines.
9. Turn rear jam nut into contact with trunnion and use two wrenches to tighten nuts, being careful not to put any binding force on the carburetor plate.

HYDRA-MATIC TRANS., REPLACE

1953-55

1. Remove propeller shaft.
2. Disconnect battery and remove starter.
3. On 1955 models, remove flywheel housing front cover.
4. If equipped with oil cooler, disconnect hoses and plug hose ends to prevent loss of coolant.
5. Remove slush deflector.
6. On models prior to 1955, remove flywheel housing lower cover.
7. Drain transmission at oil pan and torus cover.
8. Support rear of engine with a jack.
9. Remove filler tube from transmission oil pan.
10. With a separate jack, raise transmission just enough to take strain off rear engine support.
11. Disconnect rear engine support from extension housing. Remove cross member that carries support.
12. Remove control rods from side of transmission.
13. Disconnect speedometer cable.
14. Unfasten and remove torus cover from flywheel.
15. Lower jack under engine to gain access to the upper flywheel housing-to-engine bolts, and remove bolts.
16. Remove transmission and flywheel housing as a unit.
17. Reverse the foregoing procedure to install the transmission.

1959-60

1. Disconnect battery.
2. On 1957-60, remove transmission filler pipe bracket bolt from right cylinder head.
3. Remove starter motor.
4. Slide filler pipe out of sleeve in transmission case.
5. Remove lower flywheel housing front cover.
6. Drain transmission at oil pan and flywheel.
7. Remove hoses from oil cooler and plug hose ends to prevent coolant leakage.
8. Remove propeller shaft.
9. Remove cross member under flywheel housing.
10. Disconnect speedometer cable.
11. Remove rods from side of transmission.
12. Remove four nuts from flywheel-to-drive plate screws.
13. Support rear of engine with jack.
14. With a separate jack, raise transmission just enough to take strain off rear engine support.
15. Remove rear engine support and cross member that carries support.
16. Remove flywheel housing-to-engine screws.
17. Remove transmission and flywheel housing as a unit. When transmission is removed from car, take out washer from pilot hole in crankshaft and four spacer washers from drive plate screws.
18. Reverse foregoing procedure to install transmission.

1961

1. Disconnect battery and raise car.
2. Remove starter motor and slush deflector.
3. Remove front and lower flywheel housing covers.
4. Drain transmission and torus cover.
5. Remove transmission filler pipe

bracket bolt from right cylinder head.
6. Slide filler pipe out of sleeve in transmission.
7. Disconnect brake cables from parking brake relay lever. Remove retracting spring and remove relay from frame.
8. Remove propeller shaft.
9. Remove intermediate frame crossmember from below flywheel housing.

10. Disconnect speedometer cable.
11. Disconnect TV and manual rods.
12. Remove four nuts from flywheel-to-drive plate screws.
13. Support engine with jack under oil pan.
14. Raise transmission enough to take strain off rear engine support.
15. Disconnect rear engine mount at transmission extension housing.
16. Remove six screws and remove rear engine support from frame.
17. Disconnect oil cooler pipes from

adapter on transmission case.
18. Remove six screws holding flywheel housing to engine.
19. Remove transmission and flywheel housing as a unit by moving assembly toward rear of car, disengaging flywheel housing from locating dowels on engine, and then tilting front of unit downward to lower it from car. Remove washer from pilot hole in crankshaft.
20. Reverse removal procedure to install transmission.

Rear Axle and Brake Section

Refer To Hydraulic Brakes Chapter For Brake Adjustments

REAR AXLE

To remove the differential carrier assembly, disconnect the rear universal joint and remove the axle shaft as described further on. Remove the cap screws holding the carrier to the axle housing and take out the carrier.

Note — Any service on the differential carrier should be made by replacement of the complete assembly. Cadillac does not recommend any disassembly or adjustments of this unit.

Note—In case of lubricant seepage between the differential carrier and the axle housing, first make sure that the cap screws are tightened to the recommended tension of from 30 to 35 pounds feet. If this does not stop the leakage, install an extra gasket, using a good sealing compound. The additional cushioning effect of the extra gasket will prevent further seepage.

AXLE SHAFT, REPLACE

1. Remove road wheel.
2. Remove two screws holding brake drum to axle shaft flange and remove drum.
3. Remove nuts and washers holding bearing retainer and backing plate to axle housing.
4. Install axle shaft puller on axle shaft studs and, using a slide hammer, remove axle shaft.

Service Note

Before installing an axle shaft after an oil seal has been replaced, inspect rear wheel bearings for loss of lubricant, since a leaky oil seal may have permitted differential lubricant to "wash out" grease in the sealed wheel bearing. A wheel bearing that spins freely indicates a lack of grease and should be replaced at the same time a new oil seal is installed.

BRAKE MASTER CYLINDER, REPLACE

1953-55

1. To remove the cylinder, remove splash shield from flywheel housing.
2. Disconnect brake line at front of master cylinder, and on 1954-55 models, loosen remote filler reservoir pipe fitting in master cylinder cover.
3. Depress brake pedal a few times to force all fluid from cylinder.
4. Disconnect pedal operating rod at clevis on brake pedal. Disconnecting at this point retains approximate adjustment.
5. Unfasten master cylinder from frame bracket and lift unit off car.
6. Install in the reverse order. Then fill reservoir with approved brake fluid and bleed system.

POWER BRAKE, REPLACE

1954-55

To remove the power brake unit, disconnect brake lines at power cylinder end plate. Loosen vacuum line hose clamp at check valve and slide hose off check valve. Remove three nuts and lockwashers from cylinder mounting bracket and remove unit from car.

Install the power brake unit in the reverse order of removal and bleed the system as outlined below.

1956

To remove the power brake unit, disconnect relay-to-unit rod at clevis. Disconnect relay rod from push rod. Disconnect both vacuum hoses from unit, and the hydraulic line at the outlet fitting. Remove screws and nuts from the mounting bracket and remove the power brake unit from the car.

Reverse the foregoing procedure to install the power brake unit and bleed the system as outlined below.

1957-58

1. To remove the power brake unit, disconnect remote filler tube from unit.
2. Disconnect vacuum inlet from unit.
3. Disconnect hydraulic fittings from unit and cap lines.
4. Remove four bolts securing unit to cowl and remove unit from car.
5. Reverse the above precedure, check fluid level and bleed system as outlined below.

1959-61

1. Disconnect hydraulic output line from master cylinder of power unit.
2. Disconnect vacuum and hydraulic hoses from power unit.
3. Unfasten power unit push rod from brake pedal relay lever.
4. Unfasten and remove power unit from cowl.
5. Reverse removal operations to install.

BLEEDING POWER BRAKE SYSTEM

1959-61

There is no bleeder fitting at the master cylinder, the unit being self bleeding. However, the car must be on a level floor or the front end lower than the rear. *Vacuum in the reserve tank should be exhausted by several pedal applications.*

If a pressure bleeder is not available, bleed the system by first filling the master cylinder reservoir with brake fluid. Then bleed the system at the wheel cylinders in the conventional manner.

1954-55 and 1957-58

Bleeding the system is accomplished in the same manner as for conventional bleeding as outlined in the *Hydraulic Brake System Chapter* except that the power brake cylinder is bled first by attaching the bleeder hose to the fitting on the end cap. Back off the fitting ¾ turn and depress the brake pedal until bubbles cease. Next, bleed the upper fitting on the end plate above the vacuum control valve housing. Then proceed with the wheel cylinders in the usual manner.

1956

Do not run the engine while bleeding brakes. The bleeding operation should be performed by bleeding the master cylinder (part of power brake unit) first. Fill the master cylinder with approved blake fluid. Attach bleeder hose to fitting on master cylinder, apply pressure to the brake pedal, back off fitting ¾ turn and depress brake pedal until bubbles cease. Close bleeder valve before releasing pressure on brake pedal. Then proceed to bleed the wheel cylinders in the usual manner.

Front End and Steering Section

WHEEL ALIGNMENT

1961

Camber Adjustment—Adjustment is made at the camber eccentric located in the steering knuckle upper support, Fig. 1. The upper ball joint stud fits through the camber eccentric and knuckle support. Turning the eccentric repositions the upper ball joint stud.

To adjust camber, loosen the ball joint stud nut one turn and tap bottom of stud with soft mallet to loosen eccentric. Using a suitable wrench, Fig. 2, turn the eccentric as required to obtain the camber specifications listed in the *Wheel Alignment* chart. The final position of the stud should be in the rear portion of the camber eccentric in order to keep steering angle correct. After proper adjustment has been established, torque stud nut to 50-65 ft. lbs.

Caster Adjustment—Adjustment is made by turning the retaining nuts on the forward ends of the tie-struts at the frame front crossmember, Fig. 3. To gain access to the retaining nuts, it is necessary to remove the splash shield.

Proper caster adjustment is obtained by shortening or lengthening the struts between the lower suspension arms and the frame front crossmember. To provide more negative caster, lengthen the struts by loosening the front bushing retaining nuts and tightening the rear bushing retaining nuts. One turn of the nuts results in approximately ½° change in caster.

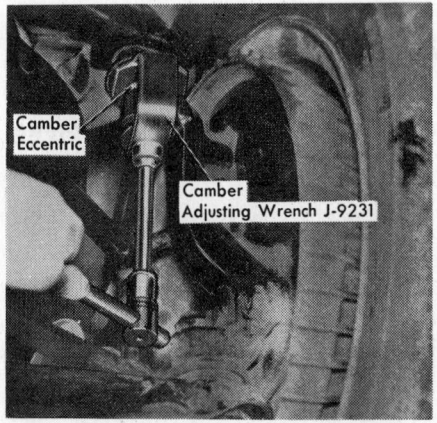

Fig. 2   Adjusting camber. 1961

To provide more positive caster, shorten the struts by loosening the rear bushing retaining nuts and tightening the front bushing retaining nuts.

After proper adjustment has been made, tighten front retaining nuts to 55-70 ft. lbs., being sure to hold the rear nut with a wrench so as not to disturb the adjustment.

Toe-In Adjustment—Toe-in is adjusted by turning the tie rod adjusters at the outer ends of each tie rod after loosening the clamp bolts. (Both right and left pivot ends have right-hand threads.) Be sure to turn both adjusters an equal amount so that the relation of the steering gear high spot to the straight ahead position of the front wheels will not be changed.

When adjustment has been completed according to the specification listed in the *Wheel Alignment* chart, tighten nuts on clamp bolts to 15-20 ft. lbs. torque. *Be sure that open side of clamps are pointed downward within 45° of vertical to prevent possible interference with the frame on maximum compression. Both the tie rod ends and joint studs should be centralized before tightening clamps.*

1957-60

Caster & Camber—These adjustments are made by adding or removing shims between the upper suspension arm mounting shaft and the frame mounting bracket.

To change caster, add or remove the correct thickness of shims at one of mounting bolts. Addition of shims at the front bolt or removal of shims at the rear bolt will decrease positive caster. Removal of shims at the front bolt or addition of shims at the rear bolt will increase positive caster.

To change camber, add or remove shims of equal total thickness at both mounting bolts. Addition of shims at both bolts will decrease positive camber. Removal of shims at both bolts will increase positive camber.

The shims for adjustment are available in three thicknesses: .0149″, .0418″ and .1046″. The shims will change caster and camber by the following amounts:

Shim Size	Caster Change (Shim at one bolt)	Camber Change (Shim at both bolts)
.0149″	1/6°	1/15°
.0418″	½°	1/5°
.1046″	1 1/6°	½°

Changing shims at one bolt to correct caster will affect camber slightly. If a large caster change is made, the resulting camber change should be taken into consideration.

The following table gives the amount of change in camber when adding shims to the front or rear bolts to change caster:

Shim Size	Camber Change When Shims are Changed At: Front Bolt	Rear Bolt
.0149″	0°	1/15°
.0418″	1/60°	1/5°
.1046″	1/30°	1/2°

When possible, make caster adjustments by changing shims at the front

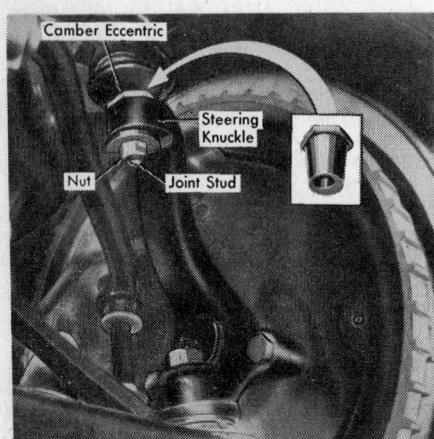

Fig. 1   Camber adjustment eccentric. 1961

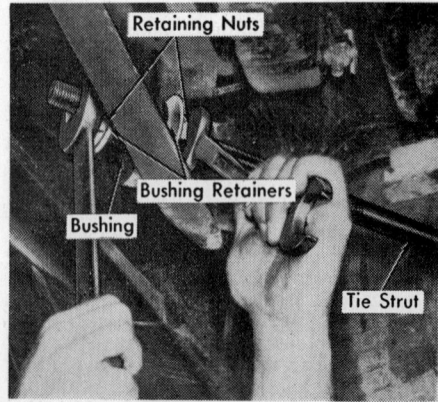

Fig. 3   Adjusting caster. 1961

bolt because the resulting camber change will be small, as can be seen in the table above.

If more than ¼" total thickness of shims are necessary to bring suspension within specifications, check for bent or damaged parts.

To adjust caster and camber, loosen the upper suspension arm mounting bolts and add or remove shims as required. Then tighten the mounting bolts 130-140 lb. ft.

NOTE: In order to avoid pulling to the right on high crowned roads, it is necessary to adjust the camber so that the left wheel is ¼° to ½° more positive camber than the right wheel.

Toe-In Adjustment—This adjustment is accomplished by turning the tie rod adjusters at the outer ends of each tie rod after loosening clamp screws. Turning the adjusters in the direction the wheels revolve when going forward decreases toe-in.

Be sure to turn both adjusters an equal amount so that the relation of the steering gear high spot to the straight ahead position of the front wheels will not be changed. When adjustment has been completed, tighten all clamp screws, *being sure open side of clamp is over open side of adjuster before tightening clamp.*

1953-56

Caster Adjustment —Loosen the clamp screw at the upper end of the steering knuckle support. Turn the eccentric bushing in complete turns only until correct caster is obtained. Tighten the clamp screw.

If it is necessary to secure a greater range of adjustment than is provided by the eccentric bushing, this can be made by removing the lower control arm inner shaft from the frame and turning the shaft so that the threaded ends move the entire suspension arm assembly forward or rearward as required. Screwing the shaft rearward moves the control arms forward and increases the amount of positive caster.

Camber Adjust—Loosen the clamp screw at the upper end of the steering knuckle support. Rotate the eccentric bushing not more than ½ turn in either direction, otherwise the caster adjustment will be affected. If correct camber adjustment cannot be obtained within ½ turn of the eccentric bushing, look for bent suspension parts.

Toe-In Adjust—This adjustment is made in the same manner outlined for 1957-60 models.

WHEEL BEARINGS, ADJUST

1960-61

When adjusting the front wheel bearings, raise the front of the car and make sure that the wheel is completely seated on the spindle. Tighten the adjusting nut to 30 ft. lbs. torque and rotate the drum to be sure all parts are properly seated and the threads are free. Then back off the nut ¼ turn. If the cotter pin cannot be installed in either of the two available holes in the spindle with the nut in this position, loosen the adjusting nut until the cotter pin can be installed. The wheel should spin freely.

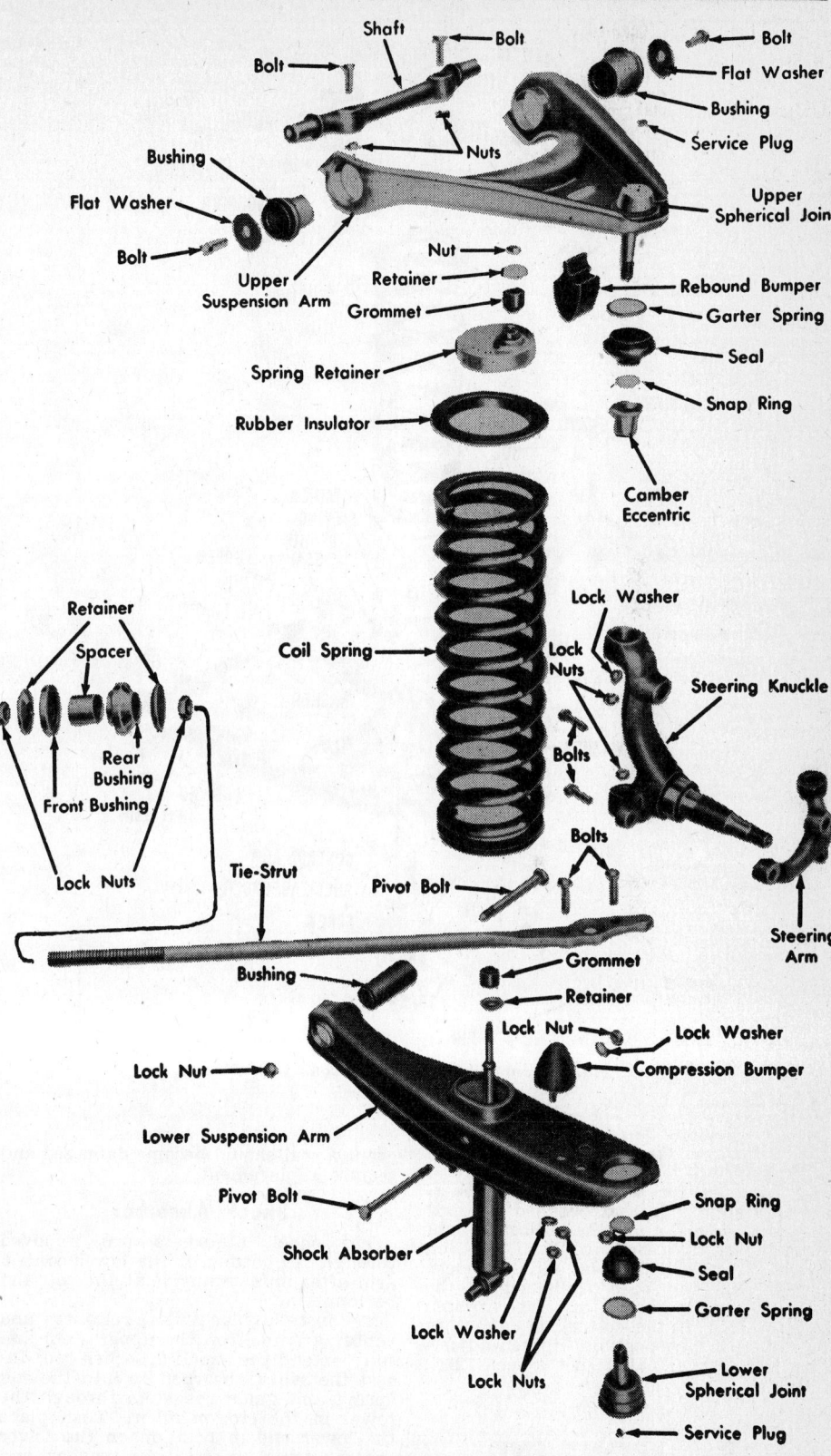

Fig. 4 Front suspension. 1961

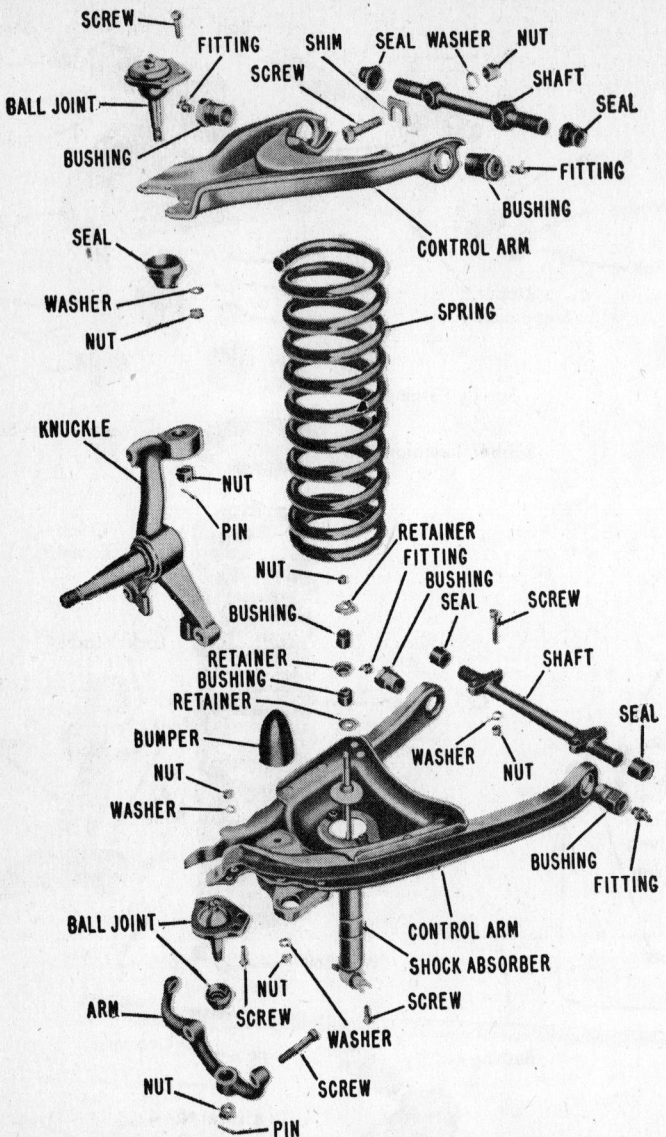

Fig. 5 Front coil spring suspension. 1957-60

moved. Remove strut and bushings as suggested by Fig. 4. Then replace as follows:

1. Insert spacer in rear bushing and install bushing and spacer in frame through rear side of crossmember.
2. Install nut on tie-strut and run nut to bottom of thread.
3. Install rear bushing retainer on strut with concave side toward nut.
4. With strut held in horizontal position, install threaded end of strut through rear bushing in frame crossmember.
5. Install front bushing on end of strut and slide bushing into position in frame crossmember. Front bushing should lock in rear bushing.
6. Install front bushing retainer on threaded end of strut with flat side against bushing. Start front nut on end of strut but do not tighten.
7. Secure opposite end of strut to lower control arm and torque bolts to 30-40 ft. lbs.
8. Connect stabilizer link.
9. Lower car and with car weight on all four wheels, tighten front nut to 55-70 ft. lbs.
10. Tighten rear nut, compressing bushing until retainer bottoms on metal spacer in bushing.
11. Adjust caster as outlined previously.
12. Install splash shield.

Upper Ball Joint & Seal

1. Remove nut from ball stud.
2. Scribe a mark on camber eccentric and steering knuckle to facilitate alignment on installation.
3. Strike bottom of ball stud with soft mallet to break it loose from knuckle.
4. Raise upper control arm and remove ball joint from knuckle.
5. Remove camber eccentric from joint stud with a suitable puller.
6. Remove seal. Clean pivot joint and stud with solvent. Inspect ball pivot for looseness or binding and replace joint if necessary.
7. Install new seal as outlined below.
8. With new seal installed, install camber eccentric on joint stud, aligning scribe marks on eccentric and knuckle.
9. Install a standard nut on joint stud and tighten nut until camber eccentric locks in knuckle. Then remove standard nut and install special lock washer and locking nut and torque nut to 50-65 ft. lbs.

Installing Joint Seal

1. Turn new seal inside out.
2. Place snap ring inside seal just over bottom hole.
3. Press in on bottom of seal until snap ring seats in groove around hole.
4. Apply a small amount of grease around hole in seal and install seal on joint stud.
5. Unroll seal until lip engages in recess around joint housing.
6. Allow air to enter seal by momentarily prying lip of seal away from joint housing with a small screwdriver.
7. Squeeze seal, sliding snap ring end up on stud.

1953-59

Procedure for adjusting wheel bearings is similar to that outlined for 1960 models except that the adjusting nut should be tightened to 25 ft. lbs. on 1959 and 16-17 ft. lbs. on earlier models. After nut has been tightened to the proper torque, back it off and retighten to 4 ft. lbs. If the cotter pin cannot be installed in this position, tighten adjusting nut further but do not exceed 12 ft. lbs.

1961 FRONT END

All lubrication fittings have been eliminated from this suspension, Fig. 4. The control arms are rubber bushed and the ball joints are packed with a special lubricant and sealed. However, service plugs are provided in the ball joint covers so that the joints may be repacked when necessary and also in the

event a seal should become damaged and require replacement.

Shock Absorber

The shock absorbers are removed through the bottom of the lower control arm after unfastening it at the top and bottom.

To install, place the retainer and rubber grommet on the upper stem and fully extend the shock absorber rod. Insert the shock absorber up into the coil spring and guide the stem through the tower in the crossmember. Then place the lower end in position on the lower control arm. Install bolt, washer and nut and torque nut to 90-110 ft. lbs. Fasten shock absorber at top.

Tie-Strut & Bushings

Raise car and jack up under frame side rails. Remove splash shield and disconnect stabilizer link from lower control arm on side tie-strut is to be re-

8. Lubricate outer surface of seal with vaseline and install garter spring on seal. Be sure spring secures lip of seal in recess all around joint housing. *If spring should separate where it is joined together, join them together and lock by twisting male end counterclockwise.*

9. After installing ball joint on car as outlined above, pry service plug from ball joint cover and discard plug. *With a suitable packing gun filled with the special lubricant for this purpose, fill joint with the lubricant, but do not permit the seal to balloon as this will shorten the seal's life. Under no circumstances should any grease but the type recommended be used in these ball joints for to do so will cause premature failure.*

10. Install new service plug in joint cover.

Lower Ball Joint & Seal

1. Remove lower control arm and coil spring.
2. Remove garter spring and seal from ball joint.
3. Press ball joint out of control arm.
4. If necessary, replace seal in a similar manner outlined for the upper seal.
5. Press new ball joint in control arm and install on car in reverse order of removal.

1957-60 FRONT END

Shock Absorber, Replace

Raise hood and remove shock absorber upper retaining nut, retainer and rubber grommet at frame mounting bracket. Remove two screws holding shock absorber to lower spring seat. Remove shock absorber from spring.

Reverse procedure to install shock absorber, Fig. 5.

Upper Ball Joint, Replace

Raise car and place stand jacks under lower suspension arms. Remove wheel. Remove nut from ball stud. Strike steering knuckle with a hammer in area of stud to loosen joint. Raise upper suspension arm so that joint clears knuckle. With a $\frac{5}{16}$" drill, drill out all ball joint rivets. Then remove ball joint.

Install new ball joint on upper suspension arm with bolts, nuts and lockwashers provided in service replacement kit. Tighten nuts to 20-25 lb. ft. Position ball joint stud in knuckle, install nut and tighten to 50-60 lb. ft. Install cotter pin.

Lower Ball Joint, Replace

Raise front of car and place jack stands under forward portion of frame side members. With a jack under spring seat, raise lower suspension arm about one inch (measured at its outer end). Remove nut from ball joint stud. Strike steering arm with a hammer to break joint loose. Remove retaining nuts and bolts and raise lower suspension arm to allow ball joint to be removed.

To install, position ball joint on suspension arm and tighten nuts to 35-40 lb. ft. Head of bolt should be under joint flange. Position joint stud in steering arm mounting hole. Lower jack to allow joint to seat itself in steering arm, and remove jack. Install ball joint nut, tighten to 50-60 lb. ft. and install cotter pin.

1953-56 FRONT END

Steering Knuckle, Remove

1. Lift front end of car from floor with jack.
2. Remove front wheel, hub, brake drum and wheel bearings.
3. Remove brake dust shield with brake shoes attached. Do not damage the hydraulic line which does not have to be removed in this operation.
4. Drive lock pin from steering knuckle support, Fig. 3.
5. Remove dust caps at upper and lower knuckle pin holes, and remove steering knuckle and thrust bearing from knuckle support.

Kingpins, Install

1. If these bushings are to be replaced, slot them lengthwise with a hacksaw and drive them out with a chisel.
2. Press new bushings into steering knuckle, being sure that the oil hole in each bushing lines up with the oil hole in the knuckle. Reaming of bushings is not necessary provided care is used when making the installation.

Steering Knuckle, Install

1. Assemble steering knuckle to support with thrust bearing in position between support and lower face of steering knuckle.
2. Drive lock pin in from front of support.
3. Use new plugs at both ends of kingpin.
4. Install grease fittings and lubricate thoroughly.
5. Install brake assembly, lubricate and adjust front wheel bearings after installing wheel.

Knuckle Support, Remove

1. Remove steering knuckle as outlined previously.
2. Place jack under lower control arm to support coil spring while disconnecting knuckle support.
3. Remove nut from rear end of upper pivot pin.
4. Remove threaded pivot pin and rubber dust seals.
5. Remove nut from rear of lower pivot pin.

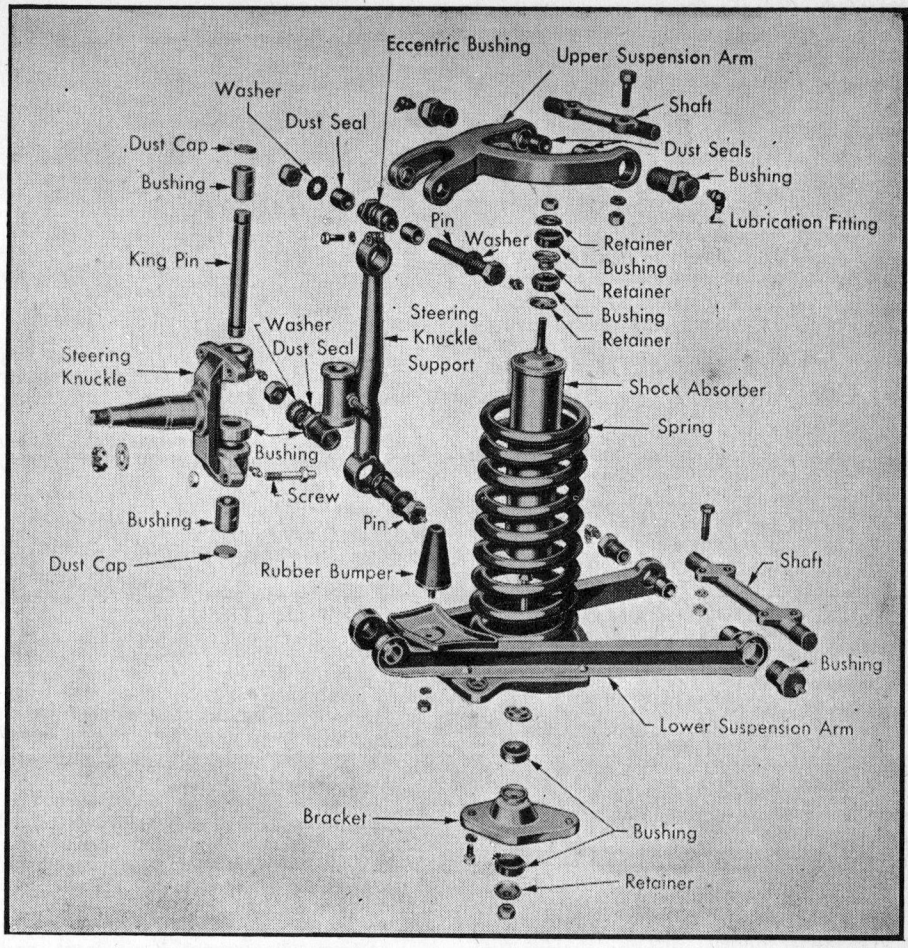

Fig. 6 Front suspension, 1953-56

6. Remove lower pivot pin and rubber dust seals.
7. Place support in vise and loosen clamp screw at upper end of knuckle support.
8. Remove upper and lower bushings from support.

Knuckle Support, Install

1. Install eccentric bushing in knuckle support so that it is centralized and install clamp screw lightly.
2. Install bushing in lower end of knuckle support, tightening bushing firmly so that there is no clearance b e t w e e n bushing shoulder and knuckle support.
3. Install lower end of knuckle support, with bushing, between outer ends of lower control arm. Install rubber dust seals between control arm and support on both sides.
4. Install threaded pivot pin, holding support so that space between support and arms is equal on both sides.
5. Install upper end of support in position between ends of upper control arms and install rubber seals.
6. Install upper pivot pin and nut with upper end of support centralized between ends of upper control arms.
7. Install steering knuckle and adjust caster, camber and toe-in.

STEERING WHEEL & HORN BUTTON

1953-55

On 1953 models, disconnect the wire from the terminal at the lower end of the steering column on *mechanical steering gears* and from the upper steering cover underneath the instrument panel on *power steering gears.* On 1954-55 cars, disconnect the wire at the lower end of the steering column.

On all models, depress the horn button, turn in either direction until locking ears are released and remove button. Remove the horn button spring and steering wheel hub nut. Take out the horn ring retainer, cushion and horn ring.

Make a mark on the steering wheel hub and steering shaft so that the wheel may be reinstalled in the correct position on the splines. Then use a suitable puller to remove the wheel.

Install the wheel and horn contact parts in the reverse order of removal, being sure to stake the wheel hub nut to the steering shaft after tightening it to 45-50 lbs. ft. torque.

1956-58

1. To remove, disconnect horn wire from terminal beneath instrument panel on steering column.
2. Loosen Allen head screws on underside of horn ring, one on each side of turn signal carrier, and remove horn ring assembly.
3. Remove steering wheel hub nut.
4. Use suitable puller to remove steering wheel.
5. Reverse the foregoing to install the wheel, being sure the punch marks

on wheel hub and steering shaft line up. Tighten wheel hub nut to a torque of 45-50 lb. ft. and stake nut in place. After tightening horn ring set screws, depress horn ring several times to make sure that it is properly seated on wheel spokes and retighten set screws.

1959

1. Disconnect horn wire from terminal on neutral safety switch beneath instrument panel on steering column.
2. Remove Phillips screw securing horn ring cap and remove cap.
3. Remove horn ring contact spring and retainer by depressing retainer and turning until retainer and spring snap out.
4. Remove two Allen screws, one under each spoke at steering column, and remove spoke ring covers.
5. Remove wheel hub nut.
6. Remove wheel with suitable puller.
7. Remove horn ring from underside of wheel.

1960

1. Remove two screws from underside of steering wheel rim at outside end of each spoke.
2. Pry off cap on steering wheel hub.
3. Remove two smallest screws (farthest from center) from hub and remove lower sections of horn control housing.
4. Disconnect horn wire from center of hub.
5. Remove two remaining screws from wheel hub and remove upper section of horn control housing.
6. To remove horn switches from upper section, disconnect horn wire and remove two screws from each switch.
7. If steering wheel is to be removed, remove wheel hub nut and use a puller to remove wheel.

1961

1. Remove cap from steering wheel hub by prying it off.
2. Disconnect horn wire from steering shaft.
3. Remove upper steering shaft nut.
4. Remove two screws securing hub to steering wheel.
5. Scribe an alignment mark on hub and on end of steering shaft to be used for alignment upon installation.
6. Use puller to remove wheel.

STEERING GEAR, REPLACE

1953

1. To remove the steering gear, raise front of car 6 in. off floor.
2. Remove steering wheel and horn contact parts as outlined previously.
3. Remove anti-rattle spring under steering wheel.
4. Remove horn wire from terminal at lower end of steering column.
5. Loosen clamp holding lower steering jacket to upper steering jacket.
6. Tap clamp down over lower jacket.

7. Disconnect steering connecting rod from pitman arm.
8. Remove three bolts holding steering gear to frame side bar.
9. Strike steering gear housing firmly with a *lead* hammer to drive the lower steering jacket down out of the upper jacket.
10. Remove steering gear, lower jacket and steering column from bottom of car.
11. Reverse the removal procedure to install the steering gear.

STEERING GEAR REPAIRS, 1953

Disassemble, Fig. 7

1. Rotate steering worm until nut is in center of travel.
2. Remove sector shaft nut.
3. Remove side cover and sector shaft from housing.
4. Turn adjuster screw in end of sector shaft down through cover.
5. Remove end cover with worm bearing, outer race and thrust washer.
6. To remove lower worm bearing, outer race and thrust washer from cover, loosen worm bearing adjuster screw lock nut and turn screw in through cover.
7. Grasp lower end of steering worm and draw steering shaft and nut assembly out of steering housing. *Be sure to keep shaft in horizontal position so that nut does not move against stops at any time, thereby causing damage to ball return mechanism. Disassembly of worm nut is not recommended.*

Assemble, Fig. 7

1. Install steering shaft and nut assembly in steering housing, keeping ball nut away from stops on worm.
2. Install worm bearing adjusting screw with lower worm bearing, outer race, and thrust washer in end cover.
3. Install end cover and attaching parts on gear housing, making sure bearings seat properly.
4. Tighten worm bearing adjusting screw until a slight drag is felt on bearings. Do not tighten lock nut.
5. Install pitman arm.
6. Install sector shaft and adjuster screw inside cover.
7. Rotate steering column until ball nut is in center of travel so that center tooth on sector shaft will enter center space on nut.
8. Install side cover and sector shaft in gear housing.
9. Tighten sector shaft adjusting screw until a slight drag is felt on bearing but do not tighten lock nut.
10. After steering gear has been installed in car, adjust gear as outlined below.

Steering Gear, Adjust

The recirculating ball type steering gear has two adjustments: the worm bearing adjustment and cross shaft end play adjustment.

Worm Bearing Adjustment—Disconnect steering connecting rod at pitman arm. Turn steering wheel to either right- or left-hand stop. Then check load to pull steering wheel back to a point not less than 90° from the straight-ahead position of the steering wheel. The load should not be less than one lb. or more than 1⅛ lb. Load is checked with a spring scale hooked to the rim of the steering wheel. To adjust, loosen lock nut and turn the worm bearing adjusting screw as required. Tighten the lock nut and recheck the adjustment.

Cross Shaft End Play—Turn the steering wheel about 90° each way through center. The pull through center should be between 1½ and 2 lbs. If an adjustment is required, loosen the lock nut and turn the cross shaft adjusting screw in the direction required to obtain the desired result. Tighten the lock nut when the adjustment is correct and recheck the adjustment.

Install the steering connecting rod. The end nut on the pitman arm ball stud should be turned up tight and backed off ⅞ to one turn.

POWER STEERING, REPLACE

1953-54 One-Piece Unit

1. To remove the power steering unit, raise front end of car 10 in. off floor and place jack stands near outer ends of lower suspension arms.
2. Remove steering wheel and horn contact parts as outlined previously.
3. Remove steering column upper and lower covers and steering column support bracket screws from instrument panel.
4. Remove three screws from steering column cover on toe board.
5. Remove heater blower motor from heater and flexible air intake hose.
6. Disconnect hydraulic steering pump-to-power unit hoses at power unit.
7. Loosen steering column lower jacket clamp.
8. Disconnect steering connecting rod at pitman arm and remove left exhaust pipe at manifold.
9. Remove three bolts holding steering gear to frame. *Remove any shims found at mounting bolts, keeping them intact for reinstallation.*
10. Carefully slide steering gear down out of upper jacket and remove complete assembly from car.
11. Reverse the foregoing procedure to install the gear. Measure gap between bottom edge of horn ring and upper edge of turn signal switch carrier. This should be 1/16 in. with the horn ring in released position. Slide steering jacket up or down as required to obtain this clearance.

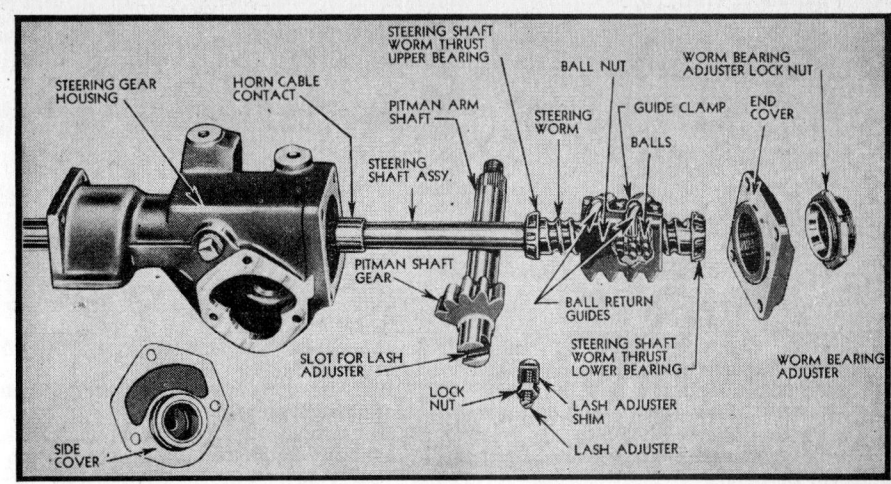

Fig. 7 Layout of manual steering gear parts. 1953

1954 Two-Piece Unit

During 1954 production at approximately Engine No. 71326, a two-piece power steering unit replaced the one-piece type. The assembly consists of two separate parts—the power steering gear and the upper shaft. They are joined together at a point just above the gear assembly by a flexible coupling. This arrangement permits the power steering gear to be removed from the vehicle without removing the steering shaft. The procedure is as follows:

1. Raise front end of car and place stand jacks near the outer ends of the lower suspension arms.
2. Disconnect hydraulic hoses at steering gear and remove fitting from valve body on side closest to frame.
3. Disconnect drag link at pitman arm.
4. With pitman arm in straight ahead position, *scribe locating marks on worm shaft flange and coupling to assure proper position of steering wheel on reassembly.*
5. Remove nuts, lockwashers and ground wires from worm shaft flange-to-coupling screws.
6. Remove steering gear from frame.
7. Installation is made in the reverse order. Tighten gear-to-frame screws 40-45 lbs. ft. torque, connect the steering linkage and bleed the system as outlined in the *Power Steering Gear* chapter.

1955

1. To remove steering gear assembly, disconnect hydraulic hoses from valve body on gear housing. Cap ends of hoses to prevent loss of oil.
2. Remove return port (large) fitting from valve body.
3. Raise front of car and place stand jacks near outer ends of lower suspension arms.

4. Disconnect pitman arm from drag link.
5. Remove lower flange-to-coupling screws.
6. Scribe marks on flange and coupling to assure correct positioning of steering wheel at assembly.
7. Unfasten gear housing from frame and remove gear housing.
8. After installing the gear in the reverse order of its removal, check the flexible coupling for distortion. The coupling must rest in a flat plane with no visible bend or twist. If it is distorted, remove lower steering column cover and lower clamp-to-jacket screw. Then loosen the steering jacket clamp screws at the instrument panel and slide the complete steering jacket up or down as required. Redrill the lower clamp and jacket, if necessary, to reinstall screw.

1956-61

1. To remove steering gear, remove tank cover from pump and discard gasket.
2. Syphon all fluid from tank.
3. Disconnect pressure and return line hoses at tank and pump, and cap ends to prevent fluid drainage.
4. Raise front end of car and place stand jacks near outer ends of lower suspension arms.
5. Disconnect pitman arm from steering gear.
6. Remove upper flange-to-shaft retaining screw.
7. Unfasten and remove gear housing from frame.
8. Reverse the foregoing to install the gear. Tighten upper flange-to-shaft retaining screw to a torque of 25-30 lb. ft. After installing the gear, check the flexible coupling for distortion. If distorted, correct as outlined for 1955 steering gear.

Instruments, Windshield Wiper and Radio

INSTRUMENT CLUSTER

1953

1. Remove lower steering column cover.
2. Remove two brackets from underside of upper steering column cover.
3. Remove transmission shift indicator-to-shifter tube screw and remove indicator.
4. Remove odometer cover from instrument cluster.
5. Pull odometer cover and upper steering column cover away from steering column far enough to disconnect transmission shift indicator bulb socket from odometer cover.
6. Disconnect shift indicator bulb.
7. Remove upper steering column cover with odometer cover and rubber anti-squeak. *It may be necessary to loosen the two screws holding steering column to cowl brace and pull steering column down to gain sufficient clearance to remove odometer cover and upper steering column cover.*
8. Remove 3 screws (1 top, 2 bottom) holding cluster to panel.
9. Remove knob and nut holding speedometer reset cable to instrument panel at right side of steering column.
10. Slide cluster an inch or so from instrument panel, disconnect speedometer cable and remove connectors from gauge terminals.
11. Cluster can now be removed.

1954

1. Remove two rear screws holding steering column to frame. Loosen front screw.
2. Remove 3 screws holding triangular steering column cover plate to toe riser.
3. Remove 5 screws holding square cover plate to toe riser.
4. Remove stop light brake switch.
5. Remove lower steering column cover.
6. Remove steering column U clamp and lower the steering column.
7. Disconnect vent cables from firewall and vent.
8. Disconnect trip odometer reset stem.
9. Remove 3 cluster mounting screws.
10. Pull cluster out far enough for access to defroster and heater control arms, and remove these parts.
11. Cluster may now be pulled further for instrument service.

1955

1. Remove 2 screws holding triangular steering column cover plate to toe riser and leave third screw in position.
2. Remove 5 screws holding square cov-

er plate to toe riser.
3. Remove brake stop light switch.
4. Disconnect speedometer cable.
5. Remove lower steering column cover and transmission dial indicator pointer.
6. Disconnect vent cables from firewall and vent.
7. Remove U clamp nuts and lower steering column.
8. Disconnect trip odometer reset stem.
9. Remove 3 cluster mounting screws.
10. Pull cluster out far enough for access to defroster and heater control arm brackets and remove these parts.
11. Cluster may now be pulled out for further service.

1956

1. Disconnect speedometer cable.
2. Remove lower steering column cover and transmission dial indicator pointer.
3. Disconnect vent cables from firewall and vent.
4. Remove U clamp nuts and lower steering column.
5. Disconnect trip odometer reset stem.
6. Remove 4 cluster mounting screws and pull cluster out far enough to gain access to defroster and heater control arm brackets and remove these parts.
7. Cluster may now be pulled out for further instrument service.

1957

1. Disconnect speedometer cable.
2. Remove lower steering column cover and transmission dial indicator pointer.
3. Remove U clamp nuts and lower steering column.
4. Disconnect trip odometer reset stem.
5. Remove 4 cluster mounting screws.
6. Cluster may now be pulled out partially for further instrument service.

1958

1. Remove lower steering column cover and transmission dial indicator pointer.
2. Remove U clamp nuts and lower steering column.
3. Remove odometer reset stem, knob and retaining nut.
4. Remove 4 cluster mounting screws.
5. Remove 2 screws from base of heater and fresh air or Air Conditioning control panels.
6. Cluster may now be partially removed for further instrument service.

1959

1. Disconnect battery ground cable.
2. Remove lower steering column cover and Hydra-Matic dial indicator pointer.

3. Remove steering column U clamp nuts and lower steering column.
4. Remove odometer reset stem, knob and retaining nut and disconnect speedometer cable.
5. Separate upper instrument cover from lower panel (6 screws).
6. Raise upper panel as high as possible to gain access to and disconnect necessary connectors linking upper cover to lower panel.
7. Unhook upper cover hooks from cowl retainers.
8. Remove upper cover with instrument cluster.
9. Separate cluster from upper cover (4 nuts) and remove instruments as required.

1960

1. Disconnect battery ground cable.
2. Remove lower steering column cover and Hydra-Matic pointer.
3. Remove 6 screws retaining panel cover to lower instrument panel.
4. Raise front edge of cover and insert wood block between cover and lower panel to provide access to components.

1961

1. Disconnect battery ground cable.
2. Remove six screws retaining upper panel cover to lower panel.
3. Raise upper panel high enough to disconnect multiple connector for map light and Guidematic (if equipped).
4. Pull cover to unhook upper cover hooks from cowl retainers and remove cover.
5. Disconnect odometer reset cable and speedometer cable.
6. Disconnect all cluster bulbs and fuel and temperature gauge wires from rear of cluster.
7. Disconnect two connectors from lighting switch.
8. Remove two screws and one bracket (above radio) that hold bezel to instrument panel.
9. Remove nut on left side of bezel near headlight switch that holds bezel to instrument panel and remove bezel.
10. Remove cluster (2 screws each side).

WINDSHIELD WIPER

1954

Remove wiper blade and arm assemblies. Hold serrated transmission shaft and loosen screw in end of shaft. Tap screw lightly with butt end of screwdriver. Spring-loaded pulleys will automatically adjust cables to proper tension. Tighten screw in end of shaft.

1955-58

The transmission cables are tensioned by spring-loaded pulleys. Tight cables cause slow wiper operation. Loose cables cause blade slap or over-travel at end of stroke. If either of these conditions exist, readjust cable tension as follows:

Remove wiper arm. Press in on end of shaft to unlock spring-loaded pulleys and hold momentarily. Then release. This automatically sets cable tension.

To remove the motor, remove the screws which attach the motor to the support and disengage the motor from the auxiliary drive assembly. Disconnect the vacuum hoses and control cable from the motor. Unfasten and remove the motor.

1959-60

1. To remove wiper motor, disconnect cable from battery.
2. Disconnect multiple connectors and washer hoses at wiper unit.
3. Remove air intake grille.
4. Disconnect wiper unit from transmission control arms at wiper unit.
5. Remove distributor cap.
6. Unfasten wiper unit by removing screws (4) through ventilator grille opening.

1961

1. Disconnect battery ground cable.
2. Disconnect multiple connectors and washer hoses at wiper unit.
3. Disconnect wiper ground strap from body.
4. Remove air intake grille.
5. Remove nut retaining upper control arm to shaft.
6. Remove screw securing lower arm to unit and remove arm.
7. Remove upper crank arm from motor shaft and remove boot from shaft.
8. Remove four screws through air intake grille opening and remove wiper assembly from under hood.

RADIO REMOVAL

1953

1. Disconnect three vacuum antenna hoses at nipples on right side of radio (left side on cars using standard push button radio).
2. Disconnect antenna lead plug from left side of radio.
3. Disconnect dial light feed wire (brown) at connector.
4. Disconnect rear speaker switch plug from left side of radio.
5. Disconnect ignition lead (black) wire at fuse connector.
6. Remove antenna control knob, spring and tone control ring from right shaft. Following same procedure, remove volume control knob and sensitivity ring from left shaft. On cars with standard push button radio, remove set screws and control knobs from right and left shafts.
7. Remove hex nut and control escutcheon marked "tone" from right control bushing. Following same procedure, remove hex nut and escutcheon

marked "sensitivity" from left control bushing.
8. On cars with standard push button radio, remove trim plates and spanner nuts from bushings.
9. Remove mounting screws from bracket and remove radio from grille.

1954-55

1. Disconnect antenna lead plug from left side of radio.
2. Disconnect rear speaker wire from connector at top of glove box.
3. Disconnect front speaker wire at right side of radio.
4. Disconnect ignition lead (black) wire at fuse connector.
5. Remove antenna control knob, spring and tone control ring from right shaft. Following same procedure, remove volume control knob and sensitivity ring from left shaft.
6. Remove hex nut control escutcheon marked "tone". Following same procedure, remove hex nut escutcheon marked "sensitivity".
7. Remove mounting screws and washers from mounting bracket to radio.
8. Remove radio from under panel. Disconnect dial light feed wire (brown) at connector.
9. Disconnect 3 vacuum antenna hoses from clip and nipples on top of radio.
10. Remove dial light from top of radio chassis.

1956

1. Disconnect radio lead (black) and antenna lead (brown) from fuse connectors.
2. Disconnect speaker unit black feed lead at connector at rear of radio.
3. Disconnect 2 shielded bayonet connections from speaker.
4. Disconnect antenna lead from right side of radio.
5. Remove manual selector knob, volume control knob and tone control ring from left shaft.
6. Remove hex nuts retaining shafts and mounting screw from radio mounting bracket.
7. Remove radio through glove compartment, disconnecting 2 dial lights from top of radio and dark green and dark blue leads from plastic connectors.

1957

1. Remove glove compartment.
2. Disconnect radio lead (black) from fuse connector.
3. Disconnect front speaker feed leads (black) at connector for speaker.
4. Disconnect shielded bayonet connection from power unit.
5. Disconnect antenna motor lead (brown) from fuse connector.
6. Disconnect rear speaker lead (green) from harness connector.
7. Remove antenna connectors at bottom left rear of radio.
8. Remove control knobs and tone control ring from left shaft.
9. Remove hex nuts retaining shafts and mounting screw from radio mounting bracket.

10. Remove radio through glove compartment opening, disconnecting 2 dial lights from top of radio.

1958 Tubes and Vibrator

It is possible to remove and install all radio tubes and the vibrator without removing the radio from the car by the following procedure.

1. Remove heater crossover duct and rubber connector. Tubes and vibrator in the radio section are now accessible from the instrument panel. To remove, reach up and pull out tube sockets.
2. Remove 4 screws accessible through glove box, securing bottom cover plate to tuner section.
3. Pull down on right side of plate and remove by pulling to right. Tubes in the tuner section are now accessible for removal and installation through glove box.

1958 Radio Unit

1. Remove glove box.
2. Disconnect front and rear speaker leads.
3. Disconnect antenna lead.
4. Disconnect multiple connector from tuner section of tuner and audio unit.
5. Remove control knobs and tone control rings.
6. Remove retaining nuts from selector and volume control shafts and remove speaker and tone escutcheons (a special wrench, Tool No. J-6968, is available for removing these nuts).
7. Remove two nuts securing radio to mounting brackets under instrument panel.
8. Remove tuner and audio unit through glove box door opening and, at same time, disconnect light from top of tuner section.

1959-60 Radio

1. Working through the glove compartment, disconnect front and rear speaker leads.
2. Disconnect antenna lead.
3. Disconnect multiple connector from radio.
4. Remove knobs, springs and speaker volume and tone control rings.
5. Unfasten radio from mounting bracket under instrument panel.
6. Remove manual selector and volume control shafts.
7. Remove radio through glove compartment.

1961

1. Disconnect battery ground cable.
2. Remove upper instrument panel cover and bezel as outlined previously.
3. Disconnect speaker leads.
4. Remove three screws retaining radio mounting panel to heater vent control bezel.
5. Remove screw retaining radio to right and rear mounting brackets and lift radio with bezel from instrument panel.

CHEVROLET & CORVETTE

INDEX OF SERVICE OPERATIONS

PAGE NO.

ACCESSORIES
Instruments 529
Windshield Wiper 529
Windshield Wiper Troubles............ 37

BODY
Air Conditioning 177
Automatic Seat Adjuster Troubles...... 36
Automatic Top Troubles............... 36
Automatic Window Lift Troubles....... 36

BRAKES (Mechanical)
Adjustments 112
Brake Cylinder Sizes..................484
Hydraulic Brake System...............112
Master Cylinder, Replace.............520
Trouble Shooting 33

BRAKES (Power)
Power Brake System, Bleed...........520
Power Unit Repairs...................128
Power Unit, Replace..................520
Trouble Shooting 32

CLUTCH
Clutch Pedal, Adjust..................503
Clutch Repairs 503
Clutch, Replace 503
Trouble Shooting 13

COOLING SYSTEM
Radiator, Replace 497
Trouble Shooting 8
Water Pump Repairs..................497
Water Pump, Replace.................497

ELECTRIC SYSTEM
Dash Gauge Service................... 85
Distributor, Replace 498
Distributor Service 46
Distributor Specifications 484
Generator Regulator Service.......... 62
Generator Regulator Specifications....483
Generator Service 62
Generator Specifications 483
Horn Button or Ring, Replace.........524
Ignition System Service.............. 46
Ignition Timing 498
Starter, Replace 498
Starter Switch Service............... 83
Starting Motor Service............... 77
Starting Motor Specifications.........485
Trouble Shooting 10
Turn Signal Troubles.................12

PAGE NO.

ENGINE
Camshaft, Replace 494
Crankcase Front End Plate............493
Crankshaft Oil Seal, Replace.........495
Crankshaft Bearing Specs.............482
Cylinder Head, Replace...............486
Engines, Replace.....................486
Main Bearings, Replace...............495
Piston Pins, Replace..................494
Piston Rings, Replace................495
Piston & Ring Specifications..........482
Pistons & Rods, Remove..............494
Piston & Rod, Assemble..............494
Pistons, Replace 494
Rocker Arm, Replace.................490
Rocker Arm Studs....................490
Rod Bearings, Replace...............495
Timing Case Cover, Replace..........492
Timing Chain, Replace...............493
Timing Gears, Replace...............493
Trouble Shooting 4
Valves, Adjust 487
Valve Arrangement 487
Valves, Grind 491
Valve Guides 490
Valve Lifters (Hydraulic) 492
Valves, Remove 490
Valve Spring Installed Height 491
Valve Spring Testing 491
Valve Specifications 481
Valve Timing Data...................493

ENGINE OILING
Oil Pan, Replace 496
Oil Pump Repairs 497
Trouble Shooting 4

FRONT SUSPENSION
Camber, Adjust 520
Caster, Adjust 520
Front End Repairs....................521
Toe-in, Adjust 521
Trouble Shooting 33
Wheel Alignment Specifications.......483

FUEL & EXHAUST SYSTEM
Carburetors 499
Fuel Pumps 96
Mufflers & Pipes.....................498
Trouble Shooting 4

OVERDRIVE 100
Trouble Shooting 14

PAGE NO.

REAR AXLE
Axle Shaft, Replace...................520
General Service 102
Non-Slip Differentials 109
Rear Axle Repairs....................517
Rear Axle Assembly, Replace.........517
Rear Axle Specifications 484
Trouble Shooting 31

SPECIFICATIONS
Brake Cylinder Sizes..................484
Capacity Data 482
Carburetors 500
Cooling System 482
Distributors 484
Crankshaft Bearings 482
Engine Tightening 480
Generator & Regulators..............483
Pistons & Rings......................482
Rear Axle 484
Starting Motors 485
Tune Up 480
Valves 481
Wheel Alignment 483

STEERING GEARS (Mechanical)
Horn Button or Ring, Replace.........524
Steering Gear, Repairs...............525
Steering Gear, Replace...............524
Steering Wheel, Replace.............524
Trouble Shooting 33

STEERING GEARS (Power)
Steering Gear, Repairs...............527
Steering Gear, Replace...............527
Trouble Shooting 34

TRANSMISSIONS (Manual Shift)
Gearshift, Adjust 509
Transmission Repairs (3 Speed).......506
Transmission Repairs (4 Speed).......507
Transmission, Replace................505
Trouble Shooting 14

TRANSMISSIONS (Automatic)
Powerglide Linkage, Adjust...........511
Powerglide, Replace..................515
Powerglide Repairs 315
Powerglide Trouble 19
Turboglide Linkage, Adjust...........516
Turboglide, Replace..................517
Turboglide Repairs 363
Turboglide Troubles 20

TUNE UP 38

Year	Model Designation	Wheelbase, Inches	Valve Location	Bore and Stroke	Piston Displacement, Cubic Inches	Compression Ratio (Standard)	Maximum Brake H.P. @ R.P.M.	Maximum Torque Lbs. Ft. @ R.P.M.	Normal Oil Pressure Pounds
1953–55	Corvette 6..............2934	102	In Head	3.5625 x 3.9375	235	8.0	150 @ 4200	223 @ 2400	45
1953	One-Fifty 6......Std. Trans.	115	In Head	3.5625 x 3.9375	235	7.1	108 @ 3600	200 @ 2000	14
	One-Fifty 6......Powerglide	115	In Head	3.5625 x 3.9375	235	7.5	115 @ 3600	204 @ 2000	45
	Two-Ten 6........Std. Trans.	115	In Head	3.5625 x 3.9375	235	7.1	108 @ 3600	200 @ 2000	14
	Two-Ten 6........Powerglide	115	In Head	3.5626 x 3.9375	235	7.5	115 @ 3600	204 @ 2000	45
	Bel-Air 6........Std. Trans.	115	In Head	3.5625 x 3.9375	235	7.1	108 @ 3600	200 @ 2000	14
	Bel Air 6........Powerglide	115	In Head	3.5625 x 3.9375	235	7.5	115 @ 3600	204 @ 2000	45
1954	One-Fifty 6......Std. Trans.	115	In Head	3.5625 x 3.9375	235	7.5	115 @ 3700	200 @ 2000	45
	One-Fifty 6......Powerglide	115	In Head	3.5625 x 3.9375	235	7.5	125 @ 4000	204 @ 2000	45
	Two-Ten 6........Std. Trans.	115	In Head	3.5625 x 3.9375	235	7.5	115 @ 3700	200 @ 2000	45
	Two-Ten 6........Powerglide	115	In Head	3.5625 x 3.9375	235	7.5	125 @ 4000	204 @ 2000	45
	Bel-Air 6........Std. Trans.	115	In Head	3.5625 x 3.9375	235	7.5	115 @ 3700	200 @ 2000	45
	Bel-Air 6........Powerglide	115	In Head	3.5625 x 3.9375	235	7.5	125 @ 4000	204 @ 2000	45
1955	6-Cyl. With Std. Trans.②	115	In Head	3.5625 x 3.9375	235	7.5	123 @ 3800	207 @ 2000	35
	6-Cyl. With Powerglide②	115	In Head	3.5625 x 3.9375	235	7.5	136 @ 4200	209 @ 2200	35
	V8 With 2-Bar. Carb.②	115	In Head	3.750 x 3.000	265	8.0	162 @ 4400	257 @ 2200	35
	V8 With 4 Bar. Carb.②	115	In Head	3.750 x 3.000	265	8.0	180 @ 4600	260 @ 2800	35
	Corvette V8	102	In Head	3.750 x 3.000	265	8.0	195 @ 5000	260 @ 3000	35
1956	6-Cylinder②	115	In Head	3.5625 x 3.9375	235	8.0	140 @ 4200	210 @ 2400	35
	V8 Std. Trans., 2-Bar. Carb.②	115	In Head	3.750 x 3.000	265	8.0	162 @ 4400	257 @ 2200	35
	V8 Powerglide, 2-Bar. Carb.②	115	In Head	3.750 x 3.000	265	8.0	170 @ 4400	257 @ 2400	35
	V8 Std. Trans., 4-Bar. Carb.②	115	In Head	3.750 x 3.000	265	9.25	205 @ 4600	268 @ 3000	35
	V8 Powerglide, 4 Bar. Carb.②	115	In Head	3.750 x 3.000	265	9.25	205 @ 4600	268 @ 3000	35
	V8 Std. Tr., 2 Four-Bar. Carbs.②	115	In Head	3.750 x 3.000	265	9.25	225 @ 5200	270 @ 3600	35
	V8 P.G., 2 Four-Bar. Carbs.②	115	In Head	3.750 x 3.000	265	9.25	225 @ 5200	270 @ 3600	35
	Corvette V8 4-Bar. Carb.	102	In Head	3.750 x 3.000	265	9.25	210 @ 5200	270 @ 3200	35
	Corvette V8 2 Four Bar. Carbs.	102	In Head	3.750 x 3.000	265	9.25	225 @ 5200	270 @ 3600	35
1957	6-Cylinder②	115	In Head	3.5625 x 3.9375	235	8.0	140 @ 4200	210 @ 2400	35
	265-V8 Two-Bar. Carb.②	115	In Head	3.750 x 3.000	265	8.0	162 @ 4400	257 @ 2400	35
	283-V8 Two-Bar. Carb.②	115	In Head	3.875 x 3.000	283	8.5	185 @ 4600	275 @ 2400	35
	283-V8 Four-Bar. Carb.②	115	In Head	3.875 x 3.000	283	9.5	220 @ 4800	300 @ 3000	35
	Corvette V8, Two 4-Bar. Carbs.	102	In Head	3.875 x 3.000	283	9.5	245 @ 5000	300 @ 3800	35
	Corvette V8, Fuel Injection	102	In Head	3.875 x 3.000	283	9.5	250 @ 5000	305 @ 3800	35
	Corvette V8, Two 4-Bar. Carbs.	102	In Head	3.875 x 3.000	283	9.5	270 @ 6000	285 @ 4200	35
	Corvette, V8 Fuel Injection	102	In Head	3.875 x 3.000	283	10.5	283 @ 6200	290 @ 4400	35
1958	6-Cylinder①	117½	In Head	3.562 x 3.94	235	8.25	145 @ 4200	215 @ 2400	35
	283-V8 Two-Bar. Carb.①	117½	In Head	3.875 x 3.00	283	8.50	185 @ 4600	275 @ 2400	35
	283-V8 Four-Bar. Carb.①	117½	In Head	3.875 x 3.00	283	8.50	230 @ 4800	300 @ 3000	35
	348-V8 Four-Bar. Carb.①	117½	In Head	4.125 x 3.25	348	9.50	250 @ 4400	355 @ 2800	35
	348-V8 Three 2-Bar. Carb.①	117½	In Head	4.125 x 3.25	348	9.50	280 @ 4800	355 @ 2800	35
	Corvette V8, 4-Bar. Carb.	102	In Head	3.875 x 3.00	283	9.50	230 @ 4800	300 @ 3000	35
	Corvette V8, Two 4-Bar. Carbs.	102	In Head	3.875 x 3.00	283	9.50	245 @ 5000	300 @ 3800	35
	Corvette V8, Fuel Injection	102	In Head	3.875 x 3.00	283	10.50	250 @ 5000	305 @ 3800	35
1959	6-Cylinder③	119	In Head	3.562 x 3.94	235	8.25	135 @ 4000	217 @ 2000	35
	283-V8③	119	In Head	3.875 x 3.00	283	8.5	185 @ 4600	275 @ 2400	35
	348-V8③	119	In Head	4.125 x 3.25	348	9.5	250 @ 4400	355 @ 2800	35
	Corvette V8, 4-Bar. Carb.	102	In Head	3.875 x 3.00	283	9.5	230 @ 4800	300 @ 3000	35
	Corvette V8, Fuel Injection	102	In Head	3.875 x 3.00	283	9.5	250 @ 5000	305 @ 3800	35
	Corvette V8, Two 4-Bar. Carb.	102	In Head	3.875 x 3.00	283	9.5	245 @ 5000	300 @ 3800	35
1960	6-Cylinder③	119	In Head	3.562 x 3.94	235	8.25	135 @ 4000	217 @ 2000	35
	283-V8③	119	In Head	3.875 x 3.000	283	8.50	170 @ 4200	275 @ 2400	35
	348-V8③	119	In Head	4.125 x 3.25	348	9.50	250 @ 4400	355 @ 2800	35
	Corvette V8-283	102	In Head	3.875 x 3.00	283	9.50	230 @ 4800	300 @ 3000	35
1961	6 Cylinder③	119	In Head	3.562 x 3.94	235	8.25	135 @ 4000	217 @ 2000	35
	V8-283③	119	In Head	3.875 x 3.00	283	8.50	170 @ 4200	275 @ 2200	45
	V8-348③	119	In Head	4.125 x 3.25	348	9.50	250 @ 4400	355 @ 2800	45
	Corvette..............867	102	In Head	3.875 x 3.00	283	9.50	230 @ 4800	300 @ 3000	35

① —Delray, Biscayne, Bel Air, Impala and Station Wagons available with any of the engines listed.

② —One-Fifty, Two-Ten and Bel Air available with any of the engines listed.

③ —Biscayne, Bel Air, Impala and Station Wagons available with any of the engines listed.

CHEVROLET & CORVETTE

TUNE UP SPECIFICATIONS

★On 1958–61 models, which have vacuum advance tube connnected to intake manifold thus producing full advance at idle speed, be sure to disconnect tube when setting ignition timing.

Year	Model	Ground Polarity and Voltage	Spark Plug Type	Spark Plug Gap Inch	Distributor Point Gap Inch	Distributor Cam Angle Degrees	Firing Order ②	Ignition Timing★ Mark	Ignition Timing★ Location	Idle Speed RPM In Drive	Compression Pressure @ Cranking Speed Minimum
1953–54	Ex. Corv.	N-6	AC 44-5	.035	⑤	38–45	153624	Ball	Flywheel	425	130
	Corvette	N-6	AC 44-5	.035	⑤	41–47	153624	Ball	Flywheel	425	130
1955	Six	N-12	AC 44-5	.035	⑤	28–35	153624	Ball	Flywheel	425	130
	V8	N-12	AC 44-5	.035	⑤	26–33	18436572	③	Damper	425	130
	Corv. 6	N-12	AC 43-5	.035	⑤	41–47	153624	Ball	Flywheel	425	130
	Corv. V8	N-12	AC 43-5	.035	⑤	26–33	18436572	③	Damper	425	130
1956	Six	N-12	AC 44-5	.035	⑤	28–35	153624	Ball	Flywheel	425	130
	V8	N-12	AC 44-5	.035	⑤	26–33	18436572	③	Damper	425	150
	Corvette	N-12	AC-C43	.035	⑤	26–33	18436572	③	Damper	425	150
1957	Six	N-12	AC 44	.035	⑤	28–35	153624	Ball	Flywheel	425	130
	V8	N-12	AC 44	.035	④	30	18436572	③	Damper	425	150
1958	Six	N-12	AC-44	.035	⑤	28–35	153624	Ball	Flywheel	425	130
	V8-283	N-12	AC-44	.035	④	30	18436572	4°BTDC	Damper	425	150
	V8-348	N-12	AC-44	.035	④	30	18436572	4°BTDC	Damper	425	160
	Corvette	N-12	AC-44	.035	④	30	18436572	4°BTDC	Damper	425	150
1959	6-Cyl.	N-12	AC-44	.035	⑤	28–35	153624	①	Flywheel	425	130
	V8-283	N-12	AC-44	.035	④	30	18436572	4°BTDC	Damper	450	140
	V8-348	N-12	AC-44N	.035	④	30	18436572	4°BTDC	Damper	450	160
	Corvette	N-12	AC-46	.035	④	30	18436572	4°BTDC	Damper	450	150
1960	6-Cyl.	N-12	AC-44	.035	⑤	28–35	153624	①	Flywheel	425	130
	V8-283	N-12	AC-44	.035	④	30	18436572	4°BTDC	Damper	450	140
	V8-348	N-12	AC-44N	.035	④	30	18436572	8°BTDC	Damper	450	150
	Corvette	N-12	AC-44	.035	④	30	18436572	4°BTDC	Damper	450	150
1961	6-Cyl.	N-12	AC-44	.035	⑤	28–35	153624	①	Flywheel	425	130
	V8-283	N-12	AC-44	.035	④	30	18436572	4°BTDC	Damper	450	140
	V8-348	N-12	AC-44N	.035	④	30	18436572	8°BTDC	Damper	450	150
	Corvette	N-12	AC-44	.035	④	30	18436572	4°BTDC	Damper	450	150

①—First short vertical line on flywheel clockwise from timing ball.
②—V8 cylinder numbering (front to rear): Left bank 1–3–5–7, right bank 2–4–6–8.
③—Second line before "O" mark on timing tab on front cover. Cars with two 4-barrel carburetors, use sixth line before "O" mark.
④—Turn adjusting screw in (clockwise) until engine misfires. Then turn screw ½ turn in opposite direction.
⑤—New points .019", used .016".

ENGINE TIGHTENING SPECIFICATIONS★

★Torque specifications are for clean and lightly lubricated threads only. Dry or dirty threads produce increased friction which prevents accurate measurement of tightness.

Year	Spark Plugs Ft. Lbs.	Cylinder Head Bolts Ft. Lbs.	Intake Manifold Ft. Lbs.	Exhaust Manifold Ft. Lbs.	Rocker Arm Shaft Bracket Ft. Lbs.	Rocker Arm Cover Ft. Lbs.	Connecting Rod Cap Bolts Ft. Lbs.	Main Bearing Cap Bolts Ft. Lbs.	Flywheel to Crankshaft Ft. Lbs.	Vibration Damper or Pulley Ft. Lbs.
1953–54 Six	20–25	90–95	①	①	25–30	6–7½	35–45	100–110	50–65	②
1955 Six	20–25	90–95	③	③	25–30	5	35–45	100–110	50–65	②
1955–56 V8	20–25	60–70	25–35	25–30	None	2½	30–35	60–70	55–65	②
1956–57 Six	20–25	90–95	③	③	25–30	④	35–45	100–110	50–65	②
1957 V8	20–25	60–70	25–35	18–22	None	④	30–35	60–70	55–65	②
1958–61 Six	25	90–95	25–35	③	20–25	④	35–45	100–110	55–65	②
1958–61 V8-283	25	60–70	25–35	⑤	None	④	30–35	60–70	55–65	②
1958–61 V8-348	25	60–70	25–35	⑤	None	④	35–45	95–105	55–65	②

①—Clamp bolts 15–20, stud nuts 25–30.
②—Pressed on.
③—End clamp bolts 15–20, center clamp bolts 25–30.
④—25 inch lbs.
⑤—Center clamp bolts 25–30, end clamp bolts 15–20.

VALVE SPECIFICATIONS

Year	Model	Valve Lash		Valve Angles		Valve Spring Installed Height	Valve Spring Pressure Lbs. @ In.	Valve Lift		Stem Clearance		Stem Diameter	
		Int.	Exh.	Seat	Face			Int.	Exh.	Intake	Exhaust	Int.	Exh.
CHEVROLET													
1953	Std. Tr.	.006H	.013H	①	①	1⁵³⁄₆₄	130 @ 1½	.2941	.3118	.001-.003	.002-.004	.3414	.3404
	Auto. Tr.	Zero	Zero	①	①	1⁵³⁄₆₄	160 @ 1½	.3275	.3275	.001-.003	.002-.004	.3414	.3404
	Corvette	.008H	.020H	①	①	1⅞	150 @ 1½	.4051	.4143	.001-.003	.003-.005	.3414	.3394
1954	Std. Tr.	.006H	.016H	①	①	1⁵³⁄₆₄	160 @ 1½	.2941	.3118	.001-.003	.002-.004	.3414	.3394
	Auto. Tr.	Zero	Zero	①	①	1²⁹⁄₃₂	182 @ 1½	.4004	.4004	.001-.003	.002-.004	.3414	.3394
	Corvette	.008H	.020H	①	①	1⅞	150 @ 1½	.4051	.4143	.001-.003	.003-.005	.3414	.3394
1955	6 Std. Tr.	.006H	.013H	①	①	1⁵¹⁄₆₄	160 @ 1½	.2941	.3118	.001-.003	.001-.003	.3414	.3414
	6 Auto. Tr.	Zero	Zero	①	①	1⁵¹⁄₆₄	202 @ 1¹⁵⁄₃₂	.4004	.4004	.001-.003	.001-.003	.3414	.3414
	V8 Std. Tr.	.008H	.016H	46	45	1⅝	150 @ 1²³⁄₆₄	.336	.343	.001-.003	.0015-.003	.3419	.3414
	V8 Auto. Tr.	Zero	Zero	46	45	1⅝	150 @ 1²³⁄₆₄	.324	.324	.001-.003	.0015-.003	.3419	.3414
	Corv. 6	.006H	.013H	①	①	1⁵¹⁄₆₄	155 @ 1¹⁵⁄₃₂	.4051	.4143	.001-.003	.001-.003	.3414	.3414
	Corv. V8	.008H	.018H	46	45	1⅝	156 @ 1⁵⁄₁₆ ②	.4043	.4136	.001-.003	.0015-.003	.3419	.3414
1956	Six	Zero	Zero	①	①	1⁵¹⁄₆₄	200 @ 1¹⁵⁄₃₂	.4004	.4004	.001-.003	.001-.003	.3414	.3414
	V8 Std. Tr.	Zero	Zero	46	45	1⅝	160 @ 1²³⁄₆₄	.3336	.3336	.001-.003	.0015-.003	.3419	.3414
	V8 Auto. Tr.	Zero	Zero	46	45	1⅝	160 @ 1²³⁄₆₄	.3732	.3732	.001-.003	.0015-.003	.3419	.3414
	Corv. ③	.008H	.018H	46	45	1⅝	165 @ 1⁵⁄₁₆	.4043	.4135	.001-.003	.0015-.003	.3419	.3414
1957	Six	Zero	Zero	①	①	1⁵¹⁄₆₄	200 @ 1¹⁵⁄₃₂	.4004	.4004	.001-.003	.001-.003	.3414	.3414
	V8-265	Zero	Zero	46	45	1⅝	160 @ 1²³⁄₆₄	.334	.334	.001-.003	.0015-.003	.3419	.3414
	V8-283	Zero	Zero	46	45	1⅝	160 @ 1²³⁄₆₄	.398	.398	.001-.003	.0015-.003	.3419	.3414
	Corv. ③	.012H	.018H	46	45	1⅝	160 @ 1²³⁄₆₄	.398	.398	.001-.003	.0015-.003	.3419	.3414
1958	Six	Zero	Zero	①	①	1⁵¹⁄₆₄	200 @ 1¹⁵⁄₃₂	.4004	.4004	.001-.003	.001-.003	.3414	.3414
	V8-283	Zero	Zero	46	45	1⅝	165 @ 1⁵⁄₁₆	.3987	.3987	.001-.003	.0015-.003	.3419	.3414
	V8-348	Zero	Zero	46	45	1¹⁹⁄₃₂	190 @ 1¹⁵⁄₆₄	.3987	.3987	.001-.003	.0025-.004	.3719	.3714
	Corvette	Zero	Zero	46	45	1⅝	165 @ 1⁵⁄₁₆	.3987	.3987	.001-.003	.0015-.003	.3419	.3414
1959	Six	Zero	Zero	①	①	1⁵¹⁄₆₄	165 @ 1¹⁷⁄₃₂	.3275	.3275	.001-.003	.001-.003	.3414	.3414
	V8-283	Zero	Zero	46	45	1⅝	165 @ 1⁵⁄₁₆	.3987	.3987	.001-.003	.0015-.003	.3419	.3414
	V8-348	Zero	Zero	46	45	1¹⁹⁄₃₂	190 @ 1¹⁵⁄₆₄	.3987	.3987	.001-.003	.0025-.004	.3719	.3714
	Corvette	Zero	Zero	46	45	1⅝	165 @ 1⁵⁄₁₆	.3987	.3987	.001-.003	.0015-.003	.3419	.3414
1960-61	④	.008H	.015H	①	①	1⁵¹⁄₆₄	163 @ 1¹⁷⁄₃₂	.3105	.3325	.001-.003	.001-.003	.3414	.3414
	6 Auto. Tr.	Zero	Zero	①	①	1⁵¹⁄₆₄	163 @ 1¹⁷⁄₃₂	.3275	.3275	.001-.003	.001-.003	.3414	.3414
	V8-283 ⑤	Zero	Zero	46	45	1⅝	160 @ 1²³⁄₆₄	.3336	.3336	.001-.003	.0015-.003	.3419	.3414
	V8-283 ⑥	Zero	Zero	46	45	1⅝	165 @ 1⁵⁄₁₆	.3987	.3987	.001-.003	.0015-.003	.3419	.3414
	V8-348	Zero	Zero	46	45	1¹⁹⁄₃₂	190 @ 1¹⁵⁄₆₄	.4005	.4119	.001-.003	.0025-.004	.3719	.3714
	Corvette	Zero	Zero	46	45	1⅝	165 @ 1⁵⁄₁₆	.3987	.3987	.001-.003	.0015-.003	.3419	.3414

①—Intake seat 31°, face 30°; exhaust seat 46°, face 45°.
②—Outer spring.
③—V8 with two 4-barrel carburetors.

④—Biscayne with manual shift transmission.
⑤—With 2-barrel carburetor.
⑥—With 4-barrel carburetor.

Year	Model	Fitting Pistons		Ring End Gap①		Wrist-pin Diameter	Rod Bearings		Main Bearings ②			
		Shim To Use	Pounds Pull On Scale	Comp.	Oil		Shaft Diameter	Bearing Clearance	Shaft Diameter	Bearing Clearance	Thrust on Bear. No.	Shaft End Play
1953-54	Corvette	.0015	7-18	.007	.005	.8662	2.311-2.312	.001-.003	③	.001-.003	3	.003-.009
1953	Std. Tr.	②	②	.007	.005	.8647	2.311-2.312	.001-.003	③	.001-.003	3	.003-.009
	Powerglide	.0015	7-18	.007	.005	.8662	2.311-2.312	.001-.003	③	.001-.003	3	.003-.009
1954	Std. Tr.	②	②	.007	.005	.8662	2.311-2.312	.001-.003	③	.001-.003	3	.003-.009
	Powerglide	.0015	7-18	.007	.005	.8662	2.311-2.312	.001-.003	③	.001-.003	3	.003-.009
1955	Corv. 6	.0015	7-18	.007	.015	.8662	2.311-2.312	.001-.003	③	.001-.003	3	.003-.009
	Corv. V8	.0015	7-18	.009	.015	.9271	1.999-2.000	.001-.003	2.2978-2.2988	.001-.003	5	.002-.006
	Six	.0015	7-18	.007	.015	.8662	2.311-2.312	.001-.003	③	.001-.003	3	.003-.009
	V8	.0015	7-18	.007	.015	.9271	1.999-2.000	.001-.003	2.2978-2.2988	.001-.003	5	.002-.006
1956	Six	.0015	7-18	.007	.015	.8662	2.311-2.312	.001-.003	③	.001-.003	3	.003-.009
	V8	.0015	7-18	.007	.015	.9271	1.999-2.000	.001-.003	2.2978-2.2988	.001-.003	5	.002-.006
	Corvette	.0015	7-18	.009	.015	.9271	1.999-2.000	.001-.003	2.2978-2.2988	.001-.003	5	.002-.006
1957	Six	.0015	7-18	.007	.015	.8662	2.311-2.312	.001-.003	③	.001-.003	3	.003-.009
	V8-265	.0015	7-18	.009	.005	.9271	1.999-2.000	.001-.003	2.2978-2.2988	.001-.003	5	.002-.006
	V8-283	.0015	7-18	.009	.005	.9271	1.999-2.000	.001-.003	2.2978-2.2988	.001-.003	5	.002-.006
1958-61	Six	.0015	7-18	.007	.015	.8662	2.311-2.312	.0007-.0027	③	.001-.003	3	.003-.009
	V8-283	.0015	7-18	.010	.015	.9271	1.999-2.000	.0007-.0027	2.2978-2.2988	.0008-.0034	5	.002-.006
	V8-348	.0015	7-18	.015	.015	.9896	2.199-2.200	.0007-.0027	2.4980-2.4990	.0006-.0032	5	.003-.007

①—Fit rings in tapered bores the clearance listed in tightest portion of ring travel.
②—Piston should pass on a .002″ feeler with light pressure, and lock on a .003″ feeler.
③—No. 1, 2.6835-2.6845. No. 2, 2.7145-2.7155. No. 3, 2.7455-2.7465. No. 4, 2.7765-2.7775.

COOLING SYSTEM & CAPACITY DATA

Year	Model	Cooling System Data			Thermostat Opening Temp.		Fuel Tank Gals.	Engine Oil			Transmissions			Rear Axle Pints
		Quarts No Heater	Quarts With Heater	Rad. Cap Relief Pressure	①	②		Refill Qts.③	Summer Grade	Winter Grade	Std. Pints	With Over-drive Pints	Auto-matic Qts.	
1953-54	Corvette	17¾	18¼	3½-4½⑥	180	160	17¼	5	20W	10W	None	None	8	3½
	Others	16	17	3½-4½⑥	180	160	16	5	20W	10W	1½	None	5④	3½
1955	Corv. 6	17¾	18¼	3½-4½	180	160	17¼	5	20W	10W	None	None	5④	4
	Corv. V8	16	17	6¼-7½	180	160	17¼	4	20W	10W	None	None	5④	4
1955-56	Six	16	17	6¼-7½	180	160	16	5	20W	10W	2	3	5④	3½
	V8	16	17	6¼-7½	180	160	16	4	20W	10W	2	3	5④	3½
1956	Corvette	16	17	6¼-7½	180	160	17¼	5	20W	10W	2	None	5④	4
1957	Six	16	17	6¼-7½	180	160	16	5	20W	10W	2	3	5④	3½
	V8	16	17	6¼-7½	180	160	16	4	20W	10W	2	3	3½④	3½
1958	Six	16	17	13	180	160	20⑤	5	20W	10W	2	3	3½④	4
	V8-283	16	17	13⑦	180	160	20⑤	4	20W	10W	2	3	3½④	4
	V8-348	22	23	13	180	160	20⑤	4	20W	10W	2	3	3½④	4
1959	Six	17	18	13	180	160	20⑤	5	20W	10W	2	3	3½④	4
	V8-283	17½	18½	13	180	160	20⑤	4	20W	10W	2	3	3½④	4
	V8-348	21	22	13	180	160	20⑤	4	20W	10W	2	None	3½④	4
1960	Six	17	18	13	170	—	20⑧	5	20W	10W	2	3	3½④	4
	V8-283	17½	18½	13	170	—	20⑧	4	20W	10W	2	3	3½④	4
	V8-348	21	22	13	170	—	20⑧	4	20W	10W	2	3	4④	4
	Corvette	15½	16½	7	—	160	16	5	20W	10W	2⑨	None	3½④	4
1961	Six	17	18	13	170	...	20⑩	5	20W	10W	2	3	9	4
	V8-283	17½	18½	13	170	...	20⑩	4	20W	10W	2	3	9	4
	V8-348	21	22	13	170	...	20⑩	4	20W	10W	2⑨	None	4④	4
	Corvette	15	16½	7	170	...	16	5	20W	10W	2⑨	None	9	4

①—For permanent type anti-freeze.
②—For alcohol type anti-freeze.
③—Add one quart with filter change.
④—Refill capacity for transmission only.
⑤—Station Wagons 17 gals.
⑥—7 lbs. on 1954 models.
⑦—7 lbs. for Corvette.
⑧—18 gallons on 9-pass. wagon. 17 gallons on 6-pass. wagon.
⑨—Four speed transmission 1½ pints.
⑩—Station Wagons 19 gals.

GENERATOR AND REGULATOR SPECIFICATIONS

★To polarize generator, reconnect the leads to the regulator; then momentarily connect a jumper wire from the "Gen" to the "Bat" terminals of the regulator.

Car & Model	Generator Number	Rotation & Ground Polarity ①	Rated Cap. Amps.	Gen. Field Ground Location ★	Brush Spring Tension, Ounces	Field Current Amperes	Regulator Number	Cutout Relay Voltage to Close Points	Cutout Relay Armature Air Gap, Inch	Voltage Regulator Setting Volts	Current Regulator Setting Amperes	Current and Voltage Armature Air Gap, Inch
1953–54	1100018	C-N	45	External	28	1.75–1.9②	1118827	6.4	.020	7.3	45	.075
1953–54	1102793	C-N	45	External	28	1.87–2.0②	1118725	6.4	.020	7.4	47	.075
1955	1100310	C-N	25	External	28	1.5–1.62③	1118945	12.8	.020	14.5	25	.075
1955	1102020	C-N	30	External	28	1.48–1.62③	1118825	12.8	.020	14.5	25	.075
1956–57	1100326	C-N	25	External	28	1.5–1.62③	1119000	12.8	.020	14.5	25	.075
1956–57	1100321	C-N	25	External	28	1.5–1.62③	1119000	12.8	.020	14.5	25	.075
1956–57	1102041	C-N	30	External	28	1.48–1.62③	1119000	12.8	.020	14.5	30	.075
1956–57	1102042	C-N	30	External	28	1.48–1.62③	1119000	12.8	.020	14.5	30	.075
1956–58	1102043	C-N	30	External	28	1.48–1.62③	1119001	12.6	.020	14.3	30	.075
1958	1102096	C-N	30	External	28	1.69–1.79③	1119001	12.6	.020	14.3	30	.075
1958	1102097	C-N	30	External	28	1.69–1.79③	1119001	12.6	.020	14.3	30	.075
1958	1102114	C-N	35	External	28	1.69–1.79③	1119002	12.6	.020	14.3	35	.075
1958	1102115	C-N	35	External	28	1.69–1.79③	1119002	12.6	.020	14.3	35	.075
1958	1102059	C-N	30	External	28	1.48–1.62③	1119001	12.6	.020	14.3	30	.075
1959 Six	1102096	C-N	30	External	28	1.69–1.79③	1119001	12.6	.020	14.3	30	.075
1959 V8	1102097	C-N	30	External	28	1.69–1.79③	1119001	12.6	.020	14.3	30	.075
1959 Corv.	1102043	C-N	30	External	28	1.48–1.62③	1119234	12.6	.020	14.3	30	.075
1959 Corv.	1102059	C-N	30	External	28	1.48–1.62③	1119235	12.6	.020	14.3	30	.075
1959 Air Cond.	1102114	C-N	35	External	28	1.69–1.79③	1119002	12.6	.020	14.3	35	.075
1959 P. Steer.	1102115	C-N	35	External	28	1.69–1.79③	1119002	12.6	.020	14.3	35	.075
1960–61 Six	1102096	C-N	30	External	28	1.69–1.79③	1119001	12.6	.020	14.3	30	.075
1960–61 V8	1102097	C-N	30	External	28	1.69–1.79③	1119001	12.6	.020	14.3	30	.075
1960–61 Corv.	1102043	C-N	30	External	28	1.69–1.79③	1119001	12.6	.020	14.3	30	.075
1960–61 V8-348	1102097	C-N	30	External	28	1.69–1.79③	1119234	12.6	.020	14.3	30	.075
1960 Air Cond.	1102174	C-N	35	External	28	1.69–1.79③	1119002	12.6	.020	14.3	35	.075
1960 V8-348	1102174	C-N	35	External	28	1.69–1.79③	1119235	12.6	.020	14.3	35	.075

①—C-Clockwise. N-Negative.   ②—At 6 volts.   ③—At 12 volts.

WHEEL ALIGNMENT SPECIFICATIONS

Year	Model	Caster, Degrees Limits	Caster, Degrees Desired	Camber, Degrees Limits	Camber, Degrees Desired	Toe-In, Inches	Toe-out on Turns, Degrees① Outer Wheel	Toe-out on Turns, Degrees① Inner Wheel	Kingpin or Steering Axis Inclination Degrees②
1953–55	Corvette	0 to + 1	+ ½	0 to + 1	+ ½	0 to ⅛	17	20	3½ to 4½
1953	All	0 to + 1	+ ½	0 to + 1	+ ½	3/16 to 5/16	20	22 to 26	3½ to 4½
1954	All	0 to + 1	+ ½	0 to + 1	+ ½	1/16 to 3/16	20	22 to 26	3½ to 4½
1955	All	− ½ to + ½	0	0 to + 1	+ ½	⅛ to 3/16	20	20½ to 24½	3 to 4
1956–57	Corvette	0 to + 1	+ ½	0 to + 1	+ ½	0 to ⅛	20	23	3½ to 4½
1956–58	All	+ ½ to + 1½	+ 1	0 to + 1	+ ½	⅛ to 3/16	18⅓	20	3½ to 4½
1958	Corvette	+ 2¼	+ 2¼	0 to + 1	+ ½	0 to ⅛	20	23	3½ to 4½
1959–61	6, V8	− ½ to + ½	0	0 to + 1	+ ½	1/16 to ⅛	17° 54′	20	7° 11′
	Corvette	+ 1½ to + 2½	+ 2	− ½ to + ½	0	0 to ⅛	17	20	3½ to 4½

①—Incorrect toe-out, when other adjustments are correct, indicates bent steering arms.
②—Incorrect kingpin angle with correct camber indicates bent suspension arms or steering knuckle support.

DISTRIBUTOR SPECIFICATIONS

Year	Model	Part No. ①	Rotation ②	Cam Angle, Degrees	Breaker Point Opening, Inch	Condenser Capacity, Mfds.③	Breaker Arm Spring Tension, Ounces	Centrifugal Advance Data Degrees @ R.P.M. of Dist.		Vacuum Advance Data		
								Advance Starts	Full Advance	Inches of Vacuum to Start Plunger Movement	Inches of Vacuum for Full Plunger Travel	Maximum Vacuum Advance, Dist. Degrees
1953	Std. Trans.	1112389	C	38–45	⑦	.18–.23	19–23	1 @ 350	17 @ 1800	4–6	7½–10	7½
	Powerglide	1112388	C	38–45	⑦	.18–.23	19–23	1 @ 375	13 @ 1750	7–8½	18½	10
1953–55	Corvette	1112314	C	40½–47½	⑦	.18–.23	19–23	1 @ 375	13 @ 1750	4–6	7½–10	7½
1954	Std. Trans.	1112388	C	38–45	⑦	.18–.23	19–23	1 @ 375	13 @ 1750	7–8½	18½	10
	Powerglide	1112396	C	38–45	⑦	.18–.23	19–23	1 @ 375	13 @ 1750	7–8½	18½	10
1955–56	Six	1112403	C	28–35	⑦	.18–.23	19–23	1 @ 375	13 @ 1750	4–6	7½–10	7½
1955	V8	1110847	C	26–33	⑦	.18–.23	19–23	1 @ 400	16 @ 1800	5–7	12–14½	11¾
1956	V8-Std.Tr.	1110847	C	26–33	⑦	.18–.23	19–23	1 @ 400	16 @ 1800	5–7	12–14½	11¾
	V8-Powerglide	1110866	C	26–33	⑦	.18–.23	19–23	1 @ 325	8½ @ 900	5–7	12–14½	11¾
	V8④	1110866	C	26–33	⑦	.18–.23	19–23	1 @ 325	8½ @ 900	5–7	12–14½	11¾
	Corvette	1110860	C	26–33	⑦	.18–.23	19–23	1 @ 350	14 @ 1750	None	None	None
1957	Six	1112403	C	28–35	⑦	.18–.23	19–23	1 @ 375	13 @ 1750	4–6	7½–10	7½
	V8	1110874	C	30	⑤	.18–.23	19–23	1 @ 400	16 @ 1800	5–7	11¾–13¾	11
	V8	1110890	C	30	⑤	.18–.23	19–23	1½ @ 400	14 @ 1850	7–9	13½–15½	11
	Corvette	1110891	C	30	⑤	.18–.23	19–23	1½ @ 400	14 @ 1850	None	None	None
1958	Six	1112403	C	28–35	⑦	.18–.23	19–23	1 @ 375	13 @ 1750	4–6	7½–10	7½
	V8-283	1110920	C	30	⑤	.18–.23	19–23	1 @ 375	14 @ 1875	7–9	15–16	7½
	V8-348	1110907	C	30	⑤	.18–.23	19–23	1½ @ 425	12 @ 2000	7–9	15–16	7½
	V8-283	1110915	C	30	⑤	.18–.23	19–23	1½ @ 400	14 @ 1850	3¾–5¾	13–15	12
1959–61	Six	1112403	C	28–35	⑦	.18–.23	19–23	1 @ 375	13 @ 1750	4–6	15–16	11
	V8	1110947	C	30	⑤	.18–.23	19–23	1 @ 375	14 @ 1875	7–9	15–16	7½
	Corvette	1110946	C	30	⑤	.18–.23	19–23	1½ @ 400	14 @ 1850	7–9	15–16	7½
	Turbo Tr.	1110891	C	⑥	⑥	.18–.23	19–23	1½ @ 400	14 @ 1850	None	None	None
	348 Eng.	1110948	C	30	⑤	.18–.23	19–23	1 @ 425	12 @ 2300	7–9	15–16	7½
	348 Eng.	1110914	C	⑥	⑥	.18–.23	19–23	1 @ 600	11 @ 3000	None	None	None
	348 Eng.	1110915	C	30	⑤	.18–.23	19–23	1½ @ 400	14 @ 1850	4¾	13½	12

①—Distributor number stamped on plate riveted to side of housing.
②—As viewed from the top. C—Clockwise.
③—Microfarads—as indicated on a condenser tester.
④—With 4-barrel carburetor and dual exhaust system.
⑤—Turn adjusting screw in (clockwise) until engine misfires. Then turn screw ½ turn in opposite direction.
⑥—Adjust cam angle of each breaker individually to 28–30 deg. which gives point opening of .014"–.018". Cam angle with both breakers should be 33–35 deg.
⑦—New points .019", used .016".

REAR AXLE AND BRAKE CYLINDER SPECIFICATIONS

Year	Model	Ring Gear & Pinion Backlash, Inch	Drive Pinion Adjustment	Drive Pinion Bearing Preload, Inch Lbs.	Drive Pinion Bearing Adjustment	Axle Shaft End Play, Inch	Hydraulic Cylinder Bore Sizes, Inch		
							Wheel Cylinder		Master Cylinder
							Front	Rear	
1953–54	All	.005–.008	Shims	⑧	None	①	1⅛	1	1
1955	All	.005–.008	Shim	⑧	None	②	1⅛	1	1
1956–59	All	.006–.009	Shim	⑧	None	②	1⅛	1	1
1960–61	All	.006–.009	Shim	⑧	None	②	1³⁄₁₆	1	1

①—Select axle shaft spacer to give free fit to .014" maximum clearance between ends of axle shaft and spacer.
②—Controlled by bearing retaining ring.
⑧—15–25 inch lbs. with new bearings, 5–15 inch lbs. with used bearings.

STARTING MOTOR SPECIFICATIONS

Year	Model	Part No.	Rotation ①	Brush Spring Tension, Ounces	No Load Test			Torque Test		
					Amperes	Volts	R.P.M.	Amperes	Volts	Torque, Lbs. Ft.
1953	All	1107109	C	24 Min.	70	5.65	5500	550	3.25	11
1954	Std. Trans.	1107109	C	24 Min.	70	5.65	5500	550	3.25	11
	Powerglide	1108035	C	24 Min.	80	5.67	5500	600	3.0	14
1955	Six	1107626	C	35 Min.	75	10.3	6900	435	5.8	10½
	V8	1107627	C	35 Min.	75	10.3	6900	435	5.8	10½
1956	Six	1107644	C	35 Min.	75	10.3	6900	435	5.8	10½
	V8 Std. Trans.	1107645	C	35 Min.	75	10.3	6900	435	5.8	10½
	V8 Powerglide	1107649	C	35 Min.	75	10.3	6900	435	5.8	10½
1957-58	Six	1107652	C	35 Min.	49–76	10.6	6200–9400	270–310	4.25	10½
	V8	1107664	C	35 Min.	49–76	10.6	6200–9400	270–310	4.25	10½
	V8	1107660	C	35 Min.	49–76	10.6	6200–9400	270–310	4.25	10½
1958	V8-348	1107668	C	35 Min.	65–100	10.6	3600–5100	300–360	3.5	10½
	V8-348	1107687	C	35 Min.	65–100	10.6	3600–5100	300–360	3.5	10½
1959-60	Six	1107652	C	35 Min.	49–76	10.6	6200–9400	270–310	4.25	10.5
	V8-283	1107664	C	35 Min.	49–76	10.6	6200–9400	270–310	4.25	10.5
	Turbo Tr.	1107694	C	35 Min.	49–76	10.6	6200–9400	270–310	4.25	10.5
	V8-348	1107688	C	35 Min.	65–100	10.6	3600–5100	300–360	3.50	....
	V8-348	1107687	C	35 Min.	65–100	10.6	3600–5100	300–360	3.50	....
	V8-348	1107712	C	35 Min.	80–120	10.6	4700–5400	290–370	2.00	....
1961	Six	1107888	C	35 Min.	49–76	10.6	6200–6900			
	V8-283	1107889	C	35 Min.	49–76	10.6	6200–9400			
	V8-283	1107892	C	35 Min.	49–76	10.6	6200–9400			
	V8-348	1107891	C	35 Min.	65–100	10.6	3600–5100			
	V8-348	1107890	C	35 Min.	65–100	10.6	3600–5100			
	Corvette	1107664	C	35 Min.	49–76	10.6	6200–9400	270–310	4.25	10.5

①—As viewed from the drive end. C—Clockwise.

SERIAL NUMBER LOCATION
Plate On Left Front Door Pillar
ENGINE NUMBER LOCATION
Sixes: Right Side Of Block At Rear Of Distributor
V8's: Front Right Side Of Block
ENGINE IDENTIFICATION

Year	Engine	Suffix Letter ①	Year	Engine	Suffix Letter ①
1957	6-235②	A	1958-61	6-235②	A
	6-235③	B		6-235③	B
	V8-265②	C		V8-283②	C
	V8-283②	E		V8-283③	D
	V8-283③	F		V8-283④	E
	V8-283④	G		V8-348②	F
				V8-348③	G
				V8-348④	H

①—Engine identified by first letter after engine number.
②—Manual shift transmission.
③—Powerglide.
④—Turboglide.

1953-55 Corvette

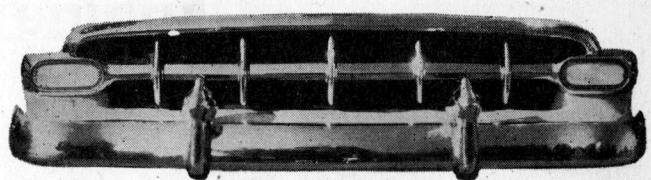
1954 Chevrolet

1953 Chevrolet

1955 Chevrolet

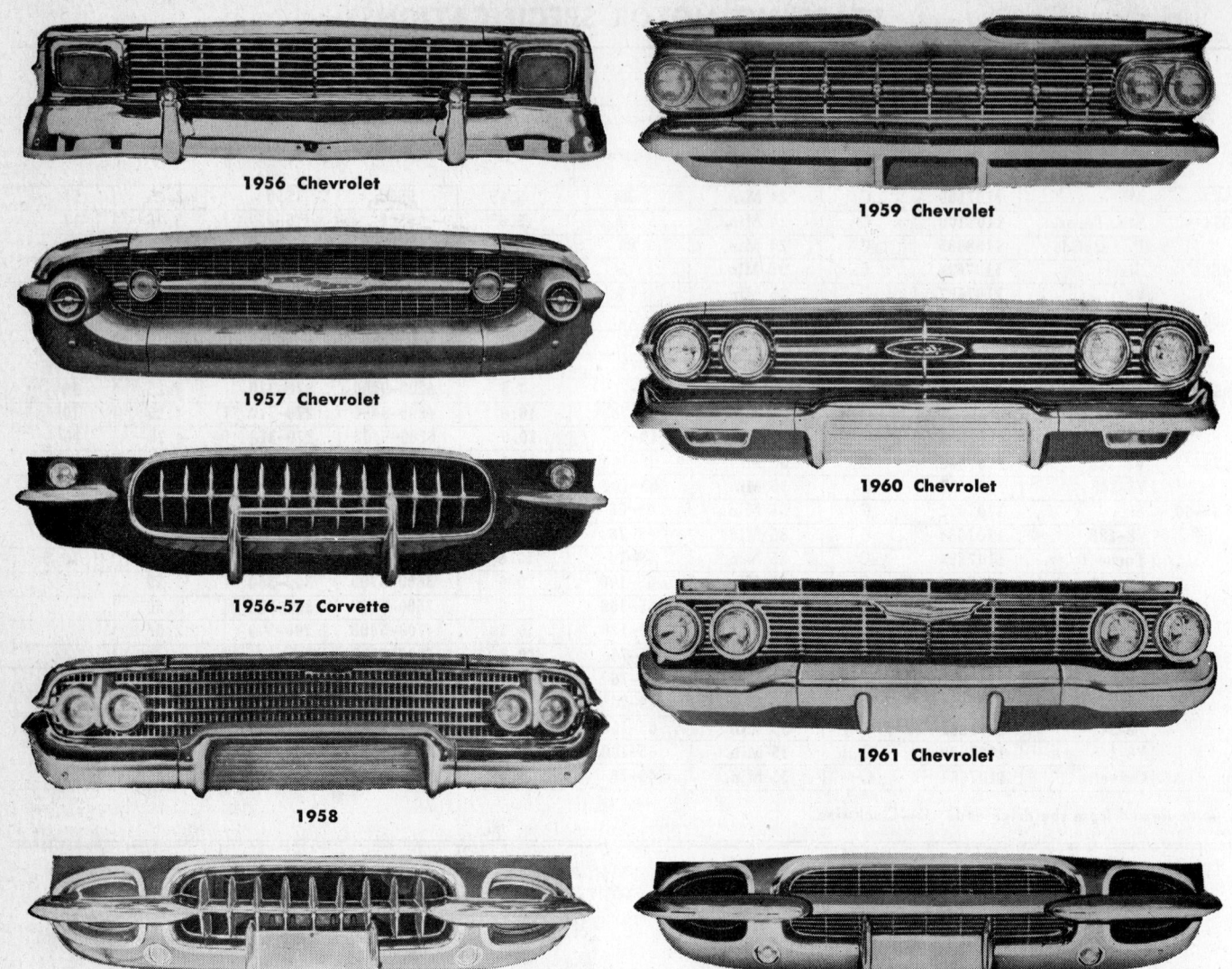

1956 Chevrolet

1959 Chevrolet

1957 Chevrolet

1960 Chevrolet

1956-57 Corvette

1958

1961 Chevrolet

1958-60 Corvette

1961 Corvette

Engine Section

ENGINE, REPLACE

In addition to the usual items such as radiator, hood, fuel and electrical lines, and linkage, it is necessary to perform the following operations:

1. On V8s, remove oil filter, distributor cap and power steering and air suspension lines (if equipped).
2. Unfasten exhaust pipe from manifolds.
3. Disconnect speedometer cable and remove propeller shaft.
4. On 1955-57 Six, disconnect R.H. headlamp, parking lamp and horn wires and remove horns. Remove battery, its support and cables. Remove windshield wiper motor.
5. Attach a suitable lifting rig and unfasten all engine and transmission

mounts. Then lift out engine and transmission as a unit.
6. Reverse above procedure to install.

CYLINDER HEAD
1955-61 V8-265, V8-283

1. Drain radiator and remove air cleaner.
2. Disconnect throttle rod from carburetor. On Powerglide or Turboglide models, disconnect lower transmission throttle lever rod.
3. Disconnect fuel, vacuum and automatic choke lines from carburetor.
4. Disconnect coil wires and remove distributor.
5. On overdrive models, disconnect

kickdown switch wires from switch.
6. Remove spark plugs.
7. Remove water outlet hose and heater hose from intake manifold.
8. Remove temperature indicator unit from intake manifold.
9. Unfasten and remove intake manifold.
10. Remove fan belt.
11. Disconnect exhaust manifold from cross-over pipe and allow cross-over pipe to drop for clearance.
12. Remove heat control valve from right bank exhaust manifold.
13. Disconnect wires from generator.
14. Remove exhaust manifolds.
15. Remove choke heat tube and rocker arm covers.
16. Back off rocker arm nuts, pivot rocker arms to clear push rods and

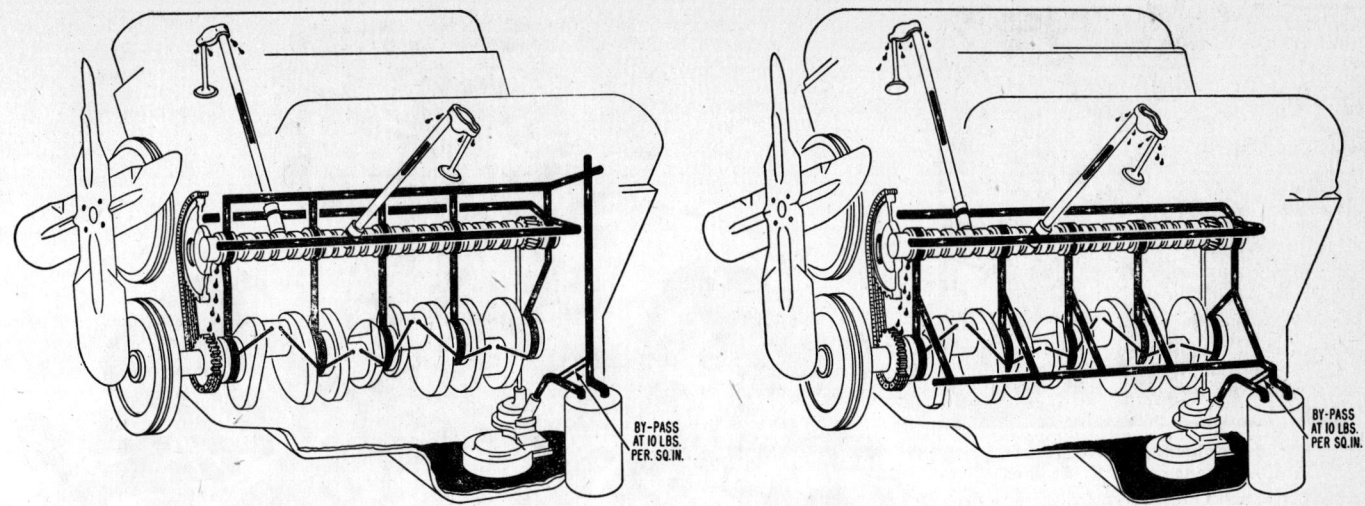

Engine lubrication, V8-283 cu. in. engine   Engine lubrication, V8-348 cu. in. engine

remove push rods. *Be certain that push rod seats on solid lifters do not come out of lifters with push rods. Snap push rod lower end to one side before lifting to break loose push rod from seat.*

17. Remove head bolts and lift off heads. *On 1960-61 models, be sure to note that the bolts in positions 17 and 14, Fig. 1, are shorter in length and must be installed in these positions upon reassembly.*

18. Reverse the above procedure to install the heads and tighten bolts in the sequence shown in Fig. 1. Torque head bolts 60-70 lb. ft., and intake and exhaust manifold bolts to 25-35 lb. ft.

1958-61 V8-348 Engine

1. When removing right head on air conditioned cars, remove air compressor, mounting brackets and lines.
2. When removing left head on cars with power steering, remove power steering pump or air suspension compressor, mounting brackets and lines.
3. Drain cooling system.
4. Remove air cleaner and disconnect choke and throttle rod.
5. Disconnect fuel and vacuum lines from carburetor.
6. Remove distributor and spark plugs.
7. Remove water outlet hose and heater hose from intake manifold.
8. Remove intake manifold.
9. Remove exhaust manifolds.
10. Remove generator.
11. Remove rocker arm covers, back off rocker arm nuts, pivot rocker

arms to clear push rods and lift out push rods.
12. Unfasten and remove cylinder heads.
13. Reverse removal procedure to install the heads and tighten them in the sequence shown in Fig. 2 to a torque of 60-70 lb. ft. Tighten intake manifold bolts and the center bolts on exhaust manifolds to a torque of 25-35 lb. ft. Exhaust manifold end bolts to 18-22 lb. ft.

1953-61 Six

1. Drain radiator, raise hood and remove air cleaner. Disconnect throttle and choke wires from carburetor.
2. Disconnect throttle rod from carburetor.
3. Disconnect gas and vacuum lines from carburetor.
4. Remove gas and vacuum line retaining clip from water outlet.
5. Remove manifold assembly.
6. Remove water outlet and thermostat from cylinder head.
7. Remove rocker arm cover.
8. Remove all spark plugs.
9. Detach coil and lay it down out of the way.
10. Remove push rod cover.
11. Disconnect oil line from rocker arm connector (none after 1957).
12. Remove temperature indicator element from cylinder head.
13. Remove rocker arm assembly.
14. Remove bolts and lift off cylinder head.
15. Reverse removal procedure to install the head and tighten bolts in the sequence shown in Fig. 3.

VALVE ARRANGEMENT

Front To Rear

V8s . . . . E-I-I-E-E-I-I-E
Sixes . . . . E-I-I-E-E-I-I-E-E-I-I-E

VALVES, ADJUST

V8 Engines

Before adjusting valve operating clearance, it is extremely important that the engine be thoroughly warmed up to normalize the expansion of all parts. This is very important because during the warm-up period the valve clearances will change considerably. To adjust the valves during or before this warm-up period will produce clearances which will be far from correct after the engine reaches normal operating temperature.

Covering the radiator will not materially hasten this normalizing process because even with the water temperature quickly raised, it does not change the rate at which the oil temperature increases and becomes stabilized, or the engine parts become normalized.

The actual temperature of the oil is not as important as stabilizing the oil temperature. The expansion or contraction of the valve mechanism, cylinder head and block are relative to this oil temperature. These parts stop expanding and valve clearance changes cease to take place only after the oil temperature is stabilized.

1. Normalize engine.
2. Remove automatic choke heat tube and remove rocker arm covers. Keep

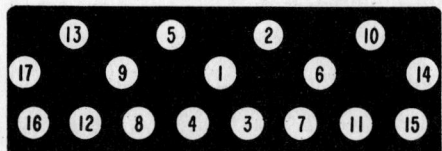

Fig. 1 Cylinder head tightening. V8-265 and V8-283

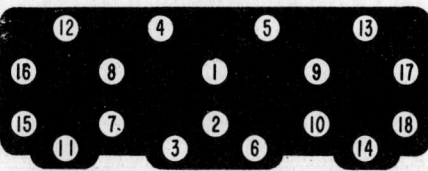

Fig. 2 Cylinder head tightening. V8-348

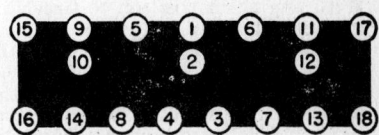

Fig. 3 Cylinder head tightening. All sixes

Fig. 4 Adjusting valve rocker arm clearance. V8 Engines

cover screws and reinforcements together.

3. Check torque of all manifold and head bolts as outlined under *Cylinder Head & Manifolds* installation.
4. Reinstall automatic choke heat tube.
5. Lubricate valve stems to assure freedom of action.

V8s With Solid Lifters

After the foregoing preliminary operations have been performed and with the engine idling, turn the self-locking rocker arm stud nuts as required to obtain the clearances given in the *Valve Data* chart (see Fig. 4).

V8s With Hydraulic Lifters

1. Crank engine until mark on harmonic balancer lines up with "O" mark on timing tab fastened to engine front cover with engine in No. 1 firing position. This may be determined by touching No. 1 valves as the balancer mark approaches the "O" mark. If these valves are not moving the engine is in No. 1 firing position. If they do move, the engine is in No. 6 firing position and should be turned over one more time to reach No. 1 firing position.
2. Valve adjustment is made by backing off the rocker arm stud nut until there is play in the valve push rod and then tightened just enough to remove all push rod-to-rocker arm clearance. This may be determined by rocking the push rod as the nut is tightened. When rod does not readily move in relation to the rocker arm, the clearance has been eliminated. *The adjusting nut should then be tightened an additional 1½ turns to place the hydraulic lifter plunger in the center of its travel. No further adjustment is required.*
3. With engine in position to fire No. 1 cylinder, the following valves may be adjusted: Exhaust 1-3-4-8. Intake 1-2-5-7.
4. Crank engine one more revolution which will bring it in the firing position for No. 6 cylinder. Then the following valves may be adjusted: Exhaust 2-5-6-7. Intake 3-4-6-8.

Turbo-Thrust 348 cu. in. engine. Note wedge-shaped combustion chamber formed in block and that underside of cylinder head is flat

V8-265 and V8-283 cylinder head and related parts

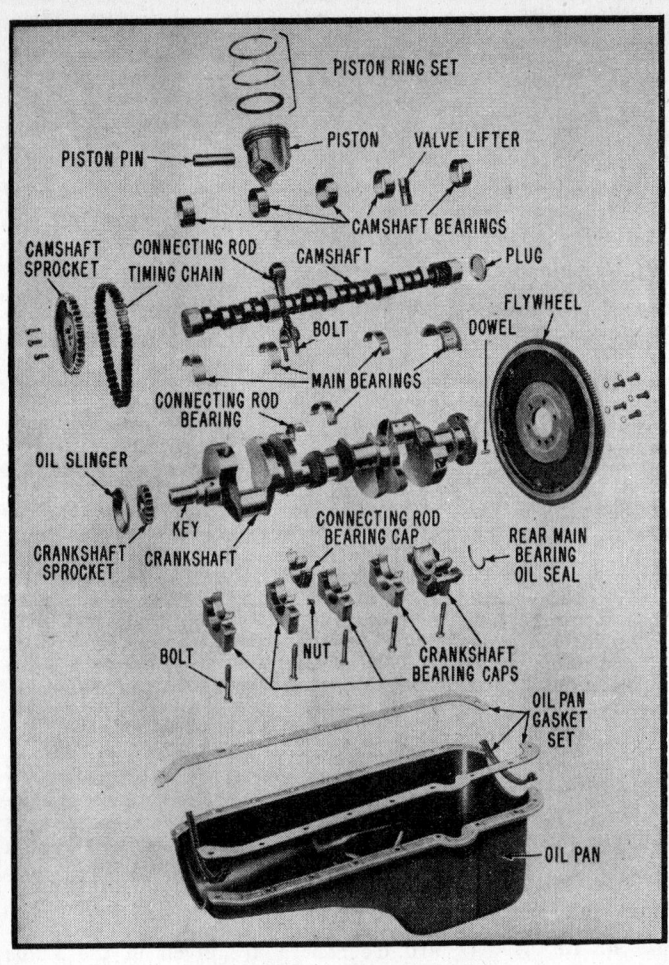

V8-265 and V8-283 internal parts

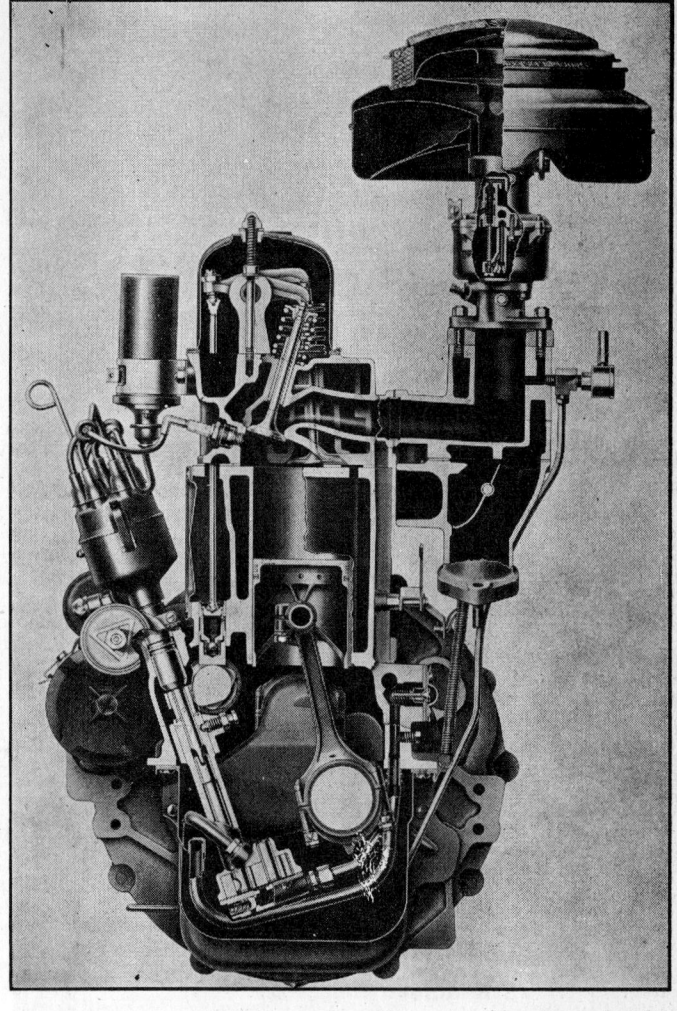

Sectional view of 6-cylinder engine. This engine features hydraulic valve lifters

Service Note

To be sure that the valves and lifters function perfectly, it is strongly recommended that a vacuum gauge be used when tightening the rocker arm nuts. With vacuum gauge connected and engine idling, tighten each rocker arm nut until the *highest and steadiest vacuum is indicated on the gauge.*

6-Cyl. With Solid Lifters

Before adjusting valves, it is extremely important that the engine be thoroughly warmed up to normalize the expansion of all parts. Tests have shown that valve clearances will vary as much as .005 in. from a cold check through the normalizing range. Consequently the engine should be run approximately 30 minutes to properly normalize all parts.

Covering the radiator will not materially hasten the normalizing process because even with the water temperature quickly raised to 185 degrees it does not change the rate at which the oil temperature increases or the engine parts become normalized.

1. Remove rocker arm cover.
2. Run engine at fast idle and check oil temperature with a thermometer at the overflow pipe on the valve rocker shaft connector. When oil temperature remains constant for five minutes, engine is normalized and ready for valve adjustment.
3. Tighten all manifold bolts, rocker arm nuts and cylinder head bolts.
4. Lubricate valve stems with engine oil to insure free movement of valves in their guides.
5. Adjust valve clearance to the specifications given in the *Valve Data* chart.
6. Install rocker arm cover, using a new gasket. Tighten cover nuts to 5 lbs. ft. torque and check for oil leaks.

6-Cyl. With Hydraulic Lifters

Anytime that the rocker arm assemblies or valve lifters are removed from the engine it is necessary to make an initial adjustment for each valve lifter. This adjustment must be made when the lifter is on the base circle of the cam according to the following procedure:

1. Remove distributor cap.
2. Crank engine until distributor rotor points to No. 1 cylinder position with the breaker points open. In this position the No. 1 piston is at the top of its compression stroke with both lifters on the base circle of the cam and both valves can be adjusted.
3. Turn the rocker arm adjusting screw down until all lash is removed from lifter to valve. This can be determined by checking push rod side play at the adjusting screw end while turning the adjusting screw. At the point where no side play of the push rod can be felt, continue turning adjusting screw down 1½ turns and tighten the lock nut securely. This places the lifter plunger in the center of its travel and no further adjustment is required.
4. Crank the engine until the distributor rotor is pointing to No. 5 cylinder position. Then adjust both valves for No. 5 cylinder in the manner described above.
5. The other valves may be adjusted by setting the engine with the distributor rotor pointing to the rest of the cylinder positions in the sequence of the firing order which is 1-5-3-6-2-4.

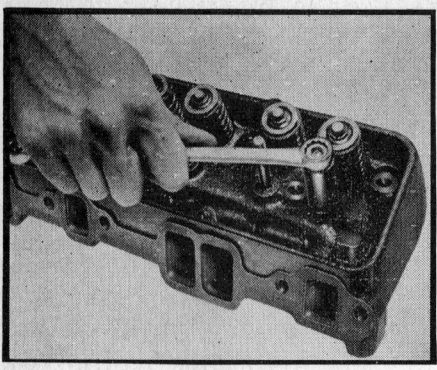

Fig. 5 Removing valve rocker stud. V8 Engines

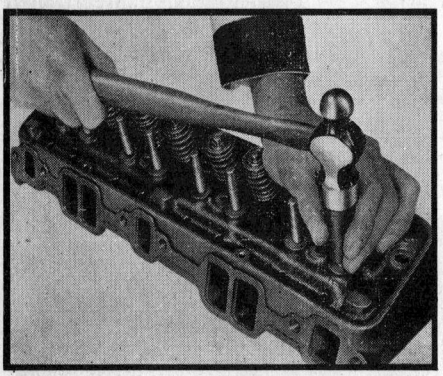

Fig. 6 Installing valve rocker stud. V8 Engines

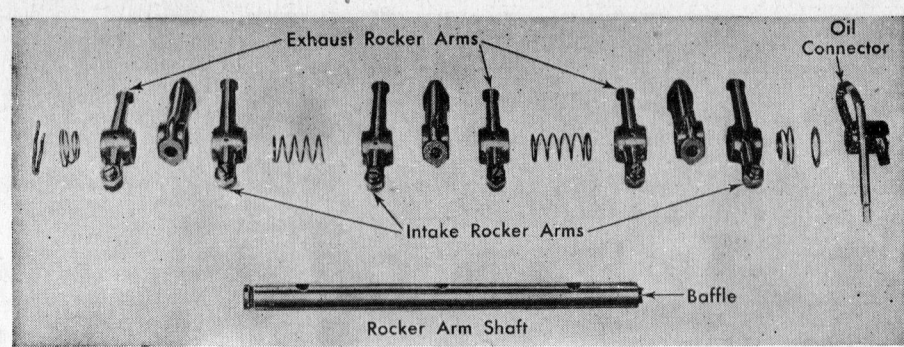

Fig. 7 Layout of rear rocker arm and shaft parts. All Sixes

ROCKER ARM STUDS

V8 Engines

Rocker arm studs that have damaged threads may be replaced with standard studs. Loose studs should be replaced with .003" oversize studs which are available for replacement.

Remove the old stud by placing a suitable spacer, Fig. 5, over the stud. Install a nut and flat washer on the stud and pull out the stud by turning the nut. After reaming the hole for an oversize stud, coat the press-fit area of the new stud with rear axle lubricant. Install the stud by driving it in until it protrudes from the head the same distance as the other studs, Fig. 6.

ROCKER ARMS

6-Cylinder Engines

Sludge and gum formation in the rocker arms and shafts will restrict the normal flow of oil to the rocker arms and valves. Each time the rocker arm and shaft assemblies are removed they should be disassembled and thoroughly cleaned.

1. Remove the support bolts, hairpin locks, springs, rocker arms and supports.
2. Clean all sludge and gum formation from the inside and outside of the shafts and from the oil distributor to valve rocker shaft tube.
3. Clean oil holes and passages in the shafts and rocker arms.

4. Clean the rocker arm shaft oil connector assembly.
5. Inspect the shafts for wear. Check the fit of the rocker arms on the shafts for excessive wear.
6. There are three each of four different types rocker arms used—right and left hand exhaust and right and left hand intake as shown in Fig. 7. Each rocker arm carries an identification number and the following chart serves to identify them.

1953-54 All; 1955-57 Std. Trans.

No. on Rocker Arm	Type Rocker Arm	For Cylinder No.
9	L. H. Exhaust 1-3-5	Exhaust
0	R. H. Exhaust 2-4-6	Exhaust
3	L. H. Intake 2-4-6	Intake
4	R. H. Intake 1-3-5	Intake

1955-57 Powerglide Transmission and All 1958-61

No. on Rocker Arm	Type Rocker Arm	For Cylinder No.
7	L. H. Intake 2-4-6	Intake
8	R. H. Intake 1-3-5	Intake
3	L. H. Exhaust 1-3-5	Exhaust
4	R. H. Exhaust 2-4-6	Exhaust

7. One end of each rocker arm shaft is plugged. The open end of each shaft must be toward the center.

VALVES, REMOVE

Place the cylinder head on its side and, with a suitable valve spring compressor, compress the valve spring and remove the valve locks. Release the tool and remove spring retainer, the valve baffle on intake valves, and seal from valve stem. Repeat operation on each valve.

Remove valves from head and place them in a board with numbered holes so they will be in proper sequence for inspection and assembly.

VALVE GUIDES

V8 Engines

Valves operate in guide holes bored directly in the cylinder head. When valve stem-to-guide clearance becomes excessive, valves with oversize stems of .003",

.015" and .030" are available for service replacement. When necessary to install valves with oversize stems the valve bores should be reamed to provide the clearance given in the *Valve Data* chart.

Check the valve stem clearance of each valve (after cleaning) in its respective valve guide. If the clearance exceeds the service limits of .004" on the intake or .005" on the exhaust, ream the valve guides to accommodate the next oversize diameter valve stem.

6-Cyl. Engines

Clean the valve guides with a wire guide brush, and clean the valves with a wire wheel brush, making sure that all carbon is removed from the top and bottom of the heads, as well as the gum which might have accumulated on the stems.

Check the clearance between valve stems and guides carefully. The standard clearances are given in the *Valve Data* chart.

Excessive clearance between valve stems and guides will cause improper seating and burned valves. When there is too much clearance between intake valve stems and guides, there is a tendency to draw oil vapor through the guide on the suction stroke, causing excessive oil consumption, fouled spark plugs and poor low speed performance.

Valve stem-to-guide clearance may be checked with special "GO" and "NO-GO" gauges. Lacking these, an alternate method is to take a new valve and place it in each valve guide and feel the clearance by moving the valve stem back and forth. If this check shows excessive clearance, it will be necessary to replace the guides that are worn as indicated by this test. If the clearance is

Fig. 8 Install valve guides as shown. 1953-54 standard 6-cylinder engine

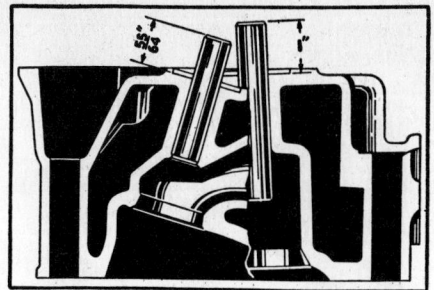

Fig. 9 Location of valve guides in 1953-54 6-cylinder engine used with Powerglide. 1955 intake 15/16", exhaust 7/8" 1956-61 intake 1", exhaust 15/16"

not excessive when checking with a new valve but is excessive when checked with the old valve, it is an indication that the old valve stem is worn and a new valve must be installed.

To remove the old guides, place the cylinder head on the table of an arbor press and, with a suitable piece of round stock, press out the guides.

Special drivers having stop collars are available to install the new guides to the correct position. Lacking these tools, install the guides so they are positioned as shown in Figs. 8 and 9. After the guides are installed, they should be finish reamed with hand reamer.

VALVE SPRING INSTALLED HEIGHT

When valves and seats are reground the position of the valve in the head is changed so as to lessen the valve spring tension. Without proper valve spring tension the valve does not seat long enough or it may not seat completely. Since the valve is cooled by transferring heat from the valve head to the seat and thence to the coolant, improper valve spring tension will cause worn, pitted and distorted valves which result in loss

of compression and power as well as poor gasoline mileage.

When valves, springs, retainers and locks are installed, measure the assembled height of the valve springs from the surface of the cylinder head spring pad to the underside of the spring retainer as shown in Figs. 9A and 10. If the assembled height is greater than the dimension given in the *Valve Specifications Chart,* install a spacer or shim of proper thickness between cylinder head spring pad and spring to bring the assembled height to specifications.

Do not install spacers unless necessary. Excessive use of spacers will result in overstressing valve springs and overloading camshaft lobes which could lead to spring breakage and worn camshaft lobes.

VALVE SPRING TESTING

Wash all springs with gasoline or other suitable solvent. Examine the springs for damage or corrosion due to acid etching, which will develop into surface cracks and cause spring failure.

Check the valve spring tension on a spring testing fixture, if one is available, Fig. 10A, and according to the specifications given in the *Valve Data* chart. If a fixture is not available, at least check the free length of each spring by standing it alongside a new spring. Any spring that does not conform to the pressure specifications within 10% should be replaced. Likewise, any spring that stands shorter than the new spring used for comparison should be discarded. Of course, cocked springs should also be scrapped.

VALVES, GRIND

Clean the valves with a wire wheel brush, making sure that all carbon is removed from the top and bottom of the heads as well as the gum which might have accumulated on the stems.

In refacing valves take off only the minimum of metal required to clean up the valve faces. If the outer edge of the

Fig. 10A Checking valve spring tension

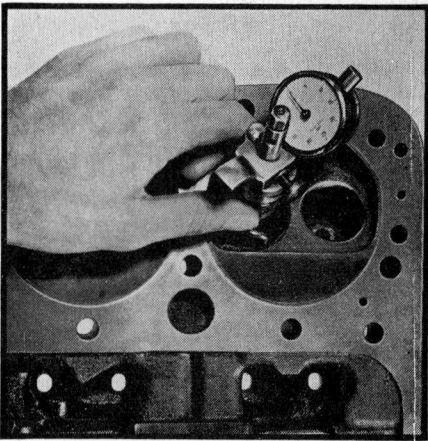

Fig. 11 Checking valve seat concentricity with dial gauge

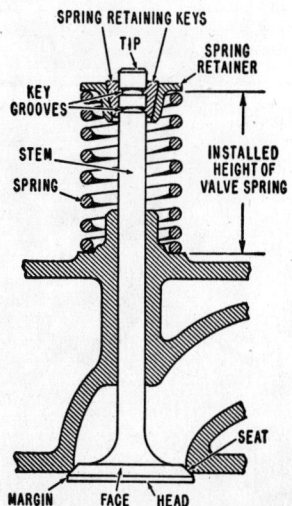

Fig. 9A Checking valve spring installed height on V8's

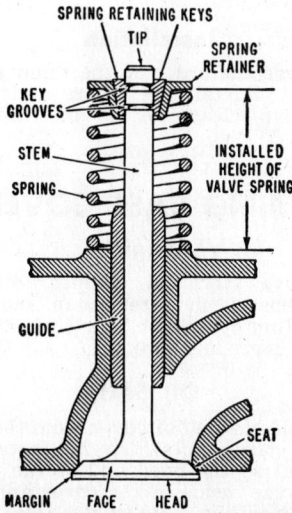

Fig. 10 Checking valve spring installed height on 6-cyl.

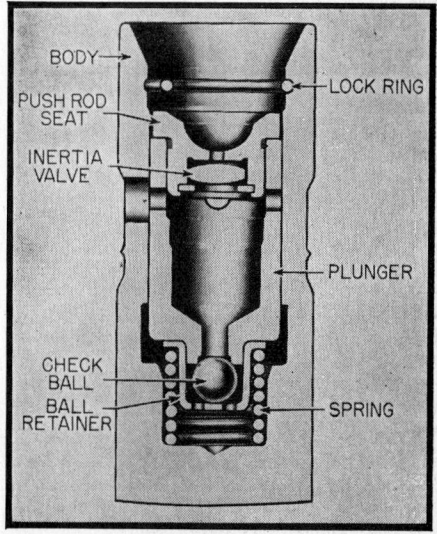

Fig. 12 Hydraulic valve lifter

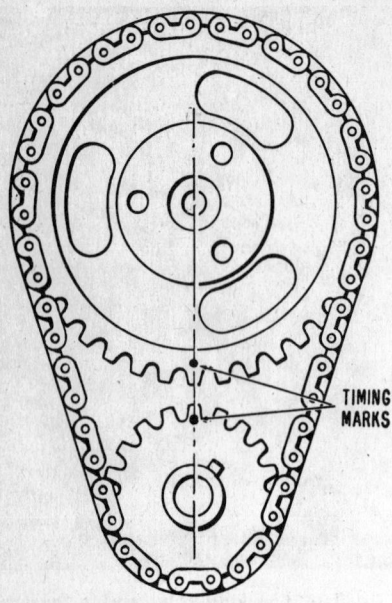

Fig. 13 Timing marks aligned for correct valve timing. V8 engines

valve becomes too thin or sharp due to excessive grinding, the valve must be replaced. This condition leads to premature breakage, burning and pre-ignition due to heat localizing on this knife edge. If the edge of the valve head is less than $\frac{1}{32}$" thick after grinding, replace the valve.

Reface valves to 44 degrees and true up seats to 45 degrees. Cutting a valve seat results in lowering valve spring pressure and increases the width of the seat. The nominal width of a valve seat is $\frac{3}{64}$ to $\frac{1}{16}$".

Test valves for concentricity with seats and for tight seating. Valves can be tested by lightly coating the valve face with prussian blue and turning the valve against its seat. This indicates whether the seat is concentric with the valve guide *but does not prove that the valve face is concentric with the valve stem, or that the valve is seating all around.* After making this test, wash all blue from the surfaces, lightly coat the *valve seat* with blue and repeat the test to see whether a full mark is obtained on the valve. *Both tests are necessary to prove that a proper seat is being obtained.*

If a dial gauge is used to check the concentricity of valve seats, Fig. 11, the concentricity should be held to within .002".

HYDRAULIC VALVE LIFTERS

The easiest method for locating a noisy valve lifter is by the use of a piece of garden hose approximately 4 feet in length. Place the end of the hose near the end of each intake and exhaust valve with the other end of the hose near the ear. In this manner, the sound is localized, making it easy to determine which lifter is at fault.

Another method is to place a finger on the face of the valve spring retainer. If the lifter is not functioning properly,

a distinct shock will be felt when the valve returns to its seat.

In most cases where noise exists in one or more lifters, all lifter units should be removed and cleaned. If dirt, varnish, carbon, etc. is found to exist in one unit, it more than likely exists in all the units.

Plungers are not interchangeable as they are selectively fitted at the factory. Should a plunger or lifter body become damaged, it is necessary to replace the entire unit, Fig. 12.

The plunger must be free in the lifter body. A simple test for this is to be sure the plunger will drop of its own weight in the body. There must be no excessive leakdown and there must be no ball check valve leakage.

Removal

Remove rocker arm covers and intake manifold. Back off rocker arm stud nuts until arms may be pivoted away from push rods. Lift out push rods and valve lifters.

Valve lifters should be placed in a rack in their proper sequence so they can be installed in the original locations in the block.

Disassemble & Assemble

1. Hold plunger down with push rod and, using a small screw driver or awl, remove plunger retainer.
2. Remove parts from lifter body.
3. Clean all parts and inspect for damage. If any parts are damaged, the entire lifter assembly should be replaced. The inertia valve in the plunger for rocker arm lubrication should move when the plunger is shaken.
4. To reassemble, invert plunger and set ball into hole in plunger. Place ball check valve retainer over ball and on plunger. Place check valve retainer spring over retainer. Assemble body over plunger assembly. Turn assembly over and install push rod seat. Compress plunger with push rod and install retainer.
5. Compress plunger to open oil holes and fill plunger with SAE 10 oil. Work plunger up and down and refill.

Installation

Reverse the order of the removal procedure to install the lifters and adjust the valve clearance as outlined previously.

TIMING CASE COVER

V8 Engines

Remove vibration damper, oil pan, heater hose from water pump, and water pump from cylinder block. Unfasten and remove cover and gaskets.

Oil Seal

Pry old seal out of cover from the front with a large screwdriver. Install the new seal so the open end of the seal is toward the inside of the cover and drive it into position with a suitable driver, being sure to support cover at sealing area.

Fig. 14 Removing camshaft gear. All sixes

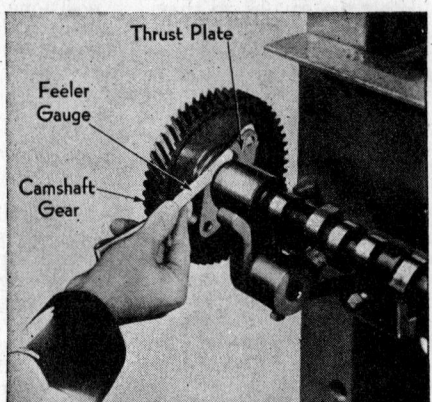

Fig. 15 Checking camshaft end play. All sixes

Fig. 16 Using puller to remove crankshaft gear. All sixes

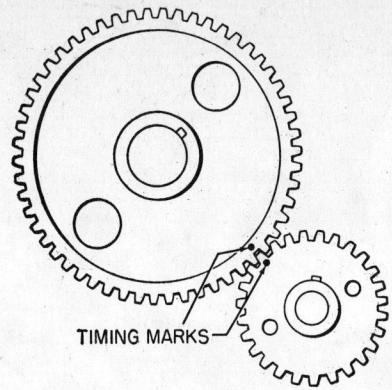

Fig. 17 Valve timing. All sixes

Installation

1. Make certain that the mating faces of cover and block are clean and flat.
2. Make certain oil slinger is in place against crankshaft sprocket.
3. Coat oil seal with light grease and, using a new cover gasket, install cover and gasket over dowel pins in cylinder block.
4. Install and tighten cover screws to 6-8 lb. ft. torque.
5. Install oil pan, harmonic balancer and water pump.
6. Start engine and check for leaks.

6-Cyl. Engines

To remove the cover, remove oil cooler lines (if used), radiator, fan belt, vibration damper and oil pan. Remove timing case cover screws *and the two bolts that are installed from the back through the front main bearing cap.* Then remove the cover.

Before installing the timing gear cover, be sure that the oil seal is seated properly in its recess in the cover, otherwise premature wear of the seal will result, causing an oil leak.

When replacing the cover, use a sleeve which is the same size as the hub of the vibration damper, slipping it over the front end of the crankshaft to act as a guide when replacing the cover.

Apply a light film of grease on the inner circumference of the seal to prevent it from being damaged when the vibration damper is being installed.

TIMING CHAIN

V8 Engines

1. Remove timing chain cover as outlined previously.
2. Remove crankshaft oil slinger.
3. Crank engine until "O" marks on sprockets are in alignment, Fig. 13.
4. Remove three camshaft-to-sprocket bolts.
5. Remove camshaft sprocket and timing chain together. Sprocket is a light press fit on camshaft for approximately ⅛". If sprocket does not come off easily, a light blow with a plastic hammer on the lower edge of the sprocket should dislodge it.
6. If crankshaft sprocket is to be re-

placed, remove it with a suitable gear puller. Install new sprocket, aligning key and keyway.
7. Install chain on camshaft sprocket. Hold sprocket vertical with chain hanging below and shift around to align the "O" marks on sprockets.
8. Align dowel in camshaft with dowel hole in sprocket and install sprocket on camshaft. *Do not attempt to drive sprocket on camshaft as welch plug at rear of engine can be dislodged.*
9. Draw sprocket onto camshaft, using the three mounting bolts. Tighten to 15-20 lb. ft. torque.
10. Lubricate timing chain and install cover.

TIMING GEARS

6-Cyl. Engines

When necessary to install a new camshaft gear, the camshaft will have to be removed as the gear is a pressed fit on the shaft. The camshaft is held in position by a thrust plate which is fastened to the crankcase by two capscrews which are accessible through two holes in the gear web.

Use an arbor press to remove the gear and when doing so, a suitable sleeve, Fig. 14, should be employed to support the gear properly on its steel hub.

Before installing a new gear, assemble a new thrust plate on the shaft and press the gear on just far enough so that the thrust plate has practically no clearance, yet is free to turn. The correct clearance is from a free fit to a maximum of .003", Fig. 15.

The crankshaft gear can be removed by utilizing the two tapped holes in conjunction with a gear puller, Fig. 16.

When the timing gears are installed, be sure the punch-marks on both gears are in mesh, Fig. 17. Backlash between the gears should be from .002" to .005", Fig. 18. Check the run-out of the gears, Fig. 19, and if the camshaft gear run-out exceeds .004" or the crank gear run-out is in excess of .003", remove the gear (or gears) and examine for burrs, dirt or some other fault which may cause the run-out. If these conditions are not the cause, replace the gear (or gears).

Fig. 18 Checking timing gear backlash. All sixes

VALVE TIMING DATA

Chevrolet

Year	Model	Intake Opens①	Intake Closes②	Exhaust Opens③	Exhaust Closes④
1953	⑤	⑦	39	42	9
	⑥	16	48	46½	17½
1954	⑤	⑦	39	42	9
	⑥	10½	53½	49	15
1955	Six⑧	⑦	39	42	9
	Six⑨	10½	53½	49	15
	V8⑧	12	54	52	14
	V8⑨	18	54	52	20
1956	Six	10½	53½	49	15
	V8⑧	18	54	52	20
	V8⑨	26½	63½	66½	23½
	V8⑩	22	61	62	24
1957	Six	10½	53½	49	15
	V8-265	18	72	52	20
	V8-283⑪	35	72	76	31
	V8-283⑫	12½	57½	54½	15½
1958	Six	10½	53½	49	15
	V8-283	12½	57½	54½	15½
	V8-348	18½	67½	68½	25½
1959	Six	16	48	46½	17½
	V8-283⑬	12½	57½	54½	15½
	V8-348	18½	60½	68½	25½
1960	Six	16	48	46½	17½
	V8-283⑭	18	54	52	20
	V8-283⑮	12½	57½	54½	15½
	V8-348	18½	67½	68½	25½
1961	Six⑬	16	48	46½	17½
	V8-283⑭	18	54	52	20
	V8-283⑮	12½	57½	54½	15½
	V8-348	18½	67½	68½	25½

Corvette

Year	Model	Intake Opens①	Intake Closes②	Exhaust Opens③	Exhaust Closes④
1953	All	19½	44½	59	5
1954	All	19½	44½	59	5
1955	Six	19½	44½	59	5
	V8	21½	63½	62½	23½
1956-60⑬		21½	63½	62½	23½

①—Degrees before top dead center.
②—Degrees after bottom dead center.
③—Degrees before bottom dead center.
④—Degrees after top dead center.
⑤—Manual shift transmission.
⑥—Automatic transmission.
⑦—One degree after top dead center.
⑧—Manual shift transmission and hydraulic valve lifters.
⑨—Automatic transmission and hydraulic valve lifters.
⑩—With two 4-barrel carburetors.
⑪—With mechanical valve lifters and two 4-barrel carburetors.
⑫—With hydraulic valve lifters and one carburetor. 42° 9°
⑬—For 1961 Biscayne Fleet Master 1°ATC, 39°.
⑭—Two-barrel carburetor.
⑮—Four-barrel carburetor.

CRANKCASE FRONT END PLATE

6-Cyl. Engines

This plate is assembled to the cylinder block with from one to three gaskets which are used for the purpose of aligning the timing gears. To check the alignment of the gears, install the front end plate to the block and use two gaskets, holding them in position with three screws. Then use a new (spare) camshaft thrust plate over the camshaft hole in the end plate and place a steel straight edge, Fig. 20, against the camshaft thrust plate and over the shoulder of the crankshaft to see whether these two surfaces are flush. If the scale strikes the shoulder on the crankshaft, add another gasket. On the other hand, if there is space between the scale and the crankshaft shoulder, remove a gasket. When the desired result is obtained, assemble the screws and bolts, using a center punch to lock the screws.

Fig. 19 Checking runout of timing gears with dial indicator. All sixes

CAMSHAFT

V8 Engines

To remove the camshaft, remove valve lifters, fuel pump and its push rod, radiator, timing chain and camshaft sprocket. Install two $\frac{5}{8}$"-18 x 4" bolts in two camshaft bolt holes. Using these bolts as a puller, remove camshaft from engine.

6-Cyl. Engines

Camshaft end play should be from a free fit to a maximum of .003" and is controlled by a thrust plate at the front end of the shaft. This clearance can be checked by inserting a feeler ribbon between the front end of the shaft and the thrust plate, Fig. 15.

If necessary to replace bearings, drive out the expansion plug at the rear of the rear bearing and use suitable equipment to remove and replace the bearings.

Caution—Be sure the oil holes in the bearings are lined up with the oil holes in the crankcase. Before reaming the bearings, insert a round-nosed punch, Fig. 21, through the oil passage from the main to the camshaft bearings and stake each bearing in place.

PISTONS & RODS, REMOVE

After removing the cylinder heads and oil pan, examine the cylinder bores above the ring travel area. If the bores are worn so that a shoulder or ridge exists at this point, remove the ridge with a ridge reamer to avoid damaging rings or cracking lands of pistons during removal.

Remove the connecting rod caps and push the pistons and rods out of the cylinders, using care to prevent rod bolts from nicking crankshaft journals. Make sure rods and pistons are properly numbered so they can be reinstalled in their proper cylinders. It is advisable to install the caps on the rods as they are removed to avoid mixing parts.

PISTONS & RODS, ASSEMBLE

V8 Engines

All pistons have an "F" cast on the front side. There is also a notch cast in the top of the piston head at the front to facilitate proper installation, Fig. 22. The piston assemblies should always be installed with the notch toward the front of the engine.

The odd numbered piston assemblies will always be installed in the left bank of cylinders, while the even numbered piston assemblies will always be installed in the right bank of cylinders.

The heavy side of the bearing end of the rod goes to the rear of the engine on the right bank. On the left bank, the heavy side of the bearing end of the rod goes to the front of the engine.

6-Cyl. Engines

The connecting rod should be assembled to the piston so that when placed in the cylinder bore, the piston pin clamp bolt faces the camshaft side of the engine.

PISTONS

High limit standard size pistons are available for service use so that proper clearances can be obtained for slightly worn cylinder bores requiring only light honing to clean up the bores.

On V8's there are four standard size pistons available for service installation. In addition, pistons are serviced in .020", .030" and .040" oversizes. On 6-cylinder engines, oversizes of .003", .010", .020", .030" and .040" are available. If the cylinders were found to have less than .005" taper or wear they can be reconditioned with a hone and fitted with high limit standard size pistons. A cylinder bore of less than .005" wear or taper may not entirely clean up when fitted to a high limit piston. If it is desired to entirely clean up the bore in these cases, it will be necessary to rebore for an oversize piston. If more than .005" taper or wear, they should be bored and honed to the smallest oversize that will permit complete resurfacing of all cylinders.

PISTON PINS

V8 Engines

Piston pins are mounted off center and are a tight press fit in the connecting rods and pivot in the pistons. Pins should be capable of supporting their own weight in either pin boss when coated with light engine oil at 60°F. temperature. Higher or lower temperatures will cause false indications. Pistons and pins are supplied as an assembly.

6-Cyl. Engines

Pistons used in these engines are aluminum and not fitted with bushings.

To remove a piston pin, remove the piston pin clamp bolt and expand the clamp slot with a screwdriver or other suitable means. Then push the pin out of the piston with hand pressure. If it

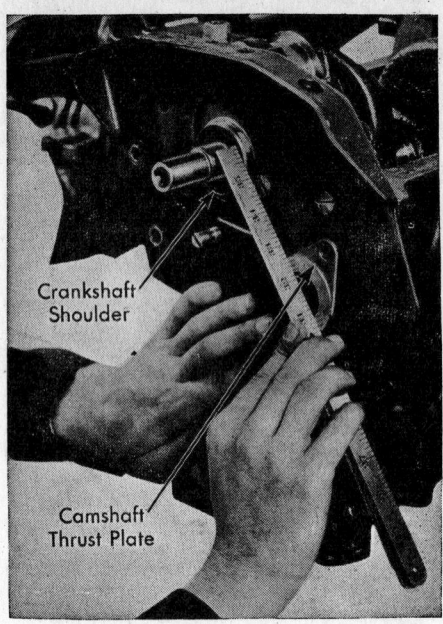

Fig. 20 Checking timing gear alignment. All sixes

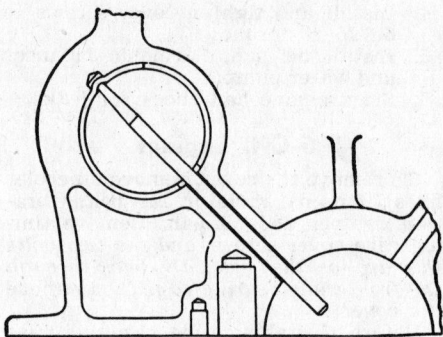

Fig. 21 Using round-nosed punch to stake camshaft bearings in place. All sixes

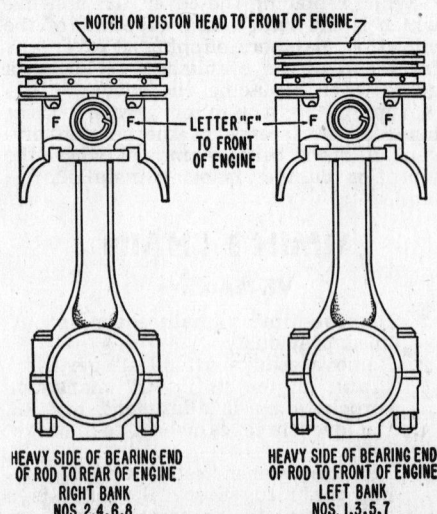

Fig. 22 Correct assembly of rod to piston. V8 Engines. On super Turbo-Thrust 348 engine, notch in piston head for cylinders 2-4-6-8 toward rear of engine

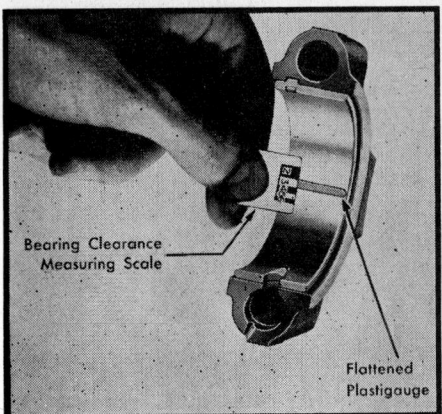

Fig. 23 Checking bearing clearance with Plastigage. V8 Engines

cannot be removed with hand pressure, use a suitable drift to drive it out.

When removing a pin with a drift, hold the piston in one hand, insert the drift and tap lightly with a hammer. Do not hold the connecting rod during this operation, otherwise misalignment of the rod may occur.

If the new pin cannot be installed in the piston with thumb pressure, enlarge the holes with an expansion reamer, Fig. 18. Take only a light cut with the reamer. Ream the holes until the pin can be pushed into the piston with the pressure of both thumbs.

PISTON RINGS

Chevrolet piston rings are furnished in standard sizes as well as .020", .030" and .040" oversizes.

When new rings are to be installed without reboring cylinders, the glazed cylinder wall should be slightly dulled but without increasing the diameter of the bore. This is done with a "Glaze-buster" or with a hone equipped with the finest grade of stones.

New rings must be checked for clearance in piston grooves and for gap in cylinder bores. The latter operation must be measured with the ring about two inches down into the bore to which it is being fitted. An inverted piston can be used to push the rings down to this position. Cylinder bores and piston grooves must be clean, dry and free from carbon and burrs.

Check the clearance of each ring in its piston groove by installing the ring and then inserting feeler gauges *under* the ring. Any wear that occurs in the piston groove forms a step or ridge at the inner portion of the lower land. If the feeler gauge is inserted above the ring, the ring may rest on the step instead of on the worn portion of the lower land, and a false measurement of clearance may result.

If the piston grooves have worn to the extent that relatively high steps or ridges exist on the lower lands, the piston should be replaced because the steps will interfere with the operation of the new rings and ring clearances will be excessive. Piston rings are not furnished in oversize widths to compensate for ring groove wear.

ROD BEARINGS

Connecting rod bearing inserts are available in standard size and undersizes of .001", .002", .010" and .020". The bearings can be replaced without removing the rod assembly by removing the cap and replacing the upper and lower halves of the bearing. The clearance between the bearing and crankshaft can be measured by the use of Plastigage as follows:

1. Remove bearing cap and wipe oil from crankshaft journal and bearing insert.
2. With crankpin at approximately bottom dead center, place a piece of Plastigage in the center of the cap.
3. Reinstall the cap and tighten to the torque value given in the *Engine Torque Data* chart.
4. Remove bearing cap and determine bearing clearance by comparing the width of the flattened Plastigage at its widest point with the graduation on the Plastigage scale, Fig. 23. The number within the graduation on the envelope indicates the clearance in thousands of an inch. If this clearance is greater than .004" on an old bearing or greater than .003" on a new bearing, or less than .001", replace the bearing.

MAIN BEARINGS

1956-61 Six and All V8's

Caution—Main bearing clearance can be checked with Plastigage in the same manner described for rod bearings. If bearings are measured with the engine in the chassis, the crankshaft must be supported in order to take up clearance between the upper bearing insert and crankshaft journal. This can be done by tightening bearing caps of adjacent bearings with .005" to .015" cardboard, (such as a calling card) between lower bearing shell and journal. Use extreme care when this is done to avoid unnecessary strain on the crankshaft or bearings or a false reading may be obtained. Do not rotate crankshaft while Plastigage is installed. *Be sure to remove cardboard.* To install new bearings, proceed as follows:

1. Remove bearing cap and worn lower shell.
2. Rotate crankshaft in normal direction to turn upper bearing shell out of crankcase. Use a cotter pin with a flattened head or the special tool made for the purpose in the crankshaft oil hole to contact the bearing and force it out, Fig. 24.
3. Place a new upper shell on the crankshaft journal with the locating notch in the correct position and rotate the shaft to turn the bearing in place.
4. Install the lower bearing snell in the cap.
5. Tighten all cap nuts to the torque value given in the *Engine Torque Data* table.

1953-55 Six

To install new main bearings, proceed as follows:

1. Remove radiator, vibration damper,

Fig. 24 Special plug for removing and installing upper main bearing inserts

fan belt, and spark plugs.

2. Loosen all rocker arm screws to relieve tension on camshaft.
3. Raise front and rear of car about 8" off floor, keeping car level.
4. Remove transmission floor pan and flywheel underpan.
5. Unfasten transmission support from cross member.
6. Uncouple gearshift selector rod from selector lever.
7. Raise rear of engine and support it with a bar across frame braces.
8. Release clutch fork from ball.
9. Unfasten transmission and slide it back about ¾".
10. Remove oil pan and timing cover.
11. Remove oil pump and screen.
12. Rotate crankshaft to best possible position for removal of all bearing caps and mark timing gear position to allow for reassembly in same position.
13. Loosen all main bearing cap bolts, allowing crankshaft to drop about ⅜".
14. Remove No. 2 and 4 bearing caps and take out upper and lower shells.
15. Install new upper bearing shells, locating dowel in hole and pressing bearings in place. If bearing has correct spread, shells should snap into place.

CRANKSHAFT REAR OIL SEAL

1955-58 V8's and 1959-61 Six

A braided oil seal is pressed into the upper and lower grooves behind the rear main bearing. Directly in front of this seal is an oil slinger which deflects the oil back into the oil pan. Should the braided seal require replacement, the installation of the lower half is accomplished as follows:

With the bearing cap and lower bearing half removed, install a new seal so that both ends protrude above the cap. Tap the seal down into position or roll it snugly in its groove with a smooth rounded tool. Then cut off the protruding ends of the seal with a sharp knife or razor blade, Fig. 25.

Installing Upper Seal

Although the usual practice is to remove the crankshaft when the upper half of the seal is to be replaced it is possible to do the job without removing the crankshaft as follows:

To remove the seal, use needle-nose pliers to grasp the end of the seal which is most accessible. Pull the seal downward while rotating the crankshaft slowly in the direction that the seal is being removed.

To install the new seal, fasten a length of wire or strong string such as fishing line securely to one end of the new seal. See that the point of fastening is not bulky and that it is not over 3/8" from the end of the seal. Coat the seal with Lubriplate. Pass the free end of the wire or string up over the crankshaft at the point where the seal is to be installed. Then exert a firm, steady pull on the wire or string and at the same time rotate the crankshaft slowly in the direction of the pull. This will help to move the seal into position. When the installation is completed, trim the ends of the seal flush with the engine block.

1959-61 V8 Rubber Seal

When necessary to correct an oil leak due to a defective seal, always replace the upper and lower seal halves as a unit. *When installing either half, lubricate the lip portion only with engine oil, keeping oil off the parting line surface as this is treated with glue.* Always clean crankshaft surface before installing a new seal. Be careful of seal retainer tang while inserting a new seal so that it doesn't cut the seal.

1. To replace the lower seal, remove seal from groove in bearing cap, using a small screwdriver to pry it out.
2. Insert new seal and roll it in place with finger and thumb.
3. To replace the upper seal (with engine in car) use a small hammer and tap a brass pin punch on one end of the seal until it protrudes far enough to be removed with pliers.
4. Insert the new seal, gradually push-

Fig. 25 Installing oil seal in bearing cap. V8 Engines

ing with a hammer handle until seal is rolled into place.
5. Install bearing cap with new seal and tighten bearing cap bolts.

OIL PAN

1959-61 V8

1. Drain crankcase and cooling system.
2. Disconnect hoses at radiator.
3. Disconnect ground strap at engine.
4. If equipped with synchromesh transmission, disconnect clutch pedal push rod at clutch pedal control, intermediate lever and shaft. Remove clutch pedal control, intermediate lever and shaft assembly at frame mounting bracket, leaving shaft assembly attached to engine.
5. Remove fuel pump.
6. If equipped with Air Suspension, disconnect hose to alcohol vaporizer bottle and hose assembly from air compressor to accumulator tank.
7. Remove accelerator control rod from its lever.
8. If equipped with power brake, remove vacuum hose at check valve at engine manifold.
9. If equipped with power steering, remove power pump from generator in order to clear power brake master cylinder.
10. Remove transmission lower control rods at transmission levers.
11. Disconnect and lower exhaust pipe and muffler assembly from exhaust manifold.
12. Remove oil filter.
13. Loosen transmission mounting bolts.
14. Remove long bolt from each front mounting.
15. Turn crankshaft so that vibration damper keyway slot is at bottom of engine. This will position crankshaft counterweights so baffle in oil pan will clear.
16. Engine will have to be raised approximately 3" to clear frame crossmember for oil pan removal. Raise engine until transmission housing comes in contact with underbody toe pan. Note clearance at fan blade and shroud while lifting engine and adjust for clearance as required.
17. Remove pan bolts and tilt oil pan while removing.

Note—Removal of the oil pan with Turboglide transmission installed is identical to the foregoing procedure except that the transmission control lever cross shaft at the transmission shifter lever and shaft assembly must be removed.

1958 V8

1. Remove distributor cap to prevent damage to it when engine is jacked up.
2. Remove exhaust crossover pipe and manifold heat valve.
3. Remove front engine mounting bolt nuts.
4. Turn crankshaft so that vibration damper keyway slot is at bottom of engine. This will index crankshaft counterweights so baffle in oil pan will clear.
5. Raise engine from below at vibra-

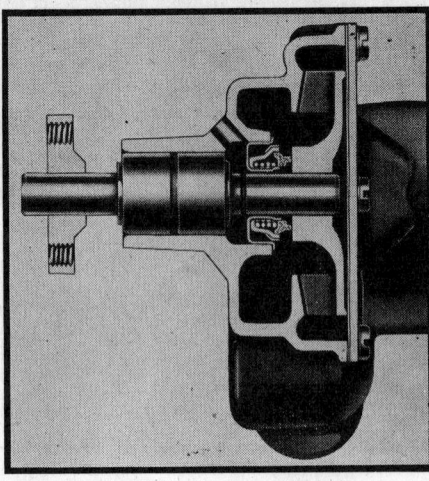

Fig. 26 V8 water pump

tion damper. Engine will have to be raised about three inches to clear frame cross member for oil pan removal. Note clearance at fan and shroud while lifting engine and adjust for clearance as required.
6. Unfasten and remove oil pan.
7. Reverse above procedure to install pan and tighten attaching bolts to a torque of 12-15 lb. ft.

1955-57 V8

To remove the oil pan, drain the oil and disconnect steering idler arm bracket from frame side rail and drop for clearance. Unfasten and remove oil pan.

After the pan is installed, tighten 5/16" bolts to a torque of 12-15 lb. ft. and 1/4" bolts to 6-9 lb. ft.

1953-54 Six

To remove the oil pan, unfasten the steering idler and third arm and bracket from the frame front cross member and let the assembly drop down. *Carefully note the number of shims used between the upper mounting bolt and cross member so the same number may be installed when replacing the assembly.* Drain the oil and remove the flywheel housing underpan, underpan extension and oil pan.

1955-57 Six

To remove the oil pan, drain the oil. Disconnect the steering idler arm bracket from the right hand frame side rail and drop for clearance. Unfasten oil pan from crankcase and remove pan. *Crankshaft may have to be turned to allow clearance at front cross member.*

1958 Six

1. Scribe alignment marks on hood around hood hinges; then remove hood.
2. Remove battery ground cable.
3. Disconnect fuel pipe at pump.
4. Remove generator lead wires and loosen fan belt.
5. Remove radiator.
6. Disconnect transmission oil cooler lines on Powerglide models.
7. Remove fan and pulley.
8. Remove rocker arm cover and at-

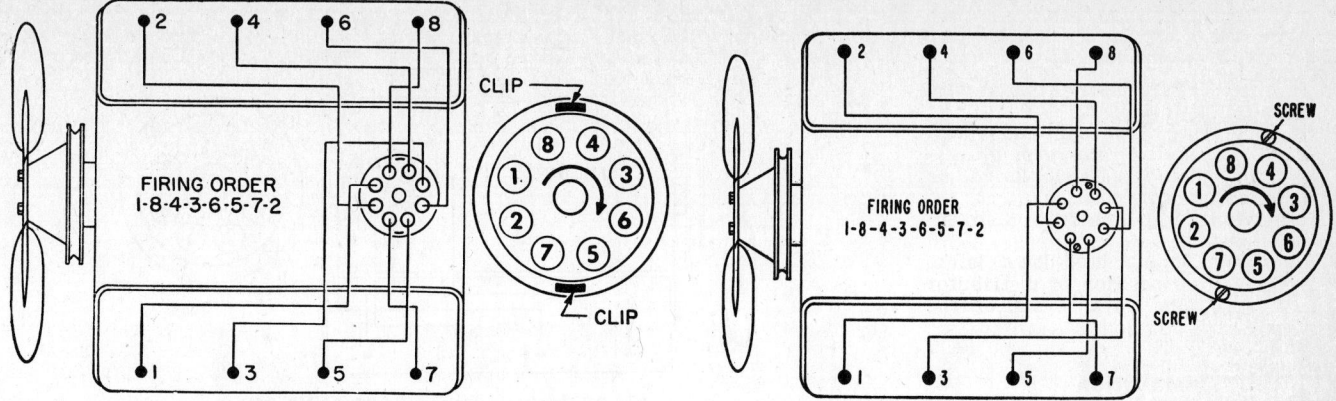

Fig. 27   Ignition details.   1955-56 V8   **Fig. 28   Ignition details.   1957-61 V8-265 and V8-283**

tach a suitable lifting rig to engine. Using a chain hoist or equivalent, lift engine only enough so that engine will be supported when front engine mounts are removed.

9. Remove center bolts from each front mount.
10. On synchromesh transmission models, disconnect clutch idler shaft bracket from engine; remove overdrive solenoid (if equipped); remove flywheel underpan extension; disconnect shifter rods at transmission.
11. On automatic transmission models, disconnect transmission oil cooler lines, and transmission control linkage at transmission.
12. Disconnect propeller shaft from rear axle, remove center mount support bolts and slide to rear until free of transmission.
13. Drain transmission and remove transmission cross member and mounting block.
14. Disconnect speedometer cable at transmission.
15. Drain crankcase oil and remove oil pan bolts.
16. Raise engine high enough so that oil pan clears cross member and pan can be removed through front of engine compartment. Crankshaft may have to be rotated to allow oil pan to clear counterweights.

1959-61 Six

1. Drain crankcase and radiator.
2. Disconnect hoses at radiator.
3. Disconnect ground strap at engine.
4. Disconnect gas tank feed pipe at fuel pump.
5. Disconnect accelerator control rod at its lever.
6. If equipped, remove overdrive solenoid.
7. Disconnect power brake hose at check valve.
8. Remove oil filter and support bracket assembly to clear power brake master cylinder.
9. Disconnect exhaust pipe from manifold.
10. Disconnect transmission lower control rods at transmission.
11. Disconnect clutch fork push rod at fork.
12. Disconnect clutch pedal control, intermediate lever and shaft from engine.

13. Loosen transmission mounting bolts and remove front engine mounting bolts.
14. Remove hood and lift engine approximately 3″ until valve rocker cover comes in contact with dash upper panel.
15. Remove bolts and oil pan. If equipped with synchromesh transmission, remove flywheel under pan extension before removing oil pan. Crankshaft may have to be turned to clear counterweights.

OIL PUMP

V8 Engines

After removing the oil pan, unfasten pump from rear main bearing cap. Disconnect pump shaft from extension by removing clip from collar. Remove pump cover and take out idler gear, drive gear and shaft.

Should any of the following conditions be found it is advisable to replace the pump assembly.

1. Inspect pump body for cracks or wear.
2. Inspect gears for wear or damage.
3. Check shaft for looseness in housing.
4. Check inside of cover for wear that would permit oil to leak past the ends of gear.
5. Check oil pick-up screen for damage to screen, by-pass valve or body.
6. Check for oil in air chamber.

6-Cyl. Engines

The pumps used in these engines are of the positive gear type. After disassembling the pump, examine the shaft and gears for excessive wear and replace where necessary, or better still, install a new pump. When assembling the pump, be sure the ground side of the idler gear is toward the cover.

Note—The gasket which is used between the pump cover and the body is special in that it controls the clearance in the pump. If the relief valve parts show wear, install new parts. Be sure that the tapered set screw which holds the pump in place is fully seated and locked with its lock nut.

RADIATOR

1. To remove the radiator, drain radiator and remove radiator-to-water outlet hose.
2. Remove radiator-to-inlet pipe hose.
3. On Powerglide or Turboglide models, remove oil cooler lines from radiator and plug lines and radiator fittings.
4. Unfasten radiator from its support and lift out.

WATER PUMP

1955-61 Six and All V8s

1. Drain radiator and remove water inlet hose from pump.
2. Remove fan belt.
3. On heater equipped models, remove hose from pump housing.
4. Unfasten pump from engine and lift off.
5. Remove fan and pulley.
6. Remove pump back plate.
7. Support fan hub on arbor press and press pump shaft out of hub.
8. Support pump on cylinder block face and press shaft and impeller out of pump, applying pressure on outer race of shaft bearing only. Shaft and bearing assembly must not be pushed out of housing by applying force on shaft or bearings will be damaged. Use a 7/8″ deep socket or a piece of tubing 1⅛″ O. D.
9. Press shaft out of impeller. Discard seal.

Assembly & Installation

Inspect all parts for wear or damage. Do not submerge shaft bearing in cleaning solvent as it is permanently sealed and lubricated.

Assemble pump in reverse order of disassembly. When installing the seal, see that it bottoms with the outer flange against the pump body. The impeller should be pressed on the shaft so that there is .010″ to .035″ clearance between impeller vanes and pump body. See Fig. 26 for position of shaft, fan hub and impeller in pump housing.

1953-54 Six

A repair kit, which consists of the seal assembly, seal washer, bearing retainer and plate gasket, is available and should be used when a leak develops.

DISTRIBUTOR

Removal

1. Disconnect distributor primary wire from coil terminal.
2. Remove distributor cap and rotor. *Mark position of rotor arm on distributor housing so distributor can be installed in same position.*
3. Remove vacuum line from distributor.
4. Remove distributor hold-down clamp.
5. Note relative position of distributor in block, then work it out of the engine.

Installation

1. Turn rotor about ⅛ of a turn counterclockwise past the mark previously placed on the distributor housing.
2. Push the distributor down into the block with the housing in the normal "installed" position. *It may be necessary to move the rotor slightly to start gear into mesh with camshaft gear, but rotor should line up with mark when distributor is down in place.*
3. Tighten distributor clamp screw snugly and connect vacuum line, primary wire to coil, and install cap. If spark plug wires were removed from cap, refer to Figs. 27, 28, 29 for correct installation. The wire grommets are numbered to show correct installation.

Service Note

If the engine was disturbed while the distributor was removed from the engine, first crank the engine to bring No. 1 piston up on its compression stroke and continue cranking until the timing mark is adjacent to the timing indicator. Then rotate the distributor cam until the rotor is in position to fire No. 1 cylinder. Install the distributor as outlined above and set the ignition timing as directed below.

IGNITION TIMING

1958-61 V8 Service Note

During mid-season of 1958 and thereafter the distributor vacuum advance tube is connected directly to the intake manifold instead of to the carburetor throttle body. This vacuum advance tube must be disconnected when setting ignition timing as full advance is present at idle speed. Do not forget to reconnect the tube after timing has been set.

To adjust the timing, crank the engine to bring No. 1 piston up on its compression stroke and stop when the mark on the harmonic balancer lines up with the proper mark on the timing tab attached to the chain cover. Loosen the distributor clamp and rotate the distributor until the points just break. Tighten the distributor clamp.

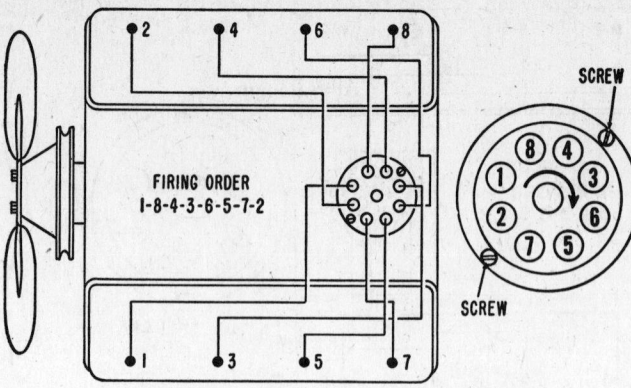

Fig. 29 Ignition details. 1958-61 V8-348

FIRING ORDER
1-8-4-3-6-5-7-2

When a timing light is used the engine should be run at hot idling speed for if it is turning faster the spark may be advanced by the centrifugal weights in the distributor and the timing will not be correct.

6-Cyl. Engines

Set the octane selector at zero. Check to see that the vacuum control operates freely, and is in full retard position. Crank the engine until No. 1 piston is coming up on its compression stroke and the steel ball in the flywheel registers with the line on the inspection hole in the flywheel housing. Loosen the distributor clamp screw and turn the housing until the points just break. Then set the octane selector so that a slight ping is heard on open throttle at 10 to 15 MPH.

When a Neon timing light is used, the engine should be run at idling speed for if it is turning faster the spark may be advanced by the centrifugal weights on the distributor and the timing will not be correct. The stroboscopic effect of the Neon light makes the ball appear to stand still in relation to the pointer at the flywheel opening. The distributor can then be rotated until the ball appears to remain exactly in line with the pointer, when the timing is correct. The factory recommends using the Neon light in timing the ignition.

STARTER REPLACE

1959-61

1. Disconnect battery ground strap and remove cable from fender clip.
2. Unplug starter motor harness dash connector.
3. Unfasten starter from its mounting.
4. Pull starter forward to clear housing and carefully lower it.

1953-58

Disconnect ground strap from battery and cable and wires from starter solenoid. Unfasten and remove starter from clutch housing.

MUFFLER & PIPES, REPLACE

1953-54

If the exhaust pipe has to be replaced it will be necessary to replace both exhaust pipe and muffler. To replace a muffler, cut exhaust pipe as close to muffler inlet as possible which will allow new muffler to be slipped over end of exhaust pipe.

There are two points to consider when installing an exhaust pipe and muffler assembly or a tail pipe: (1) There should be ⅝" clearance between the underside of the floor pan and tail pipe at the kick-up. (2) The tail pipe support must be in a vertical position otherwise it may strike the bumper.

1955-57

Convertibles carry a separate exhaust pipe and muffler. On V8s the crossover pipe may be replaced without replacing the exhaust pipe. Also be sure there is sufficient clearance between the tailpipe and shock absorber dust tube to prevent contact during operation.

1958-60

Removal of any of the exhaust system components is a obvious operation. However, the following points should be considered.

1. There should be ¾" vertical clearance between the tailpipe and the underside of the flange on the rear spring bracket.
2. The tailpipe support must be in a vertical position. If it is at an angle, the tailpipe is apt to strike the bumper.
3. There should be ¾" clearance between bumper brace and tailpipe.
4. Exhaust system should be secure and tight at all fittings and joints.

Carburetor Section

Performance Complaints

Flooding, stumble on acceleration or other performance complaints are in many instances caused by the presence of dirt, water or other foreign matter in the carburetor. To aid in diagnosing the cause of the complaint, the carburetor should be carefully removed from the engine without draining the fuel from the bowl. The contents of the fuel bowl may then be examined for contamination as the carburetor is disassembled.

Check the fuel in the bowl for contamination by dirt, water, gum or other foreign matter. A magnet moved through the fuel in the bowl will pick up and identify any iron oxide dust that may have caused intake needle and seat leakage.

Inspect gasketed surfaces between body and air horn. Small nicks or burrs should be smoothed down to eliminate air or fuel leakage. On carburetors having a vacuum piston, be especially particular when inspecting the top surface of the inner wall of the bowl around the vacuum piston passage. A poor seal at this location may contribute to a "cutting-out" on turns complaint.

Fill the carburetor bowl with clean fuel before installing on manifold. This will help prevent dirt trapped in the fuel system from being dislodged by the free flow of fuel as the carburetor is primed. The operation of the floats and intake needle and seats may be checked under pressure if a fuel pump is used at the bench to fill the carburetor bowl. Operate the throttle several times and visually check the discharge from pump jets.

Poor Mileage and Engine Loading Complaints

Cases of poor mileage and engine loading may be due in many instances to sluggish choke valve opening during cold driveaway, caused by insufficient vacuum in choke housing, a plugged or restricted heat pipe or inlet in choke cover. To check for this condition, have engine warm and running at slow idle. Remove choke heat pipe and hold a finger over the heat inlet hole (hole is on choke housing on some carburetors). If there is little or no vacuum pull on the finger, check the choke housing for gasket leaks or plugged vacuum passages. If these are OK, check choke vacuum passages in carburetor between choke housing and manifold.

Dirty or Rusty Choke Housing

In cases where it is found that the interior of the choke housing is dirty, gummed or rusty while the carburetor itself is comparatively clean, look for a punctured or eroded manifold heat tube (if one is used).

Manifold Heat Control Valve

An engine equipped with a manifold heat control valve can operate with the valve stuck in either the open or closed position. Because of this, an inoperative valve is frequently overlooked at vehicle lubrication or tune-up.

A valve stuck in the "heat-off" position can result in slow warm up, deposits in combustion chamber, carburetor icing, flat spots during acceleration, low gas mileage and spark plug fouling.

A valve stuck in the "heat-on" position can result in power loss, engine knocking, sticking or burned valves and spark plug burning.

To prevent the possibility of a stuck valve, check and lubricate the valve each time the vehicle is lubricated or tuned-up. Check the operation of the valve manually. To lubricate the valve, place a few drops of penetrating oil on the valve shaft where it passes through the manifold. Then move the valve up and down a few times to work the oil in. *Do not use engine oil to lubricate the valve as it will leave a residue which hampers valve operation.*

Cut-Out On Turns

1960 Rochester 4GC-7013004, 7013006, 7013010, 7013012—Recent changes in the design of these carburetors make new float settings necessary. These changes are the addition of a torsion spring on a new design float hanger. The torsion spring will eliminate engine cut-out that was sometimes experienced while hard cornering a vehicle with fully warmed engine. Passenger cars effected by these changes are those equipped with 283 or 348 engines with automatic transmission in combination with air conditioning.

A change has also been made for non-air conditioned cars with automatic transmission. In these carburetors only the float hanger has been redesigned. Carburetors with this change can be identified by a tag with the letter "B" stamped on it.

These carburetors can be modified to incorporate new float hangers and torsion springs by installing Kit No. 7017-804. which includes two new floats, two torsion springs, two fibre float gauges and one each of tags stamped 7015004, 7015006, 7015010 and 7015012.

Modification of carburetors 7013004 and 7013006 (with letter "B") to incorporate the torsion springs can be made by using Kit No. 7017803, which contains two torsion springs and one each of tags stamped 7015004 and 701-5006.

Acceleration Stumble During Engine Warm-up

1959-60 V8 With 2GC Units—To correct this condition a new pump modification kit (part No. 7019742) has been released. The kit includes a new pump assembly, pump return spring and a brass identification tag, code stamped "D". The duration spring on the new pump assembly and pump return spring has more tension and both springs must be installed together for best operation.

CARTER NOTES

METERING ROD

WCFB and WGD—This adjustment must be made after pump setting. Back out throttle set screw until throttle valves are fully closed and loosen metering rod arm clamp screw. With metering rods in place, press down on vacumeter link until metering rods bottom in casting. Holding rods down, revolve metering rod arm until finger on arm contacts lip on vacumeter link. Hold in place and tighten clamp screw.

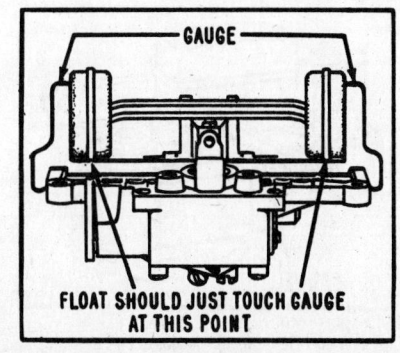

Fig. ①—WCFB float level. Adjust by bending float arms.

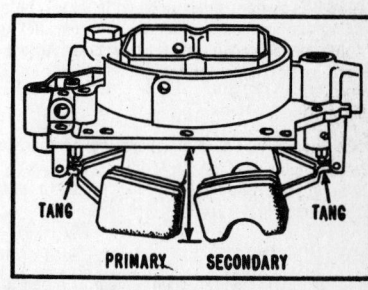

Fig. ②—WCFB float drop. Adjust by bending stop tabs on float bracket.

CARTER CARBURETOR ADJUSTMENTS

Year	Carburetor Model	Idle Adjustments				Float Level		Float Drop		Pump Travel Setting	Choke Unloader Setting	Choke Setting
		Mixture Screws Turns Open	Hot Idle Speed In Drive	Fast Idle Speed	Dashpot Plunger Clearance	Primary	Secondary	Primary	Secondary			
1959–60	WCFB-2816S	½-2	450	1700④	⑥	5/32①	9/32①	2②	2②	③	3/16⑤	Index
	WCFB-2817S	½-2	450	1700④	⑥	5/32①	9/32①	2②	2②	③	3/16⑤	Index
	WCFB-2818S	½-2	450	1700④	⑥	5/32①	9/32①	2②	2②	③	3/16⑤	Index
1958	WCFB-2669S	¼-1¾	425	1600④	.060⑫	⅛①	¼①	⅝⑦	¾⑦	③	3/16⑤	Index
	WCFB-2656S	¼-1¾	425	1800④	.060⑫	⅛①	¼①	⅝⑦	¾⑦	③	3/16⑤	Index
	WCFB-2657S	¼-1¾	425	1600④	.060⑫	⅛①	¼①	⅝⑦	¾⑦	③	3/16⑤	Index
1957	WCFB-2655S	½-1½	425	1800④	.060⑫	⅛①	¼①	⅝⑦	¾⑦	③	3/16⑤	Index
	WCFB-2626S	¼-1¼	425	None	None	⅛①	¼①	⅝⑦	¾⑦	③	None	None
	WCFB-2627S	¼-1¼	425	1800④	.060⑫	⅛①	¼①	⅝⑦	¾⑦	③	⅛⑤	Index
	WCFB-2505S-A	¾-1¾	425	1800④	.060⑫	⅛①	¼①	⅝⑦	¾⑦	③	3/16⑤	Index
	WCFB-2555S	¾-1¾	425	1600④	.060⑫	⅛①	¼①	⅝⑦	¾⑦	③	3/16⑤	Index
1956	WCFB-2362S	¼-1¼	425	1800④	None	⅛①	¼①	⅝⑦	¾⑦	③	3/16⑤	Index
	WCFB-2419S	¼-1¼	425	None	None	⅛①	¼①	⅝⑦	¾⑦	③	None	None
	WCFB-2366S-A	¼-1¼	425	1800④	None	⅛①	¼①	⅝⑦	¾⑦	③	3/16⑤	Index
	WGD-2286S	1-2	425	1800④	None	¼⑧	None	None	None	③	7/32⑤	Index
1955	WCFB-2351S	¼-1¼	425	1800④	None	⅛①	¼①	⅝⑦	¾⑦	③	3/16⑤	2 Lean
	WCFB-2218S	¼-1¼	425	1800④	None	⅛①	¼①	⅝⑦	¾⑦	③	3/16⑤	Index
1953–54	YH-2066S-A	½-1½	425	.020⑪	None	⅜⑨	None	2⑩	None	None	None	None

CARTER NOTES
Continued

Fig. ③—With pump connector link in outer hole of pump arm, flat on pump arm should be parallel with a straightedge placed on dust cover boss. Adjust by bending throttle connector rod.

④—With engine at normal operating temperature, rotate fast idle cam so fast idle screw rests on high step of cam. Adjust fast idle screw to obtain specified rpm.

⑤—With throttle wide open, clearance between upper edge of choke valve and inner wall of air horn should be as specified. Adjust by bending lip on throttle shaft lever.

⑥—Position fast idle screw on high step of fast idle cam. Adjust dashpot plunger screw so it will just contact throttle lever. Check dashpot action (engine running at hot idle speed) by snapping throttle open and shut. If engine races, turn plunger screw ½ turn clockwise; if engine stalls, turn screw ½ turn counter-clockwise.

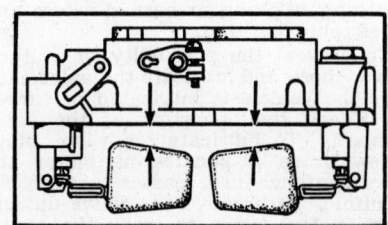

Fig. ⑦—WCFB float drop. Adjust by bending stop tabs on float bracket.

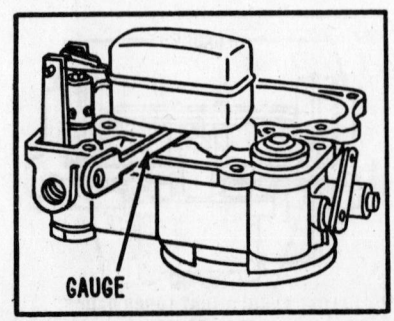

Fig. ⑧—WGD float level. Adjust by bending float lever.

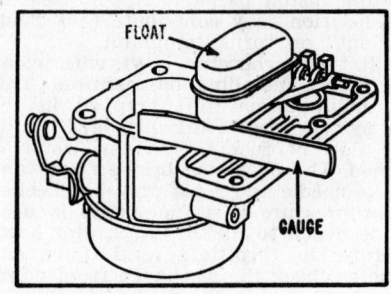

Fig. ⑨—YH float level. Adjust by bending float lever.

⑩—With bowl cover held upright, measure distance between float seam (at free end) and bowl cover. Adjust by bending stop tab on float arm.

⑪—With choke valve closed, clearance between throttle valve and carburetor bore (side opposite idle port) should be as specified. Adjust by bending choke connector rod.

⑫—Turboglide models only. With throttle valves fully closed, adjust dashpot position so that with plunger fully depressed, there should be the clearance specified between plunger and contact arm. With engine idling, test dashpot action by snapping throttle open and shut. If engine races increase clearance; if engine stalls reduce clearance.

ROCHESTER CARBURETOR ADJUSTMENTS

Year	Carburetor Model	Idle Adjustments				Float Level		Float Drop		Pump Rod Setting	Choke Unloader Setting	Choke Setting
		Mixture Screws Turns Open	Hot Idle Speed In Drive	Fast Idle Speed	Dashpot Plunger Clearance	Primary	Secondary	Primary	Secondary			
1961	BC-7013003	$2\frac{1}{2}$	425	None	None	$1\frac{9}{32}$[9]	None	$1\frac{3}{4}$[10]	None	None	.230[8]	1 Lean
	BC-7019000	$2\frac{1}{2}$	425	None	None	$1\frac{9}{32}$[9]	None	$1\frac{3}{4}$[10]	None	None	.230[8]	Index
	2GC-7019007	$1\frac{1}{2}$	450	None	[11]	$1\frac{23}{64}$[5]	None	$1\frac{29}{32}$[6]	None	$\frac{57}{64}$[7]	.360[4]	Index
	2GC-7019008	$1\frac{1}{2}$	450	None	[11]	$1\frac{23}{64}$[5]	None	$1\frac{29}{32}$[6]	None	$\frac{57}{64}$[7]	.360[4]	Index
	4GC-7019004	$1\frac{1}{2}$	450	None	[11]	$1\frac{33}{64}$[1]	$1\frac{37}{64}$[1]	$2\frac{1}{4}$[2]	$2\frac{1}{4}$[2]	$1\frac{1}{16}$[3]	.235[4]	Index
	4GC-7019006	$1\frac{1}{2}$	450	None	[11]	$1\frac{33}{64}$[1]	$1\frac{37}{64}$[1]	$2\frac{1}{4}$[2]	$2\frac{1}{4}$[2]	$1\frac{1}{16}$[3]	.235[4]	Index
1960	4GC-7015004	$1\frac{1}{2}$	450	None	[11]	$1\frac{33}{64}$[1]	$1\frac{37}{64}$[1]	$2\frac{1}{4}$[2]	$2\frac{1}{4}$[2]	$1\frac{1}{16}$[3]	.235[4]	1 Lean
	4GC-7015006	$1\frac{1}{2}$	450	None	[11]	$1\frac{33}{64}$[1]	$1\frac{37}{64}$[1]	$2\frac{1}{4}$[2]	$2\frac{1}{4}$[2]	$1\frac{1}{16}$[3]	.235[4]	Index
	4GC-7015010	$1\frac{1}{2}$	450	None	[11]	$1\frac{33}{64}$[1]	$1\frac{37}{64}$[1]	$2\frac{1}{4}$[2]	$2\frac{1}{4}$[2]	$1\frac{1}{16}$[3]	.235[4]	1 Lean
	4GC-7015012	$1\frac{1}{2}$	450	None	[11]	$1\frac{33}{64}$[1]	$1\frac{37}{64}$[1]	$2\frac{1}{4}$[2]	$2\frac{1}{4}$[2]	$1\frac{1}{16}$[3]	.235[4]	Index
1959–60	4GC-7013004	$1\frac{1}{2}$	450	None	[11]	$1\frac{43}{64}$[13]	$1\frac{47}{64}$[13]	$2\frac{1}{4}$[2]	$2\frac{1}{4}$[2]	$1\frac{1}{16}$[3]	.235[4]	1 Lean
	4GC-7013010	$1\frac{1}{2}$	450	None	[11]	$1\frac{43}{64}$[13]	$1\frac{47}{64}$[13]	$2\frac{1}{4}$[2]	$2\frac{1}{4}$[2]	$1\frac{1}{16}$[3]	.235[4]	1 Lean
	4GC-7013006	$1\frac{1}{2}$	450	None	[11]	$1\frac{43}{64}$[13]	$1\frac{47}{64}$[13]	$2\frac{1}{4}$[2]	$2\frac{1}{4}$[2]	$1\frac{1}{16}$[3]	.235[4]	Index
	4GC-7013012	$1\frac{1}{2}$	450	None	[11]	$1\frac{43}{64}$[13]	$1\frac{47}{64}$[13]	$2\frac{1}{4}$[2]	$2\frac{1}{4}$[2]	$1\frac{1}{16}$[3]	.235[4]	Index
	2GC-7013007	$1\frac{1}{4}$	450	None	None	$1\frac{23}{64}$[5]	None	$1\frac{29}{32}$[6]	None	$\frac{57}{64}$[7]	.360[4]	Index
	2GC-7013008	$1\frac{1}{2}$	450	None	None	$1\frac{23}{64}$[5]	None	$1\frac{29}{32}$[6]	None	$\frac{57}{64}$[7]	.360[4]	Index
	2GC-7013018	$1\frac{1}{4}$	450	None	[11]	$1\frac{23}{64}$[5]	None	$1\frac{29}{32}$[6]	None	$\frac{57}{64}$[7]	.360[4]	Index
	2GC-7013082	$1\frac{1}{2}$	450	None	[11]	$1\frac{23}{64}$[5]	None	$1\frac{29}{32}$[6]	None	$\frac{57}{64}$[7]	.360[4]	Index
	BC-7013000	$2\frac{1}{2}$	425	None	None	$1\frac{9}{32}$[9]	None	$1\frac{3}{4}$[10]	None	None	.230[8]	2 Rich
	BC-7013003	$2\frac{1}{2}$	425	None	None	$1\frac{9}{32}$[9]	None	$1\frac{3}{4}$[10]	None	None	.230[8]	1 Rich
	BC-7013005	$2\frac{1}{2}$	425	None	None	$1\frac{9}{32}$[9]	None	$1\frac{3}{4}$[10]	None	None	.230[8]	1 Rich
1958	BC-7011102	$1\frac{1}{2}$	425	None	None	$1\frac{9}{32}$[9]	None	$1\frac{3}{4}$[10]	None	None	.230[8]	Index
	BC-7012127	$1\frac{1}{2}$	425	None	None	$1\frac{9}{32}$[9]	None	$1\frac{3}{4}$[10]	None	None	.230[8]	1 Lean
	2GC-7012133	$1\frac{1}{2}$	425	None	.060[12]	$1\frac{19}{64}$[5]	None	$1\frac{29}{32}$[6]	None	$\frac{57}{64}$[7]	.360[8]	Index
	2GC-7012451	$1\frac{1}{2}$	425	None	.060[12]	$1\frac{19}{64}$[5]	None	$1\frac{29}{32}$[6]	None	$\frac{57}{64}$[7]	.360[8]	Index
	2GC-7012452	$1\frac{1}{2}$	425	None	.060[12]	$1\frac{19}{64}$[5]	None	$1\frac{29}{32}$[6]	None	$\frac{57}{64}$[7]	.360[8]	Index
	4GC-7012128	$1\frac{1}{2}$	425	None	.060[12]	$1\frac{5}{8}$[1]	$1\frac{11}{16}$[1]	$2\frac{1}{4}$[2]	$2\frac{1}{4}$[2]	$1\frac{1}{16}$[3]	.235[4]	1 Lean
	4GC-7011108	$1\frac{1}{2}$	425	None	.060[12]	$1\frac{5}{8}$[1]	$1\frac{11}{16}$[1]	$2\frac{1}{4}$[2]	$2\frac{1}{4}$[2]	$1\frac{1}{16}$[3]	.235[4]	Index
1957	2GC-7010647	$1\frac{1}{2}$	425	None	.060[12]	$1\frac{1}{4}$[5]	None	$1\frac{29}{32}$[6]	None	$\frac{57}{64}$[7]	.360[8]	Index
	2GC-7010648	$1\frac{1}{2}$	425	None	.060[12]	$1\frac{1}{4}$[5]	None	$1\frac{29}{32}$[6]	None	$\frac{57}{64}$[7]	.360[8]	Index
	2GC-7010719	$1\frac{1}{2}$	425	None	.060[12]	$1\frac{1}{4}$[5]	None	$1\frac{29}{32}$[6]	None	$\frac{57}{64}$[7]	.360[8]	Index
	2GC-7011131	$1\frac{1}{2}$	425	None	.060[12]	$1\frac{1}{4}$[5]	None	$1\frac{29}{32}$[6]	None	$\frac{57}{64}$[7]	.360[8]	Index
	2GC-7011224	$1\frac{1}{2}$	425	None	.060[12]	$1\frac{1}{4}$[5]	None	$1\frac{29}{32}$[6]	None	$\frac{57}{64}$[7]	.360[8]	Index
	2GC-7011149	$1\frac{1}{2}$	425	None	.060[12]	$1\frac{1}{4}$[5]	None	$1\frac{29}{32}$[6]	None	$\frac{57}{64}$[7]	.360[8]	Index
	4GC-7009846	$1\frac{1}{2}$	425	None	.060[12]	$1\frac{5}{8}$[1]	$1\frac{5}{8}$[1]	$2\frac{1}{4}$[2]	$2\frac{1}{4}$[2]	$1\frac{1}{16}$[3]	.235[4]	1 Lean
	4GC-7012126	$1\frac{1}{2}$	425	None	.060[12]	$1\frac{5}{8}$[1]	$1\frac{5}{8}$[1]	$2\frac{1}{4}$[2]	$2\frac{1}{4}$[2]	$1\frac{1}{16}$[3]	.235[4]	1 Lean
	4GC-7015711	$1\frac{1}{2}$	425	None	.060[12]	$1\frac{5}{8}$[1]	$1\frac{5}{8}$[1]	$2\frac{1}{4}$[2]	$2\frac{1}{4}$[2]	$1\frac{1}{16}$[3]	.235[4]	1 Lean
	BC-7009656	$1\frac{1}{2}$	425	None	None	$1\frac{9}{32}$[9]	None	$1\frac{3}{4}$[10]	None	None	.230[8]	3 Lean
	BC-7009657	$1\frac{1}{2}$	425	None	None	$1\frac{9}{32}$[9]	None	$1\frac{3}{4}$[10]	None	None	.230[8]	3 Lean
1956	4GC-7008737	$1\frac{1}{2}$	425	Fast	None	$1\frac{5}{8}$[1]	$1\frac{5}{8}$[1]	$2\frac{1}{4}$[2]	$2\frac{1}{4}$[2]	$1\frac{1}{16}$[3]	.235[4]	1 Lean
	2GC-7008388	$1\frac{1}{2}$	425	None	None	$1\frac{1}{4}$[5]	None	$1\frac{29}{32}$[6]	None	$\frac{57}{64}$[7]	.360[8]	Index
	2GC-7008387	$1\frac{1}{2}$	425	None	None	$1\frac{1}{4}$[5]	None	$1\frac{29}{32}$[6]	None	$\frac{57}{64}$[7]	.360[8]	Index
	BC-7009254	$2\frac{1}{2}$	425	None	None	$1\frac{9}{32}$[9]	None	$1\frac{3}{4}$[10]	None	None	.230[8]	2 Lean
	BC-7009255	$2\frac{1}{2}$	425	None	None	$1\frac{9}{32}$[9]	None	$1\frac{3}{4}$[10]	None	None	.230[8]	Index
1955	BC-7007180	$2\frac{1}{2}$	425	None	None	$1\frac{9}{32}$[9]	None	$1\frac{3}{4}$[10]	None	None	.230[8]	2 Lean
	BC-7007181	$2\frac{1}{2}$	425	None	None	$1\frac{9}{32}$[9]	None	$1\frac{3}{4}$[10]	None	None	.230[8]	Index
	2GC-7005810	$1\frac{1}{2}$	425	None	None	$1\frac{5}{32}$[5]	None	$1\frac{29}{32}$[6]	None	$\frac{15}{16}$[7]	.360[8]	Index
	2GC-7006825	$1\frac{1}{2}$	425	None	None	$1\frac{5}{32}$[5]	None	$1\frac{29}{32}$[6]	None	$\frac{15}{16}$[7]	.360[8]	Index
	2GC-7008004	$1\frac{1}{2}$	425	None	None	$1\frac{5}{32}$[5]	None	$1\frac{29}{32}$[6]	None	$\frac{15}{16}$[7]	.360[8]	Index
	2GC-7008005	$1\frac{1}{2}$	425	None	None	$1\frac{5}{32}$[5]	None	$1\frac{29}{32}$[6]	None	$\frac{15}{16}$[7]	.360[8]	Index
1954	BC-7005922	$2\frac{1}{2}$	425	None	None	$1\frac{9}{32}$[9]	None	$1\frac{3}{4}$[10]	None	None	.230[8]	2 Lean
	BC-7005921	$2\frac{1}{2}$	425	None	None	$1\frac{9}{32}$[9]	None	$1\frac{3}{4}$[10]	None	None	.230[8]	Index
1953	BC-7004478	$2\frac{1}{2}$	425	None	None	$1\frac{9}{32}$[9]	None	$1\frac{3}{4}$[10]	None	None	.166[8]	Index
	BC-7004915	$2\frac{1}{2}$	425	None	None	$1\frac{9}{32}$[9]	None	$1\frac{3}{4}$[10]	None	None	.230[8]	Index

ROCHESTER NOTES

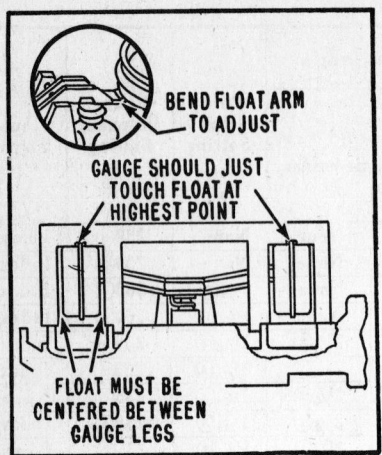

Fig. ①—4GC float level.

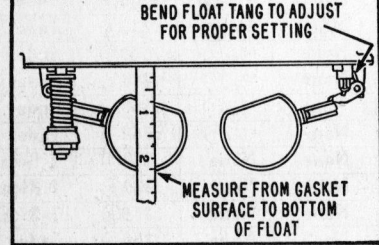

Fig. ②—4GC float drop.

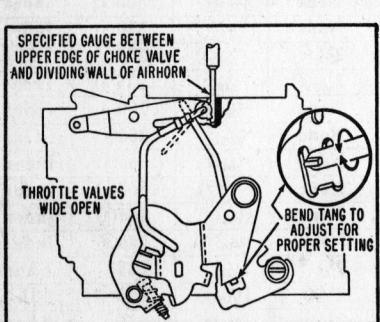

Fig. ③—With throttle valves closed, measure from top of air horn casting to bottom of pump plunger shaft. Adjust by bending pump rod.

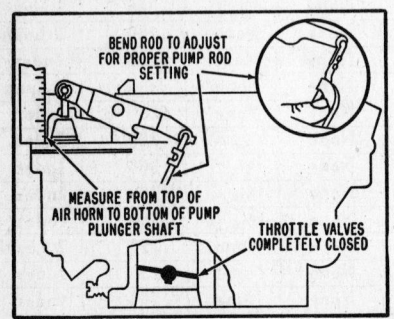

Fig. ④—Bend unloader tang on fast idle cam to obtain clearance specified between choke valve edge and dividing wall of air horn with throttle valves wide open.

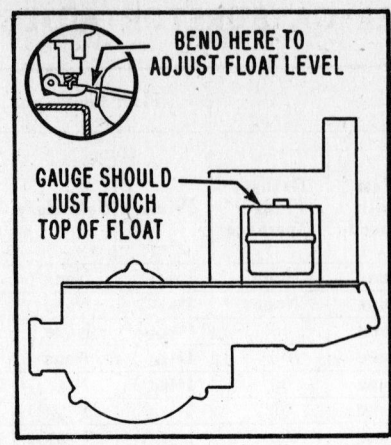

Fig. ⑤—2GC float level.

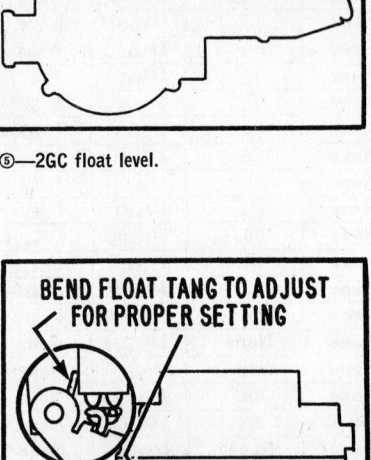

Fig. ⑥—2GC float drop.

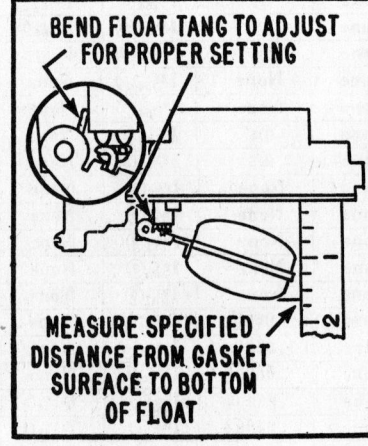

Fig. ⑦—With throttle valves fully closed, bend pump rod as necessary to obtain measurement specified from top of pump housing to top of pump rod.

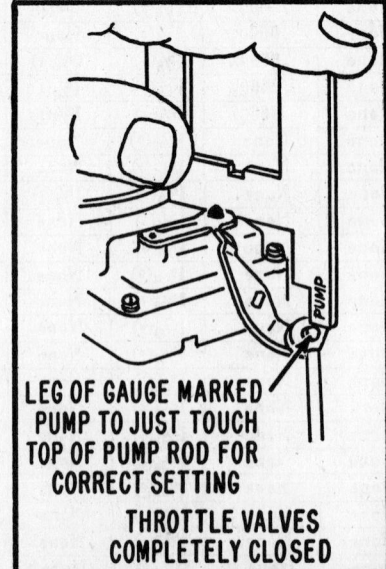

Fig. ⑧—With throttle valves wide open, choke valve must be open to the clearance specified between edge of choke valve and inner wall of air horn. Adjust by bending tang on throttle lever.

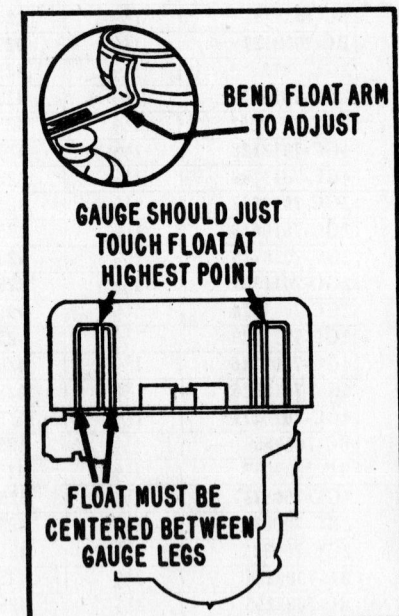

Fig. ⑨—BC float level.

(Continued next page)

ROCHESTER NOTES

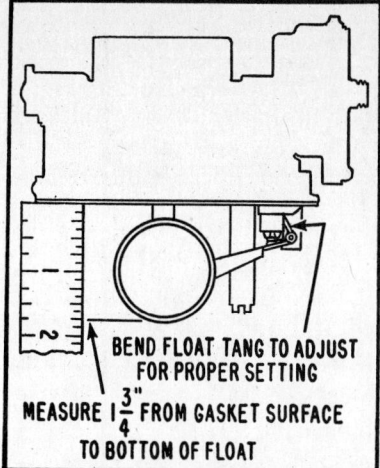

Fig. ⑩—BC float drop.

BEND FLOAT TANG TO ADJUST FOR PROPER SETTING

MEASURE 1¾" FROM GASKET SURFACE TO BOTTOM OF FLOAT

⑪—Position fast idle screw on high step of fast idle cam. Adjust dashpot plunger screw so it will just contact throttle lever. Check dashpot action (engine runnig at hot idle speed) by snapping throttle open and shut. If engine races, turn plunger screw ½ turn clockwise; if engine stalls turn screw ½ turn counter-clockwise.

⑫—Turboglide models only. With throttle valves fully closed, adjust dashpot position so that with plunger fully depressed, there should be the clearance specified between plunger and contact arm. With engine idling, test dashpot action by snapping throttle open and shut. If engine races increase clearance; if engine stalls reduce clearance.

⑬—For units with letter "B" stamped on number tag: Primary 1 33/64", secondary 1 31/64".

Clutch and Transmission Section

CLUTCH PEDAL, ADJUST

1953-54

Loosen the lock nut on the clutch fork push rod and turn the adjusting nut until free pedal travel is ¾" to 1".

1955-56

Loosen the lock nut on the clutch fork push rod and turn adjusting nut to remove all lash at the fork, then back off two turns. Tighten lock nut.

1957

Remove the cotter pin, washer and spring from the clutch fork push rod and turn the adjusting block until free pedal travel is ¾" to 1". (One turn equals about 5/16" at pedal.) Install spring, washer and cotter pin.

1958-61 With Dimple On Cross Shaft Lever

1. Disconnect forward end of clutch fork push rod from cross shaft lever.
2. Move fork push rod rearward to remove all lash. With the rod held in this position, adjust swivel on push rod so that the conical point of the swivel lines up with the "dimple" in the cross shaft lever.
3. Hold swivel position on rod and reconnect swivel to cross shaft lever.

Early 1961 With No Dimple

1. Disconnect swivel from cross shaft lever.
2. With push rod held all the way rearward, to eliminate lash between release bearing and clutch spring, check for free entry of swivel into cross shaft lever hole.
3. If swivel pin does not line up with hole, loosen jam nuts on both ends of swivel.
4. Adjust swivel to align with hole in cross shaft lever.
5. Adjust jam nuts finger tight next to swivel. Then hold rear nut and tighten front nut to a torque of 15-20 ft. lbs. to collapse the special washer.
6. Install clip into swivel. This adjustment will give ¾" to 1" free travel at the clutch pedal.

CLUTCH SERVICE

Note—*Except for 1956-57 models with Power Package and 1958 with 348 cu. in. engine, all models with standard transmission are equipped with the diaphragm spring type clutch, Fig. 1. The 1958 348 cu. in. engine and 1956-57 Power Package include a conventional coil spring type clutch.*

While it is practical to overhaul the diaphragm spring type clutch, as given below, unless special clutch rebuilding equipment is available, it is recommended that the coil spring type clutch be exchanged for a rebuilt unit should the clutch require rebuilding. The driven disc, however, may be replaced without special equipment. If special clutch rebuilding equipment is available, follow the equipment manufacturer's instructions.

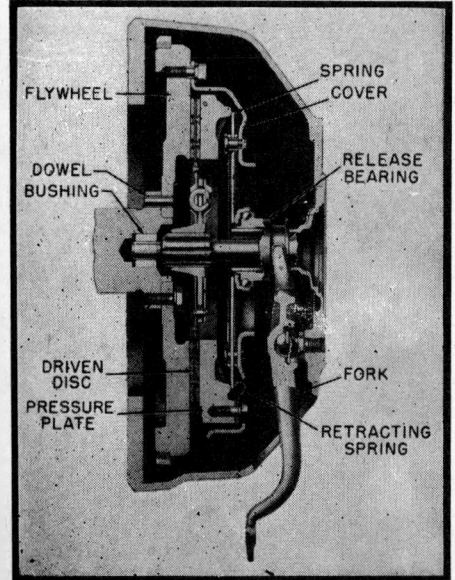

FLYWHEEL

SPRING COVER

DOWEL BUSHING

RELEASE BEARING

DRIVEN DISC

PRESSURE PLATE

FORK

RETRACTING SPRING

Fig. 1 Diaphragm spring type clutch

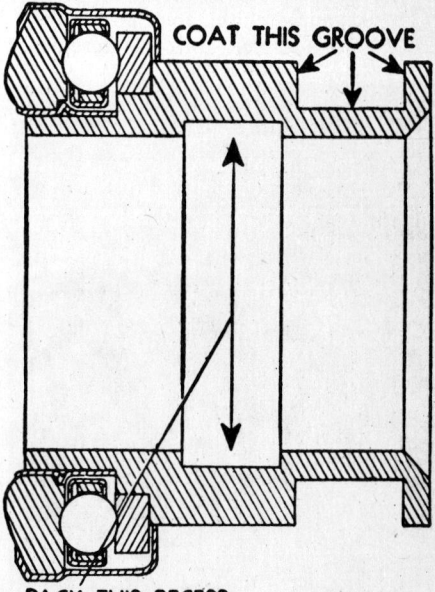

COAT THIS GROOVE

PACK THIS RECESS

Fig. 2 Clutch release bearing lubrication. All Models with diaphragm spring type clutch

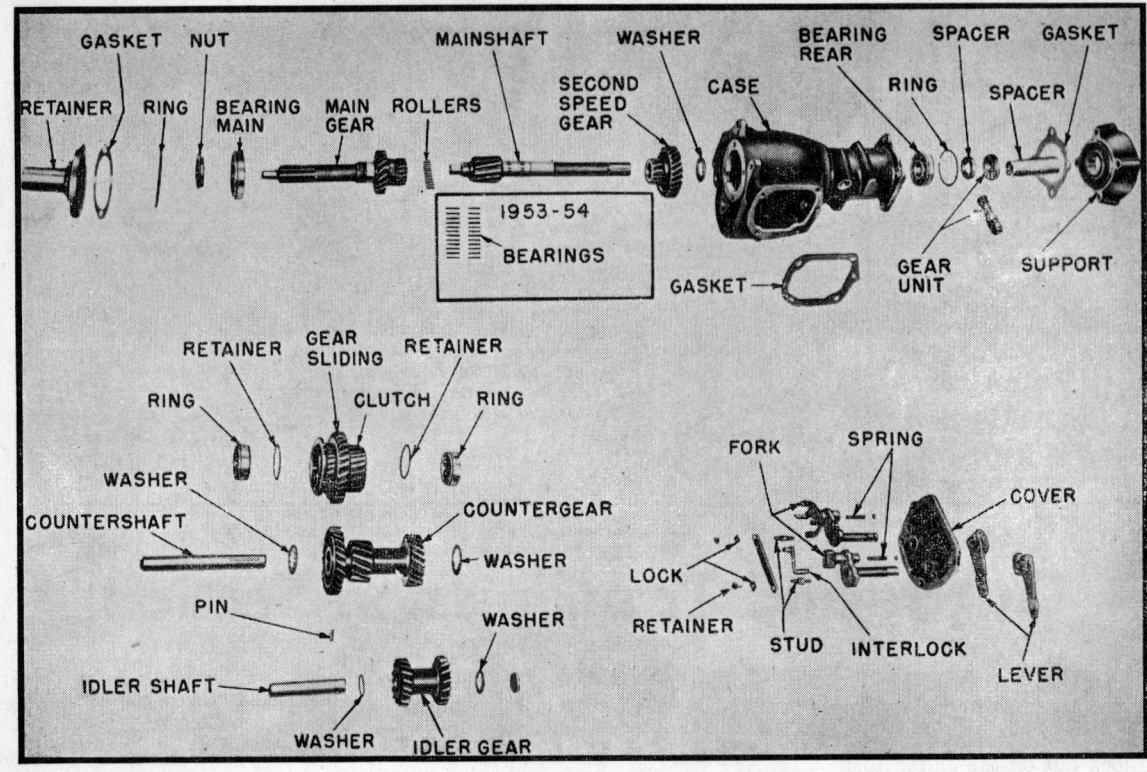

Fig. 3 Synchromesh transmission. 1953-54

DIAPHRAGM SPRING TYPE

Removal

1. **Remove** transmission as outlined further on.
2. **Remove** clutch release bearing from release fork, Fig. 1.
3. **Remove** clutch fork tension spring from fork.
4. **Disconnect** clutch fork push rod.
5. **Remove** clutch fork by forcing it forward and toward center of vehicle.

Fig. 4 Removing main drive gear and bearing with puller. 1953-55

6. Install a suitable clutch pilot tool or a spare clutch shaft to support clutch assembly during removal.
7. Loosen clutch attaching bolts one turn at a time until diaphragm spring is released.
8. Remove clutch pilot tool and take clutch assembly from vehicle.

Disassemble

1. Remove three drive strap-to-pressure plate bolts and retracting springs and remove pressure plate from clutch cover. *When disassembling, note position of grooves on edge of pressure plate and cover. These marks must be aligned at assembly to maintain balance.*
2. The diaphragm spring and two pivot rings are riveted to the clutch cover. Spring, rings and cover should be inspected for excessive wear or damage and if there is a defect, it is necessary to replace the complete cover assembly.

Inspection

1. Wash all parts except the release bearing in cleaning solvent. *The release bearing is permanently packed with lubricant and should not be soaked in cleaning solvent as this may dissolve the lubricant.*
2. Inspect pressure plate and flywheel for scores on contact surfaces.
3. Check drive-straps for looseness at the clutch cover rivets and evidence of looseness at pressure plate bolt holes.
4. Check release bearing for roughness and free fit on sleeve of clutch shaft bearing retainer.

5. Inspect clutch disc for worn, loose or oil soaked facings, broken springs, loose rivets or riding.
6. Examine splines in hub and make sure they slide freely on splines of clutch shaft. If splines are worn, clutch disc or clutch shaft should be replaced as necessary.

Assemble

1. Install pressure plate in cover, lining up groove on edge of pressure plate with groove on edge of cover.
2. Install pressure plate retracting springs and drive strap-to-pressure plate bolts and lockwashers. Tighten to 11 lb. ft. torque. The clutch is now ready to be installed.

Installation

1. Hand crank engine until "X" mark on flywheel is at bottom.

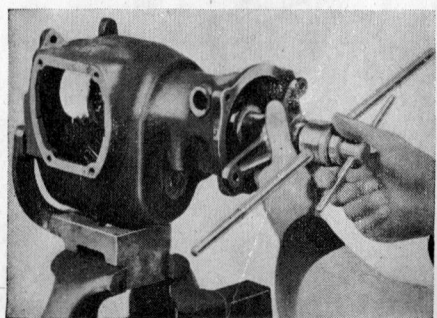

Fig. 5 Removing mainshaft. 1953-54

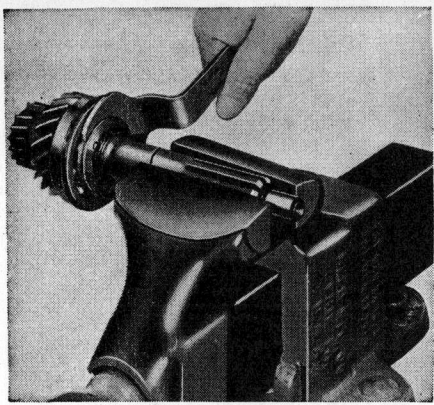

Fig. 6 Removing main drive gear retaining nut and oil slinger. 1953-55

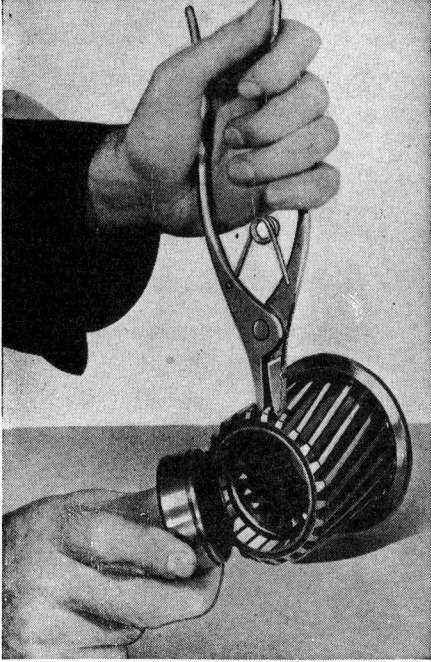

Fig. 7 Removing synchronizer ring from clutch sleeve. All models

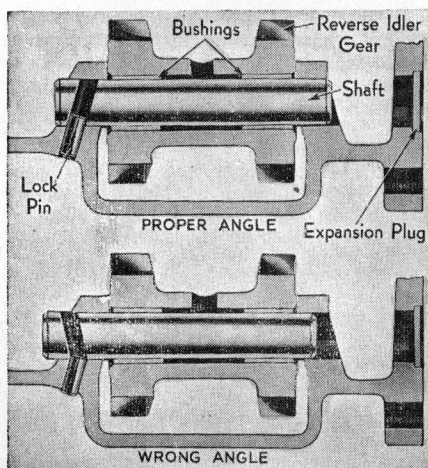

Fig. 8 Reverse idler gear, shaft and lock pin. All models

2. Install clutch disc, pressure plate and cover assembly, and support them with clutch pilot tool or spare clutch shaft.
3. Turn clutch assembly until "X" mark on cover flange lines up with "X" mark on flywheel. Align nearest bolts holes in clutch and in flywheel.
4. Install attaching bolts and tighten each one a turn at a time to prevent distorting the cover as the spring pressure is taken up.
5. Remove clutch pilot tool.
6. Pack clutch fork ball seat with a small amount of high melting point grease.
7. Install fork on ball in clutch housing.
8. Lubricate recess on inside of release bearing collar and coat release fork groove with a small amount of graphite grease, Fig. 2.
9. Install release bearing assembly to the fork and hook up linkage.
10. Install transmission.

COIL SPRING TYPE

1958 V8-348

Remove transmission as outlined further on. Then, before removing clutch from flywheel, mark with a punch the flywheel, clutch cover and one pressure plate lug so that these parts may be assembled in their same relative positions, as they were balanced as an assembly.

Disengage the clutch fork from the ball stud and remove the ball stud by screwing it rearward out of the clutch housing. Loosen the holding screws a turn or two at a time to avoid bending rim of cover. When removing clutch disc be sure to mark flywheel side. *It is advantageous to place nuts or metal spacers between the three clutch levers and the cover to hold the levers down as the holding screws are removed.*

Installation

Assemble clutch disc and clutch cover assembly to flywheel in accordance with marking on clutch disc for flywheel side. *Depress clutch levers and install spacers or nuts to hold levers down. This will facilitate installation and prevent cover distortion during tightening. Be sure to remove spacers before bolting clutch to flywheel.*

Line up the clutch disc and pilot bearing with a dummy shaft before tightening cover holding screws. Tighten holding screws before removing dummy shaft.

After transmission has been installed, adjust clutch pedal free play as directed above.

MANUAL SHIFT TRANSMISSION

Replace, 1953-54

1. Remove brake cross shaft.
2. Remove speedometer cable.
3. Detach and slide universal ball and collar back on propeller shaft.
4. Detach transmission from crossmember.
5. Remove two top transmission mounting capscrews and insert suitable guide studs in their place to prevent the transmission from hanging on the clutch disc, which may cause damage to it.
6. Remove the lower mounting capscrews and slide the transmission back and out of the vehicle.
7. Reverse the foregoing procedure to

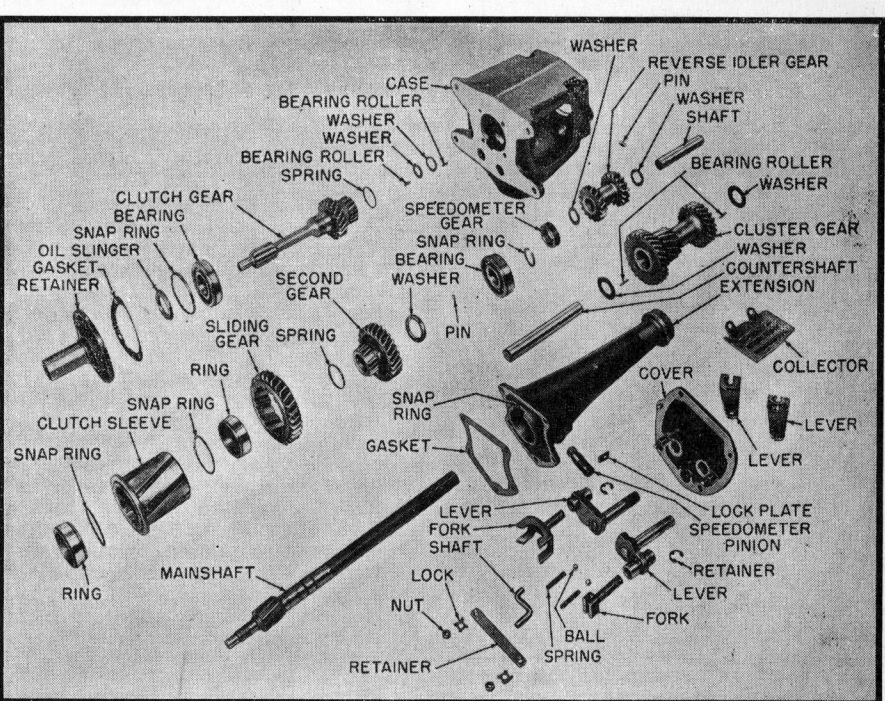

Fig. 9 Exploded view of 1955 synchromesh transmission

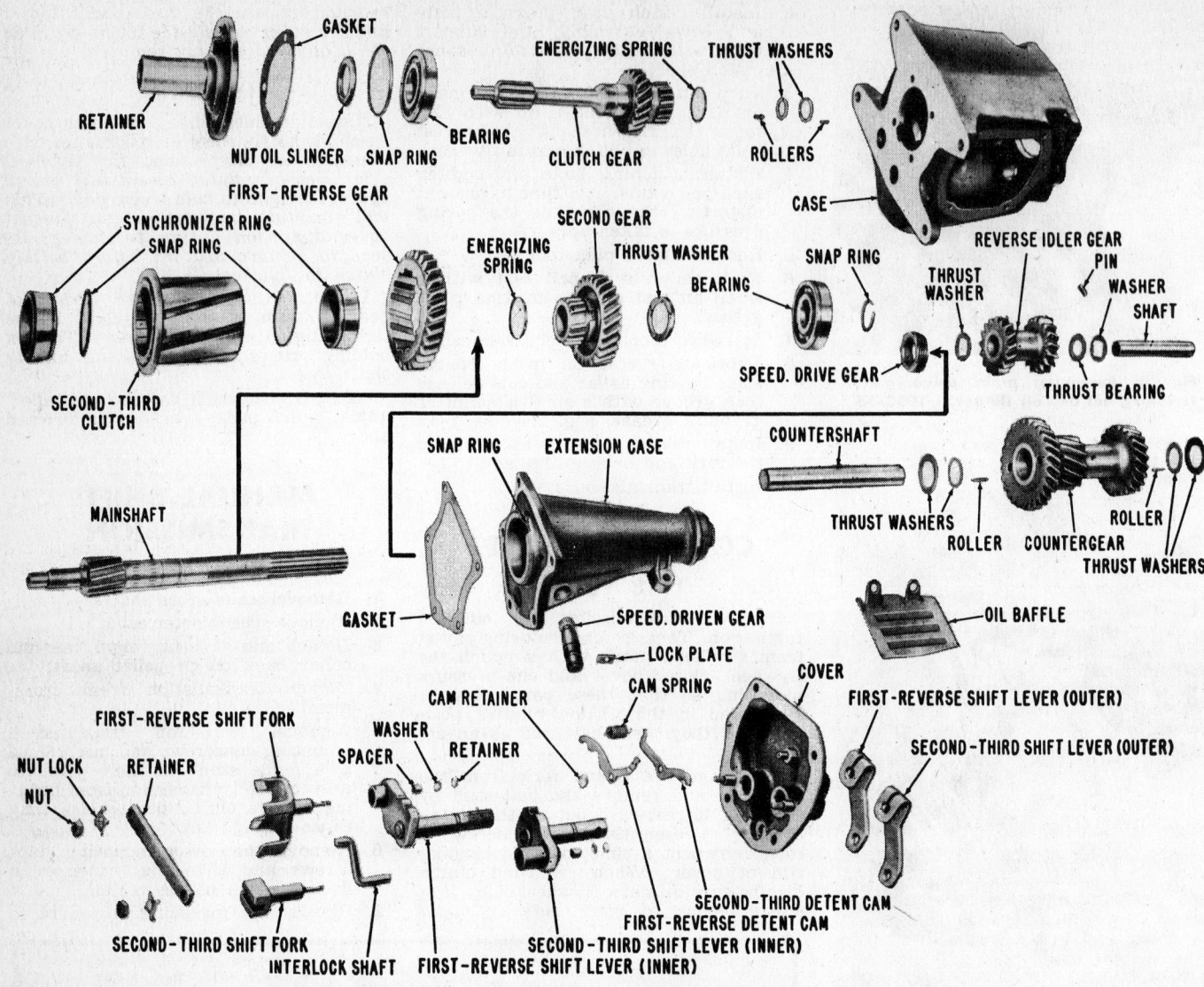

Fig. 10   Exploded view of 1956-61 three speed synchromesh transmission

install the unit, being sure to use the guide studs to guide the transmission in safely.

Replace, 1955-57

1. Disconnect speedometer cable, and the shift control rods from the levers at the transmission.
2. Split the rear universal joint and remove the propeller shaft and front universal joint.
3. Remove the two top transmission-to-clutch attaching bolts and insert guide studs in their place.
4. Remove the two lower attaching bolts and slide the transmission straight back on the guide studs until the clutch gear is free of the splines in the clutch disc.
5. Remove the transmission from under the chassis.
6. Reverse the above procedure to install the transmission, using the guide studs to prevent the weight of the transmission from hanging on the clutch disc.

Replace, 1958-61

1. Disconnect speedometer cable.
2. Disconnect shift control rods from shift levers at transmission.
3. Remove propeller shaft.
4. Support rear of engine and remove transmission mounting block-to-support bolts and washers.
5. Remove support from frame, noting number of shims present (if any) so the same amount may be installed.
6. Remove two top transmission attaching cap screws and insert guide pins in these holes. Remove two lower attaching screws.
7. Slide transmission straight back on the guide pins until the clutch gear is free of the clutch disc splines.
8. Remove transmission from under body.
9. Reverse above procedure to install the transmission.

Service Note

If high gear hop-out is experienced on Corvette V8-283 and Hi-performance 348 engines, it is probably due to the transmission-to-clutch housing bolts being too short.

To insure proper attachment of the manual transmission to the aluminum clutch housing on these engines, it is necessary that 1¾" bolts be used. It is possible for shorter bolts to loosen, resulting in transmission misalignment and high gear hop-out.

The 1¾" bolt specified for this usage is available under Part No. 427565. An installation torque of 40-50 ft. lbs. is recommended when these bolts are used in the aluminum housing.

THREE SPEED TRANSMISSION REPAIRS

Disassemble, 1953-54, Fig. 3

1. Remove cover and shifter assembly.
2. Lock transmission in two gears and remove universal yoke from mainshaft.

3. Use puller, Fig. 4, to remove main drive gear and bearing.
4. Use pusher, Fig. 5, to force mainshaft forward out of rear bearing.
5. Shift second speed gear into clutch sleeve and remove these parts together with sliding gear. Take second gear thrust washer from case.
6. Expand snap ring and tap mainshaft rear bearing toward inside of case and remove. (This bearing must be removed before attempting to remove the cluster gear.)
7. Drive countershaft out through front, and lift out cluster gear and thrust washers, and needle bearings on 1954 units.
8. Drive idler shaft lock pin into shaft and remove shaft, idler gear and thrust washers.
9. Using tool shown in Fig. 6, remove main drive gear retaining nut and oil slinger. Then press shaft out of bearing.
10. Turn synchronizer ring in clutch sleeve until ends of ring retainers can be seen through slot in sleeve. Expand retaining ring, Fig. 7, and slip ring out of sleeve.

Assembly Details

Inspect all gears for wear or damage, and see that the first and reverse sliding gear and the clutch sleeve slide freely on the mainshaft. See that the synchronizing cones are not loose in the clutch sleeve. If the cones are damaged, it will be necessary to replace the clutch sleeve assembly and both synchronizing rings.

See that the synchronizer rings are smooth and that they do not rock in the cones. Excessive rocking affects proper synchronizing of the gears during shifting.

Normally, it should not be necessary to replace the energizing springs. However, should this be necessary, the spring is assembled in its groove with its offset end between the fourth and fifth clutch teeth of either bank of teeth. This will prevent the spring from turning in its groove.

Check the countershaft bushings for excessive wear by using a narrow feeler gauge between the shaft and the bushings. The proper clearance should be from .002" to .004". (Needle bearings are used for 1954.)

When installing the reverse idler, the chamfered teeth should be placed to the rear of the case. Install the idler shaft, making sure that the lock pin hole in the shaft lines up with the hole in the case at the same angle, Fig. 8. It is well to line up these holes with a punch before installing the lock pin. Use a new lock pin and drive it in about $\frac{1}{16}$" beyond flush with the case, and peen the hole slightly.

When installing the countershaft, the step on the forward end should be flush with the front face of the case, or about $\frac{1}{64}$" below the face, to maintain proper transmission alignment.

When installing the mainshaft, the proper seating of the shoulder on the shaft against the inner race of the mainshaft rear bearing should permit .010" end play of the second speed gear.

When the assembly has been completed, check the transmission in all gears to be sure that there is no indication of binding in any position.

Disassemble, 1955-61
Fig. 9, 10

1. Remove side cover and gasket.
2. Remove main drive gear bearing retainer and, with the puller shown in Fig. 4, remove the main drive gear and bearing.
3. Remove 24 roller rear pilot bearings, 2 washers and 14 roller front bearings.
4. Unfasten extension housing from transmission case and pull extension and mainshaft out of transmission case, leaving the synchronizer and first and reverse gear in case.
5. Remove synchronizer clutch sleeve and first and reverse gear through side opening in case.
6. Remove countershaft by driving it from front to rear of case, using a soft steel drift. Remove the countergear rollers and thrust washers (and thrust bearings on 1956-61).
7. Remove the countergear.
8. Drive the idler shaft lock pin into the shaft. This pin is shorter than the diameter of the shaft so the shaft may be slipped out when the pin is driven in.
9. Using a drift pin, tap rear of idler shaft to drive out plug ahead of shaft. Do not turn the shaft while removing as the lock pin may drop down between the idler gear bushings.
10. Remove reverse idler gear and thrust washers (and bearing on 1956-61).
11. To remove the mainshaft from the extension, expand the bearing snap ring and tap the rear of the shaft with a soft hammer to bring the shaft, speedometer drive gear, second speed gear and bearing out of the extension as an assembly.

Mainshaft, Disassemble

1. Press speedometer gear off mainshaft, using suitable split plates in an arbor press.
2. Remove bearing-to-mainshaft snap ring and press bearing off shaft.
3. Remove second speed gear thrust washer, pull drive pin out of shaft and remove second speed gear.

Mainshaft, Assemble

1. Slide second speed gear on mainshaft, insert drive pin in shaft and install thrust washer against gear.
2. Install new bearing with groove in outside diameter of bearing toward second speed gear.
3. Select one of four available snap rings so end play of bearing on shaft is a maximum of .004". This may be determined by installing successively larger rings. Use the thickest ring that will enter snap ring groove on shaft.
4. Start speedometer drive gear on shaft with chamfered inside diameter of gear toward bearing. Press gear on shaft so forward face of gear is ⅞" from rear face of bearing.

Service Note

Service on the main drive gear bearing, clutch sleeve and synchronizer, reverse idler gear bushings and installation of the countergear and needle bearings is the same as for 1954 units.

Reassemble the transmission in the reverse order of disassembly, observing the precautions outlined in the assembly notes for 1954 insofar as they apply to the later units.

FOUR SPEED TRANS.
1960-61, Fig. 10A

1. To disassemble, remove side cover.
2. Remove front bearing retainer.
3. Drive lock pin from bottom side of reverse shifter lever boss and pull shifter out about ⅛". This disengages reverse shift fork from reverse gear.
4. Unfasten case extension from rear bearing retainer (5 bolts). Tap extension to rear. When reverse idler shaft is out as far as it will go, move extension to left so reverse fork clears reverse gear and remove extension.
5. Remove snap ring from end of mainshaft. Remove speedometer gear, reverse idler gear, tanged trust washer and reverse gear.
6. Remove self-locking bolt attaching rear bearing retainer to case. Then remove mainshaft assembly.
7. Lift front reverse idler gear and thrust washer from case.
8. Remove pilot rollers from main drive gear and 4th speed synchronizing ring.
9. Remove main drive gear snap ring and spacer washer. Tap drive gear from front bearing. From inside case, tap out front bearing and snap ring.
10. From front of case, tap out countershaft and remove countershaft gear and thrust washers.
11. Strip mainshaft of all parts.

Assemble
Mainshaft

1. From rear of mainshaft, assemble 1st-2nd clutch to mainshaft with sleeve taper toward rear and hub to front. Press 1st gear bushing on shaft.
2. Install 1st gear synchronizing ring so notches in ring correspond to keys in hub.
3. Install 1st gear with hub to front, and thrust washer. Make sure that grooves in washer are facing 1st gear.
4. Press rear bearing with snap ring groove toward front, making certain bearing is firmly seated against shoulder on mainshaft.
5. Choose correct selective fit snap ring and install it in mainshaft groove behind rear bearing. Snap rings are available in three thicknesses; use ring that will produce from zero to .005" clearance between rear face of bearing and front face of snap ring.
6. From front of mainshaft, install 2nd gear synchronizing ring so notches in ring correspond to keys in hub. Install 2nd speed gear with hub toward rear, and install 2nd-3rd gear thrust (bearing) washer.
7. Install 3rd gear with hub to front and 3rd gear synchronizing ring with notches to front.
8. Install 3rd-4th gear clutch (hub and sliding sleeve) with taper toward

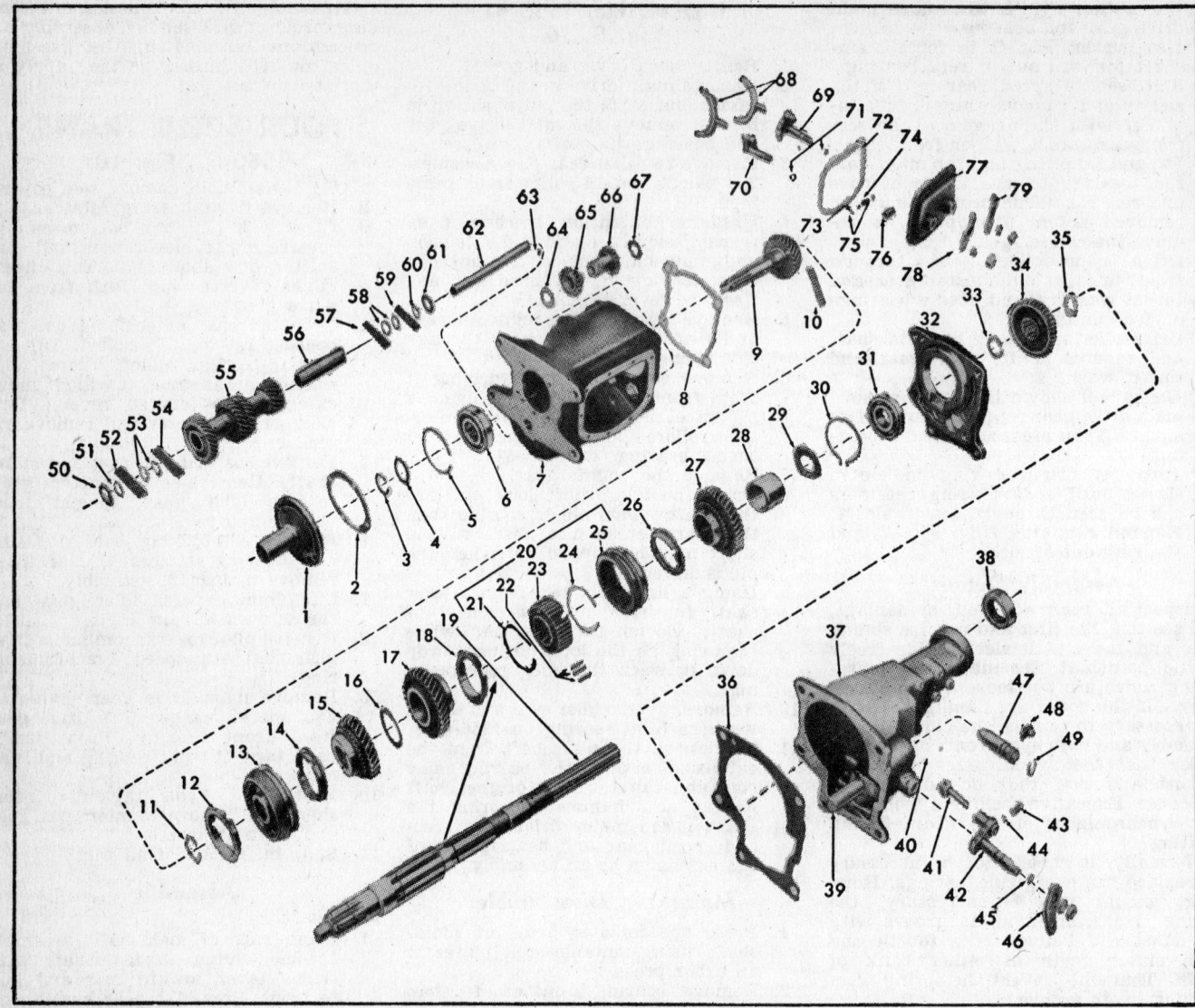

Fig. 10A   Four speed manual shift transmission.   1958-61

1. Bearing Retainer
2. Gasket
3. Selective Fit Snap Ring
4. Spacer Washer
5. Bearing Snap Ring
6. Main Drive Gear Bearing
7. Transmission Case
8. Rear Bearing Retainer Gasket
9. Main Drive Gear
10. Bearing Rollers (14)
11. Snap Ring (.086" to .088")
12. Fourth Speed Gear Synchronizing Ring
13. Third and Fourth Speed Clutch Sliding Sleeve
14. Third Speed Synchronizing Ring
15. Third Speed Gear
16. Second and Third Speed Gear Thrust Washer (Needle Roller Bearing)
17. Second Speed Gear
18. Second Speed Gear Synchronizing Ring
19. Mainshaft

20. First and Second Speed Clutch Assembly
21. Clutch Key Spring
22. Clutch Keyes
23. Clutch Hub
24. Clutch Key Spring
25. First and Second Speed Clutch Sliding Sleeve
26. First Speed Gear Synchronizing Ring
27. First Speed Gear
28. First Speed Gear Bushing
29. First Speed Gear Thrust Washer
30. Rear Bearing Snap Ring
31. Rear Bearing
32. Rear Bearing Retainer
33. Selective Fit Snap Ring
34. Reverse Gear
35. Speedometer Drive Gear
36. Rear Bearing Retainer to Case Extension Gasket
37. Case Extension
38. Rear Oil Seal
39. Reverse Idler Shaft
40. Reverse Shifter Shaft Lock Pin

41. Reverse Shift Fork
42. Reverse Shifter Shaft and Detent Plate
43. Reverse Shifter Shaft Ball Detent Spring
44. Reverse Shifter Shaft Detent Ball
45. Reverse Shifter Shaft "O" Ring Seal
46. Reverse Shifter Lever
47. Speedometer Driven Gear and Fitting
48. Retainer and Bolt
49. "O" Ring Seal
50. Tanged Washer
51. Spacer (.050")
52. Bearing Rollers (20)
53. Spacers (2—.050")
54. Bearing Rollers (20)
55. Countergear
56. Countergear Roller Spacer
57. Bearing Rollers (20)
58. Spacers (2—.050")
59. Bearing Rollers (20)
60. Spacer (.050")
61. Tanged Washer
62. Countershaft

63. Countershaft Woodruff Key
64. Reverse Idler Front Thrust Washer (Flat)
65. Reverse Idler Gear (Front)
66. Reverse Idler Gear (Rear)
67. Tanged Thrust Washer
68. Forward Speed Shift Forks
69. First and Second Speed Gear Shifter Shaft and Detent Plate
70. Third and Fourth Speed Gear Shifter Shaft and Detent Plate
71. "O" Ring Seals
72. Gasket
73. Interlock Pin
74. Poppet Spring
75. Detent Balls
76. Interlock Sleeve
77. Transmission Side Cover
78. Third and Fourth Speed Shifter Lever
79. First and Second Speed Shifter Lever

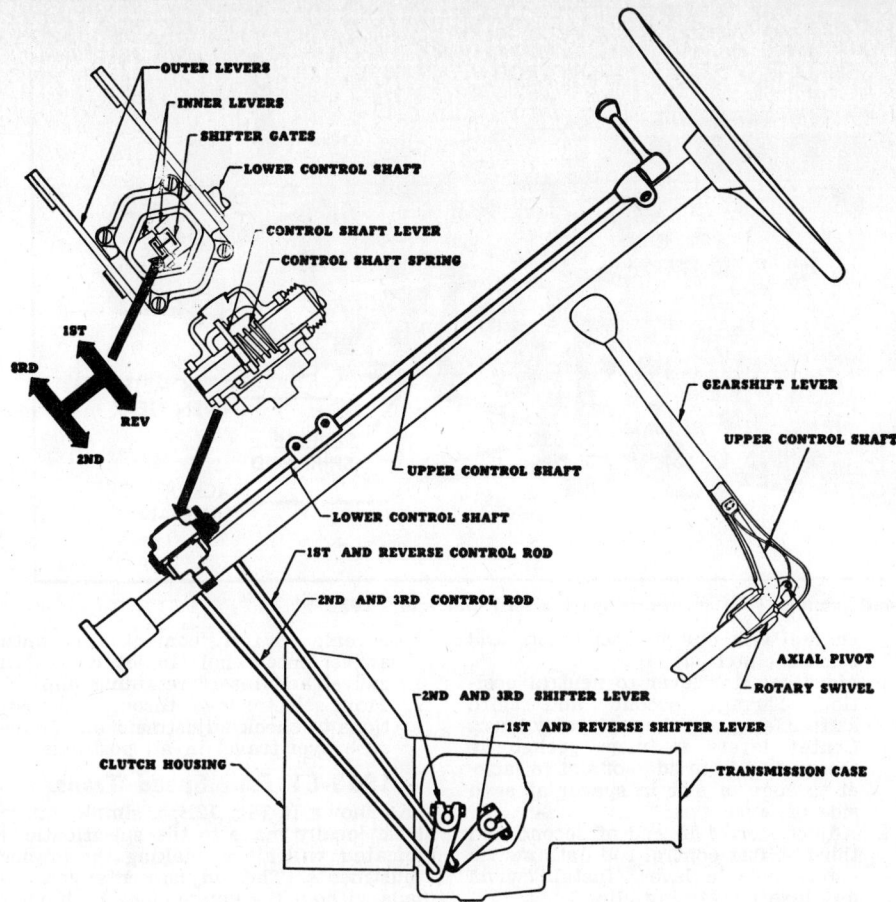

Fig. 11 1953-54 gearshift linkage

front, making sure that keys in hub correspond to notches in 3rd gear synchronizing ring. Install snap ring in mainshaft groove in front of clutch.

9. Install rear bearing retainer plate. Spread snap ring on plate to allow it to drop around rear bearing and press on end of mainshaft until snap ring engages groove in rear bearing.
10. Install reverse gear with shift collar to rear.
11. Press speedometer gear on mainshaft so it is 4½" from center of gear to flat surface of rear bearing retainer. Install snap ring in groove at rear of mainshaft.

Countershaft Gear

1. Install spacer in countergear.
2. Using grease to retain rollers, install 20 rollers in each end of gear, two .050" spacers, 20 more rollers, then one .050" spacer. Insert dummy shaft to hold parts in place during installation.

Transmission, Assemble

1. Place countershaft tanged thrust washers in place, retaining them with grease and being sure that tangs are resting in notches in case. Set counter gear in bottom of case.
2. Press bearing onto main drive gear with snap ring groove to front and firmly seat bearing against shoulder of main drive gear.
3. Install spacer washer and selective fit snap ring in groove on gear stem. Use ring that will provide zero to .005" clearance between rear face

of snap ring and front face of spacer washer.

4. Install main drive gear through side cover opening. Place snap ring in groove in front bearing.
5. With transmission resting on its front face, move countergear into mesh with main drive gear, being sure thrust washers are in place. Install key in end of countershaft and, from front of case, tap shaft until its end is flush with rear of case and dummy shaft is displaced. End play of countergear should be not more than .025".
6. Install 14 pilot rollers in main drive gear pocket, using grease to hold them in place.
7. Place a greased gasket on front face of rear bearing retainer.
8. Install 4th gear synchronizing ring on main drive gear with clutch key notches toward rear.
9. Position reverse idler gear thrust washer (untanged) on machined face of ear cast in case for reverse idler shaft. Position front reverse idler gear on top of thrust washer with hub facing rear of case.
10. Lower mainshaft assembly into case, making certain that notches on 4th gear synchronizing ring correspond to keys in clutch assembly.
11. Install self-locking bolt attaching rear bearing retainer to case, tightening it to 20-30 ft. lbs.
12. From rear of case, insert rear reverse idler gear, engaging splines with portion of gear within case.

13. Place greased gasket on rear face of rear bearing retainer.
14. Install remaining tanged thrust washer on reverse idler shaft, being sure tang is in notch in idler thrust face of extension case.
15. Place two clutches in neutral.
16. Pull reverse shifter shaft to left side of extension and rotate shaft to bring reverse shift fork to extreme forward position in extension. Line up forward and rear reverse idler gears, being sure front thrust washer is in place.
17. Start extension into transmission case by carefully inserting reverse idler shaft through reverse idler gears. Slowly push it on shifter shaft until shift fork engages reverse gear shift collar. When fork engages, rotate shifter shaft to move reverse gear rearward, permitting extension to slide onto case.
18. Install 3 extension-to-case bolts, tightening to 35-45 ft. lbs., and 2 extension-to-retainer bolts, tightening to 20 - 30 ft. lbs. Use suitable sealer on lower right attaching bolt (viewed from rear).
19. Adjust reverse shifter shaft so that groove in shaft lines up with hole in boss and drive in lock pin from top of boss.
20. Install main drive gear bearing retainer and gasket, making certain oil well lines up with oil outlet hole. Install bolts with suitable sealer and tighten to 15-20 ft. lbs.
21. Install a shift fork in each clutch sleeve. With both clutches in neutral, install side cover and gasket. Tighten cover bolts evenly to 10-20 ft. lbs. torque. Use suitable sealer when installing lower right bolt. Install shift levers.

GEARSHIFT, ADJUST
1953-54

FIG. 11—There should be ⅞" clearance between the gearshift lever and the support bracket. To adjust, remove the support from the steering column and the upper control shaft from the lower bracket. Screw the upper support up or down as required, and replace the parts.

The clearance between the gearshift lever and the lower edge of the steering wheel rim should be 2¹¹⁄₁₆". To adjust, loosen the control shaft and housing

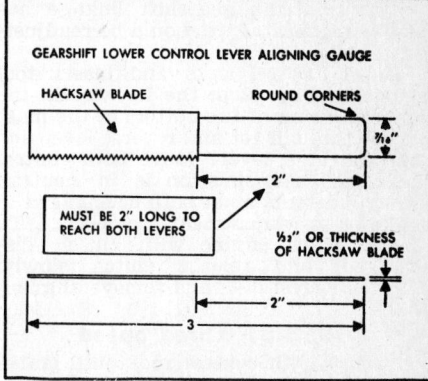

Fig. 12 Construction of keyway tool for adjusting gearshift lever. 1956-57 with synchromesh transmission

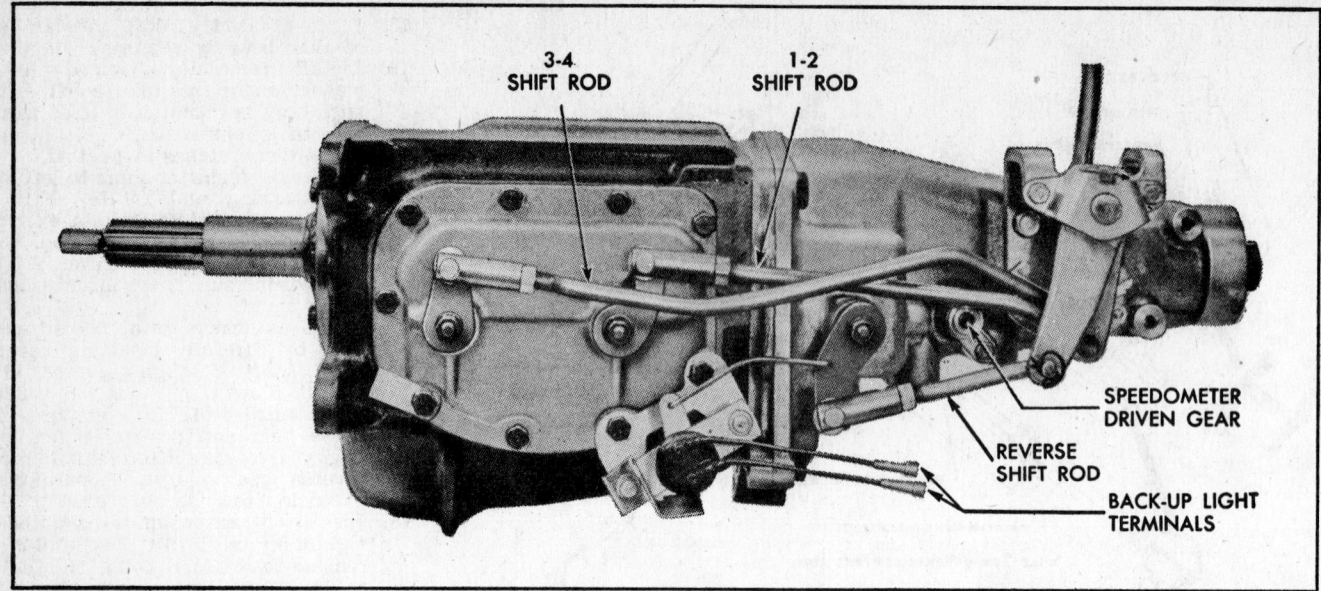

3-4 SHIFT ROD

1-2 SHIFT ROD

SPEEDOMETER DRIVEN GEAR

REVERSE SHIFT ROD

BACK-UP LIGHT TERMINALS

Fig. 12A Four speed manual shift transmission gearshift linkage. 1958-61

clamp bolts and move the housing up or down to obtain the desired clearance. Tighten bolts securely.

With transmission in neutral, gearshift lever should be horizontal. To adjust, loosen second and third speed control rod swivel clamp bolt and adjust swivel as required to bring the gearshift lever to horizontal plane. Tighten clamp bolt.

Remove the housing cover and make sure shifter gates in inner levers are aligned. If alignment is off, loosen first and reverse speed control rod swivel clamp bolt and adjust swivel until shifter gates are aligned. Tighten clamp bolt.

1955

In cases where the gearshift linkage has been disconnected, it should be adjusted when reconnecting as follows:

Slide the shifter rods into their respective swivel fittings on the levers at the control tube. Move the shifter rods through the swivel fittings until the transmission is in neutral and the 1st and reverse lever is at the midpoint of its travel (center of slot). Align the 2nd and 3rd shifter lever with 1st and reverse lever and tighten swivel fitting nuts. *Shifter tube levers must be in line or key will not enter keyway in levers.*

1956-57

Whenever the gearshift linkage has been disconnected, it should be readjusted as follows:

Loosen swivel nuts and insert tool shown in Fig. 12 in the keyway in the adjusting ring at the bottom of the mast jacket through 1st and reverse lever and 2nd and high lever. Move both control rods until transmission is in neutral. Neutral detents must both be engaged to make this adjustment correctly. To check, start engine with clutch disengaged, and release clutch slowly. Tighten swivel nuts and remove aligning tool.

1958-61 Three Speed

1. Move both control rods until transmission is in neutral. Neutral detents in transmission cover must both be engaged to make this adjustment correctly. To check, start

engine with clutch disengaged, and release clutch slowly.
2. Move selector lever to neutral position. Engage second and third shifter lever on tube with relay lever.
3. Center levers in mast jacket by measuring from edge of slot in jacket to edge of slot in spacer at each side of lever.
4. Adjust swivel on end of second and third shifter control rod until swivel enters hole in lever. Install swivel and insert retaining clip.
5. Move first and reverse lever on tube until lug on lever lines up with slot in relay lever. Pull relay lever to make sure lug will mate with slot.
6. Adjust swivel on end of first and

reverse shifter control rod until swivel enters hole in lever. Install swivel and insert retaining clip.
7. Move selector lever through all positions to check adjustment and to insure over-travel in all positions.

1960-61 Four Speed Trans.

As shown in Fig. 12B, a simple gauge block, locally made to the specifications indicated, will aid in making the proper adjustments. The adjustments can be made without the gauge block by having an assistant hold the manual shift lever in neutral position.
1. Referring to Figs. 12A and 12B, remove gearshift lever seal from floor pan.

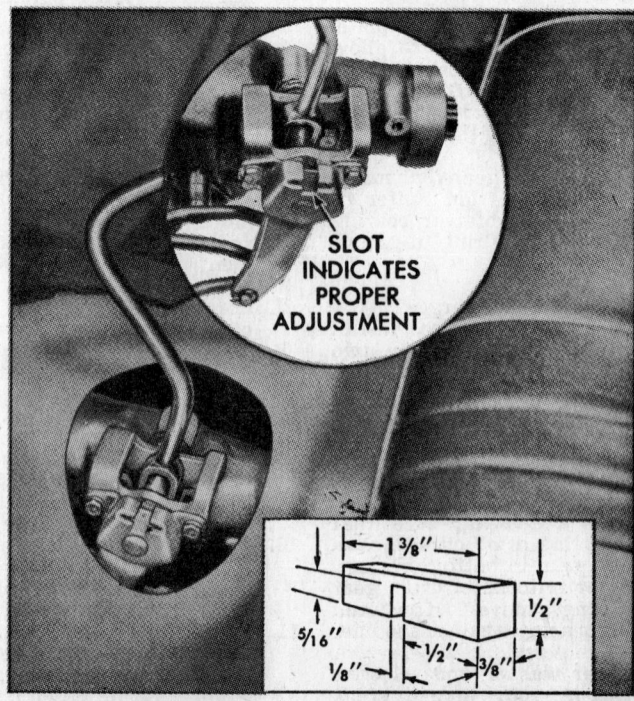

SLOT INDICATES PROPER ADJUSTMENT

1 3/8''   1/2''
5/16''   1/2''   3/8''
1/8''

Fig. 12B Four speed manual shift transmission gearshift linkage adjustments. 1958-61

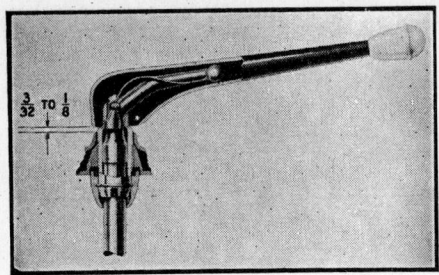

Fig. 13 Steering column upper support-to-control lever clearance. 1953 Powerglide

2. Place transmission in neutral and, if gauge block is used, position in slot.
3. Remove clevis pin at each shift lever.
4. On each shift rod, adjust threaded clevis to permit free entry of pin into hole in transmission shift lever.
5. Connect clevises to levers.
6. Remove gauge block and check shifts. If any roughness exists, one of the clevises may require adjustment of about ½ turn. Determine the rod and clevis requiring adjustment by sighting along the slot where the gauge block was used. *If transmission is removed from car, shift linkage should be adjusted before transmission is reinstalled.*

POWERGLIDE

A detailed description and service procedure on this transmission is given in the *Automatic Transmission Section* of this manual. Service adjustments and replacement procedure follows:

NEUTRAL SAFETY SWITCH

This switch prevents operation of the starter in all positions except Neutral.

1953-54

To adjust, loosen the two switch mounting screws. Place the selector lever in Neutral and, with clips over flats on end of shifter shaft, insert pin into switch mounting bracket and locating plate. Tighten screws to secure switch in this position and remove locating pin.

1955-56

Loosen one of the switch mounting screws and remove the other. Place selector lever in neutral. Center visible elongated slot in switch mounting with tapped hole in mast jacket. Then tighten screw that was loosened and tighten screw that was removed.

If the engine will not turn over after the switch is positioned as directed above, loosen the screws and rotate the switch until it does.

1957

Loosen both the switch mounting screws. Place selector lever in Neutral. Install cotter pins or similar aligning pins into two holes in switch on each side of pointer. Switch may be rotated to pointer between holes. Tighten the screws and remove cotter keys. *The slot in the switch must be set on the*

center line of the tang on the shifter tube.

If, after the switch is positioned, the engine will not turn over, loosen the screws and rotate the switch in the direction necessary until it does. Be sure selector lever is in Neutral when performing this operation.

1958-61

Place selector lever in Neutral. Loosen screws securing switch retainer, then while holding ignition switch in "Start," adjust position of switch until engine starts cranking. Hold switch in this position and tighten screws.

LINKAGE, ADJUST
1953

1. Check clearance between control lever and upper support cover, which should be as shown in Fig. 13.
2. To correct this clearance, remove screws holding upper support to mast jacket and screw upper support up or down as required to gain the desired clearance. Replace upper support screws.
3. Place selector lever in reverse and check clearance between control lever and steering wheel rim which should be 1½ in,. Fig. 14. To adjust, loosen lower support clamp bolts and move up or down as necessary.
4. With selector lever in reverse, check clearance between reverse stop on control shaft lower support and lower lever, Fig. 15. This clearance should be $\frac{3}{64}$ in.
5. To adjust, loosen transmission control rod swivel and move selector lever as necessary to obtain $\frac{3}{64}$ in. clearance and retighten the swivel. When making this adjustment, be sure transmission manual valve lever is raised to top detent position and selector lever in reverse position.

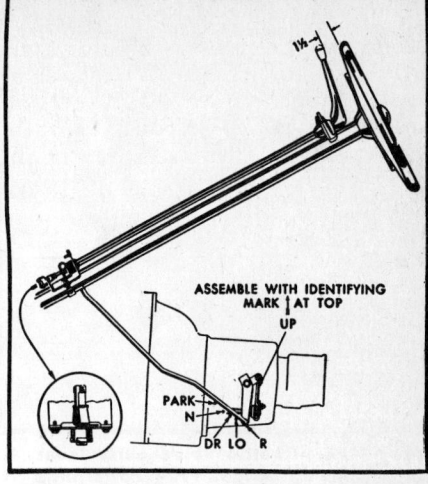

Fig. 14 Control lever to steering wheel clearance. 1953 Powerglide

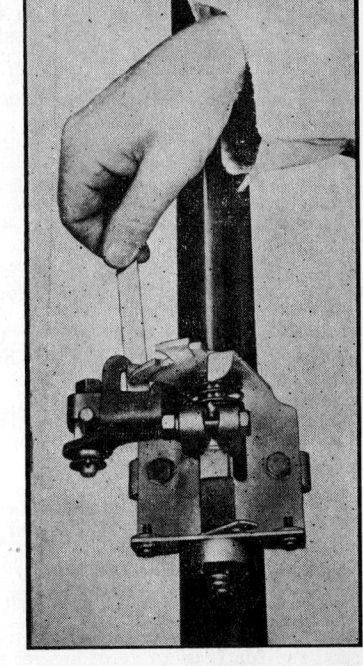

Fig. 15 Reverse stop to lower lever clearance. 1953 Powerglide

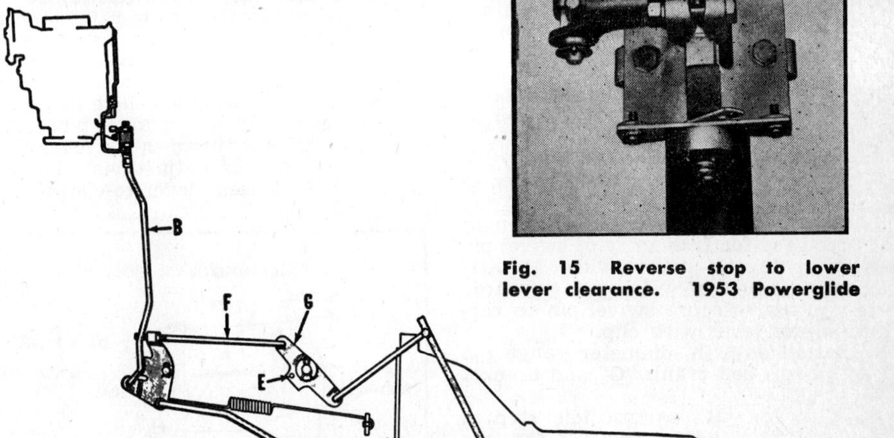

Fig. 16 Powerglide linkage. 1954

Fig. 17 Throttle valve outer lever positioning gauge. 1954 Powerglide

1954

Throttle Linkage

1. Set transmission control lever in Drive range with the hand brake set and adjust engine idle speed to 425 rpm with engine and transmission at normal operating temperature. Stop engine when normal operating temperature is attained. *The automatic choke must be entirely off and throttle stop screw against low step on fast idle cam.*
2. Remove emergency brake rod from bell crank.
3. Disconnect rod "A" from throttle lever "D", Fig. 16.
4. Remove upper rear side cover bolt and rotate clamp "C" counterclockwise to the full detent position.
5. Measure the distance between the hole in the side cover and the hole in the throttle lever "D" with Positioning Gauge J-5588, Fig. 17. If the gauge pins will enter holes, adjustment of lever "D" is correct. If not, loosen clamp bolt and adjust accordingly. *When making adjustment, clamp "C" must be rotated counterclockwise to the full detent position.*
6. Connect rod "A" to lever "D".
7. Rotate engine bell crank clockwise to set transmission lever "D" at full detent and adjust rod "B" to length required for free entry of swivel pin into throttle lever when throttle lever is held at wide open (upward) position. Secure swivel pin to carburetor lever with clip.
8. Install a $\frac{5}{16}$ in. diameter gauge pin through bell crank "G" and bracket at "E".
9. With rod "B" against idle step in carburetor, adjust rod "F" for free entry of swivel pin into throttle valve control bell crank. Hold swivel from turning and lock check nut securely.
10. Remove $\frac{5}{16}$ in. gauge pin.

Selector Linkage

1. Place selector lever in reverse and check clearance between selector lever and steering wheel rim, which should be $1\frac{11}{16}$ in. To adjust, loosen lower support clamp bolts and move

up or down as necessary. Tighten clamp bolts evenly.
2. With selector lever in reverse, check clearance between reverse stop on control shaft lower support and lower lever. This clearance should be .090 in.
3. To adjust, loosen transmission control rod swivel, making sure transmission manual lever is raised to top detent position and selector lever is in Reverse position. Move selector lever as necessary to obtain .090 in. clearance and retighten swivel.
4. On side of transmission, check proper installation of short connector rod (bell crank-to-parking lock lever)—arrow must point up.

1955-57

Positive Linkage Adjustment

1. Loosen shifter tube lever clamp nut enough to allow upper control rod to move freely in the swivel.
2. Push the control bell crank (left side of transmission case) toward the front of the car as far as it will go. This places the transmission in the Park position.
3. Place shift control lever (on steering column) in Park position.
4. Tighten shifter tube lever clamp nut securely.

Throttle Valve Linkage, 1955 Six

1. With selector lever in Drive Range and hand brake set, adjust engine idle to 425 rpm with engine at normal operating temperature and transmission warm.
2. After setting idle, shut off engine.
3. Disconnect rod "C", Fig. 19, from throttle lever "E".
4. Remove the extreme lower bolt from the rear low and drive body cover.
5. Rotate throttle valve control outer lever assembly counterclockwise to the open throttle position (to a definite stop). Hold in this position and, with the gauge shown in Fig. 20 set at 6⅜", measure distance between hole in side cover and hole in throttle lever. If the gauge pins will enter holes, adjustment of lever "E" is correct. If adjustment is not correct, loosen lever-to-clamp at-

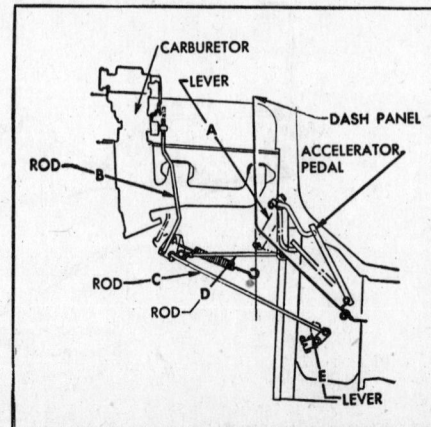

Fig. 19 Adjusting 6-cylinder throttle linkage. 1955 Powerglide

Fig. 20 Use of outer throttle valve lever gauge. 1955-56 Powerglide (6-cyl.)

taching bolt and adjust outer lever as necessary.
6. Connect rod "C" to lever "E".
7. Disconnect rod "B" from carburetor throttle valve lever and rod "D" from accelerator and throttle valve lever on cylinder block.
8. With engine idle set as in Step 1 and rod "C" forced forward against stop in transmission (open throttle), adjust rod "B" for free entry of swivel pin in carburetor throttle valve lever, with carburetor throttle valve in wide open position.
9. With carburetor throttle valve held in wide open position, and accelerator pedal fully depressed, adjust rod "D" for length required for free entry of swivel pin in bell crank.

Throttle Valve Linkage, 1956-57 Six

1. With selector lever in Drive and hand brake set, adjust engine idle to 425 rpm with engine and transmission at operating temperature.
2. After setting idle, shut off engine.
3. Disconnect rod C from lever B, Fig. 21.
4. Remove lower rear bolt from transmission side cover.
5. Rotate lever A counterclockwise to the full detent position. Hold in this position and, with gauge shown in Fig. 20 set at 7.09", measure distance between hole in side cover and hole in lever B. If gauge pins enter holes, adjustment of lever B is correct. If not, loosen clamp A and adjust lever as necessary.
6. Install rod C.
7. Disconnect rod E from carburetor throttle valve lever, and rod G from accelerator and throttle valve lever on cylinder block.
8. Move lever F to the wide open position and adjust rod E for free entry into lever D.
9. With accelerator pedal depressed placing lowest point on accelerator rod 1" above toe panel, and lever D rotated to the wide open position, adjust rod G for free entry of swivel pin in accelerator bell crank.
10. Check adjustment by releasing and depressing accelerator pedal. If lever F does not reach the wide open position it will be necessary to repeat Steps 8 and 9.

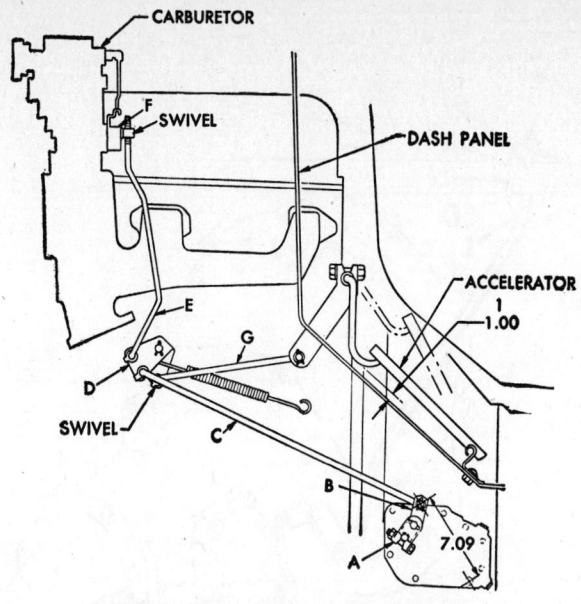

Fig. 21 Adjusting 6-cylinder throttle linkage. 1956-57 Powerglide

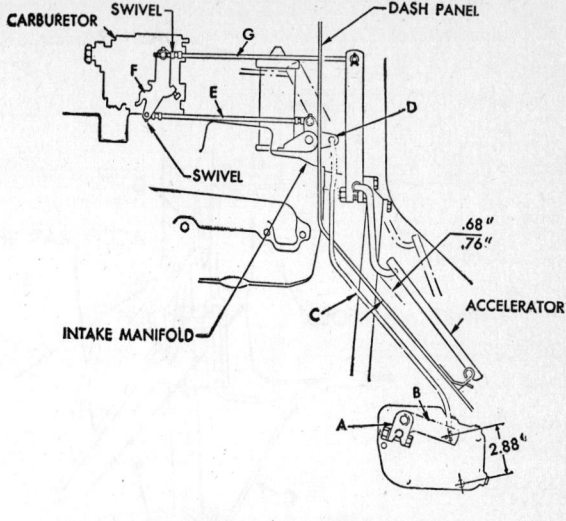

Fig. 24 Adjusting V8 (2-barrel carb.) throttle linkage. 1956 Powerglide

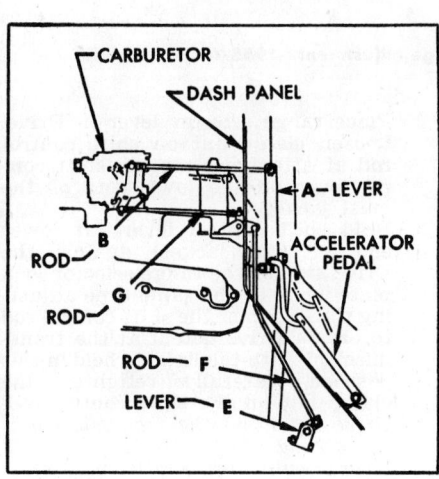

Fig. 22 Adjusting V8 throttle linkage. 1955 Powerglide

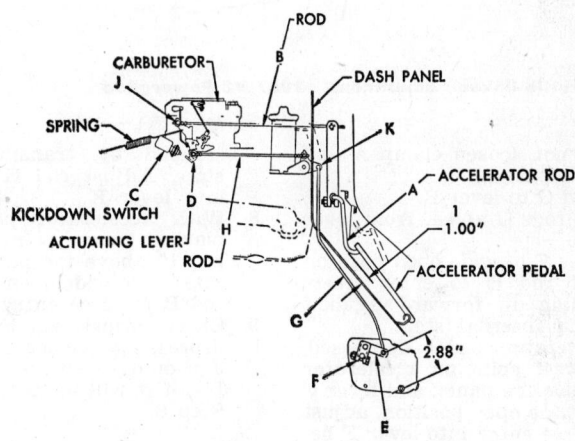

Fig. 25 Adjusting V8 (4-barrel carb.) throttle linkage. 1956 Powerglide

Fig. 23 Use of outer throttle valve lever gauge. 1955-57 Powerglide (V8)

Throttle Valve Linkage, 1955 V8

1. With engine and transmission warm and set to idle at 425 rpm, shut off engine.
2. Disconnect rod "F" from throttle lever "E", Fig. 22.
3. Remove bolt from extreme lower rear low and drive body cover.
4. Rotate throttle valve control outer lever counterclockwise to the open throttle position (to a definite stop). Hold in this position and with the gauge shown in Fig. 23 set at 2⅞", measure the distance between the hole in the side cover and hole in throttle lever,, Fig. 23. If pins of gauge will enter holes, adjustment of lever "E" is correct. If adjustment is not correct, loosen lever-to-clamp attaching screw and adjust the clamp as necessary.
5. Connect rod "F" to lever "E".
6. Disconnect rods "B" and "G" from carburetor throttle valve lever.
7. With engine idle set as recommended and rod "F" forced forward against stop in transmission, adjust rod "G" for free entry of swivel pin in carburetor throttle valve lever with carburetor throttle valve in wide open position.
8. With throttle in wide open position and accelerator pedal fully depressed, adjust rod "B" for free entry of swivel pin in throttle valve lever.

Throttle Valve Linkage. 1956 V8 With Powerglide and 2-Barrel Carburetor

1. With engine and transmission at operating temperature, set idle at 425 rpm and shut off engine.
2. Disconnect rod C from lever B, Fig. 24.
3. Remove bolt from lower rear hole of transmission left hand side cover.
4. Rotate clamp A counterclockwise to full detent position. Hold in this position and, with gauge shown in Fig. 23 set at 2.88", measure distance between hole in side cover and hole in lever B. If pins of gauge enter holes freely the adjustment is

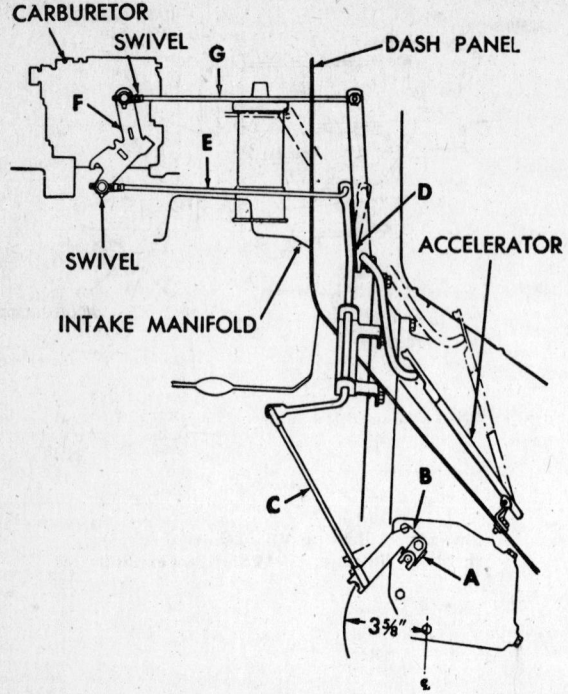

Fig. 26 Throttle linkage adjustment. 1957 V8 Powerglide

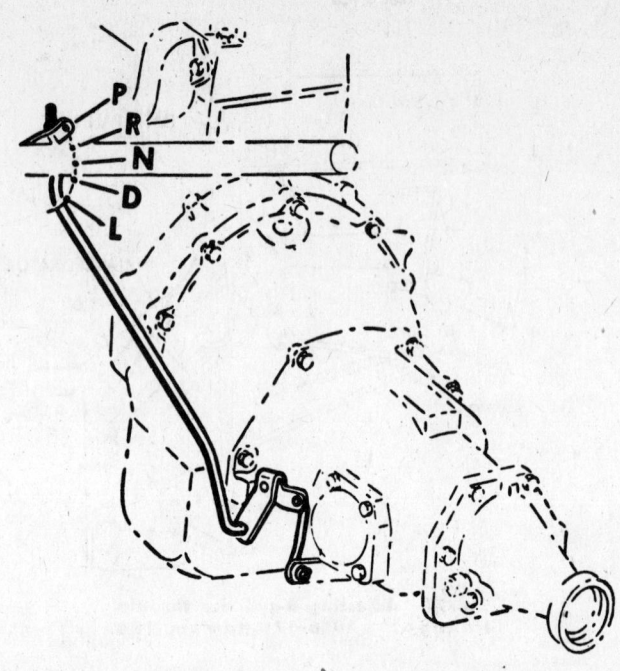

Fig. 27 Shift linkage adjustment. 1958-61 Powerglide

correct. If not, loosen clamp A and adjust as necessary.

5. Connect rod C to lever B.
6. Disconnect rods G and E from lever F.
7. Rotate lever F to wide open position and adjust rod E to enter freely while holding it forward against transmission internal stop.
8. With accelerator pedal depressed, placing lowest point on accelerator rod ¾" above toe panel, and lever F rotated to wide open position, adjust rod G for free entry into lever F before attaching it.
9. Check adjustment by releasing and depressing accelerator pedal. If lever F does not reach the wide open position it will be necessary to repeat Steps 7 and 8.

Throttle Valve Linkage. 1956 V8 With Powerglide and 4-Barrel Carburetor

1. With engine and transmission at operating temperature, set idle at 425 rpm and shut off engine.
2. Disconnect rod G from lever E, Fig. 25.
3. Remove bolt from lower hole of transmission left hand side cover.
4. Rotate clamp F counterclockwise to the full detent position. Hold in this position and, with the gauge shown in Fig. 23 set to 2.88", measure the distance from the hole in the side cover to the hole in lever E. If pins of gauge enter holes freely, adjustment is correct. If not, loosen clamp F and adjust as necessary.
5. Install rod G.
6. Disconnect rod B from lever J and rod H from lever K.
7. Place lever J to wide open position and pull rod G upward until it is

stopped by transmission internal stop. Adjust rod H for free entry into lever K.
8. With accelerator pedal depressed, placing lowest point on accelerator rod 1" above toe panel, and lever J rotated to wide open position, adjust rod B for free entry into lever J.
9. Check adjustment by releasing and depressing accelerator pedal. Lever J should reach wide open position. If not it will be necessary to repeat Step 8.

Throttle Linkage, Adjust 1957 V8 Powerglide

1. Referring to Fig. 26, remove rod C.
2. Loosely assemble lever B to clamp A.
3. With suitable gauge in place so as to obtain the 3⅝" dimension between the points indicated in Fig. 26, tighten lever B to clamp A.
4. Install rod C.
5. Install rod E in cross shaft D.
6. Place lever F in wide open position and pull rod E forward until it is stopped by transmission internal stop. Adjust swivel in rod E for easy entrance in lever F before fixing swivel in lever F.

1958-61

Shift Linkage

1. With engine stopped, lift up on range selector lever and move the lever to the position where transmission Drive detent is felt, Fig. 27. Slowly release lever to see if lever lock pin freely enters lock plate. Check Reverse range in similar manner. If the lock pin does not freely enter the lock plate in both Drive and Reverse ranges, adjust as follows:

2. Place range selector lever in Drive. Loosen clamp nut on shift control rod at attachment to the shift control lever on the lower end of the mast jacket.
3. Hold shift control lever (at lower end of mast jacket) against the Drive stop of the range selector lock plate while at the same time adjusting the length of the shift control rod to obtain Drive detent at the transmission. With the linkage held in this position, carefully retighten the clamp nut on the shift control rod. *Drive detent in the transmission is the second detent felt as the shift lever is pulled forward from its rearmost travel.*

Throttle Linkage, 6-Cyl.

1. Referring to Fig. 28, loosely assemble lever B to clamp A.
2. Insert Gauge J-5906 between transmission left hand side cover lower rear bolt and hole in lever B. Dimension between bolt and hole center lines should be 7.09 inches as shown in Fig. 28. With gauge in place, and holding clamp A counterclockwise in full detent position, tighten lever B to clamp A. Remove gauge.
3. Install rod C.
4. Install rod E in lever D. Place lever F in wide open position and pull rod E up until it is stopped by transmission internal stop. Adjust swivel in rod E for free entry in lever F before fixing swivel in lever F.
5. Check adjustment by placing linkage in idle position, then return to wide open. Position by rotating lever F upward on lever B to see if rod C deflects, meaning transmission is not on internal stop. If rod deflects, or lever F will not reach wide open position, repeat Step 4.

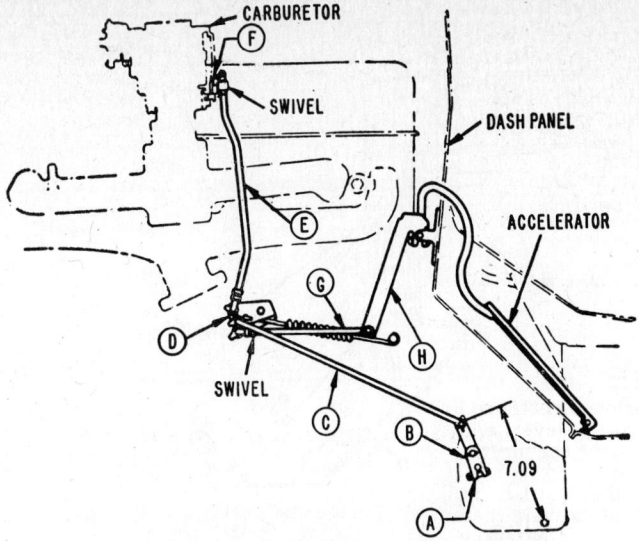

Fig. 28 Throttle linkage adjustment 1958-61 Six-cylinder Powerglide

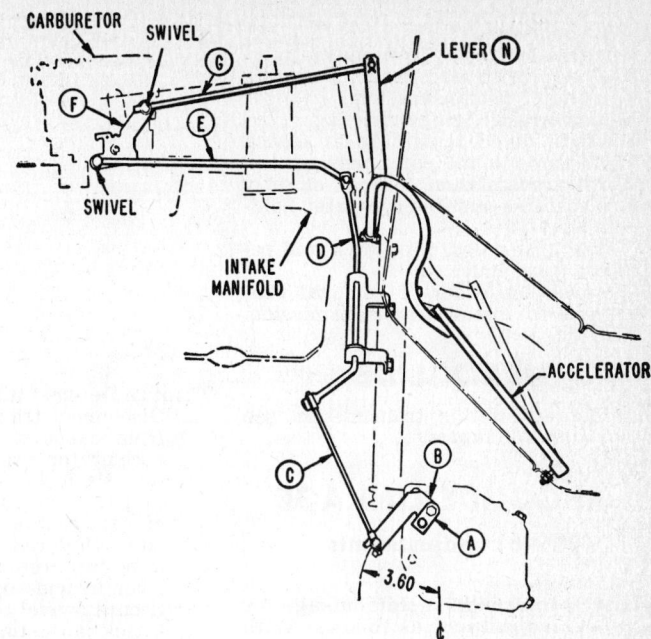

Fig. 29 Throttle linkage adjustment. 1958-61 V8 Powerglide

6. With accelerator pedal depressed until lever H contacts stop and lever D rotated to wide open position, adjust swivel or rod G for free entry into lever D before fixing swivel to lever D.

7. Check adjustment by releasing, then depressing, accelerator pedal. Check lever F for wide open position; if it doesn't reach repeat Step 6.

Throttle Linkage, V8

1. Referring to Fig. 29, loosely assemble lever B to clamp A.

2. Insert Gauge J-5906 between transmission left hand side cover lower front bolt and hole in lever B. Distance between hole center lines is 3.60″, Fig. 29. With gauge in place and holding clamp A counterclockwise in full detent position, tighten lever B to clamp A. Remove gauge.

3. Install rod C.

4. Install rod E in cross shaft D. Place lever F in wide open throttle position, adjust rod swivel on rod E for free entry in throttle bellcrank, *and then lengthen the adjustment by three turns.* Fasten swivel in bellcrank.

5. Check the adjustment by releasing linkage to its idle position, then rotate throttle bellcrank F to wide open position. While holding linkage thus, press downward on transmission outer TV lever B and check for deflection. If rod C deflects, repeat Step 4.

6. Place a ½″ wood block beneath accelerator pedal rod, depress and hold accelerator to block and then adjust swivel on rod G for free entry into throttle bellcrank F with bellcrank held fully wide open.

7. Remove wood block and depress accelerator pedal by hand to check for detent feel and check that throttle bellcrank F reaches wide open position; if it doesn't reach, repeat Step 6.

POWERGLIDE, REPLACE

1958-61

1. Drain transmission oil and remove filler pipe.

2. Disconnect oil cooler lines, vacuum modulator hose and speedometer drive cable fitting at transmission. Tie lines out of the way.

3. Disconnect body ground strap.

4. Disconnect control rods at transmission.

5. Remove propeller shaft.

6. Attach suitable transmission lifting device.

7. Disconnect engine rear mount on transmission extension, then remove transmission support crossmember.

8. Remove flywheel cover and flywheel-to-converter attaching bolts.

9. Lower rear of transmission slightly so that three upper transmission attaching bolts can be reached; use universal socket and a 39-inch extension. *Care must be taken not to lower transmission too far as the distributor housing may be forced against the dash causing damage to the distributor.*

10. Support engine at oil pan rail with a suitable jack capable of supporting weight of engine when transmission is removed.

11. Remove remaining transmission attaching bolts.

12. Move transmission slightly to the rear and downward. *Do not tip front of transmission downward as the converter could fall out as transmission is removed.* Secure converter in place with a suitable holding tool to prevent it falling out.

13. Reverse removal procedure to install transmission.

Removal, 1953-57

1. Remove toe pan plate and, on models prior to 1955, remove transmission hole cover.

2. Remove spark plugs.

3. On V8s, disconnect ground strap from battery and wires from starter solenoid.

4. Disconnect oil cooler lines at transmission and speedometer cable from driven gear fitting. Unclip cooler lines and tie them to right frame side rail.

5. Disconnect transmission control rods from levers.

6. On 1955-57 models, split rear universal joint and remove propeller shaft and front universal joint.

7. On models prior to 1955, disconnect emergency brake rod from cross shaft and drop cross shaft, cables and spring. Unfasten and slide universal ball and collar back on propeller shaft housing. Split the front universal joint and lower front end of propeller shaft.

8. Drain transmission.

9. Remove filler tube and dip stick and tape filler tube opening.

10. On V8s, remove starting motor.

11. On V8s, disconnect exhaust pipe from cross-over pipe. On 6-cylinder models, disconnect exhaust pipe from exhaust manifold.

12. Disconnect muffler from its bracket. Then move exhaust pipe and muffler to the left and tie to left frame side member.

13. Remove flywheel inspection cover.

14. Using a suitable tool to turn engine over, remove three flywheel-to-converter attaching bolts through opening in flywheel housing that is adjacent to the starting motor on V8s. On 6-cylinder models, the opening is on left side of engine.

15. Remove all converter housing-to-flywheel housing bolts except the upper most three.

16. On models prior to 1955, remove transmission support.

17. Install engine support bar or cradle to support engine.
18. Position hydraulic jack under transmission; raise and fasten handling equipment to transmission.
19. Remove rear engine mountings.
20. Remove three remaining attaching bolts through toe pan opening.
21. Move transmission to rear slightly and install a suitable converter holding tool.
22. Lower transmission on jack and remove from car.
23. Reverse the order of removal procedure to install the transmission.

TURBOGLIDE

For details on this transmission see the *Turboglide Chapter.*

TURBOGLIDE LINKAGE

1959-61 Adjustments

Shift Linkage—
1. Check transmission shift linkage for proper adjustment as follows: With engine stopped, move range selector lever to the position where Drive detent is felt. Slowly release lever to feel if lever lock pin freely enters lock plate. Check Reverse range in similar manner. If lock pin does not enter lock plate freely in both ranges, adjust as follows:
2. Position selector lever in "D". Disconnect shift control rod at its swivel attachment to the shift control lever on the lower end of the mast jacket by loosening clamp nut.
3. Place transmission shift control outer lever in Drive Position. (Drive detent in transmission is the first clockwise detent position from the fully counterclockwise detent or "GR" position, Fig. 30.)
4. Hold shift control lever (at lower end of mast jacket) against the Drive stop of the range selector lock plate while at the same time adjusting the length of the swivel on the shift control rod for free entry into the shift lever on the mast jacket. With the linkage held in this position, carefully retighten the swivel clamp nut.
5. Test transmission shifts in all ranges.

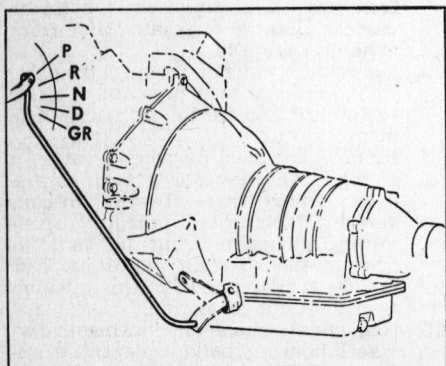

Fig. 30 Shift linkage adjustment. 1958 Turboglide. Typical of 1959-61

Throttle Detent Linkage—
1. Disconnect transmission throttle rod from carburetor throttle lever and accelerator rod from carburetor throttle lever.
2. Pull throttle valve rod toward front of car its full limit of travel, then adjust TV rod swivel for free entry into carburetor throttle lever with lever in wide open throttle position. Secure swivel to lever.
3. Check adjustment by placing carburetor throttle lever in wide open position, then pushing downward (counterclockwise) on transmission throttle valve lever and noting if transmission throttle valve rod attached to carburetor throttle lever deflects (transmission not on internal stop). If rod deflects or carburetor throttle lever will not reach wide open position, repeat adjustment.
4. Position carburetor throttle lever at wide open throttle and with an assistant depressing the accelerator pedal to hold the accelerator pedal lever in contact with the lever stop, adjust swivel on accelerator rod to permit free entry into carburetor throttle lever. Secure swivel to lever.
5. Check for detent feel by depressing accelerator pedal by hand. Detent should be felt before accelerator pedal rod strikes carpet or floor mat.

Neutral Safety Switch—
1. Place gearshift lever in neutral.
2. Loosen screws securing switch retainer. Then while holding ignition switch in "Start", adjust position of switch until engine turns over.
3. Hold switch in this position and tighten screws.
4. Check adjustment by cranking in both neutral and park.

1958 Adjustments

Shift Linkage—Follow instructions as outlined for 1959 models.

Throttle Linkage—
1. Disconnect transmission throttle valve (TV) rod at throttle bellcrank on carburetor.
2. Place wood block ½" thick beneath accelerator pedal rod and carpet or floor mat and have an assistant hold accelerator pedal fully down to block.
3. Pull transmission TV rod toward front of car its full limit of travel (through detent) and adjust rod swivel for free entry into hole in throttle bellcrank, Fig. 31.
4. Connect TV rod swivel to throttle

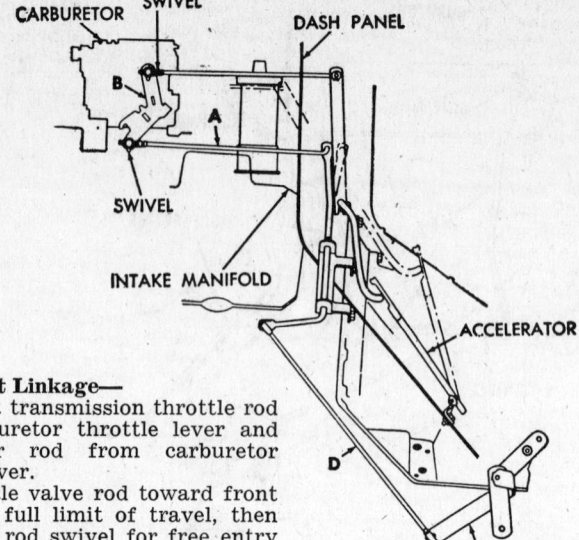

Fig. 31 Trottle linkage adjustment. 1958 Turboglide

bellcrank with clip, remove block from beneath accelerator pedal rod and check for detent "feel" by depressing accelerator pedal by hand. Transmission detent should be felt before pedal rod strikes carpet or floor mat.
5. Road test and adjust to insure that stator high angle is obtained at full throttle.

Neutral Safety Switch—This adjustment is obtained in the same manner given for 1959.

1957 Adjustments

Shift Linkage—
1. Loosen shifter tube lever clamp nut to allow upper control rod to move freely on the swivel.
2. Move selector lever on transmission toward front of car to Neutral position (3rd position forward).
3. Place hand control lever in Neutral.
4. Tighten shifter tube swivel clamp nut.
5. Check operation of linkage.

Throttle Linkage—
1. Referring to Fig. 27, remove rod A from throttle lever B.
2. Place lever B in wide open position and pull rod A forward until stator control valve spring tension is overcome and lever is bottomed.
3. Adjust swivel on rod A for easy entrance in lever B before fixing swivel in lever B.

Neutral Safety Switch—
1. Loosen switch mounting screws.
2. Place selector lever in neutral.
3. Install cotter keys into two holes in switch on each side of pointer. Switch may be rotated to place pointer between holes.
4. Tighten mounting screws and remove cotter keys.
5. If engine does not turn over after adjustment is made, loosen screws and rotate switch in the direction

necessary until it does. Be sure selector lever is in neutral when performing this operation.

TURBOGLIDE, REPLACE

1957

1. Remove toe pan plate.
2. Remove spark plugs.
3. Disconnect battery ground strap from battery and wires from starter solenoid.
4. Remove starter.
5. Remove oil filler pipe.
6. Disconnect oil cooler lines at thermal by-pass valve, remove hose from diaphragm and remove speedometer cable. Tie cooler lines to right frame side rail.
7. Disconnect linkage rods from transmission levers.
8. Remove propeller shaft and front universal joint.
9. Drain transmission fluid.
10. Disconnect muffler from its support bracket and move muffler and exhaust pipe to the left and tie to left frame side member.
11. Remove converter underpan.
12. Support rear of engine with a jack.
13. Unfasten flywheel from converter.
14. Place separate jack under transmission.
15. Remove both rear engine mounts.
16. Unfasten transmission from engine.
17. Move transmission to rear slightly and install a suitable converter holding tool.
18. Lower transmission from under car.
19. Reverse foregoing procedure to install the transmission.

1958

1. Drain oil and remove filler pipe.
2. Disconnect oil cooler lines and speedometer drive cable fitting at transmission. Tie lines out of the way.
3. Disconnect body ground strap.
4. Disconnect shift control rods from transmission.
5. Remove propeller shaft.
6. Attach a suitable transmission lifting device.
7. Disconnect engine rear mount on transmission extension and remove transmission support crossmember.
8. Remove flywheel cover and flywheel-to-converter attaching bolts.
9. Lower rear of transmission slightly so that three upper transmission-to-engine attaching bolts can be reached (use a universal socket and a 39" extension). *Care must be used not to lower the transmission too far as the distributor housing may be forced back against the dash causing damage to the distributor.*
10. Support engine at oil pan rail with a jack capable of supporting engine when transmission is removed.
11. Remove remaining attaching bolts.
12. Move transmission slightly to rear and downward and out beneath car. *Do not tilt front of transmission downward as the converter may fall out.*
13. To install, reverse removal procedure.

1959-60

1. Remove drain plug (early) or filler tube (late) to drain oil.
2. Disconnect oil cooler lines and speedometer cable.

3. Remove crankcase ventilation clamp from transmission.
4. Remove hose from vacuum modulator and from clamped attachment at side of transmission.
5. Disconnect rods from levers at transmission.
6. Disconnect propeller shaft from transmission.
7. Install suitable transmission lifting rig or other lifting device.
8. Disconnect engine rear mount on transmission extension, then remove transmission support crossmember. *If shims are present, be sure to reinstall exactly the number present as these effect drive line angles.*
9. Remove transmission underpan.
10. Mark flywheel-to-converter relationship for assembly. Then, using a jumper to turn over engine, remove flywheel-to-converter attaching bolts. *The "light" side of converter is denoted by a "blue" stripe painted across the ends of the converter cover and housing. This marking should be aligned as closely as possible with the "white" stripe painted on the engine side of the flywheel outer rim to maintain balance during assembly.*
11. Lower transmission slightly so that 3 upper transmission attaching bolts can be reached for removal. *Do not lower transmission too far as there is danger of the ignition distributor housing being forced against the dash.*
12. Support engine with jack at oil pan rail while transmission is removed.
13. Remove remaining attaching bolts and remove transmission from vehicle.

Rear Axle and Brake Section

Refer To Hydraulic Brakes Chapter For Brake Adjustments

REAR AXLE, REPLACE

1953-54 Chevrolet

1. Remove rear wheels and brake drums.
2. Hook clamps on wheel cylinders.
3. Disconnect hand brake cables.
4. Unfasten hydraulic brake line from axle housing.
5. Disconnect shock absorber links.
6. Remove spring U-bolts and shackles at rear of rear springs.
7. Remove axle from under car.
8. Reverse removal procedure to install the rear axle assembly.

1955-61 Chevrolet & 1954-61 Corvette

Major operations on this axle assembly may be performed without removing the complete assembly from the vehicle. There may be occasions, however, when it will be necessary to remove the complete assembly as a result of collision which may cause distortion of axle housing or axle shaft tubes. The following

axle housing assembly removal, therefore, is to be used only when replacement of the axle housing is necessary.

1. Raise vehicle and remove rear wheels.
2. Split rear universal joint and tape bearings to trunnion.
3. Disconnect hand brake cable at equalizer and remove cables from clamps on frame.
4. Disconnect hydraulic brake line connection at rear axle housing.
5. Disconnect shock absorber eyes from anchor plates.
6. While supporting rear axle assembly with hydraulic jack on 1955-57 cars, remove spring U-bolts and anchor plates and lower axle assembly to floor. On 1958 models, remove rear suspension upper and lower control arms and lower assembly to floor.
7. Installation is made in the reverse order of removal. Be sure to bleed hydraulic brake system.

Differential Carrier, Replace

1. Remove axle shafts. They need only to be pulled out far enough to clear

differential side gears.
2. Split rear universal joint and lower propeller shaft to floor. Tape bearings to trunnion.
3. Remove nuts which fasten differential carrier to axle housing.
4. Place a drip pan under housing and slightly separate carrier and housing and allow lubricant to drain. When drained, remove differential carrier.
5. Reinstall in the reverse order of removal.

REAR AXLE REPAIRS

1953-54 Chevrolet

Fig. 1 is a sectional view of the differential driving unit.

The drive pinion is splined and pressed in the propeller shaft, and end movement is prevented by a pin riveted through the shaft coupling and the propeller shaft.

The double-row bearing is built with no looseness or end play, nor is it adjustable for end play. If there is any looseness between the race and cone, it

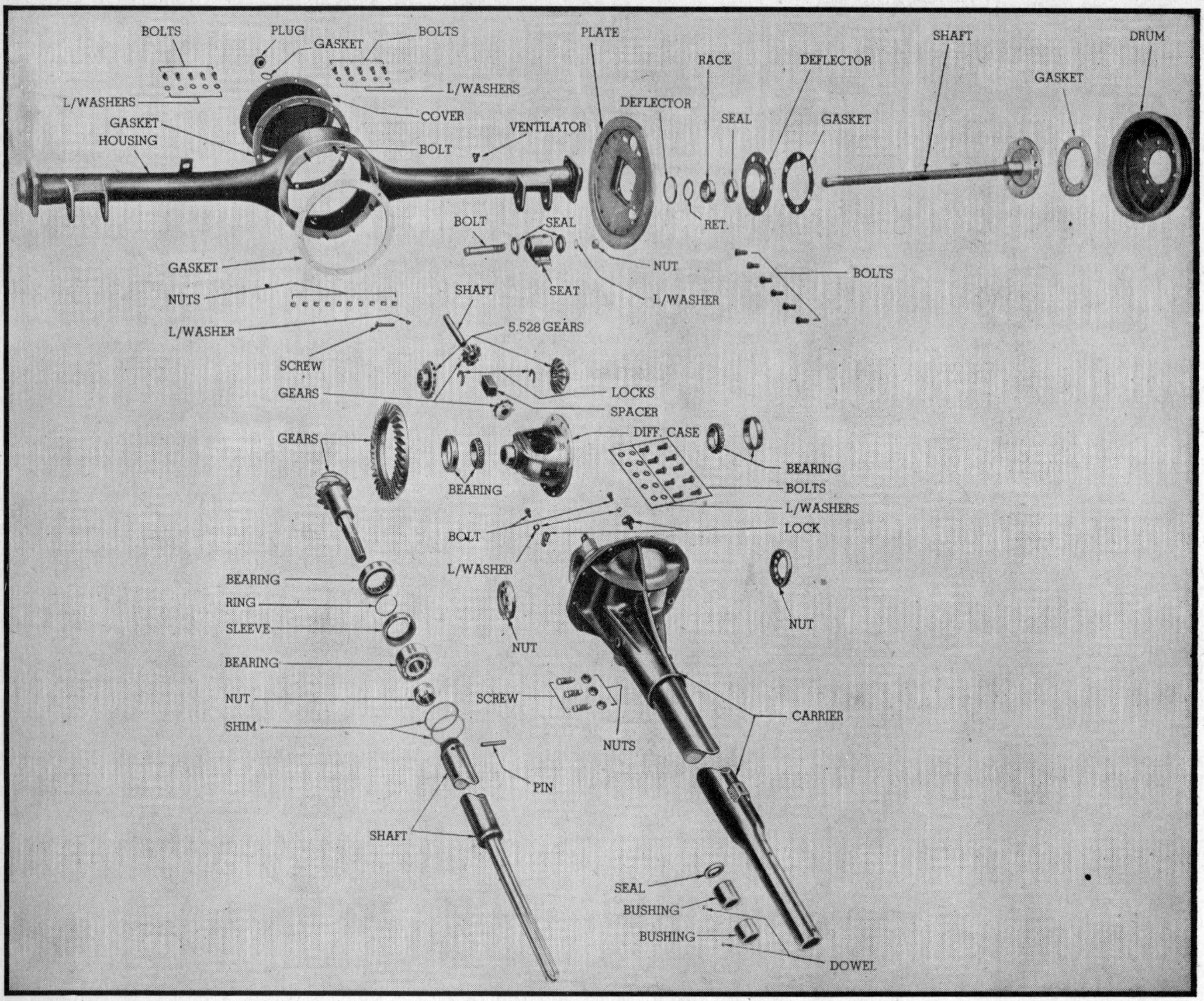

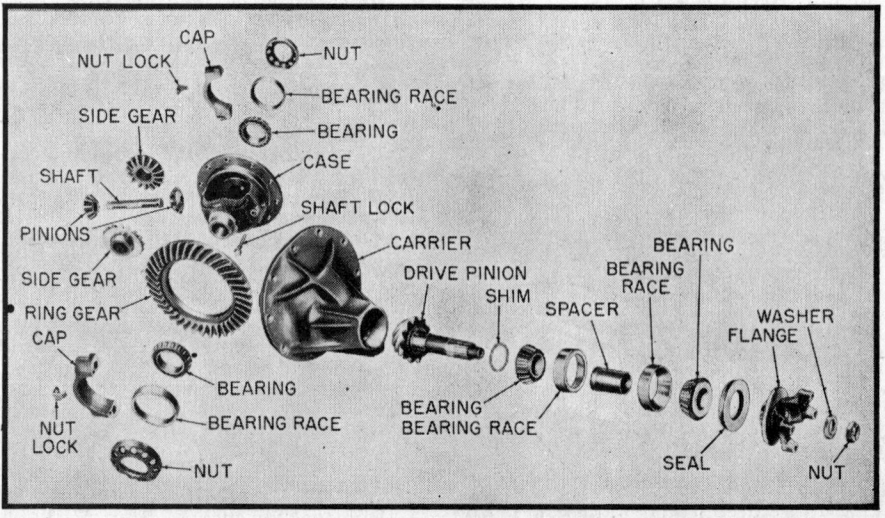

BOLTS PLUG GASKET BOLTS PLATE RACE DEFLECTOR SHAFT DRUM

L/WASHERS DEFLECTOR GASKET

GASKET COVER DEFLECTOR SEAL GASKET

HOUSING VENTILATOR SEAL

GASKET BOLT RET.

NUTS BOLT SEAL NUT BOLTS

L/WASHER SHAFT SEAT L/WASHER

SCREW 5.528 GEARS

GEARS LOCKS

SPACER

GEARS DIFF. CASE BEARING

BEARING BOLTS

L/WASHERS

BOLT LOCK

L/WASHER

BEARING NUT

RING NUT

SLEEVE

BEARING

NUT SCREW

SHIM NUTS CARRIER

PIN

SHAFT SEAL

BUSHING

BUSHING

DOWEL

Fig. 1 Rear axle. 1953-54 Chevrolet

is probably caused by abrasive matter in the lubricant which wore down the balls.

The threaded nut type of differential bearing adjustment is used. The procedure for making this adjustment, as well as the assembly of the differential case, riveting or bolting on the ring gear, checking ring gear and pinion backlash and other differential case operations, is given in the *Rear Axle Chapter*. Service standards are listed in the *Rear Axle* table.

. To replace the drive pinion and bearings, it is necessary to take out rear axle assembly, unbolt the differential carrier from the axle housing, remove the axle shafts and, after taking off the differential bearing caps and adjusting nuts, lift the differential from the carrier.

Pinion & Bearings, Replace

After removing the axle shafts and differential unit, take out the three tapered screws from the side of the housing. Jar the carrier so that the splined end of the

CAP NUT

NUT LOCK BEARING RACE

SIDE GEAR BEARING

SHAFT CASE

PINIONS SHAFT LOCK

SIDE GEAR CARRIER BEARING

DRIVE PINION BEARING

RING GEAR SHIM RACE

CAP SPACER WASHER

FLANGE

BEARING

CAP BEARING RACE

NUT BEARING SEAL

LOCK BEARING RACE NUT

NUT

Fig. 2 Rear axle. 1955-61 Chevrolet and 1954-61 Corvette

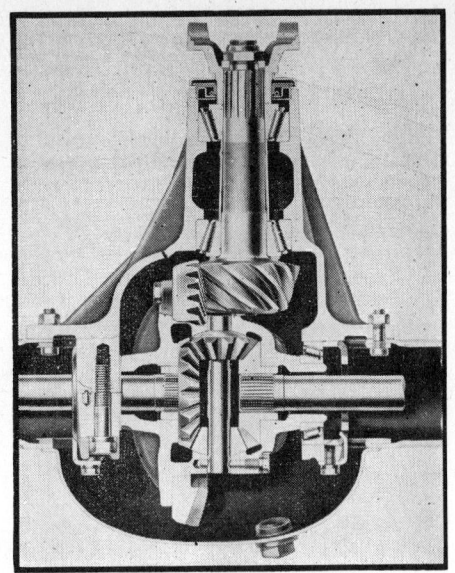

Fig. 3 Rear axle. 1955-61

propeller shaft will strike on a wooden block or wooden floor and the pinion will slide out. Remove the bearing adjusting shims from the inside of the torque tube, noting their number and total thickness.

To disassemble the pinion from the propeller shaft, file off one head of the straight pin which fastens these parts together, and drive out the pin. Pull the pinion shaft from the propeller shaft. Remove the pinion bearing lock nut and press the bearing from the pinion. Take out the bearing lock sleeve and, after releasing the rear bearing lock ring, remove this bearing.

To assemble, install the rear bearing on the pinion shaft and fit the lock ring in its groove in the shaft. Place the lock sleeve with its beveled side toward the pinion. Press the double-row bearing on the pinion shaft and install the lock nut.

The pinion assembly may now be assembled to the propeller shaft by pressing the splined end into the coupling on the end of the propeller shaft so that the rivet hole in the pinion shaft lines up with the hole in the propeller shaft. Insert a new rivet in this hole and rivet over both ends. Tighten the bearing lock nut and lock it in the milled slot in the pinion shaft.

Pinion & Propeller Shaft, Assemble

Install same thickness of shims in counterbore of the torque tube that were removed when the assembly was dismantled. Make sure the shims are flat in the counterbore and are not cocked. Shims are available in several thicknesses so that a suitable combination may be selected to replace the original ones if they are damaged, or if another combination is needed to secure proper location of the pinion if a new gear set is installed. If a new Chevrolet gear set is to be used, one .015 and one .018 inch shim should be used as this is the standard set-up.

Lubricate the bearings thoroughly and coat the bearing surface of the lock sleeve with rear axle lubricant. Install

the propeller shaft, driving it down until the bearings are seated in the housing.

Check through the lock screw holes in the side of the housing to see if the lock sleeve is in the correct position up against the back of the double-row bearing. Install the three tapered screws and draw them down evenly and tightly, then tighten the lock nuts.

If a pinion setting gauge is available, check the pinion depth as outlined in the *Rear Axle Chapter*. If a correction is necessary, disassemble the parts and, if the pinion is to be moved toward the center of the axle, add shims; if it is to be moved away from the center of the axle, remove shims.

If no pinion setting gauge is available, assemble the differential unit and check the tooth contact by painting the ring gear teeth as described in the *Rear Axle Chapter*.

When the adjustment is correct, set it securely with the lock screws and nuts as stated above.

DIFFERENTIAL CARRIER

1955-61 Chevrolet & 1954-61 Corvette

The drive pinion is mounted on preloaded taper roller bearings, Figs. 2 and 3. Adjustment of the pinion along its axis is obtained by a shim placed between the rear bearing inner race and pinion. Adjustment of preload of the two bearings is obtained by tightening the companion flange nut which compresses a spacer over the pinion stem between the bearings. Both bearing outer races are pressed into the carrier.

The threaded nut type of differential bearing adjustment is used. The procedure for making this adjustment, as

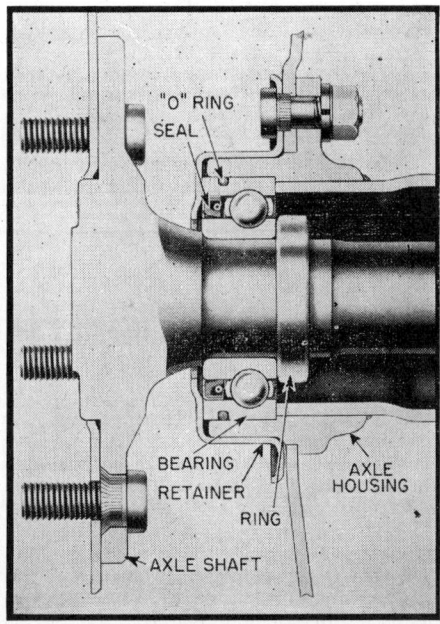

Fig. 4 Axle shaft and bearing with seal mounted outboard

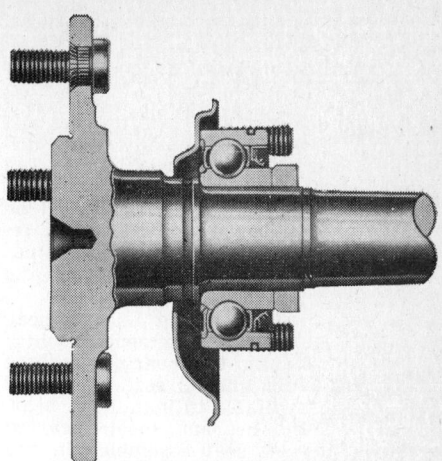

Fig. 4A Axle shaft and bearing with inboard mounted seal

well as the assembly of the differential case, replacing a ring gear, checking ring gear and pinion backlash and other differential case operations, is given in the *Rear Axle Chapter*.

Pinion & Bearings, Replace

After removing the differential unit from the carrier, unscrew the pinion flange retaining nut and pull off the flange. Press the pinion out of the front bearing and through the rear end of the carrier. The rear bearing cone, shim and bearing spacer will come out with the pinion. The bearings may then be removed and installed with suitable pulling equipment.

Reverse the operations to assemble and, after pressing on the pinion flange, slip on the washer and nut. Tighten the nut until the bearings have a preload drag of 15 to 25 inch pounds to rotate the pinion shaft.

To adjust the preload, draw up the nut until the spacer starts to buckle. Check the pull with a torque wrench or with a spring scale. This adjustment must be made every time the flange nut is removed or loosened. If the adjustment is to be made with the differential unit in the carrier, the rear wheels must be jacked off the floor.

The pinion can be moved in toward the center of the axle by installing a thinner shim. If it is to be moved away from the center of the axle, use a thicker shim.

Note—A new spacer is required between the pinion bearings when a new ring gear and pinion set is installed, either outer or inner members of either pinion bearing is changed, a new carrier casting used, or pinion adjusting shim thickness is increased. When the same pinion flange is removed and reinstalled as when an oil seal is replaced, checking for pinion bearing preload with a torque wrench is not necessary if care is taken to tighten the nut exactly to its previous position. Should a new pinion flange be required, a torque wrench reading should be taken before loosening the nut and the nut tightened to the same torque wrench reading.

AXLE SHAFT, REPLACE

1953-54 Chevrolet

To remove an axle shaft, take off the rear wheel, rear axle cover, differential pinion shaft screw, differential pinion shaft and the spacer block between the two shafts. Push inward on the outer end of the axle shaft and remove the C-shaped spacer on the inner end of the shaft. The axle shaft and brake drum may now be withdrawn.

To remove the bearing and oil seal, a special puller is recommended which removes not only the bearing but the bearing retainer and oil seal. A special tool is also available to install the bearing. With the bearing, inside bearing retainer and oil seal assembled in the tool, start the bearing in the axle housing and give the end of the tool a few light blows with a hammer. The oil seal should be staked in place with a prick-punch.

Note—Clearance between the spacer block and the axle shafts should be from a free fit to .014". If the clearance is in excess of this limit, install a new block. These spacer blocks are available in two sizes for each model, providing three different thicknesses for making this adjustment.

1955-61 Chevrolet & 1954-61 Corvette

Caution—Several types of ball and roller bearings have been used. Some ball bearings have the seal mounted outboard as shown in Fig. 4, while others have the seal mounted inboard as shown in Fig. 4A. These various installations cannot accurately be applied to specific car models. Therefore, when necessary to replace a bearing, examine the installation carefully and, if the new bearing is identical with the old, install it the same way. However, should a roller bearing be installed where the original bearing was a ball type (or vice versa) follow the installation instructions contained in the bearing package.

1. To remove an axle shaft, take off rear wheel, brake drum and gasket.
2. Remove four nuts and washers from bearing retaining bolts on inside of axle flange, Fig. 4.

3. Use a suitable puller and pull out axle shaft and bearing. Be careful not to disturb the brake backing plate. If bearing retainer and parking brake strut interfere, raise strut slightly with screw driver to obtain clearance.
4. Install bolt and nut to retain brake backing plate on axle housing.

MASTER CYLINDER, REPLACE

1953-54

To remove the master cylinder, disconnect the hydraulic line from the end of the cylinder. Remove the eccentric bolt from the brake pedal extension and master cylinder push rod. Remove the clutch link from the brake pedal extension.

Remove the plug from the forward end of the master cylinder, insert a stiff wire into the shaft lock pin and remove the pin. Remove the clutch and brake pedal extension pivot shafts from the master cylinder body. Then unfasten the cylinder from the frame and remove it from the car.

Reverse the foregoing procedure to install the unit. Then fill the reservoir with brake fluid and bleed all brake lines as outlined in the *Hydraulic Brake System Chapter*.

1955-57

To remove master cylinder, disconnect the hydraulic line from the end of the cylinder and remove the bolted brass fitting. Unfasten the cylinder from the dash panel and lift it off.

Reverse the above procedure to install the cylinder, fill the reservoir with brake fluid and bleed the system as outlined in the *Hydraulic Brake System Chapter*.

1958-61

To remove the master cylinder, disconnect the hydraulic line from the end of the cylinder. Remove clevis pin from brake pedal arm. Unfasten master cylinder from dash panel and remove from vehicle.

Reverse the above procedure to install the cylinder, fill the reservoir with brake

fluid and bleed the system as outlined in the *Hydraulic Brake System Chapter*.

POWER BRAKE UNIT

Repairs on the power brake unit are contained in the *Power Brake Chapter*. To remove and install the unit, proceed as follows:

1954

1. Disengage valve push rod from brake pedal.
2. Remove master cylinder outlet bolt from master cylinder.
3. Remove vacuum hose from check valve on power brake unit.
4. Remove vacuum reserve tank hose from valve fitting.
5. Unfasten unit from its mounting.
6. Reverse the foregoing procedure to install the unit.

1955-58

1. On engine side of dash panel, remove vacuum lines from vacuum inlet tube on intake manifold.
2. Remove vacuum line to vacuum reservoir.
3. Remove stop light wire (1955-57).
4. Remove hydraulic line from hydraulic cylinder.
5. From inside car body, disconnect lever from push rod.
6. Unfasten and remove power unit from dash panel.
7. Reverse the foregoing procedure to install the unit.

1959-61

1. Disconnect clevis at brake pedal.
2. Remove hoses from power unit.
3. Disconnect hydraulic line from master cylinder.
4. Unfasten and remove power unit from dash.
5. Installation is made in the reverse order of removal.

POWER BRAKE SYSTEM, BLEED

1954-61

The power brake system may be bled in the conventional manner as outlined in the *Hydraulic Brake System Chapter*.

Front End and Steering Section

CASTER & CAMBER

1953-54 Chevrolet & 1954-61 Corvette

Caster and camber adjustments are both performed by turning the upper control arm pivot pin. The pivot pin has a $\frac{3}{32}$ in. eccentric. To make the adjustment, proceed as follows:

1. Loosen the clamp bolt at the upper end of the steering knuckle support.

2. Remove grease fitting from the rear bushing.
3. Insert an Allen set screw wrench through the hole from which the grease fitting was removed.
4. Turn the pivot pin in the direction to obtain an exact caster setting. The camber may remain practically the same or it may move in a positive or negative direction, depending on the location of the eccentric on the pivot pin.
5. After making a slight turn of the

pivot pin, both caster and camber must be rechecked and adjustments made that will bring both angles within the limits.

1955-61 Chevrolet

The caster and camber adjustments are made by means of shims between the upper control arm inner support shaft and the support bracket attached to the frame side rail. Shims may be changed at either the front of the shaft or the

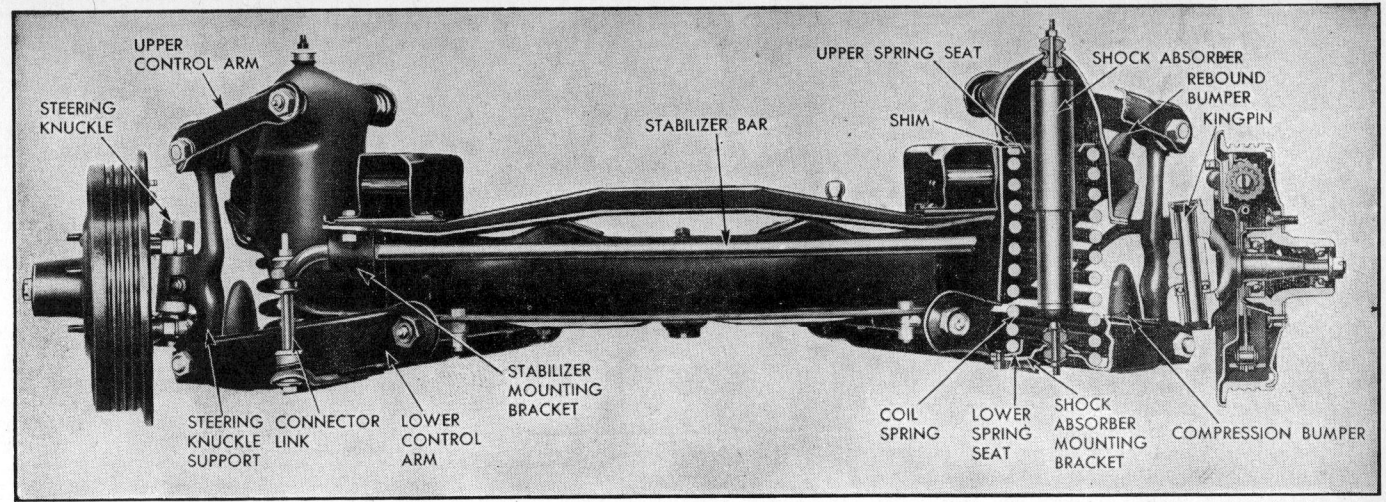

Fig. 1 Front suspension. 1953-54 Chevrolet and 1954-61 Corvette

rear of the shaft to change caster or at both points equally to change camber.

The addition of shims at the front bolt or removal of shims at the rear bolt will decrease positive caster. A $\frac{1}{32}$" shim difference (one shim) will change caster $\frac{1}{4}$°. Adding shims at both front and rear of support shaft will decrease positive camber. A $\frac{1}{32}$" shim change will move camber $\frac{1}{16}$°.

The adjustment procedure is to loosen the upper support shaft-to-bracket bolts, add or remove shims as required and re-tighten the bolts. *Both caster and camber can be performed in one operation.*

TOE-IN, ADJUST

1953-54 Chevrolet & 1954-61 Corvette

Toe-in is adjusted by loosening the clamp bolts at each end of the left-hand tie rod and turn this rod as required to obtain correct toe-in.

1955-61 Chevrolet

Toe-in can be adjusted by loosening the clamp bolts at each end of each tie rod and turning each tie rod to increase or decrease its length as necessary until proper toe-in is secured and the steering gear is on the high point for straight-ahead driving.

WHEEL BEARINGS, ADJUST

1961

To adjust the bearings, tighten the spindle nut to 20 ft. lbs. torque while rotating the wheel. Then back off one flat and install cotter pin. If cotter pin hole does not line up with nut slot, continue to back off nut just enough to install cotter pin.

1953-60

Tighten spindle nut to 28 ft. lbs. torque and rotate wheel to seat bearings. Back off adjusting nut until bearings

are loose and then re-torque to 12 ft. lbs. If cotter pin cannot be inserted, back off nut just enough to permit pin to be inserted.

FRONT END

1953-54 Chevrolet & 1954-61 Corvette

Fig. 1 shows the front suspension with telescoping shock absorbers mounted inside the coil springs.

Shock Absorber, Remove

1. With a $\frac{1}{4}$ in. open end wrench, hold the upper stem from turning and remove upper stem retaining nut, grom-

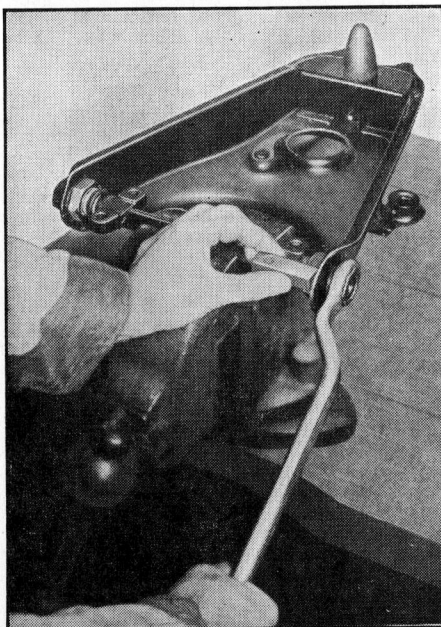

Fig. 2 Positioning lower control arm shaft with gauge J-3184. Gauge has a pin which fits into shaft bracket hole.

met retainer and grommet.

2. Remove nut and lockwasher from special bolt which retains lower bracket to control arm and pull the shock absorber and mounting bracket out through the lower control arm.

3. Place mounting bracket in a vise and remove the lower stem retaining nut, grommet retainer and grommet and remove shock absorber from bracket.

4. Inspect rubber grommets for condition and replace with new ones if necessary.

Shock Absorber, Install

1. Install grommet retainer, upper grommet, retainer bracket, lower grommet and retainer on bottom stem of shock absorber and install grommet retainer nut and tighten until it bottoms on shoulder of stem.

2. Install grommet retainer and grommet on upper stem of shock absorber and install shock absorber up through lower control arm and spring housing.

3. Index upper stud through mounting hole in top of spring housing and index hole in retainer bracket over special bolt in lower control arm.

4. Install lockwasher and nut on special bolt and tighten nut securely.

5. Install grommet and retainer over upper stem of shock absorber.

6. Install retainer nut to shock absorber upper stem, holding stem with a $\frac{1}{4}$ in. wrench. Tighten nut until it bottoms on shoulder of stem.

Front Spring, Remove

1. Disconnect stabilizer link from lower control arm.

2. Remove shock absorber as outlined previously.

3. Raise front end of car off floor and place stand jacks beneath frame side rails. Lower car until weight is carried on jacks.

4. Place an adjustable jack under the lower control arm inner shaft on side from which spring is to be removed.

5. Unfasten lower control arm inner shaft brackets from frame and drive out fastening bolts.

6. Lower jack slowly to relieve spring pressure and remove the jack. This allows the lower control arm to drop down, releasing the spring. If a shim is used, make sure it is removed from the upper spring seat.

Front Spring, Install

1. Install flat end of spring up with shim (if used) in place. Then raise lower control arm, making sure lower end of spring seats in recess in lower spring seat.
2. Place adjustable jack under lower control arm inner shaft. Slowly raise arm with jack to compress the spring. Use a long drift punch through the shaft bracket hole and hole in frame cross member to maintain alignment.
3. Install bolts through bracket and frame and tighten nuts securely.
4. Remove adjustable jack, raise car and remove stand jacks from under frame. Lower car to floor, connect stabilizer link, and install shock absorber.

Lower Arm Service

1. To remove the arm, jack up car, remove wheel, front spring and tie rod end. Unfasten control arm from outer pivot and inner shaft from frame.
2. Fasten the control arm shaft in a vise and loosen the bushing lock nuts. Remove grease fittings and bushings, and take the control arm from the shaft and remove grease seals.
3. To assemble, fasten control arm shaft in vise and install new seals over threaded ends and up onto shaft shoulders.
4. Install bushing lock nuts on shaft with chamfered side of nuts toward ends of shaft.
5. Install shaft in control arm and thread bushings onto shaft and through control arm.
6. As bushings are threaded into shaft and through control arm, thread lock nuts onto bushing.

Fig. 3 Removing upper control arm shaft with Tool J-2958. Shaft is removed from rear to front and installed from front to rear.

Fig. 4 Locate shaft in spring housing by measuring with steel scale so that shaft projects 1⅛ in.

7. Install lower control arm assembly gauge J-3184, Fig. 2, indexing pin of tool with bolt hole in shaft and tighten bushing until control arm inner face contacts end of tool.
8. Tighten lock nut securely, holding lock nut with a wrench and tighten the bushing to 150-200 lbs. ft. torque.
9. Slip seals off shaft shoulders and into their seats and install grease fittings into ends of bushings.

Upper Arm Shaft, Remove

1. Raise front of car and place stand jacks under outer end of lower control arm, allowing jack to support vehicle.
2. Remove wheel, and take grease fittings from bushings.
3. Remove bushings from outer pivot and remove seals from end of pin.
4. Remove pivot pin clamp bolt from knuckle support and slide pivot pin out of support, using an Allen wrench to assist removal.
5. Swing knuckle suport with hub and drum away from upper control arm.
6. Remove bushings from shaft and remove arm from shaft. Note that on the left side of the car it is necessary to remove the sheet metal splash guard over the steering gear housing to get at the rear bushing.
7. Remove seals from ends of shaft and, using tool J-2958, remove shaft from spring housing from *rear to front*, Fig. 11.

Upper Arm Shaft, Install

1. Install shaft in spring housing from *front to rear* using tool J 2958. Drive shaft into housing until end projects out back of spring housing 1⅛ in., Fig. 12. Replacement shafts are marked with an "F" to indicate front end. Rear end of shaft has smaller threads and care must be exercised not to drive the shaft in too far since backing it off will leave it loose in spring housing.
2. Install new seals over ends of shaft and install control arm on shaft.

3. Start both front and rear bushings onto shaft, position arm by scale measurement, Fig. 13, and start bushings into arm, making sure threads index properly.
4. Tighten bushings until they seat and then torque tighten them to 45-60 lbs. ft.
5. Install grease fittings, lubricate and check operation of control arm. Arm should fall of its own weight.
6. Install sheet metal splash guard over steering gear housing.
7. Install outer pin and bushings.

Kingpins & Bushings, Install

When replacing the floating kingpin bushings, it is not necessary to ream them to size as service bushings are machined to finished dimensions. However, when replacing these bushings, care must be exercised to make sure the oil groove in the bushing lines up with the grease fitting in the steering knuckle. These bushings should be free both on the kingpin and in the steering knuckle.

1. Install new bushings in the steering knuckle and place the knuckle on the knuckle support. Then install the thrust bearing between the lower yoke of the steering knuckle and knuckle support, making sure that the shield on the bearing is toward the top.
2. Install the kingpin from the bottom, making sure to line up the lock pin slot with the lock pin hole in the knuckle support.
3. After the kingpin is installed, check the clearance between the steering knuckle and knuckle support with a feeler gauge. If this clearance is more than .006 in., install a steel shim between the knuckle and the top of the knuckle support.
4. Install the kingpin lock pin, bearing plugs, lock rings and bearing plug covers. Install the wheel and check the toe-in and adjust if necessary.

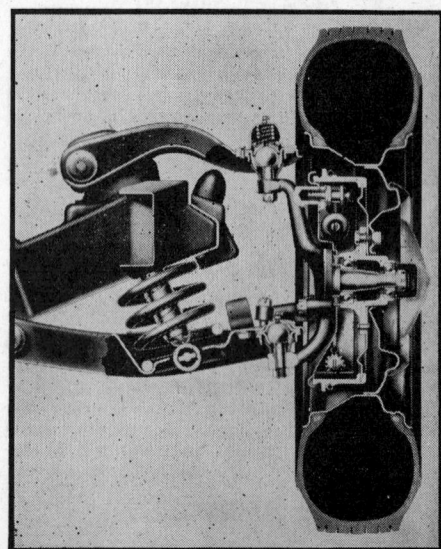

Fig. 5 Cutaway view of 1955-61 ball joint front suspension

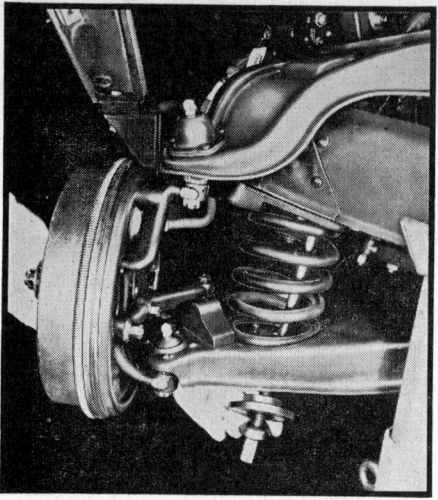

Fig. 6 Installing spring compressor to hold spring slightly compressed while removing lower control arm. 1955-61

Fig. 7 Installation of spring and lower control arm with the aid of spring compressor. 1955-61

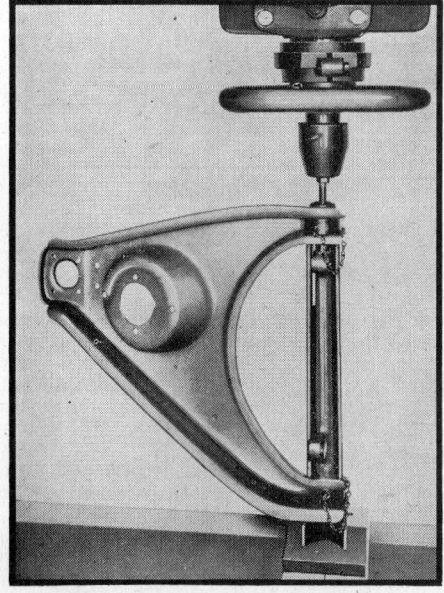

Fig. 8 Removing lower control arm bushing, using the tools shown or equivalent. 1955-61

FRONT END

1955-61 Chevrolet
Shock Absorber, Replace

Hold the shock absorber upper stem from turning with a suitable wrench and remove the nut and grommet. Unfasten the lower shock absorber pivot from the lower control arm and pull the shock absorber and mounting out at the bottom of the spring housing.

To install, reverse the removal procedure. Tighten the upper retaining nut until it bottoms on the shoulder of the stem. Torque the nut to 4-6 lb. ft. and stake in place.

Coil Spring, Replace

1. Remove shock absorber.
2. Jack up car and place stand jacks under frame side rails.
3. Remove wheel assembly to avoid damage to ball joints during spring operations.
4. Loosen 4 lower control arm cross shaft bushing bolts.
5. Install Special Spring Compressor or its equivalent through shock absorber mounting hole in front cross member and through spring. Install plate, thrust washer and nut and tighten so the spring is compressed slightly, Fig. 6.
6. Remove nut from lower ball joint. Loosen the stud by hammering on the side of the steering knuckle joint boss, backing up the knuckle with a heavy hammer.
7. Remove upper ball joint stud in similar manner, and hang drum and knuckle assembly so as not to place a strain on brake hose.
8. Unfasten lower control arm inner shaft from frame cross member.
9. Unscrew spring compressor nut and remove spring from vehicle.
10. Installation is made in the reverse order of removal with the aid of the spring compressor, Fig. 7. Rotate spring to be certain it fits the helical seats in both the cross member and lower control arm.

Lower Control Arm & Ball Joint

When replacing the lower control arm, ball joint, shaft or shaft bushings, it is necessary to remove the lower control arm from the vehicle.

The lower control arm ball joint should be replaced whenever excessive wear is indicated in the upper joint. The lower control arm ball joint stud is a loose fit in the assembly when not connected to the steering knuckle.

To replace the ball joint, chisel or drill rivet heads retaining the ball joint to the control arm and drive out the rivets. Discard the ball joint and seal. Install the new ball joint with flange against the under side of the control arm. Install and retain shield and joint in place with special bolts and nuts supplied with new joint. Tighten nuts to 10-12 lb. ft.

Lower Cross Shaft & Bushings

1. Remove bolt, washer and collar from each end of cross shaft.

2. Install 3-piece spacer of J-5888 Bushing Remover and Installer in control arm as shown in Fig. 8.
3. Thread cap screw (furnished with tool) to the bottom of the threads in the one end of the control shaft.
4. Support control arm in press as shown in Fig. 8, being sure bushing flange does not contact support.
5. Press on cap screw until bushing is free of control arm.
6. Remove cap screw and insert in other end of shaft and press out the second bushing in same manner, Fig. 9.

Bushing Installation

1. Coat outside sleeve of bushing sparingly with a lubricant, being sure not to get any on rubber bushing.
2. With cross shaft in control arm and 3-piece spacer in place, place control arm on support.
3. Press bushing into control arm until flange contacts control arm, Fig. 10.
4. Install other bushing and, after installation, shaft should be able to be rotated by hand.
5. Install collar, lock washer and nut *but do not tighten.*
6. After installing the control arm on the vehicle, bounce the front of the car to centralize the bushings and tighten bushing collar bolts securely.

Upper Control Arm & Ball Joint

1. To remove, support vehicle weight at outer end of lower control arm.
2. Remove wheel assembly.
3. Remove nut from upper ball stud and loosen stud by hammering at side of steering knuckle joint boss, backing up knuckle with heavy hammer.
4. Unfasten upper control arm from cross member, *noting the number of shims at each bolt.*
5. Remove upper arm from car.

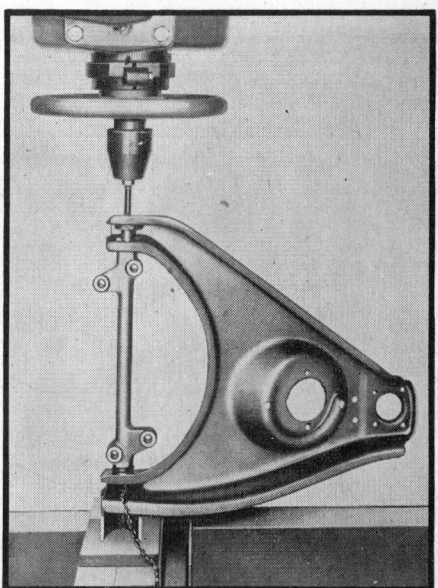

Fig. 9 Removing second bushing. 1955-61

Fig. 10 Installing lower control arm bushing. 1955-61

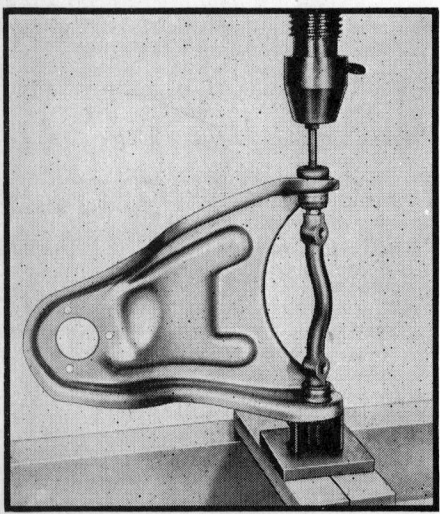

Fig. 11 Removing upper control arm bushing. 1955-61

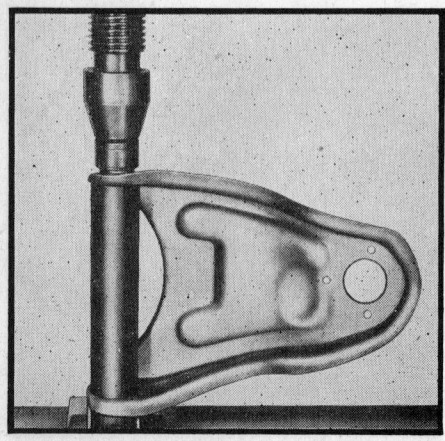

Fig. 12 Installing upper control arm bushing. 1955-61

Upper Ball Joint Inspection

The upper ball joint is checked for wear by checking the torque required to rotate the ball stud in the assembly. Install a nut on the stud and measure the torque with a torque wrench. This should be a minimum of 2 lb. ft. If excessive wear is indicated in the upper joint, both upper and lower joints should be replaced. If a tight joint is suspected, 15 lb. ft. is the maximum allowable torque.

Install the new ball joint in same manner outlined for the lower ball joint

Lower Bushing Replacement

This procedure is similar to that outlined for the lower bushings but the tools shown in Figs. 11 and 12 should be employed.

HORN BUTTON

The horn button or ornamental cap on standard wheels can be removed by prying it out of the wheel hub. On Deluxe wheels, press down on the button or cap, rotate and lift it out.

HORN RING

On 1953-54 models, remove the screws holding the pivot ring and remove ring, lock ring and spring washer.

On 1955-61 models, pry off horn button or ornamental cap and remove horn mechanism.

STEERING WHEEL

After removing the horn button or ornamental cap, unscrew the steering wheel retaining nut and use a suitable puller to take off the wheel.

STEERING GEAR, REPLACE
1953-54

1. Remove horn button or ornamental cap and take off steering wheel nut.
2. On models equipped with horn blowing ring, remove screws holding pivot ring and take off pivot ring, lock ring and horn blowing spring washer.
3. Use puller to remove steering wheel.
4. Remove upper control shaft clamp bolt from shaft connector.
5. Remove column jacket toe board grommet and seal from toe board.
6. Remove clamp which fastens column jacket to instrument panel.
7. Remove two clutch head screws that attach gearshift control upper support to column jacket. The upper control shaft and support may now be up out of engagement from shaft connector.
8. Remove clamp which retains shifter housing to column jacket. Then rotate shifter housing with lower control shaft and control rods attached away from column jacket.
9. Remove sheet metal splash guard covering steering gear housing.
10. Unfasten steering gear from frame.
11. Remove air duct from left fender skirt.

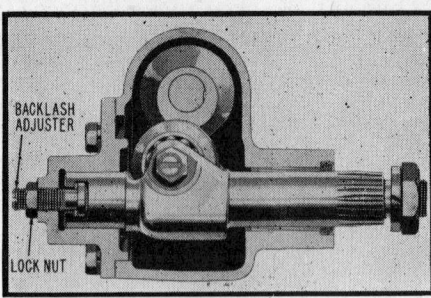

Fig. 13 Sector shaft adjustment. 1953-54

12. Rotate steering gear to clear fender skirt and raise gear, bringing it up and forward to remove it from engine compartment.

1955-57

1. Disconnect all electrical connections.
2. Remove back-up light switch (if equipped) from mast jacket.
3. Remove two rubber cover upper fasteners from inside of dash panel at mast jacket opening to permit clearance for shift levers during removal.
4. Pry off horn button or ornamental cap and remove horn mechanism.
5. Remove steering wheel.
6. Remove retaining nut, washers and bolt from dash panel attaching bracket. *Do not remove the two lower retaining bolts from dash panel attaching bracket or realignment of mast jacket-to-steering gear shaft will be necessary.*
7. Disconnect transmission control linkage from shifter levers on steering column.
8. Slide rubber seal away from covers, unfasten and remove covers.
9. Unfasten mast jacket clamp from instrument panel and remove clamp and shims.
10. On Powerglide models, disconnect indicator rod from lever, then remove transmission control selector plate.
11. Pull assembly up off steering gear shaft.
12. Disconnect pitman arm from shaft.
13. Unfasten steering gear from frame and remove gear.
14. Remove four felt seals from mainshaft of steering gear.
15. Reverse the above procedure to install the gear.

1958

The new forward position of the steering gear introduces a universal coupling into the steering shaft assembly. This coupling is packed with special grease at the factory and should not be disassembled unless absolutely necessary.

It is not necessary to remove the coupling to remove the steering gear. Simply remove the lower clamp bolt and disconnect the steering gear from the pitman arm and frame. The lower shaft and steering gear can then be pulled from the coupling.

If binding is felt after the gear is installed, the difficulty is probably due to misalignment of the shafts. Misalign-

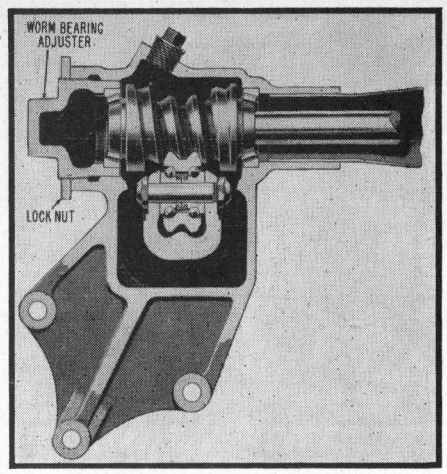

Fig. 14 Worm bearing adjustment. 1953-54

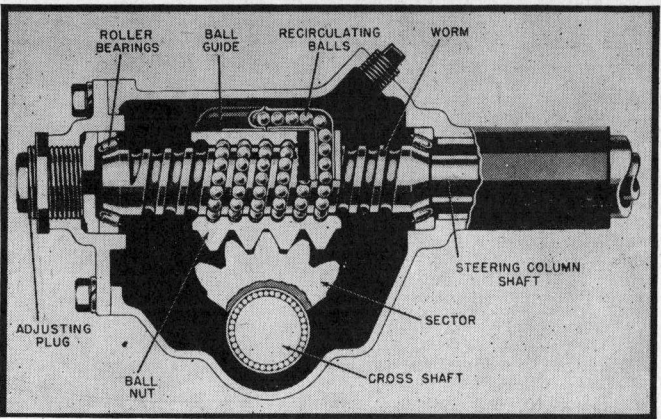

Fig. 15 Steering gear. 1955-61

ment is corrected as follows:

To correct vertical misalignment, loosen the three steering gear housing bolts. The front bolt holes in the frame are elongated to permit pivoting around the rear bolt. Pivot steering gear as required and tighten bolts.

To correct lateral misalignment, add or remove shims between the rear steering gear mounting bolt and the frame. Each $\frac{1}{32}$" shim will move the upper end of the lower shaft in or about ¼". *Standard shimming is two shims at the pivot bolt. If four shims do not correct misalignment, the lower steering shaft may be bent. Likewise, if removing all shims does not correct misalignment, the shaft may be bent.*

Coupling, Replace

1. If necessary to remove the coupling, first mark both shafts at "12 o'clock" position.
2. Remove snap ring.
3. Remove bolt from upper shaft clamp so coupling cover can be raised without interference.
4. Remove upper and lower mast jacket clamp bolts.
5. Pull steering wheel and mast jacket to rear as far as possible.

6. Raise cover and remove both bearing blocks from pin.
7. Support lower end of upper shaft and drive out pin with brass drift.
8. Remove coupling lower clamp bolt.
9. Raise coupling off serrations on lower steering shaft and remove. If necessary, shift mast jacket to one side to obtain clearance for removal.
10. Remove coupling cover and upper seal.
11. Inspect the coupling parts for damage, including the O-ring seal and upper seal.
12. Assemble the coupling, following the reverse of the removal procedure. Be sure the coupling pin is centered so the cover will slide freely over the coupling blocks. Then, before lowering the cover, pack the coupling with chassis lubricant. Lower the cover, being careful not to damage O-ring seal. Install snap ring.

1959-61

This steering gear is similar to that used in 1958 except that a second coupling has been added which will facilitate alignment of the steering gear housing. The housing is no longer shimmed for adjustment or has it got slotted holes for rotational adjustment.

To remove the lower coupling with all steering gear components in the vehicle either the steering gear has to be removed or lowered from its proper location and the upper coupling loosened, or the mast jacket, upper steering gear shaft and coupling must be loosened and pulled upward far enough to allow removal of the intermediate shaft and lower coupling.

However, if the upper steering shaft, mast jacket and upper coupling has been removed, the lower coupling may be removed as follows:

1. Remove special bolt from coupling clamp.
2. Tap coupling upward with a soft mallet to remove. The coupling is a splined part of the intermediate shaft.
3. If the coupling is to be disassembled, first scribe marks across the mating parts for proper reassembly, then separate coupling.
4. Reverse removal procedure to assemble and install the coupling and torque the special bolt into the clamp to 14-20 lb. ft.

STEERING GEAR REPAIRS, 1953-54

Disassemble

1. Remove pitman arm with a puller.
2. Loosen lock nut at end of sector shaft, Fig. 13, and turn the lash adjuster a few turns counterclockwise to remove load from bearings.
3. Loosen lock nut on worm bearing adjuster, Fig. 14, and turn cup counterclockwise a few turns.
4. Remove side cover bolts and pull cover with sector shaft from housing.
5. Remove worm bearing adjuster cup and lower worm bearing.
6. Draw worm and shaft from housing.
7. Remove lock nut from lash adjuster and screw lash adjuster through side cover. Slide lash adjuster out of slot in end of sector shaft.

Inspection

1. Wash and dry all parts.
2. With a magnifying glass, inspect roller bearings, cups, worm and sector roller.

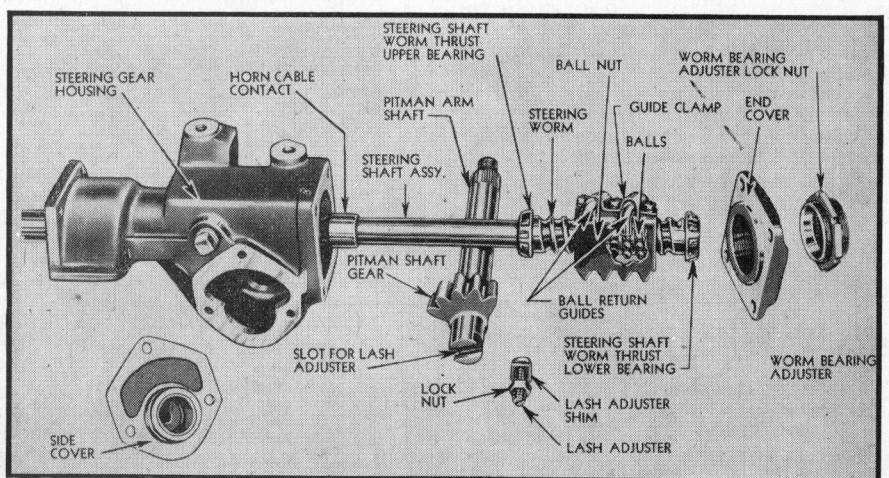

Fig. 16 Layout of steering gear parts. 1955-61

3. Check roller for any tightness or roughness of bearings.
4. Inspect sector shaft for wear. On 1952 models, check fit of shaft in housing bushing. On 1953-54 models, inspect needle bearings.
5. On 1952 models, inspect fit of sector shaft in side cover. If this area in cover or shaft is worn, a new side cover and shaft should be installed.

Assemble

1. Place upper roller bearing over worm shaft. Making sure end of horn wire is through its opening in housing, thread worm shaft into housing. Install lower bearing and worm bearing adjuster cup.
2. Assemble lash adjuster with shim in slot in end of sector shaft. Check end clearance which should not be greater than .002". For the purpose of adjusting this end clearance, a shim kit containing four shims of .063", .065", .067" and .069" thickness is available.
3. After lash adjuster end clearance has been adjusted, start sector shaft pilot into side cover. Then, using a screwdriver through hole in cover, turn lash adjuster in a counterclockwise direction to pull sector shaft pilot into side cover as far as it will go.
4. Place a new gasket on side cover. Then push side cover including sector shaft into place. After making sure there is some lash between worm and sector roller, assemble and tighten side cover bolts.

Adjustments

Adjustment of the steering gear may be accomplished on the bench or in the car. If adjusted on the bench, disregard any of the following items which obviously refer to the procedure when the gear is in the car. Follow the sequence of operations as given below:

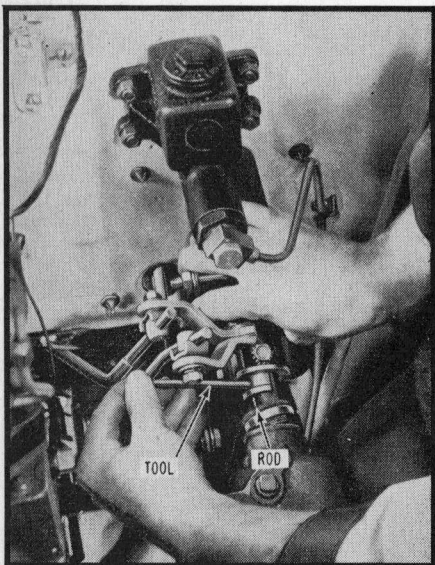

Fig. 17 Checking for concentricity of steering shaft location in mast jacket. 1955-61

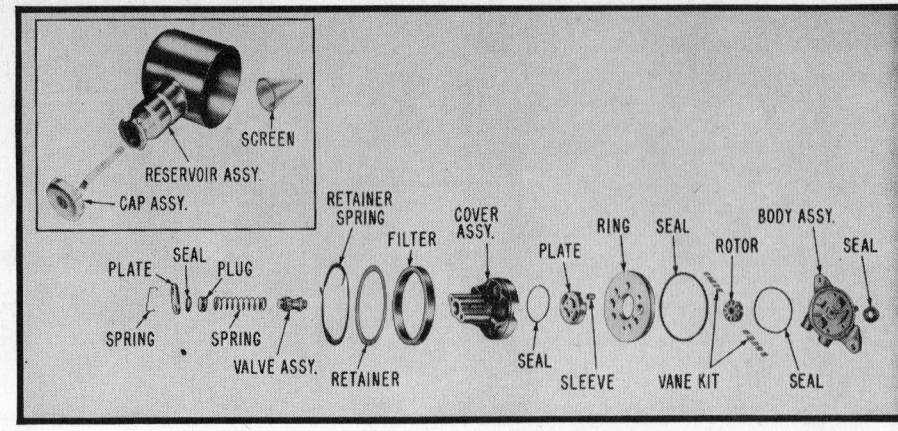

Fig. 18 Power steering pump. 1955-61

1. Disconnect steering connecting rod from pitman arm, noting relative position of steering connecting rod parts before disturbing them.
2. Remove sheet metal splash guard covering steering gear housing.
3. Referring to Fig. 13, loosen lock nut and turn lash adjuster in a counterclockwise direction.
4. Turn steering wheel gently in one direction until stopped by gear, then back away about one turn.
5. Using a spring scale hooked to the rim of the steering wheel, measure the pull required to keep the wheel in motion, which should be between ⅜ and ⅝ lb. If not within these limits, adjustment of worm bearings is necessary.
6. To adjust worm bearings, refer to Fig. 14. Loosen lock nut and turn adjuster cup until there is no perceptible end play in worm. Check pull at wheel rim, readjusting as necessary, and tighten lock nut.
7. After proper adjustment of worm bearings is obtained, and all mounting bolts are tightened to a torque of 27-40 lb. ft., adjust lash adjuster, Fig. 13. First turn steering wheel gently from one extreme to the other, carefully counting the total number of turns. Then turn wheel back exactly half way, which is the central position.
8. Turn lash adjuster clockwise to remove all lash in gear teeth and tighten lock nut 10-15 lb. ft. torque.
9. Turn steering wheel away from its central or straight-ahead position and check pull at wheel rim with spring scale when turned through its central position. This should be between ⅞ and 1⅞ lbs. If not within these limits, turn wheel ½ turn off its high spot (central position) and either tighten or loosen adjuster as necessary.

STEERING GEAR REPAIRS, 1955-61

Disassemble, Figs. 15 & 16

1. Rotate steering worm until nut is in center of travel.
2. Remove sector shaft nut.

3. Use puller to remove pitman arm.
4. Remove side cover screws and remove side cover and sector shaft from housing.
5. To remove side cover from sector shaft, turn adjuster screw in end of sector shaft down through cover.
6. Remove screws and take out end cover with worm bearing, outer race and thrust washer.
7. To remove lower worm bearing, outer race and thrust washer from cover, loosen worm bearing adjuster screw lock nut and turn screw in through cover.
8. Grasp lower end of steering worm and draw steering shaft and nut out of steering housing. *Be sure to keep shaft in horizontal position so that nut does not move against stops at any time, causing damage to ball return mechanism.* Disassembly of worm nut is not recommended.

Assemble

1. Install worm shaft and nut assembly in gear housing, keeping ball nut away from stops on worm.
2. Install worm bearing adjusting screw with lower worm bearing, outer race and thrust washer in end cover.
3. Install end cover and attaching parts on gear housing, making sure bearings seat properly.
4. Tighten worm bearing adjusting screw until a slight drag is felt on bearings. Do not tighten lock nut.
5. Install pitman arm.
6. Install sector shaft and adjusting screw inside cover.
7. Rotate steering column until ball nut is in center of travel so that center tooth on sector shaft will enter center space on nut.
8. Install side cover and sector shaft in gear housing.
9. Tighten sector shaft adjusting screw until a slight drag is felt on bearing but do not tighten lock nut.
10. After steering gear is installed in car, adjust as outlined below:

Adjustments

1. Disconnect steering relay rod from pitman arm.
2. Loosen sector shaft lash adjuster screw a few turns to relieve load from bearings.

3. Turn steering wheel in one direction until stopped by gear, then back away about one turn.

4. With a spring scale hooked to rim of steering wheel, measure pull required to keep wheel in motion; this should be ⅜ to ⅝ lb. If not within these limits, adjust worm bearings as follows:

5. Loosen worm bearing adjuster lock nut and turn adjuster until there is no perceptible end play in worm. Check pull at wheel rim, readjusting as required to obtain proper pull. Tighten lock nut and recheck pull.

6. After worm bearing adjustment is completed and all mounting bolts tightened, adjust sector shaft end play.

7. With steering wheel in straight-ahead position, turn lash adjuster screw clockwise to remove all lash and tighten lock nut.

8. Check pull at rim of steering wheel, taking highest reading on scale as wheel is turned through the central or straight-ahead position. This should be between ⅞ and 1½ lbs. *If more than 1½ lb., turn lash adjuster screw counterclockwise, then come up on the adjustment in a clockwise motion.*

9. Tighten lock nut and recheck pull.

NOTE—Due to the off-center location of the steering shaft in relation to the mast jacket, it may be necessary to adjust for concentricity as follows: With shift levers in neutral, slip the cover and spring on the steering shaft below adjusting ring towards steering gear box. Install the tool shown in Fig. 17 between the steering shaft and adjusting ring. Holding the tool at a point of contact bisecting keyway in adjusting ring as shown, insert a 5/64" drill or welding rod between steering shaft and tool. If shaft is not properly located, loosen upper dash panel bracket bolt and the two lower bracket retaining bolts. Exert slight pressure against 5/64" rod and the tool and tighten first the upper bolt and then the two lower bolts.

POWER STEERING UNIT, REPLACE

1. To remove the unit from the car, take out the horn button or ornamental cap and unscrew the steering wheel retaining nut.

2. Remove steering wheel with a suitable puller.

3. Remove upper control shaft clamp bolt from shaft connector.

4. Disconnect horn wire at connector under the instrument panel near where the horn wire comes from the mast jacket.

5. Remove steering mast jacket toe board grommet and seal from toe board.

6. Remove mast jacket clamp from instrument panel.

7. Remove two screws that attach gearshift control upper support to mast jacket. The upper control shaft and support may now be pulled up and out of engagement from shaft connector.

8. Remove clamp bolt nuts and clamp retaining the shifter housing to the mast jacket. Then rotate shifter housing, with lower control shaft and control rods attached, away from mast jacket.

9. Disconnect steering connecting rod at pitman arm, *taking care to note relative position of steering connecting rod parts before disturbing them.*

10. Disconnect steering pump-to-valve body hoses at valve body unit. *Secure the end of hoses in a raised position to prevent drainage of oil.*

11. Unfasten steering gear housing from steering support bracket.

12. Remove left air duct.

13. Rotate gear assembly to clear fender skirt and raise steering gear assembly, bringing it up and forward to remove from engine compartment.

14. Reverse the foregoing procedure to install the gear assembly. Tighten steering gear housing-to-steering support bracket bolts to 27-40 lbs. ft. torque. Also tighten steering wheel retaining nut to 35-40 lbs. ft. torque.

POWER STEERING REPAIRS, 1955-61

Power steering equipment consists of a recirculating ball type steering gear and linkage to which a hydraulic power mechanism has been added as part of the steering linkage. The hydraulic mechanism furnishes additional power to *assist* the manual operation so that the turning effort at the steering wheel is greatly reduced. The hydraulic mechanism consists of three basic units: a hydraulic pump and reservoir, a control valve, and a power cylinder.

PUMP REPAIRS

Removal, Fig. 18

1. On 6-cyl. cars only, remove fan belt and pull generator away from engine.

2. Disconnect hydraulic lines from pump, allowing fluid to drain from reservoir into a container.

3. Unfasten and remove pump.

Disassemble, Fig. 18

1. Drain remaining fluid from reservoir.

2. Remove reservoir from pump.

3. Remove pump cover and filter.

4. Disassemble pump.

Inspection, Fig. 18

1. Wash and dry all parts.

2. Inspect fit of vanes in rotor. Vanes must slide freely but snugly in slots. Tightness may be relieved by removal of irregularities.

3. Inspect flat faces of pressure plate, cam ring, pump cover, rotor and pump body. These faces may be repaired by lapping until smooth and flat. Remove all lapping compound.

4. Inspect cylindrical surface of pressure relief control valve and check fit of this valve in pump body. Slight irregularities may be corrected by polishing.

Assemble, Fig. 18

1. Lubriplate and install new O-rings in pump cover, on cam ring and in pump body.

2. Install rotor and vanes on pump body with wear patterns or beveled edge of vanes against cam ring inner diameter.

3. Install alignment sleeve in cam ring and install cam ring in pump body. *The wider edge of cam ring is correct side to pump body. Be certain to align bolt holes in cam ring and pump body. Rotor should be installed with rounded side of splines toward generator end of pump.*

4. Install pressure plate in cover.

5. Install filter and retainer.

6. Install cover to pump body.

7. Install plunger and flow spring in pump cover.

8. Install filter retainer spring in cover.

9. Install reservoir, two bolts and two sealing washers. *The brass fitting seats are the pressed-in type and are replaceable in the event of a fitting leak by tapping threads in the hole of the seat and then pulling the seat by using a bolt threaded into the tapped out seat and a flat washer and nut as an extractor.*

10. When installing new seats, align seat in its bore and press it into place, using the correct hose or tube fitting as a pressing tool.

11. Install pump on car and fill and bleed system as outlined further on.

CONTROL VALVE REPAIRS

Removal, Fig. 19

1. Loosen relay rod-to-control valve clamp.

2. Disconnect hose connections at control valve.

3. Disconnect control valve from pitman arm.

4. Unscrew control valve from relay rod.

5. Remove control valve from car.

Disassemble, Fig. 19

1. Remove dust shield from valve housing.

2. Remove retaining pin and nut from valve shaft.

3. Separate valve housing from adapter housing.

4. Remove parts from valve shaft.

5. Remove ball stud cover from adapter housing.

6. Pull ball stud to end of adapter housing and remove lock pin.

7. Remove ball plug adjuster and valve shaft.

8. Remove ball seat plug and spring.

9. Remove seats and ball stud.

10. Remove bearing sleeve.

Inspection, Fig. 19

1. Wash and dry all metal parts.

2. Inspect all parts for scratches, burrs, distortion, evidence of wear and replace all worn or damaged parts,

including mating parts where necessary.

3. Replace all seals, gaskets and covers.

Assemble, Fig. 19

1. Place ball seat in bearing sleeve and insert sleeve in housing.
2. Insert ball stud in sleeve.
3. Install other ball seat, spring and spring seat in sleeve.
4. Install valve shaft in adjuster and screw adjuster into bearing sleeve. *Adjuster should be tightened until it bottoms, and should then be backed off ¼ turn plus or minus amount necessary to insert lock pin in nearest hole. Be sure ball ends remain in correct position, otherwise there will be insufficient clearance to correctly install retaining pin.*
5. Install ball stud cover.
6. Install washer and spacer on valve shaft.
7. Install Vee seal block and ring.
8. Install annulus washer, spring and spring thrust washer with chamfered side of thrust washer toward spool side.
9. Install spool valve and retaining nut. *Spool valve is installed with Vee seal at threaded end of valve shaft.*
10. Tighten retaining nut to a torque of 25 inch lbs. and install retaining clip.
11. Insert assembled valve and adapter into valve housing and install two retaining bolts and lockwashers.
12. Fill end area with approved grease and install dust cover.

Installation

1. Install control valve on relay rod so that the distance from the center of the control valve ball stud to the center of the tie rod is approximately 3⅝".
2. Tighten control valve clamp. *Clamp should be positioned before tightening so that it will not interfere with the steering linkage.*
3. Connect four hydraulic hoses to control valve.
4. Fill reservoir and bleed system as outlined further on.

Adjust, 1960-61

1. Disconnect cylinder rod from frame bracket.
2. With car on a hoist, start the engine. One of the following two conditions will exist:
   a. If piston rod remains retracted, turn the adjusting nut clockwise until the rod begins to move out. Then turn the nut counterclockwise until the rod just begins to move in. Now turn the nut clock-

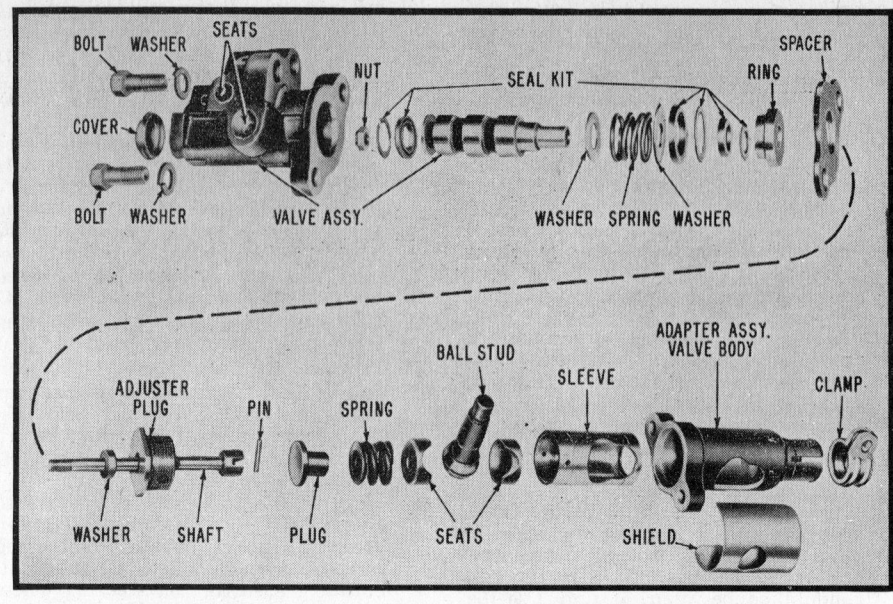

Fig. 19 Power steering control valve. 1955-61

wise to exactly one half the rotation needed to change the direction of shaft movement.
   b. If the rod extends upon starting the pump, move the nut counterclockwise until the rod begins to retract, then clockwise until the rod begins to move out again. Now turn the rod to exactly one half the rotation needed to change the direction of shaft movement. *Do not turn the nut back and forth more than is absolutely necessary to balance the valve.*
3. Restart engine. Front wheels should not turn from center if valve has been properly balanced.

POWER CYLINDER REPAIRS

Removal

1. Disconnect two hydraulic lines at power cylinder.
2. Unfasten power cylinder rod from brace at frame.
3. Unfasten power cylinder from relay rod bracket.
4. Remove power cylinder from car.

Inspection

1. Inspect seals for leaks around cylinder rod and if leaks are present, replace seals as follows:

2. Use a hook tool to remove retaining ring. Remove wiper ring, back-up washer, back-up ring and seal. *Piston rod seal should not be removed unless there are signs of leakage along the piston shaft at shaft seal.*
3. Examine brass fitting hose connection seats for cracks or damage and replace if necessary.
4. For service other than seat or seal replacement, replace the power cylinder.

Installation

1. Install power cylinder on car by reversing removal procedure.
2. Reconnect two hoses, fill system with fluid and bleed system as outlined below.

Filling & Bleeding System

1. Fill reservoir to proper level with Automatic Transmission Fluid and let fluid remain undisturbed for about two minutes.
2. Raise front wheels off floor.
3. Run engine at idle for two minutes.
4. Increase engine speed to about 1500 rpm.
5. Turn wheels from one extreme to the other, lightly contacting stops.
6. Lower wheels to floor and turn wheels right and left.
7. Recheck for leaks.
8. Check oil level and refill as required.

Instruments and Windshield Wiper

INSTRUMENT CLUSTER

1955-56

In order to remove the speedometer, first detach and pull the instrument cluster assembly from the instrument panel opening.

1957

The instrument cluster must be removed in order to remove the speedometer. On cars with automatic transmission, first disconnect the indicator rod from the lever before removing the instrument cluster.

1958

Detach and pull the instrument cluster from the instrument panel opening. Also remove all instrument lamps and high beam indicator lamp from back of speedometer. Then remove speedometer.

1959-60

1. Remove five lamp sockets and speedometer cable from back of speedometer unit.
2. From under dash, remove nut from stud at top of instrument cluster.
3. On passenger side of instrument panel, remove two screws securing bottom of housing to dash.
4. Remove speedometer head from housing by removing three screws.

1961

To remove the instrument cluster or console, two clamps must be loosened and slid up the mast jacket. The upper clamp connects the mast jacket to the instrument panel support and the lower clamp connects the lower end of the mast jacket to the firewall support.

The steering wheel and mast jacket assembly can now be lowered to provide the necessary clearance for removing the instrument console. Six screws around the console hold it in place and permit quick removal so all instruments are accessible for maintenance or installation.

WINDSHIELD WIPER

1953-54

1. On arm drive wipers, it is necessary to move the wiper arms by hand midway in their travel arc. With the arms in this position, the motor auxiliary drive lever should be in a vertical position and remain so throughout the adjustment procedure. Wipers with spiral drum drive may be adjusted in any position.
2. Remove wiper arms and blades.
3. Loosen screw in end of transmission shaft and tap slightly to insure full tension.
4. Have a helper inside the car pull the cables until one notch movement of transmission serrations can be felt or heard. While holding the cables in this position, retighten the tension screw. If wiper action is still slow, increase slack in cables by an additional notch movement of the transmission serrations.

1955-57

The wiper transmission cables are tensioned by spring loaded pulleys. The end of the transmission shaft is pushed in to unlock the pulleys. To tension the cables, push in on the transmission shaft end if blade has been removed or on the base of the wiper arm if the blade is installed.

To release cable tension for removal of component parts, push in on the transmission shaft and have a helper on the inside of the car pull on the cables to obtain the desired slack. Then release pressure on transmission shaft. *Wiper blade snap or over-travel indicates loose transmission drive cables.*

To remove the wiper motor, proceed as follows:

1. Remove the glove compartment box.
2. Adjust cables to slack position and detach them.
3. Unfasten motor from drive assembly and remove. Drive assembly can now be removed from dash panel.

1958-61

1. Make certain motor is in parked position.
2. Remove cowl vent grille from car.
3. Remove washer nozzles and disengage drive linkages from motor.
4. Under the instrument panel, disconnect electrical connector or control cable and vacuum line from wiper motor.
5. Remove retaining screws and pull motor out and down to remove.

CHRYSLER
DESOTO · IMPERIAL

INDEX OF SERVICE OPERATIONS

PAGE NO.

ACCESSORIES
Radio Replace 580
Speedometer Removal 581
Windshield Wiper 579
Windshield Wiper Troubles...........37

BODY
Air Conditioning 177
Automatic Seat Adjuster Troubles......36
Automatic Top Troubles 36
Automatic Window Lift Troubles.......36

BRAKES (Mechanical)
Adjustments 112
Brake Cylinder Sizes 538
Hydraulic Brake System.............112
Master Cylinder, Replace............573
Trouble Shooting 31

BRAKES (Power)
Power Unit, Replace.................573
Power Unit Repairs.................128
Trouble Shooting 32

CLUTCH
Clutch Pedal, Adjust...............563
Clutch Service 563
Trouble Shooting 13

COOLING SYSTEM
Radiator, Replace 556
Trouble Shooting 8
Water Distributor Tube, Replace......557
Water Pump Repairs................556
Water Pump, Replace...............556

ELECTRIC SYSTEM
Alternator Service 57
Alternator Specifications 537
Dash Gauge Service................85
Distributor, Replace 557
Distributor Service 46
Distributor Specifications 539
Generator & Regulator Service........62
Generator & Regulator Specifications...537
Horn Ring, Replace................577
Ignition System Service.............46
Ignition Timing 557
Starter Replace 558
Starter Switch Service.............83
Starting Motor Service.............77
Starting Motor Specifications........538
Trouble Shooting 10
Turn Signal Troubles 12

ENGINE
Camshaft, Replace 551
Crankshaft Oil Seal, Replace........553
Cylinder Head, Replace.............544
Engine Bearing Specifications.......535
Engine, Replace 544
Main Bearings, Replace.............553
Piston Pins, Replace...............552
Piston Rings, Replace..............553
Piston & Ring Specifications........535
Piston & Rod, Assemble............552
Pistons, Replace 552
Pistons & Rods, Remove............552
Rocker Arms, Replace..............546
Rod Bearings, Replace.............553
Timing Case Cover, Replace.........550
Timing Chain, Replace.............551
Trouble Shooting 4
Valve Arrangement 546
Valve Guides 547
Valve Lifters 549
Valve Spring Installed Height........547
Valve Spring Testing..............547
Valve Timing Data.................551
Valve Specifications 534
Valves, Adjust 545
Valves, Grind 548
Valves, Remove 547

ENGINE OILING
Oil Pan, Replace..................554
Oil Pressure Regulator.............555
Oil Pump Repairs.................555
Oil Pump, Replace................555
Trouble Shooting 4

FRONT SUSPENSION
Camber, Adjust 573
Caster, Adjust 573
Front End Repairs.................574
Toe-in, Adjust 574
Trouble Shooting 33
Wheel Alignment Specifications......540
Wheel Bearings, Adjust.............574

FUEL & EXHAUST SYSTEM
Carburetors 558
Fuel Pumps 96
Mufflers & Pipes..................558
Trouble Shooting 6

OVERDRIVES 100
Trouble Shooting 14

PAGE NO.

REAR AXLE
Axle Shaft, Replace................572
General Service 102
Non-Slip Differentials 109
Rear Axle Repairs.................570
Trouble Shooting 31

SPECIFICATIONS
Alternators 537
Brake Cylinder Sizes 538
Capacity Data 536
Carburetors 558
Cooling System Data...............536
Crankshaft & Bearings.............535
Distributors 539
Engine Tightening 535
Generators & Regulators 537
Piston, Pins & Rings..............535
Rear Axle 538
Rod Bearings 535
Starting Motors 538
Tune Up 532
Valves 534
Valve Timing 551
Wheel Alignment 540

STEERING GEARS (Mechanical)
Horn Ring, Replace................577
Steering Gear Repairs..............579
Steering Gear, Replace.............577
Steering Wheel, Replace............577
Trouble Shooting 33

STEERING GEARS (Power)
Steering Gear, Repairs.............145
Steering Gear, Replace.............578
Trouble Shooting 34

TRANSMISSIONS (Manual Shift)
Gearshift, Adjust 565
Transmission Repairs 565
Transmission, Replace 565
Trouble Shooting 14

TRANSMISSIONS (Automatic)
Powerflite, Replace................566
  Linkage, Adjust 566
  Repairs 297
  Push Buttons 567
  Trouble Shooting 21
Torqueflite, Replace...............568
  Linkage, Adjust 569
  Push Buttons 568
  Repairs, V8 Type..............341
  Repairs, 6-cyl. Type...........331
  Trouble Shooting 23

TUNE UP..........................38

GENERAL SPECIFICATIONS

Year	Model Designation	Wheelbase, Inches	Valve Location	Bore and Stroke	Piston Displacement, Cubic Inches	Compression Ratio (Standard)	Maximum Brake H.P. @ R.P.M.	Maximum Torque Lbs. Ft. @ R.P.M.	Normal Oil Pressure Pounds
CHRYSLER									
1953	Windsor 6............C60-1	125½	In Block	3.4375 x 4.750	264.5	7.0	119 @ 3600	218 @ 1600	40-60
	Windsor DeLuxe 6......C60-2	125½	In Block	3.4375 x 4.750	264.5	7.0	119 @ 3600	218 @ 1600	40-60
	New Yorker V8......C56-1	125½	In Head	3.8125 x 3.625	331.1	7.5	180 @ 4000	312 @ 2000	40-65
	New Yorker Special V8 ..C56-2	125½	In Head	3.8125 x 3.625	331.1	7.5	180 @ 4000	312 @ 2000	40-65
1954	Windsor DeLuxe 6.......C62	125½	In Block	3.4375 x 4.750	264.5	7.0	119 @ 3600	218 @ 1600	40-60
	New Yorker V8......C63-1	125½	In Head	3.8125 x 3.625	331.1	7.5	195 @ 4400	320 @ 2000	40-65
	New Yorker DeLuxe V8..C63-2	125½	In Head	3.8125 x 3.625	331.1	7.5	235 @ 4400	330 @ 2600	40-65
1955	Windsor V8............C67	126	In Head	3.6250 x 3.625	301	8.0	188 @ 4400	275 @ 2400	40-65
	New Yorker V8.........C68	126	In Head	3.8125 x 3.625	331	8.5	250 @ 4600	340 @ 2800	40-65
	Chrysler "300".........C300	126	In Head	3.8125 x 3.625	331	8.5	300 @ 5200	345 @ 3200	45-65
1956	Windsor V8 (2-Bar. Carb.) C71	126	In Head	3.8125 x 3.625	331	8.5	225 @ 4400	310 @ 2400	40-65
	Windsor V8(4 Bar. Carb.)..C71	126	In Head	3.8125 x 3.625	331	9.0	250 @ 4600	340 @ 2800	40-65
	New Yorker V8.........C72	126	In Head	3.9375 x 3.625	354	9.0	280 @ 4600	380 @ 2800	40-65
	Chrysler "300B".......C-300B	126	In Head	3.9375 x 3.625	354	9.0	340 @ 5200	385 @ 3200	40-65
1957	Windsor V8 (2-Bar. Carb.)C75-1	126	In Head	3.9375 x 3.625	354	9.25	285 @ 4600	365 @ 2400	50-65
	Windsor V8 (4 Bar. Carb.)C75-1	126	In Head	3.9375 x 3.625	354	9.25	295 @ 4600	390 @ 2800	50-65
	Saratoga V8...........C75-2	126	In Head	3.9375 x 3.625	354	9.25	295 @ 4600	390 @ 2800	50-65
	New Yorker V8........C76	126	In Head	4.0000 x 3.906	392	9.25	325 @ 4600	430 @ 2800	50-65
	300C................	126	In Head	4.0000 x 3.906	392	9.25	375 @ 5200	420 @ 4000	50-65
1958	Windsor V8...........LC1-L	122	In Head	3.9375 x 3.625	354	10.0	290 @ 4600	385 @ 2000	50-60
	Saratoga V8..........LC2-M	122	In Head	3.9375 x 3.625	354	10.0	310 @ 4600	405 @ 3200	50-60
	New Yorker V8.......LC3-H	126	In Head	4.0000 x 3.906	392	10.0	345 @ 4600	450 @ 2800	50-60
	300D V8.............LC3-S	126	In Head	4.0000 x 3.906	392	10.0	380 @ 5200	435 @ 3600②	50-60
1959	Windsor V8...........MC1-L	126	In Head	4.0312 x 3.750	383	10.0	305 @ 4600	410 @ 2400	40-65
	Saratoga V8..........MC2-M	126	In Head	4.0312 x 3.750	383	10.0	325 @ 4600	425 @ 2800	40-65
	New Yorker V8.......MC3-H	126	In Head	4.1875 x 3.750	413	10.0	350 @ 4600	470 @ 2800	40-65
	300-E V8............MC3-H	126	In Head	4.1875 x 3.750	413	10.0	380 @ 5000	450 @ 3600	40-65
1960	Windsor V8...........PC1-L	122	In Head	4.0312 x 3.750	383	10.0	305 @ 4600	410 @ 2400	40-65
	Windsor V8...........PC1-L	122	In Head	4.2500 x 3.375	383	10.0	305 @ 4600	410 @ 2400	45-65
	Saratoga V8.........PC2-M	122	In Head	4.1875 x 3.750	413	10.0	350 @ 4600	470 @ 2800	40-65
	Saratoga V8.........PC2-M	122	In Head	4.0312 x 3.750	383	10.0	325 @ 4600	425 @ 2800	40-65
	New Yorker V8 ......PC3-H	126	In Head	4.1875 x 3.750	413	10.0	350 @ 4600	470 @ 2800	40-65
	300-F V8	126	In Head	4.1875 x 3.750	413	10.0	375 @ 5000	495 @ 2800	40-65
1961	Newport V8.........RC-1	122	In Head	4.1250 x 3.375	361	9.1	265 @ 4400	380 @ 2400	40-65
	Windsor V8..........RC-2	122	In Head	4.2500 x 3.375	383	10.1	305 @ 4600	410 @ 2400	40-65
	New Yorker V8 ....RC-3	126	In Head	4.1875 x 3.750	413	10.1	350 @ 4600	470 @ 2800	40-65
	300G...........RC3-300	126	In Head	4.1875 x 3.750	413	10.1	375 @ 5000	495 @ 2800	40-65
DE SOTO									
1953	Powermaster 6...........S18	125½	In Block	3.4375 x 4.500	250.6	7.00	116 @ 3600	208 @ 1600	50
	Firedome V8.............S16	125½	In Head	3.6250 x 3.344	276.1	7.10	160 @ 4400	250 @ 2000	50
1954	Firedome V8.............S19	125½	In Head	3.6250 x 3.344	276.1	7.50	170 @ 4400	255 @ 2400	50
	Power Master Six........S20	125½	In Block	3.4375 x 4.500	250.6	7.00	116 @ 3600	208 @ 1600	50
1955	Fireflite V8.............S21	126	In Head	3.7200 x 3.344	291	7.5	200 @ 4400	274 @ 2800	50
	Firedome V8.............S22	126	In Head	3.7200 x 3.344	291	7.5	185 @ 4400	245 @ 2800	50
1956	Firedome V8.............S23	126	In Head	3.7200 x 3.800	330	8.5	230 @ 4400	305 @ 2800	50-65
	Fireflite V8.............S24	126	In Head	3.7200 x 3.800	330	8.5	255 @ 4400	350 @ 3200	50-65
	Adventurer V8...........S24	126	In Head	3.7812 x 3.800	341	9.25	320 @ 5200	356 @ 4000	50-65
1957	Firedome V8.............S25	126	In Head	3.7812 x 3.800	341	9.25	270 @ 4600	350 @ 2400	50-65
	Fireflite V8.............S26	126	In Head	3.7812 x 3.800	341	9.25	295 @ 4600	375 @ 2800	50-65
	Firesweep (2 Bar. Carb.)...S27	122	In Head	3.6875 x 3.800	325	8.5	245 @ 4400	320 @ 2400	50-65
	Firesweep (4 Bar. Carb.)...S27	122	In Head	3.6875 x 3.800	325	8.5	260 @ 4400	335 @ 2800	50-65

GENERAL SPECIFICATIONS (continued)

Year	Model Designation	Wheel-base, Inches	Valve Location	Bore and Stroke	Piston Displace-ment, Cubic Inches	Com-pres-sion Ratio (Stand-ard)	Maximum Brake H.P. @ R.P.M.	Maximum Torque Lbs. Ft. @ R.P.M.	Normal Oil Pressure Pounds
1958	Firesweep V8..........LS1-L	122	In Head	4.0625 x 3.375	350	10.0	280 @ 4600	380 @ 2400	50–65
	Firedome V8.........LS2-M	126	In Head	4.1250 x 3.375	361	10.0	295 @ 4600	390 @ 2400	50–65
	Fireflite V8...........LS3-H	126	In Head	4.1250 x 3.375	361	10.0	305 @ 4600	400 @ 2800	50–65
	Adventurer V8........LS3-S	126	In Head	4.1250 x 3.375	361	10.0	345 @ 5000	400 @ 3600	50–65
1959	Firesweep V8 ....MS1-L	122	In Head	4.1250 x 3.375	361	10.0	290 @ 4600	390 @ 2400	45–65
	Firedome V8.........MS2-M	126	In Head	4.2500 x 3.375	383	10.0	305 @ 4600	410 @ 2400	45–65
	Fireflite V8.........MS3-H	126	In Head	4.2500 x 3.375	383	10.0	325 @ 4600	425 @ 2800	45–65
	Adventurer V8........MS3-H	126	In Head	4.2500 x 3.375	383	10.0	350 @ 5000	425 @ 3600	45–65
1960	Fireflite V8	122	In Head	4.1250 x 3.375	361	10.0	295 @ 4600	390 @ 2400	45–65
	Adventurer V8	122	In Head	4.2500 x 3.375	383	10.0	305 @ 4600	410 @ 2400	45–65
1961	All V8.................	122	In Head	4.1250 x 3.375	361	9.1	265 @ 4400	380 @ 2400	40–65

IMPERIAL

Year	Model Designation	Wheel-base, Inches	Valve Location	Bore and Stroke	Piston Displace-ment, Cubic Inches	Com-pres-sion Ratio (Stand-ard)	Maximum Brake H.P. @ R.P.M.	Maximum Torque Lbs. Ft. @ R.P.M.	Normal Oil Pressure Pounds
1953	Custom V8...............C58	133½	In Head	3.8125 x 3.625	331	7.5	180 @ 4000	312 @ 2000	40–65
	Crown V8................C59	145½	In Head	3.8125 x 3.625	331	7.5	180 @ 4000	312 @ 2000	40–65
1954	Custom V8...............C64	133½	In Head	3.8125 x 3.625	331	7.5	235 @ 4400	330 @ 2600	40–65
	Crown V8................C66	145½	In Head	3.8125 x 3.625	331	7.5	235 @ 4400	330 @ 2600	40–65
1955	Custom V8...............C69	130	In Head	3.8125 x 3.625	331	8.5	250 @ 4600	340 @ 2800	40–65
	Crown V8................C70	149½	In Head	3.8125 x 3.625	331	8.5	250 @ 4600	340 @ 2800	40–65
1956	Crown V8................C70	149½	In Head	3.9375 x 3.625	354	9.0	280 @ 4600	380 @ 2800	40–65
	Custom V8...............C73	133	In Head	3.9375 x 3.625	354	9.0	280 @ 4600	380 @ 2800	40–65
1957	V8 ....IM1	129	In Head	4.0000 x 3.906	392	9.25	325 @ 4600	430 @ 2800	50–65
1958	V8 ....LY1	129	In Head	4.0000 x 3.906	392	10.0	345 @ 4600	450 @ 2800	50–60
1959	V8 ....MY1	129	In Head	4.1875 x 3.750	413	10.0	350 @ 4600	470 @ 2800	40–65
1960	V8 ....PY1	129	In Head	4.1875 x 3.750	413	10.0	350 @ 4600	470 @ 2800	40–65
1961	All....................RY-1	129	In Head	4.1875 x 3.750	413	10.1	350 @ 4600	470 @ 2800	40–65

①—Serial number 81–03167320 to 81–03168115.   ②—Serial number 82–03161884 to 82–03168116; also from 82–03166499 to 82–03168117.

TUNE UP SPECIFICATIONS

Year	Model	Ground Polarity and Voltage	Spark Plug Type Auto-Lite	Spark Plug Gap Inch	Distributor Point Gap Inch	Distributor Cam Angle Degrees	Firing Order ①	Ignition Timing Mark	Ignition Timing Location	Idle Speed RPM In Neutral	Com-pression Pressure @ Cranking Speed Minimum
CHRYSLER											
1953	Six	P-6	4S-140	.035	.020	39	153624	"O"	Damper	475	120
	V8	P-6	4GS-150	.035	.017	⑥	18436572	4° BTDC	Damper	475	135
1954	Six	P-6	4S-140	.035	.020	39	153624	2° BTDC	Damper	475	120
	V8	P-6	4GS-150	.035	.017	⑥	18436572	4° BTDC	Damper	475	135
1955	C67	P-6	4S-165	.035	.017	③	18436572	6° BTDC	Damper	475	130
	C68	P-6	4GS-175	.035	.017	③	18436572	6° BTDC	Damper	500	140
	C300	P-6	4GS-200	.035	.017	③	18436572	10° BTDC	Damper	625	140
1956	C72	N-12	AGR-42	.035	.017	②	18436572	4° BTDC	Damper	500	150
	C71	N-12	AR-52	.035	.017	31	18436572	2° BTDC	Damper	500	140
	300B	N-12	AGR-41	.035	.017	31	18436572	8° BTDC	Damper	500	150
1957	C75	N-12	AR-42	.035	.017	29	18436572	6° BTDC	Damper	500	150
	C76	N-12	AGR-42	.035	.017	④	18436572	6° BTDC	Damper	500	150
	300C	N-12	AGR-42	.035	.017	④	18436572	4° BTDC	Damper	500	150

TUNE UP SPECIFICATIONS (continued)

Year	Model	Ground Polarity and Voltage	Spark Plug Type Auto-Lite	Gap Inch	Distributor Point Gap Inch	Cam Angle Degrees	Firing Order ①	Ignition Timing Mark	Location	Idle Speed RPM In Neutral	Compression Pressure @ Cranking Speed Minimum
1958	Windsor	N-12	AR-42	.035	.017	29	18436572	8° BTDC	Damper	500	160
	Saratoga	N-12	AR-42	.035	.017	29	18436572	6° BTDC	Damper	500	160
	New Yorker	N-12	AGR-42	.035	.017	④	18436572	6° BTDC	Damper	500	160
	300D	N-12	AGR-42	.035	.017	④	18436572	6° BTDC	Damper	650	160
1959	Windsor	N-12	A-42	.035	.017	27–32	18436572	10° BTDC	Damper	500	160
	Saratoga	N-12	A-42	.035	.017	27–32	18436572	10° BTDC	Damper	500	160
	New Yorker	N-12	A-42	.035	.017	⑤	18436572	10° BTDC	Damper	500	160
	300-E	N-12	A-32	.035	.017	⑤	18436572	10° BTDC	Damper	700	160
1960	Windsor	N-12	A-42	.035	.017	27–32	18436572	10° BTDC	Damper	500	160
	Saratoga	N-12	A-42	.035	.017	27–32	18436572	10° BTDC	Damper	500	160
	New Yorker	N-12	A-42	.035	.017	27–32	18436572	10° BTDC	Damper	500	160
	300-F	N-12	A-32	.035	.017	⑤	18436572	⑧	Damper	735	160
1961	Newport	N-12	A-42	.035	.017	27–32	18436572	10°BTDC	Damper	500	135–165
	Windsor	N-12	A-42	.035	.017	27–32	18436572	10°BTDC	Damper	500	150–180
	New Yorker	N-12	A-42	.035	.017	27–32	18436572	10°BTDC	Damper	500	150–180
	300-G	N-12	A-32	.035	.017	⑤	18436572	⑧	Damper	735	150–180

DE SOTO

Year	Model	Ground Polarity and Voltage	Spark Plug Type Auto-Lite	Gap Inch	Distributor Point Gap Inch	Cam Angle Degrees	Firing Order ①	Ignition Timing Mark	Location	Idle Speed RPM In Neutral	Compression Pressure @ Cranking Speed Minimum
1953	Six	P-6	AR-8	.035	.020	39	153624	2° BTDC	Damper	475	120
	V8	P-6	4S-140	.035	.017	③	18436572	4° BTDC	Damper	475	130
1954	Six	P-6	4S-140	.035	.020	39	153624	2° BTDC	Damper	475	120
	V8	P-6	4S-140	.035	.017	③	18436572	4° BTDC	Damper	475	130
1955	S21	P-6	4S-165	.035	.017	③	18436572	4° BTDC	Damper	475	130
	S22	P-6	4S-140	.035	.017	34	18436572	10° BTDC	Damper	475	130
1956	S23	N-12	AR-52	.035	.017	31	18436572	8° BTDC	Damper	475	130
	S24	N-12	AR-52	.035	.017	31	18436572	4° BTDC	Damper	475	145
	S24 Adv.	N-12	AR-31	.035	.017	31	18436572	6° BTDC	Damper	475	150
1957	S25	N-12	AR-42	.035	.017	29	18436572	6° BTDC	Damper	500	145
	S26	N-12	AR-42	.035	.017	29	18436572	6° BTDC	Damper	500	150
	S27	N-12	AR-42	.035	.017	29	18436572	6° BTDC	Damper	500	125
1958	Adventurer	N-12	AR-32	.035	.017	④	18436572	8° BTDC	Damper	500	160
	Others	N-12	AR-42	.035	.017	29	18436572	6° BTDC	Damper	500	160
1959	Adventurer	N-12	A-32	.035	.017	⑤	18436572	10° BTDC	Damper	700	160
	Others	N-12	A-42	.035	.017	27–32	18436572	10° BTDC	Damper	500	160
1960	Fireflite	N-12	A-42	.035	.017	27–32	18436572	10° BTDC	Damper	500	160
	Adventurer	N-12	A-42	.035	.017	27–32	18436572	10° BTDC	Damper	500	160
1961	All	N-12	A-42	.035	.017	27–32	18436572	10°BTDC	Damper	500	135–165

IMPERIAL

Year	Model	Ground Polarity and Voltage	Spark Plug Type Auto-Lite	Gap Inch	Distributor Point Gap Inch	Cam Angle Degrees	Firing Order ①	Ignition Timing Mark	Location	Idle Speed RPM In Neutral	Compression Pressure @ Cranking Speed Minimum
1953	All	P-⑦	4GS-150	.035	.017	⑥	18436572	4° BTDC	Damper	475	135
1954	All	P-⑦	4GS-150	.035	.017	⑥	18436572	4° BTDC	Damper	475	135
1955	All	P-⑦	4GS-175	.035	.017	③	18436572	6° BTDC	Damper	500	140
1956	All	N-12	AGR-42	.035	.017	②	18436572	4° BTDC	Damper	500	150
1957	All	N-12	AGR-42	.035	.017	④	18436572	6° BTDC	Damper	500	150
1958	All	N-12	AGR-32	.035	.017	④	18436572	6° BTDC	Damper	500	160
1959–61	All	N-12	A-42	.035	.017	⑤	18436572	10° BTDC	Damper	500	150–180

①—Cylinder numbering (front to rear): Left bank 1–3–5–7; right bank 2–4–6–8.
②—Each set 29–32; total dwell both sets 32–36.
③—Each set 26–28; total dwell both sets 32–36.
④—Each set 29–32; total dwell both sets 36–39.
⑤—Each set 27–32; total dwell both sets 34–40.
⑥—1AZ-4001B: Each set 27–30; total dwell both sets 34–36. 1AZ-4001C: Each set 26–28; total dwell both sets 32–36.
⑦—Crown Imperial 12 volt, Custom Imperial 6 volt.
⑧—Automatic trans. 5°BTDC. With 4 speed manual trans. 10°BTDC.

VALVE SPECIFICATIONS

Year	Model	Valve Lash		Valve Angles		Valve Spring Installed Height	Valve Spring Pressure Lbs. @ In.	Valve Lift		Stem Clearance		Stem Diameter	
		Int.	Exh.	Seat	Face			Int.	Exh.	Intake	Exhaust	Int.	Exh.
CHRYSLER & IMPERIAL													
1953	Six	.008H	.010H	45	45	$1\frac{3}{4}$	115 @ $1\frac{3}{8}$	.365	.365	.001–.003	.002–.004	.341	.340
	V8	Zero	Zero	45	45	$1\frac{11}{16}$	①	.378	.361	.001–.003	.002–.004	.3725	.3715
1954	Six	.008H	.010H	45	45	$1\frac{3}{4}$	115 @ $1\frac{3}{8}$	.365	.365	.001–.003	.002–.004	.341	.340
	V8	Zero	Zero	45	45	$1\frac{11}{16}$	126 @ $1\frac{5}{16}$②	.378	.361	.001–.003	.002–.004	.3725	.3715
1955	C67	Zero	Zero	45	45	$1\frac{11}{16}$	166 @ $1\frac{5}{16}$	.381	.357	.001–.003	.002–.004	.372	.372
	C68, 69, 70	Zero	Zero	45	45	$1\frac{11}{16}$	126 @ $1\frac{5}{16}$②	.381	.357	.001–.003	.002–.004	.372	.372
	C300	.015H	.024H	45	45	$1\frac{11}{16}$	126 @ $1\frac{5}{16}$②	.444	.435	.001–.003	.002–.004	.372	.372
1956	300B	.015H	.024H	45	45	$1\frac{21}{32}$	158 @ $1\frac{7}{32}$	.444	.435	.001–.003	.002–.004	.372	.372
	Others	Zero	Zero	45	45	$1\frac{11}{16}$	166 @ $1\frac{5}{16}$	.381	.357	.001–.003	.002–.004	.372	.372
1957	300C	.015H	.024H	45	45	$1\frac{21}{32}$	158 @ $1\frac{7}{32}$②	.444	.435	.001–.003	.002–.004	.370	.370
	Others	Zero	Zero	45	45	$1\frac{11}{16}$	170 @ $1\frac{5}{16}$	.389	.389	.001–.003	.002–.004	.370	.370
1958	300D③	.015H	.024H	45	45	$1\frac{21}{32}$	158 @ $1\frac{7}{32}$②	.435	.442	.001–.003	.002–.004	.370	.370
	300D④	.015H	.024H	45	45	$1\frac{21}{32}$	158 @ $1\frac{7}{32}$②	.455	.455	.001–.003	.002–.004	.370	.370
	Others	Zero	Zero	45	45	$1\frac{11}{16}$	170 @ $1\frac{5}{16}$	.389	.389	.001–.003	.002–.004	.370	.370
1959	300E	Zero	Zero	45	45	$1\frac{55}{64}$	195 @ $1\frac{15}{32}$	.390	.390	.001–.003	.002–.004	.370	.370
	Others	Zero	Zero	45	45	$1\frac{55}{64}$	195 @ $1\frac{15}{32}$	.390	.390	.001–.003	.002–.004	.370	.370
1960–61	300	Zero	Zero	45	45	$1\frac{55}{64}$	195 @ $1\frac{15}{32}$	.430	.430	.001–.003	.002–.004	.3725	.3715
	Others	Zero	Zero	45	45	$1\frac{55}{64}$	195 @ $1\frac{15}{32}$	.389	.389	.001–.003	.002–.004	.370	.370
DE SOTO													
1953	Six	.008H	.010H	45	45	$1\frac{3}{4}$	115 @ $1\frac{3}{8}$	.365	.365	.001–.003	.002–.004	.341	.340
	V8	Zero	Zero	45	45	$1\frac{11}{16}$	105 @ $1\frac{5}{16}$②	.361	.361	.001–.003	.002–.004	.3725	.3715
1954	Six	.008H	.010H	45	45	$1\frac{3}{4}$	115 @ $1\frac{3}{8}$	.365	.365	.001–.003	.002–.004	.341	.340
	V8	Zero	Zero	45	45	$1\frac{11}{16}$	105 @ $1\frac{5}{16}$②	.361	.361	.001–.003	.002–.004	.3725	.3415
1955	All	Zero	Zero	45	45	$1\frac{11}{16}$	92 @ $1\frac{5}{16}$②	.360	.360	.001–.003	.002–.004	.372	.372
1956	Adven.	Zero	Zero	45	45	$1\frac{11}{16}$	166 @ $1\frac{5}{16}$	.381	.357	.001–.003	.002–.004	.372	.372
	Others	Zero	Zero	45	45	$1\frac{21}{32}$	160 @ $1\frac{7}{32}$②	.431	.413	.001–.003	.002–.004	.372	.372
1957	S25, 26	Zero	Zero	45	45	$1\frac{11}{16}$	175 @ $1\frac{5}{16}$	.389	.389	.001–.003	.002–.004	.370	.370
	S27	Zero	Zero	45	45	$1\frac{11}{16}$	166 @ $1\frac{5}{16}$	.389	.389	.001–.003	.002–.004	.370	.370
	Adven.	Zero	Zero	45	45	$1\frac{21}{32}$	158 @ $1\frac{7}{32}$	.430	.413	.001–.003	.002–.004	.370	.370
1958	Adven.	Zero	Zero	45	45	$1\frac{55}{64}$	195 @ $1\frac{15}{32}$	.390	.390	.001–.003	.002–.004	.370	.370
	Others	Zero	Zero	45	45	$1\frac{55}{64}$	180 @ $1\frac{15}{32}$	.390	.390	.001–.003	.002–.004	.370	.370
1959	All	Zero	Zero	45	45	$1\frac{55}{64}$	195 @ $1\frac{15}{32}$	.390	.390	.001–.003	.002–.004	.370	.370
1960–61	Ram Man.	Zero	Zero	45	45	$1\frac{55}{64}$	205 @ $1\frac{7}{16}$	.430	.430	.001–.003	.002–.004	.370	.370
	Others	Zero	Zero	45	45	$1\frac{55}{64}$	195 @ $1\frac{15}{32}$	.390	.390	.001–.003	.002–.004	.370	.370

①—Intake 128 @ $1\frac{5}{16}$, exhaust 128 @ $1\frac{9}{16}$.
②—Outer spring
③—Standard camshaft.
④—Special camshaft.

Year	Model	Fitting Pistons		Ring End Gap ①		Wrist-pin Diameter	Rod Bearings		Main Bearings			
		Shim To Use	Pounds Pull On Scale	Comp.	Oil		Shaft Diameter	Bearing Clearance	Shaft Diameter	Bearing Clearance	Thrust on Bear. No.	Shaft End Play

CHRYSLER & IMPERIAL

Year	Model	Shim To Use	Pounds Pull On Scale	Comp.	Oil	Wrist-pin Diam.	Shaft Diameter	Bearing Clearance	Shaft Diameter	Bearing Clearance	Thrust	Shaft End Play
1953-54	Six	.002	6-9	.007	.007	.8592	2.124-2.125	.0005-.0015	2.499-2.500	.0005-.0015	5	.002-.007
	V8	.002	5-12	.010	.010	.9842	2.249-2.250	.0005-.0015	2.499-2.500	.0005-.0015	3	.002-.007
1955	All	.002	5-12	.010	.010	.9842	2.249-2.250	.0005-.0015	2.499-2.500	.0005-.0015	3	.002-.007
1956	C70-72-73	.002	5-12	.010	.010	.9842	2.249-2.250	.0005-.0015	2.499-2.500	.0005-.0015	3	.002-.007
	C71	.002	5-12	.010	.010	.9842	2.249-2.250	.0005-.0015	2.499-2.500	.0005-.0015	3	.002-.007
	C300B	.002	5-12	.010	.010	.9842	2.249-2.250	.0005-.0015	2.499-2.500	.0005-.0015	3	.002-.007
1957	C75	.002	8-12	.010	.010	.9842	2.249-2.250	.0005-.0015	2.499-2.500	.0005-.0015	3	.002-.007
	C76, IMI	.002	8-12	.013	.013	.9842	2.374-2.375	.0005-.0015	2.687-2.688	.0005-.0015	3	.002-.007
	300C	.002	8-12	.013	.013	.9842	2.374-2.375	.0005-.0015	2.687-2.688	.0005-.0015	3	.002-.007
1958	LC1, LC2	.002	8-12	.010	.010	.9842	2.249-2.250	.0005-.0015	2.499-2.500	.0005-.0015	3	.002-.007
	LC3, LY1	.002	8-12	.013	.013	.9842	2.374-2.375	.0005-.0015	2.687-2.688	.0005-.0015	3	.002-.007
	300D	.002	8-12	.013	.013	.9842	2.374-2.375	.0005-.0015	2.687-2.688	.0005-.0015	3	.002-.007
1959-60	All	.0015	8-12	.013	.013	1.0936	2.374-2.375	.0005-.0015	2.749-2.750	.0005-.0015	3	.002-.007
1961	V8-361, 383	.0015	8-12	.013	.013	1.0936	2.374-2.375	.0005-.0015	2.6245-2.6255	.0005-.0015	3	.002-.007
	V8-413	.0015	8-12	.013	.013	1.0936	2.374-2.375	.0005-.0015	2.7495-2.7505	.0005-.0015	3	.002-.007

DE SOTO

Year	Model	Shim To Use	Pounds Pull On Scale	Comp.	Oil	Wrist-pin Diam.	Shaft Diameter	Bearing Clearance	Shaft Diameter	Bearing Clearance	Thrust	Shaft End Play
1953	Six	.002	5-7	.007	.007	.8592	2.124-2.125	.0005-.0015	2.499-2.500	.0005-.0015	5	.002-.007
	V8	.002	5-12	.010	.010	.9217	2.061-2.062	.0005-.0015	2.374-2.375	.0005-.0015	3	.002-.007
1954	Six	.002	8-12	.015	.015	.8592	2.124-2.125	.0005-.0015	2.499-2.500	.0005-.0015	5	.002-.007
	V8	.002	8-12	.015	.015	.9217	2.061-2.062	.0005-.0015	2.374-2.375	.0005-.0015	3	.002-.007
1955	All	.002	8-12	.015	.015	.9217	2.061-2.062	.0005-.0015	2.374-2.375	.0005-.0015	3	.002-.007
1956	All	.002	8-12	.010	.015	.9217	2.249-2.250	.0005-.0015	2.499-2.500	.0005-.0015	3	.002-.007
1957	S25-26	.002	8-12	.010	.010	.9217	2.249-2.250	.0005-.0015	2.499-2.500	.0005-.0015	3	.002-.007
	S27	.002	5-10	.010	.010	.9217	2.249-2.250	.0005-.0015	2.499-2.500	.0005-.0015	3	.002-.007
1958	All	.002	5-10	.013	.013	1.0935	2.374-2.375	.0005-.0015	2.629-2.630	.0005-.0015	3	.002-.007
1959-60	Adven.	.002	5-10	.013	.013	1.0935	2.374-2.375	.0005-.0015	2.749-2.750	.0005-.0015	3	.002-.007
	Others	.002	5-10	.013	.013	1.0935	2.374-2.375	.0005-.0015	2.629-2.630	.0005-.0015	3	.002-.007
1961	All	.0015	8-12	.013	.013	1.0936	2.374-2.375	.0005-.0015	2.6245-2.6255	.0005-.0015	3	.002-.007

①—Fit rings in tapered bores for the clearance listed in tightest portion of ring travel.

ENGINE TIGHTENING SPECIFICATIONS★

★Torque specifications are for clean and lightly lubricated threads only. Dry or dirty threads produce increased friction which prevents accurate measurement of tightness.

Year	Spark Plugs Ft. Lbs.	Cylinder Head Bolts Ft. Lbs.	Intake Manifold Ft. Lbs.	Exhaust Manifold Ft. Lbs.	Rocker Arm Shaft Bracket Ft. Lbs.	Rocker Arm Cover Ft. Lbs.	Connecting Rod Cap Bolts Ft. Lbs.	Main Bearing Cap Bolts Ft. Lbs.	Flywheel to Crankshaft Ft. Lbs.	Vibration Damper or Pulley Ft. Lbs.

CHRYSLER AND IMPERIAL

Year	Spark Plugs	Cyl Head Bolts	Intake Manifold	Exhaust Manifold	Rocker Arm Shaft Bracket	Rocker Arm Cover	Conn Rod Cap Bolts	Main Bearing Cap Bolts	Flywheel	Vibration Damper
1953-54 Six	30	70	20	20	None	None	45	85	55-60	108
1953-58 V8	30	85	30	25	85	①	45	85	60	135
1959-61	30	70	50	30	30	②	45	85	60	135

DE SOTO

Year	Spark Plugs	Cyl Head Bolts	Intake Manifold	Exhaust Manifold	Rocker Arm Shaft Bracket	Rocker Arm Cover	Conn Rod Cap Bolts	Main Bearing Cap Bolts	Flywheel	Vibration Damper
1953-54 Six	32	70	20	20	None	None	50	85	60	108
1953-55 V8	32	85	30	35	85	①	50	80-85	60	135
1956-57	30	85	30	25	③	①	45	100	60	135
1958	30	70	30	30	30	②	45	85	60	135
1959-61	30	70	50	30	30	②	45	85	60	135

①—30 Inch Lbs.   ②—40 Inch Lbs.   ③—Double rocker arm engine 85, single rocker 30.

COOLING SYSTEM & CAPACITY DATA

Year and Model	Cooling System Data			Thermostat Opening Temp.		Fuel Tank Gals.	Engine Oil			Transmissions			Rear Axle Pints
	Quarts No Heater	Quarts With Heater	Rad. Cap Relief Pressure	①	②		Refill Qts.③	Summer Grade	Winter Grade	Std. Pints	With Over- drive Pints	Auto- matic Qts.	
CHRYSLER													
1953 Six	15	16	7	180	160	17	5④	30	10W	2¾④	None	None	3¼
V8	25	26	7	180	160	20	5	30	10W	3⑤	None	None	3½
1954 Six	15	16	7	180	160	17	5	30	10W	2¾	None	11	3¼
V8	25	26	7	180	160	20	5	30	10W	None	None	11	3½
1955 Windsor	24	25	7⑥	180	160	20	5	30	10W	2¾	None	10	3¼
Others	25	26	7⑥	180	160	20	5	30	10W	None	None	11	3½
1956 Windsor	24	25	7⑥	180	160	21	5	30	10W	2¾	None	10	3¼
New Yorker	25	26	7⑥	180	160	21	5	30	10W	None	None	11	3½
300B	25	26	7⑥	180	160	21½	5	30	10W	2¾	None	11	3½
1957 New Yorker	24	25	14	180	160	23	5	30	10W	2¾	None	11½	3½
300C	24	25	14	180	160	23	5	30	10W	None	None	11½	3½
Others	21	22	14	180	160	23	5	30	10W	2¾	None	9	3½
1958 Windsor	21	22	14	180	160	23	4	30	10W	None	None	10½	3½
Saratoga	21	22	14	180	160	23	4	30	10W	None	None	10½	3½
New Yorker	24	25	14	180	160	23	5	30	10W	None	None	10½	3½
300D	24	25	14	180	160	23	5	30	10W	None	None	10½	3½
1959 Windsor	17	18	14	180	160	23	5	30	10W	None	None	10½	3½
Others	16	17	14	180	160	23	5	30	10W	None	None	10½	3½
1960–61	16	17	14⑦	180	160	23	5	30	10W	None	None	10½	3½
DE SOTO													
1953 Six	15	16	7	180	160	17	5	30	10W	2¾⑧	3½	None	3¼
V8	22	23	7	180	160	17	5④	30	10W	2¾⑧	3½	None	3½
1954 Six	15	16	7	180	160	17	5	30	10W	2¾	3½	10	3½
V8	22	23	7	180	160	17	5	30	10W	2¾	3½	10	3½
1955	23	24	7⑥	180	160	20	5	30	10W	2¾	3½	10	3½
1956	23	24	7⑥	180	160	21	4	30	10W	2¾	3½	10	3½
1957	20	21	14	180	160	23	5	30	10W	2¾	None	⑨	3½
1958 Firesweep	16	17	14	180	160	20	4	30	10W	2¾	None	10	3½
Others	16	17	14	180	160	23	4	30	10W	2¾	None	10½	3½
1959 Firesweep	16	17	14	180	160	20	5	30	10W	2¾	None	10	3½
Others	15	16	14	180	160	23	5	30	10W	2¾	None	10½	3½
1960 Fireflite	16	17	14	180	160	23	5	30	10W	2¾	None	10	3½
Adven.	15	16	14	180	160	23	5	30	10W	2¾	None	11	3½
1961	16	17	14	180	160	23	5	30	10W	2¾	None	10	3½
IMPERIAL													
1953	25	26	7	180	160	20	5	30	10W	3⑤	None	None	3½
1954–56	25	26	7⑥	180	160	20	5	30	10W	None	None	11	⑩
1957	24	25	14	180	160	23	5	30	10W	None	None	11½	3½
1958	24	25	14	180	160	23	5	30	10W	None	None	10½	3½
1959–61	16	17	14⑦	180	160	23	5	30	10W	None	None	11	3½

①—For permanent type anti-freeze.
②—For alcohol type anti-freeze.
③—Add 1 qt. with filter change.
④—Engine and torque converter have combined oiling system requiring 12 qts.
⑤—Fluid Torque Drive requires 10½ qts.
⑥—With air conditioning 14 lbs.
⑦—With air conditioning 16 lbs.
⑧—For M6 transmission 3 pints.
⑨—Powerflite 10 qts.   Torqueflite 9 qts.
⑩—Custom 3½ pints, Crown 5 pints.

IMPERIAL • DE SOTO • CHRYSLER

Year	Unit Number	Ground Polarity and Rotation	Field Coil Draw Amperes	Current Output			Operating Voltage			Voltage Regulator Point Gap	Regulator Armature Air Gap
				Engine R.P.M.	Amperes	Volts	Engine R.P.M.	Amperes	Voltage @ 120° ①		
1960–61	2095060	N-C	2.38–2.75②	1250	35③	15	1250	15	13.4–14	.015	.048–.052
	2095425	N-C	2.38–2.75②	1250	40③	15	1250	15	13.4–14	.015	.048–.052
	2095100	N-C	2.38–2.75②	1250	40③	15	1250	15	13.4–14	.015	.048–.052

①—For each 10° rise in temperature subtract .04 volt; for each 10° drop add .04 volt. Temperature is checked with a thermometer 2 inches from installed voltage regulator cover.

②—Current draw at 12 volts while turning rotor shaft by hand. ③—If output is low, stator or rectifier is shorted.

GENERATOR AND REGULATOR SPECIFICATIONS

★To polarize generator, reconnect the leads to the regulator; then momentarily connect a jumper wire from the "Arm" to the "Bat" terminals of the regulator.

Year	Generator Number ④	Rotation and Ground Polarity ①	Rated Cap. Amps.	Gen. Field Ground Location★	Brush Spring Tension, Ounces	Field Current Amperes	Regulator Number	Cutout Relay		Voltage Regulator Setting Volts	Current Regulator Setting Amperes	Current and Voltage Armature Air Gap, Inch
								Voltage to Close Points	Armature Air Gap, Inch			

CHRYSLER, DE SOTO & IMPERIAL

Year	Generator Number ④	Rotation and Ground Polarity ①	Rated Cap. Amps.	Gen. Field Ground Location★	Brush Spring Tension, Ounces	Field Current Amperes	Regulator Number	Voltage to Close Points	Armature Air Gap, Inch	Voltage Regulator Setting Volts	Current Regulator Setting Amperes	Current and Voltage Armature Air Gap, Inch
1958	GGA-6001AC	C-N	40	External	34–41	1.1–1.3③	VAT-6201A	13.1	.032	14.3	40	.050
1956	GGA-6001L	C-N	40	External	34–41	1.1–1.3③	VAT-6201A	13.1	.032	14.3	40	.050
1956	GGA-6001M	C-N	40	External	34–41	1.1–1.3③	VAT-6201A	13.1	.032	14.3	40	.050
1956–59	GGA-6001N	C-N	40	External	34–41	1.2–1.3③	VAT-6201A	13.1	.032	14.3	40	.050
1959–60	GGA-6003E	C-N	40	External	34–41	1.2–1.3③	VAT-6201A	13.1	.032	14.3	40	.050
1960	GGA-6003F	C-N	40	External	34–41	1.1–1.3③	VAT-6201A	13.1	.032	14.3	40	.050
1957–59	GGA-6007A	C-N	40	External	34–41	1.2–1.3③	VAT-6201A	13.1	.032	14.3	40	.050
1953–55	GGW-6001K	C-P	45	External	35–53	1.4–1.5②	VBE-6201A	6.5	.032	7.2	45	.050
1953	GGW-6008D	C-P	45	External	35–53	1.4–1.5②	VBE-6201A	6.5	.032	7.2	45	.050
1953–54	GGW-6008G	C-P	45	External	35–53	1.4–1.5②	VBE-6201A	6.5	.032	7.2	45	.050
1955	GGW-6016D	C-P	45	External	35–53	1.4–1.5②	VBE-6201A	6.5	.032	7.2	45	.050
1953	GGU-6006C	C-P	50	External	35–53	1.4–1.6②	VAV-6001B	6.5	.032	7.2	50	.050
1953–54	GGU-6006G	C-P	50	External	35–53	1.4–1.6②	VAV-6001B	6.5	.032	7.2	50	.050
1955	GGU-6013B	C-P	50	External	35–53	1.4–1.6②	VAV-6001B	6.5	.032	7.2	50	.050
1957–58	GHM-6001E	C-N	30	External	35–53	1.1–1.3③	VRX-6201A	13.1	.032	14.3	30	.050
1953	GHM-6002A	C-P	25	External	35–53	1.1–1.3③	VRX-6003A	13.3	.032	14.5	25	.050
1953–54	GHM-6002E	C-P	25	External	35–53	1.1–1.3③	VRX-6003A	13.3	.032	14.5	25	.050
1955	GHM-6003A	C-P	30	External	35–53	1.1–1.3③	VRX-6003B	13.1	.032	14.3	25	.050
1957–58	GHM-6004C	C-N	30	External	35–53	1.1–1.3③	VRX-6201A	13.1	.032	14.3	30	.050
1957	GHM-6010A	C-N	30	External	35–53	1.1–1.3③	VRX-6201A	13.1	.032	14.3	30	.050
1957	GHM-6010B	C-N	30	External	35–53	1.1–1.3③	VRX-6201A	13.1	.032	14.3	30	.050
1958	GHM-6010C	C-N	30	External	35–53	1.1–1.3③	VRX-6201A	13.1	.032	14.3	30	.050
1957–58	GHM-6011A	C-N	30	External	35–53	1.1–1.3③	VRX-6201A	13.1	.032	14.3	30	.050
1959	GHM-8001A	C-N	30	External	35–53	1.2–1.3③	VRX-6201A	13.1	.032	14.3	30	.050
1960	GHM-8001B	C-N	30	External	35–53	1.1–1.3③	VBO-4202C	13.1	.032	14.6	30	.050
1960	GHM-8002A	C-N	30	External	35–53	1.1–1.3③	VBO-4202C	13.1	.032	14.6	30	.050
1959	GHM-8005A	C-N	30	External	35–53	1.2–1.3③	VRX-6201A	13.1	.032	14.3	30	.050
1956	GJC-7002B	C-N	30	External	18–36	1.2–1.3③	VRX-6201A	13.1	.032	14.3	30	.050
1957	GJC-7002H	C-N	30	External	18–36	1.2–1.3③	VRX-6201A	13.1	.032	14.3	30	.050
1956	GJC-7003A	C-N	30	External	18–36	1.2–1.3③	VRX-6201A	13.1	.032	14.3	30	.050
1957	GJC-7012A	C-N	30	External	18–36	1.2–1.3③	VRX-6201A	13.1	.032	14.3	30	.050
1958	GJC-7013B	C-N	35	External	18–36	1.2–1.3③	VRX-6201A	13.1	.032	14.3	30	.050
1958	GJC-8000A	C-N	30	External	18–36	1.2–1.3③	VRX-6201A	13.1	.032	14.3	30	.050
1959	GJM-8001A	C-N	35	External	18–36	1.6–1.7③	VRX-6301A	13.1	.032	14.3	35	.050
1959	GJM-8002A	C-N	35	External	18–36	1.6–1.7③	VRX-6301A	13.1	.032	14.3	35	.050
1960	GJM-8201A	C-N	35	External	18–36	1.6–1.7③	VBO-4202BC	13.1	.032	14.6	35	.050

①—C-Clockwise. P-Positive. N-Negative. ②—At 5 volts. ③—At 10 volts. ④—Stamped on plate riveted to side of housing.

Year	Part No. ②	Rotation ①	Brush Spring Tension, Ounces	No Load Test			Torque Test		
				Amperes	Volts	R.P.M.	Amperes	Volts	Torque, Lbs. Ft.

CHRYSLER, DE SOTO & IMPERIAL

Year	Part No.	Rotation	Brush Spring	Amperes	Volts	R.P.M.	Amperes	Volts	Torque
1960–61	1889200	Clockwise	32–48	80	11.0	3800	350	4.0	8½
1953	MCL-6116	Clockwise	42–53	65	5.0	4900	410	2.0	8
1953–54	MCL-6117	Clockwise	42–53	65	5.0	4900	410	2.0	8
1953–54	MCL-6121A	Clockwise	42–53	65	5.0	4900	410	2.0	8
1955	MCL-6304	Clockwise	42–53	65	5.0	4900	410	2.0	8
1953	MDB-6001	Clockwise	42–53	31	10.0	3600	145	4.0	4
1953–54	MDB-6001A	Clockwise	42–53	31	10.0	3600	145	4.0	4
1955	MDC-6301	Clockwise	42–53	45	10.0	5800	190	4.0	5½
1955	MDD-6401	Clockwise	42–53	60	10.0	3200	240	4.0	6½
1956	MDF-6001	Clockwise	42–53	60	10.0	3200	240	4.0	6½
1957	MDL-6001	Clockwise	31–47	60	10.0	3200	225	4.0	6
1957	MDL-6002	Clockwise	31–47	60	10.0	3200	225	4.0	6
1957	MDL-6003	Clockwise	31–47	60	10.0	3200	225	4.0	6
1959	MDT-6001	Clockwise	31–47	56	10.0	3600	350	4.0	8½
1958–60	MDT-6002	Clockwise	31–47	56	10.0	3600	350	4.0	8½
1958	MDT-6003	Clockwise	31–47	56	10.0	3600	350	4.0	8½

①—As viewed from the drive end.　②—Stamped on plate riveted to side of housing.

REAR AXLE AND BRAKE CYLINDER SPECIFICATIONS

Year	Model	Ring Gear & Pinion Backlash, Inch	Drive Pinion Adjustment	Drive Pinion Bearing Preload, Inch Lbs.	Drive Pinion Bearing Adjustment	Axle Shaft End Play, Inch	Hydraulic Cylinder Bore, Sizes, Inch		
							Wheel Cylinder		Master Cylinder
							Front	Rear	

CHRYSLER & IMPERIAL

Year	Model	Backlash	Drive Pinion Adj.	Preload	Bearing Adj.	End Play	Front	Rear	Master
1953	C59	.006–.008	None	25–35②	Washer	.003–.008	1¼	1	1
	C56, 58	.006–.008	Washer	25–35②	Washer	.003–.008	1⅛	1⅛	1⅛
	C60	.006–.008	Washer	20–30②	Shims	.003–.008	1⅛	1⅛	1
1954	C62	.006–.008	Washer	20–30②	Shims	.003–.008	1⅛	1⅛	1①
	C63	.006–.008	Washer	25–35②	Washer	.003–.008	1⅛	1⅛	1⅛
	C64	.006–.008	Washer	25–35②	Washer	.003–.008	1⅛	1⅛	1①
	C66	.006–.008	None	25–35②	Washer	.003–.008	1¼	1	1
1955	C67	.006–.008	Washer	20–30②	Shims	.003–.008	1⅛	1⅛	1
	C68, 69, 300	.006–.008	Washer	25–35②	Washer	.003–.008	1⅛	1⅛	.68
	C70	.006–.008	Washer	25–35②	Washer	.003–.008	1¼	1	1
1956	C70, 72, 73	.006–.008	Washer	25–35②	Washer	.003–.008	1⅛	1⅛	1⅛
	C71	.006–.008	Washer	20–30②	Shims	.003–.008	1⅛	1⅛	1⅛
	C300B	.006–.008	Washer	25–35②	Washer	.003–.008	1⅛	1⅛	1⅛
1957–61	All	.006–.008	Washer	20–30②	Shims	.013–.023③	1⅛	1⅛	1⅛

DE SOTO

Year	Model	Backlash	Drive Pinion Adj.	Preload	Bearing Adj.	End Play	Front	Rear	Master
1953	All	.006–.008	Washer	20–30②	Shims	.003–.008	1⅛	1⅛	1
1954	Six	.006–.008	Washer	20–30②	Shims	.003–.008	1⅛	1⅛	1
	V8	.006–.008	Washer	25–35②	Washer	.003–.008	1⅛	1⅛	1
1955	Fireflite	.006–.008	Washer	25–35②	Washer	.003–.008	1⅛	1⅛	1
	Firedome	.006–.008	Washer	20–30②	Shims	.003–.008	1⅛	1⅛	1
1956	Firedome	.006–.008	Washer	20–30②	Shims	.003–.008	1⅛	1⅛	1⅛
	Fireflite	.006–.008	Washer	25–35②	Washer	.003–.008	1⅛	1⅛	1⅛
1957–61	All	.006–.008	Washer	20–30②	Shims	.013–.018	1⅛	1⅛	1⅛

①—With Power Brakes, 1½".
②—For used bearings, drag should be zero to one half that specified but with no end play of the drive pinion.
③—Adjust to .018".

DISTRIBUTOR SPECIFICATIONS

Year	Part No. ①	Rotation ②	Cam Angle, Degrees	Breaker Point Opening, Inch	Condenser Capacity, Mfds. ③	Breaker Arm Spring Tension, Ounces	Centrifugal Advance Data — Advance Starts	Full Advance	Inches of Vacuum to Start Plunger Movement	Inches of Vacuum for Full Plunger Travel	Maximum Vacuum Advance, Dist. Degrees

CHRYSLER, DE SOTO & IMPERIAL

1953-54	1AT-4102	C	39	.020	.25-.28	17-20	1 @ 450	10 @ 1425	5	15	9
1953	1AZ-4001B	C	④	.017	.25-.28	17-20	1 @ 525	11 @ 1775	5¼	17	11½
1953-54	1AZ-4001C	C	⑤	.017	.25-.28	17-20	1 @ 425	12 @ 2100	5¼	17	11½
1955	1AZ-4001D	C	⑤	.017	.25-.28	17-20	1 @ 375	17 @ 2300	5¼	17	11½
1955	1AZ-4001E	C	⑤	.017	.25-.28	17-20	1 @ 375	14 @ 2050	5¼	17	11½
1955	1AZ-4001F	C	⑤	.017	.25-.28	17-20	1 @ 375	12 @ 1725	5¼	17	11½
1955	1AZ-4001G	C	⑤	.017	.25-.28	17-20	1 @ 375	8 @ 800	5¼	11¼	7
1953-54	1AZ-4002A	C	34	.017	.25-.28	17-20	1 @ 500	11 @ 1925	5¼	17	11½
1954	1AZ-4002B	C	⑤	.017	.25-.28	17-20	1 @ 370	11 @ 1850	5¼	17	11½
1955	1AZ-4002C	C	⑤	.017	.25-.28	17-20	1 @ 375	8 @ 800	5¼	7	11¼
1956	1BJ-4302	C	31	.017	.25-.28	17-20	1 @ 380	8½ @ 2200	5½	15	12½
1956	1BJ-4302A	C	31	.017	.25-.28	17-20	1 @ 425	6 @ 800	5½	15	11½
1956	1BJ-4302B	C	31	.017	.25-.28	17-20	1 @ 400	8 @ 700	5½	15½	12½
1956	1BJ-4302C	C	31	.017	.25-.28	17-20	1 @ 425	6 @ 800	6½	16¼	11½
1956	1BJ-4302D	C	31	.017	.25-.28	17-20	1 @ 400	8 @ 700	6½	16¼	11½
1956	1BJ-4303A	C	31	.017	.25-.28	17-20	1 @ 375	14 @ 2025	6⅜	15½	11
1956	1BJ-4303C	C	31	.017	.25-.28	17-20	1 @ 375	14 @ 2025	6½	16¼	11½
1956	1BK-4301A	C	⑥	.017	.25-.28	17-20	1 @ 425	9½ @ 2400	7½	17	11½
1956	1BK-4301C	C	⑧	.017	.25-.28	17-20	1 @ 415	8 @ 1200	7½	13½	8
1956	1BK-4303	C	31	.017	.25-.28	17-20	1 @ 400	8 @ 700	7	16¼	11½
1957	1BK-4304	C	⑦	.017	.25-.28	17-20	1 @ 450	10 @ 2250	8⅛	18	11
1957	1BP-4001	C	29	.017	.25-.28	17-20	1 @ 400	10 @ 1700	10½	18	15
1957	1BP-4001A	C	29	.017	.25-.28	17-20	1 @ 435	9 @ 2300	10½	18	15
1957	1BP-4002	C	29	.017	.25-.28	17-20	1 @ 535	8½ @ 1700	7⅛	18	13
1957	1BP-4002A	C	29	.017	.25-.28	17-20	1 @ 425	13 @ 2050	10½	16	10½
1957	1BP-4002B	C	29	.017	.25-.28	17-20	1 @ 370	8 @ 850	7⅛	18	13
1958	1BP-4002F	C	29	.017	.25-.28	17-20	1 @ 460	10 @ 2100	8½	16	11
1958	1BP-4005	CC	29	.017	.25-.28	17-20	1 @ 425	10 @ 2000	8	17½	13
1959	1BP-4005B	CC	27-32	.017	.25-.28	17-20	0 @ 440	9½ @ 2150	7.2	16½	12½
1960	1BP-4005C	CC	26-32	.017	.25-.28	17-20	1 @ 450	8 @ 2200	8⅛	15	9½
1960	1BP-4005D	CC	26-32	.017	.25-.28	17-20	1 @ 385	11 @ 2150	8⅛	15	9½
1961	1BP-4005E	CC	27-32	.017	.25-.28	17-20	1 @ 450	11 @ 2050	6	16	13
1959	1BP-4006	CC	27-32	.017	.25-.28	17-20	0 @ 400	7½ @ 2350	8⅛	16⅛	11
1960	1BP-4006C	CC	27-32	.017	.25-.28	17-20	0 @ 620	11 @ 2300	8	15	11
1957	1BS-4004	C	34	.017	.25-.28	17-20	1 @ 400	8 @ 700	9⅛	18	10¼
1958	1BS-4006B	CC	⑦	.017	.25-.28	17-20	1 @ 425	10 @ 2000	7⅛	16½	13
1959	1BS-4006C	CC	⑧	.017	.25-.28	17-20	0 @ 530	9½ @ 2000	7½	18.2	14½
1960	1BS-4006E	CC	⑧	.017	.25-.28	17-20	0 @ 375	10 @ 2400	8	14½	10
1958	1BS-4007	C	⑦	.017	.25-.28	17-20	1 @ 375	6½ @ 1050	8	16	11
1958	1BS-4007A	C	⑦	.017	.25-.28	17-20	1 @ 480	10 @ 2400	8	16	11
1958	1BS-4008	C	⑦	.017	.25-.28	17-20	1 @ 375	6½ @ 1050	8	16	11
1959	1BS-4010	CC	⑧	.017	.25-.28	17-20	0 @ 400	6½ @ 1050	8⅜	18⅛	13
1959	1BS-4010A	CC	⑧	.017	.25-.28	17-20	0 @ 400	9½ @ 2300	8⅜	18⅛	13
1960	1BS-4011	CC	8	.017	.25-.28	17-20	1 @ 440	10 @ 2400	8	14½	9
1961	2095530	CC	27-32	.017	.25-.28	17-21	1 @ 490	10 @ 2300	7.4	15	11

①—Stamped on plate riveted to side of housing.
②—As viewed from the top.   C—Clockwise. CC—Counterclockwise.
③—Microfarads—As indicated on a condenser tester.
④—Each set 27½-30, total dwell both sets 34-36.
⑤—Each set 26-28, total dwell both sets 32-36.
⑥—Each set 29-32, total dwell both sets 32-36.
⑦—Each set 29-32, total dwell both sets 36-39.
⑧—Each set 27-32, total dwell both sets 34-40.

WHEEL ALIGNMENT SPECIFICATIONS

Year	Model	Caster, Degrees		Camber, Degrees		Toe-In, Inch	Toe-out on Turns, Degrees①		Kingpin or Steering Axis Inclination, Degrees②
		Limits	Desired	Limits	Desired		Outer Wheel	Inner Wheel	
CHRYSLER & IMPERIAL									
1953–54	133½" W. B. Cars	− 1 to − 3	− 2	− ⅜ to + ⅜	③	0 to 1/16	20	20½ to 22½	5 to 6½
	145½" W. B. Cars	− 1 to − 3	− 2	− ⅜ to + ⅜	③	0 to 1/16	20	20½ to 22½	5 to 6½
1955	Manual Steering	− 2 to 0	− 2	− ⅛ to + ⅝	③	0 to 1/16	20	20½ to 22½	5½ @ 0 Camber
	Power Steering	− 2 to 0	0	− ⅛ to + ⅝	③	0 to 1/16	20	20½ to 22½	5½ @ 0 Camber
1956	Manual Steering	− 2 to 0	− 2	− ⅛ to + ⅝	③	⅛	20	20½ to 22½	④
	Power Steering	− 2 to 0	0	− ⅛ to + ⅝	③	⅛	20	20½ to 22½	④
1957	Manual Steering	− 1½ to + ½	− ¾	⑤	⑤	3/32 to 5/32	20	21¾	6½ @ 0 Camber
	Power Steering	0 to + 1½	+ ¾	⑤	⑤	3/32 to 5/32	20	21¾	6½ @ 0 Camber
1958	Manual Steering	− ½ to 2	− ¾	⑤	⑤	3/32 to 5/32	18½ to 18¾	20	6½ @ 0 Camber
	Power Steering	− ¾ to + ¾	0	⑤	⑤	3/32 to 5/32	18½ to 18¾	20	6½ @ 0 Camber
1959	Manual Steering	− 1½ to 0	− ¾	⑤	⑤	⅛	⑥	20	6½ @ 0 Camber
	Power Steering	0 to + 1½	+ ¾	⑤	⑤	⅛	⑥	20	6½ @ 0 Camber
1960	Manual Steering	− 1¼ to − ¼	− ¾	⑦	⑦	⅛	⑧	20	6½ @ 0 Camber
	Power Steering	+ ¼ to + 1¼	+ ¾	⑦	⑦	⅛	⑧	20	6½ @ 0 Camber
1961	Manual Steering	− 1 to 0	− ½	⑨	⑨	⅛	20	21½	5½ to 7½
	Power Steering	+ ½ to + 1¼	+ ¾	⑨	⑨	⅛	20	21½	5½ to 7½
DE SOTO									
1953–54	All	− 1 to − 3	− 2	− ⅜ to + ⅜	③	0 to 1/16	20	20½ to 22½	5 to 6½
1955	Manual Steering	0 to − 2	− 2	− ⅛ to + ⅝	③	0 to 1/16	20	20½ to 22½	5 to 6½
	Power Steering	0 to − 2	0	− ⅛ to + ⅝	③	0 to 1/16	20	20½ to 22½	5 to 6½
1956	Manual Steering	0 to − 2	− 2	− ⅛ to + ⅝	③	3/32 to 5/32	20	20½ to 22½	5 to 6½
	Power Steering	0 to − 2	0	− ⅛ to + ⅝	③	3/32 to 5/32	20	20½ to 22½	5 to 6½
1957	Manual Steering	0 to − 1½	− ¾	⑤	⑤	3/32 to 5/32	20	21½ to 21¾	6½ @ 0 Camber
	Power Steering	0 to + 1½	+ ¾	⑤	⑤	3/32 to 5/32	20	21½ to 21¾	6½ @ 0 Camber
1958	Manual Steering	− ½ to + 2	− ¾	⑤	⑤	3/32 to 5/32	18½ to 18¾	20	6½ @ 0 Camber
	Power Steering	− ¾ to + ¾	0	⑤	⑤	3/32 to 5/32	18½ to 18¾	20	6½ @ 0 Camber
1959	Manual Steering	− 1½ to 0	− ¾	⑤	⑤	⅛	⑥	20	6½ @ 0 Camber
	Power Steering	0 to + 1½	+ ¾	⑤	⑤	⅛	⑥	20	6½ @ 0 Camber
1960	Manual Steering	− 1¼ to − ¼	− ¾	⑦	⑦	⅛	18° 42'	20	6½ @ 0 Camber
	Power Steering	+ ¼ to + 1¼	+ ¾	⑦	⑦	⅛	18° 42'	20	6½ @ 0 Camber
1961	Manual Steering	− 1 to 0	− ½	⑨	⑨	⅛	20	21½	5½ to 7½
	Power Steering	+ ½ to + 1¼	+ ¾	⑨	⑨	⅛	20	21½	5½ to 7½

①—Incorrect toe-out, when other adjustments are correct, generally indicates bent steering arms.
②—Incorrect kingpin angle with correct camber indicates bent suspension arms or steering knuckle support.
③—Left side + ½°, right side zero.
④—Crown Imperial 7° @ 0 Camber, other models 5½° @ 0 Camber.
⑤—Left side preferred + ⅜°, right side zero.
⑥—Windsor and Firesweep 18° 46', others 18° 26'.
⑦—Left side preferred + ⅜°, right side + ⅛°.
⑧—Windsor 18° 42', others 18° 44'.
⑨—Left side preferred + ½°, right side + ¼°.

SERIAL NUMBER LOCATION
Left Front Door Pillar

ENGINE NUMBER LOCATION
Sixes: Left Front Of Block
V8's: Top Of Cylinder Block

CHRYSLER GRILLE IDENTIFICATION

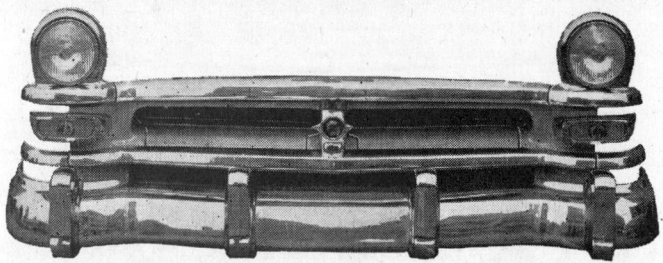

1953 Windsor

1955 New Yorker

1953 New Yorker

1955 Windsor

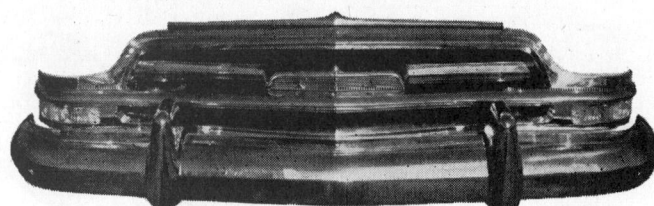

1954 Windsor

1955-56 "300"

1954 New Yorker

1956 Windsor

1954 New Yorker DeLuxe

1956 New Yorker

CHRYSLER GRILLE IDENTIFICATION continued

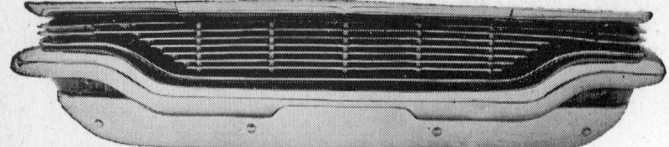

1957 Windsor

1960 Chrysler New Yorker

1957-58 "300"

1960 Chrysler Windsor and Saratoga

1958 New Yorker & Saratoga

1960 Chrysler 300F

1958 Windsor

1961 Chrysler Newport and Windsor

1959 Chrysler

1961 Chrysler New Yorker

1961 Chrysler 300G

DESOTO GRILLE IDENTIFICATION

1953 De Soto

1957 De Soto

1954 De Soto

1958 De Soto

1955 De Soto

1959 De Soto

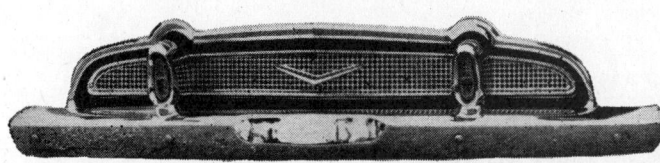

1956 De Soto

1960 De Soto

1961 De Soto

IMPERIAL GRILLE IDENTIFICATON

1953 Imperial

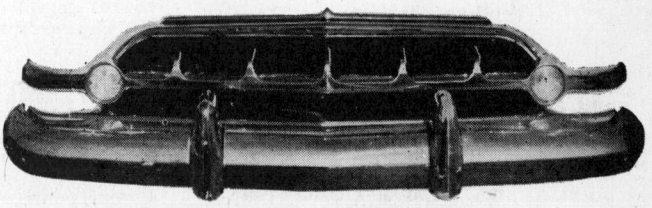

1954 Imperial

IMPERIAL GRILLE IDENTIFICATION continued

1955-56 Imperial

1958 Imperial

1957 Imperial (2 Headlamps)

1959 Imperial

1957 Imperial (4 Headlamps)

1960 Imperial

1961 Imperial

Engine Section

ENGINE, REPLACE

In addition to the usual items such as fuel lines, linkage, propeller shaft, etc., it is necessary to perform the following operations:

1. Remove hood and battery.
2. Remove radiator and exhaust pipes.
3. On 1953-55 models, support transmission and remove engine rear support and crossmember. Remove front support bolts and lift engine out toward the left front fender.
4. On 1956-59 models, support transmission and remove engine rear crossmember. Remove front support and lift engine and transmission out of chassis.
5. On 1960-61 models, remove number 6 spark plug. Then support rear of engine and remove the rear support crossmember and transmission. Remove engine front mounting and lift engine from chassis.

CYLINDER HEAD

Chrysler, De Soto, Imperial 1959-61

1. Drain cooling system.
2. Remove generator, carburetor air cleaner and fuel line.
3. Disconnect accelerator linkage.
4. Remove vacuum control tube at carburetor and distributor.
5. Disconnect heat indicator sending unit wire.
6. Remove spark plugs located under manifolds.
7. Remove intake manifold, ignition coil and carburetor as a unit.
8. Remove valve lifter chamber cover.
9. Remove rocker arm covers. *On air conditioned cars, No. 8 cylinder exhaust valve must be open to allow clearance between right-bank cylinder head cover and heater housing.*
10. Remove exhaust manifolds.

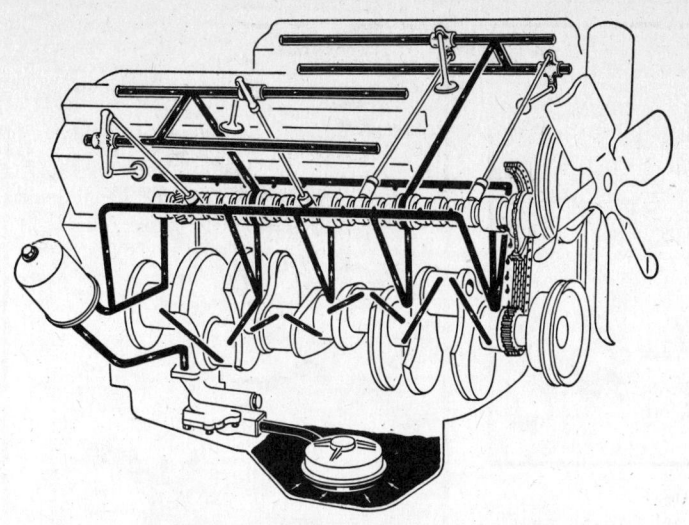

Engine lubrication. Double rocker shaft engine. Chrysler, De Soto and Imperial

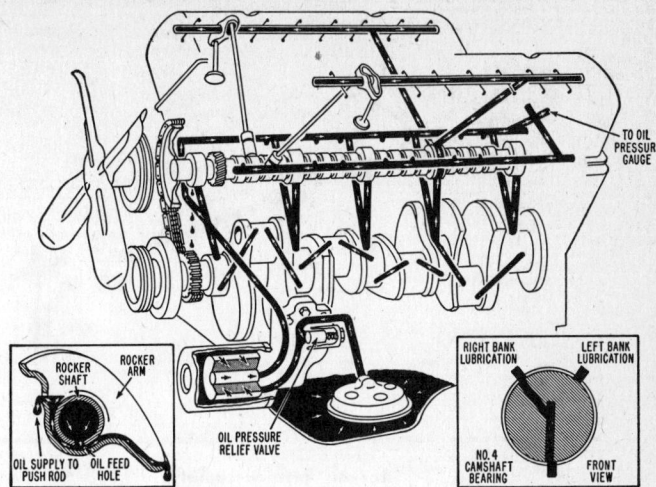

Engine lubrication. 1958-61 De Soto 1959-61 Chrysler and Imperial

11. Remove rocker arm assemblies.
12. Remove push rods.
13. Remove head attaching bolts and take off heads.
14. Installing the heads is a matter of reversing the removal procedure. Tighten attaching bolts in the sequence shown in Fig. 1.

1953-58 V8

1. Drain cooling system.
2. Remove generator, carburetor air cleaner and fuel line.
3. Disconnect accelerator linkage.
4. Remove vacuum control tube at carburetor and distributor.
5. Disconnect coil wires and heater hose.
6. Remove heat indicator sending unit wire.
7. Remove oil level dipstick.
8. Remove air tube between automatic choke and exhaust manifold.
9. On 1953-56 models, remove bolts attaching water pump housing to cylinder heads and loosen remaining water pump housing bolts to allow sufficient forward movement to facilitate installation of cylinder head-to-water pump gaskets.
10. On 1957-58 models, remove water outlet manifold and heater blower.
11. Remove ignition cable cover, spark plugs and tubes.

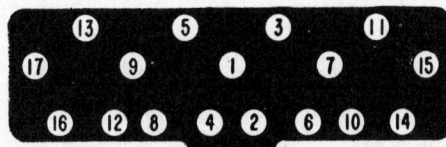

Fig. 1 Cylinder head tightening. 1959-61 Chrysler and Imperial and 1958-61 De Soto

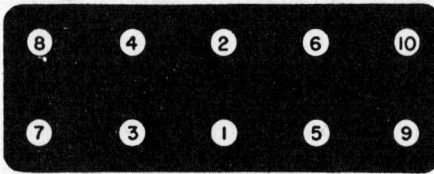

Fig. 2 Cylinder head tightening. 1953-58 Chrysler and Imperial and 1953-57 De Soto

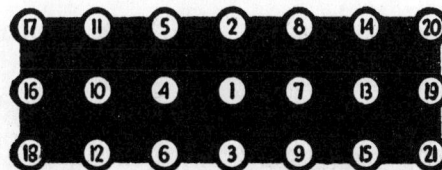

Fig. 3 Cylinder head tightening. Six-cyl.

12. Remove intake manifold, ignition coil and carburetor as an assembly.
13. Disconnect exhaust pipes at manifold flanges.
14. Remove rocker arm assemblies.
15. Remove push rods, keeping them in proper order so each will be reinstalled in its original location.
16. Lift off cylinder head.
17. Reverse foregoing procedure to install head or heads and tighten in the sequence shown in Fig. 2.

Chrysler & De Soto Six

1. Drain cooling system.
2. Remove fuel line from carburetor.
3. Remove carburetor air cleaner.
4. Remove carburetor.
5. Remove upper radiator hose, spark plugs, engine heat indicator unit and cylinder or capscrews.
6. Lift cylinder head from block, using lifting hooks in two of the spark plug holes. Do not use a screwdriver, chisel or other sharp instrument to drive between the head and block to loosen the head as damage may result.

Installation Notes—Before the cylinder head is installed, make certain that all dirt and carbon is removed from both the head and block.

If possible, use a torque wrench when tightening cylinder head nuts or capscrews. Uneven or excessive tightening may distort cylinder bores, causing compression loss and excessive oil consumption.

Tighten cylinder heads in the order shown in Fig. 3, tightening a little at a time in the proper sequence about three times around before final tightening to the torque values given in the *Tune Up Chart*. After the engine has warmed up to operating temperature, recheck the nuts and adjust torque as required.

VALVES, ADJUST
Chrysler & De Soto Six

Valve tappets should be adjusted with

Fig. 4 Rocker arm assembly. 1959-61 Chrysler and Imperial and 1958-61 De Soto

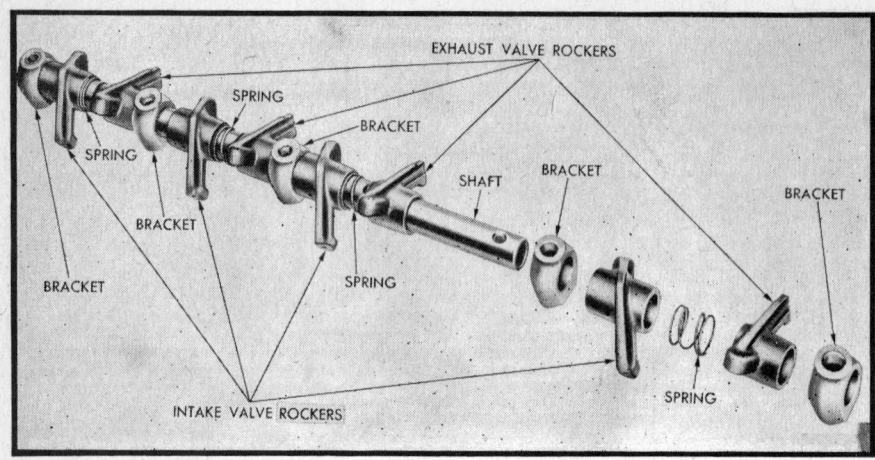

Fig. 5 Rocker arm assembly. 1953-58 Chrysler and 1953-57 De Soto single rocker shaft engines

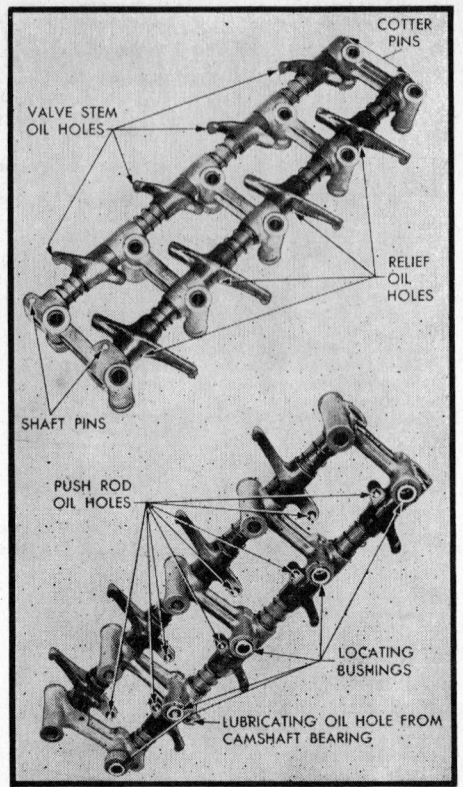

Fig. 6 Top and bottom view of 1953-58 double rocker shaft assembly

engine running and at normal operating temperature. It is important that the clearances given in *Valve Chart* be maintained to insure satisfactory engine performance. If the car is driven at continuous high speeds, and additional .002" clearance for exhaust tappets is desirable.

If the car being serviced is one wherein the valves are not accessible when the hood is raised, proceed as follows:

1. Raise right front end of car and support it with a stand.
2. Remove right front wheel and splash shield access cover if one is provided.
3. Remove valve chamber covers.
4. With engine idling and warmed up to operating temperature, adjust the intake valves and then follow through by adjusting all exhaust valves.

VALVE ARRANGEMENT

Front to Rear

1953-58 Chrysler V8	I-E-I-E-I-E-I-E
1959-61 Chrysler	E-I-I-E-E-I-I-E
1953-58 Imperial	I-E-I-E-I-E-I-E
1959-61 Imperial	E-I-I-E-E-I-I-E
1953-57 De Soto V8	I-E-I-E-I-E-I-E
1958-61 De Soto V8	E-I-I-E-E-I-I-E
6-Cylinder Engines	E-I-I-E-E-I-I-E-E-I-I-E

ROCKER ARMS

Chrysler & Imperial 1959-61 & De Soto 1958-61

Disassemble the rocker assemblies by removing the bolts from the support brackets. Then slide brackets, rocker

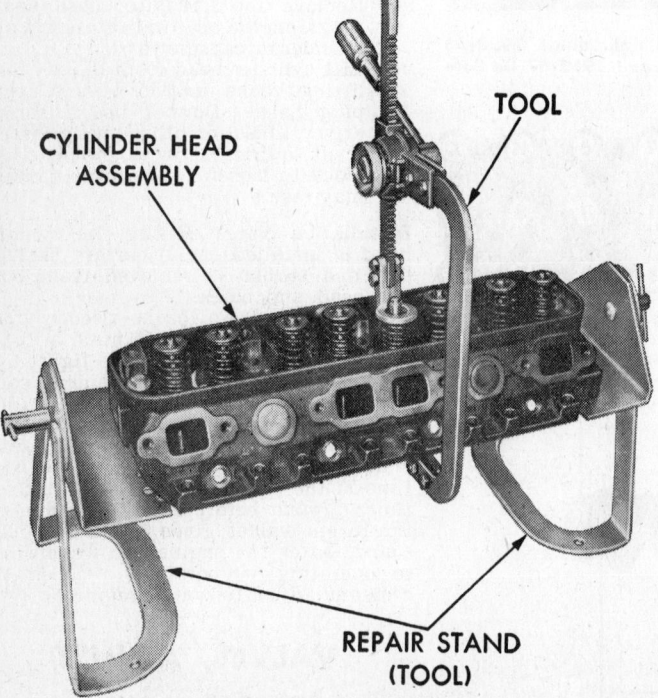

Fig. 7 Compressing valve spring to remove and install valve locks

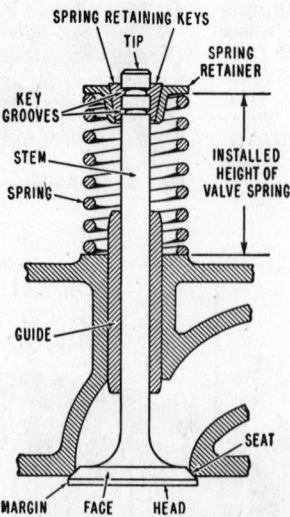

Fig. 7A Checking installed height of valve springs. Double rocker shaft engines

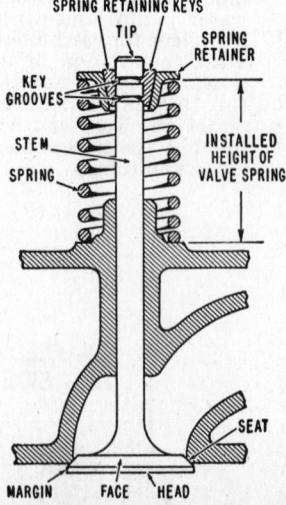

Fig. 8 Checking valve spring installed height. Single rocker shaft engines

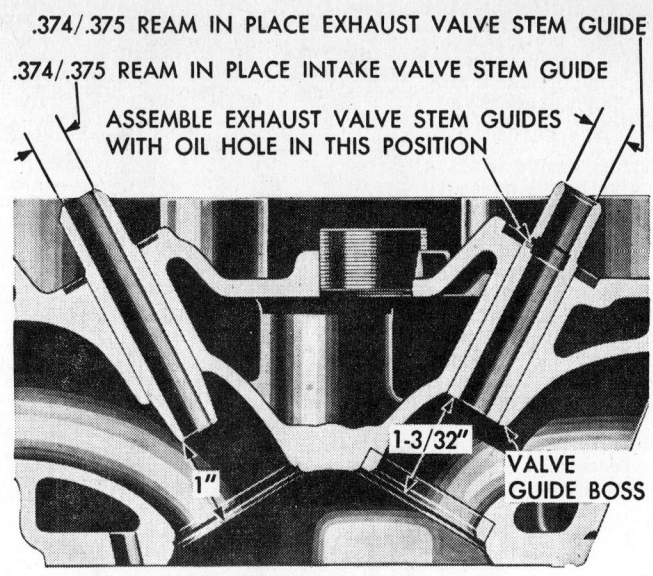

.374/.375 REAM IN PLACE EXHAUST VALVE STEM GUIDE

.374/.375 REAM IN PLACE INTAKE VALVE STEM GUIDE

ASSEMBLE EXHAUST VALVE STEM GUIDES WITH OIL HOLE IN THIS POSITION

1"

1-3/32"

VALVE GUIDE BOSS

Fig. 9 Valve guide details. De Soto engines with double rocker shafts

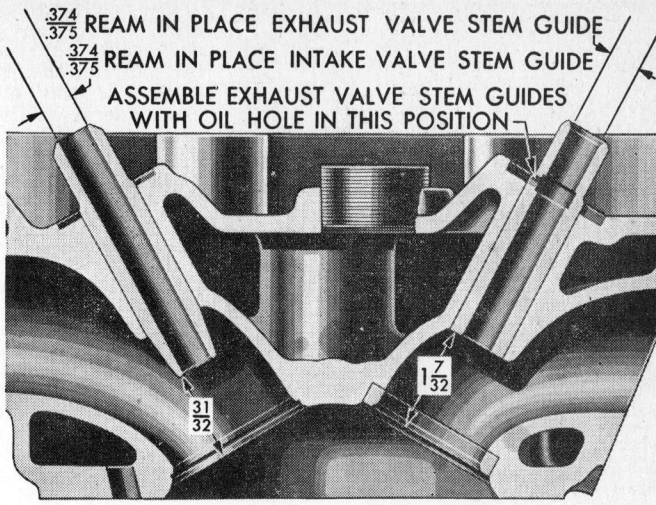

$\frac{.374}{.375}$ REAM IN PLACE EXHAUST VALVE STEM GUIDE

$\frac{.374}{.375}$ REAM IN PLACE INTAKE VALVE STEM GUIDE

ASSEMBLE EXHAUST VALVE STEM GUIDES WITH OIL HOLE IN THIS POSITION

$\frac{31}{32}$

$1\frac{7}{32}$

Fig. 10 Valve guide details. 1953-55 Chrysler and Imperial double rocker shaft engines. For 1956-58 exhaust guide measurement is 1 3/64"

arms and spacers from the shaft, Fig. 4.

Clean all parts except the oilite spacers in a suitable solvent. Keep oilite spacers soaked in engine oil until reassembled. Inspect all parts for excessive wear. Test shaft end plugs for any evidence of leaks.

When assembling, the stamped arrow near the end of the rocker shafts must be on top and pointing toward the center of the engine. The second and fourth (wide) support brackets must be placed on the shaft with the oil passages facing the center of the engine.

Assemble rocker arms in pairs between brackets with an oilite spacer between the arms. The push rod ends of all rocker arms must face in the same direction as the arrow on the shaft. Install bolts through the brackets to hold assembly together.

Chrysler & Imperial 1953-58 & De Soto 1953-57

Sludge and gum formation in the rocker arms and shafts, Figs. 5 and 6, will restrict the normal flow to the rocker arms and valves. Each time the assemblies are removed, they should be disassembled and thoroughly cleaned.

Clean all gum and sludge formation from the inside and outside of the shafts and rocker arms. Inspect the shafts for wear. Check the fit of the rocker arms on the shafts and the valve end of the rocker arms for excessive wear. If the rocker arm radius is grooved on the valve end, do not attempt grinding; replace the part.

When the assemblies are installed, make sure the rocker arms are correctly positioned to actuate the valves.

Check each push rod for a bent or damaged condition. If bent more than .020", when checked with an indicator, replace the push rod. Do not attempt to straighten a bent rod. If a dial gauge is not available, at least check the rod for straightness by rolling it on a perfectly flat surface plate.

VALVES, REMOVE

V8 Engines

With cylinder head removed as outlined previously, use a suitable valve spring compressor to compress the spring in order to take out the valve locks, Fig. 7. Then remove spring retainers, valve stem cup seal or seals and valve springs. Remove burrs from valve stem lock grooves to prevent damage to valve guides and slide valves from heads.

Place the valves in a board with numbered holes to identify their location so that, if re-used, they can be returned to the original guide holes.

Six Cylinder Engines

After taking off the cylinder head as outlined previously, take off the valve chamber covers and use cloth to block off the holes in the valve chamber to prevent the valve locks from falling into the crankcase.

With a suitable valve spring compressor, raise the springs on those valves which are closed and remove the valve locks. Then turn the crankshaft until those valves which are open are closed and remove the remaining valve locks.

Remove all valves and place them in a board with numbered holes so that they can be identified as to the valve port from which they were removed.

VALVE SPRING INSTALLED HEIGHT

When valves and seats are reground the position of the valve in the head is changed so as to lessen the valve spring tension. Without proper valve spring tension the valve does not seat long enough or it may not seat completely. Since the valve is cooled by transferring heat from the valve head to the seat and thence to the coolant, improper valve spring tension will cause worn, pitted and distorted valves which result in loss of compression and power as well as poor gasoline mileage.

When valves, springs, retainers and locks are installed, measure the assembled height of the valve springs from the surface of the cylinder head spring pad to the underside of the spring retainer as shown in Figs. 7A and 8. If the assembled height is greater than the dimension given in the *Valve Specifications Chart*, install a spacer or shim of proper thickness between cylinder head spring pad and spring to bring the assembled height to specifications.

Do not install spacers unless necessary. Excessive use of spacers will result in overstressing valve springs and overloading camshaft lobes which could lead to spring breakage and worn camshaft lobes.

VALVE SPRING TESTING

After taking out the valves, remove the springs and wash them with gasoline or other suitable solvent. Examine the springs for damage or corrosion due to acid etching, which will develop into surface cracks and cause spring failure.

Check the valve spring tension on a spring testing fixture if one is available, Fig. 8A. If a fixture is not available, at least check the free length of each spring by standing it alongside a new spring. Any spring that does not conform to the pressure specifications given in the *Valve Data* chart within 10 per cent should be replaced. Likewise, any spring that stands shorter than the new spring used for comparison should be discarded.

VALVE GUIDES

Double Rocker Shaft Engines

If necessary, remove the old guides by driving them out through the top of the

Fig. 8A Fixture and torque wrench for checking valve spring pressure

cylinder head. Drive the new guides in place up through the valve port opening to the position shown in Figs. 9 and 10.

Single Rocker Shaft Engines

Valve guides in these engines are an integral part of the head and, therefore, cannot be removed. For service, guide holes can be reamed oversize to accommodate one of three service valves with oversize stems (.005″, .015″ and .030″).

After cleaning the valve guide holes, check the clearance as follows:

Install a suitable sleeve over the valve stem to keep the valve at working height for easy checking with a dial indicator, Fig. 11. Attach the dial indicator to the head and set it at right angle to edge of valve being checked. Move the valve to and from indicator. The total indicator movement should not exceed .010″ on intake valves, or .014″ on exhaust valves. If readings exceed the above tolerances, ream the guide holes and install valves with oversize stems. Always use a .005″ reamer first and, if necessary, a .015″ then a .030″ reamer so the valve guides may be reamed true in relation to the valve seat.

Six Cylinder Engines

Clean the valve guides with a wire guide brush and check the clearance between valve stems and guides carefully. The standard clearances are given in the *Valve Data* chart.

Excessive clearance between valve stems and guides will cause improper seating and burned valves. When there is too much clearance between intake valve stems and guides, there is a tendency to draw oil vapor through the guide on the suction stroke, causing excessive oil consumption, fouled spark plugs and poor low speed performance.

To check valve stem-to-guide clearance, take a new valve and place it in each valve guide and feel the clearance by moving the valve stem back and forth. If this check shows excessive clearance, it will be necessary to replace the valve guide.

If the clearance is not excessive when checking with a new valve but is excessive when checked with the old valve, the old valve stem is worn and a new valve must be installed.

If it is necessary to replace valve guides, the tools shown in Figs. 12 and 13 should be used. If they are not available, the old guides can be driven down and out of the valve chamber; or they can be pulled out by using a suitable piece of pipe together with a long bolt and suitable washers.

After the new guides have been installed, they should be reamed, Fig. 14, to provide the clearances given in the *Valve Data* chart.

VALVES, GRIND

Clean the valves with a wire wheel brush, making sure that all carbon is removed from the top and bottom of the heads as well as the gum which might have accumulated on the stems.

If refacing valves, take off only the minimum of metal required to clean up the valve faces. If the outer edge of the valve becomes too thin or sharp due to excessive grinding, the valve must be replaced. In other words, the valve head margin must be at least $\frac{3}{64}$″, otherwise the valve must be replaced. This margin is the area above the contact surface of the valve face, Fig. 15.

Inspect the valve seats in the block for cracks, burns, pitting, ridges or improper angle. During any general engine overhaul it is advisable to reface the valve seats regardless of their condition. If new valve guides are required, they must be installed and reamed before refacing the seats if the equipment used for refacing the seats has a valve guide pilot.

The valve seat width after refacing should be a liberal $\frac{1}{16}$″ for intake seats but not more than $\frac{3}{32}$″ in any case. The width of exhaust seats should be $\frac{3}{64}$″ to a liberal $\frac{1}{16}$″.

Test valves for concentricity with seats and for tight seating. Valves can be tested by lightly coating the valve face with prussian blue and turning the valve against its seat. This indicates whether the seat is concentric with the valve guide *but does not prove that the valve face is concentric with the valve stem, or that the valve is seating all around.*

After making this test, wash all blue from the surfaces, lightly coat the *valve seat* with blue and repeat the tests to see whether a full mark is obtained on the valve. *Both tests are necessary to prove that a proper seat is being obtained.*

V8 Service Note

When valves and seats are reground the position of the valve in the head is changed so as to shorten the operating length of the hydraulic lifter. This means that the plunger is operating closer to its bottom position, and less clearance is available for the thermal expansion of

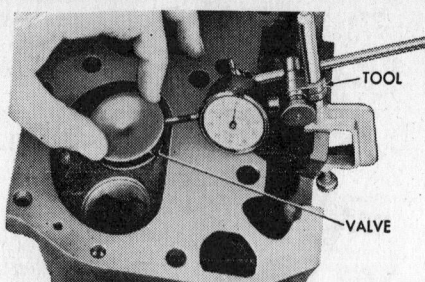

Fig. 11 Checking valve guide clearance

Fig. 12 Valve guide removing tool. 6-cyl.

Fig. 13 Valve guide installing tool. 6 cyl.

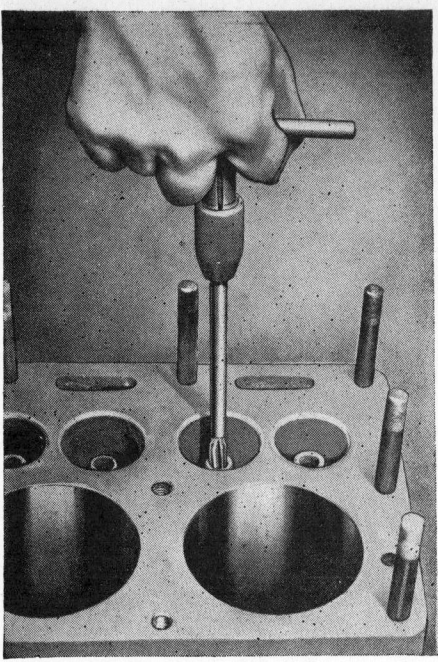

Fig. 14   Reaming valve guides. 6 cyl.

the valve mechanism during high speed driving. Design of plunger travel includes a safety factor for normal wear and refacing of valves and seats. However, if face and seat grinding is carried to the point where the valve position is changed $\frac{1}{32}$" or more from its factory installed position, the dimension from the valve spring seat in the head to the valve tip should be checked with a special gauge, Fig. 16.

There is one gauge (C-3061) for double rocker arm engines; C-3436 for single rocker arm engines prior to 1959 on Chrysler and Imperial (prior to 1958 on De Soto) and C-3648 for 1958-61 De Soto and 1959-61 on Chrysler and Imperial. These simple gauges make it possible to quickly and easily check the length of the valve stem as illustrated. The overall dimension of the gauge indicates the maximum length of the valve stem while the bottom of the slot indicates the minimum length. The valve stem must be within these limits to allow the valve to fully close and to assure the designed hydraulic action of the valve lifter linkage.

VALVE LIFTERS

Six Cylinder Engines

Since these lifters are of the mushroom type operating in guide holes bored in the cylinder block, it is necessary to remove the camshaft in order to remove the lifters.

Follow instructions for removing the camshaft. Then remove the oil pan and take the lifters out through the bottom of the engine.

Lifters are furnished in oversizes of .001, .008, .030 and .060". When reaming the lifter guides for oversize lifters, the cylinder head and valves will have to be removed so that the reamer pilot can

be inserted through the valve stem guide hole.

HYDRAULIC LIFTERS

V8 Engines

Figs. 17, 18 and 19 illustrate the types of hydraulic valve lifters used. See the *Trouble Shooting Chapter* under the heading *Engine Noises* for causes of hydraulic valve lifter noise.

The easiest method for locating a noisy valve lifter is by the use of a piece of garden hose about 4 feet long. Place one end of the hose near each valve in progression and listen through the other end. In this manner the sound is localized, making it easier to determine which lifter is at fault.

Another method is to place a finger on the valve spring retainer. If the lifter is not functioning properly, a distinct shock will be felt when the valve returns to its seat.

In most cases where noise exists in one or more lifters, all lifter units should be removed and cleaned. If dirt, varnish or carbon is found to exist in one unit, it more than likely exists in all the units.

Hydraulic Plunger, Replace

1952 and early 1953—The hydraulic plunger of the type lifter shown in Fig. 17 may be removed or installed through the push rod holes in the cylinder head.

To remove the plunger from the body of the lifter shown in Fig. 17, install a suitable valve spring compressing tool over the rocker arm as shown in Fig. 20 so the heel of the tool rests on the valve stem side. Make certain the valve is seated and that the lifter body is resting on the low point of the camshaft lobe. Using the handle of the tool for leverage, compress the valve springs sufficiently to raise the rocker arm above the push rod. While holding the rocker arm in this position, slide the rocker arm to one side along the tube. *To avoid damaging the valves, be sure that the piston head is well below the top of its travel before compressing the valve spring.*

Insert Chrysler Tool No. C-3164 over the push rod and engage the lifter plunger. Withdraw the push rod and plunger, being careful not to pull the

Fig. 16   Valve stem length gauge for checking length of valve stem after grinding valves

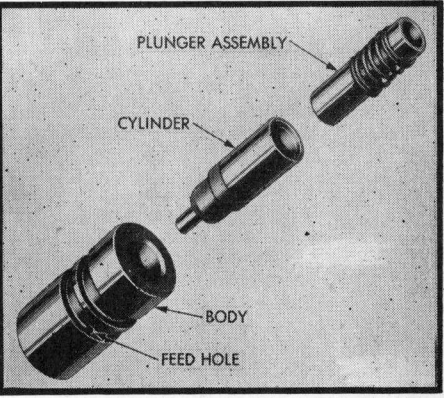

Fig. 17   Hydraulic valve lifter. 1952 and early 1953 V8

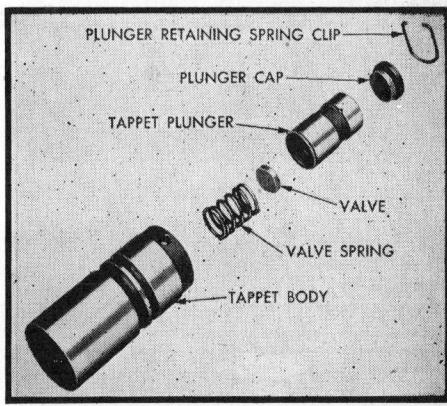

Fig. 18   Hydraulic valve lifter. 1953 (late) and 1954-55 V8

lifter body from the bore. After the tool has engaged the plunger, slightly raise the tool and shake gently. As the body drops, it can be felt leaving the plunger. Then withdraw the tool and plunger, Fig. 21.

To install a cleaned or new plunger assembly, use the tool shown in Fig. 21 to insert the push rod and plunger down through the push rod hole and into the lifter body. Make certain that the push rod is properly positioned in the plunger cap. Position the rocker arm so it is partially seated on the valve stem. Compress the valve stem and springs until the rocker arm can be slid into position over the push rod. Remove the tool.

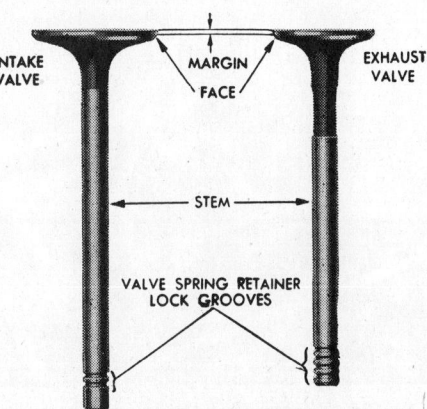

Fig. 15   Valve nomenclature

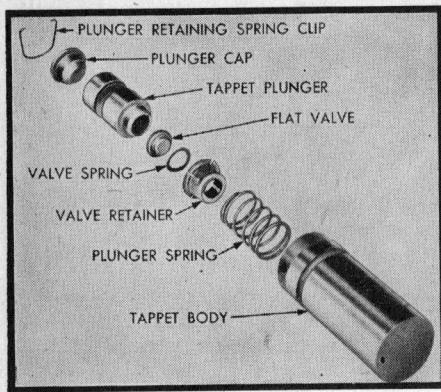

Fig. 19 Hydraulic valve lifter. 1956-61

Unit Type Lifter, Replace

Late 1953 and All 1954-60—To remove a lifter of the type shown in Fig. 18 and 19, as well as the lifter body of the type shown in Fig. 17, remove the intake manifold.

Removing Fig. 17 Type Lifter Body—Special Chrysler Tool C-3035 is available for this operation. To remove the lifter body, insert the tool through the push rod hole in the cylinder head and into the lifter body. Tighten the thumb screw on the handle of the tool and, with a twisting motion similar to that shown in Fig. 22, pull the body out of the bore. After the body has been removed, loosen the thumb screw and remove the tool and lift the body out of the lifter chamber.

When installing a new lifter body, install the plunger assembly at the same time.

Removing Fig. 18 and 19 Lifter—Chrysler Tool C-3158 is available for this operation. To remove the lifter, insert the hooked portion of the tool in the lifter body. (This portion of the tool can be used to remove lifters without a varnish build-up around the bottom of the body.) Lift the lifter out of the bore. If they are stuck, proceed as follows:

Slide the puller portion of the tool through the cylinder head push rod holes and seat it firmly in the top of the lifter. Insert the puller pin through the body and tool shaft in the holes provided, Fig. 22. Grasp the tool handle and pull the lifter out of the bore as shown. As the lifter clears the bore, withdraw the puller pin and remove the tool.

Note—When installing hydraulic lifters in the engine, fill them with light engine oil (10W) to avoid excessive time required to quiet them during initial operation of the engine.

Servicing Hydraulic Lifters

Warning—Hydraulic plungers and bodies are not interchangeable. Therefore, it is advisable to work on one lifter at a time to avoid mixing parts. *Mixed parts will not function.* Moreover, do not mix check valves as they may be slightly worn and will fit only the plungers with which they have been operating.

Testing Lifters—In testing the type lifter shown in Fig. 17, partially fill a clean pan with clean kerosene. Place the plunger and cylinder in the jaws of the special pliers shown in Fig. 23 and insert the tube end of the cylinder into the kerosene. Compress the plunger several times with the pliers before removing from the kerosene to allow the cylinder chamber to load up. Remove the unit from the kerosene and check the leakdown rate by compressing the pliers. If the plunger collapses almost instantly, the unit assembly should be replaced. When installing a new unit, first test it in the same manner.

In testing lifters shown in Fig. 18 and 19, secure a container deep enough to completely immerse the lifter assembly. Fill the container with clean kerosene. Remove the cap from the plunger and submerge the lifter. Allow the cylinder to fill with kerosene. Then remove the lifter and replace the cap.

Holding the lifter upright, insert the lower jaw of the pliers shown in Fig. 24 in the top groove of the lifter body. Engage the upper jaw of the pliers with the top of the plunger cap as shown. Check the leakdown by compressing the pliers. If the plunger collapses almost instantly, disassemble the unit, clean it again and retest. If the lifter still does not function satisfactorily, install a new unit, being sure to test the new one before installing it in the engine.

CHAIN CASE COVER

1953-54 V8

To remove the cover, proceed as follows:
1. Drain cooling system.
2. Remove all water hose.
3. Remove generator bracket.
4. On cars equipped with torque converter, remove oil cooler and tubes.
5. Remove water pump.
6. Use a suitable puller to remove vibration damper and pulley.
7. Remove felt dust seal.
8. Remove vibration damper hub key from crankshaft slot.
9. Remove left bank exhaust pipe.
10. Remove fuel pump.
11. Remove oil level dipstick.

Fig. 20 Compressing valve spring to remove push rod. 1952 and early 1953 V8

Fig. 21 Removing hydraulic plunger from lifter body. 1952 and early 1953 V8

12. Remove starting motor.
13. Drain engine oil and remove pan.
14. Remove chain case cover bolts and lockwashers.
15. Remove the bolt inside the water pump opening.
16. Drive the chain case cover off the two dowels, using a soft hammer.

1955

1. Remove radiator, fan, fan shroud and water pump housing.
2. Remove pulley and damper from hub and, with a puller, remove hub.
3. Loosen oil pan bolts and drop pan slightly to clear chain case cover.
4. Remove fuel pump.
5. Unfasten and remove chain case cover.

1956-58 Chrysler & Imperial & 1956-57 De Soto

1. Remove radiator and water pump.
2. Use a puller to remove vibration damper.
3. Remove chain cover and gasket.

1959-61 Chrysler & Imperial & 1958-61 De Soto

1. Drain cooling system.
2. Remove radiator, fan and belt.
3. Remove water pump and housing as an assembly.
4. Remove crankshaft bolt and two pulley bolts and use a puller to remove vibration damper.
5. Remove chain case cover and gasket, using extreme caution to avoid damaging oil pan gasket.
6. Remove key from crankshaft.

Six Cylinder Engines

When installing the chain case cover on these engines, place a new gasket in the cover, then drive the oil seal in position, using a drift or a flat piece of metal slightly larger than the seal to assure a tight, even contact between the seal and its seat.

When fastening the cover, care must be used to center the seal on the crankshaft before tightening the cover screws. A special centering tool, Fig. 25, is available to make the installation. When using this tool, tighten the screws only enough to hold the cover in place. Then insert the tool, holding it by the crankshaft starting jaw, tightening the jaw nut only finger tight. As the cover screws are being tightened and the gasket is being compressed, tighten the jaw nut, maintaining a slight tension between the centering tool and the seal. Then remove the tool, install the starting jaw and tighten it to a minimum of 108 lbs. ft.·torque.

TIMING CHAIN
1953-55 V8

After removing the chain case cover as outlined previously, remove the camshaft sprocket hub nut, fuel pump eccentric and dowel assembly. The camshaft sprocket and timing chain may now be taken off.

To install, rotate the crankshaft until the zero mark on the crankshaft sprocket is exactly in line with the center of the camshaft. Temporarily install the camshaft sprocket (less chain) and line up the hub dowel pin hole with the sprocket dowel pin hole, while at the same time positioning the camshaft sprocket zero mark exactly in line with the center of the crankshaft. A straight edge should be used to check the accuracy of this alignment, Fig. 26.

Remove the camshaft sprocket again and position it in the timing chain. Then place the chain on the crankshaft sprocket. Install the camshaft sprocket, being sure both zero timing marks are facing each other and in line with the center of both the camshaft and crankshaft.

1956-61

To install chain and sprockets, lay both the camshaft and crankshaft sprockets on the bench. Position the sprockets so that the timing marks are next to each other. Place the chain on both sprockets, then push the gears apart as far as the chain will permit. Use a straightedge to

form a line through the exact centers of both gears. The timing marks must be on this line, Fig. 26.

Slide the chain with both sprockets on the camshaft and crankshaft at the same time; then recheck the alignment.

Install the fuel pump eccentric on the camshaft and install cup washer and bolt. Tighten bolt to a torque of 35 lb. ft.

Six Cylinder Engines

For correct valve timing, the timing chain and sprockets should be assembled so that the marks on the sprockets line up as shown in Fig. 27. Follow the general procedure outlined for V8 engines.

VALVE TIMING DATA
Chrysler & Imperial

Year	Model	Intake Opens①	Intake Closes②	Exhaust Opens③	Exhaust Closes④
1953	Six	12	44	50	6
	V8	15	57	49	15
1954	Six	12	44	50	6
	V8	15	57	49	15
1955	C300	35	65	65	25
	Others	15	57	49	15
1956	300B	35	65	65	25
	C71	5	67	39	25
	Others	15	57	49	15
1957	300C⑤	35	65	65	25
	C76	15	57	57	15
	Others	13	59	59	17
1958	300D⑤	35	65	65	25
	LC3	15	57	57	15
	Others	13	59	59	17
1959	300E	20	60	58	22
	Others	15	57	57	15
1960-61	300	20	68	60	28
	Others	15	57	57	15

De Soto

Year	Model	Intake Opens①	Intake Closes②	Exhaust Opens③	Exhaust Closes④
1953	Six	12	44	50	6
	V8	12	52	50	14
1954	Six	12	44	50	6
	V8	12	52	50	14
1955	S21	12	52	50	14
	S22	4	76	54	10
1956	S23	4	76	54	10
	S24	15	57	49	15
	⑥	35	65	65	25
1957	S25, S26	15	57	57	15
	S27	10	58	56	16
1958	⑥	20	60	58	22
	Others	15	57	57	15
1959	⑥	20	60	58	22
	Others	15	57	57	15
1960-61	All	15	57	57	15

①—Degrees before top dead center.
②—Degrees after bottom dead center.
③—Degrees before bottom dead center.
④—Degrees after top dead center.
⑤—Special camshaft 48°, 72°, 73°, 47°.
⑥—Adventurer.

CAMSHAFT, REPLACE
1953-55 V8

To remove the camshaft, remove the valve lifter cover, then proceed as follows:

1. Remove cylinder head covers and push rods.
2. Remove valve lifters, arranging them in a board with numbered holes so they may be reinstalled in their original bores.
3. Remove ignition distributor.
4. Remove chain case cover, chain and camshaft sprocket.
5. Remove camshaft thrust plate screws.
6. Remove distributor and oil pump drive gear (tool C-3021 is available for this operation).

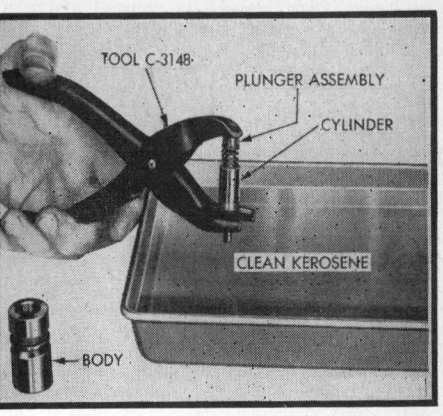

Fig. 23 Testing hydraulic lifter of the type shown in Fig. 17

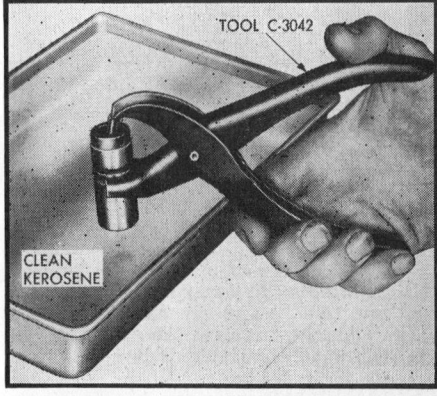

Fig. 24 Testing hydraulic lifter of the type shown in Fig. 18 and 19

Fig. 25 Showing special centering tool for chain cover oil seal. 6 cyl.

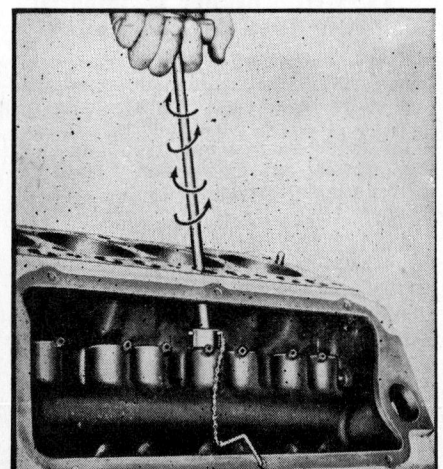

Fig. 22 Removing hydraulic valve lifter of the type shown in Fig. 18 and 19. Body of lifter shown in Fig. 17 is also removed in this manner

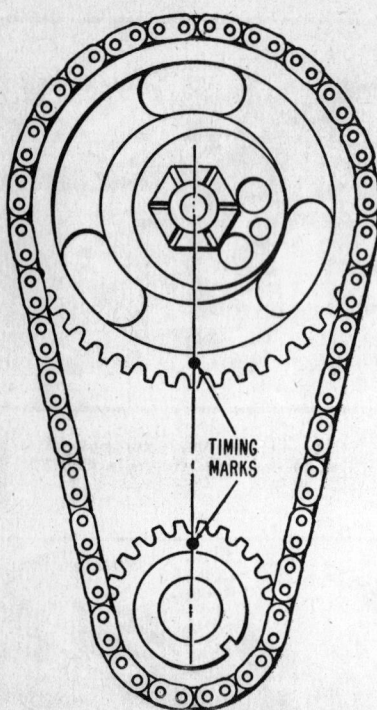

Fig. 26 Timing marks aligned for correct valve timing. V8 engines

7. Pull out the camshaft, using care not to damage the camshaft bearings with the cam lobes.
8. Remove camshaft hub and thrust plate.
9. If camshaft bearings are to be replaced at this time, it is recommended that the engine be removed and the crankshaft taken out in order that any chips or foreign material may be removed from the oil passages.

1956-58 Chrysler & Imperial & 1956-57 De Soto

To remove the camshaft, remove intake manifold, valve chamber cover, push rods, valve lifters, timing chain and sprockets. Lift out distributor drive gear and shaft. Remove camshaft thrust plate attaching bolts and oil trough. Withdraw camshaft and spacer, being careful not to damage the camshaft bearings with the cam lobes.

1959-61 Chrysler & Imperial & 1958-61 De Soto

1. To remove camshaft, remove valve lifters, timing chain and sprockets.
2. Remove distributor and oil pump drive gear.
3. Remove fuel pump to allow push rod to drop away from cam eccentric.
4. Remove camshaft, being careful not to damage camshaft bearings.

Six Cylinder Engines

The general procedure for removing the camshaft is outlined below. In addition, on some earlier models it may be necessary to take off the front end sheet metal in order to provide space to extract the camshaft from the engine. This can be determined by measuring the length of the engine and comparing it with the space available between the chain case and front grille.
1. Remove radiator, cylinder head, fuel pump, oil pump and valve cover plates.
2. Support front of engine and remove front support, chain case cover, chain and camshaft sprocket.
3. Raise valves and hold them up by inserting two wooden wedges under each valve head, Fig. 28. (This operation is not necessary if valves are to be ground as the valves will have to be removed anyway.)
4. Raise valve lifters and hold them up with wire, spring type clothes pins, Fig. 28, or other suitable means.
5. Rotate the camshaft as it is being withdrawn from the engine so that the cam lobes will clear successive obstacles.

PISTONS & RODS, REMOVE

After removing the cylinder heads and oil pan, examine the cylinder bores above the ring travel area. If the bores are worn so that a shoulder or ridge exists at this point, remove the ridge with a ridge reamer to avoid damaging rings or cracking ring lands of pistons during removal.

Remove the connecting rod caps and push the pistons and rods out of the cylinders, using care to prevent rod bolts from nicking crankshaft journals. Make sure rods and pistons are properly numbered so they can be reinstalled in their proper cylinders. It is advisable to install the caps on the rods as they are removed to avoid mixing parts.

PISTONS & RODS, ASSEMBLE

V8 Engines

When installing piston and rod assemblies in the cylinders, the compression ring gaps should be diametrically opposite one another and not in line with the oil ring gap. The oil ring expander gap should be toward the outside of the "V" of the engine. The oil ring gap should be turned toward the inside of the engine "V".

Immerse the piston head and rings in clean engine oil and, with a suitable piston ring compressor, insert the piston and rod assembly into the bore. Tap the piston down into the bore, using the handle of a hammer.

Assemble the pistons to the rods as shown in Fig. 29.

Six Cylinder Engines

When assembling the piston to the connecting rod, assemble aluminum pistons so that the slotted side is opposite the oil hole in the connecting rod.

Install the piston and rod assembly in the cylinder so that the oil hole in the connecting rod is toward the valve side of the engine.

Fig. 27 Marks on sprockets (1 and 2) should line up as shown for correct valve timing. 6 cyl.

PISTONS

Due to the necessity of maintaining piston balance, all pistons are machined to the same weight in grams, regardless of oversize. Only finished pistons are available in service and are supplied in standard and the following oversizes: .010, .020, .030, .040, .050, .060 inch.

Starting with the No. 1 cylinder, coat the bore very lightly with a light engine oil (10W). Insert the piston in the bore upside down with the feeler stock between the thrust face of the piston and cylinder wall.

While holding the piston, draw the feeler stock out straight with a spring scale attached to it. The amount of pull to withdraw the feeler stock should be as given in the charts. Fit the remaining pistons in like manner.

PISTON PINS

1959-61 Chrysler & Imperial & 1958-61 De Soto

With pistons and pins at room temperature (70°F.) the pin should be a sliding fit in the piston. The pin should be pressed into the connecting rod. Replacement is necessary if any free play exists between the pin and piston. Piston pins are available through Chrysler only with new pistons.

1953-58 Chrysler & Imperial & 1953-57 De Soto

Piston pins are supplied in standard size and oversizes of .003" and .008". The fit of the pin in both the connecting rod and piston should be a tight thumb press fit with the parts at normal room temperature.

When using an expansion reamer to fit piston pins, start off by taking a very light cut. Try the fit. Then ream and try the fit again until the pin can be pushed into the rod and piston as described above.

Six Cylinder Engines

Piston pins are available in oversizes of .003 and .008". Fit the piston pin in both the piston and rod with a thumb press fit with parts at normal room temperature (about 70°). Do not drive the pin in place, as to do so will cause distortion of the piston skirt.

PISTON RINGS

When new rings are to be installed without reboring cylinders, the glazed cylinder wall should be slightly dulled, but without increasing the bore diameter. This is done with a "Glazebuster" or with a hone equipped with the finest grade of stones.

New piston rings must be checked for clearance in piston grooves and for gap in cylinder bores. The latter operation must be measured with the ring about two inches from the bottom of the cylinder bore to which it is fitted. An inverted piston can be used to push the rings down to this position. Cylinder bores and piston grooves must be clean, dry and free from carbon and burrs.

Check the clearance of each ring in its piston groove by installing the ring and then inserting feeler gauges *under* the ring. Any wear that occurs in the piston groove forms a step or ridge at the inner portion of the lower land. If the feeler gauge is inserted above the ring, the ring may rest on the step instead of on the worn portion of the lower land, and a false measurement of clearance may result.

If the piston grooves have worn to the extent that relatively high steps or ridges exist on the lower lands, the piston should be replaced because the steps will interfere with the operation of the new rings and ring clearances will be excessive. Piston rings are not furnished in oversize widths to compensate for ring groove wear.

ROD BEARINGS

Connecting rod bearings can be replaced without removing the piston and rod assemblies merely by taking off the rod cap and replacing the upper and lower bearing halves.

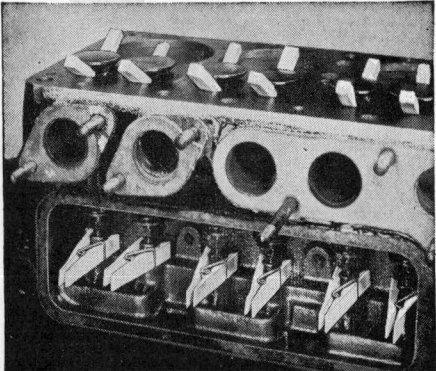

Fig. 28 Method of holding up valves and tappets for camshaft removal. 6 cyl.

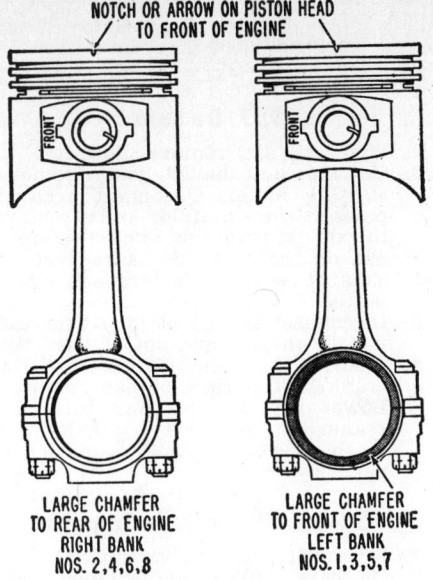

NOTCH OR ARROW ON PISTON HEAD TO FRONT OF ENGINE

LARGE CHAMFER TO REAR OF ENGINE RIGHT BANK NOS. 2,4,6,8

LARGE CHAMFER TO FRONT OF ENGINE LEFT BANK NOS. 1,3,5,7

Fig. 29 Piston and rod assembly. V8 engines

The clearance between the bearings and crankshaft can be measured with Plastigage as follows:

1. Remove bearing cap and wipe oil from crankshaft journal and bearing.
2. With crankpin at approximately bottom dead center, place a piece of Plastigage in the center of the bearing, Fig. 30.
3. Reinstall the bearing cap and tighten the bolts to the torque value given in the *Engine Torque Data* table.
4. Remove the bearing cap again and check the bearing clearance by measuring the width of the flattened Plastigage, Fig. 30. The measuring strip is supplied in the same envelope which contains the Plastigage.

MAIN BEARINGS

Caution—Main bearing clearance can be checked with Plastigage in the same manner described for rod bearings. If bearings are measured with the engine in the chassis, the crankshaft must be supported in order to take up clearance between the upper bearing insert and crankshaft journal. This can be done by tightening bearing caps of adjacent bearings with .005" to .015" cardboard, (such as a calling card) between lower bearing shell and journal. Use extreme care when this is done to avoid unnecessary strain on the crankshaft or bearings or a false reading may be obtained. Do not rotate crankshaft while Plastigage is installed. *Be sure to remove cardboard.* To install new bearings, proceed as follows:

1. Remove bearing cap and worn lower shell.
2. Rotate crankshaft in normal direction to turn upper bearing shell out of crankcase. Use a cotter pin with a flattened head or the special tool made for the purpose in the crankshaft oil hole to contact the bearing

and force it out, Fig. 31.
3. Place a new upper shell on the crankshaft journal with the locating notch in the correct position and rotate the shaft to turn the bearing in place.
4. Install the lower bearing shell in the cap.
5. Tighten all cap nuts to the torque value given in the *Engine Torque Data* table.

CRANKSHAFT OIL SEAL

V8 Engines

A braided oil seal is pressed into the upper and lower grooves behind the rear main bearing. Directly in front of this seal is an oil slinger which deflects the oil back into the oil pan. Should the braided seal require replacement, the installation of the lower half is accomplished as follows:

With the bearing cap and lower bearing half removed, install a new seal so that both ends protrude above the cap. Tap the seal down into position or roll it snugly in its groove with a smooth rounded tool. Then cut off the protruding ends of the seal with a sharp knife or razor blade.

Installing Upper Seal

Although the usual practice is to remove the crankshaft when the upper half of the seal is to be replaced it is possible to do the job without removing the crankshaft as follows:

To remove the seal, use needle-nose pliers to grasp the end of the seal which is most accessible. Pull the seal downward while rotating the crankshaft slowly in the direction that the seal is being removed.

To install the new seal, fasten a length of wire or strong string such as fishing line securely to one end of the new seal. See that the point of fastening is not bulky and that it is not over ⅜" from the end of the seal. Coat the seal with Lubriplate. Pass the free end of the wire or string up over the crankshaft at the point where the seal is to be installed. Then exert a firm, steady pull on the wire or string and at the same time rotate the crankshaft slowly in the direction of the pull. This will help to move the seal into position. When the installation is completed, trim the ends of the seal flush with the engine block.

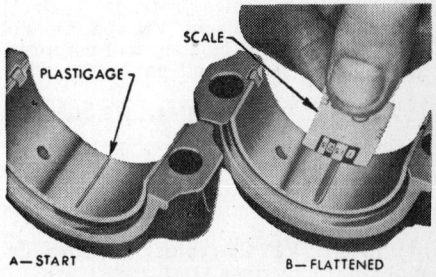

SCALE

PLASTIGAGE

A—START   B—FLATTENED

Fig. 30 Checking bearing clearance by measuring width of flattened Plastigage

Fig. 31 Using special tool (1) in oil hole to turn upper main bearing in place

Six Cylinder Engines

These models are equipped with a one-piece rubber seal for the rear main bearing, which is installed as follows:

1. Remove engine oil pan.
2. Remove lower clutch housing attaching screws.
3. Remove nuts from transmission-to-clutch housing lower studs.
4. Slide clutch pan forward, remove studs and lay pan aside.
5. Loosen all main bearing capscrews three turns.
6. Remove rear main bearing cap.
7. Slide old oil seal out of its slot.
8. Install new seal with its wiping edge forward as follows:
9. Apply soap or cup grease to one end of the seal, being careful not to get any of this lubricant between the ends so the split can close and seal properly when installed.
10. Start one end of the seal in the slot and push it in until end is near top of bearing.
11. Start other end and work into place.
12. Work seal into position so that joint or split comes together near the top.
13. Wipe a little more lubricant around the lip of the seal so that bearing flange will slip into place.

OIL PAN

Six Cylinder Engines

To remove the oil pan, take off the clutch housing lower cover to prevent damaging oil pan gaskets on the housing. Remove oil pan screws and drop pan on tie rod. Lift up on oil strainer to clear baffle inside of pan and lower pan to floor.

When installing the pan, position the end gaskets so they protrude 1/8 to 1/4 inch above the oil pan, Fig. 32. Do not cut off these ends as they will compress into place when the oil pan is installed.

1953-54 V8 Chrysler, De Soto & Imperial

Before the oil pan can be taken down, it will be necessary to remove the starting motor and exhaust crossover pipe.

1955-56 V8 Chrysler, De Soto & Imperial

After disconnecting the steering linkage at the idler arm support bracket, allow the linkage to settle away from the oil pan. Remove necessary exhaust pipes. Then unfasten and remove the oil pan.

1957 De Soto

1. Drain oil and remove dipstick.
2. On single exhaust jobs, remove starting motor, disconnect exhaust pipes at the manifolds and at clamp to exhaust extension and move pipes out of the way. Be sure rest of exhaust system is properly supported.
3. Disconnect tie rod at idler arm and pull downward and out of the way.
4. There will be interference by the crankshaft during oil pan removal. Lower the oil pan and turn the crankshaft until No. 1 crankpin is at the 8 o'clock position and lower pan.

1957-58 Chrysler & Imperial

1. Drain oil and remove dipstick.
2. On cars with single exhaust, disconnect crossover and "Y" pipe at exhaust manifolds and at clamp to exhaust extension so that crossover and "Y" pipe may be moved out of the way. Be sure rest of exhaust system is properly supported.
3. Remove converter dust shield.
4. Remove starting motor.
5. Remove nuts from front engine mounts and raise engine about 3/4 inch.
6. Rotate crankshaft so as to bring the ignition timing mark 180 degrees from the timing pointer.
7. Disconnect steering linkage at idler arm support bracket and allow linkage to settle away from bottom of oil pan.
8. Unfasten and remove pan.

1958 De Soto

1. Remove dipstick and drain oil.
2. Disconnect steering linkage from steering arm and pull linkage down and away from oil pan.
3. On single exhaust jobs, remove exhaust crossover pipe, making sure balance of exhaust system is properly supported.
4. Remove oil pan attaching screws and lower rear of pan, turning it sideways to clear crossmember. *It may be necessary to pull the brake line (running across crossmember) slightly forward to allow enough clearance for pan removal. It is not necessary to remove the brake line. The oil pan drain plug must be removed.*

1959 Chrysler & Imperial

1. Drain oil and remove dipstick.
2. Disconnect steering linkage from steering arm to allow steering linkage to be lowered.
3. On single exhaust jobs, remove exhaust crossover pipe.
4. It may be necessary to pull the brake line slightly forward to allow enough clearance for pan removal. (Do not remove brake line which runs across crossmember.)
5. On Windsor models, unfasten and lower pan.

6. On other models, disconnect throttle linkage at transmission and at carburetor. Rotate crankshaft until centerline of front counterweight is at the 10 o'clock position. Remove front engine mount nuts and raise engine one inch. Then unfasten and remove pan.

1959 De Soto

1. On all models except Firesweep, after the oil pan screws have been removed, but the pan cannot be lowered all the way, it will be necessary to rotate the crankshaft until the front crankshaft throw is at the 4 o'clock position. This will permit the pan to be removed.
2. On Firesweep models, remove the front engine mounting nuts and raise the engine about one inch. The pan may then be lowered. *Whenever it is necessary to raise the engine for any reason, always disconnect the throttle linkage at the transmission as this will prevent damage to the throttle valve lever attached to the front valve body of the automatic transmission.*

1960-61

1. Disconnect battery cable and drain crankcase.
2. Raise car on hoist and disconnect steering linkage from idler arm and pitman arm.
3. Remove number 6 spark plug.
4. Remove outlet vent pipe and disconnect exhaust pipe branches from manifolds.
5. Remove clamp attaching exhaust pipe to extension and remove exhaust pipe.
6. Remove converter dust shield.
7. On New Yorker and Imperial models, unfasten and lower pan.
8. On all other models, remove the front engine mount nuts and raise engine two inches. Remove oil pan bolts and turn flywheel until counterweight and connecting rods at the front end of crankshaft are at their

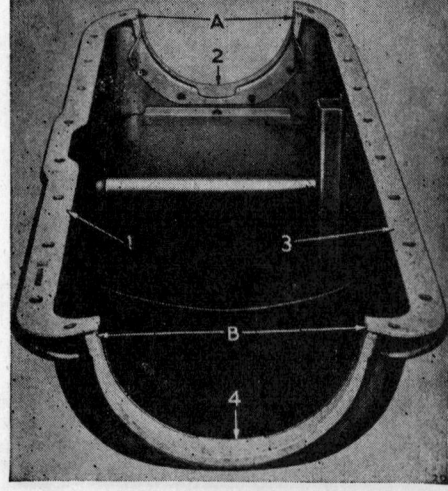

Fig. 32 Six-cylinder oil pan gaskets (1 and 4). A and B show gasket lips

highest position to provide clearance, and lower the pan. Turn the pan counterclockwise to clear oil screen and suction pipe.

OIL PUMP, REPLACE

1953-58 V8 Chrysler & Imperial & 1953-57 V8 De Soto

After removing the oil pan as outlined previously, unfasten the pump mounting bolts and drop the pump straight down and away from the engine. When installing the pump, be sure to align the drive slot in the pump shaft with the distributor drive shaft. Install new seal rings and tighten the bolts with a torque wrench 30 to 35 lbs. ft.

1959-61 Chrysler & Imperial & 1958-61 De Soto

Remove oil pump attaching bolts and remove oil pump and filter assembly from bottom side of engine.

Six Cylinder Engines

Before removing the oil pump, rotate the crankshaft and make sure the DC mark on the vibration damper or crankshaft pulley lines up with the pointer on the chain case cover and the distributor rotor is ready to fire No. 1 spark plug. After the pump is removed, do not bump the starter or let the engine turn as this will change the ignition timing.

Use a new gasket when installing the pump. If the engine crankshaft was accidentally moved while the pump was off, rotate the engine until No. 1 cylinder is in firing position. Then set the distributor rotor in No. 1 firing position and install oil pump, being sure rotor remains in correct position.

OIL PUMP REPAIRS

1959-61 Chrysler & Imperial & 1958-61 De Soto

To disassemble the pump, remove filter base and oil seal ring, Fig. 33. Remove pump rotor and shaft and lift out rotors. Remove oil pressure relief valve plug and lift out spring and plunger.

Wash all parts thoroughly. The mating surface of the oil pump cover should be smooth. Replace cover if it is scratched or grooved. Replace all worn parts and reassemble the pump.

1953-58 V8 Chrysler & Imperial & 1953-57 V8 De Soto

After removing the pump from the engine it should be disassembled, cleaned and inspected for wear or damage, Fig. 34.

1. Remove the cotter pin holding the oil strainer to the oil suction pipe. Then remove the pipe from the pump body.
2. Remove the pump cover and discard the oil seal ring.
3. Remove pump rotor and shaft and lift out rotor body.

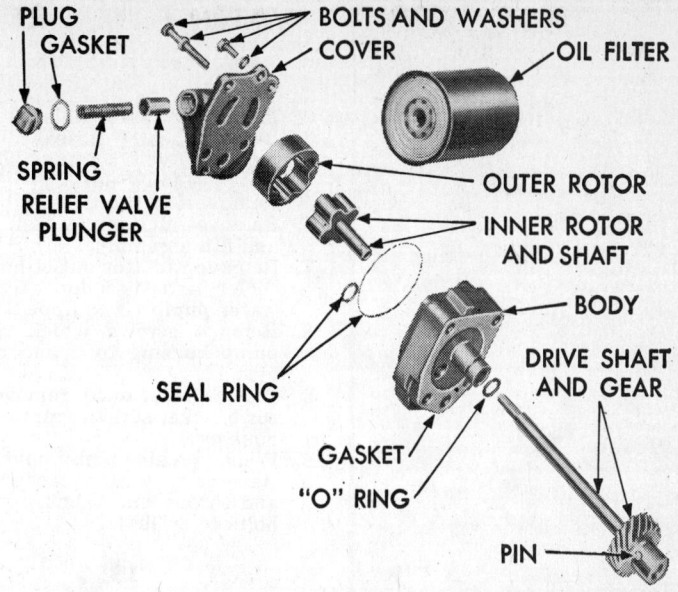

Fig. 33 Oil pump. 1959-61 Chrysler and Imperial and 1958-61 De Soto

4. Remove oil pressure relief valve plug and lift out the spring and plunger.
5. Wash all parts in cleaning solvent and inspect carefully for damage or wear.
6. The mating face of the oil pump cover should be smooth. If it is scratched or grooved, the cover should be replaced with a new one.
7. Check for excessive cover-to-rotor wear by laying a straight edge across the cover surface. If a .0015" feeler gauge can be inserted between cover and straight edge, the cover should be discarded and a new one installed.
8. Measure the diameter and thickness of the rotor body with a micrometer. If the rotor body measures less than .998" and the diameter less than 2.244", install a new rotor body.
9. Measure the thickness of the pump rotor. If it measures less than .998", a new rotor should be installed.
10. Slide rotor body and rotor into pump body and then place a straight edge across the face of the pump body between the bolt holes. If a feeler gauge of more than .004" can be inserted between the rotors and straight edge, install a new pump body.
11. Remove the pump rotor and shaft, leaving rotor body in pump cavity. Press rotor body to one side with the fingers and measure the clearance between rotor and pump bodies. If it is more than .012", install a new pump body.
12. Check the clearance between the pump rotor and rotor body. If the measurement is more than .010", install a new pump rotor and rotor body.
13. Check the oil pump relief valve plunger for scoring and free operation in its bore. If the plunger is scored, install a new one.

14. When assembling the pump, be sure to use a new oil seal ring between the cover and body. Tighten cover bolts to a torque of 10 to 12 lbs. ft.
15. Prime the pump. Then place a new oil seal ring in the pump mounting face. Install oil pump and strainer and fasten the pump in position, tightening the bolts with a torque wrench from 30 to 35 lbs. ft.

Six Cylinder Engines

To disassemble the pump, Fig. 35, remove cover and gasket. Hold hand over cover opening and, with pump upside down, turn shaft until outer rotor slips out. Drive out the straight pin securing the drive gear to the shaft. Press the shaft out of the gear and slide the shaft and inner rotor out of the body. Wash and dry all parts.

Assemble—When installing a new rotor on the drive shaft, press the rotor on until the end of the shaft is flush with the face of the gear. Install a new pin. Slide the shaft and rotor into the pump body.

Press the drive gear on the shaft until the shaft end play is from .003 to .010". Press the rotor down into the body and measure clearance from lower end of gear to pump body. Install the pin, peening over both ends. If the pin holes do not line up, drill a new hole at right angles to the other hole and install the pin.

Slide the outer rotor in place in the body. Install a new cover gasket and tighten the screws evenly.

OIL PRESSURE REGULATOR
Six Cylinder Engines

Oil pressure is controlled by a relief valve on the left side of the engine.

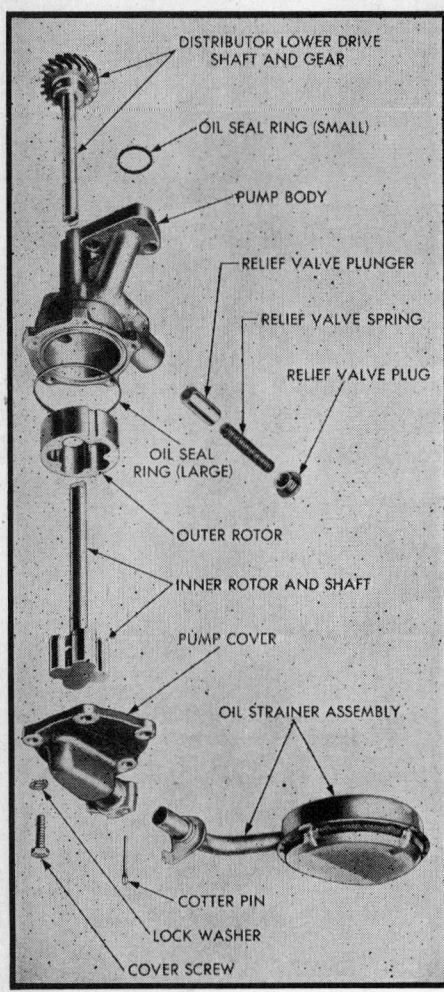

Fig. 34 Chrysler and Imperial 1953-58 and 1953-57 De Soto

Different colored springs are used in the relief valve. The standard spring is not painted. Springs lighter than standard are painted red. Springs heavier than standard are painted green. If the spring has to be changed, the same color spring should be installed.

RADIATOR, REPLACE

1953-56 V8

Drain cooling system and disconnect hoses. Remove fan blades only if additional clearance is necessary. Unfasten radiator from its support and lift it out.

1957-61

If equipped, remove the two cooler connections at the bottom of the radiator and drain the oil from the oil cooler tank. Drain cooling system and remove hoses. On air conditioned cars, remove fan shroud. Take out radiator support bolts and lift out radiator.

Six Cylinder Models

Drain cooling system and disconnect hoses. Remove fan blades only if additional clearance is necessary. Remove fan shroud (if equipped). Unfasten radiator from its support and lift it out.

WATER PUMP, REPLACE

1953-55 V8

1. Drain cooling system.
2. Remove radiator inlet hose.
3. Remove heater hoses.
4. Remove wire from temperature gauge sending unit.
5. Remove fan shroud.
6. Remove idler pulley, fan, generator and fan assembly.
7. Remove radiator outlet hose from oil cooler and disconnect cooler from water pump (if equipped).
8. Remove screws which hold water pump housing to cylinder head and block.
9. If Air Conditioned, remove compressor bracket screws from water pump housing.
10. Remove water pump housing.
11. Reverse removal procedure to install and torque pump housing attaching bolts to 30 lb. ft.

1956

Drain cooling system and remove radiator and heater hoses. Remove fan shroud and disconnect wire at temperature gauge sending unit. Remove generator, fan, idler pulley and belts. Remove oil cooler (if equipped). Remove water pump.

1957-61

Drain cooling system, and on air conditioned cars only remove upper half of fan shroud. On 1958 De Soto and all 1959-61 models it is necessary to remove the radiator. Loosen power steering pump or idler pulley, and generator. Remove all belts, fan, space and pulley.

On air conditioned cars, remove pulley from water pump fan hub, loosen all nuts from fan and remove the fluid fan drive.

On all models, remove bolts holding water pump body to housing and remove water pump.

Six Cylinder Engines

To remove the pump, drain the cooling system, remove the fan belt and disconnect water pump hose. Unfasten the pump from the engine block and lift it off with the fan.

When installing the pump, make sure all mating surfaces are clean and use a new gasket.

WATER PUMP REPAIRS

1953-55 V8

To disassemble the pump, first remove the bearing lock spring from the pump housing. Then after removing the impeller cover plate, position the pump in a suitable fixture with the impeller side up and, using a rod smaller in diameter than the bearing shaft, press downward on the shaft to remove the bearing and shaft assembly. Lift out the impeller and, after removing the impeller lock ring, take out the seal parts.

When reassembling the pump, a new seal and seal washer should be used. It is also advisable to replace the bearing

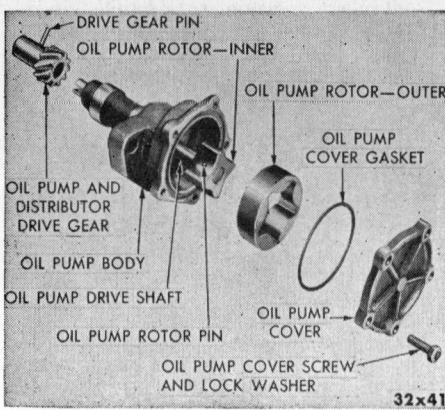

Fig. 35 Rotor type oil pump. 6 cyl.

and shaft since damage to this assembly usually results during its removal. The hub and impeller must fit tightly on the shaft; a hub that has been used previously usually does not fit tight enough.

1956

Referring to Fig. 36, remove the impeller cover plate. Press the shaft and bearing assembly out of the housing by pressing on the impeller end of the shaft. Remove the lock ring at the impeller and remove the seal parts.

The plastic impeller with which this pump is equipped cannot be re-used once it is disassembled from the pump. The impeller insert should be removed from the shaft before pushing the bearing out to prevent damage to the seal seat.

When assembling the pump, the impeller must be flush with the end of the shaft. The correct installed position of the hub is when there is .380" from the end of the fan pulley hub to the front end of the shaft.

1957-58 Chrysler & Imperial & 1957 De Soto

This pump has no cover plate nor does it use a lock pin to hold the fan pulley hub in place. To disassemble, use a suitable puller to pull the fan hub from the shaft. Remove the impeller by breaking the plastic away from the metal insert. Remove impeller insert and press the shaft and bearing assembly out of the housing from the impeller end. *Shaft and bearing assembly need not be removed to service a leaking pump.*

When assembled, the impeller should be flush with the end of the shaft. And when installing the fan pulley hub, press it on until there is .330" between the end of the shaft and the front face of the hub.

1959-61 Chrysler & Imperial & 1958-61 De Soto

If only the seal and impeller are to be replaced, support the pump assembly so that pressure is applied to the shaft. The bearings and shaft will be damaged if pressure is applied to the pump body. Fig. 37 is a disassembled view of the water pump.

To disassemble, support pump body on hub and remove impeller by breaking the plastic away from the metal insert. Remove the seal by sliding it over the shaft and insert. Remove impeller metal insert. Support body on front face (fan hub end), apply pressure to rear end of water pump shaft to press out bearing and shaft hub.

Reassemble the pump and be sure to obtain the dimensions indicated in Fig. 38.

Six Cylinder Engines

Drive pin out of fan pulley hub and use a puller to pull hub off the shaft. Remove cover and pull impeller and shaft out of body. If either impeller or shaft is to be replaced, drive out the pin holding these parts together. Drive the front bushing pin into the shaft hole of the bushing to permit removal of the bushings. Pull the bushings from the body, pulling them out toward the front. Remove the seal, spring and retainer washers from the shaft, Fig. 39.

If new bushings are to be installed, insert the thrust washer in the body with flat side facing out. Press the front bushing in with the oil groove on top and grooved end out. Press in the rear bushing, allowing $\frac{3}{32}$ inch clearance between the rear end of the bushing and the impeller housing. Drill and pin the front bushing. Remove any burrs inside the bushings and line burnish both bushings and reface the seal seat with the tool shown in Fig. 40. Then continue to assemble the pump as follows:

Install the impeller on the shaft and drill for a $\frac{1}{8}$ inch impeller pin. Install the pin and peen over both ends. Assemble the seal thrust spring, seal retainer, seal and seat retainer washer

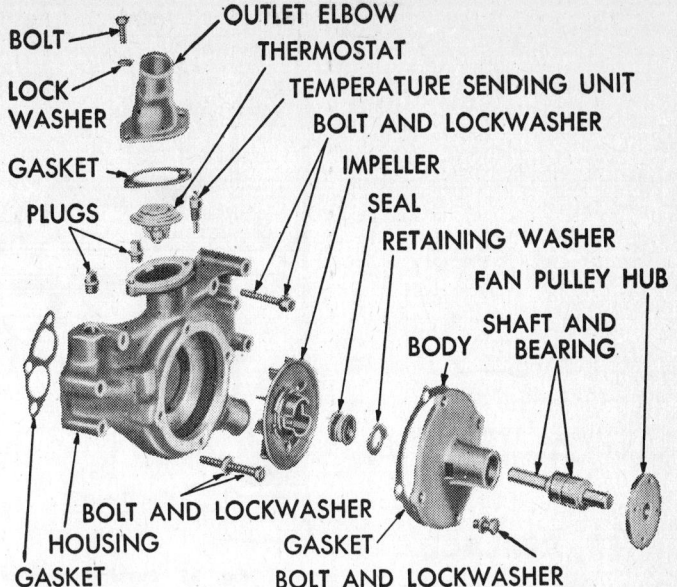

Fig. 37 Water pump. 1959-61 Chrysler and Imperial and 1958-61 De Soto

with glazed surface against seal. Install the seal retainer lock ring.

Insert the shaft and press on the fan pulley hub, leaving .003 inch clearance between the bushing and hub. Drill the shaft (if a new one is being used) and install the retaining pin. If the old shaft is being used, position the hub on the shaft so that the shaft can be drilled 90 degrees from the old hole. Remove all traces of old gaskets and install new ones. Lubricate the pump and install on the engine.

WATER DISTRIBUTOR TUBE

Six Cylinder Engines

The water distributor tube directs the flow of water from the water pump to the exhaust valve ports, which are the hottest spots in the engine. Replacement of the tube requires the removal of the radiator unless the engine is out of the chassis for repairs.

The tube should be replaced whenever the engine is completely overhauled. If the tube becomes rusted or corroded, overheating of the engine will occur due to failure of the water to circulate properly through the cylinder block.

The water distributor tube can be removed and installed after removing the water pump and spacer. A heavy rod with a hook forged on one end will facilitate removal.

DISTRIBUTOR, REPLACE

To remove the distributor, disconnect the vacuum control line and low tension wire and remove the cap and lock plate hold-down screw.

When installing the distributor, make sure that No. 1 piston is on top dead center on compression stroke and that the distributor rotor is in No. 1 firing position.

IGNITION TIMING

With the distributor properly installed on the engine as outlined previously, set ignition timing with a timing light so that with the engine idling, the timing light will flash when the pointer on the engine is opposite the timing mark on the vibration damper. Chalk-mark the spot on the vibration damper so that it stands out when the light flashes (see Figs. 41 and 42).

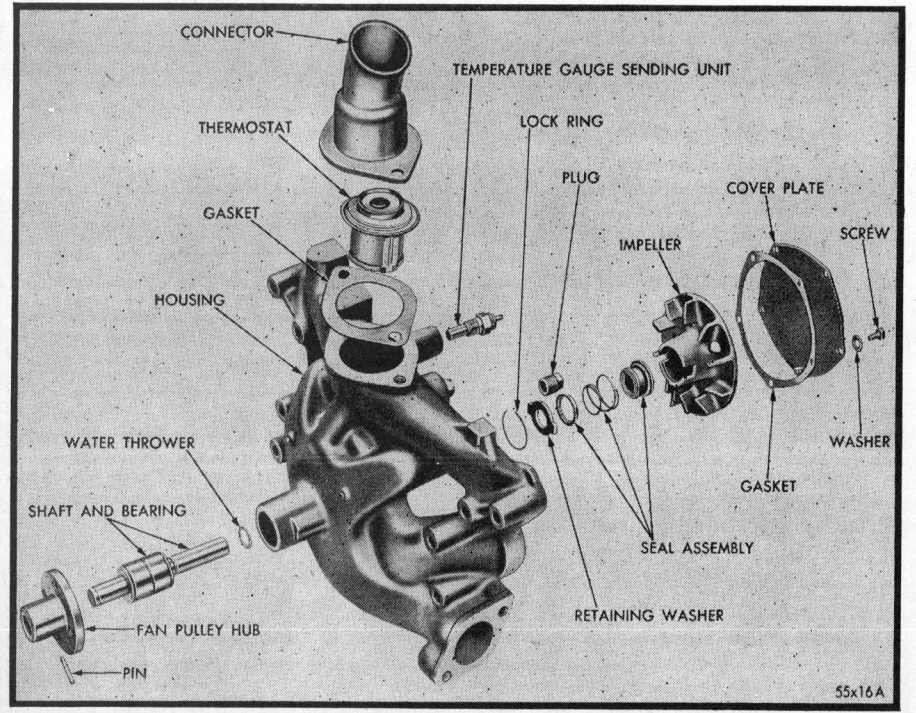

Fig. 36 Exploded view of 1956 water pump. On 1953-55 pumps a lock spring is used through a slot in the housing to position the bearing. The cover plate and fan pulley hub pin shown are not used on 1957-58 Chrysler and Imperial and 1957 De Soto pumps

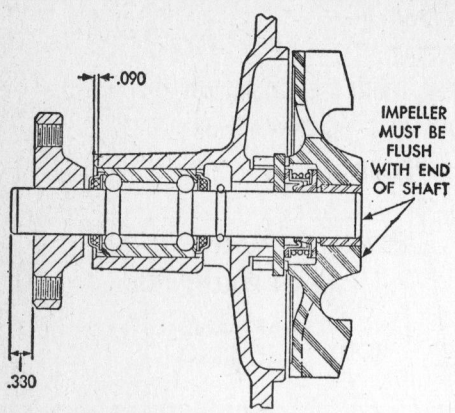

Fig. 38 Water pump. 1959-61 Chrysler and Imperial and 1958-61 De Soto

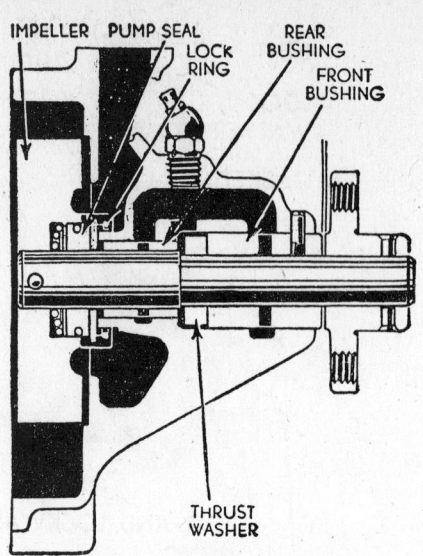

Fig. 39 Bushing type water pump. Typical of all sixes

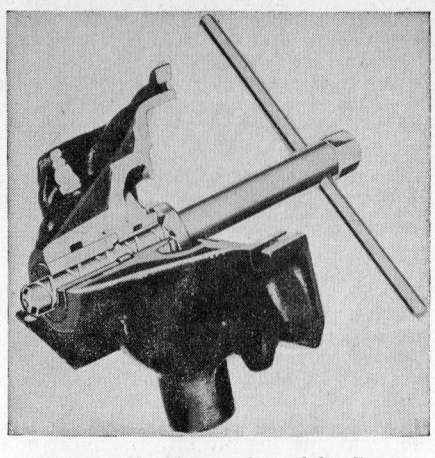

Fig. 40 Showing tool used for line-burnishing bushings and facing seal surface of housing. Six-cyl.

STARTER, REPLACE

Disconnect terminals from binding post and battery terminal or disconnect it at the battery. Then unfasten starter from flywheel housing and pull out starter.

MUFFLERS & PIPES, REPLACE

1953-54

To remove exhaust pipe on V8's and convertible, disconnect flange on left bank and spread front and rear connecting clamps. Disconnect right bank flange and lower to clear flange. Remove left pipe, then right pipe.

On all 6's except convertible, pipe is welded to muffler. Cut pipe to replace muffler. To remove tailpipe, jack up body and roll pipe to clear fuel tank and frame.

1955-61

When installing components of the exhaust system, start at the exhaust manifolds and work toward the rear until muffler is to be installed. Position tailpipe and install muffler. If the entire system or any component of it is to be replaced, clamps and brackets should be tightened only to the extent necessary to hold the exhaust system in position. The final tightening is done after the system has been properly aligned.

On 1957-59 De Soto exhaust pipe with solid crossover, cut the crossover pipe in half to facilitate removal.

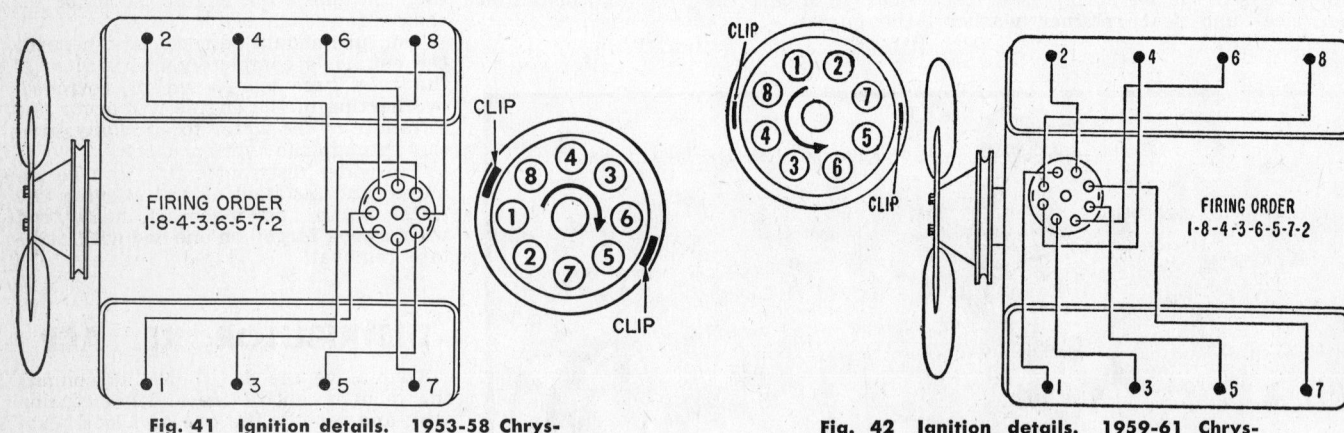

Fig. 41 Ignition details. 1953-58 Chrysler and Imperial and 1953-57 De Soto

Fig. 42 Ignition details. 1959-61 Chrysler and Imperial and 1958-61 De Soto

Carburetor Section

Performance Complaints

Flooding, stumble on acceleration or other performance complaints are in many instances caused by the presence of dirt, water or other foreign matter in the carburetor. To aid in diagnosing the cause of the complaint, the carburetor should be carefully removed from the engine without draining the fuel from the bowl. The contents of the fuel bowl may then be examined for contamination as the carburetor is disassembled.

Check the fuel in the bowl for contamination by dirt, water, gum or other foreign matter. A magnet moved through the fuel in the bowl will pick up and identify any iron oxide dust that may have caused intake needle and seat leakage.

Inspect gasketed surfaces between body and air horn. Small nicks or burrs should be smoothed down to eliminate air or fuel leakage. On carburetors having a vacuum piston, be especially particular when inspecting the top surface of the inner wall of the bowl around the vacuum piston passage. A poor seal at this location may contribute to a "cutting-out" on turns complaint.

Fill the carburetor bowl with clean fuel before installing on manifold. This will help prevent dirt trapped in the fuel system from being dislodged by the free flow of fuel as the carburetor is primed. The operation of the floats and intake needle and seats may be checked under pressure if a fuel pump is used at the bench to fill the carburetor bowl. Operate the throttle several times and visually check the discharge from pump jets.

Poor Mileage and Engine Loading Complaints

Cases of poor mileage and engine loading may be due in many instances to sluggish choke valve opening during cold driveaway, caused by insufficient vacuum in choke housing, a plugged or restricted heat pipe or inlet in choke cover. To check for this condition, have engine warm and running at slow idle. Remove choke heat pipe and hold a finger over the heat inlet hole (hole is on choke housing on some carburetors). If there is little or no vacuum pull on the finger, check the choke housing for gasket leaks or plugged vacuum passages. If these are OK, check choke vacuum passages in carburetor between choke housing and manifold.

Dirty or Rusty Choke Housing

In cases where it is found that the interior of the choke housing is dirty, gummed or rusty while the carburetor itself is comparatively clean, look for a punctured or eroded manifold heat tube (if one is used).

Manifold Heat Control Valve

An engine equipped with a manifold heat control valve can operate with the valve stuck in either the open or closed position. Because of this, an inoperative valve is frequently overlooked at vehicle lubrication or tune-up.

A stuck valve in the "heat-off" position can result in slow warm up, deposits in combustion chamber, carburetor icing, flat spots during acceleration, low gas mileage and spark plug fouling.

A valve stuck in the "heat-on" position can result in power loss, engine knocking, sticking or burned valves and spark plug burning.

To prevent the possibility of a stuck valve, check and lubricate the valve each time the vehicle is lubricated or tuned-up. Check the operation of the valve manually. To lubricate the valve, place a few drops of penetrating oil on the valve shaft where it passes through the manifold. Then move the valve up and down a few times to work in the oil. *Do not use engine oil to lubricate the valve as it will leave a residue which hampers valve operation.*

Engine Surge At Idle

Sonoramic Engines—Variations in engine idle speed may cause a loss of manifold vacuum which will actuate the anti-stall device, slightly opening the throttles. This may result in an undesirable "hunting" or surging condition. To eliminate the possibility of this condition it is recommended that the anti-stall device be adjusted as follows:

1. With accelerator linkage adjusted properly, adjust carburetor idle and mixture adjustments, being sure idle speed is 725-750 rpm in neutral with engine warmed up.
2. Disconnect vacuum tube at anti-stall device. Tape open end of the tube to prevent air leakage into the manifold. Disconnecting the vacuum tube will allow the anti-stall plunger to extend and increase engine idle speed.
3. Adjust anti-stall plunger length so engine speed is no higher than 1500 rpm.
4. Remove tape from vacuum tube and connect vacuum tube to anti-stall device. The plunger will retract and will permit engine idle to return to 725-750 rpm.

CARTER CARBURETOR ADJUSTMENTS

Year	Carburetor Model	Idle Adjustments				Float Level		Float Drop		Pump Travel Setting	Choke Unloader Setting	Choke Setting
		Mixture Screws Turns Open	Hot Idle Speed Neutral	Fast Idle Speed	Dashpot Plunger Clearance	Primary	Secondary	Primary	Secondary			
CHRYSLER & IMPERIAL												
1961	BBD-3132S	1	500	1400⑫	None	9/32⑥	None	None	None	1③	¼⑤	Index
1960–61	AFB-2927S	½–2	500	1800⑫	None	7/32①	7/32①	23/32②	23/32②	7/16③	¼⑤	2 Rich
	AFB-2950S	½–2	500	1800⑫	None	7/32①	7/32①	23/32②	23/32②	7/16③	¼⑤	2 Rich
	AFB-2968S	¼–1¾	500	1800⑫	None	7/32①	7/32①	23/32②	23/32②	7/16③	¼⑤	2 Rich
	AFB-2903S	⅛–1½	735	1800⑫	.010⑬	9/32①	9/32①	23/32②	23/32②	27/64③	¼⑤	1 Rich
	BBD-2923S-SA	½–1½	500	1400⑫	None	9/32⑥	None	None	None	1③	¼⑤	Index
1960	BBD-2924S	½–1½	500	1400⑫	None	9/32⑥	None	None	None	1③	¼⑤	Index
1959	AFB-2797S	1½–2	500	1400⑫	None	7/32①	7/32①	23/32②	23/32②	7/16③	¼⑤	Index
	BBD-2795S	¾–2¼	500	1400⑫	None	5/16⑥	None	None	None	1③	15/64⑤	Index
	BBD-2872S	¾–2¼	500	1400⑫	None	5/16⑥	None	None	None	1③	15/64⑤	Index
1958	BBD-2685S	½–1½	500	1400⑫	None	9/32⑥	None	None	None	1 1/32③	¼⑤	1 Rich
	BBD-2733S	½–1½	500	1400⑫	None	9/32⑥	None	None	None	1 1/32③	¼⑤	1 Rich
	AFB-2651S	¼–1¾	500	1400⑫	None	⑪	⑪	23/32②	23/32②	7/16③	¼⑤	1 Rich
	AFB-2806S	¼–1¾	500	1400⑫	None	⑪	⑪	23/32②	23/32②	7/32③	¼⑤	1 Rich
	AFB-2650S	¼–1¾	500	1400⑫	None	⑪	⑪	23/32②	23/32②	7/32③	¼⑤	1 Rich
	AFB-2805S	¼–1¾	500	1400⑫	None	⑪	⑪	23/32②	23/32②	7/32③	¼⑤	1 Rich
	AFB-2836S	¼–1¾	500	1400⑫	None	⑪	⑪	23/32②	23/32②	7/32③	¼⑤	1 Rich
	WCFB-2741S	1–2	650	None	None	9/32⑦	11/32⑦	23/32⑧	23/32⑧	⑨	None	None
	WCFB-2742S	1–2	650	1450㉓	None	9/32⑦	11/32⑦	23/32⑧	23/32⑧	⑨	⅛⑤	1 Rich
1957	AFB-2448S	¼–1¾	500	1475⑫	None	⑪	⑪	23/32②	23/32②	7/16③	¼⑤	1 Rich
	AFB-2686S	¼–1¾	500	1325⑫	None	⑪	⑪	23/32②	23/32②	7/16③	¼⑤	1 Rich
	WCFB-2590S	1–2	500	1375⑫	None	5/32⑦	9/32⑦	21/32⑧	25/32⑧	⑨	15/64⑤	1 Rich

CARTER CARBURETOR ADJUSTMENTS

Year	Carburetor Model	Idle Adjustments				Float Level		Float Drop		Pump Travel Setting	Choke Unloader Setting	Choke Setting
		Mixture Screws Turns Open	Hot Idle Speed Neutral	Fast Idle Speed	Dashpot Plunger Clearance	Primary	Secondary	Primary	Secondary			
CHRYSLER & IMPERIAL continued												
1957	WCFB-2589S	3/4-1 3/4	500	1375(12)	None	5/32(7)	9/32(7)	21/32(8)	25/32(8)	(9)	15/64(5)	1 Rich
	BBD-2527S	1/2-1 1/2	500	1325(12)	None	9/32(6)	None	None	None	1 1/2(3)	3/16(5)	1 Rich
1956	BBD-2312S	1/4-1 1/4	500	.020(4)	1/16(14)	1/4(6)	None	None	None	31/32(3)	3/16(5)	Index
	BBD-2313S	1/4-1 1/4	500	.020(4)	1/16(14)	1/4(6)	None	None	None	31/32(3)	3/16(5)	1 Rich
	WCFB-2367S-A	3/4-1 3/4	500	.012(10)	None	5/32(7)	7/32(7)	23/32(8)	23/32(8)	(9)	3/16(5)	1 Rich
	WCFB-2314S-A	1-2	500	.012(10)	None	5/32(7)	7/32(7)	23/32(8)	23/32(8)	(9)	3/16(5)	1 Rich
	WCFB-2444S	1/4-1 1/4	700	.008(10)	None	7/32(7)	11/32(7)	23/32(8)	27/32(8)	(15)	3/16(5)	Index
	WCFB-2445S	1/4-1 1/4	700	.008(10)	None	7/32(7)	11/32(7)	23/32(8)	27/32(8)	(15)	3/16(5)	Index
1955	WCFB-2317S	1/4-1 1/4	700	.008(10)	None	7/32(7)	11/32(7)	23/32(8)	27/32(8)	(15)	3/16(5)	Index
	WCFB-2126S	3/4-1 3/4	500	.018(10)	None	1/8(7)	3/16(7)	5/8(8)	11/16(8)	(15)	3/16(5)	Index
	BBD-2162S-A-B	1/4-1 1/4	475	.017(16)	1/16(14)	7/32(6)	None	None	None	54/64(17)	1/4(5)	Index
	BBD-2180S-A-B	1/4-1 1/4	475	.017(16)	None	7/32(6)	None	None	None	54/64(17)	1/4(5)	Index
1954	WCFB-2041S	1-2	475	.015(10)	None	1/8(7)	1/4(7)	5/8(8)	3/4(8)	(15)	3/16(5)	Index
	BB-EB91	1/2-1 1/2	475	.017(16)	(18)	5/64(19)	None	None	None	(20)	5/32(5)	Index
1953-54	WCD-2039S-A	1/2-1	475	.019(4)	3/64(22)	11/64(21)	None	None	None	17/64(15)	7/32(5)	Index
1953	WCD-935S-A	1/2-1	475	.019(4)	1/16(14)	11/64(21)	None	None	None	17/64(15)	7/32(5)	Index
	BB-E9C, E9C1	1/2-1 1/2	475	.017(16)	None	5/64(19)	None	None	None	(20)	5/32(5)	Index
	BB-E9A1	1/2-1 1/2	475	.017(16)	None	5/64(19)	None	None	None	(20)	5/32(5)	Index
DE SOTO												
1960-61	AFB-2950S	1-2	500	1800(12)	None	7/32(1)	7/32(1)	3/4(2)	3/4(2)	7/16(3)	1/4(5)	2 Rich
	AFB-2927S	1/2-2	500	1800(12)	None	7/32(1)	7/32(1)	23/32(2)	23/32(2)	7/16(3)	1/4(5)	2 Rich
	AFB-2968S	1/4-1 1/2	500	1800(12)	None	7/32(1)	7/32(1)	23/32(2)	23/32(2)	7/16(3)	1/4(5)	2 Rich
	AFB-2903S	1/8-1 1/2	735	1800(12)	.010(13)	9/32(1)	9/32(1)	23/32(2)	23/32(2)	27/64(3)	1/4(5)	1 Rich
	BBD-2923S-SA	1/2-1 1/2	500	1400(12)	None	9/32(6)	None	None	None	1(3)	1/4(5)	Index
1959	AFB-2794S	1/2-2	500	1400(12)	None	7/32(1)	7/32(1)	23/32(2)	23/32(2)	7/16(3)	1/4(5)	Index
	BBD-2924S	1/2-1 1/2	500	1400(12)	None	9/32(6)	None	None	None	1(3)	1/4(5)	Index
	BBD-2793S	1/4-1 1/4	500	1400(12)	None	5/16(6)	None	None	None	1(3)	15/64(5)	Index
	BBD-2870S	1/4-1 1/4	500	1400(12)	None	5/16(6)	None	None	None	1(3)	15/64(5)	Index
	BBD-2871S	1/4-1 1/4	500	1400(12)	None	5/16(6)	None	None	None	1(3)	15/64(5)	Index
1958	AFB-2773S	3/4-2 1/4	500	1400(12)	None	7/32(1)	7/32(1)	23/32(2)	23/32(2)	7/16(3)	1/4(5)	2 Rich
	AFB-2642S	3/4-2 1/4	500	1400(12)	None	(11)	(11)	23/32(2)	23/32(2)	7/16(3)	1/4(5)	2 Rich
	AFB-2823S	3/4-2 1/4	500	1400(12)	None	(11)	(11)	23/32(2)	23/32(2)	7/16(3)	1/4(5)	Index
	BBD-2637S	1/2-1 1/2	500	1400(12)	None	5/16(6)	None	None	None	1(3)	15/64(5)	Index
	BBD-2772S	1/2-1 1/2	500	1400(12)	None	5/16(6)	None	None	None	1(3)	15/64(5)	Index
	BBD-2822S	1/4-1 1/4	500	1400(12)	None	5/16(6)	None	None	None	1(3)	15/64(5)	Index
1957	WCFB-2532S	1/2-1 1/2	500	1375(12)	None	7/32(7)	9/32(7)	23/32(8)	25/32(8)	(15)	15/64(5)	Index
	WCFB-2588S	1/2-1 1/2	500	1325(12)	None	5/32(7)	9/32(7)	21/32(8)	25/32(8)	(9)	15/64(5)	1 Rich
	BBD-2522S-A-B	1/2-1 1/2	500	1325(12)	None	9/32(6)	None	None	None	1 1/2(3)	1/4(5)	1 Rich
1956	WCFB-2445S	1/4-1 1/4	475	1375(12)	None	7/32(7)	11/32(7)	23/32(8)	27/32(8)	(15)	11/64(5)	Index
	WCFB-2476S	1/4-1 1/4	475	1375(12)	None	7/32(7)	11/32(7)	23/32(8)	27/32(8)	(15)	11/64(5)	Index
	WCFB-2311S-A	1-2	475	1375(12)	None	5/32(7)	7/32(7)	21/32(8)	23/32(8)	(15)	3/16(5)	1 Rich
	BBD-2308S	1/2-1 1/2	475	.015(4)	1/16(14)	1/4(6)	None	None	None	1 1/32(3)	3/16(5)	Index
	BBD-2309S	1/2-1 1/2	475	.015(4)	1/16(14)	1/4(6)	None	None	None	1 1/32(3)	3/16(5)	Index
	BBD-2310S	1/2-1 1/2	475	.015(4)	1/16(14)	1/4(6)	None	None	None	1 1/32(3)	3/16(5)	Index
1955	WCFB-2210S	1-2	475	.018(4)	None	1/8(7)	3/16(7)	5/8(8)	11/16(8)	(15)	3/16(5)	Index
	BBD-2176S-A	1/4-1 1/4	475	.017(16)	None	7/32(6)	None	None	None	1(3)	1/4(5)	Index
	BBD-2177S-A	1/4-1 1/4	475	.017(16)	None	7/32(6)	None	None	None	1(3)	1/4(5)	Index
	BBD-2178S-A	1/4-1 1/4	475	.017(16)	1/16(14)	7/32(6)	None	None	None	1(3)	1/4(5)	Index
1954	BBD-2067S	1/4-1 1/4	475	.017(16)	None	(24)	None	None	None	57/64(26)	1/4(5)	Index
	BBD-2068S	1/4-1 1/4	475	.017(16)	None	(24)	None	None	None	57/64(26)	1/4(5)	Index
	BBD-2070S	1/4-1 1/4	475	.017(16)	1/16(14)	(24)	None	None	None	57/64(26)	1/4(5)	Index

CARTER CARBURETOR ADJUSTMENTS

Year	Carburetor Model	Idle Adjustments				Float Level		Float Drop		Pump Travel Setting	Choke Unloader Setting	Choke Setting
		Mixture Screws Turns Open	Hot Idle Speed Neutral	Fast Idle Speed	Dashpot Plunger Clearance	Primary	Secondary	Primary	Secondary			
DE SOTO continued												
1954	BBD-2129S	1/4-1 1/4	475	.017(16)	None	(24)	None	None	None	57/64(26)	1/4(5)	Index
	BBD-2130S	1/4-1 1/4	475	.017(16)	1/16(14)	(24)	None	None	None	57/64(26)	1/4(5)	Index
	BBD-2131S	1/4-1 1/4	475	.017(16)	None	(24)	None	None	None	57/64(26)	1/4(5)	Index
	BB-E9B1	1/2-1 1/2	475	.017(16)	(18)	5/64(19)	None	None	None	(20)	5/32(25)	Index
1953-54	BBD-2250S	1/4-1 1/4	475	.017(16)	1/16(14)	7/32(6)	None	None	None	1(3)	1/4(5)	Index
1953	BBD-2216S	1/4-1 1/4	475	.017(16)	1/16(14)	7/32(6)	None	None	None	1(3)	1/4(5)	Index
	BBD-908S	1/4-1 1/4	475	.017(16)	1/16(14)	(24)	None	None	None	57/64(26)	1/4(5)	Index
	BBD-909S	1/4-1 1/4	475	.017(16)	None	(24)	None	None	None	57/64(26)	1/4(5)	Index
	BBD-910S	1/4-1 1/4	475	.017(16)	None	(24)	None	None	None	57/64(26)	1/4(5)	Index
	BBD-911S	1/4-1 1/4	475	.017(16)	None	(24)	None	None	None	57/64(26)	1/4(5)	Index
	BBD-912S	1/4-1 1/4	475	.017(16)	None	(24)	None	None	None	57/64(26)	1/4(5)	Index
	BBD-913S	1/4-1 1/4	475	.017(16)	1/16(14)	(24)	None	None	None	57/64(26)	1/4(5)	Index

CARTER NOTES

OVERDRIVE KICKDOWN SWITCH

BBD—With throttle valves wide open, there should be 1/64" to 3/64" clearance between kickdown lever and switch stem guide. To adjust, loosen lock nuts and adjust switch.

IDLE SPEED SETTING

Some 4-barrel carburetors do not have a conventional throttle speed screw but instead use an air adjustment screw. The idle air screw is located in the throttle body and can be identified by it being larger than the idle mixture screws. Turning the air screw outward increases engine speeds but also leans the mixture. This must be compensated for by adjusting the idle mixture screws.

METERING ROD

WCFB and WCD—This adjustment must be made after the pump setting. Seat throttle valves in bores of carburetor and loosen metering rod arm clamp screw. With metering rods in place, press down on vacumeter link until metering rods bottom in casting. Holding rods down, revolve metering rod arm until finger on arm contacts lip of vacumeter link. Hold in place and tighten clamp screw.

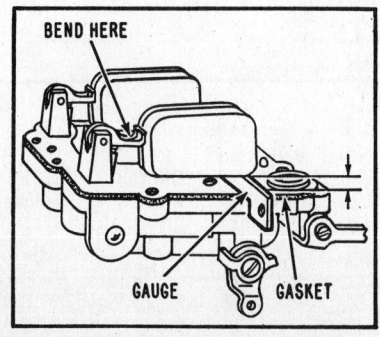

Fig. ①—AFB float level. Adjust by bending float lever.

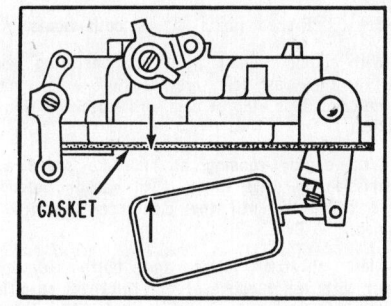

Fig. ②—AFB float drop. Adjust by bending stop tabs on float brackets.

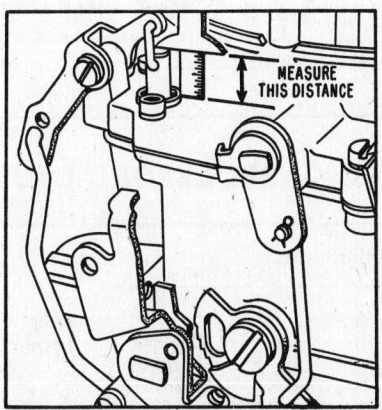

Fig. ③—Measure from top of bowl cover to top of plunger shaft with throttle connector rod in center hole of pump arm (AFB) or throttle lever (BBD). Adjust by bending throttle connector rod (AFB shown).

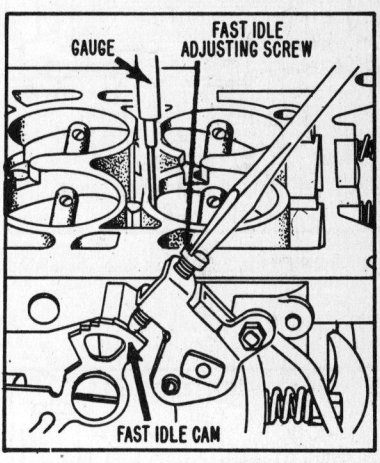

Fig. ④—With choke valve closed, tighten fast idle adjusting screw on high step of fast idle cam or on index mark until clearance between throttle valve and carburetor bore (side opposite idle port) is as specified.

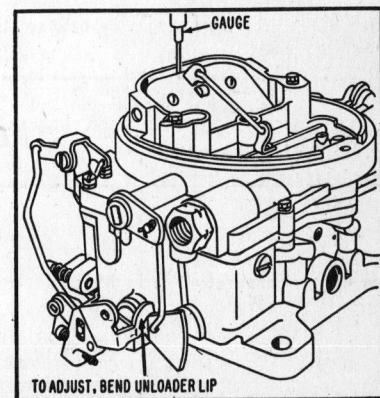

Fig. ⑤—With throttle wide open, clearance between upper edge of choke valve and inner wall of air horn should be as specified. Adjust by bending unloader lip on throttle lever (AFB shown).

CARTER NOTES
continued

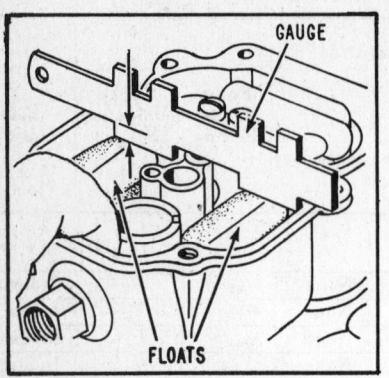

Fig. ⑥—BBD float level. Adjust by bending lip on float arm.

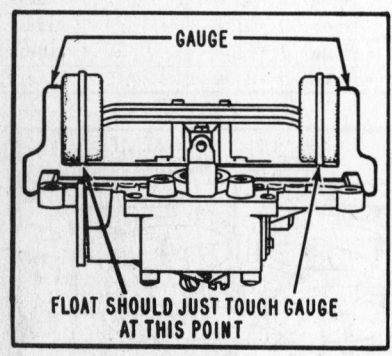

Fig. ⑦—WCFB float level. Adjust by bending float arms.

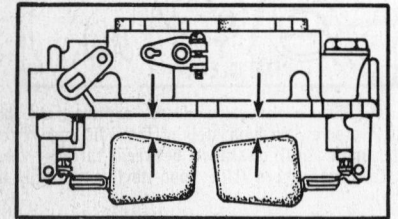

Fig. ⑧—WCFB float drop. Adjust by bending stop tabs on float bracket.

Fig. ⑨—With pump connector link in center hole of pump arm, flat on pump arm should be parallel with a straightedge placed on dust cover boss. Adjust by bending throttle connector rod.

⑩—With choke valve tightly closed, there should be the clearance specified between throttle valve and carburetor bore (side opposite idle port). Adjust by bending fast idle adjusting tang, being sure tang is on high step of cam.

⑪—See ①. Ribbed floats $\frac{7}{32}$", smooth floats $\frac{5}{16}$".

⑫—With engine running at normal operating temperature, turn fast idle screw against index mark on cam or on high step of cam until specified rpm is obtained.

⑬—With engine running at hot idle speed and transmission in drive range, turn dashpot plunger toward bellcrank until the clearance specified is obtained.

⑭—Close throttle valves and bottom dashpot plunger with feeler gauge of the thickness specified between plunger and operating lever. To adjust loosen locknut and turn dashpot in or out as required.

⑮—Same as ⑨ except connector link goes in outer hole.

⑯—With choke valve closed and fast idle cam in fast idle position, there should be the clearance specified between throttle valve and carburetor bore (side opposite idle port). Adjust by bending choke connector rod.

⑰—Same as ③ except connector rod goes in outer hole.

⑱—Tighten adjusting screw, then back it out 5 turns.

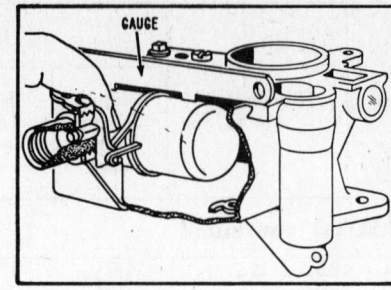

Fig. ⑩—BB float level.

⑲—Pump lifter arm should be at right angle to pump lifter shaft. Adjust by bending pump lifter arm.

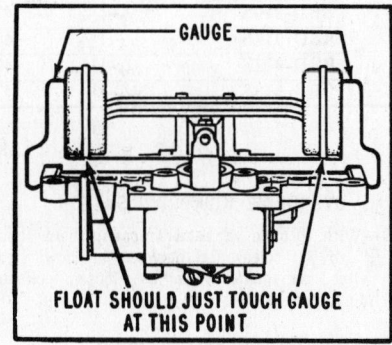

Fig. ㉑—WCD float level. Adjust by bending float arms.

㉒—With throttle valves wide open there should be the clearance specified between dashpot operating lever and the stop. Adjust by bending stop.

㉓—Hot engine with idle adjusting tang on high step of fast idle cam.

㉔—See ⑥. Flat top floats $\frac{9}{32}$", curved floats $\frac{7}{32}$".

㉕—With throttle wide open, clearance between upper edge of choke valve and inner wall of air horn should be as specified. Adjust by bending arm on choke trip lever.

㉖—Same as ③ except connector rod goes in outer hole.

STROMBERG CARBURETOR ADJUSTMENTS

Year	Carburetor Model	Idle Adjustments				Float Level	Pump Travel	Bowl Vent Valve	Choke Unloader	Choke Setting
		Mixture Screws Turns Open	Hot Idle Speed Neutral	Fast Idle Speed	Dashpot Plunger Clearance					
CHRYSLER & DE SOTO										
1961	WWC3-188	½-⅝	500	1400③	None	⅛①	⁹⁄₁₆②	⁵⁄₆₄⑤	¼④	1 Rich

STROMBERG NOTES

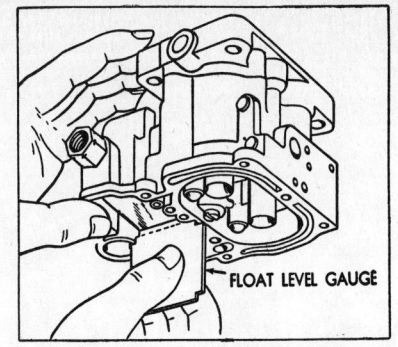

Fig. ①—WW float level. Invert main body so weight of floats only is forcing needle against its seat. There should be the distance listed from surface of fuel bowl to crown of float at center.

②—With throttle valve fully closed, measure pump travel from fully open to fully closed position. To adjust, bend pump rod.

③—With engine running at normal operating temperature, turn fast idle screw against highest step on fast idle cam until specified rpm is obtained.

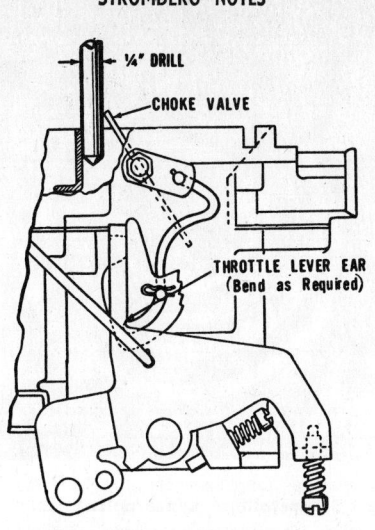

Fig. ④—With throttle valves wide open, choke valve should open dimension specified between edge of choke valve and wall of air horn. Adjust by bending ear on throttle lever.

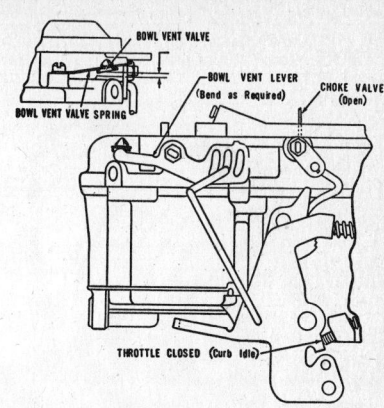

Fig. ⑤—This setting is made after pump travel setting. With throttle fully closed and choke valve wide open, test opening of bowl vent valve at center of hole with rubber valve hanging free. If not as specified, bend bowl vent lever as required.

Clutch and Transmission Section

CLUTCH PEDAL, ADJUST

1957 Chrysler & 1957-59 De Soto

To compensate for normal clutch wear, adjust the clutch release fork rod to obtain 5/32″ free play of clutch release fork outer end. This will provide a one-inch the clutch assembly be exchanged for a free pedal movement at the pedal with a total of six-inch pedal travel.

When necessary to adjust the over-center spring, back off the over-center spring adjusting nut until it is free of the "C" link. With the clutch pedal depressed to the full six-inch travel, turn the adjusting nut until the nut just contacts the "C" link. Then tighten seven full turns from the fringe-tight position.

1955-56, Fig. 1

Adjust the clutch fork rod in or out as required to secure 3/16″ free play of the clutch release fork outer end. This will provide the one inch free pedal movement at the pedal pad with a total of 7″ full pedal travel.

The upper end of the clutch pedal pivots in the lower end of the mounting bracket on needle bearings. These bearings require no periodic lubrication. However, they should be lubricated with wheel bearing grease if the pedal is removed for any reason.

1953-54

To adjust pedal free play, turn the clutch release fork rod adjusting nut until 1/8 to 3/32″ free play in the clutch fork is obtained. This adjustment, if correctly set, will give the necessary one inch free pedal play.

CLUTCH SERVICE

Unless special clutch rebuilding equipment is available, it is recommended that

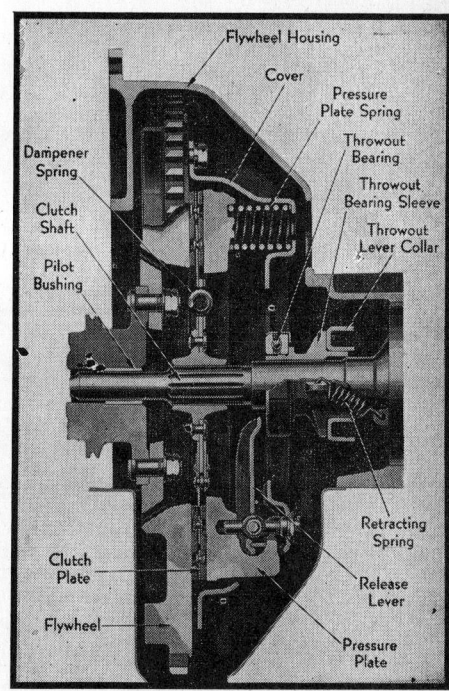

Fig. 2 Cross section of typical clutch

the clutch assembly be exchanged for a rebuilt unit should the clutch require rebuilding. The driven disc, however, may be replaced without special equipment. If clutch rebuilding equipment is available, follow the equipment manufacturer's instructions.

Fig. 1 Clutch pedal and linkage. 1955-56

Fig. 4 Shifting plates (2) fit in stop ring slots (1)

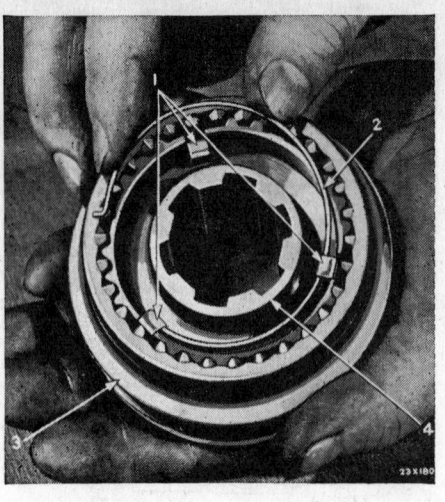

Fig. 5 Installing synchronizer shifting plates and spring spring on standard transmission. 1. Shifting plates. 2. Spreader spring. 3. Clutch sleeve. 4. Clutch gear

Fig. 6 Mainshaft and extension on standard transmission. 1. Snap ring. 2. Clutch sleeve. 3. Second speed gear. 4. Extension. 5. Clutch gear. 6. Mainshaft. 7. Sliding gear

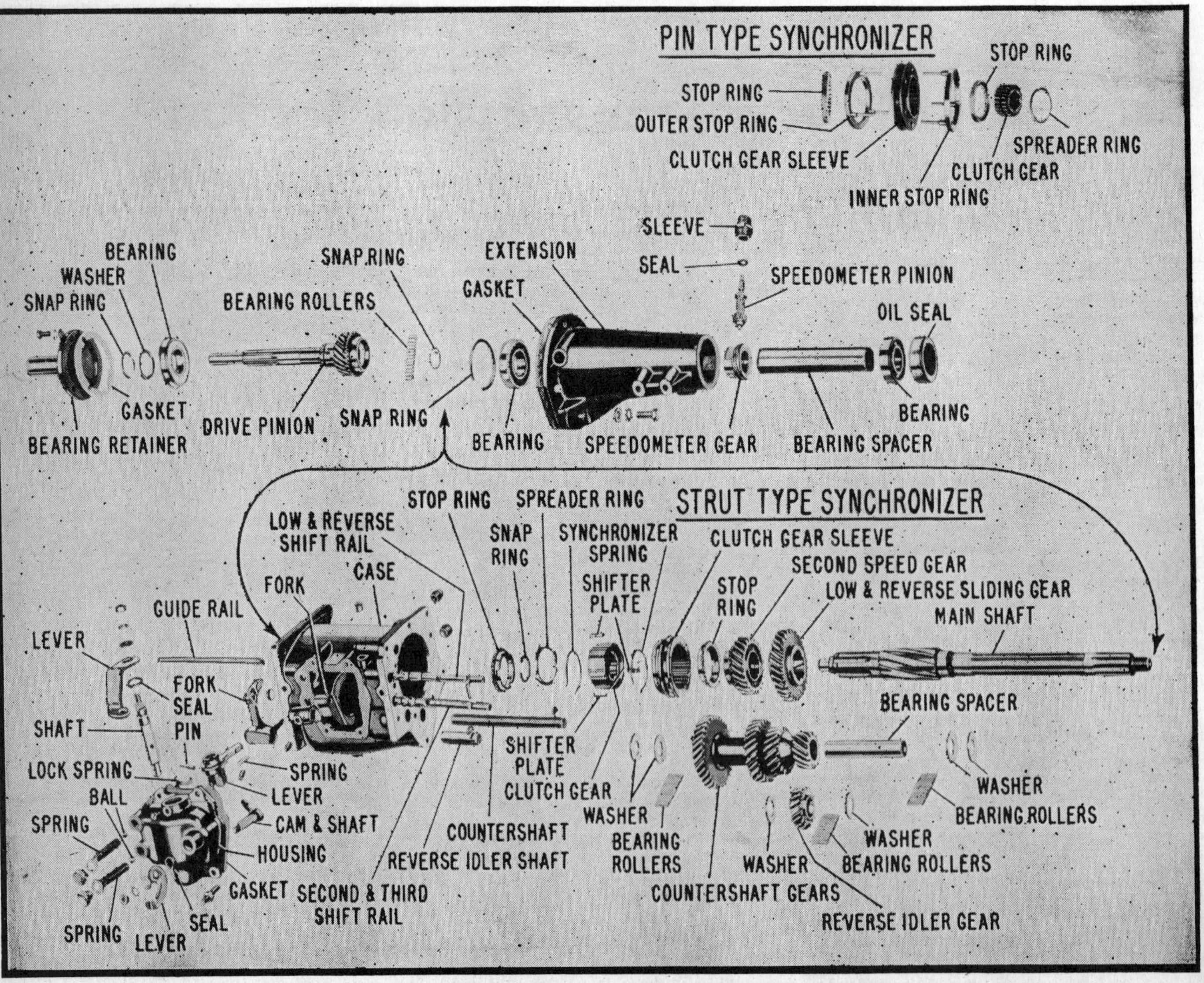

Fig. 3 Synchromesh transmission

Removal

1. Remove transmission and clutch pan.
2. Pull out clutch release bearing and sleeve.
3. Mark clutch cover and flywheel so they may be assembled in the same relative position and thus maintain original balance.
4. Remove cap screws which retain clutch cover to flywheel. Loosen each screw a few turns in succession until cover is free.
5. Clutch assembly and driven disc may now be removed from the clutch housing.

Installation

1. Coat the pilot bearing in crankshaft with wheel bearing grease.
2. Clean surfaces of flywheel and pressure plate, making certain no oil or grease remains on these parts.
3. Hold cover plate and disc in place and insert a special clutch aligning tool or a spare clutch shaft through the hub of the disc and into the crankshaft pilot bearing.
4. Bolt clutch cover loosely to flywheel, being sure marks previously made are lined up.
5. To avoid distortion of clutch cover, tighten cover bolts a few turns each in progression until all are tight. The final tightening should be 15-20 lb. ft. torque.
6. Install transmission by guiding it into place with guide studs inserted in the two top holes of the clutch housing.
7. Adjust clutch pedal free travel.

Service Note

The clutch on 1953 cars with fluid drive or torque converter is removed in the same manner as outlined for models without this equipment but the installation of the driven disc differs slightly as follows:

1. Clean surface of clutch driving plate and clutch pressure plate, making sure no oil remains on these parts.
2. Hold clutch disc in place and bolt clutch cover loosely to clutch driving plate with marks on cover and drive plate lined up.
3. Insert special clutch aligning tool or a spare clutch shaft through the hub of the driving plate and into the fluid drive runner inner bearings in the runner hub.
4. Clutch cover bolts should then be tightened a few turns at a time each

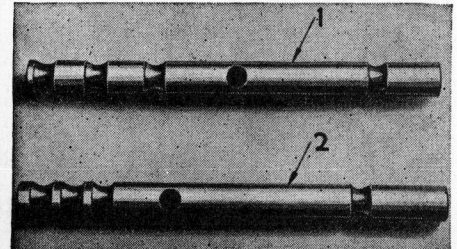

**Fig. 7 Shift rails on standard transmission.
1. First and reverse. 2. Second and high**

in progression until they are all tight.
5. Install transmission.

TRANSMISSION, REPLACE

It is not necessary to remove the floor boards.

1. On cars without overdrive, disconnect propeller shaft at front. (On cars with overdrive, remove propeller shaft and both universals. Remove solenoid and disconnect control cable.)
2. On all cars, disconnect speedometer cable, hand brake cable, and gearshift rods from transmission.
3. Remove two upper transmission mounting studs and insert guide pins in their place.
4. Remove other mounting studs and slide the transmission back and out.

When installing, use the guide studs and handle the transmission carefully to avoid damage to the clutch disc.

TRANSMISSION REPAIRS

(For detailed service on overdrive transmissions, see the *Overdrive* chapter. To disassemble the standard transmission, see Fig. 3 and proceed as follows:

1. Remove speedometer drive pinion.
2. Take off cover and gear selector, roll transmission over and remove balls.
3. Use a puller to remove mainshaft flange and brake drum.
4. Remove shifter fork guide rail.
5. With gears in neutral, remove shift fork lock screws.
6. Remove plug for lower shift rail.
7. Slide shift rails out through front of case.
8. Lift out shift forks.
9. Remove extension housing and mainshaft, being careful not to allow synchronizer to become disassembled.
10. Strip mainshaft of synchronizer, second speed gear and sliding gear.
11. Release snap ring and pull mainshaft out of extension housing.
12. Remove mainshaft bearing, spacer and speedometer drive gear.
13. Pull bearing and oil seal from extension housing.
14. Drive countershaft through rear of case, allowing cluster gear to lie in case.
15. Remove main drive gear and bearing and disassemble parts.
16. Lift out cluster gear and related parts.
17. Drive reverse idler shaft out rearward and lift out gear.

Assembly Notes

Use new gaskets, oil seals and snap rings, being sure snap rings fit snugly in their grooves.

When assembling cluster gear, place steel washer plates next to gear and bronze washers next to case. Select the proper thickness bronze washers to provide end play of from .002 to .008 inch.

If a special oil seal drift is not available, be sure that oil seal protrudes $\frac{7}{32}$

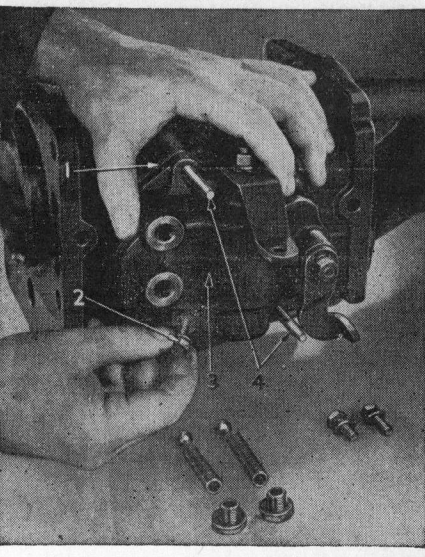

Fig. 8 Installing gearshift housing. 1953-56. 1. Gasket. 2. Screw. 3. Housing. 4. Pilot studs

inch out of the mainshaft extension housing.

Referring to Figs. 4 and 5 for synchronizer assembly, place one bent up end of synchronizer spring into pocket of shifting plate. Then install bent up end of other spring into pocket of same plate on opposite side of synchronizer. Spring on one side should leave plate in opposite direction from spring on other side.

Assemble the synchronizer unit on the mainshaft as shown in Fig. 6.

If second speed gear end play is not within .003 and .008 inch, use a snap ring of different thickness.

Install first and reverse shifter rail (1, Fig. 7) on top, other rail on bottom.

Install gearshift housing as shown in Fig. 8.

GEARSHIFT, ADJUST

1953-56 Manual Trans.

To adjust the control rod, loosen the lock bolt at the upper lever on the lower end of the steering column. Set the transmission gears in neutral and the hand control lever in the horizontal position and tighten the lock bolt.

To adjust the shift control rod, set the transmission gears in neutral and loosen the lock nut on the selector rod at the transmission end. Tighten the nut until all play is eliminated and back off ½ turn for clearance and tighten.

1957-59 Manual Trans.

This transmission incorporates an individual rod shifting mechanism, Fig. 9, which simplifies maintenance, improves shift quality and decreases shifting effort.

Cross-over adjustments and gearshift operating lever positions are adjusted by threads on the upper ends of the shift rods. Movement of the shift lever should be smooth when moving through the cross-over position.

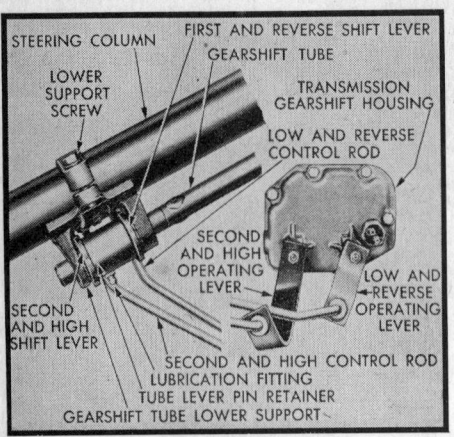

Fig. 9 Manual transmission shift linkage. 1957-59

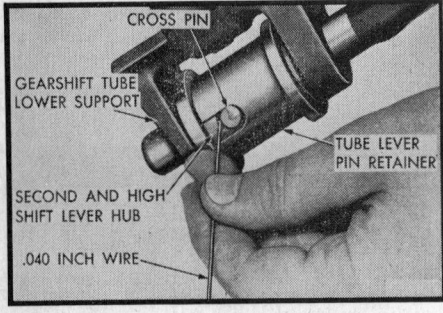

Fig. 10 Checking gearshift lever shaft in Neutral position. 1957-59

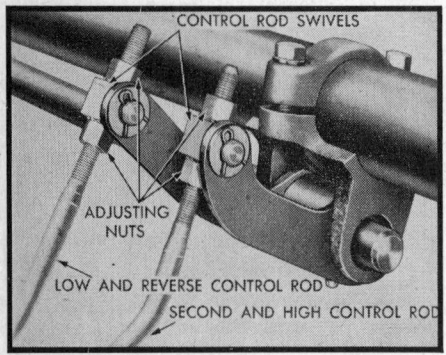

Fig. 11 Gearshift control rod adjustments. 1957-59

If an up and down motion at the hand lever is experienced during cross-over, the shift rod length should be adjusted by turning the adjusting nuts on one rod to vary the trunnion position on the rod. This will raise or lower the lever at the lower end of the steering column and thus align the cross-over. The hand lever knob must be in a horizontal position following cross-over adjustments.

If the lever binds when moving into a gear position after cross-over, check the position of the gearshift tube support at the lower end of the steering column. The support should be moved up to relieve binding on the second-to-high side and down for the low-to-reverse side.

Cross-Over Adjustments

Before making the cross-over adjustment, Fig. 10, the gearshift lever shaft must be in its normal fully returned position in neutral. Then proceed as follows:

1. Remove grease fitting from tube lever pin retainer. Rotate retainer until gearshift tube cross pin is exposed.
2. If a .040″ round feeler cannot be inserted between pin and bottom of slot as shown in Fig. 10, an adjustment at the gearshift tube lower support must be made as follows:
3. Loosen lower support screws slightly. Move support by tapping lightly with a plastic hammer.
4. Adjust support up or down as required to secure the necessary .040″ clearance.
5. Tighten support clamping screws to 150 *inch* lb. torque (90 *inch* lb. for power steering equipped cars).
6. Rotate tube-lever pin retainer to original position and install grease fitting securely. (Loss of fitting will result in loss of cross pin).

Control Rod Adjustments

After completing foregoing adjustments, be sure gearshift lever travels freely and equally up and down in either high or second gear position and low or reverse positions. Check the cross-over adjustments, Fig. 11, with the manual lever by making the cross-over from second-to-direct and from low-to-reverse. Cross-over must be free of interference. Transmission must be in neutral when making the following adjustments:

1. Loosen adjusting nuts at second-to-direct control rod swivel.
2. Turn both adjusting nuts in direction

required to locate hand lever in horizontal plane.
3. Tighten adjusting nuts securely to swivel block.
4. Loosen adjusting nuts at low-to-reverse gearshift control rod swivel.
5. Position low-to-reverse gearshift lever in direct alignment (through center of swivel lock pin) with second-to-direct gearshift lever. Tighten adjusting nuts securely to swivel block.

Caution: Failure to make this adjustment correctly will result in insufficient manual lever-to-steering column clearance or manual lever-to-operator's leg clearance. Damage to the transmission is also possible because of incomplete engagement of gears.

POWERFLITE

A detailed service procedure on this transmission is given in the *Automatic Transmission Section* of this manual.

Transmission, Replace

1. Drain transmission and converter.
2. Disconnect front universal and secure propeller shaft to frame.
3. Remove hand brake linkage.
4. Disconnect speedometer cable, neutral starter and back-up light wires from switches.
5. Disconnect throttle linkage from lever at transmission.
6. Remove push button control cable (if equipped).
7. Remove oil cooler lines (if equipped).
8. Remove nuts from rear engine mount and support engine with a suitable jack.
9. Remove crossmember, leaving engine rear support adapter attached to transmission.
10. Unfasten transmission from converter housing and slide it straight back and out of car.
11. Reverse foregoing procedure to install.

POWERFLITE LINKAGE

Selector Linkage, 1954

1. Move manual control lever at transmission to "D" position (third detent from front).
2. Check angle of gearshift control bellcrank upper lever in relation to the frame line. This should be 24 to 29 deg. to the horizontal above the frame line and pointing to the rear of the vehicle. If not at this angle, proceed as follows:
3. Disconnect front and rear gearshift control rods at the bellcrank. Locate bellcrank upper arm as described above and adjust rear control rod to the required length for a free fit in the bellcrank lower lever. Then reinstall rod.
4. Place selector lever pointer in the "D" position on the indicator dial. Check clearance between gearshift tube lever gate neutral stop land at the bottom of the steering column and gearshift lever tube. This should be .015″ to .017″ with .015″ to .030″ clearance between gate and wide

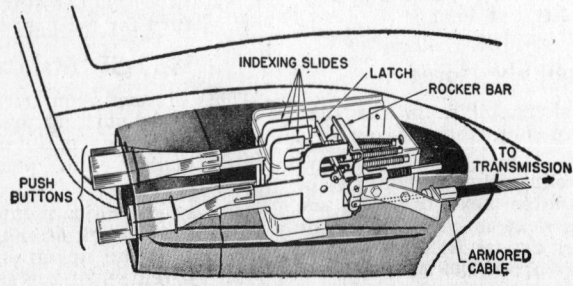

Fig. 12 Powerflite push button control unit

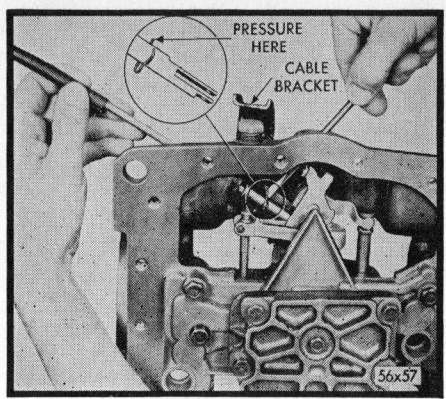

Fig. 13 Removing push button control cable from Powerflite transmission (oil pan removed to show operation)

flat face portion of lever. To adjust, loosen t h r e e attaching screws at lever gate and move gate to the desired clearance. Tighten attaching screws.

5. Make sure selector lever pointer is still in "D" position. Then adjust f r o n t gearshift rod to required length for a free fit to upper lever of bellcrank. Reinstall rod.

6. Operate selector lever through all indicator positions. Check position of pointer on indicator dial.

Selector Linkage, 1955

The selector lever is held in a gate between "N" and "D" positions under tension which is adjustable by a bracket to which it is attached behind the instrument panel. Use a spring scale and pull out the selector lever knob, which should require one to two lbs. pull on the scale to break contact between selector lever and gate. If it does not, adjust by loosening the bracket attaching bolts and slide the bracket to obtain the desired tension. Tighten bolts and recheck tension.

If correct tension cannot be obtained by adjusting the bracket, it can be corrected by removing the selector lever and mounting bracket and bending the tension spring. Bend the spring away from the gate to decrease tension and toward the gate to increase tension. If binding still exists, investigate the linkage and correct as required.

Throttle Linkage, 1953-54

Accelerator pedal angle should be 118 deg. to the horizontal. If not, adjust throttle rod length by turning the ball joint at the carburetor end of the carburetor-to-bellcrank rod to obtain the proper pedal angle. Operate linkage to be sure no binding exists.

Throttle Linkage, 1955-57

Correct any binding condition in linkage before proceeding. Engine must be at operating temperature (off fast idle) and idle speed set to 475-500 rpm. Stop engine and loosen throttle linkage adjusting screw, located on accelerator shaft-to-carburetor rod. Move rear portion of rod rearward until stopped by

the idle stop on the transmission throttle cam. With rods in line and rear portion slightly pre-loaded, lock throttle linkage adjusting screw securely.

Throttle Linkage, 1958

Correct any binding condition before making any adjustments. Engine must be at operating temperature (off fast idle) and idle speed set to 475-500 rpm in neutral.

Stop engine and loosen throttle linkage adjusting nuts on carburetor-to-bellcrank rod and on bellcrank-to-transmission rod. Adjust carburetor-to-bellcrank rod to position the lever ½" from the firewall (see "A", Fig. 17) and tighten adjusting nut. Hold a slight pre-load rearward on bellcrank-to-transmission rod while holding transmission throttle valve lever forward against the stop and tighten adjusting nut.

The accelerator pedal should be at an angle of approximately 118 deg. to the horizontal ("C" Fig. 17). If necessary to adjust pedal angle, remove accelerator pedal end of bellcrank-to-pedal rod and shorten or lengthen the rod by loosening the lock nut at the swivel end. Rotate swivel until proper rod length is obtained. Reinstall rod and tighten lock nut. The straight portion of the bell-crank-to-transmission rod is approximately 6½" long as indicated at "B", Fig. 17, measured from bellcrank end to center of bend.

Throttle Linkage, 1959-61

Throttle linkage adjustment remains essentially the same as for 1958 models with the following exception:

Placing a pin through an appropriate slot and hole (in lever and bracket) will set the correct angle of the lever for easier adjusting of the entire throttle linkage. Also, on 1960-61 models, dimension "B" as shown in Fig. 17, does not apply as the rod is shaped differently.

POWERFLITE PUSH BUTTONS
1956-61

Mechanical connection between the push button unit, Fig. 12, and the manual

Fig. 14 Control cable backlash adjustment. Powerflite

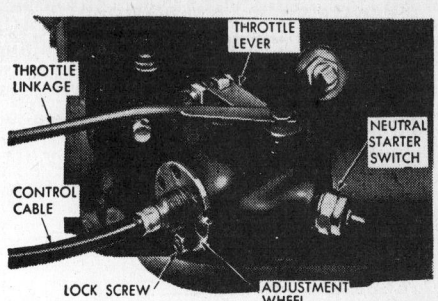

Fig. 14A Wheel-type push button cable adjustment. 1959-61 Torqueflite

control valve is obtained through the use of a single push-pull cable. One end of the wire cable is secured to the cable actuator in the speed range selector unit on the instrument panel. The other end enters the transmission case to engage the manual control valve assembly.

Cable Remove, Push Button End

Remove bezel attaching screws, then remove adjust ring and push buttons. Remove nuts holding push button unit to instrument panel and remove push button unit from rear of panel. The cable bracket is held by two screws to the push button unit. A hairpin clip secures the cable to the actuator bar.

Cable Remove, Trans. End

Remove throttle adjustment hole plug and allow transmission fluid to drain off to the level of the hole. Remove neutral starter switch to provide access to the cable lock spring. Remove cable bracket. Insert screwdriver through neutral switch hole. Push gently on projecting portion of cable lock spring and pull outward on cable, Fig. 13. On star wheel type, push "R" button in to place cable adapter near switch hole.

Cable Install, Trans. End

Push in "L" button. Place transmission manual valve lever in reverse detent by moving neutral switch contact part of lever full travel towards rear of car manually, by using a screwdriver in neutral starting switch hole. With "L" button held tightly in, insert cable into transmission case engaging cable ferrule groove with lock spring in cable adapter. Push and pull the cable, using pressure, to be sure groove in cable ferrule has engaged lock spring. Replace mounting bracket and tighten cap screw finger tight.

Cable Adjustment

Loosen and move cable and bracket assembly manually at the transmission as required, to position manual valve lever into neutral. Hold "N" button tightly in at full travel. The neutral starting switch cam should then be practically centered in its mounting hole. Use a free fitting flat nosed rod, inserted through the neutral switch mounting hole, and apply light pressure

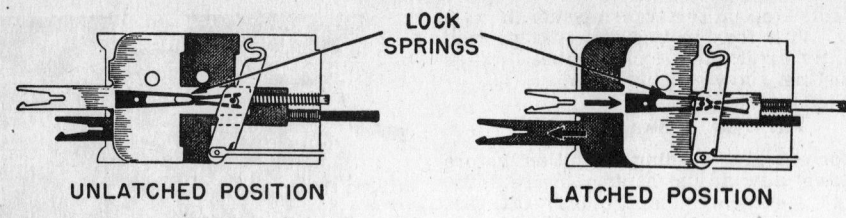

UNLATCHED POSITION | LATCHED POSITION

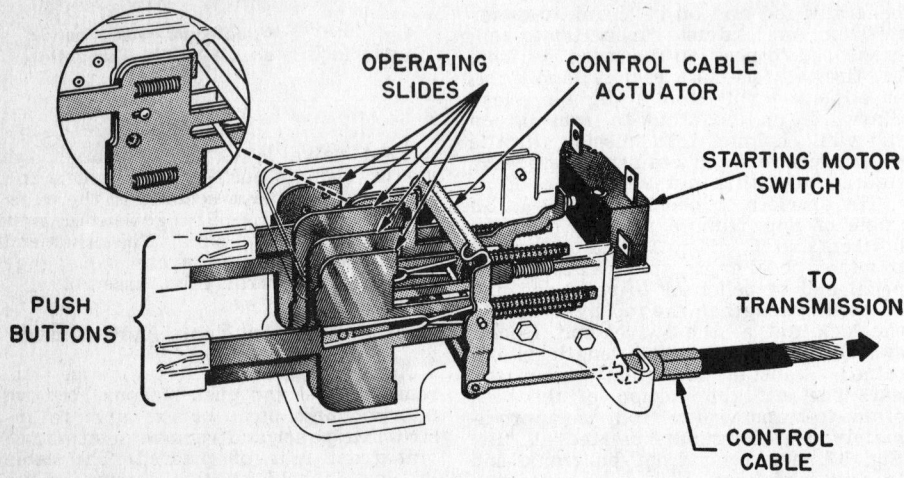

Fig. 15 Torqueflite push button control unit

against the manual valve lever to maintain the neutral detent position of the manual lever. Carefully move cable assembly in and out, without moving the manual lever, to determine total free-play travel of cable. Locate the cable in mid-position of the free-play, Fig. 14, release the pressure against the manual lever and tighten the mounting bracket securely. *Do not allow the cable to move when tightening the bracket or backlash setting will be disturbed.* Replace neutral switch and check fluid level.

TORQUEFLITE

A detailed service procedure on this transmission is given in the *Automatic Transmission Section* of this manual.

Transmission, Replace

1. Disconnect battery.
2. Place push button in "1" position ("R" position on 1960-61) so as to be able to remove cable from adapter housing on transmission.
3. Drain transmission and converter.
4. Disconnect front universal joint.
5. Disconnect hand brake linkage.
6. Disconnect speedometer cable.
7. Disconnect neutral starter switch wire.
8. Disconnect throttle control linkage at transmission.
9. Loosen push button control cable adjustable mounting bracket or adjustment wheel locking screw.
10. Remove control cable adapter housing plug, insert screwdriver through hole, release cable spring lock and remove cable from adapter housing.

11. Using same screwdriver, insert through cable opening in housing and push lever rearward to last detent. Then reinstall housing plug and tighten.
12. Remove oil cooler lines from transmission (if equipped).
13. Unfasten rear engine support from crossmember.
14. Remove starting motor.
15. Support engine with suitable jack.
16. Raise engine slightly and remove crossmember.
17. Unfasten and remove transmission from converter.
18. Reverse foregoing procedure to install transmission.

TORQUEFLITE PUSH BUTTONS

Wheel-Type Cable, 1959-61

1. To remove the cable, drain approxi-

mately three quarts of oil from the transmission.
2. Engage "1" push button.
3. Remove adjusting wheel lock screw, Fig. 14A.
4. Remove neutral starter switch, cupped washer and seal.
5. With a screwdriver inserted through neutral starter switch opening, push gently against the upward projecting portion of the control cable adapter lock spring and pull outward on cable to remove cable assembly from case.

Install and Adjust

1. Engage "R" push button. *Have an assistant hold this button firmly until the transmission end of the cable has been adjusted and locked.*
2. Back off the cable adjustment wheel (turn counter-clockwise) on cable housing until only two or three threads are showing. *Caution: do not back the wheel entirely off the guide threads because it serves as a stop to prevent the "O" ring from going too far into the case and becoming caught inside the case when the cable is installed.*
3. Push cable control housing into the transmission case with just enough force to overcome the "O" ring friction and to bottom the assembly. While holding the cable firmly into the bottomed position, rotate adjusting wheel clockwise *to just contact the transmission case.*
4. Release the inward pressure on the cable and then turn the adjusting wheel until the next adjustment hole in the wheel lines up with the lock screw hole in the case. Counting this hole as number one, continue turning the wheel clockwise until the fifth hole lines up with the screw hole in the case. Check cable adjustment to be sure of full detent in all shift ranges.
5. Install neutral starter switch and refill transmission with oil.

Non-Wheel Type Cable, 1959

1. Engage "R" button and hold in this position.
2. Loosen cable adjusting clip screw.
3. Move cable into transmission as far as it will go and turn cable adapter lock screw (left hand thread) counter-clockwise until it bottoms. This will hold lever in reverse detent position.
4. Move cable in and out and position cable in center of this free travel.
5. Tighten cable adjusting screw clip

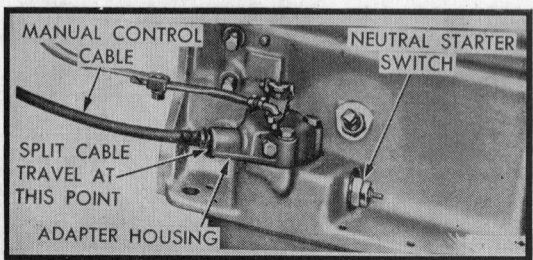

Fig. 16 Torqueflite manual control cable adjustment (non-wheel type)

to 30-50 *inch* lbs. torque.

6. Turn cable adapter lock screw out (clockwise) until it is seated at from 10-16 *inch* lbs. torque. This will seal the lock screw plug and prevent oil leakage around the lock screw threads.

Cable Adjust, 1957-58

1. Referring to Figs. 15 and 16, first engage the "R" button.
2. Drain two quarts of fluid from transmission.
3. Loosen cable adjusting clip screw.
4. Remove neutral starter switch.
5. Insert screwdriver through neutral switch hole and pry lightly on lever to hold lever in reverse detent position.
6. Move cable in and out while observing the amount of free travel, then position cable in the center of this free travel.
7. Tighten adjusting screw clip, install neutral switch and replenish transmission fluid.

TORQUEFLITE THROTTLE LINKAGE

1956-57 Four Bar. Carb.

1. Check accelerator pedal angle to make sure it is 118 degrees from the horizontal. Proper pedal angle is obtained by adjusting the pedal to shaft rod length at the ball joint on the pedal end. Check and correct any binding condition in the throttle linkage.
2. Run engine until normal operating temperature is reached. Remove air cleaner and check to see that choke valve is wide open.
3. Connect tachometer to coil and ground.
4. With engine idling in neutral, adjust engine idle screw to give 475-500 rpm, and stop engine.
5. Loosen throttle linkage adjusting nut located on the rod accelerator shaft to intermediate shaft.
6. Move rod rearward against idle stop on transmission throttle cam.
7. With rod pre-loaded and in line, lock

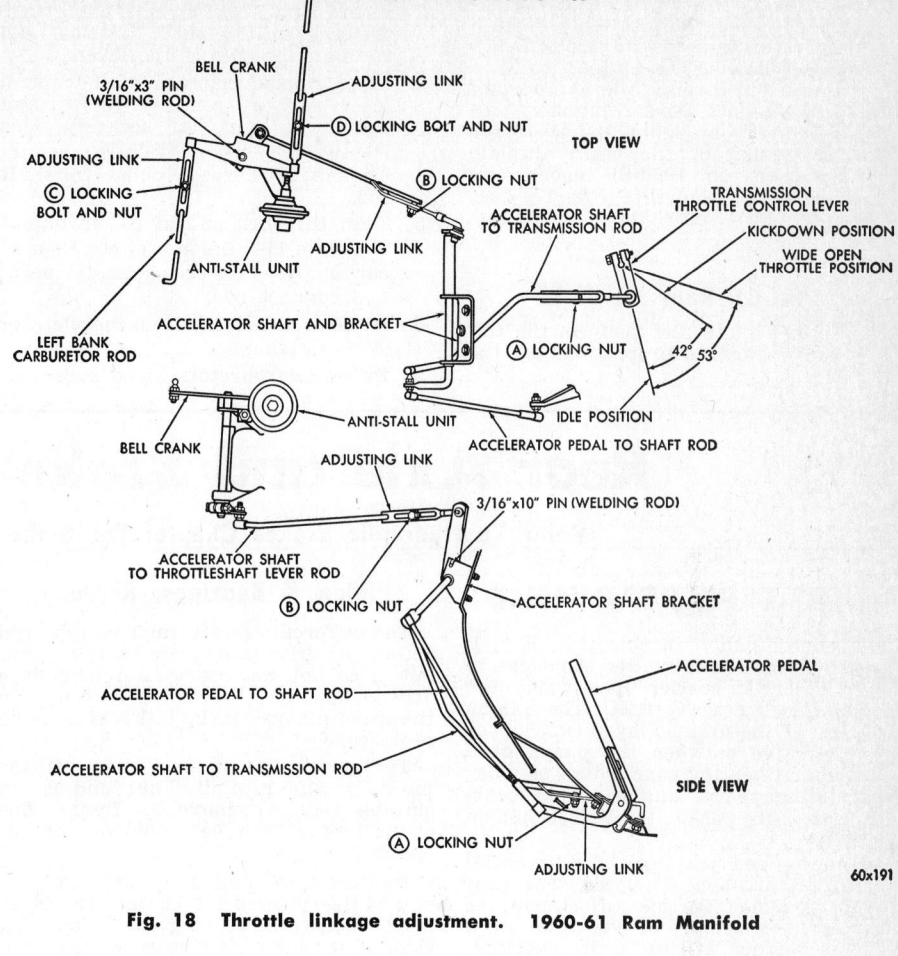

Fig. 18 Throttle linkage adjustment. 1960-61 Ram Manifold

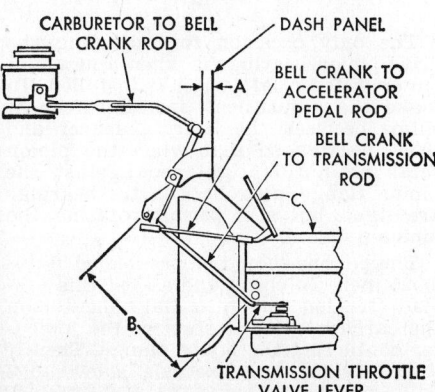

Fig. 17 Throttle linkage adjustment. 1958 Torqueflite and Powerflite

throttle linkage adjusting nut and torque to 7-9 lb. ft.

8. Start engine and recheck idle speed setting with transmission in neutral and hand brake applied.

1956-57 Two Bar. Carb.

Adjustment procedure is the same for the two-barrel carburetor except Steps 4, 6 and 7, which are performed in the following manner:

1. Loosen throttle linkage adjusting screw, located on accelerator shaft-to-carburetor rod.
2. Move rear portion of carburetor rod rearward until it is stopped by the idle stop on the transmission throttle cam.
3. With rods in line and rear portion of rod pre-loaded, lock throttle linkage adjusting screw and tighten to a torque of 7-9 lb. ft.

Note—Some vehicles may be equipped with a throttle linkage adjustment at the transmission throttle operating lever. The purpose of this adjustment is to allow for variations between chassis and engine assemblies in the manufacturing of different models and should not be used for making the throttle linkage adjustment.

1958 Four Bar. Carb.

1. With engine at operating temperature and choke valve wide open, adjust idle speed to 475-500 rpm with transmission in neutral.
2. Loosen throttle linkage adjusting nuts on carburetor-to-bell crank rod, and on bell crank-to-transmission rod.
3. Adjust carburetor-to-bell crank rod to position the lever ½" from the cowl dash panel and tighten adjusting nut (see "A", Fig. 17).
4. Dimension "B", Fig. 17, should be 8½". Hold slight pre-load rearward on bell crank-to-transmission rod while holding the transmission throttle valve lever forward against the stop, and tighten adjusting nut.
5. The accelerator pedal height should be at an angle of 115 degrees (see "C", Fig. 17) to the horizontal. If necessary to correct, shorten or lengthen pedal rod at the swivel. Reinstall rod and tighten lock nut.

1958 Two Bar. Carb.

All operations are the same as the four barrel carburetor except that, since there is no intermediate throttle control assembly, adjustment is made on the bell crank-to-carburetor rod.

1959-61

Throttle linkage adjustments remain essentially the same as for 1958 models with the following exception:

Placing a pin through the appropriate slot and hole (in lever and bracket) will set the correct angle of the lever for easier adjusting of the entire throttle linkage. Also, on 1960-61 models, dimension "B" as shown in Fig. 17, does not apply as the rod is shaped differently.

1960-61 Ram Manifold

Refer to Fig. 18 and perform the following operations to properly adjust the linkage:

1. Loosen adjusting nuts "A" and "B".
2. Insert a $\frac{5}{16}$" drill rod, 10" long into the accelerator shaft bracket and through the hole in the lever.
3. Move transmission throttle control lever forward until it stops and tighten locknut "A" securely. This positions accelerator shaft.
4. Unsnap accelerator pedal to shaft rod.
5. Turn threaded end of rod in or out to obtain 114° angle between floor of car and flat face of accelerator pedal and connect rod.
6. Remove drill rod from accelerator shaft bracket.
7. Inspect carburetors to be sure that choke valves are open, fast idle cams are released and throttle valves are closed.
8. Loosen locknuts "C" and "D" and back off anti-stall plunger far enough to allow bellcrank to be pivoted.
9. Pivot bellcrank until a $\frac{3}{16}$" drill rod, 3" long can be inserted through bellcrank hole and down into intake manifold.
10. Tighten locknuts "C" and "D" and remove the drill rod from the bellcrank.
11. Push rearward on the accelerating shaft to throttle shaft lever rod adjusting link until stop is reached and tighten locknut "B" securely.

Rear Axle and Brake Section

Refer To Hydraulic Brakes Chapter For Brake Adjustments

CAGE-TYPE REAR AXLE

The drive pinion in this unit, Fig. 1, is held in position by the shoulders in the differential carrier upon which the pinion bearing cups seat. The pinion position is maintained by a washer or shims located between the pinion head and the rear bearing cone. Shims between the bearing spacer and the front bearing cone are used to adjust pinion bearings.

The threaded nut type of differential bearing adjustment is used. The procedure for making this adjustment, as well as the assembly of the differential case, replacing a ring gear, checking ring gear and pinion backlash, and other differential case operations, is given in the *Rear Axle* chapter.

Pinion & Bearings, Replace

The differential unit must be removed before the drive pinion can be taken out, but it is not necessary to remove the drive pinion or differential unit if only the drive pinion bearing oil seal is to be replaced.

To remove the oil seal, take off the pinion flange retaining nut and use a suitable tool to remove the flange. The oil seal may then be pulled out of the carrier.

Pull the drive pinion through the gear end of the differential carrier. The bearing spacer, front bearing and shims may then be taken out. Using a bearing puller, remove the rear bearing cone from the pinion shaft and, unless the ring gear and pinion are to be replaced with new parts, use care not to allow the front and rear shim packs to become mixed.

If the differential unit was satisfactory from the standpoint of noise before the unit was dismantled, the drive pinion may be assembled with the original shims (or washer) behind the rear bearing. If new parts are used or if an adjustment was necessary, change the shims until the correct combination is obtained to locate the pinion properly.

To assemble, place the front bearing in position in its cup and install the pinion shaft oil seal, using a suitable tool. Place the washer or shims on the pinion shaft against the pinion head and press on the rear bearing. Slip the bearing spacer against the rear bearing, then place the front bearing shims ahead of the spacer. Install the pinion and assembled parts in the carrier, passing the forward end of the pinion through the front bearing. Replace the pinion flange, slip on the washer, screw on the retaining nut and tighten securely.

Pinion Bearings, Adjust

The only occasion for adjusting the drive pinion bearings is when a new pinion or differential carrier is installed. To make the adjustment, install sufficient shims between the bearing spacer and front bearing so that when the pinion retaining nut is tightened against the pinion flange, all rollers in the bearings are tight, but still permit rotating the pinion by hand.

The pinions should be pre-loaded .0015-.0025 inch. To check and adjust this preload (tension) mount a dial indicator on the carrier with the stem of the indicator contacting the pinion flange. Then if the indicator, for example shows .004 inch end play, remove the parts including .006 inch of shimming to give the necessary .002 inch draw tension or preload on the bearings.

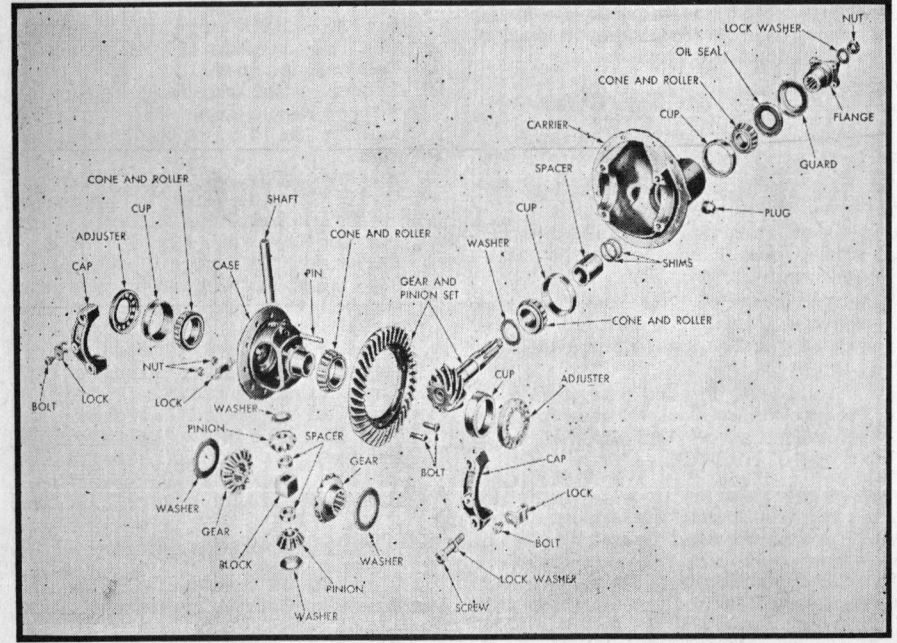

Fig. 1 Rear axle with cage-type differential. 1953-61

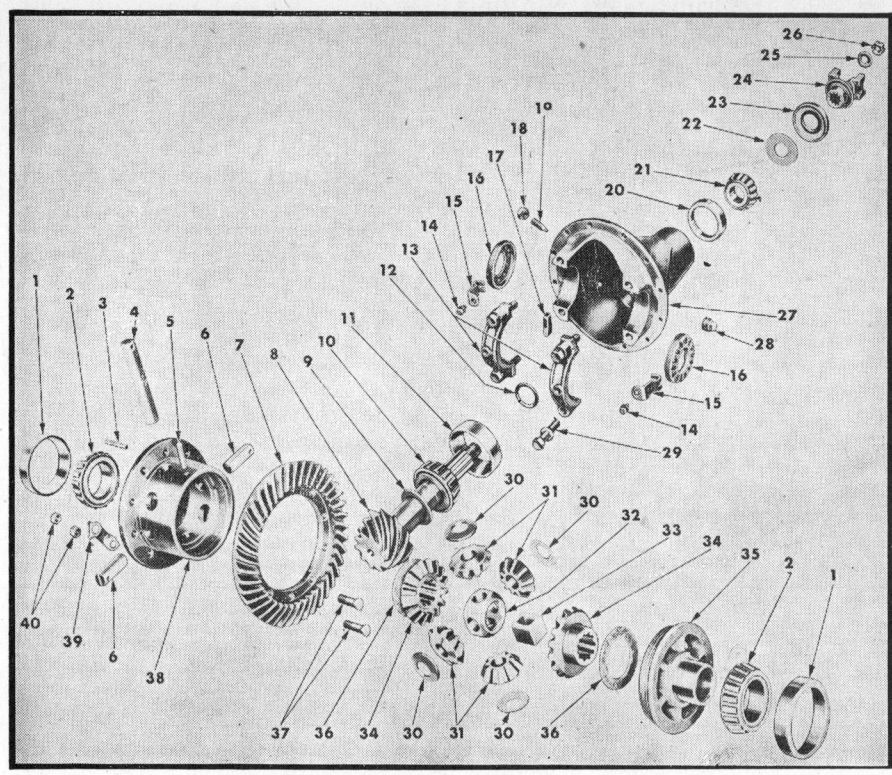

Fig. 2 Rear axle with screwed-on type barrel differential. Used on 1953-56 Crown Imperial

1—Bearing cup	11—Bearing cup	21—Bearing cone	31—Pinion
2—Bearing cone	12—Washer	22—Oil slinger	32—Block
3—Shaft lock pins	13—Carrier caps	23—Oil seal	33—Thrust block
4—Shaft	14—Lock screw	24—Yoke	34—Gear
5—Lock pin	15—Lock	25—Washer	35—Case cap
6—Shaft	16—Adjuster	26—Nut	36—Thrust washer
7—Gear	17—Thrust screw pad	27—Carrier	37—Bolts
8—Pinion	18—Check nut	28—Filler plug	38—Differential case
9—Washer	19—Thrust screw	29—Screw and washer	39—Nut lock
10—Bearing cone	20—Bearing cup	30—Thrust washer	40—Nuts

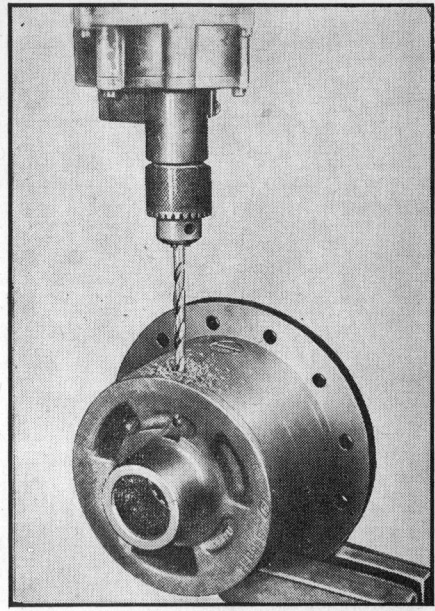

Fig. 3 Removing differential case lock pin from screw-on type differential

Fig. 4 Removing differential case cap (2) with spanner wrench (1)

Fig. 5 Removing differential pinion shaft lock pin. 1. Differential gear. 2. Lock pin. 3. Case cap. 4. Case. 5. Shaft. 6. Pinion. 7. Lock pin

Pinion, Adjust

After adjusting the pinion bearings, the position of the pinion should be checked. If a pinion setting gauge is available, check the pinion depth as outlined in the *Rear Axle* chapter. If a correction is necessary, disassemble the parts and, if the pinion is to be moved toward the center of the axle, add shims or install a thicker washer (whichever is used) between the pinion head and the rear bearing cone. If the pinion has to be moved away from the center of the axle, remove shims or install a thinner washer.

If no pinion setting gauge is available, assemble the differential unit in the carrier and check the tooth contact by painting the ring gear teeth as described in the *Rear Axle* chapter. When the adjustment is correct, install a new cotter pin in the pinion retaining nut.

SCREW-ON BARREL DIFFERENTIAL

Fig. 2 shows the differential driving unit employed on the above models. The drive pinion is held in place by the shoulders in the differential carrier, upon which the pinion bearing cups seat. A washer between the shoulder on the pinion shaft and the front bearing cone controls end play in the pinion bearings.

The ring gear and pinion are precision machined when manufactured so that no shims or washers are needed to make adjustments for pinion position.

A thrust pad, which presses against the back face of the ring gear, together with the rigid differential case design, maintain accuracy of mesh between the ring gear and pinion.

The threaded nut type of differential bearing adjustment is used. The procedure for making this adjustment, as well as replacing the ring gear and checking ring gear and pinion backlash, is given in the *Rear Axle* chapter.

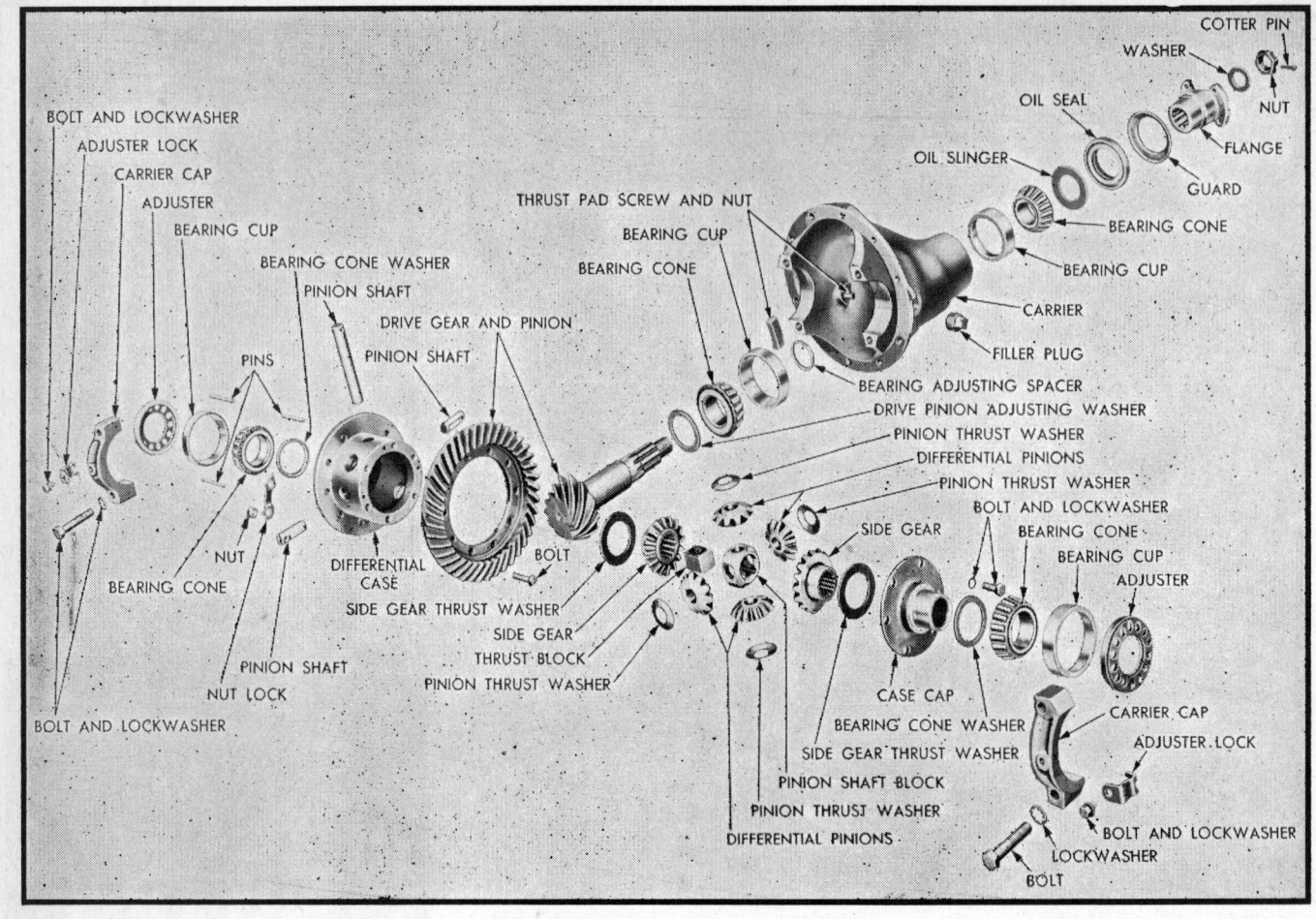

Fig. 6   Rear axle with bolt-on type barrel differential.   1953-57

Note—Except for the differential case, all service work is the same as described for the unit used on other Chrysler models.

Differential Case, Overhaul

Mount the differential case ring gear flange in a vise using copper jaws. Remove the bearing from the differential case cap side only. Remove differential case cap locking pins, Fig. 3, by center punching and drilling. Remove shell of pins left in hole with a punch.

Since the cap is a thousandth or two larger than the hole in the case which it fits into, case must be expanded for removal of cap or damage will result.

Heat the case (not cap) by playing a torch around the outside. Keep the flame moving to assure even heating. Try a piece of ordinary solder on case from time to time and when solder just starts to melt, the case is as hot as it can get without damaging inside washers.

When the case is just hot enough to melt soft solder, remove the cap, using a blunt drift and heavy hammer. If the special wrench shown in Fig. 4 is available, jar the cover loose by means of a smart blow on the wrench handle and then unscrew the cap. The parts now

can be immersed in oil to cool them for subsequent handling.

Remove the differential pinion shaft lock pin by driving it out of the case with a hammer and punch, Fig. 5. When installing this pin, be sure to peen over the outside edge of the hole to lock the pin in place.

Push the differential shaft out of the differential case. The gears, thrust washers and axle shaft thrust block will then be loose and fall out of the case.

When assembling, coat all parts with differential lubricant to facilitate holding them in place until the thrust block and differential pinion shaft are installed. Heat the case as outlined above and install the case cap, tightening it rigidly with the spanner wrench, Fig. 4, if available, or else with a punch and hammer. Drill new ¼ in. holes in the cap and install new (unused) lock pins.

Ring Gear Thrust Pad

This pad, Fig. 2, assists in maintaining the mesh of the ring gear and pinion. After all other adjustments have been made, turn the pad adjusting screw in until it just contacts the back face of the ring gear and then back it off about ⅛ turn, locking the adjustment with the lock nut.

BOLT-ON BARREL DIFFERENTIAL

Fig. 6 is a layout of the parts that make up this unit. Service-wise, it is the same as the screw-on barrel type except that the differential is unbolted from the cap. In all other respects, the unit is serviced in the same manner as the other types.

AXLE SHAFT & OIL SEALS

Fig. 7 shows the details of the new type outer oil seal employed on these models. To remove, take off the wheel, hub and drum. Then disconnect the brake tube at the wheel cylinder, and remove the brake support. Drive out the old seal and remove the burrs from the support plate to prevent damaging the new seal.

With the brake support removed, install the new seal from the outer side of the brake support plate. Then stake the plate in three places with a center punch to hold the seal in position. Install the special tool, Fig. 8, in the seal or use other suitable means to protect the leather portion of the seal from being damaged by the axle shaft keyway and

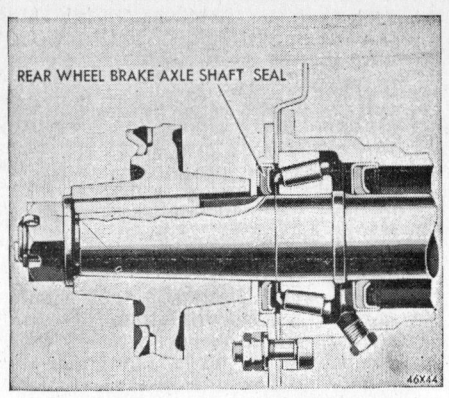

Fig. 7 Wheel bearing and axle shaft details. All models

1957-61 Service Note

As indicated in the *Rear Axle Specifications* table, the end play clearance is absolutely essential in order to allow for lengthwise expansion of axle shafts as temperatures increase during normal driving. If end play is not within the limits of .013" to .023", adjust to .018". If end play is less than .013", it is possible that the normal heat expansion of axle shafts may tend to preload the axle shaft bearings and reduce bearing life.

BRAKE MASTER CYLINDER, REPLACE

1953-54

The master cylinder is combined with the pedal bracket into a single assembly. To remove the cylinder, take out the floor mat and floor pan. Disconnect the brake line tubes from the cylinder fitting. Disconnect the clutch pedal rod at the clutch pedal and unhook the brake pedal pull back spring. Remove the three bolts from the master cylinder body. The cylinder with pedals, shaft and bracket can then be lifted off the frame bracket. Install in the reverse order of removal.

1955-61

To remove the master cylinder, remove pedal return spring. Disconnect push rod, brake line tube at master cylinder, and stop light switch wires. Unfasten cylinder from its mounting and remove from dash panel.

POWER BRAKE

1956-61 Bellows Type

To remove the unit, use a pedal depressor to depress the pedal to prevent

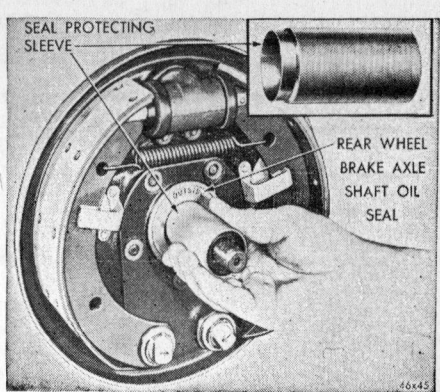

Fig. 8 Installing axle shaft outer oil seal with special sleeve

the trigger arm from extending beyond the extremities of the bracket. *If the pedal linkage is allowed to extend through the hole in the dash panel the trigger arm may be damaged.*

Disconnect the vacuum hose at the power vent. Remove the master cylinder power unit and bracket from dash panel. Use care to prevent loss of nylon bushing on pedal linkage cross pin.

Reverse foregoing procedure to install the unit.

1956 - 61 Cylinder Type

Place a wood wedge between power brake lever and forward edge of triangular hole in pedal bracket to prevent trigger arm from extending beyond extremities of bracket. *If pedal linkage is allowed to extend through dash panel the trigger arm may be damaged.*

Disconnect vacuum hose at power unit. Unfasten and remove power unit from dash.

---

install the brake support as shown. Remove the tool and complete the installation of the brake support, hub and drum and wheel.

To remove the axle shaft and inner oil seal, disconnect the brake line and remove the wheel hub and drum assembly. *Do not use a knock-out type puller or strike the ends of axle shafts to loosen wheel hubs as this may damage the bearings.* Remove the axle shaft keys and install the special sleeve shown in Fig. 8 to protect the seal while removing brake supports, seals and bearing shims. Keep each set of shims separate to assure proper assembly. Use a suitable puller to remove the axle shaft and bearing from the housing. Then pull the inner seal from the housing.

To adjust axle shaft end play, add or remove shims as required to obtain the desired end play. When adjusting bearings, remove or install an equal thickness of shims on the right and left sides of the axle housing to maintain central position of shaft thrust block.

Front End and Steering Section

CAMBER & CASTER, ADJUST

1959-61

Caster and camber adjustments are accomplished by means of the upper control arm attaching bolt and cam assemblies, Fig. 1.

To adjust caster and camber, carefully loosen the upper control arm adjusting bolt nuts while holding the bolts to prevent turning. Record caster and camber readings.

Adjustment of caster through camber readings is possible because of the consistent relation between caster change and camber change when either the front or rear cam bolt at each control arm is individually rotated.

Turning one bolt affects caster more

than camber. Turning both bolts an equal amount in the same direction affects camber directly, and caster indirectly. Turning the cams an equal amount in opposite directions will change caster with little change in camber, depending on the relative position of the cams.

By bringing caster within specifications by turning one bolt at a time, then by turning both bolts an equal amount to bring camber to the preferred reading, the caster will usually be brought close to the preferred setting.

After both caster and camber readings are correct, tighten the nuts to a torque of 65 lbs. ft. while holding the bolts from turning.

Always recheck the settings after tightening the nuts since the bolts may have turned slightly during the tightening process.

1957-58

Adjustments are performed by installing $\frac{1}{16}$" and $\frac{1}{32}$" shims between the upper control arm support brackets and the frame sub-side rails. Installing or removing shims at either the front or rear bracket changes the *caster* setting. Installing or removing shims equally at both brackets changes the *camber*.

Raise the car from the floor and loosen the upper control arm support bracket bolts. Add or remove shims as required and tighten bolts. *Adding shims equally at both front and rear support brackets will decrease positive camber. One shim $\frac{1}{16}$" thick at each bracket will change camber $\frac{5}{16}$ degree.*

Addition of shims to the front bracket or removal of shims at the rear bracket will decrease positive caster. One shim $\frac{1}{16}$" thick will change caster approximately ½ degree. Total thickness of each shim pack should not exceed $\frac{9}{16}$".

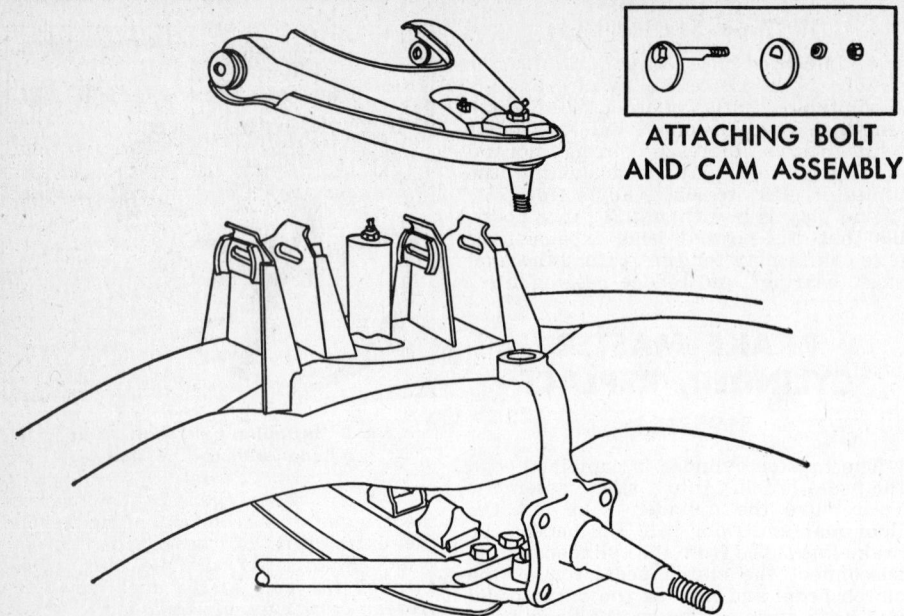

Fig. 1 Upper control arm and frame brackets. 1959-61

After lowering car, jounce front end up and down a few times before rechecking wheel alignment to allow suspension to assume normal position.

1953-56

Caster angle is not adjustable but the proper setting is obtained when assembling the camber eccentric bushing. To adjust camber, loosen the clamp screw and turn bushing to obtain the correct setting within a half revolution from the point where the correct caster setting is obtained. Do not turn the bushing until it binds against the upper control arm. Keep the steering knuckle support as nearly central as possible.

TOE-IN, ADJUST

1953-61

With the steering wheel in its mid-position, and the center spoke of the steering wheel horizontal, turn both tie rods an equal amount until the toe-in is correct.

WHEEL BEARINGS, ADJUST

1. Tighten wheel bearing adjusting nut to 90 inch pounds torque while rotating wheel.
2. Position nut lock on nut with one pair of slots in line with cotter pin hole.
3. Back off lock and adjusting nut to next slot.
4. Install cotter pin. The resulting adjustment should be zero to .003" end play.
5. Clean grease cap, coat inside with wheel bearing grease (do not fill) and install cap.

TORSION BAR SUSPENSION

1957-61
Service Notes

1. When necessary to install new torsion bars, remove all accumulated dirt, scale and moisture from inside torsion bar rear anchor.
2. Do not apply heat to anchor assembly in order to remove bar. Use an arbor press to remove bar from anchor whenever necessary.
3. Coat inside of anchor with multipurpose grease.
4. The torsion bars have a pre-set loading for right and left usage. Bars can be identified by the letter "R" or "L" stamped on one end of bar. This letter is not visible when the bar is installed. However, the last three digits of the part number can be

seen from the anchor end of the bar; the left bar is stamped with the odd number, the right bar with the even number.
5. Always install new torsion bar rear anchor seal.
6. In every case where a bar is being replaced for breakage, apparently as a result of corrosion within the rear anchor, it should be assumed that the other bar would be in a similar condition, and both bars should be replaced.
7. The torsion bar adjusting bolt should only be loosened (or tightened) with a foot pound torque wrench with vehicle supported under frame to relieve load on torsion bars. If more than 200 ft. lbs. is required to turn the adjusting bolt, then the bolt and swivel must be replaced.
8. If the vehicle is to be raised on a hoist, make sure it is lifted on the frame only so the front suspension is in full rebound under load.

TORSION BAR, REPLACE

1957-59
Removal

1. Raise vehicle by jacking under frame crossmember. Release load from torsion bar by unscrewing anchor adjusting bolt partly out of swivel.
2. Remove lock ring from rear of anchor. Slide torsion bar rearward to disengage forward end of bar from lower control arm. Then move forward to disengage bar from anchor. Remove bar, swivel and cam from frame bracket anchor.

Installation

1. Assemble anchor, swivel, bolt seat (oval side up) and bolt in frame anchor bracket. Check for torsion bar cushion in lower control arm housing. With cam bolt barely entered in cam swivel, slide bar into rear cam.
2. Rotate anchor and torsion bar until anchor is positioned as close as possible to floor pan. Engage front of bar in lower control arm shaft as far as bar will go. *Unless anchor*

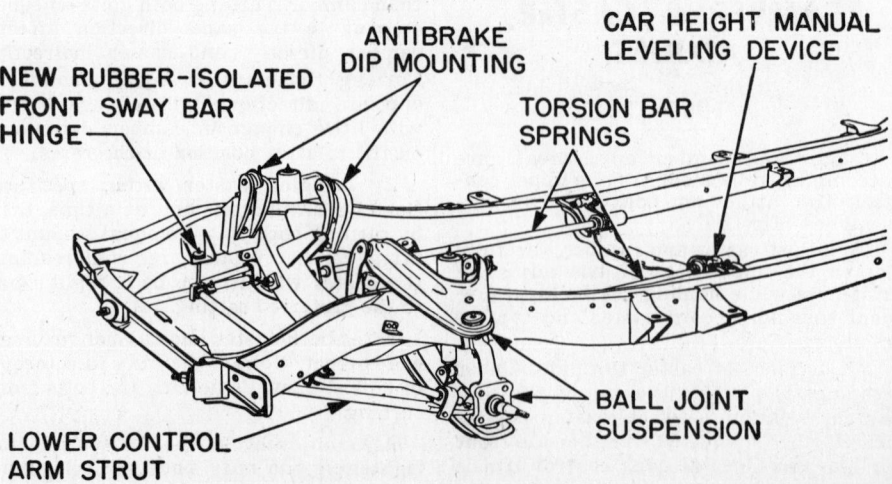

Fig. 2 Torsion bar suspension

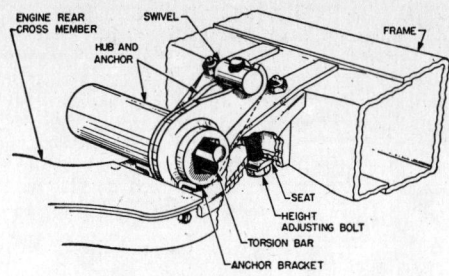

Fig 3. Torsion bar spring cam and height adjustment. 1957-59

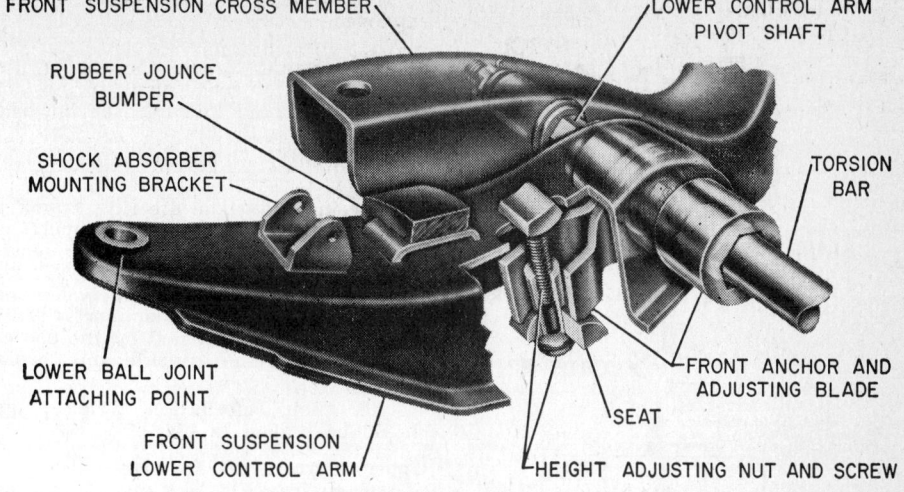

Fig. 4A Front suspension height adjustment. 1961

blade is in the position just described when installing bar, it will be impossible to adjust front suspension to the proper height.

3. Center and install lock ring in rear of anchor housing. Pressure may be applied to bar to enable lock ring to be installed.
4. After lock ring is installed, tighten cam bolt until approximately one inch of threads are showing above anchor bolt swivel. *This is an approximate setting used merely as a starting point when adjusting suspension height This setting is also necessary to place load on torsion bar before lowering vehicle to floor.*
5. Check and adjust suspension height as outlined further on.

1960-61

Removal

1. Raise vehicle by jacking under center of front crossmember.
2. Release load from torsion bar by backing off anchor adjusting bolts.
3. Remove bolt and swivel and discard.
4. Remove plastic seal from rear end of torsion bar anchor, and remove lock ring from anchor.
5. Slide torsion bar toward rear of car enough to disengage forward end from lower control arm. Slide bar forward and down, disengaging it from anchor, and remove bar.

Installation

1. Slide new anchor end seal over end of bar with cup side facing rear.

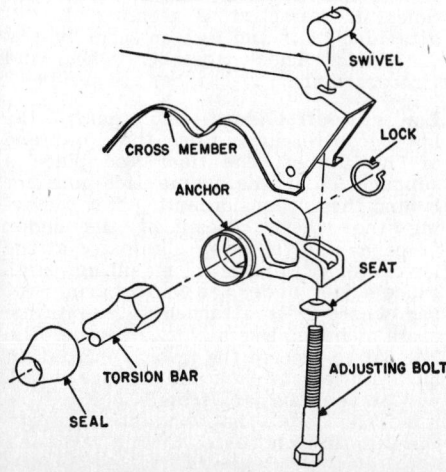

Fig. 4 Torsion bar rear support. 1960

2. Install torsion bar and position seal in groove on anchor hub.
3. Turn torsion bar until anchor is positioned approximately 120° (8 o'-clock position) down from frame. *If anchor end is not in this position when installing bar it will be impossible to adjust the suspension to the correct height.* Engage front of bar in hex opening in lower control arm.
4. Before installing lock ring, center bar so that full contact is obtained at anchor and control arm shaft. Install lock ring in groove.
5. Pack anchor seal with grease and position lip of seal in anchor hub groove. Install plastic seal in rear end of anchor.
6. Slide adjusting bolt swivel on frame and install adjusting bolt and seat. Tighten bolt into swivel until approximately one inch of threads are showing out of swivel. *This is an approximate setting used as a starting point when adjusting for correct suspension height. This setting is also necessary to place a load on the bar before lowering vehicle to floor.*
7. Lower car to floor and adjust suspension height as outlined below.

SUSPENSION HEIGHT, ADJUST

1. Jounce car so parts can assume normal position.
2. Measure from lower ball joint to floor and from bottom of lower control arm bushing housing to the floor.
3. Subtract one measurement from the other. The difference should be as listed below subject to a tolerance of plus or minus 1/8".

1957-58 Cars	1/4"
Suburbans	2¾"
C-300 Models	1¾"
1959 Cars	2⅛"
Suburbans	2½"
1960-61 Cars	2"
Suburbans	2½"

If these measurements differ more than 1/8" or if one or both of them are outside the specified limits, the suspension height of both sides must be adjusted. To adjust, turn the anchor bolt clockwise to raise the height and counterclockwise to lower it, Figs. 3 and 4.

BALL JOINT SERVICE

1. To replace ball joints, Fig. 5, raise car by jacking under lower control arm and remove wheel assembly.
2. Remove upper and lower ball stud nuts and slide tool shown in Figs. 6 and 7 down over lower stud until it rests on steering knuckle.
3. Turn threaded portion of tool, locking it against ball joint being removed. Spread tool enough to place ball stud under pressure, then strike the steering knuckle sharply with a hammer to loosen the stud. *Do not attempt to force the stud out of the knuckle with the tool alone.*
4. Remove tool, then disengage ball joint from knuckle.
5. Remove dust cover and grease seal.
6. Remove grease fitting and unscrew ball joint from control arm.
7. When installing ball joints, it is important that the threads engage those of the control arms squarely. Torque the ball joints to the control arms to 125 ft. lbs., the lower stud nut to 135 ft. lbs., and the upper stud nut to 100 ft. lbs.

FRONT END REPAIRS

Service Note, 1955-56

The front end on these models is basically the same as 1954 models except that the shock absorber is mounted within the coil spring. To remove a front shock absorber, proceed as follows, Fig. 7A.

1. Raise hood and clean the area around the upper mounting.
2. Slide a wrench over the flats on top of the shock absorber piston rod to keep the rod from turning. Then remove the nut and cup washer.

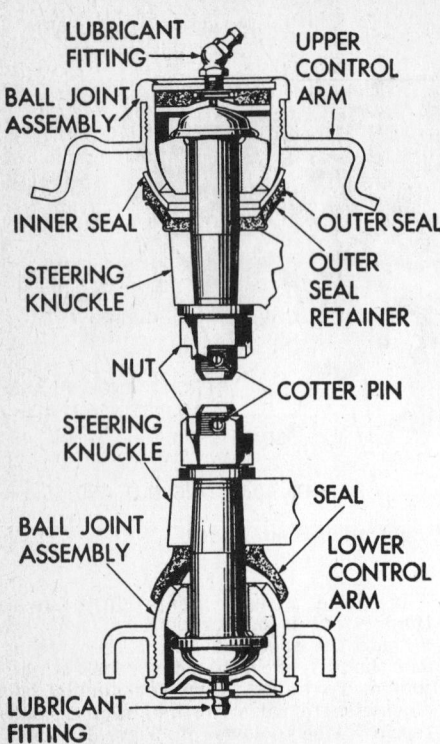

Fig. 5 Section view of upper and lower ball joints

3. Remove the two lower mounting bolts and withdraw the shock absorber through the opening in the spring seat. Lower cup washer may remain in place or drop through when shock absorber is removed.
4. Using a suitable drift, force the inner steel sleeve out of the bushing and remove the bushing from the frame opening.
5. Before installing a new bushing, dip it in soapy water and insert in the frame with a twisting motion. When installed properly, the groove in bushing will index the frame.
6. Force steel sleeve through opening in bushing and down into position.

Note—In servicing the balance of the front end, follow the procedure given for 1954 models, disregarding any items which obviously do not apply to 1955-56 models.

Kingpins & Bushings—
1. Remove wheel and hub assembly.
2. Block brake pedal so it cannot be depressed.
3. Unfasten brake support plate from knuckle.
4. Remove steering arm from knuckle.
5. Remove brake hose and connection and lift off brake support.
6. Remove kingpin lock pin.
7. Drive a punch into upper steering knuckle welch plug and pry out plug.
8. Drive kingpin downward, forcing out lower welch plug. A soft brass drift should be used in driving against top of kingpin.
9. If needle bearings are used in the knuckle they should be removed with a suitable puller. A puller should also

be used when pressed-in bushings are employed.

When installing needle bearings they must be installed from the top of the knuckle with the trade mark on top and the oil hole lined up with the oil hole in the steering knuckle.

Pressed-in type bushings must be line reamed.

After installing the steering knuckle, make sure it is free in the support as binding at this point may cause sensitive steering and car wander. There should be .008 in. clearance between the knuckle and knuckle support. This clearance can be adjusted by the use of shims between the knuckle and thrust bearing.

After their installation, welch plugs should be staked in place.

Upper Control Arm, Remove—
1. With a jack under the lower control arm spring seat, raise the car and remove the wheel.
2. Remove shock absorber.
3. Unscrew bolt from outer end of control arm.
4. Unfasten and remove control arm pivot bar.

Upper Control Arm, Assemble—
1. Position the pivot bar with seals installed in the control arm and install Tool C-608 on the pivot bar, Fig. 8. This tool has two sets of bolt holes to accommodate both sizes of upper control arm pivot bars. Be sure tool is securely fastened to pivot bar.
2. Expand the two jaws of the tool by tightening the expander wedge screw until the jaws of the tool are just snug against inside of web of control arm. Do not bring screw down more than is necessary to place jaws firmly against control arm; if tool is properly fastened to pivot bar, jaws will make proper contact on inside faces.
3. Lay a steel scale across base of expander, noting the distance between the two lines, Fig. 8. Tighten expander wedge screw until control arm has been spread 1/16 in. from its original "at rest" position.
4. Start bushings on both ends of pivot bar. Lubricate them with light engine oil or cutting oil to allow them

Fig. 6 Removing upper ball joint from steering knuckle

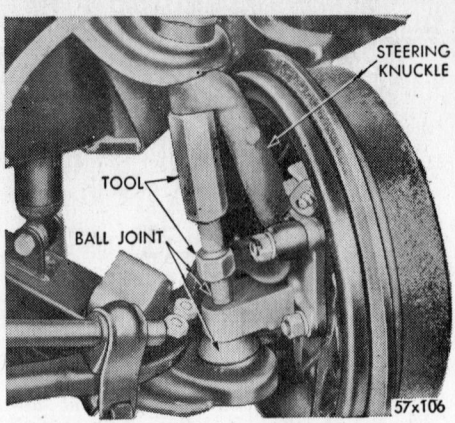

Fig. 7. Removing lower ball joint from steering knuckle

to cut their own threads in the control arm without scoring, Fig. 9.
5. Thread bushings into control arm until shoulders of bushings contact surface of control arm. Tighten with a torque wrench to at least 120-140 lbs. ft. torque.
6. Remove tool and check operation of pivot bar for freedom of movement. Only a moderate grip should be required to turn the pivot bar. Note—The pivot bar should not be rotated as this would throw it off center with the control arm and affect the caster adjustment.
7. Lubricate control arm bushings with chassis lubricant before installing on the car.

Upper Control Arm Eccentric Bushing, Install—First, install the upper control arm to the steering knuckle support as follows:

1. Install a new eccentric bushing in the steering knuckle support and place one oil seal on the bushing at the hexagon end. Oil or grease the other seal slightly and place it on the opposite boss of the control arm.
2. Slide the control arm and seal onto the steering knuckle support until the seals fit properly over the bushing and the pin hole is in proper alignment. Install pin, nut and cotter pin.
3. Using a drift, line up pivot bar holes in frame cross member. Install attaching bolts and tighten securely.
4. Install shock absorber, wheel and tire assembly.

Lower Control Arm — To remove the lower control arm, raise the front end of the car off the floor and place a support under the frame side member behind the suspension unit. After removing the wheel, disconnect the shock absorber and the sway eliminator at the lower shock absorber mounting stud. Place a jack under the control arm pivot bar where it is attached to the frame cross member. Use a block of wood, Fig. 7A, cut to receive the lower control arm bar between the jack and the bar, which will prevent the jack from slipping. Now raise the jack just enough to relieve the pressure on the pivot bar fastening bolts. Remove the bolts, placing tapered drifts in each hole, to prevent binding of the last bolt removed. Lower the jack slowly, allowing the lower control arm to come down, then lift out the spring. Remove the lower control arm pin from the knuckle support and take out the lower control arm assembly.

Lower Control Arm Bushings—To assemble the lower control arm bushings, insert the pivot bar in the control arm and place a suitable tool between the legs of the lower control arm. Start the bushings on both ends of the pivot bar, using a suitable lubricant, such as tapping compound, to cut the threads into the arm bosses without scoring. Thread the bushings into the control arm until the shoulders of the bushings contact the machined surface of the control arm, and tighten them with a force of 180 pounds feet.

Remove the tool from between the legs of the control arm and check the operation of the pivot bar for free movement in the bushings, but do not rotate it. The distance from the machined surface of the control arm to the center of the pivot bar mounting holes should be $2\frac{5}{32}''$ on 1949-54 (1.68" on 1955-56), which would be altered if the pivot bar was rotated. Lubricate the control arm bushings with semi-fluid chassis lubricant.

HORN RING
1953-61

To remove the horn ring, disconnect the battery, press down on the horn ring ornament and turn it counter-clockwise to release it. Remove mounting base screws and lift out horn ring.

STEERING WHEEL
1953-60

To remove the steering wheel, take off the horn blowing ring as outlined above. Unscrew the nut from the steering shaft. Attach a suitable puller to the steering wheel hub and pull off the wheel.

STEERING GEAR, REPLACE
1953-54 (Mechanical & Gemmer Type Power)

1. Remove horn blowing ring and steering wheel as outlined above.
2. Remove clutch, brake and accelerator pads.
3. Fold carpet back out of the way from the pedals and steering column.
4. Remove steering column draft pad.
5. Disconnect accelerator rod from bell crank just behind the fire wall in engine compartment.
6. Remove floorboard, accelerator pedal and rod assembly.
7. Remove hairpin clip and disengage rod from transmission cross-over lever.
8. Disconnect horn wire from its connector.
9. Disconnect six turn signal wires by

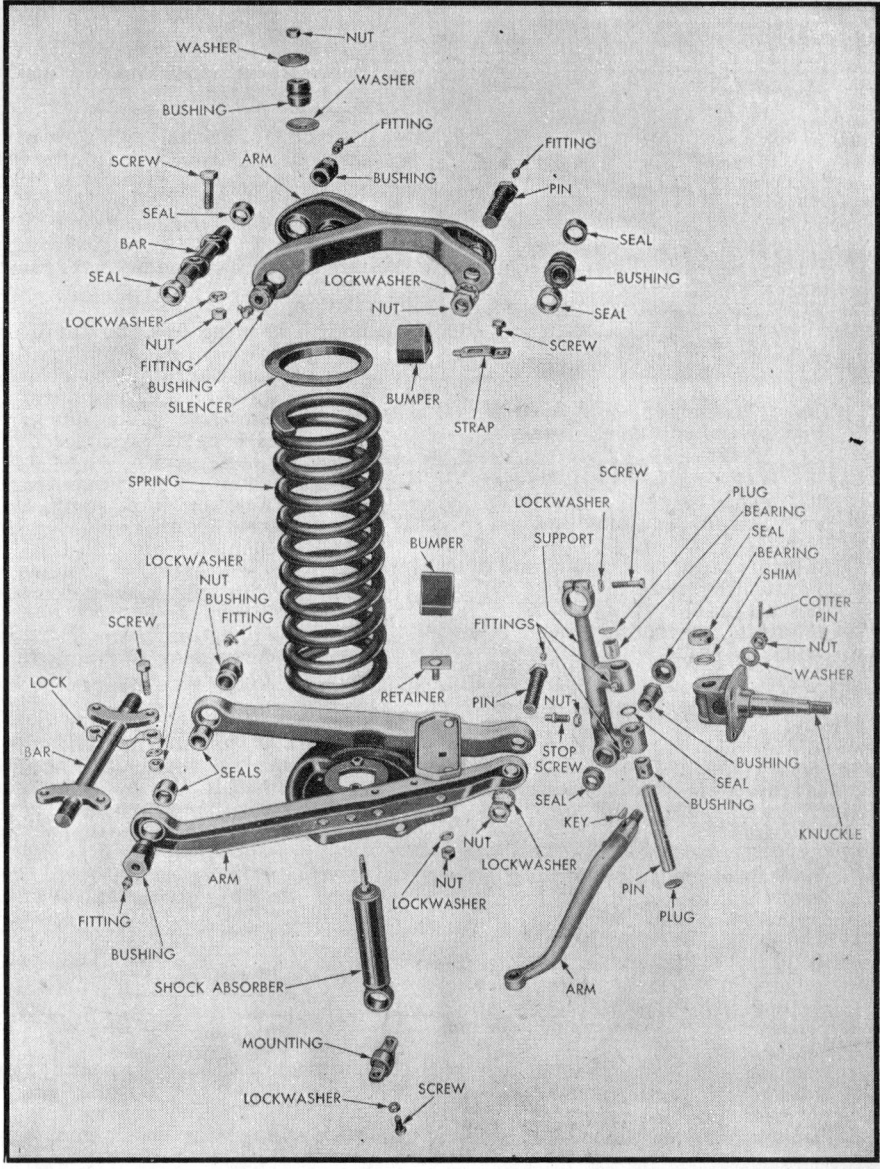

Fig. 7A   Front suspension. 1953-56

pulling three wires out of each connector plug.
10. Disconnect transmission shaft rod from shaft lever control arm.
11. Three bolts attach the steering gear assembly to the frame bracket. The two top bolts can be reached from under the hood and the bottom bolt can be reached from the front compartment through the floorboard opening. *At this point, remove only the two top bolts,* leaving the bottom bolt to hold the assembly in place until the drag link has been disconnected.
12. Remove drag link.
13. Remove starting motor and Pitman arm. *On cars with power steering, it is not necessary to remove the steering arm when removing the steering gear from the car. Remove the bolt that attaches the master cylinder push rod to the brake pedal. Remove the brake pedal bushing lock (horseshoe type) and slide the pedal outward on the shaft far enough to clear the pedal return stop screw. Now, move the pedal back toward the rear of the car, allowing sufficient clearance between the clutch and brake pedals in order to remove and install the Steering Chuck Assembly.*
14. On Power Steering cars, from under the engine compartment, disconnect the pressure and return hoses that run between the gear housing valve body assembly and the pump and reservoir, respectively. The hoses should be disconnected at the gear housing-valve body assembly and tied to the hood in an out-of-the-way-position, Thus, the ends of the hoses will be above the reservoir and will not drip oil.
15. Reach through the floorboard opening (from the driver's compartment) and remove the lower bolt

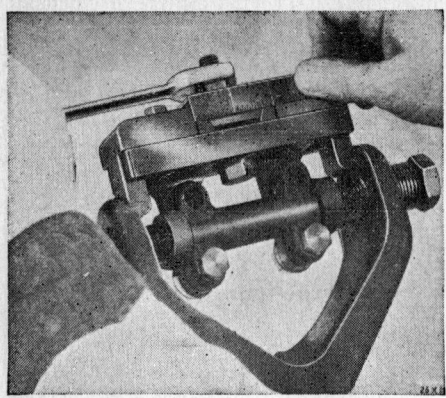

Fig. 8 Spreading upper control arm with tool C-608. 1953-54

that holds the gear assembly to the lower end of the frame bracket.

16. Remove the steering column shroud-to-instrument panel screws and take the steering gear assembly out of the car.

17. To install, reverse the foregoing procedure.

1955-56 Mechanical Type

Note—It is not necessary to remove the steering column and mast assembly to service the lower worm bearings and cross shaft assembly.

1. Disconnect battery.
2. Press down on horn ring ornament while rotating it and remove ornament.
3. Pull off steering wheel.
4. Loosen jacket-to-instrument panel bolts.
5. Remove dust pad retaining screws.
6. Remove pitman arm.
7. Loosen jacket - to - gear housing clamp bolt.
8. Remove housing-to-frame attaching bolts and work gear and cross shaft out of jacket.
9. Remove assembly from lower side of car.

1957-60 Mechanical Type

Note—It is not necessary to remove the steering column and mast assembly to service the lower worm bearings and cross shaft assembly.

1. Disconnect battery ground cable.
2. Remove steering wheel and disconnect horn and turn signal wires at instrument panel. On 1960, remove turn signal switch from jacket tube.
3. Remove jacket tube clamp at steering gear housing.
4. Remove jacket support clamp at instrument panel.
5. Remove dust shield at firewall.
6. Remove floor opening panel.
7. Remove pitman arm.
8. Remove steering gear housing-to-frame bolts.
9. Slide jacket tube and remove control units rearward through the driver's compartment as an assembly.
10. Remove brake pedal pad.
11. Remove gear from engine side of firewall.

All 1961 and Late 1960 Windsor

1. Pull off steering gear arm.
2. Remove bolt which fastens coupling to worm shaft.
3. Unfasten steering gear from frame (3 bolts) and slide gear forward to disconnect coupling from worm shaft.
4. Mark the index (master serration) position with chalk on outside of coupling hub. Then raise gear and remove it from engine compartment.

Installation

1. Locate steering gear center by rotating worm shaft from one extreme to the other while counting the number of turns. Then turn the worm shaft back ½ the number of turns, which is the exact center of steering gear travel.
2. Locate master serration in outer row of serrations on worm shaft. Mark master serration and index the gear into the engine compartment.
3. Align index mark on outside of coupling hub with master serration on worm shaft.
4. Slide coupling on worm shaft and fasten gear housing to frame, tightening bolts evenly to a torque of 50 ft. lbs.
5. Position coupling bolt hole in line with groove on worm shaft and install bolt and lockwasher; tighten bolt to 30-35 ft. lbs. *It is important that the steering tube be centered in the steering column seal and that the lip of the seal that contacts the steering tube be well lubricated with wheel bearing grease at 5000 mile intervals.*

POWER STEERING

Replace, 1954-56

1. Remove horn ring ornament by pressing it down and turning. Disconnect wire and remove horn ring.
2. Remove steering wheel, turn signal lever and plate.
3. Loosen steering column - to - instrument panel bracket.
4. Loosen steering column jacket clamp screws.
5. Remove floor mat retaining plate and rubber dust pad.
6. Remove pitman arm.
7. Loosen housing-to-frame attaching bolts.
8. Disconnect pressure and return hoses.
9. Fasten disconnected ends of hoses above oil level in reservoir to prevent further loss of oil. Cap ends of hoses to prevent the entrance of dirt.
10. Remove gear housing-to-frame attaching bolts and alignment wedge.
11. Remove gear assembly from under side of car.

Replace, 1957

1. Remove steering wheel and power steering column jacket.
2. Remove pin and disconnect steering tube from coupling.
3. Remove floor mat retaining plate.

4. Remove rubber dust pad and floor pan opening cover.
5. Remove pitman arm.
6. Loosen gear housing-to-frame attaching bolts.
7. Disconnect pressure and return hoses.
8. Cap fittings at steering gear and fasten disconnected ends of hoses above oil level in reservoir to prevent further loss of oil. Cap ends of hoses to prevent entrance of dirt.
9. Disconnect stop light switch wires from brake master cylinder.
10. Disconnect brake booster reservoir from fender side shield and move aside.
11. Remove gear housing-to-frame attaching bolts and alignment wedge.
12. Remove gear assembly by sliding unit forward and out of engine compartment.

Replace, 1958-61

1. Disconnect battery ground cable.
2. Disconnect horn wire.
3. Remove horn button and horn ring and disconnect horn wire.
4. Remove steering wheel.
5. Disconnect turn signal wires at connectors and on 1960-61 models, remove turn signal switch. Also on 1960-61 models, remove retainer snap ring from the groove in the steering tube at the top of the bearing.
6. Remove jacket tube support bracket at instrument panel. Loosen two bolts attaching jacket tube to steering housing, push jacket tube upward to expose the steering tube coupling pin and remove the pin.
7. Disconnect pressure and return hoses at steering gear. Fasten disconnected ends of hoses above oil level in reservoir. Cap ends of hoses and fittings on steering gear to prevent the entrance of dirt.
8. Use puller to remove steering arm. Unfasten and remove steering gear from frame and out through engine compartment.

Fig. 9 Installing upper control arm bushings. 1953-54

9. On cars with Ram Manifold, remove the fender opening panel. Raise lower end of gear housing and rotate the assembly in a clockwise motion towards the cowl panel until the gear shaft splines clear the frame rail, then tilt the housing toward the engine and remove the gear through inspection hole at fender side panel.

10. Reverse removal procedure to install gear.

MANUAL STEERING GEAR REPAIRS

In this type steering gear, Fig. 10, the worm is integral with the steering shaft and is supported on each end by opposed tapered roller bearings. The triple tooth roller is attached to the roller shaft by means of a steel shaft. Two needle bearing assemblies are installed between this shaft and the roller. (Some light duty models have a two tooth roller shaft).

The roller shaft is mounted in the steering gear housing on two needle bearing assemblies which are pressed into the housing. The housing cover is attached to the housing by four cap screws. An adjustment screw, mounted in the cover, controls roller shaft end play and worm and roller mesh adjustment.

The steering wheel and roller shaft arm (pitman arm) are splined to the steering shaft and roller shaft respectively. Both the pitman arm and steer-

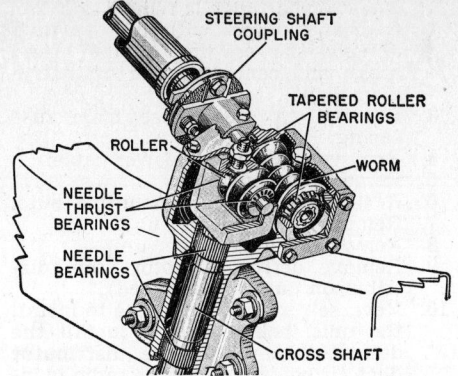

Fig. 10 Manual steering gear. 1961

ing wheel have master splines to insure correct installation.

Worm End Play, Adjust

1. Free the steering gear of all load by disconnecting the drag link and loosening the steering column braces.
2. Loosen the four cover screws about ⅛".
3. Use a knife to separate the top shim, passing the blade all the way around between the shims, being careful not to damage the remaining shims.
4. Remove one shim at a time between inspections to remove the end play.
5. The adjustment is correct when there is no end play and no stiffness in the steering gear throughout the complete range of its travel.

Roller Shaft End Play, Adjust

1. Turn the steering gear to either extreme and back off ⅛ of a turn.
2. Gripping the pitman arm at the hub, the roller shaft should rotate freely without a particle of end play.
3. If end play exists, adjust as required by means of the roller shaft adjusting screw in the side cover.
4. Be sure to tighten the lock nut securely and inspect for end play and free rotation throughout the entire range of steering gear travel.

Worm & Roller Mesh, Adjust

1. Loosen the roller shaft adjusting screw lock nut.
2. With the steering gear in its central position (drag link disconnected) tighten the roller shaft adjusting screw just enough to remove play between the roller shaft roller tooth and worm.
3. Check this by the amount of play felt at the pitman arm. It is better to leave a slight amount of play at this point than to tighten too much.
4. If tightened beyond the point where the lash is removed, serious results will occur which will cause poor steering operation.
5. Tighten the adjusting screw lock nut.

Radio, Speedometer and Windshield Wiper

WINDSHIELD WIPER

1955-56 Chrysler & Imperial

Due to the restricted room properly to assemble the eccentrics at the crank arm link ends, it will be necessary to remove the wiper assembly as a unit whenever the wiper or links are to be serviced.

Before attempting to remove the wiper motor for complete disassembly, the wiper should be operated and then shut off by turning off the ignition. *Failure to observe this precaution will result in irreparable damage to the motor switch and spring parking cam when the switch cover is removed.*

To remove the wiper, proceed as follows:

1. Disconnect wiper motor.
2. Remove right-hand fresh air door.
3. Remove clips that hold links to pivot cranks. *Clips are removed by lifting top tab and sliding sideways out of engagement with groove in pivot crank pin.*
4. Remove brass spacing washer.
5. Slip end of link containing nylon ball bushing off pivot crank pin.
6. Remove three retaining nuts and remove wiper motor bracket and links. A thick rubber gasket is assembled

between motor bracket and dash panel to reduce noise.
7. Reverse the above procedure to install the wiper assembly.
8. Adjust parking position if necessary by moving the cam adjustment lever which sticks out of the switch cover.
9. Connect wires from motor to switch as follows:
   Blue wire to "P" terminal.
   Black wire to "A" terminal.
   Red wire to "F1" terminal.
   Yellow wire to "F2" terminal.
   Hot lead wire (red) from fuel gauge is attached to circuit breaker.

1957-59 Chrysler & Imperial

To facilitate assembly and disassembly of eccentrics at the motor crank and link ends, the wiper assembly should be removed as a unit whenever wiper or links are to be serviced.

To remove the wiper on cars *not* equipped with heater and refroster ducts, first disconnect the wiper leads at the switch. Disconnect wiper links at pivot cranks by removing clips and brass washer. Remove 3 nuts which hold large motor bracket to firewall. The complete unit may now be removed by moving the bracket back

far enough to clear the studs and lowering unit down under instrument panel. *Care should be taken not to bend the links, and the battery should be disconnected to eliminate the possibility of shorts.*

To remove the wiper on cars *equipped* with heater and defroster ducts, first remove glove box and door. If car is equipped with a radio that removes from front of instrument panel, time will be saved by removing it. Disconnect wiper leads from switch. Disconnect links from pivot cranks. While holding unit in place, remove 4 self-tapping studs from motor plate to motor bracket which is attached to firewall. The unit may now be moved horizontally towards passenger side and then down from under instrument panel.

Installation is accomplished in the reverse order of removal. To readjust wiper arms, loosen wiper arm nut until a definite click is heard. Move arm to desired position and tighten. Connect the wires from the motor to the switch controls as follows:

Red wire to "F1" terminal.
Yellow wire to "F2" terminal.
Black wire to "A" terminal.
Blue wire to "P" terminal.
Hot lead from battery to circuit breaker.

1953-54 De Soto

The parking switch mounted on the motor is a simple "make" and "break" switch. The wires should be connected to the switch as follows: Green wire to "B" terminal; red to "F" terminal, and black to "A" terminal.

If both blades do not park in the same position, relocate the arms on the pivot shafts. If this fails to correct the condition, it may be necessary to disassemble the motor and reassemble the crank arms in their correct positions.

If the wiper will not stop, the condition may be due to a defective control switch. Inspect the switch to make sure the cam strikes the switch button. If necessary, open circuit the motor to stop it. Bend the cam out slightly, being careful that the cam does not strike the side of the button.

1955-59 De Soto

The wiper motor should be operated and shut off by turning off the ignition. The motor must not be disassembled when the cranks are in the parked position or damage to the motor switch and contact follower will occur when the cover is removed. To remove the wiper, proceed as follows:

1. Disconnect wires at motor.
2. Remove radio and right-hand fresh air door.
3. Disconnect links at pivot cranks. Clips are removed by lifting the top tab and sliding it sideways out of engagement with the groove in pivot crank pin.
4. Remove spacing washer and remove link from pivot crank.
5. Disconnect mounting bracket at dash panel and remove wiper motor and bracket.
6. Reverse procedure to install, being sure rubber mounting gasket is in place.
7. Adjust wiper parking position by moving cam adjustment lever which projects from switch cover.

1960-61

1. Remove glove compartment door.
2. Remove glove compartment.
3. Remove bolts attaching wiper motor bracket to the cowl panel to the instrument panel brace.
4. Disconnect wires at wiper motor.
5. Disconnect links at the pivot cranks. Clips are removed by lifting the top tab and sliding it sideways out of engagement with the groove in the pivot crank pin.
6. Remove the spacing washer and remove the link from the pivot crank.
7. Slide the complete wiper with the links far enough towards the left so the right hand link will clear the glove compartment opening in instrument panel and remove assembly using care so as not to bend the links.

RADIO REPLACE

1953-54 Chrysler & Imperial

1. Disconnect battery to prevent accidental shorts while removing radio.
2. On cars equipped with dash cowling, remove the cowling around hand brake and center section of instrument panel.
3. Remove "A" lead fuse from fuse casing.
4. Remove control unit power cable.
5. Remove antenna lead.
6. Remove control unit mounting nuts.
7. Remove radio control unit.
8. Remove speaker-power unit.
9. Remove defroster motor from distribution duct (if equipped).
10. Reverse removal procedure to install the unit, being sure to install the defroster motor in the distributor duct (if equipped) before radio is installed.

1954-56 De Soto

The radio panel must first be removed from the front of the instrument panel to gain access to the radio.

On 1956 cars equipped with cigar lighter in the ash receptacle, remove the lead wire from the junction blocks at the left support bracket.

1955-56 Chrysler & Imperial

1. Remove ash tray and cowl vent plate.
2. Remove cowl vent lever knob and cowl vent mechanism.
3. Swivel cowl vent tube back for clearance.
4. Disconnect radio and speaker lead wire.
5. Remove control knobs and mounting nuts.
6. Remove radio and speaker.
7. To install, reverse removal procedure. Adjust antenna compensator after radio is installed, being sure antenna is fully extended.

1957 Chrysler & Imperial

1. Disconnect antenna, pilot lamp lead from orange wire on harness, two wire lead from speaker, "A" lead from accessory terminal on temperature gauge.
2. Remove rear speaker wire plug.
3. Remove mounting screw from lower instrument panel-to-bracket on radio.
4. Remove radio and ash receiver housing from panel (Chrysler only).
5. Remove radio and speaker from underneath instrument panel.
6. To install, reverse removal procedure. *Do not operate radio with speaker disconnected from radio. Insert jumper wire in rear seat speaker socket, otherwise receiver will not operate.*

1957-58 De Soto

Disconnect battery ground cable and "A" lead wire at temperature gauge. On Electro-Touch Tuner models, disconnect power unit connecting plug. Disconnect speaker wires. Remove radio mounting screws on front of radio and nuts from mounting studs.

1958 Chrysler

1. Remove speaker grille and speaker.
2. Disconnect "A" lead, pilot lamp and rear seat speaker plug.

3. Remove mounting screw from lower instrument panel to bracket on radio.
4. Remove nuts from studs on rear of radio and ash receiver housing.
5. Remove two screws from bottom of radio and ash receiver housing.
6. Remove radio and ash receiver housing with radio attached from front of instrument panel.
7. Reverse above procedure to install radio. *Do not operate radio with speaker detached or damage to transistor will result. If rear seat speaker is disconnected, insert jumper wire in rear seat speaker socket, otherwise receiver will not operate.*

1958 Imperial

1. Disconnect antenna, pilot lamp lead from orange wire on harness.
2. Remove speaker grille and speaker.
3. Disconnect "A" lead from accessory terminal on temperature gauge.
4. Remove rear seat speaker wire plug.
5. Remove radio mounting nut.
6. Remove radio control knobs.
7. Remove radio from underneath instrument panel.
8. Reverse above procedure to install.

1959 De Soto

1. Disconnect battery cable.
2. Remove speaker and defroster grille.
3. Disconnect speaker leads and "A" lead wire at fuse.
4. Disconnect antenna lead and remove air deflector from distribution duct.
5. Remove screw and washer assembly from instrument panel brace-to-radio mounting bracket.
6. Remove radio knobs and nuts, and lower radio from rear of instrument panel.
7. When reinstalling radio, be sure pilot lights are firmly in place and lead wires are not pinched in any way.

1959 Chrysler

1. Remove vent deflector at heater housing.
2. Disconnect antenna, rear seat speaker plug. "A" lead to the radio terminal of fuse block and dial lamp lead to orange wire at harness.
3. Remove clutch nut and screw from radio support bracket.
4. Remove control knobs.
5. Unfasten radio from panel (2 nuts) and remove radio and mounting bracket from underneath instrument panel.
6. Remove speaker from grille.
7. Remove grille if necessary.

Precaution

Do not operate radio with speaker detached, since damage to the transistor will result. If the rear seat speaker is disconnected from the radio, insert a jumper wire in rear seat speaker socket or the receiver will not operate.

1959 Imperial

1. Disconnect antenna, and the dial lamp lead from the orange lead of harness.
2. Disconnect the two-wire lead from speaker.

3. Disconnect "A" lead from radio terminal at fuse block.
4. Remove rear seat speaker wire plug.
5. Remove mounting nut from lower instrument panel-to-bracket on radio.
6. Remove radio control knobs.
7. Remove radio from underneath instrument panel.
8. Remove speaker.

1960-61 De Soto

1. Disconnect battery.
2. Disconnect antenna "A" lead, light lead and speaker leads.
3. Remove ash tray assembly to gain access to mounting bolts.
4. Remove mounting bolts and both radio-to-dash support brackets.
5. Remove radio assembly from under instrument panel.

1960-61 Chrysler

1. Disconnect battery.
2. Remove control knobs and shaft mounting bolts.
3. Remove radio-to-dash suppport brackets.
4. Disconnect "A" lead, light lead, speaker leads, antenna lead and foot selector switch, if so equipped.
5. On models with air conditioning, remove speaker attaching screws and grille from top side of instrument panel and remove speaker and radio assembly up through opening of instrument panel.
6. On models without air conditioning, remove radio from bottom of instrument panel.

1960-61 Imperial

1. Disconnect battery.
2. Remove radio-to-dash support bracket.
3. Remove two screws attaching fuse block to instrument panel and lower the fuse block.
4. Disconnect "A" lead, light lead, speaker leads, antenna leads and foot selector switch connector, if so equipped.
5. Remove radio assembly from bottom of instrument panel.

Precaution

Do not operate radio with speaker detached, since damage to transistors may result. If rear seat speaker is disconnected from the radio, insert a jumper wire in rear speaker socker to allow receiver to operate.

SPEEDOMETER REMOVAL

1953 Chrysler

1. Disconnect battery cable.
2. Disconnect speedometer cable housing.
3. Remove instrument cluster bezel attaching screws which are accessible from face of panel.
4. Disconnect trip reset cable.

5. Move instrument cluster out of panel toward steering wheel.
6. Remove wires and connections to cluster and disengage speedometer.

1954-59 Chrysler

Disconnect battery and speedometer cable housing. Remove two nuts from rear of panel and slide speedometer out through front of instrument panel.

1957-59 Imperial

Disconnect the battery cable and remove the knob on the parking brake release handle. Disconnect the parking brake cable at the pedal assembly, then remove the assembly by working it out of the instrument panel and dash panel. Disconnect the speedometer cable and the trip mileage reset cable, and pull out the speedometer light sockets. Move the wiring harness out of the way and remove the speedometer attaching nuts. The speedometer can then be taken out by working it to the left of the steering column.

1953-56 De Soto

1. Disconnect battery.
2. Disconnect speedometer cable housing.
3. Remove three speedometer to panel attaching screws in back of panel.
4. Remove speedometer assembly from behind the dash.

1957-58 De Soto

1. Disconnect battery cable.
2. Disconnect speedometer cable housing.
3. Remove switches from speedometer bezel without disconnecting the wires. This can be done by pushing them through their mounting holes into the dash panel.
4. Remove the speedometer bezel attaching screws which are accessible from the face of the dash.
5. Move speedometer out of dash toward steering wheel.

1959 De Soto

1. Disconnect battery.
2. Disconnect speedometer cable housing.
3. Remove speedometer bezel attaching screws which are accessible through the face of the dash.
4. Move speedometer out of dash toward steering wheel.

1960-61 De Soto

1. Disconnect the battery cable.
2. Disconnect speedometer cable at speedometer.
3. Remove transmission push button bezel.
4. Remove transmission control push buttons.
5. Remove the two retainer stud nuts that hold the transmission push button housing assembly to dash, then remove housing and disconnect

back-up light wires. Move housing out of way.
6. Disconnect the three instrument panel lights.
7. Remove steering column dash support to cowl panel brace.
8. Disconnect horn and turn signal wires at the connector under dash.
9. Remove four screws that attach speedometer to instrument panel. *Hold speedometer while removing last screw, to avoid possibility of dropping and scratching the lens.*
10. When screws are removed, tilt speedometer base toward firewall and carefully lower the speedometer until the lens has cleared the instrument panel opening. Move speedometer in direction of parking brake and at same time roll the end toward the parking brake, downward, until the speedometer lens is straight up and down. Turn speedometer 180° until the base is toward the firewall, and lower speedometer to remove.

1960-61 Chrysler

1. Disconnect battery ground cable.
2. Remove steering wheel.
3. Remove steering jacket tube cover from underside of jacket tube.
4. Disconnect all wires at terminals before loosening instrument cluster attaching screws.
5. Disconnect instrument ground wire.
6. Remove instrument cluster bezel (2 nuts).
7. Disconnect speedometer cable.
8. Remove steering tube collar (2 screws).
9. Detach dome and cluster from dome support by removing two long screws and spacers located just behind steering tube collar attaching screws.
10. Detach plastic dome from instrument panel (4 screws).
11. Carefully release base of dome from supports at each side with a pointed instrument. Move dome away from opening in panel so that top of dome and cluster can be tipped outward far enough to gain access to the parking brake warning light socket. *In some cases where dome fits tightly in support it may be necessary to remove six screws that attach cluster to dome. Push cluster up into dome and carefully compress dome to clear supports on removal.*
12. Snap out lamp socket and bulb and remove dome and cluster from car.
13. Remove speedometer (4 screws).
14. Reverse removal procedure to install.

1960-61 Imperial

1. Disconnect battery ground cable.
2. Remove chrome retainer ring retaining screw at bottom of retainer.
3. Pull the bottom of the retainer forward and raise the retainer to release the upper tab located at top of retainer.
4. Remove speedometer cable, unfasten and remove speedometer.

COMET & FALCON

INDEX OF SERVICE OPERATIONS

PAGE NO.

ACCESSORIES
Radio Removal 600
Speedometer Removal 600
Windshield Wiper 600
Windshield Wiper Troubles...........37

BRAKES (Mechanical)
Adjustments 112
Brake Cylinder Sizes 585
Hydraulic Brake System..............112
Master Cylinder, Replace............597
Trouble Shooting 31

CLUTCH
Clutch Pedal, Adjust.................593
Clutch, Replace 593
Trouble Shooting 13

COOLING SYSTEM
Radiator, Replace 591
Trouble Shooting 8
Water Pump Repairs..................591
Water Pump, Replace.................591

ELECTRIC SYSTEM
Dash Gauge Service..................85
Distributor, Replace 591
Distributor Service 46
Distributor Specifications 584
Generator Regulator Service..........62
Generator Regulator Specifications.....585
Generator Service 62
Generator Specifications.............585
Horn Button, Replace................599
Ignition System Service..............46
Ignition Timing 592
Starter, Replace 592
Starter Switch Service...............83
Starting Motor Service...............77
Starting Motor Specifications........585
Trouble Shooting 10
Turn Signal Troubles 12

ENGINE
Camshaft, Replace 588
Camshaft Bearings 588
Crankshaft Bearing Specs............583
Crankshaft Oil Seal, Replace........590
Cylinder Head, Replace..............586
Engine, Replace 586
Main Bearings, Replace..............590
Piston Pins, Replace.................590
Piston Rings, Replace................590
Piston & Ring Specifications.........583
Piston & Rod, Assemble.............589
Pistons & Rods, Remove.............589
Pistons, Replace....................589
Rocker Arms 588
Rod Bearings, Replace..............590
Timing Case Cover, Replace.........588
Timing Chain, Replace..............588
Trouble Shooting 4
Valves, Adjust 587
Valve Arrangement 587
Valves, Grind 587
Valve Guides 587
Valve Lifters 588
Valves, Remove 587
Valve Spring Installed Height........587
Valve Spring Testing 587
Valve Timing Data..................588

ENGINE OILING
Oil Pan, Replace 591
Oil Pump Repairs...................591
Oil Pump, Replace..................591
Trouble Shooting 4

FRONT SUSPENSION
Camber, Adjust 597
Caster, Adjust 597
Front End Repairs 597
Toe-in, Adjust 597
Trouble Shooting 33
Wheel Alignment Specifications......585
Wheel Bearings, Adjust..............597

FUEL & EXHAUST SYSTEMS
Carburetors 592
Fuel Pumps 96
Muffler and Pipes 592
Trouble Shooting 4

OVERDRIVE 100
Trouble Shooting 14

REAR AXLE
Non-Slip Differentials 109
Axle Shaft, Replace.................595
General Service 102
Rear Axle Repairs..................596
Rear Axle Specifications............585
Trouble Shooting 31

SPECIFICATIONS
Brake Cylinder Sizes 585
Capacity Data 584
Carburetors 592
Cooling System 584
Crankshaft & Bearings.............583
Distributors 584
Engine Tightening 584
Generator & Regulators............585
Pistons, Pins & Rings..............583
Rear Axle 585
Starting Motors 585
Tune Up 583
Valves 583
Wheel Alignment 585

STEERING GEARS
Horn Button, Replace...............599
Steering Gear, Adjust...............598
Steering Gear Repairs..............599
Steering Gear, Replace.............599
Steering Wheel, Replace............599
Trouble Shooting 33

TRANSMISSIONS
Manual Shift Type:
  Gearshift Linkage, Adjust..........594
  Replace 593
  Repairs 593
  Trouble Shooting 14
Automatic Type:
  Linkage, Adjust 595
  Replace 595
  Repairs 253
  Trouble Shooting 25

TUNE UP....................38

GENERAL SPECIFICATIONS

Year	Model Designation	Wheel-base, Inches	Valve Location	Bore and Stroke	Piston Dis-place-ment, Cubic Inches	Com-pres-sion Ratio (Stand-ard)	Maximum Brake H.P. @ R.P.M.	Maximum Torque Lbs. Ft. @ R.P.M.	Normal Oil Pressure Pounds
COMET									
1960	Sedan 6 Cyl..............	114	In Head	3.500 x 2.500	144	8.7	90 @ 4200	138 @ 2000	35–55
	Sta. Wagon 6 Cyl..........	109½	In Head	3.500 x 2.500	144	8.7	90 @ 4200	138 @ 2000	35–55
1961	Six Cyl. 144 C.I. Eng........	①	In Head	3.500 x 2.500	144	8.7	90 @ 4200	138 @ 2000	35–55
	Six Cyl. 170 C.I. Eng........	①	In Head	3.500 x 2.9375	170	8.7	101 @ 4200	156 @ 2400	35–55
FALCON									
1960	All 6 Cyl.., ...	109½	In Head	3.500 x 2.500	144	8.7	90 @ 4200	138 @ 2000	35–55
1961	Six Cyl. 144 C.I. Eng........	109½	In Head	3.500 x 2.500	144	8.7	90 @ 4200	138 @ 2000	35–55
	Six Cyl. 170 C.I. Eng........	109½	In Head	3.500 x 2.9375	170	8.7	101 @ 4200	156 @ 2400	35–55

①—Sedan 114″, station wagons 109½″.

TUNE UP SPECIFICATIONS

★When using timing light, disconnect vacuum line to prevent advance mechanism from operating.

Year	Model	Ground Polarity and Voltage	Spark Plug Type	Spark Plug Gap Inch	Distributor Point Gap Inch	Distributor Cam Angle Degrees	Firing Order	★Ignition Timing Mark	★Ignition Timing Location	Idle Speed RPM In Drive	Compression Pressure @ Cranking Speed Minimum
COMET & FALCON											
1960	All	N-12	F-14Y	.034	.025	35-38	153624	①	Pulley	485	170
1961	All	N-12	F-14Y	.034	.025	35-38	153624	①	Pulley	485	170

①—Minimum 2°BTDC, maximum 10°BTDC.   Normal for standard trans. 4°BTDC, auto. trans. 10°BTDC.

PISTONS, PINS, RINGS, CRANKSHAFT & BEARINGS

Year	Model	Fitting Pistons Shim To Use	Fitting Pistons Pounds Pull On Scale	Ring End Gap ① Comp.	Ring End Gap ① Oil	Wrist-pin Diam-eter	Rod Bearings Shaft Diameter	Rod Bearings Bearing Clearance	Main Bearings Shaft Diameter	Main Bearings Bearing Clearance	Thrust on Bear. No.	Shaft End Play
COMET & FALCON												
1960-61	All	②	②	.010	.015	.912	2.1232-2.1240	.0008-.0023	2.2482-2.2490	.0006-.0025	3	.004-.008

①—Fit rings in tapered bores for clearance listed in tightest portion of ring travel area.   ②—See Piston Clearance Chart, Fig. 10.

VALVE SPECIFICATIONS

Year	Model	Valve Lash Int.	Valve Lash Exh.	Valve Angles Seat	Valve Angles Face	Valve Spring Installed Height	Valve Spring Pressure Lbs. @ In.	Valve Lift Int.	Valve Lift Exh.	Stem Clearance Intake	Stem Clearance Exhaust	Stem Diameter Int.	Stem Diameter Exh.
COMET & FALCON													
1960-61	All	.016H	.016H	45	45	1¹⁹⁄₃₂	117 @ 1⁷⁄₃₂	.344	.344	.001-.0025	.002-.0035	.310	.310

COMET & FALCON

ENGINE TIGHTENING SPECIFICATIONS★

★Torque specifications are for clean and lightly lubricated threads only. Dry or dirty threads produce increased friction which prevents accurate measurement of tightness.

Year	Spark Plugs Ft. Lbs.	Cylinder Head Bolts Ft. Lbs.	Intake Manifold Ft. Lbs.	Exhaust Manifold Ft. Lbs.	Rocker Arm Shaft Bracket Ft. Lbs.	Rocker Arm Cover Ft. Lbs.	Connecting Rod Cap Bolts Ft. Lbs.	Main Bearing Cap Bolts Ft. Lbs.	Flywheel to Crankshaft Ft. Lbs.	Vibration Damper or Pulley Ft. Lbs.
COMET & FALCON										
1960-61	15-20	65-75	None	13-18	30-35	3-5	19-24	65-75	75-85	45-55

DISTRIBUTOR SPECIFICATIONS

Year and Model	Part No. ①	Rotation ②	Cam Angle, Degrees	Breaker Point Opening, Inch	Condenser Capacity, Mfds.	Breaker Arm Spring Tension, Ounces	Centrifugal Advance Data Degrees @ R.P.M. of Dist.		Vacuum Advance Data		
							Advance Starts	Full Advance	Inches of Vacuum to Start Plunger Movement	Inches of Vacuum for Full Plunger Travel	Maximum Vacuum Advance, Dist. Degrees
COMET & FALCON											
1960 Std. Tr.	CODF-12127A	C	35-38	.025	.21-.25	17-20	None	None	.33	5.35	14
1960 Auto. Tr.		C	35-38	.025	.21-.25	17-20	None	None	.65	3.94	7
1961 Std. Tr.	144″ Engine	C	35-38	.025	.21-.25	17-20	None	None	.33	5.35	14
1961 Auto. Tr.	144″ Engine	C	35-38	.025	.21-.25	17-20	None	None	.65	3.94	7
1961 Std. Tr.	170″ Engine	C	35-38	.025	.21-.25	17-20	None	None	.43	3.00	12¼
1961 Auto. Tr.	170″ Engine	C	35-38	.025	.21-.25	17-20	None	None	.43	3.00	9¾

①—Stamped on plate riveted to side of housing. ②—Clockwise as viewed from top.

COOLING SYSTEM & CAPACITY DATA

Year and Model	Cooling System Data					Fuel Tank Gals.	Engine Oil			Transmissions			Rear Axle Pints
	Quarts No Heater	Quarts With Heater	Rad. Cap Relief Pressure	Thermostat Opening Temp.			Refill Qts. ③	Summer Grade	Winter Grade	Std. Pints	With Overdrive Pints	Automatic Qts.	
				①	②								
COMET & FALCON													
1960	8.7	9.7	14	180	160	14	3½	20	10W	2.5	None	6¼	2
1961	8.7	9.7	14	180	160	14	3½	20	10W	2.5	None	6¼	2

①—For permanent type anti-freeze. ②—For alcohol type anti-freeze. ③—Add one quart with filter change.

GENERATOR AND REGULATOR SPECIFICATIONS

★To polarize generator, disconnect field lead from regulator and momentarily flash this wire to regulator battery terminal.

Year	Generator						Regulator					
	Generator Number	Rotation and Ground Polarity ①	Rated Cap. Amps.	Gen. Field Ground Location★	Brush Spring Tension, Ounces	Field Current Amperes	Regulator Number	Cutout Relay		Voltage Regulator Setting Volts	Current Regulator Setting Amperes	Current and Voltage Armature Air Gap, Inch
								Voltage to Close Points	Armature Air Gap, Inch			
COMET & FALCON												
1960-61	CODF-10000C	C-N	25	Internal	32-40	1.2-1.8②	CODF-10505A	12.8	③	15.0	25	③
1960-61	CODF-10000D	C-N	30	Internal	32-40	1.2-1.8②	B7A-10505B	12.8	③	15.0	30	③

①—N: Negative, C: Clockwise.   ②—At 12 volts (cold).   ③—No adjustment.

STARTING MOTOR SPECIFICATIONS

Year	Model	Part No.	Rotation ①	Brush Spring Tension, Ounces	No Load Test			Torque Test		
					Amperes	Volts	R.P.M.	Amperes	Volts	Torque, Lbs. Ft.
COMET & FALCON										
1960-61	All	CODF-11001A	C	48-56	70	12		110	5	15.5

①—Clockwise.

REAR AXLE AND BRAKE CYLINDER SPECIFICATIONS

Year	Model	Ring Gear & Pinion Backlash, Inch	Drive Pinion Adjustment	Drive Pinion Bearing Preload, Inch Lbs.	Drive Pinion Bearing Adjustment	Axle Shaft End Play, Inch	Hydraulic Cylinder Bore Sizes, Inch		Master Cylinder
							Wheel Cylinder		
							Front	Rear	
COMET & FALCON									
1960-61	Sedan	.005-.010	Shims	②	Spacer	①	1¹⁄₁₆	1³⁄₁₆	1
	Sta. Wagon	.005-.010	Shims	②	Spacer	①	⅞	1⁵⁄₁₆	1

①—No adjustment.
②—17-27 inch lbs. for new bearings, 10-16 inch lbs. for used bearings.

WHEEL ALIGNMENT SPECIFICATIONS

Year	Model	Caster, Degrees		Camber, Degrees		Toe-in, Inches	Toe-out on Turns, Degrees		Steering Axis Inclination, Deg.
		Limits	Desired	Limits	Desired		Outer Wheel	Inner Wheel	
COMET & FALCON									
1960-61	All	0 to +1	+½	0 to +1	+½	¼ to ⁵⁄₁₆	20	20¾	7

ENGINE & SERIAL NUMBER LOCATION
Rear Face Of Left Front Door Inner Panel

1960 Comet

ENGINE IDENTIFICATION

Year	Engine	Ser. No. Prefix①
1960	6-144	S
1961	6-144	S
	6-170	U

①—Letter following number in serial number prefix.

1960 Falcon

1961 Comet

1961 Falcon

Engine Section

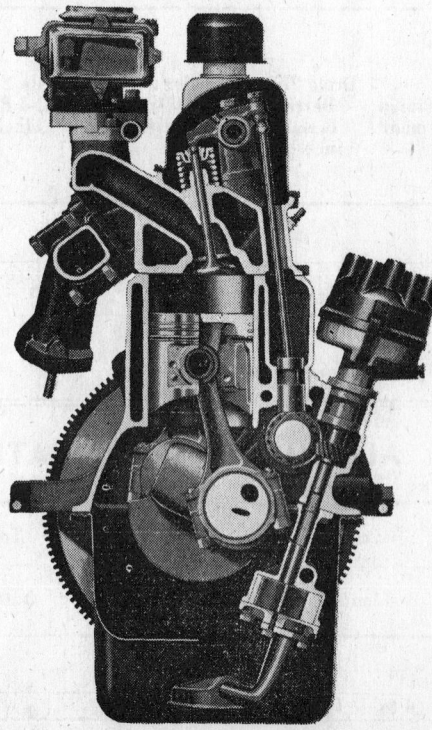

Comet and Falcon engine

ENGINE, REPLACE

1. Drain cooling system and oil pan.
2. Remove hood, air cleaner, radiator, fan and pulley, and starter.
3. Disconnect usual items such as wires, fuel and vacuum lines, carburetor linkage, etc.
4. Cars with standard transmission, disconnect clutch retracting spring. Then remove clutch equalizer shaft arm bracket at underbody rail.
5. Raise car. Remove flywheel or converter housing upper retaining bolts through access holes in floor pan.
6. Disconnect exhaust pipe at exhaust manifold.
7. Disconnect engine right and left mounts at underbody bracket.
8. Remove flywheel or converter housing cover.
9. Cars with standard transmission, remove flywheel housing lower retaining bolts.
10. Cars with automatic transmission, disconnect converter from flywheel and remove converter housing retaining bolts.
11. Lower car. Support transmission and flywheel or converter housing with a jack.
12. Attach engine lifting rig and lift engine from chassis.
13. Reverse above procedure to install the engine.

CYLINDER HEAD, REPLACE

1. Drain cooling system, remove air cleaner and disconnect battery cable at cylinder head.
2. Disconnect exhaust pipe at exhaust manifold.
3. Disconnect carburetor linkage, fuel and vacuum lines, water hoses and wires from spark plugs.
4. Remove rocker arm cover.
5. Back off valve adjusting screws to remove load from rocker arms. Then remove rocker arm shaft assembly.
6. Remove valve push rods, keeping them in proper sequence so they are returned to proper locations.
7. Remove one bolt from each end of cylinder head at opposite corners and install cylinder head guide studs ($\frac{7}{16}$"-14 x 6").
8. Remove remaining bolts and lift off cylinder head.
9. Reverse above procedure to install the cylinder head and tighten bolts in three progressive steps as follows: Tighten bolts in the sequence shown in Fig. 1 to 55 ft. lbs. torque; then tighten them to 65 ft. lbs. Finally, tighten them to 75 ft. lbs. *Once bolts have been tightened to specifications, they should not be disturbed.*

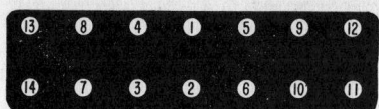

Fig. 1   Cylinder head bolt tightening sequence

VALVE ARRANGEMENT

Front to rear . . E-I-I-E-I-E-E-I-E-I-I-E

VALVES ADJUST

Before the final valve lash adjustment is made, operate the engine for 30 minutes at a fast idle to stabilize engine temperatures. To set the lash accurately, use only a step-type feeler gauge. For example, to obtain the correct setting if the clearance is .016", the .015" portion of the gauge ("go") should enter but the "no go" end (.017") should not enter.

Before starting the adjustment procedure, make two chalk marks on the crankshaft pulley. Space the marks approximately 120° apart (⅓ of circumference) so that with the timing mark the pulley is divided into three equal parts. Adjust the valves for No. 1 cylinder. Repeat the procedure for the remaining valves, turning the crankshaft ⅓ turn in the direction of normal rotation while adjusting the valves in the firing order sequence of 153624.

VALVES REMOVE

After taking off the head as outlined previously, proceed as follows:
1. Remove capscrews retaining rocker shaft brackets to head and remove shaft assembly.
2. Clean carbon out of combustion chambers before removing valves.
3. Compress valve springs with a suitable spring compressor, remove valve stem locks and release the springs. Remove sleeve, valve spring cap retainer, spring and valve. Discard intake valve seals, Fig. 2.
4. Place valves in a board with numbered holes so they can be replaced in their original positions upon reassembly.

VALVES GRIND

Clean the valves with a wire wheel brush, making sure that all carbon is removed from the top and bottom of the heads as well as the gum which might have accumulated on the stems.

In refacing valves, take off only the minimum of metal required to clean up the valve faces. If the outer edge of the valve becomes too thin or sharp due to excessive grinding, the valve must be replaced. In other words, the valve head margin must be at least $\frac{1}{32}$", otherwise the valve must be replaced.

Inspect the valve seats in the head for cracks, burns, pits, ridges or improper angle. During any general engine overhaul, it is advisable to reface the valve seats regardless of their condition.

VALVE GUIDES

Valve guides in these engines are an integral part of the head and, therefore, cannot be removed. For service, guides can be reamed oversize to accommodate one of three service valves with oversize stems (.003", .015" and .030").

Check the valve stem clearance of each valve (after cleaning) in its respective valve guide. If the clearance exceeds the service limits of .004" on the intake or .005" on the exhaust, ream the valve guides to accommodate the next oversize diameter valve.

VALVE SPRING INSTALLED HEIGHT

When valves and seats are reground the position of the valve in the head is changed so as to lessen the valve spring tension. Without proper valve spring tension the valve does not seat long enough or it may not seat completely. Since the valve is cooled by transferring heat from the valve head to the seat and thence to the coolant, improper valve spring tension will cause worn, pitted and distorted valves which result in loss of compression and power as well as poor gasoline mileage.

When valves, springs, retainers and locks are installed, measure the assembled height of the valve springs from the surface of the cylinder head spring pad to the underside of the spring retainer as shown in Fig. 3. If the assembled height is greater than the dimension given in the *Valve Specifications Chart*, install a spacer or shim of proper thickness between cylinder head spring pad and spring to bring the assembled height to specifications.

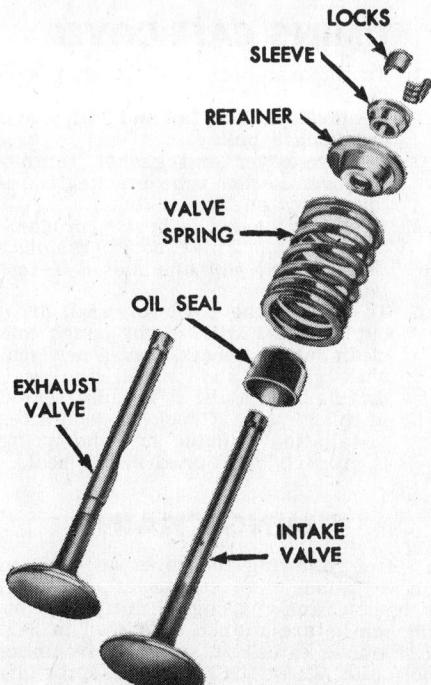

Fig. 2   Valve assembly

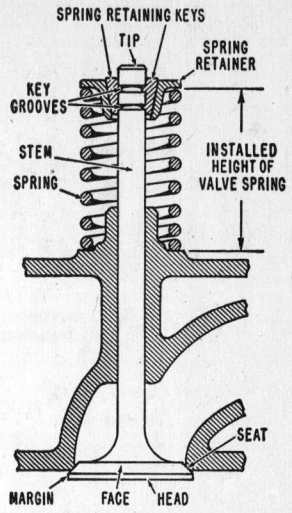

Fig. 3   Checking installed height of valve spring

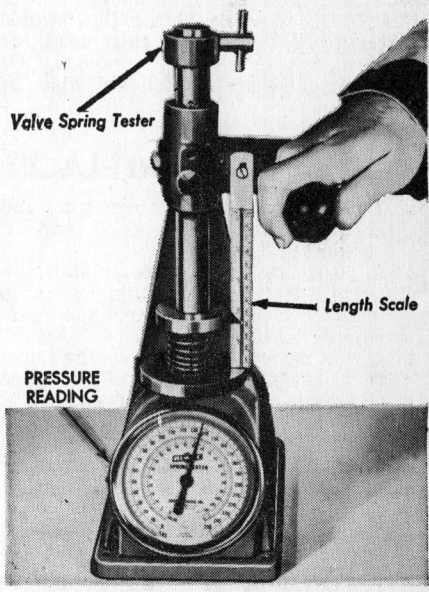

Fig. 4   Checking valve spring pressure

Do not install spacers unless necessary. Excessive use of spacers will result in overstressing valve springs and overloading camshaft lobes which could lead to spring breakage and worn camshaft lobes.

VALVE SPRING TESTING

After taking out the valve springs, wash them with gasoline or other suitable solvent. Examine the springs for damage or corrosion due to acid etching, which will develop into surface cracks and cause spring failure.

Check the valve spring tension on a spring testing fixture, if one is available, Fig. 4, and according to the specifications given in the *Valve Data Chart*. If a fixture is not available, at least check the free length of each spring by stand-

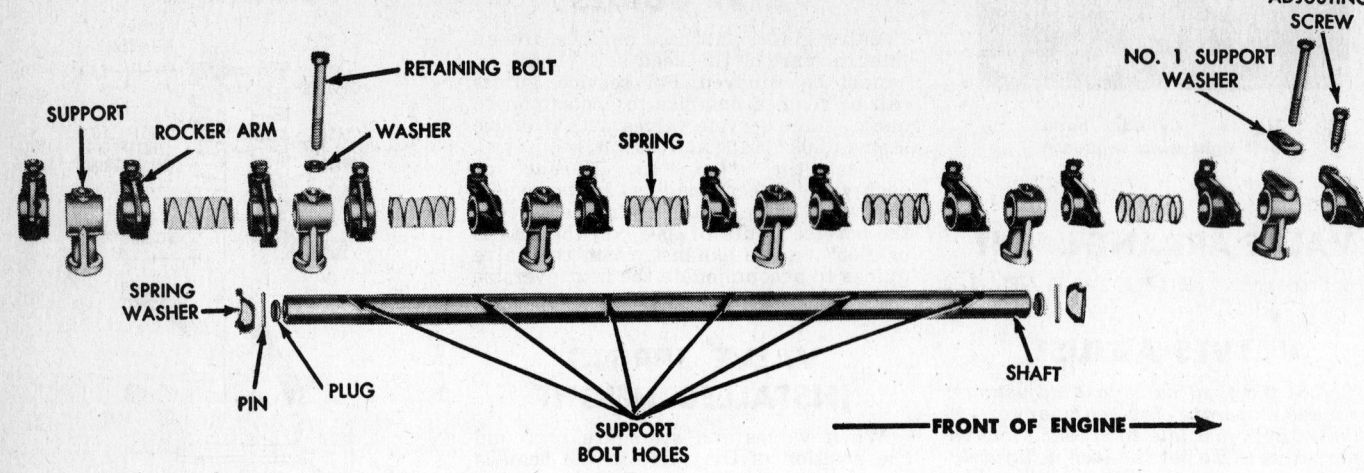

Fig. 5 Rocker arm shaft assembly

ing it alongside a new spring. Any spring that does not conform to the pressure specifications within 10% should be replaced. Likewise, any spring that stands shorter than the new spring used for comparison should be discarded. Of course, cocked springs should also be scrapped.

ROCKER ARMS REPLACE

1. To disassemble, remove pin and spring washer from each end of rocker shaft, Fig. 5.
2. Slide rocker arms, springs and supports off the shaft, being sure to identify location of parts for reassembly.
3. If it is necessary to remove the plugs from the shaft ends, drill or pierce the plug on one end. Then use a steel rod to knock out the plug on the opposite end. Working from the open end, knock out the remaining plug.

Assemble

1. Lubricate all parts with engine oil. Apply Lubriplate to the rocker arm pads.
2. If plugs were removed from shaft ends, use a blunt tool or large diameter pin punch and install a plug (cup side out) in each end of shaft.

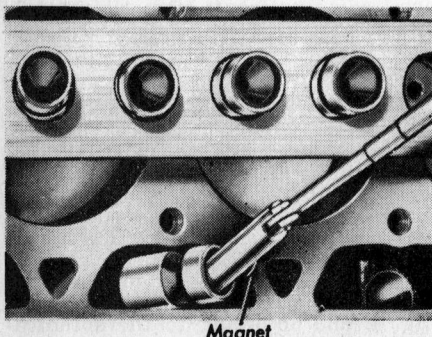

Magnet

Fig. 6 Removing valve lifter using magnetic rod

3. Install spring washer and pin on one end of shaft.
4. Install rocker arms, supports and springs in order shown in Fig. 5. *Be sure oil holes in shaft are facing downward.*
5. Complete the assembly by installing remaining spring washer and pin.

VALVE LIFTERS, REPLACE

When necessary to replace the lifters, remove the cylinder head and related parts as outlined previously. Using a magnet, remove and install one lifter at a time, Fig. 6.

When installing, apply Lubriplate to each lifter foot and coat the remainder of the lifter with engine oil before installation.

TIMING CASE COVER

1. To remove cover, drain cooling system.
2. Remove radiator, fan and pulley, and crankshaft pulley.
3. Remove cover and gasket (crankcase ventilation tube bracket is retained by one cover bolt).
4. *If oil pan gasket is broken or damaged during front cover removal, drop the oil pan and install a new gasket.*
5. To replace the cover oil seal, drive out the seal with a pin punch and clean out the recess. Coat a new seal with grease and install the seal, driving it in until it is fully seated in cover recess. Check the seal after installation to make sure the spring is properly positioned in the seal.

TIMING CHAIN

After removing the cover as outlined above, remove the crankshaft front oil slinger. Crank the engine until the timing marks are aligned as shown in Fig. 7. Remove camshaft sprocket retaining bolt and washer. Slide both sprockets and chain forward and remove them as an assembly.

Reverse the order of the foregoing

procedure to install the chain and sprockets, being sure the timing marks are aligned.

VALVE TIMING DATA

Comet & Falcon

Year Model		Intake Opens①	Intake Closes②	Exhaust Opens③	Exhaust Closes④
1960-61	All	15	37	45	7

①—Degrees before top dead center.
②—Degrees after bottom dead center.
③—Degrees before bottom dead center.
④—Degrees after top dead center.

CAMSHAFT REPLACE

To remove camshaft, remove cylinder head and related parts, radiator, oil pan, timing chain cover and valve lifters.

Remove timing chain and sprockets, camshaft thrust plate, and pull camshaft out of engine. If thrust plate shows signs of wear, install a new one.

CAMSHAFT BEARINGS REPLACE

To install new bearings it will be necessary to remove the engine from the

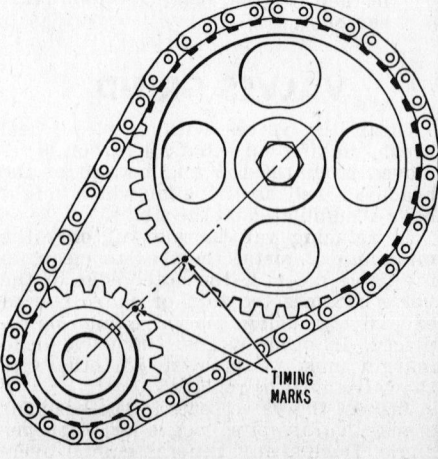

Fig. 7 Timing marks lined up for correct valve timing

car. The bearings are available pre-finished to size and require no reaming for standard and .015″ undersize journal diameters. Number 4 bearing is not interchangeable with the other bearings.

1. After removing the engine, remove the camshaft and rear bearing bore plug.
2. Remove camshaft bearings, Fig. 8.
3. To install, position the bearing at the bearing bore and press it in place. *No. 1 bearing must be pressed in .100-.140″ below front face of bearing bore. Press the remaining bearings in sufficiently to align the oil supply holes.*
4. Clean camshaft rear bearing bore plug recess and install a new plug.
5. Install parts removed and install engine in car.

PISTONS & RODS REMOVE

After removing the cylinder head and oil pan, use a ridge reamer to remove any ridge that may have formed on the cylinder wall at the top of the piston ring travel. Cutting the ridge before the piston is removed will avoid damaging rings or cracking ring lands of pistons during removal.

Remove the connecting rod cap and push the piston and rod out through the top of the bore. Use care to prevent the rod from nicking crankshaft journals. Identify the connecting rods (original rods are marked) when removing them so they may be installed in their original cylinder.

PISTON & ROD ASSEMBLE

When installed, piston and rod assembly should have the notch in piston head toward front of engine with oil squirt hole in rod positioned as shown in Fig. 9.

PISTONS

Pistons are available for service replacement in standard sizes and oversizes of .020″, .030″, .040″ and .060″.

If the pistons are to be re-used with new rings, remove the carbon from the ring grooves. A special tool is available for this work but a satisfactory job can be done by breaking an oil piston ring.

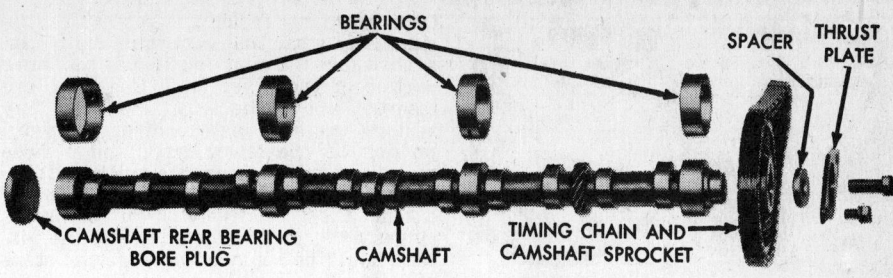

Fig. 8 Camshaft and related parts

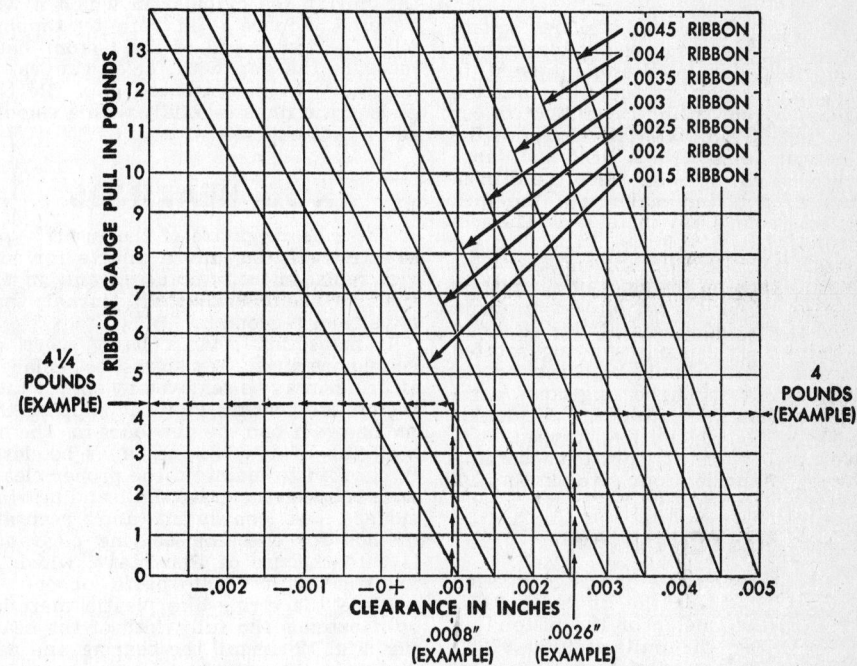

Fig. 10 Piston clearance chart

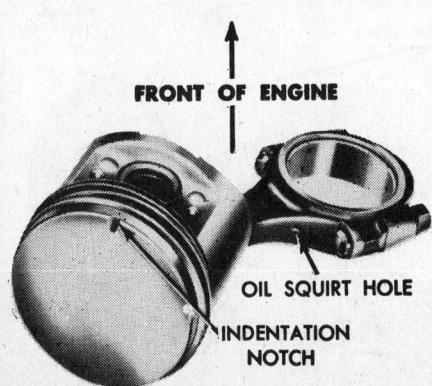

Fig. 9 Piston and rod assembly

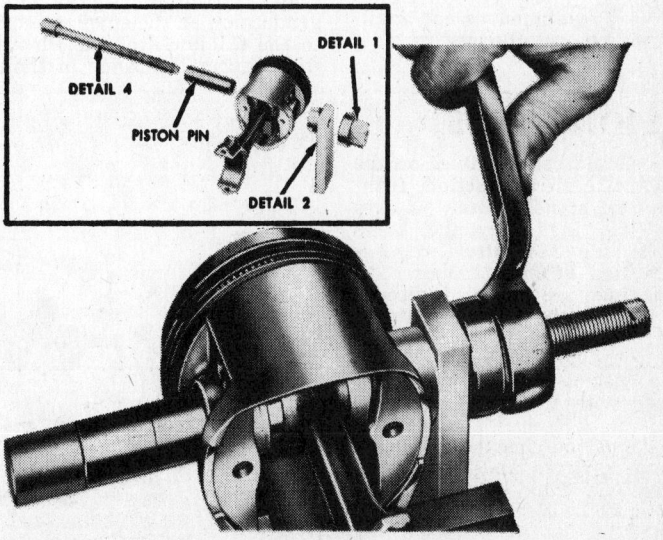

Fig. 11 Piston pin installation

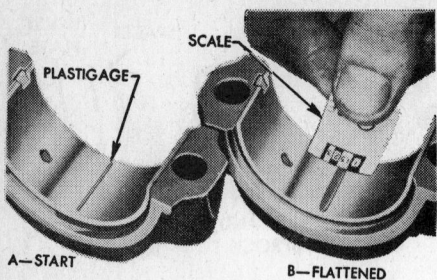

Fig. 12 Checking rod bearing clearance with Plastigage

File the broken end to a sharp, square edge and use it to scrape out the carbon. Soak the piston in cleaning solvent to loosen any carbon residue. Clean out the loosened carbon, being careful not to cut away any piston material. Clean out the oil return holes with a drill just large enough to fill the holes. Hold the drill in a tap wrench and make sure the drill does not remove any metal from the piston.

Rinse the piston in solvent and wipe off the carbon on the sides of the piston. *Never use a wire brush to clean a piston as the brush will round off the edges of the ring lands*. Pistons showing scuffed or scored skirts should be discarded for new ones. Examine the ring lands carefully for cracks. If in the least bit doubtful, the piston should be scrapped.

New pistons should be fitted according to the recommendations given in Fig. 10.

PISTON PINS

The piston pin bore of the connecting rod must be within the limits of .9107-.9112". The diameter of the piston pin must be within the limits of .9120-.9123".

Apply a light coat of engine oil to all parts. Assemble the piston to the connecting rod as shown in Fig. 9. Start the piston pin in the piston and connecting rod. Use the equipment shown in Fig. 11 and draw the pin through the piston and rod until end of pin seats in Detail 2, Fig. 11. If this equipment is not available, the pin may be installed with a suitable press.

PISTON RINGS

New rings should be assembled on the piston according to the instructions furnished by the ring manufacturer. Always use standard size rings in cylinder bores that are *standard at the bottom, regardless of the amount of cylinder wear*.

When new rings are installed without reboring cylinders the glazed cylinder walls should be slightly dulled, but without increasing the bore diameter. This is done with a "Glaze-buster" or with a hone equipped with the finest grade of stones.

New rings must be checked for clearance in piston grooves and for gap in cylinder bores. Cylinder bores and piston grooves must be clean, dry and free of carbon and burrs.

Check the clearance of each ring in its piston groove by installing the ring and then inserting feeler gauges *under* the ring. Any wear that occurs in the piston groove forms a step or ridge at the inner portion of the lower land. If gauges are inserted above the ring, the ring may rest on the step instead of on the worn portion of the lower land, and a false measurement of clearance will result.

If the piston grooves are worn to the extent that relatively high steps or ridges exist on the lower lands, the piston should be replaced because the steps will interfere with the operation of the new rings and the ring clearances will be excessive. Piston rings are not furnished in oversize widths to compensate for ring groove wear.

To check the end gap of rings, place the ring in the cylinder in which it will be used. Square it in bore by tapping with the lower end of the piston. Then measure the gap with feeler gauges. If necessary to increase the gap, file the ends of the rings carefully with a smooth file.

ROD BEARINGS

These bearings are of the insert type, selectively fitted, and available for service replacement in standard and undersizes for use on crankshaft journals that have been reground.

If inspection reveals badly worn or scored bearings, they should be replaced. Bearings may be removed by simply taking off the bearing caps and slipping the old ones out and the new ones in. The installation of new bearings must be closely checked to maintain the proper clearance between the crankshaft and bearing surface. A convenient and accurate method for checking bearing clearance is with the use of Plastigage, which is available at any auto parts jobber.

Place the string-like plastic material so it extends the full width of the bearing, Fig. 12. Install the bearing and cap and tighten the nuts to the recommended torque which is listed in the *Engine Torque Specifications* chart. Then loosen the nuts and carefully remove the cap and bearing. The widest portion of the Plastigage is then measured with the scale on the Plastigage envelope. The graduation on the envelope corresponding to the thickness of the Plastigage gives the bearing clearance in thousandths of an inch.

MAIN BEARINGS

Caution—Main bearing clearance can be checked with Plastigage in the same manner described for rod bearings. If bearings are measured with the engine in the chassis, the crankshaft must be supported in order to take up clearance between the upper bearing insert and crankshaft journal. This can be done by tightening bearing caps of adjacent bearings with .005" to .015" cardboard, (such as a calling card) between lower bearing shell and journal. Use extreme care when this is done to avoid unnecessary strain on the crankshaft or bearings or a false reading may be obtained. Do not rotate crankshaft while Plastigage is installed. *Be sure to remove cardboard*. To install new bearings, proceed as follows:

1. Remove bearing cap and worn lower shell, Fig. 13.
2. Rotate crankshaft in normal direction to turn upper bearing shell out of crankcase. Use a cotter pin with a flattened head or the special tool made for the purpose in the crankshaft oil hole to contact the bearing and force it out.
3. Place a new upper shell on the crankshaft journal with the locating notch in the correct position and rotate the shaft to turn the bearing in place.
4. Install the lower bearing shell in the cap.
5. Tighten all cap nuts to the torque value given in the *Engine Torque* table.

CRANKSHAFT OIL SEAL

A braided oil seal is pressed into the upper and lower grooves behind the rear main bearing. Directly in front of this seal is an oil slinger which deflects the oil back into the oil pan. Should the braided seal require replacement, the installation of the lower half is accomplished as follows:

With the bearing cap and lower bearing half removed, install a new seal so that both ends protrude above the cap. Tap the seal down into position or roll it snugly in its groove with a smooth rounded tool. Then cut off the protruding end of the seal with sharp knife or razor blade.

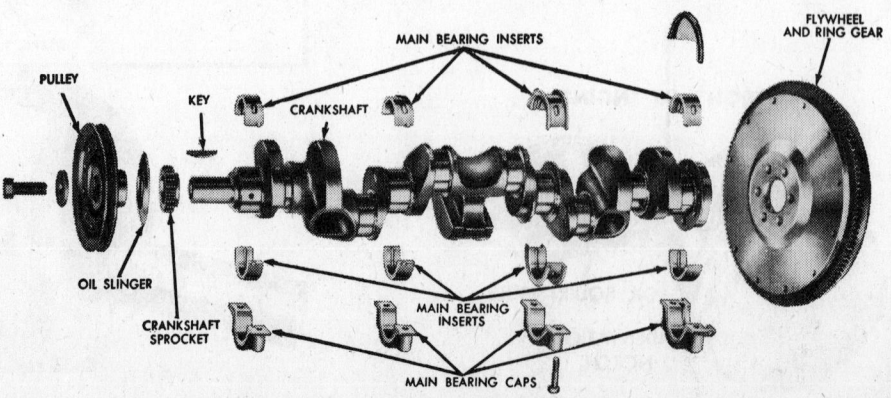

Fig. 13 Crankshaft and related parts

Installing Upper Seal

Although the usual practice is to remove the crankshaft when the upper half of the seal is to be replaced, it is possible to do the job without removing the crankshaft as follows:

To remove the old seal, use needle-nose pliers to grasp the end of the seal which is most accessible. Pull the seal downward while rotating the crankshaft slowly in the direction that the seal is being moved.

To install the new seal, fasten a length of wire or strong string such as fishing line securely to one end of the new seal. See that the point of fastening is not bulky and that it is not over ⅜" from the end of the seal. Coat the seal with Lubriplate. Pass the free end of the wire or string up over the crankshaft at the point where the seal is being installed. Then exert a firm, steady pull on the wire or string and at the same time rotate the crankshaft slowly in the direction of the pull. This will help to move the seal into position. When the installation is completed, trim the ends of the seal flush with the engine block.

OIL PAN REPLACE

1961 Falcon

1. On car with manual shift transmission, remove clutch retracting spring.
2. Remove crossmember.
3. Unfasten stabilizer bar from underbody and pull stabilizer bar downward.
4. Remove oil pan bolts and crank engine as required to obtain clearance and remove oil pan.

1960-61 Comet, 1960 Falcon

1. To remove, drain oil and remove dipstick.
2. Remove front engine mounting nuts

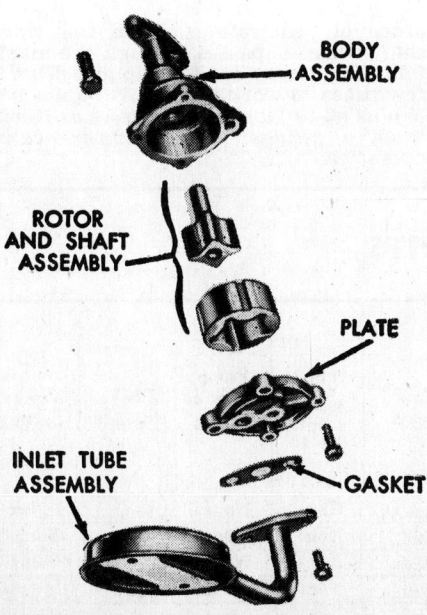

Fig. 14 Oil pump assembly

BODY ASSEMBLY

ROTOR AND SHAFT ASSEMBLY

PLATE

INLET TUBE ASSEMBLY

GASKET

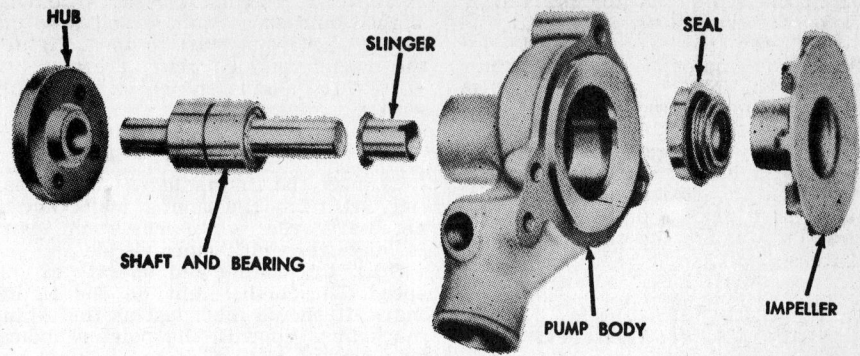

Fig. 15 Water pump assembly

HUB

SLINGER

SEAL

SHAFT AND BEARING

PUMP BODY

IMPELLER

and raise front of engine with a jack and a wood block placed under the oil pan.
3. Position 2-inch wood blocks between each engine front support and support bracket and lower engine on blocks.
4. Remove stabilizer bar-to-underbody nuts and pull stabilizer bar downward.
5. Remove oil pan retaining bolts and crank engine as required to obtain clearance for removal of pan.
6. Reverse above procedure to install.

OIL PUMP REPLACE

1. Remove oil pan as directed above.
2. Remove pump pick-up tube and screen.
3. Unfasten and remove pump from engine.
4. Reverse order of removal to install.

OIL PUMP REPAIRS

Referring to Fig. 14, disassemble pump. To remove the oil pressure relief valve, insert a self-threading sheet metal screw of the proper diameter into the oil pressure relief valve chamber cap and pull cap out of chamber. Remove spring and plunger.

The inner rotor and shaft and the outer race are serviced as an assembly. One part should not be replaced without replacing the other.

Install the pump cover and tighten to 6-9 ft. lbs. torque.

RADIATOR

Drain cooling system and disconnect upper and lower hoses at radiator. If equipped with oil cooler, disconnect lines from lower tank. Unfasten radiator from its support and lift out radiator.

WATER PUMP REPLACE

Drain cooling system and remove lower hose at water pump. Remove drive belt, fan and water pump pulley. Disconnect heater hose at water pump. Unfasten and remove water pump.

WATER PUMP REPAIRS

To disassemble pump, refer to Fig. 15 and remove hub from impeller shaft. Press shaft and bearing out of housing. Remove impeller from shaft.

To assemble, clean all gasket material from pump. If a new shaft is used, install the slinger on the shaft in the same relative position as the old slinger. Coat the bearing outer diameter with grease and press the shaft into the housing. Apply a light film of waterproof sealer on a new seal and press seal into housing. Install impeller. Lightly coat seal rubbing face of impeller with grease, then press shaft onto impeller.

Press shaft into impeller just far enough so that pump housing lightly touches face of adapter ring. The impeller-to-pump body clearance should be .005-.025" after impeller is installed.

Press water pump onto shaft until there is 3¹¹⁄₁₆" from gasket surface to outside surface of pump hub.

DISTRIBUTOR REPLACE

1. To remove the distributor, disconnect the primary wire and vacuum control pipe.
2. Remove distributor cap.
3. Scribe a mark on the distributor body indicating the position of the rotor, and scribe another mark on the body and engine block indicating position of distributor body in block. These marks can be used as guides when installing distributor in a correctly timed engine.
4. Remove hold down screw or screws and lift distributor out of block. *Do not crank engine while distributor is removed or the initial timing operation will have to be performed.*

Installation

If the crankshaft has not been disturbed, install the distributor, using the scribed marks previously made on the distributor body and engine block as guides.

If the crankshaft has been rotated while the distributor was removed from the engine, it will be necessary to retime the engine. Crank the engine to bring No. 1 piston on top dead center of its compression stroke. Align the timing mark on the crankshaft pulley with the timing pointer (see *Tune Up* chart). Install the distributor so that the rotor points to the No. 1 spark plug wire terminal in the distributor cap.

Make sure the oil pump intermediate shaft properly engages the distributor shaft. It may be necessary to crank the engine with the starter, after the distributor drive gear is properly engaged, in order to engage the oil pump intermediate shaft.

IGNITION TIMING

Align the distributor rotor with No. 1 spark plug wire terminal in the distributor cap, when No. 1 piston is on the compression stroke and timing mark on the crankshaft pulley and pointer are aligned (see *Tune Up* chart).

With the timing mark in line with the pointer, the distributor points should just start to open. It may be necessary to rotate the distributor body clockwise slightly and then counter-clockwise until the points just start to open. Tighten the distributor lock plate screw.

Start the engine and check the timing with a timing light.

Using Timing Light

Connect the timing light wires. Clean the dirt from the timing mark and if necessary use white chalk or paint to make the mark more visible.

Start the engine and operate at idle speed. Direct the light on the timing mark. It should flash just as the timing mark lines up with the pointer, indicating correct timing. If the pointer and timing mark do not line up as the light flashes, rotate the distributor as required to bring them in alignment.

STARTER REPLACE

Disconnect cable at starter. Unfasten and remove starter and rubber dust ring.

When installing the starter on a car with automatic transmission, the transmission dipstick tube bracket is mounted under the starter side mounting bolt. Snug all bolts, then tighten them starting from the middle bolt.

MUFFLER & PIPES REPLACE

When installing the exhaust pipe, slide the muffler and outlet pipe forward until the slots in the muffler extension are blocked by the exhaust pipe. The overlap should not be greater than 1¾".

When installing the muffler, have the same 1¾" overlap of the exhaust pipe and muffler extension as mentioned above. Check for possible interference between the kick-up and the floor pan.

When installing the muffler to tail pipe, slide the tail pipe on the muffler extension until the slots are blocked.

Carburetor Section

Performance Complaints

Flooding, stumble on acceleration or other performance complaints are in many instances caused by the presence of dirt, water or other foreign matter in the carburetor. To aid in diagnosing the cause of the complaint, the carburetor should be carefully removed from the engine without draining the fuel from the bowl. The contents of the fuel bowl may then be examined for contamination as the carburetor is disassembled.

Check the fuel in the bowl for contamination by dirt, water, gum or other foreign matter. A magnet moved through the fuel in the bowl will pick up and identify any iron oxide dust that may have caused intake needle and seat leakage.

Inspect gasket surfaces. Small nicks or burrs should be smoothed down to eliminate air or fuel leakage. On carburetors having a vacuum piston, be especially particular when inspecting the top surface of the inner wall of the bowl around the vacuum piston passage. A poor seal at this location may contribute to "cutting-out on turns" complaint.

Fill the carburetor bowl with clean fuel before installing on manifold. This will help prevent dirt trapped in the fuel system from being dislodged by the free flow of fuel as the carburetor is primed. The operation of the floats and intake needle and seats may be checked under pressure if a fuel pump is used at the bench to fill the carburetor bowl. Operate the throttle several times and visually check the discharge of the pump jets.

Manifold Heat Control Valve

An engine equipped with a manifold heat control valve can operate with the valve stuck in either the open or closed position. Because of this an inoperative valve is frequently overlooked at vehicle lubrication or tune-up.

A stuck valve in the "heat-off" position can result in slow warm up, deposits in combustion chamber, carburetor icing, flat spots during acceleration, low gas mileage and spark plug fouling.

A valve stuck in the "heat-on" position can result in power loss, engine knocking, sticking or burned valves and spark plug burning.

To prevent the possibility of a stuck valve, check and lubricate the valve each time the vehicle is lubricated or tuned-up. Check the operation of the valve manually. To lubricate the valve, place a few drops of penetrating oil on the valve shaft where it passes through the manifold. The move the valve up and down a few times to work in the oil. *Do not use engine oil to lubricate the valve as it will leave a residue which hampers valve operation.*

HOLLEY CARBURETOR ADJUSTMENTS

| Year | Model | Carb. Type | Idle Adjustments | | | | | Float Level | Fuel Level | Float Bowl Vent Valve | Pump Override Spring | Choke Unloader | Choke Setting |
			Mixture Screws Turns Open	Air Bypass Turns Open	Hot Idle Speed In Drive	Fast Idle Speed	Dashpot Plunger Clearance						
1960	Comet	1 Bore	1-1½	None	485	1600④	9/64③	11/64①	23/32②	None	None	¼⑤	Index
	Falcon	1 Bore	1-1½	None	485	None	5/64③	11/64①	23/32②	None	None	None	None
1961	Comet	1 Bore	1-1½	None	485	1600④	9/64③	11/64①	23/32②	None	None	¼⑤	Index
	Falcon	1 Bore	1-1½	None	485	1600④	9/64③	11/64①	23/32②	None	None	¼⑤	Index

HOLLEY NOTES

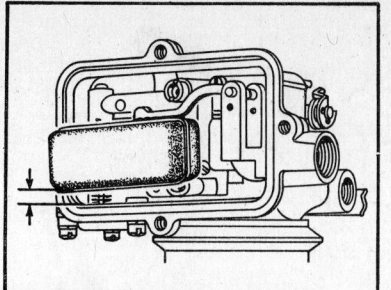

Fig. ①—Float level measured from roof of float chamber to lowest point of float with carburetor inverted.

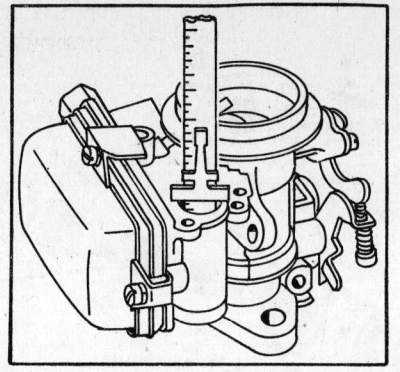

Fig. ②—Fuel level measured from power valve mounting surface.

③—With engine running at hot idle speed, hold throttle closed and depress dashpot plunger fully. Then turn adjusting screw as required to obtain the specified clearance.

④—With hot idle properly adjusted, and with fast idle screw on lowest step of fast idle cam, adjust fast idle screw to obtain RPM listed.

⑤—With throttle wide open, clearance between upper edge of choke valve and inner wall of air horn should be as listed. Adjust by bending unloader lever on throttle shaft lever.

Clutch & Transmission Section

CLUTCH

Pedal Adjustment

Adjust the clutch pedal whenever the clutch does not disengage or engage properly, or when new clutch parts are installed. Both the total travel and free travel of the pedal should be adjusted.
1. To check pedal assist spring tension, measure the distance between the end of the assist spring retainer and the rear surface of the pedal support, Fig. 1. This distance should be $1\frac{3}{16}$".
2. The total travel of the pedal should be 6 to $6\frac{1}{2}$". If the travel is less than required, move the clutch pedal bumper and bracket until the travel is within limits.
3. Pedal free travel should be $\frac{7}{8}$" to $1\frac{1}{8}$". Depress the pedal slowly until the clutch release fingers contact the release bearing and note the amount of travel. If not within specifications, loosen the equalizer rod nuts. Move the equalizer bar as required and tighten the nuts. *Both nuts must be tightened against the trunnion after the adjustment is made.*

Clutch Replace

1. Remove starter and rubber dust ring·
2. Remove propeller shaft.
3. Disconnect speedometer cable.
4. Remove transmission support bolts.
5. Remove exhaust pipe bracket bolt.
6. Disconnect shift rods at transmission levers.
7. Raise engine slightly with jack and wood block under oil pan.
8. Remove transmission-to-flywheel bolts and slide transmission back and allow it to rest on cross member.
9. Disconnect retracting spring and disconnect pedal-to-equalizer rod from equalizer bar.
10. Remove hub and release bearing.
11. Remove flywheel housing and dust cover.
12. Remove clutch from flywheel.
13. Reverse above procedure to install clutch and adjust pedal travel.

STD. TRANSMISSION

Transmission Replace

1. Remove propeller shaft.
2. Disconnect speedometer cable.
3. Disconnect gearshift rods from levers at transmission.
4. Remove bolt securing extension housing to rear support, and remove bolt from exhaust pipe bracket.
5. Place jack under flywheel housing and raise engine slightly.
6. Remove four transmission mounting bolts and thread two guide studs into the two lower bolt holes.
7. Move transmission back and out of chassis.
8. Reverse above procedure to install.

Transmission Repairs

1. Referring to Fig. 2, drain lubricant and remove cover.
2. Remove extension housing. *To prevent mainshaft from following the housing (with resultant loss of needle bearings) tap end of mainshaft with soft hammer while withdrawing housing.*

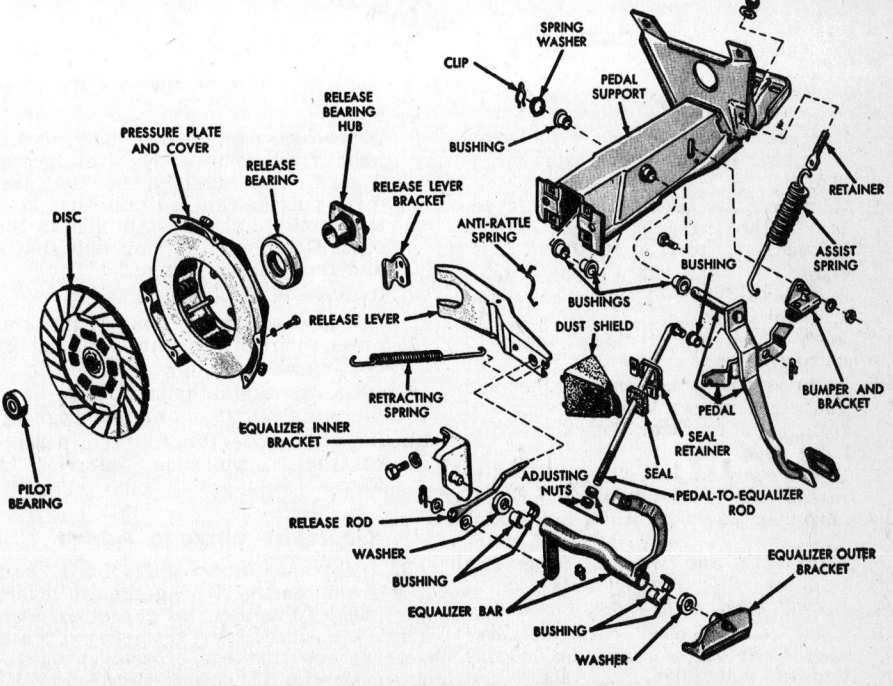

Fig. 1 Falcon clutch. 1960 mounting and linkage

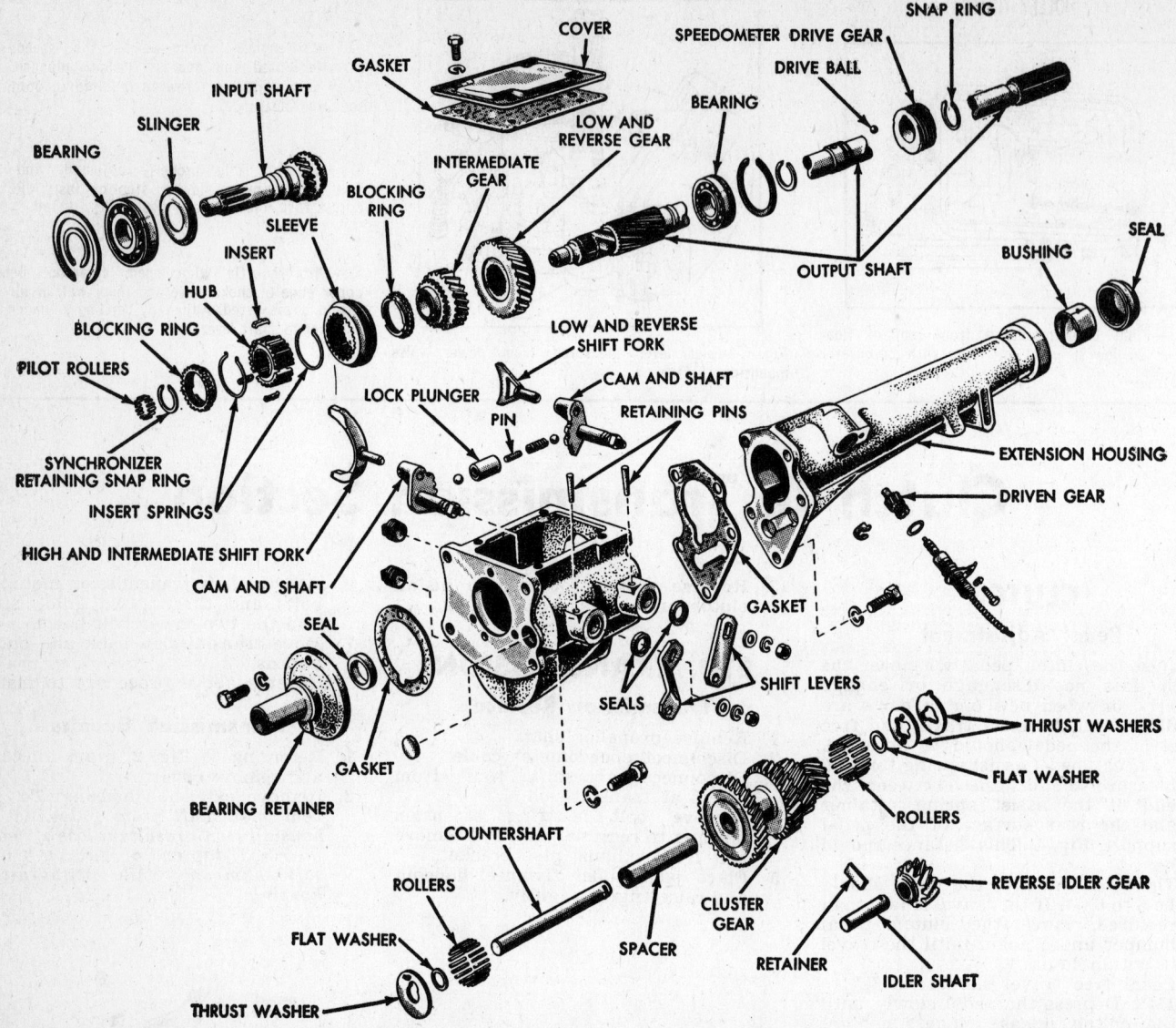

Fig. 2 Exploded view of standard transmission

3. Remove speedometer drive gear, snap ring and drive ball from mainshaft.
4. Remove idler and countershaft retainer, tapping ends of both shafts if necessary to free retainer.
5. Using a suitable arbor, drive countershaft out of cluster gear and transmission case, leaving arbor in gear. Then lower cluster gear to bottom of case.
6. After removing bearing retainer and gasket, remove main drive gear and front synchronizer blocking ring from case.
7. Remove snychronizer snap ring from mainshaft. Then, while holding synchronizer parts together, pull mainshaft out of case. Remove mainshaft parts and two shift forks. *For reference in assembly, notice which synchronizer hub faces forward.*
8. Using a soft drift, drive reverse idler shaft out of transmission case and lift out idler gear, shaft and cluster gear out of case.

9. If necessary to remove shift mechanism, first remove the shift levers. Then from the underside of the case, drive out the tapered pins that hold the cam and shaft assemblies in the case. Drive out the cam and shafts and remove the plunger.
10. Remove shift lever oil seals.
11. Remove retaining snap ring and press main drive gear shaft out of bearing and oil slinger.
12. Remove retaining snap ring and press mainshaft out of rear bearing.
13. Reverse above procedure to assemble the transmission, referring to Fig. 2.

Gearshift Linkage Adjust

If the transmission shifts hard or if it will not engage, the gearshift levers may need adjustment at the cross-over. Move the shift lever through all positions to see that the cross-over operation is smooth. If not, adjust as follows:
1. With selector lever in neutral, re-

move cotter pins and flat washers from the connecting rod adjustment sleeves and pull sleeves out of levers.
2. Loosen locknut on each sleeve and then slide sleeves up or down on the rods until smooth cross-over operation results when sleeves are attached to levers. Tighten both locknuts securely.
3. Position adjustment sleeves in shift levers and install flat washers and cotter pins.

AUTOMATIC TRANS.

For detailed repair procedure and maintenance requirements on this transmission, refer to the *Two-Speed Fordomatic* section of this manual. The following outlines the procedure for adjusting the transmission linkage and the removal of the transmission from the car.

Throttle Linkage Adjust

1. Apply parking brake and place

selector lever in neutral.

2. Run engine at a fast idle until normal operating temperature is reached. When warm, slow engine down to normal idle speed.

3. Connect tachometer to engine and adjust idle speed to 475-500 rpm with selector lever in "D".

4. Bottom the dashpot plunger against its spring and check clearance between bottomed plunger and throttle lever. Clearance must be as follows:

Falcon 1960 . . . . $\frac{5}{64}$"
Falcon 1961 . . . . $\frac{9}{64}$"
Comet 1960-61 . . . . $\frac{9}{64}$"

5. With engine stopped, disconnect throttle control rod at its clevis end, Fig. 3. Loosen clevis locknut.

6. Push throttle control rod downward to hold throttle lever against stop inside of transmission.

7. With slight downward pressure on throttle control rod, adjust its length so that the clevis pin has a free fit. From the free-fit length, *shorten* the control rod by turning the clevis 3½ turns clockwise. Install clevis pin.

8. Adjust accelerator pedal height by turning threaded trunnion on accelerator connecting link until the pedal is 4¼" from floor pan. Measure from top rear corner of pedal to floor pan.

9. If transmission operation is not satisfactory after the foregoing adjustment, the throttle control rod may be lengthened or shortened 2½ turns from the above 3½ turns. If operation is still unsatisfactory, conduct a pressure test as outlined in the *Two-Speed Fordomatic* chapter.

Manual Linkage Adjust

1. With engine stopped, loosen clamp at shift lever so that shift rod is free to slide in clamp.

2. Position selector lever so that pointer lines up in "D" position.

3. Shift manual lever at transmission into "D" detent position (second from rear).

4. Tighten clamp on shift rod and check pointer alignment in all positions.

Starter Neutral Switch Adjust

1. Check starter circuit in all selector lever positions. Circuit must be open in all positions except "N" and "P".

2. To adjust switch, loosen switch-to-

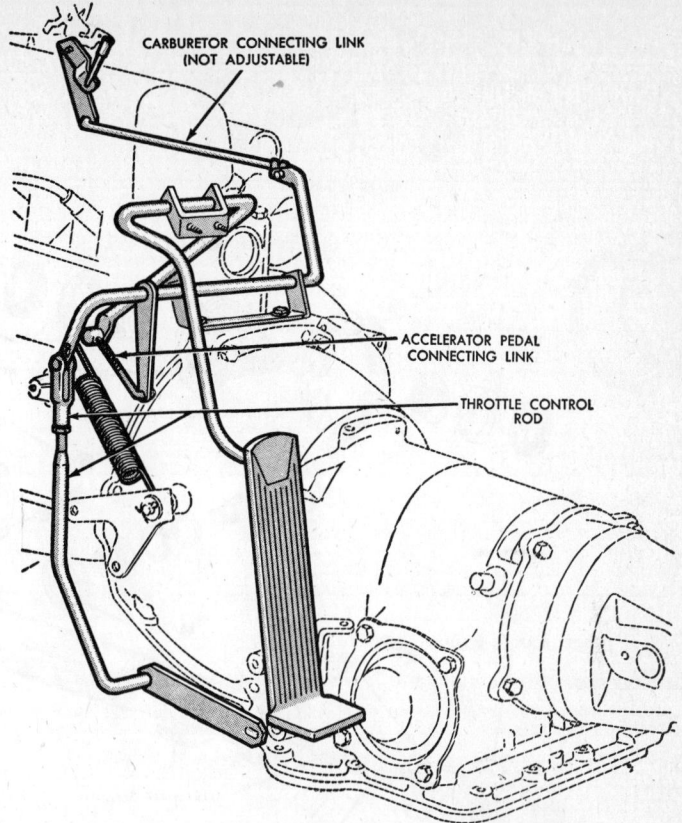

Fig. 3   Automatic transmission throttle linkage

steering column screws. Position switch so that starter circuit is closed when selector lever is at "N" and "P" only.

Automatic Trans. Replace

1. Pull back floor mat and remove converter housing-to-engine bolt access hole covers. Remove two upper bolts which attach converter housing to engine.

2. From under hood, remove two bolts attaching throttle linkage bracket to converter housing.

3. Remove starter. Then raise car on hoist.

4. Remove converter housing bottom cover.

5. Drain converter and transmission.

6. Remove propeller shaft.

7. Disconnect linkage at transmission.

8. Disconnect oil filler tube.

9. Remove engine rear support-to-extension housing bolt.

10. Disconnect parking brake cable rod at equalizer lever.

11. Place jack under transmission and raise it slightly to take weight off engine rear support member.

12. Unfasten support member from underbody (2 bolts) and remove support member.

13. Lower transmission and support engine.

14. Detach converter from flywheel (4 nuts) and remove converter away from flywheel as far as it will go.

15. Remove two lower converter housing-to-engine bolts.

16. Work converter housing off engine block dowel pins and work converter pilot out of engine crankshaft.

17. Secure converter to its housing and lower transmission.

18. Reverse above procedure to install.

Rear Axle and Brake Section
Refer To Hydraulic Brakes Chapter For Brake Adjustments

AXLE SHAFT REPLACE

1. Remove wheel and tire.

2. Back off rear brake shoe adjustments and remove brake drum.

3. Working through hole provided in axle shaft flange, remove nuts that

secure wheel bearing retainer. Then pull axle shaft out of axle housing with a slide hammer type puller. *The brake carrier plate must not be dislodged; install one nut to hold plate in place after axle shaft is removed.*

4. If the rear bearing is to be replaced,

loosen the inner retainer, Fig. 1. The retainer will become loose on the shaft if it is nicked deeply in several places with a chisel.

5. Remove bearing from shaft, using a press or puller. The new bearing should be pressed on the shaft so that it seats firmly against the

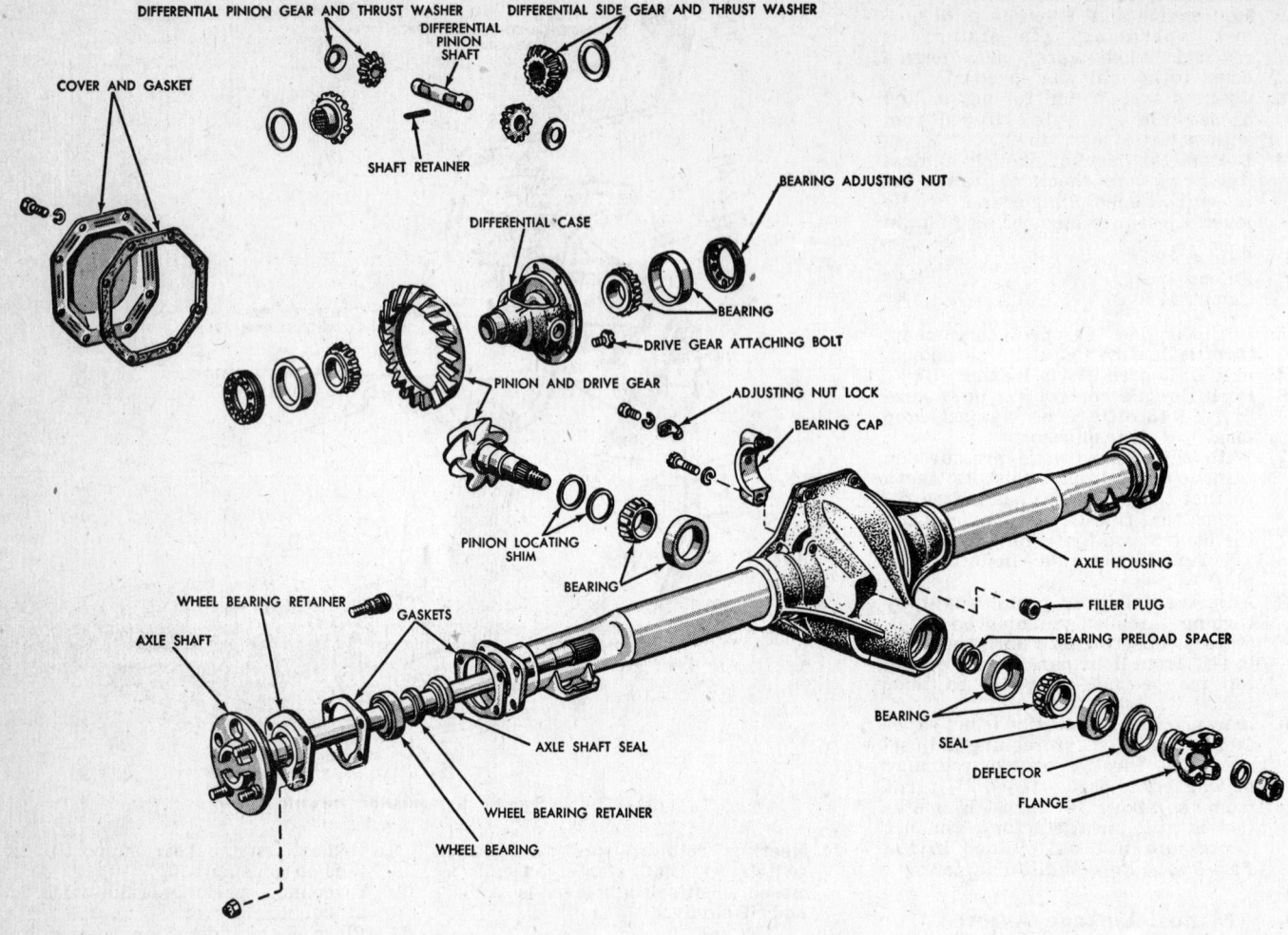

Fig. 1 Exploded view of rear axle assembly

shoulder on the shaft. Then press the retainer on the shaft until the retainer seats firmly gainst the bearing.

6. If the axle shaft oil seal is to be replaced, remove the seal with a slide hammer tool and install the new seal with a suitable driver.

7. Reverse the above procedure to install the axle shaft.

DRIVE PINION OIL SEAL REPLACE

1. Loosen but do not remove the carrier casting rear cover to drain the lubricant.

2. Referring to Fig. 1, disconnect drive shaft from drive pinion flange.

3. Mark pinion shaft nut, the end of pinion shaft, and pinion shaft splines for realignment.

4. Use a suitable tool to keep the flange from turning while removing the pinion shaft nut and flat washer.

5. Pull off flange and remove pinion oil seal.

6. Clean oil seal seat, and be sure that seal lubricant return passage is clear.

7. Coat outer edge of new seal with

oil-resistant sealer and install seal.

8. Align flange spline mark and pinion shaft spline mark and install flange.

9. Install nut and flat washer and tighten nut until marks are aligned.

10. Complete installation of remaining parts and torque cover bolts to 20-25 ft. lbs.

REAR AXLE

In this type axle, Fig. 1, the splined companion flange is fastened to the pinion shaft with a nut and flat washer which seats in the flange counterbore. The drive pinion is mounted on tapered roller bearings. Adjustment of the pinion along its axis is obtained by shims placed between the rear bearing inner race and pinion shaft shoulder. Adjustment of pinion bearings is obtained by tightening the companion flange nut which compresses a spacer over the pinion shaft between the two bearings.

The threaded nut type of differential bearing adjustment is used. The procedure for making this adjustment, as well as the assembly of the differential case, replacing a ring gear, checking ring gear and pinion backlash and other differential case operations, is given in the *Rear Axles* chapter.

All service operations on the differential case assembly and drive pinion can be performed with the housing in the car.

Inspection Before Removal

After removing the axle shafts as outlined previously, wipe the lubricant from the internal working parts and visually inspect the parts for wear or damage. Rotate the gears to see if there is any roughness which would indicate defective bearings or chipped gears. Check the gear teeth for scoring or signs of abnormal wear.

Check the differential case and drive pinion for end play. Set up a dial indicator and check backlash at several points around the drive gear. Backlash should be .005-.010". If no obvious defect is noted, check the gear tooth contact as explained in the *Rear Axles* chapter.

Loosen the differential bearing cap bolts and torque them to 5 ft. lbs. Remove the adjusting nut locks and carefully loosen one of the adjusting nuts to determine if any differential bearing preload remains. If at least one notch of preload remains, the differential bearings may be re-used provided they are not pitted or damaged.

Drive Pinion Replace

To compensate for machining tolerances, pinion and ring gears are factory tested for tooth contact and quietness. This test is conducted at a standard cone setting, using an .018″ shim between the pinion rear bearing cone and pinion gear, and varied to obtain correct tooth contact and quietness. Shims of various thicknesses are used to obtain the desired result.

Note the figures etched on the rear end of the drive pinion. One set will be found identical on both the ring gear and pinion. This denotes a matched set of gears. Another figure will be found on the end of the drive pinion which shows a plus or minus sign. This indicates the position of the pinion in relation to the center line of the axle. If there are no figures showing a plus or minus sign, it denotes a zero pinion setting and an "O" will be shown.

The gear is marked + (plus) or — (minus) the number of thousandths of an inch that the gear varies above or below standard. Thus + means the pinion is closer to the center line of the axle than standard and the — mark means farther from the center line.

When installing a new ring gear and pinion set or a new rear bearing, use new adjusting shims. Adjusting shims are available in thicknesses of .006, .007, .008, .012, .014, .016, .017 and .018 inch to obtain various thickness combinations.

The amount of shims used is determined by the amount of shims removed at disassembly and by the + or — figure etched on the pinion. For example, if the original pinion is marked +2 and had a shim pack of .015″ and the new pinion to be installed is marked —1, the shim pack must be increased by .003″ to bring the new pinion to the correct position. The new shim pack, therefore, will be .018″ thick.

Insert the drive pinion in position. At this time, install the original shim pack on the pinion shaft shoulder. For every shim added to pinion depth adjustment, subtract a like amount from the shim pack. If the pinion depth adjustment is less, add a like amount to the shim pack. This will approximate the pinion preload setting.

To adjust the preload, hold the pinion flange from turning and tighten the pinion shaft nut. As the nut is tightened, the shaft is pulled into the front bearing cone and into the flange until the cone and flange have bottomed on the collapsible spacer.

From this point a much greater torque must be applied to turn the nut since the spacer must be collapsed. From this point, also, the nut should be tightened very slowly and pinion shaft end play checked often so the pinion bearing preload does not exceed the specified limits (10-16 inch pounds on used bearings and 17-27 inch pounds on new bearings).

If the pinion nut is tightened to the point that bearing preload exceeds the limits, the pinion shaft must be removed and a new collapsible spacer installed. *Do not decrease the preload by loosening the nut as this will remove the compression between pinion front bearing cone and the collapsible spacer and may permit the front bearing cone to turn on the pinion shaft. As soon as there is preload on the bearings, turn the pinion shaft in both directions several times to seat the bearing rollers.*

MASTER CYLINDER REPLACE

1. Disconnect rubber boot from push rod end of master cylinder.
2. Disconnect brake lines from brake fitting and disconnect stop light switch wires.
3. Remove attaching bolts and remove cylinder from push rod and engine compartment.
4. Reverse above procedure to install and torque retaining bolts to 12-18 ft. lbs.

Front End and Steering Section

WHEEL ALIGNMENT

Caster and camber can be adjusted by removing or installing shims between the inner shaft of the front suspension upper arm and the underbody, Fig. 1. Both adjustments can be made at the same time by loosening the nuts on the two bolts that fasten the shaft to the underbody. After the adjustments are made, torque the nuts to 65-90 ft. lbs. *Adjusting shims are available in thicknesses of $\frac{1}{32}$″ and ⅛″. The $\frac{1}{32}$″ shims should be placed against the fender housing sheet metal or between the ⅛″ shims.*

Caster Adjust

The removal of shims at the front bolt or the installation of shims at the rear bolt will decrease caster angle. The removal of shims at the rear bolt or the installation of shims at the front bolt will increase caster angle. A $\frac{1}{32}$″ change of shim thickness will change the caster angle approximately ½ degree. The difference between the shim pack thickness at the two bolts should not exceed $\frac{1}{16}$″.

Camber Adjust

The removal of equal shims at both bolts will decrease camber angle. The installation of equal shims at both bolts will increase camber angle. A $\frac{1}{16}$″ change of shim thickness at both bolts will change camber angle ⅓°. The total shim pack thickness at each bolt should not exceed $\frac{9}{16}$″.

Toe-In Adjust

Check the steering wheel spoke position when the front wheels are in the straight-ahead position. If the spokes are not in their normal position, they can be properly adjusted while toe-in is being adjusted, Figs. 2 and 3.

1. Loosen two clamp bolts on each tie rod sleeve.
2. Adjust toe-in.
3. When toe-in and steering wheel are correct, torque the clamp bolts to 11-14 ft. lbs. *Sleeve position should not be changed when clamp bolts are tightened.*

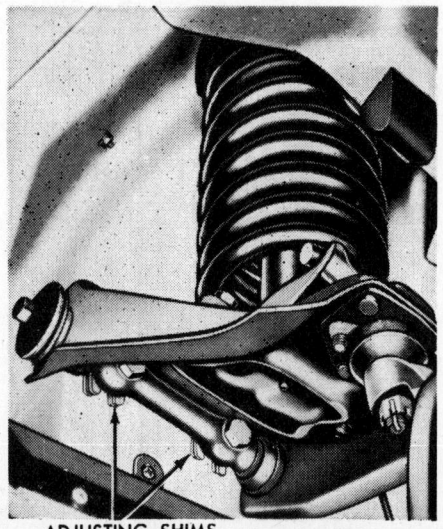

ADJUSTING SHIMS

Fig. 1   Location of caster and camber adjusting shims

WHEEL BEARINGS ADJUST

After removing wheel cover and grease cap from hub, rotate wheel hub while torquing the adjusting nut to 11-14 ft. lbs. Then back off the nut at least ⅛ turn but not more than ¼ turn.

Loosen the adjusting nut just enough to line up the nearest slot in the nut with the cotter pin hole in the spindle, and install cotter pin.

FRONT END REPAIRS
Shock Absorber Replace

1. Raise front of car and place supports under both lower suspension arms.
2. Remove shock absorber retaining nuts from spring lower retaining plate.
3. Remove shock absorber upper

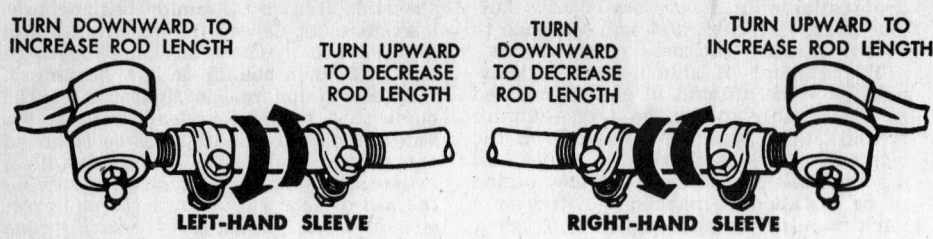

TURN DOWNWARD TO INCREASE ROD LENGTH   TURN UPWARD TO DECREASE ROD LENGTH   TURN DOWNWARD TO DECREASE ROD LENGTH   TURN UPWARD TO INCREASE ROD LENGTH

LEFT-HAND SLEEVE   **RIGHT-HAND SLEEVE**

Fig. 2   Steering tie rod sleeve adjustments

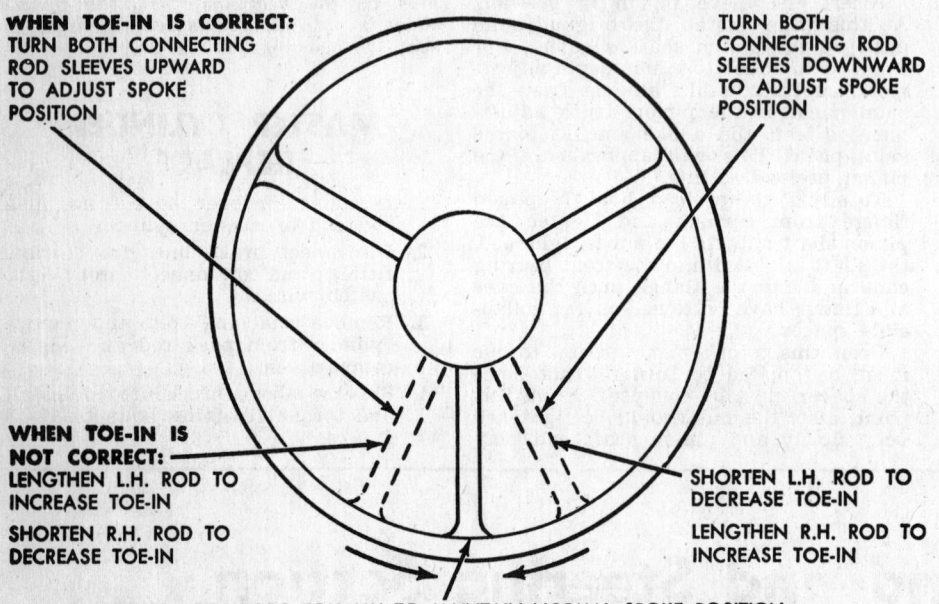

WHEN TOE-IN IS CORRECT: TURN BOTH CONNECTING ROD SLEEVES UPWARD TO ADJUST SPOKE POSITION

TURN BOTH CONNECTING ROD SLEEVES DOWNWARD TO ADJUST SPOKE POSITION

WHEN TOE-IN IS NOT CORRECT: LENGTHEN L.H. ROD TO INCREASE TOE-IN

SHORTEN R.H. ROD TO DECREASE TOE-IN

SHORTEN L.H. ROD TO DECREASE TOE-IN

LENGTHEN R.H. ROD TO INCREASE TOE-IN

ADJUST BOTH RODS EQUALLY TO MAINTAIN NORMAL SPOKE POSITION

Fig. 3   Toe-in and steering wheel spoke adjustments

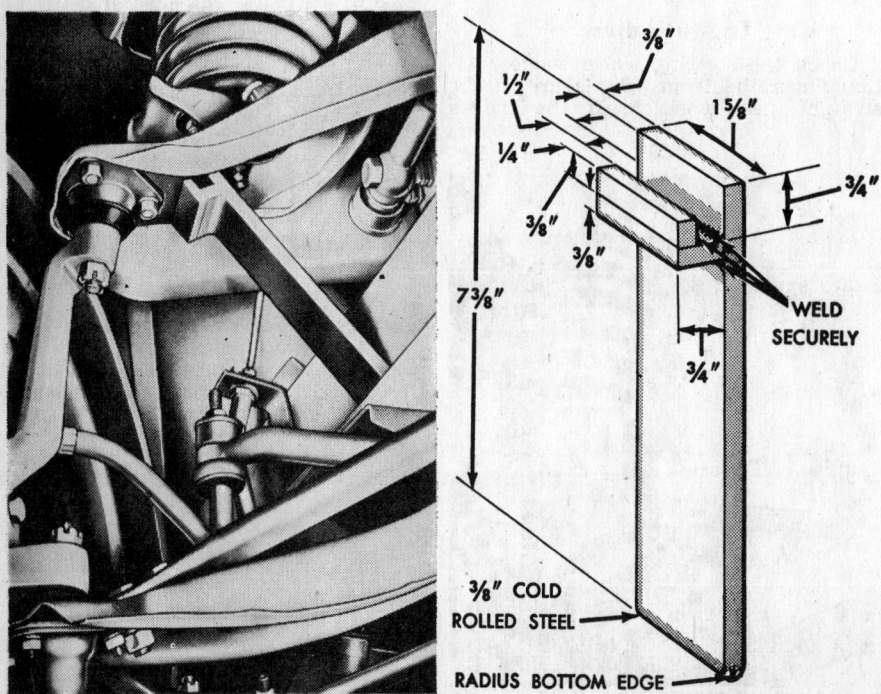

3/8" 1/2" 1/4" 3/8" 3/8" 1 5/8" 3/4" 7 3/8" 3/4"

WELD SECURELY

3/8" COLD ROLLED STEEL

RADIUS BOTTOM EDGE

Fig. 5   Upper arm support tool showing dimensions for making same and method of installation

bracket nuts and lift the bracket and shock absorber from car, Fig. 4.

4. Reverse above procedure to install.

Upper Ball Joint Replace

1. Raise car high enough to provide working space and place a support under the upper arm, Fig. 5.
2. Remove wheel and tire.
3. Cut off rivet heads with chisel.
4. Remove nut from upper stud and remove ball joint.
5. Clean end of arm and remove burrs from hole edges. Check for cracks in metal at holes and replace arm if cracked.
6. Attach new ball joint to arm, using only specified bolts, nuts and washers. *Do not rivet new ball joint to arm.*
7. Install and torque stud nut to 35 ft. lbs.
8. Lubricate ball joint and, after installing removed parts, check wheel alignment.

Wheel Spindle Replace

1. Raise car and place support tool, Fig. 5, under arm.
2. Remove wheel, drum and brake backing plate.
3. Disconnect tie rod from spindle.
4. Remove ball joints.
5. Position new spindle and torque stud nuts to 35-65 ft. lbs. Install cotter pins.
6. After installing parts removed check wheel alignment.

Front Spring Replace

1. Raise car and remove wheel.
2. Remove shock absorber.
3. Install safety stand at front end of underbody.
4. Use a suitable tool, Fig. 6, to compress the spring 2 to 2½".
5. Remove spring lower retaining nuts and remove spring.
6. Reverse above procedure to install and check wheel alignment.

Upper Arm Replace

1. Raise car and place support, Fig. 5, under the arm.
2. Remove wheel assembly.
3. Remove upper ball joint and spring.
4. Unfasten and remove arm, noting number and position of shims at each nut.
5. Reverse above procedure to install and check wheel alignment.

Lower Arm Replace

1. Raise car and place support, Fig. 5, under upper arm.
2. Remove wheel assembly.
3. Remove lower ball joint, stabilizer bar and strut retaining bolts.
4. Unfasten and remove arm.
5. Reverse above procedure to install and check wheel alignment.

STEERING GEAR

Adjustments

1. Disconnect pitman arm from steering rod.

2. Loosen steering gear housing attaching bolts at underbody side rail to relieve possible binding between steering column and worm shaft, Fig. 7.
3. Loosen steering column bracket screws at instrument panel.
4. Partially tighten steering column bracket screws.
5. Torque steering gear housing attaching bolts to 25-35 ft. lbs.
6. Loosen sector shaft adjusting screw lock nut and turn screw counterclockwise.
7. Measure worm bearing preload by attaching an inch-pound torque wrench to steering wheel nut or hook a spring scale to steering wheel rim. Read pull required to keep wheel moving for at least one complete turn. If torque or preload is not within the limits 3 to 6 inch lbs., adjust as follows:
8. Loosen steering shaft bearing adjuster lock nut and tighten or back off bearing adjuster, Fig. 7, to bring preload within specified limits.
9. Tighten steering shaft bearing adjuster lock nut and recheck preload.
10. Turn steering wheel slowly to each stop. *Turn gently against stops to avoid damage to ball return guides.* Then rotate $2\frac{5}{16}$ turns to center ball nut.
11. Turn sector adjusting screw clockwise until 8-13 inch lbs. is necessary to rotate worm past center. *No perceptible backlash is permissible at 30° on either side of center.*
12. Tighten sector adjusting screw lock nut and recheck backlash adjustment.
13. Tighten steering column bracket bolts and connect sector shaft arm to steering rod.

Horn Button

To remove, press down evenly on horn button or ring and turn counterclockwise until it lifts out from steering wheel.

Tool—T60K-5310-A

Fig. 6 Showing tool used to compress front coil spring for removal

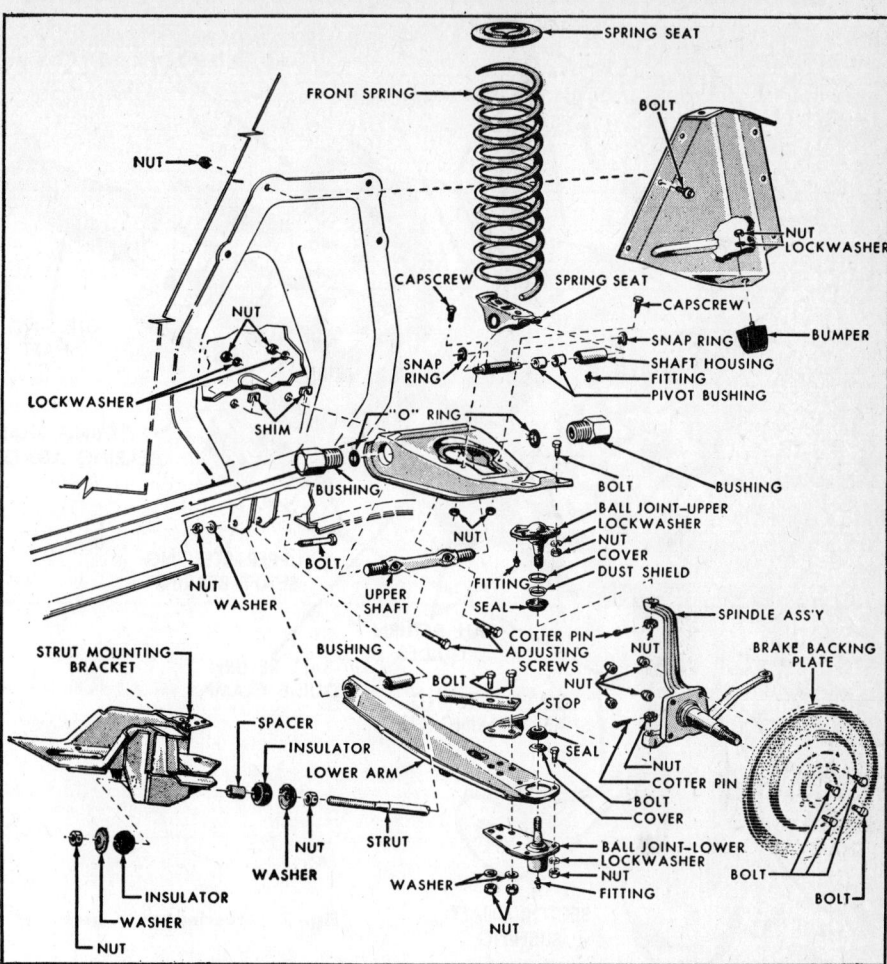

Fig. 4 Disassembled view of 1961 front suspension. Except for the threaded steel bushings for the upper control arm, the suspension is similar to 1960 which has rubber bushings.

Steering Wheel Replace

1. Remove horn ring or button and related parts.
2. Remove steering shaft nut and use a suitable puller to remove the wheel.
3. When installing, have front wheels straight ahead and position the wheel on the shaft so that the spokes are properly centered and the splines of on both parts are properly aligned. Install and stake the nut.

Steering Gear Replace

1. Raise front of car and place on safety stands.
2. Remove pitman arm from steering shaft.
3. Remove steering gear bolts from underbody and disconnect gearshift rods(s) at shift lever(s).
4. Pull rubber seal up on steering column, fold floor mat aside and move dash panel insulation out of the way.
5. Remove screws from steering column weather seal on dash panel.
6. Remove steering column cover plates and gasket.
7. Disconnect horn and turn signal wires under instrument panel. On Fordomatic cars disconnect neutral switch wires.
8. Remove steering wheel, upper bearing sleeve and spring and turn signal lever.
9. Remove steering column clamp and insulator.
10. Slide column tube off steering shaft, guiding shift lever(s) through rubber seal at dash panel.
11. Remove steering gear out the front through engine compartment.
12. Reverse above procedure to install.

Steering Gear Repairs

1. Rotate steering worm until nut is in center of travel, Fig. 7.
2. Remove sector shaft nut.
3. Use puller to remove pitman arm.
4. Remove side cover screws and remove side cover and sector shaft from housing.
5. To remove side cover from sector shaft, turn adjuster screw in end of sector shaft down through cover.
6. Remove screws and take out end cover with worm bearing, outer race and thrust washer.
7. To remove lower worm bearing, outer race and thrust washer from cover, loosen worm bearing adjuster

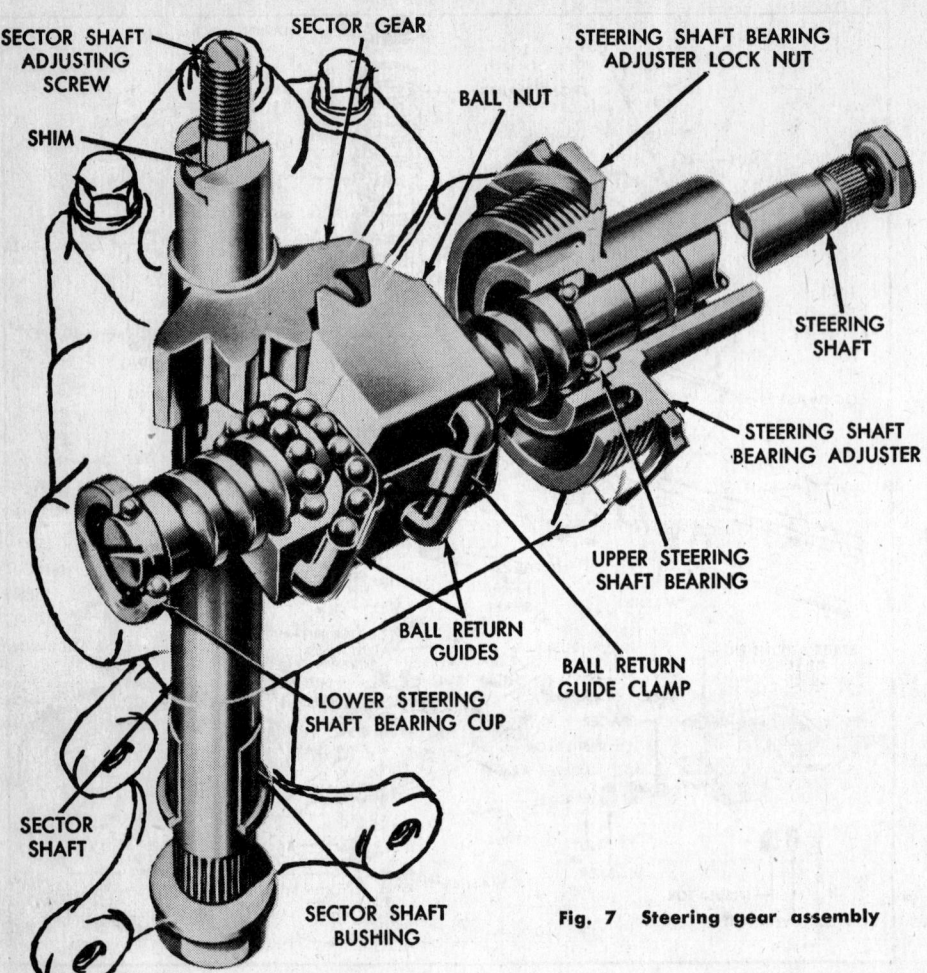

SECTOR SHAFT ADJUSTING SCREW

SHIM

SECTOR GEAR

BALL NUT

STEERING SHAFT BEARING ADJUSTER LOCK NUT

STEERING SHAFT

STEERING SHAFT BEARING ADJUSTER

UPPER STEERING SHAFT BEARING

BALL RETURN GUIDE CLAMP

BALL RETURN GUIDES

LOWER STEERING SHAFT BEARING CUP

SECTOR SHAFT

SECTOR SHAFT BUSHING

Fig. 7 Steering gear assembly

screw lock nut and turn screw in through cover.

8. Grasp lower end of steering worm and draw steering shaft and nut out of steering housing. *Be sure to keep shaft in horizontal position so that nut does not move against stops at any time, causing damage to ball return mechanism.* Disassembly of worm nut is not recommended.

Assemble

1. Install worm shaft and nut assembly in gear housing, keeping ball nut away from stops on worm.
2. Install worm bearing adjusting screw with lower worm bearing, outer race and thrust washer in end cover.
3. Install end cover and attaching parts on gear housing, making sure bearings seat properly.
4. Tighten worm bearing adjusting screw until a slight drag is felt on bearings. Do not tighten lock nut.
5. Install pitman arm.
6. Install sector shaft and adjusting screw inside cover.
7. Rotate steering column until ball nut is in center of travel so that center tooth on sector shaft will enter center space on nut.
8. Install side cover and sector shaft in gear housing.
9. Tighten sector shaft adjusting screw until a slight drag is felt on bearing but do not tighten lock nut.
10. After steering gear is installed in car, adjust as outlined previously.

Speedometer, Radio and Windshield Wiper

SPEEDOMETER, REPLACE

1. Disconnect cable at speedometer.
2. Remove screws and lift instrument cluster bezel, lens and cluster mask plate from cluster housing.
3. Remove retaining screws and remove speedometer from cluster housing.
4. Reverse above procedure to install.

RADIO, REPLACE

Comet 1960-61

1. Disconnect ground cable from battery.

2. Remove control knobs from front of receiver, and two control shaft nuts and washers.
3. Disconnect antenna lead-in cable and speaker plug.
4. Disconnect dial lamp wire and power lead at fuse panel.
5. Remove radio bracket retaining nut at left-hand side and bracket retaining screw at right-hand side. Then carefully remove radio.
6. To install radio, reverse above procedure.

Falcon 1960-61

1. Pull control knobs off and remove nuts retaining radio to instrument panel.

2. Disconnect antenna lead at right side of radio.
3. Disconnect speaker leads.
4. Disconnect radio lead wire at fuse panel and pilot light wire.
5. Remove radio right and left support bracket-to-radio retaining bolts.
6. Remove radio from panel.
7. Reverse above procedure to install.

WINDSHIELD WIPER

To remove wiper motor, disconnect wiper hose at motor. If equipped with electric wiper motor, disconnect battery ground cable. Loosen control cable retaining screw at motor. Unfasten motor from mounting bracket and remove motor.

CORVAIR

INDEX OF SERVICE OPERATIONS

PAGE NO.

ACCESSORIES
Instrument Cluster 641
Windshield Wiper 641

BRAKES
Adjustments 112
Brake Cylinder Sizes................... 604
Hydraulic Brake System................... 112
Master Cylinder, Replace................... 638
Trouble Shooting 31

CLUTCH
Clutch Linkage, Adjust................... 620
Clutch, Replace 620
Trouble Shooting 13

COOLING SYSTEM
Blower Bearing, Replace................... 617
Blower, Replace 617
Thermostat, Replace 617
Crankcase Cover, Replace................... 617

ELECTRIC SYSTEM
Dash Gauge Service................... 85
Distributor, Replace................... 617
Distributor Specifications 603
Generator Service 62
Generator, Replace 618
Generator Specifications 603
Generator Regulator Service................... 62
Generator Regulator Specifications................... 603
Ignition System Service................... 46
Ignition Timing 618
Starter, Replace................... 618
Starter Service 77
Starter Specifications 603
Trouble Shooting 10
Turn Signal Troubles................... 12

ENGINE
Camshaft, Replace 610
Cylinder Head, Assemble 612
Cylinder Head, Replace................... 612
Cylinders and Pistons................... 610
Crankcase, Replace................... 614
Crankshaft, Install 610
Engine Description 607
Engine, Dissassembly 608
Engine, Reassemble 610

PAGE NO.

Engine Rear Housing, Replace......... 616
Engine Specifications 602
Exhaust Manifold Sleeves 613
Main Bearings 615
Pistons and Cylinders................... 614
Pistons, Replace 610
Piston Pins, Replace................... 614
Piston Rings, Replace................... 614
Push Rods, Replace................... 612
Rocker Arms, Replace................... 612
Rod Bearings, Replace................... 614
Timing Gear Marks................... 610
Valves, Adjust 612
Valves, Grind 613
Valve Guides 613
Valve Lifters 613
Valves, Remove 612
Valve Seat Inserts 613
Valve Springs 613
Valve Timing Data................... 610

ENGINE OILING
Crankcase Vent Tube, Replace......... 616
Oil Pan, Replace................... 616
Oil Pump Gears, Replace................... 615
Oil Pump Repairs................... 615
Oil Pressure Regulator, Replace......... 615
Oil Cooler and By-Pass Valves................... 616
Oil Cooler, Clean................... 616
Oil Cooler, Replace................... 616
Oil Filter Adapter................... 616
Seal, Crankshaft Pulley and Engine
  Rear Housing 616
Seal, Flywheel Housing................... 617

FUEL & EXHAUST SYSTEM
Carburetors 618
Exhaust System 618
Fuel Pumps 96
Trouble Shooting 4

POWER TRAIN
Power Train, Replace................... 605
Separation of Components................... 605

REAR AXLE
Axle Shaft, Replace................... 633
Differential Carrier Repairs................... 636
Rear Axle Repairs................... 636
Rear Axle Specifications................... 604
Side Bearing Sleeve Seal, Replace................... 635
Rear Axle U-Joint, Replace................... 633

PAGE NO.

SPECIFICATIONS
Brake Cylinder Sizes................... 604
Capacity Data 604
Carburetor 619
Crankshaft 603
Distributor 603
Engine Tightening 602
General Specifications 602
Generator & Regulator 603
Main Bearings 603
Piston Pins 603
Piston Rings 603
Pistons 603
Rear Axle 604
Rod Bearings 603
Starting Motor 603
Tune Up 602
Valves 602
Wheel Alignment 604

STEERING GEAR
Steering Gear Adjustments................... 640
Steering Gear, Overhaul................... 641
Steering Gear, Replace................... 641
Steering Wheel, Replace................... 640

SUSPENSION
Front Wheel Bearings, Adjust................... 638
Front Suspension Repairs................... 639
Rear Suspension Repairs................... 639
Wheel Alignment (front)................... 638
Wheel Alignment (rear)................... 638
Wheel Alignment Specs................... 604

TRANSMISSION, AUTOMATIC
Adjustments 624
Description 624
Maintenance 624
"In Car" Repairs................... 626
Shift Lingage 624
Transmission, Overhaul 628

TRANSMISSION, MANUAL
Linkage, Adjust 621
Transmission, Assemble 623
Transmission, Disassemble 621
Transmission Repairs 622
Transmission, Replace (See Power Train
  Section)

TUNE UP SERVICE 38

GENERAL SPECIFICATIONS

Year	Model Designation	Wheel-base, Inches	Valve Location	Bore and Stroke	Piston Dis-place-ment, Cubic Inches	Com-pres-sion Ratio (Stand-ard)	Maximum Brake H.P. @ R.P.M.	Maximum Torque Lbs. Ft. @ R.P.M.	Normal Oil Pressure Pounds
1960	Standard 6..............500	108	In Head	3.375 x 2.60	140	8.0	80 @ 4400	125 @ 2400	35
	De Luxe 6..............700	108	In Head	3.375 x 2.60	140	8.0	80 @ 4400	125 @ 2400	35
	Monza 6...........900	108	In Head	3.375 x 2.60	140	8.0	95 @ 4800	125 @ 2800	35
1961	Standard 6..............500	108	In Head	3.4375 x 2.60	145	8.0	80 @ 4400	128 @ 2300	35
	De Luxe 6..............700	108	In Head	3.4375 x 2.60	145	8.0	80 @ 4400	128 @ 2300	35
	Monza 6...........900	108	In Head	3.4375 x 2.60	145	8.0	98 @ 4600	132 @ 2800	35
	Lakewood 6...........5–725	108	In Head	3.4375 x 2.60	145	8.0	80 @ 4400	128 @ 2300	35

ENGINE TIGHTENING SPECIFICATIONS★

★Torque specifications are for clean and lightly lubricated threads only. Dry or dirty threads produce increased friction which prevents accurate measurement of tightness.

Year	Spark Plugs Ft. Lbs.	Cylinder Head Bolts Ft. Lbs.	Exhaust Manifold Ft. Lbs.	Rocker Arm Stud Nut Ft. Lbs.	Rocker Arm Stud Ft. Lbs.	Rocker Arm Cover Ft. Lbs.	Connecting Rod Cap Bolts Ft. Lbs.	Crankcase Bolts Ft. Lbs.	Flywheel to Crankshaft Ft. Lbs.	Vibration Damper or Pulley Ft. Lbs.
1960-61	20–25	27–33	10–20	5–10	27–33	3–5	20–26	①	20–26	50–60

①—No caps. Torque crankcase halves to 42–48 ft. lbs. with 7/16″ bolts, for 5/16″ bolts, 7–13 ft. lbs.

TUNE UP SPECIFICATIONS

★Because of the difference in rate of expansion between aluminum head and steel spark plug it is advisable to allow engine to cool before removing plugs.

Year	Model	Ground Polarity and Voltage	Spark Plug★ Type	Spark Plug★ Gap Inch	Distributor Point Gap Inch	Distributor Cam Angle Degrees	Firing Order ①	Ignition Timing Mark	Ignition Timing Location	Idle Speed RPM In Drive	Com-pression Pressure @ Cranking Speed Minimum
1960-61	All	N-12	AC-46FF	.035	③	33	145236	②	Pulley	500	130

①—Right rear cylinder is No. 1 and left rear cylinder is No. 2. Thus reading in order from the rear, the right bank is numbered 1–3–5 and the left bank 2–4–6.

②—With distributors 1110252 and 1110258 4°BTDC; 1110259 and 1110260 13°BTDC; 1110256 and 1110257 16°BTDC.

③—New points .019″, used points .016″.

VALVE SPECIFICATIONS

Year	Model	Valve Lash Int.	Valve Lash Exh.	Valve Angles Seat	Valve Angles Face	Valve Spring Installed Height	Valve Spring Pressure Lbs. @ In.	Valve Lift Int.	Valve Lift Exh.	Stem Clearance Intake	Stem Clearance Exhaust	Stem Diameter Int.	Stem Diameter Exh.
1960-61	Std. Cam.	Zero	Zero	45	44	1½	145 @ 1 5/32	.314	.344	.001–.003	.0015–.003	.3419	①
	Spec. Cam.	Zero	Zero	45	44	1 11/16	165 @ 1 5/16	.380	.380	.001–.003	.0015–.003	.3419	①

①—Top .3414″, bottom .3404″ (.001″ taper).

PISTONS, PINS, RINGS, CRANKSHAFT & BEARINGS

Year	Model	Fitting Pistons		Ring End Gap① Minimum		Wrist-pin Diameter	Rod Bearings		Main Bearings			Shaft End Play
		Shim To Use	Pounds Pull On Scale	Comp.	Oil		Shaft Diameter	Bearing Clearance	Shaft Diameter	Bearing Clearance	Thrust on Bearing No.	
1960–61	All	②	②	.010	.010	.8001	1.799–1.800	.0007–.0027	2.0978–2.0988	.0012–.0037	1	.002–.006

①—Oversize rings not furnished. New rings should be fitted to tightest part of cylinder if cylinder is tapered.

②—Cylinder and piston must be replaced as a unit if bore is worn or tapered in excess of .005''.

DISTRIBUTOR SPECIFICATIONS

Year	Model	Part No.	Rotation①	Cam Angle, Degrees	Breaker Point Opening, Inch	Condenser Capacity, Mfds.	Breaker Arm Spring Tension, Ounces	Centrifugal Advance Data Degrees @ R.P.M. of Dist.		Vacuum Advance Data		
								Advance Starts	Full Advance	Inches of Vacuum to Start Plunger Movement	Inches of Vacuum for Full Plunger Travel	Maximum Vacuum Advance, Dist. Degrees
1960	All	1110252	C	33	②	.18–.23	19–23	2 @ 400	16 @ 1800	5–7	14½–16	11½
1960	Auto. Tr.	1110256	C	33	②	.18–.23	19–23	0 @ 850	10 @ 1800	7	16	11½
1960	Hi-Perf.	1110257	C	33	②	.18–.23	19–23	0 @ 350	12 @ 2400	8	15½	7½
1960–61	Man. Tr.	1110258	C	33	②	.18–.23	19–23	0 @ 200	16 @ 1800	6	15.2	11½
1960–61	Auto. Tr.	1110259	C	33	②	.18–.23	19–23	0 @ 850	10 @ 1800	7	16	11½
1960–61	Hi-Perf.	1110260	C	33	②	.18–.23	19–23	0 @ 350	12 @ 2400	6	15.2	11½

①—As viewed from top in installed position.　②—New points .019'', used .016''.

GENERATOR AND REGULATOR SPECIFICATIONS

★To polarize generator, reconnect the leads to the regulator; then momentarily connect a jumper wire from the "Gen" to the "Bat" terminals of the regulator.

Car & Model	Generator						Regulator					
	Generator Number	Ground Polarity	Rated Cap. Amps.	Gen. Field Ground Location★	Brush Spring Tension, Ounces	Field Current Amperes	Regulator Number	Cutout Relay		Voltage Regulator Setting Volts	Current Regulator Setting Amperes	Current and Voltage Armature Air Gap, Inch
								Voltage to Close Points	Armature Air Gap, Inch			
1960	1100357	Negative	30	External	28	1.5–1.62	1119261	12.4	.020	14.2	30	.075
1961	1102227	Negative	30	External	28	1.5–1.62	1119001	12.2	.020	14.3	30	.075

STARTING MOTOR SPECIFICATIONS

Car and Model	Part No.	Brush Spring, Tension, Ounces	No Load Test			Torque Test		
			Amperes	Volts	R.P.M.	Amperes	Volts	Torque, Lbs. Ft.
1960 Std. Trans.	1108300	35 Min.	58–80	10.6	6750–8600	280–320	4	①
1960 Powerglide	1108301	35 Min.	58–80	10.6	6750–8600	280–320	4	①
1961 Std. Trans.	1108306	35 Min.	69	10.6	7675	280–320	4	①
1961 Powerglide	1108307	35 Min.	69	10.6	7675	280–320	4	①

①—Armature locked.

CAPACITY DATA

Year	Model	Fuel Tank Gallons	Engine Oil			Transmission 3-Speed, Pints	Powerglide, Pints ②	Differential, Pints
			Refill, Qts. ①	Summer Grade	Winter Grade			
1960	All	11	4	30	10	2	②	3
1961	All	14	4	30	10	2	②	3

①—Add one quart for filter change.
②—If transmission is overhauled and if converter has not drained out, a refill will take 6 pints. A "dry" transmission will take 13–14 pints. An ordinary oil change of transmission only (not converter) will need 4½ pints.

REAR AXLE AND BRAKE CYLINDER SPECIFICATIONS

Year	Model	Ring Gear & Pinion Backlash, Inch	Drive Pinion Adjustment	Drive Pinion Bearing Preload, Inch Lbs.	Drive Pinion Bearing Adjustment	Axle Shaft End Play, Inch	Hydraulic Cylinder Bore Sizes, Inch		
							Wheel Cylinder		Mater Cylinder
							Front	Rear	
1960	All	.005–.008	Shim	①	Adj. Sleeve	None	.875	.9375	1.125
1961	All	.005–.008	Shim	①	Adj. Sleeve	None	.875	.9375	1.0

①—14–16 inch lbs. for new bearings, 9–11 inch lbs. for used bearings.

WHEEL ALIGNMENT SPECIFICATIONS

Year	Model	Caster, Degrees		Camber, Degrees		Toe-In, Inches	Toe-out on Turns. Degrees		Kingpin or Steering Axis Inclination
		Limits	Desired	Limits	Desired		Outer Wheel	Inner Wheel	
1960–61	All	+ 2½ to + 3	+ 2¾	0 to + 1	+ ½	⅛ to 3/16 ①	18	20	7

①—Rear wheels 0 to ¼" total.

SERIAL NUMBER LOCATION
Left Front Door Pillar

ENGINE NUMBER LOCATION
Top Of Engine Block Forward Of Generator- Oil Filter Adapter

ENGINE IDENTIFICATION

Year	Engine	Suffix Letter ①
1960–61	6-140 ②	Y
	6-140 ③	YD
	6-140 ④	Z

①—Engine identified by letter following engine number.
②—With manual shift transmission.
③—High performance engine.
④—With automatic transmission.

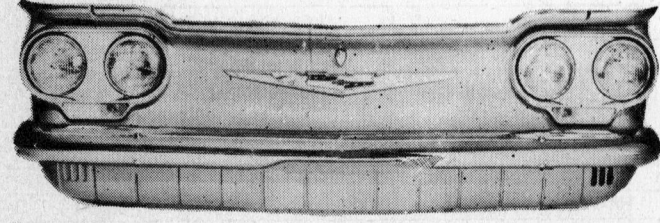

1960

1961

Power Train Section

POWER TRAIN, REPLACE

The preferred method of removal and installation described below utilizes a special Power Train Cradle (J-7894), Fig. 1, mounted on a transmission jack with the car on a hoist. Equipment limitations may require a modified approach to this operation but certain precautions must be observed.

1. The complete power train should be supported only at the engine pan rail. Under no circumstances should it be supported on the pan itself.
2. No jacking fixture or floor support should be used unless it is capable of supporting the weight of the power train (approximately 460 lbs.).
3. The center of gravity or balance point of the power train is located approximately .200" behind the front face of the cylinder block.
4. No jack should be used that does not permit the power train to be lowered *gradually*. This is essential to avoid damage to components when close clearances are encountered during removal.

Power Train Removal

When working in the engine compartment, insert a pin or bolt through the holes provided in the lid support to prevent accidentally unlocking the support.

1. Disconnect ground cable from battery and ground straps to engine.
2. Disconnect wires from coil, generator, oil pressure and temperature sending units.
3. Disconnect accelerator return spring and accelerator rod from carburetor cross shaft.
4. Raise vehicle on hoist.
5. Remove engine and rear shield seal retainers, Fig. 2.
6. Remove rear wheels and brake drums.
7. Remove axle shaft universal joints from differential carrier and remove axle shafts.
8. Remove wires from starter solenoid and disconnect speedometer cable.
9. Disconnect carburetor cross shaft rod from accelerator control idler rear lever and push rod up into engine compartment. Remove rear idler control lever rod.
10. Disconnect shift rod coupling on standard transmission jobs. On Powerglide models, disconnect flexible control cable, T.V. and accelerator rod.
11. Disconnect main fuel line and heater fuel line at hose connections. Plug lines from fuel tank.
12. On standard transmission models, disconnect clutch fork return spring and unhook clutch control cable clevis. Disconnect clutch fork pull rod. Loosen ball stud at clutch control cable cross shaft and remove cross shaft.
13. Remove emergency brake tension spring.
14. Remove rear engine grille.
15. Remove engine skid plate bolt.
16. Position transmission jack under engine, using Power Train Cradle J-7894 if available.
17. Remove two nuts from front engine mount (at transmission) and nut from rear engine mount. *If front engine mounting bracket and shims are removed from transmission, the same amount of shims must be replaced. Rear wheel toe-in will be affected if shims are altered.*
18. Lower power train gradually and watch for possible interference at the rear mounting and left rear lower control arm.
19. Remove exhaust pipe and muffler.

Power Train Installation

Reverse the removal procedure to install the power train. Be sure all harness wires, fuel lines and levers are out of the way prior to installation of the power train to prevent damage.

SEPARATION OF POWER TRAIN COMPONENTS

Remove 3-Speed Transaxle From Engine

1. With power train removed, support transaxle with chain hoist or other suitable lift and a sling.
2. Drain transmission and differential carrier.
3. Remove starting motor.
4. Remove two screws securing clutch pull rod dust seal; then remove pin attaching pull rod to clutch fork.

Fig. 1   Power train cradle (J-7894)

5. Remove bolts securing differential carrier to clutch housing. Pull transaxle away horizontally to prevent damaging clutch shaft, using care not to damage clutch fork. Remove clutch shaft.
6. To complete operation, remove clutch fork and clutch release bearing from differential carrier. The fork is attached to the carrier by a ball socket and spring retainer which is easily slipped off to allow the release bearing to be slipped off its shaft in the carrier.
7. Separate transmission from differential carrier.

Assemble 3-Speed Transaxle To Engine

1. Couple transmission to differential carrier, using new gasket. Be sure to engage splines of transmission mainshaft to internal splines of pinion in differential carrier. Install four bolts and torque them to 24-32 ft. lbs.
2. Install clutch release bearing and clutch fork on differential carrier. The bearing slips over the shaft and the fork has a spring retainer and socket which attaches to ball stud on carrier.
3. Install clutch shaft in transaxle; then check distance from end of clutch release bearing shaft to end of clutch shaft. If fully engaged, dimension should be $2\frac{9}{16}$" (plus or minus $\frac{1}{32}$").
4. Align both holes in differential carrier and clutch housing. Pilot clutch shaft splines into the clutch; then secure differential carrier to clutch housing with bolts.
5. Connect clutch push rod to clutch fork with pin; then position and secure clutch push rod dust seal to clutch housing with two screws.
6. Install starter and fill transmission and differential carrier with lubricant to the proper level.

Remove Powerglide Transaxle From Engine

1. Place a pan beneath transmission oil pan and loosen nut securing transmission filler tube to oil pan and allow transmission to drain.
2. Disconnect short length of hose connecting vacuum modulator tube to carburetor balance tube.
3. Remove engine front shield.
4. Remove starting motor.
5. Disconnect converter from engine flex plate by removing the three attaching bolts via the access hole at the 12 o'clock position in the converter housing. The converter may be rotated by prying against the starter gear teeth on the converter housing with a screwdriver.
6. Support transaxle with chain hoist or lift and sling.
7. Unfasten differential carrier from

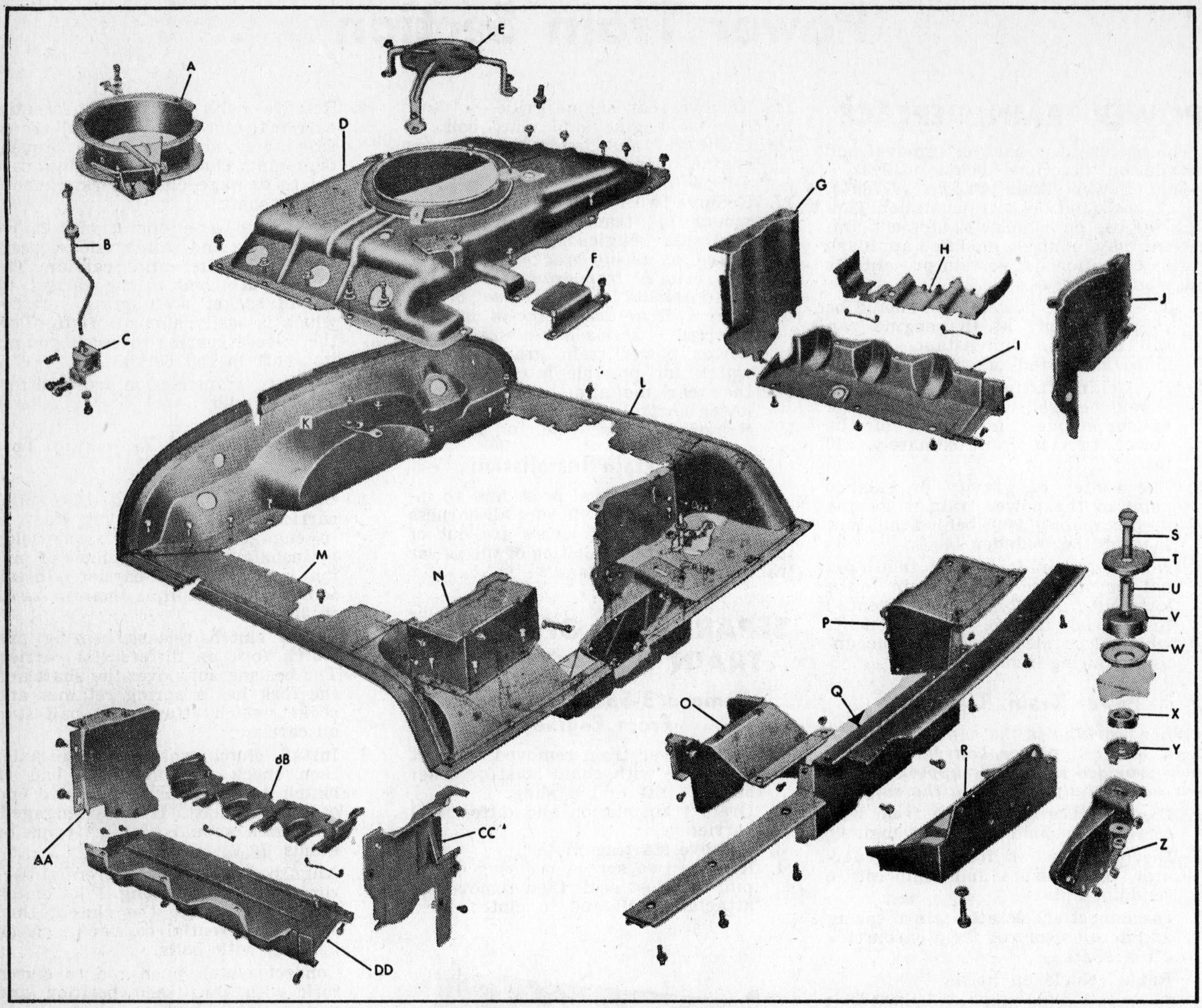

Fig. 2 Engine sheet metal components

A. Cooling Air Throttle Valve	I. Engine Lower Shroud—R. H.	Q. Engine Rear Center Shield	X. Rebound Pad
B. Thermostat Rod	J. Engine Rear Shroud—R. H.	R. Engine Skid Plate Assembly	Y. Rear Lower Mounting (Rebound Retainer)
C. Thermostat and Stop	K. Engine Front Shield	S. Rear Mount Bolt	Z. Engine Rear Mounting Bracket
D. Engine Upper Shroud	L. Engine Side Shield Assembly—R. H.	T. Rear Mount Upper Retainer	AA. Engine Front Shroud—L. H.
E. Air Cleaner Air Horn Support	M. Engine Side Shield Assembly—L. H.	U. Sleeve	BB. Engine Cylinder Air Baffle—L. H.
F. Oil Cooler Access Hole Cover	N. Oil Cooler	V. Mounting	CC. Engine Rear Shroud—L. H.
G. Front Shroud Assembly—R. H.	O. Engine Air Exhaust Duct—L. H.	W. Lower Retainer	DD. Engine Lower Shroud—L. H.
H. Engine Cylinder Air Baffle—R. H.	P. Engine Air Exhaust Duct—R. H.		

converter housing; then pull transaxle away from engine. Remove converter and turbine shaft.

Assemble Powerglide Transaxle To Engine

1. Align converter with flex plate; then pilot converter hub into crankshaft. Align bolt holes in differential carrier and converter housing; then secure transaxle to converter housing by installing top left bolt (11 o'clock position).
2. Install flex plate-to-converter bolt (at 1 o'clock position) to prevent accidental turning of converter or flex plate and loss of attaching bolt alignment.
3. Fasten remaining converter housing-to-differential carrier bolts.
4. Install starting motor.
5. Install two remaining converter-to-flex plate bolts via access hole in converter housing. The converter can then be rotated to make the attaching points accessible by turning the converter with a screwdriver against the starter gear teeth.
6. Install engine front shield.
7. If transmission filler tube was removed from engine front shield, reinsert it through the shield at this time; then connect the vacuum

Fig. 3 Dial indicator and support mounted on transmission

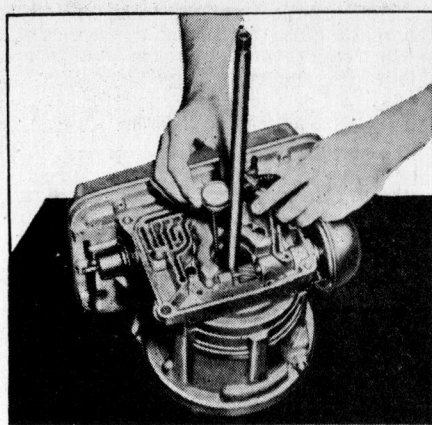

Fig. 4 Measuring mounting difference with dial indicator and support (J-8364)

lection of thrust washers of various thicknesses. In the Corvair transmission, selective thrust washers are used at two locations:

1. At the front of the transmission between the front pump body and clutch drum.
2. At the rear of the transmission between the rear face of the planet carrier hub and the front face of the governor gear.

From the serviceman's standpoint, the use of the selective thrust washers at both the front and rear is a distinct advantage as final transmission end play adjustment can be made at either end of the transmission, whichever is most advantageous. *Also, there is no condition in which the selective washers would be gauged at both locations. Thus, if the repair requires axle and transmission separation, make the washer selection at the rear. Of course, if they are not to be separated, the rear thrust washer is inaccessible and the selection must be made at the front.*

Prior to reassembly of the transmission to the differential carrier after any repair which required separation of these units, the rear selective thrust washer must be determined. *Be sure low band is properly adjusted to prevent disengagement or cocking the apply linkage before tipping the transmission in its end.*

To determine the size spacer needed a dial indicator and a special support stand is available. Install the dial indicator on the support as shown in Fig. 3. Without gasket, place support J-8364 on rear pump cavity surface of transmission case so that dial indicator tip rests on planet carrier hub. Adjust indicator on J-8364 to permit maximum indicator travel and set dial at zero.

Slowly lift J-8364 and indicator off rear pump cavity and note its range of needle deflection from *zero* position. Properly positioned on support, indicator should not deflect more than .050″ (one-half turn) when removed; otherwise raise or lower dial indicator on support post as required and again zero the gauge.

Place gauge and support on governor gear as shown in Fig. 4. Lower support slowly so that revolutions of indicator can be counted. Measurement starts once the indicator needle again reaches zero.

POWERGLIDE REAR THRUST SPACER USAGE CHART	
Indicator Reading	Spacers to Be Used
*.011—.038	NONE
.039—.053	.016
.054—.068	.031
.069—.083	.046
.084—.098	.046 + .016
.099—.113	.046 + .031
.114—.128	.046 + .046
.129—.145	.046 + .046 + .016
.146—.155	.046 + .046 + .031

*If initial indicator reading is below .011″, replace .088″ thrust washer at the clutch hub—front pump with an .076″ or .050″ thrust washer, then repeat entire rear thrust spacer selection procedure.

Spacer	Part No.
.016″	6256827
.031″	6256828
.046″	6255664

Fig. 5

modulator to the carburetor balance tube with a short length of hose.

8. Insert and secure filler tube into transmission oil pan.
9. Refill transmission with fluid.

Separate Powerglide From Differential

1. With transaxle separated from engine, place transaxle on a flat surface.
2. Pull turbine shaft carefully through transmission and carrier, being careful not to damage turbine shaft bushings on pump shaft splines.
3. Remove transmission governor.
4. Unfasten transmission from carrier and pull transmission straight away from carrier to prevent pump shaft from damaging bushings in transmission and pinion shaft.
5. Remove governor gear and selective spacer from pinion shaft of differential carrier.

Selective Thrust Washer Determination

For proper operation it is necessary that sufficient end play of the Powerglide components be maintained by selection of thrust washers of various

Fully depress support on governor gear, note indicator reading and refer to Fig. 5 for spacers to be installed on governor gear. Install spacers selected at the front face of governor gear.

Assemble Powerglide to Differential

1. With new gasket in place, align carrier and transmission on a flat surface and guide pump shaft through differential carrier so as not to damage the bushing in the pinion. Then engage pinion shaft splines with planet carrier internal splines in transmission.
2. Install governor.
3. Secure transmission to carrier with four bolts. Drive the two bolts from the carrier side first and tighten the two bolts from the carrier side first and tighten to 24-32 ft. lbs.
4. Install turbine shaft, being sure to engage the two sets of shaft splines.
5. Install converter, being sure to get full engagement of splines on stator shaft, turbine shaft and front pump shaft. *Once the converter is installed, do not tip rear of transaxle downward unless some improvised converter holding plates are used to prevent converter falling off.*

Engine Section

On all service operations where threads enter aluminum, use an anti-sieze compound, such as Permatex No. 404 or its equivalent. Such service operations that can be performed with the engine in the vehicle will be so noted directly under the unit heading.

ENGINE DESCRIPTION

The engine, Fig. 6, is the horizontal opposed air cooled six-cylinder type. The cast aluminum alloy crankcase is vertically divided into two halves which are held together by bolts at the parting line. Each crankcase half has three pilot

openings for individual cast iron cylinders which are positioned to the opening by means of four long studs at each cylinder. These studs pass freely through holes in the cylinder cooling fin structure and the cylinder head and serve to secure the cylinders and head to the crankcase.

The two opposing and identical aluminum cylinder heads incorporate cooling fins and built-in intake manifolds and contain wedge-shaped combustion chambers and valves for each cylinder. The valves are actuated by push rods through stamped rocker arms. Steel alloy valve seat inserts are provided for durability.

Steel tubes are used to house the

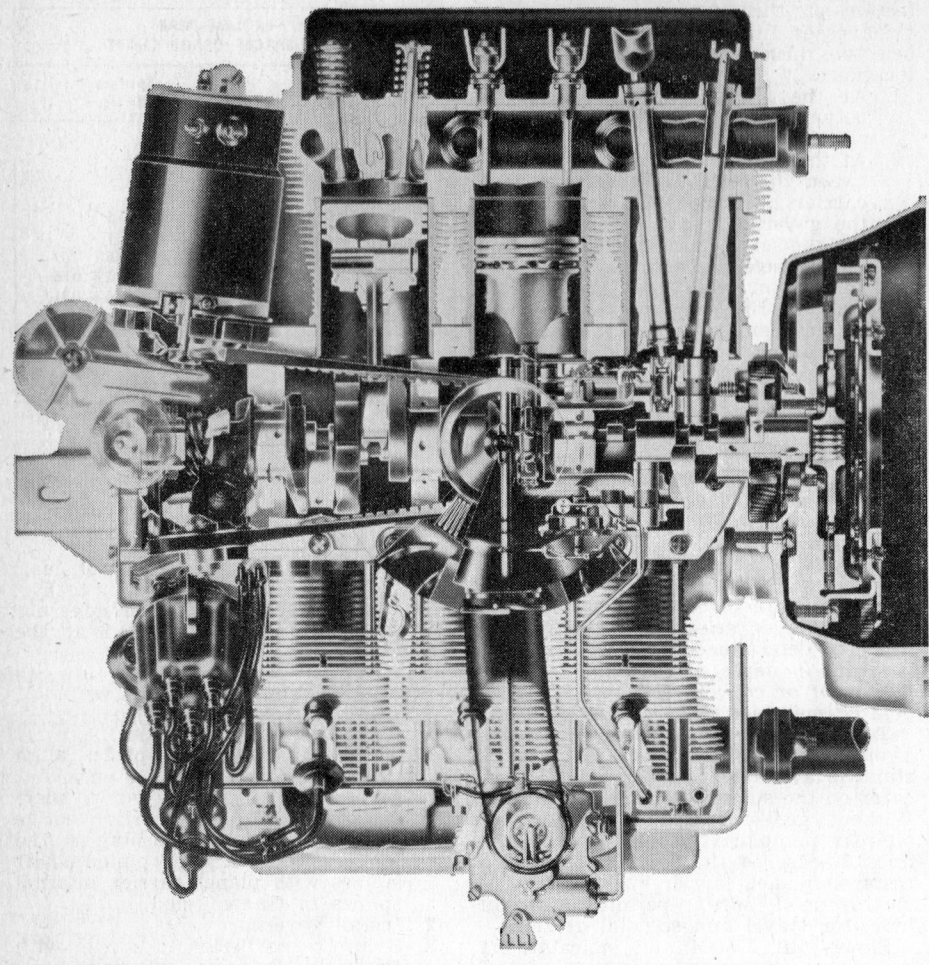

Fig. 6 Engine cross section (top view)

and idler pulley are mounted.

A rectangular crankcase cover mounts to the top of the crankcase and forms a base for the centrifugal blower.

Cooling System

The engine is entirely shrouded with sheet metal pieces that attach directly to the engine and form a plenum chamber—a condition in which the pressure of the air in an enclosed space is greater than that of the outside atmosphere.

A centrifugal blower, mounted to the top of the crankcase cover, spins on a vertical shaft to deliver cooling air outward and downward over the cylinders and heads. The air then enters a duct under each bank from where it travels rearward to be exhausted at an opening at the rear of the engine.

The rate of engine cooling is regulated by a bellows-type thermostat at the lower part of the plenum. This thermostat operates a cooling air valve which moves in and out of the eye of the blower to control the air flow. The ring closes the blower air intake until the engine has reached its correct operating temperature. In the event of a failed thermostat bellows, the ring will remain in the open position to prevent overheating of the engine.

The blower, which runs on a sealed, permanently lubricated ball bearing, is belt-driven by a pulley mounted at the extreme rear end of the crankshaft. A generator drive pulley at the left rear of the engine and an idler pulley at the right rear provide a means of changing belt direction from a vertical plane at the crankshaft pulley to a horizontal plane at the blower pulley.

An oil cooler, through which a portion of the air passes before discharge, is mounted above the air exhaust duct near the left rear corner of the engine.

push rods in the open area between the crankcase and cylinder heads adjacent to the cylinders. These tubes serve to protect the exposed push rods as well as drain back oil from the cylinder heads to a relatively shallow oil pan bolted to the bottom of the crankcase, Fig. 7.

The camshaft, which actuates the push rods through hydraulic lifters, is nested between the two halves of the crankcase below the crankshaft. This camshaft differs from the conventional design in that each of the three exhaust valve lobes are twice the width of the intake valve lobes and actuate a pair of exhaust valve lifters. The camshaft journals ride directly on the machined base metal of the crankcase. Camshaft end thrust is taken by a thrust washer located between the camshaft gear and front bearing.

No separate main bearing caps are required since the four bearings are supported entirely by the crankcase halves. The crankshaft drives the camshaft through a composition gear and drive hub. The front crankshaft seal is installed to the aluminum clutch housing (or flywheel housing) which mounts to the front of the crankcase assembly.

The engine rear housing mounts to the rear of the crankcase over four free-fitting long studs. This housing contains the oil pump, crankshaft seal and primary oil passages, Fig. 8. It provides the mounting for the distributor and the generator adapter to which the fuel pump, oil fill pipe, generator, oil filter

ENGINE DISASSEMBLY

Engine Out of Car

1. Remove transmission from power train.

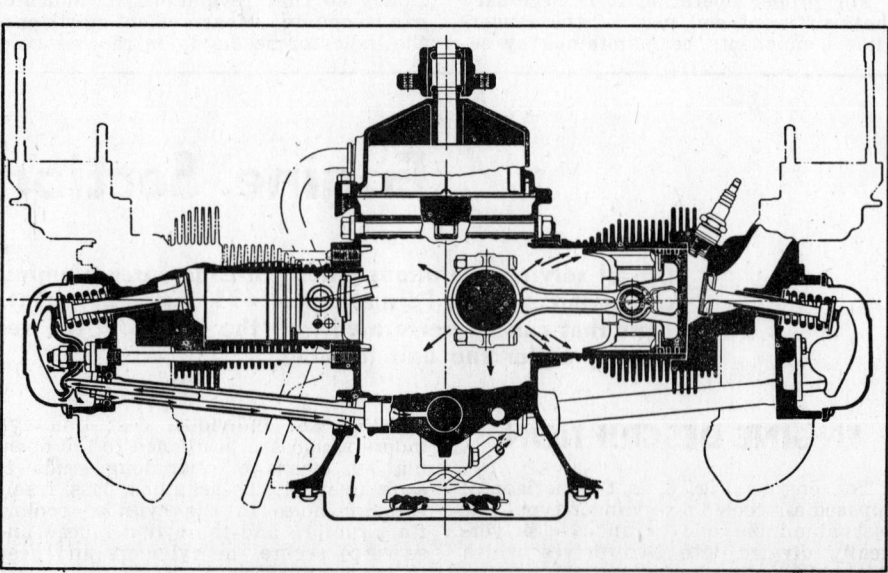

Fig. 7 Cylinder head lubrication

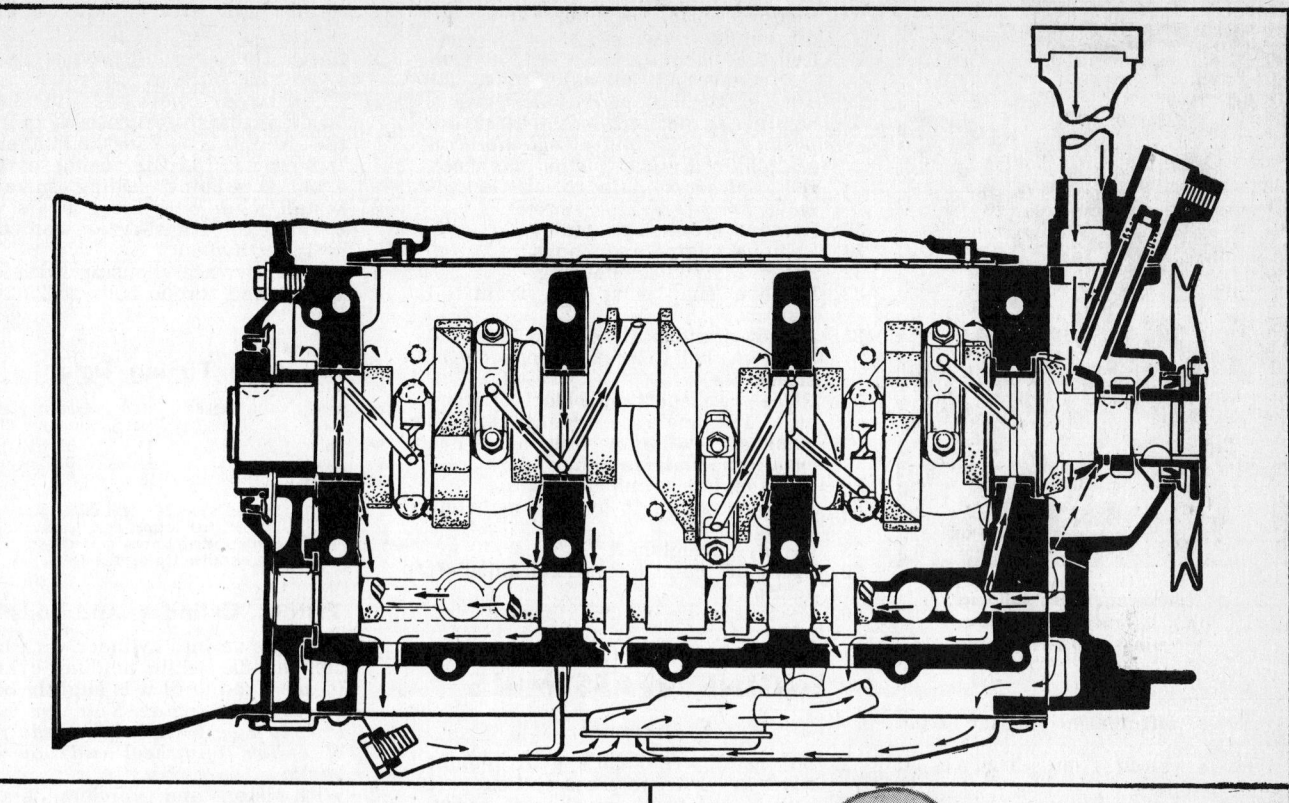

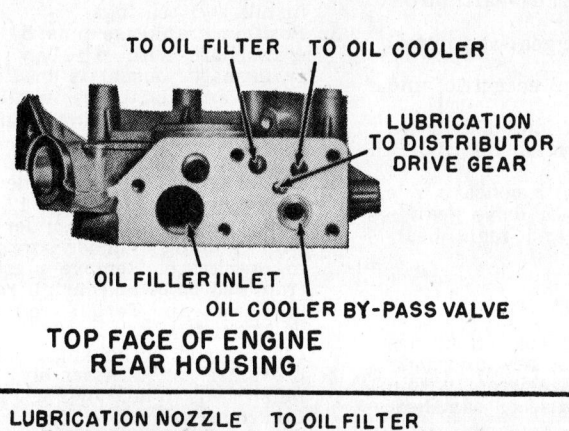

TO OIL FILTER **TO OIL COOLER**

LUBRICATION TO DISTRIBUTOR DRIVE GEAR

OIL FILLER INLET

OIL COOLER BY-PASS VALVE

TOP FACE OF ENGINE REAR HOUSING

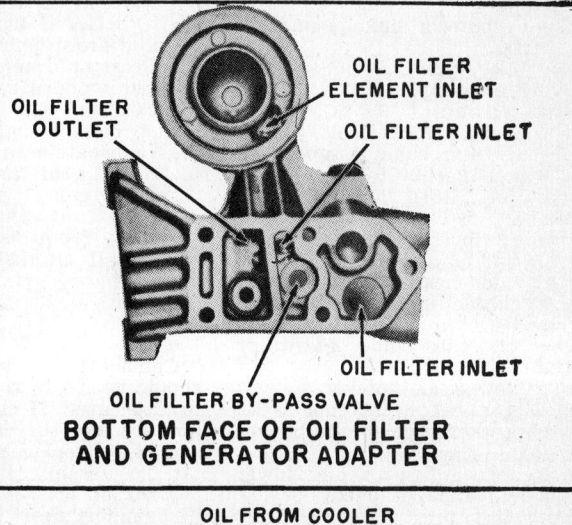

OIL FILTER OUTLET

OIL FILTER ELEMENT INLET

OIL FILTER INLET

OIL FILTER INLET

OIL FILTER BY-PASS VALVE

BOTTOM FACE OF OIL FILTER AND GENERATOR ADAPTER

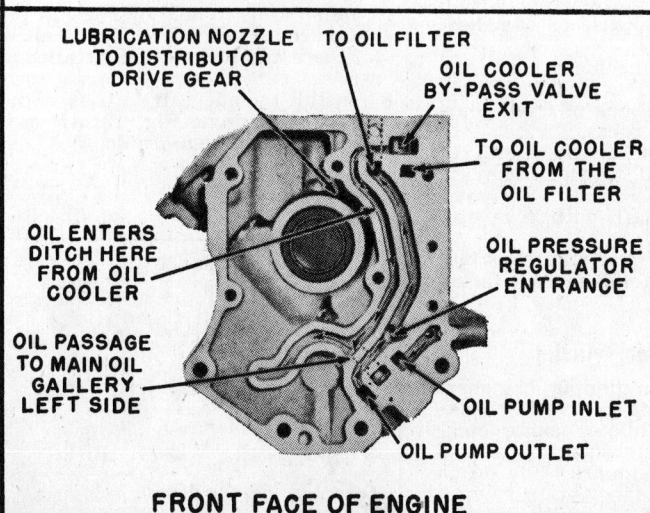

LUBRICATION NOZZLE TO DISTRIBUTOR DRIVE GEAR **TO OIL FILTER**

OIL COOLER BY-PASS VALVE EXIT

TO OIL COOLER FROM THE OIL FILTER

OIL ENTERS DITCH HERE FROM OIL COOLER

OIL PRESSURE REGULATOR ENTRANCE

OIL PASSAGE TO MAIN OIL GALLERY LEFT SIDE

OIL PUMP INLET

OIL PUMP OUTLET

FRONT FACE OF ENGINE REAR HOUSING

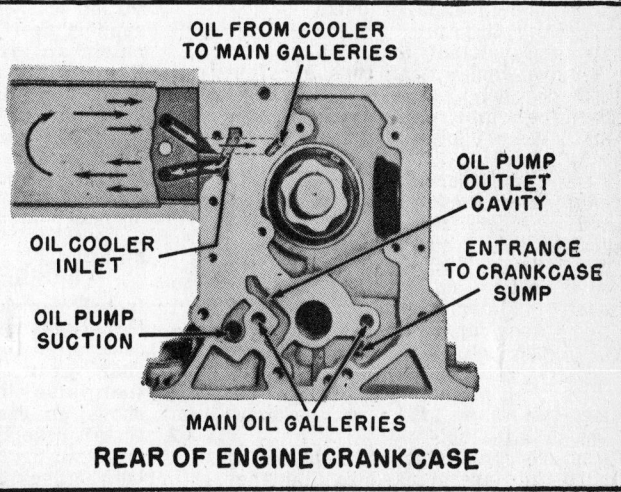

OIL FROM COOLER TO MAIN GALLERIES

OIL PUMP OUTLET CAVITY

OIL COOLER INLET

ENTRANCE TO CRANKCASE SUMP

OIL PUMP SUCTION

MAIN OIL GALLERIES

REAR OF ENGINE CRANKCASE

Fig. 8   Engine lubrication

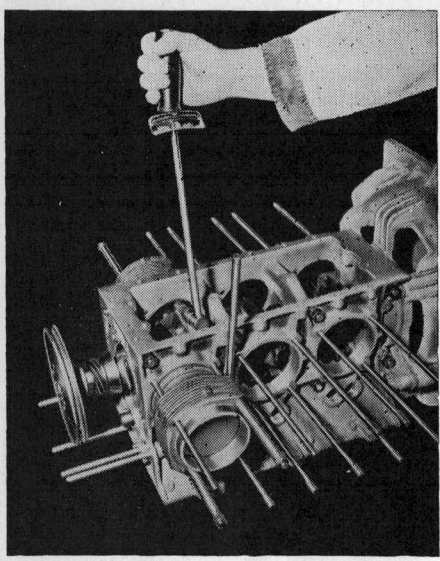

Fig. 9 Showing tubes holding opposite cylinder in place while torquing connecting rods

2. Remove differential carrier from engine.
3. Remove clutch from engine (if equipped).
4. Remove carburetor linkage and related parts.
5. Remove blower belt.
6. Remove fuel pump.
7. Remove generator.
8. Remove engine front shield.
9. Remove vacuum balance tube.
10. Remove both carburetors.
11. Remove fuel lines and oil level gauge.
12. Remove distributor and spark plugs.
13. Remove coil and generator brace from cylinder head.
14. Remove engine upper shroud and side shields.
15. Remove oil filter and generator adapter.
16. Remove blower and pulley.
17. Remove crankcase vent tube.
18. Remove crankcase cover and blower bearing.
19. Remove engine front and lower shrouds and exhaust ducts.
20. Remove oil pan.
21. Remove exhaust manifold.
22. Remove choke heat tube at right cylinder head.
23. Remove engine rear mounting bracket and skid plate at engine rear housing.
24. Remove cylinder heads. *When crankshaft is turned for further disassembly cylinders will need a holding fixture which can readily be made. Six 1/2" x 4 1/4" long steel tubes to be used on long cylinder studs (one on each cylinder) and six 1/2" x 3 1/2" long tubes for each short stud. Slip the tubes on the studs and keep them in place by means of the stud nuts, Fig. 9.*
25. Remove valve lifters with a magnet or wire hook.
26. Remove connecting rod caps, being sure they are marked so that they will be returned to the correct connecting rod.

27. Remove spring retainers and take off cylinder air baffle.
28. Remove each cylinder with piston and connecting rod as a unit.
29. Push piston out of cylinder with a hammer handle. *Ridges and/or deposits on upper end of cylinder can be removed after piston has been removed from cylinder with a cylinder mounted ridge reamer.*
30. Remove crankshaft pulley.
31. Remove engine rear housing.
32. Remove flywheel housing.
33. Remove snap ring and front oil slinger.
34. Loosen crankshaft bolts (8 long and 3 short bolts located on side of crankcase).
35. Place crankshaft on a block of wood at a 15° angle so crankshaft and camshaft will not fall out when crankcase half is removed.
36. Remove left crankcase half.
37. Remove camshaft by turning while lifting.
38. Remove crankshaft.
39. Press off camshaft and crankshaft gears.
40. Remove main bearing inserts.

ENGINE, REASSEMBLE
Crankshaft

1. To install crankshaft gear, mount shaft in an arbor press and support it between front crankshaft throw and front journal.
2. Press on crankshaft gear and install two woodruff keys.
3. Position fuel pump eccentric and spacer on shaft.
4. Lubricate crankshaft and distributor drive gear and install distributor drive gear.
5. Install oil slinger with concave side away from distributor drive gear.
6. Install crankshaft and main bearings.

Camshaft

Camshaft bearing journal clearance should be .0015" to .0035" new and .002" to .004" used. If clearance is not within limits either the crankcase or camshaft should be replaced.

1. To assemble camshaft gear and thrust washer to camshaft, firmly support shaft at back of front journal in an arbor press.
2. Place thrust washer over end of shaft and install woodruff key in keyway.
3. Lubricate camshaft with hypoid lubricant.
4. Install camshaft gear and press into place until it bottoms against thrust washer.

Timing Gear Marks

1. Install camshaft, guiding camshaft thrust washer into groove in crankcase, Fig. 10, while indexing camshaft gear to crankshaft gear so that valve timing marks line up as shown in Fig. 11.
2. Install other half of crankcase onto crankshaft and camshaft and fasten both halves together. Tighten bolts to the proper torque and in proper sequence.

3. Check camshaft end play, which should be .003" to .007".
4. Check timing gear backlash which should be .002" to .004".
5. Install front crankshaft oil slinger on crankshaft gear with flange side toward crankcase. Install slinger retaining snap ring, using care to avoid scratching sealing surface.
6. Install main oil gallery plugs with Permatex 404 anti-freeze compound or its equivalent.
7. Install flywheel housing with new gasket and torque bolts to 20-30 ft. lbs.

Valve Timing Data

Year	Model	Intake Opens①	Intake Closes②	Exhaust Opens③	Exhaust Closes④
1960	All	15	37	59	13
1961	Std.	43	93	87	69
1961	Hi-Perf.	54	118	90	82

①—Degrees before top dead center.
②—Degrees after bottom dead center.
③—Degrees before bottom dead center.
④—Degrees after top dead center.

Pistons, Cylinders and Rods

1. Push piston into cylinder with hammer handle while holding cylinder in one hand until it is slightly below top of cylinder bore. *Notch on piston top must be installed towards front of engine (flywheel end) on both banks.*
2. With pistons and cylinders installed, install rod bearings.
3. Position crankcase pins by turning crankshaft with pulley so that crankshaft journal is in line with piston and rod to be installed.
4. Place a piece of plastic hose with at least a $\frac{5}{16}$" diameter over each rod bolt to protect shaft journal.
5. Install a new copper cylinder gasket over cylinder pilot, Fig. 12.
6. Push piston with hammer handle while guiding cylinder bore pilot into crankcase. Remove plastic hose from rod bolts and install rod bearing and cap. Torque rod nuts to 20-26 ft. lbs.
7. Install cylinder holding tubes (used previously on disassembly) on cylinder studs to hold cylinder in place. Continue procedure until all cylinders and pistons are installed, Fig. 9.
8. Install cylinder air baffles with retaining springs, Fig. 12. *Air baffles are not interchangeable.*

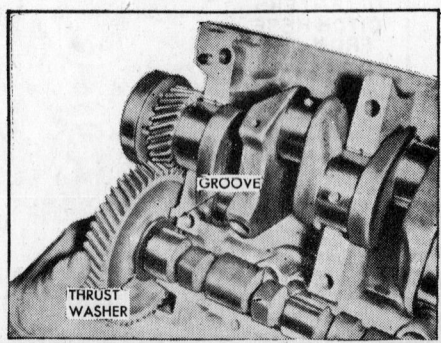

Fig. 10 Installing camshaft in crankcase

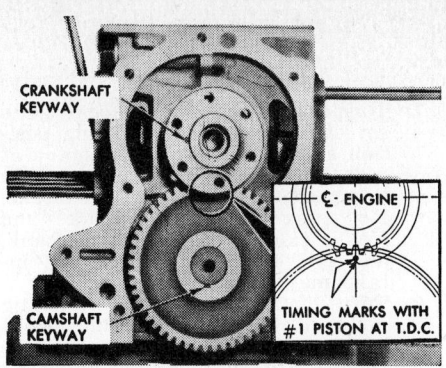

Fig. 11 Timing marks aligned for correct valve timing

Fig 12 Installing cylinder and piston. Tubes "A" and "B" are holding cylinders in place

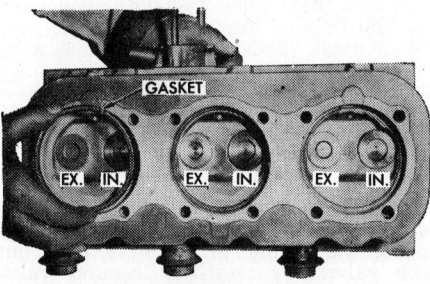

Fig. 13 Installing cylinder head gaskets

Fig. 14 Installing cylinder head

Crankcase Cover and Blower Bearing

1. Install new gasket on crankcase.
2. Install crankcase vent and another crankcase gasket.
3. Install crankcase cover and blower bearing and torque bolts to 7-13 ft. lbs.
4. Install crankcase vent tube and gasket.

Oil Pump Screen and Tube

If the original or a new oil pump screen and tube assembly is to be installed in the original crankcase, the outside diameter of the end of the tube will have to be tinned with solder before installing in crankcase.

1. Install oil pump screen and pick-up tube into cylinder case with pick-up screen positioned parallel to oil pan rails. Secure tube with clamp.
2. Coat threads on engine temperature and oil pressure sending units with anti-seize compound (Permatex 404) or its equivalent. Torque oil pressure unit to 45-65 ft. lbs. and temperature unit 35-45 ft. lbs.

Cylinder Head

Be sure all cylinder head gaskets are in cylinder head combustion chambers as shown in Fig. 13. Remove all cylinder retaining tubes from cylinder bank to which cylinder head is to be installed.

1. Install cylinder head, Fig. 14.
2. Install six flat washers and nuts on long studs, adjacent to intake manifold.
3. Install six new "O" rings, lubricated with lubriplate, in counterbore of cylinder head (location for rocker arm studs) and coat rocker stud bore with anti-sieze compound.
4. Install rocker arm studs, Fig. 15, with threads coated with anti-sieze compound.
5. Tighten nuts and rocker studs in sequence shown in Fig. 16. Torque nuts and rocker studs to 27-33 ft. lbs.

Push Rod Oil Drain Tubes

1. Lightly oil hydraulic lifters and install in their proper bores.
2. Install push rod oil drain tubes through cylinder head, Fig. 17. Place "O" rings, one on each end of drain tube as shown. Oil "O" rings and push in place at lifter bore in crankcase and cylinder head.
3. Install push rods with side oil hole up into valve rocker socket, Fig. 18 (blue band end).
4. On early production engines, install push rod guides in place over rocker studs and push rods and tighten bolts. *On late production engines, push rod guides are installed under valve rocker studs.*
5. Install rocker arms, balls and nuts loosely in place. Adjust valve lash as outlined elsewhere in this section, after installing distributor.

Final Assembly

1. Install engine rear housing.
2. Install crankshaft pulley. After pulley bottoms in place, back off retaining bolt one turn and then torque it to 60-80 ft. lbs. *Do not drive pulley*

Fig. 15 Installing rocker arm studs

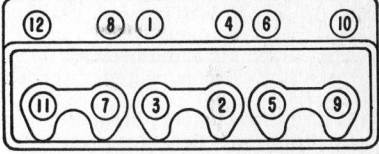

Fig. 16 Cylinder head tightening sequence

Fig. 17 Installing push rod drain tubes

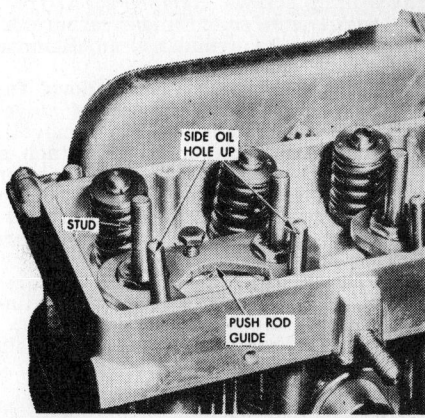

Fig. 18 Push rod installation

Fig. 19 Checking installed height of valve springs

in place as this will damage crankshaft thrust bearing and crankcase.

3. Install oil cooler.
4. Install exhaust manifolds.
5. Install oil filter and generator adapter.
6. Install sheet metal removed.
7. Install wires, fuel lines, etc.
8. Install spark plugs.
9. Install oil pan. Check parting line to see if flywheel housing gasket is far enough up for good sealing.
10. Install fuel pump and add engine oil.

CYLINDER HEAD REPLACE

Engine In Car

Left Bank Head:
1. Drain crankcase oil.
2. Disconnect battery cables and ground connection to engine.
3. Disconnect radio ground strap.
4. Remove carburetor intake hose (connected to air cleaner and carburetor).
5. Remove carburetor accelerator return spring and disconnect accelerator rod from carburetor.
6. Disconnect left-side carburetor cross-shaft support (2 screws) from carburetor.
7. Disconnect fuel line at carburetor.
8. Remove carburetor.
9. Remove long stud from carburetor mounting.
10. Remove wires and spark plugs.
11. *Loosen* all engine side shield retaining screws. *Remove* screw from engine side shield under carburetor, attached to cylinder head. Remove engine side shield.
12. Remove oil cooler (this allows engine rear shroud freedom of movement during cylinder head removal).
13. Raise car on a hoist and attach a suitable lifting fixture to power train. *See requirements for lifting and supporting power train as outlined at the beginning of this section.*
14. Remove both engine side seal retainers and engine rear seal retainers.
15. Remove engine rear center shield and seal assembly.
16. Remove lower engine shroud.
17. Remove exhaust pipe-to-manifold nuts.
18. Open french locks on exhaust manifold and remove holding clamp nuts.
19. Remove exhaust manifold.
20. Remove engine rear mounting cotter pin, nut and washer from below body rear mounting bracket.
21. Remove rocker arm cover while holding a pan below to catch oil draining from cylinder head.
22. Remove rocker arms, push rods and push rod guides. *Present production engines require removal of valve rocker studs to remove push rod guides.*
23. Remove rocker arm studs, washers and "O" rings from head. Also, remove push rod guides from late production engines.
24. Remove "O" rings from bottom of push rod drain tubes with a pair of hooked tweezers.

To remove No. 5 exhaust push rod drain tube, it is necessary to remove the right side exhaust manifold.

25. Remove retaining nuts and washers retaining head.
26. Carefully lower engine assembly approximately 3" to clear cylinder head carburetor flange.
27. Remove cylinder head from crankcase studs.
28. Reverse above procedure to install the head and tighten head nuts in the sequence shown in Fig. 16.

Right Bank Head: Removal and installation of the right bank head is essentially the same as the left head, except the coil, oil pressure and oil temperature sending units must be disconnected. Also remove the choke heat pipe and choke fresh air pipe from the exhaust manifold.

CYLINDER HEAD ASSEMBLE

Cylinder heads are identical except for location of vacuum balance tube hose connector which is on one side of the carburetor mounting pad on the right bank and the other side on the left bank.

1. Install each valve coated with SAE 30 engine oil in the valve guide from which it was removed or to the valve guide it was fitted.
2. Lightly coat valve spring shim with petrolatum to hold shim in place and place on valve spring seat.
3. Set valve spring in place on shim. Place valve cap in position, compress valve spring and install valve locks. *Each valve spring must have a hardened shim (.020" minimum) under it to protect aluminum surface. Service shims are available in .030" thickness.*
4. Check installed height of valve springs, Fig. 19. Reseating valves raises the installed height of valve springs and, if excessive, will have the effect of weak valve springs. If installed height of springs do not come within the limits illustrated, install a .030" shim. At no time should the spring be shimmed to give an installed height of less than the minimum limits.
5. Coat cylinder head and cylinder counterbore pilot with petrolatum to retain gasket and install new head gaskets, Fig. 13.

VALVES ADJUST

Engine In Car

1. Turn crankshaft counterclockwise to set distributor in No. 1 firing position and crankshaft pulley notch at "O" timing mark on timing pad. In this position valves for No. 1 intake, No. 1 exhaust, No. 3 intake and No. 5 exhaust on the right bank, and No. 4 exhaust and No. 6 intake may be adjusted.
2. Turn down rocker arm adjusting nut until there is no axial movement of the push rod as felt with the fingers, Fig. 20. Then turn adjusting nut ¾ turn more.
3. Turn crankshaft counterclockwise and set distributor to fire No. 2 cylinder and adjust remaining valves.

ROCKER ARMS REPLACE

Engine In Car

1. Remove rocker cover and gasket.
2. Remove rocker arm nuts, balls and rocker arms.
3. Replace parts and adjust valve lash.
4. Install cover and gasket.

PUSH RODS REPLACE

Engine In Car

1. Remove valve cover and gasket.
2. Loosen valve rocker arms, balls and nuts from cylinder requiring push rod replacement.
3. Remove push rod and guide and install new push rod with .050" side oil hole up into cylinder head.
4. Adjust valve lash and replace cover and gasket.

VALVES, REMOVE

Head Removed

With cylinder head removed, use a suitable valve spring compressor to compress the spring in order to take out the valve locks. Then remove valve spring cap, spring, shim and valve. Repeat this operation on each valve assembly. Place valves in a board with numbered holes to identify their location so that, if re-used, they can be returned to the original guide holes.

Fig. 20 Adjusting valves

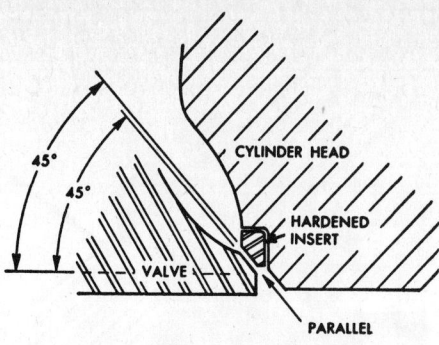

Fig. 21 Relation of valve and seat angles

VALVE SPRINGS REPLACE

Engine In Car

1. Drain crankcase oil.
2. Remove valve cover and gasket.
3. Remove rocker arm nut, ball and rocker arm.
4. Remove spark plug from cylinder requiring valve spring replacement and use compressed air to hold valves in closed position.
5. Install a nut on rocker stud and use a forked tool as a lever to compress valve spring far enough to remove valve locks. Then remove spring cap and spring.
6. Install spring on spring seat shim with cap. Compress spring and install valve locks.
7. Install rocker arm, ball and nut and adjust valve lash.
8. Install valve cover and gasket.
9. Install engine oil.

Head Removed

After taking out the valve springs, wash them with gasoline or other suitable solvent. Examine the springs for damage or corrosion due to acid etching, which will develop into surface cracks and cause spring failure.

Check the valve spring tension on a spring testing fixture if one is available. Spring should be compressed to 1½" at which height it should check 58 to 64 lbs. Weak springs affect power and economy and should be replaced if not within 5 lbs. of the above limit.

If a testing fixture is not available, at least check the free length of each spring by standing it alongside a new spring. Any spring that stands shorter than the new spring used for comparison should be scrapped. Of course, cocked springs should also be discarded.

VALVE GUIDES

Head Removed

Valve guides are an integral part of the head and, therefore, cannot be removed. For service, guide holes can be reamed oversize to accommodate one of three service valves with oversize stems (.003", .005" and .010").

After cleaning the valve guide holes, check the clearance with a dial indicator. Intake valve stem clearance should be .001" to .004" while exhaust stem clear-

ance should be .002" to .005".

Clamp the dial indicator on one side of the rocker cover gasket rail, arranging the indicator so that movement of the valve stem from side to side (crosswise to head) will cause a direct movement of the indicator stem. The indicator must contact the side of the valve stem just above the cylinder head. With the valve head about $\frac{1}{16}$" off its seat, move the stem of the valve from side to side with light pressure to obtain a clearance. By trying new valves in the guide holes it can be determined whether the valves should be replaced or the bores reamed and oversize valves installed.

VALVES, GRIND

Head Removed

In refacing valves take off only the minimum of metal required to clean up the valve faces. If the outer edge of the valve becomes too thin or sharp due to excessive grinding, the valve must be replaced. In other words the valve head margin must be at least $\frac{1}{32}$" otherwise the valve must be replaced. The margin is the area above the contact surface of the valve face. The valve seat width after refacing should be $\frac{1}{32}$" to $\frac{3}{32}$" for intake valves and $\frac{1}{16}$" to $\frac{1}{8}$" for exhaust valves. Valve seat angle on all valves should be 45° and should be concentric within .002" dial indicator reading. Valve face to seat angles are parallel as shown in Fig. 21.

VALVE SEAT INSERTS

Head Removed

When reconditioning valves, the exhaust valve seat inserts in the cylinder head should be inspected. If either valve seat inserts or valve guide bores are beyond repair, the cylinder head should be discarded and replaced with a new one.

VALVE LIFTERS REPLACE

Engine In Car

1. Drain crankcase oil.
2. Remove valve cover and gasket.
3. Remove engine lower shroud.
4. Remove rocker arms, balls, push rod guides, push rods and push rod drain tubes from cylinder from which valve lifter is to be removed.
5. Remove lifter with a strong magnet or:
   a. Remove snap ring retaining push rod seat and remove seat. Then remove lifter with a pair of pliers inserted in valve lifter snap ring groove.
   b. Remove oil pan and squirt lifter body with solvent to remove varnish from lifter body.
6. Install valve lifters well lubricated with engine oil.
7. Install push rod drain tubes with new "O" rings and set push rods in place on lifter seats with side oil hole up next to rocker arms.
8. Install push rod guides, rocker arms,

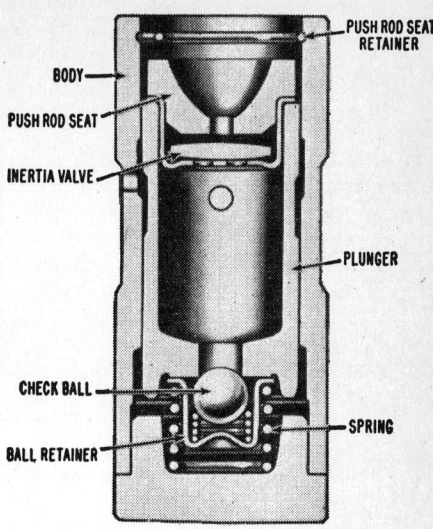

Fig. 22 Hydraulic valve lifter

balls and nuts, valve cover and gasket.
9. Install engine oil.

Lifters Out of Engine

1. Referring to Fig. 22, hold plunger down with a push rod and, using a small screwdriver or awl, remove push rod seat retainer.
2. Remove push rod seat and inertia valve, plunger and spring from lifter body.
3. Pull check ball retainer from plunger and remove ball and spring.
4. Clean all parts in solvent. If any parts are damaged, the entire lifter assembly should be replaced. The inertia valve in the push rod seat should move when the plunger is shaken.
5. Assemble lifter in reverse order of disassembly. Then compress plunger to open oil holes and fill plunger with SAE 10 oil. Work plunger up and down and refill.

EXHAUST MANIFOLD SLEEVES

1961

The exhaust sleeves are a press fit into the exhaust manifold.

Fig. 23 Removing exhaust sleeves. 1960

Fig. 24 Removing ridge and/or carbon from cylinder with ridge reamer

1960

1. Remove exhaust manifold sleeves with a pipe wrench by turning gradually, Fig. 23. *Do not tap or pry sleeves from cylinder head.*
2. Check exhaust manifold sleeve installation holes in cylinder head for nicks or damage.
3. Coat new sleeves with anti-sieze compound and locate flat side parallel to exhaust push rod drain tube hole. Sleeves are installed with a press fit and must be started into place square with the exhaust bore in head. Sleeves are available in standard, .002" and .010" oversize for service.
4. Place sleeves in a container of dry ice for about 10 minutes.
5. Warm cylinder head to about 200° in boiling water or a suitable oven if one is available. *Do not use an open flame.*
6. Remove sleeves one at a time from the dry ice and tap into place.

PISTONS & CYLINDERS

Engine Disassembled

1. Using a block of wood for a fixture, drill two holes, spaced to provide a location for two long bolts. Holes should be small enough to require driving the bolts into the wood block. Clamp wood block in vise.
2. Install cylinder over bolts on wood fixture. Holding cylinder with one hand, Fig. 24, insert ridge reamer and remove ridge and/or carbon from cylinder.
3. Check cylinder walls for out-of-round or excessive ridge at top of ring travel. If cylinders are found to have taper or wear in excess of .005", the cylinder and piston must be replaced.

PISTON RINGS REPLACE

Engine In Car

Bear in mind that cylinders and pistons are serviced as a unit and the operation outlined below is for replacing one or more pistons in one bank requir-

---

ing ring replacement. It is not intended for complete piston and ring replacement.

1. Drain crankcase oil and remove cylinder head.
2. Remove cylinder from piston requiring new rings.
3. Remove old and install new rings. *Position oil control ring gap towards top of engine and compression rings with gap 45° from oil ring gap location. Rings must be installed with markings and inside bevel toward top of piston. Lubricate piston rings with engine oil and slide ring compressing tool, Fig. 25, over rings just enough to compress rings into piston.*
4. Reverse above procedure to install parts removed. Add engine oil, start engine and check for oil leaks.

PISTON PINS

Engine Disassembled

Piston pins should be capable of supporting their own weight in either piston boss when coated with light engine oil at 70° temperature. Higher or lower temperatures will cause false indications. *Pistons, pins and cylinders are serviced as assemblies.*

ROD BEARINGS REPLACE

Engine In Car

1. Remove air cleaner element and carburetor intake hose.
2. Remove choke heat tube, choke fresh air hose and carburetor linkage.
3. Disconnect fuel lines at carburetor.
4. Remove left bank carburetor.
5. Disconnect choke link to choke assembly. Remove choke and air horn by removing nuts at legs of air horn support.
6. Disconnect spark plug wires.
7. Remove blower drive belt.
8. Disconnect fuel lines at fuel pump.
9. Remove carburetor cross shaft and vacuum balance tube.

Fig. 25 Installing piston rings with aid of ring compressor (J-8356)

Fig. 26 Installed length of crankcase and rear housing studs

10. Remove all engine upper shroud bolts and screws.
11. Remove screws on each side of front engine shield.
12. Disconnect cooling air throttle valve thermostat rod and remove cooling air throttle valve.
13. Remove all fuel lines.
14. Remove engine upper shroud, tipping front lip up so it clears front engine shield.
15. Remove blower pulley and blower.
16. Remove crankcase cover, gaskets and crankcase vent.
17. Remove spark plug from cylinder requiring new rod bearing and remove rod cap and bearing insert. Use a piece of $\frac{5}{16}$" plastic hose on each rod bolt to protect crankshaft journals from being scratched or marred.
18. Reverse above procedure to install parts removed. While tightening upper shroud bolts, rotate blower and check for interference at blower to upper shroud. Add engine oil, start engine and check for oil leaks.

Engine Disassembled

Rod bearing inserts are available in standard sizes and undersizes of .001", .002", .010" and .020". These bearings are not shimmed and when clearance becomes excessive the next undersize bearing insert should be used. *Do not file rod or caps in an attempt to fit bearings.*

Rod bearing clearance is checked with Plastigage in the same manner outlined for main bearings. If flattened Plastigage measurement is not over .003" (worn) or .002" (new) or not less than .001" the fit is satisfactory.

CRANKCASE

Engine Disassembled

1. Remove two oil gallery plugs located at flywheel housing end of crankcase. These passages should be cleaned with solvent.
2. Check cylinder pilot bores and bearing surfaces in each half of crankcase for nicks, cracks or other damage that would interfere with the proper fit of component parts.

Fig. 27 Crankcase tightening sequence

3. Do not use scrapers or other sharp tools to clean gasket surfaces. A good cleaning solvent should be used to dissolve gasket material or varnish that may adhere to the surfaces.

Stud and Thread Repairs

Always use anti-seize compound (Permatex 404 or equivalent) on all threads entering aluminum.

To replace crankcase studs, install long and short studs as indicated in Fig. 26. Studs are available in oversizes of .003", .006" and .009".

It should require a torque of 10 to 30 ft. lbs. to install studs. If torque is less than 10, another selected stud should be used.

Heli-coils for thread repairs are available at local auto parts jobbers and should be installed to Heli-Coil prescribed methods.

All cylinder studs installed in crankcase adjacent to the main bearing webs have blind holes while the others do not.

MAIN BEARINGS

Engine Disassembled

Whenever the crankcase is parted, the bearings and crankshaft journals should be inspected. If upon inspection one half shows evidence of fatigue, distress, abrasion, erosion, scoring or the like, both crankcase halves should be replaced. *Never should one half be replaced without replacing the other half.*

If the running clearance of a bearing is too great with used bearing inserts, it will be necessary to replace both bearing halves. Should this become necessary, the crankshaft journal should be checked with a micrometer for out-of-round, taper or undersize dimensions.

Main Bearing Clearance

Main bearing clearance is checked with Plastigage, a wax-like material, available at auto parts jobbers.

To assure proper seating of the bearings, all crankcase bolts must be at their specified torque. Eight long $\frac{7}{16}$"

bolts 42-48 ft. lbs., and three $\frac{5}{16}$" bolts 7-13 ft. lbs. Hold bolt head on $\frac{7}{16}$" bolts while tightening the nut. Do not tighten at bolt head. Fig. 27 shows tightening sequence. To check main bearing clearance, proceed as follows:

1. Starting with rear main bearing, remove one half of the crankcase while the other is supported on its side. Wipe oil from bearings and journal.
2. Place a strip of Plastigage the full width of the bearing (parallel to crankshaft on journal). *Crankcase split line surfaces must be free of nicks and foreign matter.*
3. Install other half of crankcase with bearings and evenly tighten crankcase bolts to proper torque. *Do not rotate crankshaft while Plastigage is between bearing and journal.*
4. Remove one half of crankcase. Then measure the width of the flattened Plastigage with the graduated scale on the edge of the Plastigage envelope.
5. If the flattened Plastigage is not over .004" (worn) or .003" (new) or less than .001" the bearing insert is satisfactory. If not within these limits replace bearing insert.
6. A .002" undersize bearing may produce the proper clearance. If not, it will be necessary to regrind the crankshaft journal for use with the next undersize bearing. Bearings are available in undersizes of .001", .002", .010" and .020".
7. Proceed to the next bearing. After all bearings have been checked and installed, rotate the crankshaft to see that there is no excessive drag.
8. Check the end play by forcing the crankshaft to the extreme forward position. End play should be .002" to .006".

OIL PAN REPLACE

Engine In Car

1. Drain crankcase oil and remove all bolts retaining oil pan to crankcase. Remove pan and discard gasket.
2. Install oil pan and torque retaining bolts to 3½-5 ft. lbs.

OIL PUMP GEARS REPLACE

Engine In Car

1. Drain crankcase oil.
2. Place a piece of hardwood between oil pan rail and Power Train Cradle (J-7894). Install wood block adjacent to engine skid plate. Installation of wood block will allow easy removal of skid plate.
3. Disconnect engine rear mount and remove engine rear shield seal and center shield. Remove bolts from exhaust air ducts connected to the engine rear center shield plate.
4. Lower engine about 1" to clear rear mount.
5. Remove rear mounting bracket and engine skid plate.

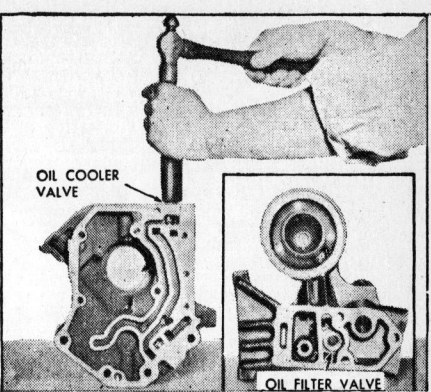

Fig. 28 Oil filter and oil cooler by-pass valve installation

6. Remove oil pump cover and gears.
7. Reverse above procedure to replace parts removed. Torque mounting bracket nuts to 20-30 ft. lbs. and torque rear mounting nut to 40-60 ft. lbs.
8. After completing installation of remaining parts, add engine oil, start engine and check for leaks.

OIL PUMP REPAIRS

Engine Disassembled

1. When assembling the oil pump to the engine rear housing, install the idler gear on the shaft. Idler gear shaft should be .010" to .020" below gasket surface.
2. Place drive gear and shaft in pump housing.
3. Check projection of oil pump gears above gasket surface; this should be .0045" maximum and .0025" minimum. Clearance between gears and housing should be .005".
4. Lubricate pump gears before installation. Install pump cover and tighten bolts.
5. Install a long screwdriver down the distributor mounting hole in the engine rear housing and turn oil pump drive shaft to see that pump turns freely.
6. Install pressure regulator valve, spring, gasket and plug.

OIL PUMP PRESSURE REGULATOR REPLACE

Engine In Car

1. Drain crankcase oil.
2. Remove right side exhaust air duct.
3. Remove pressure regulator plug, nylon gasket, spring and valve.
4. Install regulator parts, exhaust air duct and crankcase oil. *To check oil pressure, remove plug on top of oil filter and generator adapter, and install an oil pressure gauge. Start engine, check pressure, which should be 35 psi, and check for oil leaks.*

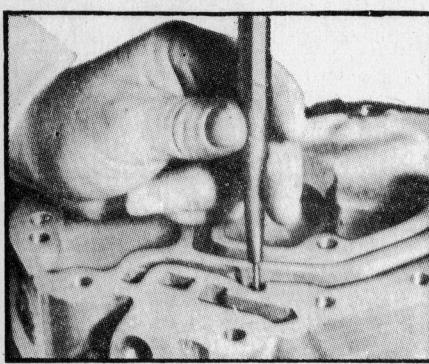

Fig. 29 Installing oil pressure regulator stop groove pin

OIL COOLER & BY-PASS VALVES

Engine Disassembled

1. Referring to Fig. 28, remove oil filter by-pass valve by catching the inner edge of the valve with a suitable hook or small screwdriver.
2. Install the new filter valve with the spring *up* in the adapter housing.
3. Remove the coil cooler valve in the same manner as the filter valve. However, the valve spring should be installed *down*.

OIL COOLER, CLEAN

Engine In Car

Remove the cooler access hole cover (under generator) and brush foreign particles away from oil cooler fins. Insert an air hose gun under the cooler and blow up through cooler fins.

OIL COOLER REPLACE

Engine In Car

1. Remove screws retaining oil cooler to engine shrouds, shields and cylinder head.
2. Remove cooler access hole cover (beneath generator) and remove long oil cooler mounting bolt and cooler.
3. Remove and discard worn seals from oil cooler adapter.
4. Invert cooler and allow oil to drain. Clean cooler fins with an air hose before and after cleaning in solvent.
5. Reverse above procedure to install. Tighten long retainer bolt 8-12 ft. lbs. Start engine and check for oil leaks around cooler and seal location.

OIL PAN

Engine In Car

1. Drain crankcase oil.
2. Remove bolts securing oil pan to crankcase.
3. Remove oil pan and discard gasket.
4. Installation is done in reverse order and bolts are tightened to *40-60 inch lbs.*

OIL FILTER & GENERATOR ADAPTER

Engine In Car

1. To remove, release pulley belt tension at idler pulley and remove blower pulley belt. Disconnect battery ground and generator harness.
2. Remove generator and bracket.
3. Disconnect fuel lines at pump.
4. Remove bolts around oil filler tube; then remove all remaining bolts from adapter.
5. Remove adapter with fuel pump, oil filter and idler pulley as a unit.
6. Remove adapter gasket.
7. Reverse above procedure to install and torque adapter bolts to 7-13 ft. lbs.

CRANKCASE VENT TUBE REPLACE

Engine In Car

1. Remove engine upper shroud and blower pulley.
2. Remove retaining bolts and remove vent tube.
3. Install a new cork gasket over vent tube end, and insert in crankcase cover.
4. Install vent tube clamp and tighten bolt securely.
5. Install blower pulley and engine upper shroud assembly.

CRANKSHAFT PULLEY & ENGINE REAR HOUSING SEAL REPLACE

Engine In Car

On some engines the rear housing seal is installed with the flange on the inside, in which case the engine will have to be removed from the car and rear housing removed. If the flange is on the outside, proceed as follows:

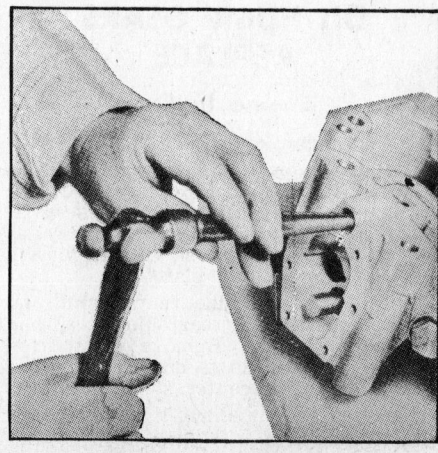

Fig. 30 Installing oil gallery plug

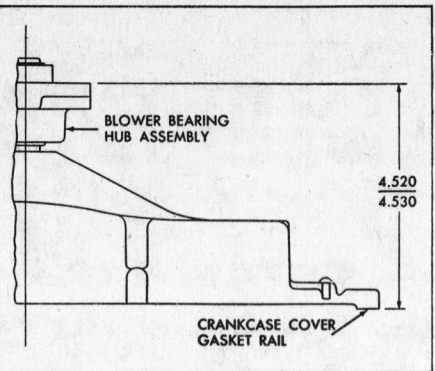

Fig. 31 Blower bearing and crankcase cover

BLOWER BEARING HUB ASSEMBLY

4.520
4.530

CRANKCASE COVER GASKET RAIL

1. Drain crankcase oil.
2. Disconnect battery cable to engine.
3. Remove all side shield seal retainers.
4. Remove engine rear center shield.
5. Remove engine skid bolt and attach Power train Cradle (J-7894) to bottom of engine with car on a hoist.
6. Remove engine rear body grille and engine rear mount.
7. On standard transmission cars remove clutch return spring and disconnect clutch control cable and clutch pull rod.
8. Loosen outboard stud nut and slide it part way out of engine front mounting bracket slot.
9. Remove shift rod coupling.
10. Loosen front mounting nuts and lower engine until nuts are flush with end of studs (do not remove nuts).
11. Lower engine far enough to remove engine rear mounting bracket.
12. Remove oil filter and pulley belt.
13. Remove crankshaft pulley with a suitable puller. *Install bolts in pulley hub a depth of ¼" only, otherwise the bolts will damage the rear housing seal.*
14. Remove engine rear housing seal by prying on its outer edge with a couple of screwdrivers. *The lips of seal are packed with high melting cup grease for the life of the seal.*
15. Reverse above procedure to install parts removed. Add engine oil, start engine and check for oil leaks.

ENGINE REAR HOUSING

Engine Disassembled

When replacing the engine rear housing as a new unit, the following operations are required.

1. Install groove pin, Fig. 29, which holds oil pump pressure regulator valve in place.
2. Install oil pump gallery plug flush with counterbore, using sealing compound, Fig. 30.
3. Install new rear housing seal.
4. Install distributor holding stud 1⅛" measured from distributor pad on engine rear housing.

FLYWHEEL HOUSING SEAL

Engine Disassembled

1. Tap seal out of housing with a wood or fibre drift.
2. Clean flywheel housing seal surface with solvent and check surface for nicks or damage.
3. Lubricate outer seal surface (beaded area) with lubriplate or petrolatum and install with suitable driver. *If seal is removed and still usable, pack sealing lips with a good grade of cup grease with a high melting point (350°). New seals are packed with this type grease to last the life of the seal.*

BLOWER BEARING, BLOWER & CRANKCASE COVER

Engine In Car

1. Disconnect battery ground cable.
2. Disconnect accelerator linkage and fuel lines.
3. Remove oil level gauge and fresh air choke at air cleaner. Remove choke pipe.
4. Remove air cleaner, air horn and support.
5. Remove carburetor vacuum balance tube and retaining strap at engine upper shroud.
6. Remove pulley belt and distributor wire harness.
7. Disconnect cooling air throttle valve lever swivel.
8. Remove engine upper shroud and thermostat rod as a unit. An alternate method is to remove the lower left shroud and remove clip from thermostat rod; then remove thermostat rod from engine upper shroud.
9. Remove blower pulley and blower (4 bolts) from blower bearing hub assembly.
10. Remove crankcase cover bolts and washers.
11. Remove crankcase - to - crankcase vent gasket and crankcase vent.

Blower Bearing Replace

1. While supporting crankcase cover,

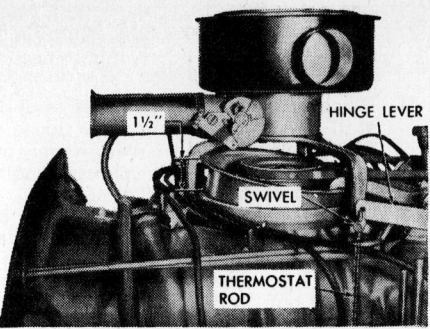

Fig. 33   Cooling air throttle valve adjustment

press blower bearing shaft out of blower.
2. Install new blower bearing hub assembly in crankcase cover, using hypoid lubricant on bearing shaft.
3. Press on shaft of blower bearing to a height shown in Fig. 31. *Do not press on bearing outer or inner race.*

Installation of Blower

1. Assemble crankcase cover, vent and gaskets as shown in Fig. 32.
2. Install blower and pulley bolts and torque to 20-25 ft. lbs.
3. Install engine upper shroud fuel lines and cooling air throttle valve assembly and tighten all retaining bolts. *When tightening upper shroud bolts, turn blower several times to make sure blower edge does not rub against upper shroud.*
4. Install remaining parts in the reverse order of removal.

BLOWER BEARING REPLACE

Crankcase Cover Removed

1. While supporting crankcase cover press blower shaft out of cover.
2. Install a new blower bearing hub in cover, using hypoid lubricant on bearing shaft.
3. Press on shaft of blower bearing and press assembly in place to a height

of 4.520" to 4.530" parallel to cover gasket rails. Do not press on bearing inner or outer race.

COOLING SYSTEM THERMOSTAT

Engine In Car

In the event of a failed thermostat bellows, the cooling air throttle valve will remain in the open position allowing a maximum air flow over the engine to prevent overheating.

When installing a new thermostat it is necessary to adjust the cooling air throttle valve opening to provide the correct air flow. This adjustment must be made with the engine at normal operating temperature so the thermostat rod can easily be pulled up against the pull of the thermostat bellows. The adjustment is as follows:

1. With swivel inserted in hinge lever, pull up on thermostat rod until the bellows is stopped within its mounting bracket.
2. Measure the opening of the cooling air valve as shown in Fig. 33 and adjust the swivel to produce a 1½" opening. This measurement is to be made below the center line of the air horn. *Do not pull up on the air throttle valve while making this adjustment—pull on thermostat rod only.*

DISTRIBUTOR REPLACE

Engine In Car

To remove distributor, disconnect primary wire from coil. Remove distributor cap and vacuum line from distributor. Mark position of rotor arm on housing so that distributor may be reinstalled in same position. Unfasten and remove distributor from engine.

If necessary to remove secondary leads from distributor cap, mark position on cap tower for lead to No. 1 cylinder or see Fig. 34.

When installing distributor, turn rotor about ⅛ turn counterclockwise past the mark previously placed on distributor housing. Push distributor down into posi-

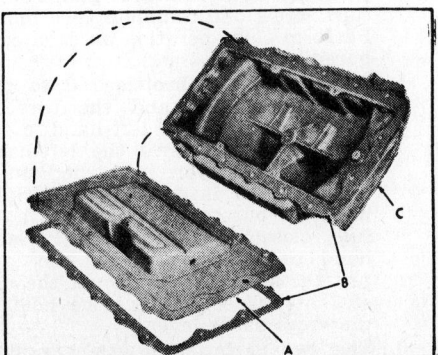

Fig. 32 Crankcase cover and vent.
A. Vent.   B. Cover.   C. Gaskets.

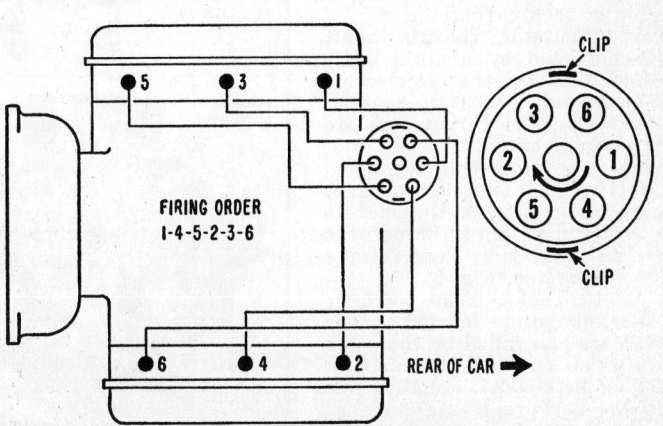

Fig. 34   Ignition wiring

tion in block with housing in normal installed position. It may be necessary to move the rotor slightly to start gear into mesh with camshaft gear but rotor should line up with mark when distributor is down in place. Fasten distributor in place and check ignition timing.

IGNITION TIMING

Connect a timing light to No. 1 spark plug and battery. Start engine and run it at slow idling speed. Aim timing light at timing mark as shown. Adjust as required to bring the timing notch on the pulley in line with the dotted lines indicated for the timing marks present on the timing plate. Loosen distributor clamp bolt and rotate distributor body until timing is correct and tighten clamp bolt.

GENERATOR REPLACE

Engine In Car

Disconnect ground cable from battery, and wires from generator terminals.

Remove drive belt, three attaching bolts and remove generator from engine.

Installation

1. Place generator in position and install bracket, leaving nuts loose.
2. Place blower belt over generator pulley but do not tighten idler bracket at this time.
3. Tighten two generator-to-engine oil filter attaching bolts and torque to 15-22 ft. lbs.
4. Snug up mounting bracket-to-generator bolt and nut (at commutator end) but do not tighten so that the bracket cannot move. Then finger tighten bracket-to-cylinder head bolts.
5. Tighten generator bracket-to-engine rear bolt to 15-22 ft. lbs.
6. Tighten mounting bracket-to-generator bolt (at commutator end) to 8-11 ft. lbs.
7. Tighten generator bracket-to-engine front bolt to 15-22 ft. lbs.
8. Adjust idler pulley so that there will be a ⅜" deflection with a 15 lb. push midway between blower and idler pulley. Tighten idler pulley.
9. Connect generator wires to their proper terminals. On radio equipped cars, connect radio by-pass condenser to the armature (A) terminal —not to field (F) terminal.

STARTER REPLACE

Engine In Car

Disconnect wires and cable from starter. Unfasten and remove starter by pulling it forward to clear housing.

Reverse removal procedure and check starter operation.

EXHAUST SYSTEM

The exhaust system is a single unit consisting of the exhaust pipes, muffler and tail pipe. Remove the four mounting nuts connecting the exhaust pipes to the manifolds. Carefully pull muffler and pipes from under car.

When replacing the muffler, cut it off as close to the exhaust pipe as possible. The service muffler will have a flange over which the cut end of the exhaust pipe can be clamped.

Carburetor Section

1961

The carburetor system is the same as 1960 models except that a manually-operated choke is used in place of the automatic device used formerly.

1960

The Corvair engine makes use of two identical Rochester "H" single barrel carburetors, one located on each intake manifold, Fig. 1. Each carburetor is separated from the engine manifold by an insulator block. Neither carburetor is equipped with an automatic choke, since the choke is in the centrally located air horn-air cleaner assembly at the top of the engine, Fig. 2. From the air cleaner assembly two air tubes direct filtered air to the top of each carburetor.

The two carburetor throttle shaft levers are connected by a cross shaft which is actuated by the accelerator linkage. Careful adjustment is imperative to insure that the carburetors are properly synchronized.

The air horn assembly, while separated from the carburetors, is a definite part of the carburetion system. Outside air passes through the air horn, through the air cleaners and arrives as clean filtered air at each carburetor, Fig. 3.

The automatic choke, choke modifier and fast idle linkage are located on the air horn and are controlled by the same cross shaft which operates the carburetors. Many adjustments normally performed at the carburetor are done at the air horn assembly.

The automatic choke vacuum source is located at the mid-point of the balance tube which extends between the two engine manifolds. The choke outside air source is located on the air cleaner. Clean filtered air is passed from the air cleaner, through the tubing beside the engine manifold to be heated, and thence back to the automatic choke housing.

Synchronizing Carburetors

1. Detach and lift off air cleaner and air hoses as a unit.
2. Disconnect throttle rods from each carburetor.
3. Fully back off each idle speed screw on each carburetor so that each throttle valve is fully closed.
4. Place a .003" feeler between idle speed screw and throttle lever, Fig. 4. Turn screw down until it just holds gauge. Remove gauge and turn screw one complete turn more. Perform this operation on each carburetor.
5. Reconnect the throttle rod to the right carburetor and the throttle rod swivel to the left-hand cross shaft lever. Be sure the left-hand cross shaft lever is turned fully clockwise to insure that the right hand carburetor throttle valve is fully closed. Lifting up on the left-hand carburetor throttle rod, adjust the swivel at the top of the rod so that it freely enters the hole in the cross shaft lever.
6. The two carburetors are now synchronized. Any further curb idle speed screw adjustment must be duplicated on both carburetors.

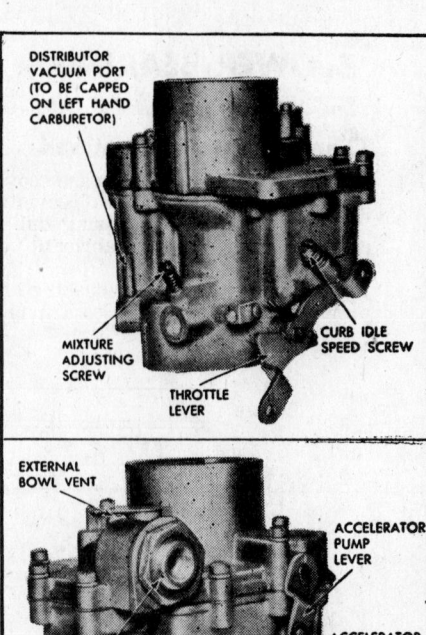

Fig. 1   Rochester type "H" carburetor

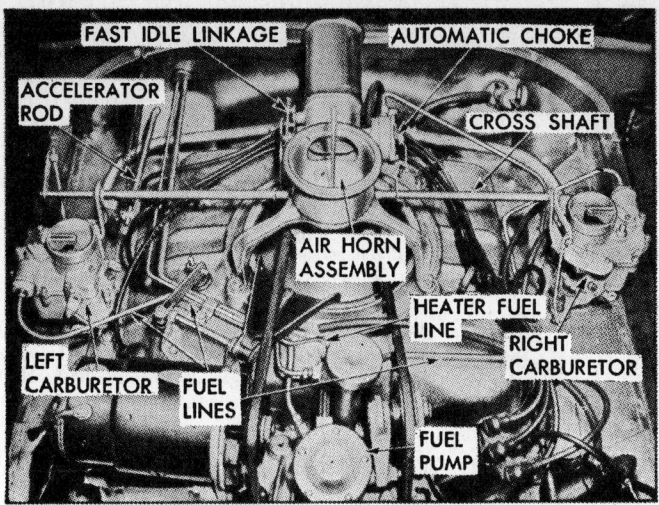

Fig. 2 Carburetion system. 1960

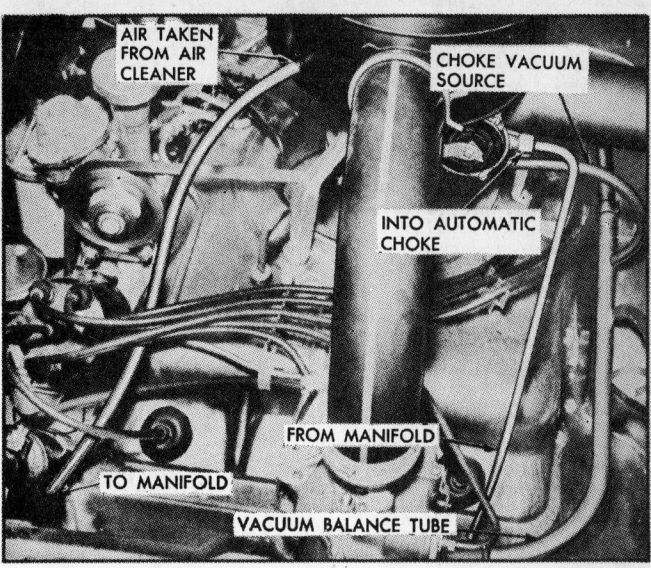

Fig. 4 Choke heat source and routing. 1960

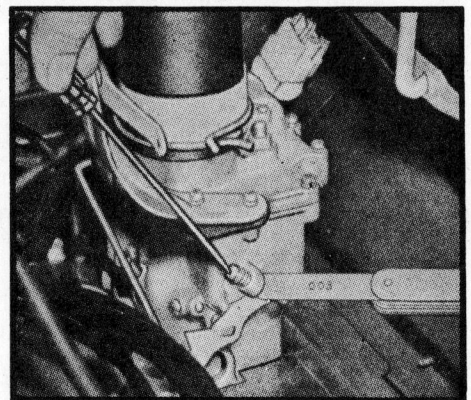

Fig. 5 Adjusting idle screw during carburetor synchronization. Note feeler gauge inserted between idle screw and throttle lever

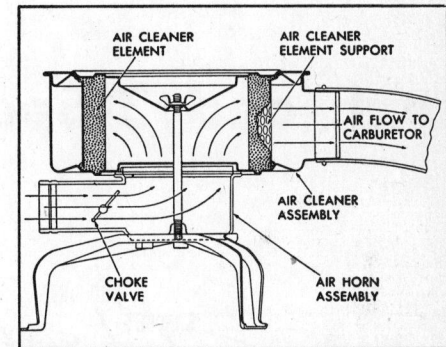

Fig. 3 Air routing to carburetor. 1960

ROCHESTER CARBURETOR ADJUSTMENTS

Year	Carburetor Model	Idle Adjustments				Float Level		Float Drop		Pump Rod Setting	Choke Unloader Setting	Choke Setting
		Mixture Screws Turns Open	Hot Idle Speed In Drive	Fast Idle Speed	Dashpot Plunger Clearance	Primary	Secondary	Primary	Secondary			
1961	H-7019100	1½	500	⑧	None	1¹³⁄₆₄②	None	1¾④	None	⑤	None	None
	H-7019101	1½	500	⑧	None	1¹³⁄₆₄②	None	1¾④	None	⑤	None	None
	H-7019107	1½	500	⑧	None	1¹³⁄₆₄②	None	1¾④	None	⑤	None	None
1960	H-7015300	2	500	2200①	None	1¹³⁄₆₄②	None	1¾④	None	⑤	¼⑥	Index⑦
	H-7015310	2	500	2200①	None	1¹³⁄₆₄②	None	1¾④	None	⑤	¼⑥	Index⑦
	H-7015311	2	500	2200①	None	1¹³⁄₆₄②	None	1¾④	None	⑤	¼⑥	Index⑦
	H-7015312	2	500	2200①	None	⁷⁄₁₆③	None	1¾④	None	⑤	¼⑥	Index⑦
	H-7015313	2	500	2200①	None	⁷⁄₁₆③	None	1¾④	None	⑤	¼⑥	Index⑦

ROCHESTER NOTES

①—Turn adjusting screw against high step of fast idle cam until the specified engine RPM is obtained.

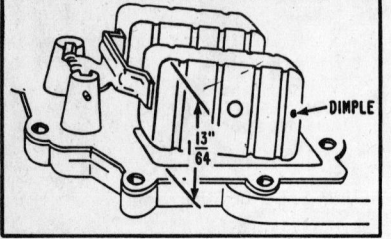

Fig. ②—Float level. If float has no dimple, take measurement from center of float.

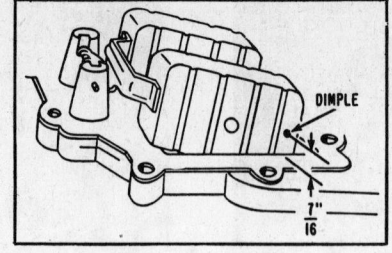

Fig. ③—Float level.

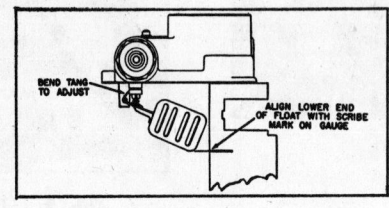

Fig. ④—Float drop.

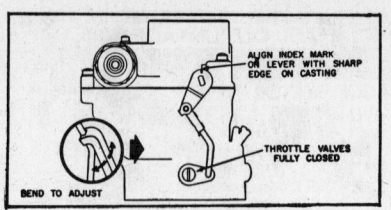

Fig. ⑤—With throttle valves completely closed, bend pump rod as shown until index line on upper pump lever just aligns with sharp edge of air horn casting.

⑥—With throttle valves wide open there should be the clearance listed between top of choke valve and adjacent wall of air horn. To adjust, bend unloader tang.

⑦—Adjust so that pointer lines up with index mark on choke housing cover.

⑧—With choke wide open, clearance between fast idle screw and pad (tang) on throttle lever should be .010" on manual transmission and .030" on automatic transmission jobs. Adjust fast idle screw as required.

Clutch and 3-Speed Transmission Section

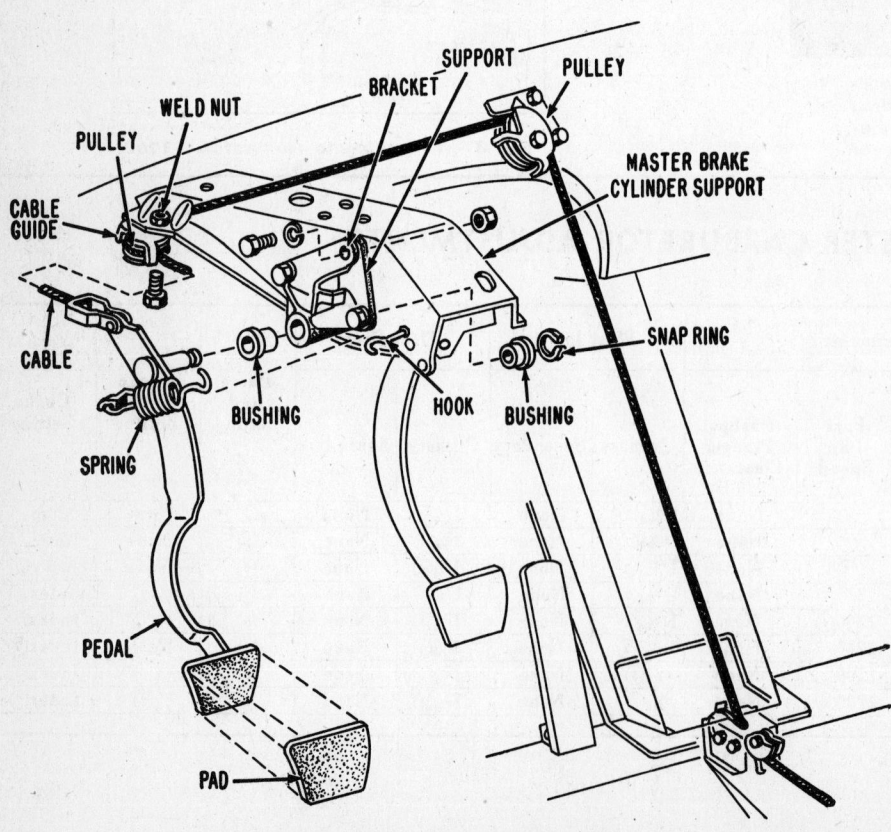

Fig. 1   Clutch pedal components

CLUTCH LINKAGE

The pedal should have at least ¾" travel before the clutch release bearing engages the clutch diaphragm spring. Check the clutch control cable and make sure that it is well anchored at the clutch pedal, Fig. 1, and engaged in each pulley.

1. Attach return spring, Fig. 2, to the cross shaft outboard lever lower hole. Clutch fork pull rod must be disconnected from cross shaft lever.
2. Adjust cable clevis, Fig. 2, until the outboard lever has a clearance of ⅛" to ⅜" as shown.
3. Manually pull clutch fork pull rod, Fig. 3, until slack is taken up at clutch fork.
4. With pull rod in this position, align swivel, Fig. 3, with upper hole in outboard lever. Back off swivel 3 complete turns and assemble to lever.
5. If service is required on the clutch linkage, refer to Figs. 1 and 4.

CLUTCH REPLACE

1. Remove engine, axle and transmission from the car and separate the axle and transmission from the engine as outlined in the *Power Train Section*.
2. The clutch fork, ball stud and clutch release bearing are removed with the axle housing.

3. Disconnect clutch fork from ball stud and remove clutch release bearing from shaft.
4. Remove 6 clutch attaching bolts, one turn at a time, until clutch spring pressure is released. Then remove clutch from engine.
5. Reverse above procedure to install the clutch, being sure the cushion springs of the clutch disc are located on the flywheel side of the driven plate hub.

MANUAL TRANSMISSION

In essence the Corvair transmission is a conventional synchromesh type except for the use of concentric input and output shafts and its mounting on the differential carrier, Fig. 5.

Because of its mounting on the differential carrier, the mainshaft is hollow to permit the passage of the clutch shaft to the front of the transmission to the clutch gear. The clutch gear drives the counter gear and the remaining power flow sequence is identical to the conventional three speed transmission.

Shift Linkage Adjust

After any service operation in which the shift control rod in the tunnel has been replaced or it has been found that transmission response is improper to the shift pattern, adjust the linkage as follows:
1. Loosen U-joint clamp nut and move transmission shift shaft so that the transmission is in Reverse. If position is doubted, start engine with clutch disengaged and then slowly release the clutch.
2. With an assistant holding the gearshift lever in Reverse, tighten the U-joint clamp nut.
3. Test shifts in all ranges.

Gearshift Lever Replace

1. Remove tunnel front plate.
2. Unfasten shift lever from floor pan

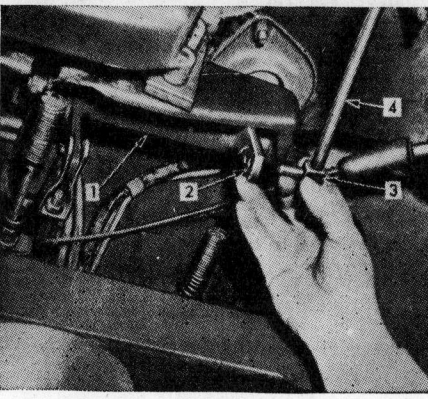

Fig. 2   Adjusting clutch cable.

1. **Locking nut**
2. **Cable clevis**
3. **Outboard lever**
4. **Return Spring**

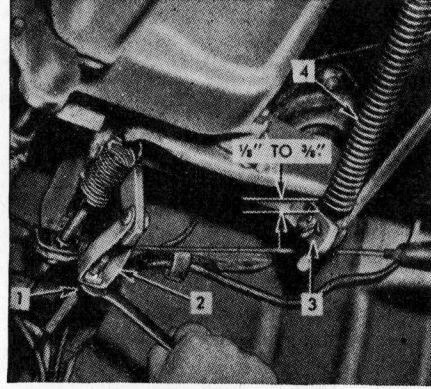

Fig. 3   Adusting clutch fork pull rod.

1. **Cross shaft**
2. **Outboard lever**
3. **Clutch fork pull rod swivel**
4. **Clutch fork pull rod**

(4 nuts). *The two rear nuts also secure the shift control shaft front mounting bracket.*
3. From driver's compartment, lift shift lever up until its studs clear the floor pan; then remove the unit by lifting the floor mat at the center of the seat.
4. If repairs are to be made, refer to Fig. 6.
5. Reverse above procedure to install lever assembly.

Shift Control Rod Replace

1. With tunnel cover removed, Fig. 7, fold back rubber boot covering control shaft U-joint at transmission end of shaft enough to expose connecting pin.
2. Remove connecting pin by pushing out with channel lock pliers.
3. Separate control shaft U-joint from transmission shift shaft by pushing control shaft out toward front of case.
4. Complete removal of shaft by removing two nuts attaching control shaft front mounting bracket; then remove control shaft, U-joint and mounting bracket as an assembly.
5. Reverse above procedure to install.

Transmission Replace

Instructions for the removal of the power train from the vehicle and the separation of the transmission from the power train are provided in the *Power Train Section.*

Transmission Disassemble

1. Remove front cover plate and clutch gear bearing snap ring, Fig. 8.
2. Remove clutch gear and bearing (special puller J-8136).
3. Remove top cover.
4. Remove snap ring from mainshaft groove.
5. Drive or press mainshaft out of transmission.
6. Remove mainshaft parts by lifting out through top of case.

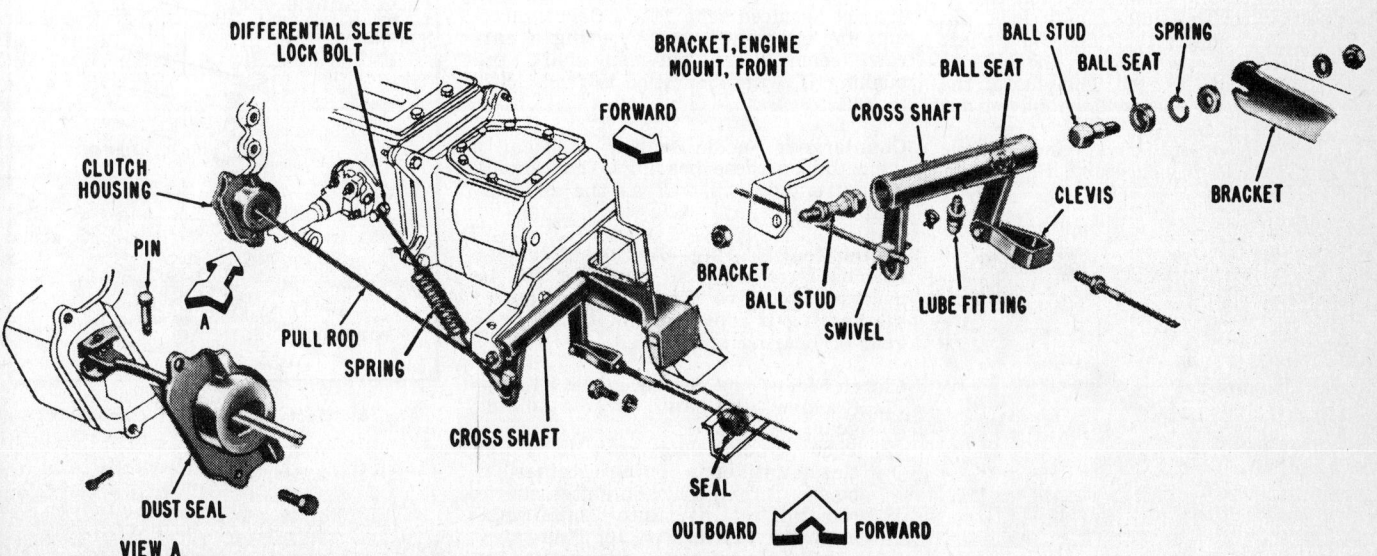

Fig. 4   Clutch linkage components

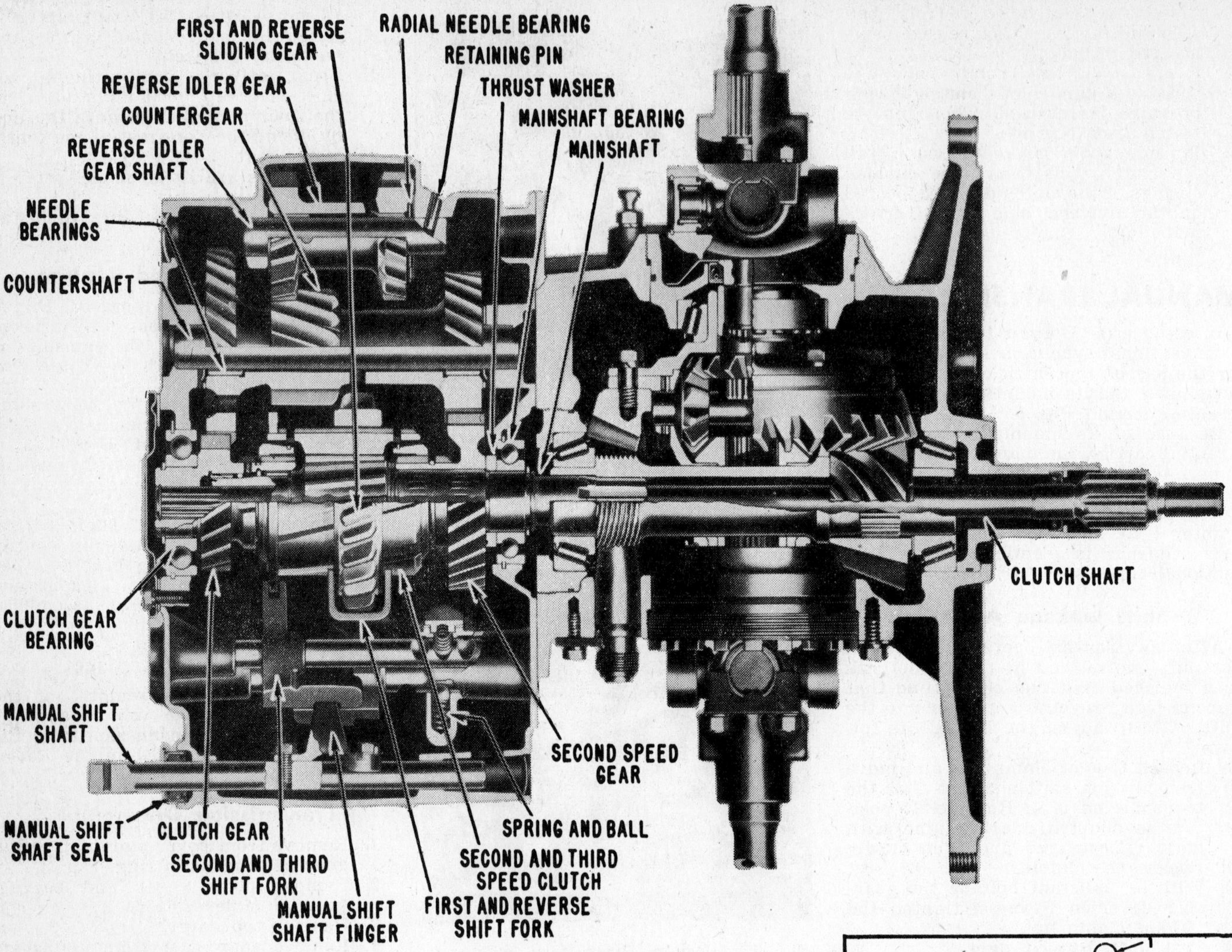

FIRST AND REVERSE SLIDING GEAR
REVERSE IDLER GEAR
COUNTERGEAR
REVERSE IDLER GEAR SHAFT
NEEDLE BEARINGS
COUNTERSHAFT
RADIAL NEEDLE BEARING
RETAINING PIN
THRUST WASHER
MAINSHAFT BEARING
MAINSHAFT
CLUTCH SHAFT
CLUTCH GEAR BEARING
MANUAL SHIFT SHAFT
MANUAL SHIFT SHAFT SEAL
CLUTCH GEAR
SECOND AND THIRD SHIFT FORK
MANUAL SHIFT SHAFT FINGER
SECOND SPEED GEAR
SPRING AND BALL
SECOND AND THIRD SPEED CLUTCH
FIRST AND REVERSE SHIFT FORK

Fig. 5 Three speed transaxle (transmission and axle)

7. Expand snap ring and remove mainshaft rear bearing.
8. Drive countershaft out from hole in front of case, being sure to account for 25 needle rollers at each end.
9. Drive reverse idler shaft lock pin into the shaft; then drive the shaft out of the case through the hole at the rear of the case. The plug at the front of the case will be driven out by the shaft.
10. Remove detent cover and remove shift forks if necessary, Fig. 9.

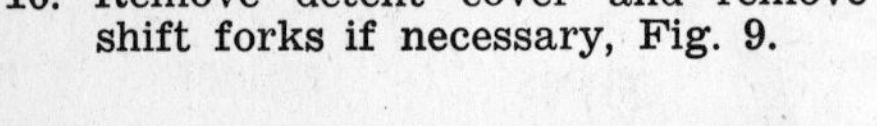

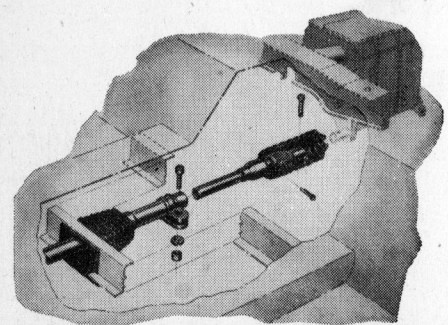

Fig. 7 Tunnel shaft components

Transmission Repairs

Reverse Idler Gear Bushings—Because of the high degree of accuracy to which these parts are machined, the bushings are not serviced separately. Check bushings for excessive wear by using a narrow feeler gauge between shaft and bushing. Proper clearance is from .002" to .004."

Countergear Needle Bearing—If wear is indicated on these bearings, they should all be replaced as well as the countershaft.

Clutch Gear Bearing—As the clutch gear bearing is removed as a unit, it will be necessary to drive the clutch gear out of the bearing if replacement of either the gear or bearing is required.

Clutch Sleeve and Synchronizer Rings—
1. Remove first and reverse sliding gear.
2. Turn synchronizer ring in clutch sleeve until ends of ring retainer can be seen through slot in clutch sleeve.
3. Expand retainer into counterbore in clutch sleeve, Fig. 10. This raises retainer from groove in ring so ring may be slipped out.

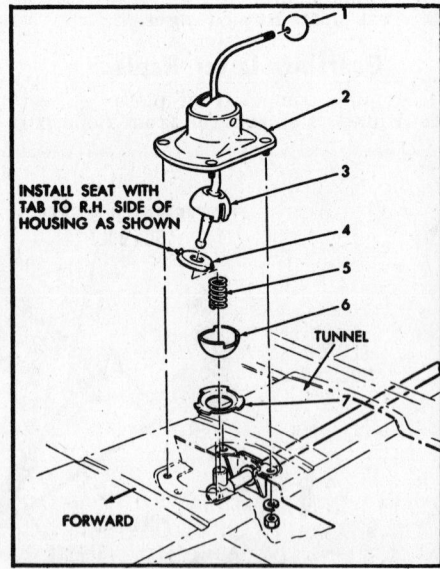

INSTALL SEAT WITH TAB TO R.H. SIDE OF HOUSING AS SHOWN

TUNNEL

FORWARD

Fig. 6 Gearshift lever components.

1. Knob
2. Housing
3. Lever
4. Seat
5. Spring
6. Spherical joint
7. Retainer

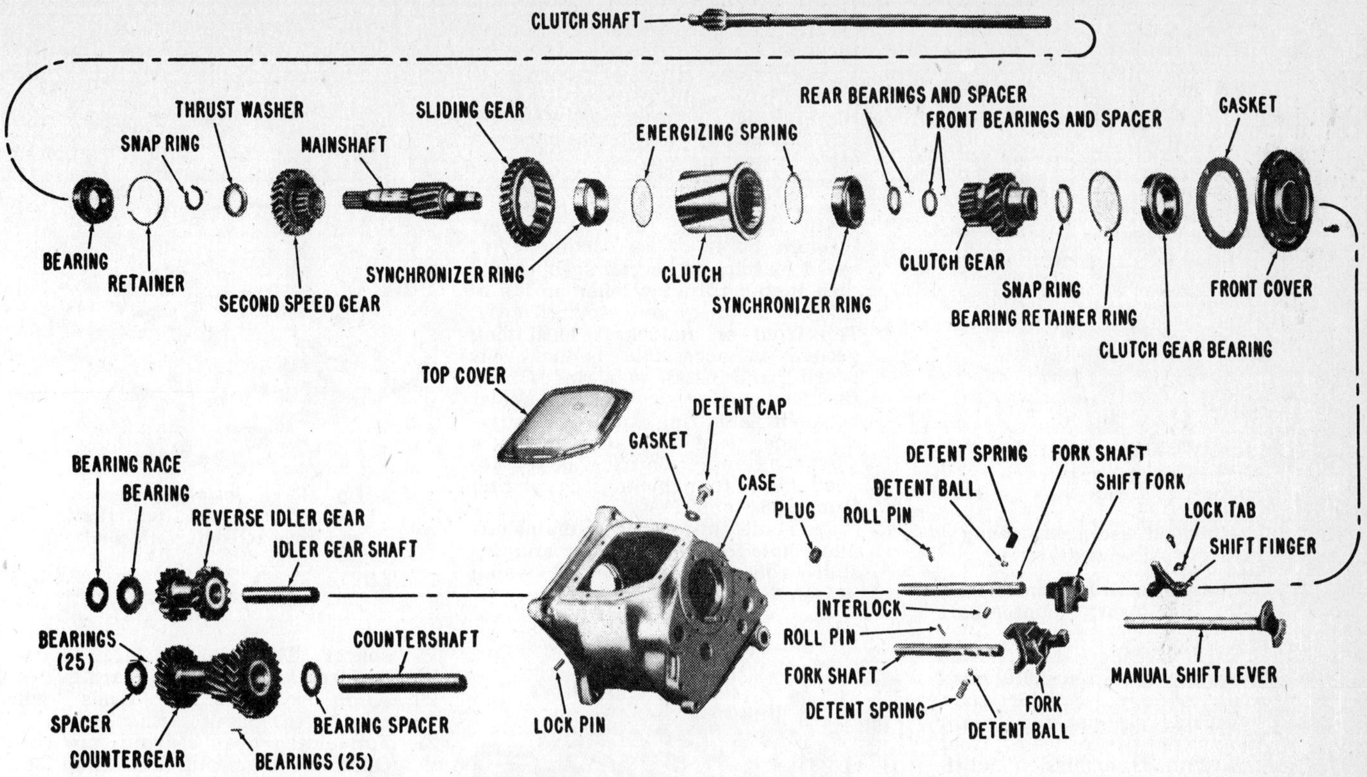

CLUTCH SHAFT

THRUST WASHER   SLIDING GEAR   REAR BEARINGS AND SPACER   GASKET
SNAP RING   ENERGIZING SPRING   FRONT BEARINGS AND SPACER
MAINSHAFT

BEARING   SYNCHRONIZER RING   CLUTCH   CLUTCH GEAR   FRONT COVER
RETAINER   SECOND SPEED GEAR   SYNCHRONIZER RING   SNAP RING
BEARING RETAINER RING   CLUTCH GEAR BEARING

TOP COVER
DETENT CAP
GASKET   DETENT SPRING   FORK SHAFT
BEARING RACE   CASE   DETENT BALL   SHIFT FORK
BEARING   PLUG   ROLL PIN   LOCK TAB
REVERSE IDLER GEAR   SHIFT FINGER
IDLER GEAR SHAFT   INTERLOCK
ROLL PIN
BEARINGS   COUNTERSHAFT   FORK SHAFT   MANUAL SHIFT LEVER
(25)   DETENT SPRING   FORK
SPACER   BEARING SPACER   LOCK PIN   DETENT BALL
COUNTERGEAR   BEARINGS (25)

Fig. 8   Manual shift three speed transmission components

4. Check synchronizer cones for wear or for being loose in clutch sleeve. If cones are damaged in any way, it will be necessary to replace the clutch sleeve and both synchronizer rings. Clutch sleeve should be replaced if there is more than .030" end play between cone and snap ring.
5. Inspect synchronizer rings for smoothness.
6. Place the synchronizer rings in the cones and check with thumbs to see that rings do not rock. Excessive rocking indicates a poor fit between rings and cone, which will not permit proper synchronizing of gears during shifting.

7. Assemble synchronizer parts, being certain retainers seat in groove all the way around rings so rings will turn freely.

Synchronizer Energizing Springs—Under normal operation it should never be necessary to replace the energizing springs. However, should a spring be removed for any reason, a new spring should be installed. The spring may be removed by slipping a thin blade under the spring and raising it sufficiently to slide it off over the clutch gear teeth.

Install the new spring as shown in Fig. 11, thus keeping the spring from turning in its groove.

Transmission Assemble

1. Referring to Fig. 8, lubricate manual control shaft with oil and insert through seal in case. Position actuating finger and secure to shaft with two lock tabs and capscrews.
2. Install detent spring and ball, Fig. 12, in detent cavity. Tap to insure spring is resting on bottom of cavity.
3. Insert first and reverse shift fork through case, slip fork on shaft and secure fork to shaft with roll pin.
4. Insert interlock in detent cavity.
5. Insert second and third fork shaft through case and slip fork onto shaft. Twist shaft so its interlock groove is 90 degrees from the interlock; then fully insert shaft and twist shaft so interlock notch is engaged by interlock. Secure shift fork to shaft with roll pin.
6. Insert detent ball and spring for

second and third shift fork, and install detent cavity cover and gasket.
7. Place some cup grease in roller bearing area of each end of countergear and install 25 rollers in each end. Grease will hold rollers in place while installing.
8. Apply grease to bearing thrust washers and countergear thrust washer and place one at each end of countergear. Tab on each washer should be positioned so as to align with notches in case.

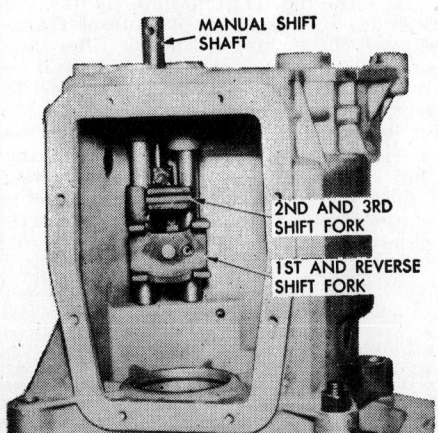

MANUAL SHIFT SHAFT

2ND AND 3RD SHIFT FORK

1ST AND REVERSE SHIFT FORK

Fig. 9   Shift forks installed

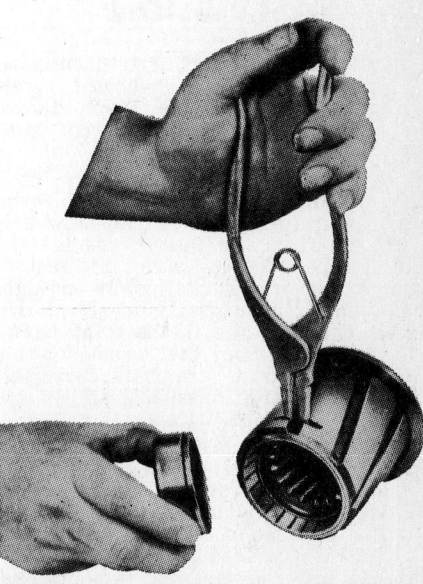

Fig. 10   Removing synchronizing ring

LOCATE OFFSET END OF SPRING BETWEEN
3RD AND 4TH TEETH OF EITHER BANK OF TEETH

Fig. 11   Position of energizing spring

9. Insert countergear in bottom of case.
10. Lubricate and insert countershaft in case.
11. Coat thrust washer and needle thrust bearing with grease and position them on reverse idler gear. Needle bearing against end (rear) with chamfered gear teeth. Coat bushings with transmission lubricant.
12. Place reverse idler gear in case with thrust bearing toward rear.
13. Install reverse idler shaft from rear, making sure lock pin hole in shaft lines up with hole in case at same angle.

14. Use new idler shaft lock pin and drive it in approximately $\frac{1}{16}$" beyond flush with case.
15. Install mainshaft rear bearing in case until bearing contacts retainer ring in case. Then expand retainer and tap bearing until retainer ring seats in bearing groove.
16. Assemble mainshaft components, Fig. 13.
17. From the front, insert mainshaft through bores of second and third speed clutch and second speed gear; then install thrust washer on mainshaft with oil grooves toward gear.
18. Tap front of mainshaft until ring groove is accessible behind rear bearing and install snap ring. Check fit of snap ring by inserting feeler between snap ring and bearing inner race. End clearance must be .004" maximum. Thrust washers are available in four thicknesses ranging from .086" to .097".
19. Place some cup grease in mainshaft pilot hole of clutch gear and install roller bearings and small

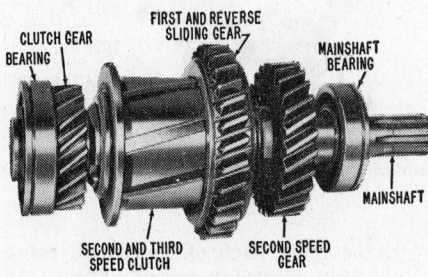

Fig. 13   Mainshaft components

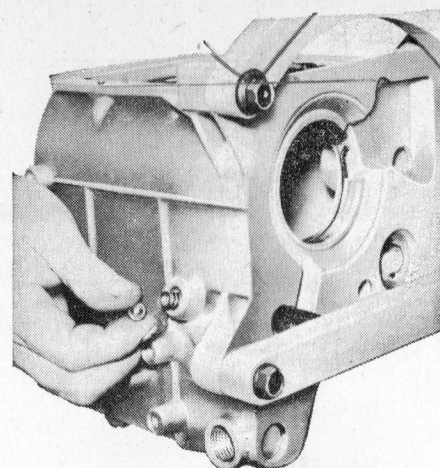

Fig. 12   Installing detent spring and ball for first and reverse shift fork shaft

spacer. Then install large spacer and remaining roller bearings.
20. Align synchronizer lands with clutch gear blank teeth.
21. Tap clutch gear bearing into case. Open retainer ring and fully seat bearing as indicated by seating of retainer ring in bearing groove.
22. Install front cover plate and gasket.
23. Install top cover and gasket.
24. Install expansion plugs in case openings at rear of manual shift shaft and reverse idler gear.

Powerglide Section

DESCRIPTION

The Corvair Powerglide transmission, Fig. 1, consists of an air-cooled, three element torque converter which drives through an automatic, two-speed planetary transmission.

As shown, the transmisison is integrated to the differential carrier to form a Transaxle. As a result, the converter is remote from the main transmission, being separated by the differential carrier. Two shafts run axially through the hollow pinion shaft; one from the converter cover hub to the front pump and the other from the turbine to the input sun gear to transmit converter torque to the transmission gear box.

Excepting the converter location, mechanical components of the Corvair Powerglide are generally scaled-down versions of comparable parts in the conventional Powerglides used on Chevrolet cars. The use of a plate-type reverse clutch and a welded converter with integral starter driven gear are obvious exceptions.

MAINTENANCE & ADJUSTMENTS

Adding Oil

Oil level should be checked every 1000 miles. Oil should be added only when the level is near the "ADD" mark on the dipstick with oil at normal operating temperature. The oil level dipstick is located in the right front of the engine compartment. *The difference in oil level between "FULL" and "ADD" is one pint.*

To check oil level accurately, the engine should be idled with the transmission oil at normal operating temperature and the control lever in Neutral position. Oil level should be maintained no higher than the "FULL" mark on the dipstick. Do not overfill as foaming and aerating of the oil will result because the planetary unit will be running in oil, causing improper application of the band or clutches.

Draining and Refilling

No periodic draining of the trans-mission oil is recommended.

When the transmission requires repairs, drain the oil by loosening the filler tube attaching nut in the oil pan and allow the oil to drain (no drain plug is provided).

To refill the transmission, tighten the filler tube nut and add 4 pints of transmission fluid, using a suitable filler tube and funnel. Start engine and allow it to idle in Neutral for 3 to 5 minutes to warm the transmission fluid. Then add oil as required to bring the level to the "FULL" mark on the dipstick. Assuming that the converter was not drained (since it is welded) and allowing for nominal spillage or draindown, approximately 6 pints are required for a refill.

SHIFT LINKAGE

Check Operation

If improper shift linkage adjustment is suspected, a check can be made quickly without any disassembly as follows:

1. Start engine and allow to run for

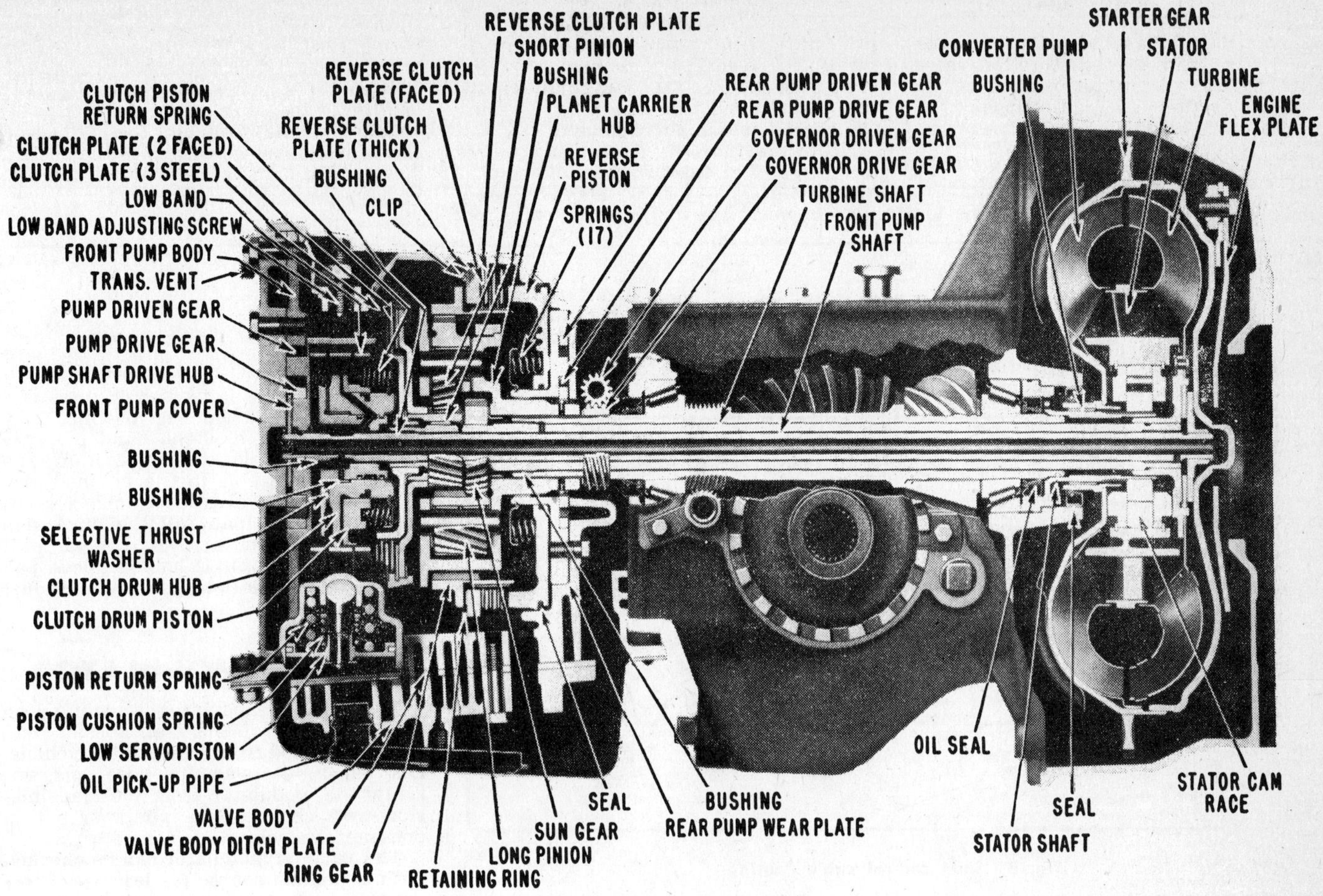

CLUTCH PISTON RETURN SPRING
CLUTCH PLATE (2 FACED)
CLUTCH PLATE (3 STEEL)
LOW BAND
LOW BAND ADJUSTING SCREW
FRONT PUMP BODY
TRANS. VENT
PUMP DRIVEN GEAR
PUMP DRIVE GEAR
PUMP SHAFT DRIVE HUB
FRONT PUMP COVER

BUSHING
BUSHING
SELECTIVE THRUST WASHER
CLUTCH DRUM HUB
CLUTCH DRUM PISTON

PISTON RETURN SPRING
PISTON CUSHION SPRING
LOW SERVO PISTON
OIL PICK-UP PIPE
VALVE BODY
VALVE BODY DITCH PLATE
RING GEAR
RETAINING RING

REVERSE CLUTCH PLATE (FACED)
REVERSE CLUTCH PLATE (THICK)
BUSHING
CLIP

REVERSE CLUTCH PLATE
SHORT PINION
BUSHING
PLANET CARRIER HUB
REVERSE PISTON
SPRINGS (17)

SEAL
SUN GEAR
LONG PINION

REAR PUMP DRIVEN GEAR
REAR PUMP DRIVE GEAR
GOVERNOR DRIVEN GEAR
GOVERNOR DRIVE GEAR
TURBINE SHAFT
FRONT PUMP SHAFT

BUSHING
REAR PUMP WEAR PLATE

STARTER GEAR
STATOR
TURBINE
ENGINE FLEX PLATE

CONVERTER PUMP
BUSHING

OIL SEAL
SEAL
STATOR SHAFT
STATOR CAM RACE

Fig. 1 Corvair Powerglide

2 to 3 minutes to warm up the transmission fluid.

2. With engine at normal idle speed, very slowly move range selector lever up from "N" to "R" and note by feel the point at which the reverse clutch applies. Properly adjusted, the reverse clutch should apply at the peak of the tooth separating Neutral and Reverse detents, Fig. 2.

3. Make the same check as in Step 2 while moving the selector lever from "N" toward "D". Properly adjusted, the low band should apply as the selector lever follower is felt to be at the tooth peak separating Neutral from Drive and full Drive detent.

4. Unless the shifts are obtained at the points illustrated, the shift linkage should be adjusted with Gauge J-8365, Fig. 3.

Adjustment

1. Drain oil and remove oil pan.
2. Place selector lever in "D".
3. Insert Gauge J-8365 into manual valve bore as shown in Fig. 3 with tab of gauge upward so it engages to forward port of valve body as shown in inset.
4. With gauge in place, push forward on manual valve levers. Properly adjusted, the gauge will be held in place horizontally without being supported.
5. If readjustment is required, loosen lock screw and push manual valve levers forward so that gauge is held in this attitude. Recheck adjustment as in Step 4.
6. When satisfactory adjustment is obtained, install oil pan and filler tube; then refill transmission with oil as described above.

Neutral Safety Switch Adjustment

Properly adjusted the neutral safety switch should prevent engine cranking when the ignition switch is turned to "Start" with the selector lever in any position other than "N."

To adjust, loosen switch mounting screws and place range selector lever in "N". Push switch in a direction towards front of vehicle as far as possible to extend plunger. Insert gauge (.680-.685") between end of plunger and switch; then move switch tightly against gauge and plunger and tighten two attaching screws while holding in this position. *A gauge 1"x1⅛"x.680-.685" can be made from steel stock.*

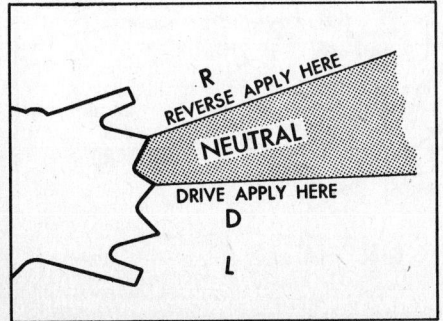

R
REVERSE APPLY HERE
NEUTRAL
DRIVE APPLY HERE
D
L

Fig. 2 Shift linkage check diagram

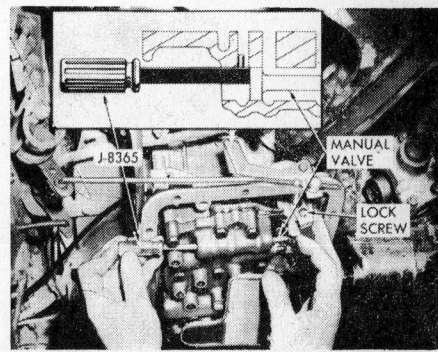

J-8365

MANUAL VALVE

LOCK SCREW

Fig. 3 Adjusting manual valve linkage

Throttle Valve Linkage

As special linkage is not used to actuate the transmission throttle valve, refer to the carburetor portion of the *Engine Section* for adjustment procedure.

Low Band Adjustment

As no periodic adjustment of the low band is recommended, access to the adjusting screw has been provided from inside the vehicle via the parcel compartment area behind the rear seat.

To gain access to the low band, remove the parcel shelf and the plug covering the access hole in the floor pan.

Adjustment of the low band requires an improvised tubular hex ¾" socket approximately 4½ to 6" long. Probably the simplest way to fabricate this tool would be to weld two ¾" tubular stamped steel spark plug wrenches together.

To adjust, loosen the lock nut and tighten the adjusting screw *to 35 to 45 inch lbs., then back off 4 complete turns exactly.* While holding the adjusting screw stationary by means of the socket, inserted through the improvised wrench, tighten the lock nut securely.

"In Car" Repairs

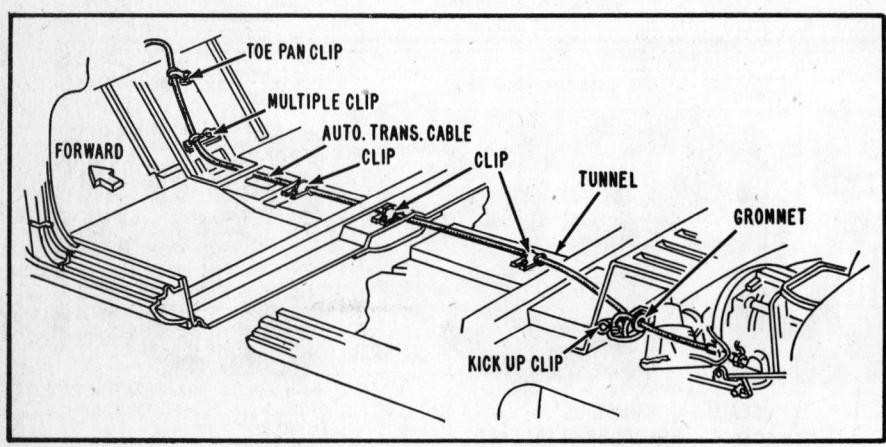

Fig. 4 Shift control cable routing

CONTROL CABLE REPLACE

Remove tunnel covers and detach cable as suggested by Fig. 4. Install new cable as follows:

1. Lay cable out beneath car in its correct relationship.
2. Insert cable up into passenger compartment. Cable must then be routed *under* parking brake cable and then *over* parking brake pipe to prevent possibility of brake cable riding against shift cable.
3. Connect shift cable to range selector.
4. Shift range selector to "D" and secure cable to base of toe-pan.
5. Complete installation as shown in Fig. 4, being sure to bow cable to center line of vehicle to guide cable through hole in engine front support.

Cable-to-Transmission Installation

Early Design, Fig. 5—With throttle rods disconnected from throttle valve lever on transmission, rotate throttle valve lever its full limit counterclockwise and insert cable ball into slot of transmission manual valve lever while guiding cable sheath stop into slot. Insert and tighten cable sheath nut 8-10 ft. lbs. *Torque is provided only as a guide but care must be exercised as overtightening can crack case at this area.*

Later Design, Fig. 6—Install O-ring seal on cable, having lubricated it with Lubriplate. With throttle rods disconnected from throttle valve lever on transmission, rotate throttle valve lever its full limit counterclockwise and insert cable ball into slot of manual valve lever. Fully seat O-ring and secure installation by installing capscrew and lockwasher.

Checking Installation, Fig. 7—Once fully tightened, exert a slight hand pressure in the counterclockwise direction and check that the hole in the notched arm of the throttle valve lever is *below* the transmission oil pan rail the dimension indicated by the arrows, Fig. 7 (⅜" plus or minus $\frac{1}{16}$"). If hole is above pan rail, cable installation is faulty and must be rechecked.

VACUUM MODULATOR

The vacuum modulator is mounted on the right side of the transmission and can be serviced from beneath the vehicle. Disconnect the vacuum hose and unscrew the modulator from the transmission with channel lock pliers or a thin one-inch wrench.

The vacuum modulator can be checked with a vacuum source for leakage. However, leakage normally results in transmission oil pull-over and results in oil smokey exhaust and continually low transmission oil level. No repairs are possible on the modulator; replace with new unit.

When installing, center the gasket in place with vaseline and hold it centered

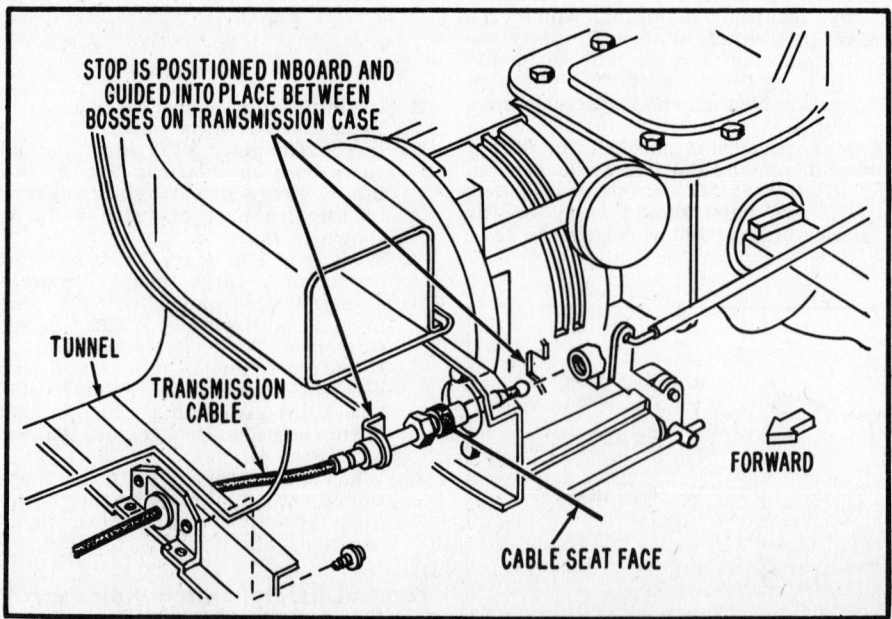

Fig. 5 Cable-to-case installation (early design)

during installation to prevent an external oil leak.

GOVERNOR

Governor is accessible from beneath the vehicle and is mounted on the left side of the transmission. To remove, unscrew lock screw and pull the unit out of the transmission.

The only part replaceable is the driven gear. Drive out the roll pin with a punch and pull out the gear. Drill a new hole in the governor 90 degrees from the original; then insert a new gear and roll pin.

When installing, use a new O-ring seal on the governor. Then insert the governor in the transmission with a slight twist to engage the gear teeth.

VALVE BODY & LOW SERVO

Removal

1. Drain oil pan and disconnect throttle valve rods from TV lever on transmission.
2. Remove oil pan and oil pick-up pipe.
3. Make an improvised sheet metal strap, Fig. 7A, and loosely install with one pan bolt.
4. Remove bolts securing valve body to transmission, tap valve body lightly with a soft hammer to loosen from its dowels in transmission case, then carefully lower the valve body about $\frac{1}{16}$", rotate improvised strap into place so it spans the servo piston hub and secure strap with pan bolt. This eliminates possibility of servo piston slipping down out of its bore and the loss of low band engagement with its apply components.
5. To remove the low servo piston, pull downward on the hub of the piston shaft with a screwdriver. *Do not remove piston in vehicle unless low band screw is first tightened fully.*

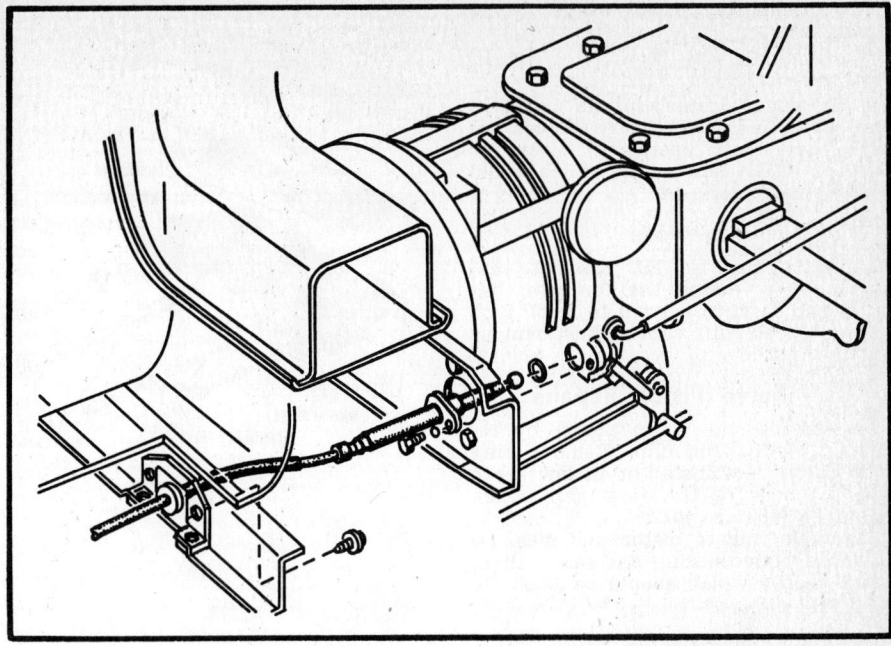

Fig. 6 Cable-to-case installation (later design)

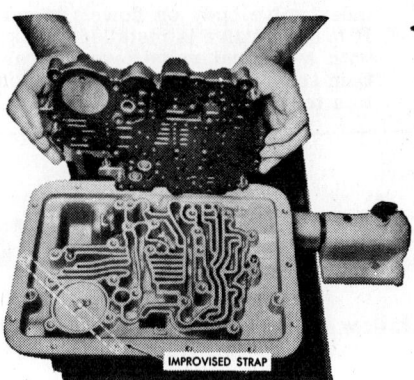

Fig. 7A Remove valve body

Valve Body Repairs

Referring to Fig. 7B, disassemble valve body as follows:

1. If installed, remove manual valve.
2. Remove screws and separate modulator valve body from main valve body. *Modulator body should be held during removal of screws as it is under spring pressure from the pressure regulator valve spring.*
3. Remove pressure regulator valve spring retainer, spring, and pressure regulator valve.
4. From the modulator body, remove rear pump priming ball and the front and rear pump check valves and springs. Also remove modulator valve.
5. To remove line pressure limiting valve, drive roll pin from modulator valve body with a punch, then remove line pressure limiting valve spring and valve from their bore in the modulator body.
6. Remove screws and separate the transfer plate and gasket from the main valve body.
7. To remove the low drive shift valve components, remove retainer ring, then release the pressure and remove low drive regulator valve sleeve, regulator valve, spring seat and inner and outer springs. Lightly tap main valve body with a plastic mallet to remove the low drive shift valve from its bore.
8. To remove the TV valve components, remove retaining pin by wedging a thin screwdriver between its head and the surface of the main valve body, then remove detent valve assembly and throttle valve spring. Complete disassambly of the throttle body by removing the "E" ring from the throttle valve, then remove throttle valve from main valve body

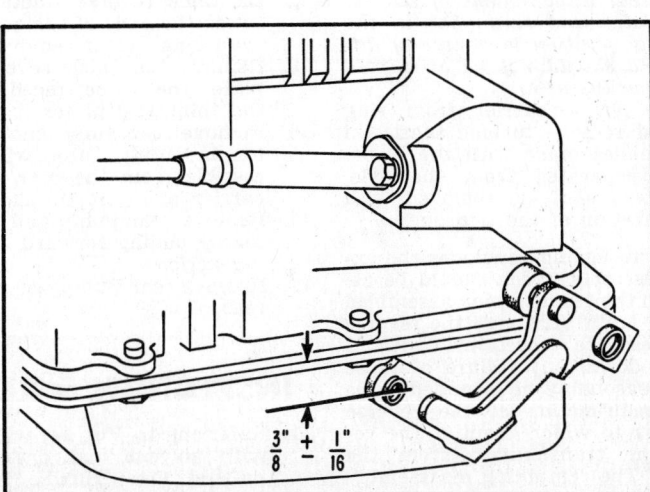

Fig. 7 Cable installation check diagram

$$\frac{3}{8}" \pm \frac{1}{16}"$$

by tapping valve body with a plastic hammer.

Inspection

A thorough cleaning of all parts in clean solvent is mandatory. Check all valves and their operating bores for burrs or other deformities which could result in valve hang-up.

Assemble

Referring to Fig. 7B, complete assembly by reversing the foregoing instructions. Tighten screws to 38-50 *inch lbs.* and check shift cable adjustment as described earlier.

Low Servo Piston Repairs

Disassemble the servo piston by removing the hairpin clip. Remove ring from piston and install it in low servo bore to measure the ring gap which should be .002″ to .012″.

Assemble ring to piston and measure clearance between ring and one wall of piston groove which should be .0005″ to .005″.

Installation

1. Install low servo piston and return spring in transmission bore and engage notch in piston shaft with low band apply strut, loosening low band screw slightly to permit piston ring to seat in case bore.
2. Install valve body in transmission while simultaneously loosening low band screw until it is possible to

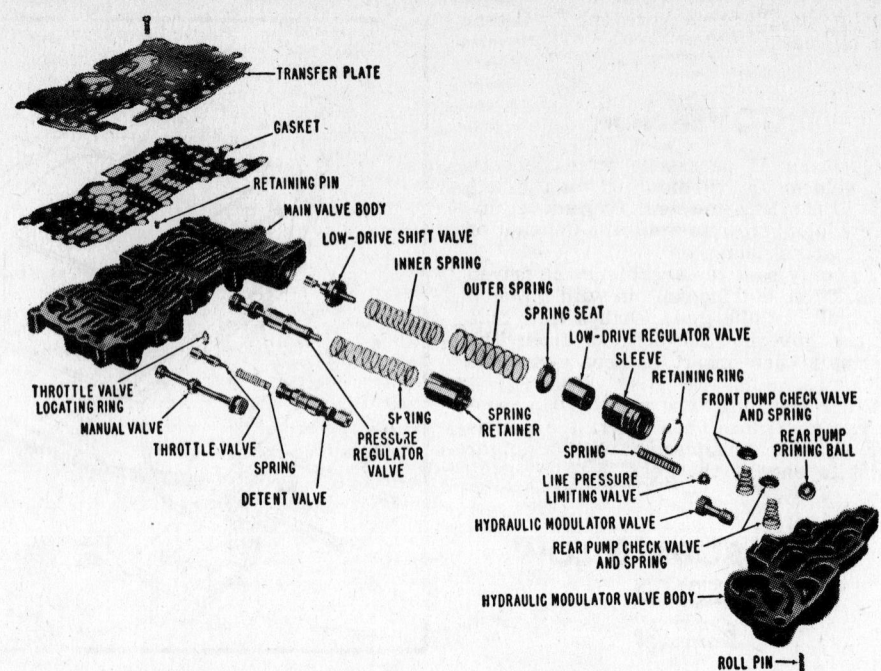

Fig. 7B Valve body exploded

index valve body on dowels in case. If manual valve is installed, index it with a manual valve lever in case; then secure valve body with 20 bolts to a torque of 9-11 ft. lbs.

3. Install O-ring in valve body and install oil pick-up pipe and secure with screw.
4. Complete installation and adjust low band as outlined previously.

Service Operations, Power Train Removed

All operations which follow must be performed with the power train removed from the vehicle and mounted on the fixture used for its removal.

TRANSMISSION DISASSEMBLE

1. Drain oil and remove 12 bolts securing front pump to case.
2. *If overhaul is being made with the transmission installed on power train, loosen low band adjusting screw jam nut and fully tighten the adjusting screw. This will prevent the case components from being pulled out when front pump is removed, Fig. 8.*
3. Remove front pump cover and pull out pump shaft, Fig. 9. Remove front pump body from case, using care not to drop pump gears. Remove pump gasket.
4. Loosen low band adjusting screw and remove low band and related parts, Fig. 10.
5. Remove clutch drum, Fig. 11. *If operations are being performed with the transmission attached to the power train, care should be taken not to disengage the ring gear from the reverse clutch face*

plates unless replacement of either the ring gear or reverse plates is anticipated. Engagement of the reverse plates and ring gear in the horizontal position is generally difficult and should not be attempted unnecessarily.

6. Remove planet carrier from ring gear and remove turbine shaft. On disassemblies made with the transmission separated from the axle, the turbine shaft is removed with the separation of the two units.

NOTE—The foregoing concludes the extent of disassembly which should be attempted with the transmission assembled to the power train. Although the reverse clutch plates are accessible without further tear-down, any failure of these plates can reasonably be assumed to be caused by malfunction of the reverse clutch, access to which requires the removal of the transmission from the power train. The remaining disassembly operations can only be performed with the transmission separated from the power train.

7. Remove ring gear, Fig. 12.
8. Remove clip, Fig. 13, mounted on the thick reverse reaction plate between the ends of the reverse clutch snap ring. Then remove snap ring.
9. Remove the thick reverse reaction plate, the three faced plates and the thin steel plates.
10. Remove rear pump and reverse piston mounting bolts, which are accessible from the rear (differential carrier side) of transmission case.
11. Remove rear pump and reverse piston by pulling forward with a twisting action.
12. Remove rear pump wear plate from rear of case.

INSPECTION & REPAIRS

1. Referring to Fig. 14, wash all parts with solvent and dry with compressed air. Handle transmission case carefully to avoid damaging finished surfaces as such damage could result in oil leakage.

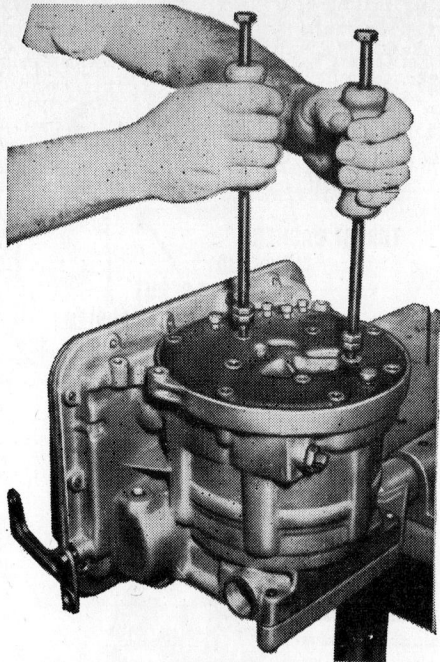

Fig. 8 Removing front pump with slide hammers

Fig. 9 Removing front pump drive shaft

Fig. 10 Low band components

INPUT SUN GEAR TO LOW SUN GEAR THRUST WASHER

Fig. 11 Removing clutch drum

2. Inspect all mating surfaces of the transmission case for nicks and other damage and repair as required. Be especially careful to check the area around the manual shift cable as over-tightening the cable nut could possibly crack the case at this point. Check case bores for wear and grooves.
3. Inspect condition of ring gear teeth and splines.
4. Inspect governor drive gear, splines and teeth for wear.
5. Inspect rear pump wear plate for wear and abrasion.
6. If clutch drive plate facings are worn or show signs of intensive heat, replace plates. Reaction (steel) plates, unless external tangs are peened or damaged, are generally serviceable even after failure of drive plates.
7. In the valve body area of the transmission case, check that the priming ball is retained by its wire retainer and see that the ball and its seat in the case is not deformed. Repair any seat deformation and if ball is damaged, replace it.
8. Check manual valve and TV valve linkage. If damaged replace as required.
9. If necessary, remove valve body oil pick-up tube and clean screen. Also check that the O-ring seal used between the pick-up and valve body is in good condition.
10. Inspect condition of low band. If it shows signs of excessive heat, brittleness of facing can be expected and the band should be replaced.
11. Individual inspection and repair procedures are covered in the following text. The seven bushings used in the transmission are indicated in Fig. 15 together with the applicable bushing installer.

Front Pump

1. Wash all parts and blow out oil passages.
2. If inspection shows that pump gears are serviceable, install gears and check:
   a. Clearance between OD of driven gear and body should be .0025-.005".
   b. Clearance between driven gear and crescent should be .003-.009".
   c. With scale and feeler gauge check

Fig. 12 Removing ring gear

Fig. 13 Reverse clutch pack retainer ring and clip

gear end clearance, which should be .0005-.0015".
   d. Inspect pump drive gear teeth for interference between tops of teeth and crescent in pump.
6. Replace gasket and square cut seal ring in OD of front pump cover. Also check condition of cast iron seal rings on pump body hub.
7. Check condition of front pump body bushing and replace if necessary.

Clutch Drum

1. Referring to Fig. 16, disassemble clutch drum as picture suggests.
2. Inspect clutch drum band surface for excessive scoring or burning. Also check drum bushing for scoring or excessive wear.
3. Check steel ball in clutch drum that acts as a relief valve. Be sure that it is free to move in the hole and that the orifice leading to the front of the drum is open. If the ball is loose enough to rattle, replace clutch drum as an assembly. Replacement or staking of the ball should not be attempted.
4. Check fit of clutch flange in drum slots. There should be no appreciable radial play between these two parts. Also check low sun gear for nicks or burrs and bushing for wear.
5. Check clutch plates for burning, pitting or metal pick-up. Also check to

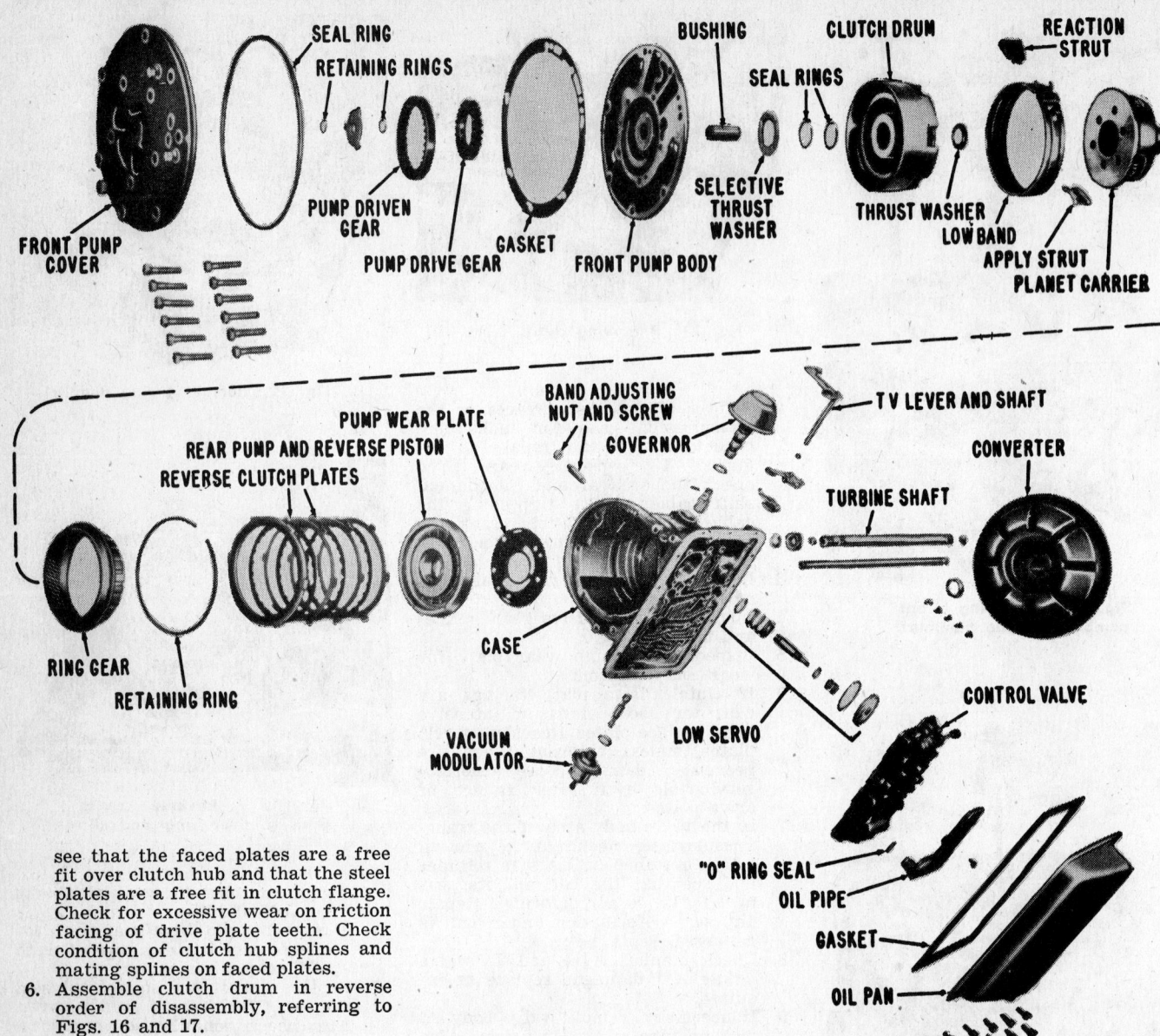

Fig. 14 Corvair Powerglide transmission

see that the faced plates are a free fit over clutch hub and that the steel plates are a free fit in clutch flange. Check for excessive wear on friction facing of drive plate teeth. Check condition of clutch hub splines and mating splines on faced plates.

6. Assemble clutch drum in reverse order of disassembly, referring to Figs. 16 and 17.

Planet Carrier

Currently, no service operations are recommended for the planet carrier. If a component fails, replace the planet carrier as an assembly.

Turbine Shaft

Check the shaft for nicks and cracks and check the splined areas for wear. Check that the two lube holes are open. Also inspect the bushings and replace if necessary.

Pump Shaft

Check the splines at the converter end of the shaft for wear or damage. Inspect the bronze faced drive lugs for peened edges and wear of its splined connection to the shaft by twisting to check for looseness. Be especially careful to check that the drive hub is tightly retained by the snap ring. If bronze hub is worn, remove top snap ring and replace hub.

Rear Pump and Reverse Piston

1. Referring to Fig. 18, disassemble as picture suggests. The tools shown in Fig. 19, together with a press aids in disassembly.
2. Check fit of pump gears as described for the front pump. Fits and tolerances are identical.
3. Inspect pump body for leaks and scoring. Check hub of pump body for smoothness. Any burrs on the surface would cause leakage and could result in a jammed reverse piston.
4. Check for broken return springs and make a comparative check of spring heights by standing all springs in a row. If appreciable variance of spring height is noted, replace springs.
5. Check condition of rear pump body bushing and replace if necessary.

Converter

It is not necessary to drain the converter as it is welded and no internal repairs can be made.

Check the starter gear for worn or broken teeth and for broken welds at its attachment to the converter assembly. If starter gear is undamaged but welds are loose or broken, re-weld as required.

Check converter seams for stress or breaks and either replace converter or repair welds as required. If welds are repaired, keep added material to a minimum by carefully chipping off all scale and filing away any unnecessary weld to obtain converter balance as close to original as possible. Replace the converter if roughness due to unbalance is noted after reassembly to engine. Check converter bushing for wear and replace if necessary.

TRANSMISSION ASSEMBLE

The following steps apply only if the transmission is separated from the Power Train.

1. Install two improvised guide pins in rear pump bolt holes. Install rear pump wear plate on guide pins, using a small amount of vaseline to hold plate in place.

2. Insert rear pump and reverse piston. Then insert a length (½" to ¾" wide) of .010-.015" shim stock between piston outer seal and case. With rear of case downward, running the shim stock around the entire diameter of the seal will seat the seal quickly. Remove guide pins and install rear pump mounting bolts, torquing them to 9-11 ft. lbs.

3. Install reverse clutch drive and reaction plates alternately starting with a steel plate, and finishing with a faced plate. The notched lug in each steel plate is installed so it is at the top of the groove at the 4 o'clock position in the case. Then install the thick reaction plate; it has a square "dimple" on its lug which engages the 4 o'clock case groove.

4. Install reverse clutch retainer ring in such a manner so that the open ends of the ring are at the 12 o'clock position; then install retainer clip (Fig. 13) on thick reaction plate between ends of snap ring.

5. With rear of transmission case downward, align internal lands and grooves of reverse face plates.

6. Engage ring gear to reverse drive plates, Fig. 12. Engagement must

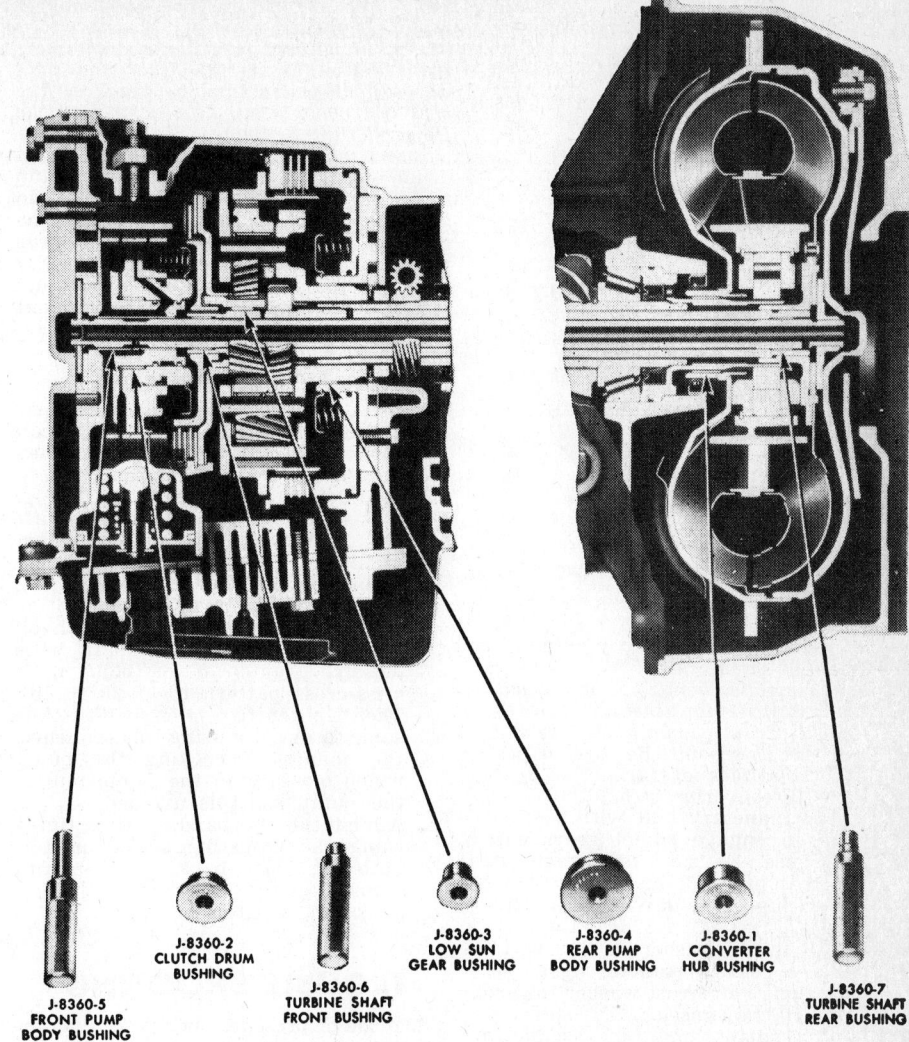

J-8360-5
FRONT PUMP
BODY BUSHING

J-8360-2
CLUTCH DRUM
BUSHING

J-8360-6
TURBINE SHAFT
FRONT BUSHING

J-8360-3
LOW SUN
GEAR BUSHING

J-8360-4
REAR PUMP
BODY BUSHING

J-8360-1
CONVERTER
HUB BUSHING

J-8360-7
TURBINE SHAFT
REAR BUSHING

Fig. 15   Powerglide bushings and installers

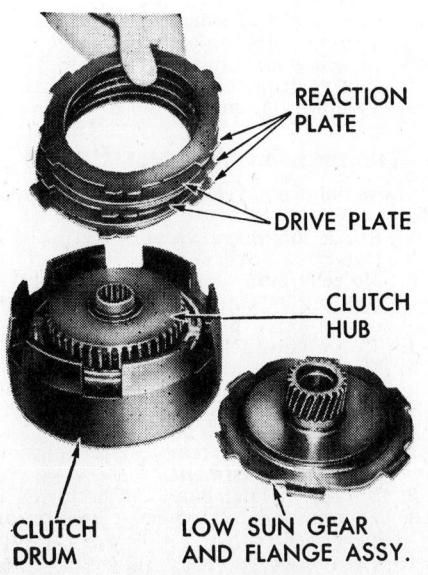

REACTION PLATE

DRIVE PLATE

CLUTCH HUB

CLUTCH DRUM

LOW SUN GEAR AND FLANGE ASSY.

Fig. 17   Installing clutch drum plates

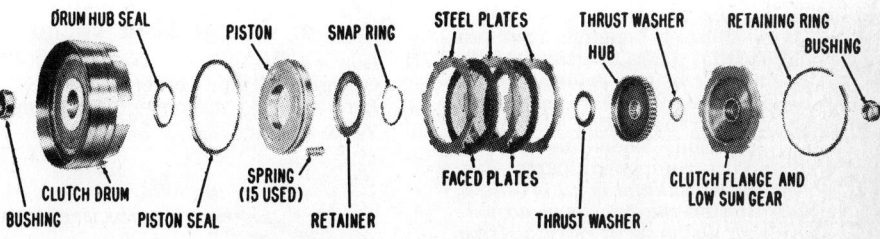

DRUM HUB SEAL

PISTON

SNAP RING

STEEL PLATES

THRUST WASHER

RETAINING RING

BUSHING

HUB

CLUTCH DRUM

BUSHING

PISTON SEAL

SPRING (15 USED)

RETAINER

FACED PLATES

THRUST WASHER

CLUTCH FLANGE AND LOW SUN GEAR

Fig. 16   Clutch drum and component parts

SNAP RING

PISTON INNER SEAL

BUSHING

PUMP BODY

PUMP DRIVE GEAR

SPRING RETAINER

SPRINGS (17 USED)

REVERSE PISTON

PISTON OUTER SEAL

PUMP DRIVEN GEAR

Fig. 18   Rear pump and reverse piston

Fig. 19 Removing reverse piston return spring retainer

be made by feel while jiggling the drive plates laterally.

7. *On assemblies being performed with the transmission installed on the Power Train, install the turbine shaft at this point. Be sure to fully engage splines of turbine shaft to those in converter turbine.*

8. Install planetary unit with a slight twist to engage planet gears with ring gear. Be sure to engage the two rear pump drive lugs on planet hub with grooves in rear pump drive gear.

9. Install thrust washer on captive input sun gear in planetary gear set with flange of thrust washer toward front of transmission. If necessary, apply a small amount of vaseline to keep thrust washer centered, especially if the work is being performed with the transmission assembled to the Power Train.

10. Install clutch drum assembly, using a slight twist to engage low sun gear to planet gears in gear set.

11. If assembly is being performed with transmission removed from Power Train, turn transmission to a horizontal position. Then install low band and its component parts, Fig. 20. *When the linkage is all installed, snugly tighten the low band adjusting screw to prevent struts from falling out of place.* Then jiggle clutch drum slightly to center band and linkage.

Front Selective Thrust Washer Determination

At this point, prior to the installation of the front pump when overhauling the transmission while assembled to the Power Train, the thrust washer selection must be determined with the tool shown in Fig. 21 as described below. *The use of this tool and the following procedure is absolutely limited to overhauls performed while the transmission is assembled to the differential carrier. At this point, during overhauls with the transmission*

separated from the differential carrier, install the original (unless necessary to replace) thrust washer on the front pump hub without gauging, and complete transmission assembly. Final end play adjustment would then be made at the rear (governor gear) as described in the Power Train Section.*

Insert pilot of tool into bore of clutch drum and secure with two front pump mounting bolts. Tighten bolts fully to compress pilot spring. See that the plunger is fully seated. Then observe plunger action and select thrust washer as instructed in Fig. 21. Remove tool and install thrust washer selected on front pump hub.

Final Assembly

1. Install front pump body with new gasket, being careful not to break cast iron oil ring on pump hub when they are indexed to clutch drum.

2. Install front pump drive shaft, Fig. 9. Use care when inserting shaft not to damage bushings in transmission.

3. Install a new square cut seal ring in front pump cover; then position pump cover. Dip bolt heads in oil impervious sealer and install bolts loosely. Tighten outer bolts in a criss-cross pattern to 18-20 ft. lbs. Then tighten five inner bolts to the same torque. By using this sequence, the chance of cocking the pump which would bind the pump hub to the pump shaft is avoided.

4. Adjust the low band by first tightening the adjusting screw until it bottoms; then back off four full turns exactly. Holding adjusting screw and tighten lock nut.

TROUBLE SHOOTING

The use of pressure checks for diagnosis of Corvair Powerglide malfunctions is not recommended at this time; therefore pressure test data are not provided.

No Drive In Any Selector Position; Cannot Load Engine

1. Low oil level.
2. Clogged oil pipe screen.
3. Broken or disconnected manual valve cable.

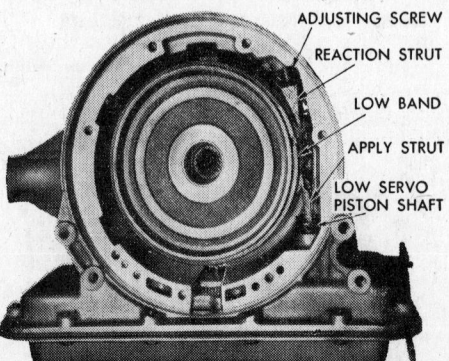

Fig. 20 Installing low band components

ADJUSTING SCREW
REACTION STRUT
LOW BAND
APPLY STRUT
LOW SERVO PISTON SHAFT

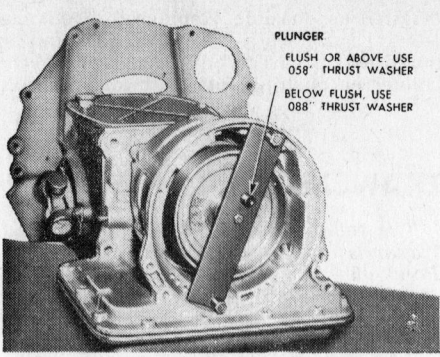

PLUNGER
FLUSH OR ABOVE USE .058" THRUST WASHER
BELOW FLUSH, USE .088" THRUST WASHER

Fig. 21 Gauging clutch drum thrust washer with J-8371

4. Front pump defective.
5. Front pump shaft disengaged at either converter or pump gear.
6. Front pump priming ball not seating.
7. Defective pressure regulator valve.
8. Defective line pressure limit valve.
9. Rear pump check valve and rear pump priming ball not seating. Both must occur for possible malfunction.

Engine Speed Flares On Standstill Starts But Acceleration Lags

Low band partially applied due to any of the following:
1. Low oil level.
2. Clogged pick-up pipe screen.
3. Improper band adjustment.
4. Servo piston apply passage blocked.
5. Servo piston ring broken or leaking.
6. Band facing worn.
7. Low band apply linkage disengaged or broken.
8. Converter stator not holding (rare).

Engine Speed Flares On Upshift

1. Low oil level.
2. Clogged oil screen or pipe.
3. High clutch partially applied (blocked feed orifice).
4. Clutch plates worn.
5. Clutch seals leak.
6. Clutch piston hung up.
7. Clutch drum relief ball not seating.
8. Vacuum modulator hose collapsed.

Transmission Will Not Upshift

Low band not releasing, probably due to:
1. Stuck low-drive valve.
2. Defective governor.
3. No rear pump output such as stuck priming ball, drive pins not engaged, or defective pump.
4. TV valve stuck or maladjusted.
5. Maladjusted manual valve lever.

Upshifts Harsh

1. Incorrect carburetor-to-transmission TV rod adjustment.
2. Improper low band adjustment.
3. Vacuum modulator hose broken or disconnected.
4. Vacuum modulator diaphragm leaks.
5. Vacuum modulator valve stuck.
6. Hydraulic modulator valve stuck.

Closed Throttle (Coast) Downshifts Harsh

1. Improper low band adjustment.
2. Vacuum modulator hose disconnected or broken.
3. Vacuum modulator diaphragm ruptured.
4. Vacuum modulator valve stuck.
5. Engine idle speed too high.
6. Sticking valves in valve body (pressure regulator or hydraulic modulator valves).

Car Creeps In Neutral

1. Incorrect manual valve lever adjustment.
2. High clutch or low band not released.

No Drive In Reverse

1. Manual valve lever improperly adjusted.
2. Cable linkage adjustment.
3. Reverse clutch piston stuck.
4. Reverse clutch plates worn out.
5. Reverse clutch leaking excessively.
6. Blocked reverse clutch apply orifice.

Improper Shift Points

1. Incorrectly adjusted carburetor-to-transmission linkage.
2. Incorrectly adjusted TV valve.
3. Governor defective.
4. Rear pump priming ball stuck.

Oil Forced Out of Filler Tube

1. Oil level too high causing planet carrier to run in oil and cause foam.
2. Oil pick-up pipe split or not sealed.

Unable To Push Start

1. Rear pump drive gear not engaged with drive pins on planet carrier hub.
2. Rear pump defective.
3. Rear pump priming ball not seating.

TRANSMISSION SHIFT POINT

Upshifts	M.P.H.
Minimum throttle	10-12½
Full throttle	41-47
Part throttle	34-41

Downshifts	M.P.H.
Closed throttle	8-12
Full throttle	38-44
Part throttle	23-30
Manual low	41-46

Rear Axle and Brake Section

Refer To Hydraulic Brakes Chapter For Brake Adjustments

AXLE DESCRIPTION

The Corvair rear axle is of the straddle-mounted hypoid type which embodies a differential carrier mounted rigidly to the engine; no rear axle housing is used, Figs. 1 and 2. Independently suspended axle shafts are attached to universal joints which, in turn, are splined into the differential side gears.

A hollow shaft is used with the drive pinion to permit passage of the engine output shaft forward to the transmission. To permit the axial hole in the pinion shaft, the drive pinion and gear are two pieces coupled together. The drive pinion shaft is directly connected to the transmission output member. Preloaded tapered roller bearings support the drive pinion at fore and aft locations in the differential carrier. The ring gear is bolted to the differential case which is mounted on preloaded tapered roller bearings on each side of the differential carrier.

Components of the differential assembly are conventional with the exception of the side gears which have integral elongated splined hubs which project to the outboard extremity of the differential case and cover to receive the axle shaft universal joints.

AXLE SHAFT, BEARING & U-JOINT

Removal

1. Remove wheel and brake drum.
2. Unfasten bearing retainer from backing plate (four nuts accessible through hole in axle shaft flange).

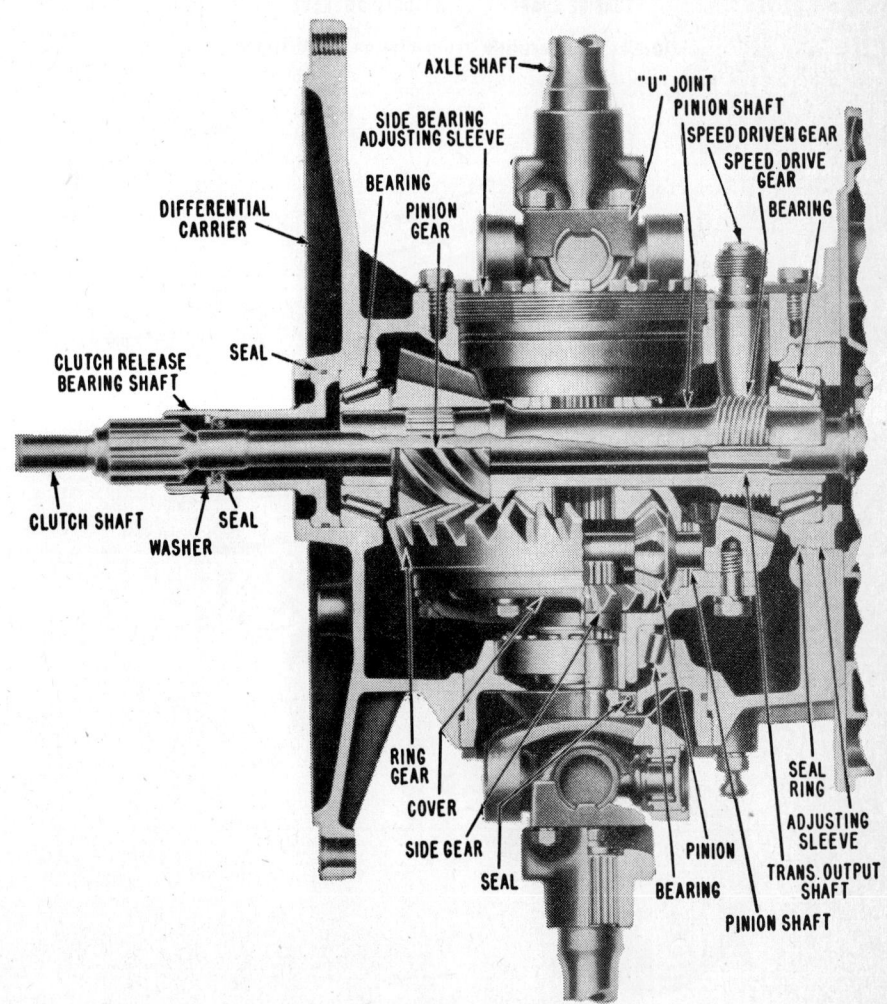

Fig. 1 Three speed transmission rear axle

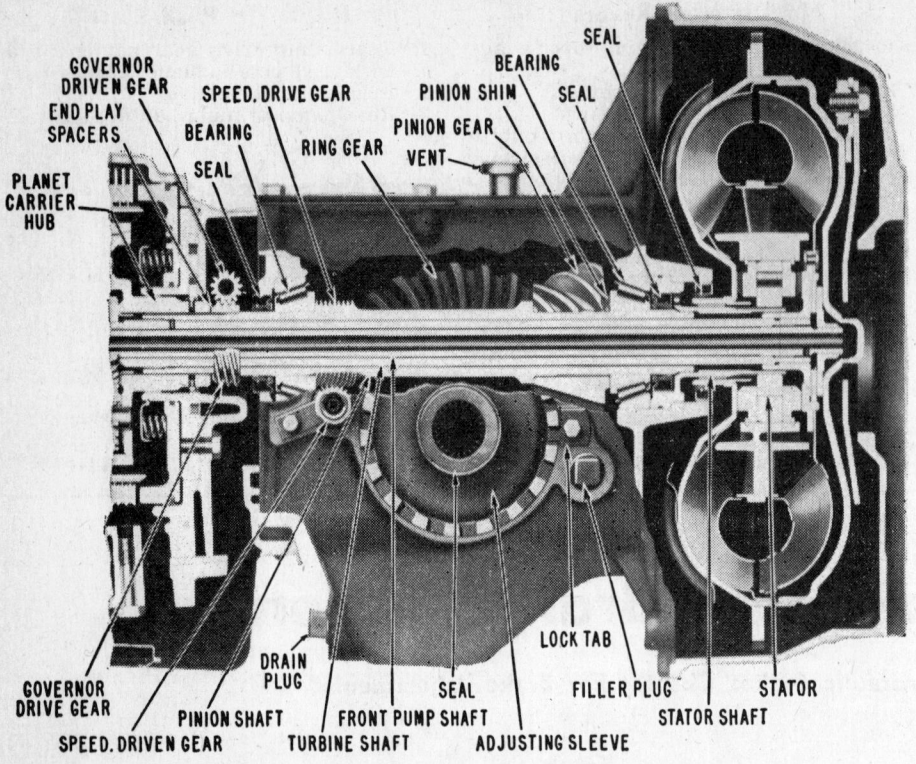

GOVERNOR DRIVEN GEAR
END PLAY SPACERS
PLANET CARRIER HUB
SPEED. DRIVE GEAR
BEARING
SEAL
RING GEAR
PINION SHIM
PINION GEAR
VENT
BEARING
SEAL
SEAL

GOVERNOR DRIVE GEAR
SPEED. DRIVEN GEAR
PINION SHAFT
DRAIN PLUG
TURBINE SHAFT
FRONT PUMP SHAFT
SEAL
ADJUSTING SLEEVE
LOCK TAB
FILLER PLUG
STATOR SHAFT
STATOR

Fig. 2   Powerglide transmission rear axle

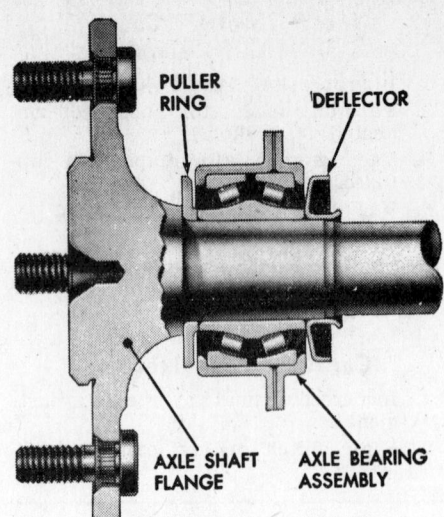

PULLER RING
DEFLECTOR
AXLE SHAFT FLANGE
AXLE BEARING ASSEMBLY

Fig. 3   Axle shaft bearing

Fig. 5   Removing side bearing adjusting sleeve

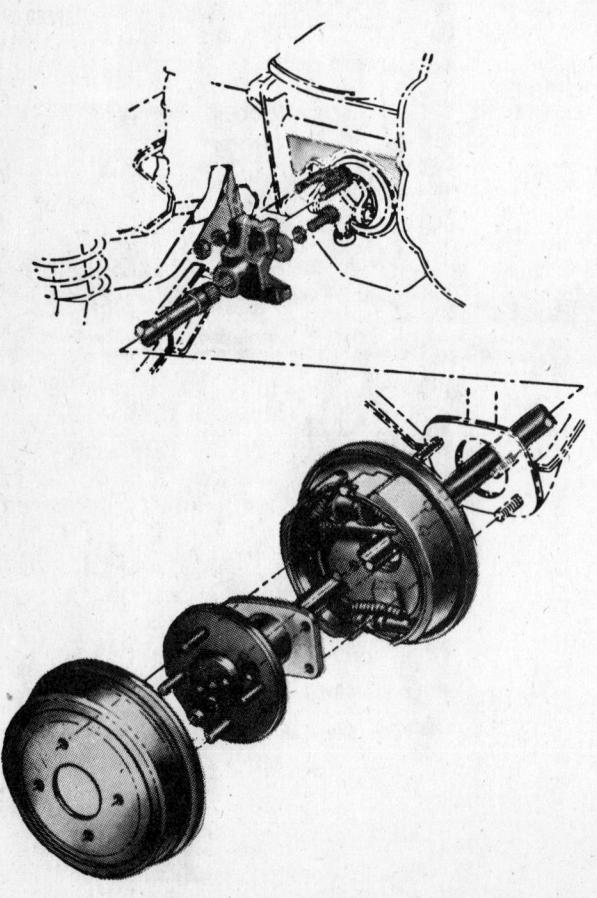

Fig. 4   Axle shaft components

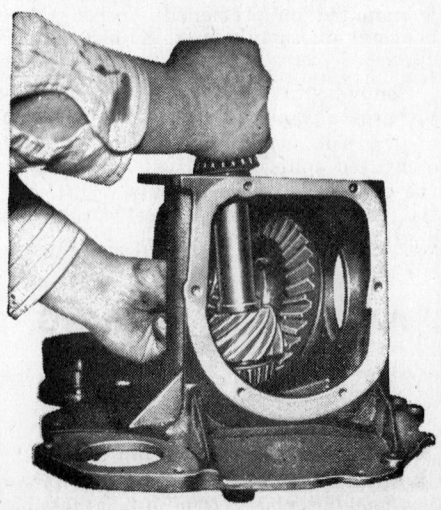

Fig. 7   Removing pinion from carrier

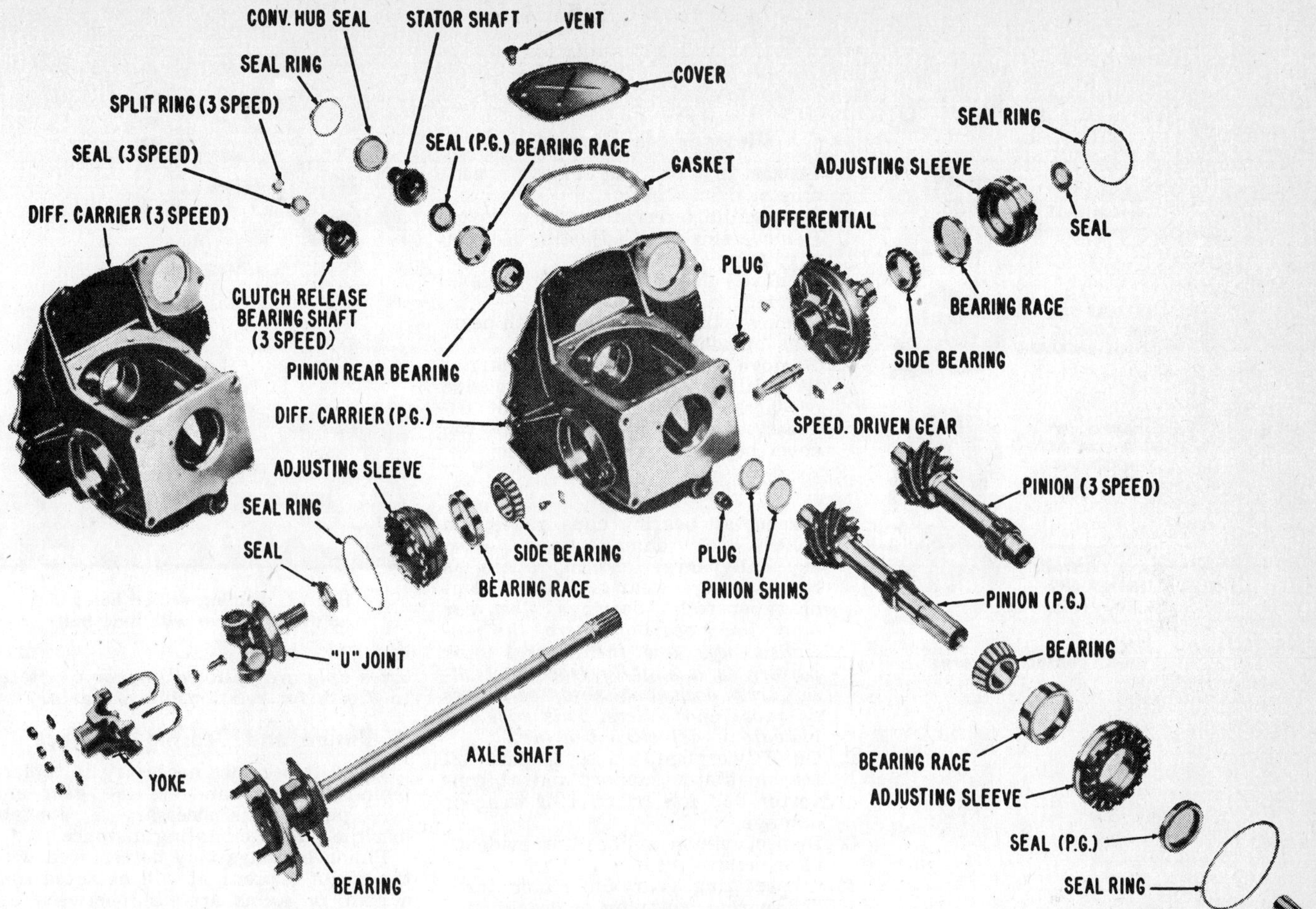

CONV. HUB SEAL STATOR SHAFT VENT

SEAL RING

SPLIT RING (3 SPEED)

SEAL (3 SPEED)

DIFF. CARRIER (3 SPEED)

COVER

SEAL (P.G.) BEARING RACE

GASKET

SEAL RING

ADJUSTING SLEEVE

SEAL

DIFFERENTIAL

PLUG

BEARING RACE

CLUTCH RELEASE
BEARING SHAFT
(3 SPEED)

SIDE BEARING

PINION REAR BEARING

DIFF. CARRIER (P.G.)

SPEED. DRIVEN GEAR

ADJUSTING SLEEVE

SEAL RING

SEAL

PINION (3 SPEED)

SIDE BEARING

PLUG

BEARING RACE

PINION (P.G.)

PINION SHIMS

"U" JOINT

BEARING

AXLE SHAFT

BEARING RACE

ADJUSTING SLEEVE

YOKE

SEAL (P.G.)

SEAL RING

BEARING

BUSHING (P.G.)

Fig. 8   Differential carrier

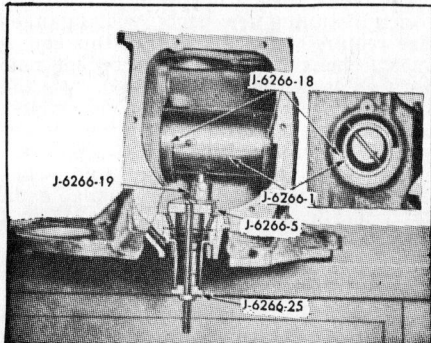

Fig. 9   Pinion depth shim selection gauges

Fig. 6 Removing pinion adjusting sleeve

3. Pull backing plate outward slightly then push it back onto the control arm studs to break away from the bearing retainer. The axle shaft can now be pulled outward sufficiently to free the U-joint splines from the differential side gears.

4. Remove U-joint from axle shaft (4 nuts from U-bolts).

5. Remove yoke from axle shaft.

Axle Shaft Bearings, Replace

1. Place axle shaft in a press with puller plate below the puller ring, Fig. 3.

2. Remove oil deflector, bearing and puller ring.

3. To install, place a new puller ring, bearing and oil deflector on axle shaft. *To prevent damaging bearing during installation of the new parts, place the old puller ring with its flat side against the bearing inner race and then press the puller ring and bearing onto the axle shaft.*

4. Remove old puller ring and install oil deflector.

Installation, Fig. 4

1. Insert axle shaft through lower control arm and install U-joint yoke on splines of axle shaft. It may be

necessary to lightly tap yoke onto splines if original pieces are being installed. *When assembling new pieces for the first time, it is good practice to assemble and disassemble the yoke to the axle shaft with a press to ease the assembly of the pieces in the vehicle.*

2. Secure U-joint flange to axle shaft.

3. Attach U-joint to yoke on shaft with U-bolts.

4. With bearing retainer holes lined up with control arm studs, insert U-joint splines through seals in side bearing adjusting sleeves and index with side gear splines.

5. Secure bearing retainer to brake backing (4 nuts) via access hole in axle shaft flange.

6. Position brake drum control arm studs and secure wheel and drum.

SIDE BEARING SLEEVE SEAL

The side bearing adjusting sleeve seal may be replaced while installed in the vehicle. Remove the U-joint from the side bearing adjusting sleeve. Pry out the seal, then install the new seal using any flat object as a driver as the seal mounts flush. *Seal lips must be inward.*

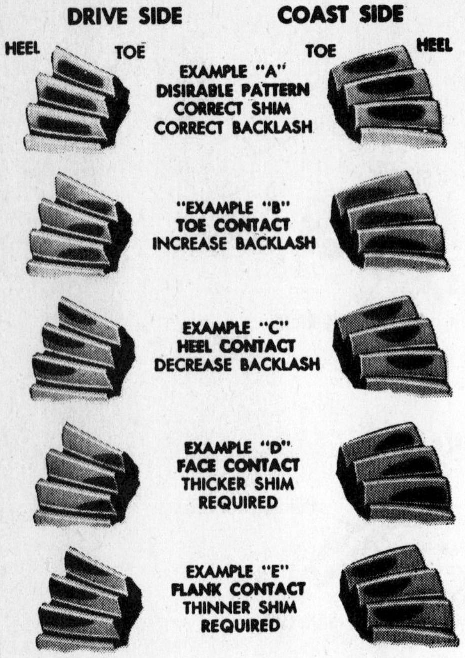

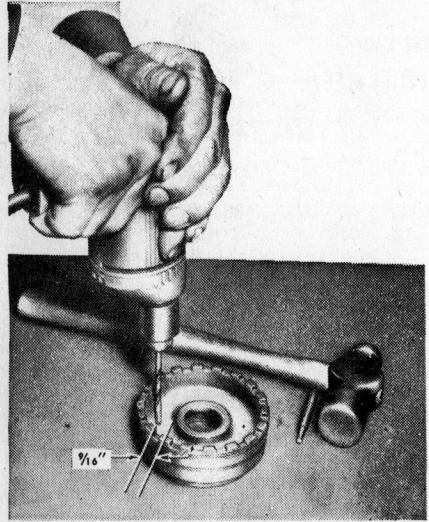

DRIVE SIDE   COAST SIDE

HEEL   TOE   TOE   HEEL

EXAMPLE "A" DISIRABLE PATTERN CORRECT SHIM CORRECT BACKLASH

"EXAMPLE "B" TOE CONTACT INCREASE BACKLASH

EXAMPLE "C" HEEL CONTACT DECREASE BACKLASH

EXAMPLE "D" FACE CONTACT THICKER SHIM REQUIRED

EXAMPLE "E" FLANK CONTACT THINNER SHIM REQUIRED

Fig. 10 Ring gear contact patterns

Fig. 12 Sealing drilled holes in adjusting sleeve with lead balls

DIFFERENTIAL CARRIER

For removal and installation of the differential carrier, refer to the *Power Train Section.*

Disassemble Carrier

1. Loosen lock tab and remove speedometer driven gear.
2. Remove differential carrier cover.
3. Remove side gear adjusting sleeves, Fig. 5.
4. Remove pinion adjusting sleeve, Fig. 6.
5. Remove pinion drive gear with bearings attached, Fig. 7.
6. Remove differential from carrier by shifting differential to one side of carrier and then turning 90 degrees in order to remove via the cover hole in carrier.

Inspection

1. Inspect all bearing cups, races and rollers for damage and wear, especially large end of rollers as this is where wear is most evident on taper roller bearings. *The rear axle pinion bearings are of the pre-loaded type, and the natural wear pattern is a slightly frosted condition with occasional slight scratches on races and rollers. This does not indicate a defective bearing.*
2. On Powerglide axles, inspect oil seal in stator support and at converter hub for evidence of wear or damage.
3. Inspect pinion splines for evidence of excessive wear.
4. Inspect ring gear and pinion teeth for scoring, chipping or cracking.
5. Check fit of differential side gears in case.
6. Check fit of side gear and U-joint shaft splines.
7. Inspect differential pinion shaft for scoring or evidence of excessive wear.
8. Inspect differential carrier for cracks or crossed threads.

AXLE REPAIRS

For Three Speed and Powerglide Axles

Note—Repairs required on three speed axles only, and those for Powerglide axles only are outlined further on. Refer to Fig. 8 for relationship of parts.

Pinion and Bearing, Replace

When it becomes necessary to replace pinion bearings and/or ring gear and drive pinion, it is necessary to re-establish the pinion mounting distance.

Pinion bearings may be removed with the aid of a press. It will be noted that a shim or shims are used between the pinion rear bearing and pinion. To determine the shim thickness to be used when installing new parts special gauges are required. Fig. 9. Lacking this equipment, check the ring gear contact pattern as shown in Fig. 10. To do this the differential carrier must be assembled. If a change is indicated, disassemble the parts and change the shimming as required to obtain the proper tooth contact pattern. Shims are available in thicknesses of .006, .009, .012, .015 and .018".

Pinion Front Bearing Race

Remove the old race with a punch. On Powerglide models it is necessary to remove the seal. Install a new race in the pinion adjusting sleeve using a suitable driver to push the race in place. Install a new seal on Powerglide units.

Side Bearing Adjusting Sleeve Bearing Race

1. Punch mark the side bearing adjusting sleeve at two places $\frac{9}{16}$" outboard from the seal bore 180° apart, Fig. 11.
2. Using a $\frac{9}{16}$" or smaller drill, drill through the adjusting sleeve at the punch mark locations until the drill is stopped by the bearing race.
3. Drive out the bearing race with a small pin punch.
4. Install a new bearing race in the sleeve with a suitable flat plate as a driver until the bearing race is flush.

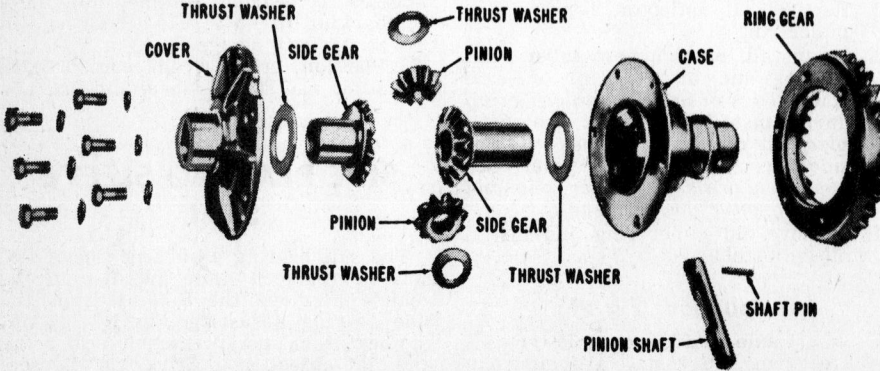

THRUST WASHER   THRUST WASHER   RING GEAR

COVER   SIDE GEAR   PINION   CASE

PINION   SIDE GEAR

THRUST WASHER   THRUST WASHER

SHAFT PIN

PINION SHAFT

Fig. 13 Differential assembly

Fig. 11 Drilling side bearing adjusting sleeves for bearing race removal

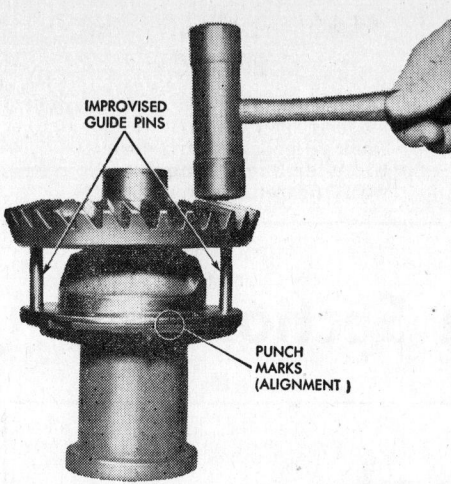

Fig. 14 Installing ring gear on differential case and cover, using improvised guide pins

5. Seal the drilled holes by using lead balls of at least .225″ diameter, Fig. 12. Balls of this type are commercially available for carburetor repair kits.

Differential Overhaul

Disassemble the differential as suggested by Fig. 13. To remove the differential pinions after the case has been separated, drive out the roll pin securing the differential pinion shaft to the case. *Before separating the differential case halves, punch mark the rim of both halves so that they may be attached in the original position, Fig. 14.* When securing the ring gear to the case, tighten all bolts to a torque of 40-60 ft. lbs. in a criss-cross pattern.

REPAIRS ON 3 SPEED TRANS. AXLES ONLY

Clutch Release Bearing Shaft Seal

Remove split ring and old seal from clutch release bearing shaft by prying out with a punch. Install the new seal, open side inward, using a suitable socket (¾″) and socket extension. Drive seal until it bottoms, then install split ring in clutch release bearing shaft.

Clutch Release Bearing Shaft and/or Pinion Bearing Rear Race

1. Place differential carrier in arbor press and press out shaft and race.
2. If a new shaft is being installed, first install the inner seal. Install a new seal ring in groove on outer diameter of bearing shaft and lubricate with vaseline.
3. Support differential carrier only on boss at clutch release bearing location with a suitable cylinder; then place bearing race on shaft and press both into differential carrier. Press until cup is flush with adjacent surface inside carrier.

REPAIRS ON POWER-GLIDE AXLES ONLY

Pinion Shaft Front Oil Seal and/or Converter Hub Oil Seal

The pinion shaft front oil seal and the converter hub oil seal are located diametrically opposite fore and aft. respectively, in the differential carrier.

Remove the oil seal by prying out with a punch or similar tool. Coat outer diameter of new seal with a non-hardening sealer and install seal. The converter hub seal is mounted flush. A special driver is available to install the pinion seal. A stop is provided on this driver which insures the seal being installed to the proper depth. This same driver (J-8340) is also used to drive the converter hub seal.

Pinion Shaft Rear Oil Seal

Drive out the old seal with a pin punch inserted through access hole in stator shaft. Install new seal as shown in Fig. 15 until it bottoms.

Pinion Shaft Bushing

Remove old bushing from inside diameter of pinion shaft using a chisel or other suitable tool. Use care not to damage the bushing mating surfaces in pinion shaft during removal.

Install new bushing with a suitable driver. Special tool J-8333 is available for this operation; it has a stop provided thereon to press the bushing to the proper depth.

Stator Shaft and/or Pinion Rear Bearing Race

1. Remove stator shaft and pinion bearing cup from carrier by placing carrier in a press and pressing downward on end of stator shaft. Replace parts removed.

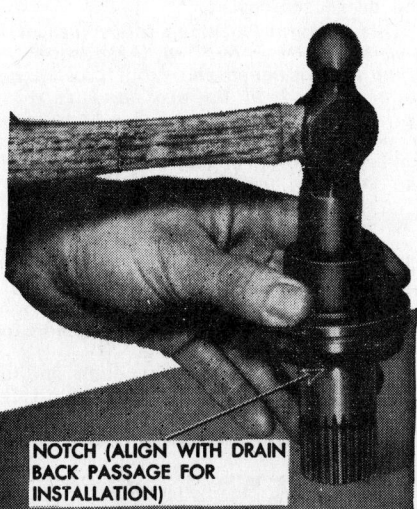

Fig. 15 Installing pinion rear oil seal in stator shaft

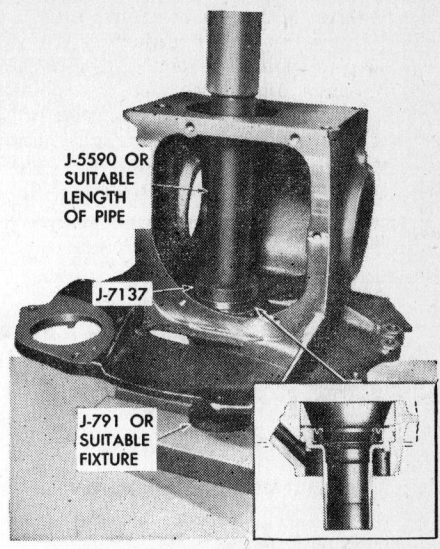

Fig. 16 Installing stator shaft and pinion rear bearing race

2. Install seal ring in groove on outside diameter of stator shaft and lubricate with vaseline. *Outer diameter seal is not used on later production stator shafts.*

3. If a new stator shaft is being installed, it will be necessary to install a new pinion rear oil seal as previously described.

4. Align notch in stator shaft, Fig. 15, with drain back passage boss in differential carrier. Place bearing race on stator shaft and press race and shaft into housing, Fig. 16. *Carrier must be supported only at stator shaft boss for this operation.*

ASSEMBLE DIFFERENTIAL CARRIER

1. Referring to Fig. 8, insert differential into carrier with side bearing cones installed on differential hubs.

2. While differential is loose in carrier, insert pinion into carrier through cover hole. Then engage pinion with ring gear and carefully position pinion rear bearing in race. On Powerglide models, care must be used not to damage seal at this location when pinion is installed.

3. Install new O-ring seals in side bearing adjusting sleeves. Coat adjusting sleeve threads with a non-hardening pipe thread compound. Loosely install sleeves in carrier with side bearings positioned in sleeves.

4. On Powerglide models, install a new O-ring seal in pinion adjusting sleeve. Position pinion so that its front bearing will pick up the bearing race in sleeve and loosely install sleeve in carrier. Use care not to damage seal lips when inserting pinion shaft over adjusting sleeve.

5. Tighten both side bearing adjusting sleeves and pinion adjusting sleeve to the point of contact between bearings and races. At this point, there should be no preload on any of the bearings and ring gear and pinion backlash should be just enough so that the pinion and dif-

ferential can be rotated easily and smoothly. The assembly is now ready for ring gear and pinion adjustment. *This adjustment, as well as checking ring gear and pinion backlash and other differential case operations is described in the Rear Axles Chapter.* Also refer to Fig. 10.

MASTER CYLINDER, REPLACE

1. Disconnect hydraulic lines from outlet end of cylinder.
2. Remove pedal return spring.
3. Unfasten 3 mounting nuts from dash wall and remove cylinder.

Suspension and Steering Section

SUSPENSION ADJUSTMENTS

Front Wheel Bearings

1. Raise car and remove cotter pin from spindle.
2. Tighten spindle nut to 80 inch lbs. (6 to 7 ft. lbs.) while rotating wheel.
3. Back off nut one flat (1/6 turn).
4. Insert cotter pin if slot in nut and hole in spindle align. If not, back off an additional ½ flat or less and insert cotter pin.
5. Spin wheel to make certain it rolls freely. *Wheel bearings should have .000" to .004" end play when properly adjusted.*

Front Wheel Camber

This is the first adjustment to be performed on the front suspension. The adjustment is made by means of shims between the upper control arm inner shaft and the front crossmember, Fig. 2. Although shims can be changed at either the front or rear attachment, it is important that the shimming be done equally so as to have no effect on caster. Adding shims at both front and rear of support shaft will decrease positive camber.

The procedure for adjustment is to loosen the upper support shaft-to-crossmember bolts and add or remove shims equally as required and retighten bolts. *It may be necessary to remove the wheel to secure these bolts.*

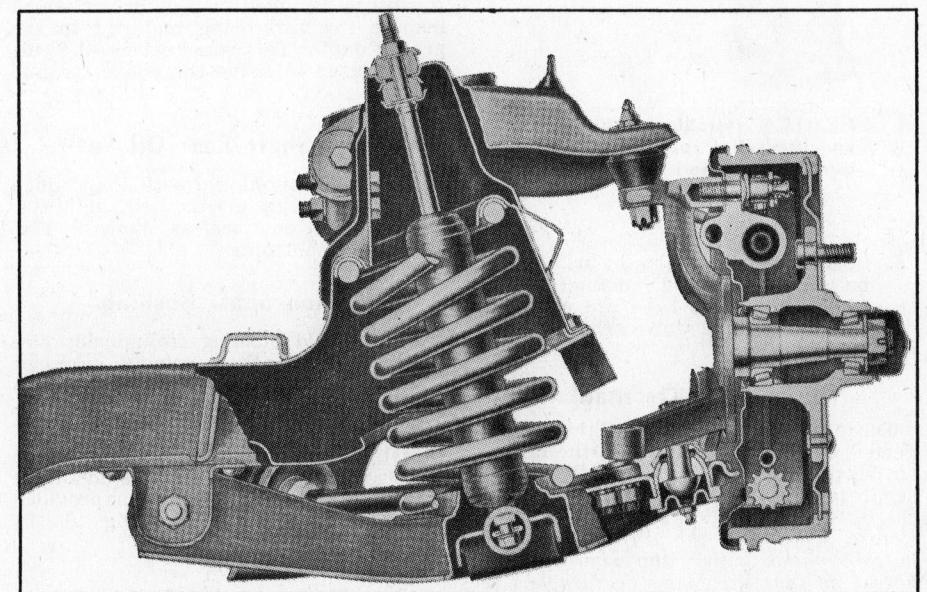

Fig. 1   Front suspension

Front Wheel Caster

Caster is adjusted by turning the two nuts at the rear of the strut rod, Fig. 3. Lengthening this rod by turning the nuts increases caster while shortening the rod decreases caster.

Due to manufacturing tolerances, it is possible to "run out" of threads on the strut rod or cause the front coil spring to be cocked in its seat and rub the spring tower. Only when this happens is it permissible to shim unevenly at the upper control arm. However, if this is the case, camber must be rechecked.

Front Wheel Toe-In

1. Set steering gear on high point, with "saw cut" in steering shaft coupling at 6 o'clock position and steering wheel positioned for straight ahead driving.
2. Loosen clamp bolt at each end of each tie rod individually and adjust toe-in to specifications. Tighten clamp bolts and remove equipment.

Rear Wheel Toe-In

Due to the design of this independently sprung rear axle and suspension, it will be necessary to check and adjust rear

wheel toe-in. *If drive on type equipment is used, reverse the vehicle and back it into position. Toe-in will be read as toe-out when vehicle is backwards because readings will be taken from the rear of the tires rather than the front. A tram may also be used in a similar procedure as that used on the front wheels except both sides will be adjusted at the same time. It must be pointed out, however, that since the wheels are adjusted by adding or removing shims at the front edge of the transmission, both wheels are adjusted at the same time.*

A $\frac{1}{16}$" shim added to each side will increase toe-in. Removal of a $\frac{1}{16}$" shim from each side will decrease toe-in. Shims must be added or removed in pairs so that there is always the same number at each point.

Toe-in should be 0" or minus ¼" per wheel. Due to manufacturing tolerances and parts "stack-up" it is possible to have toe-out on one wheel and toe-in on the opposite wheel. In this case, adjust the suspension to bring the wheel with the toe-out as close to specifications as possible but not letting the opposite wheel go out of specifications. For example, if one wheel toes-out by ¼", then the opposite wheel must toe in enough to give 0" to ¼" overall toe-in.

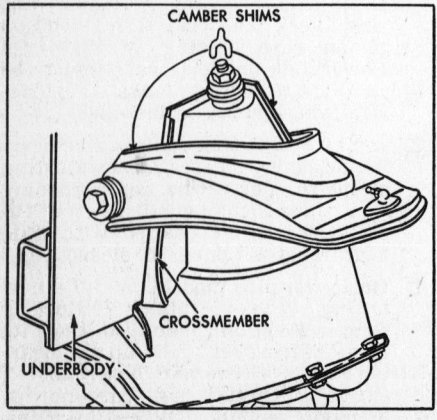

Fig. 2   Camber shim

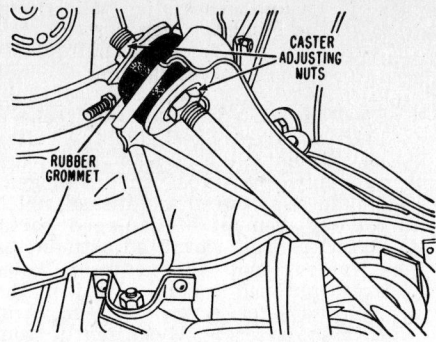

Fig. 3 Caster adjustment

Rear Wheel Camber

Rear wheel camber should be 1½° positive (plus or minus ½°). There is no provision for adjustment of this item and it is provided as a checking specification only.

If camber is not within limits, either the crossmember is out of alignment with the body or has become distorted due to collision, etc., or else the control arm has become distorted, bent, etc.

FRONT END REPAIRS

In servicing the front suspension, it will be desirable to raise the car on a hoist and the suspension allowed to swing free. If a twin post hoist or similar equipment is used, support the front of the vehicle at the forward end of the body side rail extension (each side) with jackstands and lower front of hoist.

Shock Absorber, Replace

1. With vehicle supported and front end hanging free, remove upper attaching nut, cup washer and grommet.
2. Remove two lower attaching bolts.
3. Withdraw shock absorber through lower control arm.
4. Reverse above procedure to install, extending shock absorber shaft to its full length to facilitate installation.

Upper Ball Joint

The upper ball joint is inspected for wear by checking the torque required to rotate the ball stud in the assembly. Support vehicle at outer end of lower control arm and remove wheel. Remove nut from upper control arm ball stud. Remove stud from steering knuckle. Raise control arm to clear knuckle and install a nut on the stud and measure torque required to turn stud. This should be a minimum of 2 ft. lbs. If excessive wear is indicated in upper joint, both upper and lower joints should be replaced. If a tight joint is suspected, 15 ft. lbs. is the maximum allowable torque with the joint well lubricated.

Lower Ball Joint

The lower ball joint is a loose fit in the assembly when not connected to the

steering knuckle. If inspection reveals that the upper joints are serviceable, inspect lower ball joints for excessive wear as follows:

1. With wheels resting on floor, measure distance from top of lube fitting to bottom of ball stud. Record dimensions for each side.
2. Now jack up car under outer end of each lower control arm and take same measurement.
3. If the difference in dimensions on either side is greater than $\frac{3}{32}$", the joint is excessively worn and both lower joints should be replaced. Another indication of lower joint wear is when difficulty is experienced when lubricating the joint. If the metal liner has worn to the point where the lubrication grooves in the liner have worn away, then abnormal pressure is required to force lubricant through the joint. This is another reason for replacing both lower joints.

   To test whether or not the stud is loose in the knuckle, remove the cotter pin and prick punch a mark on the nut and stud to identify relative location later. Then tighten nut to original position and observe torque reading. If less than 45 ft. lbs., stud may have been loose in the knuckle and both lower joints should be replaced.

Coil Spring, Replace

1. Raise vehicle and allow front control arms to swing free.
2. Remove shock absorber.
3. Remove strut rod nuts (pressed in).
4. *Loosen but do not remove* lower control arm inner pivot nut.
5. Place jackstand under inner end of control arm under bushing.
6. Remove control arm pivot nut and tap out pivot pin.
7. Lower hoist or jackstand until spring is free and take it out. *A bar placed through control arm and into spring tower will retain spring and keep it from slipping until free. Otherwise, keep clear of suspension until all compression is removed from spring.*

Reverse above procedure to replace the spring. When installing, place rubber

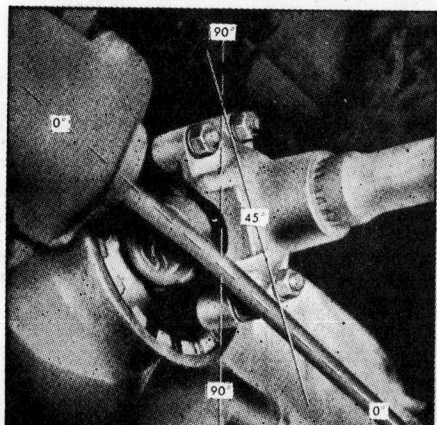

Fig. 4 Rear axle positioning for rear spring removal

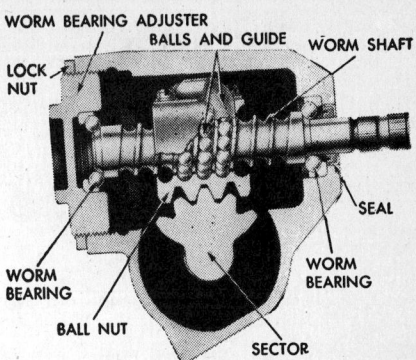

Fig. 5 Steering gear worm nut and ball circuits

spacer in place on top of spring and secure it friction tape. Step in spacer must contact end of spring.

The tension in the strut rod is due to the rubber grommet at the opposite end of the rod. Do not touch the large nuts at the grommet end as these control caster adjustment, Fig. 3.

Lower Control Arm and Ball Joint, Replace

To remove these parts, take out the coil spring as outlined above. Then remove lower ball joint nut and tap control arm to remove it and joint from knuckle. Use a suitable wrench to remove self-tapping joint from lower control arm. Reverse above procedure to install parts removed.

Upper Control Arm and Ball Joint, Replace

With wheel removed, remove nut from upper ball joint stud. Remove stud from knuckle. Remove two nuts retaining upper control arm shaft to crossmember. *Note number of shims at each bolt.*

To remove ball joint from control arm, cut off rivet heads, being careful not to enlarge holes in control arm. Tap out rivets and remove joint from control arm.

Install new joint, using special alloy bolts and nuts furnished with new ball joint. Tighten nuts to a torque of 20-25 ft. lbs.

When control arm has been installed, bounce front end of car to centralize bushings and tighten cross shaft bolts to a torque of 35-40 ft. lbs.

If ball joint was replaced or if proper number of shims were not reinstalled, recheck camber and caster.

REAR SUSPENSION REPAIRS

Shock Absorber, Replace

The attachment of the rear shock absorber is identical to the mounting of the front suspension. However, the rear shock absorber holds all of the rear spring compression. For this reason, the weight of the vehicle must be resting on the tires.

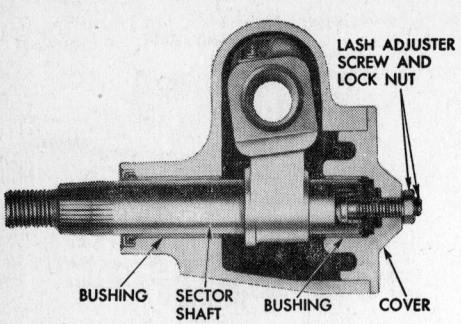

LASH ADJUSTER
SCREW AND
LOCK NUT

BUSHING SECTOR BUSHING COVER
SHAFT

Fig. 6 Steering gear pitman (sector) shaft

Place the car on a drive-on type hoist, frame contact hoist or place jack stands under the body at each side rail, just forward of the rear wheel openings. The body should be raised high enough so that the wheels hang free and a floor jack can be placed under the tire. With a second jack, raise tire so that it is in normal position. This will allow shock absorber to be removed without interfering with the floor.

Coil Spring, Replace

1. Raise vehicle by body side rails so that control arms may swing free. Vehicle must be raised enough to allow a rolling floor jack to be placed under brake drum.
2. Loosen control arm cross shaft bolts (in ends of shaft). Remove bolt that holds brake hose bracket to underbody. It may also be necessary to disconnect and plug fuel line and heater fuel supply line (on left side only). Remove wheel. Replace nuts on studs to hold drum in place.
3. Position axle as shown in Fig. 4 to allow axle shaft and control arm to swing down far enough to remove spring.
4. Place rolling jack under brake drum. Raise jack slightly to place a light load on spring. Remove shock absorber.
5. Carefully lower floor jack until spring is free. *Do not remove or lower jack too far as this places too much strain on axle shaft and brake hose.*
6. Reverse above procedure to install and lower vehicle to floor. Bounce rear end several times and tighten cross shaft bolts to a torque of 45-55 ft. lbs.

Lower Control Arm, Replace

1. Remove coil spring as outlined above.
2. Before removing floor jack from under drum, support control arm with a jack stand without placing strain on brake hose.
3. Remove brake drum.
4. With a screwdriver, shift upper end of a brake shoe onto the brake anchor, which will allow axle flange plate and axle shaft to be pulled out past parking brake strut.
5. Remove backing plate nuts.
6. Pry between axle flange plate and

backing plate until axle shaft and U-joint can be pulled out of case.
7. Remove U-joint bolts.
8. Remove bolt from end of axle shaft.
9. Remove U-joint yoke and withdraw axle shaft.
10. Remove backing plate from lower control arm studs. Tie backing plate up to crossmember.
11. Unfasten control arm from crossmember (4 bolts). A parking brake cable is also attached to two of these bolts. Remove control arm.
12. Reverse above procedure to install parts removed.

STEERING GEAR

Adjustments

Before attempting steering gear adjustments in an attempt to correct such conditions as shimmy, loose or hard steering or road shocks, make a careful check of front end alignment, shock absorbers, wheel balance and tire pressure for possible causes.

Only two adjustments are possible on the steering gear, Fig. 5, but they must be made in the following manner, step by step, in the order given.

1. Loosen pitman shaft lash adjuster screw lock nut, Fig. 6, and turn lash adjuster screw a few turns counterclockwise to remove over-center load (increase lash). Gently turn the wheel in one direction until stopped by the gear and then back off one turn of the steering wheel.
2. Pry off the horn button. Using a suitable size socket and a low reading (inch lb.) torque wrench on the steering shaft nut, measure the torque needed to keep the wheel in motion. This should be 2 to 6 inch lbs. If the torque does not fall within these limits, adjustment of the worm bearing is necessary.
3. To adjust the worm bearing, Fig. 5, loosen the worm bearing adjuster

lock nut and turn the adjuster down until there is no perceptible end play in the worm. Check the pull at the torque wrench, readjusting the nut as necessary to obtain proper pull. Tighten the lock nut and recheck pull. If the gear feels "lumpy" after adjustment, the bearings are probably damaged and the gear should be removed and disassembled for replacement of damaged parts.
4. After proper worm adjustment is obtained, and all mounting bolts are tightened securely, adjust the lash adjuster screw, Fig. 6. First turn the steering wheel gently from one stop all the way to the other, counting the total number of turns. Then turn the wheel back exactly half way to the center position. The mark on the worm shaft should be at the 6 o'clock position. The sawcut in the coupling should be lined up with this mark. Turn the lash adjuster screw clockwise to take out all lash in the gear teeth, then tighten lock nut. Check the highest torque needed to turn the wheel through the center position. Torque should be between 7 and 12 inch lbs.
5. Tighten lock nut and recheck. *Always make the final lash adjustment in the clockwise direction.*
6. Make sure wheels are straight ahead and connect pitman arm to pitman shaft.

Steering Wheel, Replace

1. Pry out horn button.
2. Remove three screws attaching receiver cup and bushing spacer to steering wheel, then remove flat belleville spring.
3. Remove nut and washer from steering shaft.
4. Use puller to remove wheel. *Do not lose spring or seat located under steering wheel.*
5. Turn signal canceling cam may be removed if desired.

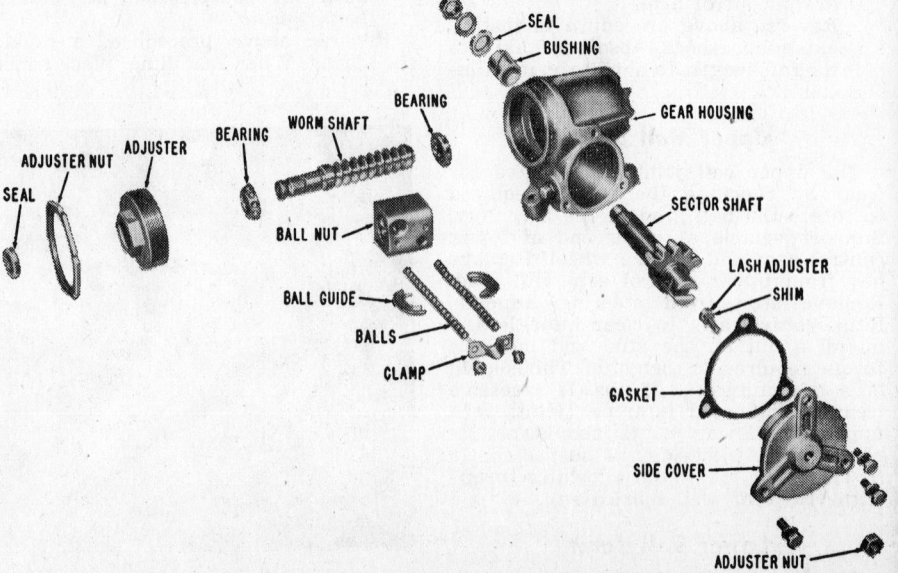

SEAL
BUSHING
BEARING
WORM SHAFT
BEARING
GEAR HOUSING
ADJUSTER NUT
ADJUSTER
BEARING
SEAL
BALL NUT
SECTOR SHAFT
LASH ADJUSTER
SHIM
BALL GUIDE
BALLS
CLAMP
GASKET
SIDE COVER
ADJUSTER NUT

Fig. 7 Exploded view of steering gear

6. Reverse above procedure to install, making sure that mark on steering shaft lines up with mark on steering wheel.

Steering Gear, Replace

1. Disconnect pitman arm from pitman shaft.
2. Unfasten steering gear from frame (3 bolts).
3. Unfasten steering shaft coupling (3 bolts) and slide steering gear forward and down, removing it from car.
4. Reverse above procedure to install steering gear.

Steering Gear, Overhaul

1. Referring to Fig. 7, turn pitman shaft adjuster a few turns counterclockwise. This will remove load from worm bearings caused by the close meshing of rack and sector teeth.
2. Turn worm bearing adjuster counterclockwise a few turns.
3. Unfasten and remove side cover and pitman shaft. *If sector does not clear opening in housing easily, turn worm shaft by hand until sector will pass through opening in housing.*
4. Remove worm bearing adjuster, lock nut and lower bearing from housing.
5. Draw worm shaft and nut assembly from housing. Remove upper bearing. *Use care that ball nut does not run down to either end of worm. Damage will be done to ends of ball guides if nut is allowed to rotate until stopped at end of worm.*
6. Unscrew lash adjuster from side cover. Slide adjuster and shim out of slot in end of pitman shaft.
7. If the ball bearing nut is perfectly free with no indication of binding or tightness when rotated on worm, do not disassemble. However, if these conditions exist, remove clamp and draw guide out of nut. Turn nut upside down and rotate worm shaft back and forth until all 36 balls have dropped out of nut. With balls removed, nut can be pulled endwise off worm.
8. Reverse above procedure to assemble the steering gear and adjust as outlined previously. When assembling lash adjuster, place shim in slot in end of sector shaft. Check end clearance which should not exceed .002. For adjusting purposes, shims of four thicknesses (.063, .065, .067 and .069″) are available.

Instruments & Windshield Wiper

INSTRUMENT CLUSTER

1. Disconnect battery ground cable from battery.
2. Remove the connectors from back of instrument cluster and pull harness out of retaining clips on back of cluster.
3. Disconnect speedometer cable.
4. Remove light switch and from beneath dash remove nut attaching lighter (if equipped) and withdraw lighter.
5. Lower mast jacket and steering wheel assembly from instrument panel or remove steering wheel on 3-speed models or steering wheel and turn signal housing on automatic transmission models to give clearance for cluster removal.
6. Remove cluster attaching screws and remove the cluster, instrument center panel and seal by pulling straight out, turning slightly to clear transmission range selector.
7. Remove two harness clips from back of cluster.
8. Remove screws attaching the cluster back to the cluster.
9. Remove instruments and speedometer as required.

WINDSHIELD WIPER

1. Remove retainer securing drive link to wiper motor drive arm.
2. If equipped with a washer, note location of washer hoses to wiper motor, then remove hoses from motor from inside front compartment. Also remove electrical connectors from motor.
3. Remove screws securing motor to the body and remove motor.
4. To install, reverse above procedure. *It is important that the three screws attaching motor be fully tightened so that the sleeves surrounding the screws bottoms to prevent "floating" of the motor.*

DODGE & DART

INDEX OF SERVICE OPERATIONS

PAGE NO.

ACCESSORIES
Radio Removal 695
Speedometer 695
Windshield Wiper 694
Windshield Wiper Troubles...........37

BODY
Air Conditioning 177
Automatic Seat Adjuster Troubles......36
Automatic Top Troubles.............36
Automatic Window Lift Troubles......36

BRAKES (Mechanical)
Adjustments 112
Brake Cylinder Sizes...............646
Hydraulic Brake System.............112
Master Cylinder, Replace...........688
Trouble Shooting 31

BRAKES (Power)
Power Unit, Replace...............688
Power Unit Repairs.................128
Trouble Shooting 32

CLUTCH
Clutch Pedal, Adjust...............677
Clutch Service 677
Trouble Shooting 13

COOLING SYSTEM
Radiator, Replace 669
Trouble Shooting 8
Water Distributor Tube, Replace......670
Water Pump Repairs................669
Water Pump, Replace...............669

ELECTRIC SYSTEM
Alternator Specifications 666
Alternator Service 57
Dash Gauge Service 85
Distributor, Replace...............670
Distributor Service 46
Distributor Specifications...........649
Generator Regulator Service 62
Generator Regulator Specifications....650
Generator Service 62
Generator Specifications...........650
Horn Button or Ring, Replace.......692
Ignition System Service............46
Ignition Timing 671
Starter, Replace 671
Starter Switch Service............83
Starting Motor Service 77
Starting Motor Specifications........647
Trouble Shooting 10
Turn Signal Troubles..............12

PAGE NO.

ENGINE
Camshaft 663
Crankshaft Oil Seal, Replace........666
Cylinder Head, Replace............652
Engine Bearing Specifications.......646
Engine, Replace..................652
Main Bearings, Replace............665
Piston Pins, Replace..............664
Piston Rings, Replace.............665
Piston & Ring Specifications........646
Pistons & Rods, Remove...........664
Piston & Rod, Assemble...........664
Pistons, Replace.................664
Rocker Arm, Replace.............656
Rod Bearings, Replace............665
Timing Case Cover, Replace........661
Timing Chain, Replace............662
Trouble Shooting 4
Valve Arrangement 656
Valves, Adjust 655
Valves, Grind 660
Valve Guides 659
Valve Lifters 660
Valves, Remove 658
Valve Seat Inserts, Replace........660
Valve Spring Installed Height.......658
Valve Spring Testing..............659
Valve Timing Data 663
Valve Specifications 645

ENGINE OILING
Oil Pan, Replace.................666
Oil Pressure Regulator............669
Oil Pump Repairs................668
Oil Pump, Replace...............667
Trouble Shooting 4

FRONT SUSPENSION
Camber, Adjust 688
Caster, Adjust 688
Front End Repairs...............689
Toe-in, Adjust 689
Trouble Shooting 33
Wheel Alignment Specifications.......651
Wheel Bearings, Adjust...........689

FUEL & EXHAUST SYSTEM
Carburetors 671
Fuel Pumps 96
Mufflers And Pipes..............671
Trouble Shooting 4

OVERDRIVE 100
Trouble Shooting 14

PAGE NO.

REAR AXLE
Non-Slip Differentials 109
Axle Shaft, Replace...............687
General Service 102
Rear Axle Repairs................686
Rear Axle Specifications...........646
Trouble Shooting 31

SPECIFICATIONS
Alternator 666
Brake Cylinder Sizes..............646
Capacity Data 648
Carburetors 673
Cooling System 648
Crankshaft 646
Distributors 649
Engine Tightening 647
Generator & Regulators...........650
Main Bearings 646
Pistons, Pins & Rings 646
Rear Axle 646
Rod Bearings 646
Starting Motors 647
Tune Up 644
Valves 645
Valve Timing 663
Wheel Alignment 651

STEERING GEARS (Mechanical)
Horn Button or Ring, Replace.......692
Steering Gear Repairs.............693
Steering Gear, Replace............693
Steering Wheel, Replace..........692
Trouble Shooting 33

STEERING GEARS (Power)
Steering Gear Repairs.............145
Steering Gear, Replace............694
Trouble Shooting 34

TRANSMISSION
(Manual Shift)
Gearshift, Adjust 680
Transmission Repairs 678
Transmission, Replace 678
Trouble Shooting 14

TRANSMISSION (Automatic)
Powerflite, Replace 681
  Linkage, Adjust 681
  Push Button Control 683
  Repairs 297
  Trouble Shooting 21
Torqueflite V8, Replace...........683
Torqueflite V8 Repairs............341
Torqueflite 6, Replace...........684
Torqueflite 6 Repairs............331
  Linkage, Adjust 685
  Push Button Control 684
  Trouble Shooting 23

TUNE UP 38

GENERAL SPECIFICATIONS

Year	Model Designation	Wheelbase, Inches	Valve Location	Bore and Stroke	Piston Displacement, Cubic Inches	Compression Ratio (Standard)	Maximum Brake H.P. @ R.P.M.	Maximum Torque Lbs. Ft. @ R.P.M.	Normal Oil Pressure Pounds
DODGE									
1953	Coronet V8 . . . . D44	119	In Head	3.4375 x 3.250	241.3	7.1	140 @ 4400	220 @ 2000	45
	Coronet V8 . . . . D48	114	In Head	3.4375 x 3.250	241.3	7.1	140 @ 4400	220 @ 2000	45
	Coronet 6 . . . . D46	119	In Block	3.2500 x 4.625	230.2	7.0	103 @ 3600	190 @ 1200	45
	Meadowbrook 6 . . . . D46	119	In Block	3.2500 x 4.625	230.2	7.0	103 @ 3600	190 @ 1200	45
	Meadowbrook 6 . . . . D47	114	In Block	3.2500 x 4.625	230.2	7.0	103 @ 3600	190 @ 1200	45
1954	Meadowbrook V8 . . D-50-1, 1A	119	In Head	3.4375 x 3.250	241.3	7.10	140 @ 4400	220 @ 2000	45
	Coronet V8 . . . . D-50-2	119	In Head	3.4375 x 3.250	241.3	7.50	150 @ 4400	222 @ 2400	45
	Royal V8 . . . . D-50-3	119	In Head	3.4375 x 3.250	241.3	7.50	150 @ 4400	222 @ 2400	45
	Meadowbrook 6 . . . . D-51-1, 1A	119	In Block	3.2500 x 4.625	230.2	7.25	110 @ 3600	190 @ 1600	45
	Coronet 6 . . . . D-51-2	119	In Block	3.2500 x 4.625	230.2	7.25	110 @ 3600	190 @ 1600	45
	Coronet Suburban 6 . . . . . . D-52	①	In Block	3.2500 x 4.625	230.2	7.25	110 @ 3600	190 @ 1600	45
	Coronet Sport Coupe V8 D-53-2	114	In Head	3.4375 x 3.250	241.3	7.50	150 @ 4400	222 @ 2400	45
	Royal Sport Coupe V8 . . D-53-3	114	In Head	3.4375 x 3.250	241.3	7.50	150 @ 4400	222 @ 2400	45
1955	Coronet 6 . . . . D-56-1	120	In Block	3.2500 x 4.625	230	7.4	123 @ 3600	194 @ 1600	45
	Coronet V8 . . . . D-55-1	120	In Head	3.6250 x 3.250	270	7.6	175 @ 4400	240 @ 2400	45
	Royal V8 . . . . D-55-2	120	In Head	3.6250 x 3.250	270	7.6	175 @ 4400	240 @ 2400	45
	Custom Royal V8 . . . . . . D-55-3	120	In Head	3.6250 x 3.250	270	7.6	183 @ 4400	245 @ 2400	45
1956	Coronet 6 . . . . D-62-1	120	In Block	3.2500 x 4.625	230	7.6	131 @ 3800	203 @ 2000	40–45
	Coronet V8 . . . . D-63-1	120	In Head	3.6250 x 3.250	270	8.0	189 @ 4400	266 @ 2400	50–65
	Royal V8 (2-Bar. Carb.) . D63-2	120	In Head	3.6250 x 3.812	315	8.0	218 @ 4400	309 @ 2000	50–65
	Royal V8 (4-Bar. Carb.) . D63-2	120	In Head	3.6250 x 3.812	315	8.0	230 @ 4400	316 @ 2400	50–65
	Cust. Roy.(2-Bar. Carb.) . D63-3	120	In Head	3.6250 x 3.812	315	8.0	218 @ 4400	309 @ 2000	50–65
	Cust. Roy.(4-Bar. Carb.) . D63-3	120	In Head	3.6250 x 3.812	315	8.0	230 @ 4400	316 @ 2400	50–65
	"500" V8 . . . . D-500	120	In Head	3.6250 x 3.812	315	9.25	260 @ 4800	330 @ 3000	50–65
1957	Coronet 6 . . . . D72	122	In Block	3.2500 x 4.625	230	8.0	138 @ 4000	208 @ 1600	50–65
	Coronet V8 . . . . D66	122	In Head	3.6875 x 3.797	325	8.5	245 @ 4400	320 @ 2400	50–65
	Royal V8 . . . . D67-1	122	In Head	3.6875 x 3.797	325	8.5	245 @ 4400	320 @ 2400	50–65
	Custom Royal V8 . . . . . . D67-2	122	In Head	3.6875 x 3.797	325	8.5	260 @ 4400	335 @ 2800	50–65
	Suburban V8 . . . . D70-71	122	In Head	3.6875 x 3.797	325	8.5	245 @ 4400	320 @ 2400	50–65
	"500" D500	122	In Head	3.6875 x 3.797	325	9.25	285 @ 4800	345 @ 2800	50–65
	"500" (Special Kit) D500	122	In Head	3.6875 x 3.797	325	9.25	310 @ 4800	350 @ 3200	50–65
1958	Coronet 6 . . . . LD1-L	122	In Block	3.2500 x 4.625	230	8.0	138 @ 4000	208 @ 1600	40–65
	Coronet V8 . . . . LD2-L	122	In Head	3.6875 x 3.797	325	9.0	252 @ 4400	345 @ 2400	40–65
	Royal V8 . . . . LD2-M	122	In Head	3.6875 x 3.797	325	9.0	265 @ 4400	355 @ 2800	40–65
	Custom Royal V8 . . . . . LD3-H	122	In Head	4.0625 x 3.375	350	10.0	295 @ 4600	385 @ 2800	50–65
	Custom Sierra V8 . . . . . LD3-H	122	In Head	4.0625 x 3.375	350	10.0	295 @ 4600	385 @ 2800	50–65
	Suburban V8 . . . . LD3-L	122	In Head	4.0625 x 3.375	350	10.0	295 @ 4600	385 @ 2800	50–65
	Sierra V8 . . . . LD3-L	122	In Head	4.0625 x 3.375	350	10.0	295 @ 4600	385 @ 2800	50–65
	D500 (Engine Package)	122	In Head	4.1250 x 3.375	361	10.0	320 @ 4800	400 @ 2800	50–65
1959	Coronet 6 . . . . MD1-L	122	In Block	3.2500 x 4.625	230	8.0	135 @ 3600	205 @ 1200	40–45
	Coronet V8 . . . . MD2-L	122	In Head	3.9531 x 3.312	326	9.2	255 @ 4400	350 @ 2400	45–65
	Royal V8 . . . . MD3-M	122	In Head	4.1250 x 3.375	361	10.1	295 @ 4600	390 @ 2400	45–65
	Custom Royal V8 . . . . . MD3-H	122	In Head	4.1250 x 3.375	361	10.1	305 @ 4600	400 @ 2800	45–65
	Std. Sierra V8 . . . . . . MD3-L	122	In Head	4.1250 x 3.375	361	10.1	295 @ 4600	390 @ 2400	45–65
	Cust. Sierra V8 . . . . . MD3-H	122	In Head	4.1250 x 3.375	361	10.1	305 @ 4600	400 @ 2800	45–65
	D-500 (Engine Package)	122	In Head	4.2500 x 3.375	383	10.0	320 @ 4600	420 @ 2800	45–65
	Super D-500 (Engine Package)	122	In Head	4.2500 x 3.375	383	10.0	345 @ 5000	420 @ 3600	45–65
1960	Matador V8	122	In Head	4.1250 x 3.375	361	10.0	295 @ 4600	390 @ 2400	45–65
	Polara V8	122	In Head	4.2500 x 3.375	383	10.0	325 @ 4800	420 @ 2800	45–65
	D-500 (Engine Package)	122	In Head	4.2500 x 3.375	383	10.0	330 @ 4800	460 @ 2800	45–65
1961	V8-361 . . . . 2 Bar. Carb.	122	In Head	4.1250 x 3.375	361	9.0	265 @ 4400	380 @ 2400	45–65
	V8-383 . . . . 4 Bar. Carb.	122	In Head	4.2500 x 3.375	383	10.0	325 @ 4600	425 @ 2800	45–65
	V8-383 . . . . Ram Induction	122	In Head	4.2500 x 3.375	383	10.0	330 @ 4800	460 @ 2800	45–65

GENERAL SPECIFICATIONS continued

Year	Model Designation	Wheelbase, Inches	Valve Location	Bore and Stroke	Piston Displacement, Cubic Inches	Compression Ratio (Standard)	Maximum Brake H.P. @ R.P.M.	Maximum Torque Lbs. Ft. @ R.P.M.	Normal Oil Pressure Pounds
DART									
1960	Seneca & Pioneer 6..........	②	In Head	3.4062 x 4.125	225	8.5	145 @ 4000	215 @ 2800	40–65
	Seneca & Pioneer V8........	②	In Head	3.9062 x 3.312	318	9.0	230 @ 4400	340 @ 2400	50
	Phoenix V8.................	118	In Head	3.9062 x 3.312	318	9.0	230 @ 4400	340 @ 2400	50
	Phoenix V8 ③.............	118	In Head	4.1250 x 3.375	361	10.0	310 @ 4800	435 @ 2800	45–65
	Phoenix V8 ③.............	118	In Head	4.2500 x 3.375	383	10.0	330 @ 4800	420 @ 2800	45–65
1961	Six Cylinder④.............	②	In Head	3.4062 x 4.125	225	8.2	145 @ 4000	215 @ 2800	40–65
	V8-318④........2 Bar. Carb.	②	In Head	3.9062 x 3.312	318	9.0	230 @ 4400	340 @ 2400	50
	V8-318④........4 Bar. Carb.	②	In Head	3.9062 x 3.312	318	9.0	260 @ 4400	345 @ 2800	50

①—Two door, 114″; four door, 119″.　　②—Cars 118″, Station Wagons 122″.　　③—D-500 power package with two 4-barrel carburetors.
④—This engine available in all models.

TUNE UP SPECIFICATIONS

Year	Model	Ground Polarity and Voltage	Spark Plug Type ①	Spark Plug Gap Inch	Distributor Point Gap Inch	Distributor Cam Angle Degrees	Firing Order ②	Ignition Timing Mark	Ignition Timing Location	Idle Speed RPM In Neutral	Compression Pressure @ Cranking Speed Minimum
DODGE											
1953	Six	P-6	AR-8	.035	.020	39	153624	2° BTDC	Damper	475	120
	V8	P-6	4S-140	.035	.017	⑧	18436572	4° BTDC	Pulley	475	125
1954	Six	P-6	4S-140	.035	.020	39	153624	2° BTDC	Damper	475	120
	V8	P-6	4S-140	.035	.017	⑧	18436572	4° BTDC	Pulley	475	125
1955	Six	P-6	4S-140	.035	.020	39	153624	2° BTDC	Damper	475	120
	V8	P-6	4S-165	.035	.017	⑧	18436572	4° BTDC	Pulley	475	125
1956	Six	N-12	AR-80	.035	.020	39	153624	2° BTDC	Damper	475	120
	Coronet V8	N-12	AR-52	.035	.017	31	18436572	4° BTDC	Pulley	475	125
	Royal V8	N-12	AR-52	.035	.017	31	18436572	6° BTDC	Pulley	475	125
	D-500	N-12	4S-250	.035	.017	④	18436572	2° BTDC	Damper	475	125
1957	Six	N-12	AR-51	.035	.020	39	153624	TDC	Damper	475	120
	Red Ram	N-12	AR-42	.035	.017	29	18436572	4° BTDC	Pulley	475	125
	Super R. R.	N-12	AR-42	.035	.017	29	18436572	6° BTDC	Pulley	475	125
	D-500	N-12	AR-42	.035	.017	④	18436572	2° BTDC	Pulley	475	125
1958	LD1	N-12	AR-51	.035	.020	39	153624	2° BTDC	Damper	475	120
	LD2	N-12	AGR-42	.035	.017	29	18436572	6° BTDC	Pulley	475	125
	LD3	N-12	AR-42	.035	.017	④	18436572	6° BTDC	Damper	475	160
	D500	N-12	AR-32	.035	.017	④	18436572	8° BTDC	Damper	475	160
1959	MD1	N-12	AR-51	.035	.020	39	153624	2½° BTDC	Damper	475	120
	MD2	N-12	AR-42	.035	.017	29	18436572	10° BTDC	Pulley	475	125
	MD3	N-12	A-42	.035	.017	29	18436572	10° BTDC	Damper	475	160
	D-500	N-12	A-32	.035	.017	29	18436572	10° BTDC	Damper	475	160
1960	Matador	N-12	A-42	.035	.017	27–32	18436572	⑥	Damper	485	160
	Polara	N-12	A-42	.035	.017	27–32	18436572	⑥	Damper	485	160
	D-500	N-12	A-32	.035	.017	27–32	18436572	7½° BTDC	Damper	530⑤	160
1961	V8-361	N-12	A-42	.035	.017	27–32	18436572	10° BTDC	Damper	500	160

Year	Model	Ground Polarity and Voltage	Spark Plug Type ①	Spark Plug Gap Inch	Distributor Point Gap Inch	Distributor Cam Angle Degrees	Firing Order ②	Ignition Timing Mark	Ignition Timing Location	Idle Speed RPM In Neutral	Compression Pressure @ Cranking Speed Minimum
DART											
1960	6-Cylinder	N-12	AG-42	.035	.020	36–42	153624	2½°BTDC	Damper	485	120
	V8-318 Std.Tr.	N-12	A-42	.035	.017	27–32	18436572	5° BTDC	Pulley	545	125
	V8-318 Auto.Tr.	N-12	A-42	.035	.017	27–32	18436572	10° BTDC	Pulley	485	125
	V8-361	N-12	A-32	.035	.017	27–32	18436572	7½°BTDC	Damper	530⑤	160
	V8-383	N-12	A-32	.035	.017	27–32	18436572	⑥	Damper	530⑤	160
1961	Six Cyl	N-12	AG-52	.035	.020	40–45	153624	2½°BTDC	Damper	550	120
	V8 Std. Tr.	N-12	A-42	.035	.017	27–32	18436572	5° BTDC	Pulley	500	125
	V8 Auto Tr.	N-12	A-42	.035	.017	27–32	18436572	10° BTDC	Pulley	500	125

①—Auto-Lite.
②—V8 cylinder numbering (front to rear): Left bank 1-3-5-7, right bank 2-4-6-8.
③—Each set 26–28, total dwell both sets 32–36.
④—Each set 29–32, total dwell both sets 36–39.
⑤—In Drive.
⑥—With IBP-4005C distributor 12½°BTDC; with IBP-4005D 10°BTDC.

VALVE SPECIFICATIONS

Year	Model	Valve Lash Int.	Valve Lash Exh.	Valve Angles Seat	Valve Angles Face	Valve Spring Installed Height	Valve Spring Pressure Lbs. @ In.	Valve Lift Int.	Valve Lift Exh.	Stem Clearance Intake	Stem Clearance Exhaust	Stem Diameter Int.	Stem Diameter Exh.
DODGE													
1953	Six	.010H	.010H	45	45	1¾	115 @ 1⅜	.350	.350	.001–.003	.001–.003	.3405	.3405
	V8	Zero	Zero	45	45	1¹¹⁄₁₆①	105 @ 1⁵⁄₁₆①	.360	.364	.001–.003	.002–.004	.3725	.3715
1954	Six	.010H	.010H	45	45	1¾	115 @ 1⅜	.365	.365	.001–.003	.003–.005	.3405	.3405
	V8	Zero	Zero	45	45	1¹¹⁄₁₆①	105 @ 1⁵⁄₁₆①	.365	.365	.001–.003	.002–.004	.3725	.3715
1955	Six	.010H	.010H	45	45	1¾	115 @ 1⅜	.365	.365	.001–.003	.003–.005	.340	.340
	D55-1, 2	Zero	Zero	45	45	1¹¹⁄₁₆	140 @ 1⁵⁄₁₆	.360	.360	.001–.003	.002–.004	.370	.370
	D55-3	Zero	Zero	45	45	1¹¹⁄₁₆①	105 @ 1⁵⁄₁₆①	.360	.360	.001–.003	.002–.004	.370	.370
1956	Six	.010H	.010H	45	45	1¾	115 @ 1⅜	.379	.365	.001–.003	.003–.005	.340	.340
	D63	Zero	Zero	45	45	1¹¹⁄₁₆	140 @ 1⁵⁄₁₆	.360	.360	.001–.003	.002–.004	.370	.370
	D500	.012H	.022H	45	45	1²¹⁄₃₂①	158 @ 1⁷⁄₃₂①	.400	.409	.001–.003	.002–.004	.370	.370
1957	Six	.010H	.010H	45	45	1¾	115 @ 1⅜	.365	.365	.001–.003	.003–.005	.340	.340
	V8	Zero	Zero	45	45	1¹¹⁄₁₆	166 @ 1⁵⁄₁₆	.389	.389	.001–.003	.002–.004	.370	.370
	D500	Zero	Zero	45	45	1¹¹⁄₁₆	175 @ 1⁵⁄₁₆	.388	.388	.001–.003	.002–.004	.370	.370
	D500-1	.015H	.024H	45	45	1²¹⁄₃₂①	158 @ 1⁷⁄₃₂①	.444	.435	.001–.003	.002–.004	.370	.370
1958	Six	.010H	.010H	45	45	1¾	115 @ 1⅜	.365	.365	.001–.003	.003–.005	.340	.340
	LD-2	Zero	Zero	45	45	1¹¹⁄₁₆	166 @ 1⁵⁄₁₆	.389	.389	.001–.003	.002–.004	.370	.370
	LD-3, D500	Zero	Zero	45	45	1⁵⁵⁄₆₄	195 @ 1¹⁵⁄₃₂	.390	.390	.001–.003	.002–.004	.370	.370
1959	Six	.010H	.010H	45	45	1¾	115 @ 1⅜	.365	.365	.001–.003	.003–.005	.340	.340
	MD2	Zero	Zero	45	45	1¹¹⁄₁₆	166 @ 1⁵⁄₁₆	.390	.386	.001–.003	.002–.004	.373	.372
	MD3, D500	Zero	Zero	45	45	1⁵⁵⁄₆₄	195 @ 1¹⁵⁄₃₂	.390	.390	.001–.003	.002–.004	.373	.372
1960–61	D500	Zero	Zero	45	45	1⁵⁵⁄₆₄	205 @ 1⁷⁄₁₆	.430	.430	.001–.003	.002–.004	.373	.372
	Others	Zero	Zero	45	45	1⁵⁵⁄₆₄	195 @ 1¹⁵⁄₃₂	.389	.389	.001–.003	.002–.004	.373	.372
DART													
1960	Six	.010H	.020H	④	④	1¹¹⁄₁₆	177 @ 1⁵⁄₁₆	.362	.345	.001–.003	.002–.004	.373	.372
	V8-318②	.010H	.018H	45	45	1¹¹⁄₁₆	177 @ 1⁵⁄₁₆	.370	.368	.001–.003	.002–.004	.373	.372
	V8-318②	.010H	.018H	45	45	1¹¹⁄₁₆	177 @ 1⁵⁄₁₆	.390	.389	.001–.003	.002–.004	.373	.372
	V8-361	Zero	Zero	45	45	1⁵⁵⁄₆₄	195 @ 1¹⁵⁄₃₂	.389	.389	.001–.003	.002–.004	.370	.370
	V8-383	Zero	Zero	45	45	1⁵⁵⁄₆₄	205 @ 1⁷⁄₁₆	.430	.430	.001–.003	.002–.004	.373	.372
1961	Six	.010H	.020H	④	④	1¹¹⁄₁₆	177 @ 1⁵⁄₁₆	.371	.364	.001–.003	.002–.004	.373	.372
	V8 2 Bar.Carb.	.010H	.018H	45	45	1¹¹⁄₁₆	177 @ 1⁵⁄₁₆	.370	.368	.001–.003	.002–.004	.373	.372
	V8 4 Bar.Carb.	.010H	.018H	45	45	1¹¹⁄₁₆	177 @ 1⁵⁄₁₆	.390	.390	.001–.003	.002–.004	.373	.372

①—Outer spring.
②—Seneca and Pioneer.
③—Phoenix.
④—Intake face and seat 45°, exhaust seat 45°. exhaust face 47°.

PISTONS, PINS, RINGS, CRANKSHAFT & BEARINGS

Year	Model	Fitting Pistons		Ring End Gap ①		Wrist-pin Diameter	Rod Bearings		Main Bearings			
		Shim To Use	Pounds Pull On Scale	Comp.	Oil		Shaft Diameter	Bearing Clearance	Shaft Diameter	Bearing Clearance	Thrust on Bear. No.	Shaft End Play
DODGE												
1953–54	Six	.002	6–10	.010	.010	.8592	2.061–2.062	.0005–.0015	2.499–2.500	.0005–.0015	5	.002–.007
	V8	.0015	5–10	.007	.007	.8592	1.936–1.937	.0005–.0015	2.374–2.375	.0005–.0015	3	.002–.007
1955	Six	.002	6–10	.010	.010	.8592	2.061–2.062	.0005–.0015	2.499–2.500	.0005–.0015	5	.002–.007
	Red Ram	.0015	5–10	.010	.010	.8592	1.936–1.937	.0005–.0015	2.374–2.375	.0005–.0015	3	.002–.007
	Super R. R.	.0015	5–10	.007	.007	.8592	1.936–1.937	.0005–.0015	2.374–2.375	.0005–.0015	3	.002–.007
1956	Six	.002	6–10	.010	.010	.8592	2.249–2.250	.0005–.0015	2.499–2.500	.0005–.0015	5	.002–.007
	Coronet V8	.0015	5–10	.010	.010	.8592	1.936–1.937	.0005–.0015	2.374–2.375	.0005–.0015	3	.002–.007
	Royal V8	.0015	5–10	.010	.010	.9216	2.249–2.250	.0005–.0015	2.499–2.500	.0005–.0015	3	.002–.007
	D-500	.0015	5–10	.010	.010	.9216	2.249–2.250	.0005–.0015	2.499–2.500	.0005–.0015	3	.002–.007
1957	Six	.002	6–10	.010	.010	.8592	2.061–2.062	.0005–.0015	2.499–2.500	.0005–.0015	5	.002–.007
	V8	.0015	5–10	.010	.010	.9216	2.249–2.250	.0005–.0015	2.499–2.500	.0005–.0015	3	.002–.007
1958	Six	.002	6–10	.010	.010	.859	2.061–2.062	.0005–.0015	2.499–2.500	.0005–.0015	5	.002–.007
	LD2	.0015	5–10	.010	.010	.922	2.249–2.250	.0005–.0015	2.499–2.500	.0005–.0015	3	.002–.007
	LD3, D500	.001	5–10	.013	.013	1.0935	2.379–2.380	.0005–.0015	2.629–2.630	.0005–.0015	3	.002–.007
1959	6-Cyl.	.0015	5–10	.010	.010	.859	2.061–2.062	.0005–.0015	2.499–2.500	.0005–.0015	5	.002–.007
	MD2	.0015	5–10	.010	.010	.984	2.124–2.125	.0002–.0022	2.499–2.500	.0005–.0015	3	.002–.007
	MD3, D500	.001	5–10	.013	.013	1.093	2.374–2.375	.0005–.0015	2.629–2.630	.0005–.0015	3	.002–.007
1960–61	All	.001	5–10	.013	.013	1.093	2.374–2.375	.0005–.0015	2.629–2.630	.0005–.0015	3	.002–.007
DART												
1960	6-Cyl.	.001	5–10	.010	.010	.9008	2.186–2.187	.0005–.0015	2.749–2.750	.0005–.0015	3	.002–.007
	V8-318	.001	5–10	.010	.010	.9842	2.124–2.125	.0005–.0015	2.499–2.500	.0005–.0015	3	.002–.007
	V8-361, 383	.001	5–10	.013	.013	1.093	2.374–2.375	.0005–.0015	2.629–2.630	.0005–.0015	3	.002–.007
1961	Six	.001	5–10	.010	.010	.9008	2.186–2.187	.0005–.0015	2.749–2.750	.0005–.0015	3	.002–.007
	V8	.001	5–10	.010	.010	.9842	2.124–2.125	.0005–.0015	2.499–2.500	.0005–.0015	3	.002–.007

①—Fit rings in tapered bores for clearance listed in tightest portion of ring travel.

REAR AXLE AND BRAKE CYLINDER SPECIFICATIONS

Year	Model	Ring Gear & Pinion Backlash, Inch	Drive Pinion Adjustment	Drive Pinion Bearing Preload Inch Lbs.	Drive Pinion Bearing Adjustment	Axle Shaft End Play, Inch	Hydraulic Cylinder Bore Sizes, Inch		
							Wheel Cylinder		Master Cylinder
							Front	Rear	
1953–54	Six	.006–.010	Washer	20–30①	Shims	.013–.018	1⅛	1⅛	1⅛
	V8	.006–.010	Washer	25–35①	Washer	.013–.018	1⅛	1⅛	1⅛
1955	Synchromesh	.006–.010	Washer	15–25①	Shims	.013–.018	1⅛	1⅛	1⅛
	Powerflite	.006–.010	Washer	20–30①	Washer	.013–.018	1⅛	1⅛	1⅛
1956	Synchromesh	.006–.010	Washer	15–25①	Shims	.013–.018	1⅛	1⅛	1⅛
	Powerflite 6	.006–.010	Washer	15–25①	Shims	.013–.018	1⅛	1⅛	1⅛
	Powerflite V8	.006–.010	Washer	20–30①	Shims	.013–.018	1⅛	1⅛	1⅛
1957–61	All	.006–.010	Washer	20–30①	Shims	.013–.023②	1⅛	1⅛	1⅛

①—For used bearings, drag should be zero to one half that specified but with no end play of the drive pinion.
②—Adjust to .018″.

ENGINE TIGHTENING SPECIFICATIONS★

★Torque specifications are for clean and lightly lubricated threads only. Dry or dirty threads produce increased friction which prevents accurate measurement of tightness.

Year	Spark Plugs Ft. Lbs.	Cylinder Head Bolts Ft. Lbs.	Intake Manifold Ft. Lbs.	Exhaust Manifold Ft. Lbs.	Rocker Arm Shaft Bracket Ft. Lbs.	Rocker Arm Cover Ft. Lbs.	Connecting Rod Cap Bolts Ft. Lbs.	Main Bearing Cap Bolts Ft. Lbs.	Flywheel to Crankshaft Ft. Lbs.	Vibration Damper or Pulley Ft. Lbs.
DODGE										
1953–59 Six	30	85	20	20	None	None	45	85	60	135
1953 V8	30	85	30	35	85	①	45	85	55	135
1954 V8	30	85	30	25	85	②	45	85	55	135
1955–57 V8⑤	30	85	30	25	30	②	45	85	55	135
1955–57 V8⑥	30	85	30	25	85	②	45	85	55	135
1958 V8⑤	30	85	30	25	30	②	45	85	55	135
1958 V8⑥	30	70	30	30	30	③	45	85	55	135
1959 V8-326	30	85	30	25	85	③	45	85	55	135
1959–61 V8-361, 383	30	70	40	25	30	③	45	85	55	135
DART										
1960–61 Six	30	65	④	10	30	③	45	85	55	⑦
1960–61 V8-318	30	85	30	25	85	③	45	85	55	135
1960 V8-361, 383	30	70	40	25	30	③	45	85	55	135

①—12-17 inch lbs. ②—30 inch lbs. ③—40 inch lbs. ④—200 inch lbs. ⑤—Red Ram Engine. ⑥—Super Red Ram Engine. ⑦—Press fit.

STARTING MOTOR SPECIFICATIONS

Year and Model	Part No.	Rotation ①	Brush Spring Tension, Ounces	No Load Test			Torque Test		
				Amperes	Volts	R.P.M.	Amperes	Volts	Torque, Lbs. Ft.
DODGE									
1953–54	MCH-6205	C	42–53	65	5	4300	335	2	6
1953–55	MCH-6206	C	42–53	65	5	4300	335	2	6
1954–55	MCH-6305	C	42–53	65	5	4300	335	2	6
1956	MDF-6002	C	42–53	60	10	3200	240	4	6.5
	MDF-6007	C	42–53	60	10	3200	240	4	6.5
	MDG-6001	C	42–53	50	10	4400	210	4	5
	MDG-6002	C	42–53	50	10	4400	210	4	5
1957–58	MDM-6001	C	31–47	50	10	4400	210	4	5
	MDL-6003	C	31–47	60	10	3200	225	4	6
	MDL-6004	C	31–47	60	10	3200	225	4	6
1958	MDT-6001	C	31–47	56	10	3600	350	4	8½
1959	MDU-6003	C	31–47	50	10	5300	280	4	6.2
	MDT-6001	C	31–47	56	10	3600	350	4	8.5
1960	MDT-7001	C	31–47	58	11	3800	350	4	8½
1961	1889200	C	32–48	78	11	3800	350	4	8.5
DART									
1960	MTD-7002	C	31–47	58	11	3800	350	4	8½
	MDU-7001	C	31–47	50	11	5500	355	4	9
	MTD-7001	C	31–47	58	11	3800	350	4	8½
1961	MDT-7002	C	32–48	58	11	3800	350	4	8.5
	1889100	C	32–48	78	11	3800	350	4	8.5

①—As viewed from the drive end. C—Clockwise.

DODGE & DART

COOLING SYSTEM & CAPACITY DATA

Year and Model	Cooling System Data					Fuel Tank Gals.	Engine Oil			Transmissions			Rear Axle Pints
	Quarts No Heater	Quarts With Heater	Rad. Cap Relief Pressure	Thermostat Opening Temp. ①	②		Refill Qts.③	Summer Grade	Winter Grade	Std. Pints	With Over-drive Pints	Auto-matic Qts.	

DODGE

Year and Model	Quarts No Heater	Quarts With Heater	Rad. Cap Relief Pressure	①	②	Fuel Tank Gals.	Refill Qts.③	Summer Grade	Winter Grade	Std. Pints	With Over-drive Pints	Auto-matic Qts.	Rear Axle Pints
1953 Six	14	15	7	180	160	17	5	30	10W	2¾④	3½	None	3¼
1953 V8	19	20	7	180	160	17	5⑤	30	10W	2¾④	3½	None	3¼⑥
1954 Six	14	15	7	180	160	17	5	30	10W	2¾④	3½	None	3¼
1954 V8	19	20	7	180	160	17	5	30	10W	2¾④	3½	11	3¼⑦
1955 Six	13	14	7⑩	180	160	17	5	30	10W	2¾④	3½	10	3¼
1955 V8	19	20	7⑩	180	160	17	5	30	10W	2¾	3½	10	3¼
1956 D62	13	14	7	180	160	17	5	30	10W	2¾	3½	10	3¼
1956 D63-1	19	20	7	180	160	17	5	30	10W	2¾	3½	10	3¼
1956 D63-2, 3	20	21	14	180	160	17	5	30	10W	2¾	3½	10	3¼
1956 D-500	20	21	14	180	160	17	5	30	10W	2¾	None	10	3¼
1957 D72	13	14	14	180	160	20	5	30	10W	2¾	None	10	3¼
1957 D66	20	21	14	180	160	20	5	30	10W	2¾	None	⑧	3¼
1957 D67	20	21	14	180	160	20	5	30	10W	2¾	None	9	3¼
1957 D70, D71	20	21	14	180	160	22	5	30	10W	2¾	None	9	3¼
1958 Six	13	14	14	180	160	20⑨	5	30	10W	2¾	None	10	3¼
1958 LD2	20	21	14	180	160	20⑨	5	30	10W	2¾	None	10	3½
1958 LD3	16	17	14	180	160	20⑨	4	30	10W	2¾	None	10½	3½
1958 D-500	16	17	14	180	160	20⑨	4	30	10W	2¾	None	10½	3½
1959 Six	13	14	14	180	160	20⑨	5	30	10W	2¾	None	10	3¼
1959 MD2	20	21	14	180	160	20⑨	5	30	10W	2¾	None	⑧	3½
1959 MD3	16	17	14	180	160	20⑨	5	30	10W	2¾	None	10½	3½
1959 D-500	16	17	14	180	160	20⑨	5	30	10W	None	None	10½	3½
1960 Matador	16	17	14	180	160	20⑨	5	30	10W	2¾	None	11	3½
1960 Polara	16	17	14	180	160	20⑨	5	30	10W	3¼	None	11	3½
1960 D-500	16	17	14	180	160	20⑨	5	30	10W	None	None	11	3½
1961	16	17	14	180	160	20⑫	5	30	10W	4¼	None	9½	4

DART

Year and Model	Quarts No Heater	Quarts With Heater	Rad. Cap Relief Pressure	①	②	Fuel Tank Gals.	Refill Qts.③	Summer Grade	Winter Grade	Std. Pints	With Over-drive Pints	Auto-matic Qts.	Rear Axle Pints
1960 Six	14	14.7	14	180	160	20⑨	4	30	10W	5	None	⑪	3¼
1960 V8-318	20	21	14	180	160	20⑨	5	30	10W	2¾	None	⑪	3½
1960 V8-361, 383	16	17	14	180	160	20⑨	5	30	10W	3¼	None	⑪	3½
1961 Six	13	14	14	180	160	20⑫	4	30	10W	5	None	7½	3¼
1961 V8	20	21	14	180	160	20⑫	5	30	10W	5	None	10	4

①—For permanent type anti-freeze.
②—For alcohol type anti-freeze.
③—Add one quart with filter change.
④—Semi-automatic transmission 3 pints.
⑤—With torque converter, engine and converter have combined oiling system requiring 12 qts. with extra quart for filter change.
⑥—With Gyromatic. Overdrive or Easyshift use 3½ pints.
⑦—With Easyshift or Overdrive use 3½ pints.
⑧—With Powerflite 10 qts. with Torqueflite 9 qts.
⑨—Station Wagons 22 gals.
⑩—14 lbs. with Air Conditioning.
⑪—Powerflite 10 qts., Torqueflite 9 qts.
⑫—Station Wagons 21 gals.

DISTRIBUTOR SPECIFICATIONS

Year	Part No. ①	Rotation ②	Cam Angle, Degrees	Breaker Point Opening, Inch	Condenser Capacity, Mfds. ③	Breaker Arm Spring Tension, Ounces	Centrifugal Advance Data Degrees @ R.P.M. of Dist.		Vacuum Advance Data		
							Advance Starts	Full Advance	Inches of Vacuum to Start Plunger Movement	Inches of Vacuum for Full Plunger Travel	Maximum Vacuum Advance, Dist. Degrees
DODGE & DART											
1953	1AT-4101	C	36–42	.020	.25–.28	17–20	1 @ 450	10 @ 1425	4¼	14	8
1954–56	1AT-4101B	C	36–42	.020	.25–.28	17–20	1 @ 525	8 @ 1350	4¾	14	8
1956	1AT-4103	C	36–42	.020	.25–.28	17–20	1 @ 525	8 @ 1350	4¾	14	8
1953	1AZ-4003	C	④	.017	.25–.28	17–20	1 @ 375	15 @ 1750	5¼	17	11½
1953–54	1AZ-4003A	C	④	.017	.25–.28	17–20	1 @ 425	11 @ 1625	5¼	17	11½
1954	1AZ-4003B	C	④	.017	.25–.28	17–20	1 @ 375	15 @ 1650	5¼	17	11½
1955	1AZ-4003C	C	④	.017	.25–.28	17–20	1 @ 375	18 @ 1900	5¼	17	11½
1955	1AZ-4003D	C	④	.017	.25–.28	17–20	1 @ 375	12 @ 1625	5¼	17	11½
1955	1AZ-4003E	C	④	.017	.25–.28	17–20	1 @ 375	18 @ 1900	5¼	11¼	7
1955	1AZ-4003F	C	④	.017	.25–.28	17–20	1 @ 375	12 @ 1625	5¼	11¼	7
1955	1AZ-4003G	C	④	.017	.25–.28	17–20	1 @ 375	16 @ 1650	5¼	8½	4
1955	1AZ-4003H	C	④	.020	.25–.28	17–20	1 @ 375	16 @ 1650	5¼	17	11½
1956	1BJ-4301A	C	31	.017	.25–.28	17–20	1 @ 400	15 @ 2150	5½	15	12½
1956	1BJ-4303	C	31	.017	.25–.28	17–20	1 @ 415	16 @ 2350	6⅜	15	11
1956	1BJ-4303B	C	31	.017	.25–.28	17–20	1 @ 415	15 @ 2350	.5¼	12	8
1957	1BP-4002	C	27–32	.017	.25–.28	17–20	1 @ 535	8½ @ 1700	7⅛	18	13
1957	1BP-4002D	C	27–32	.017	.25–.28	17–20	1 @ 455	9 @ 2400	10½	17½	13
1958	1BP-4002E	C	27–32	.017	.25–.28	17–20	1 @ 410	9 @ 1650	6¾	14	11
1957	1BP-4003	C	26–32	.017	.25–.28	17–20	1 @ 575	9½ @ 2200	7⅛	18	13
1957	1BP-4003A	C	26–32	.017	.25–.28	17–20	1 @ 370	11 @ 950	7⅛	13½	9½
1957	1BP-4003B	C	26–32	.017	.25–.28	17–20	1 @ 415	11½ @ 2200	7⅛	18	13
1959	1BP-4003J	C	27–32	.017	.25–.28	17–20	0 @ 450	6½ @ 2300	6¾	13¼	10
1960	1BP-4003L	C	27–32	.017	.25–.28	17–20	0 @ 335	9 @ 2300	8	17	15
1960	1BP-4003N	C	27–32	.017	.25–.28	17–20	0 @ 350	8 @ 2400	8	17	15
1960	1BP-4003T	C	26–32	.017	.25–.28	17–20	1 @ 430	11½ @ 2300	8¼	17	13
1958	1BP-4005	CC	27–32	.017	.25–.28	17–20	1 @ 425	10 @ 2000	8	13	17½
1959	1BP-4005B	CC	27–32	.017	.25–.28	17–20	0 @ 350	9½ @ 2150	8⅛	16⅛	11
1960	1BP-4005C	CC	27–32	.017	.25–.28	17–20	0 @ 500	8 @ 2200	8	15	11
1960	1BP-4005D	CC	26–32	.017	.25–.28	17–20	1 @ 425	10 @ 2000	7⅛	16½	13
1957–59	1BR-4001	C	36–42	.020	.25–.28	17–20	1 @ 460	8½ @ 1800	6	16	9½
1957	1BS-4005	C	⑤	.017	.25–.28	17–20	1 @ 415	8 @ 1200	9⅛	18	10¼
1958	1BS-4006B	C	⑤	.017	.25–.28	17–20	1 @ 425	10 @ 2000	7⅛	13	16½
1959	1BS-4006C	CC	⑥	.017	.25–.28	17–20	0 @ 450	9½ @ 2000	8⅜	18⅛	13
1960	1BS-4006E	CC	⑥	.017	.25–.28	17–20	0 @ 375	10 @ 2400	8	14½	10
1958	1BS-4009	C	⑥	.017	.25–.28	17–20	1 @ 425	10 @ 2000	7⅛	13	16½
1960	2095270	C	36–42	.020	.25–.28	17–21	0 @ 350	11½ @ 2200	6	12	12
1961	IBP-4005E	CC	27–32	.017	.25–.28	17–21	0 @ 375	11 @ 2050	7	16	13
	2095270	C	36–42	.020	.25–.28	17–21	0 @ 350	11½ @ 2200	6	12	12
	2095647	C	27–32	.017	.25–.28	17–21	0 @ 300	12 @ 2300	7	17	13
	1838505		27–32	.017	.25–.28	17–21	0 @ 350	9 @ 2300	7	17	13
	1889710		27–32	.017	.25–.28	17–21	0 @ 300	8½ @ 2200	6	13	10

① —Stamped on plate riveted to side of housing.
② —As viewed from the top. C—Clockwise. CC—Counterclockwise.
③ —Microfarads—as indicated on a condenser tester.

④ —Each set 26–28, total dwell both sets 32–36.
⑤ —Each set 29–32, total dwell both sets 36–39.
⑥ —Each set 27–32, total dwell both sets 34–40.

GENERATOR AND REGULATOR SPECIFICATIONS

★ To polarize generator, reconnect the leads to the regulator; then momentarily connect a jumper wire from the "Arm" to the "Bat" terminals of the regulator.

	Generator						Regulator					
								Cutout Relay		Voltage Regulator Setting Volts	Current Regulator Setting Amperes	Current and Voltage Armature Air Gap, Inch
Year	Generator Number ④	Rotation and Ground Polarity ①	Rated Cap. Amps.	Gen. Field Ground Location★	Brush Spring Tension, Ounces	Field Current Amperes	Regulator Number	Voltage to Close Points	Armature Air Gap, Inch			
1957–59	GGA-6001AC	C-N	40	External	34–41	1.1–1.3③	VAT-6201A	13.1	.032	14.3	40	.050
1956	GGA-6001K	C-N	40	External	34–41	1.1–1.3③	VAT-6201A	13.1	.032	14.3	40	.050
1956	GGA-6001L	C-N	40	External	34–41	1.1–1.3③	VAT-6201A	13.1	.032	14.3	40	.050
1956–58	GGA-6001N	C-N	40	External	34–41	1.1–1.3③	VAT-6201A	13.1	.032	14.3	40	.050
1958–60	GGA-6003E	C-N	40	External	34–41	1.1–1.3③	VAT-6201A	13.1	.032	14.3	40	.050
1958	GGA-6003F	C-N	40	External	34–41	1.1–1.3③	VAT-6201A	13.1	.032	14.3	40	.050
1959–60	GGA-6007A	C-N	40	External	34–41	1.1–1.3③	VAT-6201A	13.1	.032	14.3	40	.050
1960	GGA-6009AC	C-N	40	External	34–41	1.1–1.3③	VAT-6201A	13.1	.032	14.3	40	.050
1953–55	GGW-6001J	C-P	45	External	35–53	1.4–1.5②	VBE-6201A	6.5	.032	7.2	45	.050
1953–54	GGW-6001K	C-P	45	External	35–53	1.4–1.5②	VBE-6201A	6.5	.032	7.2	45	.050
1954	GGW-6008BA	C-P	45	External	35–53	1.6–1.7②	VBE-6001A	6.5	.032	7.2	45	.050
1954	GGW-6008F	C-P	45	External	35–53	1.4–1.5②	VBE-6201A	6.5	.032	7.2	45	.050
1954	GGW-6008G	C-P	45	External	35–53	1.4–1.5②	VBE-6201A	6.5	.032	7.2	45	.050
1953	GGW-6009A	C-P	45	External	35–53	1.4–1.5②	VBE-6201A	6.5	.032	7.2	45	.050
1953	GGW-6009B	C-P	45	External	35–53	1.4–1.5②	VBE-6201A	6.5	.032	7.2	45	.050
1953	GGW-6010A	C-P	45	External	35–53	1.4–1.5②	VBE-6201A	6.5	.032	7.2	45	.050
1953	GGW-6010B	C-P	45	External	35–53	1.4–1.5②	VBE-6201A	6.5	.032	7.2	45	.050
1953–54	GGW-6012A	C-P	45	External	35–53	1.4–1.5②	VBE-6201A	6.5	.032	7.2	45	.050
1953–55	GGW-6012B	C-P	45	External	35–53	1.4–1.5②	VBE-6201A	6.5	.032	7.2	45	.050
1953–54	GGW-6014A	C-P	45	External	35–53	1.4–1.5②	VBE-6201A	6.5	.032	7.2	45	.050
1953–54	GGW-6014B	C-P	45	External	35–53	1.4–1.5②	VBE-6201A	6.5	.032	7.2	45	.050
1955	GGW-6016A	C-P	45	External	35–53	1.4–1.5②	VBE-6201A	6.5	.032	7.2	45	.050
1955	GGW-6016C	C-P	45	External	18–36	1.6–1.7②	VBE-6201A	6.5	.032	7.2	45	.050
1955	GGW-6017A	C-P	45	External	35–53	1.6–1.7②	VBE-6201A	6.5	.032	7.2	45	.050
1956	GJC-7001A	C-P	30	External	18–36	1.2–1.3③	VRX-6201A	13.1	.032	14.3	30	.050
1956	GJC-7001C	C-N	30	External	18–36	1.2–1.3③	VRX-6201A	13.1	.032	14.3	30	.050
1957	GJC-7001D	C-N	30	External	18–36	1.2–1.3③	VRX-6201A	13.1	.032	14.3	30	.050
1956	GJC-7002A	C-N	30	External	18–36	1.2–1.3③	VRX-6201A	13.1	.032	14.3	30	.050
1957	GJC-7002H	C-N	30	External	18–36	1.2–1.3③	VRX-6201A	13.1	.032	14.3	30	.050
1956	GJC-7003B	C-N	30	External	18–36	1.2–1.3③	VRX-6201A	13.1	.032	14.3	30	.050
1957–58	GJC-7012A	C-N	30	External	18–36	1.2–1.3③	VRX-6201A	13.1	.032	14.3	30	.050
1959	GJM-8001A	C-N	35	External	18–36	1.6–1.7③	VRX-6301A	13.1	.032	14.3	35	.050
1960	GJM-8201A	C-N	35	External	18–36	1.6–1.7③	VBO-4202BC	13.1	.032	14.6	35	.050
1960	GJM-8302A	C-N	35	External	18–36	1.6–1.7③	VBO-4202B	13.1	.032	14.6	35	.050
1957–58	GHM-6004C	C-N	30	External	18–36	1.2–1.3③	VRX-6201A	13.1	.032	14.3	30	.050
1960	GHM-8001B	C-N	30	External	35–53	1.2–1.3③	VBO-4202C	13.1	.032	14.6	30	.050
1960	GHM-8002A	C-N	30	External	35–53	1.2–1.3③	VBO-4202C	13.1	.032	14.6	30	.050
1959	GHM-8005A	C-N	30	External	35–53	1.1–1.3③	VRX-6201A	13.1	.032	14.3	30	.050

①—C-Clockwise. P-Positive. N-Negative. ②—At 5 volts. ③—At 10 volts. ④—Stamped on plate riveted to side of housing.

Year	Model	Caster, Degrees		Camber, Degrees		Toe-In, Inches	Toe-out on Turns, Degrees①		Kingpin or Steering Axis Inclination②
		Limits	Desired	Limits	Desired		Outer Wheel	Inner Wheel	
DODGE									
1953–54	All	— 1 to + 1	0	— 3/8 to + 3/8	③	0 to 1/16	20	20½ to 22½	5 to 6½
1955	Manual Steering	— 2 to 0	— 2	— 1/8 to + 5/8	④	0 to 1/16	20	20½ to 22½	5½ @ 0 Camber
	Power Steering	— 2 to 0	0	— 1/8 to + 5/8	④	0 to 1/16	20	20½ to 22½	5½ @ 0 Camber
1956	Manual Steering	— 2 to 0	— 2	— 1/8 to + 5/8	④	3/32 to 5/32	20	20½ to 22½	5½ @ 0 Camber
	Power Steering	— 2 to 0	0	— 1/8 to + 5/8	④	3/32 to 5/32	20	20½ to 22½	5½ @ 0 Camber
1957	Manual Steering	0 to — 1½	— ¾	⑤	⑤	3/32 to 5/32	20	21½	6½ @ 0 Camber
	Power Steering	0 to + 1½	+ ¾	⑤	⑤	3/32 to 5/32	20	21½	6½ @ 0 Camber
1958	Manual Steering	0 to + ½	+ ¼	⑤	⑤	3/32 to 5/32	18¾	20	6½ @ 0 Camber
	Power Steering	0 to + 1½	+ ¾	⑤	⑤	3/32 to 5/32	18¾	20	6½ @ 0 Camber
1959	Manual Steering	— 1½ to 0	— ¾	⑤	⑤	1/8	18°46'	20	6½ @ 0 Camber
	Power Steering	0 to + 1½	+ ¾	⑤	⑤	1/8	18°46'	20	6½ @ 0 Camber
1960	Manual Steering	— 1½ to 0	— ¾	⑥	⑥	1/8	18°42'	20	6½ @ 0 Camber
	Power Steering	0 to + 1½	+ ¾	⑥	⑥	1/8	18°42'	20	6½ @ 0 Camber
1961	Manual Steering	— 1 to 0	— ½	⑦	⑦	1/8	18°42'	20	6½ @ 0 Camber
	Power Steering	+ ¼ to + 1¾	+ ¾	⑦	⑦	1/8	18°42'	20	6½ @ 0 Camber
DART									
1960	Manual Steering	— 1½ to 0	— ¾	⑥	⑥	1/8	18°42'	20	6½ @ 0 Camber
	Power Steering	+ 1½ to 0	+ ¾	⑥	⑥	1/8	18°42'	20	6½ @ 0 Camber
1961	Manual Steering	— 1 to 0	— ½	⑦	⑦	1/8	18°42'	20	6½ @ 0 Camber
	Power Steering	+ ¼ to + 1¾	+ ¾	⑦	⑦	1/8	18°42'	20	6½ @ 0 Camber

①—Incorrect toe-out, when other adjustments are correct, generally indicates bent steering arms.
②—Incorrect kingpin angle with correct camber indicates bent suspension arms or steering knuckle support.
③—Left side ¼° to ½° higher than right side within these limits.
④—Left side + ½°, right side 0°.
⑤—Left side preferred + 3/8°, right side zero.
⑥—Left side preferred + 3/8°, right side + 1/8°.
⑦—Left side preferred + ½°, right side + ¼°.

SERIAL NUMBER LOCATION
Left Front Door Pillar

ENGINE NUMBER LOCATION

Sixes:	Left Front Of Block
1954-57 V8:	Pad Between No. 2 and 3 Cylinders
V8-325:	Pad Between No. 2 and 3 Cylinders
V8-350:	Right Side Of Block Below Distributor
V8-318:	Left Front Face Of Block
V8-361, 383:	Right Side Of Block Next To Water Pump

ENGINE IDENTIFICATION

Year	Engine	Eng. No. Prefix
1958	V8-325	LD2
	V8-350	LD3
1959	V8-325	MD2
	V8-361	MD3
1960	V8-318	P318
	V8-361	P36
	V8-383	P38
1961	V8-318	R318
	V8-361	R36
	V8-383	R38

1953 All and 1954 Models D50-1A, D51-1A

1954 Except D50-1A and D51-1A

1956

1955

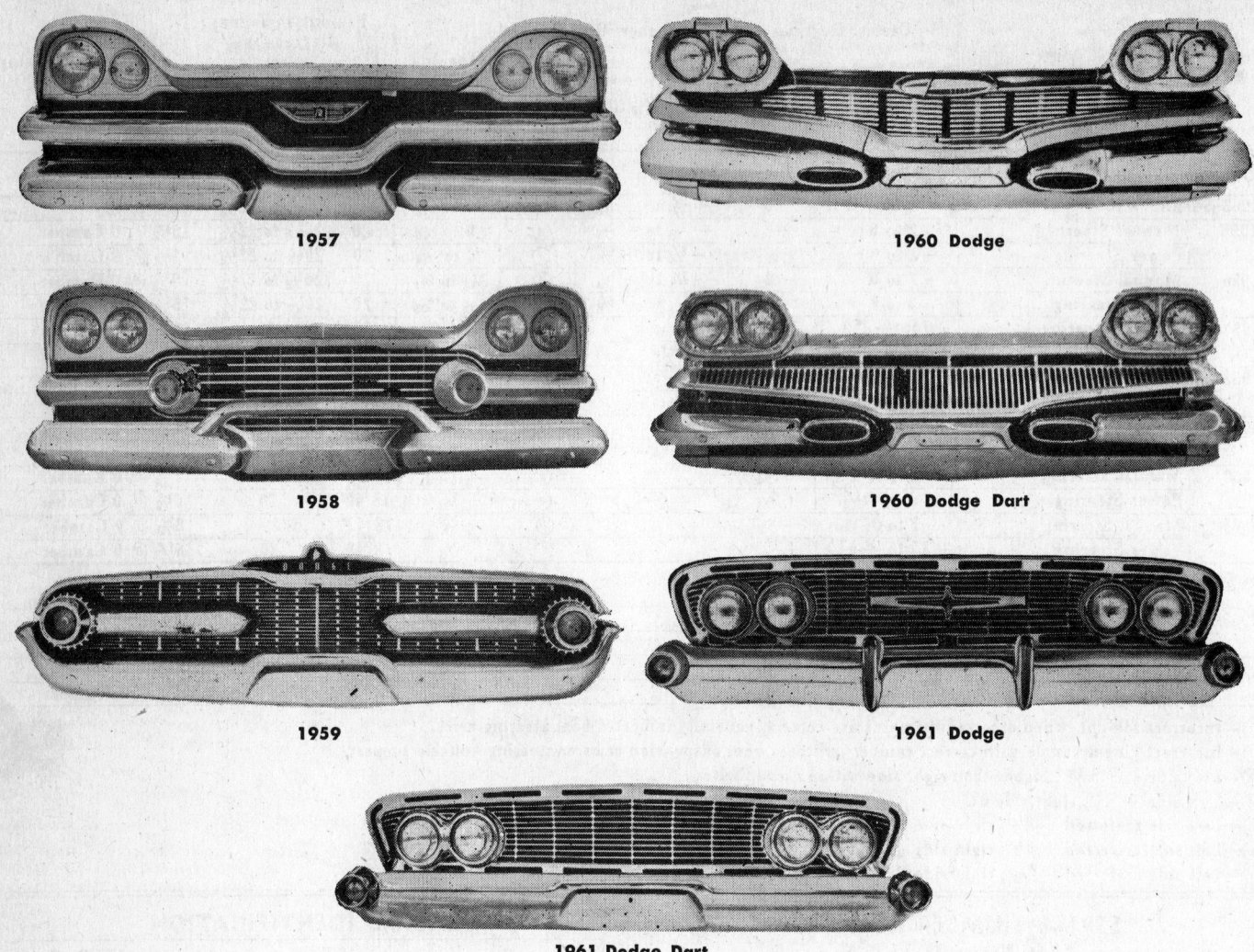

1957

1960 Dodge

1958

1960 Dodge Dart

1959

1961 Dodge

1961 Dodge Dart

Engine Section

ENGINE, REPLACE

In addition to the usual items such as fuel lines, linkage, propeller shaft, etc., it is necessary to perform the following operations:

1. Remove hood and battery.
2. Remove radiator and exhaust pipes.
3. On 1953-55 V8, support transmission and remove engine rear support and crossmember. Remove front support bolts and lift engine from chassis.
4. On 1953-59 Sixes, remove transmission, front and rear engine supports and lift out engine.
5. On 1956-57 V8 and 1958 Red Ram, support transmission and remove rear engine support crossmember. Remove front supports and lift engine and transmission out of car.
6. On 1958 Super Red Ram and all 1959-61 V8's, support rear of engine and remove engine rear support crossmember. Remove transmission. Remove engine front mounting nuts and lift engine out of chassis.

7. On 1960-61 Six, support rear of engine and remove rear engine support crossmember. Disconnect converter from flex plate and remove transmission and converter as an assembly. Remove front engine mounting bolts and lift engine out of chassis.

CYLINDER HEAD

1960-61 Dart Six

1. To remove head, drain cooling system.
2. Remove carburetor air cleaner and fuel line.
3. Disconnect accelerator linkage.
4. Remove vacuum control tube at carburetor and distributor.
5. Disconnect spark plug wires, heater hose and clamp holding by-pass hose.
6. Disconnect heat indicator sending unit wire.
7. Disconnect exhaust pipe at manifold.
8. Remove intake and exhaust manifold and carburetor as a unit.
9. Remove outlet vent tube and rocker arm cover.
10. Remove thermostat housing and thermostat.
11. Remove rocker arms and push rods.
12. Remove head bolts and lift off heads.
13. Install head in reverse order of removal and tighten bolts in the sequence shown in Fig. 1A, and to the torque listed in the *Engine Tightening* chart. *When installing the manifolds, loosen the three bolts holding the intake manifold to the exhaust manifold. This is required to maintain proper alignment.* Install manifolds and carburetor as a unit with the cup side of the conical washers against the manifolds. Tighten the nuts to 10 ft. lbs. Then tighten the three bolts holding the intake manifold to exhaust manifold to 15 ft. lbs.

1953-59 Six

1. Drain cooling system.

2. Remove fuel line from carburetor.
3. Remove carburetor air cleaner.
4. Remove carburetor.
5. Remove upper radiator hose, spark plugs, engine heat indicator unit and cylinder or capscrews.
6. Lift cylinder head from block, using lifting hooks in two of the spark plug holes. Do not use a screwdriver, chisel or other sharp instrument to drive between the head and block to loosen the head as damage may result.

Installation

Before the cylinder head is installed, make certain that all dirt and carbon is removed from both the head and block.

If possible, use a torque wrench when tightening cylinder head nuts or capscrews. Uneven or excessive tightening may distort cylinder bores, causing compression loss and excessive oil consumption.

Tighten cylinder heads in the order shown in Fig. 1, tightening a little at a time in the proper sequence about three times around before final tightening to the torque values given in the *Engine Tightening* chart. After the engine has warmed up to operating temperature, recheck the nuts and adjust torque as required.

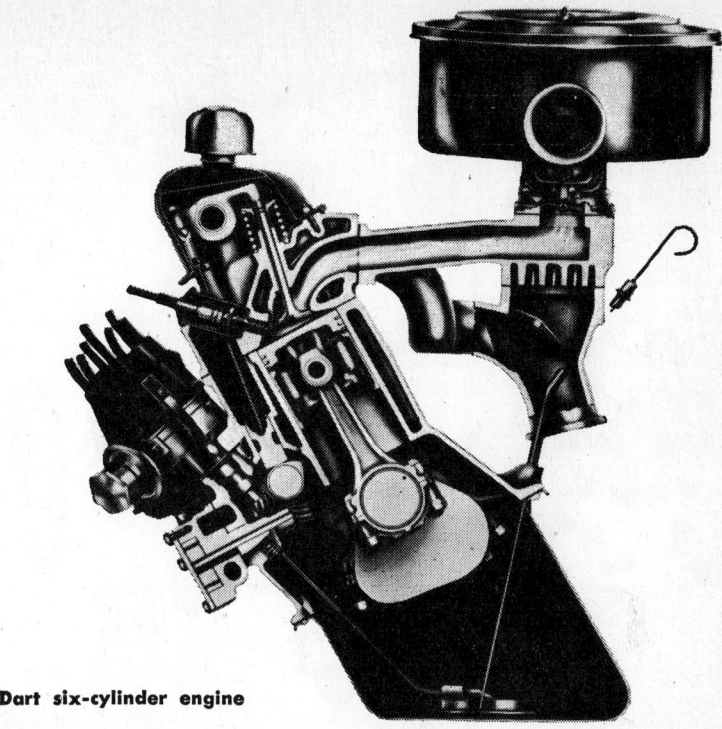

Dart six-cylinder engine

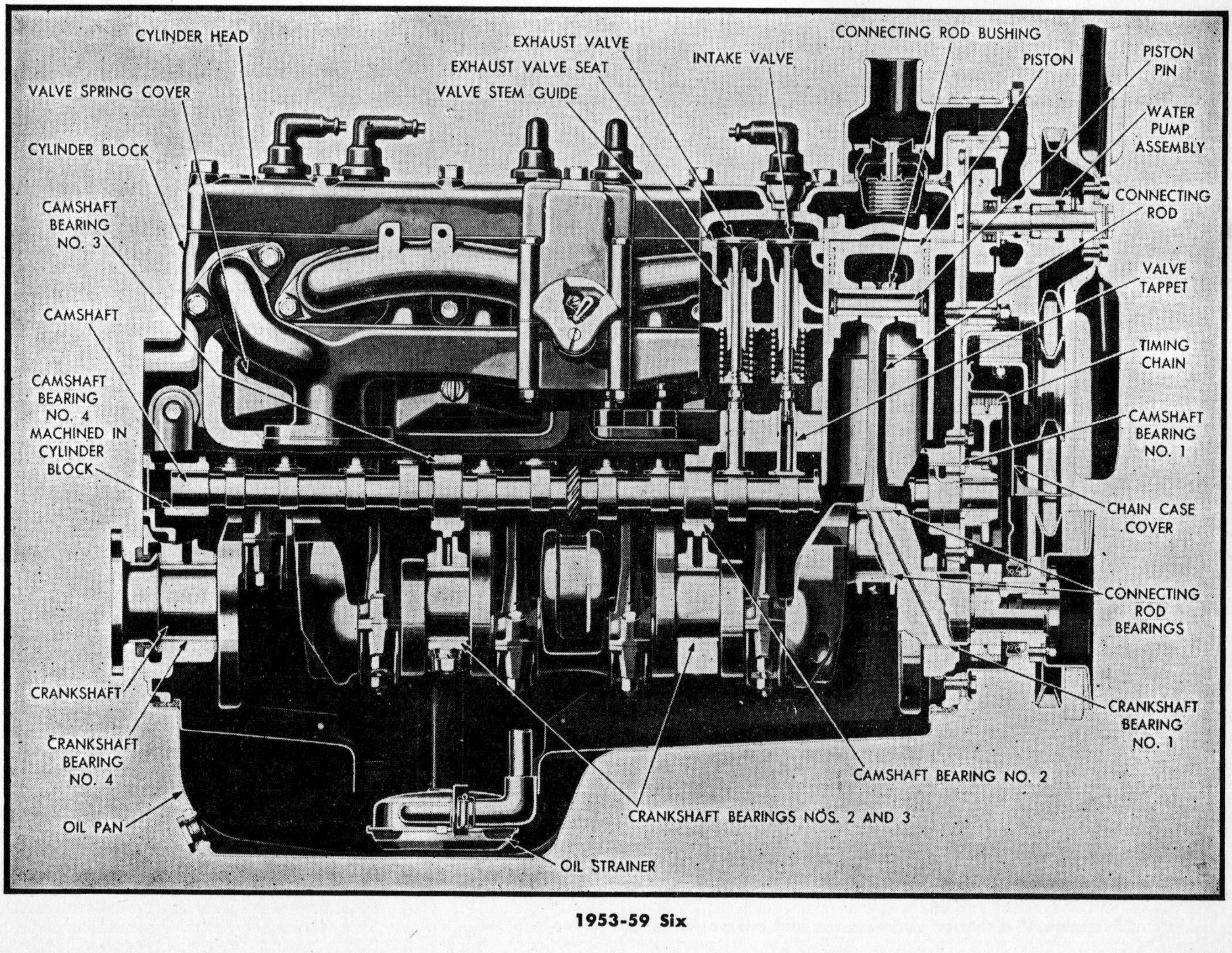

1953-59 Six

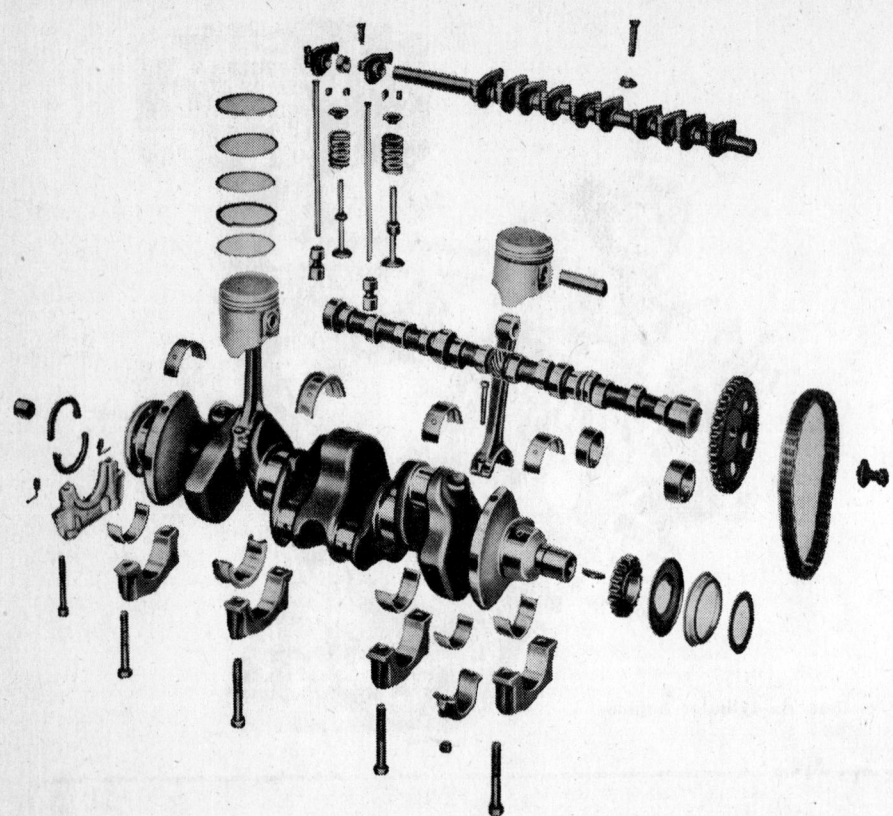

Internal engine parts. Dart Six

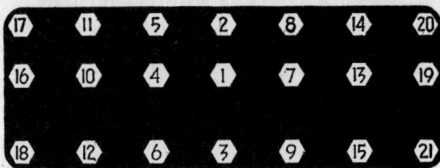

Fig. 1 Cylinder head tightening. 1953-59 Six

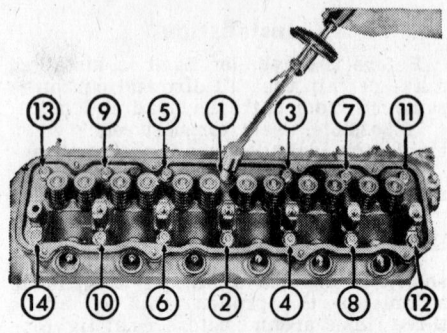

Fig. 1A Cylinder head tightening sequence. Dart Six

1959-61 V8-318, 326

1. Drain cooling system.
2. Remove carburetor air cleaner.
3. Disconnect pump-to-carburetor fuel line.
4. Remove distributor vacuum tube.
5. Remove generator.
6. Disconnect throttle linkage at carburetor.
7. Remove distributor cap, coil wires, heat indicator sending unit wire and heater hoses at engine.
8. Remove spark plugs and cables.
9. Remove engine ventilator pipe.
10. Remove intake manifold, carburetor and coil as an assembly.
11. Remove exhaust manifolds.
12. Remove rocker arm covers.
13. Remove cylinder heads and push rods.
14. Reverse order of removal to install heads and tighten bolts in the sequence shown in Fig. 2.

1958-61 V8-350, 361, 383

Rocker arm assemblies can be removed without disturbing the cylinder heads or cooling system. To remove the heads, proceed as follows:

1. Drain cooling system, remove air cleaner, fuel line from pump and carburetor, distributor vacuum tube and generator.
2. Disconnect throttle linkage at carburetor, distributor cap, coil wires, heat indicator sending unit wire and heater hoses at engine.
3. Remove spark plugs and cables, and engine ventilating outlet pipe.
4. Remove intake manifold, carburetor and coil as an assembly.
5. Remove exhaust manifolds.
6. Remove cylinder head covers and spark plug cable support brackets.
7. Remove rocker shaft assemblies. *Do not remove bolts from end brackets.*

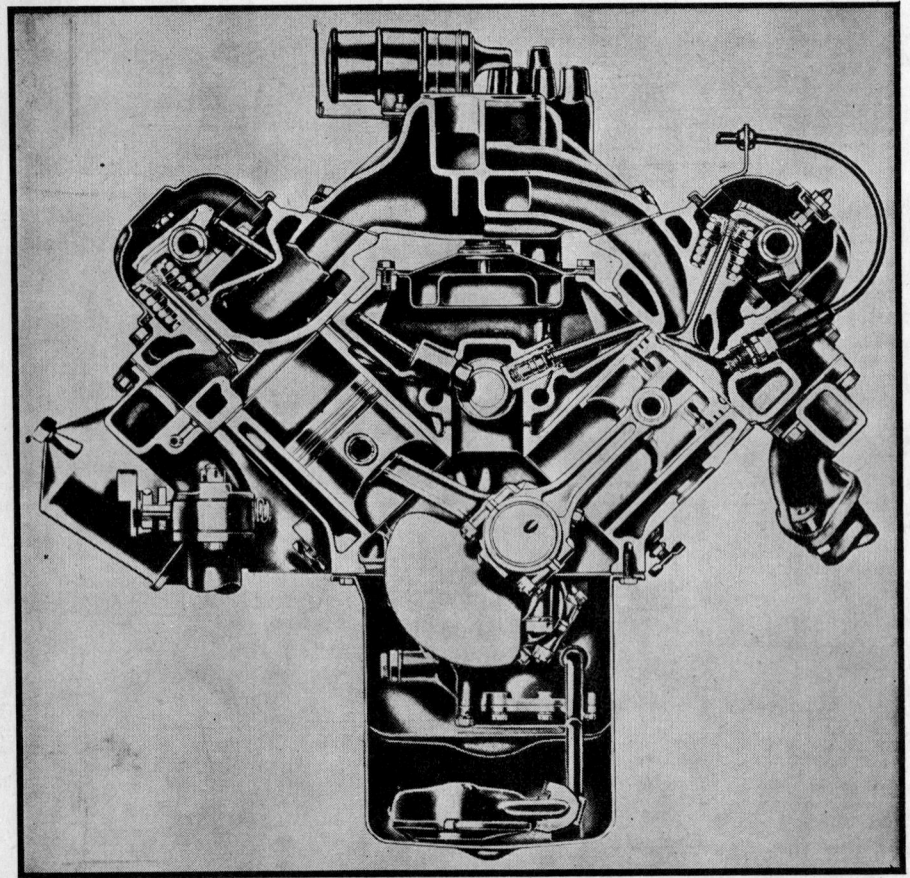

1953-58 engine with forged rocker arms and one rocker shaft for each bank

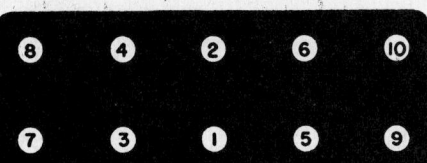

Fig. 2 Cylinder head tightening. 1953-57 and 1958-61 V8-318, 326

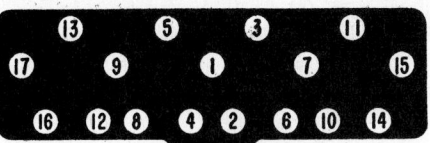

Fig. 3 Cylinder head tightening. 1958-61 V8-350, 361, 383

8. Remove push rods and valve lifter chamber cover.
9. Remove attaching bolts and lift off heads.
10. Reverse the foregoing procedure to install the heads and tighten the bolts in the sequence shown in Fig. 3 to a torque 70 lb. ft. Tighten intake and exhaust manifold bolts to to a torque of 30 lb. ft.

1953-57 & 1958 Red Ram

1. Remove air cleaner.
2. Remove generator.
3. Disconnect fuel and vacuum lines at carburetor.
4. Disconnect carburetor kickdown switch (if equipped).
5. Disconnect linkage at carburetor.
6. Disconnect coil wires.
7. Remove heat indicator bulb.
8. Disconnect heater hose.
9. Remove intake manifold, carburetor and coil as a unit.
10. Disconnect exhaust manifold-to-exhaust pipe flange.
11. Remove bolts holding water pump housing to cylinder heads.
12. Remove distributor cap and cables.
13. Remove rocker arm assemblies.
14. Lift out push rods.
15. Remove cylinder heads.
16. Reverse removal procedure and tighten the heads in the sequence shown in Fig. 2.

VALVES, ADJUST

1960-61 Dart Six

Before the final valve lash adjustment is made, operate the engine for 30 minutes at a fast idle to stabilize engine temperatures. Before starting the adjustment, make two chalk marks on the vibration damper. Space the marks about 120 degrees apart (⅓ of circumference) so that with the timing mark the damper is divided into three equal parts. Adjust the valves for No. 1 cylinder. Repeat the procedure for the remaining valves, turning the crankshaft ⅓ turn in the direction of normal rotation while adjusting the valves in the firing order sequence of 153624.

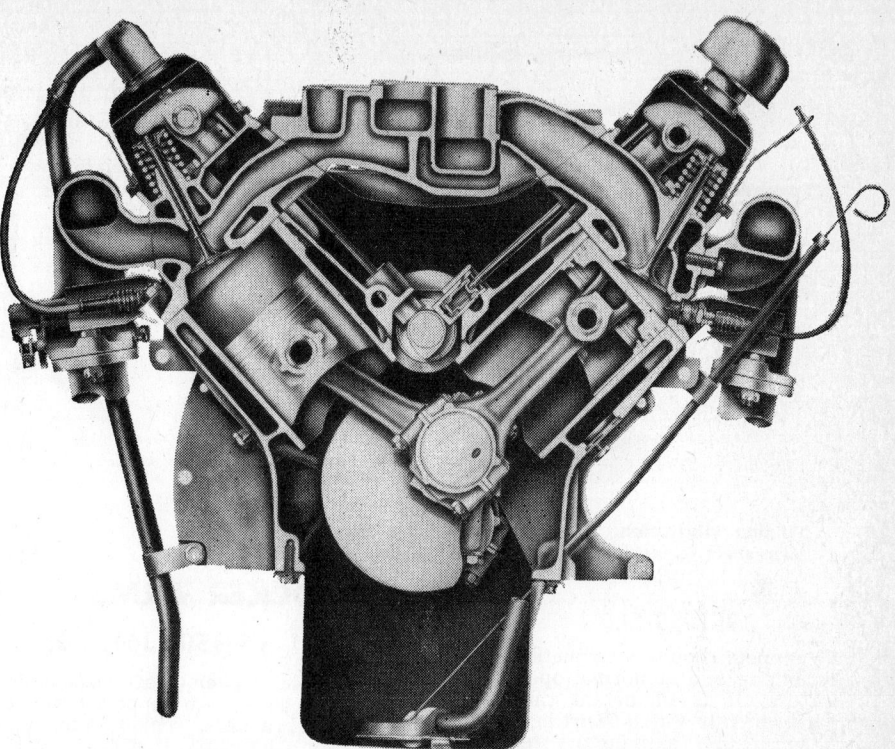

V8-350, 361, 383 with stamped steel rocker arms

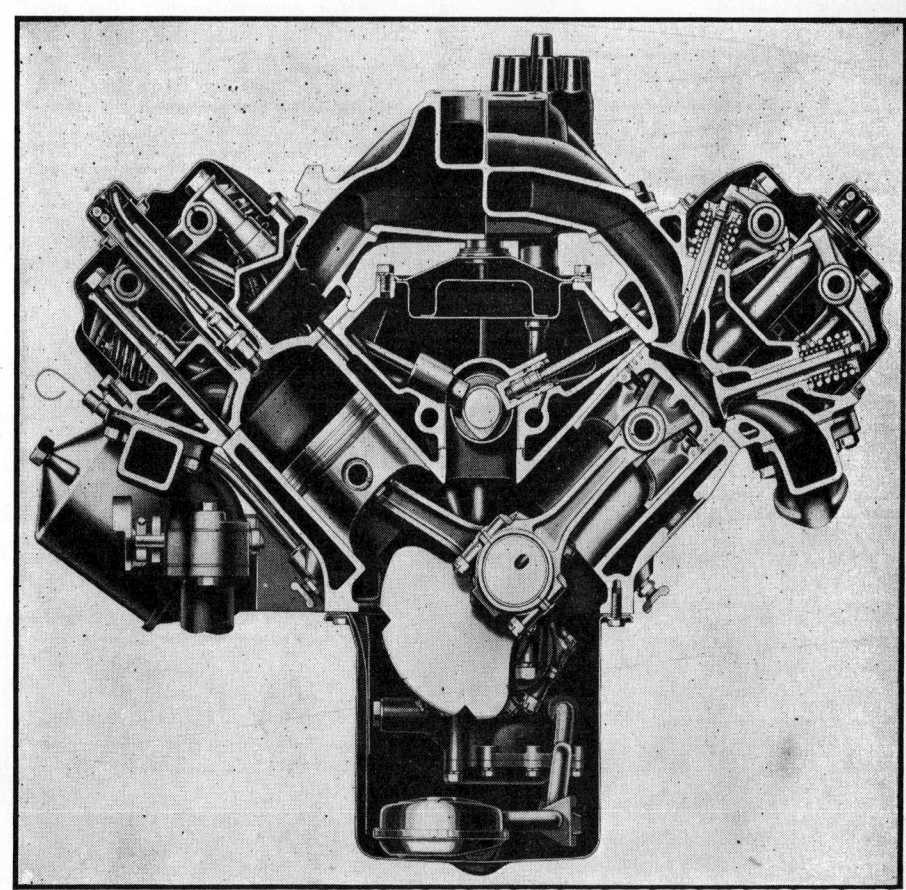

1953-57 engine with two rocker arm shafts for each bank, exhaust valve seat inserts and two springs for each valve

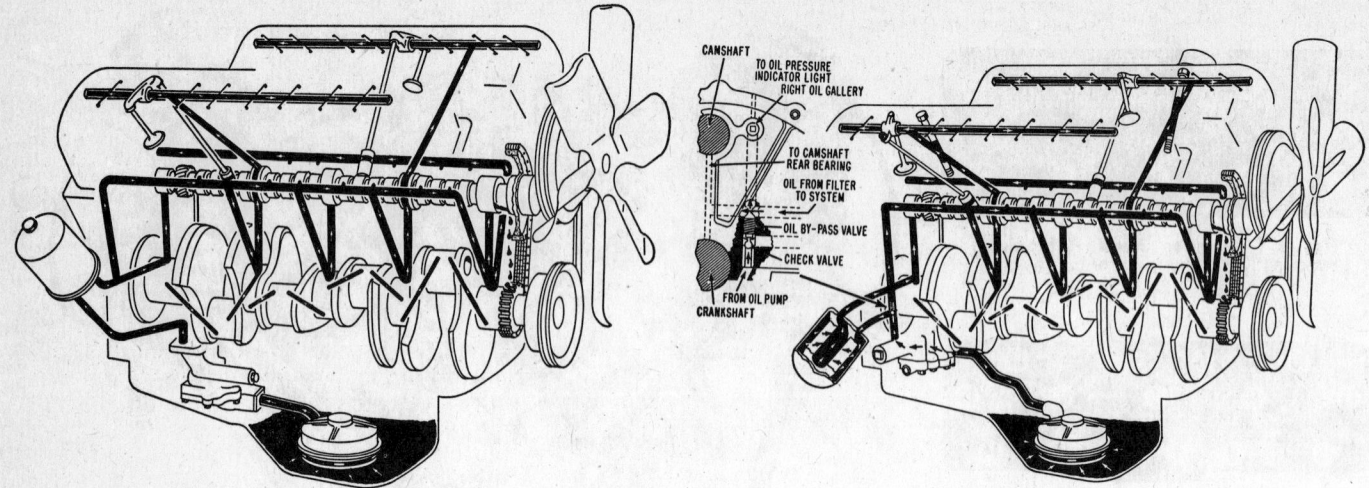

Engine lubrication. 1953-58 with single rocker arm shaft for each bank and forged rocker arms

Engine lubrication. V8-318, 326

1953-59 Six

Valve tappets should be adjusted with engine running and at normal operating temperature. It is important that the clearances given in *Valve Chart* be maintained to insure satisfactory engine performance. If the car is driven at continuous high speeds, an additional .002″ clearance for exhaust tappets is desirable.

If the car being serviced is one wherein the valves are not accessible when the hood is raised, proceed as follows:

1. Raise right front end of car and support it with a stand.
2. Remove right front wheel and splash shield access cover if one is provided.
3. Remove valve chamber covers.
4. With engine idling and warmed up to operating temperature, adjust the intake valves and then follow through by adjusting all exhaust valves.

V8s With Mechanical Lifters

Engines with mechanical lifters can be identified by the rocker arm adjusting screws. These screws are self-locking and when turning them during the process of adjustment they should indicate some resistance to turning (a minimum of 3 lb. ft. tension). If any screw turns too easily it should be replaced and, if necessary, the rocker arm as well.

Valve clearances should be set up after the engine is warmed up to operating temperature and to the clearances listed in the *Valve Specifications* table.

VALVE ARRANGEMENT

Front to Rear

1958-61 V8-350, 361, 383	E-I-I-E-E-I-I-E
1958-61 V8-318, 326	I-E-I-E-I-E-I-E
1953-57 V8	I-E-I-E-I-E-I-E
1953-59 Six	E-I-I-E-E-I-I-E-E-I-I-E
1960-61 Six	E-I-E-I-E-I-E-I-E-I-E

ROCKER ARMS

1958-61 V8-350, 361, 383

Disassemble rocker shaft assemblies by removing bolts from support brackets and sliding brackets, rocker arms and spacers from the shaft, Fig. 4. Clean all parts *except the oilite spacers* in a suitable solvent. Keep oilite spacers soaked in engine oil until reassembled. Inspect all parts for excessive wear. Test shaft end plugs for evidence of leaks.

When assembling, rocker shaft outlet holes must face away from the center of the engine. The second and fourth (wide) support brackets must be placed on the shaft with the oil passages facing the center of the engine. This is necessary to provide proper lubrication to the rocker assemblies.

Assemble rocker arms in pairs between brackets with an oilite spacer between the arms and with the push rod socket section of each arm close together rather than far apart. Install bolts through the brackets to hold the assembly together until ready to install on cylinder heads.

1953-57 & 1958-61 V8-318, 326

Sludge and gum formation in the rocker arms and shafts, Figs. 5 and 6, will restrict the normal flow to the rocker arms and valves. Each time the assemblies are removed (see *Cylinder Heads*), they

should be disassembled and thoroughly cleaned.

Clean all gum and sludge formation from the inside and outside of the shafts and rocker arms. Inspect the shafts for wear. Check the fit of the rocker arms on the shafts and the valve end of the rocker arms for excessive wear. If the rocker arm radius is grooved on the valve end, do not attempt grinding; replace the part.

When the assemblies are installed, make sure the rocker arms are correctly positioned to actuate the valves.

Check each push rod for a bent or damaged condition. If bent more than .020″, when checked with an indicator, replace the push rod. Do not attempt to straighten a bent rod. If a dial gauge is not available, at least check the rod for straightness by rolling it on a perfectly flat surface plate.

1960-61 Dart Six

To remove rocker arms, take off head cover outlet tube, rocker arm cover and rocker shaft bolts and retainers. Lift off rocker arm and shaft assembly.

Clean all parts. Be sure the inside of the shaft is clean and the oil holes are open. The drilled hole in the bore of the rocker arm must be open to the trough and valve end of the arms. The trough also feeds oil to the adjusting screw and push rod. Assemble and install as follows:

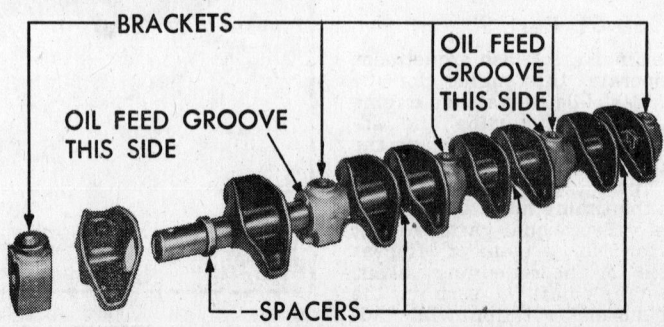

Fig. 4 Rocker arm shaft assembly. 1958-61 V8-350, 361, 383

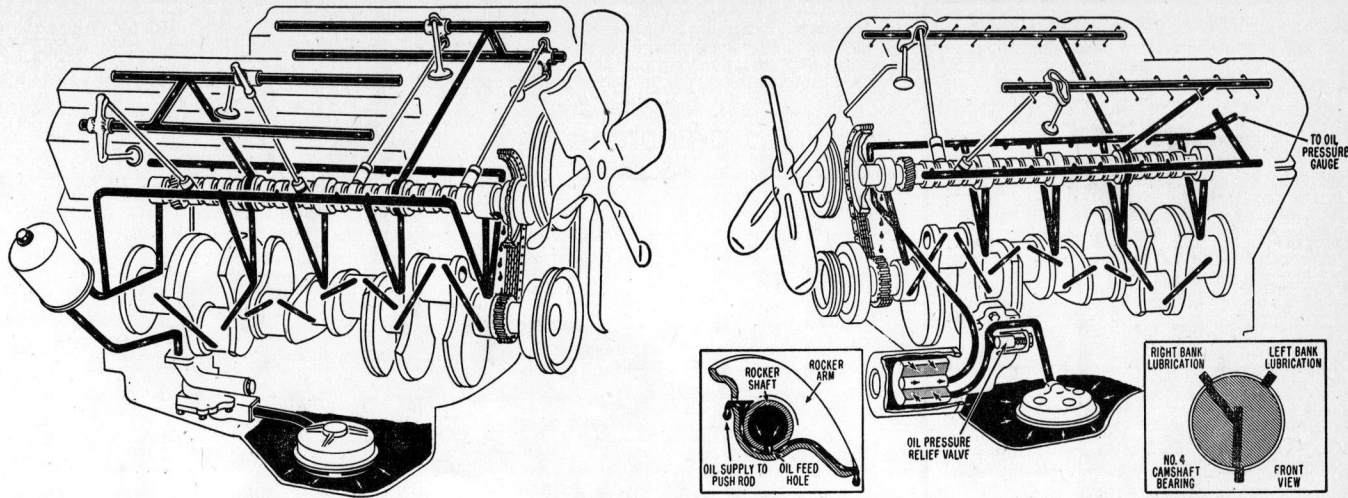

Engine lubrication. 1953-57 with two rocker arm shafts for each bank

Engine lubrication. V8-350, 361, 383

1. Referring to Fig. 6A, note flat on forward end of rocker shaft. The flat also denotes the upper side of the shaft. Rocker arms must be put on the shaft with the adjusting screw to the right side of the engine. Place one of the small retainers on the one long bolt and install the bolt in the rear hole in the shaft from the top side.

2. Install one rocker arm and one spacer; then two rocker arms and a spacer. Continue in same sequence until all rocker arms and spacers are on the shaft.

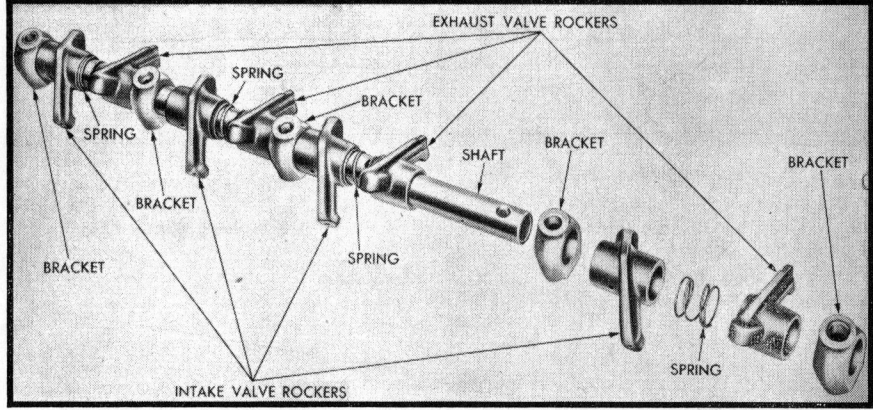

Fig. 6 Layout of rocker arm parts. 1953-58 Red Ram engines

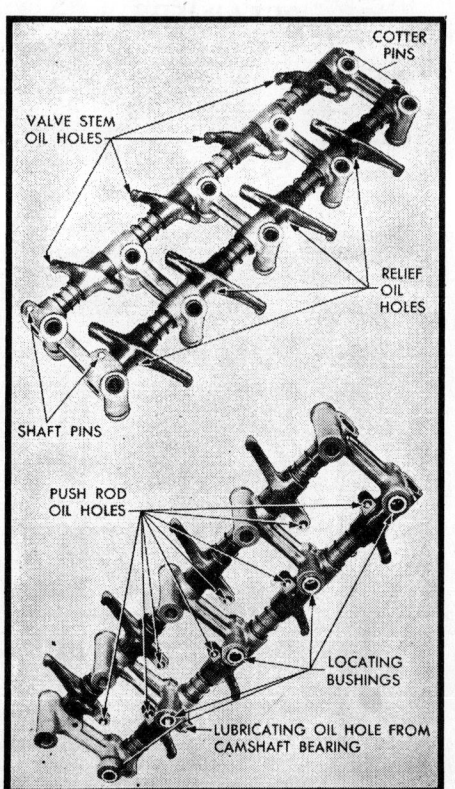

Fig. 5 Top and bottom view
1953-57 Super Red Ram

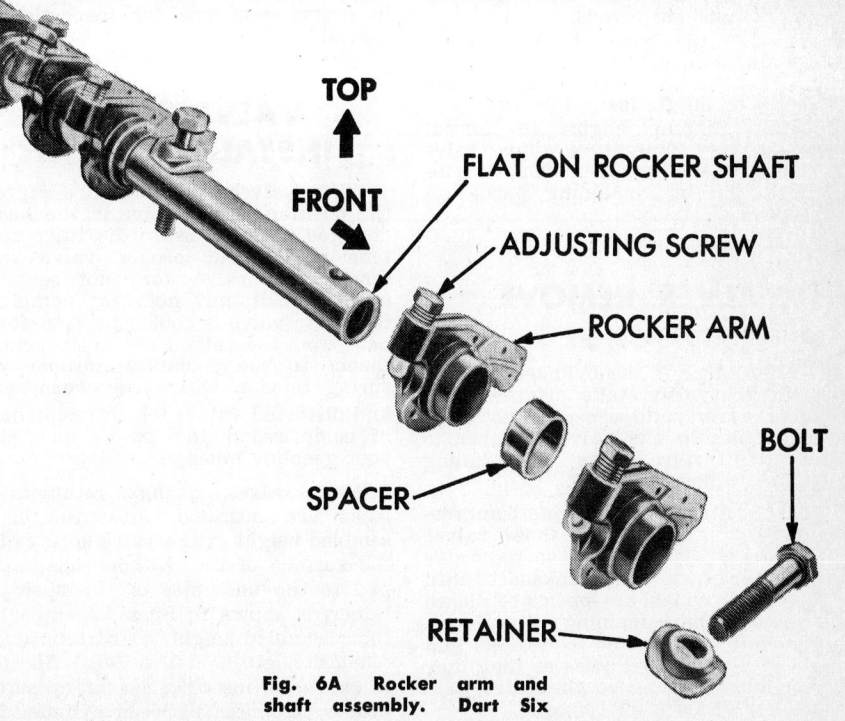

Fig. 6A Rocker arm and shaft assembly. Dart Six

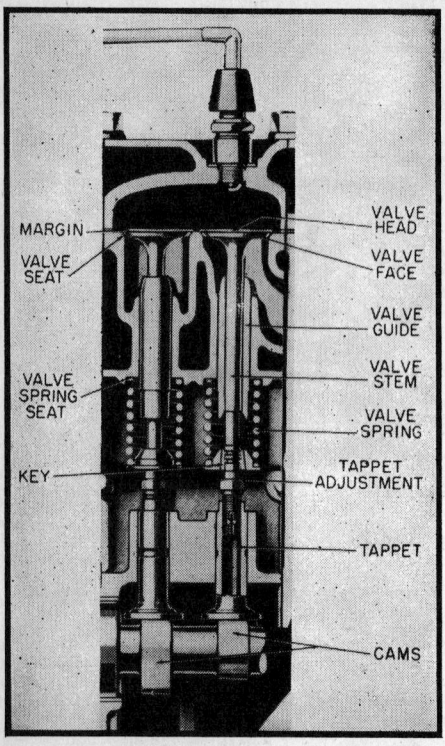

Fig. 7 Valve details. 1953-59 Six

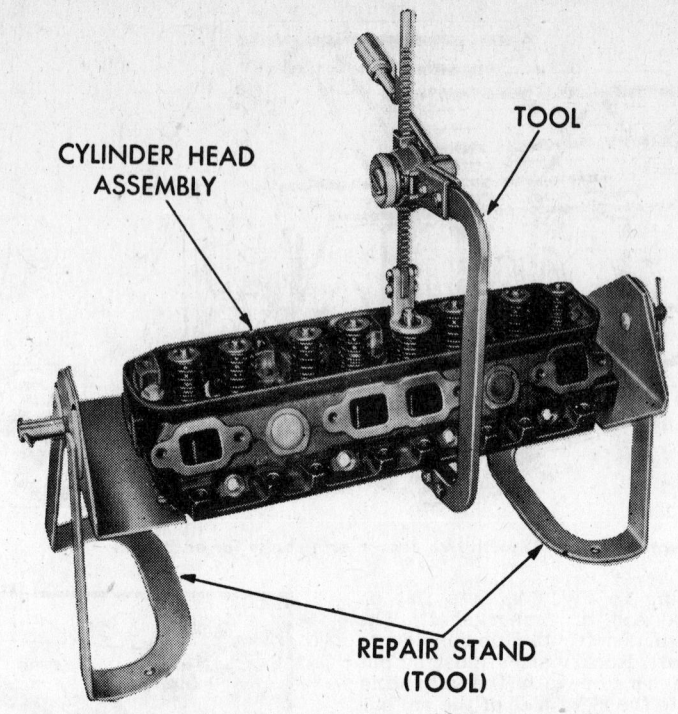

Fig. 8 Compressing valve spring

3. Place a bolt and small retainer in front hole in shaft.
4. Place a bolt and the one *wide* retainer through the center hole in the shaft with six rocker arms on each side of center.
5. Install remaining bolts and retainers, separating the four pairs of rocker arms.
6. Locate assembly on cylinder head and position rocker arm adjusting screws in push rods.
7. Tighten bolts finger tight, bringing retainers in contact with shaft *between rocker arms*. Then tighten bolts to 30 ft. lbs.
8. After running engine to normal operating temperature, adjust valve lash to specifications. Complete installation of remaining parts removed.

VALVES, REMOVE

1953-59 Six

After taking off the cylinder head as outlined previously, take off the valve chamber covers and use cloth to block off the holes in the valve chamber to prevent the valve locks from falling into the crankcase, Fig. 7.

With a suitable valve spring compressor, raise the springs on those valves which are closed and remove the valve locks. Then turn the crankshaft until those valves which are open are closed and remove the remaining valve locks.

Remove all valves and place them in a board with numbered holes so that they can be identified as to the valve port from which they were removed.

V8's and Dart Six

Place the cylinder head on its side and with a suitable valve spring compressor, compress the valve spring and remove the valve locks, Fig. 8. Release the tool and remove spring retainer and spring. Remove any burrs or sharp edges on the valve stem before removing the cup seal and valve. As the valves are removed, k e e p them in a numbered board or rack in the same order as they were in the head so they will be in proper sequence for inspection and assembly, Fig. 9.

VALVE SPRING INSTALLED HEIGHT

When valves and seats are reground the position of the valve in the head is changed so as to lessen the valve spring tension. Without proper valve spring tension the valve does not seat long enough or it may not seat completely. Since the valve is cooled by transferring heat from the valve head to the seat and thence to the coolant, improper valve spring tension will cause worn, pitted and distorted valves which result in loss of compression and power as well as poor gasoline mileage.

When valves, springs, retainers and locks are installed, measure the assembled height of the valve springs from the surface of the cylinder head spring pad to the underside of the spring retainer as shown in Figs. 9A and 9B. If the assembled height is greater than the dimension given in the *Valve Specifications Chart*, install a spacer or shim of proper thickness between cylinder head

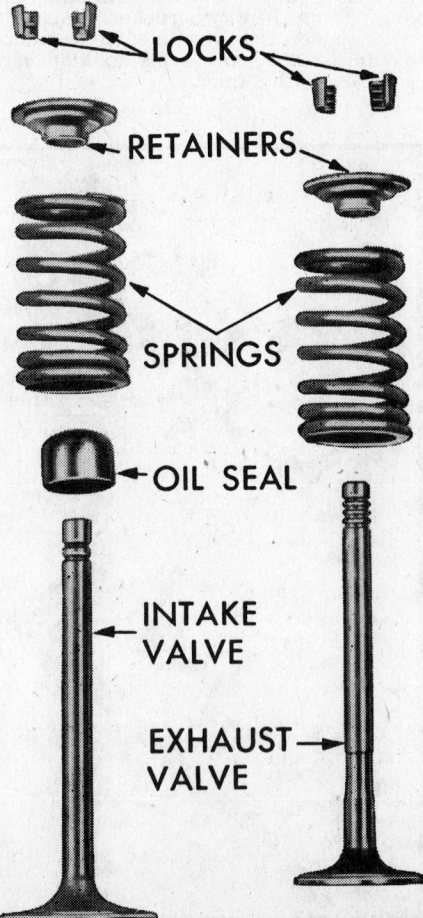

Fig. 9 Valves and related parts. Typical of all models

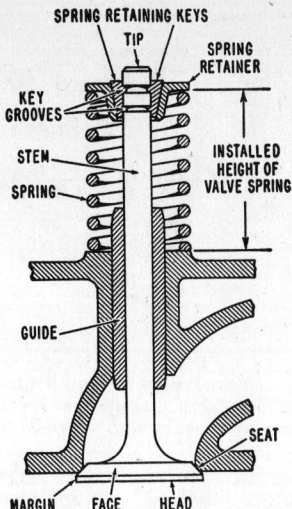

Fig. 9A Checking valve spring installed height on engines with removable valve guides

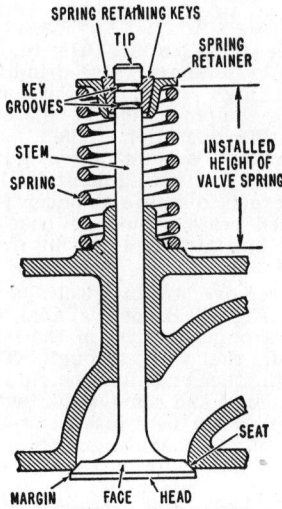

Fig. 9B Checking valve spring installed height on engines with integral valve guides

spring pad and spring to bring the assembled height to specifications.

Do not install spacers unless necessary. Excessive use of spacers will result in overstressing valve springs and overloading camshaft lobes which could lead to spring breakage and worn camshaft lobes.

VALVE SPRING TESTING

After taking out the valves, remove the springs and wash them with gasoline or other suitable solvent. Examine the springs for damage or corrosion due to acid etching, which will develop into surface cracks and cause spring failure.

Check the valve spring tension on a spring testing fixture if one is available, Fig. 10. If a fixture is not available, at least check the free length of each

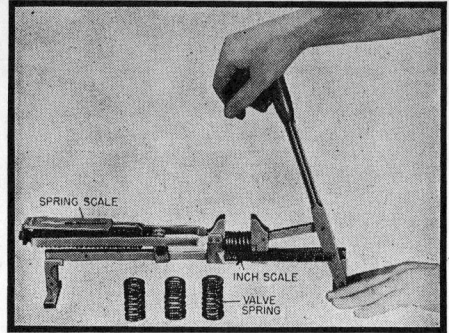

Fig. 10 Fixture for checking valve spring pressure

spring by standing it alongside a new spring. Any spring that does not conform to the pressure specifications given in the *Valve Data* chart within 10 per cent should be replaced. Likewise, any spring that stands shorter than the new spring used for comparison should be discarded.

1960-61 Dart Six

To check the length of the valve spring when installed, install the valve, spring retainer and locks (without the spring). With the locks seated in the retainer and the valve seated, the space between the spring seat on the cylinder head and the underside of the retainer should be $1\frac{5}{8}''$ to $1\frac{11}{16}''$. If more than $1\frac{11}{16}''$, use a $\frac{1}{16}''$ spacer under the spring when assembling.

VALVE GUIDES

1953-59 Six

Clean the valve guides with a wire guide brush and check the clearance between valve stems and guides carefully. The standard clearances are given in the *Valve Data* chart.

Excessive clearance between valve stems and guides will cause improper seating and burned valves. When there is too much clearance between intake valve stems and guides, there is a tendency to draw oil vapor through the guide on the suction stroke, causing excessive oil consumption, fouled spark plugs and poor low speed performance.

To check valve stem-to-guide clearance, take a new valve and place it in each valve guide and feel the clearance by moving the valve stem back and forth. If this check shows excessive clearance, it will be necessary to replace the valve guide.

If the clearance is not excessive when checking with a new valve but is excessive when checked with the old valve, the old valve stem is worn and a new valve must be installed.

If it is necessary to replace valve guides, the tool shown in Fig. 11 should be used. If not available, the old guides can be pulled out by using a suitable piece of pipe together with a long bolt and suitable washers.

After the new guides have been installed, they should be reamed, Fig. 12, to provide the clearances given in the *Valve Data* chart.

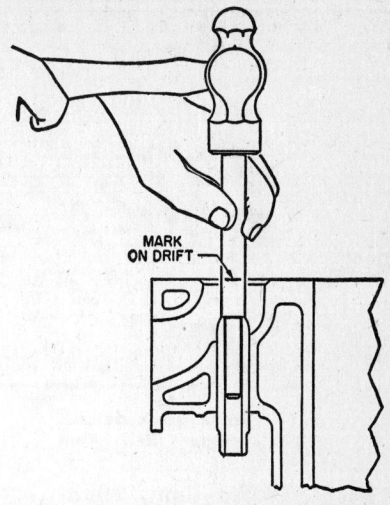

Fig. 11 Showing drift with pilot extending into valve guide for removing and installing guides. Mark drift as shown to indicate depth to which the guide must be driven in. 1953-59 Six

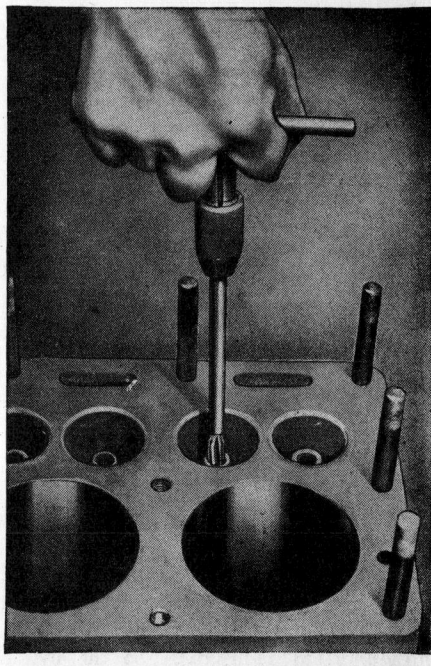

Fig. 12 Reaming valve guide. 1953-59 Six

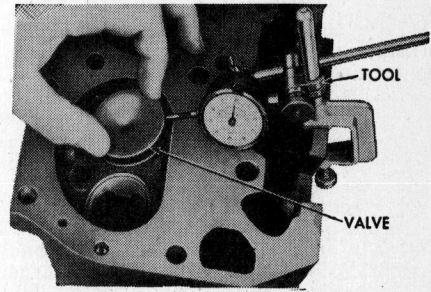

Fig. 13 Measuring valve guide wear with dial gauge

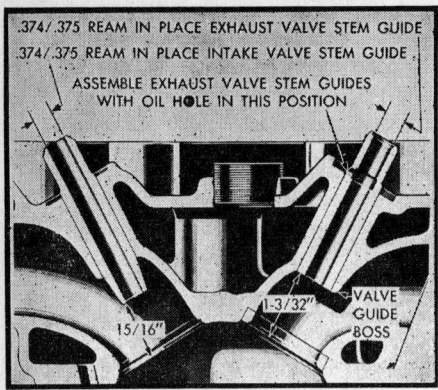

Fig. 14 Valve guide details. 1953-57 Super Red Ram

1955-57 Red Ram, 1958-61 V8, 1960-61 Dart Six

Valve guides in these engines are an integral part of the cylinder heads and, therefore, cannot be removed. For service, guide holes can be reamed oversize to accommodate one of three service valves with oversize stems (.005", .015" and .030").

Test the valve guides for wear as shown in Fig. 13. Install a suitable sleeve over the valve stem to hold the valve at working height in the head. Attach a dial indicator having valve stem at right angle with edge of valve. Move valve to and from indicator. Total movement should not exceed .010" on intake valves and .014" on exhaust valves. If tolerance is excessive, ream guide holes and install valves with overside stems. Always use a .005" reamer first, then (if necessary) a .015" reamer and finally a .030" reamer so the guides remain true in relation to the seat.

1953-57 Super Red Ram

Remove the old guides by driving them out through the top of the cylinder head. Drive the new guides in place by driving them up through the valve port opening. To determine how far the guides should be driven in, see Fig. 14.

When installing exhaust valve guides, make certain that the oil holes in the top of the guides are facing up.

After valve guides are properly installed, ream each guide so the inside diameter measures .374-375", Fig. 14.

VALVES, GRIND

Clean the valves with a wire wheel brush, making sure that all carbon is removed from the top and bottom of the heads as well as the gum which might have accumulated on the stems.

If refacing valves, take off only the minimum of metal required to clean up the valve faces. If the outer edge of the valve becomes too thin or sharp due to excessive grinding, the valve must be replaced. In other words, the valve head margin must be at least $\frac{3}{64}$", otherwise the valve must be replaced. This margin is the area above the contact surface of the valve face, Fig. 15.

Inspect the valve seats in the block for cracks, burns, pitting, ridges or improper angle. During any general engine overhaul it is advisable to reface the valve seats regardless of their condition, If new valve guides are required, they must be installed and reamed before refacing the seats if the equipment used for refacing the seats has a valve guide pilot.

The valve seat width after refacing should be a liberal $\frac{1}{16}$" for intake seats but not more than $\frac{3}{32}$" in any case. The width of exhaust seats should be $\frac{3}{64}$" to a liberal $\frac{1}{16}$".

Test valves for concentricity with seats and for tight seating. Valves can be tested by lightly coating the valve face with prussian blue and turning the valve against its seat. This indicates whether the seat is concentric with the valve guide *but does not prove that the valve face is concentric with the valve stem, or that the valve is seating all around.* After making this test, wash all blue from the surfaces, lightly coat the *valve seat* with blue and repeat the test to see whether a full mark is obtained on the valve. *Both tests are necessary to prove that a proper seat is being obtained.*

V8 Service Note

When valves and seats are reground the position of the valve in the head is changed so as to shorten the operating length of the hydraulic lifter. This means that the plunger is operating closer to its bottom position, and less clearance is available for the thermal expansion of the valve mechanism during high speed driving. Design of plunger travel includes a safety factor for normal wear and refacing of valves and seats. However, if face and seat grinding is carried to the point where the valve position is changed $\frac{1}{32}$" or more from its factory installed position, the dimension from the valve spring seat in the head to the valve tip should be checked with a special gauge, Fig. 16.

There is one gauge (C-3061) for double rocker arm engines; C-3436 for single rocker arm engines prior to 1958; and C-3648 for 1958 and later engines with stamped steel rocker arms. These simple gauges make it possible to quickly and easily check the length of the valve stem as illustrated. The overall dimension of the gauge indicates the maximum length of the valve stem while the bottom of the

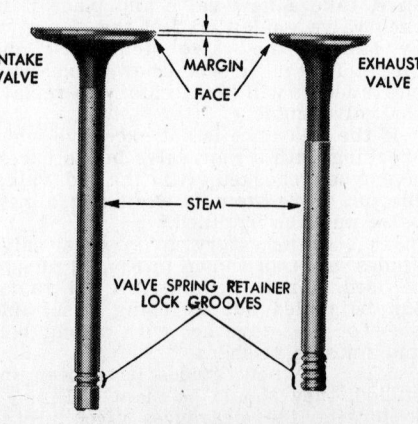

Fig. 15 Valve nomenclature

Fig. 16 Valve stem length gauge for checking length of valve stem after grinding valves. V8s

slot indicates the minimum length. The valve stem must be within these limits to allow the valve to fully close and to assure the designed hydraulic action of the valve lifter linkage.

VALVE SEAT INSERTS

1953-59 Six

Since these inserts are too hard to reface by ordinary valve grinding methods, a high speed grinder or special lapping equipment should be used to perform this operation. When using this equipment, be sure valve guides are clean and the valve guide pilot is a snug fit in order to assure a concentric finish. Finished seats should be checked with a dial indicator and runout should not exceed .001".

To remove an insert (if a suitable puller, Fig. 17, is not available) drill two holes at opposite sides of the insert, but not all the way through. Then cut through the undrilled portion with a sharp chisel and remove the two pieces.

To install a new insert, first remove all burrs and sharp edges from the seat recess. Then chill the new insert with dry ice to obtain maximum contraction and place it in the recess.

If a standard insert is too loose (less than .002" press fit) a .010" oversize seat is available. Before it can be installed, however, the recess in the block must be machined to fit the seat.

VALVE LIFTERS

1953-59 Six

Since these lifters are of the mushroom type operating in guide holes bored in the cylinder block, it is necessary to remove the camshaft in order to remove the lifters.

Follow instructions for removing the camshaft. Then remove the oil pan and take the lifters out through the bottom of the engine.

Lifters are furnished in oversizes of .001, .008, .030 and .060". When reaming the lifter guides for oversize lifters, the cylinder head and valves will have to be removed so that the reamer pilot can be inserted through the valve stem guide hole.

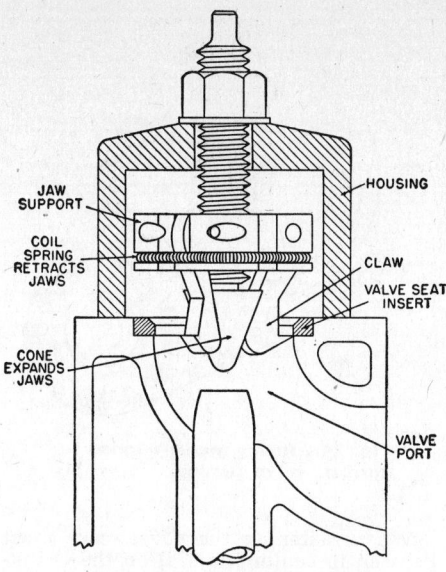

Fig. 17 Valve seat insert puller

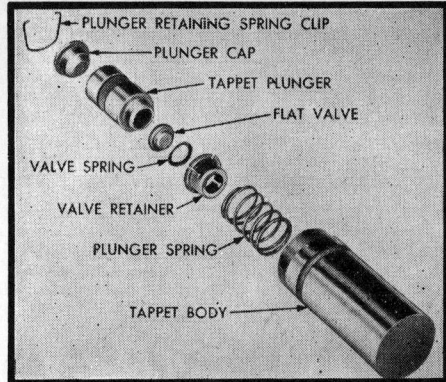

Fig. 19 Hydraulic valve lifter

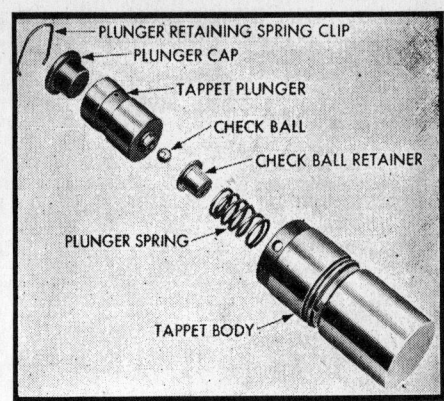

Fig. 20 Layout of ball valve type hydraulic lifter

1960-61 Dart Six

After taking off the rocker arm and shaft assembly, lift out push rods. The valve lifters may then be removed with a suitably long magnet rod. If the lifters cannot be removed with the magnet rod, a special tool (C-3661) may be used. Insert the tool through the push rod opening in the cylinder head and into lifter. Turn the handle to expand the tool in the lifter, then with a twisting motion remove the lifter from its bore. Place lifters in a board or rack with numbered holes since each lifter must be reinstalled in its original location.

Inspect the lifters for scores and the lower ends for pits and rough surfaces. Check crowned faces of lifters with a straightedge. If any negative crown (dish) is observed, the lifter should be replaced.

HYDRAULIC LIFTERS

V8 Engines

Figs. 18, 19, 20 illustrate the types of hydraulic valve lifters used. See the *Trouble Shooting Chapter* under the heading *Engine Noises* for causes of hydraulic valve lifter noise.

The easiest method for locating a noisy valve lifter is by the use of a piece of garden hose about 4 feet long. Place one end of the hose near each valve in progression and listen through the other end. In this manner the sound is localized, making it easier to determine which lifter is at fault.

Another method is to place a finger on the valve spring retainer. If the lifter is not functioning properly, a distinct shock will be felt when the valve returns to its seat.

In most cases where noise exists in one or more lifters, all lifter units should be removed and cleaned. If dirt, varnish or carbon is found to exist in one unit, it more than likely exists in all the units.

Removing Lifters

On the Super Red Ram engine the valve lifters can be removed through the push rod holes in the cylinder heads by the use of a tool of the type shown in Fig. 21, after removing the rocker shaft assemblies and push rods.

On 1953-57 and Red Ram engines the lifters may be removed after taking off the intake manifold. If the lifters are stuck in the bores due to carbon or varnish build-up, use a tool of the type shown in Fig. 21 and use a twisting motion to pull the lifter out of the bore. The sharp edge at the bottom of the lifter bore will shave the varnish and carbon deposits off the lifter as it is being withdrawn.

Servicing Lifters

Hydraulic plungers and bodies are not interchangeable. Therefore, it is advisable to work on one lifter at a time to avoid mixing parts. *Mixed parts will not function.*

In testing a lifter, secure a container deep enough to completely immerse the lifter assembly. Fill the container with clean kerosene. Remove the cap from the plunger and submerge the lifter. Allow the cylinder to fill with kerosene. Then remove the lifter and replace the cap.

Holding the lifter upright, insert the lower jaw of the pliers shown in Fig. 22 in the top groove of the lifter body. Engage the upper jaw of the pliers with the top of the plunger cap as shown.

Check the leakdown by compressing the pliers. If the plunger collapses almost instantly, disassemble the unit, clean it again and retest. If the lifter still does not function satisfactorily, install a new unit, being sure to test the new one before installing it in the engine.

CHAIN CASE COVER

1953-55 V8

To remove the chain case cover on these engines, proceed as follows:
1. Drain cooling system and disconnect water hoses.
2. Remove generator and mounting bracket and fan belt.
3. Remove radiator.
4. Use a suitable puller to remove crankshaft pulley.
5. With a chain hoist fastened to the intake manifold, slightly relieve engine weight on front motor support. Then remove the four motor support bolts.
6. Remove fan blades and hub.
7. Remove bolts that hold water pump housing to the cylinder block and heads. Then lift water pump, housing, front motor support and insulator up and away from the engine.

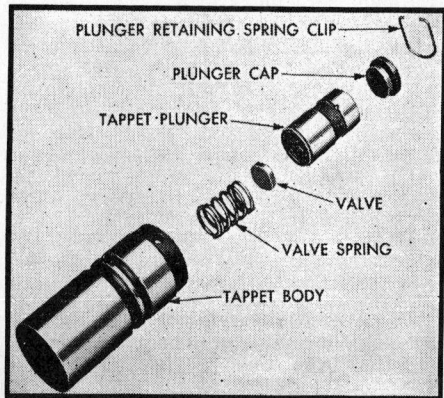

Fig. 18 Layout of flat valve type hydraulic lifter

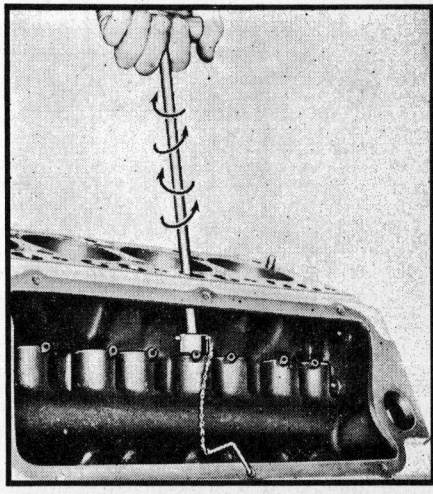

Fig. 21 Removing hydraulic valve lifter

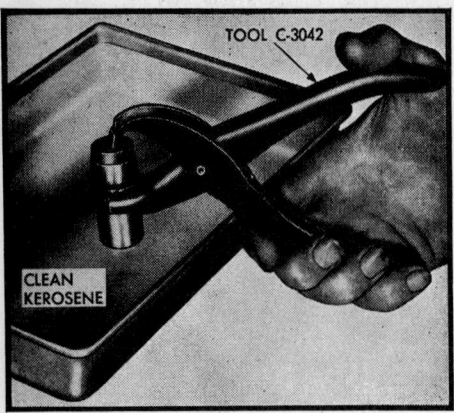

Fig. 22 Testing hydraulic valve lifter

Fig. 23 Special centering tool for chain case cover oil seal. 1953-59 Six

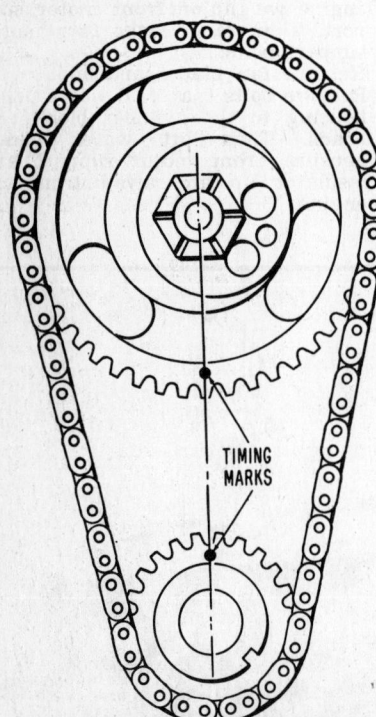

Fig. 24 Timing marks aligned for correct valve timing. V8s

8. Loosen the bolts that hold the oil pan to the cylinder block. Then drop the pan slightly to clear the chain case cover.
9. Disconnect fuel lines at fuel pump.
10. Remove fuel pump from chain case cover.
11. Unfasten chain case cover from cylinder block and pull the cover out and away from the block.
12. Replace the cover oil seal.
13. Reinstall the cover in the reverse order from which it was removed, being sure to guard against water and oil leaks.

1958-61 V8-350, 361, 383

1. Drain cooling system.
2. Remove radiator, fan and belt.
3. Remove water pump and housing as an assembly.
4. Remove crankshaft bolt and pulley from vibration damper and remove damper with a puller.
5. Remove key from crankshaft.
6. Remove chain case cover and gasket. *Use extreme caution to avoid damaging the oil pan gasket; if damaged it will be necessary to remove the oil pan in order to install a new pan gasket.*

1956-57 & 1958 Red Ram

1. Disconnect water hoses.
2. Remove generator.
3. Remove radiator.
4. Remove retaining bolt and slide crankshaft pulley off end of crankshaft.
5. Remove fan blades and hub.
6. Remove water pump.
7. Loosen oil pan bolts and drop pan slightly to clear chain case cover.
8. Remove fuel pump.
9. Remove chain case cover.

1959-61 V8-318, 326

1. Remove radiator, fan and belt.
2. Remove water pump and housing as a unit.
3. Remove crankshaft pulley.
4. Remove key from crankshaft.
5. Remove fuel pump.
6. Remove chain case cover and gasket, *using extreme caution to avoid damaging oil pan gasket otherwise oil pan will have to be removed. It is normal to find particles of neoprene collected between crankshaft seal retainer and oil slinger.*

1960-61 Dart Six

1. To remove cover, drain cooling system and remove radiator and fan.
2. Remove vibration damper with a puller.
3. Loosen oil pan bolts to allow clearance and remove chain case cover.
4. Reverse above procedure to install cover.

1953-59 Six

When installing the chain case cover on these engines, place a new gasket in the cover, then drive the oil seal in position, using a drift or a flat piece of metal slightly larger than the seal to assure a tight, even contact between the seal and its seat.

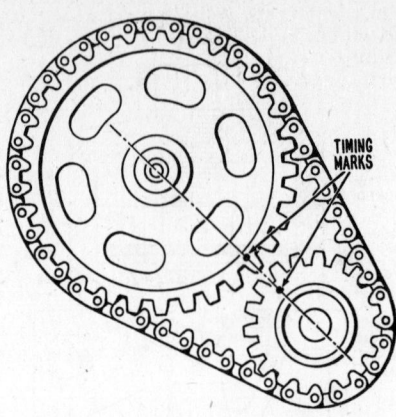

Fig. 24A Timing marks aligned for correct valve timing. Dart Six

When fastening the cover, care must be used to center the seal on the crankshaft before tightening the cover screws. A special centering tool, Fig. 23, is available to make the installation. When using this tool, tighten the screws only enough to hold the cover in place. Then insert the tool, holding it by the crankshaft starting jaw, tightening the jaw nut only finger tight. As the cover screws are being tightened and the gasket is being compressed, tighten the jaw nut, maintaining a slight tension between the centering tool and the seal. Then remove the tool, install the starting jaw and tighten it to a minimum of 108 lbs. ft. torque.

TIMING CHAIN

1953-55 V8

After removing the chain case cover as outlined previously, remove the camshaft sprocket hub nut, fuel pump eccentric and dowel assembly. The camshaft sprocket and timing chain may now be taken off.

To install, rotate the crankshaft until the zero mark on the crankshaft sprocket is exactly in line with the center of the camshaft. Temporarily install the camshaft sprocket (less chain) and line up the hub dowel pin hole with the sprocket dowel pin hole, while at the same time positioning the camshaft sprocket zero mark exactly in line with the center of the crankshaft. A straight edge should be used to check the accuracy of this alignment, Fig. 24.

Remove the camshaft sprocket again and position it in the timing chain. Then place the chain on the crankshaft sprocket. Install the camshaft sprocket, being sure both zero timing marks are facing each other and in line with the center of both the camshaft and crankshaft.

1956-61 V8

To install chain and sprockets, lay both the camshaft and crankshaft sprockets on the bench. Position the sprockets so that the timing marks are next to each other. Place the chain on both sprockets, then push the gears apart as far as the chain will permit. Use a straightedge to form a line through the exact centers of both gears. The timing marks must be on this line, Fig. 24.

This is the same procedure as in previous models, except that now the alignment is done on the bench rather than on the engine.

Slide the chain with both sprockets on the camshaft and crankshaft at the same time; then recheck the alignment.

1960-61 Dart Six

1. After removing chain case cover as outlined above, take off camshaft sprocket attaching bolt.
2. Remove chain with camshaft sprocket.
3. Clean all parts and dry with compressed air.
4. Inspect chain for broken or damaged links. Inspect sprockets for cracks and chipped, worn or damaged teeth.

Installation

1. Turn crankshaft so sprocket timing mark is toward and directly in line with centerline of camshaft.
2. Temporarily install camshaft sprocket. Rotate camshaft to position sprocket timing mark toward and directly in line with centerline of crankshaft; then remove camshaft sprocket.
3. Place chain on crankshaft sprocket and position camshaft sprocket in chain so sprocket can be installed with timing marks aligned without moving camshaft, Fig. 24A.
4. Install parts removed in reverse order of removal.

1953-59 Six

For correct valve timing, the timing chain and sprockets should be assembled so that the marks on the sprockets line up as shown in Fig. 25. Follow the general procedure outlined for V8 engines.

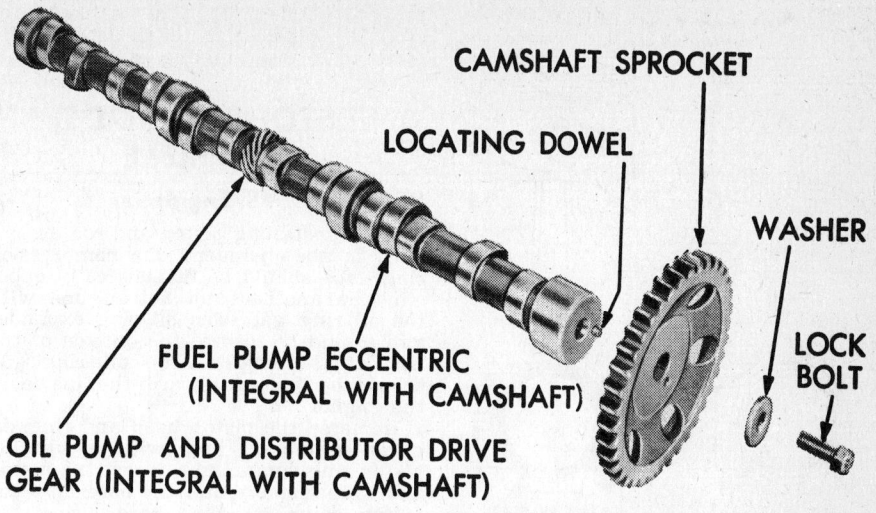

Fig. 26A   Camshaft and sprocket.   Dart Six

VALVE TIMING DATA

Dart

Year	Model	Intake Opens①	Intake Closes②	Exhaust Opens③	Exhaust Closes④
1960	Six	0	52	40	8
	V8-318⑤	17	47	55	9
	V8-318⑥	13	55	51	17
	V8-383	20	68	60	28
1961	Six	8	44	48	TDC
	V8⑦	17	47	55	9
	V8⑧	13	55	51	17
	D500	24	64	64	24

Dodge

Year	Model	Intake Opens	Intake Closes	Exhaust Opens	Exhaust Closes
1953	All	8	36	37	7
1954	Six	12	44	50	6
	V8	17	47	55	9
1955	Six	12	44	50	6
	V8	14	50	52	12
1956	D62-1	12	44	50	6
	D63-1	14	50	52	12
	D63-2, D63-3	11	53	49	15
	D500	12	60	54	18
1957	Six	12	44	50	6
	V8	10	58	56	16
	D500	20	56	58	18
1958	Six	12	44	50	6
	V8	10	58	56	16
	D500	15	57	57	15
1959	MD1	12	44	50	6
	MD2	14	54	56	12
	MD3	15	57	57	15
	D500	20	60	58	22
1960	D500	20	60	58	22
	Others	15	57	57	15
1961	D500 Polara	24	64	64	24
	D500 Ram Ind.	20	68	68	20
	Others	15	57	57	15

① —Degrees before top dead center.
② —Degrees after bottom dead center.
③ —Degrees before bottom dead center.
④ —Degrees after top dead center.
⑤ —Seneca and Pioneer.
⑥ —Phoenix.
⑦ —Two barrel carburetor.
⑧ —Four barrel carburetor.

CAMSHAFT

1953-59 Six

The general procedure for removing the camshaft is outlined below. In addition, on some earlier models it may be necessary to take off the front end sheet metal in order to provide space to extract the camshaft from the engine. This can be determined by measuring the length

of the engine and comparing it with the space available between the chain case and front grille.

1. Remove radiator, cylinder head, fuel pump, oil pump and valve cover plates.
2. Support front of engine and remove front support, chain case cover, chain and camshaft sprocket.
3. Raise valves and hold them up by inserting two wooden wedges under each valve head, Fig. 26. (This operation is not necessary if valves are to be ground as the valves will have to be removed anyway).
4. Raise valve lifters and hold them up with wire, spring type clothes pins, Fig. 26, or other suitable means.
5. Rotate the camshaft as it is being withdrawn from the engine so that the cam lobes will clear successive obstacles.

1960-61 Dart Six

The camshaft is supported by four precision type, steel-backed, babbitt-lined bearings. Rearward thrust is taken by the rear face of the sprocket hub, contacting the front of the engine block.

The camshaft, Fig. 26A, can be removed after removing the grille, radiator and timing chain. To remove the cam-

Fig. 25 For correct valve timing, marks on sprockets should line up as shown. If there is more than ¾" slack in the chain, it should be replaced. 1953-59 Six

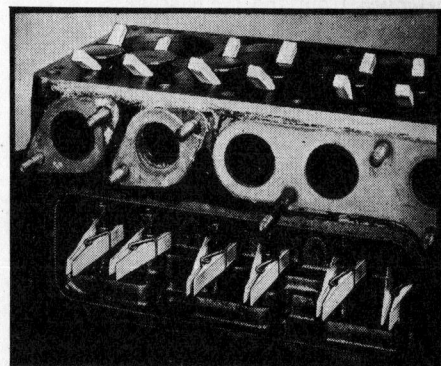

Fig. 26 One method of holding up valves and tappets for camshaft removal. 1953-59 Six

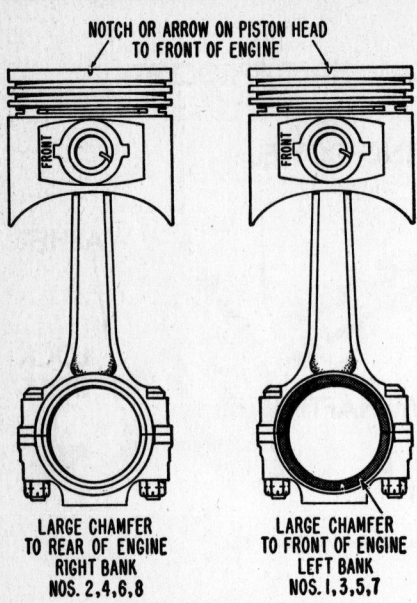

NOTCH OR ARROW ON PISTON HEAD
TO FRONT OF ENGINE

FRONT

LARGE CHAMFER
TO REAR OF ENGINE
RIGHT BANK
NOS. 2,4,6,8

LARGE CHAMFER
TO FRONT OF ENGINE
LEFT BANK
NOS. 1,3,5,7

**Fig. 27 , Correct assembly
of pistons and rods. V8s**

shaft bearings the torque converter or flywheel must also be removed.

1. Remove valve lifters, oil pump and distributor.
2. Slide camshaft out of engine.
3. Remove welch plug back of rear camshaft bearing.
4. Remove bearings with suitable puller equipment.
5. Install new bearings, being sure the oil holes in bearings line up with corresponding oil holes in crankcase.

V8 Engines

To remove the camshaft, remove all valve lifters, timing chain and sprockets. Remove distributor and oil pump-distributor drive gear. Remove fuel pump and see that push rod has moved away from eccentric drive cam. Withdraw the camshaft from the engine, using care to see that the cam lobes do not damage the camshaft bearings.

If camshaft bearings are to be replaced, it is recommended that the engine be removed from the chassis and the crankshaft taken out in order that any chips or foreign material may be removed from the oil passages.

PISTONS & RODS, REMOVE

After removing the cylinder heads and oil pan, examine the cylinder bores above the ring travel area. If the bores are worn so that a shoulder or ridge exists at this point, remove the ridge with a ridge reamer to avoid damaging rings or cracking ring lands of pistons during removal.

Remove the connecting rod caps and push the pistons and rods out of the cylinders, using care to prevent rod bolts from nicking crankshaft journals. Make sure rods and pistons are properly numbered so they can be reinstalled in their proper cylinders. It is advisable to install the caps on the rods as they are removed to avoid mixing parts.

PISTONS & RODS, ASSEMBLE

V8 Engines

When installing piston and rod assemblies in the cylinders, the compression ring gaps should be diametrically opposite one another and not in line with the oil ring gap. The oil ring expander gap should be toward the outside of the "V" of the engine. The oil ring gap should be turned toward the inside of the engine "V".

Immerse the piston head and rings in clean engine oil and, with a suitable piston ring compressor, insert the piston and rod assembly into the bore. Tap the piston down into the bore, using the handle of a hammer.

Assemble the pistons to the rods as shown in Fig. 27.

1960-61 Dart Six

Piston and rod assemblies must be installed with the notch on the piston head toward the front of the engine, and the oil hole in the connecting rod toward the manifold side of the engine.

1953-59 Six

When assembling the piston to the connecting rod, assemble aluminum pistons so that the slotted side is opposite the oil hole in the connecting rod.

Install the piston and rod assembly in the cylinder so that the oil hole in the connecting rod is toward the valve side of the engine.

PISTONS

Due to the necessity of maintaining piston balance, all pistons are machined to the same weight in grams, regardless of oversize. Only finished pistons are available in service and are supplied in standard and the following oversizes: .010, .020, .030, .040, .050, .060 inch.

The recommended clearance between the thrust face of the piston and cylinder wall is .00075" to .00175" when meas-

Fig. 29 Using special tool (1) in crankshaft oil hole to turn upper main bearing in place

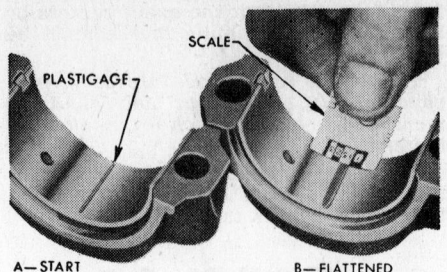

PLASTIGAGE
SCALE

A—START   B—FLATTENED

Fig. 28 Checking bearing clearance by measuring width of flattened Plastigage

ured with a micrometer and a dial indicator. Or the clearance can be checked with a ½" wide feeler .0015" thick.

Starting with the No. 1 cylinder, coat the bore very lightly with a light engine oil (10W). Insert the piston in the bore upside down with the feeler stock between the thrust face of the piston and cylinder wall.

While holding the piston, draw the feeler stock out straight with a spring scale attached to it. The amount of pull to withdraw the feeler stock should be as given in the chart. Fit the remaining pistons in like manner.

PISTON PINS

1960-61 Dart Six

Piston pins should be a very light thumb press fit in the piston with the parts at room temperature (70°). Piston pins are supplied in standard size only. If excessive clearance is noted, both piston and pin should be replaced.

1958-61 V8-350, 361, 383

With new pistons and new pins at room temperature (70°), the pin should be a very light thumb press fit in the piston. The pin is tightly (pressed) fitted in the connecting rod. Replacement is necessary after any noticeable free play has developed between the pin and piston. Pins are available through Chrysler only with new pistons. New pistons are supplied with properly fitted pins.

1953-57 V8 & 1958-61 V8-318, 326

Piston pins are supplied in standard size and oversizes of .003" and .008". The fit of the pin in both the connecting rod and piston should be a tight thumb press fit with the parts at normal room temperature.

When using an expansion reamer to fit piston pins, start off by taking a very light cut. Try the fit. Then ream and try the fit again until the pin can be pushed into the rod and piston as described above.

1953-59 Six

To remove a piston pin, take off the lock rings and heat the piston in a container of hot water. Push the pin out with hand pressure. If it cannot be removed with hand pressure, use a suitable drift to drive it out.

When removing the pin with a drift, hold the piston in one hand, insert the drift and tap lightly with a hammer.

Do not hold the connecting rod during this operation, otherwise misalignment of the rod may occur.

If the new pin cannot be installed in the piston with thumb pressure, enlarge the holes with an expansion reamer.

Take only a light cut with the reamer. Ream the holes until the pin can be pushed into the piston with the pressure of both thumbs.

The fit of the pin in the connecting rod should be a tight thumb press fit with the parts at normal room temperature of 70°F.

PISTON RINGS

When new rings are to be installed without reboring cylinders, the glazed cylinder wall should be slightly dulled, but without increasing the bore diameter. This is done with a "Glaze-buster" or with a hone equipped with the finest grade of stones.

New piston rings must be checked for clearance in piston grooves and for gap in cylinder bores. The latter operation must be measured with the ring about two inches from the bottom of the cylinder bore to which it is fitted. An inverted piston can be used to push the rings down to this position. Cylinder bores and piston grooves must be clean, dry and free from carbon and burrs.

Check the clearance of each ring in its piston groove by installing the ring and then inserting feeler gauges *under* the ring. Any wear that occurs in the piston groove forms a step or ridge at the inner portion of the lower land. If the feeler gauge is inserted above the ring, the ring may rest on the step instead of on the worn portion of the lower land, and a false measurement of clearance may result.

If the piston grooves have worn to the extent that relatively high steps or ridges exist on the lower lands, the piston should be replaced because the steps

Fig. 31 Screws (1) must be removed from chain case cover before front bearing cap can be taken off. 1953-59 Six

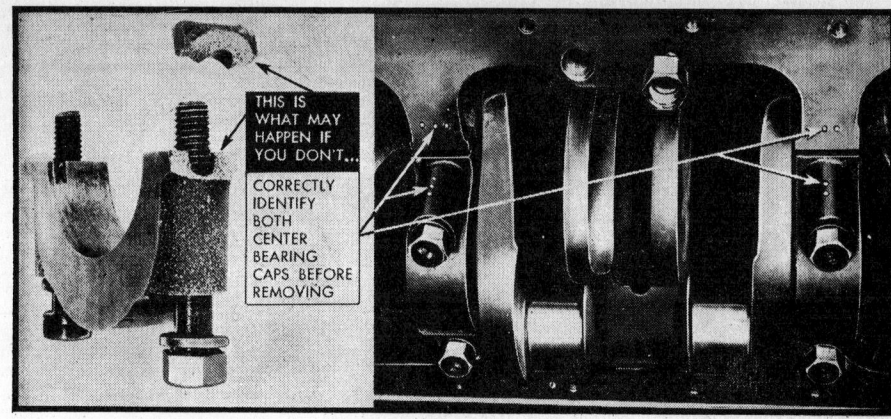

THIS IS WHAT MAY HAPPEN IF YOU DON'T...

CORRECTLY IDENTIFY BOTH CENTER BEARING CAPS BEFORE REMOVING

Fig. 30 Method of identifying main bearing caps. 1953-59 Six

will interfere with the operation of the new rings and ring clearances will be excessive. Piston rings are not furnished in oversize widths to compensate for ring groove wear.

See the *Piston and Ring Data* chart for ring groove clearances and end gap clearances.

ROD BEARINGS

Connecting rod bearings can be replaced without removing the piston and rod assemblies merely by taking off the rod cap and replacing the upper and lower bearing halves.

The clearance between the bearings and crankshaft can be measured with Plastigage as follows:

1. Remove bearing cap and wipe oil from crankshaft journal and bearing.
2. With crankpin at approximately bottom dead center, place a piece of Plastigage in the center of the bearing, Fig. 28.
3. Reinstall the bearing cap and tighten the bolts to the torque value given in the *Engine Tightening* table.
4. Remove the bearing cap again and check the bearing clearance by measuring the width of the flattened Plastigage, Fig. 28. The measuring strip is supplied in the same envelope which contains the Plastigage.

MAIN BEARINGS

V8 & Dart Six Engines

Caution—Main bearing clearance can be checked with Plastigage in the same manner described for rod bearings. If bearings are measured with the engine in the chassis, the crankshaft must be supported in order to take up clearance between the upper bearing insert and crankshaft journal. This can be done by tightening bearing caps of adjacent bearings with .005" to .015" cardboard, (such as a calling card) between lower bearing shell and journal. Use extreme care when this is done to avoid unnecessary strain on the crankshaft or bearings or a false reading may be obtained. Do

not rotate crankshaft while Plastigage is installed. *Be sure to remove cardboard.* To install new bearings, proceed as follows:

1. Remove bearing cap and worn lower shell.
2. Rotate crankshaft in normal direction to turn upper bearing shell out of crankcase. Use a cotter pin with a flattened head or the special tool made for the purpose in the crankshaft oil hole, to contact the bearing and force it out, Fig. 29.
3. Place a new upper shell on the crankshaft journal with the locating notch in the correct position and rotate the shaft to turn the bearing in place.
4. Install the lower bearing shell in the cap.
5. Tighten all cap nuts to the torque value given in the *Engine Tightening* table.

1953-59 Six

Main bearings can be replaced after removal of the oil pan. Both standard and undersize bearings are available for service replacement (see Fig. 30).

Never use a new bearing half with an old bearing half. Never file or shim original bearing caps in an attempt to fit bearings.

To install a new set of bearings, proceed as follows:

1. Remove oil pan, clutch housing pan and oil suction pipe.
2. Disconnect chain case cover from the oil pan seal and remove oil pan gasket seal plate, Fig. 31.
3. Loosen bearing caps slightly.
4. Remove one cap at a time and replace both upper and lower bearing shells.
5. Before installing bearings, be sure crankshaft is not nicked or scored.
6. Measure clearance between bearing and crankshaft when installing either old or new bearings.
7. Plastigage may be used to measure clearance as shown in Fig. 12. Lacking Plastigage, however, coat a piece of .0015" brass shim stock (½" wide and 1" long) with oil and place it between the bearing and crankshaft.

ALTERNATOR & REGULATOR

Year	Unit Number	Ground Polarity and Rotation	Field Coil Draw Amperes	Current Output			Operating Voltage			Voltage Regulator Point Gap	Regulator Armature Air Gap
				Engine R.P.M.	Amperes	Volts	Engine R.P.M.	Amperes	Voltage @ 120° ①		

DODGE & DART

Year	Unit Number	Ground Polarity and Rotation	Field Coil Draw Amperes	Engine R.P.M.	Amperes	Volts	Engine R.P.M.	Amperes	Voltage @ 120° ①	Voltage Regulator Point Gap	Regulator Armature Air Gap
1961	2095060	Neg.–C	2.38–2.75②	1250	35③	14.6	1250	15	13.5–14.1④	.015	.048–.052
	2095425	Neg.–C	2.38–2.75②	1250	40③	14.6	1250	15	13.5–14.1④	.015	.048–.052
	2095100	Neg.–C	2.38–2.75②	1250	40③	14.6	1250	15	13.5–14.1④	.015	.048–.052

①—For each 10° rise in temperature subtract .04 volt; for each 10° drop in temperature add .04 volt. Temperature is checked with a thermometer 2 inches from installed voltage regulator cover.

②—Current draw at 12 volts while turning rotor shaft by hand.

③—If output is low, stator or rectifier is shorted.

④—At 2200 RPM there should be a voltage increase of .2 to .7 volt.

---

8. Install the bearing cap and draw it up tight.

9. If the clearance is not excessive, there will be a slight drag when the crankshaft is turned. The desired clearance is given in the *Engine Bearing Data* chart.

10. Tighten caps to the recommended torque.

NOTE—The tool shown in Fig. 29 or a flattened cotter pin head may be used in the crankshaft oil hole to contact the upper bearing half and force it out.

Replacement Caps—In case of warpage or other damage to main bearing caps, replacement caps are available which have stud holes 1/64″ larger than the original caps and 1/16″ shorter. This permits shimming or filing to adjust for variations between original and replacement caps. Never file, dress down or shim original bearing caps.

CRANKSHAFT REAR OIL SEAL

1953-59 Six

The rear main bearing cap contains oil seals and gaskets to prevent leakage of oil at this point. The seals and gaskets should be carefully located in the cap before installation, Fig. 32.

The seal retainer bolts should be left loose until the bearing cap is tightened in order to properly locate the seal to the crankshaft.

When replacing the upper half of the two-piece seal, it will be necessary to remove the transmission and clutch and fluid drive.

V8 & Dart Six Engines

A braided oil seal is pressed into the upper and lower grooves behind the rear main bearing. Directly in front of this seal is an oil slinger which deflects the oil back into the oil pan. Should the braided seal require replacement, the installation of the lower half is accomplished as follows:

With the bearing cap and lower bearing half removed, install a new seal so that both ends protrude above the cap. Tap the seal down into position or roll it snugly in its groove with a smooth rounded tool. Then cut off the protruding ends of the seal with a sharp knife or razor blade.

Installing Upper Seal

Although the usual practice is to remove the crankshaft when the upper half of the seal is to be replaced it is possible to do the job without removing the crankshaft as follows:

To remove the seal, use needle-nose pliers to grasp the end of the seal which is most accessible. Pull the seal downward while rotating the crankshaft slowly in the direction that the seal is being removed.

To install the new seal, fasten a length of wire or strong string such as fishing line securely to one end of the new seal. See that the point of fastening is not bulky and that it is not over 3/8″ from the end of the seal. Coat the seal with Lubriplate. Pass the free end of the wire or string up over the crankshaft at the point where the seal is to be installed. Then exert a firm, steady pull on the wire or string and at the same time rotate the crankshaft slowly in the direction of the pull. This will help to move the seal into position. When the installation is completed, trim the ends of the seal flush with the engine block.

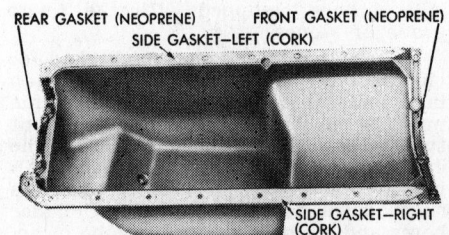

Fig. 32A Location of oil pan gaskets. Dart Six

Fig. 32 Crankshaft rear oil seals. 1953-59 Six

OIL PAN

1960-61 V8-361, 383

1. Disconnect battery cable.
2. Disconnect steering linkage from idler arm and steering arm.
3. Remove outlet vent pipe and disconnect exhaust pipe branches from manifolds.
4. Remove clamp attaching exhaust pipe to extension and remove exhaust pipe.
5. Drain engine oil and remove converter dust shield.
6. Remove oil pan bolts and lower pan, turning it counterclockwise to clear oil pick up assembly.

1960-61 Six

1. Remove tie rod at steering and idler arms.
2. Remove front engine mounting bolts.
3. Remove left side support, connecting converter housing and cylinder block.
4. Raise engine about 2″.
5. Drain oil.

6. Remove oil pan bolts and lower pan down and to the rear. *Do not turn oil pick up out of position.* Install pan in the reverse order placing gaskets as shown in Fig. 32A.

1959-61 V8-318, 326

1. Remove dipstick and drain oil.
2. Disconnect steering linkage from steering arm.
3. Remove starter.
4. On single exhaust jobs, remove exhaust crossover pipe.
5. Remove converter dust shield.
6. Raise engine about 1¼" after disconnecting front engine mounts.
7. Unfasten and remove pan, turning it sideways to clear crossmember.

1958-59 V8-350, 361, 383

1. Remove oil level dipstick.
2. Drain oil (leave plug out).
3. Disconnect steering linkage from steering arm.
4. On single exhaust system, remove crossover exhaust pipe.
5. Remove attaching screws and lower rear of pan, turning it sideways to clear crossmember.
6. Before installing the pan, clean the oil strainer and check it for alignment. The bottom of the strainer must be parallel with the lower, machined surface of the engine block.

1957 & 1958 Red Ram With Dual Exhaust

1. Drain oil and remove dipstick.
2. Disconnect steering linkage at idler arm support bracket and allow linkage to settle away from bottom of oil pan.
3. Remove starting motor.
4. Rotate crankshaft so as to bring ignition timing marks to 5 o'clock position (this will place crankshaft counterweights up in block out of the way).
5. Unfasten and drop pan as far as possible and work out over top of crossmember.

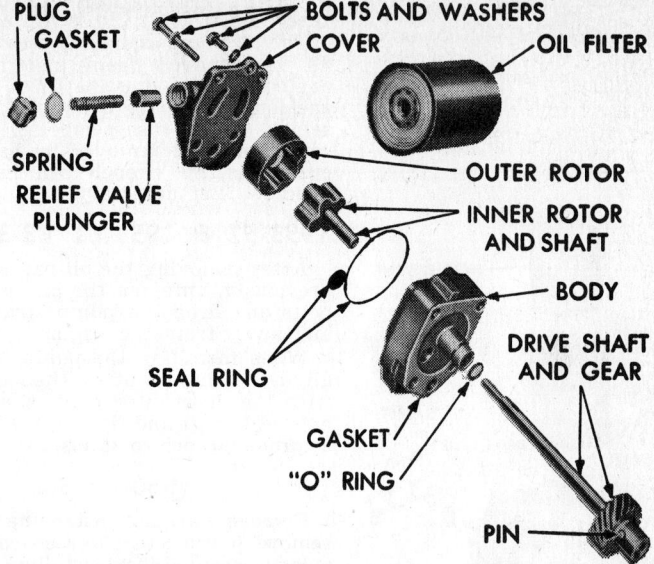

Fig. 33 Oil pump disassembled. 1958-61 V8-350, 361, 383

1957 & 1958 Red Ram With Single Exhaust

1. Disconnect "Y" pipe at exhaust manifolds.
2. Remove manifold heat control valve.
3. Place ignition timing marks at 5 o'clock position.
4. Loosen tail pipe and rear muffler support clamps.
5. Remove clamp that connects exhaust pipe to "Y" pipe.
6. Pull exhaust system rearward to break the exhaust-to-"Y" pipe connection. Work the "Y" pipe out of the way.
7. Remove starting motor.
8. Disconnect steering linkage at idler arm support bracket and allow to settle.
9. Remove engine front support attaching nuts.
10. Jack up front of engine about ½".
11. Unfasten and lower pan as far as possible and work out of position from over top of crossmember.

1953-56 V8

On 1953-54, remove starter and exhaust cross-over pipe. On 1955-56, disconnect steering linkage at idler arm support bracket and allow linkage to settle away from oil pan. Then unfasten and remove pan.

1953-56 Six

To remove the oil pan, remove the clutch housing lower pan to prevent damaging the oil pan gaskets on the housing. Lower the pan part way, lift up the oil strainer and take down the pan.

Before installing the oil pan, clean the pan and the pan rail of the block thoroughly and install new gaskets. Four gaskets are used as a seal between the pan and block. The gaskets are fitted into the fold-over slots of the oil pan ends to allow a more secure fit.

The right and left oil pan side gaskets may be installed with sealing compound applied on both sides. The end gaskets

should be installed so that the ends of the gaskets stick out above the oil pan at least ⅛". Do not cut off the gasket ends as they will compress against the block and form a better seal as the oil pan is tightened against the block.

1957-59 Six

1. Raise car on hoist and drain engine oil.
2. Disconnect pitman arm from steering gear and idler arm from idler arm bracket.
3. Remove dust shield.
4. Remove starter motor.
5. Disconnect front engine mounts and raise front of engine approximately 2 inches. Install small block under mounts to support engine.
6. Remove pan bolts and pan.

OIL PUMP, REPLACE

1953-59 Six

Before removing the oil pump, rotate the crankshaft and make sure the "DC" mark on the crankshaft pulley lines up with the pointer on the chain case cover

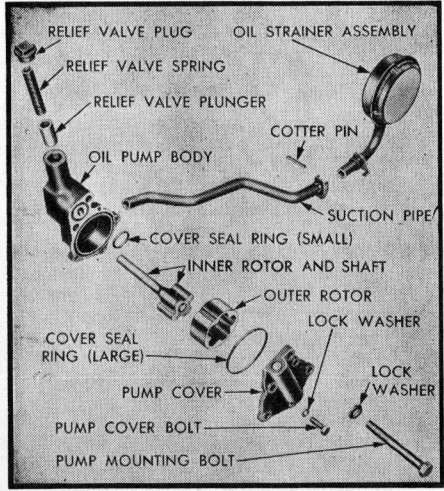

Fig. 34 V8 oil pump. 1953-57 and 1958 Red Ram

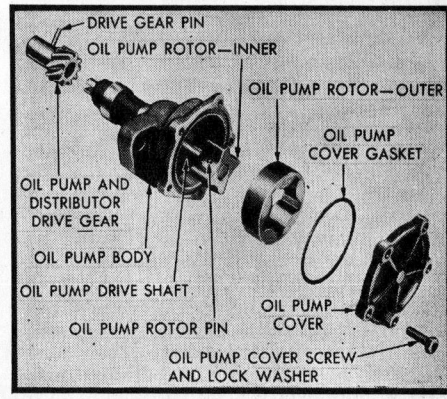

Fig. 35 Layout of oil pump parts. 1953-59 Six

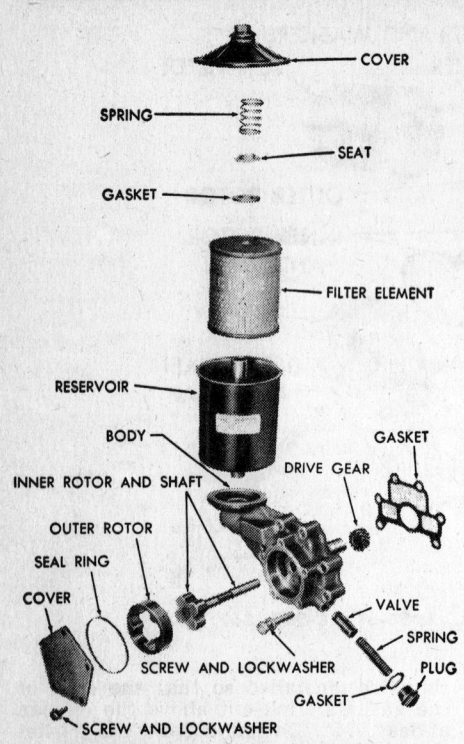

Fig. 35A   Oil pump and filter disassembled.   1960-61   Six

and that the distributor rotor is ready to fire No. 1 spark plug. After the pump is removed, do not bump the starter or let the engine turn as this will change the igniton timing.

On 1953 models, it may be necessary to remove the two upper capscrews of the oil pump cover to provide sufficient clearance to remove the pump.

On 1954-59 Models it is necessary to remove the front engine mount "U" bolts and loosen the two rear support bolts. Then, using a suitable bar, pry the engine straight over far enough to remove the oil pump after the attaching bolts have been removed.

Use a new gasket when installing the oil pump. Line up the slots on the end of the pump shaft with the mounting holes in the pump flange. Turn the drive gear counter-clockwise one tooth and slip the oil pump into position. Check the position of the distributor rotor. It should be ready to fire No. 1 spark plug (rotor in seven o'clock position).

If the position of No. 1 piston was accidentally changed while the oil pump was removed, take out the spark plug. Rotate the crankshaft and check the compression of No. 1 cylinder. Do this by holding the thumb tightly over the spark plug hole. When the compression is felt by the thumb, turn the crankshaft until the piston is at top dead center, as indicated when the pointer lines up with the DC mark on the crankshaft pulley.

Turn the pump drive shaft until the slot in its end lines up the cap screws holes in the mounting flange. Then turn the drive gear one tooth counter-clockwise, and carefully install the pump. Do not turn the drive gear while installing the pump.

1958-60 V8-350, 361, 383

The oil pump and filter assembly, Fig. 33, is removed from underneath the engine by removing the three short and one long attaching bolts. Clean the assembly before disassembling. The filter can usually be removed by hand. However, a strap wrench can be used to unscrew it if necessary.

1953-57 & 1958-61 V8-318, 326

After removing the oil pan as outlined previously, unfasten the pump mounting bolts and drop the pump straight down and away from the engine.

When installing the pump, be sure to align the drive slot in the pump shaft with the distributor drive shaft. Install new seal rings and tighten the bolts with a torque wrench to 35 lbs. ft.

1960-61 Six

Remove oil pump attaching bolts and remove pump and filter assembly from side of engine. When installing the pump tighten the attaching bolts to 200 inch lbs.

OIL PUMP REPAIRS
1953-59 Six & 1953-61 V8

After removing the pump from the engine it should be disassembled, cleaned and inspected for wear, Figs. 33, 34, 35.

1. Remove the cotter pin holding the oil strainer to the oil suction pipe. Then remove the pipe from the pump body.
2. Remove the pump cover and discard the oil seal ring.
3. Remove pump rotor and shaft and lift out rotor body.
4. Remove oil pressure relief valve plug and lift out the spring and plunger.
5. Wash all parts in cleaning solvent and inspect carefully for damage or wear.
6. The mating face of the oil pump cover should be smooth. If it is scratched or grooved, the cover should be replaced with a new one.
7. Check for excessive cover-to-rotor wear by laying a straight edge across the cover surface. If a .0015" feeler gauge can be inserted between cover and straight edge, the cover should be discarded and a new one installed.
8. Slide rotor body and rotor into pump body and then place a straight edge across the face of the pump body between the bolt holes. If a feeler gauge of less than .003" or more than .006" can be inserted between the rotors and straight edge, install a new pump body.
9. Remove the pump rotor and shaft, leaving rotor body in pump cavity. Press rotor body to one side with the fingers and measure the clearance between rotor and pump bodies. If it is more than .012", install a new pump body.
10. Check the clearance between the pump rotor and rotor body. If the measurement is more than .012",

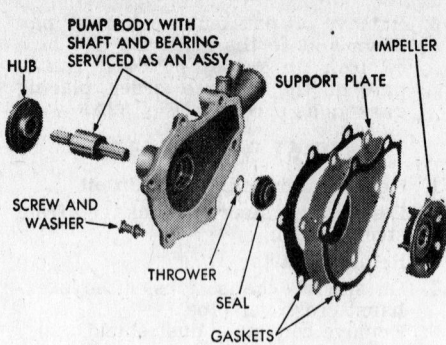

Fig. 36A   Water pump disassembled.   1960-61   Six

install a new pump rotor and rotor body.
11. Check the oil pump relief valve plunger for scoring and free operation in its bore. If the plunger is scored, install a new one.

1960-61 Six

Refer to Fig. 35A and remove the pump cover seal ring. Press off the drive gear, supporting the gear to keep load off aluminum body. Remove rotor and shaft and lift out outer pump rotor. Remove oil pressure relief valve plug and lift out spring and plunger.

Inspection

1. The rotor contact area and the bores of the shaft and valve in the pump body should be smooth, free from scratches, scoring or excessive wear.
2. The pump cover should be smooth, flat and free from scoring or ridges. Lay a straightedge across the cover. If a .0015" feeler gauge can be inserted under the straightedge, the cover should be replaced.
3. All surfaces of the outer rotor should be smooth and uniform, free from ridges, scratches or uneven wear. Discard a rotor less than .649" thick and/or less than 2.469" in diameter.
4. The inner rotor and shaft assembly should be smooth, free from scoring and uneven wear. Discard rotors less than .649" thick.
5. Place outer rotor in pump body and measure clearance between rotor and body. Discard pump body if clearance is more than .012".
6. Install inner rotor and shaft in pump body. Shaft should turn freely but without side play. If clearance between rotor teeth is more than .010", replace both rotors.
7. Measure rotor end clearance. If feeler gauge of more than .004" can be inserted between straightedge and rotors, install a new pump body.
8. The oil pressure relief valve should be smooth, free from scratches or scoring, and should be a free fit in its bore.
9. Relief valve springs are painted either gray, red or brown to denote free lengths of $2\frac{3}{16}$, $2\frac{19}{64}$ and $2\frac{5}{64}$ inches. Rather than change the length, replace a spring with one of the same color.

OIL PRESSURE REGULATOR

1953-59 Six

Oil pressure is controlled by a relief valve located on the left side of the engine.

Inspect the relief valve plunger and spring after removing the valve cap and gasket. If the plunger is scratched, remove the scratches by polishing, or install a new plunger. If the old plunger is to be reinstalled, clean it and flush out the bore with engine oil by cranking the engine with the starter.

If the spring is to be replaced, use a new one of the same type. Do not use a heavier spring or a steel ball or washers behind the spring to raise the oil pressure. If oil pressure is low, check the fit of crankshaft bearings or look for other causes of possible loss of oil pressure.

Different colored springs are used in the relief valve. The medium spring is unpainted; the light spring is red, and the heavy spring is green. If it is necessary to replace a spring, install a spring of the same color.

RADIATOR, REPLACE

To remove radiator, drain cooling system and disconnect hoses. Remove fan shroud (if equipped). Unfasten radiator from its support and lift it out.

WATER PUMP, REPLACE

1958-61

Drain cooling system and then remove fan shroud (if equipped). Loosen fan belt and remove fan, spacer and pulley. Remove the water pump to housing retaining bolts and remove the pump.

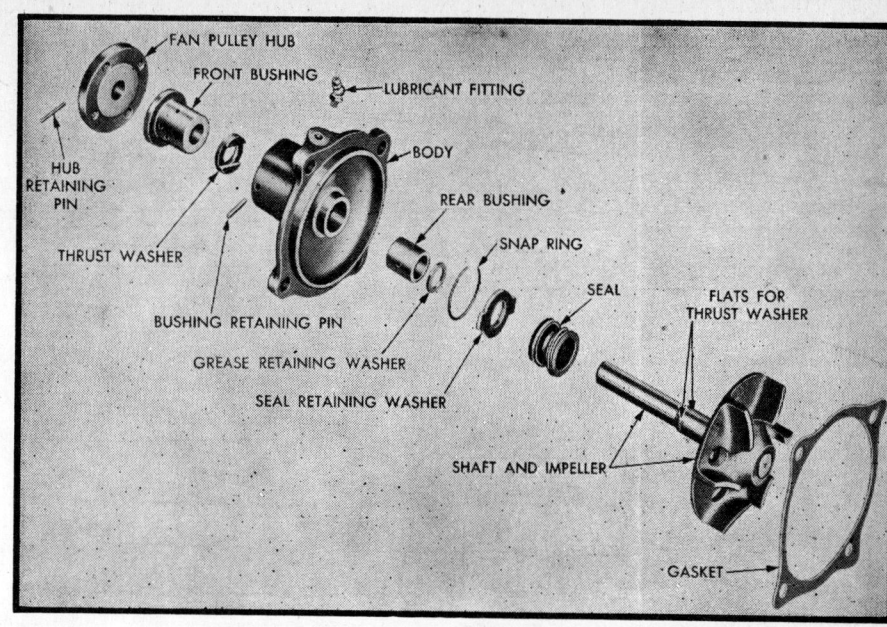

Fig. 38 Layout of 1953-56 V8 water pump parts

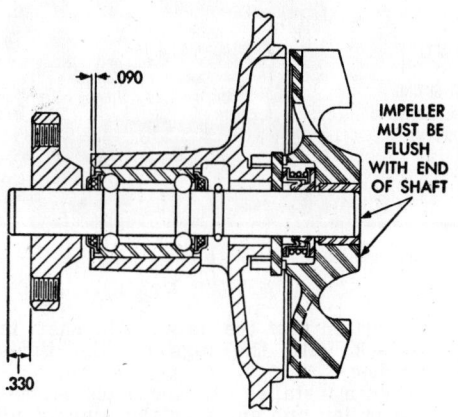

Fig. 37 Water pump assembly details. 1957-61 V8

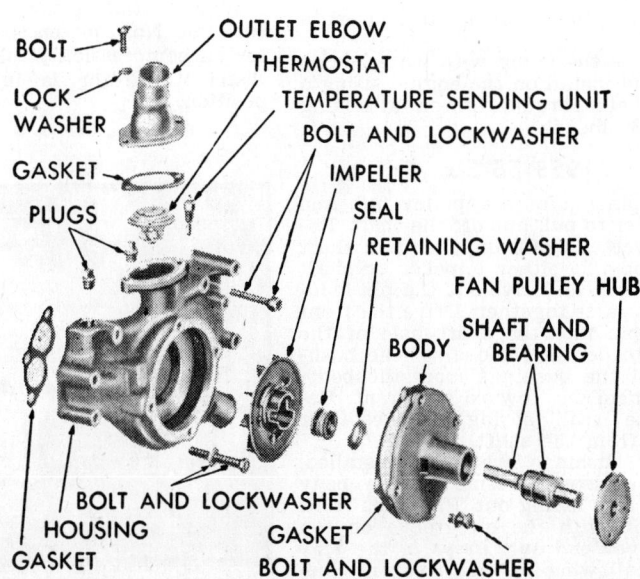

Fig. 36 Water pump disassembled. 1958-61 V8-350, 361, 383

1953-57 V8

Remove the fan and belt and disconnect water pump hose. Unfasten the water pump from the engine and lift it off.

1953-57 Six

Remove the fan and belt and disconnect water pump hose. Unfasten the water pump from the engine and lift out the pump assembly.

When installing the pump, make sure all mating surfaces are clean, and use new gaskets.

WATER PUMP REPAIRS

1960-61 Six

With the exception of the seal and impeller, this pump, Fig. 36A, is serviced only as an assembly. When replacing the impeller or seal, install hub to obtain a dimension of .41" between end of shaft and face of hub.

1957-59 Six & 1957-61 V8

To disassemble this type pump, use a suitable puller to pull the fan hub from the shaft. Remove the impeller by breaking the plastic away from the metal insert. Remove impeller insert and press the shaft and bearing assembly out of the housing from the impeller end, Fig. 36. *Shaft and bearing assembly need not be removed to service a leaking water pump.*

When assembled, the impeller should be flush with the end of the shaft. And when installing the fan pulley hub, press it on until there is .330" between the end of the shaft and the front face of the hub, Fig. 37. On 1957-59 Six, install hub flush with end of shaft.

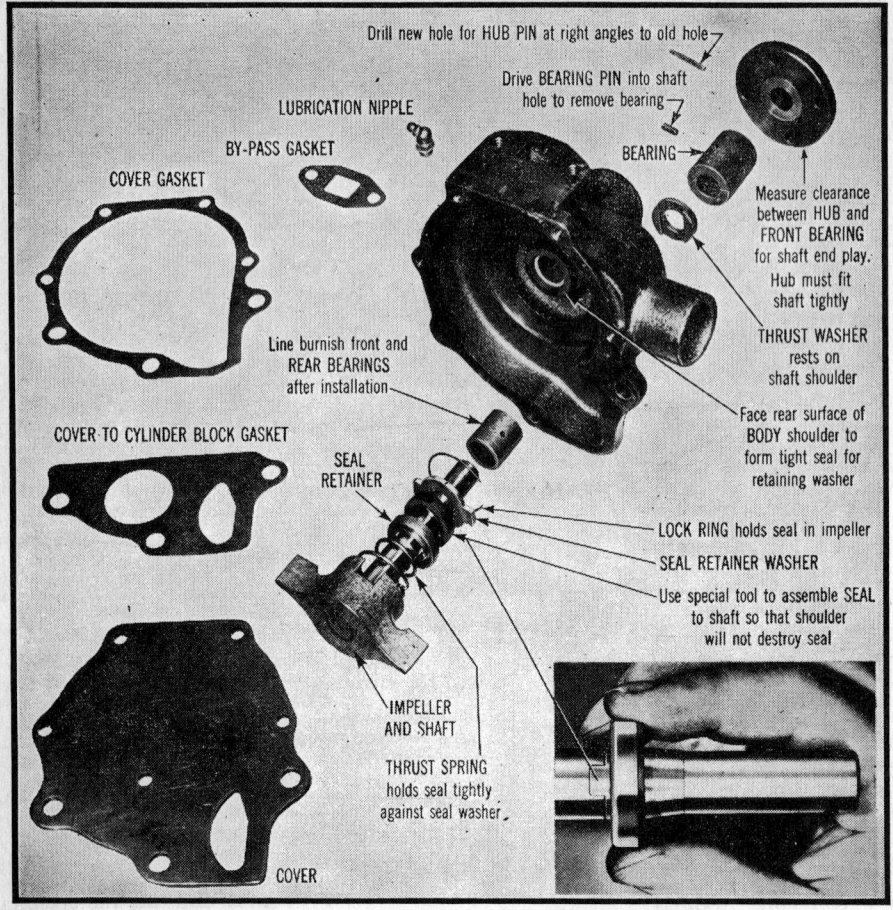

Drill new hole for HUB PIN at right angles to old hole

Drive BEARING PIN into shaft hole to remove bearing

LUBRICATION NIPPLE

BY-PASS GASKET

BEARING

COVER GASKET

Measure clearance between HUB and FRONT BEARING for shaft end play. Hub must fit shaft tightly

THRUST WASHER rests on shaft shoulder

Line burnish front and REAR BEARINGS after installation

Face rear surface of BODY shoulder to form tight seal for retaining washer

COVER-TO-CYLINDER BLOCK GASKET

SEAL RETAINER

LOCK RING holds seal in impeller

SEAL RETAINER WASHER

Use special tool to assemble SEAL to shaft so that shoulder will not destroy seal

IMPELLER AND SHAFT

THRUST SPRING holds seal tightly against seal washer

COVER

Fig. 39   Servicing 1953-56 six cylinder water pump

1953-56 V8

1. Drive out fan hub retaining pin and pull off hub, Fig. 38.
2. Remove impeller and shaft.
3. Drive front bushing retaining pin through bushing and into shaft bore. Then drop out pin.
4. Use a suitable puller to remove rear bushing, thrust washer and front bushing.
5. Remove snap ring holding retainer washer and seal in impeller cavity. Slide retainer washer and seal off shaft.

Assembly—When installing the rear bushing, press it into the bore .130-.155" beyond seat surface. Press in front bushing far enough to seat the shoulder. Install a suitable flat washer so as not to damage the bearing surface as the bushing is pressed into position.

Drill a hole in the front bushing (No. 13 drill) and install the retaining pin. Drive the pin flush with the pump body surface.

The bushings should be burnished if a burnisher is available. If not, line ream the rear bushing .6704-.6714" and the front bushing .595-.596". When using the reamer, be careful not to engage the thrust washer between the bushings as damage to the washer and bushings may result. Use a suitable tool to reface the seal seat.

When inserting the shaft and impeller, be certain that the flats on the shaft interlock with the lugs on the thrust washer.

When installed, the clearance between the pulley hub and front bushing should be .0005-.005". Measure with feeler gauge.

Drill a hole through the fan pulley hub and shaft (No. 22 drill) and insert a new pin.

Lubricate the pump with water pump grease and install on the engine, using a new gasket. Torque tighten attaching bolts 25-30 lbs. ft.

1953-56 Six

Drive pin out of fan pulley hub and use a puller to pull hub off the shaft. Remove cover and pull impeller and shaft out of body. If either impeller or shaft is to be replaced, drive out the pin holding these parts together. Drive the front bushing pin into the shaft hole of the bushing to permit removal of the bushings. Pull the bushings from the body, pulling them out toward the front. Remove the seal, spring and retainer washers from the shaft, Fig. 39.

If new bushings are to be installed, insert the thrust washer in the body with flat side facing out. Press the front bushing in with the oil groove on top and grooved end out. Press in the rear bushing, allowing 1/32 inch clearance between the rear end of the bushing and the impeller housing. Drill and pin the

front bushing. Remove any burrs inside the bushings and line burnish both bushings and reface the seal seat. Then continue to assemble the pump as follows:

Install the impeller on the shaft and drill for a 1/8 inch impeller pin. Install the pin and peen over both ends. Assemble the seal thrust spring, seal retainer, seal and seat retainer washer with glazed surface against seal. Install the seal retainer lock ring.

Insert the shaft and press on the fan pulley hub, leaving .003 inch clearance between the bushing and hub. Drill the shaft (if a new one is being used) and install the retaining pin. If the old shaft is being used, position the hub on the shaft so that the shaft can be drilled 90 degrees from the old hole. Remove all traces of old gaskets and install new ones. Lubricate the pump and install on the engine.

WATER DISTRIBUTOR TUBE

1953-59 Six

The water distributor tube, located in the water jacket on the valve side of the engine, should be replaced whenever the engine is completely overhauled. If the tube becomes rusted or corroded, overheating of the engine may occur due to failure of the water to circulate properly through the cylinder block.

To replace the tube, remove the radiator and water pump. Pull the tube out of the cylinder block with a stiff hooked rod, Fig. 40.

Install the new tube with the slots up and be sure it is inserted far enough into the block so that the water pump will seat properly against the block.

DISTRIBUTOR, REPLACE

To remove the distributor, disconnect the vacuum control line and low tension wire and remove the cap and lock plate hold-down screw.

When installing the distributor, make sure that No. 1 piston is on top dead center on compression stroke and that the distributor rotor is in No. 1 firing position.

Fig. 40   Using hooked rod (2) to pull out water distributor tube. 1953-59 Six

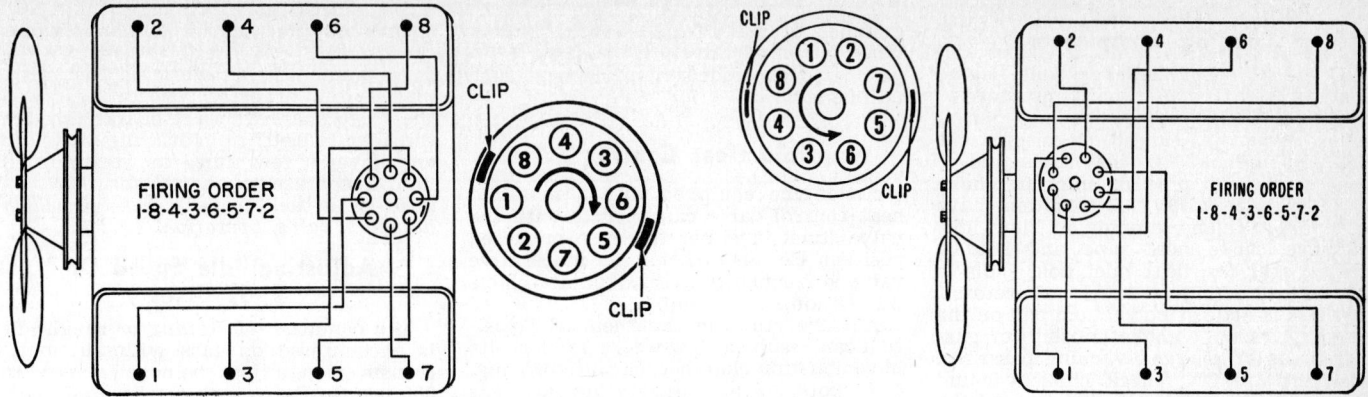

Fig. 41 Ignition details. 1953-57 and 1958-61 V8-318, 326   Fig. 42 Ignition details. 1958-61 V8-350, 361, 383

IGNITION TIMING

With the distributor properly installed on the engine as outlined below, set the ignition timing with a timing light so that with the engine idling, the timing light will flash when the pointer on the engine is opposite the timing mark on the vibration damper. Chalk-mark the spot on the vibration damper so that it stands out when the light flashes (see Figs. 41 and 42).

STARTER, REPLACE

Disconnect wires and cables from starter. Then unfasten starter from flywheel housing and pull out the starter.

Service Note

Noisy or erratic starter operation may be caused by lack of lubrication or deposits of foreign material on the Bendix driveshaft.

To correct this condition, remove the inspection plate at the bottom of the torque converter or clutch housing. Then apply a suitable upper-cylinder rust inhibitor or SAE 5W or SAE 10W oil to the shaft by means of a 7" piece of tubing attached to the spout of a pressure oil can. In extreme cases, it may be necessary to remove, disassemble and clean the starter.

MUFFLER & PIPES, REPLACE

1953 V8

The exhaust pipe and muffler are individual units, the pipe sliding into the muffler and secured by a double bolt clamp.

1954-56 V8

On all models except Convertible, the exhaust pipe and muffler are a welded assembly. In order to remove either the "Y" pipe or the muffler, it will only be necessary to disconnect the extension joint at the "Y" pipe. On the Convertible, the disconnection can be made at either the "Y" pipe or the muffler.

On all models except Convertible, the muffler and extension pipe to the "Y" are serviced as an assembly.

1957-59 V8 Single Exhaust

Removing "Y" Exhaust Pipe
1. Cut crossover pipe as close to "Y" as possible.
2. Remove left-hand exhaust pipe.
3. Unfasten steering idler arm from bracket, allowing idler arm and link to drop.
4. Unfasten exhaust pipe from right-hand exhaust manifold.
5. Work "Y" pipe past torsion bar spring and out through bottom of car.

6. When replacing exhaust pipes a 2" O.D. piece of steel tubing may be used to close area where cut was made.

Removing Muffler
1. Work tailpipe out of muffler.
2. Unfasten exhaust extension pipe from "Y" pipe.
3. Work exhaust extension out of "Y" pipe.

1955-59 Dual Exhaust

The service procedure for the dual exhaust system is comparable to the exhaust system for six-cylinder models, except that there is an individual system for each side.

1953-59 Six

The exhaust pipe and muffler are a welded assembly. To replace either part, cut the pipe at or near the welded joint. When installing either part, use a double bolt clamp to secure the joint.

1960-61 V8

When assembling exhaust system work from rear to front of car. The ball joint flange lower surface should be parallel to each other and perpendicular to pipe axis. On 383" engine with single exhaust, adjust converter housing bracket so it is flat against converter housing and in proper contact with the pipe tab.

Carburetor Section

Performance Complaints

Flooding, stumble on acceleration or other performance complaints are in many instances caused by the presence of dirt, water or other foreign matter in the carburetor. To aid in diagnosing the cause of the complaint, the carburetor should be carefully removed from the engine without draining the fuel from the bowl. The contents of the fuel bowl may then be examined for contamination as the carburetor is disassembled.

Check the fuel in the bowl for contamination by dirt, water, gum or other foreign matter. A magnet moved through the fuel in the bowl will pick up and identify any iron oxide dust that may have caused intake needle and seat leakage.

Inspect gasketed surfaces between body and air horn. Small nicks or burrs should be smoothed down to eliminate air or fuel leakage. On carburetors having a vacuum piston, be especially particular when inspecting the top surface of the inner wall of the bowl around the vacuum piston passage. A poor seal at

this location may contribute to a "cutting-out" on turns complaint.

Fill the carburetor bowl with clean fuel before installing on manifold. This will help prevent dirt trapped in the fuel system from being dislodged by the free flow of fuel as the carburetor is primed. The operation of the floats and intake needle and seats may be checked under pressure if a fuel pump is used at the bench to fill the carburetor bowl. Operate the throttle several times and visually check the discharge from pump jets.

Poor Mileage and Engine Loading Complaints

Cases of poor mileage and engine loading may be due in many instances to sluggish choke valve opening during cold driveaway, caused by insufficient vacuum in choke housing, a plugged or restricted heat pipe or inlet in choke cover. To check for this condition, have engine warm and running at slow idle. Remove choke heat pipe and hold a finger over the heat inlet hole (hole is on choke housing on some carburetors). If there is little or no vacuum pull on the finger, check the choke housing for gasket leaks or plugged vacuum passages. If these are OK, check choke vacuum passages in carburetor between choke housing and manifold.

Dirty or Rusty Choke Housing

In cases where it is found that the interior of the choke housing is dirty, gummed or rusty while the carburetor itself is comparatively clean, look for a punctured or eroded manifold heat tube (if one is used).

Manifold Heat Control Valve

An engine equipped with a manifold heat control valve can operate with the valve stuck in either the open or closed position. Because of this, an inoperative valve is frequently overlooked at vehicle lubrication or tune-up.

A valve stuck in the "heat-off" position can result in slow warm up, deposits in combustion chamber, carburetor icing, flat spots during acceleration, low gas mileage and spark plug fouling.

A valve stuck in the "heat-on" position can result in power loss, engine knocking, sticking or burned valves and spark plug burning.

To prevent the possibility of a stuck valve, check and lubricate the valve each time the vehicle is lubricated or tuned-up. Check the operation of the valve manually. To lubricate the valve, place a few drops of penetrating oil on the valve shaft where it passes through the manifold. Then move the valve up and down a few times to work the oil in. *Do not use engine oil for this purpose as it will leave a residue which hampers valve operation.*

Adjusting Idle Speed On 1961 Sixes

If a condition of stalling or rough idle is encountered on cars with automatic transmission, adjust the hot idle speed to 500 rpm in Drive *with the headlights on*. It is important to make this adjustment with the headlights on so the alternator will be under full load condition. There is a variation up to 65 engine rpm between "light" and "full" charge conditions of the alternator.

CARTER NOTES

OVERDRIVE KICKDOWN SWITCH

BB—With throttle valves wide open, there should be $\frac{1}{64}''$ to $\frac{3}{64}''$ clearance between kickdown lever and switch stem guide. To adjust, loosen lock nuts and adjust switch.

METERING RODS

WCFB—This adjustment must be made after pump setting. Seat throttle valves in bores of carburetor and loosen metering rod arm clamp screw. With metering rods in place, press down on vacumeter link until metering rods bottom in casting. Holding rods down, revolve metering rod arm until finger on arm contacts vacumeter link. Hold in place and tighten clamp screw.

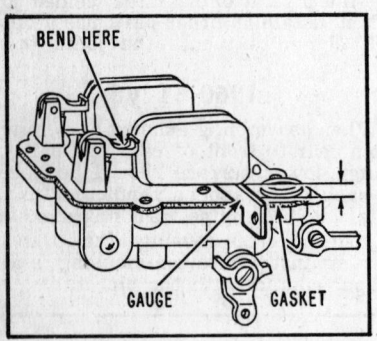

Fig. ①—AFB float level. Adjust by bending float lever.

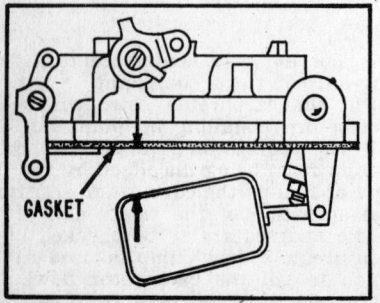

Fig. ②—AFB float drop. Adjust by bending stop tabs on float brackets.

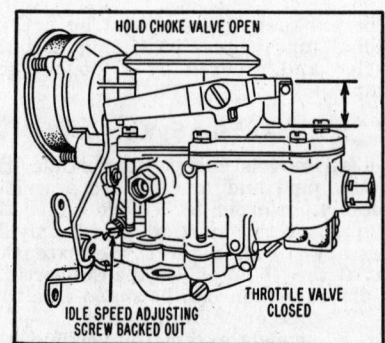

Fig. ③—Measure from top of bowl cover to top of plunger shaft with throttle connector rod in center hole of pump arm. Adjust by bending throttle connector rod (BBS shown).

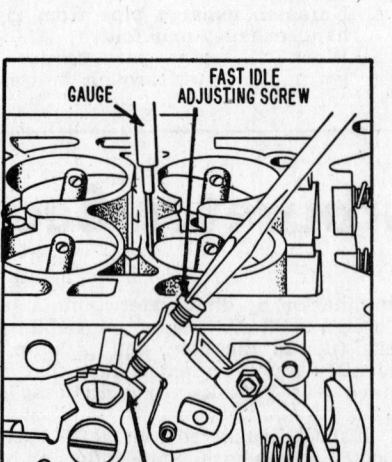

Fig. ④—With choke valve closed, tighten fast idle adjusting screw on high step of fast idle cam until clearance between throttle valve and carburetor bore (side opposite idle port) is as specified (AFB shown).

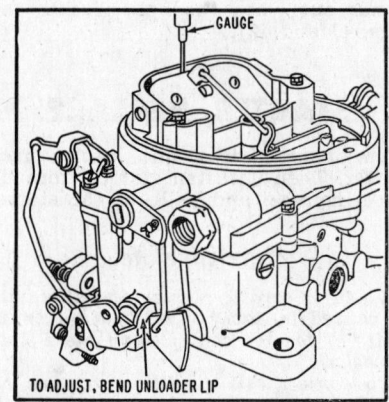

Fig. ⑤—With throttle wide open, clearance between upper edge of choke valve and inner wall of air horn should be as specified. Adjust by bending unloader lip on throttle lever (AFB shown).

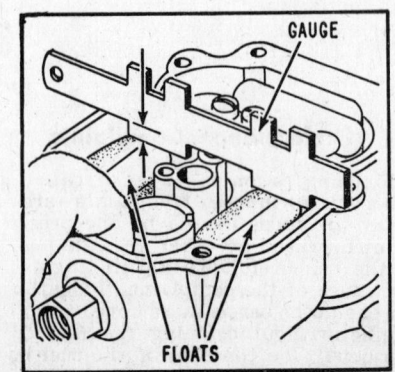

Fig. ⑥—BBD and BBS float level. Adjust by bending lip on float arm.

CARTER CARBURETOR ADJUSTMENTS

Year	Carburetor Model	Idle Adjustments				Float Level		Float Drop		Pump Travel Setting	Choke Unloader Setting	Choke Setting
		Mixture Screws Turns Open	Hot Idle Speed Neutral	Fast Idle Speed	Dashpot Plunger Clearance	Primary	Secondary	Primary	Secondary			
1961	BBS-3098S	1	550	1800[11]	None	$7/32$[6]	None	None	None	$27/32$[8]	$3/16$[12]	Index
	BBS-3099S	1	550	1600[11]	None	$7/32$[6]	None	None	None	$27/32$[8]	$3/16$[12]	Index
	BBS-3128S	1	550	1600[11]	None	$7/32$[6]	None	None	None	$27/32$[8]	$3/16$[12]	Index
	BBD-3132S	1	500	1400[11]	None	$9/32$[6]	None	None	None	1[8]	$1/4$[5]	Index
	AFB-3103S	$1\frac{1}{2}$	500	1800[11]	None	$7/32$[1]	$7/32$[1]	$9/16$[2]	$9/16$[2]	$7/16$[8]	$1/4$[5]	Index
	AFB-3131S	$1\frac{1}{2}$	500	1800[11]	None	$7/32$[1]	$7/32$[1]	$9/16$[2]	$9/16$[2]	$7/16$[8]	$1/4$[5]	Index
	AFB-3105S	$1\frac{1}{2}$	500	1700[11]	None	$7/32$[1]	$7/32$[1]	$9/16$[2]	$9/16$[2]	$7/16$[8]	$1/4$[5]	Index
	AFB-3106S	$1\frac{1}{2}$	500	1800[11]	None	$7/32$[1]	$7/32$[1]	$9/16$[2]	$9/16$[2]	$7/16$[8]	$1/4$[5]	Index
	AFB-3140S	$1\frac{1}{2}$	500	1700[11]	None	$7/32$[1]	$7/32$[1]	$9/16$[2]	$9/16$[2]	$7/16$[8]	$1/4$[5]	Index
	AFB-3152S	$1\frac{1}{2}$	500	1800[11]	None	$7/32$[1]	$7/32$[1]	$9/16$[2]	$9/16$[2]	$7/16$[8]	$1/4$[5]	2 Rich
	AFB-2968S	$1\frac{1}{2}$	500	1800[11]	None	$7/32$[1]	$7/32$[1]	$9/16$[2]	$9/16$[2]	$7/16$[8]	$1/4$[5]	2 Rich
	AFB-3133S	$1\frac{1}{2}$	500	1800[11]	None	$7/32$[1]	$7/32$[1]	$9/16$[2]	$9/16$[2]	$7/16$[8]	$1/4$[5]	2 Rich
	AFB-2903S	$1\frac{1}{2}$	750	1500[11]	.010[14]	$9/32$[1]	$9/32$[1]	$3/4$[2]	$3/4$[2]	$1/4$[8]	$1/4$[5]	1 Rich
1960-61	BBD-2921S	1	485	1400[11]	None	$7/16$[6]	None	None	None	1[8]	$15/64$[12]	Index
	BBD-2922S	1	485	1400[11]	None	$7/16$[6]	None	None	None	1[8]	$15/64$[12]	Index
1960	BBS-2985S	1	485	1300[11]	None	$7/16$[6]	None	None	None	$27/32$[8]	$9/64$[12]	Index
	BBS-2986S	1	485	1300[11]	None	$7/16$[6]	None	None	None	$27/32$[8]	$9/64$[12]	Index
	AFB-2948S	1-2	485	1250[11]	None	$7/32$[1]	$7/32$[1]	$3/4$[2]	$3/4$[2]	$7/16$[8]	$1/4$[5]	Index
	AFB-2991S	1-2	485	1250[11]	None	$7/32$[1]	$7/32$[1]	$3/4$[2]	$3/4$[2]	$7/16$[8]	$1/4$[5]	Index
	AFB-2903S	$1\frac{1}{2}$	530[13]	1800[11]	.010[14]	$9/32$[1]	$9/32$[1]	$3/4$[2]	$3/4$[2]	$1/4$[8]	$1/4$[5]	1 Rich
1959	BBS-2567S	$\frac{1}{2}$-$1\frac{1}{2}$	475	1300[11]	None	$7/32$[6]	None	None	None	$27/32$[8]	$9/64$[12]	Index
	BBS-2569S	$\frac{1}{2}$-$1\frac{1}{2}$	475	1300[11]	None	$7/32$[6]	None	None	None	$27/32$[8]	$9/64$[12]	Index
	BBD-2822S	1	475	1400[11]	None	$9/32$[6]	None	None	None	1[8]	$15/64$[5]	Index
	BBD-2870S	1	475	1400[11]	None	$9/32$[6]	None	None	None	1[8]	$15/64$[5]	Index
	AFB-2773S	$1\frac{1}{2}$	475	1400[11]	None	$7/32$[1]	$7/32$[1]	$23/32$[2]	$23/32$[2]	$7/16$[8]	$1/4$[5]	Index
	AFB-2787S	$1\frac{1}{2}$	475	1400[11]	None	$7/32$[1]	$7/32$[1]	$23/32$[2]	$23/32$[2]	$7/16$[8]	$1/4$[5]	Index
	AFB-2794S	$1\frac{1}{2}$	475	1400[11]	None	$7/32$[1]	$7/32$[1]	$23/32$[2]	$23/32$[2]	$7/16$[8]	$1/4$[5]	Index
1958	AFB-2642S	$3/4$-$1\frac{3}{4}$	475	1400[11]	None	[10]	[10]	$23/32$[2]	$23/32$[2]	$7/16$[8]	$1/4$[5]	2 Rich
	WCFB-2660S	$\frac{1}{2}$-$1\frac{1}{2}$	475	1400[11]	None	$7/32$[7]	$9/32$[7]	$23/32$[8]	$23/32$[8]	[9]	$11/64$[5]	Index
1957	WCFB-2622S	$3/4$-$1\frac{3}{4}$	475	1375[11]	None	$7/32$[7]	$9/32$[7]	$23/32$[8]	$25/32$[8]	[9]	$11/64$[5]	Index
	WCFB-2532S	$\frac{1}{2}$-$1\frac{1}{2}$	475	1375[11]	None	$7/32$[7]	$9/32$[7]	$23/32$[8]	$25/32$[8]	[15]	$15/64$[5]	Index
1956	WCFB-2432S	$\frac{1}{2}$-$1\frac{1}{2}$	475	.012[4]	None	$1/8$[7]	$3/16$[7]	$5/8$[8]	$11/16$[8]	[15]	$3/16$[5]	Index
	WCFB-2474S	$\frac{1}{2}$-$1\frac{1}{2}$	475	.012[4]	None	$1/8$[7]	$3/16$[7]	$5/8$[8]	$11/16$[8]	[15]	$3/16$[5]	Index
	WCFB-2443S-A	$3/4$-$1\frac{3}{4}$	475	.012[4]	None	$7/32$[7]	$9/32$[7]	$23/32$[8]	$25/32$[8]	[15]	$11/64$[5]	Index
	WCFB-2303S-A-B	$\frac{1}{2}$-$1\frac{1}{2}$	475	.012[4]	None	$7/32$[7]	$9/32$[7]	$23/32$[8]	$25/32$[8]	[15]	$11/64$[5]	1 Rich
1955	WCFB-2181S	$\frac{1}{2}$-$1\frac{1}{2}$	475	.012[4]	None	$1/8$[7]	$3/16$[7]	$5/8$[8]	$11/16$[8]	[15]	$3/16$[5]	Index
	WCFB-2253S	$\frac{1}{2}$-$1\frac{1}{2}$	475	.012[4]	None	$1/8$[7]	$3/16$[7]	$5/8$[8]	$11/16$[8]	[15]	$3/16$[5]	Index
1954	WCFB-2191S	1-2	475	.015[4]	None	$1/8$[7]	$3/16$[7]	$5/8$[8]	$11/16$[8]	[15]	$3/16$[5]	3 Lean
	BB-E9N1	$\frac{1}{2}$-$1\frac{1}{2}$	475	None	None	$5/64$[17]	None	None	None	[18]	None	None
	BB-E9T1	$\frac{1}{2}$-$1\frac{1}{2}$	475	None	None	$5/64$[17]	None	None	None	[18]	None	None
	BB-E9U1	$\frac{1}{2}$-$1\frac{1}{2}$	475	None	$4\frac{1}{2}$[16]	$1/16$[17]	None	None	None	[18]	None	None
	BB-E9V1	$\frac{1}{2}$-$1\frac{1}{2}$	475	None	None	$5/64$[17]	None	None	None	[18]	None	None
1953	BB-D6V1	$\frac{1}{2}$-$1\frac{1}{2}$	475	None	$4\frac{1}{2}$[16]	$5/64$[17]	None	None	None	None	None	None
	BB-D6U1	$\frac{1}{2}$-$1\frac{1}{2}$	475	None	None	$5/64$[17]	None	None	None	None	None	None
	BB-D6H2	$\frac{1}{2}$-$1\frac{1}{2}$	475	None	None	$5/64$[17]	None	None	None	None	None	None
	BB-D6P1	$\frac{1}{2}$-$1\frac{1}{2}$	475	None	5[16]	$5/64$[17]	None	None	None	None	None	None
	BB-D6P2	$\frac{1}{2}$-$1\frac{1}{2}$	475	None	$4\frac{1}{2}$[16]	$5/64$[17]	None	None	None	None	None	None
	BB-D6M1	$\frac{1}{2}$-$1\frac{1}{2}$	475	None	None	$5/64$[17]	None	None	None	None	None	None

DODGE & DART

CARTER NOTES
continued

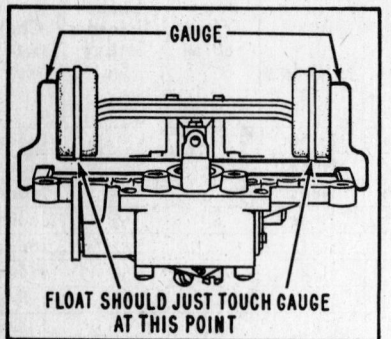

Fig. ⑦—WCFB float level. Adjust by bending float lever.

Fig. ⑨—With pump connector link in center hole flat on pump arm should be parallel with a straightedge on dust cover boss. Adjust by bending throttle connector rod.

⑩—See ①. Ribbed floats $\frac{7}{32}$", smooth floats $\frac{5}{16}$".

⑪—Hot engine with fast idle screw on index mark or high step of fast idle cam.

⑬—In drive range.

⑭—With engine running at hot idle speed and transmission in drive range, turn dashpot plunger toward bellcrank until specified clearance is obtained.

⑮Same as ⑥ except connector link goes in outer hole.

⑯—Tighten adjusting screw, then back off the number of turns specified.

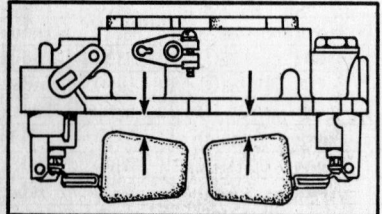

Fig. ⑧—WCFB float drop. Adjust by bending stop tabs on float bracket.

⑫—With throttle wide open, clearance between upper edge of choke valve and inner wall of air horn should be as specified. Adjust by bending choke trip lever.

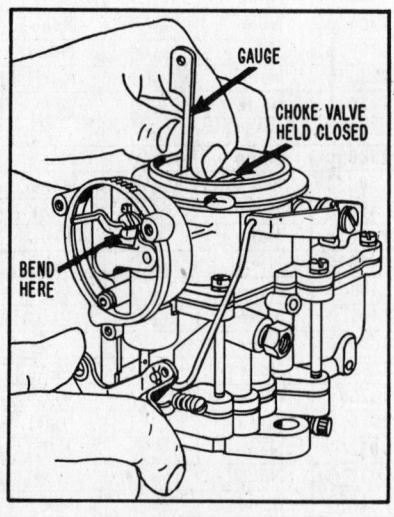

Fig. ⑰—BB float level.

⑱—Pump lifter arm should be at right angle to pump lifter shaft. Adjust by bending pump lifter arm.

HOLLEY CARBURETOR ADJUSTMENTS

| Year | Model | Carb. Type | Idle Adjustments | | | | | Float Level | Fuel Level | Float Bowl Vent Valve | Pump Override Spring | Choke Unloader | Choke Setting |
			Mixture Screws Turns Open	Air Bypass Turns Open	Hot Idle Speed Neutral	Fast Idle Speed	Dashpot Plunger Clearance						
1960-61	V8-383	4 Bore	1④	1⑤	500	.015③	None	①	②	.060⑥	.015⑦	$\frac{3}{16}$⑧	1 Rich

---

HOLLEY NOTES

FUEL BOWL INVERTED
ADJUST FLOAT PARALLEL TO BOWL FLOOR
ADJUSTING NUT

Fig. ①—Invert fuel bowl. Then loosen lock screw enough to allow adjusting nut to rotate. Turn adjusting nut until base of float is parallel with floor of bowl. Adjust both floats in same manner.

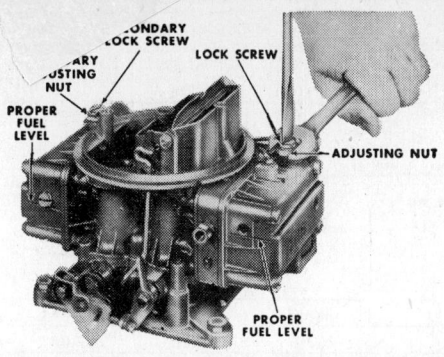

Fig. ②—With engine idling, turn adjusting nut as required until fuel just dribbles out of sight plug hole. Adjust both floats in same manner.

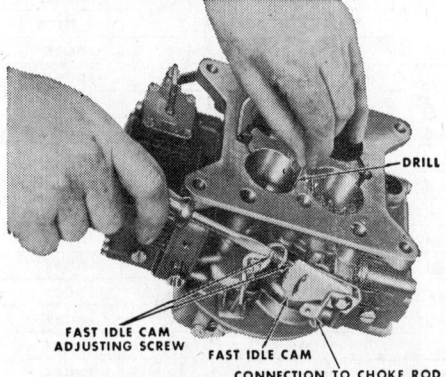

Fig. ③—With fast idle screw in contact with high step of cam, adjust screw to open primary throttle plates the dimension listed (side toward center of carburetor).

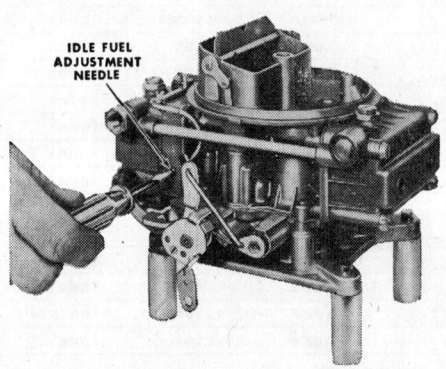

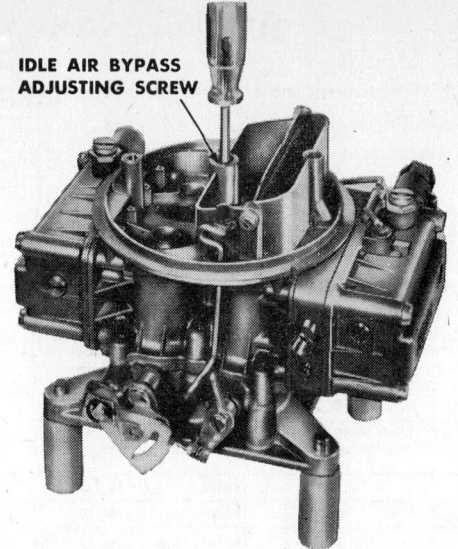

Fig. ⑤—This adjustment eliminates idle instability due to icing. Turn the screw in until it seats lightly, then back it off one full turn.

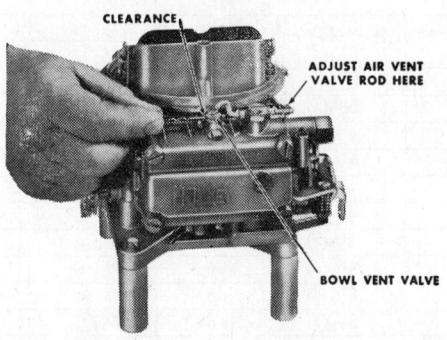

Fig. ⑥—This adjustment is important in high temperature operation. With throttle closed, center of valve should clear bowl by the dimension specified. Adjust by changing the arc in rod near contact with throttle lever.

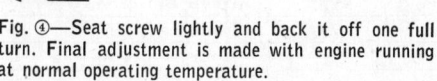

Fig. ④—Seat screw lightly and back it off one full turn. Final adjustment is made with engine running at normal operating temperature.

HOLLEY NOTES

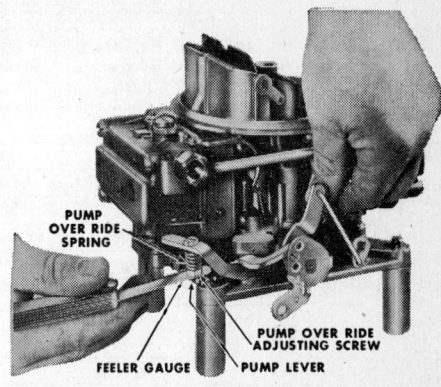

Fig. ⑦—With both throttles held wide open and pump held down, clearance between nut and pump lever should be as specified.

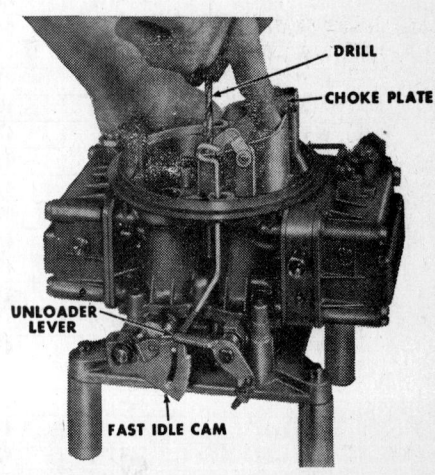

Fig. ⑧—Hold choke plate closed and throttle wide open. Correct clearance from choke plate to back of main body should be as specified. Adjust by bending unloader lever.

STROMBERG NOTES

CARBURETOR BALL CHECKS

Whenever it becomes necessary to dismantle a carburetor be sure to account for the ball check valves that may be found under pump plungers and compensating or power valves.

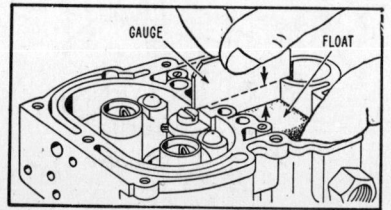

Fig. ①—WW float level. Adjust by bending float lever.

Fig. ②—With choke valve held open, pump travel from fully closed to fully open position should be as specified. Adjust by bending pump rod.

③—With throttle valves closed, turn fast idle screw out until it rests on high step of fast idle cam. Then turn screw in the number of turns specified.

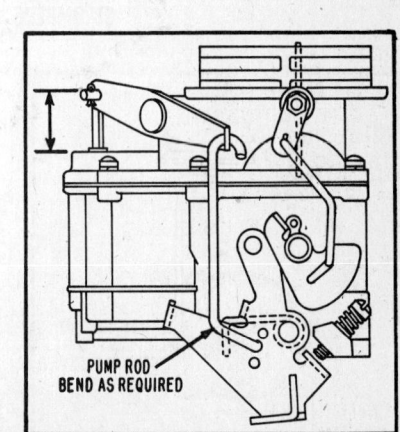

STROMBERG CARBURETOR ADJUSTMENTS

Year	Carburetor Model	Idle Adjustments				Float Level	Pump Travel	Bowl Vent Valve	Choke Unloader	Choke Setting
		Mixture Screws Turns Open	Hot Idle Speed Neutral	Fast Idle Speed	Dashpot Plunger Clearance					
1961	WW15-43	1¼	500	1250(5)	None	7/32(6)	(9)	5/64(10)	15/64(4)	Index
	WW15-44	1¼	500	1250(5)	None	7/32(6)	(9)	5/64(10)	15/64(4)	Index
	WW15-45	1¼	500	1250(5)	None	7/32(6)	(9)	5/64(10)	15/64(4)	Index
	WWC3-188A	½–⅝	500	1400(5)	None	1/8(6)	9/16(2)	5/64(8)	¼(4)	1 Rich
1960	WW15-41A	1¼	500	1400(5)	None	7/32(1)	19/64(2)	3/32(8)	15/64(4)	Index
	WW15-42	1¼	500	1400(5)	None	7/32(1)	19/64(2)	3/32(8)	15/64(4)	Index
	WWC3-188	½–⅝	500	1400(5)	None	1/8(1)	9/16(2)	3/32(8)	¼(4)	1 Rich
1959	WW3-164	¾–1¼	475	8(3)	None	7/32(2)	19/64(2)	None	15/64(4)	Index
	WW3-181	¾–1¼	475	8(3)	None	7/32(2)	19/64(2)	None	15/64(4)	Index
	WW3-182	¾–1¼	475	8(3)	None	7/32(2)	19/64(2)	None	15/64(4)	Index
	WW3-183	¾–1¾	475	8(3)	None	7/32(2)	19/64(2)	None	15/64(4)	Index
1958	WW3-159	¾–1¾	475	5½(3)	None	3/16(1)	13/64(2)	None	.166(4)	Index
	WW3-160	¾–1¾	475	5½(3)	None	3/16(1)	13/64(2)	None	.166(4)	Index
	WW3-163	¾–1¾	475	8(3)	None	7/32(2)	19/64(2)	None	15/64(4)	Index
	WW3-164	¾–1¾	475	8(3)	None	7/32(2)	19/64(2)	None	15/64(4)	Index
1957	WW3-149	¾–1¼	475	5½(3)	None	7/32(2)	19/64(2)	None	.166(4)	Index
	WW3-150	¾–1¼	475	5½(3)	None	7/32(2)	19/64(2)	None	.166(4)	Index
	WW3-159	¾–1¼	475	5½(3)	None	3/16(2)	13/64(2)	None	.166(4)	Index
	WW3-160	¾–1¼	475	5½(3)	None	3/16(2)	13/64(2)	None	.166(4)	Index
1956	WW3-135	¾–1¼	475	4½(3)	None	3/16(1)	15/64(2)	None	.166(4)	Index
	WW3-136	¾–1¼	475	4½(3)	None	3/16(1)	15/64(2)	None	.166(4)	Index
	WW3-137	¾–1¼	475	4½(3)	None	3/16(1)	15/64(2)	None	.166(4)	Index
	WW3-138	¾–1¼	475	4½(3)	None	3/16(1)	15/64(2)	None	.166(4)	Index
	WW3-139	¾–1¼	475	4½(3)	None	3/16(1)	15/64(2)	None	.166(4)	Index
	WW3-140	¾–1¼	475	4½(3)	None	3/16(1)	15/64(2)	None	.166(4)	Index
1955–56	WW3-124	¾–1¼	475	5⅛(3)	None	3/16(1)	13/64(2)	None	.166(4)	Index
	WW3-125	¾–1¼	475	5⅛(3)	None	3/16(1)	13/64(2)	None	.166(4)	Index
	WW3-126	¾–1¼	475	5⅛(3)	None	3/16(1)	13/64(2)	None	.166(4)	Index
1955	WW3-131	¾–1¼	475	4½(3)	None	3/16(1)	15/64(2)	None	.166(4)	Index
	WW3-132	¾–1¼	475	4½(3)	None	3/16(1)	15/64(2)	None	.166(4)	Index
	WW3-133	¾–1¼	475	4½(3)	None	3/16(1)	15/64(2)	None	.166(4)	Index
	WW3-120	¾–1¼	475	4½(3)	None	3/16(1)	15/64(2)	None	.166(4)	Index
	WW3-121	¾–1¼	475	4½(3)	None	3/16(1)	15/64(2)	None	.166(4)	Index
	WW3-122	¾–1¼	475	4½(3)	None	3/16(1)	15/64(2)	None	.166(4)	Index
1953–54	WW3-105	¾–1¼	475	4½(3)	None	3/16(1)	3/4(2)	None	.166(4)	Index
	WW3-108	¾–1¼	475	4½(3)	None	3/16(1)	3/4(2)	None	.166(4)	Index
	WW3-109	¾–1¼	475	4½(3)	None	3/16(1)	3/4(2)	None	.166(4)	Index

STROMBERG NOTES continued

⑤—With engine running at normal operating temperature, turn fast idle screw against highest step on fast idle cam until specified rpm is obtained.

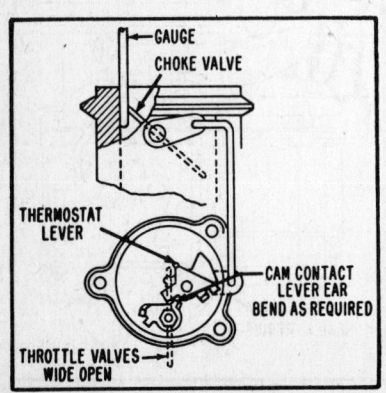

Fig. ④—With throttle valves wide open, choke valve should open the dimension specified between edge of choke valve and wall of air horn. Adjust by bending tang on throttle lever.

Fig. ①—WW float level. Invert main body so weight of floats only is forcing needle against its seat. There should be the distance listed from surface of fuel bowl to crown of float at center.

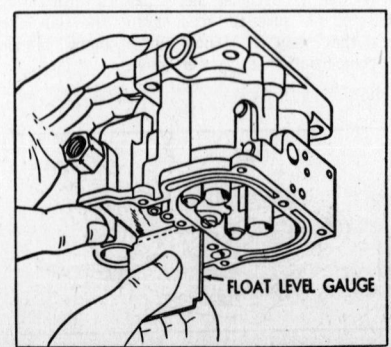

FLOAT LEVEL GAUGE

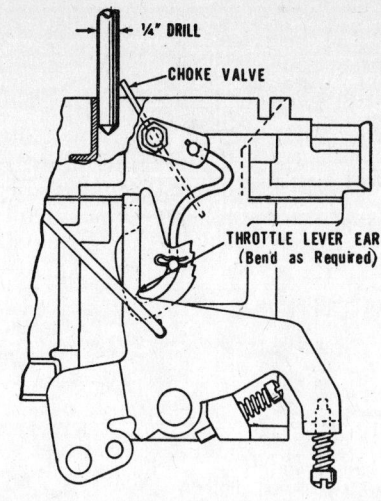

¼" DRILL
CHOKE VALVE
THROTTLE LEVER EAR
(Bend as Required)

Fig. ⑦—With throttle valves wide open, choke valve should open the dimension specified between edge of choke valve and wall of air horn. Adjust by bending ear on throttle lever.

Fig. ⑧—This setting is made after pump travel setting. With throttle fully closed and choke valve wide open, test opening of bowl vent valve at center of hole with rubber valve hanging free. If opening is not as specified, bend bowl vent lever as required.

⑨—Pump travel is automatically taken care of when bowl vent valve is properly adjusted.

⑩—With throttle valves tightly closed it should be possible to insert a drill of the size listed between bowl vent and vent seat protruding through air horn. Adjust by bending pump rod as required.

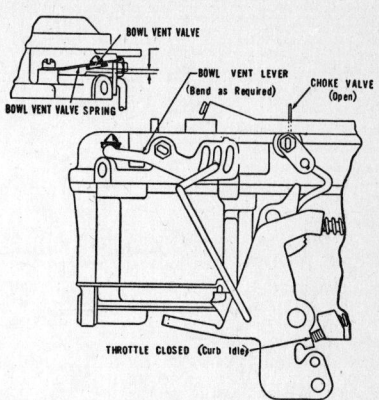

BOWL VENT VALVE
BOWL VENT LEVER
(Bend as Required)
CHOKE VALVE
(Open)
BOWL VENT VALVE SPRING
THROTTLE CLOSED (Curb Idle)

Clutch and Transmission Section

CLUTCH PEDAL, ADJUST

1960-61

The procedure for adjusting the clutch is the same as that outlined for 1957-59 with the following exception. When adjusting the overcenter spring the adjusting nut should be turned up five turns on 10, 10½ and 11" clutches and three turns tighter than finger tight for 9¼" clutch.

1957-59

To compensate for normal clutch wear, adjust the clutch release fork rod to obtain $\frac{5}{32}$" free play of clutch release fork outer end. This will provide a one-inch free pedal movement at the pedal with a total of six-inch pedal travel.

When necessary to adjust the over-center spring, back off the over-center spring adjusting nut until it is free of the "C" link. With the clutch pedal depressed to the full six-inch travel, turn the adjusting nut until the nut just contacts the "C" link. Then tighten seven full turns for the 10" clutch or five full turns for the 9¼" clutch—*no more*—from the finger-tight position.

1955-56

Adjust the clutch fork rod in or out as required to secure $\frac{3}{16}$" free play of the clutch release fork outer end. This will provide the one inch free pedal movement at the pedal pad with a total of 7" full pedal travel, Fig. 1.

The upper end of the clutch pedal pivots in the lower end of the mounting bracket on needle bearings in the V8 and nylon bushings in the Six. These bearings require no periodic lubrication. However, they should be lubricated with wheel bearing grease if the pedal is removed for any reason.

1953-54

To adjust pedal free play, turn the clutch release fork rod adjusting nut until ⅛ to $\frac{3}{32}$" free play in the clutch fork is obtained. This adjustment, if correctly set, will give the necessary one inch free pedal play.

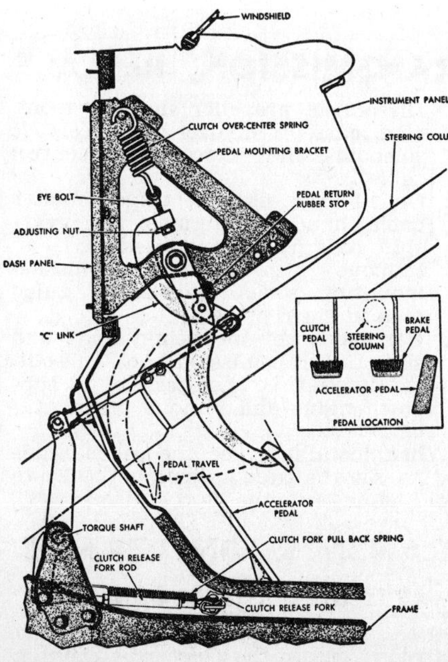

CLUTCH SERVICE

Unless special clutch rebuilding equipment is available, it is recommended that the clutch assembly be exchanged for a rebuilt unit should the clutch require rebuilding. The driven disc, however, may be replaced without special equipment. If clutch rebuilding equipment is available, follow the equipment manufacturer's instructions, Fig. 2.

Removal

1. Remove transmission and clutch pan.
2. Pull out clutch release bearing and sleeve.
3. Mark clutch cover and flywheel so they may be assembled in the same relative position and thus maintain original balance.
4. Remove capscrews which retain clutch cover to flywheel. Loosen each

WINDSHIELD
INSTRUMENT PANEL
CLUTCH OVER-CENTER SPRING
STEERING COLUMN
PEDAL MOUNTING BRACKET
EYE BOLT
PEDAL RETURN RUBBER STOP
ADJUSTING NUT
DASH PANEL
"C" LINK
CLUTCH PEDAL
STEERING COLUMN
BRAKE PEDAL
ACCELERATOR PEDAL
PEDAL LOCATION
PEDAL TRAVEL "7"
ACCELERATOR PEDAL
TORQUE SHAFT
CLUTCH FORK PULL BACK SPRING
CLUTCH RELEASE FORK ROD
CLUTCH RELEASE FORK
FRAME

Fig. 1 Clutch pedal and linkage. 1955-56

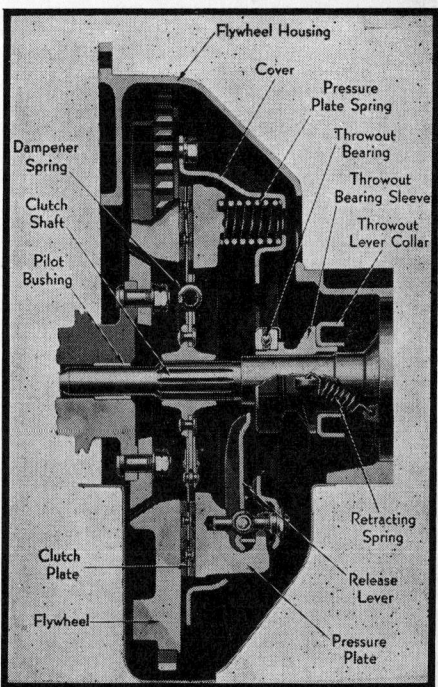

Flywheel Housing
Cover
Pressure Plate Spring
Dampener Spring
Throwout Bearing
Clutch Shaft
Throwout Bearing Sleeve
Pilot Bushing
Throwout Lever Collar
Retracting Spring
Clutch Plate
Release Lever
Flywheel
Pressure Plate

Fig. 2 Clutch. 1953-59

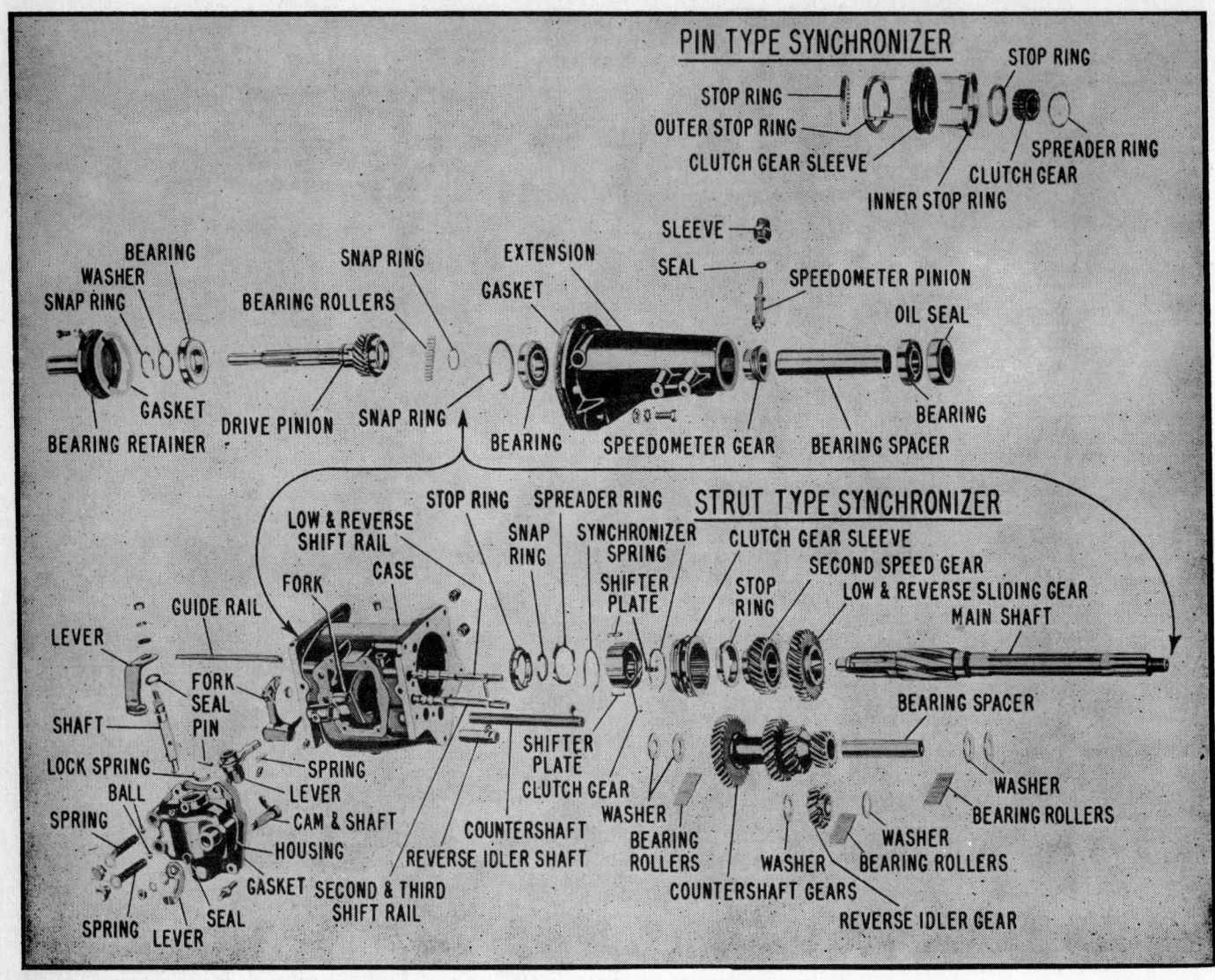

Fig. 3 Manual shift transmission. 1953-61 Dodge and Dart V8

screw a few turns in succession until cover is free.

5. Clutch assembly and driven disc may now be removed from the clutch housing.

Installation

1. Coat the pilot bearing in crankshaft with wheel bearing grease.
2. Clean surfaces of flywheel and pressure plate, making certain no oil or grease remains on these parts.
3. Hold cover plate and disc in place and insert a special clutch aligning tool or a spare clutch shaft through the hub of the disc and into the crankshaft pilot bearing.
4. Bolt clutch cover loosely to flywheel, being sure marks previously made are lined up.
5. To avoid distortion of clutch cover, tighten cover bolts a few turns each in progression until all are tight. The final tightening should be 15-20 lb. ft. torque.
6. Install transmission by guiding it into place with guide studs inserted in

the two top holes of the clutch housing.

7. Adjust clutch pedal free travel.

Service Note

The clutch on 1952-53 cars with fluid drive or torque converter is removed in the same manner as outlined for models without this equipment but the installation of the driven disc differs slightly as follows:

1. Clean surface of clutch driving plate and clutch pressure plate, making sure no oil remains on these parts.
2. Hold clutch disc in place and bolt clutch cover loosely to clutch driving plate with marks on cover and drive plate lined up.
3. Insert special clutch aligning tool or a spare clutch shaft through the hub of the driving plate and into the fluid drive runner inner bearings in the runner hub.
4. Clutch cover bolts should then be tightened a few turns at a time each in progression until they are all tight.
5. Install transmission.

TRANSMISSION, REPLACE

1. Disconnect propeller shaft at front. (On cars with overdrive, remove solenoid and disconnect control cable).
2. On all cars, disconnect speedometer cable, hand brake cable, and gear-shift rods from transmission.
3. Remove two upper transmission mounting studs and insert guide pins in their place.
4. Remove other mounting studs and slide the transmission back and out. On 1958-61, it is necessary to support engine and remove crossmember.

When installing, use the guide studs and handle the transmission carefully to avoid damage to the clutch disc.

TRANSMISSION REPAIRS

1953-61 Dodge & Dart V8

(For detailed service on overdrive transmission, see the *Overdrive* chapter. To disassemble the standard transmission, see Fig. 3 and proceed as follows:

1. Remove speedometer drive pinion.
2. Take off cover and gear selector, roll transmission over and remove balls.
3. Use a puller to remove mainshaft flange and brake drum.
4. Remove shifter fork guide rail.
5. With gears in neutral, remove shift fork lock screws.
6. Remove plug for lower shift rail.
7. Slide shift rails out through front of case.
8. Lift out shift forks.
9. Remove extension housing and mainshaft, being careful not to allow synchronizer to become disassembled.
10. Strip mainshaft of synchronizer, second speed gear and sliding gear.
11. Release snap ring and pull mainshaft out of extension housing.
12. Remove mainshaft bearing, spacer and speedometer drive gear.
13. Pull bearing and oil seal from extension housing.
14. Drive countershaft through rear of case, allowing cluster gear to lie in case.
15. Remove main drive gear and bearing, and disassemble parts.
16. Lift out cluster gear and related parts.
17. Drive reverse idler shaft out rearward and lift out gear.

Assembly Notes—Use new gaskets, oil seals and snap rings, being sure snap rings fit snugly in their grooves.

When assembling cluster gear, place steel washer plates next to gear and bronze washers next to case. Select the proper thickness bronze washers to provide end play of from .002 to .008 inch.

If a special oil seal drift is not available, be sure that oil seal protrudes $\frac{7}{32}$ inch out of the mainshaft extension housing.

Referring to Figs. 4 and 5 for synchronizer assembly, place one bent up end of synchronizer spring into pocket of shifting plate. Then install bent up end of other spring into pocket of same plate on opposite side of synchronizer. Spring on one side should leave plate in opposite direction from spring on other side.

Assemble the synchronizer unit on the mainshaft as shown in Fig. 6.

Fig. 4 Shifting plates (2) fit in stop ring slots (1). Standard transmission

If second speed gear end play is not within .003 and .008 inch, use a snap ring of different thickness.

Install first and reverse shifter rail on top, other rail on bottom, Fig. 7.

Install gearshift housing as shown in Fig. 8.

1960-61 Six

1. Referring to Fig. 8A, remove transmission flange.
2. Remove extension housing.
3. Remove transmission cover.
4. Remove clutch shaft bearing retainer.
5. Grasp clutch shaft with hand and pull assembly out of case. *Be careful not to bind inner synchronizer ring on clutch teeth.*
6. With transmission in reverse, remove outer center bearing snap ring, using a hook or a flat blade, then partially remove mainshaft.
7. Cock mainshaft; then remove synchronizer sleeve, rings and 2-3 shift fork.
8. Remove clutch gear snap ring, using snap ring pliers. Slide clutch gear off end of mainshaft.
9. Slide second speed gear, stop ring and synchronizer spring off mainshaft.
10. Remove low-reverse sliding gear and shift fork as mainshaft is withdrawn from case.
11. Using a feeler gauge, check end play of cluster gear, which should be .004″ to .012″. This measurement will determine if new thrust washers are to be installed at reassembly.
12. Drive countershaft rearward and out of case. Remove key from end of shaft.
13. Lift cluster gear and thrust washers out of case. Disassemble cluster gear by removing needle bearings (22 each end) and spacer.
14. Using a suitable drift, drive reverse idler gear shaft towards rear and out of case. Remove key from shaft.
15. Lift out reverse idler gear, thrust washers and needle bearings (22) out of case. Remove needle bearings from gear.

Assembly Notes

Reassembling the transmission is accomplished by reversing the disassembly procedure. However, observe the following:

1. When installing the reverse idler gear, have the bevelled ends of the gear teeth forward. Raise the idler gear slightly to align with shaft; then drive shaft into case, through thrust washer and gear, until end of shaft is approximately $\frac{1}{64}″$ below surface of case.
2. Cluster gear thrust washers are available in two sizes marked "A" and "B". Make a selection to give .004″ to .012″ total end play of cluster gear. Make sure tabs on thrust washers slide into grooves in case. Countershaft should be installed until approximately $\frac{1}{64}″$ below surface of case.
3. When installing mainshaft, have offset of low-reverse fork to rear. Engage fork in low-reverse gear,

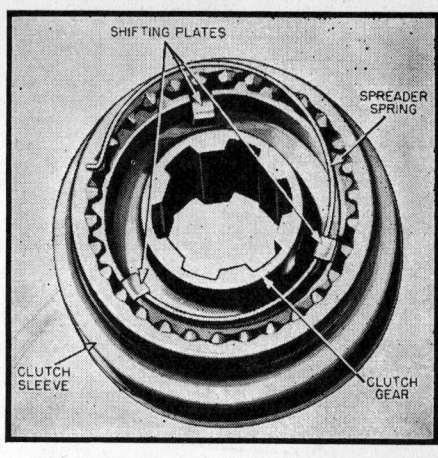

Fig. 5 Installing synchronizer shifting plates and spreader spring.

Fig. 6 Mainshaft and extension housing assembly

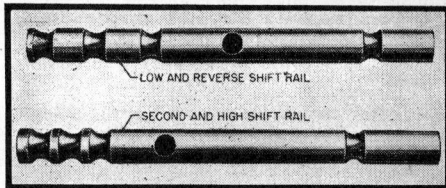

Fig. 7 Shifter rails

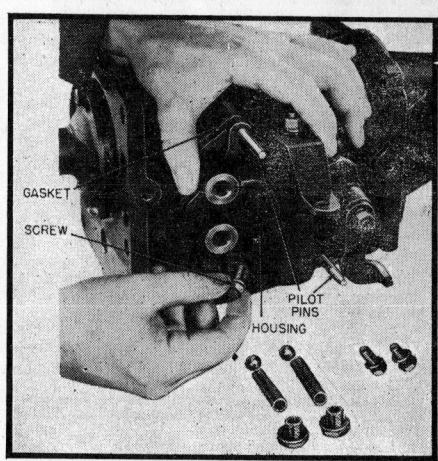

Fig. 8 Installing gearshift housing

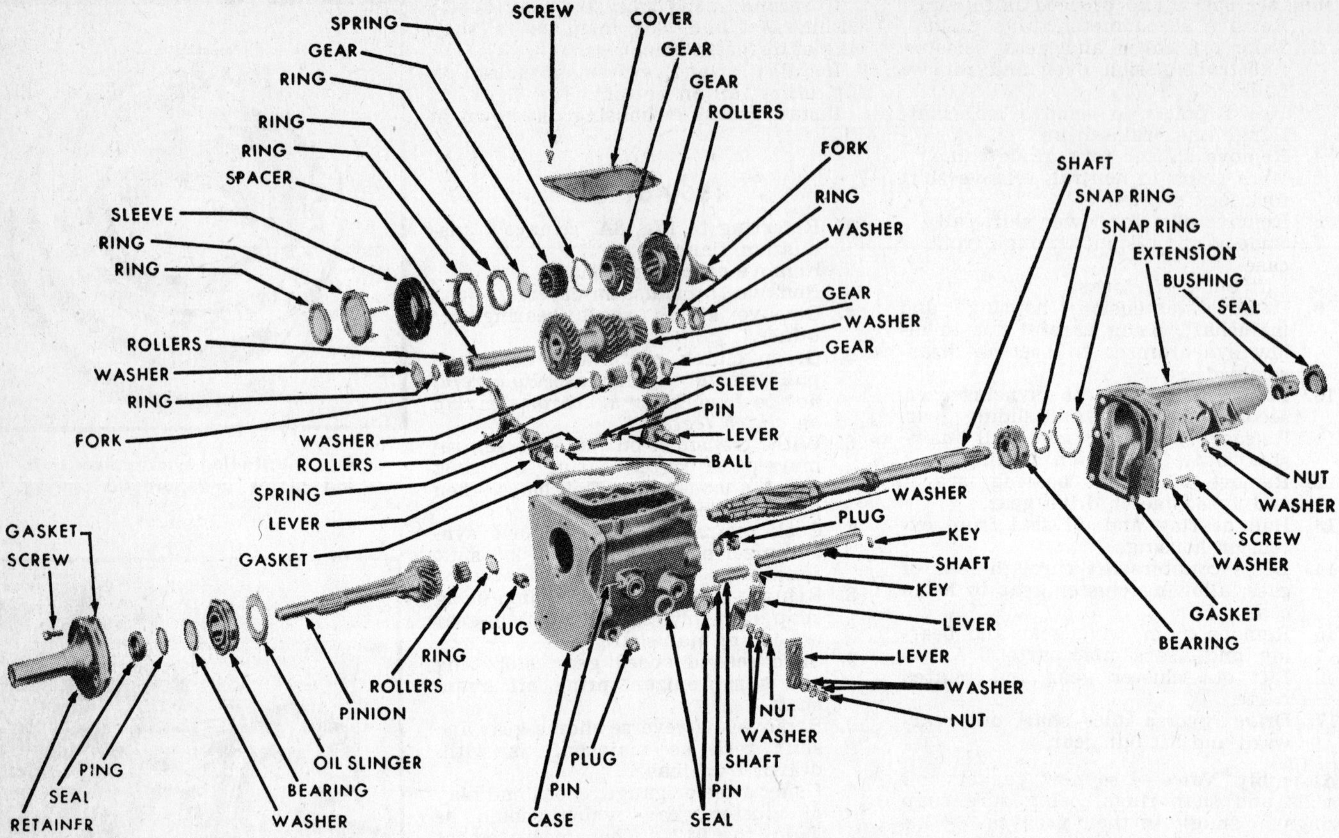

Fig. 8A   **Manual shift transmission. 1960-61 Six**

(Labels on exploded diagram, clockwise/around:)
SPRING, GEAR, RING, RING, RING, SPACER, SLEEVE, RING, RING, ROLLERS, WASHER, RING, FORK — SCREW, COVER, GEAR, GEAR, GEAR, ROLLERS, FORK, RING, WASHER, GEAR, WASHER, GEAR, SLEEVE, PIN, LEVER, BALL — WASHER, ROLLERS, SPRING, LEVER, GASKET — SHAFT, SNAP RING, SNAP RING, EXTENSION, BUSHING, SEAL, NUT, WASHER, SCREW, WASHER, GASKET, BEARING — WASHER, PLUG, KEY, SHAFT, KEY, LEVER, LEVER, WASHER, NUT — GASKET, SCREW, RING, ROLLERS, PINION, OIL SLINGER, BEARING, WASHER, PING, SEAL, RETAINER — PLUG, RING, PLUG, PIN, CASE, NUT, WASHER, SHAFT, PIN, SEAL

---

4. After sliding the synchronizer clutch gear on mainshaft and down against second speed gear, select a snap ring of the correct thickness and install. *Snap ring should eliminate end play and must be a snug fit.*

5. Check clearance between clutch gear and second speed gear, which should be .003" to .008". *End play in excess of .008" will permit gear "jump out."*

then position in case by shifting into reverse.

6. After mainshaft is properly positioned, select a snap ring that will be a snug fit at the rear bearing.

GEARSHIFT, ADJUST
1953-56

To adjust the control rod, loosen the lock bolt at the upper lever on the lower end of the steering column. Set the transmission gears in neutral and the hand control lever in the horizontal position and tighten the lock bolt.

To adjust the shift control rod, set the transmission gears in neutral and loosen the lock nut on the selector rod at the transmission end. Tighten the nut until all play is eliminated and back off ½ turn for clearance and tighten.

1957-58, 1960-61 Manual Trans.

This transmission incorporates an individual rod shifting mechanism, Fig. 9, which simplifies maintenance, improves shift quality and decreases shifting effort.

Cross-over adjustments and gearshift operating lever positions are adjusted by threads on the upper ends of the shift rods. Movement of the shift lever should be smooth when moving through the cross-over position.

If an up and down motion at the hand lever is experienced during cross-over, the shift rod length should be adjusted by turning the adjusting nuts on one rod to vary the trunnion position on the rod.

This will raise or lower the lever at the lower end of the steering column and thus align the cross-over. The hand lever knob must be in a horizontal position following cross-over adjustments.

If the lever binds when moving into a gear position after cross-over, check the position of the gearshift tube support at the lower end of the steering column. The support should be moved up to relieve binding on the second-to-high side and down for the low-to-reverse side.

Cross-Over Adjustments

Before making the cross-over adjustment, Fig. 10, the gearshift lever shaft must be in its normal fully returned position in neutral. Then proceed as follows:

1. Remove grease fitting from tube lever pin retainer. Rotate retainer until gearshift tube cross pin is exposed.

2. If a .040" round feeler cannot be inserted between pin and bottom of slot as shown in Fig. 10, an adjustment at the gearshift tube lower support must be made as follows:

3. Loosen lower support screws slightly. Move support by tapping lightly with a plastic hammer. On cars with power steering, do not attempt to separate lower support after loosening.

4. Adjust support up or down as required to secure the necessary .040" clearance.

5. Tighten support clamping screws to 150 *inch* lb. torque (90 *inch* lb. for power steering equipped cars).

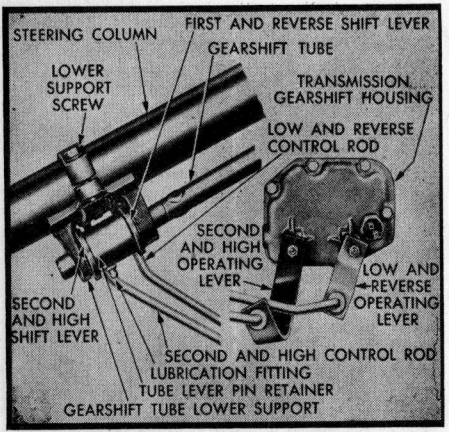

Fig. 9   **Manual transmission shift linkage. 1957-58, 1960-61**

(Labels on photo:)
STEERING COLUMN, FIRST AND REVERSE SHIFT LEVER, GEARSHIFT TUBE, LOWER SUPPORT SCREW, TRANSMISSION GEARSHIFT HOUSING, LOW AND REVERSE CONTROL ROD, SECOND AND HIGH OPERATING LEVER, LOW AND REVERSE OPERATING LEVER, SECOND AND HIGH SHIFT LEVER, SECOND AND HIGH CONTROL ROD, LUBRICATION FITTING, TUBE LEVER PIN RETAINER, GEARSHIFT TUBE LOWER SUPPORT

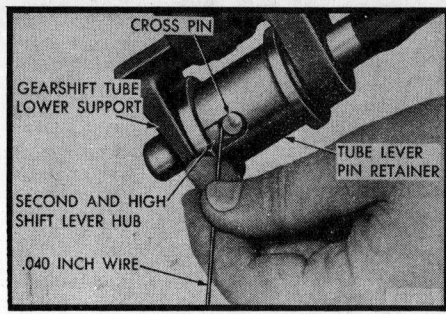

Fig. 10 Checking gearshift lever shaft in Neutral position. 1957-58, 1960-61

6. Rotate tube-lever pin retainer to original position and install grease fitting securely. (Loss of fitting will result in loss of cross pin).

Control Rod Adjustments

After completing foregoing adjustments, be sure gearshift lever travels freely and equally up and down in either high or second gear position and low or reverse positions. Check the cross-over adjustments, Fig. 11, with the manual lever by making the cross-over from second-to-direct and from low-to-reverse. Cross-over must be free of interference. Transmission must be in neutral when making the following adjustments:

1. Loosen adjusting nuts at second-to-direct control rod swivel.
2. Turn both adjusting nuts in direction required to locate hand lever in horizontal plane.
3. Tighten adjusting nuts securely to swivel block.
4. Loosen adjusting nuts at low-to-reverse gearshift control rod swivel.
5. Position low-to-reverse gearshift lever in direct alignment (through center of swivel lock pin) with second-to-direct gearshift lever. Tighten adjusting nuts securely to swivel block.

Caution: Failure to make this adjustment correctly will result in insufficient manual lever-to-steering column clearance or manual lever-to-operator's leg clearance. Damage to the transmission is also possible because of incomplete engagement of gears.

1959 Manual Trans.

Check position of steering column jacket. Gearshift and turn signal levers must have adequate clearance under steering wheel. If necessary, loosen jacket clamps, position jacket and tighten clamps. Check gearshift tube for interference or drag at instrument panel bracket, the floor pad and the tube support lower bracket. Eliminate any looseness of control rods in operating levers at transmission. Levers must be in neutral when making the following adjustments:

1. Lever travel (free play) up and down (toward or away from steering wheel) in first or reverse should equal the lever travel in second and

high. Adjust by loosening the lower bracket clamp and moving the bracket up or down. Tighten clamp to 40 inch-pounds.
2. Outer (knob) section of control lever should be horizontal with transmission in neutral and lever at rest (away from steering wheel). Adjust length of rod attached to tube lower lever (2-3 shift).
3. Shifting through crossover should be smooth. Adjust length of rod attached to tube upper lever (1-R shift) to attain smooth crossover; then shorten rod an additional two turns to insure disengagement from low when fast shift is made.

POWERFLITE

A detailed service procedure on this transmission is given in the *Automatic Transmission Section* of this manual.

Transmission, Replace

1. Drain transmission and converter.
2. Disconnect front universal and secure propeller shaft to frame.
3. Remove hand brake linkage.
4. Disconnect speedometer cable, neutral starter and back-up light wires from switches.
5. Disconnect throttle linkage from lever at transmission.
6. Remove push button control cable (if equipped).
7. Remove oil cooler lines (if equipped).
8. Remove nuts from rear engine mount and support engine with a suitable jack.
9. Remove crossmember, leaving engine rear support adapter attached to transmission.
10. Unfasten transmission from converter housing and slide it straight back and out of car.
11. Reverse foregoing procedure to install.

POWERFLITE LINKAGE

Selector Linkage, 1954

1. Move manual control lever on transmission (long lever toward rear) to Neutral position, which is the second detent position from the rear of the vehicle.

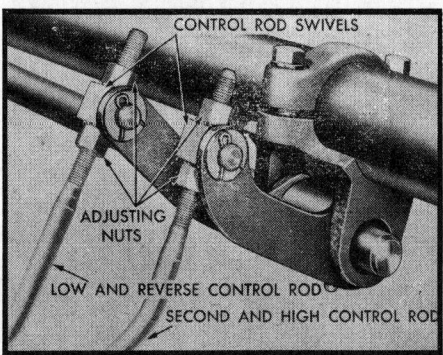

Fig. 11 Gearshift control rod adjustments. 1957-58, 1960-61

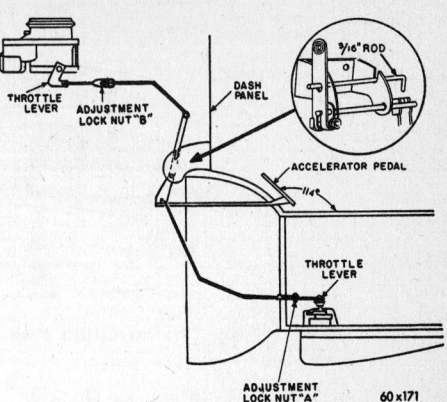

Fig. 11A Throttle linkage. 1960-61 V8

2. Check angle of upper lever of gearshift control bellcrank mounted to the frame. It should be about 40 to 45 degrees above the horizontal line of the frame. The lower arm should point slightly toward the rear of the vehicle.
3. Disconnect front and rear gearshift control rods at gearshift control bellcrank.
4. Locate gearshift control bellcrank short arm as described above and adjust the control rod to the required length for a free fit in the bellcrank lower lever. Reinstall rod.
5. Put selector lever pointer in Neutral position on the indicator dial at the top of the steering column, then proceed as follows:
6. Check clearance between gearshift tube lever and end of neutral position gate. This clearance should be .015″ to .017″. *Failure to provide this clearance will affect the proper section of Neutral.*
7. Check the clearance between the flat gearshift lever and side of gate. This should be .015″ to .030″. *Failure to provide adequate clearance will cause binding on the gate which will affect ease of selection.*
8. In the event adjustment is necessary, loosen the clamp holding the selector gate to steering column jacket. Move the gate as necessary to obtain the desired clearance. Then tighten clamp and recheck clearance.
9. With selector lever still in Neutral, adjust front gearshift rod to the required length to provide a free fit in the upper lever of the bellcrank; then reinstall rod.
10. Operate the selector lever through all selective positions and check accuracy of the pointer on the dial indicator.

Selector Linkage, 1955

The selector linkage is held in the gate between "N" and "D" positions under tension which is adjustable by a bracket to which it is attached behind the instrument panel.

Use a spring scale and pull out the selector lever knob, which should require

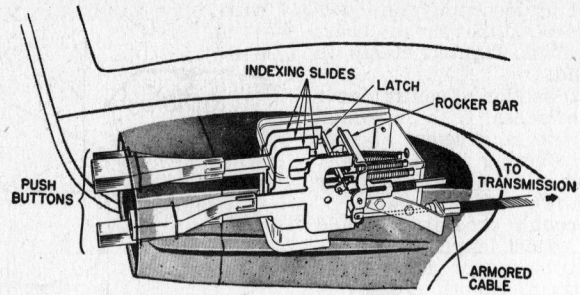

Fig. 12 Powerflite push button controls (typical)

Fig. 14 Powerflite control cable backlash adjustment

one to two pounds pull on the scale to break contact between selector lever and gate. If it does not, adjust by loosening the bracket attaching bolts and slide the bracket to obtain the proper tension. Tighten bolts and recheck tension.

If correct tension cannot be obtained by adjusting the bracket, it can be corrected by removing the selector lever and mounting bracket and bending the tension spring. Bend the spring away from the gate to decrease tension and toward the gate to increase tension.

The selector must go into the gate without interference when shifting. Do not use force. If any binding exists, investigate the linkage and correct as required.

Throttle Linkage, 1954

1. With carburetor off fast idle speed adjusted to 475-500 rpm in neutral, adjust linkage as follows:
2. Loosen Allen lock screw in throttle control rod swivel.
3. Disconnect clip from throttle control rod and move swivel and throttle control lever as far forward as they will go.
4. Slowly move swivel and throttle control lever rearward until a slight resistance to travel (caused by a detent) is felt.
5. Holding swivel and lever at the exact position where resistance was felt, push slightly forward on throttle rod to remove free play. Lock swivel in this position.

Throttle Linkage, 1955-58 V8

1. Be sure there is no bind in the throttle linkage; if there is, correct this condition before proceeding.
2. Run engine until normal operating temperature is reached.
3. Remove air cleaner to make definitely sure choke valve is fully opened.
4. Connect tachometer leads to coil and ground.
5. Adjust engine idle speed to 475-500 rpm with transmission in neutral.
6. Loosen throttle linkage adjusting screw (located on accelerator shaft-to-carburetor rod.
7. Move rear portion of this rod rearward until it is stopped by the idle stop on the transmission throttle cam.
8. With rods in line and rear portion of rod pre-loaded, lock throttle linkage adjusting screw securely.

Throttle Linkage, 1954-58 Six

The operations outlined for the V8 engines apply to 6-cylinder models except Steps 6, 7 and 8, which are as follows:
1. Loosen throttle linkage adjusting screw, located on throttle control rod from engine to carburetor.
2. While holding throttle control rod against closed throttle stop, move bellcrank arm just enough to start extending the accelerator return spring. *Do not extend spring more than* $\frac{1}{8}$" *in opposite direction.*
3. With control rods in line and preloaded slightly, lock throttle rod adjusting screw securely.

Throttle Linkage, 1959 V8

1. With engine shut off and carburetor off fast idle, disconnect transmission throttle rod at carburetor.
2. With rod held to limit of travel rearward, the distance from the dash to the bellcrank should be $\frac{1}{2}$" to $\frac{9}{16}$". If correct, the balance of the linkage is properly adjusted and all that is necessary is to adjust the throttle rod length to fit between bellcrank (held to rear) and carburetor lever. If dimension is correct, proceed as follows:
3. Connect throttle rod to carburetor.
4. With engine running at operating temperature and carburetor off fast idle, adjust idle speed to 475-500 rpm with transmission in neutral.
5. Loosen adjusting lock nuts on transmission throttle rod and the rod at transmission.
6. Adjust throttle rod to correct length

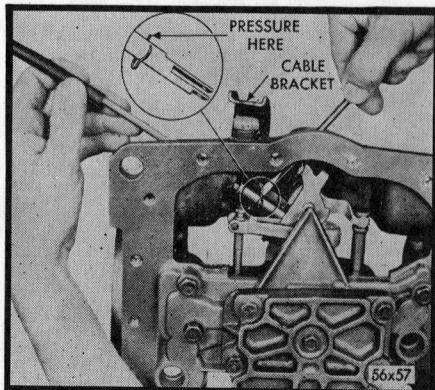

Fig. 13 Removing Powerflite push button control cable from transmission (oil pan removed to show operation)

by holding bellcrank $\frac{1}{2}$" to $\frac{9}{16}$" from dash while tightening lock nut on rod.
7. Accelerator pedal should be 115 deg. from horizontal, measured from rear of pedal. If necessary, adjust accelerator rod under slanting toe-board.
8. Adjust length of rod at transmission by holding transmission lever forward against internal stop while tightening lock nut on rod.

Throttle Linkage, 1959 Six

1. With carburetor choke valve fully open and throttle off fast idle, the distance from heater housing to center of bellcrank ball stud should be approximately $2\frac{1}{4}$". Length of linkage spring should be $8\frac{1}{4}$".
2. Only when heater housing to ball stud distance is correct can the throttle rod be adjusted to produce $8\frac{1}{4}$" spring length. If heater housing to ball stud distance is incorrect, proceed as follows:
3. With engine at operating temperature and carburetor off fast idle, adjust idle speed to 475-500 rpm with transmission in neutral.
4. Loosen lock nuts on throttle rod above cylinder head and the rod at the transmission.
5. While holding heater housing-to-bellcrank ball stud distance at $2\frac{1}{4}$", adjust throttle rod to produce the $8\frac{1}{4}$" spring length.
6. Adjust accelerator pedal-to-bellcrank rod to hold the pedal 115 deg. from the horizontal.
7. Adjust length of rod at transmission by holding transmission lever forward against internal stop while tightening lock nut on rod.

Throttle, Linkage, 1960-61

1. With engine at operating temperature, carburetor off fast idle cam and transmission in neutral, adjust idle speed to 475-500 rpm.
2. Loosen throttle adjusting lock nuts on both carburetor rod and the transmission throttle rod.
3. Insert a $\frac{3}{16}$" rod in the hole and open slot of accelerator shaft bracket end into the elongated hole of the throttle lever.
4. With rod in position, hold transmis-

sion throttle valve lever all the way forward and tighten transmission to accelerator lever assembly rod adjusting lock nut "A", Fig. 11A.

5. Remove rod from accelerator lever, shaft and bracket assembly.

6. With carburetor throttle lever off fast idle cam and against the idle stop screw, move the rear half of the carburetor rod rearward until the stop in the transmission is felt, tighten lock nut "B", Fig. 11A.

7. The accelerator pedal should be at an angle of 114° to the horizontal. If necessary to adjust, remove accelerator pedal end of the bell crank to pedal rod, and shorten or lengthen the rod by loosening lock nut at the swivel end and rotate the swivel. Reinstall the rod and tighten the lock nut. *Be sure the rod is properly aligned to prevent binding. Poor engine performance due to carburetor throttle not opening fully or lack of kickdown may result if pedal angle is incorrect.*

POWERFLITE PUSH BUTTONS

1954-61

Mechanical connection between push button unit, Fig. 12, and the manual control valve is obtained through the use of a single push-pull cable. One end of the wire cable is secured to the cable actuator in the speed range selector unit on the instrument panel. The other end enters the transmission case to engage the manual control valve assembly.

Cable Remove, Push Button End

Remove bezel attaching screws, then remove bezel and push buttons. Remove nuts holding push buttons unit to instrument panel and remove push button unit from rear of panel. The cable bracket is held by two screws to the push button unit. A hairpin clip secures the cable to the actuator bar.

Cable Remove, Trans. End

Remove throttle adjusting hole plug and allow transmission fluid to drain off to the level of the hole. Remove neutral starter switch to provide access to the cable lock spring. Remove cable bracket. On star wheel type, push "R" button in to place cable adapter near switch hole. Insert screwdriver through neutral

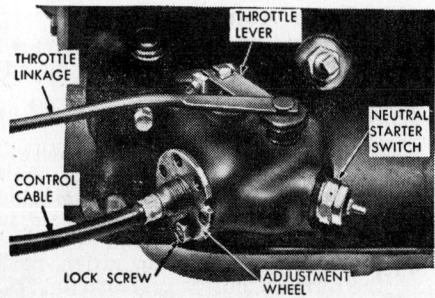

Fig. 14A   Wheel type push button cable adjustment. 1959-61 V8 Torqueflite

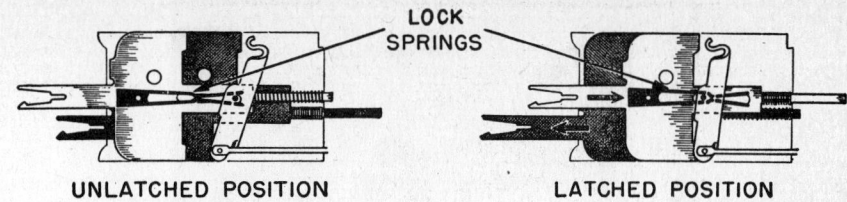

UNLATCHED POSITION   LATCHED POSITION

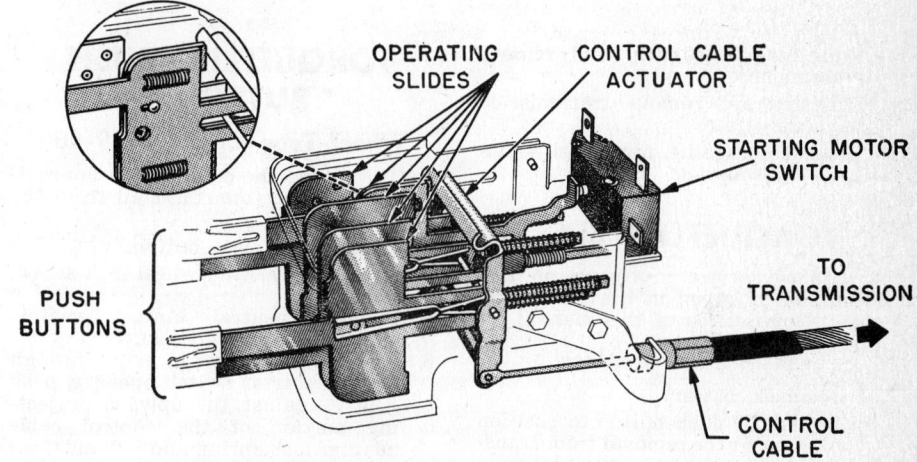

Fig. 15   Torqueflite gearshift control unit (typical)

switch hole. Push gently on projecting portion of cable lock spring and pull outward on cable, Fig. 13.

Cable Install, Trans. End

Push in "L" button. Place transmission manual valve lever in reverse detent by moving neutral switch contact part of lever full travel towards rear of car manually, by using a screwdriver in neutral switch hole. With "L" button held tightly in, insert cable into transmission case engaging cable ferrule groove with lock spring in cable adapter. Push and pull the cable, using pressure, to be sure groove in ferrule has engaged lock spring. Replace mounting bracket and tighten cap screw finger tight.

Cable Adjustment

Loosen and move cable bracket assembly manually at the transmission as required, to position manual valve lever into neutral. Hold "N" button tightly in at full travel. The neutral starting switch cam should then be practically centered in its mounting hole. Use a free fitting flat nosed rod, inserted throught the neutral switch mounting hole, and then apply light pressure against the manual valve lever to maintain the neutral detent position of the manual lever. Carefully move cable assembly in and out, without moving the manual lever, to determine total freeplay travel of cable. Locate the cable in mid-position of the free-play, Fig. 14, release the pressure against the manual lever and tighten the mounting bracket securely. *Do not allow the cable to move when tightening the bracket or backlash*

setting will be disturbed. Replace neutral switch and check fluid level.

V8 TORQUEFLITE

A detailed service procedure on this transmission is given in the *Automatic Transmission Section* of this manual.

Transmission, Replace

1. Disconnect battery.
2. Place push button in "1" position ("R" position on 1960-61) so as to be able to remove cable from adapter housing on transmission.
3. Drain transmission and converter.
4. Disconnect front universal joint.
5. Disconnect hand brake linkage.
6. Disconnect speedometer cable.
7. Disconnect neutral starter switch wire.
8. Disconnect throttle control linkage at transmission.
9. Loosen push button control cable adjustable mounting bracket or adjustment wheel locking screw.
10. Remove control cable adapter housing plug, insert screwdriver through hole, release cable spring lock and remove cable from adapter housing.
11. Using same screwdriver, insert through cable opening in housing and push lever rearward to last detent. Then reinstall housing plug and tighten.
12. Remove oil cooler lines from transmission (if equipped).
13. Unfasten rear engine support from crossmember.
14. Remove starting motor.
15. Support engine with suitable jack.

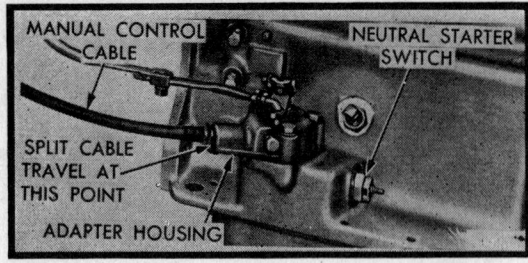

Fig. 16 Torqueflite manual control cable adjustment (non-wheel type)

16. Raise engine slightly and remove crossmember.
17. Unfasten and remove transmission from converter.
18. Reverse foregoing procedure to install transmission.

TORQUEFLITE SIX

A detailed service procedure on this transmission is given in the *Automatic Transmission Section* of this manual.

Transmission, Replace

1. Disconnect battery.
2. Depress "L" push button to position control cable for removal from transmission.
3. Remove starting motor.
4. Drain transmission and converter.
5. Disconnect neutral switch wire and remove switch.
6. Remove control cable to transmission adjusting screw, insert screwdriver through neutral switch opening and push gently against upper projecting portion of cable lock spring and pull outward on cable to remove cable from adapter and case.
7. Loosen clamp screw and remove throttle link and lever assembly from throttle shaft.
8. Disconnect oil cooler lines at transmission and remove filler tube.
9. Remove speedometer pinion and sleeve from transmission and disconnect front universal joint.
10. Remove parking brake cable from brake support.
11. Remove nuts securing transmission extension housing insulator to the crossmember.
12. Support engine with suitable jack.
13. Raise engine slightly and remove crossmember.
14. Place transmission jack under transmission.
15. Mark converter and flex plate to assure correct assembly. Remove converter to flex plate mounting screws and attach a small "C" clamp to edge of bell housing to hold converter in place during transmission removal.
16. Remove bell housing bolts and carefully work transmission rearward off engine block dowels and to disengage converter hub from end of crankshaft.
17. Lower transmission jack and remove transmission and converter.
18. Reverse foregoing procedure to install transmission.

TORQUEFLITE PUSH BUTTONS

Wheel-Type Cable, 1959-60

1. To remove the cable, drain approximately three quarts of oil from the transmission.
2. Engage "1" push button.
3. Remove adjusting wheel lock screw, Fig. 14A.
4. Remove neutral starter switch, cupped washer and seal.
5. With a screwdriver inserted through neutral starter switch opening, push gently against the upward projecting portion of the control cable adapter lock spring and pull outward on cable to remove cable assembly from case.

Install and Adjust

1. Engage "R" push button. *Have an assistant hold this button firmly until the transmission end of the cable has been adjusted and locked.*
2. Back off the cable adjustment wheel (turn counter-clockwise) on cable housing until only two or three threads are showing. *Caution: do not back the wheel entirely off the guide threads because it serves as a stop prevent the "O" ring from going too far into the case and becoming caught inside the case when the cable is installed.*
3. Push cable control housing into the transmission case with just enough force to overcome the "O" ring friction and to bottom the assembly. While holding the cable firmly into the bottomed position, rotate adjusting wheel clockwise *to just contact the transmission case.*
4. Release the inward pressure on the cable and then turn the adjusting wheel until the next adjustment hole in the wheel lines up with the lock screw hole in the case. Counting this hole as number one, continue turning the wheel clockwise until the fifth hole lines up with the screw hole in the case. Check cable adjustment to be sure of full detent in all shift ranges.
5. Install neutral starter switch and refill transmission with oil.

Non-Wheel Type Cable, 1959

1. Raise vehicle on hoist and drain 2 quarts of fluid from transmission.
2. Engage "L" push button.
3. Remove control cable lock clip.

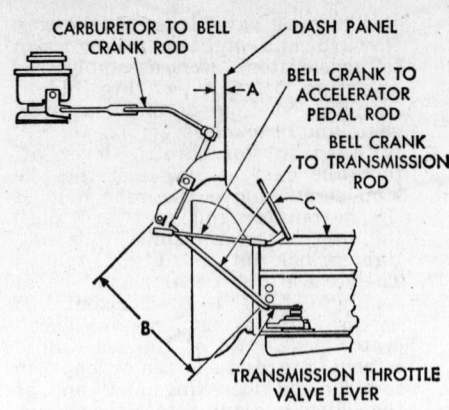

Fig. 17 Throttle linkage adjustment. 1958 Torqueflite

4. Remove plug and locking screw.
5. With screwdriver inserted through plug hole, push gently against upward projecting portion of control cable adapter spring and pull outward on cable to remove cable from adapter housing.
6. Insert screwdriver into cable entrance hole in cable adapter housing and push cable adapter to limit of travel to the reverse detent position. Remove screwdriver.
7. Reinstall plug and locking screw in adapter housing.
8. Turn locking screw with screwdriver counter-clockwise until locking screw contacts adapter. Tighten locking screw firmly against adapter to cause adapter to bind against adapter housing. *Do not over-tighten screw as adapter housing may be damaged.*
9. Engage "R" button.
10. Hold cable in alignment with hole in adapter housing.
11. Push cable into housing until adapter spring engages groove in cable end.
12. With a helper firmly holding the "R" button in at full travel position, carefully position cable housing at the midpoint of cable backlash.
13. While continuing to hold "R" button firmly, tighten cable adjusting clip screw securely, being careful not to move cable during tightening process.
14. With screwdriver, turn adapter locking screw clockwise to limit of travel. Tighten 10 to 16 inch lbs. In this position, locking screw seats against inner end of plug and prevents oil leakage at this point.

Cable Adjust, 1957-58

1. "R" push button must be depressed and held all the way in during adjustment.
2. Loosen cable lock clip screw at transmission.
3. Push cable in until it stops; then release cable.
4. Tighten cable clip screw, making sure cable housing is not forced in or out during adjustment.
5. To check for proper operation, push the various buttons, return to "N" each time while checking starter operation. Engine should start only when "N" button is depressed.

TORQUEFLITE THROTTLE LINKAGE

1957 Four Bar. Carb.

1. With engine at operating temperature and idle speed adjusted to 475-500 rpm, loosen throttle linkage adjusting nut on rod from bell crank to intermediate throttle control.
2. Hold light pre-load rearward on rod so that throttle valve lever is against the stop in the transmission.
3. Tighten throttle adjusting nut.
4. Adjust accelerator pedal rod by removing rod at pedal arm. Loosen lock nut and turn ball and socket end of rod in direction required so that pedal can be depressed just down to floor mat without compressing mat.

1957 Two Bar. Carb.

All operations are the same as four barrel carburetor except that, since there is no intermediate throttle control, adjustment is made on the bell crank to carburetor rod.

1958-59 Four Bar. Carb.

1. With engine at operating temperature and idle speed set at 475-500 rpm, loosen throttle linkage adjusting nuts on carburetor-to-bell crank rod, and on bell crank-to-transmission rod.
2. Adjust carburetor-to-bell crank rod to position the lever ½" from cowl dash panel (see "A", Fig. 17) and tighten adjusting nut.
3. Dimension "B" should be 8½". Hold slight pre-load rearward on bell crank-to-transmission rod while holding transmission throttle valve lever forward against the stop, and tighten adjusting nut.
4. The accelerator pedal should be at an angle of 115 degrees to the horizontal (see "C", Fig. 17). If necessary to correct, remove the rod and rotate the swivel as required. Reinstall rod and tighten lock nut.

1958-59 Two Bar. Carb.

All operations are the same as the four barrel carburetor except that since there is no intermediate throttle control assembly, the adjustment is made on the bell crank-to-carburetor rod.

1960-61 Six

1. With engine at operating temperature and carburetor off fast idle cam, adjust idle speed to 500 rpm.
2. Loosen lock nut and move transmission throttle control lever forward until it stops. Tighten lock nut.
3. Check accelerator pedal angle. It

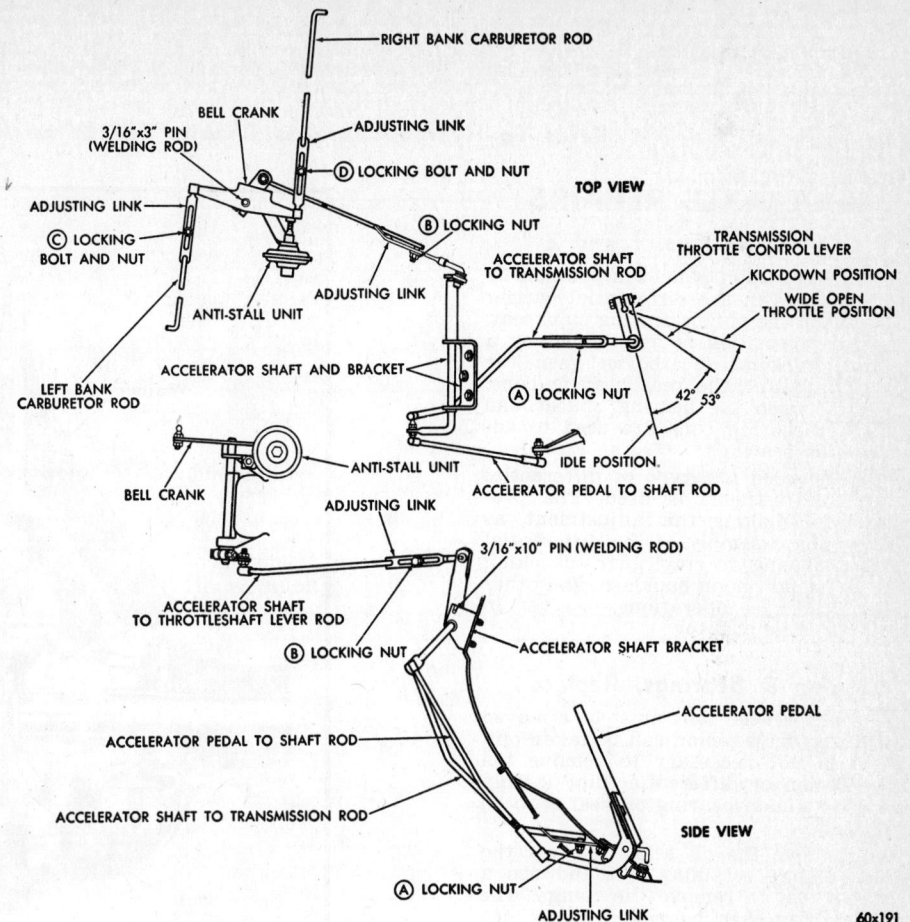

Fig. 18   Throttle linkage.   1960-61 Ram Manifold engine

60x191

should be 115°. To adjust, disconnect pedal and adjust rod length. When correct, reconnect pedal.

1960-61 V8

The procedure is the same as that outlined previously for the 1960 Powerflite.

1960-61 Ram Manifold

Refer to Fig. 18 and perform the following operations to properly adjust the linkage:

1. Loosen adjusting nuts "A" and "B".
2. Insert a 3/16" drill rod, 10" long into the accelerator shaft bracket and through the hole in the lever.
3. Move transmission throttle control lever forward until it stops and tighten locknut "A" securely. This positions accelerator shaft.
4. Unsnap accelerator pedal to shaft rod.
5. Turn threaded end of rod in or out to obtain 114° angle between floor of car and flat face of accelerator pedal and connect rod.
6. Remove drill rod from accelerator shaft bracket.
7. Inspect carburetors to be sure that choke valves are open, fast idle cams are released tnd throttle valves are closed.
8. Loosen locknuts "C" and "D" and back off anti-stall plunger far enough to allow bellcrank to be pivoted.
9. Pivot bellcrank until a 3/16" drill rod, 3" long can be inserted through bellcrank hole and down into intake manifold.
10. Tighten locknuts "C" and "D" and remove the drill rod from the bellcrank.
11. Push rearward on the accelerating shaft to throttle shaft lever rod adjusting link until stop is reached and tighten locknut "B" securely.

Rear Axle and Brake Section

Refer To Hydraulic Brakes Chapter For Brake Adjustments

REAR AXLE REPAIRS

Cage Type, Figs. 1 and 2

The drive pinion is held in position by the shoulders in the differential carrier upon which the pinion bearing cups seat. The pinion position is maintained by a washer or shims located between the pinion head and the rear bearing cone. Shims between the bearing spacer and the front bearing cone are used to adjust pinion bearings.

The threaded nut type of differential bearing adjustment is used. The procedure for making this adjustment, as well as the assembly of the differential case, replacing a ring gear, checking ring gear and pinion backlash, and other differential case operations, is given in the *Rear Axle* chapter.

Pinion & Bearings, Replace

The differential unit must be removed before the drive pinion can be taken out, but it is not necessary to remove the drive pinion or differential unit if only the drive pinion bearing oil seal is to be replaced.

To remove the oil seal, take off the pinion flange retaining nut and use a suitable tool to remove the flange. The oil seal may then be pulled out of the carrier.

Pull the drive pinion through the gear end of the differential carrier. The bearing spacer, front bearing and shims may then be taken out. Using a bearing puller, remove the rear bearing cone from

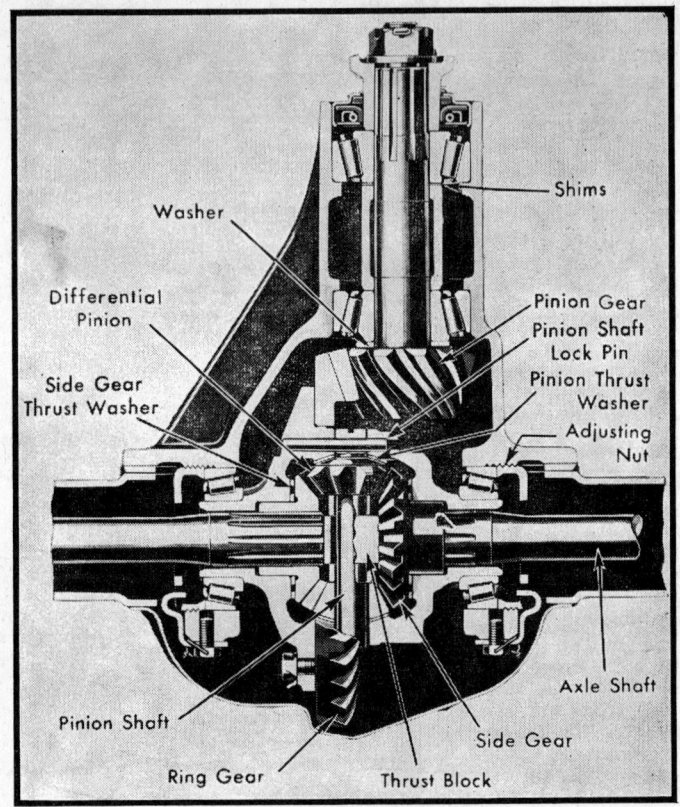

Fig. 1 Cage-type rear axle

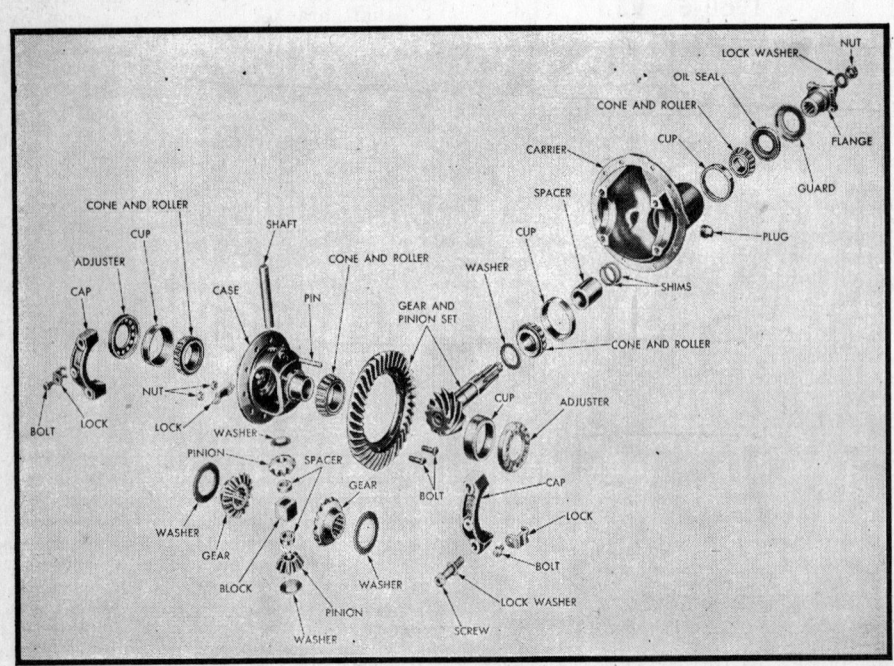

Fig. 2 Rear axle with cage-type differential

the pinion shaft and, unless the ring gear and pinion are to be replaced with new parts, use care not to allow the front and rear shim packs to become mixed.

If the differential unit was satisfactory from the standpoint of noise before the unit was dismantled, the drive pinion may be assembled with the original shims (or washer) behind the rear bearing. If new parts are used, or if an adjustment was necessary, change the shims until the correct combination is obtained to locate the pinion properly.

To assemble, place the front bearing in position in its cup and install the pinion shaft oil seal. Place the washer or shims on the pinion shaft against the pinion head and press on the rear bearing. Slip the bearing spacer against the rear bearing, then place the front bearing shims ahead of the spacer. Install the pinion and assembled parts in the carrier, passing the forward end of the pinion through the front bearing. Replace the pinion flange, slip on the washer, screw on the retaining nut and tighten securely.

Pinion Bearings, Adjust

The only occasion for adjusting the drive pinion bearings is when a new pin-

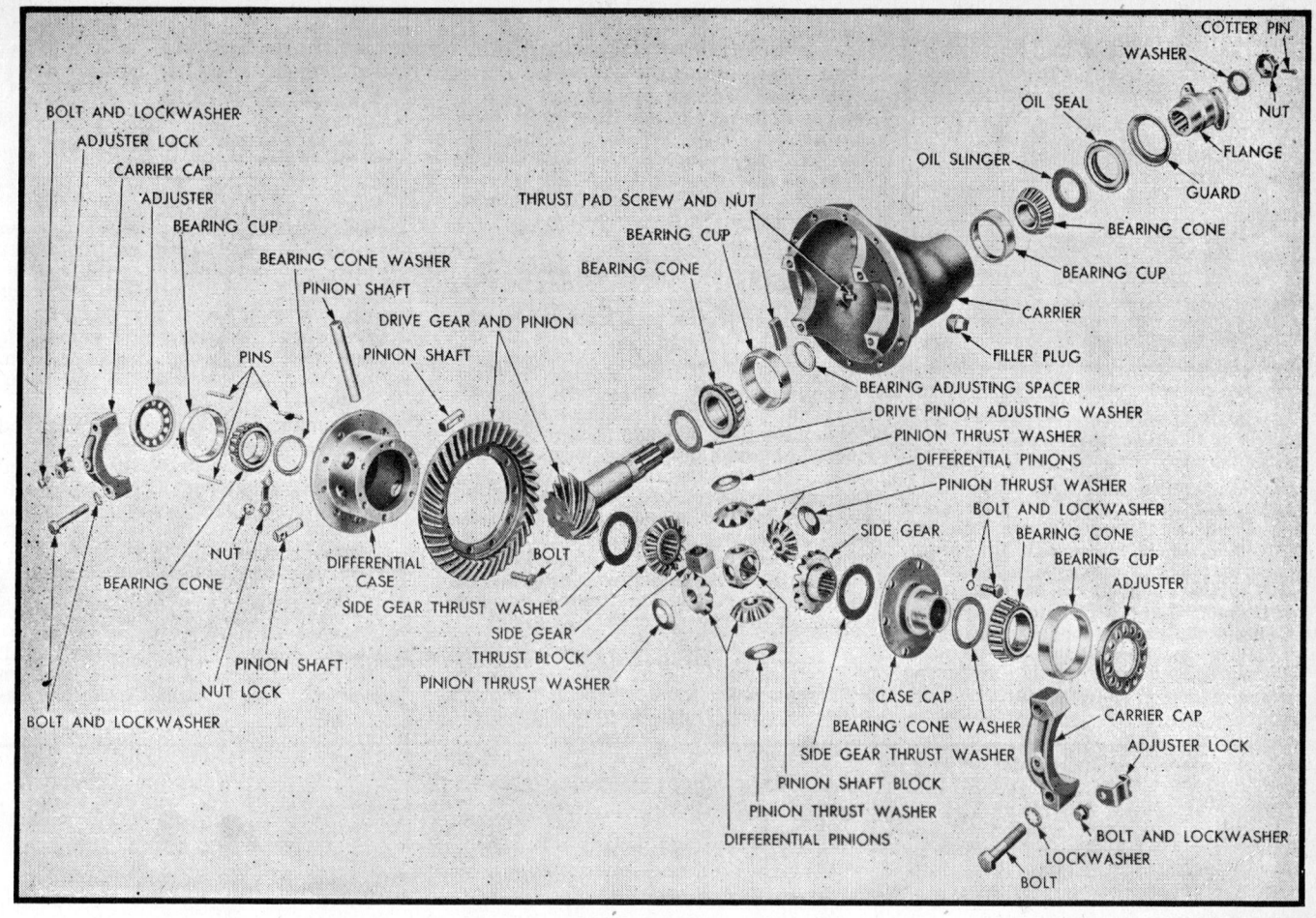

Fig. 3 Bolted barrel-type differential

ion or differential carrier is installed. To make the adjustment, install sufficient shims between the bearing spacer and front bearing so that when the pinion retaining nut is tightened against the pinion flange, all rollers in the bearings are tight, but still permit rotating the pinion by hand.

The bearings should be pre-loaded .0015 to .0025 inch. To check and adjust this pre-load (tension) mount a dial indicator on the carrier with the stem of the indicator contacting the pinion flange. Then if the indicator, for example shows .004 inch end play, remove the parts including .006 inch of shimming to give the necessary .002 inch draw tension or pre-load on the bearings.

Pinion, Adjust

After adjusting the pinion bearings, the position of the pinion should be checked. If a pinion setting gauge is available, check the pinion depth as outlined in the *Rear Axle* chapter. If a correction is necessary, disassemble the parts and, if the pinion is to be moved toward the center of the axle, add shims or install a thicker washer (whichever is used) between the pinion head and the rear bearing cone. If the pinion has to be moved away from the center of the axle, remove shims or install a thinner washer.

If no pinion setting gauge is available, assemble the differential unit in the carrier and check the tooth contact by painting the ring gear teeth as described in the *Rear Axle* chapter. When the adjustment is correct, install a new cotter pin in the pinion retaining nut.

BARREL TYPE DIFFERENTIAL

In general, the service procedure is the same as the cage-type previously described except for repairs on the differential case.

As shown in Fig. 3, the differential case houses a four-pinion differential, the case being closed by a bolted-on cap.

To dismantle the differential case, remove the attaching bolts and tap the cap lightly with a soft hammer to remove it. Drive out the three differential pinion shaft lock pins. Drive the long pinion shaft out of the case, using a brass drift and hammer. Lift out the axle shaft thrust block. Drive the short pinion shafts out of the case, lift out the pinion shaft block, and pick out the pinion gears, side gears and thrust washers.

Assemble in the reverse order and tighten the case cap bolts to 35-40 lbs. ft. torque.

Ring Gear Thrust Pad—This pad, Fig. 3, is located in the differential carrier and assists in maintaining the mesh of the ring gear and pinion. After all other adjustments have been made, break the weld on the thrust screw lock nut and tighten the thrust pad screw until the pad drags on the ring gears. Then back off ⅛ turn to create a .006-.008" clearance, tighten the lock nut and weld into position.

AXLE SHAFT & OIL SEAL

To remove the outer oil seal on these models, take off the wheel, hub and drum. Then disconnect the brake tube at the wheel cylinder, and remove the brake support. Drive out the old seal and remove the burrs from the support plate to prevent damaging the new seal.

With the brake support removed, install the new seal from the outer side of the brake support plate. Then stake the plate in three places with a center punch to hold the seal in position. Install the special tool, Fig. 4, in the seal or use other suitable means to protect the leather portion of the seal from being damaged by the axle shaft keyway and install the brake support as shown. Remove the tool and complete the installation of the brake support, hub and drum and wheel.

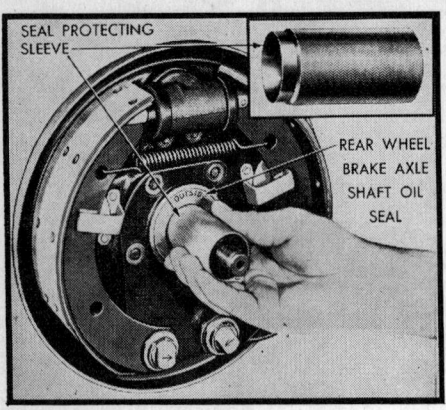

Fig. 4 Installing axle shaft outer oil seal with special sleeve

To remove the axle shaft and inner oil seal, disconnect the brake line and remove the wheel hub and drum assembly. *Do not use a knock-out type puller or strike the ends of the axle shafts to loosen wheel hubs as this may damage the bearings.* Remove the axle shaft keys and install the special sleeve shown in Fig. 4 to protect the seal while removing brake supports, seals and bearing shims. Keep each set of shims separate to as-

sure proper assembly. Use a suitable puller to remove the axle shaft and bearing from the housing. Then pull the inner oil seal from the housing.

To adjust axle shaft end play, add or remove shims to obtain the desired end play of .003 - .008″. When adjusting bearings, remove or install an equal thickness of shims on the right and left sides of the axle housing to maintain central position of shaft thrust block.

BRAKE MASTER CYLINDER, REPLACE

1953-54

The master cylinder is combined with the pedal bracket into a single assembly. To remove the cylinder, take out the floor mat and floor pan. Disconnect the brake line tubes from the cylinder fitting. Disconnect the clutch pedal rod at the clutch pedal and unhook the brake pedal pull back spring. Remove the three bolts from the master cylinder body. The cylinder with pedals, shaft and bracket can then be lifted off the frame bracket. Install in the reverse order of removal.

1955-59

To remove the master cylinder, remove pedal return spring. Disconnect push rod

by removing shoulder bolt and nut. Disconnect brake line tube at master cylinder, and stop light switch wires. Unfasten cylinder from its mounting and remove from dash panel.

POWER BRAKE UNIT

1955-61

1. To remove the unit, insert a wooden wedge or block between the power lever and bracket (this will prevent damage to the ramp of the trigger arm).
2. Scratch alignment marks across the power unit adjacent to the vacuum test port and across the mounting bracket.
3. Disconnect vacuum hose from end of power unit.
4. Remove master cylinder push rod eye bolt from pedal.
5. Remove stop light switch wires and master cylinder brake tube from master cylinder.
6. Remove master cylinder.
7. Unfasten the power unit from the dash panel and slide the unit and bracket straight out.
8. Reverse above procedure to install the power unit, being sure to align the scribe marks made before removal.

Front End and Steering Section

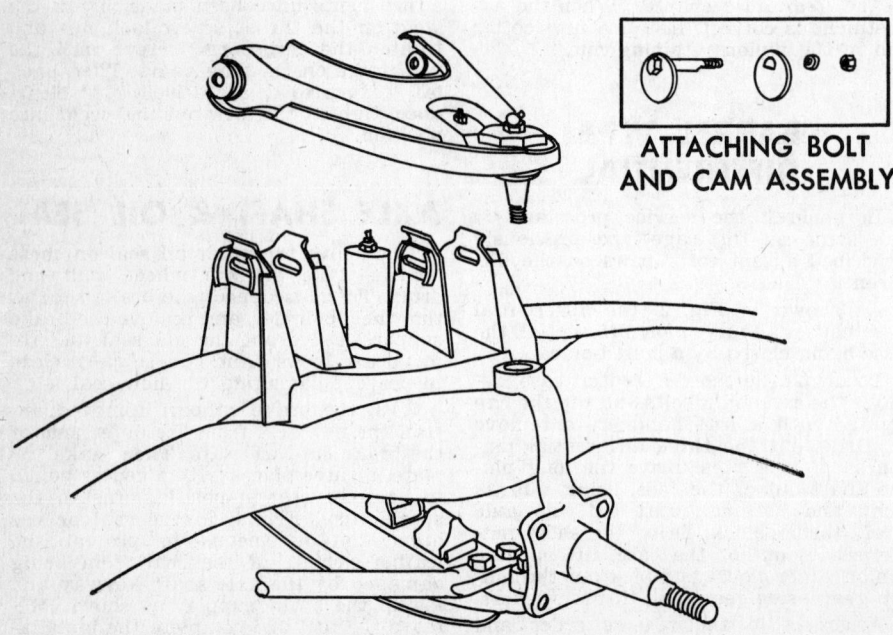

ATTACHING BOLT AND CAM ASSEMBLY

Fig. 1 Upper control arm and frame brackets. 1959-61

CASTER & CAMBER, ADJUST

1959-61

Caster and camber adjustments are accomplished by means of the upper control arm attaching bolt and cam assemblies, Fig. 1.

To adjust caster and camber, carefully loosen the upper control arm adjusting bolt nuts while holding the bolts to prevent turning. Record caster and camber readings.

Adjustment of caster through camber readings is possible because of the consistent relation between caster change and camber change when either the front or rear cam bolt at each control arm is individually rotated.

Turning one bolt affects caster more than camber. Turning both bolts an equal amount in the same direction affects camber directly, and caster indirectly. Turning the cams an equal amount in opposite directions will change caster with little change in camber, depending on the relative position of the cams.

By bringing caster within specifications by turning one bolt at a time, then by turning both bolts an equal amount to bring camber to the preferred reading, the caster will usually be brought close to the preferred setting.

After both caster and camber readings are correct, tighten the nuts to a torque of 65 lbs. ft. while holding the bolts from turning.

Always recheck the settings after tightening the nuts since the bolts may have turned slightly during the tightening process.

1957-58

Adjustments are performed by installing $\frac{1}{16}''$ and $\frac{1}{32}''$ shims between the upper control arm support brackets and the frame sub-side rails. Installing or removing shims at either the front or rear bracket changes the *caster* setting. Installing or removing shims equally at both brackets changes the *camber*.

Raise the car from the floor and loosen the upper control arm support bracket bolts. Add or remove shims as required and tighten bolts. *Adding shims equally at both front and rear support brackets will decrease positive caster.* One shim $\frac{1}{16}''$ thick at each bracket will change camber $\frac{5}{16}$ degree.

Addition of shims to the front bracket or removal of shims at the rear bracket will decrease positive caster. One shim $\frac{1}{16}''$ thick will change caster approximately $\frac{1}{2}$ degree. Total thickness of each shim pack should *not* exceed $\frac{9}{16}''$.

After lowering car, jounce front end up and down a few times before rechecking wheel alignment to allow suspension to assume normal position.

1953-56

Caster is not adjustable but the proper setting is obtained when assembling the camber eccentric bushing. To adjust camber, loosen the clamp screw and turn the bushing to obtain the correct setting within a half revolution from the point where the correct caster setting is obtained. Do not turn the bushing until it binds against the upper control arm.

TOE-IN, ADJUST

With the steering wheel in mid-position, loosen the clamps on the end of both rods and turn both ends until the wheels are straight ahead. Then, without disturbing the steering wheel, turn both tie rods an equal amount until the toe-in is correct and equal at each wheel.

WHEEL BEARINGS, ADJUST

1. Tighten wheel bearing adjusting nut to 90 inch pounds torque while rotating wheel.
2. Position nut lock on nut with one pair of slots in line with cotter pin hole.
3. Back off lock and adjusting nut to next slot.
4. Install cotter pin. The resulting adjustment should be zero to .003" end play.
5. Clean grease cap, coat inside with wheel bearing grease (do not fill) and install cap.

TORSION BAR SUSPENSION

Service Notes

1. When necessary to install new torsion bars, remove all accumulated dirt, scale and moisture from inside torsion bar rear anchor.
2. Do not apply heat to anchor assembly in order to remove bar. Use an arbor press to remove bar from anchor whenever necessary.
3. Coat inside of anchor with multi-purpose grease.
4. The torsion bars have a pre-set loading for right and left usage. Bars can be indentified by the letter "R" or "L" stamped on one end of bar. This letter is not visible when the

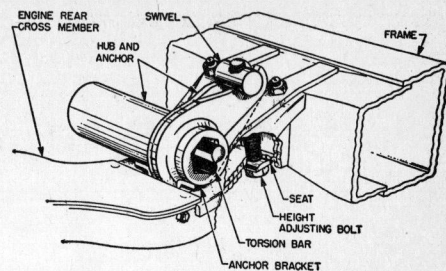

Fig. 3 Torsion bar spring cam and height adjustment. 1957-59

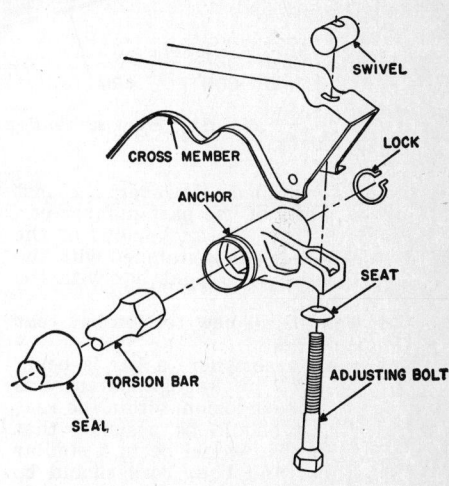

Fig. 4 Torsion bar rear support. 1960

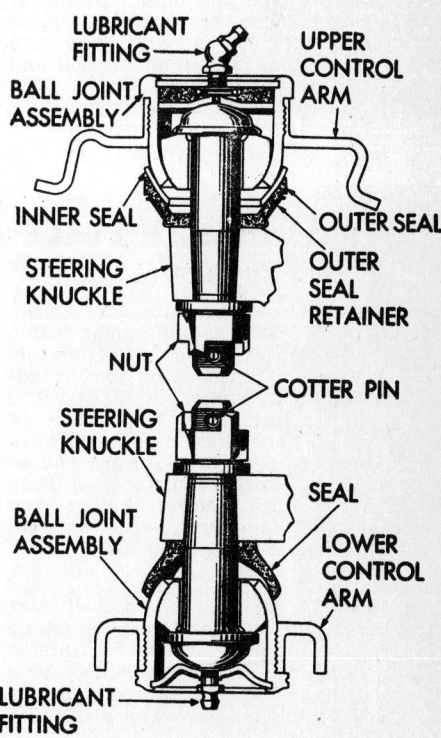

Fig. 5 Sectional view of upper and lower ball joints

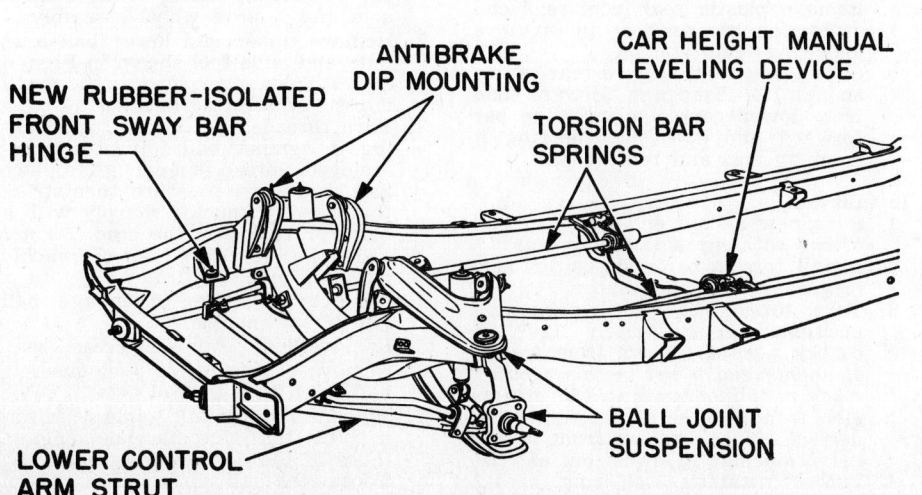

Fig. 2 Torsion Bar Suspension

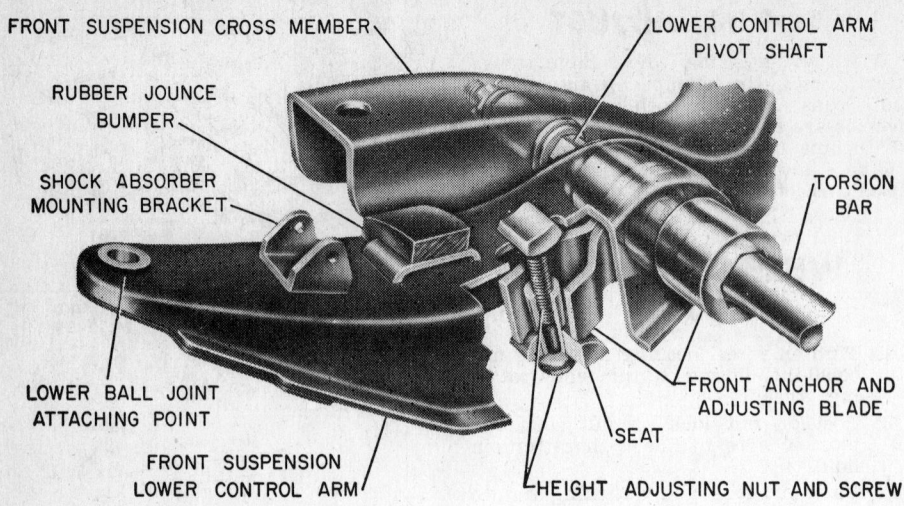

FRONT SUSPENSION CROSS MEMBER

RUBBER JOUNCE BUMPER

SHOCK ABSORBER MOUNTING BRACKET

LOWER BALL JOINT ATTACHING POINT

FRONT SUSPENSION LOWER CONTROL ARM

LOWER CONTROL ARM PIVOT SHAFT

TORSION BAR

FRONT ANCHOR AND ADJUSTING BLADE

SEAT

HEIGHT ADJUSTING NUT AND SCREW

Fig. 4A Front suspension height adjustment. 1961

bar is installed. However, the last three digits of the part number can be seen from the anchor end of the bar; the left bar is stamped with the odd number, the right bar with the even number.

5. Always install new torsion bar rear anchor seal.
6. In every case where a bar is being replaced for breakage, apparently as a result of corrosion within the rear anchor, it should be assumed that the other bar would be in a similar condition, and both bars should be replaced.
7. The torsion bar adjusting bolt should only be loosened (or tightened) with a foot pound torque wrench with vehicle supported under frame to relieve load on torsion bars. If more than 200 ft. lbs. is required to turn the adjusting bolt, then the bolt and swivel must be replaced.
8. If the vehicle is to be raised on a hoist, make sure it is lifted on the frame only so the front suspension is in full rebound under load.

TORSION BAR, REPLACE

1957-59

Removal

1. Raise vehicle by jacking under frame crossmember. Release load from torsion bar by unscrewing anchor adjusting bolt partly out of swivel.
2. Remove lock ring from rear of anchor. Slide torsion bar rearward enough to disengage foward end of bar from lower control arm. Then move forward to disengage bar from anchor. Remove bar, swivel and cam from frame bracket anchor.

Installation

1. Assemble anchor, swivel, bolt seat (oval side up) and bolt in frame anchor bracket. Check for torsion bar cushion in lower control arm housing. With cam bolt barely entered in cam swivel, slide bar into rear cam.
2. Rotate anchor and torsion bar until anchor is positioned as close as possible to floor pan. Engage front

of bar in lower control arm shaft as far as bar will go. *Unless anchor blade is in the position just described when installing bar, it will be impossible to adjust front suspension to the proper height.*

3. Center and install lock ring in rear of anchor housing. Pressure may be applied to bar to enable lock ring to be installed.
4. After lock ring is installed, tighten cam bolt until approximately one inch of threads are showing above anchor bolt swivel. *This is an approximate setting used merely as a starting point when adjusting suspension height. This setting is also necessary to place load on torsion bar before lowering vehicle to floor.*
5. Check and adjust suspension height as outlined further on.

1960-61

Removal

1. Raise vehicle by jacking under center of front crossmember.
2. Release load from torsion bar by backing off anchor adjusting bolts.
3. Remove bolt and swivel and discard.
4. Remove plastic seal from rear end of torsion bar anchor, and remove lock ring from anchor.
5. Slide torsion bar toward rear of car enough to disengage forward end from lower control arm. Slide bar forward and down, disengaging it from anchor, and remove bar.

Installation

1. Slide new anchor end seal over end of bar with cup side facing rear.
2. Install torsion bar and position seal in groove on anchor hub.
3. Turn torsion bar until anchor is positioned approximately 120° (8 o'clock position) down from frame. *If anchor end is not in this position when installing bar it will be impossible to adjust the suspension to the correct height.* Engage front of bar in hex opening in lower control arm.
4. Before installing lock ring, center bar so that full contact is obtained at anchor and control arm shaft. Install lock ring in groove.

5. Pack anchor seal with grease and position lip of seal in anchor hub groove. Install plastic seal in rear end of anchor.
6. Slide adjusting bolt swivel on frame and install adjusting bolt and seat. Tighten bolt into swivel until approximately one inch of threads are showing out of swivel. *This is an approximate setting used as a starting point when adjusting for correct suspension height. This setting is also necessary to place a load on the bar before lowering vehicle to floor.*
7. Lower car to floor and adjust suspension height as outlined below.

SUSPENSION HEIGHT, ADJUST

1. Jounce car so parts can assume normal position.
2. Measure from lower ball joint to floor and from bottom of lower control arm bushing housing to the floor.
3. Subtract one measurement from the other. The difference should be as listed below subject to a tolerance of plus or minus 1/8".

1957 Sedans and Coupes	2 1/8"
Suburbans	2 5/8"
Sports Models	1 5/8"
1958 Sedans and Coupes	2 3/16"
Suburbans	2 11/16"
Sports Models	1 11/16"
1959 Sedans and Coupes	2 1/8"
Suburbans	2 1/2"
1960-61 Sedans and Coupes	2"
Suburbans	2 1/2"

If these measurements differ more than 1/8" or if one or both of them are outside the specified limits, the suspension height of both sides must be adjusted. To adjust, turn the anchor bolt clockwise to raise the height and counterclockwise to lower it, Figs. 3, 4 and 4A.

BALL JOINT SERVICE

1. To replace ball joints, Fig. 5, raise car by jacking under lower control arm and remove wheel assembly.
2. Remove upper and lower ball stud nuts and slide tool shown in Figs. 6 and 7 down over lower stud until it rests on steering knuckle.
3. Turn threaded portion of tool, locking it against ball joint being removed. Spread tool enough to place ball stud under pressure, then strike the steering knuckle sharply with a hammer to loosen the stud. *Do not attempt to force stud out of knuckle with tool alone.*
4. Remove tool, then disengage ball joint from knuckle.
5. Remove dust cover and grease seal.
6. Remove grease fitting and unscrew ball joint from control arm.
7. When installing ball joints, it is important that the threads engage those of the control arms squarely. Torque the ball joints to the control arms to 125 ft. lbs., the lower stud nut to 135 ft. lbs., and the upper stud nut to 100 ft. lbs.

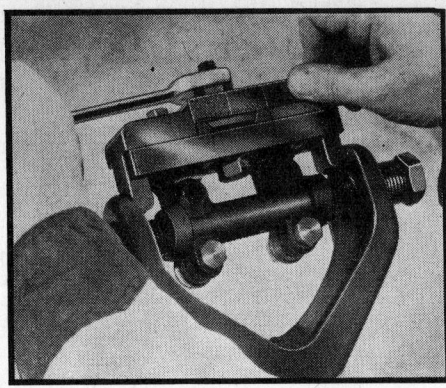

Fig. 8 Spreading upper control arm with Tool C-608. Typical of all 1953-54

FRONT END REPAIRS

Service Note, 1955-56

The front end on these models is basically the same as 1954 models except that the shock absorber is mounted within the coil spring. To remove a front shock absorber, proceed as follows:

1. Raise hood and clean the area around the upper mounting.
2. Slide a wrench over the flats on top of the shock absorber piston rod to keep the rod from turning. Then remove the nut and cup washer.
3. Remove the two lower mounting bolts and withdraw the shock absorber through the opening in the spring seat. Lower cup washer may remain in place or drop through when shock absorber is removed.
4. Using a suitable drift, force the inner steel sleeve out of the bushing and remove the bushing from the frame opening.
5. Before installing a new bushing, dip it in soapy water and insert in the frame with a twisting motion. When installed properly, the groove in bushing will index the frame.
6. Force steel sleeve through opening in bushing and down into position.

NOTE—In servicing the balance of the front end, follow the procedure given for 1954 models, disregarding any items which obviously do not apply to 1955-56 models, Fig. 6.

1953-54

Kingpins & Bushings

1. Remove wheel and hub assembly.
2. Block brake pedal so it cannot be depressed.
3. Unfasten brake support plate from knuckle.
4. Remove steering arm from knuckle.
5. Remove brake hose and connection and lift off brake support.
6. Remove kingpin lock pin.
7. Drive a punch into upper steering knuckle welch plug and pry out plug.
8. Drive kingpin downward, forcing out lower welch plug. A soft brass

drift should be used in driving against top of kingpin.
9. If needle bearings are used in the knuckle they should be removed with a suitable puller. A puller should also be used when pressed-in bushings are employed.

When installing needle bearings they must be installed from the top of the knuckle with the trade mark on top and the oil hole lined up with the oil hole in the steering knuckle.

Pressed-in type bushings must be line reamed.

After installing the steering knuckle, make sure it is free in the support as binding at this point may cause sensitive steering and car wander. There should be .008 in. clearance between the knuckle and knuckle support. This clearance can be adjusted by the use of shims between the knuckle and thrust bearing.

After their installation, welch plugs should be staked in place.

Upper Control Arm

1. With a jack under the lower control arm spring seat, raise the car and remove the wheel, Fig. 7.
2. Remove shock absorber.
3. Unscrew bolt from outer end of control arm.
4. Unfasten and remove control arm pivot bar.

To assemble the upper control arm, proceed as follows:

1. Position the pivot bar with seals installed in the control arm and install Tool C-608 on the pivot bar, Fig. 8. This tool has two sets of bolt holes to accommodate both sizes of upper control arm pivot bars. Be sure tool is securely fastened to pivot bar.
2. Expand the two jaws of the tool by tightening the expander wedge screw until the jaws of the tool are just snug against inside of web of control arm. Do not bring screw down more than is necessary to place jaws firmly against control arm; if tool is properly fastened to pivot bar, jaws will make proper contact on inside faces.
3. Lay a steel scale across base of expander, noting the distance between

Fig. 6 Removing upper ball joint from steering knuckle

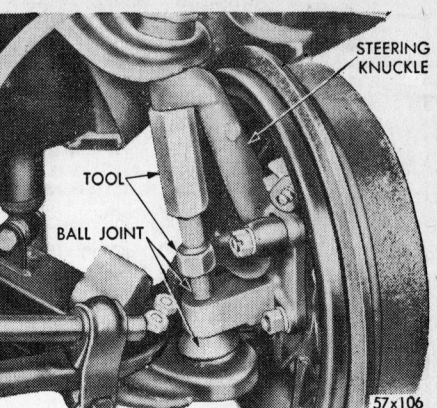

Fig. 7 Removing lower ball joint from steering knuckle

the two lines, Fig. 8. Tighten expander wedge screw until control arm has been spread $\frac{1}{16}$ in. from its original "at rest" position.
4. Start bushings on both ends of pivot bar. Lubricate them with light engine oil or cutting oil to allow them to cut their own threads in the control arm without scoring, Fig. 9.
5. Thread bushings into control arm until shoulders of bushings contact surface of control arm. Tighten with a torque wrench to at least 120-140 lbs. ft. torque.
6. Remove tool and check operation of pivot bar for freedom of movement. Only a moderate grip should be required to turn the pivot bar. *The pivot bar should not be rotated as this would throw it off center with the control arm and affect the caster adjustment.*
7. Lubricate control arm bushings with chassis lubricant before installing on the car.

Upper Arm Eccentric Bushing

First, install the upper control arm to the steering knuckle support as follows:

1. Install a new eccentric bushing in the steering knuckle support and place one oil seal on the bushing at the hexagon end. Oil or grease the other seal slightly and place it on the opposite boss of the control arm.
2. Slide the control arm and seal onto the steering knuckle support until the seals fit properly over the bushing and the pin hole is in proper alignment. Install pin, nut and cotter pin.
3. Using a drift, line up pivot bar holes in frame cross member. Install attaching bolts and tighten securely.
4. Install shock absorber, wheel and tire assembly.

Lower Control Arm

Lower Control Arm — To remove the lower control arm, raise the front end of the car off the floor and place a support under the frame side member behind the suspension unit. After removing the wheel, disconnect the shock absorber and the sway eliminator at the lower shock

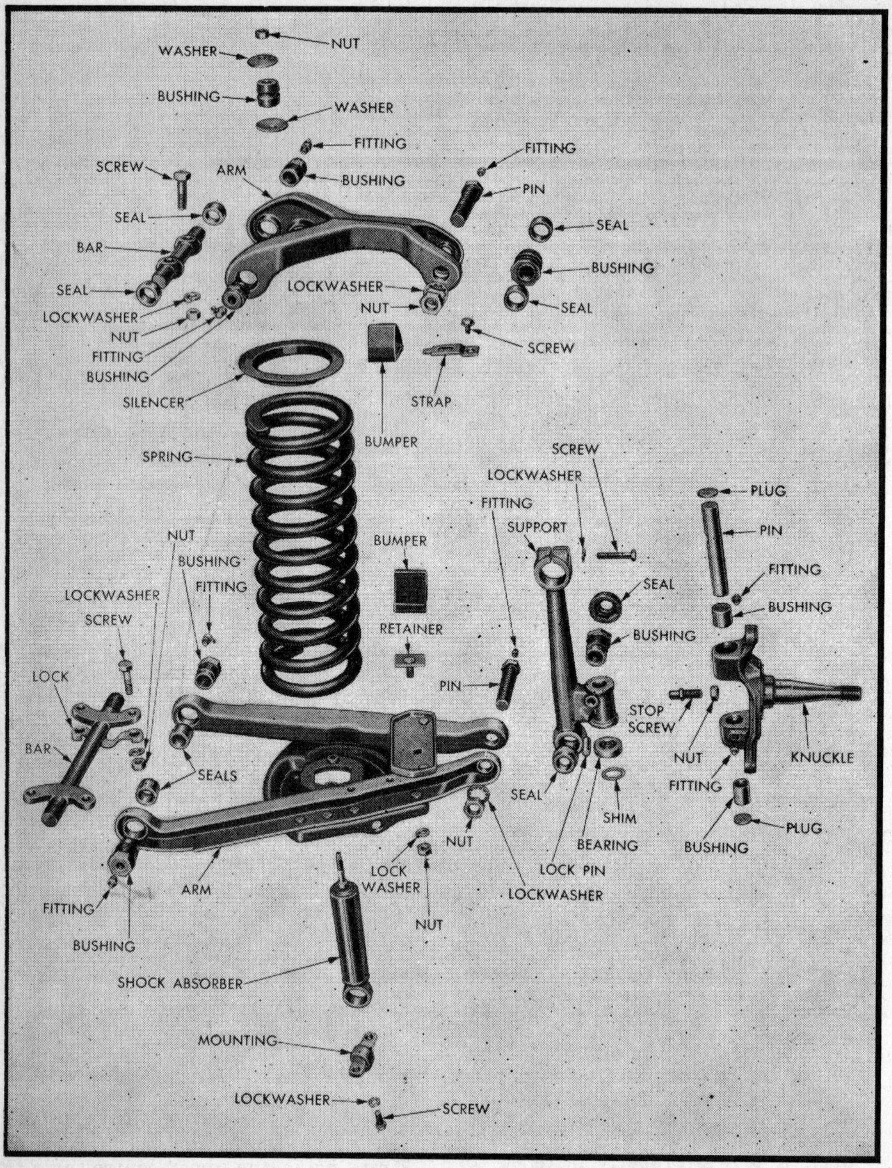

Fig. 8 labels (front suspension diagram):

NUT, WASHER, BUSHING, WASHER, FITTING, FITTING, SCREW, ARM, BUSHING, PIN, SEAL, SEAL, BAR, BUSHING, SEAL, LOCKWASHER, SEAL, LOCKWASHER, NUT, NUT, SCREW, FITTING, BUSHING, SILENCER, STRAP, BUMPER, SPRING, SCREW, LOCKWASHER, PLUG, FITTING, PIN, SUPPORT, FITTING, NUT, BUMPER, SEAL, BUSHING, BUSHING, LOCKWASHER, FITTING, RETAINER, BUSHING, LOCK, PIN, STOP SCREW, BAR, SEALS, NUT, KNUCKLE, SHIM, PLUG, FITTING, ARM, BEARING, BUSHING, FITTING, NUT, LOCK PIN, SEAL, LOCK WASHER, LOCKWASHER, BUSHING, NUT, SHOCK ABSORBER, MOUNTING, LOCKWASHER, SCREW

Fig. 8   Front suspension, 1953-56 (typical)

absorber mounting stud. Place a jack under the control arm pivot bar where it is attached to the frame cross member. Use a block of wood cut to receive the lower control arm bar between the jack and the bar, which will prevent the jack from slipping. Now raise the jack just enough to relieve the pressure on the pivot bar fastening bolts. Remove the bolts, placing tapered drifts in each hole, to prevent binding of the last bolt removed. Lower the jack slowly, allowing the lower control arm to come down, then lift out the spring. Remove the lower control arm pin from the knuckle support and take out the lower control arm assembly.

Lower Control Arm Bushings—To assemble the lower control arm bushings, insert the pivot bar in the control arm and place a suitable tool between the legs of the control arm, Fig. 10. Start the bushings on both ends of the pivot bar, using a suitable lubricant, such as tapping compound, to cut the threads into the arm bosses without scoring. Thread the bushings into the control arm until the shoulders of the bushings contact the machined surface of the control arm, and tighten them with a force of 180 pounds feet.

Remove the tool from between the legs of the control arm and check the operation of the pivot bar for free movement in the bushings, but do not rotate it. The distance from the machined surface of the control arm to the center of the pivot bar mounting holes should be $2\frac{5}{32}''$ on 1949-54 Sixes ($2\frac{7}{32}''$ on all other models), which would be altered if the pivot bar was rotated. Lubricate the control arm bushings with semi-fluid chassis lubricant.

HORN BUTTON
1953-54, Fig. 11

1. Disconnect the horn wire at the connector near the bottom of the steer-

ing column (on some models) or at the horn relay.
2. Turn the horn button medallion retainer ⅛ turn counter-clockwise and lift off the button, button retainer, contact spring and plate.
3. Pull out the horn wire and spacer bushing from the center of the steering tube.
4. If the steering wheel is to be replaced, remove the steering wheel retaining nut and lift out the horn button contact cup. Then remove the screws that hold the horn button retainer fastening plate and base to the steering wheel.

HORN BLOWING RING
1953-61, Fig. 12

1. Disconnect the horn wire at the connector at the base of the steering column.
2. On 1953-54, push down on the horn blowing ring medallion and turn it counter-clockwise. Remove the medallion, retainer spring and cushion. On 1955-61, remove two screws on underside of medallion and take off medallion.
3. Loosen and remove the three horn ring retainer screws and spacer bushings. Then lift out the horn ring, travel plate and insulator assembly, wire, contact spring plate and ground plate.
4. On reassembly, be sure to contact spring plate is installed with the colored dot appearing on the top side.

STEERING WHEEL

To remove the steering wheel, take off the horn button or blowing ring and related parts as outlined above. Remove the nut and washer which holds the steering wheel to the steering tube. Attach a suitable puller to the steering wheel, utilizing the tapped holes provided in the wheel hub, and pull the

Fig. 9   Installing upper control arm bushings. 1953-54

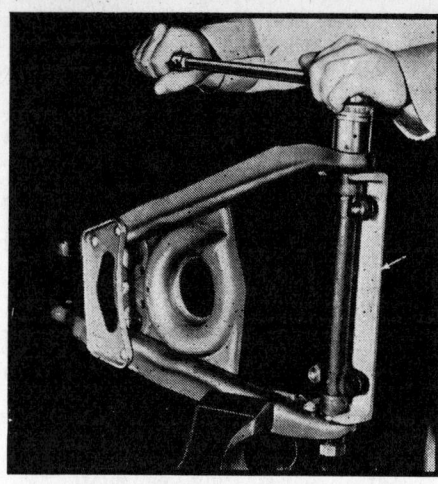

Fig. 10 Installing lower control arm bushings, using spreader tool to keep arms in proper position. 1953-54

wheel off the steering tube.

When installing the wheel, be sure that the master serration on the steering tube (if present) is in alignment with the serration on the steering wheel hub before installing.

MANUAL STEERING GEAR, REPLACE
1953-60

1. Remove horn button or blowing ring

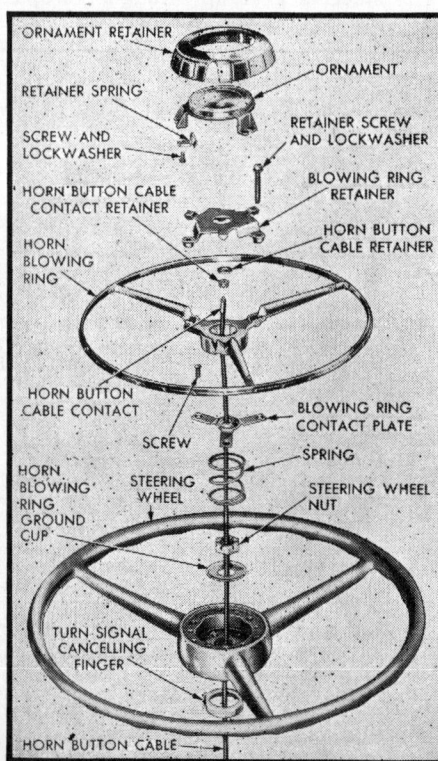

Fig. 11 Horn button and related parts. Typical of all 1953-54 Sixes

and steering wheel as outlined previously.

2. Remove left front wheel.
3. Remove front seat cushion and floor mat after sliding draft pad up on column.
4. Remove floor pan pedal opening cover.
5. Disconnect turn signal control wires (if equipped) at connections under instrument panel. *Time will be saved if a length of wire is attached to the loose ends of the turn signal wires before withdrawing through the jacket tube. This will enable all wires to be drawn back through the tube at reassembly.*
6. Remove transmission shifting mechanism at steering column.
7. Unfasten gear housing from frame.
8. Disconnect Pitman arm.
9. Remove steering gear post bracket cap at instrument panel.
10. On 1953-54 6-cylinder models, remove steering gear from *top* side of car by lifting up as far as possible and withdrawing from right side of car.
11. On 1955-56 models, remove steering gear from bottom side of car by withdrawing as far as possible and bending to right side of car.
12. On 1957-59 models, remove steering gear by withdrawing it up through opening in floor pan.
13. On 1960-61 models, slide steering gear jacket tube rearward and remove through drivers compartment. Remove tapered retainer and spring fom the column tube. Unfasten the steering gear from the frame and slide the gear toward rear of car and at the same time raise the lower end of the gear and remove through hood opening.

MANUAL STEERING GEAR REPAIRS

In this type steering gear, Fig. 13, the worm is integral with the steering shaft and is supported on each end by opposed tapered roller bearings. The triple tooth roller is attached to the roller shaft by means of a steel shaft. Two needle bearing assemblies are installed between this shaft and the roller. (Some light duty models have a two tooth roller shaft).

The roller shaft is mounted in the steering gear housing on two needle bearing assemblies which are pressed into the housing. The housing cover is attached to the housing by four cap screws. An adjustment screw, mounted in the cover, controls roller shaft end play and worm and roller mesh adjustment.

The steering wheel and roller shaft arm (pitman arm) are splined to the steering shaft and roller shaft respectively. Both the pitman arm and steering wheel have master splines to insure correct installation.

Worm End Play, Adjust

1. Free the steering gear of all load by disconnecting the drag link and loosening the steering column braces.

2. Loosen the four cover screws about 1/8".
3. Use a knife to separate the top shim, passing the blade all the way around between the shims, being careful not to damage the remaining shims.
4. Remove one shim at a time between inspections to remove the end play.
5. The adjustment is correct when there is no end play and no stiffness in the steering gear throughout the complete range of its travel.

Roller Shaft End Play, Adjust

1. Turn the steering gear to either extreme and back off 1/8 of a turn.
2. Gripping the pitman arm at the hub, the roller shaft should rotate freely without a particle of end play.
3. If end play exists, adjust as required by means of the roller shaft adjusting screw in the side cover.
4. Be sure to tighten the lock nut securely and inspect for end play and free rotation throughout the entire range of steering gear travel.

Worm & Roller Mesh, Adjust

1. Loosen the roller shaft adjusting screw lock nut.
2. With the steering gear in its central position (drag link disconnected) tighten the roller shaft adjusting screw just enough to remove play between the roller shaft roller tooth and worm.
3. Check this by the amount of play felt at the pitman arm. It is better to leave a slight amount of play at this point than to tighten too much.
4. If tightened beyond the point where the lash is removed, serious results

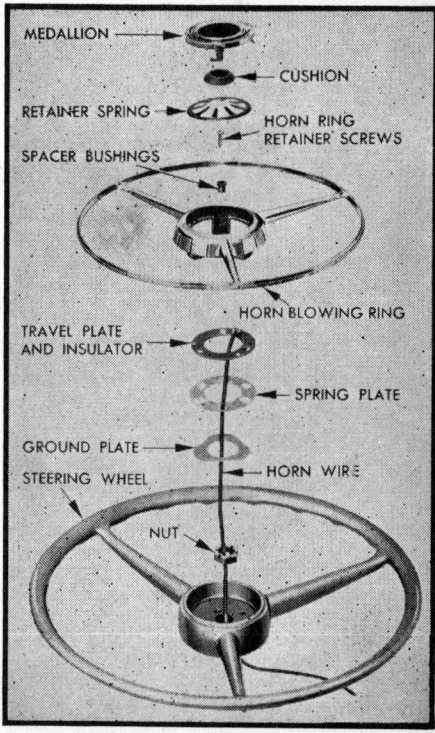

Fig. 12 Horn ring and related parts. 1953-54

will occur which will cause poor steering operation.

5. Tighten the adjusting screw lock nut.

POWER STEERING, REPLACE

1958-61

1. To remove the unit, disconnect battery ground cable.
2. Disconnect horn wire.
3. Remove horn button, horn ring and horn wire.
4. Remove steering wheel.
5. Disconnect turn signal wires at connectors and on 1960-61 models, remove turn signal switch and also remove retainer snap ring from groove in steering tube at top of bearing.
6. Remove jacket tube support brackets at instrument panel.
7. Loosen two bolts attaching jacket tube to steering housing, push jacket tube upward to expose steering coupling pin and remove pin.
8. Remove nut at drag link-to-steering arm ball joint.
9. Disconnect pressure and return hoses at steering gear. Fasten disconnected ends of hoses above oil level in reservoir. Cap hose ends and fittings on steering gear to prevent entrance of dirt.
10. Remove steering arm with puller.
11. Unfasten gear housing from frame and remove steering gear at engine compartment.
12. On cars with Ram Manifold, remove left front wheel and fender opening panel. Raise lower end of gear housing in a clockwise motion towards cowl panel until the gear shaft end of the housing and shaft will clear

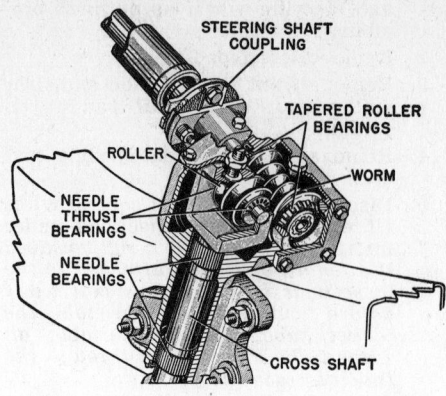

Fig. 13 Manual steering gear. 1961

the "A" frame of front suspension. Then tilt gear assembly towards engine slightly to allow swinging the gear downward through opening at fender side panel.

13. Reverse foregoing procedure to install the steering gear.

1961

1. Disconnect battery ground terminal.
2. Pull steering arm from steering gear.
3. Remove bolt attaching lower coupling to steering gear worm shaft.
4. Unfasten steering gear from frame (3 bolts) and slide gear assembly toward front of car to disengage column tube flexible coupling from steering worm shaft.
5. Remove gear through engine compartment.
6. When installing the gear, align the index mark on the outside of the

flexible coupling hub with the master spline on the steering worm shaft.

1955-1957

1. Remove two screws from horn ring ornament and remove ornament from steering wheel.
2. Disconnect horn wire, remove three horn ring screws and remove horn ring.
3. On 1957 models, remove front seat cushion.
4. Remove steering wheel.
5. Remove turn signal lever.
6. Remove steering column-to-instrument panel bracket and shroud.
7. Loosen steering column jacket clamp screws.
8. Raise front of car and disengage drag link from pitman arm.
9. Use suitable puller to remove pitman arm from steering gear shaft.
10. Loosen three gear housing-to-frame attaching bolts and lower front of car to floor.
11. Pull jacket from steering shaft.
12. Remove floor mat retaining plate, dust pad and access plate.
13. Place a large pan underneath unit. Then disconnect pressure and return hoses and drain gear by rotating it until all oil is expelled from unit.
14. Fasten disconnected ends of hoses above oil level in reservoir to prevent further loss of oil and cap ends to prevent any foreign matter from entering.
15. On 1955-56 models, raise front of car from floor and remove gear housing-to-frame attaching bolts and alignment wedge. Then remove the gear from the lower side of the car.
16. On 1957 models, remove steering gear attaching bolts. Then lift the steering gear up through the opening in the floor pan.

Speedometer, Radio & Windshield Wiper

WINDSHIELD WIPER

1953-54

The parking switch mounted on the motor is a simple "make" and "break" switch. The wires should be connected to the switch as follows: Green wire to "B" terminal; red to "F" terminal, and black to "A" terminal.

If both blades do not park in the same position, relocate the arms on the pivot shafts. If this fails to correct the condition, it may be necessary to disassemble the motor and reassemble the crank arms in their correct positions.

If the wiper will not stop, the condition may be due to a defective control switch. Inspect the switch to make sure the cam strikes the switch button. If necessary, open circuit the motor to stop it. Bend the cam out slightly, being careful that the cam does not strike the side of the button.

1955-59

The wiper motor should be operated and shut off by turning off the ignition. The motor must not be disassembled when the cranks are in the parked position or damage to the motor switch and contact follower will occur when the cover is removed. To remove the wiper, proceed as follows:

1. Disconnect wires at motor.
2. Remove radio and right-hand fresh air door.
3. Disconnect links at pivot cranks. Clips are removed by lifting the top tab and sliding it sideways out of engagement with groove in pivot crank pin.
4. Remove spacing washer and link from pivot crank.
5. Disconnect mounting bracket at dash panel and remove wiper motor and bracket.
6. Reverse procedure to install, being

sure rubber mounting gasket is in place.

7. Adjust wiper parking position by moving cam adjustment lever which projects from switch cover.

1960-61

1. Remove glove compartment door.
2. Remove glove compartment.
3. Remove bolts ataching wiper motor bracket to cowl panel to instrument panel brace.
4. Disconnect wire at wiper motor.
5. Disconnect links at pivot cranks. Clips are removed by lifting the top tab and sliding it sideways out of engagement with the groove in the pivot crank pin.
6. Remove spacing washer and remove link from pivot crank.
7. Slide wiper motor, with links, far enough towards the left so that right hand link will clear glove compartment opening in panel and remove

assembly. *Use care so as not to bend the links.*

RADIO REMOVAL

1953-56

Disconnect radio and speaker wires. Unfasten radio from its mounting and remove from instrument panel.

1957-59

Disconnect battery ground cable and "A" terminal lead wire at temperature gauge. Disconnect radio and speaker wires. Unfasten radio from its mounting and remove from instrument panel.

1960-61

Disconnect battery, antenna "A" lead, light lead and front and rear speaker leads. Remove ash tray assembly to gain access to mounting bolts. Remove mounting bolts and remove radio-to-dash support bracket. *Do not operate radio with speaker detached since damage to transistors may result. If rear seat speaker is disconnected from radio, insert a jumper wire in speaker socket to allow the radio to operate.*

SPEEDOMETER

1953-56

1. Disconnect battery.
2. Disconnect speedometer cable housing.
3. Remove four speedometer to panel attaching screws in back of panel.
4. Remove speedometer assembly from behind the dash.

1957-59

1. Disconnect battery.
2. Disconnect speedometer cable housing.
3. Remove four speedometer bezel retaining screws, accessible from the face of the instrument panel.
4. Move speedometer out of dash toward steering wheel.

1960-61

1. Disconnect battery.
2. Cover front and back of speedometer lens with masking tape to prevent marring finish.
3. Remove instrument panel gear selector bezel.
4. Remove gearshift buttons and covers.
5. Remove steering column bracket on manual transmission equipped cars.
6. Loosen gearshift control housing and cable.
7. Remove gear selector bracket.
8. Disconnect speedometer cable.
9. With a long shank Phillips screwdriver, remove speedometer panel instrument housing.
10. Reverse above procedure to install.

FORD
THUNDERBIRD · EDSEL

INDEX OF SERVICE OPERATIONS

PAGE NO.

ACCESSORIES

Radio Removal 751
Speedometer Removal 751
Windshield Wiper 752
Windshield Wiper Troubles.......37

BODY

Air Conditioning 177
Automatic Seat Adjuster Troubles......36
Automatic Top Troubles..............36
Automatic Window Lift Troubles........36

BRAKES (Mechanical)

Adjustments 112
Brake Cylinder Sizes............705
Hydraulic Brake System..........112
Master Cylinder, Replace........741
Trouble Shooting 31

BRAKES (Power)

Power Unit Repairs..............128
Power Unit, Replace.............741
Trouble Shooting 32

CLUTCH

Clutch Pedal, Adjust............729
Clutch Service 730
Trouble Shooting 13

COOLING SYSTEM

Radiator, Replace 722
Trouble Shooting 8
Water Pump Repairs.............723
Water Pump, Replace............722

ELECTRIC SYSTEM

Dash Gauge Service 85
Distributor, Replace...........723
Distributor Service 46
Distributor Specifications 702
Generator Regulator Service ...62
Generator Regulator Specifications....703
Generator Service 62
Generator Specifications 703
Horn Button or Ring, Replace...746
Ignition System Service........46
Ignition Timing 723
Starter, Replace...............723
Starter Switch Service.........83
Starting Motor Service.........77
Starting Motor Specifications..700
Trouble Shooting 10
Turn Signal Troubles...........12

PAGE NO.

ENGINE

Camshaft, Replace 717
Camshaft Bearings 718
Crankshaft Bearing Specs.......701
Crankshaft Oil Seal, Replace...720
Cylinder Head, Replace.........708
Engine, Replace 708
Main Bearings, Replace.........719
Piston Pins, Replace...........719
Piston Rings, Replace..........719
Piston, Pin & Ring Specs.......701
Pistons & Rods, Remove.........718
Piston & Rod, Assemble.........718
Pistons, Replace 718
Rocker Arms, Replace...........713
Rod Bearings, Replace..........719
Timing Case Cover, Replace.....714
Timing Chain, Replace..........716
Timing Gears, Replace..........716
Trouble Shooting 4
Valves, Adjust 711
Valve Arrangement 711
Valves, Remove 712
Valves, Grind 713
Valve Guides 713
Valve Lifters 713
Valve Specifications 699
Valve Spring Installed Height........713
Valve Spring Testing...........713
Valve Timing Data 717

ENGINE OILING

Oil Pan, Replace...............720
Oil And Vacuum Pump............721
Oil Pump Repairs...............721
Trouble Shooting 4

FRONT SUSPENSION

Camber, Adjust 742
Caster, Adjust 742
Front End Repairs..............743
Toe-in, Adjust 743
Trouble Shooting 33
Wheel Alignment Specifications........705
Wheel Bearings, Adjust.........743

FUEL & EXHAUST SYSTEMS

Carburetors 725
Fuel Pumps 96
Mufflers And Pipes.............724
Trouble Shooting 4

OVERDRIVE 100

Trouble Shooting 14

PAGE NO.

REAR AXLE

Axle Shaft, Replace............741
General Service 102
Non-Slip Differentials 109
Rear Axle Repairs..............737
Rear Axle, Replace.............737
Rear Axle Specifications.......705
Trouble Shooting 31

SPECIFICATIONS

Brake Cylinder Sizes...........705
Capacity Data 704
Carburetors 725
Cooling System 704
Crankshaft Bearings 701
Distributors 702
Engine Tightening 700
Generator & Regulators 703
Pistons, Pins & Rings 701
Rear Axle 705
Starting Motors 700
Tune Up 698
Valves 699
Valve Timing 717
Wheel Alignment 705

STEERING GEARS (Mechanical)

Horn Button or Ring, Replace...746
Steering Gear Repairs..........748
Steering Gear, Replace.........746
Steering Wheel, Replace........746
Trouble Shooting 33

STEERING GEARS (Power)

Repairs, Linkage Type..........749
Repairs, Integral Type.........145
Replace, Integral Type.........749
Trouble Shooting 34

TRANSMISSION (Manual Shift)

Gearshift, Adjust 731
Transmission Repairs 731
Transmission, Replace..........730
Trouble Shooting 14

TRANSMISSIONS (Automatic)

Linkage, Adjust 731
Transmission, Replace..........737
Cruise-O-Matic Repairs 240
Ford-O-Matic Repairs (3 Speed)......240
Ford-O-Matic Repairs (2 Speed)......253
Trouble Shooting 24, 25

TUNE UP 38

Year	Model Designation	Wheel-base, Inches	Valve Location	Bore and Stroke	Piston Displacement, Cubic Inches	Compression Ratio (Standard)	Maximum Brake H.P. @ R.P.M.	Maximum Torque Lbs. Ft. @ R.P.M.	Normal Oil Pressure Pounds
FORD									
1953	Six Cylinder..............A3	115	In Head	3.5625 x 3.600	215	7.00	101 @ 3500	185 @ 1500	57
	V8.....................B3	115	In Block	3.1875 x 3.750	239	7.20	110 @ 3800	196 @ 2000	57
1954	Six Cylinder..............A4	115½	In Head	3.6250 x 3.600	223	7.20	115 @ 3900	193 @ 1000	50
	V8.....................U4	115½	In Head	3.5000 x 3.100	239	7.20	130 @ 4200	214 @ 1800	50
1955	Six Cylinder..............A5	115½	In Head	3.6250 x 3.600	223	7.50	120 @ 3900	195 @ 1200	50
	V8.....................U5	115½	In Head	3.6250 x 3.600	272	7.60	162 @ 4200	258 @ 2200	50
1956	Six Cylinder..............A6	115½	In Head	3.6250 x 3.600	223	8.00	137 @ 4200	202 @ 1600	50
	V8①.....................U6	115½	In Head	3.6250 x 3.300	272	8.40	176 @ 4400	264 @ 2400	50
	V8②.....................M6	115½	In Head	3.7500 x 3.300	292	8.40	202 @ 4600	289 @ 2600	50
1957	Six Cylinder.............③	③	In Head	3.6250 x 3.600	223	8.60	144 @ 4200	212 @ 2400	50
	Custom and "300"......V8	116	In Head	3.6250 x 3.300	272	8.60	190 @ 4500	270 @ 2700	50
	Fairlane, "500", Sta. Wag..V8	118	In Head	3.7500 x 3.300	292	9.10	212 @ 4500	297 @ 2700	50
1958	Six Cylinder.............③	③	In Head	3.6250 x 3.600	223	8.60	145 @ 4200	212 @ 2100	45–50
	Custom and "300"......V8	116	In Head	3.7500 x 3.300	292	9.10	205 @ 4500	295 @ 2400	45–50
	Fairlane, "500", Sta. Wag..V8	116	In Head	4.0000 x 3.300	332	9.50	265 @ 4600	360 @ 2800	45–50
1959	Six Cylinder.............③	③	In Head	3.6250 x 3.600	223	8.40	145 @ 4000	206 @ 2200	45–50
	Standard V8 Engine......③	118	In Head	3.7500 x 3.300	292	8.80	200 @ 4400	285 @ 2200	45–55
	Special V8 Option........③	118	In Head	4.0000 x 3.300	332	8.90	225 @ 4400	325 @ 2200	43–54
	Power V8 Option.........③	118	In Head	4.0000 x 3.500	352	9.60	300 @ 4600	380 @ 2800	43–54
1960	Six Cylinder.............③	119	In Head	3.6250 x 3.600	223	8.40	145 @ 4000	206 @ 2000	45–50
	Standard V8 Engine......③	119	In Head	3.7500 x 3.300	292	8.80	185 @ 4200	292 @ 2200	45–55
	Special V8 Option........③	119	In Head	4.0000 x 3.500	352	8.90	235 @ 4400	350 @ 2400	43–54
	Power V8 Option.........③	119	In Head	4.0000 x 3.500	352	9.60	300 @ 4600	381 @ 2800	43–54
1961	Six Cylinder.............③	119	In Head	3.6250 x 3.600	223	8.40	135 @ 4000	200 @ 2000	35–55
	Standard V8-292........③	119	In Head	3.7500 x 3.300	292	8.80	175 @ 4200	279 @ 2200	35–55
	Optional V8-352........③	119	In Head	4.0000 x 3.500	352	8.90	220 @ 4400	336 @ 2400	35–55
	Optional V8-390.......③	119	In Head	4.0468 x 3.781	390	9.60	300 @ 4600	427 @ 2800	35–55
THUNDERBIRD									
1955	V8.....................P5	102	In Head	3.7500 x 3.300	292	8.50	198 @ 4400	285 @ 2500	50
1956	V8 With Std. Trans.......P6	102	In Head	3.7500 x 3.300	292	8.40	202 @ 4600	289 @ 2600	50
	V8 With Overdrive........P6	102	In Head	3.8000 x 3.440	312	8.40	215 @ 4600	317 @ 2600	50
	V8 With Auto. Trans......P6	102	In Head	3.8000 x 3.440	312	9.00	225 @ 4600	324 @ 2600	50
1957	V8 With Std. Trans........	102	In Head	3.7500 x 3.300	292	9.10	206 @ 4500	297 @ 2700	50
	V8 With 4-Bar. Carb......	102	In Head	3.8000 x 3.440	312	9.70	245 @ 4500	332 @ 3200	50
	V8 With Two 4-Bar. Carbs.....	102	In Head	3.8000 x 3.440	312	9.70	265 @ 4800	336 @ 3400	50
1958	V8.......................	113	In Head	4.0000 x 3.500	352	10.20	300 @ 4600	395 @ 2800	45–50
1959–60	V8 Std. Engine..........	113	In Head	4.0000 x 3.500	352	9.60	300 @ 4600	380 @ 2800	43–54
	V8 Optional Engine.........	113	In Head	4.3000 x 3.700	430	10.10	350 @ 4800	490 @ 3100	45–55
1961	All.....................	113	In Head	4.0468 x 3.781	390	9.60	300 @ 4600	427 @ 2800	35–55
EDSEL									
1958	Ranger..........E-400 Eng.	118	In Head	4.0469 x 3.500	361	10.5	303 @ 4600	405 @ 2900	45–50
	Pacer...........E-400 Eng.	118	In Head	4.0469 x 3.500	361	10.5	303 @ 4600	405 @ 2900	45–50
	Corsair.........E-475 Eng.	124	In Head	4.2031 x 3.703	410	10.5	345 @ 4600	472 @ 2600	45–50
	Citation........E-475 Eng.	124	In Head	4.2031 x 3.703	410	10.5	345 @ 4600	472 @ 2600	45–50
	Sta. Wagons......E-400 Eng.	116	In Head	4.0469 x 3.500	361	10.5	303 @ 4600	405 @ 2900	45–50
1959	6-Cyl.④..............	120	In Head	3.6250 x 3.594	223	8.4	145 @ 4000	206 @ 2200	45–50
	Ranger V8-292.............	120	In Head	3.7500 x 3.297	292	8.8	200 @ 4400	285 @ 2200	45–50
	Corsair V8-332............	120	In Head	4.0000 x 3.297	332	8.9	225 @ 4000	325 @ 2200	45–50
	V8-361⑤................	120	In Head	4.0469 x 3.500	361	9.6	303 @ 4600	390 @ 2900	45–50
1960	Ranger With 6-223 Engine④..	120	In Head	3.6250 x 3.594	223	8.4	145 @ 4000	206 @ 2000	45–50
	Ranger With V8-292 Eng....	120	In Head	3.7500 x 3.297	292	8.8	185 @ 4200	292 @ 2200	45–50
	Ranger With V8-352 Eng....	120	In Head	4.0000 x 3.500	352	9.6	300 @ 4000	381 @ 2800	45–50

①—Mainline and Customline.   ③—Available in any model.   ④—Optional engine on Ranger and Villager models.

②—Fairlane and Station Wagon.   ⑤—Power option on all models.

TUNE UP SPECIFICATIONS

★Disconnect vacuum line at carburetor to make vacuum advance inoperative when using timing light.

Year	Model	Ground Polarity and Voltage	Spark Plug		Distributor		Firing Order ②	Ignition Timing★		Idle Speed RPM In Neutral	Compression Pressure @ Cranking Speed Minimum
			Type ①	Gap Inch	Point Gap Inch	Cam Angle Degrees		Mark	Location		
FORD											
1953	Six		P-6	H-10	.035	.025	35–38	153624	Groove	Damper	475	130
	V8		P-6	H-10	.030	.015	26–38	15486372	Groove	Pulley	475	125
1954	Six		P-6	H-10	.035	.025	35–38	153624	3°BTDC	Damper	475	120
	V8		P-6	H-10	.035	.015	26–28	15486372	③	Pulley	475	130
1955	Six		P-6	870	.034	.025	35–38	153624	3°BTDC	Damper	475	125
	V8		P-6	F-14-Y	.034	.015	26–28	15486372	③	Damper	475	130
1956–57	Six		N-12	870	.034	.025	35–38	153624	⑤	Damper	475	150
	V8		N-12	F-14-Y	.034	.015	26–28	15486372	③	Damper	475	155
1958	Six		N-12	870	.034	.025	35–38	153624	⑤	Damper	475	150
	V8-292		N-12	F-14-Y	.034	.015	26–28	15486372	③	Damper	475	160
	V8-332		N-12	F-11-Y	.034	.015	26–28	15426378	③	Damper	500	180
1959–60	Six		N-12	870	.034	.025	35–38	153624	⑤	Damper	475	150
	V8-292		N-12	F-14-Y	.034	.015	26–28	15486372	⑦	Damper	475	160
	V8-332		N-12	F-11-Y	.034	.015	26–28	15426378	③	Damper	500	180
	V8-352		N-12	F-11-Y	.034	.015	26–28	15426378	③	Damper	500	190
1961	Six		N-12	860	.034	.025	35–38	153624	⑥	Damper	465	150
	V8-292		N-12	F-14-Y	.034	.015	26–28	15486372	⑦	Damper	465	160
	V8-352		N-12	F-11-Y	.034	.015	26–28	15426378	③	Damper	515	180
	V8-390		N-12	F-11-Y	.034	.015	26–28	15426378	③	Damper	515	180
THUNDERBIRD											
1955	All		P-6	F-14-Y	.034	.015	26–28	15486372	③	Damper	475	135
1956–57	All		N-12	F-14-Y	.034	.015	26–28	15486372	③	Damper	475	155
1958	All		N-12	F-11-Y	.034	.015	26–28	15426378	③	Damper	500	180
1959–60	V8-352		N-12	F-11-Y	.034	.015	26–28	15426378	④	Damper	500	180
	V8-430		N-12	F-11-Y	.034	.015	26–28	15426378	④	Damper	475	190
1961	V8-390		N-12	F-11-Y	.034	.015	26–28	15426378	③	Damper	515	180
EDSEL											
1958	E-400 Engine		N-12	F-11-Y	.034	.015	26–28½	15426378②	③	Damper	475–500	180
	E-475 Engine		N-12	F-11-Y	.034	.015	26–28½	15426378②	③	Damper	475–500	200
1959	6-Cylinder		N-12	870	.034	.025	35–38	153624	⑤	Damper	475–500	150
	V8-292		N-12	F-14-Y	.034	.015	26–28	15486372②	③	Damper	475–500	160
	V8-332		N-12	F-11-Y	.034	.015	26–28	15426378②	③	Damper	475–500	180
	V8-361		N-12	F-11-Y	.034	.015	26–28	15426378②	③	Damper	475–500	180
1960	6-223		N-12	F-14-Y	.034	.025	35–38	153624	⑤	Damper	475–500	150
	V8-292		N-12	F-14-Y	.034	.015	26–28	15486372②	③	Damper	475–500	160
	V8-352		N-12	F-11-Y	.034	.015	26–28	15426378②	③	Damper	475–500	180

①—Champion.
②—V8 cylinder numbering (front to rear): Right bank 1-2-3-4, left bank 5-6-7-8.
③—Standard trans. 3°BTDC, automatic trans. 6°BTDC.
④—Standard trans. 3°BTDC, automatic trans. 7°BTDC.
⑤—Standard trans. 4°BTDC, automatic trans. 6°BTDC.
⑥—Standard trans. 4°BTDC, automatic trans. 10°BTDC.
⑦—Standard trans. 3°BTDC, automatic trans. 10°BTDC.

VALVE SPECIFICATIONS

Year	Model	Valve Lash		Valve Angles		Valve Spring Installed Height	Valve Spring Pressure Lbs. @ In.	Valve Lift		Stem Clearance		Stem Diameter	
		Int.	Exh.	Seat	Face			Int.	Exh.	Intake	Exhaust	Int.	Exh.
FORD													
1953	Six	.015H	.015H	45	45	1⁵³⁄₆₄	132 @ 1½	.329	.324	.001–.002	.002–.003	.3420	.3410
	V8	.014C	.018C	45	45	1⁵⁷⁄₆₄	82 @ 1¹⁹⁄₃₂	.319	.315	.001–.003	.0015–.0035	.3415	.3410
1954	Six	.015H	.019H	45	45	1⁵³⁄₆₄	132 @ 1½	.329	.325	.001–.002	.002–.003	.3420	.3410
	V8	.019H	.019H	45	45	1⁵³⁄₆₄	132 @ 1½	.331	.331	.001–.002	.002–.003	.3415	.3410
1955	Six	.015H	.019H	45	45	1⁵³⁄₆₄	132 @ 1½	.329	.325	.001–.002	.002–.003	.3420	.3410
	V8	.019H	.019H	45	45	1⁵³⁄₆₄	132 @ 1½	.331	.331	.001–.002	.002–.003	.3420	.3410
1956	Six	.019H	.019H	45	45	1¾	165 @ 1²⁵⁄₆₄	.370	.370	.001–.002	.002–.003	.3420	.3410
	V8	.019H	.019H	45	45	1¾	165 @ 1²⁵⁄₆₄	.386	.384	.001–.002	.002–.003	.3420	.3410
1957	Six	.019H	.019H	45	45	1¾	165 @ 1²⁵⁄₆₄	.370	.370	.001–.0025	.0025–.0035	.3420	.3407
	V8	.019H	.019H	45	45	1¾	165 @ 1²⁵⁄₆₄	.401	.421	.001–.0025	.0025–.0035	.3420	.3407
1958	Six	.019H	.019H	45	45	1¾	165 @ 1²⁵⁄₃₂	.370	.370	.001–.0025	.0025–.0035	.3420	.3407
	V8-292	.019H	.019H	45	45	1¾	165 @ 1²⁵⁄₃₂	.401	.421	.001–.0025	.0025–.0035	.3420	.3407
	V8-332	.026H①	.026H①	②	②	1¹³⁄₁₆	185 @ 1²⁷⁄₆₄	.408	.408	.001–.0025	.003–.004	.3715	.3697
1959	Six	.019H	.019H	45	45	1¾	165 @ 1²⁵⁄₃₂	.369	.369	.001–.0025	.003–.004	.3420	.3402
	V8-292	.018H	.018H	45	45	1¾	165 @ 1²⁵⁄₃₂	.359	.357	.001–.0025	.0025–.004	.3420	.3402
	V8-332	Zero	Zero	②	②	1¹³⁄₁₆	185 @ 1²⁷⁄₆₄	.408	.408	.001–.0025	.003–.004	.3715	.3697
	V8-352	Zero	Zero	②	②	1¹³⁄₁₆	185 @ 1²⁷⁄₆₄	.408	.408	.001–.0025	.003–.004	.3715	.3697
1960	Six	.019H	.019H	45	45	1¾	165 @ 1²⁵⁄₆₄	.369	.369	.001–.0025	.003–.004	.3420	.3402
	V8-292	.019H	.019H	45	45	1¾	165 @ 1²⁵⁄₆₄	.358	.356	.001–.0025	.003–.004	.3420	.3402
	V8-352	Zero④	Zero④	②	②	1¹³⁄₁₆	185 @ 1²⁷⁄₆₄	.408	.408	.001–.0025	.003–.004	.3715	.3697
1961	Six	.019H	.019H	45	44	1¾	165 @ 1²⁵⁄₆₄	.369	.369	.001–.0024	.003–.004	.3420	.3402
	V8-292	.019H	.019H	45	44	1¾	165 @ 1²⁵⁄₆₄	.358	.356	.001–.0024	.003–.004	.3420	.3402
	V8-352	Zero	Zero	③	③	1¹³⁄₁₆	185 @ 1²⁷⁄₆₄	.408	.408	.001–.0024	.003–.004	.3715	.3697
	V8-390	Zero④	Zero④	45	44	1¹³⁄₁₆	200 @ 1²⁷⁄₆₄	.408	.408	.001–.0024	.003–.004	.3715	.3697
THUNDERBIRD													
1955	All	.019H	.019H	45	45	1⁵³⁄₆₄	132 @ 1½	.331	.331	.001–.002	.002–.003	.3420	.3410
1956	All	.019H	.019H	45	45	1²⁵⁄₃₂	125 @ 1²⁵⁄₆₄	.386	.384	.001–.002	.002–.003	.3420	.3410
1957	All	.019H	.019H	45	45	1²⁵⁄₃₂	165 @ 1²⁵⁄₆₄	.401	.421	.001–.0025	.0025–.0035	.3420	.3407
1958	All	Zero	Zero	②	②	1⁵³⁄₆₄	185 @ 1²⁷⁄₆₄	.399	.404	.001–.0025	.003–.004	.3715	.3697
1959	V8-352	Zero	Zero	②	②	1⁵³⁄₆₄	185 @ 1²⁷⁄₆₄	.408	.408	.001–.0025	.003–.004	.3715	.3697
	V8-430	Zero	Zero	45	45	1⁵³⁄₆₄	250 @ 1⁷⁄₁₆	.408	.408	.001–.0025	.0025–.004	.3715	.3697
1960	V8-352	Zero	Zero	②	②	1⁵³⁄₆₄	185 @ 1²⁷⁄₆₄	.408	.408	.001–.0025	.003–.004	.3715	.3697
	V8-430	Zero	Zero	45	45	1⁵³⁄₆₄	250 @ 1⁷⁄₁₆	.408	.408	.001–.0025	.0025–.004	.3715	.3697
1961	V8-390	Zero	Zero	45	44	1¹³⁄₁₆	200 @ 1²⁷⁄₆₄	.408	.408	.001–.0024	.003–.004	.3715	.3697
EDSEL													
1958	E-400	Zero	Zero	②	②	1⁵³⁄₆₄	185 @ 1²⁷⁄₆₄	.399	.399	.001–.0025	.003–.004	.3715	.3697
	E-475	Zero	Zero	②	②	1⁵³⁄₆₄	250 @ 1²⁵⁄₆₄	.441	.441	.001–.0025	.003–.004	.3715	.3697
1959	Six	.019H	.019H	45	45	1²⁵⁄₃₂	165 @ 1²⁵⁄₆₄	.369	.369	.001–.0025	.003–.004	.3420	.3402
	V8-292	.019H	.019H	45	45	1²⁵⁄₃₂	165 @ 1²⁵⁄₆₄	.359	.357	.001–.0025	.0025–.004	.3420	.3407
	V8-332	Zero	Zero	②	②	1⁵³⁄₆₄	185 @ 1²⁷⁄₆₄	.408	.408	.001–.0025	.003–.004	.3715	.3697
	V8-361	Zero	Zero	②	②	1⁵³⁄₆₄	185 @ 1²⁷⁄₆₄	.408	.408	.001–.0025	.003–.004	.3715	.3697
1960	Six	.019H	.019H	45	45	1²⁵⁄₃₂	165 @ 1²⁵⁄₆₄	.369	.369	.001–.0025	.003–.004	.3420	.3402
	V8-292	.019H	.019H	45	45	1²⁵⁄₃₂	165 @ 1²⁵⁄₆₄	.358	.356	.001–.0025	.003–.004	.3420	.3402
	V8-352	Zero	Zero	②	②	1⁵³⁄₆₄	185 @ 1²⁷⁄₆₄	.408	.408	.001–.0025	.003–.004	.3715	.3697

①—Hydraulic lifter jobs having adjusting screws, see text for adjustment procedure.
②—Intake 30°, exhaust 45°.
③—Intake 29°, exhaust 44°.
④—High performance engines with mechanical valve lifters, valve lash .020″ hot.

ENGINE TIGHTENING SPECIFICATIONS★

★Torque specifications are for clean and lightly lubricated threads only. Dry or dirty threads produce increased friction which prevents accurate measurement of tightness.

Year	Spark Plugs Ft. Lbs.	Cylinder Head Bolts Ft. Lbs.	Intake Manifold Ft. Lbs.	Exhaust Manifold Ft. Lbs.	Rocker Arm Shaft Bracket Ft. Lbs.	Rocker Arm Cover Ft. Lbs.	Connecting Rod Cap Bolts Ft. Lbs.	Main Bearing Cap Bolts Ft. Lbs.	Flywheel to Crankshaft Ft. Lbs.	Vibration Damper or Pulley Ft. Lbs.
FORD & THUNDERBIRD										
1953 Six	25–30	65–70	23–28	23–28	45–55	2–2½	45–50	95–105	75–85	45–55
1953 V8	25–30	65–70	23–28	25–30	None	None	45–50	95–105	75–85	45–55
1954 Six	25–30	65–75	23–28	23–28	45–55	2–2½	45–50	95–105	75–85	85–95
1954 V8	25–30	65–75	23–28	23–28	12–15	2–2½	45–50	95–105	75–85	85–95
1955–60 Six	15–20	65–75	23–28	23–28	45–55	4–7	45–50	95–105	75–85	85–95
1955–57 V8-272	15–20	65–75	23–28	23–28	12–15	2–2½	45–50	95–105	75–85	85–95
1955–57 V8-292	15–20	65–75	23–28	23–28	12–15	2–2½	45–50	95–105	75–85	85–95
1956 V8-312	15–20	65–75	23–28	23–28	12–15	2–2½	45–50	120–130	75–85	130–145
1957 V8-312	15–20	65–75	23–28	23–28	12–15	2–2½	45–50	95–105	75–85	130–145
1958–60 V8-292	15–20	65–75	23–28	23–28	12–15	2–2½	45–50	95–105	75–85	85–95
1958–60 V8-332	15–20	80–90	12–15	23–28	40–45	4–7	45–50	95–105	75–85	130–145
1958–60 V8-352	15–20	80–90	23–28	23–28	40–45	4–7	45–50	95–105	75–85	130–145
1959–60 V8-430	15–20	95–105	23–28	23–28	40–45	4–7	45–50	95–105	75–85	75–90
1961 Six	15–20	105–115	23–28	23–28	45–55	4–7	40–45	95–105	75–85	70–90
1961 V8-292	15–20	65–75	23–28	23–28	12–15	2–2½	40–45	80–90	75–85	70–90
1961 V8-352	15–20	80–90	32–35	23–28	40–45	4–7	40–45	95–105	75–85	70–90
1961 V8-390	15–20	80–90	32–35	23–28	40–45	4–7	40–45	95–105	75–85	70–90
EDSEL										
1958 E-400 Eng.	15–20	75	23–28	23–28	45–50	2–2½	45–50	95–105	75–85	130–145
1958 E-475 Eng.	15–20	90	23–28	23–28	45–50	2–2½	45–50	95–105	75–85	130–145
1959–60 Six	15–20	65–75	23–28	23–28	45–55	2–2½	45–50	95–105	75–85	85–95
1959–60 V8-292	15–20	65–75	23–28	23–28	45–55	2–2½	45–50	95–105	75–85	85–95
1959 V8-332	15–20	80–90	23–28	23–28	45–50	2–2½	45–50	95–105	75–85	130–145
1959 V8-361	15–20	80–90	23–28	23–28	45–50	2–2½	45–50	95–105	75–85	130–145
1960 V8-352	15–20	80–90	23–28	23–28	45–50	2–2½	45–50	95–105	75–85	130–145

STARTING MOTOR SPECIFICATIONS

Year and Model	Part No.	Rotation ①	Brush Spring Tension, Ounces	No Load Test			Torque Test		
				Amperes	Volts	R.P.M.	Amperes	Volts	Torque, Lbs. Ft.
1953 Std. Trans.	FAD-11002A	C	48–56	70	6	3000	700	3.5	16
1953 Fordomatic	FAJ-11002A	C	48–56	70	6	3000	700	3.5	16
1954–55 Ford, T-Bird	FAC-11002G	C	48–56	70	6	3000	700	3.5	16
1956–57 Ford, T-Bird	B6A-11002A	C	48–56	120	12	4800	550	5.0	15½
1958 All	FAR-11002A	C	48–56	80	12	4800	550	5.0	15½
1959–60 All	FAR-11001A	C	48–56	85	12	4500	550	5	15.5
1961		C	48–56	80–110	12		580	5	14.8

①—As viewed from the drive end. C—Clockwise.

PISTONS, PINS, RINGS, CRANKSHAFT & BEARINGS

Year	Model	Fitting Pistons		Ring End Gap ①		Wrist-pin Diameter	Rod Bearings		Main Bearings			
		Shim To Use	Pounds Pull On Scale	Comp.	Oil		Shaft Diameter	Bearing Clearance	Shaft Diameter	Bearing Clearance	Thrust on Bear. No.	Shaft End Play
FORD												
1953	Six	.0015	5–10	.007	.007	.9121	2.2984–2.2988	.0005–.002	2.4984–2.4988	.0005–.002	3	.004–.008
	V8	.0015	6–12	.007	.007	.7502	2.1384–2.1388	.0005–.003	2.4984–2.4988	.0005–.002	3	.002–.006
1954	Six	②	②	.010	.010	.9121	2.2984–2.2988	.0005–.002	2.4984–2.4988	.0005–.002	3	.004–.008
	V8	②	②	.010	.010	.9121	2.1884–2.1888	.0005–.002	2.4984–2.4988	.0005–.002	3	.002–.006
1955	Six	②	②	.010	.010	.9121	2.2984–2.2988	.0005–.002	2.4984–2.4988	.0005–.003	3	.004–.008
	V8	②	②	.010	.010	.9121	2.1884–2.1888	.0005–.002	2.4984–2.4988	.0005–.003	3	.002–.006
1956–57	Six	②	②	.010	.015	.9121	2.2984–2.2988	.0005–.002	2.4984–2.4988	.0005–.003	3	.004–.008
	V8-272	②	②	.010	.015	.9121	2.1884–2.1888	.0005–.003	2.4984–2.4988	.0005–.003	3	.002–.006
	V8-292	②	②	.010	.015	.9121	2.1884–2.1888	.0005–.003	2.4984–2.4988	.0005–.003	3	.002–.006
	V8-312	②	②	.012	.015	.9121	2.1884–2.1888	.0005–.003	2.6235–2.6243	.0005–.003	3	.002–.006
1958	Six	②	②	.010	.015	.9121	2.2984–2.2988	.0004–.0023	2.4984–2.4988	.0005–.0025	3	.004–.008
	V8-292	②	②	.010	.015	.9121	2.1884–2.1888	.0008–.0027	2.4984–2.4988	.0006–.0032	3	.002–.006
	V8-332	②	②	.013	.015	.9751	2.4384–2.4388	.0009–.0028	2.7484–2.7492	.0007–.0029	3	.002–.006
1959–60	Six	②	②	.010	.015	.9121	2.2984–2.2988	.0004–.0023	2.4984–2.4988	.0005–.0025	3	.004–.008
	V8-292	②	②	.010	.015	.9121	2.1884–2.1888	.0008–.0027	2.4984–2.4988	.0006–.0032	3	.002–.006
	V8-332	②	②	.013	.015	.9752	2.4384–2.4388	.0009–.0028	2.7484–2.7492	.0007–.0029	3	.002–.006
	V8-352	②	②	.013	.015	.9752	2.4384–2.4388	.0009–.0028	2.7484–2.7492	.0007–.0029	3	.002–.006
1961	Six	②	②	.010	.015	.9121	2.2984–2.2988	.0006–.0025	2.4984–2.4988	.0006–.0028	3	.004–.008
	V8-292	②	②	.010	.015	.9121	2.1884–2.1888	.0005–.0024	2.4984–2.4988	.0006–.0032	3	.004–.008
	V8-352	②	②	.015	.015	.9752	2.4384–2.4388	.0006–.0026	2.7488–2.7492	.0006–.0031	3	.004–.008
	V8-390	②	②	.015	.015	.9752	2.4384–2.4388	.0006–.0026	2.7488–2.7492	.0006–.0031	3	.004–.008
THUNDERBIRD												
1955	All	②	②	.010	.010	.9121	2.1884–2.1888	.0005–.002	2.4984–2.4988	.0005–.003	3	.002–.006
1956–57	V8-292	②	②	.010	.015	.9121	2.1884–2.1888	.0005–.003	2.4984–2.4988	.0005–.003	3	.002–.006
	V8-312	②	②	.012	.015	.9121	2.1884–2.1888	.0005–.003	2.6235–2.6243	.0005–.003	3	.002–.006
1958	V8-352	②	②	.013	.015	.9751	2.4384–2.4388	.0009–.0028	2.7484–2.7492	.0007–.0029	3	.002–.006
1959–60	V8-352	②	②	.013	.015	.9752	2.4384–2.4388	.0009–.0028	2.7484–2.7492	.0007–.0029	3	.002–.006
	V8-430	②	②	.015	.015	.9752	2.5992–2.6000	.0006–.0026	2.8994–2.9002	.0009–.0029	3	.002–.006
1961	V8-390	②	②	.015	.015	.9752	2.4384–2.4388	.0006–.0026	2.7488–2.7492	.0006–.0031	3	.004–.008
EDSEL												
1958	E-400 Engine	.002	5–10	.013	.015	.975	2.4380–2.4388	.0006–.0024	2.7484–2.7492	.0006–.0024	3	.002–.006
	E-475 Engine	.002	5–10	.013	.015	.975	2.5992–2.6000	.0007–.0025	2.8994–2.9002	.0008–.0026	3	.004–.008
1959	6-Cyl.	.002	5–10	.010	.015	.9121	2.298–2.299	.0004–.0023	2.498–2.499	.0005–.0025	3	.004–.008
	V8-292	.002	5–10	.010	.015	.9121	2.188–2.189	.0008–.0027	2.498–2.499	.0006–.0032	3	.002–.006
	V8-332	.002	5–10	.013	.015	.9752	2.438–2.439	.0009–.0028	2.7484–2.7492	.0007–.0029	3	.002–.006
	V8-361	.002	5–10	.013	.015	.9752	2.438–2.439	.0009–.0028	2.7484–2.7492	.0007–.0029	3	.002–.006
1960	6-223	.002	5–10	.010	.015	.9121	2.2980–2.2988	.0004–.0018	2.4980–2.4988	.0005–.0025	3	.004–.008
	V8-292	.002	5–10	.010	.015	.9121	2.1880–2.1888	.0007–.0027	2.4980–2.4988	.0006–.0032	3	.002–.006
	V8-352	.002	5–10	.013	.015	.9752	2.4380–2.4388	.0009–.0028	2.7484–2.7492	.0007–.0029	3	.002–.006

①—Fit rings in tapered bores for clearance listed in tightest portion of ring travel.

②—Refer to Piston Clearance chart, Fig. 19.

DISTRIBUTOR SPECIFICATIONS

Year	Model	Part No.	Rotation ①	Cam Angle, Degrees	Breaker Point Opening, Inch	Condenser Capacity, Mfds.	Breaker Arm Spring Tension, Ounces	Centrifugal Advance Data Degrees @ R.P.M. of Dist.		Vacuum Advance Data		
								Advance Starts	Full Advance	Inches of Vacuum to Start Plunger Movement	Inches of Vacuum for full Plunger Travel	Maximum Vacuum Advance, Dist. Degrees
1958	Edsel	B8E-12127E	CC	26–28	.015	.21–.25	17–20	½ @ 375	9 @ 2000	1	15	5–7
1959	V8-292	B9FA-12127A	CC	26–28	.015	.21–.25	17–20	1 @ 450	15½ @ 2000	6½	15	12½
1960	T-Bird	B9MF-12127B	CC	26–28	.015	.21–.25	17–20	1 @ 500	15 @ 2000	6½	15	12½
1960	V8-292	COAF-12127A	CC	26–28	.015	.21–.25	17–20	1¾ @ 800	11 @ 2000	7	20	12½
1960	V8-352	COAF-12127B	CC	26–28	.015	.21–.25	17–20	1½ @ 500	14½ @ 2000	5	15	11½
1960–61	V8-352	COAF-12127D	CC	26–28	.015	.21–.25	17–20	1¼ @ 500	12½ @ 2000	5	17	12½
1960–61	V8-352	COAF-12127E	CC	26–28	.015	.21–.25	17–20	1½ @ 775	12¼ @ 2000	5	17	12½
1960	Six	COAF-12127F	C	35–38	.025	.21–.25	17–20	None	None	.42	6½	13
1961	Six	COAF-12127G	C	35–38	.025	.21–.25	17–20	None	None	.38	5.99	13
1961	Six	CISF-12127D	C	35–38	.025	.21–.25	17–20	None	None	1.08	6.50	13
1961	V8-390	CISF-12127A	CC	26–28	.015	.21–.25	17–20	1½ @ 400	11 @ 2000	9	17	9
1953–54	Six	FAA-12127C	C	35–38	.025	.21–.25	17–20	None	None	.50	6.0	11¾
1954	V8	FAE-12127A	CC	26–28	.015	.21–.25	17–20	None	None	.72	4.4	14½
1955	Six	FDH-12127A	C	35–38	.025	.21–.25	17–20	None	None	.50	6.0	11¾
1955	V8	FDJ-12127C	CC	26–28	.015	.21–.25	17–20	None	None	.40	4.6	15¾
1956	Six	FDR-12127A	C	35–38	.025	.21–.25	17–20	None	None	.50	6.0	13¾
1956	V8	FDS-12127A	CC	26–28	.015	.21–.25	17–20	None	None	.28	4.6	16½
1956	V8	FDS-12127B	CC	26–28	.015	.21–.25	17–20	None	None	.29	2.19	13½
1955	T-Bird	FEA-12127E	CC	26–28	.015	.21–.25	17–20	None	None	.19	1.95	14¾
1957	Six	FEG-12127B	C	35–38	.025	.21–.25	17–20	None	None	2¼	4¼	12¾
1958	Six	FEG-12127D	C	35–38	.025	.21–.25	17–20	None	None	.55	3.38	12½
1957	T-Bird	FEH-12127A	CC	26–28	.015	.21–.25	17–20	1¼ @ 425	17½ @ 2000	5	20	11
1957	T-Bird	FEK-12127A	CC	26–28	.015	.21–.25	17–20	1 @ 450	12¾ @ 2000	5	20	12
1958	Six	FET-12127B	C	35–38	.025	.21–.25	17–20	None	None	.55	3.38	12½
1959	Six	FET-12127C	C	35–38	.025	.21–.25	17–20	None	None	.38	5.99	13
1960	Six	FET-12127D	C	35–38	.025	.21–.25	17–20	None	None	.38	5.99	13
1958	V8-292	FEV-12127A	CC	26–28	.015	.21–.25	17–20	2 @ 450	17 @ 2000	6	20	11½
1959	V8-361	FEV-12127D	CC	26–28	.015	.21–.25	17–20	1 @ 500	14 @ 2000	8	14	10½
1958	T-Bird	FEV-12127H	CC	26–28	.015	.21–.25	17–20	1½ @ 450	11 @ 2000	6	20	11½
1959–60	Edsel	FEV-12127J	CC	26–28	.015	.21–.25	17–20	1 @ 500	15 @ 2000	6	16	12½
1958–59	V8-292	FEV-12127M	CC	26–28	.015	.21–.25	17–20	2 @ 450	17 @ 2000	6	20	11½
1958–59	T-Bird	FEV-12127N	CC	26–28	.015	.21–.25	17–20	1 @ 500	14 @ 2000	8	14	10
1958	Edsel	FEW-12127D	CC	26–28	.015	.21–.25	17–20	1 @ 400	10½ @ 2000	1	14	9
1959	V8-430	FEW-12127H	CC	26–28	.015	.21–.25	17–20	1 @ 525	15 @ 2000	6½	16	12½
1953	V8	8BA-12127	C	26–28	.015	.21–.25	17–20	None	None	.30	3.7	10½
1953	V8	OBA-12127	C	26–28	.015	.21–.25	17–20	None	None	.30	3.7	10½

GENERATOR AND REGULATOR SPECIFICATIONS

★To polarize generator disconnect field lead from regulator and momentarily flash this lead to regulator battery terminal.

Year	Generator Number①	Rated Cap. Amps.	Gen. Field Ground Location★	Brush Spring Tension Ounces	Regulator Number	Cutout Relay Closing Voltage	Voltage Setting	Current Setting
1961	30 Ampere	30	Internal	32–40		12.0–12.8	14.6–15.4	28–32
1961	35 Ampere	35	Internal	32–40		12.4–13.2	14.6–15.4	33–37
1958–60	2900231	35	Internal	26–34	COMF-10505A	12.4–13.2	14.6–15.4	33–37
1958–60	2900278	35	Internal	26–34	B8E-10505B	12.4–13.2	14.6–15.4	33–37
1958–60	2900430	35	Internal	26–34	COMF-10505A	12.4–13.2	14.6–15.4	33–37
1959	2900643	30	Internal	32–40	2900424	12.4–13.2	14.6–15.4	28–32
1959–60	2900650	30	Internal	32–40	2700015	12.4–13.2	14.6–15.4	28–32
1958–60	2900693	35	Internal	26–34	COMF-10505A	12.4–13.2	14.6–15.4	33–37
1959–60	B9FM-10000A	35	Internal	26–34	COMF-10505A	12.4–13.2	14.6–15.4	33–37
1958–60	COAF-10000A	35	Internal	32–40	COMF-10505A	12.4–13.2	14.6–15.4	33–37
1958–60	COAF-10000D	35	Internal	32–40	COMF-10505A	12.4–13.2	14.6–15.4	33–37
1959–60	COSF-10000A	35	Internal	32–40	COMF-10505A	12.4–13.2	14.6–15.4	33–37
1953–55	FAA-10000A	35	Internal	30	FAC-10505A	6.0–6.6	7.4–7.8	34–38
1953–55	FAA-10000B	35	Internal	30	FAC-10505A	6.0–6.6	7.4–7.8	34–38
1953–55	FAA-10000E	35	Internal	30	FAC-10505A	6.0–6.6	7.4–7.8	34–38
1956–57	FAR-10000B	30	Internal	26–34	FAP-10505B,C	12.0–12.8	14.6–15.4	28–32
1958	FAR-10000B	30	Internal	26–34	②	12.4–13.2	14.6–15.4	28–32
1956–57	FAS-10000B	30	Internal	26–34	FAP-10505B,C	12.0–12.8	14.6–15.4	28–32
1956–57	FAS-10000C	30	Internal	26–34	FAP-10505B,C	12.0–12.8	14.6–15.4	28–32
1956–60	FAS-10000E	30	Internal	26–34	②	12.4–13.2	14.6–15.4	28–32
1956–60	FAS-10000G	30	Internal	26–34	②	12.4–13.2	14.6–15.4	28–32
1953–56	FAT-10000A	35	Internal	30	FAC-10505A	6.0–6.6	7.4–7.8	34–38
1955	FBA-10000C	40	Internal	30	FAD-10505A,C	6.0–6.6	7.4–7.8	38–42
1953–56	FBC-10000A	35	Internal	30	FAC-10505A	6.0–6.6	7.4–7.8	34–38
1953–56	FBC-10000E	35	Internal	30	FAC-10505A	6.0–6.6	7.4–7.8	34–38
1953–55	FBM-10000A	35	Internal	30	FAC-10505A	6.0–6.6	7.4–7.8	34–38
1956–57	FBT-10000B	30	Internal	26–34	FAP-10505B,C	12.0–12.8	14.6–15.4	28–32
1956–57	FBT-10000C	30	Internal	26–34	FAP-10505B,C	12.0–12.8	14.6–15.4	28–32
1956–57	FBU-10000B	30	Internal	26–34	FAP-10505B,C	12.0–12.8	14.6–15.4	28–32
1956–57	FBV-10000B	30	Internal	26–34	FAP-10505B,C	12.0–12.8	14.6–15.4	28–32
1958	FGV-10000A	40	Internal	26–34	FAR-10505A	12.0–12.8	14.6–15.4	38–42
1959–60	FHA-10000A	30	Internal	32–40	②	12.4–13.2	14.6–15.4	28–32
1953	FAA-10002A	35	Internal	30	FAC-10505A	6.0–6.6	7.4–7.8	34–38
1953–56	FAD-10002A	60	Internal	30	8BA-10505A	5.9–6.2	7.1–7.3	55–60
1953–56	FGB-10002A	35	Internal	30	FAC-10505A	6.0–6.6	7.4–7.8	34–38

①—Stamped on plate riveted to side of housing.
②—Uses either 2900424 or 2700015 regulator.

COOLING SYSTEM & CAPACITY DATA

| Year and Model | Cooling System Data | | | | | Fuel Tank Gals. | Engine Oil | | | Transmissions | | | Rear Axle Pints |
	Quarts No Heater	Quarts With Heater	Rad. Cap Relief Pressure	Thermostat Opening Temp. ①	②		Refill Qts. ③	Summer Grade	Winter Grade	Std. Pints	With Over-drive Pints	Auto-matic Qts.	
FORD													
1953 Six	15	16	7	180	160	17④	4	20W	10W	3	4½	9¾	3½⑥
1953 V8	22	23	7	180	160	17④	4	20W	10W	3	4½	9¾	3½⑥
1954–55 Six	15	16	7⑨	180	160	17④	4	20W	10W	3	4½	9¾	3½⑥
1954–55 V8	20	21	7⑨	180	160	17④	5	20W	10W	3	4½	9¾	3½
1956 Six	14½	15½	12–15	180	160	17④	4	20W	10W	3	3⑤	9¼	4⑦
1956 V8	19	20	12–15	180	160	17④	5	20W	10W	3	3⑤	9¾	4⑦
1957 Six	15	16	12–15	180	160	19④	4	20W	10W	3	3	9¼	4½
1957 V8	19	20	12–15	180	160	19④	5	20W	10W	3	3	9¾	4½
1958 Six	15	16	12–15	180	160	20⑧	4	20W	10W	3	3	9	5½
1958 V8-292	19	20	12–15	180	160	20⑧	5	20W	10W	3	3	9	5½
1958 V8-332	19	20	12–15	180	160	20⑧	5	20W	10W	3	4½	10	5½
1959 Six	15	16	12–15	180	160	20	4	20W	10W	3	4¼	10	4½
1959 V8-292	19	20	12–15	180	160	20	5	20W	10W	3	4¼	10	4½
1959 V8-332	19	20	12–15	180	160	20	5	20W	10W	3	4¾	10	4½
1959 V8-352	19	20	12–15	180	160	20	5	20W	10W	3	4¾	10	4½
1960 Six	15	16	12–15	180	160	20	4	20W	10W	3½	4¼	⑩	4½
1960 V8-292	19	20	12–15	180	160	20	5	20W	10W	3½	4¼	⑩	4½
1960 V8-352	19	20	12–15	180	160	20	5	20W	10W	3½	4¾	⑩	4½
1961 Six	15	16	12–15	180	160	20	4	20W	10W	3½	4¼	⑩	4½
1961 V8-292	19	20	12–15	180	160	20	5	20W	10W	3½	4¼	⑩	4½
1961 V8-352	19	20	12–15	180	160	20	5	20W	10W	3½	4¾	⑩	4½
1961 V8-390	19	20	12–15	180	160	20	5	20W	10W	3½	4¾	⑩	4½
THUNDERBIRD													
1955 All	20	21	12–15	180	160	17	5	20W	10W	3	4½	9¾	3½
1956 All	20	21	12–15	180	160	17	5	20W	10W	3½	4½	10¼	3
1957 All	20	21	12–15	180	160	20	5	20W	10W	3	4½	10	4½
1958 All	20	21	12–15	180	160	20	5	20W	10W	3¾	4½	10	5½
1959 V8-352	19	20	12–15	180	160	20	5	20W	10W	3	4¾	10	4½
1959 V8-430	20	21	12–15	180	160	20	5	20W	10W	None	None	10	5½
1960	20	21	12–15	180	160	20	5	20W	10W	3½	4¾	10	4½
1961	19½	20½	12–15	180	160	20	5	20W	10W	None	None	10	4½
EDSEL													
1958 Ranger	18½	19½	13	180	160	20	5	20W	10W	3½	5	10	4½
1958 Pacer	18½	19½	13	180	160	20	5	20W	10W	3½	5	10	4½
1958 Corsair	22	23	13	180	160	20	5	20W	10W	3½	5	10	4½
1958 Citation	22	23	13	180	160	20	5	20W	10W	3½	5	10	4½
1958 Sta. Wags.	18½	19½	13	180	160	20	5	20W	10W	3½	5	10	4½
1959 Six	15	16	12–15	180	160	20	4	20W	10W	3	None	11	4½
1959 V8-292	19	20	12–15	180	160	20	5	20W	10W	3¼	None	11	4½
1959 V8-332	19	20	12–15	180	160	20	5	20W	10W	3¼	None	11	4½
1959 V8-361	19	20	12–15	180	160	20	5	20W	10W	3¼	None	11	4½
1960 Six	15	16	12–15	180	160	20	4	20W	10W	3	None	⑩	4½
1960 V8-292	19	20	12–15	180	160	20	5	20W	10W	3¼	None	⑩	4½
1960 V8-352	19	20	12–15	180	160	20	5	20W	10W	None	None	⑩	4½

①—For permanent type anti-freeze.
②—For alcohol type anti-freeze.
③—Add one quart with filter change.
④—Station Wagons and Couriers, 19 gallons.
⑤—Station Wagons 4½ pints.
⑥—Station Wagons, 3 pints.
⑦—Station Wagons and Couriers, 3 pints.
⑧—Retractable hardtop 17½ gallons.
⑨—12-15 lbs. on 1955 models.
⑩—Fordomatic 9, Cruiseomatic 10.

REAR AXLE AND BRAKE CYLINDER SPECIFICATIONS

Year	Model	Ring Gear & Pinion Backlash, Inch	Drive Pinion Adjustment	Drive Pinion Bearing Preload, Inch Lbs.	Drive Pinion Bearing Adjustment	Axle Shaft End Play, Inch	Hydraulic Cylinder Bore Sizes, Inch: Wheel Cylinder Front	Wheel Cylinder Rear	Master Cylinder
FORD									
1953–56	Pass. Car	.003–.008	Shim	18–24③	Spacer	None	1⅛	⅞	1
	Sta. Wagon	.003–.008	Shim	10–30	Spacer	None	1⅛	15/16	1
1957	All	.004–.009	Shim	17–27④	Spacer	None	1⅛	⅞	1①
1958–59	Pass. Car	.004–.009	Shim	17–27④	Spacer	None	1⅛	⅞	1①
	Sta. Wagon	.004–.009	Shim	17–27④	Spacer	None	1⅛	15/16	1①
1960–61	All	.004–.009	Shim	17–27④	Spacer	None	1 3/32	15/16	1
THUNDERBIRD									
1955–56	All	.003–.008	Shim	18–24③	Spacer	None	1⅛	⅞	1
1957–59	All	.004–.009	Shim	17–27④	Spacer	None	1⅛	⅞	1①
1960–61	All	.004–.009	Shim	17–27④	Spacer	None	1 3/32	29/32	1
EDSEL									
1958	All	.004–.009	Shim	17–27④	Spacer	None	1⅛	29/32	1②
1959	All	.004–.009	Shim	17–27④	Spacer	None	1⅛	15/16	21/32①
1960	Pass. Car	.004–.009	Shim	17–27④	Spacer	None	1⅛	15/16	1
	Sta. Wagon	.004–.009	Shim	17–27④	Spacer	None	1⅛	31/32	1

①—Power brake 1⅛″.
②—Power brake .656″.
③—For used bearings 13–18 inch lbs.
④—For used bearings 8–12 inch lbs.

WHEEL ALIGNMENT SPECIFICATIONS

Year	Model	Caster, Degrees: Limits	Caster, Degrees: Desired	Camber, Degrees: Limits	Camber, Degrees: Desired	Toe-In, Inches	Toe-out on Turns, Degrees ①: Outer Wheel	Toe-out on Turns, Degrees ①: Inner Wheel	Kingpin Angle, or Steering Axis Degrees ②
FORD									
1953	All	— 1 to + ½	— ¼	0 to + 1	+ ½	1/16 to ⅛	20	22½	4¾ to 5¾
1954	All	0 to + 1	+ ½	+ ¼ to + 1¼	+ ¾	1/16 to ⅛	20	24½	7° 7′
1955	All	+ ½ to + 1½	+ 1	+ ¼ to + 1¼	+ ¾	1/16 to ⅛	20	24½	7° 7′
1956	All	+ ½ to + 1½	+ 1	+ ¼ to + 1¼	+ ¾	1/16 to ⅛	20	24½	7° 7′
1957	All	+ ½ to + 1½	+ 1	+ ½ to + 1½	+ 1	1/16 to ⅛	20	24¼	7° 1′
1958	All	0 to + 1	+ ½	+ ½ to + 1½	+ 1	1/16 to ⅛	20	24¼	7° 1′
1959	All	0 to + 1	+ ½	+ ½ to + 1½	+ 1	1/32 to ⅛	20	24½	6° 45′
1960	All	— ½ to + ½	0	+ ½ to + 1½	+ 1	⅛ to 5/32	20	24¼	6¾ @ 1 Camber
1961	All	— ½ to + ½	0	+ ¼ to + 1	+ ⅜	⅛ to ¼	20	24¼	6¾ @ 1 Camber
THUNDERBIRD									
1955	All	+ ½ to + 1½	+ 1	+ ¼ to + 1¼	+ ¾	1/16 to ⅛	20	24½	7° 7′
1956	All	+ ½ to + 1½	+ 1	+ ¼ to + 1¼	+ ¾	1/16 to ⅛	20	24½	7° 7′
1957	All	+ ½ to + 1½	+ 1	+ ½ to + 1½	+ 1	1/16 to ⅛	20	25	7° 1′
1958	All	+ ½ to + 1½	+ 1	+ ½ to + 1½	+ 1	1/16 to ⅛	20	17° 7′	7° 7′
1959	All	+ ½ to + 1½	+ 1	+ ½ to + 1½	+ 1	1/16 to ⅛	20	24¼	7° 7′
1960	All	+ ½ to + 1½	+ 1	+ ½ to + 1½	+ 1	1/16 to ⅛	20	17⅛	6¾ @ 1 Camber
1961	All	— ¼ to — 1¼	— ¾	0 to + 1	+ ½	1/16 to ⅛	20	20½	

WHEEL ALIGNMENT SPECIFICATIONS continued

Year	Model	Caster, Degrees		Camber, Degrees		Toe-In, Inches	Toe-out on Turns, Degrees (1)		Kingpin Angle, or Steering Axis Degrees(2)
		Limits	Desired	Limits	Desired		Outer Wheel	Inner Wheel	
EDSEL									
1958	Ranger	+ ½ to + 1½	+ 1	+ ½ to + 1½	+ 1	$\frac{1}{32}$ to $\frac{1}{8}$	20	23½	7 @ 0 Camber
	Pacer	+ ½ to + 1½	+ 1	+ ½ to + 1½	+ 1	$\frac{1}{32}$ to $\frac{1}{8}$	20	23½	7 @ 0 Camber
	Corsair	0 to − 1½	− ¾	0 to + ¾	+ ⅜	$\frac{1}{16}$ to $\frac{3}{16}$	20	24¾	7 @ 0 Camber
	Citation	0 to − 1½	− ¾	0 to + ¾	+ ⅜	$\frac{1}{16}$ to $\frac{3}{16}$	20	24¾	7 @ 0 Camber
	Wagons	+ ½ to + 1½	+ 1	+ ½ to + 1½	+ 1	$\frac{1}{32}$ to $\frac{1}{8}$	20	23½	7 @ 0 Camber
1959	All	+ 1 to + 2	+ 1½	+ ¼ to + 1¼	+ ⅞	$\frac{1}{32}$ to $\frac{1}{8}$	17	20	6¾ @ 1° Camber
1960	All	0 to + 1	+ ½	+ ½ to + 1½	+ 1¼	$\frac{1}{16}$ to $\frac{1}{8}$	17¼	20	6¾ @ 1° Camber

①—Incorrect toe-out, when other adjustments are correct, indicates bent steering arms.

②—Incorrect king pin or spindle support angle with correct camber indicates bent suspension arms or spindle support.

ENGINE & SERIAL NUMBER LOCATION
Plate On Left Front Door Pillar
ENGINE IDENTIFICATION

Ford & Thunderbird

Year	Engine	Ser. No. Prefix
1953	6-215	A3
	V8-239	B3
1954	6-215	A4
	V8-239	U4
1955	6-223	A5
	V8-272②	M5
	V8-272①	U5
	V8-292	P5
1956	6-223	A6
	V8-272	U6
	V8-292	M6
	V8-312	P6
1957	6-223	A7
	V8-272	B7
	V8-292	C7
	V8-312②	D7
	V8-312③	E7
	V8-312④	F7

Year	Engine	Ser. No. Prefix
1958	6-223	A8
	V8-292	C8
	V8-332①	B8
	V8-332②	G8
	V8-352	H8
1959	6-223	A9
	V8-292	C9
	V8-332	B9
	V8-352	H9
	V8-430	J9
1960	6-223	OV
	V8-292	OW
	V8-352①	OX
	V8-352②	OY
	V8-430	OJ
1961	6-223	IV
	V8-292	IW
	V8-352	IX
	V8-390	IZ

Edsel

Year	Engine	Ser. No. Prefix
1958	V8-361	W8
	V8-410	X8
1959	6-223	A9
	V8-292	C9
	V8-332	B9
	V8-361	W9
1960	6-223	OV
	V8-292	OW
	V8-352	OY

①—Two barrel carburetor.

②—Four barrel carburetor.

③—Two 4 barrel carburetors.

④—With supercharger.

1953

1955 FORD

1954

1955-56 Thunderbird

1956 Ford

1959 Thunderbird

1957 Ford

1959 Edsel

1957 Thunderbird

1960 Ford

1958 Ford

1960 Thunderbird

1958 Thunderbird

1960 Edsel

1958 Edsel

1961 Ford

1959 Ford

1961 Thunderbird

Engine Section

ENGINE, REPLACE

1953-61

Because of engine compartment tolerances, the engine should not be removed and installed with the transmission attached.

1. Drain cooling system and crankcase.
2. Remove radiator and air cleaner.
3. Remove hood on 1953-56 Sixes, 1955-56 V8, 1958-60 V8-332, 352, 361, all 1961 models and all Thunderbirds.
4. Remove fuel and vacuum lines and all hoses, wires and linkage attached to engine.
5. Disconnect exhaust pipe from manifolds.
6. Remove starter and automatic transmission filler tube (if equipped).
7. Remove converter or flywheel housing lower cover.
8. Remove clutch release linkage (if equipped).
9. Support transmission with jack.
10. Unfasten converter or flywheel housing from engine.
11. Remove engine mounting bolts and lift engine out of chassis.

CYLINDER HEAD REPLACE

Service Note

In instances where cylinder head gasket leakage is hard to control, aluminum paint can be applied to the gasket as a sealer.

Spray one coat of the aluminum paint on both sides of the gasket and allow the paint to dry. Then spray a second coat on both sides and, while the paint is still wet, install the gasket. Torque the head and manifold bolts to specifications to complete the job.

V8-332, 352, 390 engines

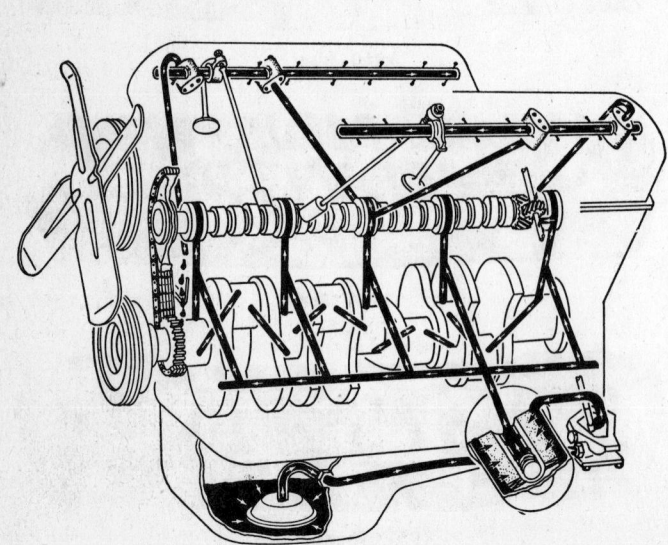

Engine lubrication. V8-239, 272, 292 and 312 engines

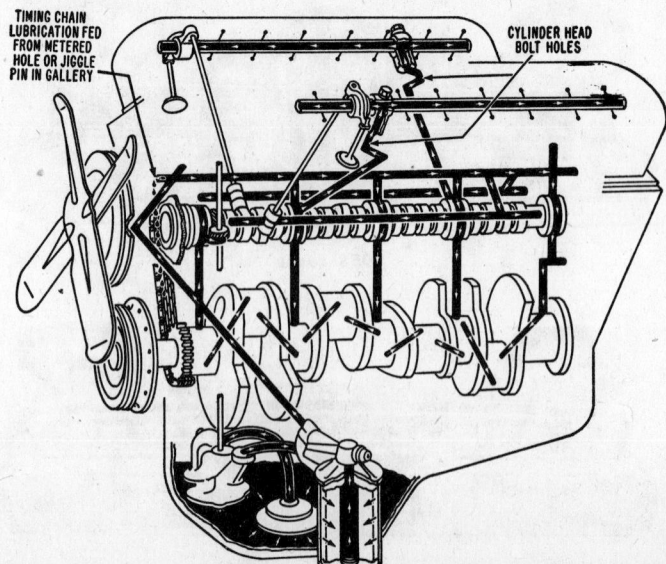

TIMING CHAIN LUBRICATION FED FROM METERED HOLE OR JIGGLE PIN IN GALLERY

CYLINDER HEAD BOLT HOLES

Engine lubrication. V8-332, 352, 361, 390, 410 and 430 engines

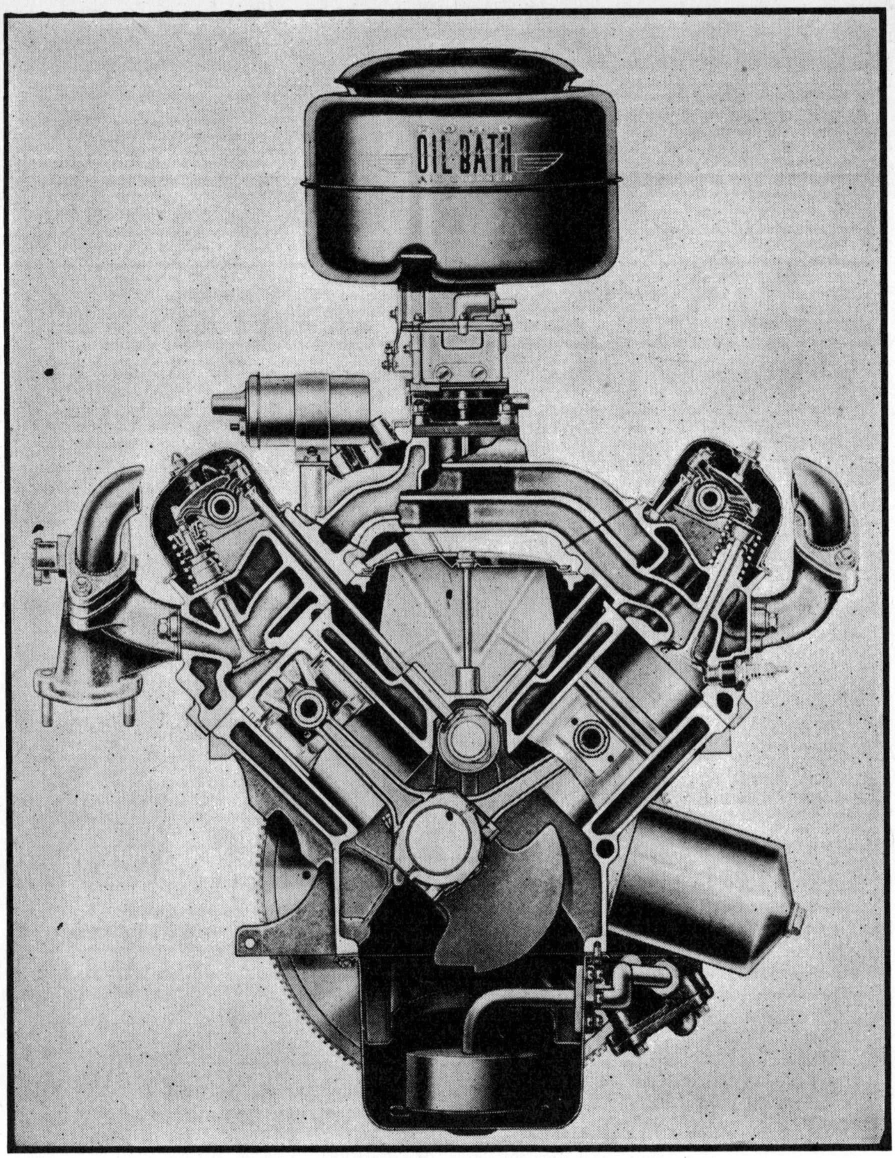

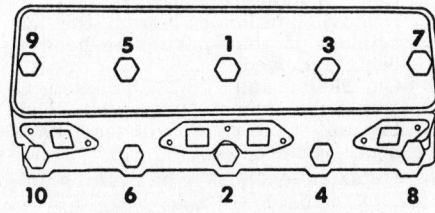

1958-61 V8-292 engine and all 1954-57 V8s

1961 Ford & T-Bird 352, 390

1. Remove intake manifold, carburetor and radiator supply tank as an assembly.
2. Disconnect exhaust pipes from exhaust manifolds.
3. Remove bolts and lift off head.
4. Install cylinder heads in the reverse order of removal and tighten bolts in the sequence shown in Fig. 1 three times around. The final tightening should be done to the torque given in the *Engine Tightening* table.

1960-61 Ford V8-292

1. Remove intake manifold, carburetor, coil and radiator supply tank as an assembly.
2. Remove valve rocker arm shaft assembly. Remove and identify push rods to be sure they are returned to their original locations.

3. To remove the right-hand head, disconnect battery ground cable and oil level dipstick tube bracket.
4. Remove generator drive belt and move generator out of the way. Remove ignition harness bracket from head.
5. To remove left head, disconnect temperature sending unit wire and ground strap from head.
6. Remove distributor cap and spark plug wires at plugs.

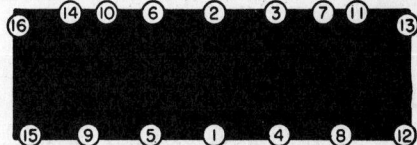

Fig. 1 Cylinder head tightening sequence. 1954-61 V8

7. Disconnect exhaust pipe from exhaust manifold.
8. Remove cylinder head bolts and lift off head.
9. Install heads in reverse order of removal and tighten bolts in the sequence shown in Fig. 1 three times around. Final tightening should be to the torque listed in the *Engine Tightening* table.

1961 Six

1. Drain cooling system and remove air cleaner.
2. Disconnect hoses, tubes, wires and linkage attached to head.
3. Remove coil, distributor cap and spark plugs.
4. On engine with positive crankcase ventilation, disconnect exhaust tube at regulator valve and crankcase outlet. Remove exhaust tube.
5. Remove valve rocker arm shaft assembly. Lift out push rods and identify them as to location so they can be installed in their original position.
6. Unfasten and pull manifold away from cylinder head.
7. Remove radiator supply tank.
8. Remove all cylinder head bolts and lift head off engine.
9. Reverse removal procedure to install and tighten head in the sequence shown in Fig. 2 three times around. Final tightening should be to the torque listed in the *Engine Tightening* table.

1958-60 Ford and T-Bird V8-332, V8-352

1. Drain cooling system.
2. Remove air cleaner.
3. Remove intake manifold and carburetor as a unit.
4. Remove exhaust manifolds and spark plugs.
5. If left head is to be removed, remove ignition coil.
6. Unfasten and remove cylinder head.
7. Install cylinder heads in the reverse order of removal. Tighten the heads in the sequence shown in Fig. 1 in three steps. Tighten the bolts first to 60-70 lb. ft., then to 70-80 lb. ft., and finally to 80-90 lb. ft. in the same sequence.

1959-60 V8-430 T-Bird

1. Remove intake manifold.
2. Remove coil and wire loom from left rocker arm cover.
3. Remove distributor
4. Remove valve push rod cover.
5. Remove rocker arm covers.
6. Rotate engine to bring No. 1 piston on T.D.C. on compression stroke.

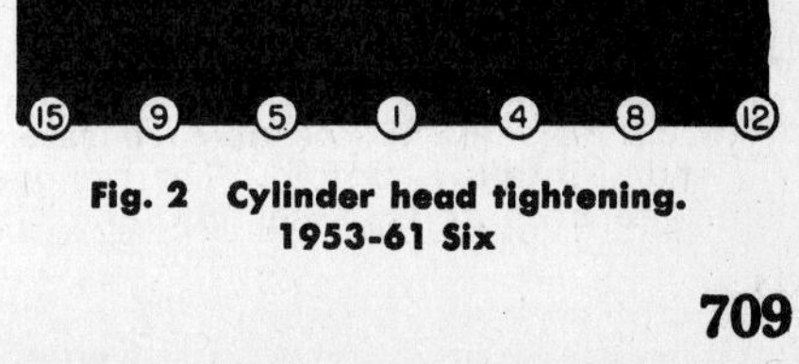

Fig. 2 Cylinder head tightening. 1953-61 Six

Continue rotation for 45° further. Then starting at No. 4 valve rocker support, loosen support bolts in sequence, two turns at a time. After bolts are all loosened, remove rocker arm assembly and then the push rods. Starting at No. 1 valve rocker support, follow same procedure on left support bolts.

7. Disconnect exhaust manifolds from pipes.
8. Unfasten and remove heads.
9. When installing, tighten head bolts in three progressive steps. First tighten bolts in sequence shown in Fig. 1 to 75 ft. lbs., then to 85 and finally to 95-105 ft. lbs.

1958-59 V8-292 Engine

1. Drain cooling system and remove air cleaner.
2. Remove intake manifold, carburetor and coil as a unit.
3. Remove rocker arm cover.
4. Remove exhaust manifolds.
5. To remove right head, disconnect battery ground cable and oil level dipstick tube bracket. Loosen generator mounting bolts and drive belt adjusting arm bolt at generator. Then pivot generator and remove drive belt. Loosen generator and move out of the way. Remove ignition harness bracket from head.
6. To remove left head, disconnect temperature sending unit wire and engine ground strap.
7. Release spring tension on rocker arms by loosening adjusting screws and remove rocker arm assembly. Remove and identify push rods so they can be replaced in their original positions.
8. Remove bolts and lift off head.
9. Reverse procedure to install head and tighten the bolts in the sequence shown in Fig. 1 in three steps. First tighten to 55 lb. ft., then to 65 lb. ft. and finally to 75 lb. ft. in the same sequence.

1958-60 Six

1. Drain cooling system.
2. Remove air cleaner and tape carburetor air horn closed.
3. Disconnect upper hose at radiator, heater hose at water outlet housing, oil pressure and water temperature sending unit wires at sending units, and battery ground cable at cylinder head.
4. Disconnect carburetor fuel inlet line and vacuum line at fuel pump, and distributor vacuum line at distributor.
5. Remove ignition coil and move it to one side.
6. Remove distributor cap and spark plugs.
7. On cars with automatic transmission, disconnect throttle control rod and accelerator connecting link at accelerator bracket. Remove accelerator bracket from block.
8. On cars with synchromesh transmission, disconnect accelerator rod at bell crank.
9. Disconnect fuel inlet line and distributor vacuum line at carburetor, and at intake manifold. Then remove three lines as an assembly.

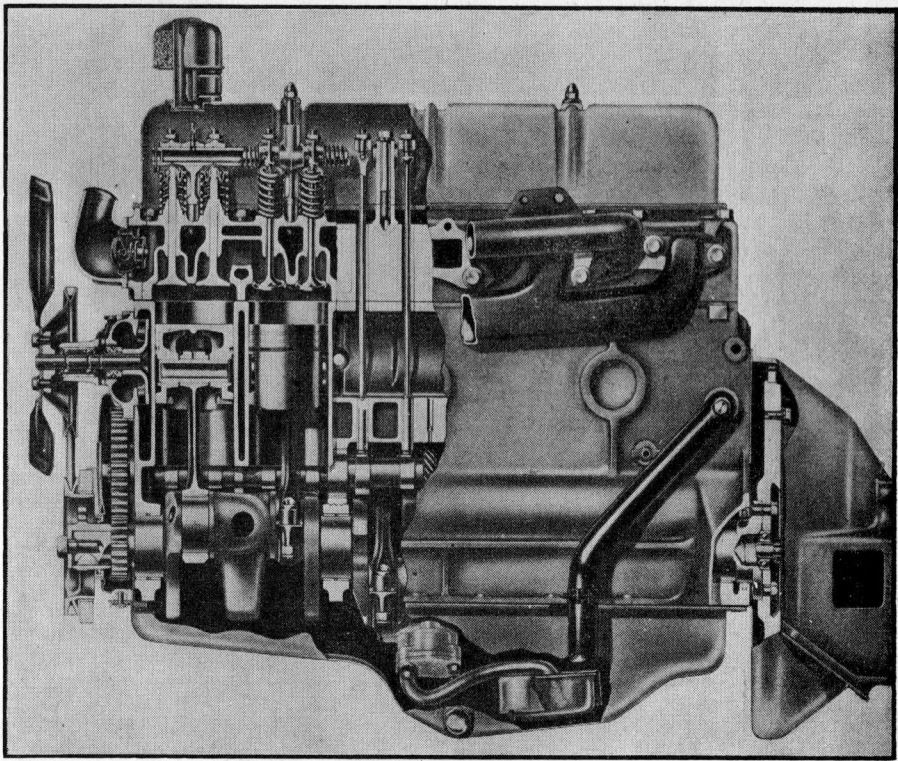

Six-cylinder overhead valve engine. 1953-61

10. Disconnect choke control cable at carburetor.
11. Remove rocker arm cover. Remove cap screw and bracket from No. 6 rocker arm support. Pull oil inlet line out of support and out of block with pliers.
12. Remove cap screw from No. 1 rocker arm support and remove oil outlet line and bracket.
13. Loosen all rocker arm adjusting screws to remove valve spring tension before removing rocker arm assembly.
14. Remove push rods and identify them so they can be installed in their original positions.
15. Unfasten and pull manifold away from cylinder head. Then unfasten and lift off head.
16. Reverse procedure to install the head and tighten it down in three steps in the sequence shown in Fig. 2. Tighten bolts first to 55 lb. ft., then to 65 lb. ft. and finally to 75 lb. ft. in the same sequence.

1958-60 Edsel V8-332, 352, 361, E-400, E-475

1. Drain cooling system.
2. Remove rocker arms and push rods.
3. Remove intake manifold.
4. Remove ignition coil from the left cylinder if that particular head is being removed.
5. On E-400 and V8-361, disconnect wire from temperature gauge sending unit if the right cylinder head is being removed.
6. Unfasten exhaust pipe from manifold.
7. Unfasten and remove cylinder head and exhaust manifold as a unit. *The*

exhaust manifolds should not be separated from the cylinder heads unless the head is to be replaced or the valves are to be ground.

8. Reverse the removal procedure to install and tighten the bolts in the sequence shown in Fig. 1 to the torque values given in the *Engine Tightening* chart.

1954-57 V8

1. Drain cooling system.
2. Remove valve chamber cover.
3. Remove exhaust manifolds.
4. Remove spark plugs.
5. Remove intake manifold.
6. Remove ignition harness bracket.
7. On Thunderbird, remove distributor cap when removing right-hand cylinder head.
8. When removing the right cylinder head on all other vehicles, disconnect the battery ground cable and the oil dip stick tube bracket from the cylinder head.
9. Loosen and move the generator out of the way.
10. Release the spring tension on the rocker arms by loosening the adjusting screws, then remove the rocker arm assemblies and baffle plates.
11. Remove the push rods, keeping them in their order of removal for proper installation.
12. Disconnect wire from temperature sending unit in left cylinder head.
13. Remove the attaching bolts and lift off the heads.
14. Install heads in the reverse order of removal and tighten the bolts in the sequence shown in Fig. 1.

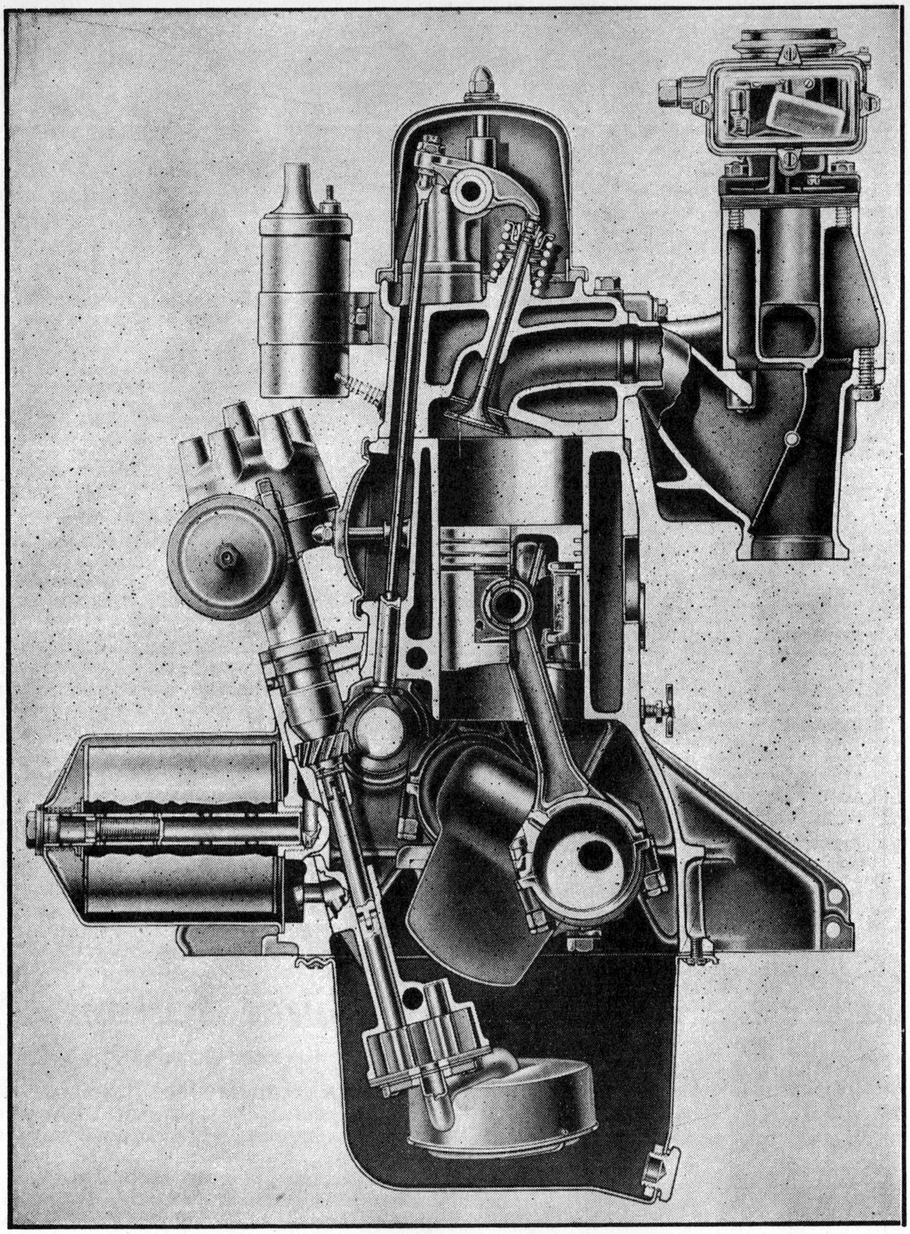

Six-cylinder overhead valve engine. 1953-61

1953 V8

If available, always tighten cylinder heads with a torque wrench to the values given in the *Engine Tightening* chart. If equipped with cast iron heads, make a final tightening after the engine has been warmed up. With aluminum heads, the final tightening should be made after the engine has been warmed up and allowed to cool, Fig. 3.

Cylinder head gaskets are stamped with the word "front" and should be so installed. Improper installation of head gaskets will block some of the water passages, causing improper water circulation with the consequent overheating of the engine.

1953-57 Six

1. Drain cooling system and disconnect radiator and heater hose at

cylinder head outlet elbow.
2. Disconnect windshield wiper vacuum line from manifold.
3. Remove air cleaner and disconnect battery cable at head, and accelerator rod and choke cable at carburetor.
4. Remove valve chamber cover.
5. Disconnect fuel line at fuel pump and carburetor and distributor vacuum line at distributor and carburetor.
6. Remove spark plugs.
7. Disconnect coil from head and allow coil to hang from distributor.
8. Disconnect engine temperature sending unit wire.
9. Remove fan assembly.
10. Remove capscrew and clip from No. 6 rocker arm support bracket.
11. Pull oil feed line out of bracket and block.
12. Loosen all rocker arm adjusting

screws to remove valve spring load from rocker arms.
13. Slide rocker arms away from push rods and remove rods. The rocker arms at each end of the engine cannot be moved so they should be left in place.
14. Tag the push rods so they can be reinstalled in the same place from which they were removed.
15. Unfasten the manifold and pull it away from the head, allowing it to be supported by the muffler inlet pipe.
16. Remove all cylinder head bolts. Install guide studs, and lift the head assembly off the engine.
17. Reverse the removal procedure to install the head and tighten it down in the sequence shown in Fig. 2.

VALVE ARRANGEMENT

Front to Rear

Six Cyl	E-I-I-E-I-E-E-I-E-I-I-E
V8-239, 272, 292, 312	E-I-I-E-E-I-I-E
V8-332, 352, 361, 390	E-I-E-I-I-E-I-E
V8-430 Right Bank	I-E-I-E-I-E-I-E
V8-430 Left Bank	E-I-E-I-E-I-E-1
E-400	E-I-E-I-I-E-I-E
E-475 Right Bank	I-E-I-E-I-E-I-E
E-475 Left Bank	E-I-E-I-E-I-E-I

VALVES, ADJUST

Overhead Valve Engines

Prior to 1957, rocker arm adjusting screws are provided with a lock nut. Starting with 1957 engines self-locking adjusting screws are used.

If the cylinder head or rocker arm assemblies have been removed and installed, a preliminary (cold) valve lash adjustment should be made before starting the engine. If the adjustment is made in connection with an engine tune-up, the valve lash adjustment should be made with the engine at operating temperature.

To make the "hot" adjustment, operate the engine for a minimum of 30 minutes at a fast idle to stabilize engine temperatures. With the engine idling, check the valve lash with the proper feeler gauge between valve stem and rocker arm. Adjust the lash by means of the adjusting screw to the clearance given in the *Valve Specifications* table.

To make the "cold" adjustment, first turn over the engine to bring No. 1 piston up on its compression stroke, which will be indicated by the TDC mark on the vibration damper. Then proceed as follows:

1953-61 Six Cylinder

Make two chalk marks on the vibra-

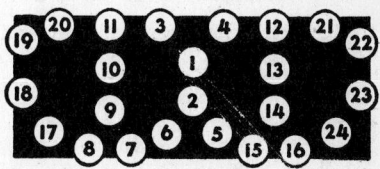

Fig. 3 Cylinder head tightening. 1953 V8

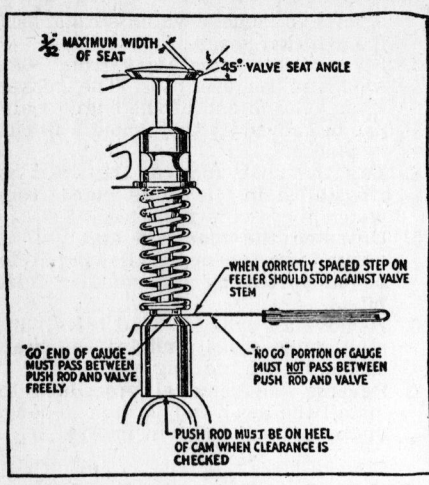

Fig. 4 Valve adjustment data on 1953 V8

tion damper. Space the marks approximately 120 degrees apart (⅓ of circumference) so that with the timing mark the damper is divided into three equal parts. Adjust the valves for No. 1 cylinder. Repeat this procedure for the remaining set of valves, turning the crankshaft ⅓ turn at a time in the direction of normal rotation, while adjusting the valves in the firing order sequence, which is 153624.

V8-239, 272, 292, 312

Make three chalk marks on the vibration damper. Space the marks 90 degrees apart (¼ of circumference) so that with the timing mark the damper is divided into four equal parts. Rotate the crankshaft until No. 1 piston is near TDC at the end of the compression stroke and adjust the following valves:

No. 1 intake and exhaust
No. 2 intake
No. 4 exhaust
No. 5 exhaust
No. 7 intake

Rotate the crankshaft 180 degrees (½ turn) which puts No. 4 piston on TDC. Then adjust the following valves:

No. 4 intake
No. 5 intake
No. 6 exhaust
No. 8 exhaust

Rotate the crankshaft 270 degrees (¾ turn), which puts No. 3 piston on TDC. Then adjust the following valves:

No. 2 exhaust
No. 3 intake and exhaust
No. 6 intake
No. 7 exhaust
No. 8 intake

V8-332, 352, 390 With Mechanical Lifters

Chalk mark the vibration damper into four equal parts as suggested above for other V8 engines. Then with No. 1 piston on TDC of its compression stroke, adjust the following valves:

No. 1 intake and exhaust
No. 4 exhaust
No. 5 exhaust
No. 7 intake

No. 8 intake

Rotate crankshaft 180 degrees (½ turn) which puts No. 4 piston up on TDC. Then adjust the following valves:

No. 2 exhaust
No. 4 intake
No. 5 intake
No. 6 exhaust

Rotate the crankshaft 270 degrees (¾ turn) which puts No. 3 piston on TDC. Then adjust the following valves:

No. 2 intake
No. 3 intake and exhaust
No. 6 intake
No. 7 exhaust
No. 8 exhaust

V8-332 and 352 With Rocker Arm Adjusting Screws and Hydraulic Lifters

These engines may be identified by a daub of orange paint on the engine front cover visible from the left side of the engine. In making an adjustment on these valves, follow the procedure outlined above for engines with mechanical lifters insofar as positioning the valves. Then proceed as follows:

1. With lifter being adjusted on base circle of cam on camshaft, turn adjusting screw so that clearance is obtained between push rod and rocker arm adjusting screw.
2. Adjust screw until clearance is just removed.
3. Tighten screw an additional 2½ turns.
4. Apply steady force to the push rod end of the rocker arm, depress the arm until the push rod bottoms in the lifter.
5. Check clearance between end of valve stem and rocker arm. A clearance of at least .060″ should exist. If less than .060″, back off the adjusting screw until at least .060″ clearance is obtained.
6. Repeat adjustment on all other valves in the sequence given for mechanical lifter jobs.

V8-332, 352, 390 With Non-Adjustable Hydraulic Lifters

For these engines a .060″ shorter push rod (color coded white) or a .060″ longer push rod (color coded yellow) are available for service to provide a means of compensating for dimensional changes in the valve mechanism. Valve stem-to-rocker arm clearance should be .078-.218″ with the hydraulic lifter completely collapsed. Repeated valve grind jobs will decrease this clearance to the point that if not compensated for the lifters will cease to function.

To check the clearance, bring the piston of the cylinder being checked on top dead center of the compression stroke. Then with hydraulic lifter collapsed, check the clearance between valve stem and rocker arm. If the clearance is less than .078″, the .060″ shorter push rod should be used. If clearance is more than .218″ the .060″ longer push rod should be used.

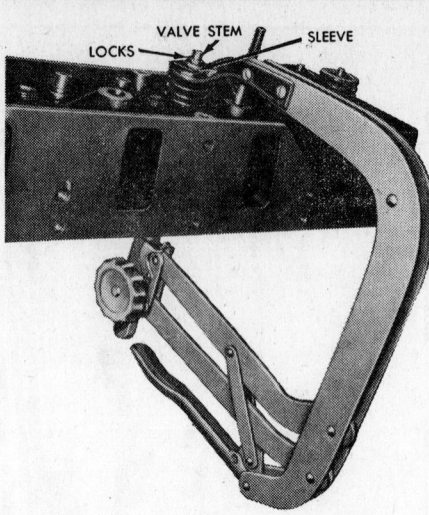

Fig. 5 Removing or installing valves. Overhead valve engines

1953 V8

Since there are no means of adjusting valves when these engines are assembled, this operation must be performed after the valves have been refaced and before assembling the valve guides and springs.

To check the valve clearance, turn over the engine until the valve being checked is fully closed. Slip a feeler gauge between the valve stem and the valve lifter, Fig. 4. If the clearance is not according to that given in the *Valve Specifications* table, remove the valve and grind the end of the valve stem, being sure that the valve stem is ground perfectly square.

VALVES, REMOVE
V8 Engines (Except '53)

With the cylinder head removed as outlined previously, use a suitable valve spring compressor, Fig. 5, to compress each spring. Remove the valve locks and sleeve, tapping the sleeve with a soft hammer if necessary. Remove the neoprene sleeve from the valve stem and release the pressure on the spring. Remove the spring compressor and lift off the valve retainer sleeve, retainer, spring and valve. Repeat for the remaining valves. Keep the valves and related parts together so they may be installed in their respective positions if found in satisfactory condition.

Six Cylinder

After taking off the head as outlined previously, proceed as follows:

1. Remove capscrews retaining rocker shaft brackets to head and remove shaft assembly.
2. Clean carbon out of combustion chambers before removing valves.
3. Compress valve springs with a suitable spring compressor, remove valve stem locks and release the springs. Remove sleeve, valve spring cap retainer, spring and valve. Discard intake valve seals.
4. Place valves in a board with num-

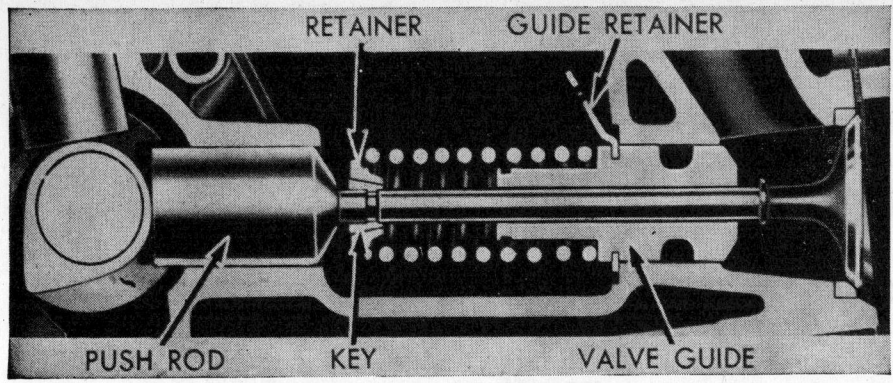

Fig. 6   1953 V8 valve details

bered holes so they can be replaced in their original positions upon reassembly.

1953 V8

The valve, guide, spring and retainer are assembled and installed in the engine as one unit, Fig. 6.

To remove the assembly, insert a bar type valve lifter through the valve spring and to the flange on the lower end of the valve guide, Fig. 7. Using the top of the valve chamber as a fulcrum, pull down on the valve guide and withdraw the guide retainer. Then with the valve lifter tool, push the assembly up and remove it from above.

When replacing valve and guide assemblies in the block, be sure to have the joint in the valve guide at *right angles* to the camshaft.

VALVES, GRIND

Clean the valves with a wire wheel brush, making sure that all carbon is removed from the top and bottom of the heads as well as the gum which might have accumulated on the stems.

In refacing valves, take off only the minimum of metal required to clean up the valve faces. If the outer edge of the valve becomes too thin or sharp due to excessive grinding, the valve must be replaced. In other words, the valve head margin must be at least $\frac{1}{32}$″, otherwise the valve must be replaced.

Inspect the valve seats in the head for cracks, burns, pits, ridges or improper angle. During any general engine over-

haul, it is advisable to reface the valve seats regardless of their condition.

VALVE GUIDES

Overhead Valve Engines

Valve guides in these engines are an integral part of the head and, therefore, cannot be removed. For service, guides can be reamed oversize to accommodate one of three service valves with oversize stems (.003″, .015″ and .030″).

Check the valve stem clearance of each valve (after cleaning) in its respective valve guide. If the clearance exceeds the service limits of .004″ on the intake or .005″ on the exhaust, ream the valve guides to accommodate the next oversize diameter valve.

1953 V8

See *Valves, Remove* inasmuch as the valve, guide, spring and retainer are assembled and installed in the engine as one unit.

VALVE SPRING INSTALLED HEIGHT

When valves and seats are reground the position of the valve in the head is changed so as to lessen the valve spring tension. Without proper valve spring tension the valve does not seat long enough or it may not seat completely. Since the valve is cooled by transferring heat from the valve head to the seat and thence to the coolant, improper valve spring tension will cause worn, pitted and distorted valves which result in loss of compression and power as well as poor gasoline mileage.

When valves, springs, retainers and locks are installed, measure the assembled height of the valve springs from the surface of the cylinder head spring pad to the underside of the spring retainer as shown in Fig. 7A. If the assembled height is greater than the dimension given in the *Valve Specifications Chart*, install a spacer or shim of proper thickness between cylinder head spring pad and spring to bring the assembled height to specifications.

Do not install spacers unless necessary. Excessive use of spacers will result in overstressing valve springs and over-

loading camshaft lobes which could lead to spring breakage and worn camshaft lobes.

VALVE SPRING TESTING

After taking out the valve springs, wash them with gasoline or other suitable solvent. Examine the springs for damage or corrosion due to acid etching, which will develop into surface cracks and cause spring failure.

Check the valve spring tension on a spring testing fixture, if one is available, Fig. 8, and according to the specifications given in the *Valve Data Chart*. If a fixture is not available, at least check the free length of each spring by standing it alongside a new spring. Any spring that does not conform to the pressure specifications within 10% should be replaced. Likewise, any spring that stands shorter than the new spring used for comparison should be discarded. Of course, cocked springs should also be scrapped.

ROCKER ARMS

To disassemble the rocker arms, remove cotter pins from each end of the shaft and remove the flat washers and spring washers. Slide rocker arms, springs and supports off shaft, being sure to identify all parts so they can be assembled in the same position.

If it is necessary to remove the plugs from each end of the shaft, drill or pierce one plug, then insert a steel rod through the plug and knock out the plug on the opposite end. Working from the open end, knock out the remaining plug.

Assemble the rocker arms and related parts as indicated by Figs. 9, 10 and 11.

HYDRAULIC VALVE LIFTERS

The internal parts of each hydraulic valve lifter assembly are a matched set.

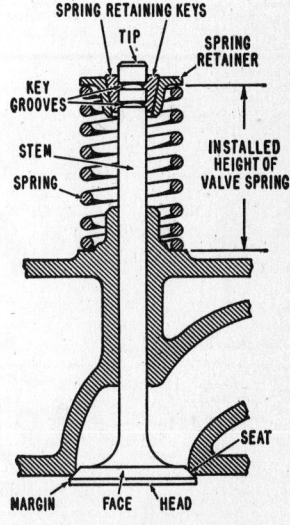

Fig. 7A   Checking valve spring installed height

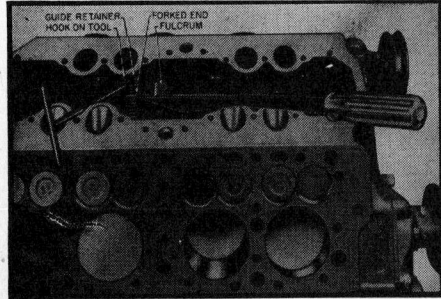

Fig. 7   Removing valve guide retainer. 1953 V8

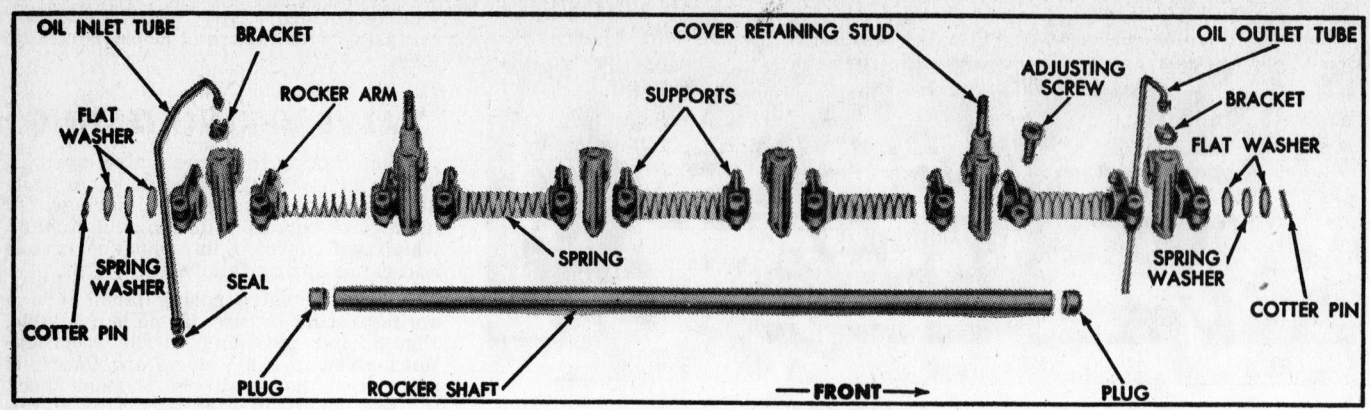

Fig. 9 Six cylinder rocker arm shaft assembly

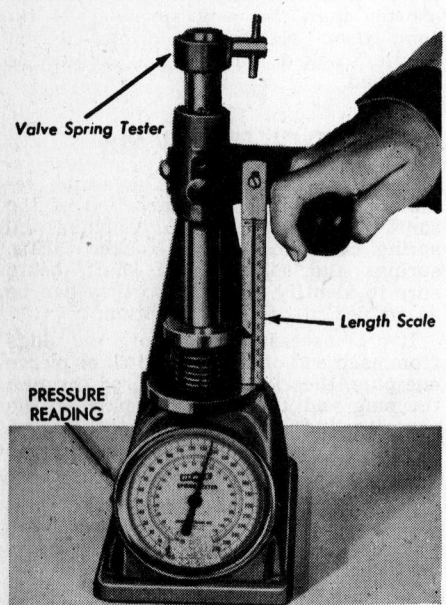

Fig. 8 Checking valve spring pressure

If these are mixed, improper valve operation may result. Therefore, disassemble, inspect and test each assembly separately to prevent mixing the parts.

Fig. 12 illustrates the type of hydraulic lifter used. See the *Trouble Shooting Chapter* under the heading *Engine Noises* for causes of hydraulic valve lifter noise.

The easiest method of locating a noisy valve lifter is by the use of a piece of garden hose about 4 feet long. Press one end of the hose near each valve in progression and listen through the other end. In this manner the sound is localized, making it easier to determine which lifter is at fault.

Another method is to place a finger on the valve spring retainer. If the lifter is not functioning properly, a distinct shock will be felt when the valve returns to its seat.

In most cases where noise exists in one or more lifters, all lifter units should be removed and cleaned. If dirt, varnish or carbon is found to exist in one unit, it more than likely exists in all the units.

To disassemble, first immerse the lifters in solvent and remove all traces of carbon and varnish. Remove the lock ring from the lifter body and disassemble as shown in Fig. 12. Wash all parts in solvent and wipe dry with a lint-free cloth.

To assemble, hold the plunger inverted and assemble the valve disc, small spring, valve disc retainer and large spring on the plunger. Slip the body over the plunger, then install the push rod cup and lock ring in the body.

TIMING CASE COVER

1959-60 V8-430 T-Bird

1. Remove hood, air cleaner, radiator, radiator supply tank, fuel pump and fuel pump push rod.
2. Remove water pump, pulley and fan.
3. Remove vibration damper.
4. Remove engine right and left support-to-underbody nuts. Raise engine with jack and wood block placed under oil pan. Position one-inch wooden blocks between engine front support brackets on underbody and block. Then remove jack from under oil pan.
5. Remove oil pan.
6. Unfasten and remove cover.

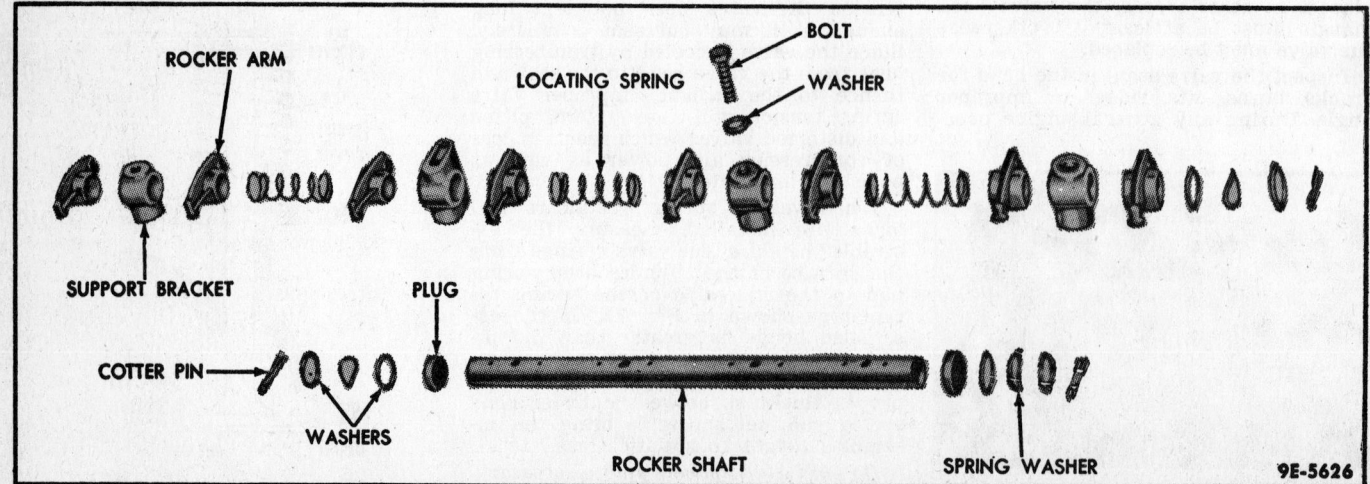

Fig. 10 Rocker arm shaft assembly. V8-332, 352, 361, 390, 410 and 430 engines

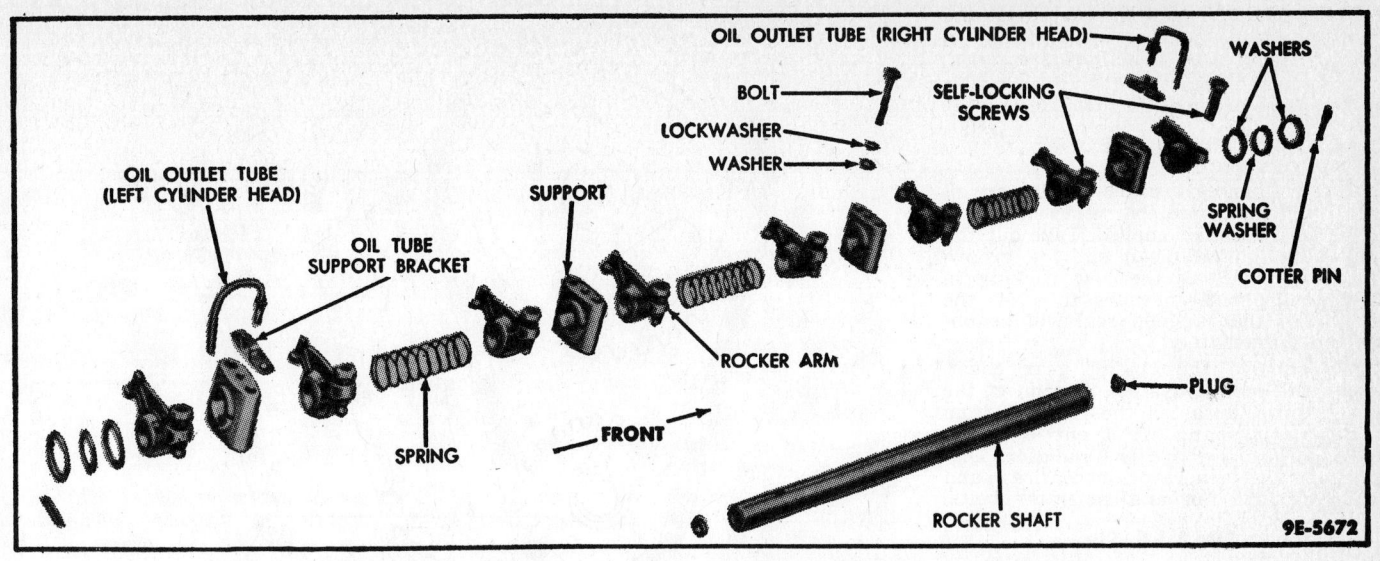

Fig. 11 Rocker arm shaft assembly. V8-239, 272, 292 and 312 engines

1958 T-Bird & 1959-60 V8-352 T-Bird

1. Drain cooling system and crankcase.
2. Remove hood, air cleaner, radiator, fuel pump, radiator supply tank, water pump, vibration damper and oil pan.
3. Unfasten and remove cover.

V8-332, 352, 361, 390, 410

1. Remove radiator and fuel pump.
2. On cars with power steering, disconnect pump bracket from water pump.
3. Remove water pump.
4. Remove vibration damper with puller.
5. Unfasten and remove front cover. *If oil pan gasket is broken or damaged in removing cover, remove oil pan and install new gasket.*
6. Install a new cover oil seal and reinstall the cover in the reverse order of removal.

V8-272, 292, 312

1. Remove radiator and fuel pump.
2. Remove vibration damper.
3. Unfasten front cover from block and oil pan and remove cover and water pump as a unit. *If the oil pan gasket is broken during removal of front cover, remove oil pan and install new gasket.*
4. Install a new cover oil seal and reinstall cover in reverse order of removal.

1956-61 Six Cylinder

To remove front cover, remove radiator, fan, drive belt, pulley, vibration damper and water pump. Unfasten front cover from cylinder block and oil pan and remove cover. *If oil pan gasket is broken or damaged during front cover removal, drop the oil pan and install a new gasket.*

1955 V8

1. To remove the cover, drain cooling system and remove radiator.
2. Loosen fan blades and hub.
3. Remove fuel pump.
4. Remove fan belt.
5. Unfasten generator mounting bracket and move it out of the way.
6. Loosen generator adjusting bracket and move it out of the way.
7. Remove crankshaft pulley.
8. Remove engine front steady rest.
9. Remove four bolts that fasten front cover to oil pan.
10. Disconnect water by-pass tube.
11. Remove seven remaining front cover bolts then remove the water pump and front cover as a unit.
12. Install a new front cover oil seal if necessary and reinstall the cover in the reverse order of its removal.

1954 V8

1. To remove the cover, drain radiator and crankcase.
2. Loosen fan attaching bolts.
3. Loosen fan belt and take it off together with blade, pulley, spacer and fan bolts.
4. Remove upper radiator hose and disconnect water by-pass tube at water pump.
5. Remove water pump, crankshaft pulley and engine steady rest.
6. Remove fuel pump.
7. Swing generator support bracket and generator adjusting arm out of the way.

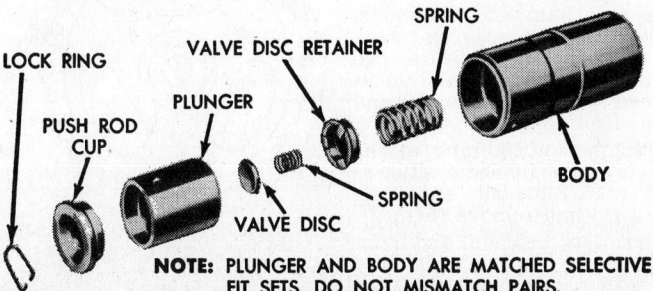

NOTE: PLUNGER AND BODY ARE MATCHED SELECTIVE. FIT SETS. DO NOT MISMATCH PAIRS.

Fig. 12 Hydraulic valve lifter disassembled

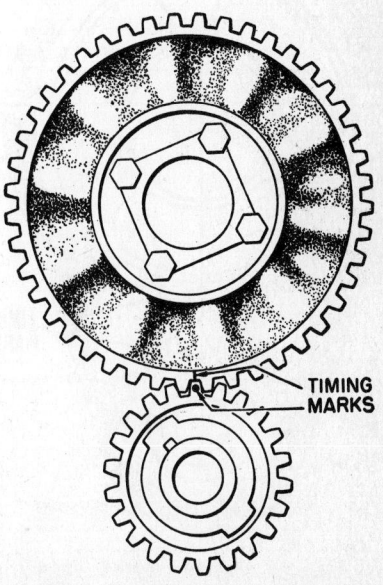

Fig. 13 Valve timing. 1953 V8s

8. Remove the timing case cover and crankshaft pulley spacer.

9. Install a new cover oil seal if necessary and reinstall the cover in the reverse order of its removal.

1953 V8

The timing case cover carries an oil seal which should be renewed every time the cover is removed. Take out the old packing and clean out the groove thoroughly. Soak the new packing in oil for about 30 minutes to swell the fabric so that a good seal will be obtained immediately.

To remove the timing gear cover, drain the cooling system, disconnect the water hose, unfasten the radiator from its mountings and lift it out. *It is not necessary to remove the radiator.* Disconnect the generator lead wires, and take off the fan and generator belts.

1953-55 Six

To remove the front cover, take off the radiator and vibration damper. Remove the two screws which fasten the oil pan to the front cover and loosen the other oil pan screws slightly. Remove the remaining cover screws and take off the cover and gasket.

Install a new cover oil seal and reinstall the cover in the reverse order of its removal, being sure to tighten the oil pan screws.

TIMING GEARS

1953 V8

When installing a camshaft gear, the cap screw holes are unevenly spaced so that the gear can be attached in one position only. Before installing the gear,

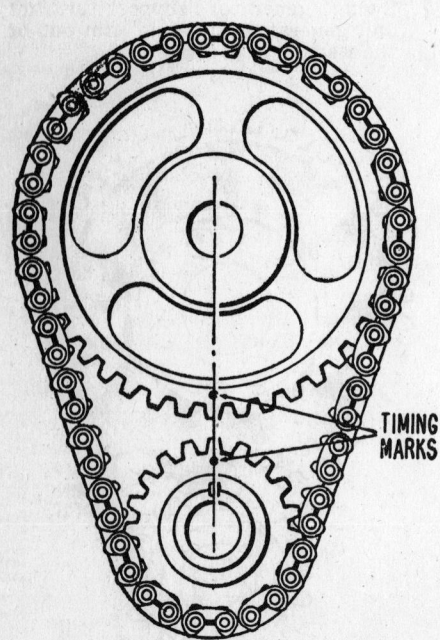

Fig. 14 Timing Marks lined up for correct valve timing. V8-332, 352, 361, 390, 410, 430

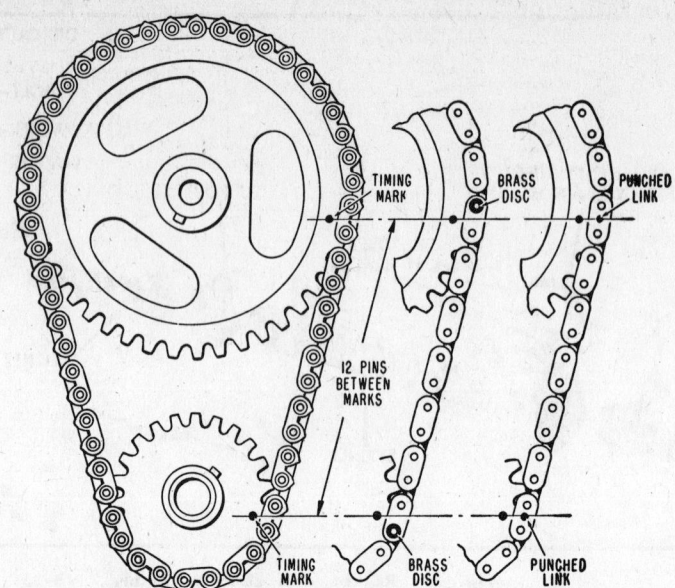

Fig. 15 Timing marks lined up for correct valve timing. V8-239, 272, 292, 312. The punch link type chain was used on some 1954 V8 engines

however, turn over the engine so that the timing mark on the crankshaft gear is facing up. Then turn the camshaft so that when the camshaft gear is installed, the timing marks on both gears will be meshed. In other words, the mark on the tooth of the crankshaft gear should be meshed between the two teeth on the camshaft gear at the mark, Fig. 13.

TIMING CHAIN

V8-332, 352, 361, 390, 410

1. To remove the chain, first take off the front cover as outlined previously.
2. Crank engine until timing mark on camshaft sprocket is adjacent to timing mark on crankshaft sprocket, Fig. 14.
3. Remove camshaft sprocket cap screw and fuel pump eccentric.
4. Slide both sprockets and chain forward and remove as an assembly.
5. Reverse foregoing procedure to install the chain, being sure to align the timing marks as shown.

V8-272, 292, 312

To remove the chain and sprockets, take off radiator, fan blades and hub, timing chain cover and oil pan. Remove camshaft sprocket capscrew and lockwasher. Remove fuel pump eccentric and counterweight from camshaft.

Crank the engine until timing marks on the sprockets and chain are positioned as shown in Fig. 15. Slide both sprockets and chain forward and remove them.

To install, position the chain and camshaft sprocket on the camshaft. Be sure the timing marks are positioned as shown in Fig. 15. Install the other parts removed.

1954-55 V8

Remove the front cover, water pump and fan as a unit. Crank the engine until the timing marks on the sprockets are positioned as shown in Fig. 15. Remove the fuel pump eccentric and camshaft sprocket cap screw. Remove the eccentric and counterweight from the camshaft. Slide both sprockets and the chain forward, and remove the camshaft sprocket and chain and a unit.

To install, position the chain and camshaft sprocket on the camshaft. Be sure the timing marks are positioned as shown in Fig. 15. Install the other parts removed.

Six Cylinder Engines

To make the sprocket and chain accessible, remove the radiator, vibration damper and cylinder front cover. Before removing the crankshaft sprocket, align the timing marks as shown in Fig. 16. Remove the camshaft sprocket retaining

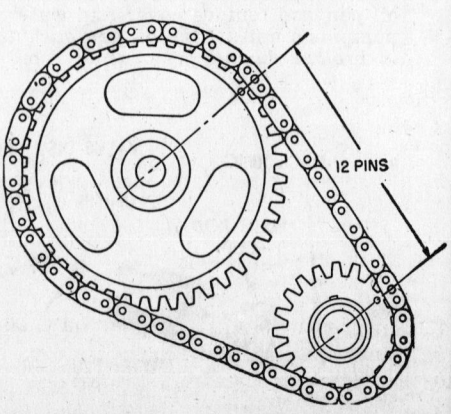

Fig. 16 Valve timing. Six cylinder

bolt and washer. Slide the camshaft sprocket, timing chain and crankshaft sprocket forward until the camshaft sprocket comes off the camshaft.

To install, place the chain over the crankshaft sprocket and insert the camshaft sprocket in the chain so the timing marks on both sprockets are aligned as shown in Fig. 16. Align the keyway in the camshaft with the camshaft sprocket keyway and slide the assembly into position.

VALVE TIMING DATA

FORD & T-BIRD

Year	Model	Intake Opens[1]	Intake Closes[2]	Exhaust Opens[3]	Exhaust Closes[4]
1953	Six	23	79	65	33
	V8	21	68	56	11
1954	Six	13	68	55	22
	V8	8	44	47	5
1955	Six	13	68	55	22
	V8	12	54	58	8
1956	Six	24	46	68	2
	V8	12	54	58	8
1957	Six	17	53	61	9
	V8	18	58	66	10
1958	Six	17	53	61	9
	V8-292	18	58	66	10
	V8-332	21	51	67	9
	V8-352	21	51	67	9
1959	Six	17	53	61	9
	V8-292	12	54	58	8
	V8-332	17	57	59	19
	V8-352	22	68	68	22
	V8-430	22	68	68	22
1960	Six	17	53	61	9
	V8-292	12	54	58	8
	V8-352[5]	22	68	68	22
	V8-352[6]	26	64	67	23
	V8-430	22	68	63	27

EDSEL

Year	Model	Intake Opens[1]	Intake Closes[2]	Exhaust Opens[3]	Exhaust Closes[4]
1958	E400 Eng.	17	59	57	19
	E475 Eng.	27	69	69	27
1959	Six	17	53	61	9
	V8-292	12	54	58	8
	V8-332	17	59	57	19
	V8-361	22	68	68	22
1960	Six	17	53	61	9
	V8-292	12	54	58	8
	V8-352	26	64	67	23

[1]—Degrees before top dead center.
[2]—Degrees after bottom dead center.
[3]—Degrees before bottom dead center.
[4]—Degrees after top dead center.
[5]—Two-barrel carburetor.
[6]—Four-barrel carburetor.

CAMSHAFT, REPLACE

1960-61 Ford & Edsel Six

1. Remove timing chain cover and oil pan.
2. On 1961 remove headlamp trim rings.
3. Remove grille.
4. Remove rocker arm assembly.
5. Remove push rods.
6. Remove distributor.
7. Remove push rod cover. Raise valve lifters clear of camshaft lobes and secure them with spring-type clothes pins or window regulator clips.
8. Remove fuel pump.
9. Remove timing chain and sprockets.
10. Remove camshaft thrust plate and spacer.
11. Slide camshaft out of engine.

1960-61 Ford & Edsel V8-292

1. Remove timing chain cover and water pump as an assembly.
2. Remove intake manifold and oil pan.
3. Remove grille.
4. Remove rocker arm assembly.
5. Remove push rods.
6. Remove distributor.
7. Remove timing chain and sprockets.
8. Raise valve lifters clear of camshaft lobes and secure them with spring-type clothes pins or window regulator clips.
9. Remove camshaft thrust plate and spacer.
10. Slide camshaft out of engine.

1960-61 Ford V8-352, 390

1. Remove timing chain cover, chain, sprockets and intake manifold.
2. Remove grille and distributor.
3. Remove rocker arm assembly.
4. Remove push rods.
5. Position an inspection light through push rod opening and into valve push rod valley. Remove valve lifters with a magnet through push rod openings. *It may be necessary in some cases to transfer the lifter over to an adjoining push rod opening in order to remove it.*
6. Remove oil pan.
7. Slide camshaft out of engine.

1958-60 Edsel V8 (Exc. 292)

1. Remove timing chain cover, chain and sprockets.
2. Remove intake manifold.
3. Remove push rod cover.
4. Remove valve lifters.
5. On 1958 with 410 engine remove vertical mesh grille.
6. Slide camshaft out of engine.

1959-60 V8-352 T-Bird

1. Remove radiator, radiator supply tank and hood.
2. Remove vibration damper, timing case cover, chain and sprockets and intake manifold.
3. Remove hydraulic lifters.
4. Remove camshaft.

1959-60 V8-430 T-Bird

1. Remove hood, radiator, radiator supply tank and grille.
2. Remove vibration damper, timing case cover, chain and camshaft sprocket and oil pan.
3. Remove distributor.
4. Remove rocker arm assemblies and push rods.
5. Remove hydraulic valve lifters with a magnet through the valve push rod holes in cylinder heads.
6. Remove camshaft.

1959-60 V8-332 Ford

1. Remove air cleaner, radiator, water pump, vibration damper, fuel pump and timing case cover.
2. Unfasten power steering pump and lay it on front engine splash shield.
3. Remove camshaft sprocket and chain.

4. Remove coil and distributor.
5. Disconnect transmission linkage.
6. Remove rocker arms and push rods.
7. Remove intake manifold and carburetor.
8. Remove baffle from push rod chamber and lift hydraulic lifters from block.
9. Withdraw camshaft from engine.

1958-60 Thunderbird

1. Remove timing chain cover and chain as outlined previously.
2. Remove intake manifold and valve lifters.
3. Remove retaining bolts from top center of grille and three bolts from bottom of grille and push top of grille forward.
4. Remove the camshaft.

1958 V8-332 Ford

1. Drain cooling system and oil pan.
2. Remove intake manifold and carburetor as an assembly.
3. Remove radiator, fuel pump and drive belts.
4. Remove water pump, fan and pulley as an assembly.
5. Remove timing case cover, stabilizer bar, oil pan and oil pump.
6. Crank engine until timing marks are positioned as shown in Fig. 14. Then remove timing chain and sprockets.
7. Remove valve lifters and camshaft.
8. Reverse removal procedure to install.

1958-59 V8-292, 1956-57 V8

1. Drain cooling system and oil pan.
2. Remove intake manifold, carburetor and ignition coil as an assembly.
3. Remove radiator (also grille support on 1956), fuel pump, fan, spacer, pulley, vibration damper, timing case cover, stabilizer bar and oil pan.
4. Crank engine to bring timing marks in position shown in Fig. 15.
5. Remove distributor cap and scribe a line on the distributor housing and cylinder block to mark the position of the rotor and distributor housing for installation. Then remove distributor.
6. Remove timing chain and sprockets.
7. Remove rocker arm assemblies, push rods and push rod chamber cover.
8. Turn camshaft until valve lifters can be lifted with the fingers or with a magnet. Raise lifters clear of camshaft lobes and hold them up with spring-type clothes pins.
9. Carefully remove camshaft by pulling it forward out of engine.
10. Reverse removal procedure to install.

1956-59 Six

1. Drain cooling system and oil pan.
2. Remove radiator and grille (also grille support bar on 1956-57).
3. Remove fan, belt(s), pulley, vibration damper and water pump.
4. Remove oil level dipstick, crankcase ventilation tube, stabilizer bar on 1957-59, flywheel housing inspection cover and oil pan.
5. Remove rocker arms and push rods.

6. Remove distributor cap.
7. Remove push rod cover.
8. Remove fuel pump. Crank engine to line up timing marks as shown in Fig. 16.
9. Scribe a line on distributor housing and cylinder block to mark position of rotor and distributor housing for installation. Then remove distributor.
10. Remove timing chain and sprockets.
11. Turn camshaft until valve lifters can be raised and secured with spring-type clothes pins.
12. Slide camshaft out of engine.
13. Reverse removal procedure to install.

1954-55 V8

1. Remove radiator, radiator grille, crankshaft pulley, fuel pump, water pump and fan blade assembly and timing case cover.
2. Remove intake manifold, carburetor and ignition coil as a unit.
3. Remove rocker arm assemblies and push rods.
4. Crank engine until timing marks on sprockets are aligned as shown in Fig. 15 depending upon the type of chain used.
5. Remove distributor cap and scribe a line on the distributor housing and cylinder block to mark the position of the rotor and distributor housing. Then remove distributor.
6. Remove camshaft sprocket and timing chain.
7. Remove camshaft thrust plate, key and spacer ring.
8. Use a magnetic lifter to lift the tappets and install clothes pins or other suitable holders to keep the tappets up.
9. Carefully remove the camshaft by pulling it toward the front of the engine.
10. Reverse the foregoing procedure to install the camshaft.

1953 V8

After the valves and lifters have been removed from the engine, insert a screw-

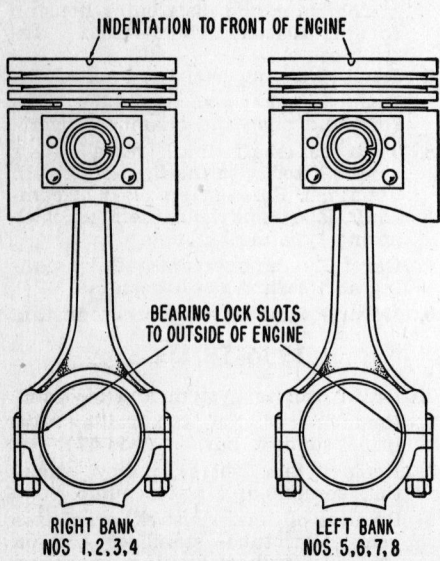

INDENTATION TO FRONT OF ENGINE

BEARING LOCK SLOTS TO OUTSIDE OF ENGINE

RIGHT BANK NOS 1,2,3,4

LEFT BANK NOS 5,6,7,8

Fig. 17 Piston and rod assembly. All V8's

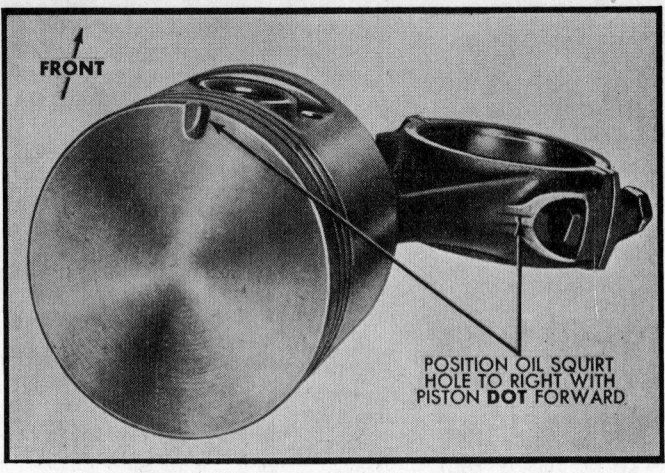

FRONT

POSITION OIL SQUIRT HOLE TO RIGHT WITH PISTON **DOT** FORWARD

Fig. 18 Correct assembly of piston and rod. Six cylinder

driver behind the camshaft gear to start the shaft forward. Then pull out the shaft, using great care not to allow the cam lobes to damage the camshaft bearings as the shaft is being withdrawn.

If it is desired to remove the camshaft without taking off the cylinder heads, remove the valve chamber covers and oil baffles. Then use a bar type valve lifter to pull down the valve spring in order to remove the valve guide retainer. Raise the valve assembly enough so that the opening in the side of the valve lifter is across the boss in the valve chamber. Raise all the lifters in this manner and insert the valve guide retainers in these openings. With the lifters held up in this manner, the camshaft may be withdrawn.

1953-55 Six

To remove the camshaft, take off the radiator. (On 1953-54 remove the grille.) Remove the crankshaft damper and timing case cover. Remove the rocker arm cover and valve push rod covers. Lift the tappets and hold them up with clothes pins or rubber bands.

Note—If the engine is removed from the vehicle and mounted on a work stand, position it front end up and pull the tappets away from the camshaft to facilitate camshaft removal. Be sure the oil pan is either drained or removed before inverting engine.

Take off the distributor, fuel pump, camshaft sprocket and timing chain. Remove the screws retaining the camshaft thrust plate and take off the plate. Then carefully pull the camshaft out of the engine.

CAMSHAFT BEARINGS

All Except 1953 V8

When necessary to replace camshaft bearings, the engine will have to be removed from the vehicle and the plug at the rear of the cylinder block will have to be removed in order to utilize the special camshaft bearing removing and installing tools required to do this job. If properly installed, camshaft bearings

require no reaming—nor should this type bearing be reamed or altered in any manner in an attempt to fit bearings.

1953 V8

The camshaft in these engines are supported on three split sleeve bearings and are replaced in the same manner suggested for 1954 engines.

PISTONS & RODS, REMOVE

After removing the cylinder heads and oil pan, use a ridge reamer to remove any ridge that may have formed on the cylinder wall at the top of the piston ring travel. Cutting the ridge before the piston is removed will avoid damaging rings or cracking ring lands of pistons during removal.

Remove the connecting rod cap and push the piston and rod out through the top of the bore. Use care to prevent the rod from nicking crankshaft journals. Identify the connecting rods (original rods are marked) when removing them so they may be installed in their original cylinder.

PISTON & ROD, ASSEMBLE

All V8's

Assemble the pistons to the rods as shown in Fig. 17.

All Sixes

Piston heads are marked for location on the forward side, Fig. 18. Rods and caps are numbered on the same side as the piston they serve.

PISTONS

Pistons are available for service replacement in standard sizes and oversizes of .005", .020", .030", .040" and .060".

If the pistons are to be re-used with new rings, remove the carbon from the ring grooves. A special tool is available

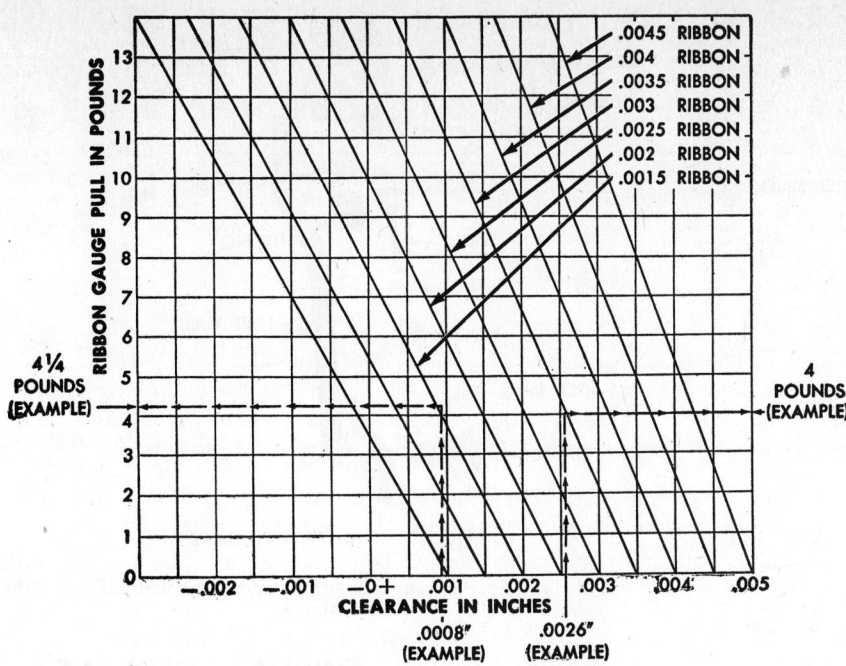

Fig. 19 Piston clearance chart

for this work but a satisfactory job can be done by breaking an old piston ring. File the broken end to a sharp, square edge and use it to scrape out the carbon. Soak the piston in cleaning solvent to loosen any carbon residue. Clean out the loosened carbon, being careful not to cut away any piston material. Clean out the oil return holes with a drill just large enough to fill the holes. Hold the drill in a tap wrench and make sure the drill does not remove any metal from the piston.

Rinse the piston in a clean solvent and wipe off the carbon on the sides of the piston. *Never use a wire brush to clean a piston as the brush will round off the edges of the ring lands.* Pistons showing scuffed or scored skirts should be discarded for new ones. Examine the ring lands carefully for cracks. If in the least bit doubtful, the piston should be scrapped.

New pistons should be fitted according to the recommendations given in Fig. 19.

PISTON PINS

All V8's (Except 430)

It is recommended procedure to replace piston pins whenever new rings are installed. Pins that have been relatively quiet when the old rings were in service may be noisy after new rings are installed.

Use a suitable reamer to ream the piston for oversize pins. The pins are retained by snap rings, one located at each end of the pin. When installing the retainers, make sure each one enters the groove in the piston pin boss.

T-Bird V8-430 Engine

Piston pins in these engines are a pressed fit in the piston, no snap rings being used to retain the pin in the piston.

Pistons and pins are furnished by Ford only as an assembly.

PISTON RINGS

New rings should be assembled on the piston according to the instructions furnished by the ring manufacturer. Always use standard size rings in cylinder bores that are *standard at the bottom, regardless of the amount of cylinder wear.*

When new rings are installed without reboring cylinders the glazed cylinder walls should be slightly dulled, but without increasing the bore diameter. This is done with a "Glaze-buster" or with a hone equipped with the finest grade of stones.

New rings must be checked for clearance in piston grooves and for gap in cylinder bores. Cylinder bores and piston grooves must be clean, dry and free of carbon and burrs.

Check the clearance of each ring in its piston groove by installing the ring and then inserting feeler gauges *under* the ring. Any wear that occurs in the piston groove forms a step or ridge at the inner portion of the lower land. If gauges are inserted above the ring, the ring may rest on the step instead of on the worn portion of the lower land, and a false

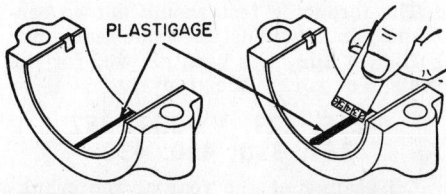

PLASTIGAGE IN PLACE BEFORE BEARING CAP IS TORQUED

PLASTIGAGE AFTER BEARING CAP IS REMOVED

Fig. 20 Checking bearing clearance with Plastigage

measurement of clearance will result.

If the piston grooves are worn to the extent that relatively high steps or ridges exist on the lower lands, the piston should be replaced because the steps will interfere with the operation of the new rings and the ring clearances will be excessive. Piston rings are not furnished in oversize widths to compensate for ring groove wear.

To check the end gap of rings, place the ring in the cylinder in which it will be used. Square it in the bore by tapping with the lower end of the piston. Then measure the gap with feeler gauges. If necessary to increase the gap, file the ends of the rings carefully with a smooth file.

ROD BEARINGS

These bearings are of the insert type, selectively fitted, and available for service replacement in standard and undersizes for use on crankshaft journals that have been reground.

If inspection reveals badly worn or scored bearings, they should be replaced. Bearings may be removed by simply taking off the bearing caps and slipping the old ones out and the new ones in. The installation of new bearings must be closely checked to maintain the proper clearance between the crankshaft and bearing surface. A convenient and accurate method for checking bearing clearance is with the use of Plastigage, which is available at any auto parts jobber.

Place the string-like plastic material so it extends the full width of the bearing, Fig. 20. Install the bearing and cap and tighten the nuts to the recommended torque which is listed in the *Engine Torque Specifications* chart. Then loosen the nuts and carefully remove the cap and bearing. The widest portion of the Plastigage is then measured with the scale on the Plastigage envelope. The graduation on the envelope corresponding to the thickness of the Plastigage gives the bearing clearance in thousandths of an inch.

1959-60 Ford & T-Bird Service Note

A new connecting rod bolt, identified by a small projection at the center of the bolt head, is available to replace an obsolete type used in certain 1959-60 engines. When performing service operations that require removing the connecting rod bolts from one of these engines, all bolts should be checked, and any bolt that does not have the projection should be replaced with the new type.

MAIN BEARINGS

Caution—Main bearing clearance can be checked with Plastigage in the same manner described for rod bearings. If bearings are measured with the engine in the chassis, the crankshaft must be supported in order to take up clearance between the upper bearing insert and crankshaft journal. This can be done by tightening the bearing caps of adjacent bearings with .005" to .015" cardboard, (such as a calling card) between lower bearing

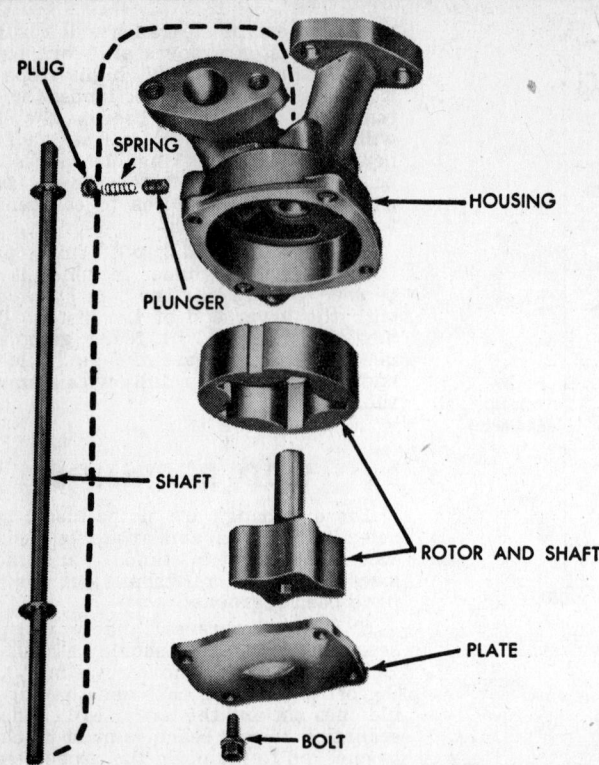

Fig. 22   Rotor type oil pump

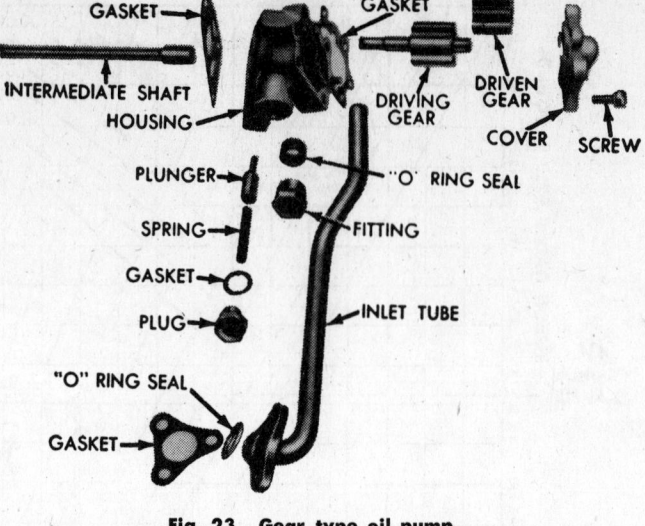

Fig. 23   Gear type oil pump

shell and journal. Use extreme care when this is done to avoid unnecessary strain on the crankshaft or bearings or a false reading may be obtained. Do not rotate crankshaft while Plastigage is installed. *Be sure to remove cardboard.* To install new bearings, proceed as follows:

1. Remove bearing cap and worn lower shell.
2. Rotate crankshaft in normal direction to turn upper bearing shell out of crankcase. Use a cotter pin with a flattened head or the special tool made for the purpose in the crankshaft oil hole to contact the bearing and force it out.
3. Place a new upper shell on the crankshaft journal with the locating notch in the correct position and rotate the shaft to turn the bearing in place.
4. Install the lower bearing shell in the cap.
5. Tighten all cap nuts to the torque valve given in the *Engine Torque Specifications* table.

CRANKSHAFT OIL SEAL

1953 V8

Oil sealing is controlled by a two-piece metal retainer having a groove which returns excess oil to the crankcase. These retainers can be replaced without removing the crankshaft by simply taking off the rear main bearing cap. The upper half of the retainer can be pushed around and taken out through the bottom.

V8-239 (1954), 272, 292, 312

Oil sealing at the rear of the crank-

shaft is obtained by a wick-type seal half in the block and a similar seal fitting into the groove of the seal retainer for the lower half. Seals are also used in the vertical grooves in the sides of the seal retainer.

When necessary to install new seals, press the seal half in the block and seal retainer and cut the ends of the seals flush. Coat the seal retainer-to-block mating surface with sealer, install the retainer and tighten the bolts to a torque of 23-28 ft. lbs.

Dip the retainer side seals in light engine oil, then immediately install them in the grooves. It may be necessary to tap the seals into place for the last ½" of travel. *Do not cut the seal projecting ends, and do not use sealer on the side seals as they are designed to expand when dipped in oil.*

Check the retainer side seals for leaks by squirting a few drops of oil into the parting lines between the retainer and cylinder block from the outside. Blow compressed air against the seals from the inside of the block. If air bubbles appear in the oil, it indicates possible oil leakage.

The foregoing test should *not* be performed on newly installed side seals until sufficient time has been allowed for the seals to expand in the grooves.

6-215, 223, V8-332, 352, 361, 390, 410, 430

Oil sealing at the rear of the crankshaft is obtained by seal halves in the cylinder block and rear bearing cap. Side seals are also used in the vertical grooves in the bearing cap. Install and test seals

in the same manner outlined for other models above.

OIL PAN, REPLACE

1960-61 Ford & Edsel Six

1. Drain crankcase.
2. Remove flywheel housing lower cover and oil level dipstick.
3. On Station Wagons, unfasten stabilizer bar from lower control arm and frame and position the bar as far forward as possible.
4. On engines with vent tube type crankcase ventilation system, remove ventilation tube.
5. Remove oil pan bolts and turn crankshaft as required to gain clearance to remove the pan.
6. After removing the pan, remove oil pump inlet tube and screen.

1960-61 Ford & Edsel V8-292

1. Drain crankcase and disconnect oil pump inlet tube at oil pump.
2. Remove oil pan retaining bolts and drop pan.
3. Remove nut securing inlet tube to oil pan; then remove screen and inlet tube from pan.

1960-61 Ford V8-352, 390

1. Drain oil from crankcase and remove oil level dipstick.
2. Remove flywheel housing lower cover.
3. Unfasten and lower oil pan to frame crossmember.
4. Crank engine to obtain necessary clearance between crankshaft counterweight and rear of oil pan.
5. If oil pump is to be removed, remove retaining bolts and allow pump to fall into oil pan. If pump is not to be removed, loosen pump inlet tube upper bolt and remove lower bolt; then swing inlet tube clear of pan.
6. Remove oil pan by bringing it forward and tilting it down.

1958-60 Edsel V8 (Exc. 292)

1. Crank the engine to place the No. 1 or 5 piston on top dead center.
2. Remove oil level dipstick.
3. Drain crankcase.
4. Remove stabilizer bar.
5. Unfasten front engine mounts and raise engine approximately two inches and block it in this position.
6. Remove oil pan retaining bolts. Then lower pan and allow it to set on the frame crossmember.
7. Reach into the crankcase and remove the two bolts that attach the oil pump screen pickup tube to the pump. Allow the screen and tube assembly to drop into the oil pan.
8. Move oil pan forward and lower it from chassis.

1959-60 V8-430 T-Bird

1. Crank engine until the 14° mark on the vibration damper is aligned with the timing pointer.
2. Drain oil pan.
3. Remove engine right and left front insulators.
4. Remove engine right and left support-to-underbody nuts. Raise engine with a jack and wood block placed under oil pan. Position a one-inch wood block between engine front support brackets and underbody. Remove jack from under oil pan and allow engine to rest on blocks.
5. Unfasten and lower oil pan to underbody crossmember.
6. Remove oil pump inlet tube and screen lower retaining screw and loosen upper screw so that inlet tube can swing freely.
7. Remove oil pan in a lowering forward motion.

1958 T-Bird & 1959-60 V8-352 T-Bird, 1961 T-Bird

1. Drain cooling system and crankcase.
2. Disconnect radiator upper hose.
3. Unfasten and lower oil pan to underbody cross member.
4. Position crankshaft so that counterweight will clear pan and move pan forward.
5. Unfasten and position ignition coil out of the way.
6. Install engine lifting sling.
7. Remove engine front mounting bolts.
8. Raise engine high enough to permit removal of oil pump bolts.
9. Remove oil pan and pump.

1958-60 V8-332, 352 Ford

1. Crank engine to bring No. 1 piston up on TDC to obtain necessary clearance between crankshaft counterweight and rear of oil pan.
2. Remove stabilizer bar (1958).
3. Unfasten oil pan and lower it to frame cross member.
4. Loosen oil pump inlet tube upper bolt and remove lower bolt. Swing inlet tube clear of oil pan. Remove pan by bringing it forward and tilting it down.

1957 V8 Ford & 1958-59 Ford & Edsel V8-292

1. Drain oil from crankcase.
2. On 1958-59 car, remove stabilizer bar.
3. Disconnect oil pump inlet tube at oil pump.
4. Remove screws and oil pan.

1957-59 Ford & Edsel Six

1. Remove oil level dipstick, stabilizer bar and flywheel housing inspection cover.
2. Unfasten and remove oil pan.

1956 V8

1. To remove the pan, drain crankcase and remove oil level indicator.
2. Remove engine front splash pans (except Thunderbird).
3. On Fordomatic cars, remove converter housing cover.
4. Disconnect oil inlet tube at oil pump.
5. Remove O-ring seal from pump end of tube.
6. Remove attaching screws and lower pan. *On all cars except Thunderbird, No. 5 piston must be at the top of its cylinder before pan can be removed.*

1954-55 V8

To remove the oil pan, drain the crankcase and remove the front engine splash pans (except on Thunderbird). Take off the oil pump-to-oil pan pipe. On 1954 Fordomatic cars only, remove converter housing dust cover. Turn engine over to bring No. 1 piston up on top dead center. Then remove the attaching bolts and take down the pan.

1953 V8

To remove the pan, remove the two bolts holding the steering idler arm support to the frame, and pull down on the steering linkage. Take off the starter motor. Remove the front flywheel housing cover. This comes straight down after the removal of the necessary nuts and bolts. Remove the oil level indicator tube from the pan, and the bottom section of the road draft tube. Remove the pan attaching screws and lower the pan.

It is not necessary to raise the front end of the engine although the proper combination of standard tools are necessary to reach the two forward screws holding the pan to the block.

1953-54 Six

Drain the crankcase. Remove the front crossmember guard and splash shield. Remove the bolts which attach the engine front supports to the frame. Take out the oil level dipstick. Raise the front end of the engine about 2". Then remove oil pan screws and pan.

Note—The oil pan on early models is retained by slotted head screws. Retainer screw springs must be installed under the head of these screws to provide adequate pressure against the pan flange for a good seal. Tighten the screws until they are snug, then tighten the screws from the center outward in each direction with a large screwdriver.

1956 Six

To remove the oil pan, drain crankcase and remove oil level indicator. Remove engine left and right splash aprons. Remove flywheel housing inspection cover. Remove retaining screws and take down pan.

1955 Six

1. To remove the pan, drain crankcase and remove oil dip stick.
2. Drain cooling system and disconnect upper hose at engine.
3. Remove engine front support bolts.
4. Remove engine steady rest.
5. Raise front of engine about 2".
6. Remove right and left engine front splash aprons.
7. Lower engine on a suitable block.
8. Remove flywheel housing cover.
9. Unfasten and remove oil pan.

OIL & VACUUM PUMP

1959-60 V8-430

A vacuum pump is integral with the oil pump and is used as a booster for windshield wiper operation. If the vacuum section of the pump is damaged replace it with a new unit.

The oil pump is the rotor type and is serviced as described below.

OIL PUMP REPAIRS

Rotor Type Pump, Fig. 22

1. With all parts clean and dry, check the inside of the pump housing and the outer race and rotor for damage or excessive wear.
2. Check the mating surface of the pump cover for wear. If this surface is worn, scored or grooved, replace the cover.
3. Measure the clearance between the outer race and rotor. This clearance should be .006-.009".
4. With the rotor assembly installed in the housing, place a straight edge over the rotor assembly and housing. Measure the clearance between the straight edge and the rotor and outer race. Recommended limits are .001-.0035". *The outer race, shaft and rotor are furnished only as an assembly.*
5. Check the drive shaft-to-housing bearing clearance by measuring the O.D. of the shaft and the I.D. of the housing bearing. The recommended clearance limits are .0015-.0029".
6. Inspect the relief valve spring for a collapsed or worn condition.
7. Check the relief valve piston for scores and free operation in the bore. The specified piston clearance is .0015-.0029".

Gear Type Pump, Fig. 23

After all parts are clean and dry, inspect the pump body and gear teeth for damage or wear. Check the gear end clearance with a dial indicator or Plastigage. The Plastigage method is as follows:

Position the gasket on the housing, then place a strip of Plastigage on the gears and install the cover. Remove the

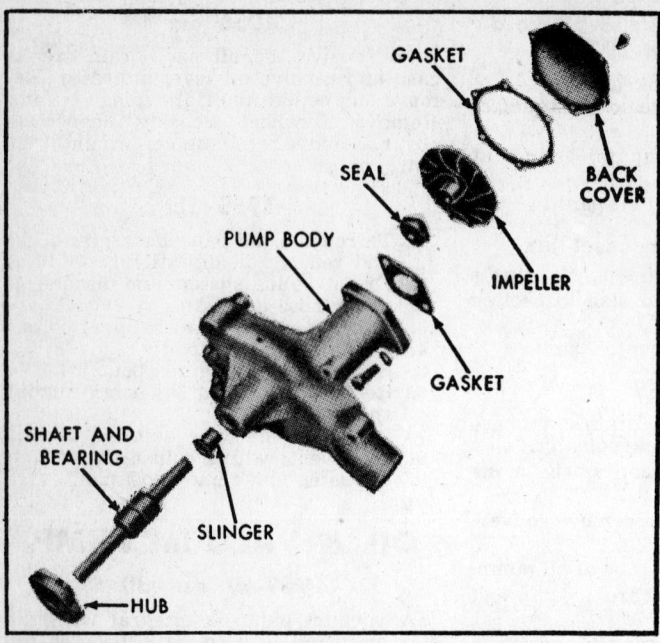

Fig. 24 Water pump. V8-332, 352, 361, 390, 410, 430

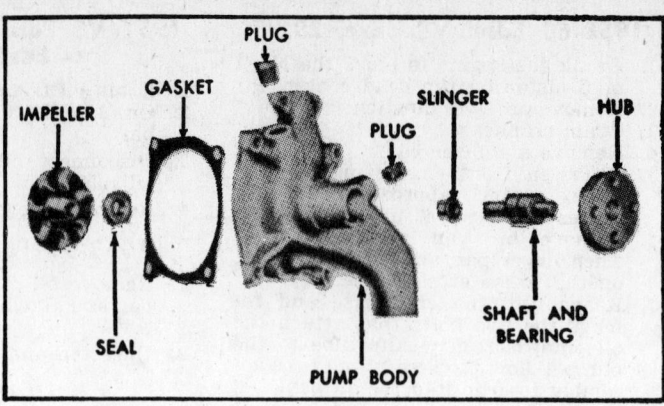

Fig. 25 Water pump. V8-239, 272, 292, 312

cover and check the Plastigage reading. The clearance is .0015-.006".

Check the gears for freedom of rotation. Inspect the relief valve spring for a collapsed or worn condition. Check the relief valve piston for scores and free operation in the bore.

RADIATOR

1960-61 Ford

1. Drain cooling system and disconnect upper and lower hoses at radiator.
2. Disconnect automatic transmission fluid cooler lines at radiator.
3. Remove radiator retaining bolts at upper support and loosen bolts at lower support. Remove fan guard upper retaining bolts.
4. Remove radiator, upper supports and fan guard as an assembly.

1958-61 Thunderbird

1. Disconnect oil cooler lines at radiator (if used).
2. On 1961, remove fan shroud.
3. On 1958-60, remove fan and spacer if equipped, then disconnect upper and lower hoses at radiator.
4. Unfasten radiator support bolts and lift out radiator. The radiator supply tank need not be removed unless necessary.

1958-60 Ford & Edsel

1. Drain cooling system and disconnect upper and lower radiator hoses.
2. On V8 cars with automatic transmission, disconnect oil cooler lines at radiator.
3. Unfasten radiator from its support and remove it from the chassis.
4. When installing the radiator on V8 cars with automatic transmission do not tighten the support bolts until

after the oil cooler lines are connected.

1955-57 Except Thunderbird

To remove the radiator, drain cooling system and remove upper and lower hoses. On 6-cylinder cars, remove radiator support cross bar. On all models, unfasten radiator from its support and lift it out of the vehicle.

1955-57 Thunderbird

To remove the radiator, raise the front of the vehicle and position safety stands. Drain cooling system and remove water hoses. On 1956-57, remove fan lower shroud. Unfasten the radiator from its support and lift it out the radiator and shroud as a unit.

1954

To remove the radiator, drain the cooling system and remove all water hoses. Unfasten the radiator from the support (U-frame) and lift it out.

1953

To remove the radiator, drain the cooling system and remove the hoses from the radiator. Release the strap that secures the generator to the generator bracket. Tilt the generator forward and remove the belt. Remove the two capscrews that secure the fan to the generator, lower the fan and remove the belt. Take the fan off the engine from the left side. Then remove the three screws that secure each side of the radiator to its support and lift out the radiator.

WATER PUMP, REPLACE

1960-61 Ford & Edsel Six

1. Drain cooling system and disconnect hoses at pump.

2. Remove fan, pulley and drive belt.
3. Remove water pump back plate bolt which retains radiator supply tank support bracket and generator bracket.
4. Unfasten and remove pump.

1960-61 Ford & Edsel V8-292, 352, 390

1. Drain cooling system and disconnect hoses from water pump.
2. Remove fan, belt and pulley (also spacer on 292 engine).
3. Remove bolts retaining pump to cylinder front cover (V8-292) or to block.
4. Remove pump from engine.

1958-59 Edsel V8

1. Drain cooling system and disconnect hoses from pump.
2. Remove drive belts, fan and pulley (also spacer on V8-410).
3. Slide front pump hose clamp rearward and remove pump from engine.

1958-61 Thunderbird

Remove fan belt. Disconnect radiator lower hose and heater hose at water pump.

On 352 and 390 engines, loosen fuel pump bolts and slide pump out of bolts one inch for access to the water pump lower left retaining bolt.

Loosen and move generator bracket away from water pump. Then unfasten and remove pump from engine.

1958-59 V8 Ford

Drain cooling system and disconnect radiator lower hose and heater hose at water pump. Remove fan, belt and pulley (also fan spacer on V8-292). Unfasten pump and remove it from the engine.

1954-57 V8

To remove the pump, drain the cooling system and disconnect the lower radiator hose and heater hose. Remove the fan belt, fan, spacer and pulley. Unfasten the pump from the timing case cover and lift out the pump and timing pointer.

On Thunderbirds, it will be necessary to remove the engine left-hand splash shield. Also the generator support brac-

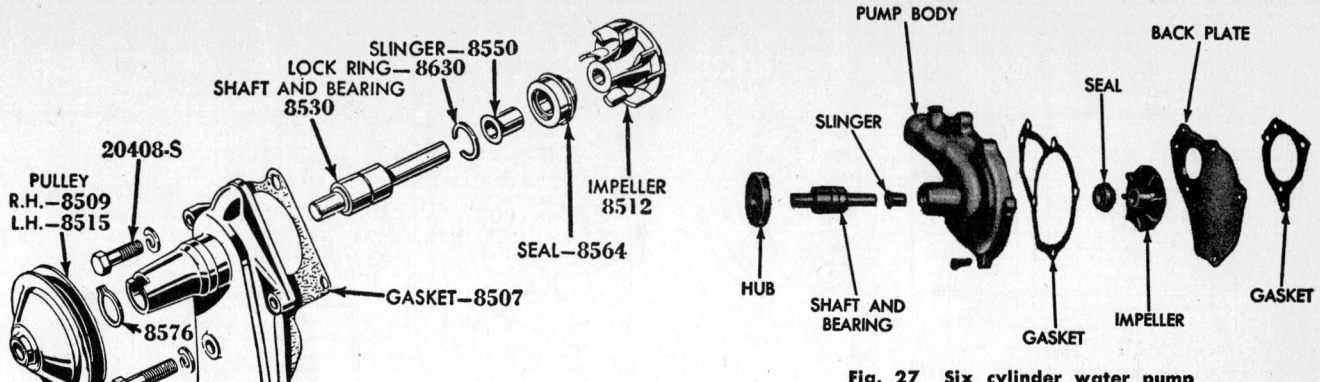

Fig. 26   Water pump.   1953 V8

Fig. 27   Six cylinder water pump

ket must be moved out of the way.

1953 V8

To remove the pump, drain the cooling system and remove the upper hoses. On the right-hand pump, remove the heater hose. Remove the generator belt. On the right-hand pump only, remove the fan belt.

To prevent damage when raising the engine, remove the throttle lever rod from the "Z" bar. Remove the nut that secures each water pump housing to the engine front support brackets. Place a jack under the oil pan until the front engine support studs are clear of the water pump housing. Unfasten the water pump from the cylinder block. And remove the cap screw from the inside of the water pump inlet that secures the water pump housing to the cylinder block.

1953-59 Six

Drain the cooling system and disconnect the lower radiator hose and heater hose. Remove the fan belt and fan. Unfasten the pump from the engine and lift it off.

WATER PUMP REPAIRS

These water pumps, Figs. 24 to 27, are of the sealed type and repair kits are available for making repairs.

To disassemble, remove the snap ring from the groove in front of the pump housing, directly behind the pulley. Remove the pulley and, with a suitable puller, press the shaft out of the impeller. Press the bearing assembly from the pump housing. Press seal and sleeve assembly from pump housing. The snap ring in the center of the housing need not be removed unless damaged.

When assembling the pump, be sure to maintain the clearances listed below between the impeller and pump housing.

1953-59 Six	.020-.030"
1953-59 Ford V8	.030-.040"
1958-59 V8-410	.105-.115"
1958-59 V8-430	.095-.105"
1960 Six	.030-.040"

1960 V8-292	.030-.040"
1960 V8-332, 352, 361	.080-.090"
1961 Six	.015-.025"
1961 V8-292	.025-.035"
1961 V8-352, 390	.070-.080"

DISTRIBUTOR, REPLACE

Removal

1. To remove the distributor, disconnect the primary wire and vacuum control pipe. On some models the work may be made easier if the accelerator pull back spring is disconnected.

2. Remove distributor cap.

3. Scribe a mark on the distributor body indicating the position of the rotor, and scribe another mark on the body and engine block indicating position of distributor body in block. These marks can be used as guides when installing distributor in a correctly timed engine.

4. Remove hold down screw or screws and lift distributor out of block. *Do not crank engine while distributor is removed or the initial timing operation will have to be performed.*

Installation

If the crankshaft has not been disturbed, install the distributor, using the scribed marks previously made on the distributor body and engine block as guides.

If the crankshaft has been rotated while the distributor was removed from the engine, it will be necessary to retime the engine. Crank the engine to bring No. 1 piston on top dead center of its compression stroke. Align the timing mark on the vibration damper or pulley with the timing pointer (see *Tune Up*) chart). Install the distributor so that the rotor points to the No. 1 spark plug wire terminal in the distributor cap, Figs. 28, 29, 30.

Note—On all overhead valve engines, make sure the oil pump intermediate shaft properly engages the distributor shaft. It may be necessary to crank the engine with the starter, after the distributor drive gear is properly engaged, in order to engage the oil pump intermediate shaft.

IGNITION TIMING

All Models

Align the distributor rotor with No. 1 spark plug wire terminal in the distributor cap, when No. 1 piston is on the compression stroke and timing mark on the crankshaft pulley or vibration damper and pointer are aligned (see *Tune Up* chart).

With the timing mark in line with the pointer, the distributor points should just start to open. It may be necessary to rotate the distributor body clockwise slightly and then counter-clockwise until the points just start to open. Tighten the distributor lock plate screw.

Start the engine and check the timing with a timing light.

Using Timing Light

When using a power timing light, *be sure to disconnect the distributor vacuum line before checking timing,* otherwise the timing will be affected due to the fact that the vacuum opening is above the throttle plate.

Connect the timing light high tension lead to the No. 1 spark plug and the other two leads to the proper battery terminals. Clean the dirt from the timing mark and if necessary use white chalk to make the mark more visible.

Start the engine and operate at idle speed. Direct the light on the timing mark. It should flash just as the timing mark lines up with the pointer, indicating correct timing. If the pointer and timing mark does not line up as the light flashes, rotate the distributor as required to bring them in alignment.

STARTER REPLACE

1953-54

1. Disconnect starter cable at starter terminal.

2. On V8's with manual shift transmission, remove starter-to-oil pan attaching bracket screw.

3. On 6-Cylinder and Fordomatic cars, remove flywheel to starter screw.

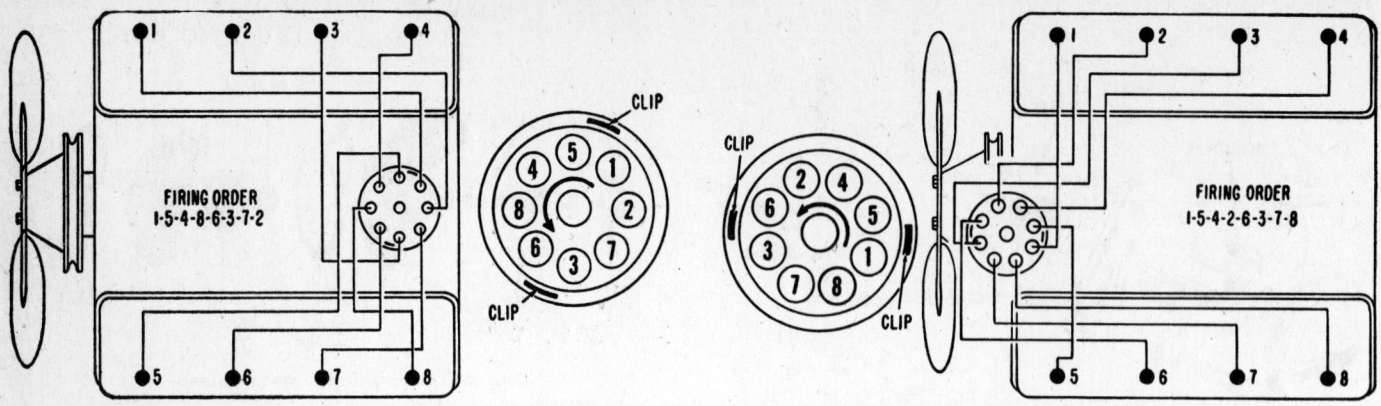

Fig. 29 Ignition details. V8-239 (1954), 272, 292, 312   **Fig. 30 Ignition details. V8-332, 352, 361, 390, 410, 430**

4. On all models, loosen through bolts and lift out starter. *It may be necessary to tilt the starter slightly to clear the starter drive around flywheel.*

5. When removing the starter on 1954 V8's, it may be necessary to drop the steering idler arm bracket in order to facilitate removal of the starter.

1955-61 Ford & T-Bird

Disconnect cable at starter terminal. Remove clutch housing-to-starter screws and remove starter. It may be necessary to tilt the starter slightly to clear the starter drive around the flywheel.

1958-60 Edsel

1. Disconnect battery ground cable.
2. Raise vehicle.
3. Disconnect cable from starter.
4. On some models additional clearance is required to remove starter. If so, unfasten steering idler arm bracket from frame and lower linkage. Unfasten right-hand exhaust pipe from manifold, pry pipe downward until it clears studs, then move pipe to right as far as possible.

5. Unfasten starter from flywheel housing.
6. Move starter forward and downward past steering linkage and exhaust pipe.

MUFFLER & PIPES REPLACE

1953-54 All and 1955-61 Six

Replacing any of the components of the exhaust system is an obvious operation. However, it is advisable to loosen all the attaching bracket clamps to relieve twists in the system; then tighten the clamps.

1955 V8

Replacing the muffler and tailpipe are obvious operations. However, to remove

the exhaust pipe on cars with standard or overdrive transmissions, remove the clutch retracting spring.

On cars with single exhaust system or when replacing the right-hand exhaust pipe on a dual exhaust system, remove the heater inlet duct and motor, starter motor and seal and No. 2 spark plug. On Thunderbirds remove the muffler. Then, on all models, remove the pipe through the bottom of the car.

1956-61 Ford V8 and 1956-57 T-Bird

No difficulty should be experienced in replacing muffler and tailpipe on these cars. When replacing the right exhaust pipe on dual exhaust jobs, it is necessary first to remove the muffler. Upon installation, install the pipe and exhaust gas control valve, then install the muffler.

1958-61 Thunderbird

The right and left exhaust pipe front sections are serviced as one piece. Disconnect and remove the pipe assembly from the exhaust manifolds. On 352 engines, remove the exhaust gas control valve from the right exhaust manifold.

When installing, connect the front and rear exhaust pipe sections. Then on 352 engines position the exhaust gas control valve on the right exhaust manifold, using new gasket. Connect and fasten exhaust pipe sections to manifolds.

1958-60 Edsel

When necessary to replace the right-hand exhaust pipe on cars with the E-400 engine, remove the thermostatic exhaust control valve from right-hand exhaust manifold.

When replacing a muffler and/or tailpipe, jack up the frame to provide clearance at the axle for removal of the tailpipe. When installing a tailpipe, check for possible interference between the tailpipe "kick-up" and floor pan.

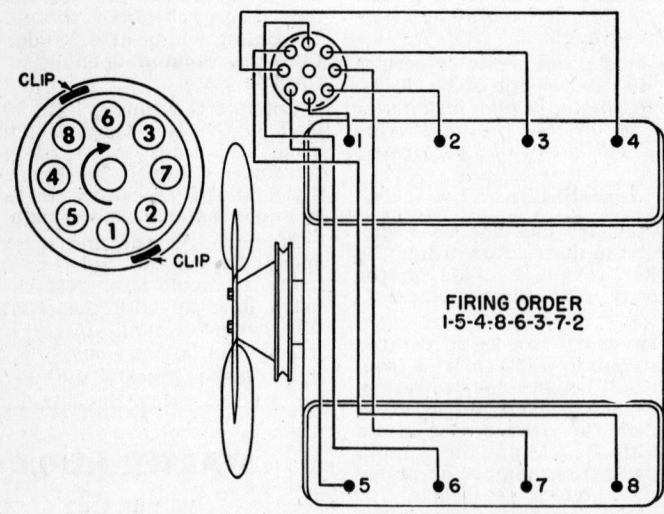

Fig. 28 Ignition details. 1953 V8

Carburetor Section

Performance Complaints

Flooding, stumble on acceleration or other performance complaints are in many instances caused by the presence of dirt, water or other foreign matter in the carburetor. To aid in diagnosing the cause of the complaint, the carburetor should be carefully removed from the engine without draining the fuel from the bowl. The contents of the fuel bowl may then be examined for contamination as the carburetor is disassembled.

Check the fuel in the bowl for contamination by dirt, water, gum or other foreign matter. A magnet moved through the fuel in the bowl will pick up and identify any oxide dust that may have caused intake needle and seat leakage.

Inspect gasketed surfaces between body and air horn. Small nicks or burrs should be smoothed down to eliminate air or fuel leakage. On carburetors having a vacuum piston, be especially particular when inspecting the top surface of the inner wall of the bowl around the vacuum piston passage. A poor seal at this location may contribute to a "cutting-out" on turns complaint.

Fill the carburetor bowl with clean fuel before installing on manifold. This will help prevent dirt trapped in the fuel system from being dislodged by the free flow of fuel as the carburetor is primed. The operation of the floats and intake needle and seats may be checked under pressure if a fuel pump is used at the bench to fill the carburetor bowl. Operate the throttle several times and visually check the discharge from pump jets.

Poor Mileage and Engine Loading Complaints

Cases of poor mileage and engine loading may be due in many instances to sluggish choke valve opening during cold driveaway, caused by insufficient vacuum in choke housing, a plugged or restricted heat pipe or inlet in choke cover. To check for this condition, have engine warm and running at slow idle. Remove choke heat pipe and hold a finger over the heat inlet hole (hole is on choke housing on some carburetors). If there is little or no vacuum pull on the finger, check the choke housing for gasket leaks or plugged vacuum passages. If these are OK, check choke passages in carburetor between choke housing and manifold.

Dirty or Rusty Choke Housing

In cases where it is found that the interior of the choke housing is dirty, gummed or rusty while the carburetor itself is comparatively clean, look for a punctured or eroded manifold heat tube (if one is used).

Manifold Heat Control Valve

An engine equipped with a manifold heat control valve can operate with the valve stuck in either the open or closed position. Because of this, an inoperative valve is frequently overlooked during vehicle lubrication or tune-up.

A valve stuck in the "heat-off" position can result in slow warm up, deposits in combustion chamber, carburetor icing, flat spots during acceleration, low gas mileage and spark plug fouling.

A valve stuck in the "heat-on" position can result in power loss, engine knocking, sticking or burned valves and spark plug burning.

To prevent the possibility of a stuck valve, check and lubricate the valve each time the vehicle is lubricated or tuned-up. Check the operation of the valve manually. To lubricate the valve, place a few drops of penetrating oil on the valve shaft where it passes through the manifold. Move the valve up and down a few times to work in the oil. *Do not use engine oil for this purpose as it will leave a residue which hampers valve operation.*

CARTER CARBURETOR ADJUSTMENTS

Year	Carburetor Model	Idle Adjustments				Float Level		Float Drop		Pump Travel Setting	Choke Unloader Setting	Choke Setting
		Mixture Screws Turns Open	Hot Idle Speed Neutral	Fast Idle Speed	Dashpot Plunger Clearance	Primary	Secondary	Primary	Secondary			
1960	AFB-2292S	$1\frac{1}{2}$-$2\frac{1}{2}$	475	550④	$\frac{7}{16}$⑥	$\frac{3}{16}$①	$\frac{3}{16}$①	$\frac{23}{32}$②	$\frac{23}{32}$②	$\frac{11}{32}$③	$\frac{1}{8}$⑤	Index
1959	AFB-2853S	$1\frac{1}{2}$-$2\frac{1}{2}$	475	550④	$\frac{7}{16}$⑥	$\frac{3}{16}$①	$\frac{3}{16}$①	$\frac{23}{32}$②	$\frac{23}{32}$②	$\frac{17}{32}$③	$\frac{1}{8}$⑤	Index
1958	AFB-2640S-A-C	$\frac{1}{4}$-$1\frac{3}{4}$	500	650④	$\frac{7}{16}$⑥	$\frac{5}{16}$①	$\frac{5}{16}$①	$\frac{23}{32}$②	$\frac{23}{32}$②	$\frac{15}{32}$③	.067⑤	2 Lean
1957	AFB-2441S	$\frac{1}{2}$-$1\frac{1}{2}$	475	1900⑦	$\frac{7}{16}$⑥	$\frac{5}{32}$①	$\frac{5}{32}$①	$\frac{23}{32}$②	$\frac{23}{32}$②	$\frac{15}{32}$③	.067⑤	1 Rich

CARTER NOTES

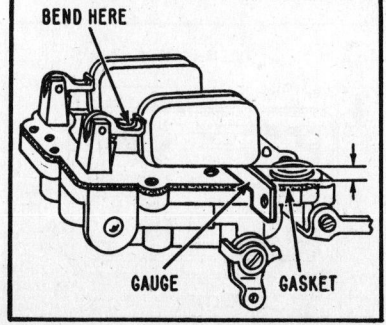

Fig. ①—AFB float level. Adjust by bending float lever.

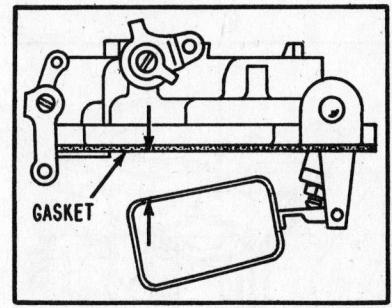

Fig. ②—AFB float drop. Adjust by bending stop tabs on float brackets.

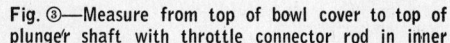

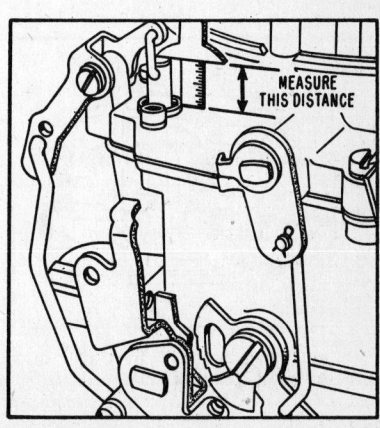

hole of pump arm. Adjust by bending throttle connector rod.

Fig. ③—Measure from top of bowl cover to top of plunger shaft with throttle connector rod in inner

CARTER NOTES
continued

④—With engine at normal operating temperature, turn fast idle screw against lowest step of fast idle cam until specified rpm is obtained.

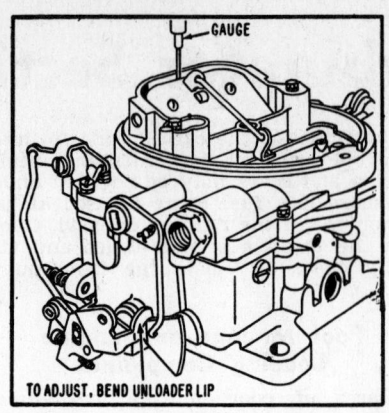

TO ADJUST, BEND UNLOADER LIP

Fig. ⑧—With throttle wide open, clearance between upper edge of choke valve and inner wall of air horn should be as specified. Adjust by bending unloader lip on throttle lever.

⑥—With primary throttle valves wide open, there should be the clearance specified from top of bowl cover to top of dashpot plunger. Adjust by bending stop lug on flat lever.

⑦—With engine at normal operating temperature, turn fast idle screw against high step of fast idle cam until the specified rpm is obtained.

HOLLEY CARBURETOR ADJUSTMENTS

Year	Model	Carb. Type	Idle Adjustments					Float Level	Fuel Level	Float Bowl Vent Valve	Pump Override Spring	Choke Unloader	Choke Setting
			Mixture Screws Turns Open	Air Bypass Turns Open	Hot Idle Speed Neutral	Fast Idle Speed	Dashpot Plunger Clearance						
FORD													
1961	Six	1 Bore	1-1½	None	465	None	.075[6]	3/32-7/32[1]	11/16[2]	None	None	None	None
	V8-390	4 Bore	1[23]	1[24]	515	.015[22]	.075[6]	[20]	[21]	.060[25]	.015[26]	3/16[27]	Index
1960	Six	1 Bore	3/4-1¾	None	475	None	.075[6]	3/16-7/32[1]	11/16[2]	None	None	None	None
	V8-352	4 Bore	1[23]	1[24]	515	.015[22]	.075[6]	[20]	[21]	.060[25]	.015[26]	3/16[27]	Index
1959	Six	1 Bore	3/4-1¾	None	475	None	.055[6]	3/16-7/32[1]	11/16[2]	None	None	None	None
	V8	2 Bore	3/4-1¾	None	475	[9]	.045[6]	7/8[3]	[7]	.060[6]	.015[17]	None	1 Rich
1958	Six	1 Bore	3/4-1¾	None	475	None	.055[6]	3/16-7/32[1]	11/16[2]	None	None	None	None
	V8-292	2 Bore	3/4-1¾	None	475	1800[18]	.055[6]	3/4[3]	[10]	1/16[12]	.015[17]	None	Index
	V8-332	2 Bore	3/4-1¾	None	500	1800[18]	.055[6]	3/4[3]	1/2[11]	1/16[12]	.015[17]	None	Index
	V8-352	4 Bore	1-1½	None	500	1800[18]	.055[6]	3/4[3]	[13]	1/16[12]	.015[17]	None	Index
1957	Six	1 Bore	1-1½	None	475	None	.055[6]	5/16[1]	11/16[2]	None	None	None	None
	V8	2 Bore	1-1½	None	475	2250[18]	.005[6]	3/4[3]	1/2[11]	1/16[12]	.015[17]	None	Index
	V8	4 Bore	1-1½	None	475	2250[18]	.055[6]	13/16[3]	[14]	1/16[12]	.015[17]	None	Index
1956	Six	1 Bore	1-1½	None	475	None	.055[16]	5/16[1]	11/16[2]	None	None	None	None
	V8	2 Bore	1-1½	None	475	[19]	.055[16]	1½[5]	11/16[15]	None	None	None	Index
1955-56	V8	4 Bore	1-1½	None	475	[19]	.055[16]	1/4[4]	1/2[15]	None	None	None	Index
1953-55	Six	1 Bore	1-1½	None	475	[19]	.055[16]	5/16[1]	11/16[2]	None	None	None	None
	V8	2 Bore	1-1½	None	475	[19]	.055[16]	9/32[5]	5/8[15]	None	None	None	Index

HOLLEY NOTES

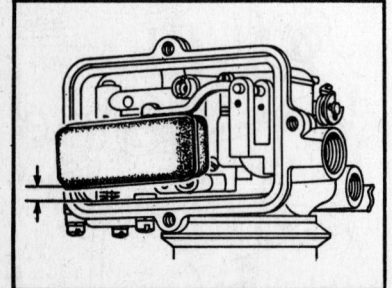

Fig. ①—Float level measured from roof of float chamber to lowest point of float with carburetor inverted.

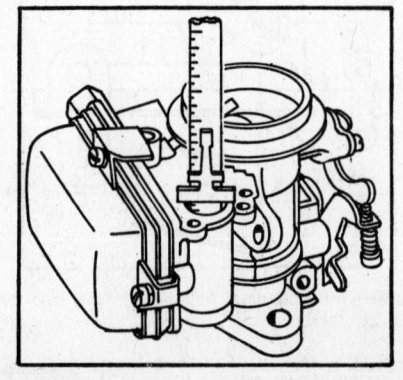

Fig. ②—Fuel level measured from power valve mounting surface.

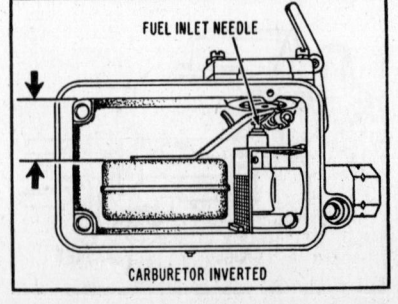

FUEL INLET NEEDLE

CARBURETOR INVERTED

Fig. ③—Float level measured from floor of fuel bowl to bottom of float with fuel bowl inverted.

HOLLEY NOTES
continued

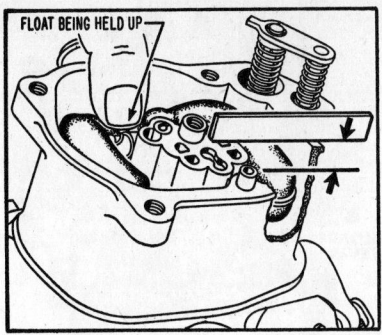

Fig. ④—Float level measured from machined surface of main body to top of free end of float with float in uppermost position.

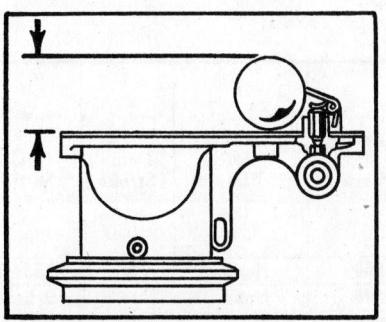

Fig. ⑤—Float level measured from air horn gasket to bottom of float with air horn inverted.

⑥—With engine running at hot idle speed, loosen dashpot screw. Hold throttle closed and depress dashpot plunger fully. Turn dashpot in its bracket as required to obtain the specified clearance between plunger and accelerator lever.

⑦—Stop engine after having been warmed up to operating temperature. Then remove sight plug. Fuel within bowl should be at lower edge of sight plug hole. Adjust by loosening lock screw on top of fuel bowl just enough to allow rotation of nut. Adjust as required and tighten screw.

⑧—Bend vent rod at angle as required to obtain specified clearance between vent button and machined surface of fuel bowl with throttle in hot idle position.

⑨—With hot idle speed properly adjusted, turn fast idle screw in until it just touches lowest step on fast idle cam; then back off one turn.

⑩—With engine stopped, fuel within bowl should be at lower edge of sight plug hole. Raise or lower float as required to obtain proper fuel level (see ③).

⑪—Below centerline of main discharge nozzle.

⑫—With throttle plates closed, clearance between vent button and top of fuel bowl should be as specified. Adjust by bending horizontal arm on accelerating pump operating lever.

⑬—With engine running at normal operating temperature, fuel level is correct if fuel just dribbles out of both sight plug holes. If not, adjust both floats.

⑭—Measured from bowl cover upper screw. Primary ½", secondary ⅝".

⑮—Below machined surface of float bowl.

⑯—With throttle fully closed, hold dashpot plunger in to the limit of its travel. Then turn adjusting screw as required to obtain the specified clearance between screw and plunger.

⑰—With throttle plates held wide open, there should be the clearance listed between pump arm and hex nut on accelerating lever with pump held fully depressed. To adjust, hold hex nut and turn adjusting screw as required.

⑱—With fast idle screw on highest step of fast idle cam.

⑲—Turn fast idle adjusting screw in until it just touches lowest step on fast idle cam.

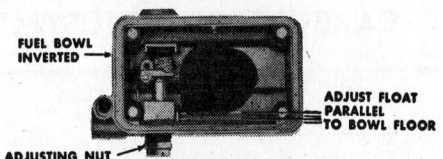

Fig. ⑳—Invert fuel bowl. Then loosen lock screw enough to allow adjusting nut to rotate. Turn adjusting nut until base of float is parallel with floor of bowl. Adjust both floats in same manner.

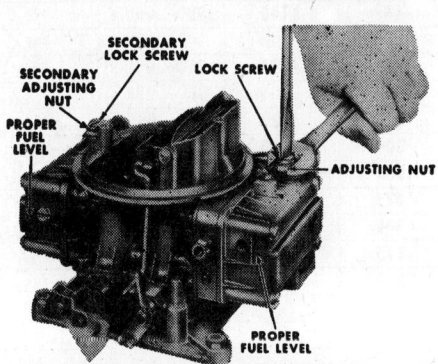

Fig. ㉑—With engine idling, turn adjusting nut as required until fuel just dribbles out of sight plug hole. Adjust both floats in same manner.

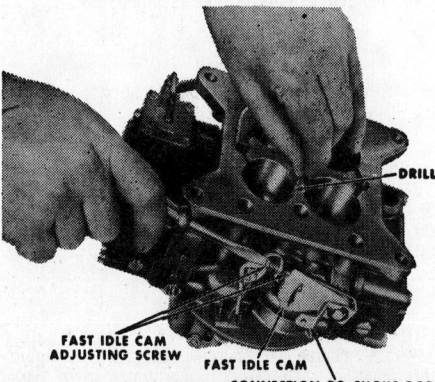

Fig. ㉒—With fast idle screw in contact with high-step of cam, adjust screw to open primary throttle plates the dimension listed (side toward center of carburetor).

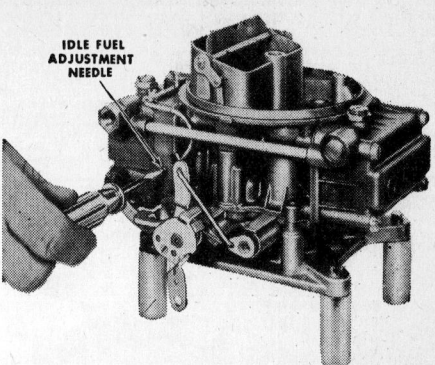

Fig. ㉓—Seat screw lightly and back it off one full turn. Final adjustment is made with engine running at normal operating temperature.

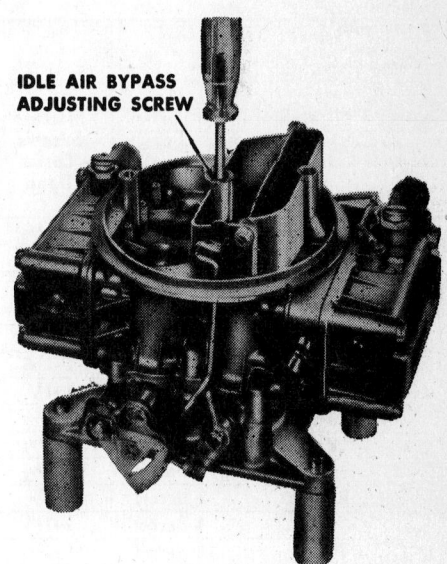

Fig. ㉔—This adjustment eliminates idle instability due to icing. Turn screw in until it seats lightly, then back it off one full turn.

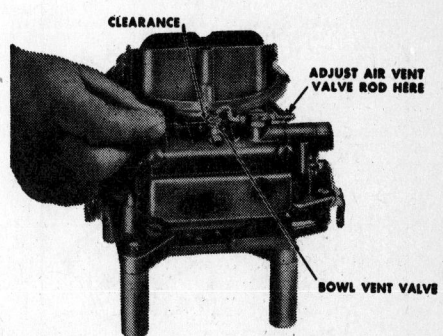

Fig. ㉕—This adjustment is important in high temperature operation. With throttle closed, center of valve should clear bowl by the dimension specified. Adjust by changing the arc in rod near contact with throttle lever.

HOLLEY NOTES
continued

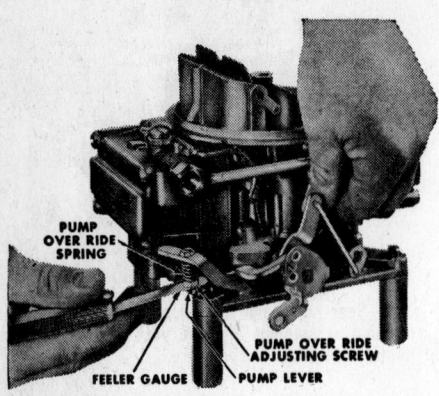

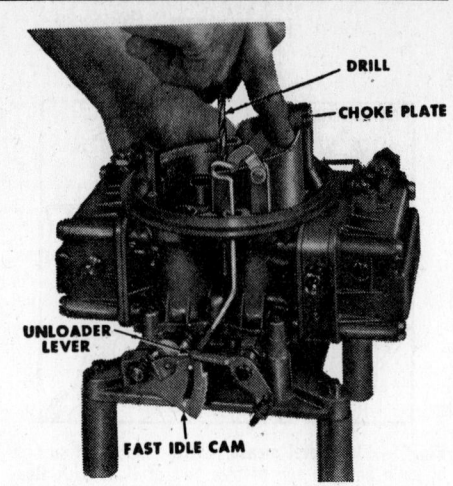

Fig. ㉖—With both throttles held wide open and pump held down, clearance between nut and pump lever should be as specified.

Fig. ㉗—Hold choke plate closed and throttle wide open. Clearance from back of choke plate to back of main body should be as specified. Adjust by bending unloader lever.

FORD CARBURETOR ADJUSTMENTS

Year	Model	Carb. Type	Idle Adjustments				Float Level	Fast Idle Cam	Secondary Throttle Plate	Pump Stroke	Choke Setting
			Mixture Screws Turns Open	Hot Idle Speed In Neutral	Fast Idle Speed	Dashpot Setting					
1961	292 Std. Tr.	2 Barrel	1-1½	515	1500③	None	$29/64$①	.040⑥	None	②	Index
	292 Auto Tr.	2 Barrel	1-1½	465	1700③	.060-.090⑤	$29/64$①	.040⑥	None	②	2 Lean
	352 Std. Tr.	2 Barrel	1-1½	515	1500③	None	$29/64$①	.040⑥	None	②	Index
	352 Auto Tr.	2 Barrel	1-1½	515	1700③	.060-.090⑤	$29/64$①	.040⑥	None	②	2 Lean
	V8-390	4 Barrel	1-1½	515	1700③	.060-.090⑤	$21/32$①	.040⑥	.009⑧	②	2 Lean
1960	V8-292	2 Barrel	1-1½	475	1800③	.060-.090⑤	$7/16$-$15/32$①	.030⑥	None	②	2 Rich
	V8-352	2 Barrel	1-1½	500	1800③	.060-.090⑤	$7/16$-$15/32$①	⑦	None	②	3 Lean
	V8-352	4 Barrel	1-1½	500	1800③	.060-.090⑤	$7/16$-$15/32$①	⑦	.009⑧	②	3 Lean
1959	V8	2 Barrel	1-1½	475	④	.035-.050⑤	$7/16$-$15/32$①	⑦	None	②	Index
	V8	4 Barrel	1-1½	500	④	.035-.050⑤	$7/16$-$15/32$①	⑦	.009⑧	②	Index
1958	V8	2 Barrel	1-1½	475	④	.060-.090⑤	$7/16$-$15/32$①	⑦	None	②	Index
	V8	4 Barrel	1-1½	500	④	.060-.090⑤	$7/16$-$15/32$①	⑦	.005⑧	②	Index
1957	V8	2 Barrel	1-1½	475	④	.045-.064⑤	$9/16$①	⑦	None	②	Index
	V8	4 Barrel	1-1½	475	④	.045-.064⑤	$9/16$①	⑦	.005⑧	②	Index

FORD NOTES

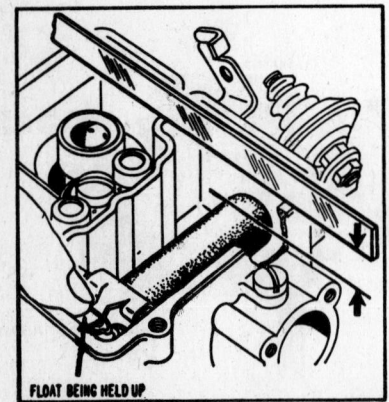

Fig. ①—Float level measured from top surface of main body to top of free end of float with float in uppermost position.

②—Pump lever has four holes and pump link has two holes to control pump stroke. Install pump rod in top hole for winter operation, and second hole from bottom for summer operation. Install pump operating rod in outside hole in pump link.

③—With fast idle screw on high step of fast idle cam.

④—Turn fast idle screw in until it just touches the lowest step on fast idle cam. Then back off ¼ to ½ turn.

⑤—With engine at normal operating temperature and hot idle speed properly adjusted, loosen dashpot locknut. Hold throttle closed and depress plunger. Clearance between throttle lever and plunger should be as listed. To adjust, turn dashpot in its bracket as required.

⑥—Open throttle plates halfway. Hold choke plate closed by means of choke housing shaft. Clearance between cast stop on back of choke housing and edge of fast idle cam should be as listed. To adjust, loosen bellcrank lever screw and turn lever as required to obtain correct clearance.

⑦—With choke plate fully closed, adjust bellcrank lever so that fast idle stop screw seats on next to highest step on fast idle cam.

⑧—Hold secondary throttle plates closed. Turn secondary throttle shaft lever out until the plates stick in throttle bores and there is the clearance listed between screw and throttle lever. Then turn screw in one full turn.

Clutch and Transmission Section

CLUTCH PEDAL, ADJUST

1953-61

A clutch pedal adjustment should be made whenever the clutch does not disengage or engage properly, or when new clutch parts are installed. Both the total travel and the free travel of the pedal should be adjusted.

Measure the total travel of the pedal which should be as follows:

Ford 1953-58	6⅜″ to 6⅝″
Ford 1959-61	6⅝″ to 6⅞″
T-Bird 1955-58	6⅞″ to 7⅛″
T-Bird 1959-60	6⅝″ to 6⅞″
Edsel 1958	6⅜″ to 6⅝″
Edsel 1959-60	6⅝″ to 6⅞″

If the correct dimension does not obtain move the clutch pedal bumper and bracket up or down until the travel is within correct limits. Adjust the assist spring link to give the spring the proper length as follows:

Edsel 1958-60	10 3/32″
Ford 1953-58	6⅝″
Ford 1959-60	9⅞″
Ford 1961	10″
T-Bird 1955-58	6¹³⁄₁₆″
T-Bird 1959-60	9⅞″

After the correct total travel has been established, check the pedal free travel. Depress the clutch pedal by hand, then measure the distance the clutch pedal travels before the clutch begins to disengage. The free travel should be a minimum of one inch.

If an adjustment is necessary, loosen the lock nut on the clutch pedal release rod and turn the adjusting nut. When the adjusting nut is turned clockwise, free travel is increased, and vice versa. Tighten lock nut after adjustment has been made.

1956-61 Service Note

The centrifugal weights in the clutch at high speed will move the release levers closer to the release bearing and reduce the pedal free travel by as much as ¾″. Therefore, it is recommended that the pedal free travel be checked while the engine is running at approximately 3000 rpm. This check can be made while the car is standing and transmission is in neutral. The free pedal travel under these conditions must be at least ½″. Readjust if necessary to obtain at least ½″ free pedal travel with engine running at approximately 3000 rpm.

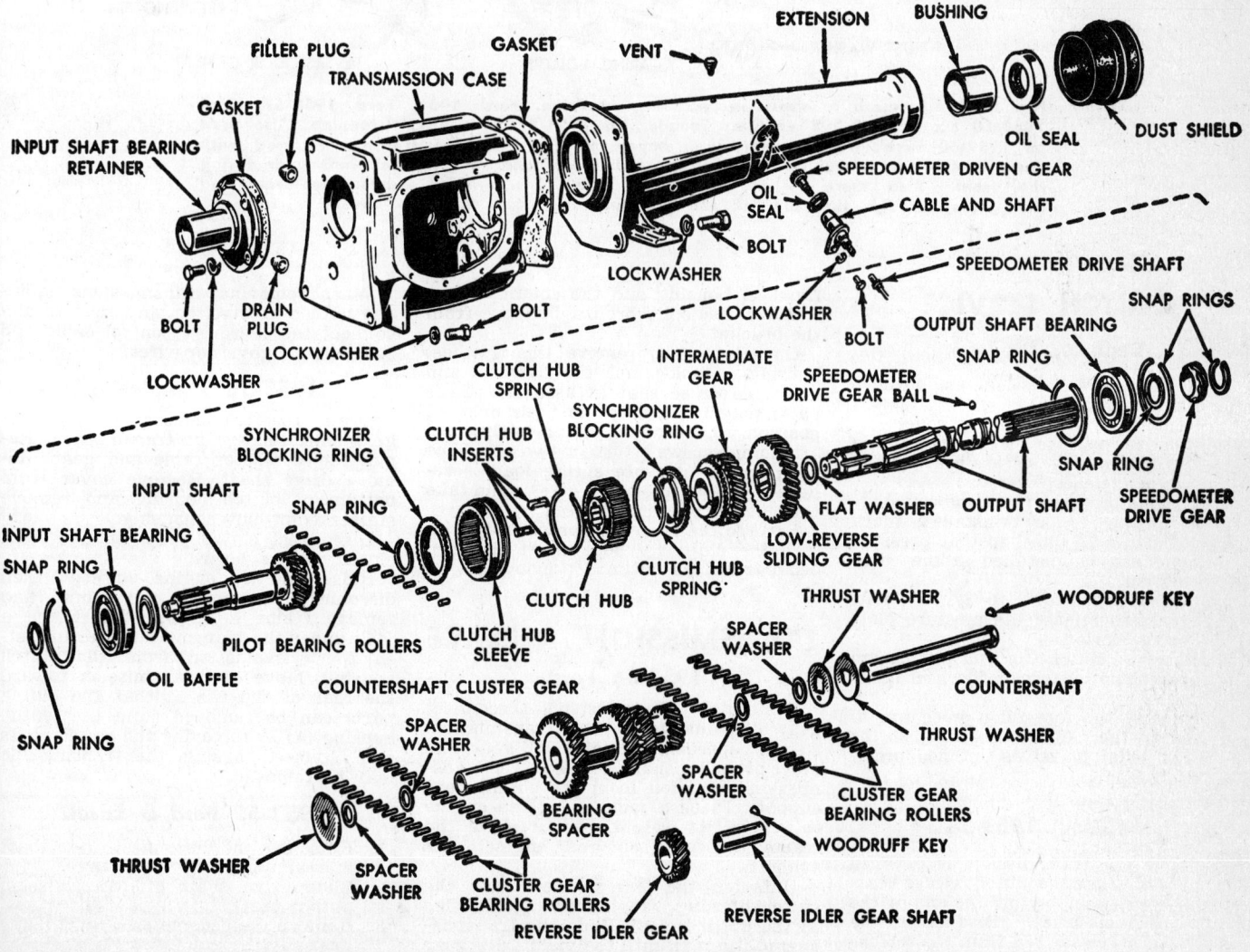

Fig. 1 Synchromesh transmission without overdrive on 1958-60 Ford with 332 and 352 engines, 1956-60 Thunderbird and 1958 Edsel. Also used on 1958 and 1960 Edsel with overdrive.

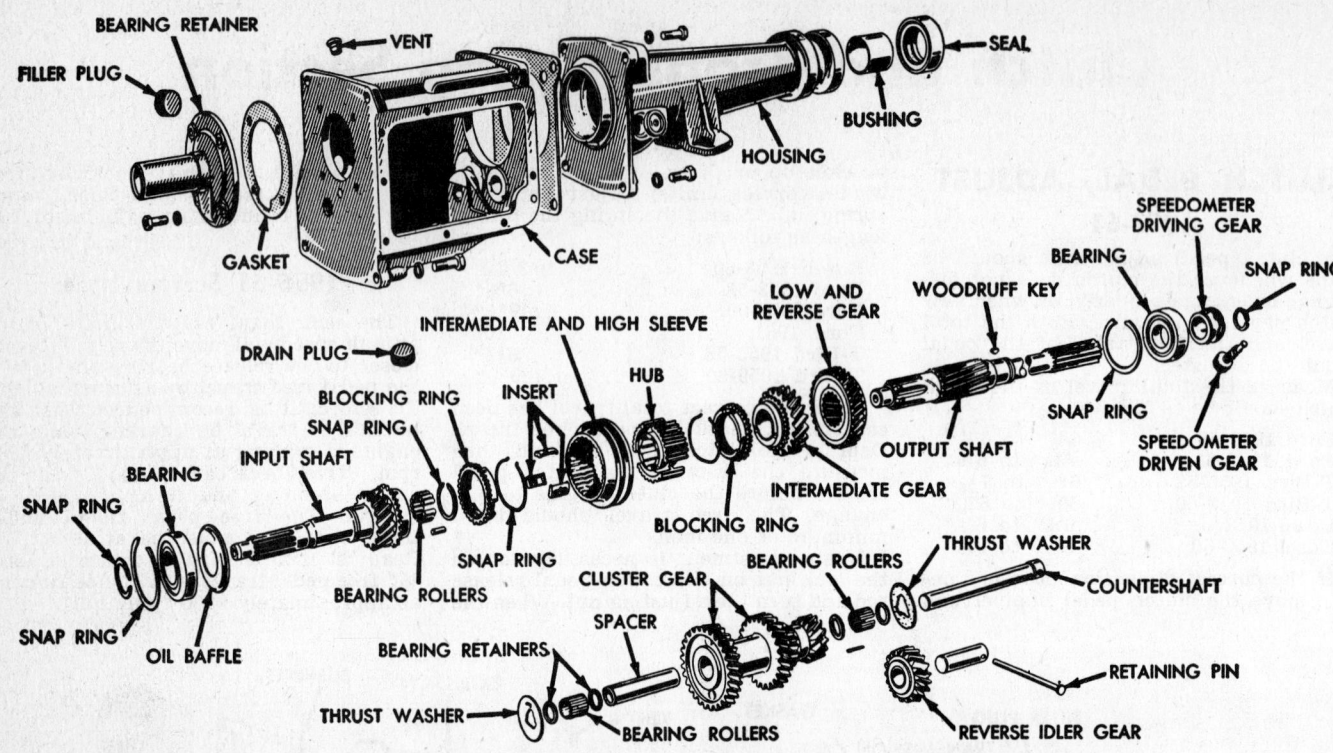

Fig. 2 Synchromesh transmission without overdrive. Ford 1961, Ford 1953-57, Ford 1958-60 Six and V8-292 engines, Thunderbird 1955-57 with V8-292 engine. Also used on 1959-60 Edsel, without overdrive. Important: The overdrive transmission used with these models has the shift fork groove on the low and reverse mainshaft gear facing the front. Also there is no removable side cover, which necessitates removing the gears through the top of the transmission after the top cover is removed

CLUTCH SERVICE

Replace, 1957-61

1. Remove transmission as outlined further on.
2. Remove flywheel housing cover.
3. Remove release lever retracting spring and slide release bearing and hub off release lever.
4. If same pressure plate and cover assembly is to be reinstalled, mark cover and flywheel so that pressure plate can be installed in the same position.
5. Loosen clutch cover-to-flywheel bolts evenly to release the pressure plate spring tension.
6. Remove clutch and disc through opening in bottom of flywheel housing.
7. Reverse the foregoing procedure to install the clutch. Then adjust the free pedal travel as outlined previously.

Replace, 1953-56

Remove the transmission as outlined further on. Slide the clutch release bearing and hub assembly off the end of the clutch release lever. Disconnect the clutch pedal release rod from the release lever assembly.

On 1953-56 models, remove the clutch release equalizer bar bracket from the flywheel housing and the equalizer bar. Remove the split bronze bushing from the bracket.

On all models, remove the flywheel housing. Prick-punch the flywheel and clutch cover so that at assembly these parts may be installed in their original position. Loosen the clutch-to-flywheel attaching screws a turn or two at a time until clutch pressure spring load is relieved. Then remove the screws and take the clutch from the flywheel.

Reverse the foregoing procedure to install the clutch. Then adjust the free pedal travel as outlined previously.

TRANSMISSION, REPLACE

1953-56 Ford

Drain the transmission. Disconnect gearshift linkage at the transmission. Remove speedometer cable and gear. Remove propeller shaft. Unfasten the transmission extension from the engine rear support. Place a jack under the engine to relieve its weight, then remove the frame crossmember and engine rear support.

Unfasten the transmission from the clutch housing. Install two guide pins in the upper holes. Slide the transmission to the rear until the main drive gear clears the clutch housing. Then lower the transmission and pull forward to remove it from the vehicle.

When removing transmissions equipped with overdrive, be sure first to disconnect the overdrive control cable and solenoid and governor wires.

1955-56 Thunderbird

Drain the transmission. Disconnect gear shift linkage at transmission. Remove speedometer cable and gear. Remove drive shaft. Remove cover from bottom of clutch housing and remove starter from clutch housing.

Disconnect clutch pedal linkage from clutch release lever.

Raise rear of engine slightly, then disconnect the engine rear mount and remove frame cross member. Place a jack under the transmission and unfasten the transmission from the clutch housing. Move the transmission toward the rear of the car so that the clutch parts can be removed from the clutch housing. After removing the clutch parts and flywheel housing, the transmission may be removed.

1957-59 Ford & Edsel

1. Raise car and disconnect drive shaft at rear universal joint flange.
2. Slide drive shaft off transmission output shaft.
3. Remove speedometer cable and gear.
4. Disconnect gearshift rods at transmission.
5. Unfasten engine rear support from

transmission extension housing.

6. Disconnect parking brake adjusting rod from equalizer bracket.
7. Raise rear of engine to relieve weight on frame crossmember, then remove crossmember.
8. Lower engine and transmission for clearance, then unfasten transmission from flywheel housing.
9. Install guide pins in the two lower transmission bolt holes.
10. Move transmission back and out of chassis.
11. Reverse foregoing procedure to install transmission.

1957 Thunderbird

1. Raise car and disconnect drive shaft at rear universal joint flange.
2. Slide drive shaft off transmission output shaft.
3. Remove speedometer cable and gear.
4. Disconnect gearshift linkage at transmission.
5. Unfasten engine rear support from extension housing.
6. Raise rear of engine and remove rear support.
7. Lower engine and remove bolts from transmission to flywheel housing.
8. Move transmission toward rear so that clutch pressure plate and cover can be removed.
9. Remove cover from bottom of flywheel housing.
10. Remove starter.
11. Disconnect clutch linkage at release lever, then remove release bearing and hub and clutch assembly.
12. Unfasten flywheel housing from engine block. Turn flywheel housing upside down and remove it from car.
13. Transmission can now be removed from car.
14. Reverse foregoing procedure to install transmission and clutch.

1958-60 Thunderbird

1. Disconnect drive shaft at rear U-joint.
2. Disconnect parking brake adjusting rod and parking brake cables from equalizer.
3. Remove exhaust pipes.
4. Remove two bolts that secure transmission to engine rear support.
5. Jack up transmission enough to take weight off crossmember.
6. Remove crossmember.

7. Disconnect speedometer cable bracket and cable at transmission.
8. Remove gearshift rods from transmission levers.
9. Unfasten transmission from clutch housing and remove.

1960-61 Ford & Edsel

1. Remove drive shaft.
2. Disconnect speedometer cable.
3. Disconnect gearshift rods from transmission levers.
4. Disconnect parking brake cable and support engine with a jack.
5. Unfasten extension housing from rear engine support.
6. Raise rear end of engine and remove engine rear support and frame crossmember as a unit.
7. Support transmission with a jack. Then unfasten transmission from clutch housing and install guide pins in the two lower holes.
8. Move transmission and jack rearward until input shaft clears clutch housing. If necessary, lower engine enough to get clearance for transmission removal. *Do not depress clutch pedal while transmission is removed.*
9. Reverse removal procedure to install transmission.

TRANSMISSION REPAIRS

The following describes the procedure for units without overdrive. For detailed service on the overdrive, consult the *Overdrive* chapter. To disassemble the transmission, see Figs. 1 and 2 and proceed as follows:
1. Remove gearshift housing.
2. Drive out the pin that retains the countershaft and idler gear shaft to the transmission case.
3. Unfasten the extension housing and twist it ¼ turn counterclockwise to permit removal of countershaft.
4. Drive countershaft out the rear of case, using a cluster gear roller retainer shaft tool or a spare countershaft cut to the length of the cluster gear. Leave cluster gear and dummy shaft in case until after main drive gear and mainshaft have been removed. Remove extension and mainshaft assembly from case.
5. Drive reverse idler shaft out of case and lift out reverse idler gear.

6. Unfasten and remove main drive gear bearing retainer.
7. Tap main drive gear out through front of case.
8. To disassemble mainshaft, remove snap ring that holds it to the extension housing. Tap mainshaft out of extension. Remove snap ring from in front of synchronizer and strip mainshaft of all parts.
9. After cleaning and inspecting parts, reassemble transmission by reversing the order of the foregoing procedure.

STD. TRANS. SHIFT LINKAGE, ADJUST

The gearshift rods are adjusted so that with the transmission gears in neutral, the two levers on the steering column are in line with each other. In this position, the shift lever can be moved up or down in neutral without binding.

AUTOMATIC TRANS. LINKAGE MANUAL LINKAGE

1953-54 Ford

Disconnect the upper end of the manual control rod from the selector arm. Position the selector lever so that the indicator on the steering wheel is down *against the stop* in the DR position. Position the transmission manual lever in the DR position (second position from bottom).

On all models except 1954 V8, adjust the rod length so that the pin on the sleeve trunnion freely enter the grommet on the selector arm. Lengthen the rod by turning the sleeve one full turn counterclockwise. Reassemble the rod to the selector arm and lock the sleeve in place with the lock nut. Check the alignment of the pointer for all positions of the selector lever.

On 1954 V8, rotate the manual shift rod clevis until the clevis pin freely enters the grommet in the selector arm. Lengthen the manual shift rod assembly by rotating the clevis two full turns counterclockwise. Install the clevis pin and tighten the lock nut. Check the alignment of the pointer at all positions on the selector dial.

1955-57 Ford

1. With engine shut off, disconnect upper end of manual shift rod from selector lever.
2. Position selector lever so that indicator is down against stop in DR position.
3. Place transmission manual lever in DR detent (second from bottom).
4. Rotate manual shift rod clevis to obtain shortest rod length that will permit clevis pin to enter grommet in selector lever.
5. Turn clevis two additional turns counterclockwise and install clevis pin.

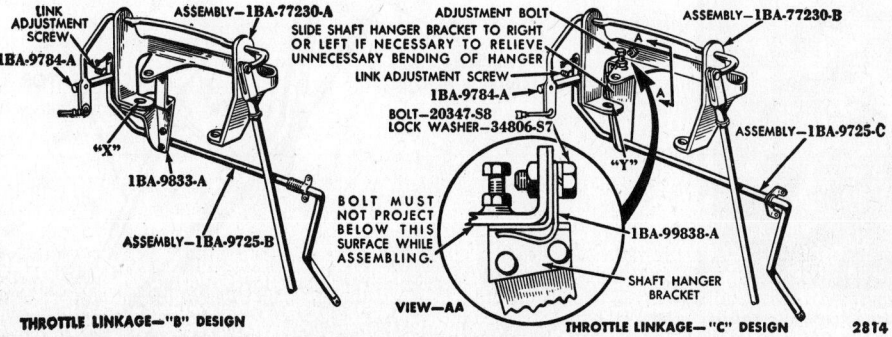

THROTTLE LINKAGE—"B" DESIGN

LINK ADJUSTMENT SCREW
1BA-9784-A
ASSEMBLY-1BA-77230-A
SLIDE SHAFT HANGER BRACKET TO RIGHT OR LEFT IF NECESSARY TO RELIEVE UNNECESSARY BENDING OF HANGER
LINK ADJUSTMENT SCREW
1BA-9784-A
BOLT-20347-S8
LOCK WASHER-34806-S7
ASSEMBLY-1BA-77230-B
"X"
1BA-9833-A
ASSEMBLY-1BA-9725-B
BOLT MUST NOT PROJECT BELOW THIS SURFACE WHILE ASSEMBLING.
VIEW-AA
"Y"
ASSEMBLY-1BA-9725-C
1BA-99838-A
SHAFT HANGER BRACKET
THROTTLE LINKAGE—"C" DESIGN
2814

Fig. 3 Throttle linkage. 1953

6. Lock clevis with lock nut.
7. Check pointer alignment for all positions of selector lever.

1955-57 Thunderbird

1. Disconnect manual shift rod from selector lever.
2. Position selector so that indicator at quadrant is against stop in DR position.
3. Position transmission manual lever in DR position (second from bottom).
4. Adjust length of manual shift rod by turning clevis lock nuts until clevis pin enters selector lever.
5. Turn clevis lock nuts one turn counterclockwise, then install clevis pin.
6. Lock clevis with lock nuts.
7. Check pointer alignment for all positions of selector lever.

1958 Ford

1. Disconnect upper end of manual shift rod and clevis from shift selector lever.
2. Position selector lever so that pointer is down against the steering column stop in the DR (Fordomatic) or D1 (Cruise-O-Matic) position.
3. Shift the manual lever on the transmission to the second detent from the bottom.
4. Rotate the clevis on the manual shift rod until the clevis pin can easily be inserted in the lever insulator.
5. Lock the clevis in place and connect the rod and clevis to the selector lever.
6. Check the pointer alignment for all positions of the selector lever.

1958-60 Thunderbird

1. With engine stopped, disconnect upper end of manual shift rod and clevis from shift selector lever.
2. Position selector lever so that pointer is down against the steering column stop in the D1 position.
3. Shift manual lever on transmission

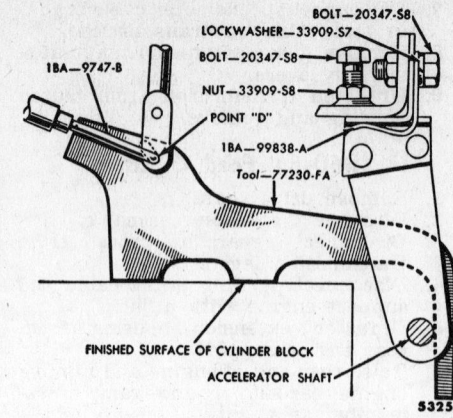

Fig. 4 Throttle linkage adjustment. 1953

to the second position from bottom (D1 detent).
4. Rotate clevis on manual shift rod until it can easily be installed on the selector lever pin.

1959-61 Fordomatic & Mileomatic

1. With engine stopped, loosen clamp at shift lever so that shift rod is free to slide in clamp.
2. Position selector lever in D position against steering column stop.
3. Shift manual lever at transmission into D detent position (second from rear).
4. Tighten clamp on shift rod.
5. Check pointer alignment for all selector lever positions.

1959-61 Cruiseomatic & Dual Power

1. With engine stopped, loosen clamp at shift lever so that shift rod is free to slide in clamp.
2. Position selector lever in D1 position.
3. Shift manual lever at transmission

into second position from rear (D1 detent).
4. Tighten clamp on shift rod.

THROTTLE LINKAGE, ADJUST

1953 Ford

Fig. 3 illustrates the "B" and "C" designs of throttle linkages for these models. To make the adjustment, first check the position of the accelerator-to-carburetor connecting link (9784). This link must be parallel to a line drawn through the centerline of the engine. If the link is not parallel, loosen the lock nut on the link adjusting screw and turn the link as required to position the link correctly. Tighten the lock nut.

After adjusting the engine idle speed and dashpot, place the linkage adjustment tool, Fig. 4, on the end of the carburetor-to-Z-bar rod so the tool rests on the clean finished surface of the cylinder block. Hold the rod at the bottom of the slot in the tool. Then loosen the lock nut on the adjustment bolt, Fig. 3. Turn the bolt until the leg of the tool just touches the accelerator shaft, Fig. 4. Tighten the lock nut to secure the adjustment.

Loosen the lock nut on the carburetor-to-Z-bar rod and turn the barrel of the rod until the idle adjustment screw just touches its stop when the rod is held at the bottom of the tool slot. Tighten the lock nut and remove the tool.

Remove the clevis pin from the upper end of the Z-bar-to-transmission rod and pull upward on the rod to hold the transmission lever against its internal stop. Adjust the clevis until the pin will enter the holes in the clevis and Z-bar. Then lengthen the Z-bar rod 2½ turns and assemble it to the Z-bar with the clevis pin. Tighten lock nut.

If clutch or band slippage occurs at part throttle, lengthen the Z-bar rod adjustment another ½ turn but do not exceed 3½ turns.

If accelerator height is insufficient to

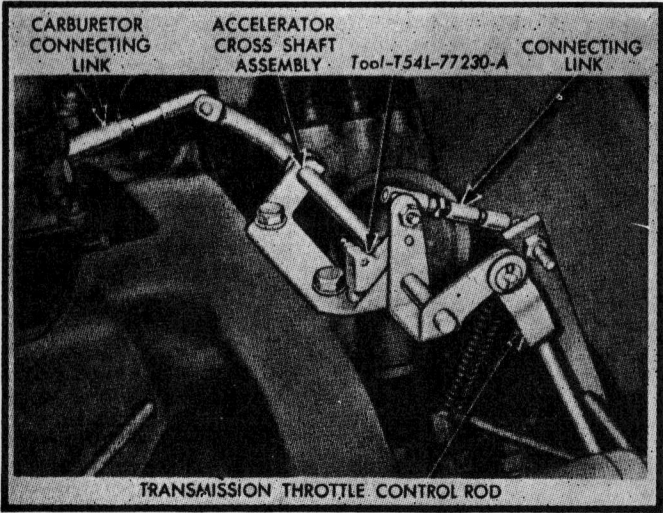

Fig. 5 Throttle linkage adjustment. 1954 V8

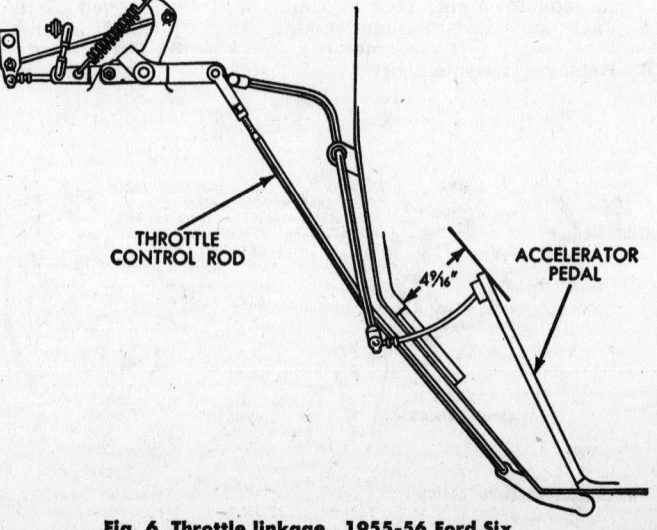

Fig. 6 Throttle linkage. 1955-56 Ford Six

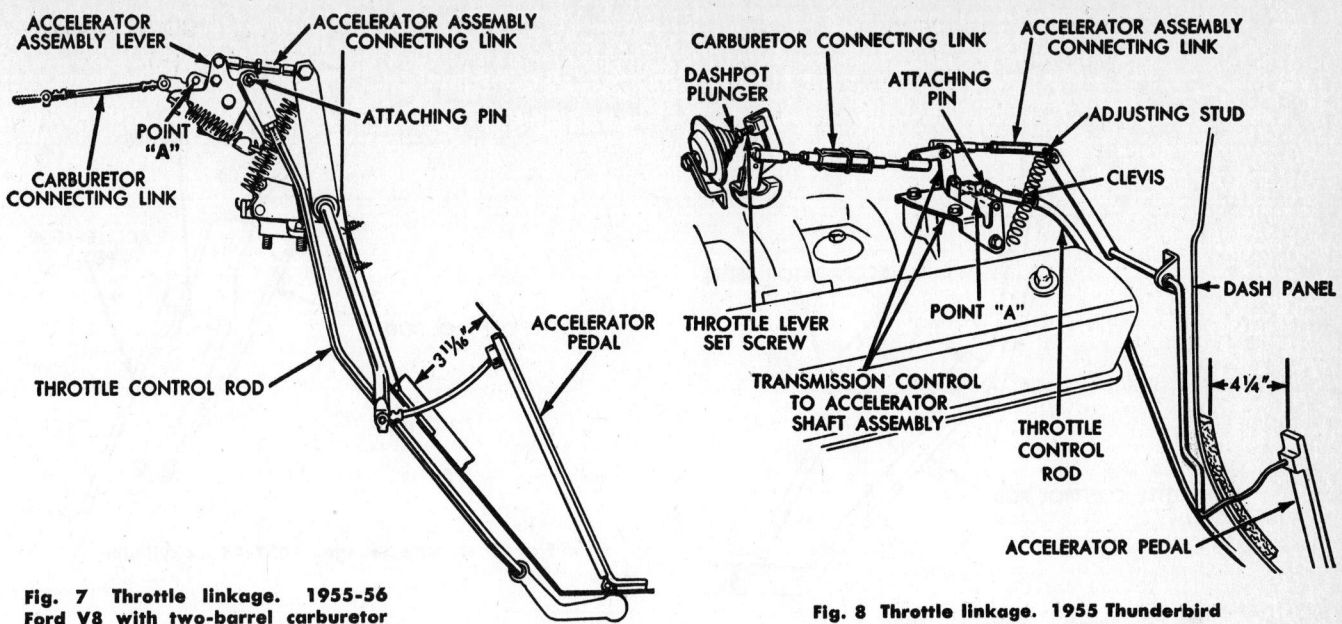

Fig. 7 Throttle linkage. 1955-56 Ford V8 with two-barrel carburetor

Fig. 8 Throttle linkage. 1955 Thunderbird

give kickdown, adjust the carburetor rod length with the rod end positioned at the top of the slot and the tool in the same position as before, Fig. 4.

1954 V8 Ford

To adjust the throttle linkage, first adjust the carburetor idle speed and dashpot as outlined previously and make the adjustment as follows:

Thoroughly clean the flat surface of the accelerator rod mounting bracket. Then position the throttle linkage adjustment tool, Fig. 5. The upper pin of the tool should freely enter the hole in the accelerator cross shaft lever. If not, loosen the lock nut and rotate the connecting link barrel until it does.

Remove the clevis pin from the upper end of the transmission throttle control rod at the accelerator rod lever and pull on the rod to hold the transmission lever against its internal stop. Rotate the clevis until the pin enters the holes in the clevis and lever. Then lengthen the transmission control rod by rotating the clevis 3 turns counterclockwise.

If this adjustment permits clutch or band slippage, increase the length of the rod another ½ turn *but do not exceed 4 turns.*

Adjust the accelerator cross shaft lever connecting link stud until the connecting link is parallel with the flat spring riveted to the mounting bracket on the engine block.

Adjust the length of the link to provide a pedal height of $3\frac{11}{16}$ in. from the toe board to the center of the pedal ball.

1954 Six

To adjust the throttle linkage on these models, remove the clevis pin from the upper end of the transmission control rod. Pull up firmly on the rod to hold the transmission lever against its in-

ternal stop. Adjust the clevis until the pin can freely enter the clevis pin holes and accelerator shaft lever. Then lengthen the rod by 3 turns and install the clevis pin.

1955-56 Six

1. Remove clevis pin from upper end of throttle control rod, Fig. 6.
2. Pull upward firmly but gently on throttle control rod to hold transmission lever against its internal stop.
3. Rotate throttle rod clevis until clevis pin enters clevis and accelerator shaft.
4. Lengthen throttle control rod by rotating clevis 3 turns counterclockwise.
5. Assemble throttle control rod to accelerator shaft.
6. Check throttle linkage and relieve any binding conditions.
7. Road test car. And if band or clutch slippage is evident, increase rod length to 3½ turns but do not exceed 4 turns of the clevis.
8. If band or clutch slippage is not eliminated after 4 turns of the clevis, refer to *Oil Pressure Check* in *Fordomatic Chapter*.
9. Check transmission for kickdown action. If there is no kickdown, disconnect accelerator connecting link from accelerator cross shaft lever. Then adjust accelerator pedal height by turning threaded trunnion on accelerator connecting link until top surface of accelerator pedal is $4\frac{5}{16}$" from floor pan.

1955-56 Ford V8
(2-Bar. Carb.)

1. Disconnect throttle control rod from accelerator assembly, Fig. 7.
2. Insert a ¼" drill rod through holes in "Point A".

3. Adjust length of carburetor connecting link to close the carburetor against its stop.
4. Adjust accelerator assembly connecting link to obtain a pedal height of $3\frac{11}{16}$".
5. Remove ¼" rod and check the alignment at "A". The pin must re-enter freely.
6. With ¼" rod removed, adjust throttle control rod. Pull upward gently but firmly on the rod to hold the transmission against its internal stop.
7. Rotate clevis until its pin freely fits on accelerator assembly lever.
8. Then lengthen throttle control rod by rotating clevis 3 turns counterclockwise.
9. Assemble throttle control rod to accelerator assembly lever, and tighten clevis lock nut.
10. Check throttle linkage and relieve any binding condition.
11. Road test car. If band or clutch slippage is evident, increase length of throttle control rod to 3½ turns but do not exceed 4 turns of clevis.
12. If band or clutch slippage is evident after 4 turns of the clevis, check oil pressure as directed in the *Fordomatic Chapter*.

1955 Thunderbird

1. Disconnect throttle control rod from transmission control-to-accelerator assembly, Fig. 8.
2. Insert a ¼" drill rod at point "A".
3. Adjust length of carburetor connecting link to close carburetor against its stop.
4. Adjust accelerator assembly connecting link to obtain a pedal height of 4¼".
5. Remove ¼" rod and check alignment at point "A". Pin must re-enter holes freely.
6. With ¼" rod removed, pull upward

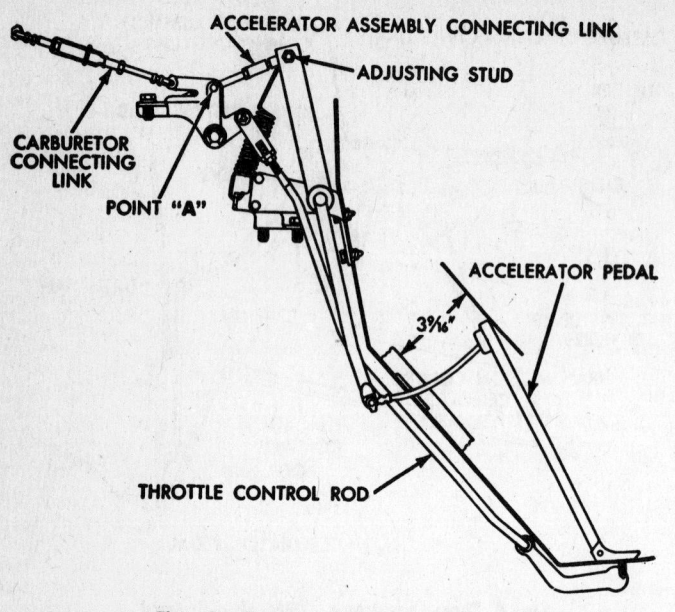

Fig. 9 Throttle linkage. 1955 Ford Special V8 with four-barrel carburetor

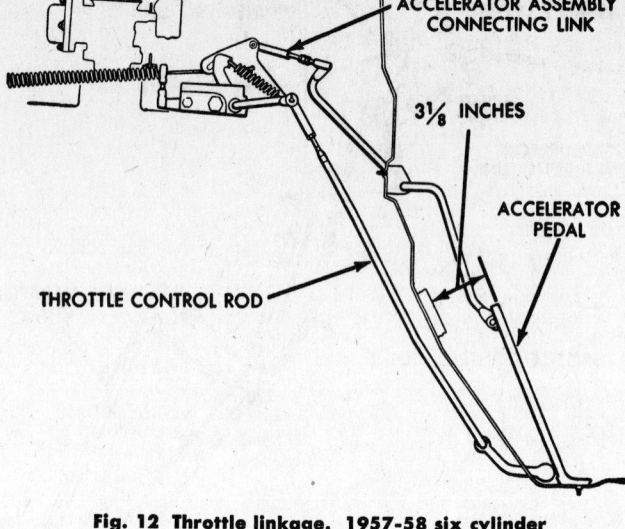

Fig. 12 Throttle linkage. 1957-58 six cylinder

gently but firmly on the rod to hold transmission lever against its internal stop

7. Rotate clevis until its pin fits freely.
8. Then lenghten throttle control rod by rotating clevis 3 turns counterclockwise. Hold clevis in alignment and tighten lock nut.
9. Road test car. And if band or clutch slippage is evident, increase length of rod to 3½ turns (not over 4) of the clevis.
10. If band or clutch slippage is not eliminated at 4 turns of clevis, check oil pressure as outlined in the *Fordomatic Chapter.*

1955 Ford Special V8 With 4-Barrel Carb.

1. Disconnect throttle rod from accelerator assembly, Fig. 9.
2. Insert ¼" drill rod through holes in accelerator assembly and bracket.
3. Adjust length of carburetor connecting link to close carburetor against its stop.
4. Adjust accelerator assembly connecting link to obtain a pedal height of 3 9/16".
5. Remove ¼" rod and check align-

ment; rod must re-enter freely.

6. With ¼" rod removed, pull upward gently but firmly on the rod to hold transmission lever against its internal stop.
7. Rotate clevis until its pin fits freely in accelerator assembly lever.
8. Then lengthen throttle control rod by rotating clevis 3 turns counterclockwise.
9. Assemble throttle rod to accelerator assembly lever with clevis pin.
10. Hold clevis in alignment and tighten lock nut.
11. Check throttle linkage and relieve any binding condition.
12. Road test car. And if band or clutch slippage is evident, increase length of throttle rod to 3½ turns (not over 4) of the clevis.
13. If band or clutch slippage is not eliminated at 4 turns of clevis, check oil pressure as outlined in *Fordomatic Chapter.*

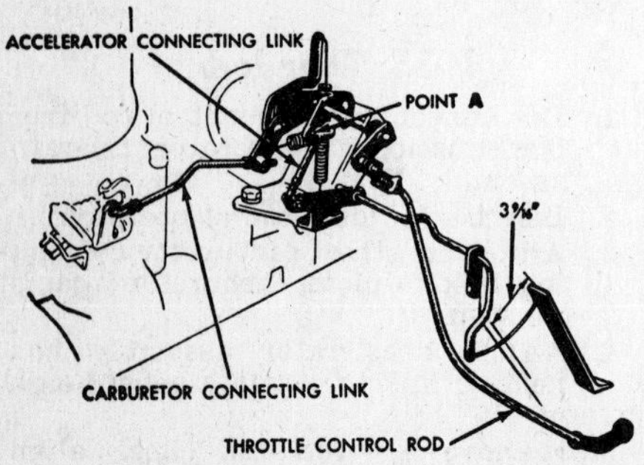

1956 Ford V8 With 4-Barrel Carburetor

1. Disconnect throttle rod from accelerator assembly, Fig. 10.
2. Insert a ¼" drill rod through holes at point "A".
3. Adjust length of carburetor connecting link to close carburetor against its stop.
4. Adjust accelerator assembly connecting link to obtain a pedal height of 3 9/16".
5. Remove ¼" rod and check for alignment at "A". Pin must reenter freely.
6. Remove drill rod and adjust throttle control rod. Pull upward gently but firmly on rod to hold transmission lever against its normal stop.
7. Rotate clevis until it freely fits pin on accelerator lever.
8. Lengthen throttle control rod by ro-

tating clevis three turns counterclockwise.

9. Assemble throttle rod to accelerator lever. Hold clevis in alignment to prevent binding and tighten lock nut.
10. Check throttle linkage and relieve any binding condition.
11. Road test car. If band or clutch slippage is evident, increase length of throttle rod to 3½ turns but not over four turns of clevis. If band or clutch slippage is still not eliminated, make an oil pressure check.

1956 Thunderbird

Fig. 11 illustrates the linkage used on 1956 Thunderbird. The adjustment procedures are the same as the other 8-cylinder engines with 4-barrel carburetor except for pedal height, which should be 4¼".

1957-58 Six-Cylinder

1. Remove clevis from upper end of throttle control rod. Pull throttle control rod upward to hold throttle lever against main control stop.
2. Turn clevis until its pin will enter hole in throttle lever. Then lengthen rod 2½ turns.
3. Connect throttle rod to accelerator shaft and secure it with cotter pin temporarily.

Fig. 10 Throttle linkage. 1956 Ford V8 with four-barrel carburetor

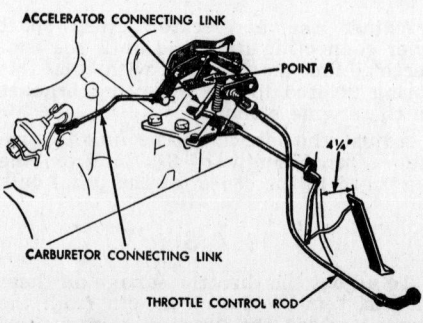

Fig. 11 Throttle linkage. 1956 Thunderbird

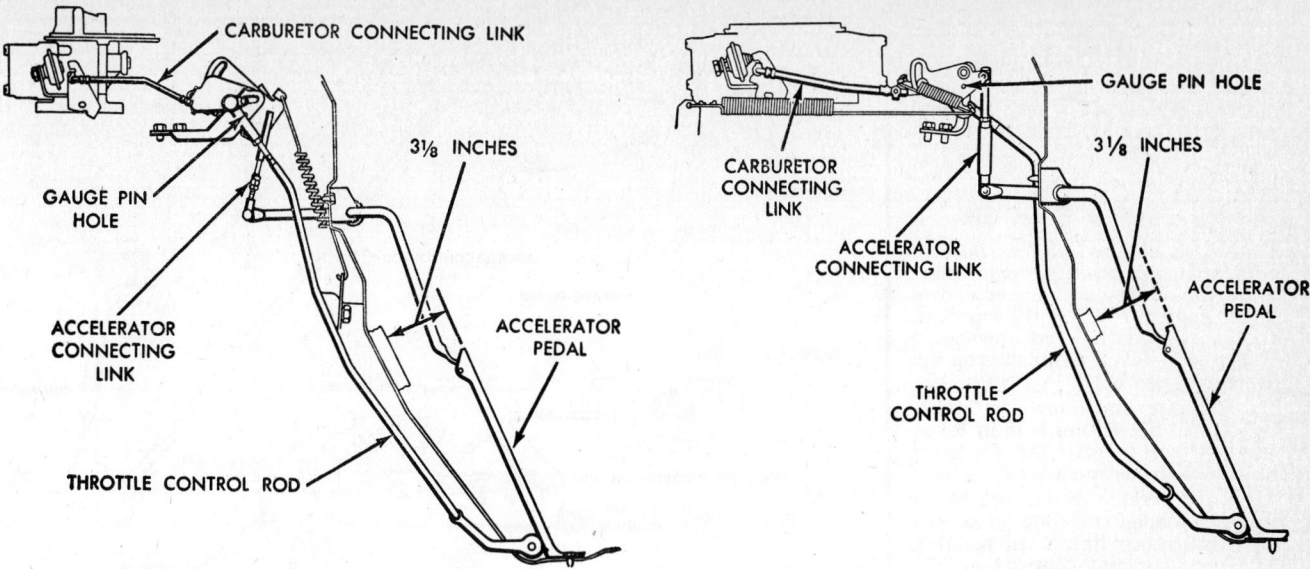

Fig. 13 Throttle linkage. 1957-58 Ford V8 with two barrel carburetor

Fig. 14 Throttle linkage. 1957-58 with four barrel carburetor

4. Adjust accelerator pedal height by turning threaded trunnion on accelerator connecting link until the point where linkage connects to accelerator pedal is 3⅛" from floor mat, Fig. 12.

1957-58 V8 Ford & T-Bird

1. Referring to Figs. 13 and 14, disconnect throttle rod from accelerator.
2. Insert a ¼" drill rod through gauging holes. Adjust length of car-

buretor connecting link so that carburetor lever is held against its hot idle stop.
3. Adjust accelerator connecting link to obtain a pedal height of 3⅛" (4½" on 1958 T-Bird).
4. Remove drill rod and check alignment of holes.
5. Pull upward gently but firmly on throttle control rod to hold transmission lever against its internal stop.
6. Rotate clevis until it freely fits pin on accelerator lever. Then lengthen

throttle control rod by rotating clevis 3 turns counterclockwise.
7. Connect throttle rod to lever.

Edsel Push Buttons, 1958

1. Turn on ignition switch and depress N button. Then turn ignition off.
2. Disconnect selector motor control rod from manual lever on transmission, Figs. 15 and 16.
3. Move manual lever on transmission to the rear or front until lever contacts the stop. Then move lever

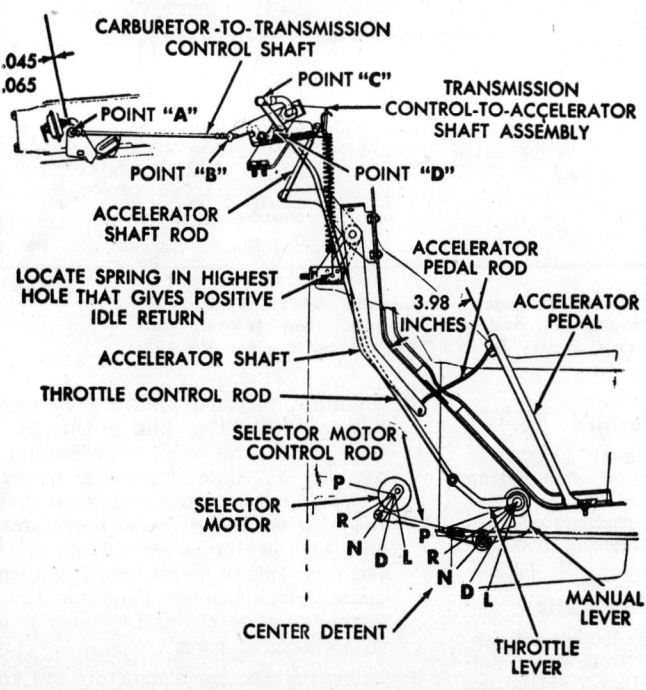

Fig. 15 Throttle linkage. Edsel 1958 Corsair and Citation

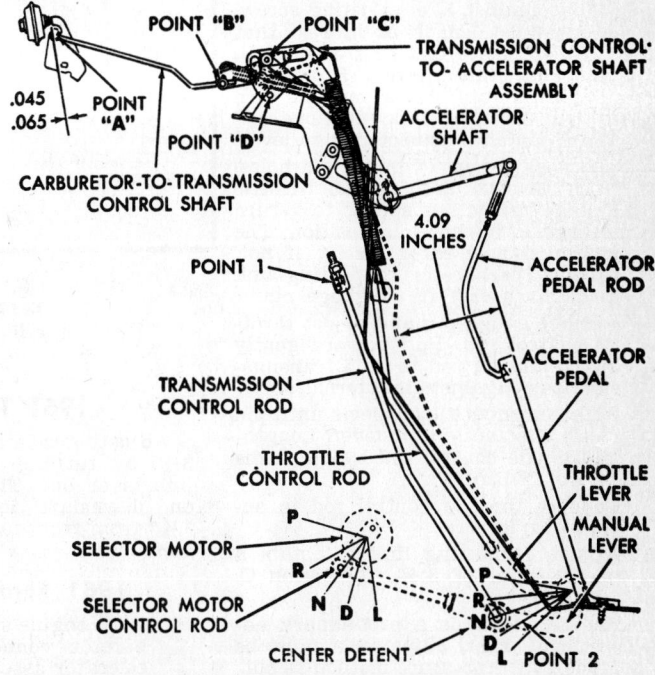

Fig. 16 Throttle linkage. Edsel 1958 Ranger, Pacer and Wagons

to the center of its travel (3 detents).

4. Loosen selector motor control rod lock nut and turn clevis until clevis pin can be inserted freely through clevis and manual lever on transmission. Then tighten lock nut.

1959-61 Ford & Edsel Six

1. With engine stopped and carburetor at its hot idle position, disconnect turnbuckle or clevis at upper end of throttle control rod, Fig. 17 top view. Pull throttle control rod upward to hold throttle lever against stop inside transmission.

2. Turn throttle rod clevis or turnbuckle until pin enters hole in lever. Then lengthen throttle rod 3½ turns and secure adjustment.

3. Adjust accelerator pedal height by turning threaded trunnion on accelerator connecting link until pedal is 3½" from floor mat (dimension "C", Fig. 17 top view).

4. The foregoing is a preliminary adjustment. Final adjustment must be made by the pressure method as outlined in the automatic transmission chapter.

1961 V8 With Fordomatic and 1959-60 V8 Ford, T-Bird, Edsel

1. With engine stopped, disconnect throttle control rod and carburetor connecting link from accelerator assembly, Fig. 17 (center and bottom views).

2. Insert a ¼" gauge pin through gauging holes at "A", Fig. 17.

3. Lift carburetor connecting link to its normal operating position. Maintain forward pressure on it so that carburetor throttle lever is held solidly against idle adjusting screw. Then adjust length of link so that threaded sleeve can be freely fitted into accelerator lever. From this position, rotate sleeve one full turn to lengthen the link. Remove ¼" gauge pin and connect link to lever.

4. Check alignment of gauge pin holes. Open throttle and permit throttle linkage retracting spring to return linkage to its hot idle position. The pin must now enter freely; if not, readjust carburetor connecting link to obtain a free fit of gauge pin.

5. Remove gauge pin and adjust throttle control rod. Pull upward gently but firmly on rod to hold transmission lever against its internal stop.

6. Rotate turnbuckle or clevis until pin freely fits accelerator lever. Lengthen throttle control rod by 3½ turns (4½ on T-Bird).

7. Connect throttle control rod to accelerator lever.

8. Adjust connecting link to obtain a pedal height of 3½" (dimension C, Fig. 17).

9. The foregoing is a preliminary adjustment. Final adjustment must be made by the pressure method as outlined in the automatic transmission chapter.

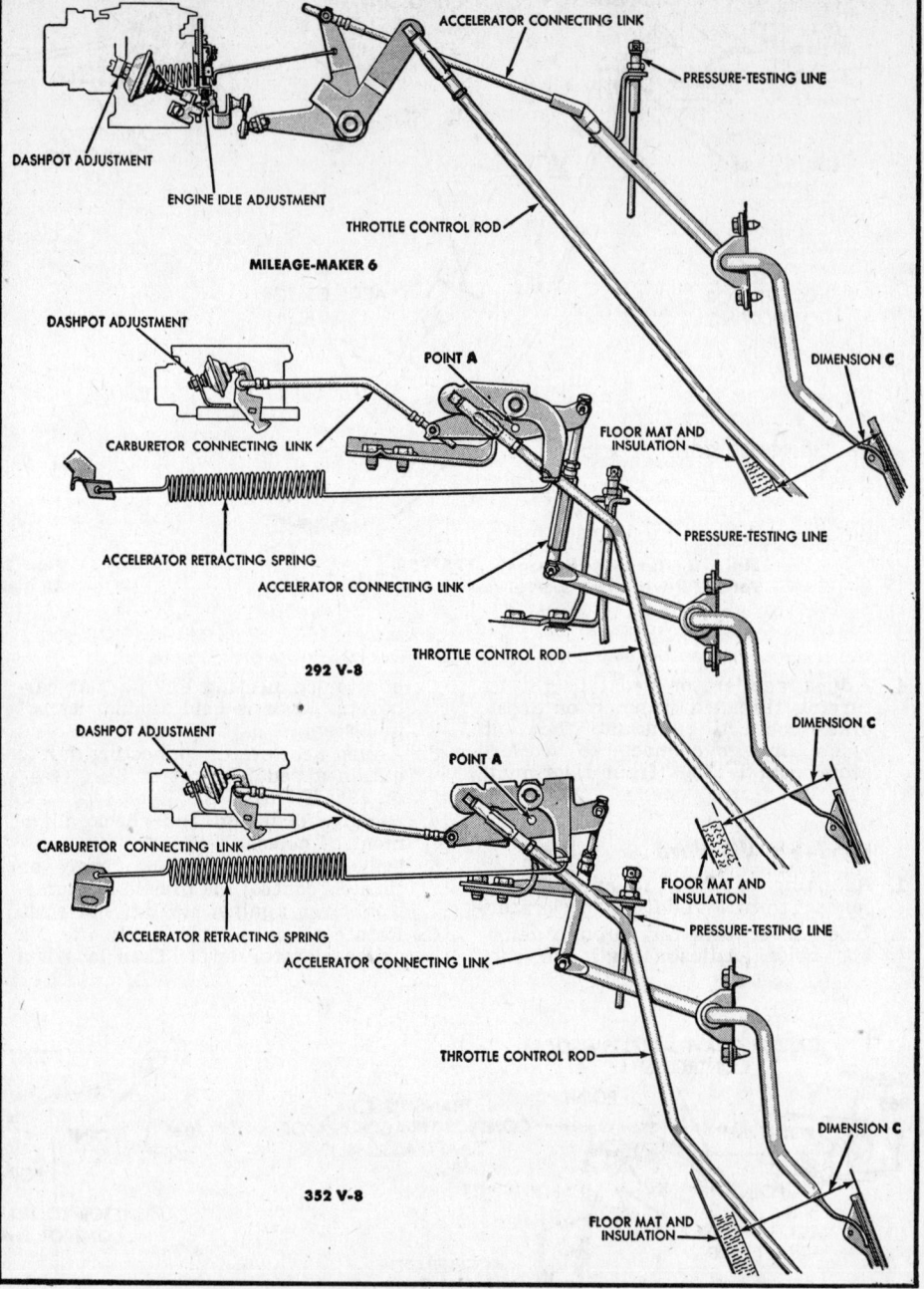

Fig. 17 Throttle linkage. Fordomatic 1961. Typical of 1959-60 Fordomatic and Cruiseomatic. Top is for six-cylinder models, center for V8-292 and bottom for V8-352

1961 Thunderbird

Adjust accelerator pedal height to 3¹¹⁄₁₆" by turning carburetor connecting link in or out. Then position speed nut on downshift lever-to-carburetor rod 1¼" from front face of bushing in downshift lever.

1961 Ford Cruiseomatic

1. With engine stopped, disconnect carburetor connecting link from accelerator assembly. Insert ¼" gauge pin through gauge holes at "A", Fig. 18.

2. Maintain forward pressure on carburetor connecting link so that carburetor throttle lever is held solidly against hot idle adjusting screw. Then adjust carburetor link so that the sleeve can be freely fitted into the accelerator lever. From this position, rotate sleeve one full turn counterclockwise to lengthen link. Remove gauge pin and connect link to accelerator lever.

3. Adjust carburetor connecting link to obtain a pedal height of 3¹¹⁄₁₆" as indicated at dimension "C".

TRANS. & CONV. REPLACE

Two Speed Units

1. Remove cover from bottom of converter housing.
2. Drain transmission and converter.
3. Remove drive shaft.
4. Disconnect linkage, speedometer cable and oil cooler lines at transmission.
5. Disconnect oil filler tube.
6. On 1961 models, disconnect pressure test line from transmission.
7. Remove starter motor.
8. Disconnect parking brake cable.
9. Remove engine rear support bolts.
10. Support transmission with jack and remove crossmember.
11. Unfasten converter from flywheel and converter housing from engine.
12. Secure converter to transmission so it will not fall out when transmission is separated from engine.
13. Work transmission off engine block dowel pins and toward rear until converter pilot clears crankshaft.
14. Lower transmission from car.
15. Reverse foregoing procedure to install the transmission. Then fill transmission with fluid and adjust control linkage as outlined previously.

1955-57 Thunderbird & All Convertibles

The frame construction of these models will not permit the transmission to be moved rearward far enough to clear the turbine shaft from the converter; therefore, the transmission and converter must be removed as a unit. The general procedure is as follows:

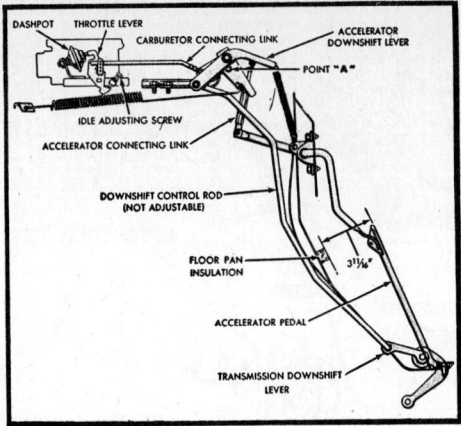

Fig. 18 Cruiseomatic throttle linkage. 1961 Ford

1. Drain transmission and converter.
2. Remove fluid filler tube.
3. On 1961 models, disconnect vacuum hose from vacuum diaphragm unit at transmission.
4. Remove flywheel-to-converter nuts. Install converter housing front plate to hold converter in place when transmission is removed.
5. Remove starter motor.
6. Disconnect oil cooler lines from transmission. Remove transmission vent tube (if equipped).
7. Disconnect linkage and speedometer cable from transmission.
8. Remove drive shaft.
9. On cars with single exhaust system it may be necessary to loosen and drop the exhaust to allow converter to clear exhaust pipe.
10. Remove engine support-to-transmission bolts. Support transmission with a jack and remove crossmember. Support rear of engine.
11. Unfasten converter housing from engine and move transmission assembly to the rear and down to remove it from the car.
12. Reverse removal procedure to install the transmission. Then fill with fluid and adjust controls as outlined previously.

TRANS. LESS CONV. REPLACE

Three-Speed Units
Except Convertibles & 1955-57 T-Bird

1. On 1961 models, disconnect hose from vacuum diaphragm unit at transmission.
2. Disconnect fluid tube and drain fluid.
3. Remove drive shaft.
4. Disconnect oil cooler lines.
5. Remove vent tube (if equipped).
6. Disconnect linkage and speedometer cable at transmission.
7. Remove engine rear support-to-transmission bolts. Support transmission with a jack and remove crossmember.
8. Support engine and remove transmission-to-converter housing bolts.
9. Tilt rear of transmission upward and move assembly toward rear until clear of turbine shaft. Then lower and remove assembly from car.
10. Reverse removal procedure to install the transmission. Fill with fluid and adjust controls as outlined previously.

Rear Axle and Brake Section

Refer To Hydraulic Brakes Chapter For Brake Adjustments

REAR AXLE, REPLACE

1957-61

It is not necessary to remove the entire rear axle assembly to service the differential carrier assembly. After removing the drive shaft and axle shafts, remove the nuts that retain the differential carrier to the axle housing and remove it from the housing.

1953-56 Ford Pass. Car

It is not necessary to remove the entire rear axle assembly to service the differential assembly. After removing the axle shafts as described further on, unfasten the differential carrier from the axle housing and lift it out.

1953-56 Ford Station Wagon & Thunderbird

Inasmuch as the differential carrier is part of the rear axle housing, it is advisable to remove the entire rear axle assembly if the differential is to be overhauled. The procedure is as follows:
1. Lift the rear of the car with a chain hoist attached to the bumper.
2. Set chassis support stands under the frame side rails ahead of the spring front hangers.
3. Drain differential housing.
4. Remove axle shafts and propeller shaft.
5. Remove hydraulic brake line clips from axle housing and free brake line from differential housing. Wire hydraulic line to frame.
6. Raise axle housing with a jack until shock absorbers start to compress. Remove nut holding shock absorber to spring seat.
7. Remove U-bolts attaching axle housing to springs.
8. Lower rear axle assembly to the floor.

REAR AXLE REPAIRS

1957-61

This rear axle, Fig. 1, is a banjo-housing hypoid in which the drive pinion

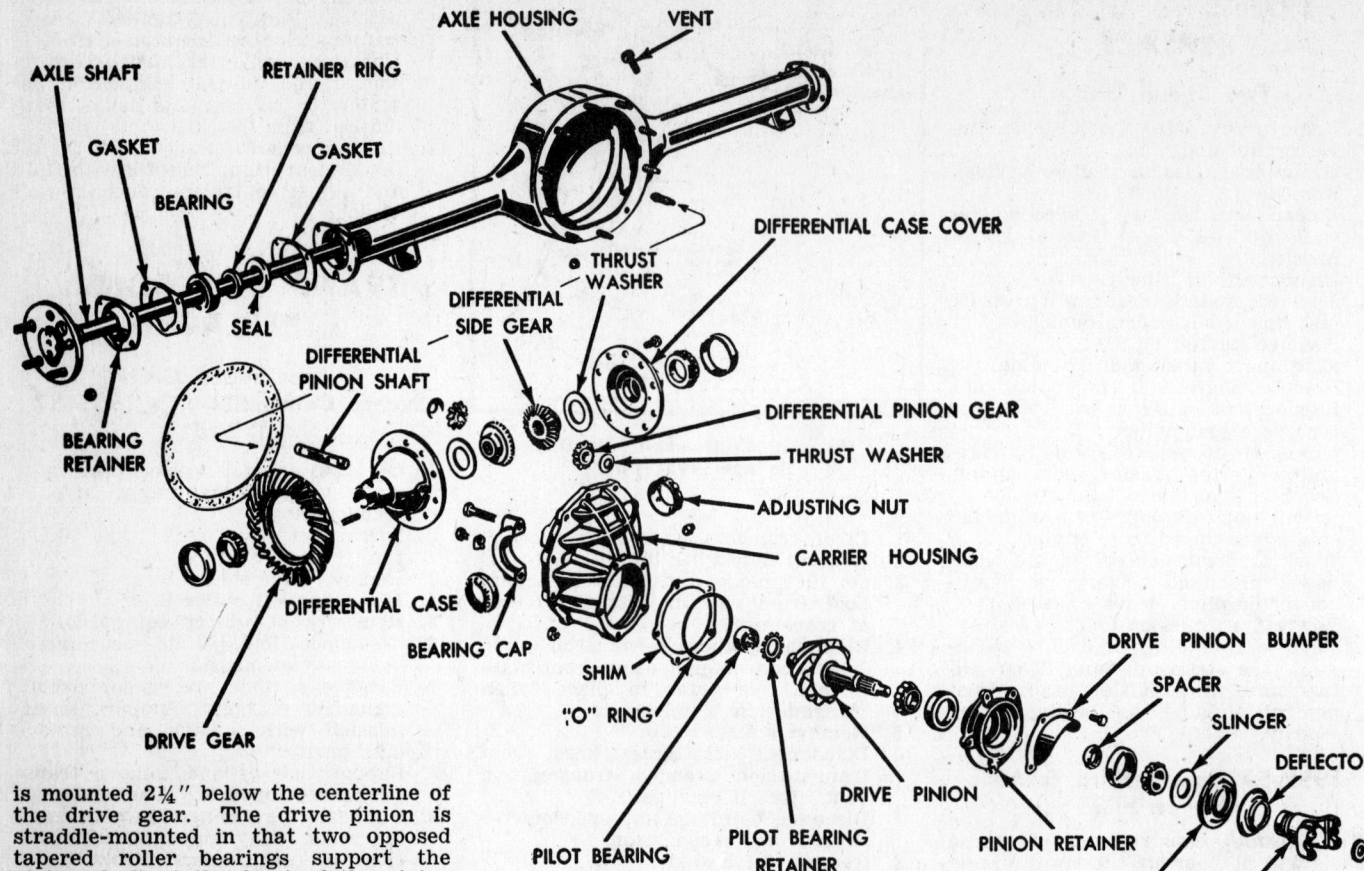

Fig. 1 Exploded view of 1957-61 rear axle

is mounted 2¼″ below the centerline of the drive gear. The drive pinion is straddle-mounted in that two opposed tapered roller bearings support the pinion shaft at the front of the pinion gear and a straight roller bearing supports the pinion shaft at the rear of the pinion gear.

The pinion shaft and gear are assembled in the pinion retainer which is bolted to the carrier housing. Two carrier and differential cases are used to accommodate two bearing sizes. The right and left axle shafts are not interchangeable since the left shaft is shorter than the right.

Disassembly

1. Mark one differential bearing cap and bearing support to ensure proper assembly. Remove adjusting nut locks, bearing caps and adjusting nuts. Lift differential out of carrier.
2. Remove drive gear from differential case.
3. Drive out differential pinion shaft retainer and separate the differential pinion shaft and remove gears and thrust washers.
4. Remove drive pinion retainer from carrier. Remove O-ring from retainer.
5. Remove pinion locating shim. Measure shim thickness with micrometer.
6. If the drive pinion pilot bearing is to be replaced, drive the pilot end and bearing retainer out at the same time. When installing, drive the bearing in until it bottoms. Install a new retainer with the concave side up.
7. Mount the drive pinion retainer assembly in a holding fixture and remove pinion shaft nut and flat washer. Then remove universal joint flange, oil seal and slinger.

8. Remove pinion retainer from fixture and place a protective sleeve or hose on the pinion pilot bearing surface. Then press the pinion shaft out of front bearing cone and remove spacer.
9. Remove pinion rear bearing cone.
10. Do not remove pinion bearing cups from retainer unless they are worn or damaged. The flange and pilot are machined by locating on these cups after they are installed in the bores. If new cups are to be installed, make sure they are seated in the retainer by trying to insert a .0015″ feeler gauge between cup and bottom of bore.

Assembly

Differential Case—Place a side gear and thrust washer in the differential case bore. *Lubricate all parts liberally with axle lubricant during assembly.* With a soft-faced hammer, drive pinion shaft into case only far enough to retain a pinion thrust washer and pinion gear. Place the second pinion and thrust washer in position. Drive the pinion shaft into place. Be careful to line up pinion shaft retainer holes. Place second side gear and thrust washer in position and install differential case cover. Install retainer. A pinion or axle shaft spline can be inserted in side gear spline to check for free rotation of differential gears.

Insert two ⁷⁄₁₆″ x 2″ bolts through differential flange and thread them 3 or 4 turns into the drive gear as a guide in aligning the drive gear bolt holes. Press or tap the drive gear into position. Install and tighten the drive gear bolts evenly and alternately across the gear to 60-65 lb. ft. torque.

If the differential bearings have been removed, use a suitable press to install them.

Pinion and Retainer—Install the pinion rear bearing cone on the pinion shaft and install a new spacer on the shaft. Place the bearing retainer on the pinion shaft, then install the front bearing cone. *As the bearing is pressed into position, rock the pinion retainer. Do not press the bearing on the shaft until all play is removed between retainer and bearings as the spacer may be compressed too much.*

Lubricate both bearings with axle lubricant. Place oil slinger in position. Coat the outside edge of a new oil seal with an oil-resistant sealer and press it into the bearing retainer. New seals need not be soaked before installation. Install the universal joint flange. Place the flat washer over the pinion shaft and start the pinion shaft nut.

Hold the flange and tighten the pinion shaft nut until a torque required to turn the pinion is 8-12 *inch* lbs. with used bearings or 17-27 *inch* lbs. with new bearings. As the pinion shaft nut is

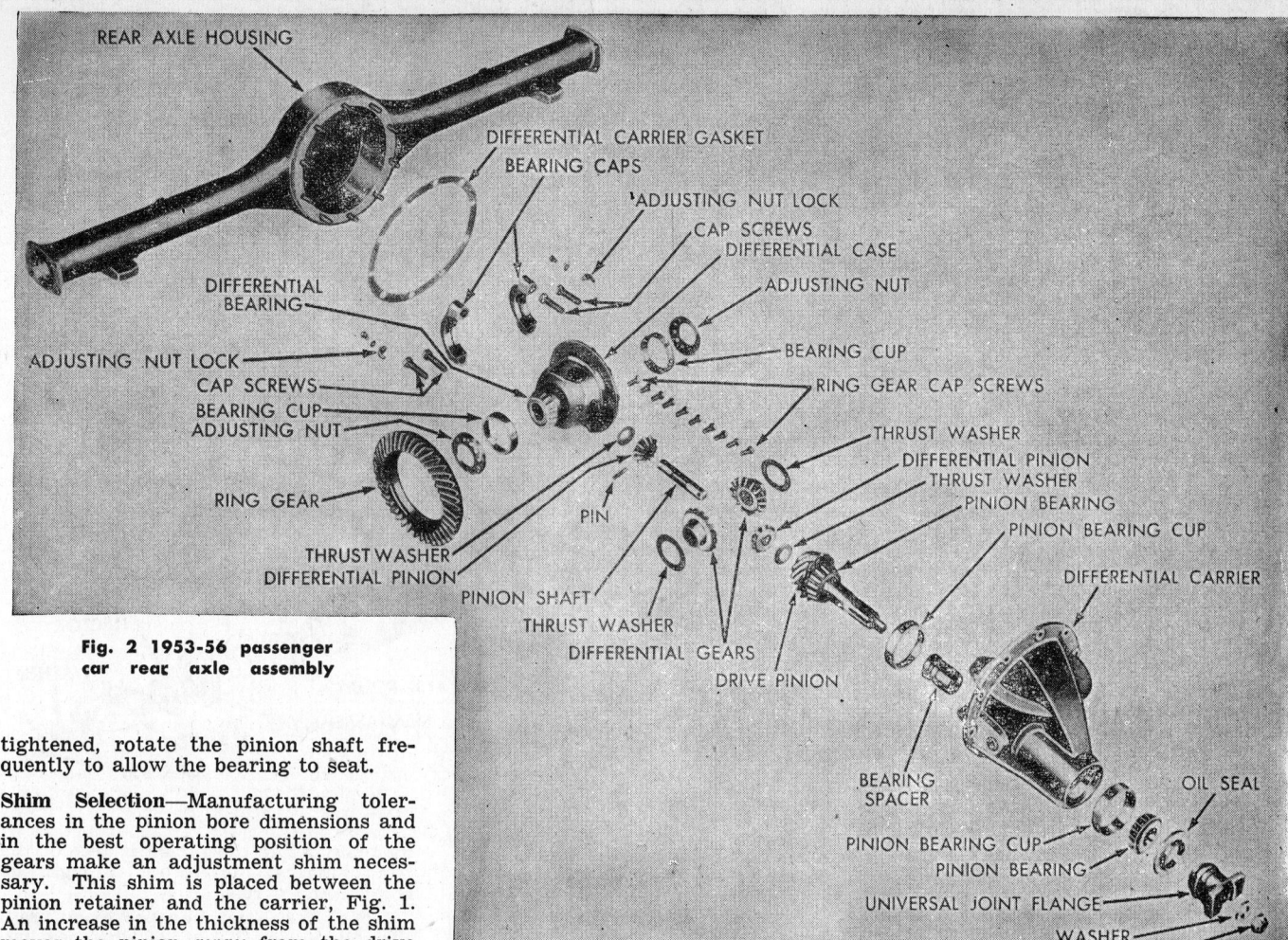

Fig. 2 1953-56 passenger car rear axle assembly

tightened, rotate the pinion shaft frequently to allow the bearing to seat.

Shim Selection—Manufacturing tolerances in the pinion bore dimensions and in the best operating position of the gears make an adjustment shim necessary. This shim is placed between the pinion retainer and the carrier, Fig. 1. An increase in the thickness of the shim moves the pinion *away* from the drive gear. Manufacturing objectives are to make axles requiring a .0015″ shim and if a new assembly is being built, a .0015″ shim should be used for a tentative build-up. Shims are available in .010″ to .021″ thicknesses in steps of .001″.

Pinions and drive gears are marked, when matched, with the same number. Following the number on the pinion is a minus (—) or plus (+) followed by a number. If the pinion is marked "—1" it indicates that a shim .001″ thinner than a standard shim for this carrier is required. A minus number means the pinion should be moved closer to the drive gear and a thinner shim is required. A plus number means the pinion should be moved farther from the drive gear and a thicker shim is required. A pinion marked zero (0) is a standard pinion.

To select a shim, measure the original shim with a micrometer. Note the dimensional mark on the original pinion. Compare the mark on the original pinion with the mark on the new pinion to determine how the original shim should be modified.

For example, if the original shim is .015″ and the original pinion is marked "—1", the new pinion requires a +1 shim. Therefore, the new pinion requires a .002″ thicker shim, and a .017″ shim should be used. If the new pinion is marked the same as the old pinion, no shim change is required.

Backlash Adjustment—The threaded nut type of differential bearing adjustment is used. The procedure for making this adjustment and checking drive gear and pinion backlash is given in the *Rear Axle Service* chapter.

1953-56 Ford Pass. Car

Fig. 2 illustrates the rear axle assembly used on passenger cars only.

Before the differential carrier assembly can be taken out, the axle shafts must be removed (how this is done is explained further on).

The splined universal joint flange is fastened to the pinion shaft with a nut which seats directly on the counterbore in the flange.

The drive pinion is mounted on taper roller bearings. Adjustment of the pinion along its axis is obtained by shims placed between the rear bearing outer race and a shoulder in the carrier. Preload of the two bearings is obtained by tightening the universal flange nut which compresses a spacer over the pinion shaft between the bearings. Both bearing outer races are pressed into the carrier, the rear race against pinion adjusting shims, the front race against the shoulder in the carrier. The rear bearing inner race

is pressed onto the pinion shaft to a shoulder at the pinion end. The front bearing is a light press fit to a close sliding fit on the pinion shaft.

The threaded nut type of differential bearing adjustment is used. The procedure for making this adjustment, as well as the assembly of the differential case, replacing a ring gear, checking ring gear and pinion backlash, and other differential case operations, is given in the *Rear Axle* chapter.

Pinion & Bearings, Replace

After removing the differential unit from the carrier, unscrew the pinion flange retaining nut and pull off the flange. Press the pinion out of the front bearing and through the rear end of the carrier. The rear bearing cone and bearing spacer will come out with the pinion. The bearings may then be removed and installed with suitable pulling equipment.

Reverse the operations to assemble and, after pressing on the flange, slip on the washer and nut. Tighten the nut until the bearings have a preload drag of 22 to 28 inch pounds of torque to rotate the pinion shaft.

To adjust the preload, draw up the nut with a torque wrench until the spacer starts to buckle. This adjustment must be made every time the flange nut is re-

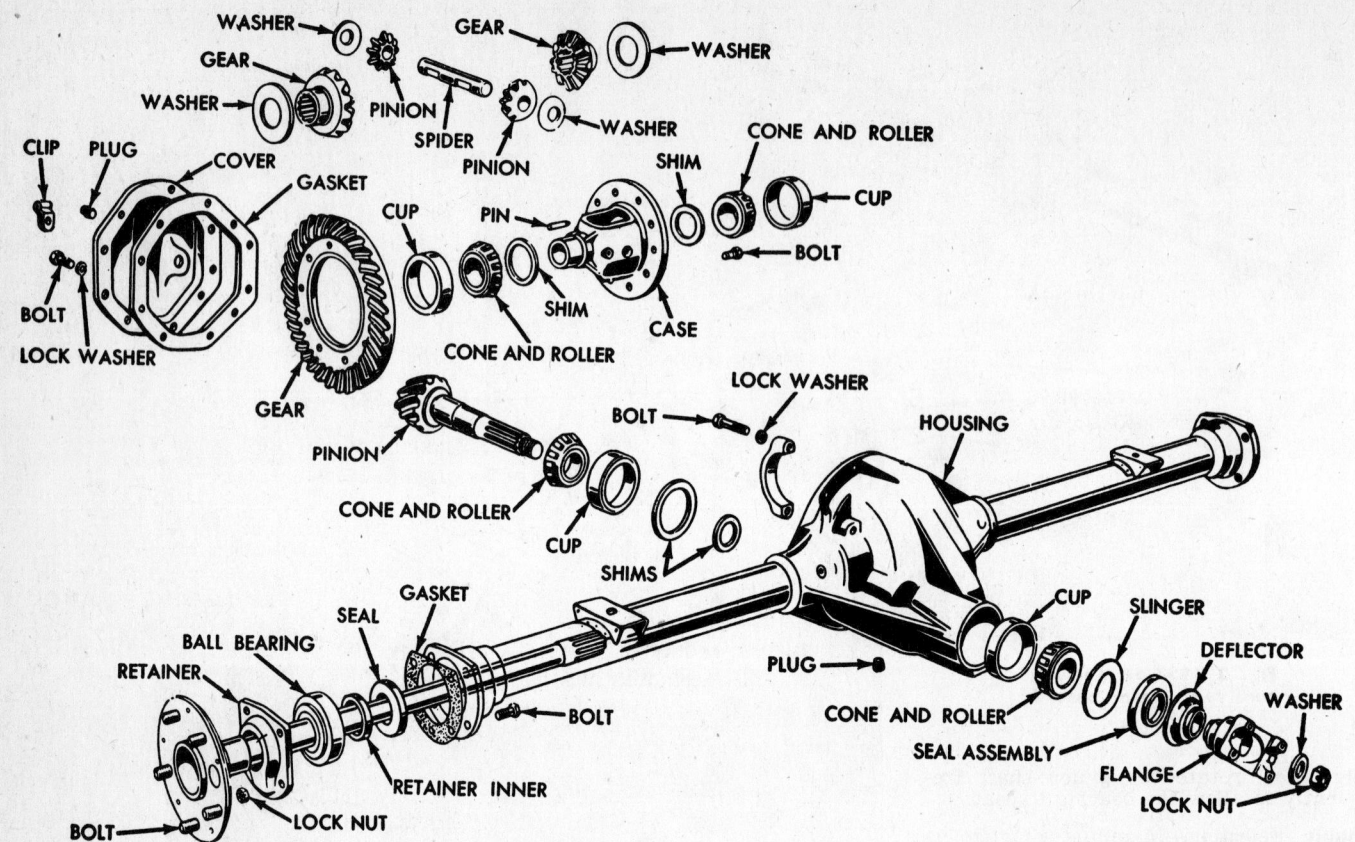

Fig. 3 Integral housing rear axle. 1953-56 Thunderbird and Ford Station Wagon

moved or loosened. If the adjustment is to be made with the differential in the carrier, the rear wheels must be jacked off the floor.

Drive Pinion Position

The drive pinion position usually does not require adjustment other than the bearing preload unless a new pinion bearing cup is installed. If a new rear bearing cup is installed, check the pinion position by using a micrometer depth gauge as outlined in the *Rear Axle* chapter. If the depth of the pinion measures more than 2.000" (plus or minus .002") it will be necessary to install shims in back of the pinion shaft rear bearing cup. Shims are available in .003, .005, .010, and .020" thicknesses for this purpose.

Note—A new pinion bearing spacer is required when a new ring gear and pinion set is installed, when any part of either pinion bearing is changed, when a new carrier casting is used, or when pinion adjusting shim thickness is increased. When the same universal joint flange is removed and reinstalled (as when an oil seal is replaced) checking for pinion bearing preload with a torque wrench is not necessary if care is taken to tighten the nut exactly to its previous position. Should a new flange be required, a torque wrench reading should be taken before loosening the nut and the nut tightened to the same torque wrench reading.

1953-56 Station Wagon and Thunderbird

In this type axle, Fig. 3, the drive pinion is held in position by shoulders in the differential carrier, upon which the pinion bearing cups seat. The pinion position is maintained by shims located between the rear bearing and the rear shoulder in the differential carrier. Shims between the bearing spacer and the front bearing cone are used to adjust pinion bearings.

The shimmed type of differential bearing adjustment is employed. The procedure for making this adjustment, as well as the assembly of the differential case, replacing the ring gear, checking ring gear and pinion backlash, and other differential case operations, is given in the *Rear Axle* chapter.

The axle tubes are pressed into the differential carrier to form a one-piece housing. To overhaul the unit, therefore, the rear axle assembly must be removed from the chassis.

Pinion & Bearings, Replace

After removing the axle shafts and differential unit, unscrew the pinion flange retaining nut and pull off the flange. The pinion may then be removed from the carrier by driving it out of the front bearing with a brass drift and

hammer. After the pinion is free of the front bearing, pull it out through the rear of the carrier.

Mount the pinion in a press and press the pinion shaft out of the bearing. When replacing the bearing select a suitable sleeve or length of pipe of the same diameter as the cone so the rollers or cage will not be damaged when being forced on the shaft.

Drive the front bearing cup and oil seal out of the forward end of the carrier. If the rear bearing cup is to be replaced or if the pinion setting is to be changed, remove the rear bearing cup.

To change the pinion setting, the shims behind the rear bearing cup should be measured with a micrometer. The necessary shims may then be removed or added to obtain the proper pinion setting as indicated when a pinion setting gauge is used (see *Rear Axle* Chapter). After the required shims have been added or subtracted, replace the rear bearing cup.

When making a pinion adjustment, the same thickness of pinion bearing adjusting shims should be added or removed at the rear bearing cup to retain the proper pinion bearing adjustment.

To install the pinion, support it under the head with a wood block while the pinion flange is reinstalled. The pinion oil seal should not be replaced until **after** the pinion setting has been checked.

Pinion Bearings, Adjust

The only occasion for adjusting the drive pinion bearings is when a new pinion or differential carrier is installed.

To make the adjustment, install sufficient shims between the bearing spacer and front bearing so that when the pinion retaining nut is tightened against the pinion flange, all rollers in the bearing are tight, but still permit rotating the pinion by hand.

Pinion, Adjust

After adjusting the pinion bearings, the position of the pinion may be checked. If a pinion setting gauge is available, check the pinion depth as outlined in the *Rear Axle* Chapter. If a correction is necessary, disassemble the pinion and, if it is to be moved toward the center of the axle, add shims between the rear bearing and rear shoulder in the carrier. If the pinion has to be moved away from the center of the axle, remove shims from this point.

If no pinion setting gauge is available, assemble the differential unit in the carrier and check the tooth contact by painting the ring gear teeth as described in the *Rear Axle* Chapter. After satisfactory tooth contact has been established, remove the pinion flange to install the seal.

AXLE SHAFT

Axle shafts are mounted on sealed ball bearings pressed to a shoulder on the axle shaft, and held in place by a pressed-on bearing retainer ring. The shaft bearings are pre-lubricated and require no additional lubrication. The shafts are held in place in the axle housing by a retainer plate. The wheel hub and brake drum flange are forged integral with the axle shaft. The flange provides the brake drum and wheel mounting and eliminates the need for a keyed hub.

To remove an axle shaft, take off the wheel and unfasten the brake drum from the axle shaft flange. Through the hole provided in the flange, remove the nuts which secure the brake support plate to the axle housing. Then with a suitable puller, pull the shaft out of the housing, using care not to dislodge the brake support plate or damage the oil seal in the housing. Install one nut to hold the brake plate in position.

Axle shaft bearings should be removed only when necessary to install a new bearing. A bearing once removed must be discarded.

If necessary to disassemble, loosen the axle shaft bearing retainer ring and remove the retainer. The bearing may be removed with a bearing puller, after which remove the retainer plate.

To assemble, place the retainer plate on the shaft. Press the bearing up against the shoulder on the shaft. Install the bearing retainer ring and press it firmly against the bearing. Before installing the shaft examine the oil seal and replace it if necessary.

Before installing a new oil seal it should be thoroughly soaked in oil for at least ½ hour to make it soft and pliable. When installing the seal, use a suitable seal driver, driving the seal into the axle housing with the axis of the shaft and tight against the shoulder. After installing the seal, check the outer

diameter for tightness in the housing to avoid possible leaks.

To install the shaft, remove the temporary nut holding the brake plate, and lubricate the bearing bore in the housing. Clean the brake plate surface and install new gaskets between the retainer plate and brake plate. Slide the shaft into the housing, using care not to damage the oil seal. Push the shaft in until its bearing is tight against the shoulder in the housing. Complete the job by tightening the axle shaft nuts to 30-35 pounds feet torque, and install the brake drum and wheel.

MASTER CYLINDER, REPLACE

1953-56

1. Disconnect wires at stop light switch and remove switch.
2. Disconnect brake line from master cylinder and depress brake pedal a few times to force out all fluid.
3. Remove eccentric bolt which attaches master cylinder push rod to brake pedal.
4. Remove master cylinder from dash panel.
5. Reverse removal procedure to install and bleed the brakes as outlined in the *Hydraulic Brakes* chapter.

1957-61 Ford, 1957 T-Bird, 1958 Edsel

1. Disconnect rubber boot from rear end of master cylinder in passenger compartment.
2. Disconnect brake line from master cylinder fitting. If stop light switch is attached to cylinder, disconnect wires from switch.
3. On 1957-59, force as much brake fluid as possible from cylinder into a suitable container by pushing down brake pedal all the way several times.
4. Unfasten cylinder from dash panel and lift cylinder away from push rod and out of engine compartment. On 1960-61, remove rubber boot from push rod.

1958-60 Thunderbird

1. Disconnect stop light switch wires from switch. Remove brake bolt and two copper gaskets from master cylinder.
2. Force as much fluid as possible from cylinder into a suitable container by pushing down several times on the brake pedal.
3. Remove four nuts that attach cylinder to dash panel; then lift cylinder and boot away from push rod and out of engine compartment.

1959 Edsel

1. Working inside passenger compartment, remove eccentric bolt, bushings and lock nut which secure master cylinder push rod to brake pedal.
2. Working inside engine compartment, remove hollow nut attaching stop light switch and hydraulic line outlet fitting to master cylinder.

3. Unfasten and remove master cylinder from dash panel.

1960 Edsel

1. Working inside passenger compartment, remove the "C" washer and spring washer that secures the master cylinder push rod to the brake pedal. Remove push rod and bushing from pedal.
2. Remove hydraulic line outlet fitting from master cylinder.
3. Remove stop light switch.
4. Remove two capscrews which secure master cylinder to engine side of dash panel and remove cylinder.

POWER BRAKE UNIT, REPLACE

1957-60 Ford (Bellows Type)

Removal—

1. Disconnect vacuum hose at top of power unit.
2. Remove nut from valve-adjusting eccentric and take off flat washer, spring and bushing.
3. Remove valve-adjusting eccentric.
4. Remove nylon bushing from power unit valve housing.
5. Unfasten power unit from dash panel.

Installation—

1. Pull brake pedal back toward car seat until master cylinder push rod comes out of master cylinder. Let push rod hang free.
2. Position power unit mounting bracket on dash panel. Be sure brake pedal trigger is in position against the air valve button before tightening attaching nuts and screws.
3. Install valve-adjusting eccentric and bumper through brake pedal, power lever and valve housing of power unit.
4. Slide eccentric bushing over eccentric and into valve housing.
5. Install eccentric spring with larger coils toward housing. Install washer and nut.
6. Tighten eccentric nut to the point that the eccentric bolt is firmly locked to power lever, but can still be turned for adjustment.
7. Attach vacuum hose and start engine.
8. Turn eccentric until unit chatters when pedal is depressed. Then turn eccentric until chatter disappears. Do not turn eccentric more than necessary or the unit "cut-in" will be excessively high. After adjustment, tighten eccentric nut. Check adjustment after nut is tightened.
9. Disconnect mounting bracket from dash.
10. Pull pedal and power unit back and insert master cylinder push rod in cylinder boot. Install nuts and screws that attach mounting bracket to dash panel.
11. Loosen push rod eccentric lock nut only enough to turn eccentric.
12. Rotate eccentric clockwise to its maximum travel. This will shorten push rod, permitting master cylinder

piston to return to fully released position.

13. Rotate eccentric in a counterclockwise direction until master cylinder piston starts to resist movement of push rod. Hold eccentric and tighten lock nut.

14. Check master cylinder for bubbles or spurt at compensator port, which indicates push rod is properly adjusted.

1960-61 Ford (Piston Type)

1. Working inside the vehicle under the instrument panel, remove and discard the horseshoe-type retaining clip. Push the retaining bolt through the brake pedal and power brake push rod.
2. Open the hood. Disconnect wires from stop light switch at brake master cylinder. Remove brake line from master cylinder outlet fitting.
3. Remove vacuum hoses from power unit.
4. Unfasten and remove power brake unit from cowl panel.
5. Reverse above procedure to install the unit; then bleed the system.

1960 T-Bird (Piston Type)

1. Working inside of car under instrument panel, remove eccentric bolt lock nut and push eccentric bolt out through brake pedal and power brake push rod.
2. Open hood. Disconnect wires from stop light switch and remove brake bolt from master cylinder outlet.
3. Remove vacuum hoses from brake unit.
4. Unfasten and remove power unit from cowl panel.
5. Reverse above procedure to install; then bleed system.

1958-60 T-Bird (Bellows Type)

Removal—
1. Remove master cylinder.

2. Remove headlamp beam selector switch and left cowl trim panel.
3. Remove hood control cable from bracket, and then remove bracket.
4. On cars with overdrive, remove overdrive control handle and bracket.
5. After detaching left vent-air register panel (6 screws and 3 bolts), lower parking brake handle, tilt panel outward at bottom and remove panel.
6. Disconnect vacuum hose at power unit. Detach and slide valve adjusting eccentric to the left until head of eccentric contacts brake pedal.
7. Detach power unit from its mounting bracket (2 bolts and 2 self-tapping screws) and remove power unit from trigger and out of car.

Installation—
1. Position power unit mounting bracket on dash panel, being sure brake pedal trigger is positioned against air valve button to avoid damage to button. Fasten power unit in place.
2. Slide valve adjusting eccentric and bumper through brake pedal extension, power lever and valve housing.
3. Slide eccentric bushing (either end) over valve adjusting eccentric and into valve housing.
4. Install eccentric spring with larger coils toward housing. Install washer and nut.
5. Tighten valve adjusting eccentric nut to a point that the eccentric bolt is firmly locked to power lever but can still be turned for adjustment.
6. Attach vacuum hose.

Adjustments—Start engine. Turn valve adjusting eccentric until unit chatters when pedal is applied. Then turn eccentric until chatter disappears. *Do not turn eccentric more than necessary or the unit "cut-in" will be excessively high.* If a satisfactory adjustment cannot be obtained, the pedal trigger may be bent.

1958-60 Edsel

1. Working inside the front passenger compartment, disconnect the push rod from the brake pedal lever.
2. Working in the engine compartment, remove the hydraulic cylinder outlet connector bolt. *It is not necessary to remove the stop light switch, wires or brake line from the outlet fitting.*
3. Disconnect the two vacuum hoses from the vacuum inlet tubes attached to the side of the cylinder.
4. Remove the four screws that attach the power brake unit to the adapter on the dash panel, then remove the unit.
5. Installation is made in the reverse order of removal. When installed, fill and bleed the brake system.

1957 Thunderbird

To remove the unit, depress brake pedal several times to remove all vacuum from system. Disconnect hydraulic lines and vacuum hose at booster. Remove booster unit from mounting bracket.

Install the unit in the reverse order and bleed the air from the brake system.

1954-56

To remove the unit, depress the brake pedal several times to remove all vacuum from the system. Disconnect hydraulic lines and vacuum hose at the power unit. Disconnect the stop light switch wires at the switch. Remove the power unit from the mounting bracket.

Install the power unit on the mounting bracket. Connect the stop light switch wires. Bleed the brake system. Connect the vacuum hose and tighten the clamps securely. Connect the hydraulic lines.

Front End and Steering Section

CAMBER & CASTER, ADJUST

1961 Thunderbird

Camber—Adjust camber by removing or installing shims between pivot bracket of lower control arm and mounting bracket on underbody in engine compartment, Fig. 1.

Removal of shims will increase camber; installing shims will decrease camber. A $\frac{1}{16}$″ shim change will change camber angle $\frac{1}{3}$°.

Caster—Adjustment is made by repositioning strut on lower control arm as shown in Fig 1. Adjust caster by loosening rear retaining bolts and lift strut so that strut serrations will be free from serrations on lower arm.

Lengthen distance of "Dimension A", Fig. 1, to decrease caster and shorten distance to increase caster angle. Tighten rearward nuts that retain strut to lower control arm and recheck caster and camber.

1954-61 Ford & Edsel

To adjust caster, loosen the two bolts that secure the upper suspension arm shaft to the frame and insert shims between the shaft and frame. A $\frac{1}{16}$″ shim at the front bolt will add a positive caster of $\frac{1}{2}$ degree. A $\frac{1}{16}$″ shim removed at the front bolt will produce a negative caster of $\frac{1}{2}$ degree. Shims are available in thicknesses of $\frac{3}{32}$″ and $\frac{1}{8}$″. When caster is correct, tighten bolts securely.

To adjust camber, insert or remove an equal number of shims from between the shaft and frame at both the front and rear bolts. Each $\frac{1}{16}$″ of shim will change camber $\frac{1}{4}$ degree.

1958-60 Thunderbird

Camber and caster is adjusted in the same manner as outlined above for Ford except that the shims are located between the inner shaft of the suspension upper arm and the mounting bracket on the underbody in the engine compartment.

1955-57 Thunderbird

Camber and caster is adjusted in the same manner outlined for Ford except that the shims are located on the engine side of the bracket. Thus, when adjusting caster on these cars, the removal of shims at the front bolt will produce a positive caster. A shim added to the front bolt will produce a negative caster. To adjust camber insert or remove an equal number of shims at both bolt positions.

TOE-IN, ADJUST

Position the front wheels in their straight-ahead position. Then turn both tie rod adjusting sleeves an equal amount until the desired toe-in setting is obtained.

WHEEL BEARINGS, ADJUST

Pack the wheel bearings with the proper lubricant. Install the wheel, hub and drum as a unit. Tighten the spindle nut with a 12″ wrench, while rotating the wheel back and forth, until there is a noticeable drag or bind. This assures that the bearing cones are properly seated. Then back off the spindle nut to line up to the nearest cotter pin hole which will allow the hub to rotate freely with no perceptible end play. Lock the spindle nut in this position with a cotter pin and install the grease cap and hub cap.

Remove the support stands and check the wheel alignment as previously outlined.

FRONT END REPAIRS

1961 Thunderbird Ball Joints

1. Remove ball joint from arm. If ball joint is riveted to arm, drill a ⅛″ pilot hole completely through each rivet. Then drill off the rivet head through the pilot hole with a ⅜″ drill. Drive all rivets out of holes.
2. Clean end of arm and remove all burrs from hole edges. Check for cracks in metal at the holes and replace arm if cracked.
3. Install new ball joint, *using the special bolts, nuts and washers supplied with the ball joint. Do not attempt to rivet new ball joint to arm.*
4. Torque ball joint stud nuts to 60-80 ft. lbs. Lubricate ball joints and check caster and camber angles.

Shock Absorber

When installing, position the shock absorber and upper mounting plate in place and install mounting plate bolts and dash panel brace nuts. Lower car slightly with safety stands under lower control arm. This will raise upper arm enough to position lower shock absorber stud through hole at bottom of spring lower seat. Secure shock absorber to spring seat by installing insulator, washer and retaining nut.

Front Spring

1. With safety stand under lower control arm, remove wheel, shock absorber and upper control arm bumper and bracket.
2. Raise car slightly in order to lower upper control arm.
3. Insert a lock bar through top of spring and position bar on 7th coil

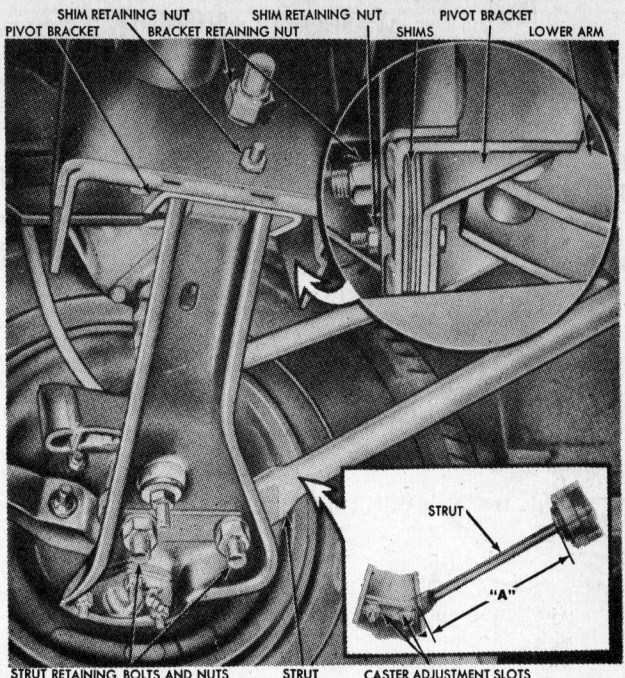

Fig. 1   Caster and camber adjustments. 1961 Thunderbird

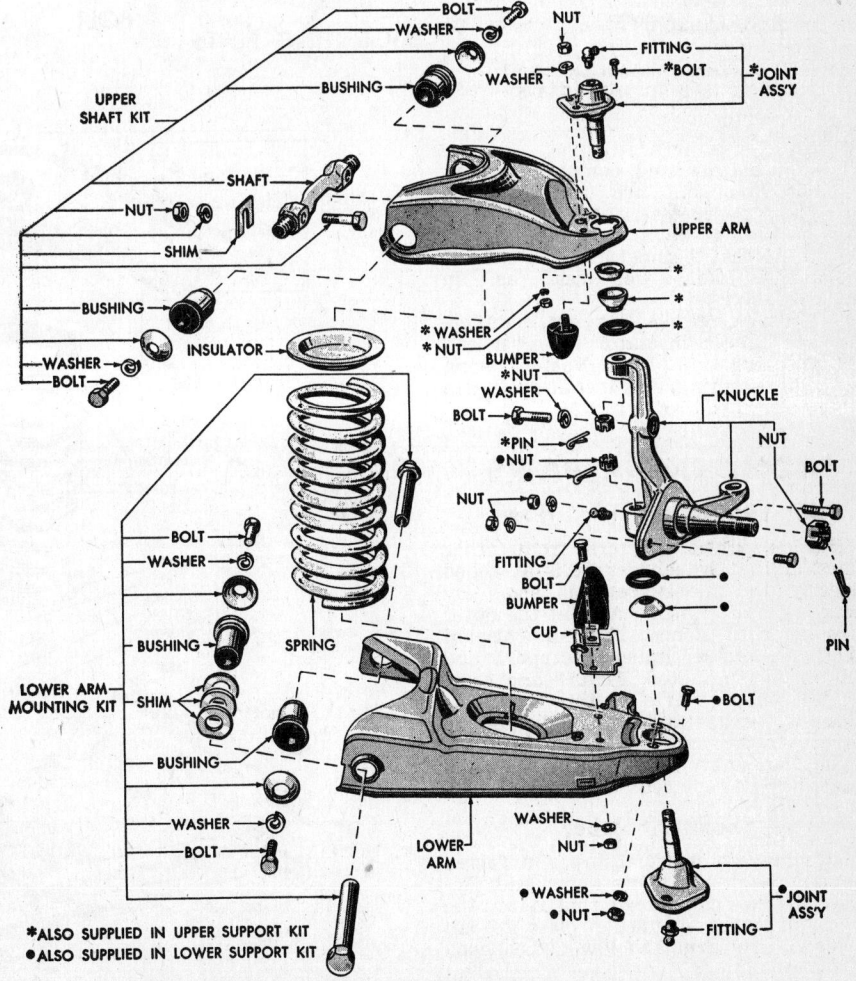

Fig. 3   Front suspension on Ford 1957-59, Edsel 1958 and T-Bird 1958-59.   For 1960-61 Ford, 1960 T-Bird and 1959-60 Edsel, the upper control arm shaft bushings are the screw type

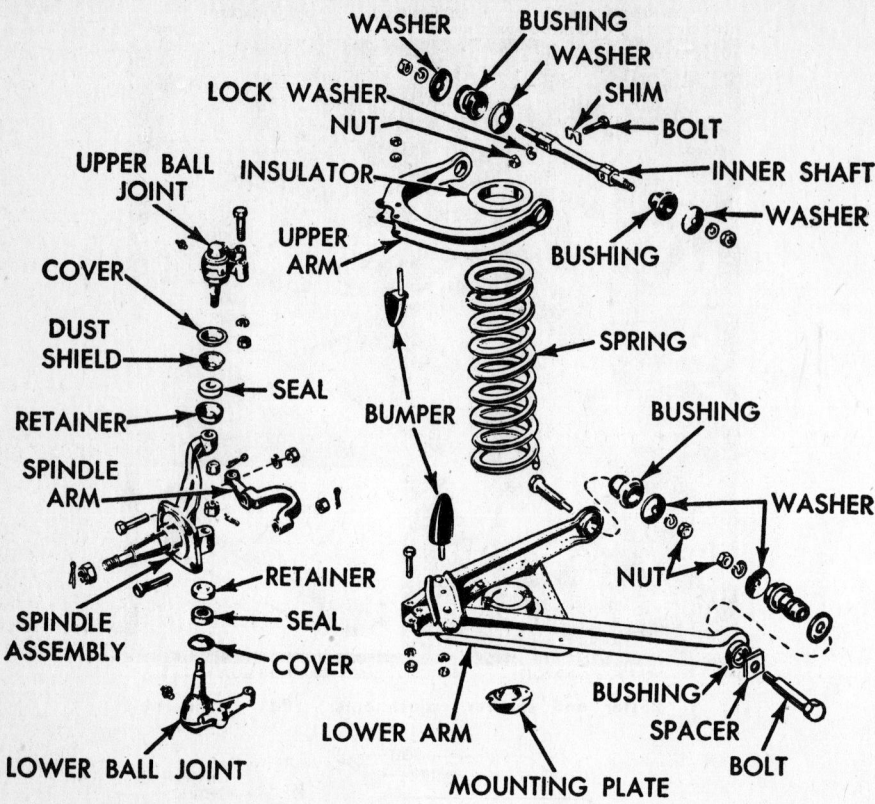

Fig. 4 Front suspension. Ford 1954-56 and T-Bird 1955-57

Lower Arm & Spring, Remove

Raise the front of the car and place a support stand under each frame side rail to the rear of the lower control arm. Remove the hub cap and pry off the grease cap. Remove the nut from the wheel spindle and pull off the wheel assembly with hub and brake drum.

Remove the shock absorber as outlined above and detach the stabilizer (stabilitor) bar from the lower control arm.

Loosen the slotted nut which attaches the lower ball joint stud to the lower spindle boss one or two turns. Then with a brass bar and hammer, strike the lower spindle boss to pop the stud loose against its nut. Place a jack under the outer end of the lower arm and raise the jack until the upper arm rebound bumper is clear of the frame. The nut can then be removed and the spindle and brake assembly lifted off the ball joint stud and moved out of the way.

Lower the jack until the coil spring is free and can be removed. Note the rubber insulators at the upper and lower ends of the spring.

Unfasten the lower control arm from the frame and remove the arm. Inspect the bushings on the inner end of each arm leg and replace if defective.

When installing bushings, do not attempt to press them beyond the edge of the shoulder ribs as severe distortion will result, which will affect the operation of the suspension unit. Under no circumstances should only one bushing be replaced.

from bottom and compress spring until top coils are drawn out of spring upper seat.

4. Remove 4 bolts attaching lower spring seat to upper arm and remove spring and lower seat as an assembly.

5. If a new spring is being installed, tape rubber insulator to upper end of spring in 3 places. Fasten spring seat to spring and install spring in reverse order of removal.

FRONT END REPAIRS

All 1954-60 & 1961 Ford

This suspension differs from other types in that wheel spindle is attached directly to the suspension arms by means of ball joints located at the outer ends of both arms. The conventional steering knuckle, knuckle support and kingpin is eliminated, Figs. 3 and 4.

The working parts of this type suspension are assembled directly to the vehicle frame and cannot be removed as an assembly. However, individual parts may be replaced as outlined below.

Shock Absorber

To remove a shock absorber, unfasten it from the frame at its upper end. Remove the two cap screws that retain the shock absorber mounting plate to the lower control arm and lower the shock absorber unit.

To install, reverse the removal procedure and tighten the two lower cap screws to 13-18 lbs. ft. torque.

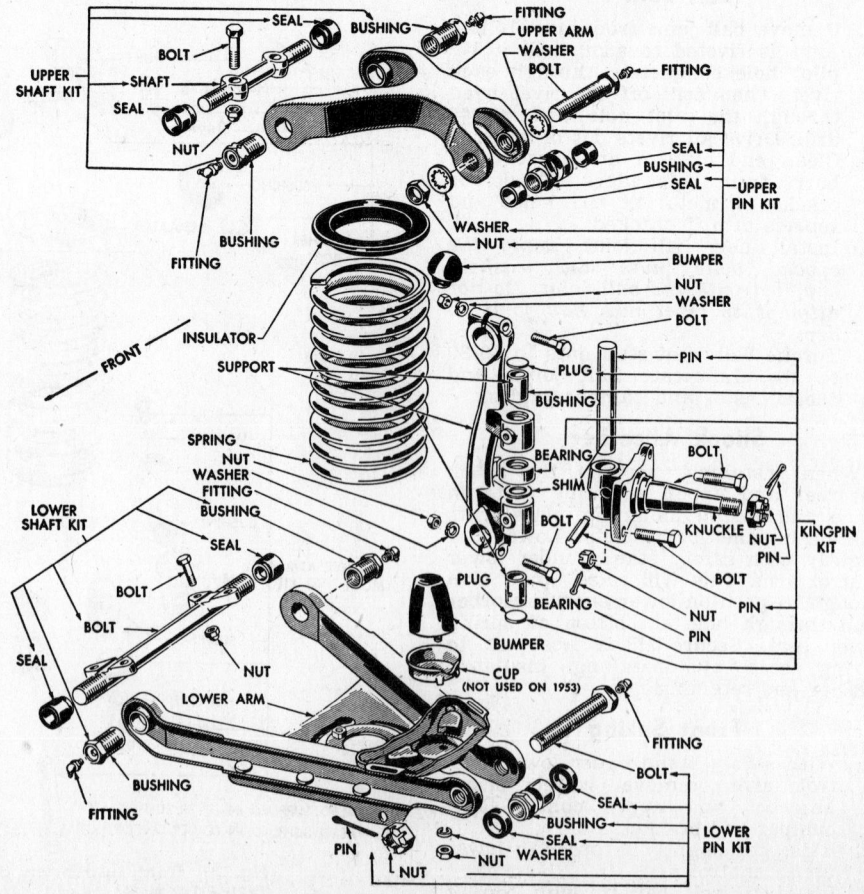

Fig. 5 Front suspension. 1953

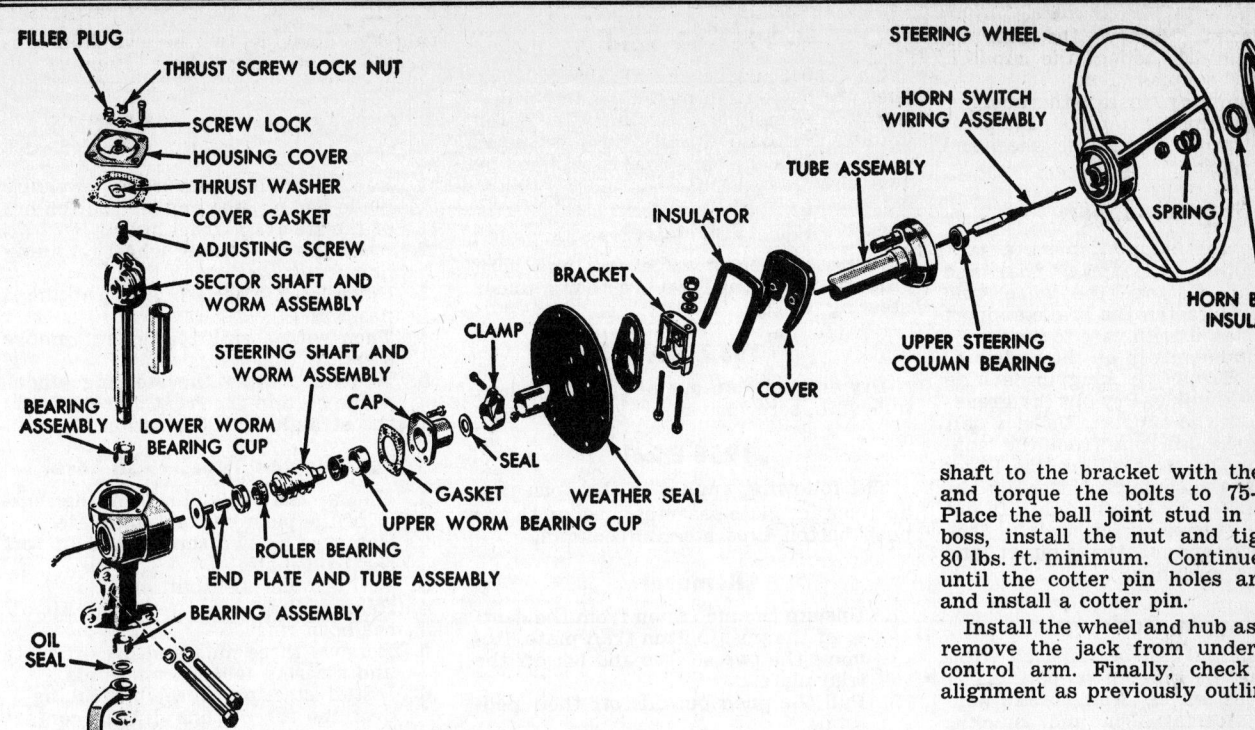

FILLER PLUG
THRUST SCREW LOCK NUT
SCREW LOCK
HOUSING COVER
THRUST WASHER
COVER GASKET
ADJUSTING SCREW
SECTOR SHAFT AND WORM ASSEMBLY
STEERING SHAFT AND WORM ASSEMBLY
BEARING ASSEMBLY
LOWER WORM BEARING CUP
CLAMP
CAP
SEAL
GASKET
UPPER WORM BEARING CUP
ROLLER BEARING
END PLATE AND TUBE ASSEMBLY
BEARING ASSEMBLY
OIL SEAL
SECTOR SHAFT ARM (PITMAN ARM)
BRACKET
INSULATOR
WEATHER SEAL
COVER
TUBE ASSEMBLY
INSULATOR
HORN SWITCH WIRING ASSEMBLY
STEERING WHEEL
SPRING
HORN RING
HORN BUTTON INSULATOR
UPPER STEERING COLUMN BEARING

Fig. 6 Conventional steering gear, 1953-57 Ford and T-Bird

Ball Joint Service

Remove the cover and seal from the ball joint. Inspect the joint and replace if found defective. If the joint is still serviceable, *do not* wash it in solvent as it will be extremely difficult to lubricate it again. Do not hammer the ball joint bodies as binding will result. Inspect the metal seal parts for damage and replace if necessary. Replace the sponge rubber seal, making sure it is stuffed into the metal seal cup before pushing it down over the ball joint stud.

Lower Arm & Spring, Install

To install the lower control arm, secure the rearward leg to the frame crossmember tube, running the nut up finger tight. With the arm forced firmly against the tube, install enough shims to fill the space between the forward arm leg bushing and front crossmember. Then install the bolt and washers and run the nut up finger tight. With the arm in curb load position (approximately horizontal) with the outer end slightly lower than the inner, tighten the nuts to 80-100 lbs. ft. torque.

Place the coil spring with the rubber insulators in position on the lower control arm. Then with a jack under the lower arm, compress the coil spring. Care must be taken to see that the upper and lower ends of the spring are properly seated and the rubber insulators are in place. Guide the spindle boss over the ball joint stud. Install the nut and torque it to 100 lbs. ft. Continue to tighten until the cotter pin holes are lined up and install the cotter pin.

Remove the jack from under the arm and install the shock absorber. Secure the stabilizer bar to the lower suspension arm.

Upper Arm, Remove

Remove the shock absorber. Place a jack under the lower control arm spring seat and raise it until some of the tension has been removed from the upper bumper. Remove the wheel and tire assembly.

Wire the spindle to the frame to avoid possible damage to the brake hose from undue tension. Loosen the ball joint stud by backing the nut off one or two turns and striking the spindle boss. Remove the stud nut completely and then remove the two bolts that secure the inner shaft to the frame. Note the number of shims between the shaft and frame at each of the bolt locations. Then take off the upper control arm.

When installing bushings, be sure to use a spacer tool of the proper dimensions between the arm legs so that the arm will not be distorted or bent. When both bushings are in place, install the nut and washer on each end of the shaft and tighten finger tight. Position the shaft in the arm so that the shaft bolt holes are parallel with the arm. Then tighten the nuts from 80-100 lbs. ft. torque. Under no circumstances should only one bushing be replaced.

Note—The upper ball joint is serviced in exactly the same way as the lower.

Upper Arm, Install

Position the arm on the frame crossmember. Use the same number of shims that were originally used between the shaft and frame bracket. Secure the shaft to the bracket with the two bolts and torque the bolts to 75-90 lbs. ft. Place the ball joint stud in the spindle boss, install the nut and tighten it to 80 lbs. ft. minimum. Continue to tighten until the cotter pin holes are lined up and install a cotter pin.

Install the wheel and hub assembly and remove the jack from under the lower control arm. Finally, check the wheel alignment as previously outlined.

FRONT END REPAIRS

1953

The working parts of the suspension system, Fig. 5 are assembled directly to the car frame and cannot be removed as an assembly. Therefore to remove any part for replacement, it is necessary to disassemble the part from the car.

Lower Arm & Spring

To replace either of these parts, jack up the car until the wheels clear the floor and place a stationary jack under the frame. Remove the shock absorber, and stabilizer end clip. Place a jack under the lower arm pivot shaft and exert enough pressure on the jack to keep the pivot shaft tight to the frame. Unfasten the pivot shaft and lower the jack slowly. When the spring is fully extended, lift it out of the lower arm. Remove the nut from the lower bushing pin and screw out the pin. The lower arm can then be lifted out.

To install, position the lower arm, screw in the bushing pin and tighten the nut. Place the flat end of the spring upward and the lower end in the spring seat in the arm. With the jack in position under the pivot shaft, raise the lower arm to the frame. Use a drift to align the holes in the pivot shaft and cross member for easy installation of bolts. Install the shock absorber, fasten the stabilizer end with clip on lower arm and remove jacks.

Upper Control Arm

To replace the upper control arm, place a jack under the lower spring seat and raise the car. Remove the wheel. Run a strong wire from the kingpin support to the frame to avoid damage to the hydraulic brake hose from undue tension. Unfasten the upper pivot shaft from the frame. Remove the nut and bushing pin at the top of the support, and lift off the upper arm.

When assembling, install the bushing pin before attempting to fasten the pivot shaft to the frame. Install the wheel and remove the jack.

Kingpin Support

To replace this support, place a jack under the lower arm spring seat and raise the car. Remove the wheel and brake drum. Unfasten the brake support plate and fasten it with wire to the frame to prevent undue strain on the hydraulic brake hose. Drive the kingpin locking pin from the knuckle. Pry out the grease seal plug from the support. Using a soft drift, drive the kingpin from the support and knuckle, forcing out the lower grease seal at the same time. Remove the upper and lower pivot pins and lift out the kingpin support. Loosen the lock bolts at each end of the support and press out the bushings.

Kingpin Bushings

These bushings can be replaced without removing the kingpin support. After taking off the wheel, drum, brake support plate, steering arm and knuckle, press out the bushings. After pressing in the new bushings, they can be reamed from below.

Pivot Shaft Bushing

It is necessary to remove the upper control arm to replace these bushings. When screwing in the new bushings, insert a hard wood block between the ends of the arm at the pivot shaft to keep the ends in the proper position.

The lower control arm pivot shaft bushings can be replaced without removing the arm from the car.

Pivot Pin or Bushing

To replace either the upper or lower pivot pin or bushing, place a jack under the spring seat of the lower arm and remove the wheel. Remove the pivot pin nut and screw out the pin. To remove the bushing from the support, loosen the lock bolt and press out the bushing.

Note — After replacing any part of the suspension, check and adjust camber and caster.

HORN BUTTON OR RING

1961 Thunderbird

Unsnap hub cap from horn ring. Remove steering wheel nut and pull off steering wheel and horn ring.

1958-60 Thunderbird

To remove the horn ring, pull off the decorative cover at the center of the steering wheel and remove the wheel from the steering shaft. Remove the turn signal cancelling cam and ground contact ring. Removal of the three retaining screws then allows complete disassembly of the remaining parts.

1960-61 Ford

On 1960 Fairlane and all 1961 models, the horn button can be removed by pressing down evenly and turning the button counterclockwise until it lifts out. On the other models the horn ring is retained by two screws.

1960 Edsel

Remove steering wheel cap and horn ring by removing two screws under steering wheel.

1959 Edsel

Pry emblem cap out of steering wheel hub with screwdriver or knife blade.

1958 Edsel

The following applies to the horn ring and contact plate assembly used with the push button type steering column.

Removal

1. Unsnap the medallion from the center of the push button trim plate. Remove the two screws and lift off the trim plate.
2. Pull the push buttons off their pedestals.
3. Remove the three screws from inside the horn ring hub and lift off the horn ring.
4. Unscrew the three nuts that attach the horn contact plate and steering wheel to the wheel hub.
5. Lift off the horn contact plate assembly. *The horn wire in the push button switch and tube assembly is not replaceable. Therefore, should trouble occur in this assembly, replace the complete tube assembly.*

Installation

1. Install contact plate on the three steering wheel studs. Install and tighten the three nuts.
2. Secure horn ring to contact plate with three screws.
3. Press push buttons on their proper pedestals.
4. Install push button trim plate.
5. Snap medallion in slots in trim plate.

1953-59

The horn button can be removed by pressing down evenly and turning the button counterclockwise until it lifts out.

Thunderbird 1955-57

On Thunderbird the horn ring is removed by first removing the two screws at the back of the steering wheel.

STEERING WHEEL

Ford & T-Bird

After removing the horn button or emblem from the steering wheel as outlined above, take off the steering wheel nut and use a suitable puller to remove the wheel.

1960 Edsel

Remove steering wheel cap and horn ring by removing two screws from underside of steering wheel. Remove retaining nut and pull off steering wheel.

Conventional Type, 1958-59 Edsel

1. Use a small screwdriver or knife blade and pry the emblem button out of the steering wheel hub.
2. Remove the steering wheel retaining nut.
3. Place front wheels in straight-ahead position.
4. Then with a suitable puller, remove steering wheel.
5. When installing the steering wheel, make certain the front wheels are in the straight-ahead position.

Push Button Type, 1958 Edsel

1. Unsnap the medallion from the center of the push button trim plate.
2. Remove the two screws and lift off the trim plate.
3. Pull off the push buttons.
4. Remove the three screws and lift off the horn ring.
5. Remove three nuts and lift off plate and steering wheel from studs.
6. Install steering wheel by placing it over the three studs. Install contact plate and tighten nuts.
7. Install horn ring and retaining screws.
8. Press on push buttons and install trim plate and medallion.

STEERING GEAR, REPLACE

1953-56 Ford

To remove the steering wheel, disconnect the horn wire at the connector at the bottom of the gear housing. Remove the horn button or ring by pressing down and turning the button or ring counterclockwise. Pull the horn wire out of the steering gear shaft. Remove the nut and, with a suitable puller, remove the steering wheel.

To remove the steering gear, disconnect the steering column from the instrument panel. Disconnect the gearshift levers from the gearshift rods. Remove the capscrew from the bracket that secures the gearshift tube to the steering column tube and remove the bracket. Remove the gearshift tube pin and the gearshift levers.

Loosen the steering column clamp and pull the column tube off the steering gear shaft. Disconnect the steering arm from the linkage and use a puller to remove the steering arm from the steering gear. Unfasten the steering gear housing from the frame and take the gear out of the car. (It may be necessary to raise the car before the gear can be taken out.)

1955-57 Thunderbird

To remove the steering gear, disconnect the wires at the bottom of the steering gear housing. Loosen the lower steering column clamp, then remove the two screws from the upper steering column bracket.

Remove the horn ring from the steering wheel. Remove the upper steering column, upper steering shaft, and steering wheel as an assembly from the car.

Raise the front of the car. Remove the steering arm from the steering gear shaft. Unfasten the steering gear housing from the frame and remove the lower steering gear assembly from the car.

1957 Ford

On all cars except those with Fordomatic, the steering gear must be removed through the engine compartment. On cars with Fordomatic, remove the steering gear through the passenger compartment.

1. Remove steering wheel.
2. Disconnect turn signal wires under instrument panel.
3. Remove two screws that fasten steering column bracket to instrument panel. On cars without Fordomatic, remove turn indicator lever and gearshift lever from steering column.
4. Pull rubber weather seal up on steering column, then fold floor mat back from steering column.
5. Remove retaining screws from cover plate on engine compartment wall. Disconnect speedometer cable from instrument panel and remove right-hand cover plate from cable.
6. Disconnect Fordomatic or gearshift rods from levers on steering column.
7. On Fordomatic cars, disconnect neutral switch wires at bottom of column.
8. On cars with cynchromesh transmission, remove clutch return spring bracket.
9. Remove sector shaft arm nut and use a suitable puller to remove arm from shaft. On cars with single exhaust system, muffler inlet pipe must be removed before removing sector shaft arm.
10. Unfasten steering gear from frame and remove from car.

Ford 1958-60 Six and V8-292 With Synchromesh Transmission

1. Remove steering wheel.
2. Disconnect turn indicator wires under instrument panel.
3. Unfasten steering column bracket from instrument panel.
4. Remove turn indicator lever and gearshift lever.
5. Pull rubber seal up on steering column and fold mat away from steering column.
6. Remove screws from steering column weather seal on engine compartment wall.
7. Disconnect speedometer cable from instrument panel, remove right-hand cover plate and feed cable through cover plate.
8. Disconnect clutch pedal release rod at clutch pedal and remove cover plate from rod.
9. Disconnect clutch return spring.
10. Disconnect gearshift linkage at steering column bracket.
11. Remove nut and pull pitman arm from steering shaft.
12. Unfasten steering gear from frame and remove gear through engine compartment.

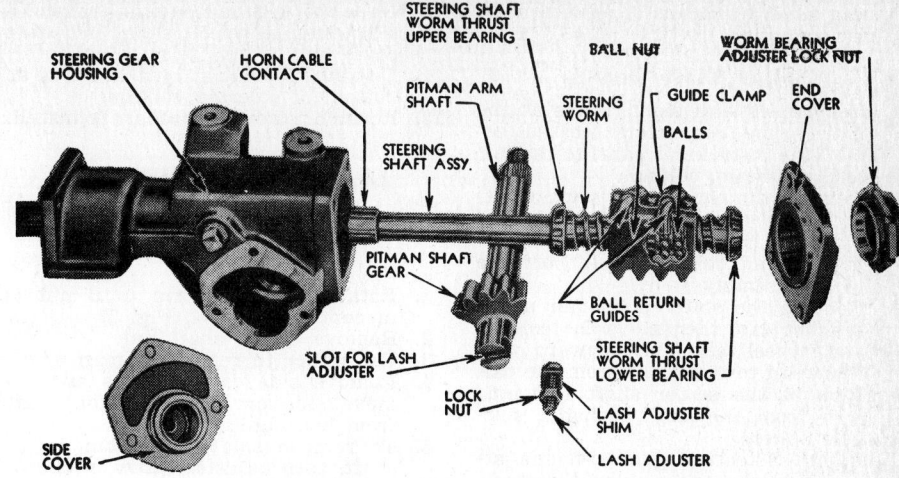

Fig. 7 Disassembled view of 1958-61 steering gear

13. Reverse removal procedure to install.

Ford 1958-60 V8-332 Conventional Drive and All Models with Automatic Transmission

1. Remove steering wheel.
2. Disconnect turn indicator wires under instrument panel.
3. On cars with automatic transmission, remove selector dial indicator cover and control selector indicator.
4. Unfasten steering column bracket from instrument panel.
5. Remove screws from steering column weather seal, disconnect speedometer cable at speedometer, remove steering column opening cover plates and route cable through weather seal.
6. Disconnect manual control linkage at steering gear.
7. On synchromesh transmission cars, disconnect clutch equalizer bar.
8. Disconnect neutral switch wires at bottom of steering column (if equipped).
9. Place front of car on safety stands.
10. Pull pitman arm off steering shaft.
11. Unfasten steering gear housing from frame and remove steering gear through inside of car.
12. Reverse removal procedure to install the gear.

1958-60 Thunderbird

1. Remove steering wheel.
2. Disconnect parking brake handle bracket and remove cowl side trim panel and left vent control handle.
3. Disconnect hood lock release cable bracket.
4. On cars with Cruise-O-Matic, remove starter neutral switch screws and move switch to one side.
5. Disconnect horn wire, and wiring assembly from steering column.
6. Unfasten and move instrument panel lower panel to one side.
7. Pull aside steering column cover plate insulation and disconnect parking brake bracket.

8. Remove steering column cover plate and parking brake handle.
9. Unfasten steering column from instrument panel.
10. On cars with conventional shift transmission, disconnect clutch linkage as necessary to provide clearance for steering gear removal through inside of car.
11. Disconnect shift lever(s) near steering column.
12. Pull off Pitman arm.
13. Unfasten and remove steering gear from inside car.

1961 Ford

1. Remove Pitman arm.
2. If necessary, disconnect exhaust pipe from manifold.
3. Remove steering gear housing attaching bolts. *If car has a flexible joint at the steering shaft, remove flexible joint clamp bolt and remove the gear.* Otherwise continue with the following steps.
4. With automatic transmission, disconnect neutral switch wires at switch.
5. Loosen steering column lower clamp.
6. Disconnect shift levers from rods.
7. Remove steering wheel, disconnect horn and turn signal wires and remove steering shaft upper bearing sleeve and spring.
8. Disconnect steering column-to-instrument panel bracket and remove selector dial indicator cover and control indicator.
9. After removing screws from steering column weather seal, position both halves of steering column opening cover plate out of the way.
10. Remove steering column tube assembly and then remove steering gear through passenger compartment.
11. Reverse foregoing procedure to install gear.

1958 Edsel

The steering gear worm is integral with the steering shaft on some models. On other models, a "stub" type worm shaft is used and is connected to the steering shaft by means of an internally splined coupling.

Stub Shaft Gear

1. Disconnect turn signal wires at the bullet type connectors located behind the instrument panel to the left of the steering column.
2. Remove the three screws which attach the selector switch terminal block to the lower side of the steering column tube, then lift off the block assembly.
3. Remove the steering column upper bracket cap, then move the column and wheel assembly upward and rearward to remove it from the car.
4. Remove the sector shaft (pitman) arm from the shaft, using a suitable puller.
5. Remove steering gear-to-frame attaching bolts and remove the steering gear.
6. Reverse the foregoing procedure to install the gear.

Long Shaft Gear

1. Remove steering wheel.
2. Disconnect turn signal wires under the instrument panel.
3. Disconnect automatic transmission neutral switch wires (if equipped).
4. Slide rubber weather seal up on steering column and fold floor mat away from column.
5. Disconnect speedometer cable at speedometer.
6. Remove clutch pedal release rod, clutch equalizer shaft, bushing and bracket.
7. Remove floor panel cover plate.
8. Remove sector shaft (pitman) arm with suitable puller.
9. Disconnect transmission or gear shift rods from levers on steering column.
10. Remove steering gear housing-to-frame attaching bolts.
11. Remove steering gear through front passenger compartment.
12. Reverse foregoing procedure to install the steering gear.

1959-60 Edsel

1. Remove steering wheel.
2. Disconnect turn indicator wires under instrument panel.
3. Remove two screws that fasten steering column bracket to instrument panel.
4. Remove turn indicator lever and gearshift lever from steering column.
5. Remove retaining screws from steering column weather seal on engine compartment wall and fold floor mat away from steering column.
6. Disconnect speedometer cable from instrument panel, remove right-hand cover plate and feed cable through cover plate.
7. Disconnect clutch pedal release rod at pedal and remove plate from rod.
8. Disconnect clutch return spring.
9. Disconnect gearshift linkage at steering column bracket.
10. Remove pitman arm from steering shaft.
11. Unfasten steering gear from frame and remove gear through engine compartment.

12. On cars with automatic transmission, remove selector dial indicator cover and control selector indicator. Disconnect neutral switch wires at bottom of steering column.
13. Reverse removal procedure to install.

MANUAL STEERING GEAR REPAIRS

1958-61

1. Rotate steering worm until nut is in center of travel, Fig. 7.
2. Remove sector shaft nut.
3. Use puller to remove pitman arm.
4. Remove side cover screws and remove side cover and sector shaft from housing.
5. To remove side cover from sector shaft, turn adjuster screw in end of sector shaft down through cover.
6. Remove screws and take out end cover with worm bearing, outer race and thrust washer.
7. To remove lower worm bearing, outer race and thrust washer from cover, loosen worm bearing adjuster screw lock nut and turn screw in through cover.
8. Grasp lower end of steering worm and draw steering shaft and nut out of steering housing. *Be sure to keep shaft in horizontal position so that nut does not move against stops at any time, causing damage to ball return mechanism.* Disassembly of worm nut is not recommended.

Assemble

1. Install worm shaft and nut assembly in gear housing, keeping ball nut away from stops on worm.
2. Install worm bearing adjusting screw with lower worm bearing, outer race and thrust washer in end cover.
3. Install end cover and attaching parts on gear housing, making sure bearings seat properly.
4. Tighten worm bearing adjusting screw until a slight drag is felt on bearings. Do not tighten lock nut.
5. Install pitman arm.
6. Install sector shaft and adjusting screw inside cover.
7. Rotate steering column until ball nut is in center of travel so that center tooth on sector shaft will enter center space on nut.
8. Install side cover and sector shaft in gear housing.
9. Tighten sector shaft adjusting screw until a slight drag is felt on bearing but do not tighten lock nut.
10. After steering gear is installed in car, adjust as outlined below:

Adjustments

1. Disconnect steering relay rod from pitman arm.
2. Loosen sector shaft lash adjuster screw a few turns to relieve load from bearings.
3. Turn steering wheel in one direction until stopped by gear, then back away about one turn.
4. With a spring scale hooked to rim

of steering wheel, measure pull required to keep wheel in motion; this should be $\frac{1}{4}$ to $\frac{3}{4}$ lbs. on a 9" radius. If not within these limits, adjust worm bearings as follows:
5. Loosen worm bearing adjuster lock nut and turn adjuster until there is no perceptible end play in worm. Check pull at wheel rim, readjusting as required to obtain proper pull. Tighten lock nut and recheck pull.
6. After worm bearing adjustment is completed and all mounting bolts tightened, adjust sector shaft end play.
7. With steering wheel in straight-ahead position, turn lash adjuster screw clockwise to remove all lash and tighten lock nut.
8. Check pull at rim of steering wheel, taking highest reading on scale as wheel is turned through the central or straight-ahead position. This should be between 1 to 1$\frac{5}{8}$ lbs. *If more than 1$\frac{5}{8}$ lbs., turn lash adjuster screw counterclockwise, then come up on the adjustment in a clockwise motion.*
9. Tighten lock nut and recheck pull.

1953-57 Adjustments

Before proceeding with the adjustments, loosen the gear housing from the frame side rail to relieve any possible vertical strain. Loosen the steering column clamp to relieve any possible horizontal strain. Then tighten the mounting and clamp bolts which will relieve any misalignment in the steering gear mounting.

Steering gear adjustments must be made in the order given below to insure satisfactory results.

Worm Bearing Preload

The worm bearing preload is controlled by the shim pack installed between the steering gear housing and the housing upper cap. The shim pack contains shims of various thicknesses; the thinner shims are installed on the top of the pack, and the adjustment is made as follows:

Disconnect the sector shaft arm from the steering linkage. Turn the steering wheel two complete turns from the straight-ahead position. Hook a spring scale to the steering wheel rim. Rotate the wheel at least one turn with the aid of the scale. The pull required to keep the wheel moving should be between $\frac{1}{8}$ and $\frac{5}{8}$ lbs., which is the worm bearing preload. If the reading is high, a shim or shims should be added. If reading is too low, remove a shim or shims.

If an adjustment is required, unfasten the upper cap from the housing and work the cap and column jacket upward to allow clearance for removing or adding shims. For additional working clearance it may be necessary to remove the steering wheel.

To add a shim, split the shim at one point and install the shim with the split in the upward position. Make sure the split ends do not overlap as this could lead to a false adjustment.

To remove a shim separate the first shim from the pack with a knife blade. Pass the blade all around the shim, being careful not to damage the shims.

The steering column and upper housing cap must be assembled on the gear housing each time the preload is checked.

Worm & Roller Mesh

This adjustment is controlled by the adjustment screw mounted on the sector shaft cover. Adjustment is made as follows:

Disconnect the sector shaft arm from the steering linkage. Attach a spring scale to the steering wheel rim. Pull the wheel through the straight-ahead position and note reading on scale. The scale reading should be at least ½ lb. above that of the worm bearing preload previously determined, but the total reading must not exceed 1⅝ lbs. If the scale reading does not exceed the worm bearing preload by at least ½ lb., the worm and roller mesh should be adjusted.

Place the steering wheel in the straight-ahead position. Remove the adjusting screw cover and lock washer. Rotate the adjusting screw clockwise while moving the steering gear arm back and forth until all backlash is removed.

Install the lock washer and cover and check the preload with the spring scale as previously described. The reading should be between 1 and 1⅝ lbs. If the reading is too high, turn the adjusting screw slightly counterclockwise. If too low, turn the screw slightly clockwise.

Disassemble

Fig. 6 illustrates the conventional steering gear used on 1956 models. But inasmuch as it is typical of earlier models the following procedure will mainly apply to these models.
1. Drain lubricant from housing.
2. Remove sector shaft and cover.
3. Remove cover from sector shaft.
4. Unfasten and slide housing cap off steering shaft.
5. Pull shaft out of housing.
6. Slide housing upper cap gaskets (shim pack), bearing cup, and upper worm bearing out of housing.
7. Use suitable puller to remove lower worm bearing cup.
8. Press sector shaft needle bearings and oil seal through steering arm end of housing.

Inspect & Assemble

After cleaning all parts, inspect worm and rollers for scores, cracks or for signs of chipping. Inspect steering shaft bearing cups and bearings for wear, cracks or damage. Check sector shaft for wear at needle bearing locations. Replace all parts that are damaged enough to impair steering gear operation, and assemble the steering gear in the reverse order of disassembly.

INTEGRAL POWER STEERING

1961 Thunderbird

The Ford Torsion Bar Power Steering unit is used. For repairs see the *Power Steering Chapter.* The following material outlines the removal and installation procedure.

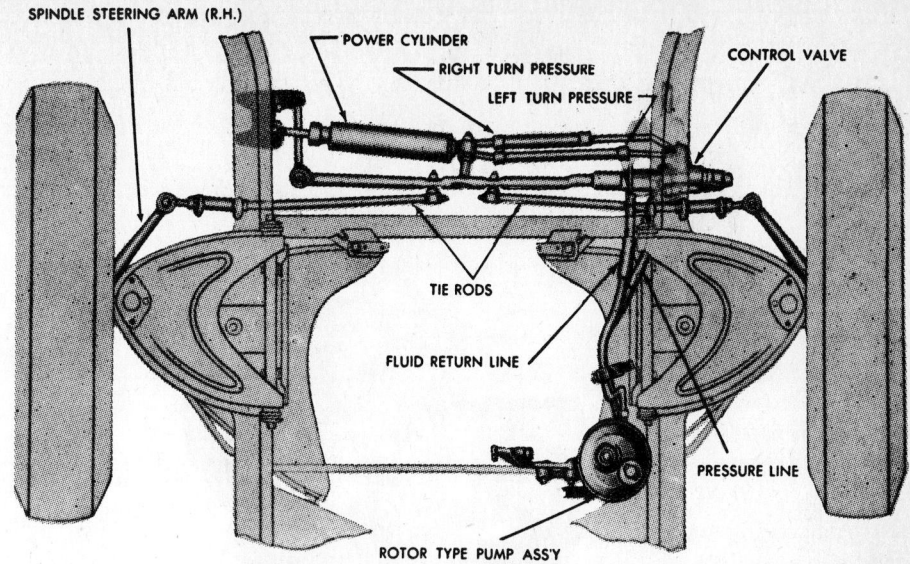

Fig. 8 Power steering components. 1954-61

Fixed Column Type

1. Disconnect hydraulic lines from gear housing. Plug openings and cap lines.
2. Disconnect steering shaft flexible joint by driving out tapered pin that retains joint flange to steering shaft.
3. Raise car and disconnect pitman arm from steering gear.
4. Remove gear housing bolts and remove gear.
5. Reverse removal procedure to install steering gear. Then, with engine idling, check for leaks by twice cycling steering wheel from one extreme to the other. Do not hold wheel against the stops. Add fluid to reservoir as required.

Movable Column Type

1. Disconnect hydraulic lines from gear housing. Plug openings and cap lines.
2. Remove 5 pivot bracket clamp bolts, remove bracket upper nut and remove pivot bracket.
3. Remove steering shaft retainer pin.
4. Disconnect pitman arm from steering gear.
5. Remove attaching bolts and remove gear from car.
6. Reverse removal procedure to install gear. Then with engine idling, check for leaks by twice cycling steering wheel from one extreme to the other. Do not hold wheel against stops. Add fluid to reservoir as required.

LINKAGE TYPE POWER STEERING

1954-61

The power steering system, Fig 8, combines a conventional type steering gear with a power-assisted steering linkage. The power-assist mechanism consists of a pump and fluid reservoir, a control valve, a power cylinder, the connecting fluid lines and the steering linkage. Figs. 9, 10 and 11 illustrate the main components of the system.

Before performing service operations on the power steering system, make certain that the trouble is not caused by the lack of fluid.

Fluid Pressure Test

A fluid pressure test will show whether the pump or some other unit in the power steering system is causing trouble in the system. Disconnect the pressure line hose from the pump outlet and install a pressure testing tool between the hose and pump outlet. *Be sure the pressure gauge is between the pump and shut-off valve on the tool.*

Open the shut-off valve on the testing tool and run the engine at idle speed. If the pump normally operates quietly, ignore the louder pump noise when the tester is connected to the system. Allow at least two minutes for the fluid to warm up before starting the pressure tests.

1. Turn the front wheels all the way to the right, then to the left, and note the fluid pressure reading on the gauge when the wheels are against the stops. Normal fluid pressure at both positions is 975-1100 lbs. *Do not hold the wheels against the stops for more than 30 seconds at a time as the fluid may overheat.*
2. If the fluid pressure is less than specified with the wheels against the stops, turn the wheels away from the stops. Slowly close the tester shut-off valve and watch the gauge for an increase in pressure. *Do not leave the valve closed for more than 15 seconds.*
3. If the fluid pressure is less than specified with the shut-off valve closed, the pump is causing the trouble. If the pressure increases but does not reach the minimum pressure specified, the pump, control valve and the power cylinder all should be inspected. If the pressure is within limits, the trouble is either

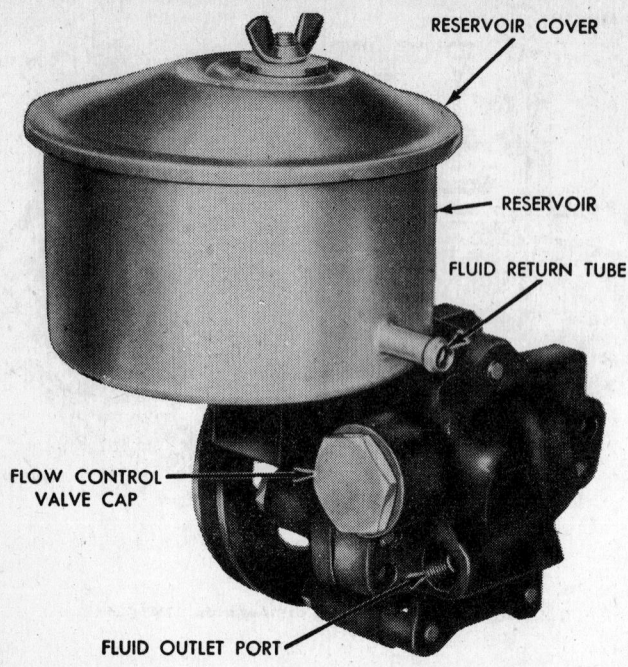

RESERVOIR COVER

RESERVOIR

FLUID RETURN TUBE

FLOW CONTROL
VALVE CAP

FLUID OUTLET PORT

Fig. 9 Power steering pump and reservoir

3. Measure distance between center of ball stud in sector shaft arm and the center of the stud at the inner end of the left-hand spindle connecting rod. *Be sure that measurement is taken parallel to the centerline of the control valve.* The distance should be as follows:

Ford 1961	$11\frac{15}{16}''$
1960	12''
1957-59	$10\frac{7}{8}''$
1954-56	9''
Thunderbird 1960	$10\frac{3}{4}''$
1959	$9\frac{1}{2}''$
1958	$10\frac{7}{8}''$
1955-57	$9\frac{1}{2}''$
Edsel 1960	$11\frac{15}{16}''$
1959	$10\frac{15}{16}''$
1958 Ranger, Pacer	$10\frac{7}{8}''$
1958 Citation, Corsair	$11\frac{1}{4}''$

4. When the correct distance is obtained, install the roll pin in the rod hole to lock the valve on the rod.
5. Tighten the valve sleeve clamp bolt to 30-35 lbs. ft. torque.
6. Install and tighten ball stud nut to a torque of 56-60 lbs. ft.
7. Connect and tighten four hoses on control valve.
8. Fill fluid reservoir to within ½" from top with automatic transmission fluid.
9. Start engine and run at idle speed for about two minutes to warm up fluid.
10. Turn steering wheel to both extremes several times and check for leaks.
11. Increase engine speed to a fast idle and again turn steering wheel several times to both extremes.
12. Stop engine and check system for leaks.
13. Hook a spring scale to steering wheel rim and measure pull required to turn wheel in both directions with engine idling and wheels on dry concrete. The pull should be about equal in both directions with tires inflated at specified pressures.

in the control valve or the power cylinder.
4. After completing the test, shut off the engine, remove the tester and make the necessary repairs.

Pump Removal

1. Remove reservoir cover and draw as much fluid from the reservoir as possible with a suction gun.
2. Disconnect hoses at pump and reservoir and fasten them in a raised position to prevent fluid draining out.
3. Remove pump drive belt.
4. Unfasten and remove pump.

Pump, Install

1. Mount pump on engine and install attaching bolts finger tight.
2. Install and tighten drive belt.
3. Check alignment of crankshaft pulley with pump pulley. If two pulleys are not aligned, the pump may be incorrectly installed or it may be necessary to install spacers to align the pulleys.
4. Adjust pump belt tension as outlined below.
5. Connect hoses at pump and reservoir.
6. Fill reservoir with automatic transmission fluid to ½" from top of reservoir.
7. Start engine and run at idle speed for about two minutes to warm up fluid in steering system.
8. Turn steering wheel to right and left extremes several times.
9. Check system for fluid leaks.
10. Increase engine speed to a fast idle and again turn steering wheel to both extremes several times.
11. Stop engine and check entire steering system for leaks.

Pump Belt Tension

1. Check belt tension with a torque wrench and socket on the pump pulley bolt. Pull the wrench slowly as if tightening the bolt. The torque required to slip the pulley against the belt friction should be within 14-16 lbs. ft.
2. If the belt is too loose or too tight, loosen the bracket adjusting bolts enough to permit moving the pump and bracket.
3. Reposition the pump until the pulley slips against the belt friction within 14-16 lbs. ft. torque. The belt tension should be as close as possible to the higher torque limit.

Control Valve Removal

1. Remove reservoir cover and, using a suction gun, draw as much fluid as possible from reservoir.
2. Disconnect four hoses at control valve and drain fluid from hoses.
3. Turn front wheels to extreme right and left several times to force all fluid from system.
4. Loosen clamp bolt and nut at right-hand end of sleeve.
5. Pull roll pin out of steering arm-to-idler arm rod through slot in sleeve.
6. Remove control valve ball stud nut.
7. Remove nut from end of ball stud, then raise control valve high enough to remove ball stud from sector shaft arm.
8. Turn wheels fully to left, then turn control valve counterclockwise to remove it.

Control Valve, Install

1. Thread valve on steering arm-to-idler arm rod until about four threads are still visible on the rod.
2. Position ball stud in sector shaft arm.

Power Cylinder Removal

1. Disconnect the two hoses from power cylinder. Fasten open ends of hoses in raised position to prevent fluid draining out.
2. Place a container under the ports of the power cylinder, then slowly move the front wheels to the left and right several times to force fluid from cylinder.
3. Remove nut, washer and insulator from outer end of piston rod. Do not remove rod from idler arm bracket at this time.
4. Remove nut, washer and insulator from end of stud in steering arm-to-idler arm rod.
5. Pull piston rod out of idler arm bracket and remove power cylinder.

Power Cylinder, Install

1. Install inner washer and bushing on mounting stud in steering arm-to-idler arm rod.

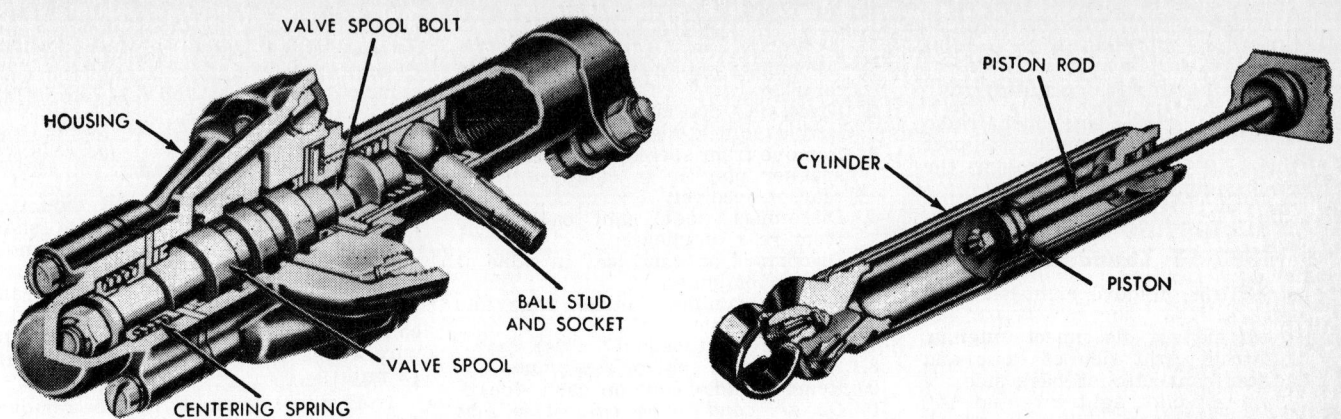

Fig. 10 Power steering control valve   Fig. 11 Power steering power cylinder

2. Install inner insulator and washer on power cylinder piston rod, then position the cylinder on the mounting stud with the piston rod in the idler arm bracket.
3. Install outer bushing, washer and nut on mounting stud. If a new nut is installed, tighten it to a torque of 60-70 lbs. ft. If a used nut is installed, tighten it to 50-60 lbs. ft.

4. Install the outer insulator, washer and nut on the piston rod, and tighten the nut to a torque of 40-50 lbs. ft.
5. Connect and tighten two hoses to control valve.
6. Fill reservoir to proper level.
7. Start engine and run at idle speed for about two minutes to warm

fluid.
8. Turn steering wheel to right and left extremes several times and check system for fluid leaks.
9. Increase engine speed to a fast idle and again turn steering wheel to both extremes several times.
10. Stop engine and check for fluid leaks.

Speedometer, Radio and Windshield Wiper

SPEEDOMETER, REPLACE

1954

Remove various light units and speedometer cable. Remove the hold down clamp and two mounting screws. Remove speedometer from above instrument panel.

1955

1. Remove speedometer dome (4 nuts).
2. Remove temperature and fuel gauges.
3. Remove speedometer back plate (4 screws).
4. Unfasten front housing from upper housing (2 screws) and remove front housing.
5. Remove lower housing (2 screws).
6. Speedometer may now be removed from upper housing (2 screws).

1956

Disconnect speedometer cable and remove four speedometer mounting screws. Rotate speedometer ¼ turn clockwise and remove it from cluster.

1957 All, 1958-60 Ford

Remove instrument cluster from front of panel. Remove cluster back plate. Speedometer may now be removed.

1958-60 Thunderbird

Pull speedometer bezel from instrument panel. Remove four mounting screws and pull speedometer far enough from panel to disconnect cable and remove pilot lights.

1961 Ford

1. Disconnect battery cable.
2. Remove instrument cluster.
3. Unfasten and remove speedometer from instrument cluster.

1961 Thunderbird

Remove screw retaining chrome trim ring and remove ring. Remove mounting screws and pull speedometer far enough from instrument panel to disconnect cable and remove pilot lights.

Make certain all pilot lights are secure in their mounting holes when installing speedometer. The top pilot light is the high beam indicator.

1958 Edsel

1. Disconnect battery ground cable.
2. Unfasten left-hand fresh air duct from instrument panel.
3. Lower duct, remove cable and remove duct.
4. Remove speedometer light sockets.
5. Disconnect cable housing from speedometer.
6. Unhook wiring harness from clips and move harness downward out of the way.
7. Unfasten speedometer (4 screws), tip unit downward and remove from rear of cluster.

1959 Edsel

1. Disconnect battery ground cable.
2. Remove hi-beam indicator and speedometer lamp socket and bulb assemblies.
3. Remove oil pressure and charge indicator lamp sockets and bulbs.
4. Disconnect speedometer cable.
5. Disconnect two wires from constant voltage (C.V.) regulator.
6. Remove five screws from speedometer retainer plate and carefully remove speedometer from cluster.

1960 Edsel

1. Remove upper instrument cluster.
2. Remove six speedometer case-to-cluster screws and remove speedometer and case.
3. Remove speedometer from case.

RADIO REPLACE

1960-61 Ford

1. Pull off radio knobs and remove nuts retaining radio to instrument panel.
2. Disconnect antenna lead at right side of radio.
3. Disconnect speaker leads and pilot light wire at wiring harness.
4. Disconnect radio lead wire at fuse panel and wire from retaining clips.
5. Remove radio support bolt and nut.
6. Lift radio out of instrument panel.

7. Reverse removal procedure to install.

1960-61 Ford Air Conditioned

Remove the glove box liner, radio speaker, right radio mounting support and then lift the radio through the speaker opening.

1953-59 Ford
1955-57 Thunderbird

1. On 1957-58, remove right-hand air duct.
2. On all models, disconnect antenna, lead from right side of radio and speaker connector at back side.
3. Disconnect pilot light wire and "A" lead from radio.
4. Remove fuse and two panel mounting screws.
5. Remove nut from stud on each side of radio and press brackets away from studs.
6. Push radio forward and tilt it toward toeboard until it clears instrument panel.

1958-60 Thunderbird

Radio Receiver — Remove the control knobs and two mounting nuts. Remove radio access cover and rear support bracket-to-instrument panel mounting bolt. Lower receiver through access hole and disconnect pilot light lead, "A" lead and audio chassis cable.

Audio Chassis—To gain access, remove left heater control trim panel extension. Disconnect audio chassis cable from receiver control chassis. Disconnect speaker and remove chassis (4 screws).

Speaker—Remove heater control trim panel and tunnel trim panel. Remove four mounting nuts and disconnect speaker cable from audio chassis and remove speaker.

1961 Thunderbird

1. With ignition switch off, remove speaker grille and speaker.
2. Remove control knobs, two hex mounting nuts, the bezel, and two radio mounting nuts and washers.
3. Remove radio access cover and radio lower center support screw.
4. Remove radio through speaker opening.

1958 Edsel

1. Remove both fresh air ducts from under instrument panel.
2. Disconnect antenna and speaker wires from radio. *Never turn radio on while speaker is disconnected as this will damage the transistors.*
3. Disconnect pilot light at bullet connector and the "A" lead at fuse panel.
4. Remove control knobs, serrated ring controls, bezel and radio retaining nuts.
5. Remove bracket nuts from each side of radio and press brackets away from studs.
6. Work radio out of instrument panel, then tilt it toward toeboard until unit clears intrument panel.

1959 Edsel

1. Disconnect ground cable from battery.
2. Disconnect dial lamp and "A" power lead at quick disconnect.
3. Remove front speaker plug, and rear speaker plug if so equipped, from rear of receiver.
4. Disconnect audio unit cable plug from rear of chassis.
5. Disconnect antenna lead in cable at bottom of chassis.
6. Remove tuning, volume, tone and speaker knobs.
7. Remove escutcheon (2 nuts).
8. Remove two control shaft nuts.
9. Remove radio (nut on each side).
10. *On air conditioned cars it will be necessary to remove glove box, clock, ash receiver and evaporator cover plate. Radio may then be removed from under right side of instrument panel.*

1960 Edsel

1. Disconnect battery ground cable.
2. Remove control knobs, nuts and washers from front of radio.
3. Disconnect antenna lead-in cable and front seat speaker plug.
4. Disconnect dial lamp wire at bullet connector and "A" power lead at fuse mounting block.
5. Remove nut from radio bracket at right side and screw from bracket at left side. Then remove radio. *On cars with air conditioning, it is necessary to remove ash tray and spot cooler.*
6. To install, reverse removal procedure.

WINDSHIELD WIPER

1953-56

1. To remove wiper motor, first take out radio.
2. Remove linkage and vacuum line from motor.
3. Remove motor from mounting bracket (2 screws).
4. Remove cable from motor.

1957

The wiper motor operates through two sets of cables. Tension on the cables is maintained by two cable tensioners. The wiper motor is removed in the same manner as on earlier models except that the radio *need not* be removed. To remove the cables and tensioners, it will be necessary to remove the cowl top ventilator grille and weatherstrip.

To assemble the cables, first connect them to the motor pulley. Pull the cable tension ratchet spring away from the ratchet, wind up the cable tension spring and insert a cotter pin in the hole temporarily. Position cables over tension pulleys and install tensioners. Remove holding cotter pin, install pivot shaft idler pulley water shields, and ventilator grille and weatherstrip.

1958 Ford

When service is required on the wiper motor, control assembly or pivot shaft assemblies, they may be removed separately. To gain access to the motor and linkage, however, first take out the radio and remove the cowl top ventilator grille and weatherstrip.

1959 Ford

To remove the motor and mounting plate, first disconnect the pivot shaft links from the motor shaft arm (under instrument panel). On vacuum motor jobs disconnect control cable and vacuum hose. On electric motor jobs disconnect control cable and motor supply wire. Remove motor and mounting plate (2 nuts).

The control assembly may be removed from the instrument panel by removing the bezel nut after loosening and removing the control knob.

To remove the pivot shafts, first lift off the wiper arms and blades. Remove the link retaining clips from the motor shaft. Remove pivot attaching nuts, spacers and washers. The pivots may then be removed.

1960-61 Ford

To remove the wiper motor on car with air conditioner, remove the glove box liner, radio, speaker, and right defroster nozzle-to-instrument panel brace (if equipped). Then remove the wiper motor through the speaker opening.

To remove the wiper motor on cars without air conditioning, proceed as follows:

1. Remove two bolts retaining motor and lower the motor.
2. Disconnect wiper motor vacuum line at motor or at bullet connector.
3. Loosen screw retaining wiper control cable at motor and disconnect cable.
4. Reverse above procedure to install motor and adjust control cable.

1958-60 Thunderbird

When service is required on the wiper motor, control assembly or pivot shaft assemblies, they may be removed separately. To remove any of the wiper assemblies it will first be necessary to remove the glove box. To remove the wiper motor, in addition to the glove box, the right defroster air duct must also be removed. And to gain access to the left pivot shaft the speedometer must be removed.

Before installing a new wiper motor, loosen the motor drive pulley tension clamp nut, compress the tension arms and tighten the nut. When the motor is installed, loosen the tension arms clamp nut to put tension on the cables then tighten the nut.

Before installing new pivot shaft assemblies, loosen the motor drive pulley tension arms clamp nut, compress the tension arms with a "C" clamp and tighten the nut. After installing the cables and pivot shafts, release the tension arms clamp nut, then tighten it.

1958-59 Edsel

If service is required on the wiper motor, control assembly or pivot shaft and cable tensioners, they can be removed separately. Removal of the wiper motor and control assembly is obvious. The following outlines the requirements on the pivot shaft and cable tensioners:

1. Remove nine screws and lift off cowl top ventilator grille.
2. Remove rubber plugs from access holes in cowl panel above cable tensioners.
3. Remove nuts and screws from tensioner mounting brackets. Remove tensioners from cowl panel, leaving them in cowl compartment.
4. Remove wiper arms and blades.
5. Unfasten and lower pivot assemblies into cowl compartment.
6. Reach through cowl top ventilator opening and disconnect cables from auxiliary drive.
7. Remove wiper pivot and cable and tensioner assemblies from cowl compartment.
8. Bend cable guide tabs slightly to release cables from tensioner pulleys. *The cable tensioner always winds to its tightest position when cables are removed from pulleys. Therefore, it is important that the tensioners be reset before they are installed.*
9. Clamp the tensioner in a vise to pre-set the spring. While holding the leaf spring away from the ratchet, wind up the cable tension spring until the locking pin hole is in line with the bracket. Insert a cotter pin in the hole to hold the tensioner in the pre-set position temporarily.
10. Install the cables on the pulleys and bend cable guide tabs to their original position so that they barely clear the pulleys.
11. Install the assemblies, *noting that the cable tips and cable attaching tabs on the auxiliary drive pulley are color coded to facilitate assembly of cables in proper grooves on the drive.*
12. When installed and tightened, insert a hooked tool through the access hole in the cowl and pull the cotter pins out of the tensioners.

1960 Edsel

1. Disconnect battery ground cable on cars with electric wiper and/or air conditioning.
2. Disconnect control cable from motor.
3. Disconnect vacuum hose from motor, and windshield washer control cable (if equipped).
4. Unfasten and remove wiper motor from dash panel.
5. On air conditioned cars, remove radio and spot cooler in order to remove wiper motor.
6. Reverse above procedure to install.

LANCER & VALIANT

INDEX OF SERVICE OPERATIONS

PAGE NO.

ACCESSORIES

Speedometer, Replace 774
Radio, Replace 774
Windshield Wiper 774
Windshield Wiper Troubles 37

BODY

Air Conditioning 177
Automatic Seat Adjuster Troubles 36
Automatic Top Troubles 36
Automatic Window Lift Troubles 36

BRAKES (Mechanical)

Adjustments 112
Brake Cylinder Sizes.................. 757
Hydraulic Brake System 112
Master Cylinder, Replace..............770
Trouble Shooting 31

BRAKES (Power)

Power Unit Repairs....................128
Power Unit, Replace...................770
Trouble Shooting 32

CLUTCH

Clutch Pedal, Adjust..................765
Clutch, Replace 765
Clutch Service 765
Trouble Shooting 13

COOLING

Radiator, Replace 763
Trouble Shooting 8
Water Pump Repairs...................763
Water Pump, Replace..................763

ELECTRIC SYSTEM

Alternator Specifications 757
Alternator Service 57
Dash Gauge Service................... 85
Distributor, Replace..................764
Distributor Service................... 46
Distributor Specifications 756
Ignition System Service............... 46
Ignition Timing 764
Starter Switch Service 83
Starting Motor Service 77
Starting Motor Specifications.........756
Starter, Replace 764
Trouble Shooting 10
Turn Signal Troubles 12

ENGINE

Camshaft & Bearings...................761
Crankshaft & Bearing Specs............755
Crankshaft Oil Seal, Replace..........762
Cylinder Head, Replace................758
Engine, Replace 758
Main Bearings, Replace................762
Piston Pins, Replace..................762
Piston Rings, Replace.................762
Piston, Pin & Ring Specs..............755
Pistons & Rods, Remove...............761
Piston & Rod, Assemble...............761
Pistons, Replace 762
Rocker Arms, Replace.................759
Rod Bearings, Replace.................762
Timing Case Cover, Replace...........761
Timing Chain, Replace................761
Trouble Shooting 4
Valve Arrangement 759
Valves, Adjust 759
Valves, Grind 760
Valve Guides, Replace................760
Valve Lifters 761
Valves, Remove 760
Valve Spring Installed Height..........760
Valve Spring Testing..................761
Valve Specifications 756
Valve Timing Data....................761

ENGINE OILING

Oil Pan, Replace......................763
Oil Pump Repairs.....................763
Trouble Shooting 9

FRONT SUSPENSION

Camber, Adjust 770
Caster, Adjust 770
Front End Repairs....................771
Riding Height, Adjust.................770
Toe-in, Adjust 770
Trouble Shooting 33
Wheel Alignment Specifications.......757
Wheel Bearings, Adjust...............770

FUEL SYSTEM

Carburetors 764
Fuel Pumps 96
Trouble Shooting 4

OVERDRIVE 100

Trouble Shooting 14

REAR AXLE

Axle Shaft, Replace...................770
General Service 102
Non-Slip Differentials.................109
Rear Axle Repairs....................768
Rear Axle Specifications..............757
Trouble Shooting 31

SPECIFICATIONS

Alternator 757
Brake Cylinder Sizes..................757
Capacity Data 756
Carburetors 765
Cooling System 756
Crankshaft & Bearings................755
Distributors 756
Engine Tightening 758
Pistons, Pins & Rings.................755
Rear Axle 757
Starting Motors 756
Tune Up 755
Valve Timing ....
Valves 756
Wheel Alignment 757

STEERING GEARS, MANUAL

Horn Button & Ring...................773
Repairs 773
Replace 773
Steering Wheel, Replace..............773
Trouble Shooting 33

STEERING GEAR, POWER

Repairs 145
Replace 773
Trouble Shooting 34

TRANSMISSION, MANUAL

Gearshift, Adjust 767
Repairs 766
Replace 766
Trouble Shooting 14

TRANSMISSION, AUTOMATIC

Linkage, Adjust 767
Repairs 331
Replace 767
Trouble Shooting 23

TUNE UP 38

GENERAL SPECIFICATIONS

Year	Model Designation	Wheelbase, Inches	Valve Location	Bore and Stroke	Piston Displacement, Cubic Inches	Compression Ratio (Standard)	Maximum Brake H.P. @ R.P.M.	Maximum Torque Lbs. Ft. @ R.P.M.	Normal Oil Pressure Pounds
LANCER									
1961	Models 170, 770..........Six	106½	In Head	3.4062 x 3.125	170	8.2	101 @ 4400	155 @ 2400	40–65
	Power Package..........Six	106½	In Head	3.4062 x 4.125	225	8.2	145 @ 4000	215 @ 2800	40–65
VALIANT									
1960	All...................Six	106½	In Head	3.4062 x 3.125	170	8.6	101 @ 4400	155 @ 2400	40–65
1961	All...................Six	106½	In Head	3.4062 x 3.125	170	8.2	101 @ 4400	155 @ 2400	40–65

TUNE UP SPECIFICATIONS

★When using a timing light, disconnect vacuum line to prevent advance mechanism from functioning.

Year	Model	Ground Polarity and Voltage	Spark Plug Type ①	Spark Plug Gap Inch	Distributor Point Gap Inch	Distributor Cam Angle Degrees	Firing Order	Ignition Timing★ Mark	Ignition Timing★ Location	Idle Speed RPM In Neutral	Compression Pressure @ Cranking Speed Minimum
LANCER											
1961	All	N-12	AG-52	.035	.020	40–45	153624	2½°BTDC	Pulley	500	130
VALIANT											
1960	All	N-12	AG-52	.035	.020	40–45	153624	2½°BTDC	Pulley	500	130
1961	All	N-12	AG-52	.035	.020	40–45	153624	2½°BTDC	Pulley	500	130

①—Auto-Lite.

PISTONS, PINS, RINGS, CRANKSHAFT & BEARINGS

Year	Model	Fitting Pistons Shim To Use	Fitting Pistons Pounds Pull On Scale	Ring End Gap ① Minimum Comp.	Ring End Gap ① Minimum Oil	Wrist-pin Diameter	Rod Bearings Shaft Diameter	Rod Bearings Bearing Clearance	Main Bearings Shaft Diameter	Main Bearings Bearing Clearance	Main Bearings Thrust on Bear. No.	Shaft End Play
LANCER & VALIANT												
1960–61	All	②	②	.010	.010	.9008	2.1865–2.1875	.0005–.0015	2.7495–2.7505	.0005–.0015	3	.002–.007

①—Fit rings in tapered bores for clearance listed in tightest portion of ring travel.
②—Fit pistons to a clearance of .0005–.0015″ at top of piston skirt with parts at room temperature (70°).

LANCER & VALIANT

VALVE SPECIFICATIONS

Year	Model	Valve Lash Int.	Valve Lash Exh.	Valve Angles Seat	Valve Angles Face	Valve Spring Installed Height	Valve Spring Pressure Lbs. @ In.	Valve Lift Int.	Valve Lift Exh.	Stem Clearance Intake	Stem Clearance Exhaust	Stem Diameter Int.	Stem Diameter Exh.
LANCER													
1961	All	.010H	.020H	①	①	1¹¹⁄₁₆	165 @ 1⁵⁄₁₆	.375	.360	.001–.003	.002–.004	.3725	.3715
VALIANT													
1960	All	.010H	.020H	①	①	1¹¹⁄₁₆	177 @ 1⁵⁄₁₆	.375	.368	.001–.003	.002–.004	.3725	.3715
1961	All	.010H	.020H	①	①	1¹¹⁄₁₆	165 @ 1⁵⁄₁₆	.375	.360	.001–.003	.002–.004	.3725	.3715

①—Intake face and seat 45°, exhaust seat 45°, exhaust face 47°.

DISTRIBUTOR SPECIFICATIONS

Year	Model	Part No. ①	Rotation ②	Cam Angle, Degrees	Breaker Point Opening, Inch	Condenser Capacity, Mfds.	Breaker Arm Spring Tension, Ounces	Centrifugal Advance Data Degrees @ R.P.M. of Dist. Advance Starts	Centrifugal Advance Data Degrees @ R.P.M. of Dist. Full Advance	Vacuum Advance Data Inches of Vacuum to Start Plunger Movement	Vacuum Advance Data Inches of Vacuum for Full Plunger Travel	Vacuum Advance Data Maximum Vacuum Advance, Dist. Degrees
LANCER & VALIANT												
1960-61	All	1889750	C	40-45	.020	.25–.28	17–21	0 @ 325	12 @ 1925	5	14½	11

①—Stamped on distributor housing.   ②—Viewed from top.

STARTING MOTOR SPECIFICATIONS

Year	Model	Part No.	Rotation ①	Brush Spring Tension, Ounces	No Load Test Amperes	No Load Test Volts	No Load Test R.P.M.	Torque Test Amperes	Torque Test Volts	Torque Lbs. Ft.
LANCER & VALIANT										
1960-61	All	MDT-7009	C	32-48	58	11	3800 Min.	350	4	8½

①—Viewed from drive end.   C: Clockwise.

COOLING SYSTEM & CAPACITY DATA

Year and Model	Cooling System Data Quarts No Heater	Cooling System Data Quarts With Heater	Cooling System Data Rad. Cap Relief Pressure	Cooling System Data Thermostat Opening Temp. ①	Cooling System Data Thermostat Opening Temp. ②	Fuel Tank Gals.	Engine Oil Refill Qts. ③	Engine Oil Summer Grade	Engine Oil Winter Grade	Transmissions Std. Pints	Transmissions With Over-drive Pints	Transmissions Automatic Qts.	Rear Axle Pints
LANCER & VALIANT													
1960-61	13	14	14	180	160	13	4	30	10W	5	None	6½	2

①—For permanent type anti-freeze.   ②—For alcohol type anti-freeze.   ③—Add one quart with filter change.

WHEEL ALIGNMENT SPECIFICATIONS

Year	Model	Caster, Degrees Limits	Caster, Degrees Desired	Camber, Degrees Limits	Camber, Degrees Desired	Toe-in, Inch	Toe-out on Turns, Degrees[1] Outer Wheel	Toe-out on Turns, Degrees[1] Inner Wheel	Knuckle Support Angle
LANCER									
1961	Manual Steer.	0 to —1	—½	[3]	[2]	3/32 to 5/32	17⅔	20	6½ to 8½
	Power Steer.	+ ¼ to + 1¼	+ ¾	[3]	[2]	3/32 to 5/32	17⅔	20	6½ to 8½
VALIANT									
1960–61	Manual Steer.	0 to — 1	—½	[2]	[2]	⅛	17⅔	20	7½° @ 0° Camber
	Power Steer.	+ ¼ to + 1¼	+ ¾	[2]	[2]	⅛	17⅔	20	7½° @ 0° Camber

[1]—Incorrect toe-out, when other adjustments are correct, generally indicates bent steering arms.
[2]—Right preferred + ⅛°, left preferred + ⅜°.
[3]—Right preferred + ¼°, left + ½°.

REAR AXLE AND BRAKE CYLINDER SPECIFICATIONS

Year	Model	Ring Gear & Pinion Backlash, Inch	Drive Pinion Adjustment	Drive Pinion Bearing Preload, Inch Lbs.	Drive Pinion Bearing Adjustment	Axle Shaft End Play, Inch	Hydraulic Cylinder Bore Sizes, Inch — Wheel Cylinder Front	Hydraulic Cylinder Bore Sizes, Inch — Wheel Cylinder Rear	Master Cylinder
LANCER & VALIANT									
1960–61	All	.004–.006	Washer	15–25[1]	Washer	.013–.023[2]	1.00	13/16	1.00

[1]—For used bearings, 0–13 inch lbs. with no pinion end play.
[2]—Adjust to .018″.

ALTERNATOR AND REGULATOR SPECIFICATIONS

Year	Unit Number	Ground Polarity and Rotation	Field Coil Draw Amperes	Current Output Engine R.P.M.	Current Output Amperes	Current Output Volts	Operating Voltage Engine R.P.M.	Operating Voltage Amperes	Operating Voltage Voltage @ 120°[1]	Voltage Regulator Point Gap	Regulator Armature Air Gap
LANCER & VALIANT											
1960–61	2095060	Neg.-C	2.38–2.75[2]	1250	28[3]	14.6	1250	15	13.48–14.08[4]	.015	.048–.052

[1]—For each 10° rise in temperature subtract .04 volt; for each 10° drop add .04 volt. Temperature is checked with a thermometer 2 inches from installed voltage regulator cover.
[2]—Current draw at 12 volts while turning rotor shaft by hand.
[3]—If output is low, stator or rectifier is shorted.
[4]—At 2200 R.P.M. there should be a voltage increase of .2 to .7 volt.

ENGINE TIGHTENING SPECIFICATIONS★

★Torque specifications are for clean and lightly lubricated threads only. Dry or dirty threads produce increased friction which prevents accurate measurement of tightness.

Year	Spark Plugs Ft. Lbs.	Cylinder Head Bolts Ft. Lbs.	Intake Manifold Ft. Lbs.	Exhaust Manifold Ft. Lbs.	Rocker Arm Shaft Bracket Ft. Lbs.	Rocker Arm Cover Ft. Lbs.	Connecting Rod Cap Bolts Ft. Lbs.	Main Bearing Cap Bolts Ft. Lbs.	Flywheel to Crankshaft Ft. Lbs.	Vibration Damper or Pulley Ft. Lbs.
LANCER & VALIANT										
1960–61	30	65	①	10	30	③	45	85	60	②

①—200 inch lbs. ②—Press fit. ③—40 inch lbs.

SERIAL NUMBER LOCATION:
Left front door hinge pillar.

ENGINE NUMBER LOCATION:
Boss on right side of block.

ENGINE IDENTIFICATION:

1960 Valiant

Eng. No. Prefix

1960 Six (6-170) P17①
1961 Six (6-170) R17①
1961 Six (6-225) R22①

①—Additional numerals denote month and day of production.

1961 Lancer

1961 Valiant

Engine Section

ENGINE, REPLACE

1. Scribe hood hinge outlines on hood and remove hood.
2. Drain cooling system and remove battery and carburetor air cleaner.
3. Disconnect transmission cooler lines at radiator (if equipped).
4. Remove radiator and hoses.
5. Remove outlet vent pipe.
6. Disconnect fuel lines, carburetor linkage and wiring to engine.
7. Disconnect exhaust pipe at manifold.
8. Disconnect propeller shaft and tie out of the way.
9. Remove speedometer cable and gearshift rods.
10. Remove clutch torque shaft, brake cables and rods.
11. Remove converter cover plate.
12. Drain converter and transmission. Remove oil cooler lines, filler tube and push button cable.
13. Support rear of engine.
14. Remove engine rear support crossmember.
15. Disconnect converter from flexible mounting plate.
16. Remove transmission bolts from clutch housing.
17. Remove transmission and converter as an assembly. *Do not remove converter from transmission.*
18. Attach lifting fixture to cylinder head and attach chain hoist.
19. Remove engine support and front engine mounting bolts and lift engine from chassis.
20. Reverse above procedure to install.

CYLINDER HEAD

1. To remove head, drain cooling system.
2. Remove carburetor air cleaner and fuel line.
3. Disconnect accelerator linkage.
4. Remove vacuum control tube at carburetor and distributor.
5. Disconnect spark plug wires, heater hose and clamp holding by-pass hose.
6. Disconnect heat indicator sending unit wire.
7. Disconnect exhaust pipe at manifold.
8. Remove intake and exhaust manifold and carburetor as a unit.
9. Remove outlet vent tube and rocker arm cover.
10. Remove thermostat housing and thermostat.
11. Remove rocker arms and push rods.
12. Remove head bolts and lift off head.
13. Check all surfaces of head with a straightedge if there is any reason to suspect leakage. *Cylinder head warpage should not exceed .005" lengthwise or .003" crosswire.* If there is any reason to suspect restricted water passages, the large recessed screw plug in the rear of the head can be removed.
14. Clean the oil return passages in the head and block.

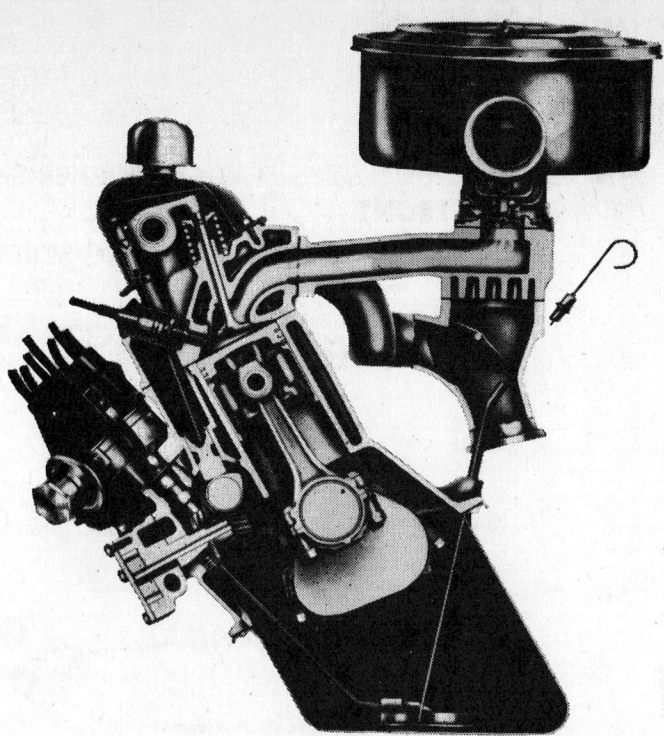

Lancer and Valiant engine

2. Remove rocker arm cover.
3. Remove rocker shaft bolts and retainers.
4. Lift off rocker arms and shaft.

Inspection

Clean all parts with a suitable solvent. Be sure the inside of the shaft is clean and the oil holes are open. The drilled oil hole in the bore of the rocker arm must be open to the trough and valve end of the arms. The trough also feeds oil to the adjusting screw and push rod.

The shaft should be free from excessive wear in arm contact areas. The shaft should be smooth in retainer contact areas. The adjusting screws in the rocker arms should have a uniform round end. The drag torque should be smooth and uniform. The retainers should be smooth and undamaged in the shaft contact area.

Assemble and Install

1. Referring to Fig. 4, note flat on forward end of rocker shaft which denotes the upper side of the shaft. Rocker arms must be put on the shaft with the adjusting screw to the right side of the engine. Place one of the small retainers on the one long bolt and install the bolt in the rear hole in the shaft from the top side.
2. Install one rocker arm and one spacer; then two rocker arms and a spacer. Continue in same sequence until all rocker arms and spacers are on the shaft.

15. Install the head in the reverse order of removal and tighten the bolts in the sequence shown in Fig. 3 and to the torque listed in the *Engine Torque* table.
16. *When installing the manifolds, loosen the three bolts holding the intake manifold to the exhaust manifold. This is required to maintain proper alignment.* Install intake and exhaust manifold with carburetor with the cup side of the conical washers against the manifolds. Tighten the nuts to 10 ft. lbs. Then tighten the three bolts holding the intake manifold to the exhaust manifold to 15 ft. lbs.

ROCKER ARMS

1. To remove rocker arms, take off head cover outlet tube.

VALVE ARRANGEMENT

Front to Rear

1960-61 . . . . E-I-E-I-E-I-I-E-I-E-I-E

VALVES ADJUST

Before the final valve lash adjustment is made, operate the engine for 30 minutes at a fast idle to stabilize engine temperatures.

Before starting the adjustment procedure, make two chalk marks on the vibration damper. Space the marks approximately 120° apart (⅓ of circumference) so that with the timing mark the damper is divided into three equal parts. Adjust the valves for No. 1 cylinder. Repeat the procedure for the remaining valves, turning the crankshaft ⅓ turn in the direction of normal rotation while adjusting the valves in the firing order sequence of 153624.

Fig. 2   Internal parts of engine

3. Place a bolt and small retainer in front hole in shaft.
4. Place a bolt and the one *wide* retainer through the center hole in the shaft with six rocker arms on each side of center.
5. Install remaining bolts and retainers, separating the four pairs of rocker arms.
6. Locate the assembly on the cylinder head and position rocker arm adjusting screws in push rods.
7. Tighten bolts finger tight, bringing retainers in contact with the shaft *between rocker arms.*
8. Tighten bolts to 30 ft. lbs.
9. After running engine to normal operating temperature, adjust valve lash to specifications.
10. Complete the job by installing the remaining parts removed.

VALVES, REMOVE

Place the cylinder head on its side and, with a suitable valve spring compressor, compress the valve spring and remove the valve locks. Release the tool and remove spring retainer and spring. Remove any burrs or sharp edges on the valve stem before removing the cup seal and valve. As the valves are removed, keep them in a numbered board or rack in the same order as they were in the head so they will be in proper sequence for inspection and assembly.

VALVES, GRIND

Clean the valves with a wire wheel brush, making sure all carbon is removed from the top and bottom of the valve heads as well as the gum which might have accumulated on the valve stems.

In refacing valves, take off only the minimum of metal required to clean up the valve faces. If the outer edge of the valve becomes too sharp or thin due to excessive grinding, the valve must be scrapped. This condition leads to premature breakage, burning and pre-ignition due to the heat localizing on this knife edge. If the edge of the valve head is less than $\frac{3}{64}$" thick after grinding, discard the valve.

Reface intake valves to 45 degrees and exhaust valves to 47 degrees. Reseat the cylinder head to 45 degrees for both intake and exhaust valves.

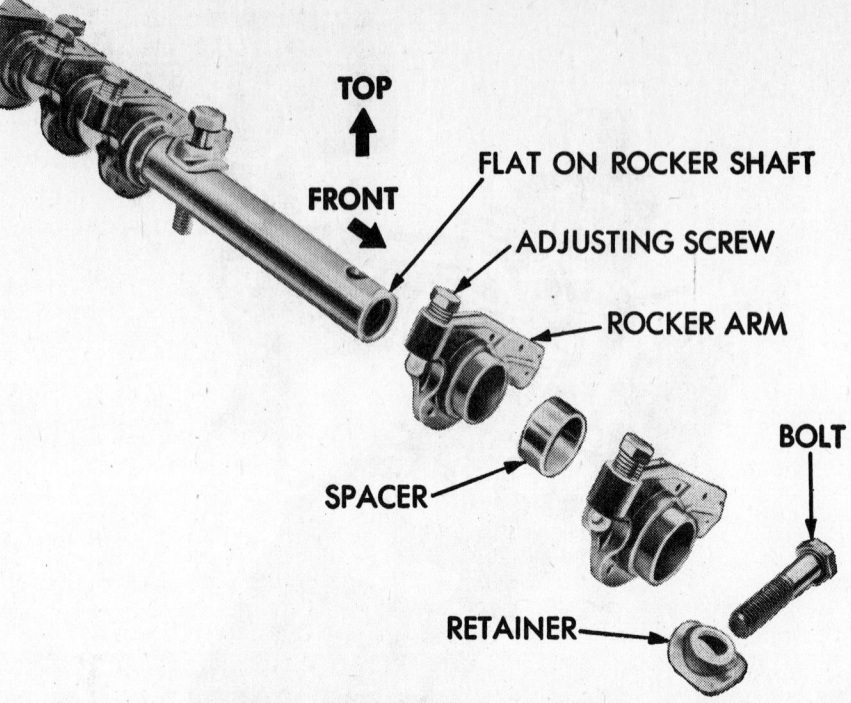

Fig. 4 Rocker arm and shaft assembly

Try each valve (with Prussian Blue) in its proper seat to determine the contact with the seat. The position of the contact should be near the center of the reground area of the valve and the seat should be $\frac{5}{64}$" to $\frac{3}{32}$" wide for intake, and $\frac{3}{64}$" to $\frac{1}{16}$" for exhaust valves. To move the contact toward the head of the valve (and narrow the seat) use a 60-degree stone. To move the contact away from the head of the valve (and narrow the seat) use a 20-degree stone.

VALVE GUIDES

Valves operate in guide holes bored directly in the cylinder head. When valve stem-to-guide clearance becomes excessive, valves with oversize stems of .005" .015" and .030" are available for service replacement. When necessary to install valves with oversize stems the valve bores should be reamed to provide the proper operating clearance.

Check the valve stem clearance of each valve (after cleaning) in its respective valve guide. If the clearance exceeds the service limits of .004" on the intake or .005" on the exhaust, ream the guides to accomodate the next oversize diameter valve stem.

VALVE SPRING INSTALLED HEIGHT

When valves and seats are reground the position of the valve in the head is changed so as to lessen the valve spring tension. Without proper valve spring tension the valve does not seat long enough or it may not seat completely. Since the valve is cooled by transferring heat from the valve head to the seat and

thence to he coolant, improper valve spring tension will cause worn, pitted and distorted valves which result in loss of compression and power as well as poor gasoline mileage.

When valves, springs, retainers and locks are installed, measure the assembled height of the valve springs from the surface of the cylinder head spring pad to the underside of the spring retainer as shown in Fig. 4A. If the assembled height is greater than the dimension given in the *Valve Specifications Chart,* install a spacer or shim of proper thickness between cylinder head spring pad and spring to bring the assembled height to specifications.

Do not install spacers unless necessary.

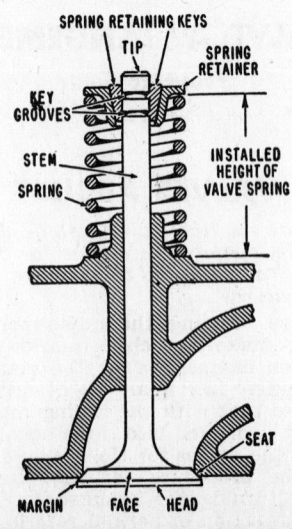

Fig. 4A Checking installed height of valve spring

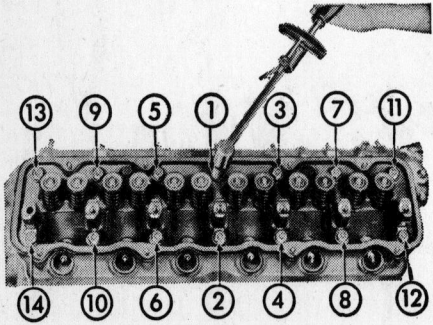

Fig. 3 Cylinder head tightening sequence

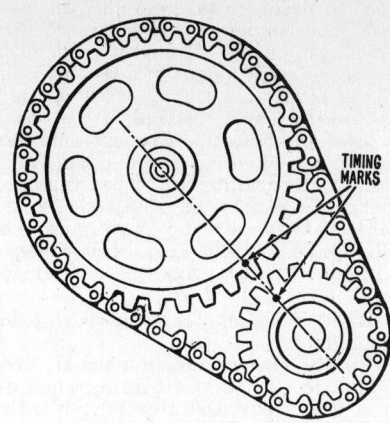

Fig. 5 Valve timing marks aligned for correct valve timing

Excessive use of spacers will result in overstressing valve springs and overloading camshaft lobes which could lead to spring breakage and worn camshaft lobes.

VALVE SPRING TESTING

Wash all springs with a suitable solvent. Examine the springs for damage or corrosion due to acid etching, which will develop into surface cracks and cause spring failure.

Check the valve spring tension on a spring testing fixture, if one is available, and according to the specifications listed in the *Valve Specifications* table. If a fixture is not available, at least check the free length of each spring by standing it alongside a new spring. Any spring that does not conform to the pressure specifications within 10% should be discarded. Likewise, any spring that stands shorter than the new spring used for comparison should be replaced. Of course, cocked springs should also be scrapped.

VALVE LIFTERS

After taking off rocker arm and shaft assembly, lift out push rods. The valve lifters may then be removed with a suitably long magnet rod. If the lifters cannot be removed with the magnet rod, a special tool (C-3661) may be used. Insert the tool through the push rod opening in the cylinder head and into lifter. Turn the handle to expand the tool in the lifter, then with a twisting motion remove the lifter from its bore. Place lifters in a board with numbered holes since each lifter must be installed in its original location.

Inspect the lifters for scores and the lower ends for pits and rough surfaces. Check crowned faces of lifters with a straightedge. If any negative crown (dish) is observed, the lifter should be replaced.

TIMING CHAIN COVER

1. To remove cover, drain cooling system and remove radiator and fan.

2. Remove vibration damper with a puller.
3. Loosen oil pan bolts to allow clearance and remove chain case cover.
4. Reverse above procedure to install cover.

TIMING CHAIN

1. After removing chain case cover as outlined above, take off camshaft sprocket attaching bolt.
2. Remove chain with camshaft sprocket.
3. Clean all parts and dry with compressed air.
4. Inspect timing chain for broken or damaged links. Inspect sprockets for cracks and chipped, worn or damaged teeth.

Installation

1. Turn crankshaft so sprocket timing mark is toward and directly in line with centerline of camshaft.
2. Temporarily install camshaft sprocket. Rotate camshaft to position sprocket timing mark toward and directly in line with centerline of crankshaft; then remove camshaft sprocket.
3. Place chain on crankshaft sprocket and position camshaft sprocket in chain so sprocket can be installed with timing marks aligned without moving camshaft, Fig. 5.
4. Install parts removed in reverse order of removal.

VALVE TIMING DATA

Lancer & Valiant

Year	Model	Intake Opens①	Intake Closes②	Exhaust Opens③	Exhaust Closes④
1960-61	All	8	44	48	⑤

① — Degrees before top dead center.
② — Degrees after bottom dead center.
③ — Degrees before bottom dead center.
④ — Degrees after top dead center.
⑤ — Top dead center.

CAMSHAFT & BEARINGS

The camshaft is supported by four precision type, steel-backed, babbitt-lined bearings. Rearward thrust is taken by the rear face of the sprocket hub, contacting the front of the engine block. The camshaft, Fig. 6, can be removed after removing the grille, radiator and timing chain. To remove the camshaft bearings, the torque converter (or flywheel) must also be removed.

1. Remove valve lifters, oil pump and distributor.
2. Slide camshaft out of engine.
3. Remove welch plug back of rear camshaft bearing.
4. Remove bearings with suitable puller equipment.
5. Install new bearings, being sure the oil holes in bearings line up with the corresponding oil holes in the crankcase.

PISTONS & RODS, REMOVE

1. Drain cooling system and remove the cylinder head.
2. Drain oil and remove oil pan.
3. Remove top ridge from cylinder bores, using a suitable ridge reamer.
4. Rotate crankshaft so connecting rod being removed is centered with cylinder bore; then remove rod cap.
5. Use protector sleeves over connecting rod bolts and push pistons and rods out through top of cylinder block.
6. Install caps on their mating rods.

PISTON & ROD, ASSEMBLE

Piston and rod assemblies must be installed with the notch on the piston head toward the front of the engine, and the oil hole in the connecting rod toward the manifold side of the engine.

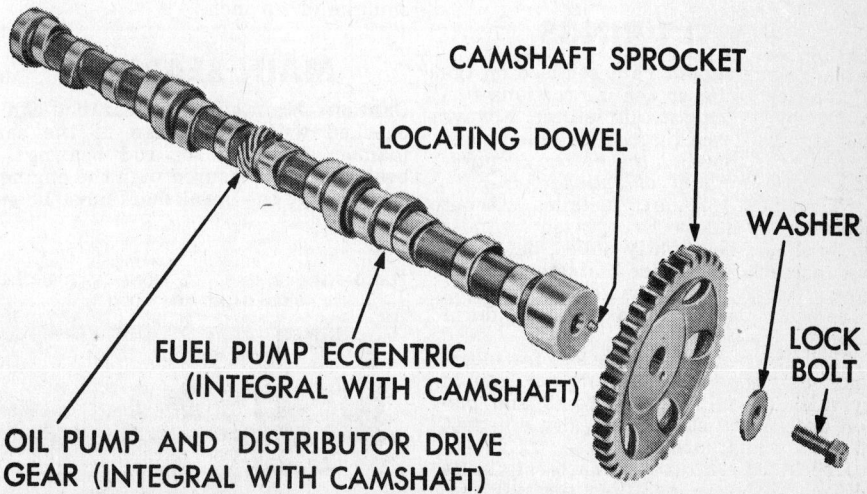

CAMSHAFT SPROCKET

LOCATING DOWEL

WASHER

LOCK BOLT

FUEL PUMP ECCENTRIC (INTEGRAL WITH CAMSHAFT)

OIL PUMP AND DISTRIBUTOR DRIVE GEAR (INTEGRAL WITH CAMSHAFT)

Fig. 6 Camshaft and sprocket

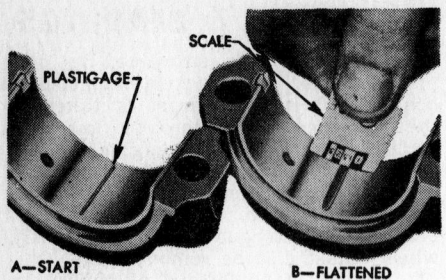

Fig. 7 Checking bearing clearing with Plastigage

PISTONS

If the pistons are to be re-used with new rings, remove the carbon from the ring grooves. A special tool is available for this work but a satisfactory job can be done by breaking an old piston ring. File the broken end to a sharp, square edge and use it to scrape out the carbon. Soak the piston in cleaning solvent to loosen any carbon residue. Clean out the loosened carbon, being careful not to cut away any piston material. Clean out the oil return holes with a drill just large enough to fill the holes. Hold the drill in a tap wrench and make sure the drill does not remove any metal from the piston.

Rinse the piston in solvent and wipe off the carbon on the sides of the piston. *Never use a wire brush to clean a piston as the brush will round off the edges of the ring lands.* Pistons showing scuffed or scored skirts should be discarded for new ones. Examine the ring lands carefully for cracks. If in the least bit doubtful, the piston should be scrapped.

PISTON PINS

Piston pins should be a very light thumb press fit in the piston with the parts at room temperature (70°). Piston pins are supplied in standard size only. If excessive clearance is noted, both piston and pin should be replaced.

PISTON RINGS

New rings should be assembled on the piston according to the instructions furnished by the ring manufacturer. Always use standard size rings in cylinder bores that are *standard at the bottom, regardless of the amount of cylinder wear.*

When new rings are installed without reboring cylinders the glazed cylinder walls should be slightly dulled, but without increasing the bore diameter. This is done with a "Glaze-buster" or with a hone equipped with the finest grade of stones.

New rings must be checked for clearance in piston grooves and for gap in cylinder bores. Cylinder bores and piston grooves must be clean, dry and free of carbon and burrs.

Check the clearance of each ring in its piston groove by installing the ring and then inserting feeler gauges *under* the ring. Any wear that occurs in the piston groove forms a step or ridge at the inner portion of the lower land. If gauges are inserted above the ring, the ring may rest on the step instead of on the worn portion of the lower land, and a false measurement of clearance will result.

If the piston grooves are worn to the extent that relatively high steps or ridges exist on the lower lands, the piston should be replaced because the steps will interfere with the operation of the new rings and the ring clearances will be excessive. Piston rings are not furnished in oversize widths to compensate for ring groove wear.

To check the end gap of rings, place the ring in the cylinder in which it will be used. Square it in bore by tapping with the lower end of the piston. Then measure the gap with feeler gauges. If necessary to increase the gap, file the ends of the rings carefully with a smooth file.

ROD BEARINGS

These bearings are of the insert type, selectively fitted, and available for service replacement in standard and undersizes for use on crankshaft journals that have been reground.

If inspection reveals badly worn or scored bearings, they should be replaced. Bearings may be removed by simply taking off the bearing caps and slipping the old ones out and the new ones in. The installation of new bearings must be closely checked to maintain the proper clearance between the crankshaft and bearing surface. A convenient and accurate method for checking bearing clearance is with the use of Plastigage, which is available at any auto parts jobber.

Place the string-like plastic material so it extends the full width of the bearing, Fig. 7. Install the bearing and cap and tighten the nuts to the recommended torque which is listed in the *Engine Torque Specifications* chart. Then loosen the nuts and carefully remove the cap and bearing. The widest portion of the Plastigage is then measured with the scale on the Plastigage envelope. The graduation on the envelope corresponding to the thickness of the Plastigage gives the bearing clearance in thousandths of an inch.

MAIN BEARINGS

Caution—Main bearing clearance can be checked with Plastigage in the same manner described for rod bearings. If bearings are measured with the engine in the chassis, the crankshaft must be sup-

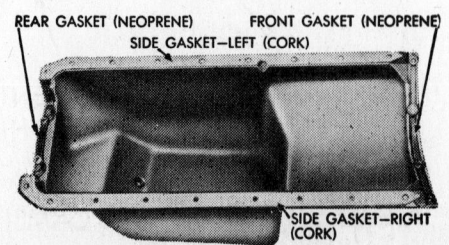

Fig. 8 Oil Pan and gaskets

ported in order to take up clearance between the upper bearing insert and crankshaft journal. This can be done by tightening bearing caps of adjacent bearings with .005" to .015" cardboard, (such as a calling card) between lower bearing shell and journal. Use extreme care when this is done to avoid unnecessary strain on the crankshaft or bearings or a false reading may be obtained. Do not rotate crankshaft while Plastigage is installed. *Be sure to remove cardboard.* To install new bearings, proceed as follows:

1. Remove bearing cap and worn lower shell.
2. Rotate crankshaft in normal direction to turn upper bearing shell out of crankcase. Use a cotter pin with a flattened head or the special tool made for the purpose in the crankshaft oil hole to contact the bearing and force it out.
3. Place a new upper shell on the crankshaft journal with the locating notch in the correct position and rotate the shaft to turn the bearing in place.
4. Install the lower bearing shell in the cap.
5. Tighten all cap nuts to the torque value given in the *Engine Torque* table.

CRANKSHAFT OIL SEAL

A braided oil seal is pressed into the upper and lower grooves behind the rear main bearing. Directly in front of this seal is an oil slinger which deflects the oil back into the oil pan. Should the braided seal require replacement, the installation of the lower half is accomplished as follows:

With the bearing cap and lower bearing half removed, install a new seal so that both ends protrude above the cap. Tap the seal down into position or roll it snugly in its groove with a smooth rounded tool. Then cut off the protruding end of the seal with sharp knife or razor blade.

Installing Upper Seal

Although the usual practice is to remove the crankshaft when the upper half of the seal is to be replaced, it is possible to do the job without removing the crankshaft as follows:

To remove the old seal, use needle-nose pliers to grasp the end of the seal which is most accessible. Pull the seal downward while rotating the crankshaft slowly in the direction that the seal is being moved.

To install the new seal, fasten a length of wire or strong string such as fishing line securely to one end of the new seal. See that the point of fastening is not bulky and that it is not over ⅜" from the end of the seal. Coat the seal with Lubriplate. Pass the free end of the wire or string up over the crankshaft at the point where the seal is being installed. Then exert a firm, steady pull on the wire or string and at the same time rotate the crankshaft slowly in the direction of the pull. This will help to move

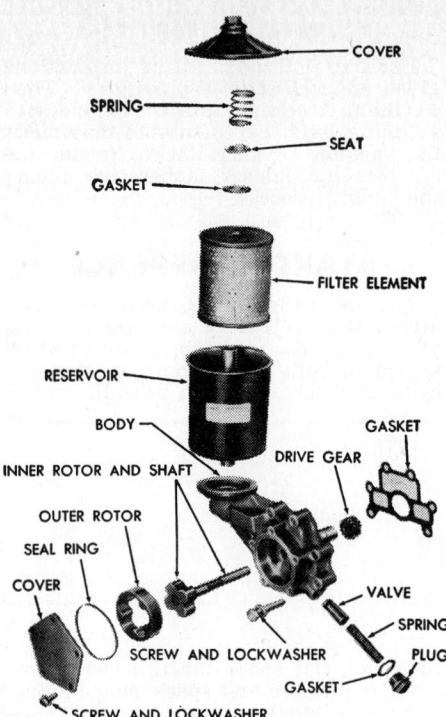

Fig. 9 Oil pump and filter disassembled

the seal into position. When the installation is completed, trim the ends of the seal flush with the engine block.

OIL PAN, REPLACE

1. Disconnect battery ground cable.
2. Drain cooling system and disconnect both radiator hoses.
3. Loosen alternator adjuster strap and move alternator toward engine as far as possible.
4. Disconnect throttle rod at carburetor by pulling it out of rubber bushing in carburetor lever.
5. Disconnect exhaust pipe at manifold.
6. Disconnect any other tubes, hoses or wires in engine compartment that might interfere or be damaged by raising front end of engine.
7. Remove steering and idler arm ball joints from steering linkage center link.
8. Remove bolts attaching the two engine supports to the "K" member.
9. Using a block of wood positioned under forward end of oil pan (over bolt heads) raise front of engine approximately two inches with a jack against the wood block. *Do not jack up engine under vibration damper.*
10. After engine is raised, place short pieces of 2x4 wood blocks between engine supports and "K" member. Lower engine and remove jack.
11. Remove clutch lower and front covers, or converter cover plate.
12. Drain oil and remove oil pan.
13. Maneuver oil pan down and forward, then lower rear end of pan and remove.

14. Note position of oil screen and pipe; then unscrew the assembly from crankcase.
15. Reverse removal procedure to install the pan, noting the location of the pan gaskets as shown in Fig. 8.

OIL PUMP REPAIRS

In order to gain access to the oil pump, it will be necessary to perform Steps 1 through 10 for removing the oil pan. Then remove oil pump cover, outer rotor and oil pump, Fig. 9.

To disassemble, remove the pump cover seal ring. Press off the drive gear, supporting the gear to keep load off aluminum body. Remove rotor and shaft and lift out outer pump rotor. Remove oil pressure relief valve plug and lift out spring and plunger. Remove oil pressure sending unit.

Inspection

1. The rotor contact area and the bores for the shaft and valve in the pump body should be smooth, free from scratches, scoring or excessive wear.
2. The pump cover should be smooth, flat and free from scoring or ridges. Lay a straightedge across the cover. If a .0015″ feeler gauge can be inserted under the straightedge, the cover should be replaced.
3. All surfaces of the outer rotor should be smooth and uniform, free from ridges, scratches or uneven wear. Discard a rotor less than .649″ thick and/or less than 2.469″ in diameter.
4. The inner rotor and shaft assembly should be smooth, free from scoring and uneven wear. Discard rotors less than .649″ thick.
5. Place outer rotor in pump body and measure clearance between rotor and body. Discard pump body if clearance is more than .012″.
6. Install inner rotor and shaft in pump body. Shaft should turn freely but without side play. If clearance between rotor teeth is more than .010″, replace both rotors.
7. Measure rotor end clearance. If feeler gauge of more than .004″ can be inserted between straightedge and rotors, install a new pump body.
8. The oil pressure relief valve should be smooth, free from scratches or scoring, and should be a free fit in its bore.
9. Relief valve springs are painted either gray, red or brown to denote free lengths of 2.19, 2.29 and 2.39 inches. Rather than change the length, replace a spring with one of the same color.

Assemble and Install

1. With pump rotors in body, press drive gear on shaft, flush with end of shaft.
2. Install seal ring in groove in body and install cover. Tighten bolts to 10 ft. lbs. Test pump for free turning.
3. Install oil pressure relief valve spring. Use new washer (gasket)

and tighten plug securely.
4. If pump shaft turns freely, remove pump cover and outer rotor before installation of pump on engine.
5. Install oil pressure sending unit and tighten to 60 inch lbs. (5 ft. lbs.)
6. Using a new gasket, install pump on engine and tighten bolts to 200 inch lbs. (16 ft. lbs.)
7. Install oil filter reservoir on pump. Install filter element and tighten cover nuts to 25 ft. lbs.
8. Connect oil pressure sending unit wire.
9. Complete the installation by reversing Steps 1 through 10 as given under *Oil Pan, Replace.*

RADIATOR

To remove radiator, drain cooling system and disconnect hoses. On cars so equipped, disconnect oil cooler lines and cap them to prevent loss of fluid. Remove radiator attaching bolts and lift radiator straight up and out of chassis.

WATER PUMP REPLACE

To remove the water pump, drain cooling system and loosen the fan belt. Remove the fan, spacer, pulley and belt. Remove the pump inlet hose and the heater hose. Remove clamp from bypass hose. Remove water pump bolts and push pump body down and off the by-pass hose.

WATER PUMP REPAIRS

The water pump body and the shaft are serviced only as an assembly. It is not necessary to remove the hub unless a new pump assembly is to be installed. Replacement of the impeller and the seal, Fig. 10, is done as follows:

1. Support pump on the hub end of shaft and break plastic impeller away from metal insert.
2. Remove support plate and gaskets.
3. Split impeller metal insert and remove from shaft.
4. Remove rubber portion of shaft seal and the spring. Use a puller to remove retainer portion of seal, then remove thrower from shaft. *Do not pry retainer portion of seal out of pump body.*
5. Pump shaft should rotate freely without binding and pump body

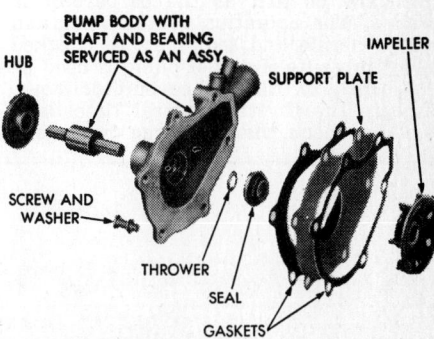

Fig. 10 Water pump disassembled

should be free of corrosion and damage. If a new shaft and body is necessary, remove hub from shaft with a puller. To install the hub on new pump, support the pump on the impeller end of the shaft only. Press the hub 13/32" beyond flush.

6. Complete assembly by reversing the disassembly procedure.

DISTRIBUTOR, REPLACE

The distributor rotates clockwise. To remove, take off cap, disconnect primary wire and vacuum line. Remove hold-down bolt and lift out distributor. Install in the following manner:

1. Rotate crankshaft until mark on inner edge of crankshaft pulley is in line with the "O" (TDC) mark on timing chain cover.
2. With distributor gasket in position, hold distributor over mounting pad.
3. Turn rotor to point forward, corresponding to 4 o'clock position.
4. Install distributor so that when fully seated on engine, the gear has spiraled to bring rotor to 5 o'clock position.
5. Turn housing until ignition points are separating and rotor is under No. 1 cap tower.
6. Install hold-down bolt.
7. Adjust timing with timing light.

IGNITION TIMING

For initial timing, follow instructions given under *Distributor, Replace*. Then for the final setting, time the engine with a timing light, being sure to disconnect the vacuum advance line to render the advance mechanism inoperative during the timing process.

STARTER, REPLACE

To remove the starter, disconnect negative cable at battery and starter cable at starter. Remove starter-to-flywheel attaching bolts and remove starter and cylinder block seal from beneath engine.

Carburetor Section

Performance Complaints

Flooding, stumble on acceleration or other performance complaints are in many instances caused by the presence of dirt, water or other foreign matter in the carburetor. To aid in diagnosing the cause of the complaint, the carburetor should be carefully removed from the engine without draining the fuel from the bowl. The contents of the fuel bowl may then be examined for contamination as the carburetor is disassembled.

Check the fuel in the bowl for contamination by dirt, water, gum or other foreign matter. A magnet moved through the fuel in the bowl will pick up and identify any iron oxide dust that may have caused intake needle and seat leakage.

Inspect gasketed surfaces between body and air horn. Small nicks or burrs should be smoothed down to eliminate air or fuel leakage. On carburetors having a vacuum piston, be especially particular when inspecting the top surface of the inner wall of the bowl around the vacuum piston passage. A poor seal at this location may contribute to a "cutting-out" on turns complaint.

Fill the carburetor bowl with clean fuel before installing on manifold. This will help prevent dirt trapped in the fuel system from being dislodged by the free flow of fuel as the carburetor is primed. The operation of the float and intake needle and seat may be checked under pressure if a fuel pump is used at the bench to fill the carburetor bowl. Operate the throttle several times and visually check the discharge from jets.

Poor Mileage and Engine Loading Complaints

Cases of poor mileage and engine loading may be due in many instances to sluggish choke valve opening during cold driveaway, caused by insufficient vacuum in choke housing, a plugged or restricted heat pipe or inlet in choke cover. To check for this condition, have engine warm and running at slow idle. Remove choke heat pipe and hold a finger over the heat inlet hole (hole is on choke housing on some carburetors). If there is little or no vacuum pull on the finger, check the choke housing for gasket leaks or plugged vacuum passages. If these are OK, check choke vacuum passages in carburetor between choke housing and manifold.

Dirty or Rusty Choke Housing

In case where it is found that the interior of the choke housing is dirty, gummed or rusty while the carburetor itself is comparatively clean, look for a punctured or eroded manifold heat tube (if one is used).

Manifold Heat Control Valve

An engine equipped with a manifold heat control valve can operate with the valve stuck either in the open or closed position. Because of this, an inoperative valve is frequently overlooked at vehicle lubrication or tune-up.

A valve stuck in the "heat-off" position can result in slow warm up, deposits in combustion chamber, carbure-

tor icing, flat spots during acceleration, low gas mileage and spark plug fouling.

A valve stuck in the "heat-on" position can result in power loss, engine knocking, sticking or burned valves and spark plug burning.

To prevent the possibility of a stuck valve, check and lubricate the valve each time the vehicle is lubricated or tuned-up. Check the operation of the valve manually. To lubricate the valve, place a few drops of penetrating oil on the valve shaft where it passes through the manifold. Move the valve up and down a few times to work in the oil. *Do not use engine oil for this purpose as it will leave a residue which hampers valve operation.*

Hesitation On Light Acceleration

1960—If this condition is encountered after an engine tune-up, it can be corrected by repositioning the air cleaner inlet tube at 90° to the right across the valve cover.

Adjusting Idle Speed

1961—If a condition of stalling or rough idle is encountered on cars with automatic transmission, adjust the hot idle speed to 500 rpm in Drive *with the headlights on.* It is important to make this adjustment with the headlights on so the alternator will be under full load condition. There is a variation up to 65 engine rpm between "light" and "full" charge conditions of the alternator.

CARTER CARBURETOR ADJUSTMENTS

Year	Carburetor Model	Idle Adjustments				Float Level		Float Drop		Pump Travel Setting	Choke Unloader Setting	Choke Setting
		Mixture Screws Turns Open	Hot Idle Speed Neutral	Fast Idle Speed	Dashpot Plunger Clearance	Primary	Secondary	Primary	Secondary			
1961	BBS-3093S	1	550	③	None	$7/32$①	None	None	None	$27/32$②	$3/16$④	Index
	BBS-3094S	1	550	③	None	$7/32$①	None	None	None	$27/32$②	$3/16$④	Index
	BBS-3127S	1	550	③	None	$7/32$①	None	None	None	$27/32$②	$3/16$④	Index
1960	BBS-2900S	$1/2$-$1\frac{1}{2}$	500	③	None	$7/32$①	None	None	None	$27/32$②	$9/64$④	Index
	BBS-2901S	$1/2$-$1\frac{1}{2}$	500	③	None	$7/32$①	None	None	None	$27/32$②	$9/64$④	Index
	BBS-3053S	$1/2$-$1\frac{1}{2}$	500	③	None	$7/32$①	None	None	None	$27/32$②	$9/64$④	Index

CARTER NOTES

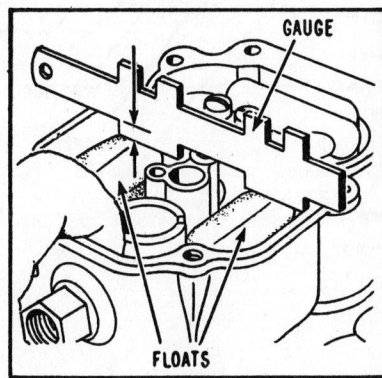

Fig. ①—BBS float level. Adjust by bending lip **on** float arm.

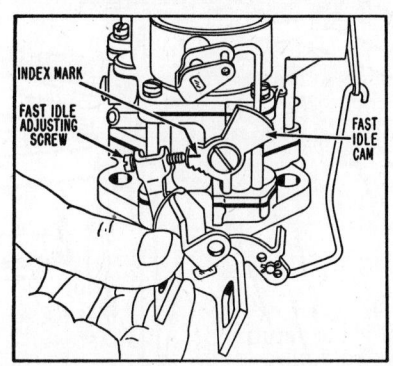

Fig. ③—Open throttle valve and hold choke valve fully closed. Now close throttle valve which will position fast idle cam to fast idle position. Release choke valve only. The index mark on cam should split center of fast idle screw. Adjust by bending fast idle connector rod.

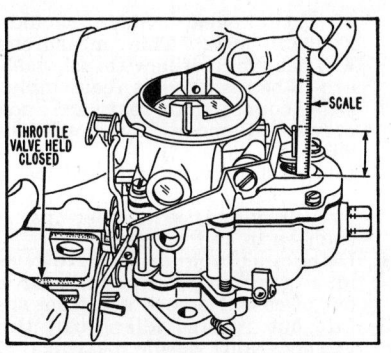

Fig. ②—Open choke valve so that throttle valve can be fully seated in carburetor bore, then close throttle valve lightly. With pump connector rod in center hole of throttle lever, measure distance from top of air horn to end of pump plunger shaft. Adjust by bending pump connector rod.
Note: If pump rod is installed in either long or short stroke hole, remove hair pin clip (directly under bowl vent valve) either up or down to obtain correct bowl vent clearance.

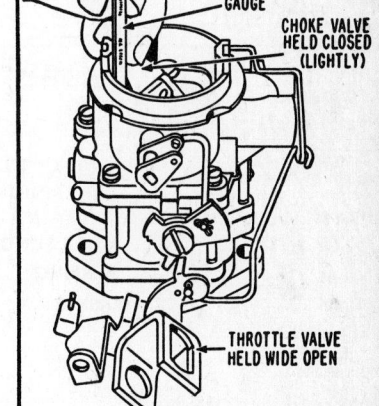

Fig. ④—With throttle valve held wide open, clearance between upper edge of choke valve and inner **wall** of air horn should be as specified. Adjust by bending unloader tang on throttle lever.

Clutch and Transmission Section

CLUTCH PEDAL, ADJUST

Shorten or lengthen the clutch release fork rod by turning the adjusting nut until there is $\frac{5}{32}$" free movement of the clutch fork outer end. This adjustment, if correctly set, will give the necessary one inch free play at the pedal.

CLUTCH SERVICE

Unless special clutch rebuilding equip-ment is available, it is recommended that the clutch assembly be exchanged for a rebuilt unit should the clutch re-quire rebuilding. The driven disc, how-ever, may be replaced without special equipment. If clutch rebuilding equip-ment is available, follow the equipment manufacturer's instructions.

Removal

1. Remove transmission and clutch pan.
2. Pull out clutch release bearing and sleeve.
3. Mark clutch cover and flywheel so they may be assembled in the same relative position and thus maintain original balance.
4. Remove capscrews which retain clutch cover to flywheel. Loosen each screw a few turns in succession until cover is free.
5. Clutch assembly and driven disc may now be removed from clutch housing.

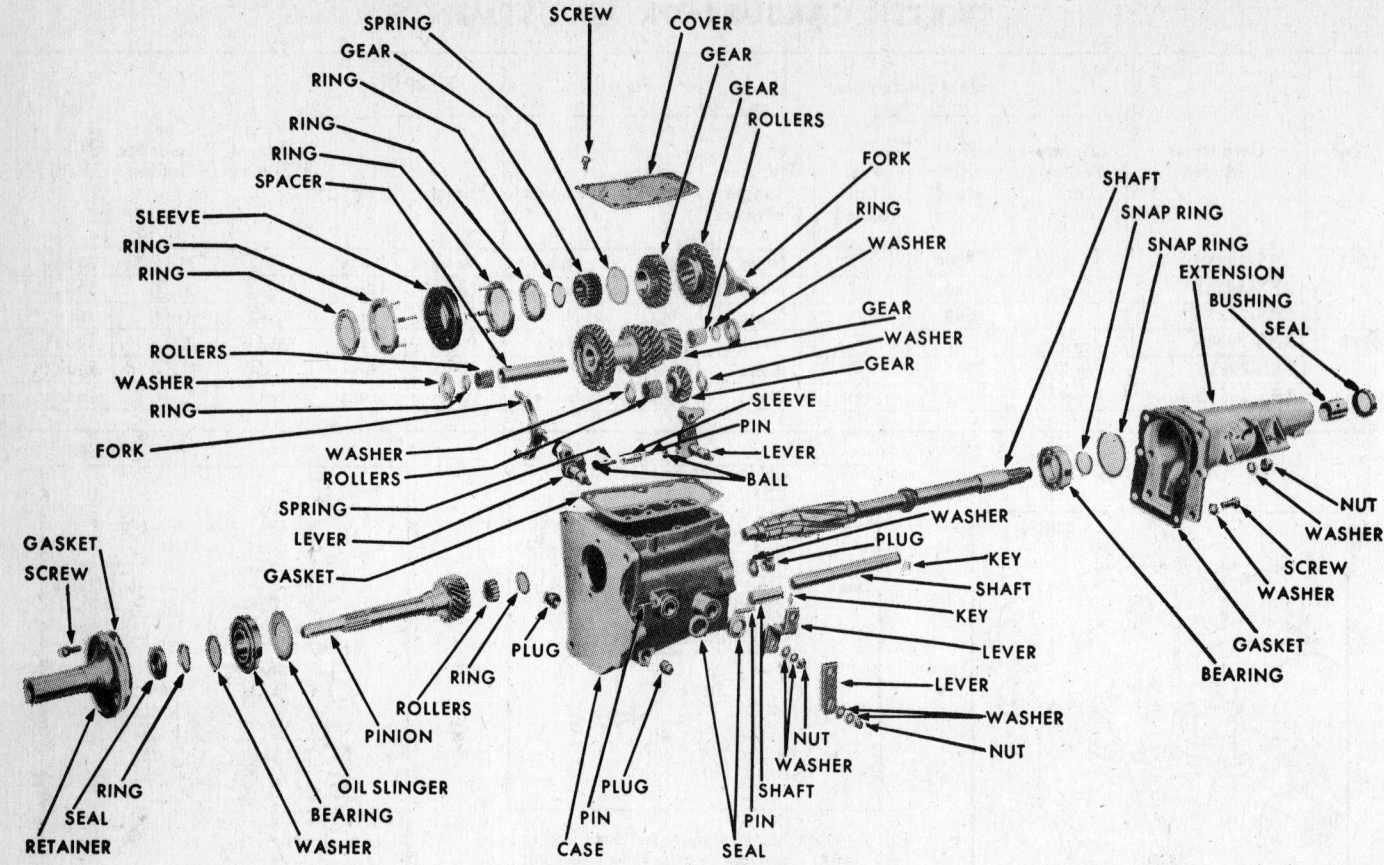

Fig. 1 Manual shift transmission

Installation

1. Coat pilot bearing in crankshaft with wheel bearing grease.
2. Clean surfaces of flywheel and pressure plate, making certain no oil or grease remains on these parts.
3. Hold cover plate and disc in place and insert a special clutch aligning tool or spare clutch shaft through hub of disc and into crankshaft pilot bearing.
4. Bolt clutch cover loosely to flywheel, being sure marks previously made are lined up.
5. To avoid distortion of clutch cover, tighten cover bolts a few turns each in progression until all are tightened securely.
6. Adjust clutch pedal free travel.

MANUAL SHIFT TRANSMISSION

Transmission, Replace

1. Drain lubricant.
2. Disconnect propeller shaft, speedometer cable and housing, gearshift control rods and hand brake controls. *Remove speedometer cable with hand so that housing is not crushed.*
3. Remove back-up light switch.
4. Support rear end of engine.
5. Raise engine slightly and remove crossmember attaching bolts.

6. Support transmission; then remove transmission-to-clutch housing bolts.
7. Slide transmission rearward until clutch shaft clears clutch disc before lowering transmission.
8. Reverse above procedure to install the transmission and adjust gearshift control.

Transmission Repairs

1. Referring to Fig. 1, remove transmission flange.
2. Remove extension housing.
3. Remove transmission cover.
4. Remove clutch shaft bearing retainer.
5. Grasp clutch shaft with hand and pull assembly out of case. *Be careful not to bind inner synchronizer ring on clutch teeth.*
6. With transmission in reverse, remove outer center bearing snap ring, using a hook or a flat blade, then partially remove mainshaft.
7. Cock mainshaft; then remove synchronizer sleeve, rings and 2-3 shift fork.
8. Remove clutch gear snap ring, using snap ring pliers. Slide clutch gear off end of mainshaft.
9. Slide second speed gear, stop ring and synchronizer spring off mainshaft.
10. Remove low-reverse sliding gear and shift fork as mainshaft is withdrawn from case.
11. Using a feeler gauge, check end play

of cluster gear, which should be .004" to .012" This measurement will determine if new thrust washers are to be installed at reassembly.
12. Drive countershaft rearward and out of case. Remove key from end of shaft.
13. Lift cluster gear and thrust washers out of case. Disassemble cluster gear by removing needle bearings (22 each end) and spacer.
14. Using a suitable drift, drive reverse idler gear shaft towards rear and out of case. Remove key from shaft.
15. Lift out reverse idler gear, thrust washers and needle bearings (22) out of case. Remove needle bearings from gear.
16. To remove gearshift mechanism, remove operating levers from their shafts, Fig. 2.
17. Drive out tapered retaining pin from either of the two lever shafts, then withdraw lever shaft from inside transmission case. *As the shaft is being withdrawn, detent balls will drop to bottom of case.*
18. Remove interlock sleeve, spring, pin and both balls from case. Drive out remaining tapered pin, then slide lever shaft out of transmission.

Assembly Notes

Reassembling the transmission is accomplished by reversing the disassembly procedure. However, observe the following:

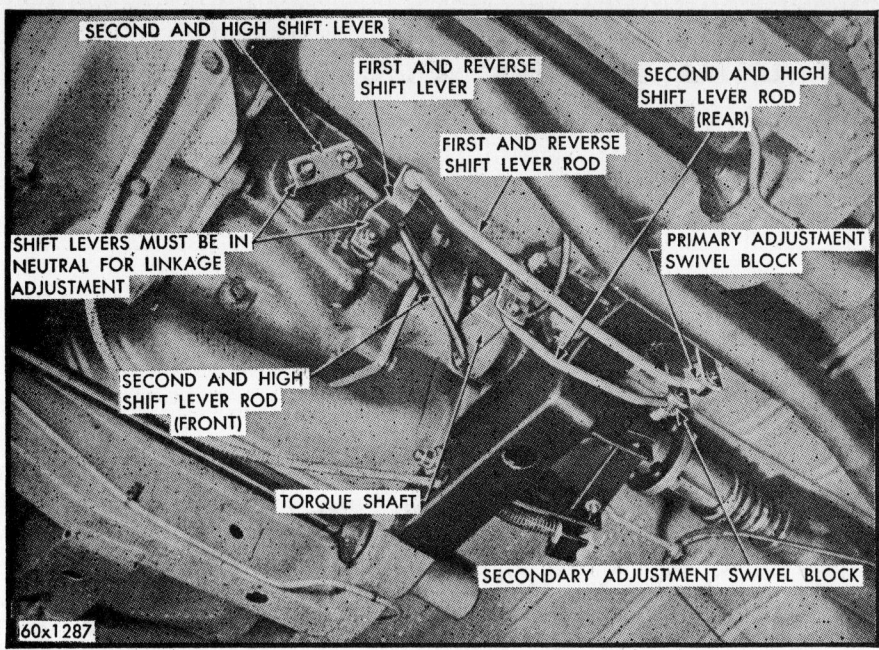

SECOND AND HIGH SHIFT LEVER
FIRST AND REVERSE SHIFT LEVER
SECOND AND HIGH SHIFT LEVER ROD (REAR)
FIRST AND REVERSE SHIFT LEVER ROD
SHIFT LEVERS MUST BE IN NEUTRAL FOR LINKAGE ADJUSTMENT
PRIMARY ADJUSTMENT SWIVEL BLOCK
SECOND AND HIGH SHIFT LEVER ROD (FRONT)
TORQUE SHAFT
SECONDARY ADJUSTMENT SWIVEL BLOCK
60x1287

Fig. 2 Gearshift linkage

1. When installing the reverse idler gear, have the bevelled ends of the gear teeth forward. Raise the idler gear slightly to align with shaft; then drive shaft into case, through thrust washer and gear, until end of shaft is approximately $\frac{1}{64}''$ below surface of case.
2. Cluster gear thrust washers are available in two sizes marked "A" and "B". Make a selection to give .004" to .012" total end play of cluster gear. Make sure tabs on thrust washers slide into grooves in case. Countershaft should be installed until approximately $\frac{1}{64}''$ below surface of case.
3. When installing mainshaft, have offset of low-reverse fork to rear. Engage fork in low-reverse gear, then position in case by shifting into reverse.
4. After sliding the synchronizer clutch gear on mainshaft and down against second speed gear, select a snap ring of the correct thickness and install. *Snap ring should eliminate end play and must be a snug fit.*
5. Check clearance between clutch gear and second speed gear, which should be .003" to .008". *End play in excess of .008" will permit gear "jump out."*
6. After mainshaft is properly positioned, select a snap ring that will be a snug fit at the rear bearing.

GEARSHIFT, ADJUST

1. Remove screws that retain upper boot and retaining ring to floor pan.
2. Remove retaining ring, then slide boot up on gearshift lever far enough to expose the shift mechanism.
3. Disconnect low-reverse shift rod and

disengage rod from lever.
4. Disconnect 2-3 shift rod and disengage rod from lever.
5. Place transmission shift levers in neutral, Fig. 2.
6. Slide a suitable tool over cross-over pin on 2-3 lever side. This will position cross-over pin so that shift levers are locked in neutral position.
7. Preset length of low-reverse shift rod by loosening lock nut on end of rod, which is threaded through swivel block. Turn swivel block either in or out to properly position hand lever and shift levers in neutral position. *Correct neutral position is where shift levers are in a direct vertical position with floor pan.*
8. After correct vertical position of both levers have been obtained, secure low-reverse rod to its lever.
9. Loosen clamp nut holding 2-3 shift rod in swivel block.
10. Slide swivel block either to front or rear on rod until stub shaft on block can be inserted into its lever. Install washer and clip.
11. With levers on transmission in neutral, tighten clamp nut that holds 2-3 rod in swivel.
12. Complete assembly and check shift in all gears. Cross-over action should be smooth, and shifting into gears should be crisp without binding.

TORQUEFLITE 6

A detailed service procedure on this transmission is given in the *Automatic Transmission Section* of this manual.

Transmission, Replace

1. Disconnect battery ground cable.

2. Depress "L" button to position control cable for removal from transmission.
3. Remove starting motor.
4. Raise vehicle on a hoist or support with stands.
5. Remove cover plate from in front of converter to provide access to converter drain plugs and mounting bolts.
6. Drain converter and transmission.
7. Remove neutral starter switch.
8. Remove cable adjusting wheel lock screw at transmission.
9. Insert screwdriver through neutral starting switch opening. Push screwdriver gently against upper projecting portion of cable lock spring, and pull cable out of transmission.
10. Loosen clamp screw and remove throttle link and lever from throttle shaft.
11. Disconnect oil cooler lines at transmission and remove oil filler tube.
12. Remove speedometer driven gear and sleeve.
13. Loosen transmission parking brake cable clamp bolt where cable enters cover. Remove housing cover lower plug. Insert screwdriver through hole, then gently exert pressure against projecting portion of cable lock spring and withdraw brake cable.
14. Disconnect front universal joint and secure out of the way.
15. Remove nut securing extension housing insulator to crossmember.
16. Raise engine slightly.
17. Disconnect rear wheel brake cable from lever and crossmember. Then remove crossmember.
18. Support transmission with a jack.
19. Mark converter and flex driving plate so they can be assembled in the same relative position. Remove converter to flex plate screws.
20. Attach a small "C" clamp to edge of bell housing to hold converter in place during transmission removal.
21. Remove bell housing retaining bolts.
22. Carefully work transmission rearward off engine block dowels and to disengage converter hub from end of crankshaft.
23. Lower transmission jack and remove transmission and converter.
24. Reverse above procedure to install the assembly.

THROTTLE LINKAGE

1. With engine at operating temperature and carburetor off the fast idle cam, adjust idle speed to 500 rpm.
2. Loosen lock nut and move transmission throttle control lever forward until it stops. Then tighten lock nut securely.
3. Adjust a spirit level protractor to 115 degrees; then place protractor lengthwise on flat face of accelerator pedal.
4. With car on level floor, disconnect accelerator pedal rod and adjust length of rod to center the bubble in spirit level. After correct pedal angle is obtained, reconnect pedal rod.

Rear Axle and Brake Section
Refer To Hydraulic Brakes Chapter For Brake Adjustments

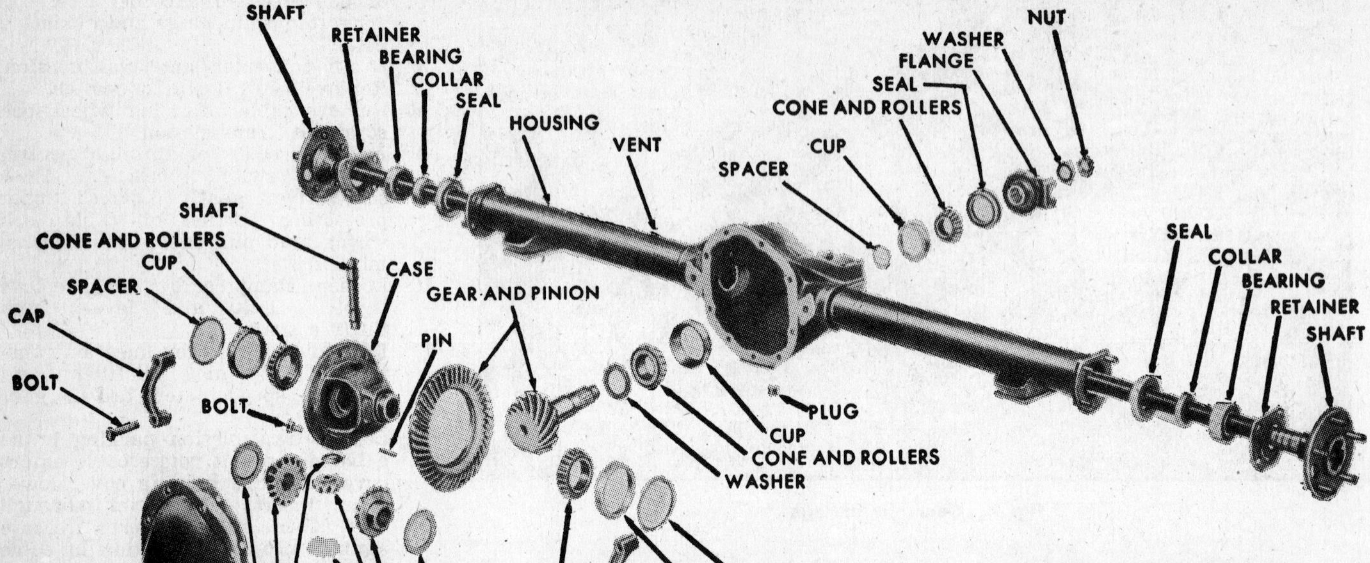

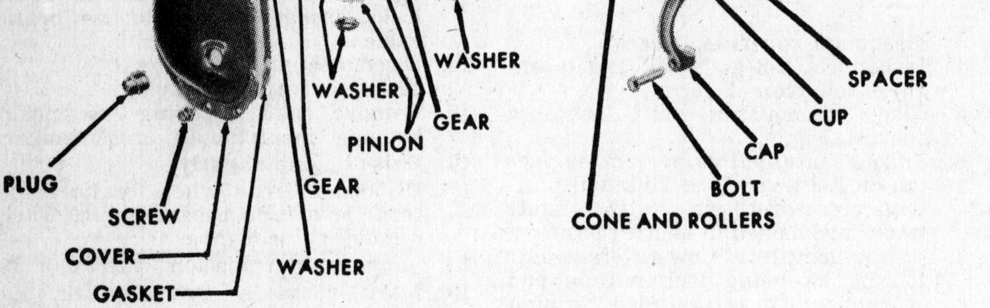

Fig. 1   Rear axle differential and carrier

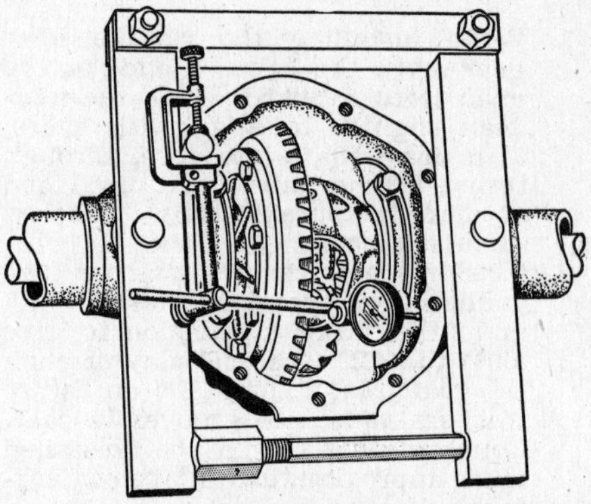

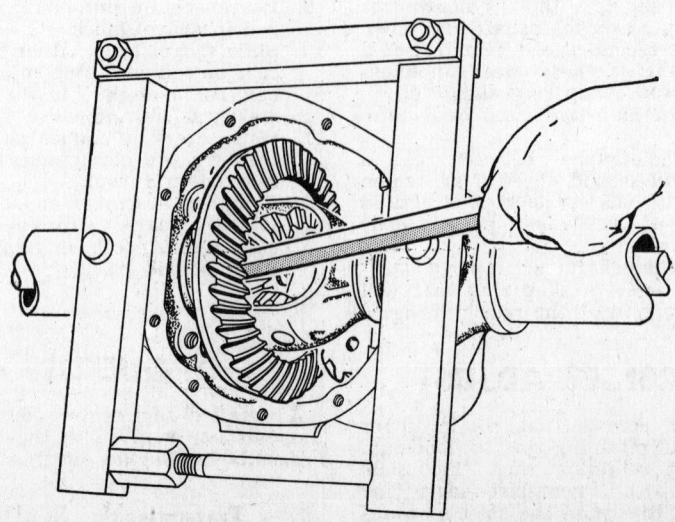

Fig. 2   Checking ring gear runout, using a spread tool and dial indicator

REAR AXLE REPAIRS

The rear axle is an integral type design with the axle housing and differential carrier housing integrated into one component. Access to the differential carrier is obtained by removal of housing cover, Fig. 1.

Differential bearing preload is adjusted by a spacer located between the end of the differential side bearings and the housing.

Drive pinion depth is adjusted by a spacer located back of the rear pinion bearing.

Pinion bearing preload is adjusted by a spacer located between the front pinion bearing and the shoulder on the pinion shaft.

Disassemble

1. Remove rear axle assembly from car.
2. Drain lubricant and remove cover.
3. Remove pinion yoke.
4. Remove pinion oil seal.
5. Check ring gear and differential case runout by placing a dial indicator against machined surface on back face of ring gear. Rotate ring

Fig. 3   Prying differential out of housing

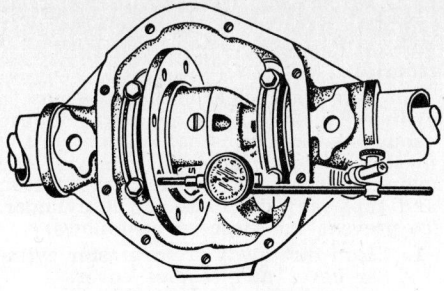

Fig. 4 Checking differential case runout with dial indicator

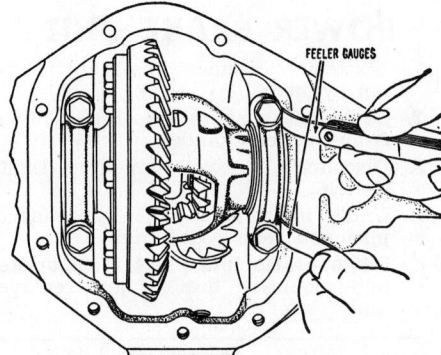

Fig. 5 Checking differential end play

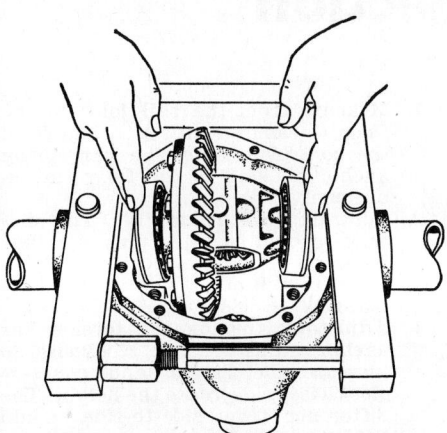

Fig. 6 Installing differential assembly

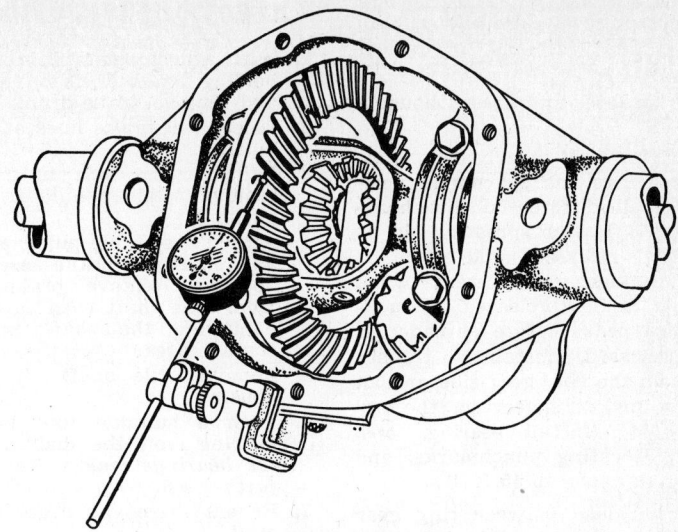

Fig. 7 Checking ring gear backlash

gear slowly and check reading. If runout exceeds .005″, check case after ring gear is removed to determine if runout is in the case or in drive gear, as described later on.

6. If differential bearing caps have no identifying marks, punchmark the caps and housing to identify right and left caps on reassembly. Then remove caps.

7. Install spreader tool and dial indicator as shown in Fig. 2 and check ring gear runout. Tighten spreader and spread housing .012-015″. *Do not spread housing in excess of .020″ as permanent distortion of housing may result.*

8. Remove dial indicator and pry dif-ferential case out of housing with a pry bar, Fig. 3.

9. Remove drive pinion and bearings.

10. Remove ring gear.

11. If ring gear runout was excessive when checked in Step 5, check the case to determine if the runout is in the gear or the case.

12. Reinstall differential case with spacers in housing. Remove spreader and install bearing caps and torque to 45 ft. lbs.

13. Mount dial indicator as shown in Fig. 4. Rotate case several times to seat bearings. Then turn case slowly and check indicator for runout. If the same reading is obtained as made with the ring gear and case, runout is in the case and not the drive gear.

14. Remove bearing caps, install spreader and spread housing .012-.015″.

15. Remove differential case, then the spreader.

16. Remove differential bearings if necessary.

17. Drive out lock pin which secures differential pinion shaft in case.

18. Drive out pinion shaft and remove pinions, side gears and thrust washers.

19. Remove rear pinion bearing and spacer from shaft. If bearing cups are to be removed, drive out with a brass drift.

20. Wash all parts and check bearings, cups, gears and thrust washers for nicks, burrs or damage and replace as required.

Assemble

1. Assemble differential by placing side gears and thrust washers into place. Mesh pinions with side gears. Install pinion thrust washers and rotate gears until pinions line up with pinion shaft holes. Install pinion shaft and lock pin.

2. Install ring gear and tighten bolts to 35 ft. lbs.

3. Install differential bearings.

Differential Bearing Preload, Adjust

1. Install spreader and spread case .012-.015″. Position differential bearing cups over bearings and install differential in carrier housing. Then remove spreader.

2. Measure original spacer thickness. Select a spacer approximately .012″ thinner for end play trial spacer. Install spacers between bearing cups and housing. Force differential to one side. On the other side, see how much shim stock will go between bearing cup and housing with a slight drag.

3. Measure total thickness of spacers plus feeler gauge stock to give the thickness of spacers needed to bring clearance to zero, Fig. 5. Then add .003″ to .006″ to the total for correct preload. Install spreader and remove differential from housing; then remove spreader.

Drive Pinion Depth

1. Look at the end of the new pinion to see if it has a plus or minus marking on it. Then if the new pinion has a different marking than the old pinion, use a thicker or thinner spacer by the amount that the new pinion differs from the old. Spacers are available in thickness steps of .002″ from .074″ to .106″. Pinions are marked 0, +1, +2, +3, —1, —2, —3.

2. Install pinion into carrier.

3. Install selected spacer on shaft with chamfer on spacer toward pinion gear.

4. Install front pinion bearing. Install yoke (not oil seal) and torque nut to 220 ft. lbs.

5. With pinion in vertical position, rotate pinion several times to seat bearings. Then, using an inch pound torque wrench, check rotating torque which should be 15-25 inch lbs. If not enough preload is present, install a thinner spacer; if too much, install a thicker spacer.

6. After correct spacer has been installed, install pinion shaft oil seal. Then install yoke and torque nut 220 ft. lbs.

7. Install spreader and spread housing .012-.015″.

8. With differential side bearing cups over bearings and spacers in position, install differential into housing, Fig. 6. Loosen spreader; but as spreader is released, make sure that some backlash is present when spreader is fully released. If backlash disappears before spreader is fully released, install a thinner spacer on the ring gear side and an equally thicker spacer on the opposite side. Install bearing caps, aligning locating punchmarks, and tighten cap bolts to 45 ft. lbs.

9. Check backlash between ring gear and pinion at least in four points, Fig. 7. The backlash at the lowest point must be from .004-.006″. There can be no more than .003″ difference from the lowest backlash point to the highest.

10. Install housing cover.

AXLE SHAFT & OIL SEALS

1. With wheel removed, remove clips holding brake drum on wheel studs and remove brake drum.

2. Disconnect brake lines at wheel cylinders.

3. Using access hole in axle flange, remove retainer nuts from end of housing.

4. Attach a suitable puller and remove axle shaft and brake assembly from housing. Remove brake assembly from axle shaft with care, to avoid damaging the shaft in the seal contact area.

5. Remove axle shaft oil seal from housing.

6. With a suitable tool, remove the bearing from the shaft. *Removal of the bearings makes them unfit for further use.*

7. Reverse removal procedure to install.

BRAKE MASTER CYLINDER, REPLACE

To remove the master cylinder, disconnect the master cylinder push rod from brake pedal. Disconnect brake line and stop light wires from cylinder. Remove attaching nuts and remove cylinder from car.

On cars with power brakes, the master cylinder push rod is a part of the vacuum brake and is not retained in the master cylinder piston. On removing the cylinder from the booster, the piston and cups may drop out of the cylinder. To prevent this proceed as follows:

1. Clean dirt away from master cylinder cover and remove cover.

2. Lightly depress brake pedal and insert a 1/8″ wire or drill through the large hole in the brake reservoir to retain the piston in the cylinder.

POWER BRAKE UNIT

1. Disconnect vacuum line from vacuum cylinder.

2. Disconnect hydraulic brake line from master cylinder.

3. Disconnect wires from stop light switch.

4. Under instrument panel, disconnect push rod from pedal linkage.

5. Remove attaching nuts from brake unit mounting bracket and remove unit from car.

Front End & Steering Section

WHEEL ALIGNMENT

Before checking and adjusting wheel alignment, make sure the front wheel bearings are properly adjusted and that the front suspension height is correct. These adjustments are given further on.

Camber and Caster

Camber and caster adjustments are accomplished by means of the upper control arm attaching bolt and cam assemblies, Fig. 1.

To adjust caster and camber, carefully loosen the upper control arm adjusting bolt nuts while holding the bolts to prevent turning.

Adjustment of caster through camber readings is possible because of the consistent relation between caster change and camber change when either the front or rear cam bolt at each control arm is individually rotated.

Turning one bolt affects caster more than camber. Turning both bolts an equal amount in the same direction affects camber directly, and caster indirectly. Turning the cams an equal amount in opposite directions will change caster with little change in camber, depending on the relative position of the cams.

By bringing caster within specifications by turning one bolt at a time, then by turning both bolts an equal amount to bring camber to the preferred reading, the caster will usually be brought close to the preferred setting.

After both caster and camber readings are correct, tighten the nuts to a torque of 65 ft lb while holding the bolts from turning.

Always recheck the settings after tightening the nuts since the bolts may have turned slightly during the tightening process.

Toe-In Adjustment

Take toe-in readings with front wheels in straight ahead position. When necessary to adjust, loosen the clamps at each end of both tie rod adjusting tubes, Fig. 2.

Adjust toe-in by turning the tie rod tube which will "center" the steering wheel spokes. If the steering wheel was centered, make the toe-in adjustment by turning both tubes an equal amount. Before tightening the clamps, turn tie rod so ball sockets are either against the front or back sides of studs. Torque bolts to 15 ft lb.

RIDING HEIGHT

Before taking measurements, grasp the bumpers at the center (rear bumper first) and jounce the car up and down several times. Jounce the car at the front bumper the same number of times and release the bumper at the same point in the cycle each time.

1. Measure from the ball joint to the floor (measurement "A"), and from the control arm torsion bar spring anchor housing to the floor (measurement "B").

2. Subtract "A" from "B". The distance should be 1¾″ (plus or minus 1/8″).

3. Measure the other side in the same manner.

4. Adjust by turning the torsion bar anchor adjusting nut *clockwise to increase* the height and *counterclockwise to decrease* the height. The difference from side-to-side should not exceed 1/8″.

5. After adjusting, jounce the car and recheck the measurements on both sides, even if only one side may have been adjusted.

WHEEL BEARINGS

1. To adjust bearings, tighten wheel bearing adjusting nut to 15 ft lb while rotating the wheel.

2. Position nut lock on nut with one pair of slots in line with cotter pin hole.

3. Back off lock and adjusting nut 1½ slots (cotter pin hole will be covered).

4. Remove lock and re-position it so the cotter pin can be inserted. *Do not move adjusting nut.* Install cotter pin.

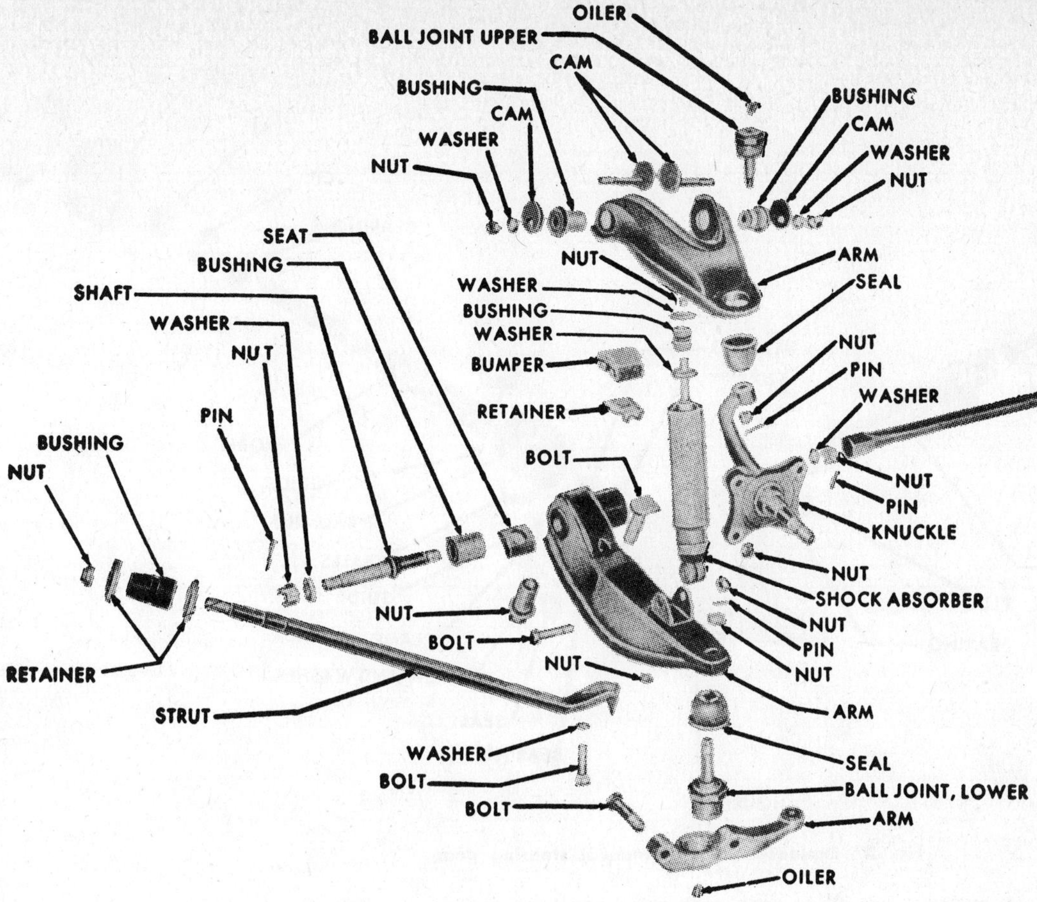

OILER
BALL JOINT UPPER
CAM
BUSHING
CAM
WASHER
NUT
BUSHING
CAM
WASHER
NUT
SEAT
BUSHING
SHAFT
WASHER
NUT
NUT
WASHER
BUSHING
WASHER
BUMPER
RETAINER
ARM
SEAL
NUT
PIN
WASHER
PIN
BUSHING
NUT
BOLT
SEAL
LOCK
BAR OR SPRING
NUT
PIN
KNUCKLE
RETAINER
STRUT
BOLT
NUT
NUT
SHOCK ABSORBER
NUT
PIN
NUT
ARM
WASHER
BOLT
SEAL
BOLT
BALL JOINT, LOWER
ARM
OILER

Fig. 1 Exploded view of front suspension

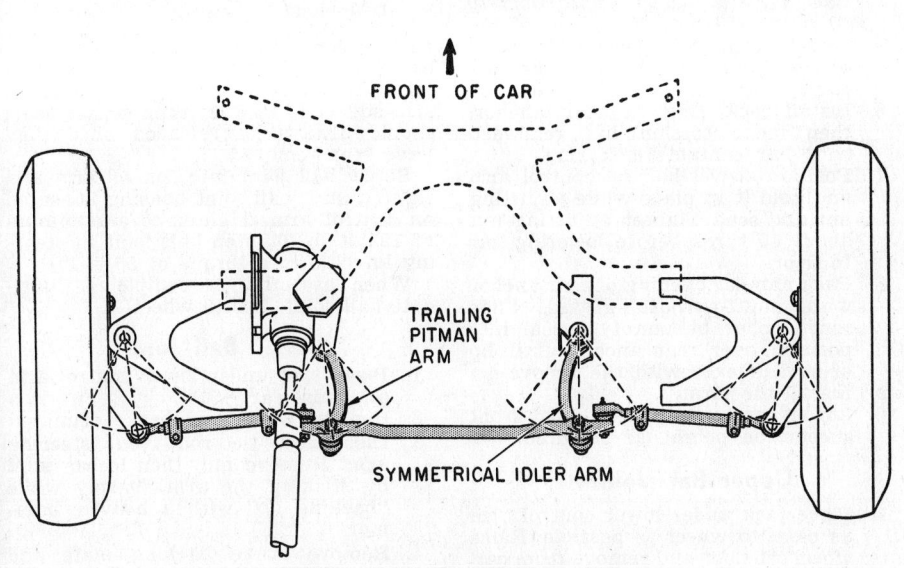

FRONT OF CAR

TRAILING PITMAN ARM

SYMMETRICAL IDLER ARM

ALL ARMS AND LINKS SWING THROUGH SIMILAR ARCS
MINIMIZING EFFORT THROUGHOUT THE ENTIRE STEERING RANGE

Fig. 2 Steering linkage

FRONT END REPAIRS

Lower Control Arm Strut

1. Remove mounting bolts.
2. Remove nut and bushing retainer from forward end of strut at crossmember.
3. Slide strut and inner bushing retainer from bushing.
4. Pry bushing from "K" member with screwdriver.

Installation

1. Dip new bushing in water and with tapered portion toward rear of car, install in "K" member, using a twisting motion until groove in bushing seats properly with support member.
2. With cupped side out, slide bushing retainer over threaded end of strut. Push strut through bushing in crossmember, position outer bushing over end of strut (cupped side in) and install nut *finger tight only.*
3. Install strut-to-control arm bolts and torque nuts to 100 ft lb.
4. Lower car to floor and jounce car to permit bushing to assume its normal position on strut.
5. Tighten nut on forward end of strut to 40 ft lb.

Torsion Bar Springs

The torsion bars are not interchangeable from side to side. The bars are

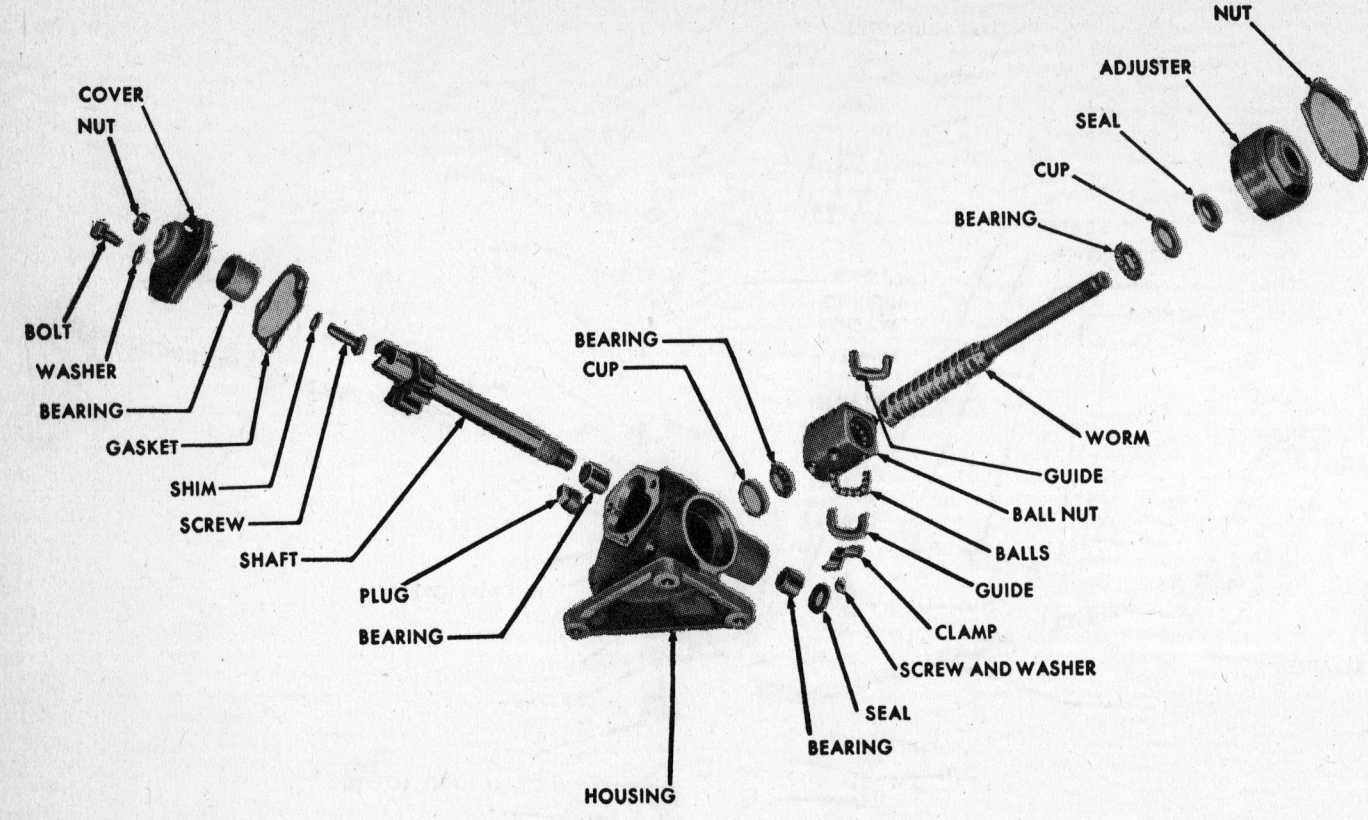

Fig. 3 Exploded view of manual steering gear

marked as either right or left by an "R" or an "L" stamped on one end of the bars. *Do not lift by the front suspension control arms for this operation.*

1. If car is to be raised on a hoist, make sure it is lifted on the body so that the front suspension is in full rebound (under no load). If the car is to be raised on a jack, place jack under center of "K" member and raise car off floor so front suspension is under no load.
2. Release load from torsion bar by backing off anchor adjusting nuts. Remove adjusting nut and swivel bolt.
3. Remove strut.
4. Remove lock ring from rear of torsion bar rear anchor.
5. To facilitate removal of torsion bars, install Tool C-3728 on the torsion bar and move bar rearward by holding tool firmly and hitting pad on tool with a hammer. *Do not apply heat to front and rear anchors. The surface of the torsion bar must not be scratched or marred in any manner.*
6. Remove tool and slide rear anchor balloon type seal off front end of torsion bar.
7. Remove torsion bar by sliding it rearward and out through rear anchor.

Installation

1. Clean hex openings in anchors and from hex ends of torsion bar springs.
2. Insert torsion bar through rear anchor.

3. Slide rear anchor balloon type seal over torsion bar, with large cupped side of seal facing rearward.
4. Coat both ends of torsion bar with multi-purpose grease.
5. When inserting torsion bar into anchor in lower control arm, *position adjusting arm approximately 60 degrees below the plane of the control arm, otherwise adjustment of the front suspension to the correct height will not be possible.*
6. Install lock ring in rear anchor, then move torsion bar rearward until bar contacts lock ring.
7. Position swivel bolt on control arm and hold it in place while adjusting nut and seat. Tighten adjusting nut about 10 turns before lowering car to floor.
8. Pack annular opening of rear anchor with multi-purpose grease. Slide rear anchor balloon type seal into position over rear anchor until lip of seal indexes with the groove.
9. Install the strut.
10. Lower car to floor and adjust front suspension height as required.

Upper Ball Joints

1. Place jack under lower control arm as close to wheel as possible. Raise wheel off floor and remove from car.
2. Remove ball joint stud nut.
3. Place spreader tool C-3711 or equivalent down on flat section of lower control arm. Turn threaded portion of tool, locking it securely against upper stud. Spread tool enough to place upper stud under pressure,

then strike steering knuckle sharply with a hammer to loosen stud.
4. Remove tool and disengage ball joint from knuckle. Remove ball joint balloon seal by prying metal retainer edge loose with a screwdriver.
5. Unscrew ball joint from upper control arm.

Installation—When installing a new ball joint, it is important that the ball joint threads engage those of the control arm squarely. Balloon type grease seals should always be replaced once they have been removed.

Screw ball joint into control arm and tighten until ball joint housing is seated on control arm. Tighten to a minimum of 125 ft lb. Tighten ball joint in steering knuckle to a torque of 55 ft lb.

When assembly is completed, lubricate ball joint. Install wheel.

Lower Ball Joint

1. Place jack under lower control arm and raise car.
2. Remove wheel and brake drum.
3. Disconnect tie rod from steering arm. Remove nut, then loosen stud by striking the arm sharply while "backing up" with a heavier hammer.
4. Remove brake backing plate and support it so no strain is put on brake hose.
5. Disconnect ball joint from lower control arm and remove knuckle arm.
6. Place assembly in vise and remove balloon seal and ball joint.

Installation

1. Screw ball joint into steering arm as far as possible by hand. Then tighten ball joint housing to a minimum of 300 ft lb until ball joint is seated in steering knckle arm.
2. Slide a new balloon seal into position, using extreme care not to pinch the rubber or deform metal retainer of seal.
3. Lubricant ball joint.
4. Install steering knuckle arm on brake support plate and connect ball joint to lower control arm, and tie rod end to steering knuckle arm. Tighten ball joint stud nut to 90 ft. lb. and tie rod end to 50 ft. lb.
5. Install drum and wheel and adjust front wheel bearings.

Lower Control Arm

1. Place jack under "K" member and raise car so that both wheels are clear of floor.
2. Disconnect strut from lower control arm.
3. Remove torsion bar.
4. Remove wheel and brake drum.
5. Disconnect shock absorber at lower control arm bracket; then push shock absorber up out of the way.
6. Disconnect lower ball joint stud from lower control arm.
7. Support brake support plate so as not to put strain on brake hose.
8. Remove nut attaching lower control arm shaft to "K" member. Reinstall nut until flush with end of shaft to protect the threads.
9. Using hammer and brass drift, loosen shaft (tapered fit) and remove nut.
10. Slide lower control arm and shaft out from rear of crossmember.
11. Remove old and install new bushings as required.

Installation

1. Position shaft and control arm in the "K" member in approximate operating position. Install washer and nut finger tight only.
2. Connect ball joint to steering knuckle and tighten nut to 55 ft. lb.
3. Connect shock absorber and tighten nut to 55 ft. lb.
4. Install torsion bar, strut, and wheel and drum assembly.
5. Lower car to floor. Then jounce car and set front suspension heights.
6. Tighten lower control arm shaft nut to 160 ft. lb.
7. Check and adjust front suspension as necessary.

Upper Control Arms

The upper control arm support mounting brackets are welded to the shock absorber tower and to the body horizontals (side rails).

1. Place jack under lower control arm as close to wheel as possible.
2. Raise car and remove wheel.
3. Remove upper ball joint stud from steering knuckle.
4. Remove nuts, cams and cam bolts. Lift control arm away from support.
5. Remove balloon type seal by prying retainer loose with screwdriver.

6. Remove old and install new bushings as required.

Installation

1. Slide control arm into position and install cam bolts, cams and nuts. Tighten nuts in preparation for final adjustment.
2. Slide upper ball joint stud into position in steering knuckle. Install washer and nut and tighten to 55 ft. lb.
3. Install wheel and remove jack.
4. Check and adjust car height and alignment, then tighten control arm cam bolt nuts to 65 ft. lb.

HORN BUTTON & RING

1. Disconnect battery ground cable.
2. Rotate horn button ¼ turn counterclockwise and remove the button.
3. Remove three screws and bushings from button base and lift out base or horn ring.

STEERING WHEEL

Remove horn button or ring as outlined previously. Disconnect wire from horn switch and remove switch. Remove steering wheel nut and washer, then attach puller and remove wheel.

MANUAL STEERING GEAR

Replace

1. Unscrew sector shaft arm retaining nut and remove arm with a puller.
2. Remove bolts attaching gear to frame.
3. Remove bolt from coupling clamp at upper end of steering gear worm shaft.
4. While supporting the gear, tap the coupling assembly upward with a mallet until it is free from worm shaft splines. Then lift out steering gear.

MANUAL STEERING GEAR REPAIRS

A worm and recirculating ball type steering gear is used with the manual steering gear system, Fig. 3. The steering worm shaft is a "stub" type and is connected to the steering shaft with a universal joint type coupling. The worm shaft is supported on each end by ball type thrust bearings. The sector shaft rotates in two needle bearings in the steering housing and a needle bearing in the housing cover.

Adjustments

Two adjustments are required: worm bearing pre-load, and ball nut and sector gear mesh. These adjustments must be made carefully and in the order given to ensure satisfactory results.

Worm Bearing Pre-load

1. Disconnect steering gear arm from sector shaft.

2. Loosen sector shaft adjusting screw lock nut and back out adjusting screw approximately two turns. This relieves the load imposed by the closely meshed ball nut and sector gear teeth.
3. Turn steering wheel two complete turns from straight-ahead position. *Do not turn steering wheel hard against stops in gear when steering gear arm is disconnected as internal damage might result.*
4. Hook a spring scale to the steering wheel and rotate the wheel at least one turn (toward straight-ahead position) with the scale. The pull required to keep the wheel moving should be between ¼ and ¾ lb. If the reading is not within these limits, adjustment of the worm bearing pre-load is necessary.
5. To adjust the pre-load, loosen the lock nut on the large adjuster nut which threads into the housing. Turn the adjuster clockwise to increase pre-load or counter-clockwise to decrease the pre-load.

Ball Nut and Sector Gear Mesh

The sector shaft adjusting screw, located in the housing cover, raises or lowers the shaft to provide the proper mesh load between the tapered teeth of the sector gear and tapered teeth of the ball nut. This adjustment is made only after the proper worm bearing pre-load has been obtained.

1. Turn steering wheel gently from one stop all the way to the other, carefully counting the number of turns. Then turn the wheel back exactly half way, to the center position.
2. Turn the sector shaft adjusting screw clockwise to take out all lash between the gear teeth, then tighten the adjusting screw lock nut.
3. Turn the steering wheel about ¼ turn away from center and, using a spring scale, check the pull required to move the wheel through the high spot (center) position. The scale reading should be between 1 and 1⅝ lb. This represents the total of the worm bearing pre-load and the gear mesh load. Readjust, if necessary to obtain proper pull.
4. After the adjustments have been completed, align front wheels in the straight-ahead position. Then install steering arm on sector shaft and tighten retaining nut to 120-130 ft lb.

POWER STEERING

The power steering gear used is the Constant Control type used on other Chrysler cars but built on a smaller scale. However, servicing the gear is essentially the same.

To remove the steering gear, proceed as follows:

1. Unscrew gear shaft arm retaining nut and remove arm with a puller.
2. Disconnect hydraulic lines from steering gear valve.
3. Remove bolts attaching gear to frame.
4. Remove bolt from coupling clamp at

upper end of steering gear worm shaft.

5. While supporting gear, tap coupling assembly upward with a mallet until

it is free from worm shaft splines. Then lift gear out of car.

Instruments, Radio & Windshield Wiper

INSTRUMENT CLUSTER

1961 Lancer

1. Remove heater switch trim plate.
2. Remove transmission push button trim plate.
3. Remove steering wheel.
4. Loosen (do not remove) steering column jacket tube clamp and steering jacket to lower instrument panel screws.
5. Disconnect speedometer cable at speedometer.
6. Unfasten and pull instrument cluster and casting from panel housing.
7. Separate cluster panel from panel cluster casting.
8. Disconnect all wires and remove instrument cluster and remove instrument bezel from cluster base.
9. Remove all gauges.
10. Remove speedometer from cluster base.

1960-61 Valiant

1. Disconnect battery ground cable.
2. Remove headlamp switch knob.
3. Unfasten and pull top of instrument cluster forward.
4. Disconnect speedometer cable from speedometer and electrical connections.
5. Remove instrument cluster.
6. Remove speedometer from cluster.

RADIO

Lancer and Valiant, 1960-61

1. Disconnect battery ground cable.
2. Remove radio speaker grille.
3. Disconnect "A" antenna lead and speaker leads.
4. Remove nuts from radio mounting studs.
5. Remove radio opening cover plate.
6. Unfasten radio from support housing.
7. Remove radio through opening between radio support and speaker.

WINDSHIELD WIPER

1961 Lancer

1. Remove heater switch trim plate.
2. Remove transmission push button trim plate.
3. Remove steering wheel.
4. Loosen (do not remove) steering column jacket tube clamp and steering jacket to lower instrument panel screws.

5. Disconnect speedometer cable at speedometer.
6. Unfasten and pull instrument cluster and casting from panel housing.
7. Separate cluster panel from panel cluster casting.
8. Disconnect all electrical connections and remove instrument cluster.
9. Remove radio speaker grille and speaker.
10. Unfasten and remove wiper motor through instrument panel opening.

1960-61 Valiant

1. Disconnect battery cable.
2. Remove glove compartment.
3. Pry radio speaker grille away from instrument panel.
4. Unfasten and lower radio speaker to gain access to wiper motor bracket.
5. Disconnect wires to wiper motor.
6. Remove headlamp switch pull knob.
7. Unfasten and pull top of instrument cluster forward to gain access to wiper pivot on left side.
8. Disconnect speedometer cable and wiper motor wires at panel switch.
9. Disconnect links at pivot cranks.
10. Slide wiper with links far enough toward left so that right hand link will clear glove compartment opening and remove wiper bracket with wiper and links as an assembly, being careful not to bend links.

LINCOLN & CONTINENTAL

INDEX OF SERVICE OPERATIONS

ACCESSORIES PAGE NO.

Instruments 803
Radio Removal 804
Windshield Wiper 804
Windshield Wiper Troubles...........37

BODY

Air Conditioning 177
Automatic Seat Adjuster Troubles......36
Automatic Top Troubles..............36
Automatic Window Lift Troubles.......36

BRAKES (Mechanical)

Adjustments 112
Brake Cylinder Sizes.................778
Hydraulic Brake System.............112
Trouble Shooting 31

BRAKES (Power)

Power Unit Repairs..................128
Power Unit, Replace.................798
Trouble Shooting 32

COOLING SYSTEM

Radiator, Replace 788
Trouble Shooting 8
Water Pump Repairs................789
Water Pump, Replace...............788

ELECTRIC SYSTEM

Dash Gauge Service.................85
Distributor, Replace.................789
Distributor Service 46
Distributor Specifications...........777
Generator Regulator Service..........62
Generator Regulator Specifications.....779
Generator Service 62
Generator Specifications 777
Horn Ring, Replace..................801
Ignition System Service.............46
Ignition Timing 789
Starter Replace 789
Starter Switch Service...............83
Starting Motor Service...............77
Starting Motor Specifications.........779
Trouble Shooting 10
Turn Signal Troubles................12

ENGINE PAGE NO.

Camshaft, Replace 785
Camshaft Bearings 785
Crankshaft & Bearing Specs........777
Crankshaft Oil Seal, Replace.........786
Cylinder Head, Replace.............781
Engine, Replace 780
Main Bearings, Replace.............786
Piston Pins, Replace................786
Piston Rings, Replace...............786
Piston, Pins, & Ring Specs..........777
Piston & Rod, Assemble............785
Pistons & Rods, Remove...........785
Pistons, Replace 785
Rocker Arms 782
Rod Bearings, Replace.............786
Timing Case Cover, Replace........784
Timing Chain, Replace.............785
Trouble Shooting 4
Valves, Adjust 782
Valve Arrangement 782
Valves, Grind 783
Valve Guides 783
Valve Lifters 784
Valves, Remove 783
Valve Spring Installed Height........783
Valve Spring Testing 783

ENGINE OILING

Oil Pan, Replace 787
Oil Pump Repairs..................787
Trouble Shooting 9

FRONT SUSPENSION

Camber, Adjust 799
Caster, Adjust 799
Front End Repairs..................800
Toe-in, Adjust 800
Trouble Shooting 33
Wheel Alignment Specifications......778
Wheel Bearings, Adjust............800

FUEL & EXHAUST SYSTEMS

Carburetors 790
Fuel Pumps 96
Muffler and Pipes..................790
Trouble Shooting 4

OVERDRIVE 100

Trouble Shooting 14

REAR AXLE PAGE NO.

Axle Shaft, Replace.................798
General Service 102
Non-Slip Differentials...............109
Rear Axle Repairs..................798
Rear Axle, Replace.................798
Rear Axle Specifications............778
Trouble Shooting 31

SPECIFICATIONS

Brake Cylinder Sizes...............778
Capacity Data 778
Carburetors 791
Cooling System 778
Crankshaft & Bearings.............777
Distributors 777
Engine Tightening 776
Generator & Regulators............779
Pistons, Pins & Rings..............777
Rear Axle 778
Starting Motors 779
Tune Up 776
Valve Timing 785
Valves 777
Wheel Alignment 778

STEERING GEARS (Mechanical)

Horn Ring, Replace.................801
Steering Gear, Adjust 803
Steering Gear Repairs..............803
Steering Gear, Replace.............801
Steering Wheel, Replace............801
Trouble Shooting 33

STEERING GEARS (Power)

Steering Gear Repairs..............145
Steering Gear, Replace.............802
Trouble Shooting 34

TRANSMISSIONS (Automatic)

Hydra-Matic Linkage, Adjust........793
Hydra-Matic, Replace 793
Hydra-Matic Repairs 283
Hydra-Matic Trouble Shooting.......25
Turbo-Drive Linkage, Adjust........794
Turbo-Drive, Replace 795
Turbo-Drive Repairs 240
Turbo-Drive Trouble Shooting.......24

TUNE UP 38

GENERAL SPECIFICATIONS

Year	Model Designation	Wheelbase, Inches	Valve Location	Bore and Stroke	Piston Displacement, Cubic Inches	Compression Ratio (Standard)	Maximum Brake H.P. @ R.P.M.	Maximum Torque Lbs. Ft. @ R.P.M.	Normal Oil Pressure Pounds
1953	Lincoln V8..............All	123	In Head	3.8000 x 3.500	317	8.0	205 @ 4200	305 @ 2300	40
1954	Lincoln V8..............All	123	In Head	3.8000 x 3.500	317	8.0	205 @ 4200	305 @ 2300	40
1955	Lincoln V8..............All	123	In Head	3.9375 x 3.500	341	8.5	225 @ 4400	332 @ 2500	40
1956	Continental V8......Mark II	126	In Head	4.0000 x 3.660	368	9.0	285 @ 4600	402 @ 3000	40
	Lincoln V8..............All	126	In Head	4.0000 x 3.660	368	9.0	285 @ 4600	402 @ 3000	40
1957	Continental V8......Mark II	126	In Head	4.0000 x 3.660	368	10.1	300 @ 4800	415 @ 3000	45
	Lincoln V8..............All	126	In Head	4.0000 x 3.660	368	10.1	300 @ 4800	415 @ 3000	45
1958	Continental V8......Mark III	131	In Head	4.3000 x 3.700	430	10.5	375 @ 4800	490 @ 3100	35–50
	Lincoln V8..............All	131	In Head	4.3000 x 3.700	430	10.5	375 @ 4800	490 @ 3100	35–50
1959	Continental V8......Mark IV	131	In Head	4.3000 x 3.700	430	10.5	375 @ 4800	490 @ 3100	35–50
	Lincoln V8..............All	131	In Head	4.3000 x 3.700	430	10.5	375 @ 4800	490 @ 3100	35–50
1960	Continental V8......Mark V	131	In Head	4.3000 x 3.700	430	10.0	315 @ 4100	465 @ 2200	35–50
	Lincoln V8..............All	131	In Head	4.3000 x 3.700	430	10.0	315 @ 4100	465 @ 2200	35–50
1961	Lincoln Continental V8.....All	123	In Head	4.3000 x 3.700	430	10.0	315 @ 4100	465 @ 2200	52–62

TUNE UP SPECIFICATIONS

★Disconnect vacuum line when using a timing light to set timing.

Year	Model	Ground Polarity and Voltage	Spark Plug Type ①	Spark Plug Gap Inch	Distributor Point Gap Inch	Distributor Cam Angle Degrees	Firing Order ②	Ignition Timing★ Mark	Ignition Timing★ Location	Idle Speed RPM In Drive	Compression Pressure @ Cranking Speed Minimum
1953–54	All	P-6	H-10	.035	.015	26–28	15486372	3°BTDC	Damper	425	125
1955	All	P-6	F-14Y	.034	.015	26–28	15486372	5°BTDC	Damper	425	125
1956	All	N-12	F-14Y	.034	.015	26–28	15486372	5°BTDC	Damper	465	140
1957	All	N-12	F-14Y	.034	.015	26–28	15486372	5°BTDC	Damper	465	150
1958–59	All	N-12	F-11Y	.034	.015	26–28	15426378	6°BTDC	Damper	465	200
1960–61	All	N-12	F-11Y	.034	.015	26–28	15426378	6°BTDC	Damper	465	160

①—Champion.   ②—Cylinder numbering (front to rear): Right bank 1-2-3-4, left bank 5-6-7-8.

ENGINE TIGHTENING SPECIFICATIONS★

★Torque specifications are for clean and lightly lubricated threads only.   Dry or dirty threads produce increased friction which prevents accurate measurement of tightness.

Year	Spark Plugs Ft. Lbs.	Cylinder Head Bolts Ft. Lbs.	Intake Manifold Ft. Lbs.	Exhaust Manifold Ft. Lbs.	Rocker Arm Shaft Bracket Ft. Lbs.	Rocker Arm Cover Ft. Lbs.	Connecting Rod Cap Bolts Ft. Lbs.	Main Bearing Cap Bolts Ft. Lbs.	Flywheel to Crankshaft Ft. Lbs.	Vibration Damper or Pulley Ft. Lbs.
1953–55	24–30	80–90	23–28	23–28	12–15	2–2½	45–50	120–130	75–85	130–145
1956–57	15–20	90	23–28	23–28	22–25	2–2½	45–50	120–130	75–85	130–145
1958–61	15–20	85–105	23–28	23–28	45–50	2–2½	45–50	95–105	75–85	75–90

VALVE SPECIFICATIONS

Year	Model	Valve Lash Int.	Valve Lash Exh.	Valve Angles Seat	Valve Angles Face	Valve Spring Installed Height	Valve Spring Pressure Lbs. @ In.	Valve Lift Int.	Valve Lift Exh.	Stem Clearance Intake	Stem Clearance Exhaust	Stem Diameter Int.	Stem Diameter Exh.
1953	All	Zero	Zero	45	45	1 51/64	150 @ 1 7/16	.354	.354	.001–.002	.003–.004	.3420	.3410
1954	All	Zero	Zero	45	45	1 51/64	140 @ 1 15/32	.354	.354	.001–.002	.002–.003	.3420	.3410
1955	All	Zero	Zero	45	45	1 51/64	170 @ 1 27/64	.384	.384	.001–.002	.002–.003	.3420	.3410
1956	All	Zero	Zero	45	45	1 51/64	190 @ 1 3/8	.417	.417	.001–.002	.002–.003	.3420	.3410
1957	All	Zero	Zero	45	45	1 51/64	190 @ 1 3/8	.417	.417	.001–.0025	.0025–.004	.3420	.3407
1958	All	Zero	Zero	①	①	1 53/64	250 @ 1 25/64	.441	.441	.001–.0025	.003–.004	.3715	.3697
1959	All	Zero	Zero	45	45	1 53/64	250 @ 1 7/16	.408	.408	.001–.0025	.003–.004	.3715	.3697
1960	All	Zero	Zero	45	45	1 53/64	250 @ 1 7/16	.408	.408	.001–.0025	.0025–.004	.3715	.3697
1961	All	Zero	Zero	45	45	1 41/64	190 @ 1 5/64	.408	.408	.001–.002	.002–.003	.3715	.3705

①—Intake 30°, exhaust 45°.

PISTONS, PINS, RINGS, CRANKSHAFT & BEARINGS

Year	Model	Fitting Pistons Shim To Use	Fitting Pistons Pounds Pull On Scale	Ring End Gap ① Comp.	Ring End Gap ① Oil	Wristpin Diameter	Rod Bearings Shaft Diameter	Rod Bearings Bearing Clearance	Main Bearings Shaft Diameter	Main Bearings Bearing Clearance	Thrust on Bear. No.	Shaft End Play
1953–54	All	.002	6–12	.010	.010	.9122	2.248–2.249	.0005–.002	2.6235–2.6243	.001–.003	3	.004–.008
1955	All	.002	6–12	.010	.010	.9122	2.248–2.249	.0005–.003	2.6235–2.6243	.001–.003	3	.004–.008
1956–57	All	.002	6–12	.013	.010	.9122	2.248–2.249	.0005–.003	2.6235–2.6243	.001–.003	3	.004–.008
1958–60	All	.002	5–10	.015	.015	.9752	2.599–2.600	.0006–.0026	2.8994–2.9002	.0009–.0029	3	.004–.008
1961	All	.002	5–10	.015	.015	.9750	2.599–2.600	.0005–.0017	2.8994–2.9003	.0007–.0019	3	.004–.008

①—Fit rings in tapered bores for clearance listed in tightest portion of ring travel.

DISTRIBUTOR SPECIFICATIONS

Year and Model	Part No.①	Rotation ②	Cam Angle, Degrees	Breaker Point Opening, Inch	Condenser Capacity, Mfds.③	Breaker Arm Spring Tension, Ounces	Centrifugal Advance Data Degrees @ R.P.M. of Dist. Advance Starts	Centrifugal Advance Data Degrees @ R.P.M. of Dist. Full Advance	Vacuum Advance Data Inches of Vacuum to Start Plunger Movement	Vacuum Advance Data Inches of Vacuum for Full Plunger Travel	Vacuum Advance Data Maximum Vacuum Advance, Dist. Degrees
1953	FAF-12127A	CC	26–28	.015	.21–.25	17–20	None	None	.55⑦	4.85⑤	14 1/4–15 1/2
1954	FAF-12127B	CC	26–28	.015	.21–.25	17–20	None	None	.51⑦	2.65⑤	15–15 1/2
1955	FDL-12127B	CC	26–28	.015	.21–.25	17–20	None	None	.62⑦	2.35⑤	12 1/4–13 1/2
1956	FDU-12127B	CC	26–28	.015	.21–.25	17–20	None	None	.46④	1.88⑤	12 3/4–14
	FER-12127A	CC	26–28	.015	.21–.25	17–20	None	None	.46④	1.88⑤	12 3/4–14
1957	FEL-12127A	CC	26–28	.015	.21–.25	17–20	0 @ 300	12 @ 2000	5	20	8
1958	FEW-12127A	CC	26–28	.015	.21–.25	17–20	0 @ 300	13 @ 2000	6	20	11 1/2
	FEW-12127D	CC	26–28	.015	.21–.25	17–20	1/2 @ 300	13 @ 2000	6	20	11 1/2
1959–60	FEW-12127E	CC	26–28	.015	.21–.25	17–20	1 @ 400	13 @ 2000	6	18	11 1/2
1961	CIVF-12127A	CC	26–28	.015	.21–.25	17–20	2 @ 500	15 @ 2000	6	18	11

①—Stamped on plate riveted to housing.

②—As viewed from top. C—Clockwise. CC—Counter clockwise.

③—Microfarads—as indicated on a condenser tester.

④—At 600 RPM. ⑤—At 2000 RPM. ⑥—At 400 RPM. ⑦—At 500 RPM.

COOLING SYSTEM & CAPACITY DATA

Year and Model	Cooling System Data					Fuel Tank Gals.	Engine Oil			Transmissions			Rear Axle Pints
	Quarts No Heater	Quarts With Heater	Rad. Cap Relief Pressure	Thermostat Opening Temp.			Refill Qts. ③	Summer Grade	Winter Grade	Std.	With Over-drive	Auto-matic Qts.	
				①	②								
LINCOLN													
1953–54	22½	24	12–15	170	160	20	5	20	10W	None	None	11	4
1955	23	24	12–15	170	160	20	5	20	10W	None	None	10	4
1956	23	25.2	12–15	180	160	20	5	20	10W	None	None	10	4
1957	22	25.2	12–15	180	160	20	5	20	10W	None	None	11.3	4
1958	23	26	12–15	180④	160	23	5	20	10W	None	None	12	4
1959	23	26	12–15	180④	160	22	5	20	10W	None	None	11½	4
1960	23	26	12–15	180④	160	25	5	20	10W	None	None	10½	4.8
1961	22	25	12–15	180④	160	21	5	20	10W	None	None	11	4.8
CONTINENTAL													
1956	23	25.4	12–15	180	160	25	5	20	10W	None	None	10	4
1957	22	25.4	12–15	180	160	20	5	20	10W	None	None	11.3	4
1958	23	26	12–15	180④	160	23	5	20	10W	None	None	12	4
1959	23	26	12–15	180④	160	22	5	20	10W	None	None	11½	4
1960	23	26	12–15	180④	160	25	5	20	10W	None	None	10½	4.8

①—For permanent type anti-freeze.
②—For alcohol type anti-freeze.
③—Add one quart with filter change.
④—Thermostats (2) in front face of each block 142°.

WHEEL ALIGNMENT SPECIFICATIONS

Year	Model	Caster, Degrees③		Camber, Degrees④		Toe-In, Inch	Toe-out on Turns, Degrees①		Kingpin or Steering Axis Inclination②
		Limits	Desired	Limits	Desired		Outer Wheel	Inner Wheel	
1953–55	All	− 1½ to 0	− ¾	0 to + ¾	+ ⅜	3/32 to 5/32	20	23	7 @ ¾ Camber
1956–57	Lincoln	0 to − 1½	− ¾	0 to + ¾	+ ⅜	⅛ to 3/16	20	25° 48′	7 @ ¾ Camber
	Continental	+ ¾ to + 1¼	+ 1	+ ½ to + 1	+ ¾	3/32 to 5/32	20	25° 48′	7 @ ¾ Camber
1958–60	All	0 to − 1½	− ¾	0 to + ¾	+ ⅜	⅛ to 3/16	17° 20′	20	7° 26′ @ ¾ Camber
1961	All	− 1½ to 0	− ¾	0 to + ¾	+ ⅜	1/16 to 3/16	17° 48′	20	7 @ ¾ Camber

①—Incorrect toe-out, when other adjustments are correct, indicates bent steering arms.
②—Incorrect kingpin or knuckle support angle with correct camber indicates bent suspension arms or knuckle support.
③—Within ½° one side of car to other.   ④—Within ¼° one side of car to other.

REAR AXLE AND BRAKE CYLINDER SPECIFICATIONS

Year	Model	Ring Gear & Pinion Backlash, Inch	Drive Pinion Adjustment	Drive Pinion Bearing Preload Inch Lbs.	Drive Pinion Bearing Adjustment	Axle Shaft End Play, Inch	Hydraulic Cylinder Bore Sizes, Inch		Master Cylinder
							Wheel Cylinder		
							Front	Rear	
1953–55	All	.003–.008	Shims	18–20②	Shims	None	1⅛	15/16	1
1956–57	All	.003–.008	Shims	18–20②	Shims	None	1 3/32	15/16	1①
1958–60	All	.003–.008	Shims	18–20②	Shims	None	1 3/32	15/16	21/32
1961	All	.003–.008	Shims	18–20②	Shims	None	1 3/32	15/16	⅞

①—Conventional.   Power brake .656″.
②—For used bearings 8–12 inch lbs.

STARTING MOTOR SPECIFICATIONS

Year	Model	Part No.	Rotation ①	Brush Spring Tension, Ounces	No Load Test			Torque Test		
					Amperes	Volts	R.P.M.	Amperes	Volts	Torque, Lbs. Ft.
1953–55	All	FAC-11002G	C	48–56	70	6	5500	700	3.5	14
1956	All	B6A-11002A	C	48–56	120	12	4800	550	5.0	15½
1957	All	FAR-11001A	C	48–56	85	12	4500	550	5.0	15½
1958–59	All	2900550	C	48–56	85	12	4500	550	5.0	15½
1960	All	FAY-11001A	C	48–56	85	12	4500	550	5.0	15½
1961	All	CIVF-11001C	C	48–56	70	12	9500	525	4.0	14

①—As viewed from the drive end. C—Clockwise.

GENERATOR AND REGULATOR SPECIFICATIONS

★To Polarize Generator: For internally grounded systems, disconnect field lead from regulator and momentarily flash this lead to the regulator battery terminal. For externally grounded systems, reconnect leads to the regulator; then momentarily connect a jumper wire from the "Gen" or "Arm" to the "Bat" terminals of the regulator.

	Generator						Regulator					
Year	Generator Number	Rotation and Ground Polarity ③	Rated Cap. Amps.	Gen. Field Ground Location★	Brush Spring Tension, Ounces	Field Current	Regulator Number	Cutout Relay		Voltage Regulator Setting Volts	Current Regulator Setting Amperes	Current and Voltage Armature Air Gap, Inch
								Voltage to Close Points	Armature Air, Gap, Inch			
1953	FAB-10002A	C-P	40	Internal	26–34	1.7–2.0③	B5A-10505C	6.3	....	7.6	40	....
1954–55	FBB-10002A	C-P	50	Internal	26–34	2.5–2.8③	FAJ-10505A	6.3	....	7.6	50	....
1956	B6A-10002A	C-N	30	Internal	26–34	1.5–1.6①	B6A-10505A	12.4	....	15.0	30	....
1957	FGP-10000B	C-N	40	Internal	26–34	1.5–1.6①	FEL-10505	12.4	....	15.0	40	....
1958	FGV-10000A	C-N	40	Internal	32–40	1.5–1.6①	2900423	12.4	....	15.0	40	....
1959	FGV-10000A	C-N	40	Internal	32–40	1.48④	2700017	12.4	....	15.0	40	....
1959	FGV-10000A	C-N	40	Internal	32–40	1.48④	2900563	12.4	....	15.0	40	....
1960	B9LF-10000A	C-N	40	Internal	32–40	1.0–1.1④	2900563	12.4	....	15.0	40	....
1960	B9LF-10000B	C-N	50	External	28	2.0–2.5④	COLF-10505A	12.4	....	14.8⑤	48	....
1961	CIVF-10000A	C-N	40	Internal	32–40	1.5–2.0	CIVF-10505A	12.6	....	15.6	40	....

①—At 15 volts. ②—At 6 volts. ③—C-Clockwise. P-Positive. N-Negative. ④—At 10 volts. ⑤—Lower contacts should be .3–.5 volt less than the upper.

SERIAL & ENGINE NUMBER LOCATION
1953-54: Right Front Door Pillar
1955-61: Left Front Door Pillar

1954

1953

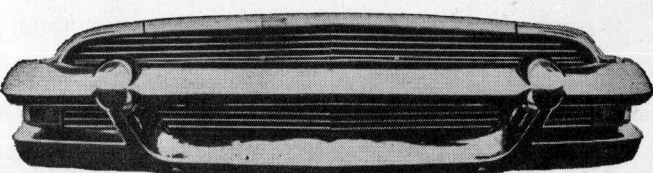

1955

1956 Lincoln

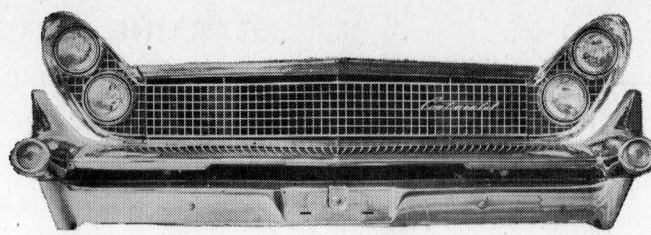

1959 Continental

1956-57 Continental

1959 Lincoln

1957 Lincoln

1960 Continental

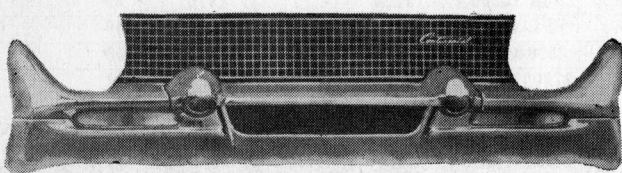

1958 Continental

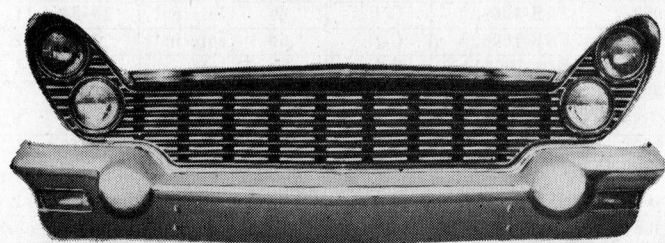

1960 Lincoln

1958 Lincoln

1961

Engine Section

ENGINE, REPLACE

In addition to the usual items such as fuel lines, linkage and radiator hoses, the following operations must be performed:

1. Remove hood, radiator and air cleaner.
2. On 1953-57 models, remove defroster blower motor and on 1953-55, the oil filter.
3. Remove power steering pump and starter.
4. Disconnect exhaust pipes from manifolds.
5. On 1956-57 models, remove radiator splash shield and radio speaker.
6. Support transmission with a suitable jack.
7. Unfasten engine mountings and attach lifting rig to engine.
8. Remove bell housing to engine attaching bolts and carefully lift engine out of chassis. *Be sure to support transmission with front end tilted up to prevent converter from falling out.*

CYLINDER HEADS

1953-57

1. Disconnect throttle linkage at carburetor and remove capscrews holding linkage brackets to cylinder block and intake manifold.
2. Disconnect fuel and vacuum lines from fuel pump, intake manifold and carburetor and remove lines and fuel pump.
3. Remove vacuum line from carburetor and distributor. Disconnect high tension lead and primary ignition wire from coil and take off coil.
4. Remove distributor cap and wiring harness brackets and take off these parts as a unit.
5. Disconnect automatic choke arm from carburetor and remove choke assembly.
6. Loosen heater tube connections at

1958-61 engine. Note wedge-shaped combustion chamber formed in block and that underside of cylinder head is flat

Fig. 1   Removing rocker arm assembly.   1953-57

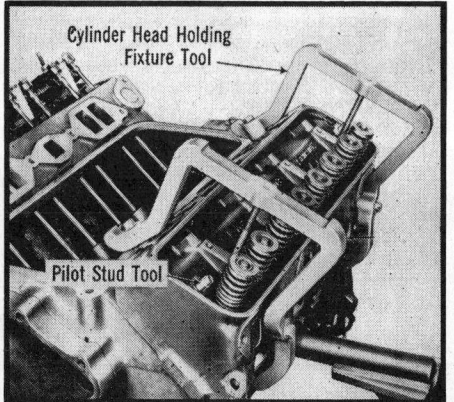

Fig. 2   Showing use of special fixture and pilots to remove and install cylinder head.   1953-57

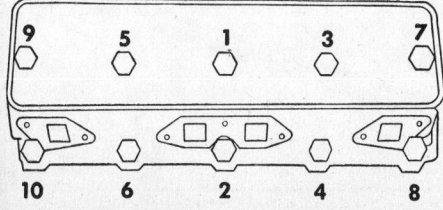

Fig. 3   Cylinder head tightening

intake manifold and carburetor. Take off carburetor and pull heater tube straight up from manifold.

7. Remove front exhaust cross-over pipe and both exhaust manifolds. *Caution*—Do not scratch surfaces of exhaust ports since gaskets are not used at these locations.
8. Remove oil filler cap and pipe and oil dipstick and tube. If the tube is tight, tap it lightly on the welded bracket with a hammer.
9. Remove rocker arm covers and gaskets by removing two acorn nuts and lockwashers.
10. Remove distributor retaining bracket and pull distributor gently from block. Notice the distance the rotor turns as the distributor is removed. This will be very helpful when distributor is reinstalled as the helical gears turn the shaft.
11. Remove intake manifolds and gaskets. When this operation is done, make sure the cover is cleaned first so dirt does not fall into the push rod chamber.
12. Loosen push rod adjusting nuts and screws to relieve tension on push rods.
13. Remove capscrews and nuts holding rocker arm assemblies to cylinder heads.
14. Remove oil overflow pipe from end support at front on right bank and at rear on left bank.

15. Remove rocker arm assemblies, Fig. 1, and lift out push rods. Retain push rods in correct order to assure proper assembly.
16. Remove two end cylinder head capscrews and install pilot studs, Fig. 2.

Note—It is strongly recommended that the cylinder head holding fixture shown in Fig. 3 be used as it has been designed so all work operations may be performed with the fixture in place. Thus, the machined surfaces are being protected from being scratched or marred which would require extensive repair work to prevent a gasket leak.

17. Install the fixture as shown in Fig. 2, using intake manifold bolts. Remove remaining cylinder head capscrews and lift the heads off the two locating dowels and pilot studs.
18. Install the heads in the reverse order of removal and tighten the holddown bolts in the sequence shown in Fig. 3 and to the torque values given in the *Engine Tightening* chart.

1958-61

1. Drain cooling system.
2. Remove rocker arms and push rods.
3. Remove intake manifold.
4. Remove ignition coil from the left cylinder if that particular head is being removed.

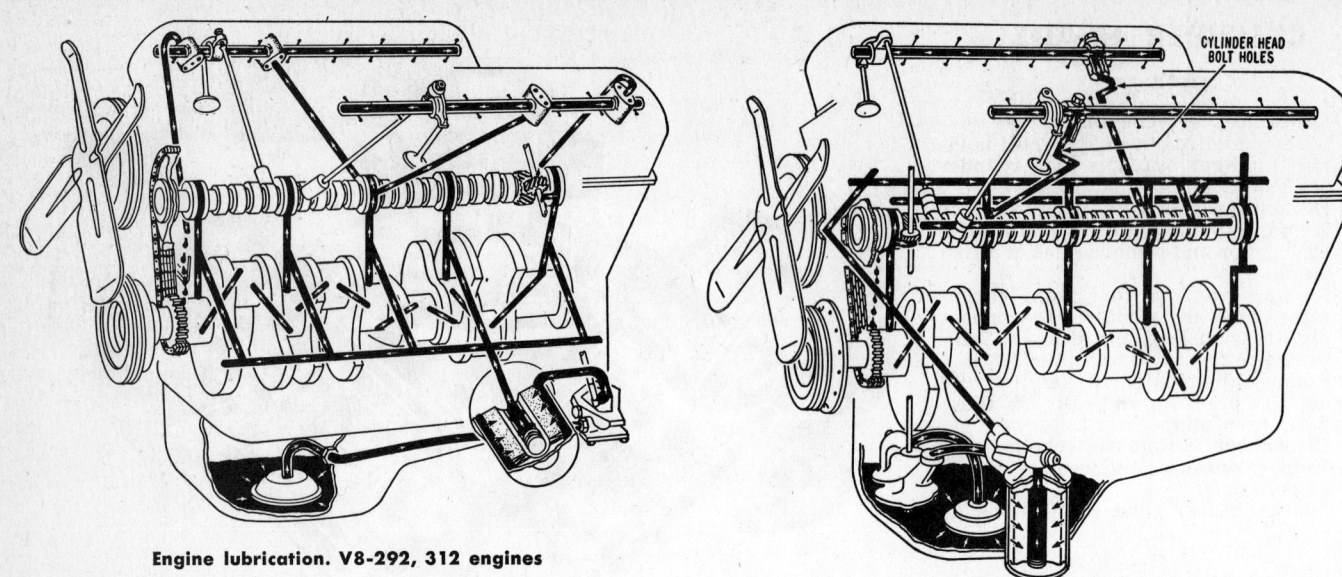

Engine lubrication. V8-292, 312 engines

Engine lubrication. 1958-61

5. Unfasten exhaust pipe from manifold.
6. Unfasten and remove cylinder head and exhaust manifold as a unit. *The exhaust manifolds should not be separated from the cylinder heads unless the head is to be replaced or the valves are to be ground.*

Installation

Install the cylinder heads in the reverse order of removal. Tighten the heads in the sequence shown in Fig. 3. The bolts must be tightened in three steps. The bolts must be tightened first to 70, then 80 and finally to 90 lbs. ft. torque.

VALVE ARRANGEMENT
Front to Rear

1953-57 . . . . E-I-I-E-E-I-I-E
1958-61 Right Bank . . . . . I-E-I-E-I-E-I-E
1958-61 Left Bank . . . . . E-I-E-I-E-I-E-I

VALVES, ADJUST
1953-57

Take off the distributor cap and turn the engine until the distributor rotor is at the firing position for No. 1 cylinder. When this is done, the following valves will be fully closed and, therefore, can be adjusted:

No. 1 intake and exhaust.
No. 2 intake and exhaust.
No. 5 intake and exhaust.
No. 4 exhaust; No. 7 intake.

After setting up the above valves, turn the engine so the distributor rotor is at the firing position for No. 6 cylinder. Then the rest of the valves can be adjusted. These are:

No. 3 intake and exhaust.
No. 6 intake and exhaust.
No. 8 intake and exhaust.
No. 4 intake; No. 7 exhaust.

To make the adjustment, turn the adjusting screw clockwise while moving the push rod up and down until all slack is removed (do not force the hydraulic plunger down into the lifter body). After removing all slack, turn the adjusting screw an additional 2 turns, Fig. 4 on 1952-53 and 2½ turns on 1954-57. Hold the adjusting screw and tighten the lock nut. If any lifter is noisy during subsequent operation, the adjustment may be varied by turning the adjusting screw an additional ¼ turn from the two-turn setting on 1952-53 and ½ turn on 1954-57.

ROCKER ARMS

Sludge and gum formation in rocker arms and shafts, Figs. 5 and 6, will restrict the normal flow of oil to the rocker arms and valves. Each time the assemblies are removed (see *Cylinder Head*) they should be disassembled and thoroughly cleaned.

Remove the support bracket bolts, cotter pins, washers, springs, support brackets, and shafts. Clean all gum and sludge formation from the inside and outside of the shafts and rocker arms. Inspect the shafts for wear. Check the fit of the rocker arms on the shafts and the valve end of the rocker arms for excessive wear. If the rocker arm radius is grooved on the valve end, do not attempt grinding; replace the part.

When the assemblies are installed, make sure the rocker arms are correctly positioned to actuate the valves. The oil overflow pipe hole in the shaft should

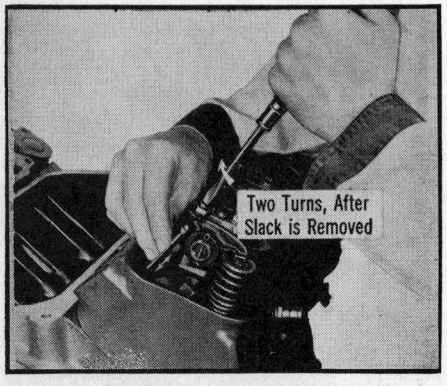

Fig. 4 Adjusting valve clearance for zero lash. 2½ turns on 1954-57

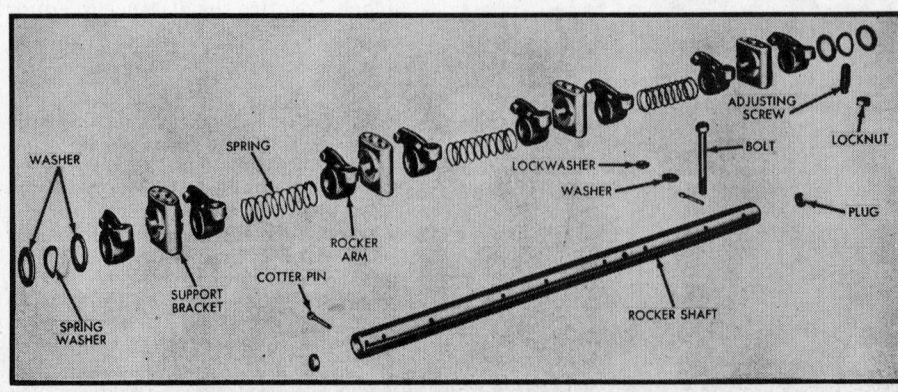

Fig. 5 Layout of rocker arm assembly. 1953-57

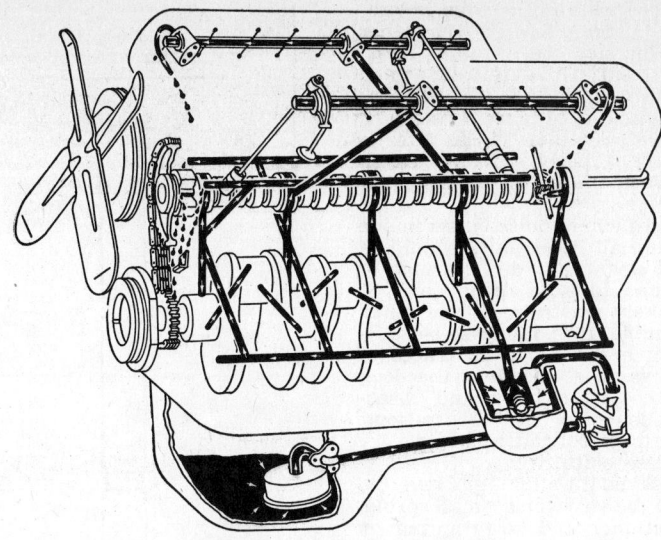

Engine lubrication. 1953-57

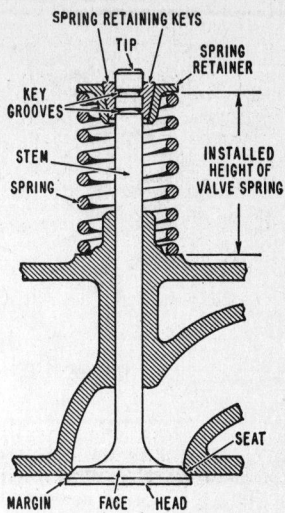

Fig. 7A Checking valve spring installed height

be seen through the center hole of the front support on the right bank and the rear support on the left bank. If the hole cannot be seen, turn the shaft until the holes line up.

Check each push rod for a bent or damaged condition. If bent more than .020" when checked with an indicator, replace the rod; do not attempt to straighten a bent rod. If a dial gauge is not available, at least check the rod for straightness by rolling it on a perfectly flat surface plate.

VALVES, REMOVE

With the cylinder head removed as outlined previously, use a suitable valve spring compressor, Fig. 7, to compress each spring. Remove the valve locks and sleeve, tapping the sleeve with a soft hammer if necessary. Remove the sleeve from the valve stem and release the pressure on the spring. Remove the spring compressor and lift off the valve retainer sleeve, retainer, spring and valve. Repeat for the remaining valves. Keep the valves and related parts together so they may be installed in their respective positions if found in satisfactory condition.

VALVE GUIDES

Valve guides in these engines are an integral part of the head and, therefore,

cannot be removed. For service, guides can be reamed oversize to accommodate one of three service valves with oversize stems (.003", .015" and .030").

Check the valve stem clearance of each valve (after cleaning) in its respective valve guide. If the clearance exceeds the service limits of .004" on the intake or .005" on the exhaust, ream the valve guides to accommodate the next oversize diameter valve.

VALVE SPRING INSTALLED HEIGHT

When valves and seats are reground the position of the valve in the head is changed so as to lessen the valve spring tension. Without proper valve spring tension the valve does not seat long enough or it may not seat completely. Since the valve is cooled by transferring heat from the valve head to the seat and thence to the coolant, improper valve spring tension will cause worn, pitted and distorted valves which result in loss of compression and power as well as poor gasoline mileage.

When valves, springs, retainers and locks are installed, measure the assembled height of the valve springs from the surface of the cylinder head spring pad to the underside of the spring retainer as shown in Fig. 7A. If the assembled height is greater than the dimension

given in the *Valve Specifications Chart*, install a spacer or shim of proper thickness between cylinder head spring pad and spring to bring the assembled height to specifications.

Do not install spacers unless necessary. Excessive use of spacers will result in overstressing valve springs and overloading camshaft lobes which could lead to spring breakage and worn camshaft lobes.

VALVE SPRING TESTING

After taking out the valve springs, wash them with gasoline or other suitable solvent. Examine the springs for damage or corrosion due to acid etching, which will develop into surface cracks and cause spring failure.

Check the valve spring tension on a spring testing fixture, if one is available, Fig. 8, and according to the specifications given in the *Valve Data Chart*. If a fixture is not available, at least check the free length of each spring by standing it alongside a new spring. Any spring that does not conform to the pressure specifications within 10% should be replaced. Likewise, any spring that stands shorter than the new spring used for comparison should be discarded. Of course, cocked springs should also be scrapped.

VALVES, GRIND

Clean the valves with a wire wheel brush, making sure that all carbon is removed from the top and bottom of the heads as well as the gum which might have accumulated on the stems.

In refacing valves, take off only the minimum of metal required to clean up the valve faces. If the outer edge of the valve becomes too thin or sharp due to excessive grinding, the valve must be replaced. In other words, the valve head margin must be at least $\frac{1}{32}$", otherwise the valve must be replaced, Fig. 9.

Inspect the valve seats in the head for

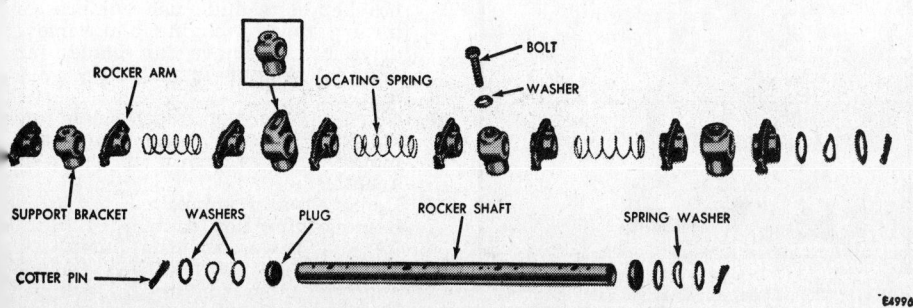

Fig. 6 Rocker arm assembly 1958-61 engines

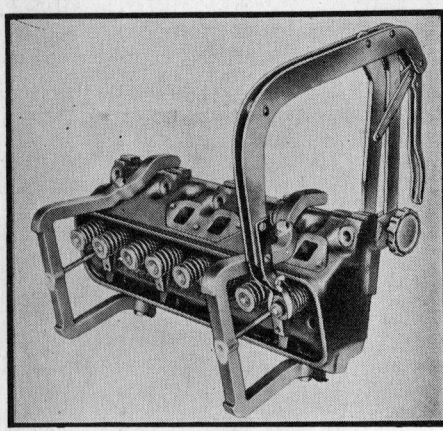

Fig. 7 Showing use of cylinder head holding fixture and valve spring compressor

cracks, burns, pits, ridges or improper angle. During any general engine overhaul, it is advisable to reface the valve seats regardless of their condition.

1958-61 Service Note

Whenever a complaint of hydraulic lifter noise is encountered, and also after performing a valve grind job or replacing a cylinder head the hydraulic lifters should be collapsed and the valve stem to rocker arm clearance checked. Each lifter should be checked individually to guard against differences in machining or wear variables.

Valve stem to rocker arm clearance should check between .078" and 218". If it does the existing push rod should be retained. If the actual measured clearance is less than .078", a .060" *shorter* push rod (color coded white) should be installed. When the actual measured clearance is more than .218", a .060" *longer* push rod (color coded yellow) should be installed.

To check the clearance a special spanner-type tool is available to apply pressure on the rocker arm to bleed down the hydraulic lifter until the plunger is completely bottomed. Of course, checking must be done with lifter on heel of cam. If the special tool is not available, a stiff rod such as a socket extension and a length of wire can be used to collapse the lifter. Wire one end of the rod to the rocker arm as close to the valve stem as possible and apply pressure to the other end.

HYDRAULIC VALVE LIFTERS

The internal parts of each hydraulic valve lifter assembly are a matched set. If these are mixed, improper valve operation may result. Therefore, disassemble, inspect and test each assembly separately to prevent mixing the parts.

Figs. 10 and 11 illustrate the type of hydraulic lifter used. See the *Trouble Shooting Chapter* under the heading *Engine Noises* for causes of hydraulic valve lifter noise.

The easiest method of locating a noisy valve lifter is by the use of a piece of garden hose about 4 feet long. Press one

end of the hose near each valve in progression and listen through the other end. In this manner the sound is localized, making it easier to determine which lifter is at fault.

Another method is to place a finger on the valve spring retainer. If the lifter is not functioning properly, a distinct shock will be felt when the valve returns to its seat.

In most cases where noise exists in one or more lifters, all lifter units should be removed and cleaned. If dirt, varnish or carbon is found to exist in one unit, it more than likely exists in all the units.

To disassemble, first immerse the lifters in solvent and remove all traces of carbon and varnish. Remove the lock ring from the lifter body and disassemble as shown in the illustrations. Wash all parts in solvent and wipe dry with a lint-free cloth.

To assemble, hold the plunger inverted and assemble the valve disc, small spring, valve disc retainer and large spring on the plunger. Slip the body over the plunger, then install the push rod cup and lock ring in the body.

TIMING CASE COVER

1953-57

1. Drain cooling system.
2. Remove top radiator air deflector, hood latch support brackets, horns, radiator and hoses.
3. Disconnect generator wires, and water by-pass tube from water pump and outlet connection.
4. Remove fan blades.
5. Loosen generator adjusting bracket and take off fan belt.
6. Unfasten generator bracket from front cover and cylinder block and remove generator.
7. Remove seven cap screws which

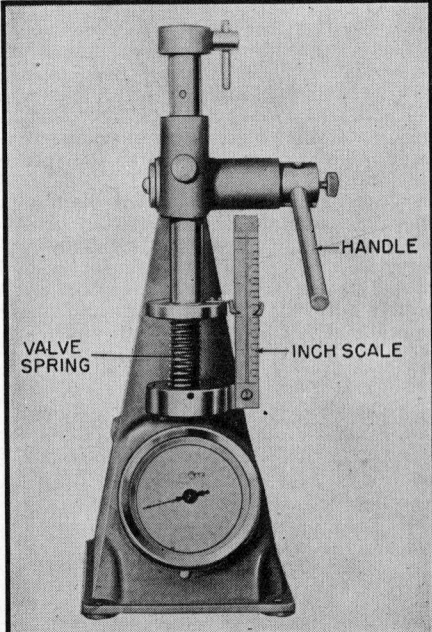

Fig. 8 Special fixture for checking valve spring pressure. All models

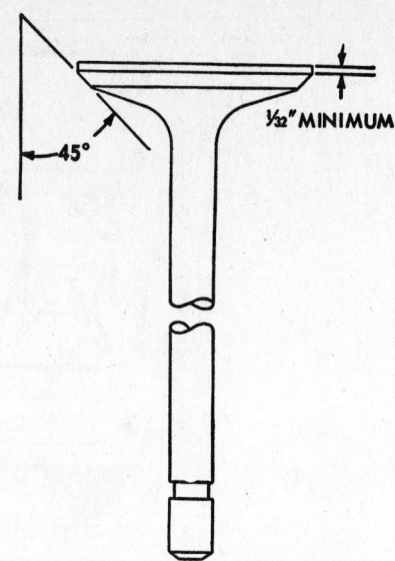

Fig. 9 Refaced valve requirements. Intake valves for 1958 have 30° angle

fasten water pump and heat deflection plate to front cover.
8. Use a suitable puller to remove vibration damper.
9. Remove front cover and timing pointer by taking out five remaining cap screws.

1958-60

1. Remove the radiator.
2. Remove power steering pump and mounting bracket from engine.
3. Remove generator adjusting bracket and belt or belts.
4. Remove fuel pump.
5. Remove water pump.
6. Remove vibration damper with a suitable puller. Also spacer.
7. Unfasten timing chain cover from engine block and oil pan. *If oil pan gasket is broken or damaged during disassembly or assembly, remove the oil pan and install new gasket.*
8. Install a new cover oil seal if necessary and reinstall the cover in the reverse order of removal.

1961

1. Drain cooling system and disconnect water hoses. Remove radiator supply tank, thermostat and gasket.
2. Disconnect wires from coil, engine ground strap and battery ground cable at water pump.
3. Remove fan shield from radiator.
4. On air conditioned cars, loosen bracket bolts and push compressor inward toward engine and remove drive belt. Remove fan blade, fan and compressor drive pulley as a unit.
5. Remove generator splash shield and drive belts. Remove fan, spacer and mounting bolts from water pump as a unit.
6. Remove water pump.
7. Remove vibration damper.
8. Remove power steering pump.
9. Remove fuel pump. Then remove cup-type plug from top of cylinder front cover with a long punch.

10. Raise front of car and unfasten front cover from oil pan and cylinder block. Remove front cover. *If oil pan gasket is damaged during removal of front cover, it will be necessary to replace the gasket before installing front cover.*

TIMING CHAIN

1953-57

Valve timing is set by aligning the two sprocket timing marks together on a center-to-center line between camshaft and crankshaft, Fig. 13.

1958-61

1. To remove the chain, first take off the timing chain cover as outlined previously.
2. Crank the engine until the timing mark on the camshaft sprocket is adjacent to the timing mark on the crankshaft sprocket, Fig. 13.
3. Remove cap screws, lock plate and fuel pump eccentric from front of camshaft.
4. Place a screwdriver behind the camshaft sprocket and carefully pry the sprocket and chain off the camshaft.
5. Reverse the foregoing procedure to install the chain, being sure to align the timing marks as shown in Fig. 13.

VALVE TIMING DATA

Year	Model	Intake Opens①	Intake Closes②	Exhaust Opens③	Exhaust Closes④
1953	All	18	58	56	20
1954	All	18	58	56	20
1955	All	12	54	58	8
1956	All	18	72	59	31
1957	All	18	72	59	31
1958	All	27	69	69	27
1959	All	22	68	63	27
1960	All	22	68	63	27
1961	All	22	68	63	27

①—Degrees before top dead center.
②—Degrees after bottom dead center.
③—Degrees before bottom dead center.
④—Degrees after top dead center.

CAMSHAFT, REPLACE

1953-57

After removing the rocker arms, push rods, valve lifters and timing case cover, carefully withdraw the camshaft from

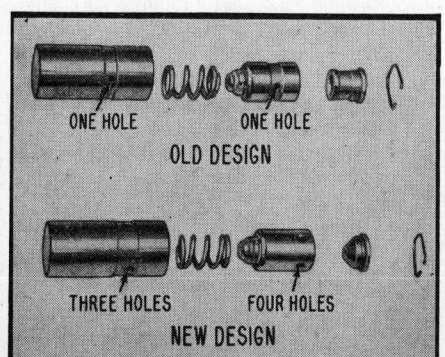

Fig. 10 Two designs of hydraulic valve lifters. 1953-57

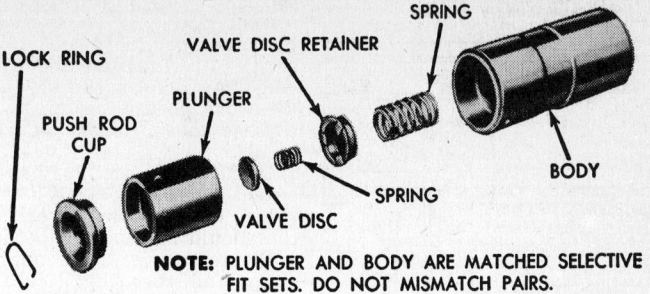

Fig. 11 Hydraulic valve lifter disassembled. 1958-61

the engine, being careful not to damage the camshaft bearings.

1958-61

If it is necessary to replace the camshaft only it may be accomplished without removing the engine from the chassis. But if the camshaft bearings are to be replaced the engine will have to be removed. To remove the camshaft, proceed as follows:

1. Remove the timing chain cover and chain as outlined previously.
2. Remove intake manifold.
3. Remove valve lifter cover.
4. Remove the hydraulic valve lifters and place them in a rack so they may be reinstalled in their respective bores. It may be necessary to remove the carbon from the top of the lifter bore before the lifters can be removed.
5. Remove grille.
6. Carefully slide camshaft out of engine.

CAMSHAFT BEARINGS

The camshaft is supported on five babbitt-lined, steel-backed bearing inserts. When necessary to replace these bearings, the engine will have to be removed from the vehicle and the plug at the rear of the cylinder block will have to be removed in order to utilize the special camshaft bearing removing and installing tools required to do this job. If properly installed, camshaft bearings require no reaming—nor should this type bearing be reamed or altered in any manner in an attempt to fit bearings.

PISTONS & RODS, REMOVE

After removing the cylinder heads and oil pan, use a ridge reamer to remove any ridge that may have formed on the cylinder wall at the top of the piston ring travel. Cutting the ridge before the piston is removed will avoid damaging rings or cracking ring lands of pistons during removal.

Remove the connecting rod cap and push the piston and rod out through the top of the bore. Use care to prevent the rod from nicking crankshaft journals. Identify the rods (original rods are marked) when removing them so they may be installed in their original cylinders.

PISTON & ROD, ASSEMBLE

If the old pistons are serviceable, make certain that they are installed on the rods from which they were removed. The assembly must be made as shown in Fig. 14.

PISTONS

If the pistons are to be reused with new rings, remove the carbon from the ring grooves. A special tool is available for this work but a satisfactory job can be done by breaking an old piston ring. File the broken end to a sharp, square edge and use it to scrape out the carbon. Soak the piston in cleaning solvent to loosen any carbon residue. Clean out the loosened carbon, being careful not to cut away any piston material. Clean out the oil return holes with a drill just large enough to fill the holes. Hold the drill in a tap wrench and make sure the drill does not remove any metal from the piston.

Rinse the piston in solvent and wipe off the carbon on the sides of the piston. Never use a wire brush to clean a piston

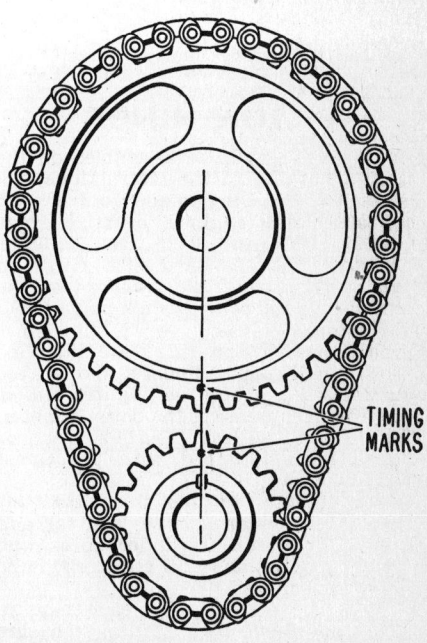

Fig. 13 Valve timing

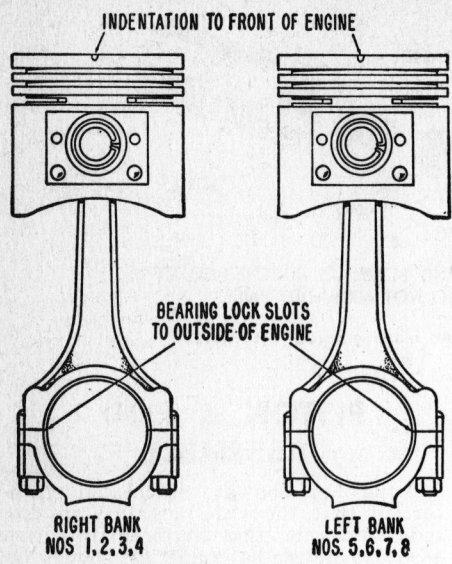

INDENTATION TO FRONT OF ENGINE

BEARING LOCK SLOTS TO OUTSIDE OF ENGINE

RIGHT BANK NOS 1,2,3,4

LEFT BANK NOS 5,6,7,8

Fig. 14 Piston and rod assembly

as the brush will round off the edges of the ring lands. Pistons showing scuffed or scored skirts should be replaced by new ones. Examine the ring lands carefully for cracks. If in the least bit doubtful, the piston should be discarded.

PISTON PINS

1953-57

It is recommended procedure to replace piston pins whenever new piston rings are installed. Pins that have been relatively quiet when the old rings were in service may be noisy after new rings are installed. The pin should fit in the piston and rod by pushing it in with both thumbs with the parts at normal room temperature.

1958-61

Pins are a press fit and no snap rings are used to retain them in place.

PISTON RINGS

New rings should be assembled on the piston according to the instructions furnished by the ring manufacturer. On 1949 and later engines, oversize rings of .020", .030" and .040" are available. Always use standard size rings in cylinder bores that are *standard at the bottom, regardless of the amount of cylinder wear.*

When new piston rings are installed without reboring cylinders, the glazed cylinder walls should be slightly dulled, but without increasing the bore diameter. This is done with a "Glaze-buster" or with a hone equipped with the finest grade of stones.

New piston rings must be checked for clearance in piston grooves and for gap in cylinder bores. Cylinder bores and piston grooves must be clean, dry and free of carbon and burrs.

Check the clearance of each ring in its piston groove by installing the ring and then inserting feeler gauges *under*

the ring. Any wear that occurs in the piston groove forms a step or ridge at the inner portion of the lower land. If gauges are inserted above the ring, the ring may rest on the step instead of on the worn portion of the lower land, and a false measurement of clearance will result.

If the piston grooves have worn to the extent that relatively high steps or ridges exist on the lower lands, the piston should be replaced because the steps will interfere with the operation of new rings and the ring clearances will be excessive. Piston rings are not furnished in oversize widths to compensate for ring groove wear.

To check the end gaps of rings, place the ring in the cylinder in which it will be used. Square it in the bore by tapping with the lower end of the piston, then measure the gap with feeler gauges. If necessary to increase the gap, file the ends of rings carefully with a smooth file.

ROD BEARINGS

These bearings are of the insert type, selectively fitted and requiring no reaming on installation. The bearings are available for service in standard and undersizes for use on journals that have been reground.

If inspection reveals badly worn or scored bearings, they should be replaced. Both main and rod bearings may be replaced by simply taking off the bearing caps and slipping the old ones out and the new ones in. The installation of new bearings must be closely checked to maintain the proper clearance between the crankshaft and bearing surface. A convenient and accurate method for checking bearing clearance is with the use of Plastigage, which is available at any auto parts jobber.

Place the string-like plastic material so it extends the full width of the bearing. Install the bearing and cap and tighten the nuts or bolts to the recommended torque which is listed in the *Engine Torque Specifications* chart. Then, loosen the nuts or bolts and carefully remove the cap and bearing. The widest portion of the Plastigage is then measured with the scale on the Plastigage envelope, Fig. 16. The graduation on the envelope corresponding to the thickness of the Plastigage gives the bearing clearance in thousands of an inch.

MAIN BEARINGS

Caution—Main bearing clearance can be checked with Plastigage in the same manner described for rod bearings. If bearings are measured with the engine in the chassis, the crankshaft must be supported in order to take up clearance be-crankshaft journal. This can be done by tightening bearing caps of adjacent bearings with .005" to .015" cardboard, (such as a calling card) between lower bearing shell and journal. Use extreme care when this is done to avoid unnecessary strain on the crankshaft or bearings or a false reading may be obtained. Do not rotate crankshaft while Plastigage is installed. *Be sure to remove cardboard.* To install new bearings, pro-

ceed as follows:

1. Remove bearing cap and worn lower shell.
2. Rotate crankshaft in normal direction to turn upper bearing shell out of crankcase. Use a cotter pin with a flattened head or the special tool made for the purpose in the crankshaft oil hole to contact the bearing and force it out.
3. Place a new upper shell on the crankshaft journal with the locating notch in the correct position and rotate the shaft to turn the bearing in place.
4. Install the lower bearing shell in the cap.
5. Tighten all cap nuts to the torque value given in the *Engine Torque* table.

CRANKSHAFT REAR OIL SEAL

A braided oil seal is pressed into the upper and lower grooves behind the rear main bearing. Directly in front of this seal is an oil slinger which deflects the oil back into the oil pan. Should the braided seal require replacement, the installation of the lower half is accomplished as follows:

With the bearing cap and lower bearing half removed, install a new seal so that both ends protrude above the cap. Tap the seal down into position or roll it snugly in its groove with a smooth rounded tool. Then cut off the protruding end of the seal with a sharp knife or razor blade.

Installing Upper Seal

Although the usual practice is to remove the crankshaft when the upper half of the seal is to be replaced, it is possible to do the job without removing the crankshaft as follows:

To remove the oil seal, use needle-nose pliers to grasp the end of the seal which is most accessible. Pull the seal downward while rotating the crankshaft slowly in the direction that the seal is being removed.

To install the new seal, fasten a length of wire or strong string such as fishing line securely to one end of the new seal. See that the point of fastening is not bulky and that it is not over ⅜" from the end of the seal. Coat the seal with Lubriplate. Pass the free end of the wire or string up over the crankshaft at the point where the seal is being installed. Then exert a firm, steady pull on the

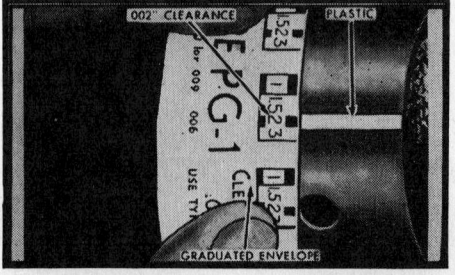

Fig. 16 Checking bearing clearance with Plastigage. All models

wire or string and at the same time rotate the crankshaft slowly in the direction of the pull. This will help to move the seal into position. When the installation is completed, trim the ends of the seal flush with the engine block.

OIL PAN, REPLACE

1953-57

To remove the pan, disconnect any steering linkage that seems necessary. Remove the external oil supply tube. Unfasten the oil pan attaching screws and lower the pan.

1958

1. Crank engine to bring No. 1 piston at approximately 14° BTDC to obtain clearance between crankshaft counterbalances.
2. Remove battery ground cable.
3. Remove oil level dipstick.
4. Raise car on hoist and drain oil pan.
5. Remove front engine support nuts.
6. Position jack under front edge of oil pan, using a block of wood between pan and jack.
7. Lower vehicle enough to raise front of engine about 2".
8. Place a block of wood (1" thick) between front engine support insulators and supports.
9. Raise car and remove jack.
10. Unfasten and lower oil pan to frame crossmember.
11. With pan resting on crossmember, remove lower and loosen upper oil pump inlet tube and screen retaining screws. This allows tube and screen to swing freely, permitting oil pan baffle clearance.
12. Oil pan may now be removed in a lowering forward motion.

1959-60

1. Crank engine to bring No. 1 piston at approximately 14 deg. BTDC to obtain clearance between crankshaft counterbalances (observe timing marks on damper).
2. Disconnect ground cable from battery.
3. Drain oil and remove dipstick.
4. Unfasten and lower pan to frame crossmember.
5. Remove oil pump inlet tube and screen retaining screws.
6. Remove pan.

1961

1. Remove hood and oil level dipstick.
2. Revolve engine to position No. 1 piston 15°BTDC for oil pan clearance purposes (refer to timing marks on vibration damper).
3. Set parking brake and raise car.
4. Drain oil pan.
5. Remove generator splash shield. Remove bolt securing automatic transmission oil inlet and outlet transfer line bracket to cylinder block.
6. To allow clearance for oil pan removal, remove engine front support retaining nut. Place a block of wood on a floor jack and position jack under front leading edge of oil pan. Raise engine about one inch and insert a ¾" block of wood between

support insulators and underbody engine support pad. Then remove floor jack.
7. Unfasten and pull stabilizer arms downward to gain additional clearance.
8. Remove engine mounting bolts and bolt load spreaders. Free oil pan from block. Remove two mounting bolts securing oil pump pick-up tube and screen assembly to oil pump, and allow pump to drop into oil pan. Then remove oil pan.

OIL-VACUUM PUMP

1958-60

Vacuum booster pump and oil pump combination units, Fig. 17, are only used on engines equipped with vacuum windshield wipers. Electric windshield wiper equipped vehicles do not have the vacuum booster feature.

The oil pump section is serviced in the same manner as the pump without the vacuum pump. If the vacuum pump parts are damaged with score marks, wear or breakage, replace the complete vacuum pump.

OIL PUMP

1958 and 1961

To remove the pump, drop the oil pan as outlined above. Then remove the two bolts that attach the pump to the crankcase and remove pump, gasket and the intermediate shaft.

To disassemble, remove the pump cover plate, Fig. 18, and lift out the rotor and shaft. Scrape the stake marks that hold the relief valve in the pump housing until the retainer can be removed. Then remove the retainer, spring and relief

valve from the pump housing. Inspect the pump as follows:

1. With all parts clean and dry, check the inside of the pump housing and the outer race and rotor for damage or excessive wear.
2. Check the mating surface of the pump cover for wear. If this surface is worn, scored or grooved, replace the cover.
3. Measure the clearance between the outer race and housing. This clearance should be .006-.012".
4. With the rotor assembly installed in the housing, place a straight edge over the rotor assembly and housing. Measure the clearance between the straight edge and the rotor and outer race. Recommended limits are 0015-.004".
5. Check the drive shaft-to-housing bearing clearance by measuring the O.D. of the shaft and the I.D. of the housing bearing. The recommended clearance limits are .0015-0029".
6. Inspect the relief valve spring for a collapsed or worn condition.
7. Check the relief valve piston for scores and free operation in the bore.

1953-57

The oil pump is mounted on the outside of the engine where it can be easily removed. When servicing the 1956-57 pump, refer to the procedure given for 1958 pump.

To disassemble the 1952-55 pump, remove cover. Tap cover gently with a soft hammer if stuck. Do not tap on the end of the drive shaft. Remove the gears from the body and take out the relief valve parts. Replace andy damaged parts and reassemble the pump.

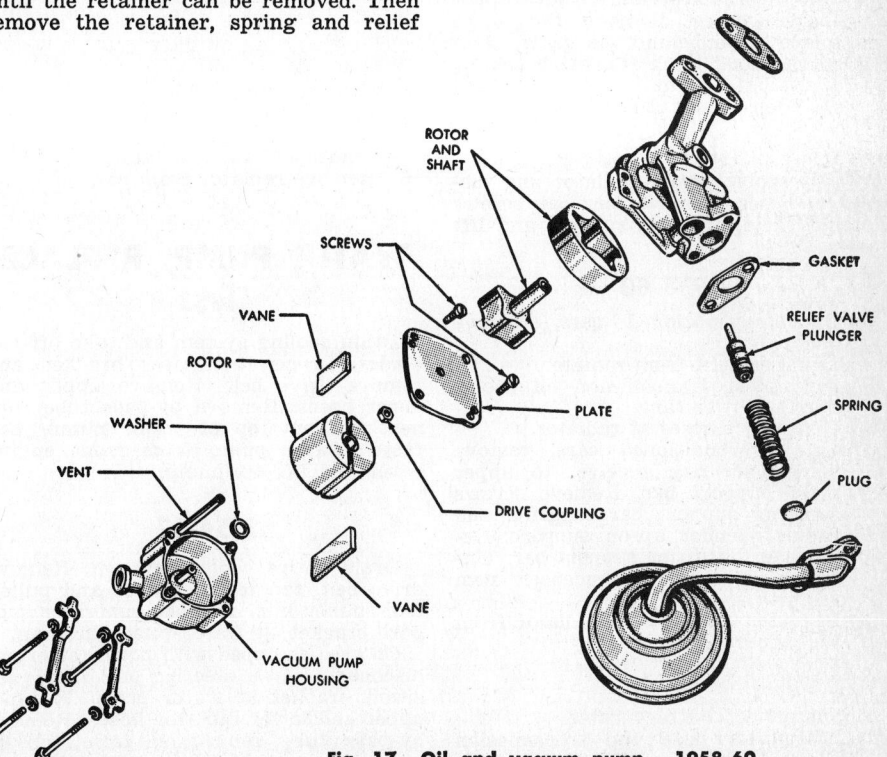

Fig. 17 Oil and vacuum pump. 1958-60

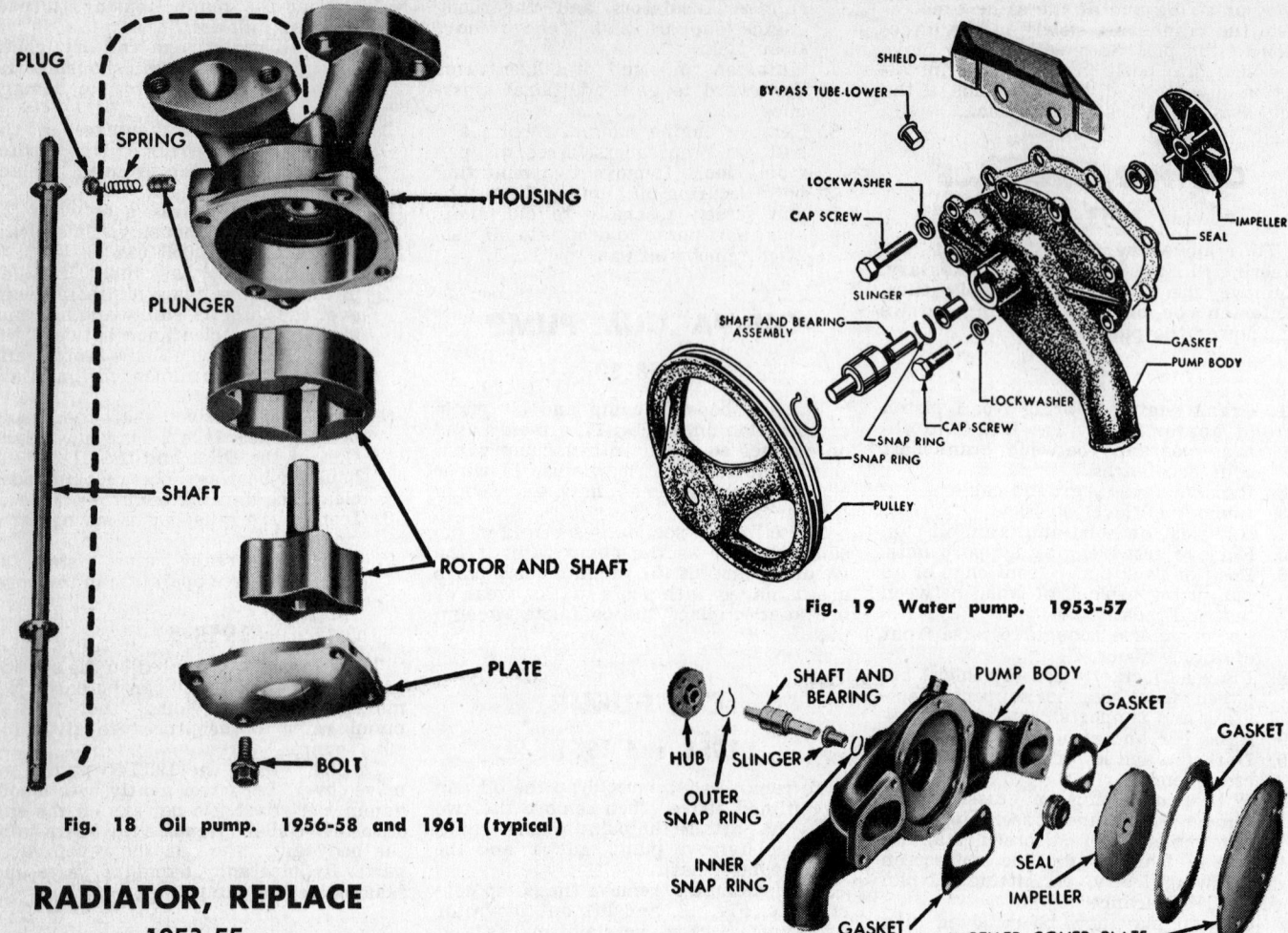

Fig. 18 Oil pump. 1956-58 and 1961 (typical)

Fig. 19 Water pump. 1953-57

Fig. 20 Water pump. 1958-61

RADIATOR, REPLACE

1953-55

Drain the radiator and remove upper and lower hoses. Remove the horns and place them behind the grille. Unfasten the hood latch support brackets, and the radiator from its support on both sides. Then lift out the radiator.

1956-57

Drain coolant from radiator and disconnect hoses. Remove four cap screws holding radiator to its support and lift out radiator.

1958-60

1. On air-conditioned cars, remove hood.
2. Drain coolant from radiator.
3. Disconnect transmission oil cooler lines at lower tank.
4. Disconnect hoses at radiator.
5. On air conditioned cars, remove screws securing receiver to upper grille support bar. Remove screws securing support bar to grille and radiator-fender apron support. Remove grille upper support bar. Unfasten and remove condenser from radiator.
6. Unfasten and remove radiator from its support.

1961

1. Disconnect battery cable.
2. Disconnect hose and transmission cooler lines from radiator.

3. Remove fan shield.
4. Remove radiator mounting bolts.
5. On air conditioned cars, unfasten condenser from radiator.
6. Remove radiator from car.

WATER PUMP, REPLACE

1953

Drain cooling system and take off fan blades. Loosen generator bracket and remove drive belt. Remove upper and lower hoses. Remove by-pass tube connection from top of water pump. Unfasten water pump from front engine cover and lift off pump.

1954-57

Drain entire cooling system. Remove drive belt, fan blade, spacer and pulley from pulley hub. Remove generator support bracket at water pump housing.

On cars equipped with power steering, disconnect power steering pump and reservoir bracket at water pump. Remove upper and lower radiator hoses. Remove by-pass tube connection from top of water pump, and heater outlet tube con-

nections at water pump. Unfasten water pump from engine front cover.

1958-60

1. On air-conditioned cars, remove hood and radiator.
2. Remove battery.
3. Disconnect hoses from water pump.
4. Remove belts from water pump.
5. On air-conditioned cars, unfasten power steering pump and air conditioner compressor brackets from engine.
6. Remove fan and pulleys from pump hub.
7. Remove screws attaching dipstick tube bracket, water pump and gaskets to engine. Remove pump and gaskets.

1961

1. Disconnect battery cable.
2. On air conditioned cars, remove fan shield, power booster clutch, fan and compressor drive pulley.
3. With standard cooling system, remove fan shield, fan and spacer.
4. Remove radiator supply tank.
5. Loosen clamp securing by-pass hose to water pump.

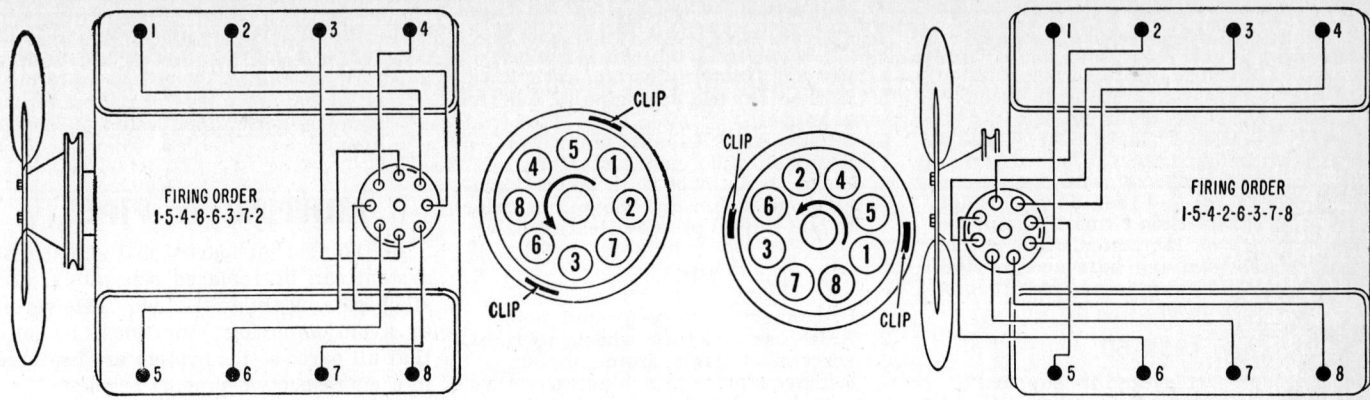

Fig. 21   Ignition details. 1953-57

Fig. 22   Ignition details. 1958-61

6. Remove generator splash shield.
7. Remove drive belts.
8. Remove hose from pump.
9. Remove pump mounting bolts. Then after positioning oil dipstick tube bracket and power steering pump bracket to allow removal of water pump, remove water pump.

WATER PUMP REPAIRS

1953-57

Fig. 19. Remove the snap ring from the groove in the front of the pump housing behind the pulley. (If the pump has a pressed steel pulley, remove the pulley before taking out the snap ring.) Press the shaft and bearing and pulley from the impeller. Then press the shaft and bearing and pulley from the housing. Press shaft and bearing from pulley. Press seal and sleeve from pump housing. (It is not necessary to remove the snap ring from the center of the pump housing.)

Assemble the pump in the reverse order, coating all parts lightly with cup grease. When pressing the shaft into the housing, stop applying the pressure when resistance is felt or the snap ring inside the housing will be broken. When assembled, there should be .025" to .035" clearance between the impeller and housing as measured with a feeler gauge.

1958-61

Disassemble, Fig. 20

1. Remove impeller cover plate.
2. Press shaft and bearing assembly out of impeller and pump housing.
3. Press seal out of pump housing.
4. Press shaft and bearing assembly out of hub.
5. If slinger is damaged, mark its position on shaft and then remove slinger.

Assembly

1. Remove all gasket material from mounting faces of pump and engine block.
2. If slinger was removed, install a new one, using the locating marks made before slinger was removed as a guide.
3. Coat the bearing outer diameter lightly with grease and press the

shaft and bearing assembly into the pump housing.
4. Apply a thin film of waterproof sealer on a new seal and press the seal into the housing.
5. Inspect the seal rubbing face of the impeller for grooves. Replace the impeller if it is worn or damaged. Coat the rubbing face of the impeller lightly with grease.
6. Press impeller on shaft. The clearance between the impeller and impeller cover gasket surface must be 030" to .040" (⅛" on 1961).
7. Position the fan hub on the shaft, then press the hub on the shaft.
8. Install a new gasket on the impeller cover and install the cover.
9. Install the pump on the engine in the reverse order of its removal.

DISTRIBUTOR, REPLACE

1. Disconnect distributor primary wire from coil terminal and remove distributor cap.
2. Unscrew vacuum line connection from vacuum advance unit.
3. Remove tachometer drive cable retaining screw and clip and pull cable and driven gear from distributor housing on models so equipped.
4. Unscrew distributor clamp bolt and remove lock washer and clip.
5. As the distributor is lifted from engine the shaft and rotor will turn counterclockwise part of a revolution. Lift distributor only far enough to disengage the gear.
6. When rotor stops turning, scribe a mark on the manifold or on engine casting to indicate the rotor position, then remove the distributor. *Do not crank the engine after the distributor is removed, otherwise the distributor will have to be initially timed to the engine.*
7. Install the distributor in the reverse order of its removal. Then start the engine, check the oil pressure and adjust the ignition timing, Figs. 21, 22.

IGNITION TIMING

Align the distributor rotor with No. 1 spark plug wire terminal in the distributor cap, when No. 1 piston is on the compression stroke and timing marks on

the crankshaft pulley and pointer are aligned.

With the timing mark in line with the pointer, the distributor points should just start to open. It may be necessary to rotate the distributor body clockwise slightly and then counter-clockwise until the points just start to open. Tighten the distributor lock plate screw.

Start the engine and check the timing with a timing light.

Using Timing Light

When using a timing light, *be sure to disconnect the distributor vacuum line before checking timing*, otherwise the timing will be affected due to the fact that the vacuum opening is above the throttle plate.

Connect the timing light high tension lead to the No. 1 spark plug and the other two leads to the proper battery terminals. Clean the dirt from the timing mark and if necessary use white chalk to make the mark more visible.

Start the engine and operate at idle speed. Direct the light on the timing mark. It should flash just as the timing mark lines up with the pointer, indicating correct timing. If the pointer and timing mark does not line up as the light flashes, rotate the distributor as required to bring them in alignment.

STARTER, REPLACE

1953-55

1. Disconnect ground cable from battery.
2. Remove cable from starter.
3. Remove two bolts attaching steering idler arm to frame lower support.
4. Remove capscrews holding end plate to converter housing.
5. Remove starter by pulling it out and down until starter drive clears housing.

1956-57

1. Disconnect cable from starter.
2. Unfasten starter from flywheel housing.
3. Turn front wheels to extreme right position and remove starter.

1958

1. Remove ground cable from battery.
2. Remove two top drive end plate-to-

flywheel capscrews.
3. Raise vehicle.
4. Remove nut from rear engine support bracket stud and raise rear of engine approximately one inch.
5. Remove cable from starter.
6. Remove lower drive end plate-to-flywheel capscrew.
7. Remove starter by working assembly forward and then down through lower suspension arms. *If equipped with power lubricator, remove two bracket retaining nuts and position power lubricator to one side to provide clearance.*

1959-60

1. Remove battery and its support.

2. Disconnect transmission control rod at accelerator shaft bracket lever.
3. Drain coolant from cylinder block.
4. Remove front engine mounting nuts.
5. Raise front end of engine as high as possible.
6. Remove right exhaust manifiiold.
7. Unfasten and remove starter.
8. If car is equipped with power lubricator, unfasten and move lubricator to one side to provide clearance.

1961

1. Disconnect battery ground cable.
2. Raise car and turn wheels to right.
3. Disconnect cable from starter.
4. Remove starter attaching capscrews.

5. Work starter forward and upward until clear of flywheel housing.
6. Tilt up rear of starter and with a turning motion lower assembly outward and down between No. 2 crossmember and transmission oil cooler line.

MUFFLER & PIPES

All component parts of the exhaust system can be replaced separately, and all operations are quite obvious. However, to avoid annoying vibrations, be sure that all parts of the system are centered in their respective support brackets.

Carburetor Section

Performance Complaints

Flooding, stumble on acceleration or other performance complaints are in many instances caused by the presence of dirt, water or other foreign matter in the carburetor. To aid in diagnosing the cause of the complaint, the carburetor should be carefully removed from the engine without draining the fuel from the bowl. The contents of the fuel bowl may then be examined for contamination as the carburetor is disassembled.

Check the fuel in the bowl for contamination by dirt, water, gum or other foreign matter. A magnet moved through the fuel in the bowl will pick up and identify any iron oxide dust that may have caused intake needle and seat leakage.

Inspect gasketed surfaces between

body and air horn. Small nicks or burrs should be smoothed down to eliminate air or fuel leakage. On carburetors having a vacuum piston, be especially particular when inspecting the top surface of the inner wall of the bowl around the vacuum piston passage. A poor seal at this location may contribute to a "cutting-out" on turns complaint.

Fill the carburetor bowl with clean fuel before installing on manifold. This will help prevent dirt trapped in the fuel system from being dislodged by the free flow of fuel as the carburetor is primed. The operation of the floats and intake needle and seats may be checked under pressure if a fuel pump is used at the bench to fill the carburetor bowl. Operate the throttle several times and visually check the discharge from pump jets.

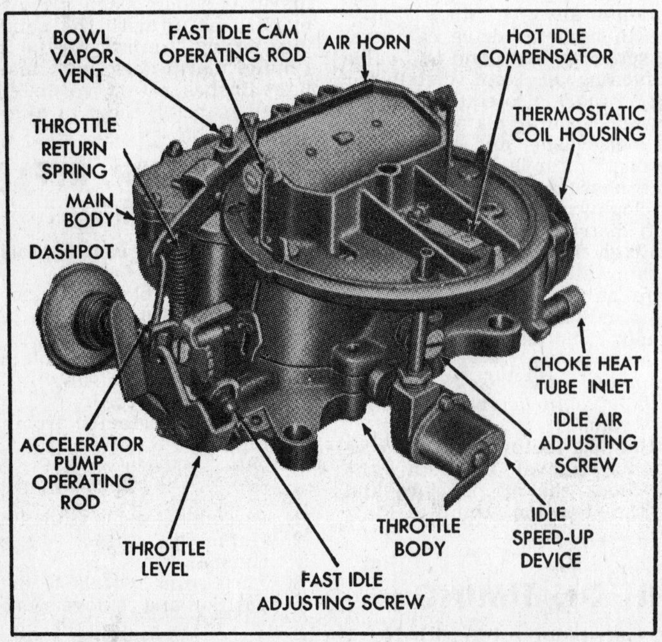

Poor Mileage and Engine Loading Complaints

Cases of poor mileage and engine loading may be due in many instances to sluggish choke valve opening during cold driveaway, caused by insufficient vacuum in choke housing, a plugged or restricted heat pipe or inlet in choke cover. To check for this condition, have engine warm and running at slow idle. Remove choke heat pipe and hold a finger over the heat inlet hole (hole is on choke housing on some carburetors). If there is little or no vacuum pull on the finger, check the choke housing for gasket leaks or plugged vacuum passages. If these are OK, check choke vacuum passages in carburetor between choke housing and manifold.

Dirty or Rusty Choke Housing

In cases where it is found that the interior of the choke housing is dirty, gummed or rusty while the carburetor itself is comparatively clean, look for a punctured or eroded manifold heat tube (if one is used).

Manifold Heat Control Valve

An engine equipped with a manifold heat control valve can operate with the valve stuck either in the open or closed position. Because of this, an inoperative valve is frequently overlooked at vehicle lubrication or tune-up.

A valve stuck in the "heat-off" position can result in slow warm up, deposits in combustion chamber, carburetor icing, flat spots during acceleration, low gas mileage and spark plug fouling.

A valve stuck in the "heat-on" position can result in loss of power, engine knocking, sticking or burned valves and spark plug burning.

To prevent the possibility of a stuck valve, check and lubricate the valve each time the vehicle is lubricated or tuned-up. Check the operation of the valve manually. To lubricate the valve, place a few drops of penetrating oil on the valve shaft where it passes through the manifold. Move the valve up and down a few times to work in the oil. *Do not*

Fig. 1 Carter ABD for 1961. Note location of idle speed-up device and idle air adjusting screw

use engine oil for this purpose as it will leave a residue which hampers valve operation.

Idle Speed-Up Device

1961 Carter ABD—On air conditioned cars, a mechanism is used to increase engine speed sufficiently to overcome the additional load incurred when the air conditioning unit is working, Fig. 1. This device is an electrical solenoid switch that operates an air valve in an external by-pass system of the carburetor to increase air flow. As long as the air conditioning switch is on, the solenoid is activated and holds the needle off the seat, allowing air to be admitted below the throttle plates. The solenoid is not affected by throttle position or by mani-fold vacuum and is controlled only by the air conditioning switch. With the incorporation of this device, it is no longer necessary to operate the air conditioning system when adjusting hot idle speed.

If there is reason to believe that the device is not functioning, check for proper vacuum by placing a finger on the air passage tube projecting through the air horn. When the unit is in operation, the vacuum pull will be felt by finger application. *Vacuum should be felt only when the air conditioning clutch is engaged.*

If engine rpm does not decrease approximately 30-40 rpm with finger applied to air inlet tube, check for current at solenoid terminals. If current is present, remove solenoid and check valve and seat. If seat is damaged, replace entire assembly. If valve is damaged, replace valve only. If both valve and seat are undamaged, and the unit is free of dirt, replace the solenoid.

Idle Air Adjustment

1961 Carter ABD—The idle air adjustment screw, Fig. 1, is used to adjust engine idle speed in a similar manner as the hot idle speed adjustment screw on conventional carburetors. Turning the air adjustment screw outward increases speed, but also leans the mixture supplied to the manifold which is compensated for by adjustment of the idle mixture adjustment screws. The initial setting of the idle speed adjustment screw is 3½ turns open.

CARTER CARBURETOR ADJUSTMENTS

Year	Carburetor Model	Idle Adjustments				Float Level		Float Drop		Pump Travel Setting	Choke Unloader Setting	Choke Setting
		Mixture Screws Turns Open	Hot Idle Speed In Drive	Fast Idle Speed	Dashpot Plunger Clearance	Primary	Secondary	Primary	Secondary			
1961	ABD-31495	1–1½	465	625④	.075⑫	5/16⑨	None	None	None	17/32⑩	1/8⑪	Index
1960	ABD-2965S	1½	465	525④	.075⑫	1/4⑨	None	None	None	7/16⑩	1/8⑪	1 Lean
1959	AFB-2853S	1½–2½	465	550④	7/16⑬	3/16①	3/16①	23/32②	23/32②	17/32③	1/8⑤	Index
1957	WCFB-2404S-A	1/2–1½	465	800④	1/16⑭	1/16⑥	3/16⑥	9/16⑦	11/16⑦	⑧	1/8⑤	1 Rich

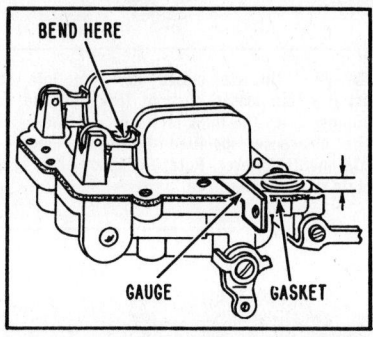

Fig. ①—AFB float level. Adjust by bending float lever.

CARTER NOTES

METERING ROD

WCFB—Metering rod adjustment must be made after pump adjustment. With throttle valves fully closed, loosen metering rod arm clamp screw. With metering rods in place, press down on vacumeter link until metering rods bottom in casting. Holding rods down, revolve metering rod arm until finger on arm contacts lip of vacumeter link. Hold in place and tighten clamp screw.

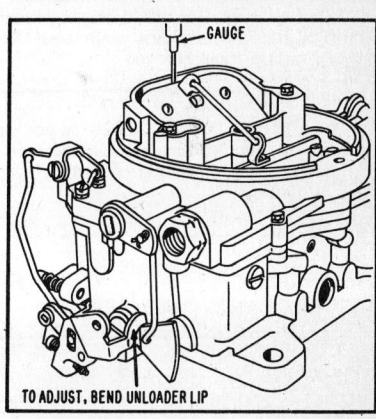

Fig. ⑤—With throttle wide open, clearance between upper edge of choke valve and inner wall of air horn should be as specified. Adjust by bending unloader lip on throttle lever.

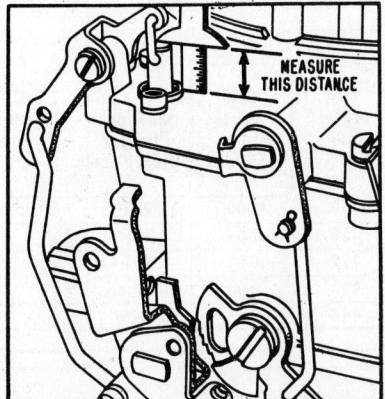

Fig. ③—Measure from top of bowl cover to top of plunger shaft with throttle connector rod in inner hole of pump arm. Adjust by bending throttle connector rod.

④—With engine at normal operating temperature, turn fast idle screw against low step on fast idle cam until the specified rpm is obtained.

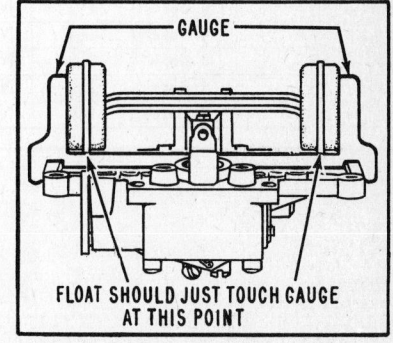

Fig. ⑥—WCFB float level. Adjust by bending float lever.

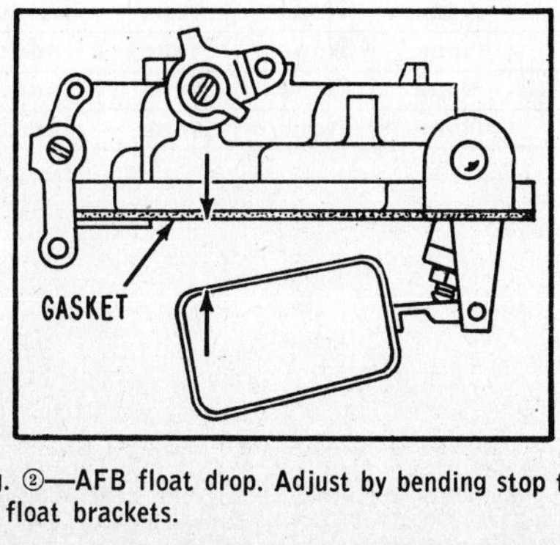

Fig. ②—AFB float drop. Adjust by bending stop tabs on float brackets.

CARTER NOTES
continued

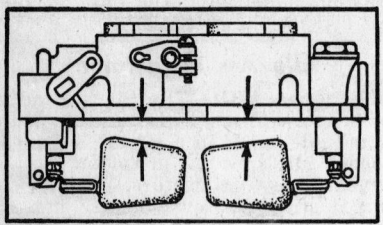

Fig. ⑦—WCFB float drop. Adjust by bending stop tabs on float bracket.

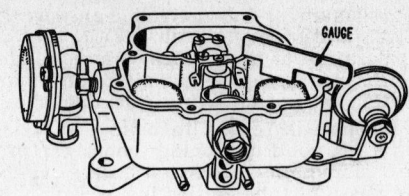

Fig. ⑨—Measured from top surface of main body to top of free end of float in uppermost position.

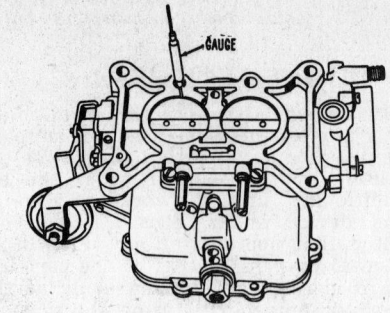

Fig. ⑪—With throttle wide open there should be the clearance specified between upper edge of choke valve and inner wall of air horn. Adjust by bending tang on choke unloader lever.

Fig. ⑧—Flat on pump arm should be parallel with a straightedge placed across dust cover boss. Adjust by bending throttle connector rod.

⑬—With primary throttle valves wide open, there should be the clearance specified between top of bowl cover to top of plunger. Adjust by bending stop lug on flat lever.

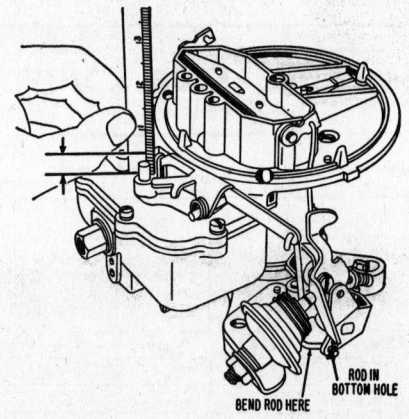

Fig. ⑩—Measured from top of air horn to top of plunger shaft with pump operating rod in bottom hole. Adjust by bending pump operating rod as required.

⑭—Dashpot plunger shaft should bottom with the gauge size listed between shaft and operating lever with throttle valves fully closed. Adjust by turning dashpot in or out as required.

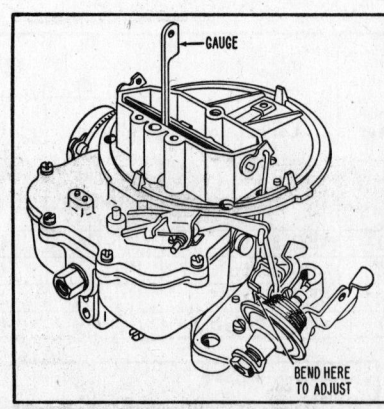

Fig. ⑫—With throttle closed and hot idle screw against its stop, loosen dashpot locknut. Hold dashpot plunger in to the limit of its travel. There should be the clearance specified between plunger and throttle operating lever. Rotate dashpot in its bracket to obtain desired clearance.

HOLLEY CARBURETOR ADJUSTMENTS

Year	Model	Carb. Type	Idle Adjustments					Float Level	Fuel Level	Float Bowl Vent Valve	Pump Override Spring	Choke Unloader	Choke Setting
			Mixture Screws Turns Open	Air Bypass Turns Open	Hot Idle Speed In Drive	Fast Idle Speed	Dashpot Plunger Clearance						
1958	All	4 Bore	$1\frac{1}{4}$	None	450	1800④	.067⑤	①	⑥	.067⑦	.015⑨	None	1 Rich
1956	All	4 Bore	$1\frac{1}{4}$	None	450	⑩	.055⑧	$\frac{1}{4}$②	$\frac{1}{2}$③	None	None	None	Index
1955	All	4 Bore	$1\frac{1}{4}$	None	450	⑩	.055⑧	$\frac{1}{4}$②	$\frac{1}{2}$③	None	None	None	Index
1954	All	4 Bore	$1\frac{1}{4}$	None	440	⑩	None	$\frac{1}{4}$②	$\frac{1}{2}$③	None	None	None	Index
1953	All	4 Bore	$1\frac{1}{4}$	None	440	⑩	None	$\frac{1}{4}$②	$\frac{1}{2}$③	None	None	None	Index

HOLLEY NOTES

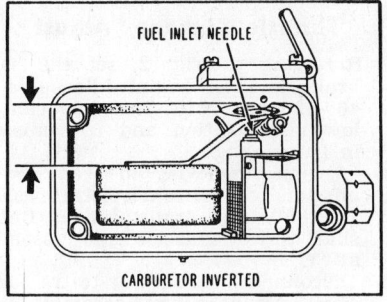

Fig. ①—Float level measured from bottom of float to floor of float bowl with bowl inverted; primary float $1\frac{1}{16}''$, secondary $\frac{9}{16}''$.

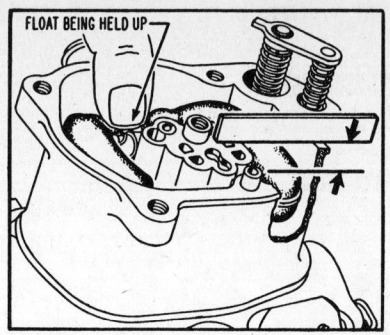

Fig. ②—Float level measured from machined surface of float bowl.

③—Below machined surface of float bowl.

④—With fast idle screw against highest step on fast idle cam.

⑤—With throttle fully closed and dashpot plunger held in to the limit of its travel, there should be the clearance listed between plunger and throttle lever. Adjust by rotating dashpot in its bracket as required.

⑥—With engine running at hot idle speed, remove plugs from both sight holes. If fuel just dribbles out of sight holes, fuel level is correct. If not, adjust float level.

⑦—With primary throttle plates closed, there should be the clearance listed between the unseated bowl vent valve and vent valve seat. Adjust by bending vent arm of accelerating pump lever (not valve rod).

⑧—With throttle fully closed, hold dashpot plunger in to the limit of its travel. Then turn adjusting screw as required to obtain the clearance listed between end of screw and plunger.

⑨—With primary throttle plates held wide open, there should be the clearance listed between pump arm and hex nut on accelerating lever with pump held fully depressed. To adjust, hold hex nut and turn adjusting screw as required.

⑩—Turn fast idle screw in until it just touches low step on fast idle cam.

Automatic Transmission Section

HYDRA-MATIC DRIVE

Note—A detailed step-by-step service procedure is given in the *Hydra-Matic Drive* chapter. The following outlines the procedure for adjusting the control linkage.

1953-54 Linkage, Adjust

Before attempting any linkage adjustments it is necessary that the timing, idle mixture and idle speed (400-425 rpm) be checked to maintain best operation. Engine must be at normal operating temperature.

Throttle Linkage Adjustment—Fig. 1.

1. Raise car and disconnect throttle rod at transmission throttle lever at point "1".
2. Check transmission throttle lever, using Gauge 7919. Bend lever if necessary.
3. Connect throttle rod to transmission throttle lever and lower car.
4. Remove clevis pin from point "D".
5. Adjust rod between points "A" and "B" as follows: carburetor throttle rod at point "A" to be set at low idle and control shaft to be at stop position at "C". Tighten lock nuts so ends are aligned with each other.
6. While holding carburetor arm at "A" in low idle position, push down gently but firmly on transmission throttle rod, against stop position. and adjust clevis at point "D" so clevis pin enters clevis and shaft freely.
7. Remove clevis pin and shorten transmission throttle rod three complete turns. Reinstall clevis pin and install cotter pin. Tighten clevis lock nut on throttle rod.
8. Road test car and check shift points.

Manual Linkage Adjustment—Fig. 1.

1. Disconnect manual control rod from arm at point "3".
2. Position selector lever on steering column against stop in "DR" position.
3. Set manual lever at transmission, point "2", at second position from top ("DR" position).
4. Adjust manual rod so sleeve enters grommet hole freely. Then lengthen rod by one full turn.
5. Secure sleeve assembly and check position of selector lever in all ranges.

Hydramatic, Replace, 1953-54

1. To remove the unit, disconnect throttle rod at foot accelerator.
2. Remove front seat clevis pins and tip seat.
3. Remove floor carpet.
4. Remove transmission floor pan cover.
5. Disconnect drive shaft at rear universal and remove shaft and front universal from transmission shaft.
6. Remove starting motor.
7. Remove flywheel housing pan and engine plate.

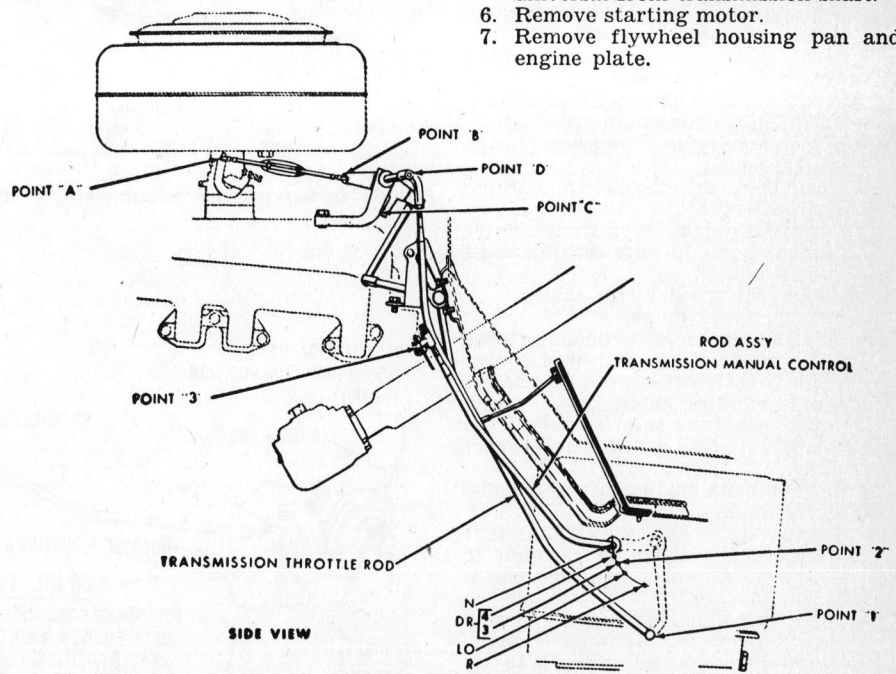

Fig. 1 Hydra-Matic control linkage. 1953-54

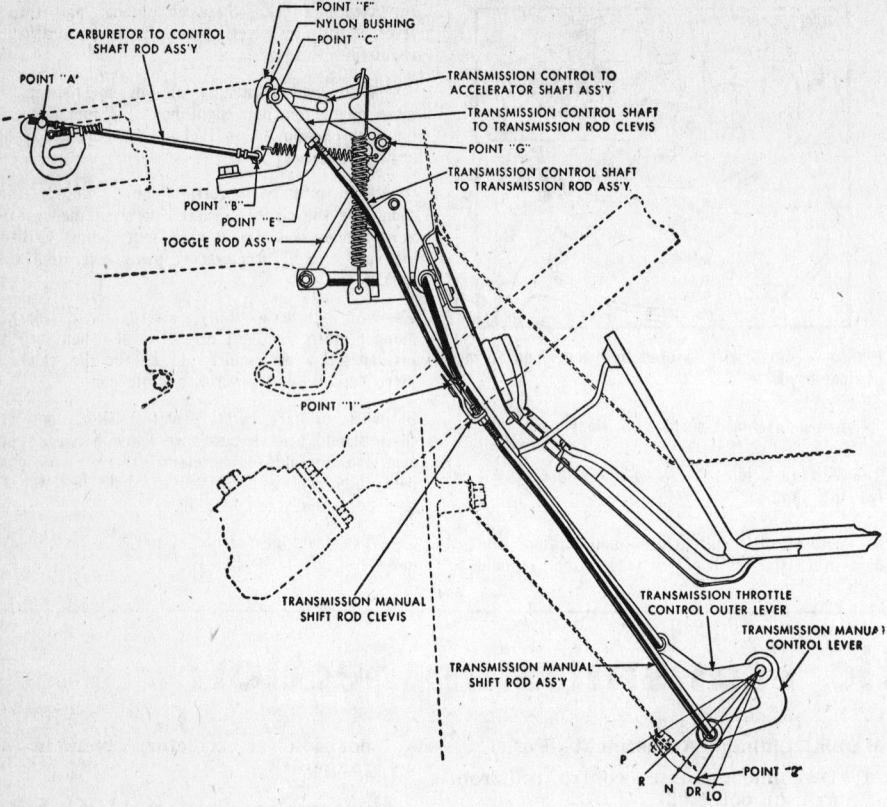

Fig. 2 Turbo-Drive throttle linkage adjustments. 1955-57

8. Drain transmission and fluid coupling.
9. Disconnect rear mount from frame cross member. Remove bottom half of rubber mount.
10. Place jack at rear of engine oil pan, using a wooden block to protect the pan and raise engine far enough to install an engine support.
11. Remove detachable cross member from frame X member.
12. Lower jack under engine and allow engine to rest on engine support.
13. Attach a suitable lifting hoist to the transmission.
14. Disconnect control rods from transmission levers.
15. Remove throttle lever from side of transmission to prevent damage from bending.
16. Disconnect speedometer cable.
17. Remove spark plugs.
18. Remove cap screws holding torus cover to flywheel and push cover toward rear of car to disengage dowels locating it on the flywheel. *Cover should not be pried away from flywheel as this will damage gasket surface.*
19. Remove bolts holding flywheel housing to engine.
20. Remove transmission by sliding unit toward rear of car far enough to disengage flywheel housing dowels and mainshaft from pilot bearing.
21. The front end of the transmission must be lowered below the engine flywheel and pulled forward to remove the transmission bearing extension from the frame cross member.

22. Position a dolly under the transmission and remove the unit from under the car.
23. Reverse the order of the above procedure to install the transmission.

1955-57 TURBO-DRIVE

Throttle Linkage, Adjust

1. Referring to Fig. 2, set the hand brake and set engine idle speed to 400-425 rpm with fast idle cam in low idle position and transmission in Drive range.
2. Disconnect clevis pin from transmission control-to-accelerator shaft assembly and transmission control shaft-to-transmission rod assembly at "C".
3. Disconnect carburetor-to-transmission control shaft rod assembly.
4. Insert gauge pin at point "E".
5. Adjust carburetor-to-transmission control shaft rod so that it fits freely at points "A" and "B".
6. Connect rod and remove gauge pin.
7. Pull upward on transmission control shaft-to-transmission rod to position throttle lever against its internal stop. Adjust clevis at point "C" so that clevis pin enters clevis and lever freely. Lengthen rod by turning clevis 2½ turns and reassemble.
8. With ignition off and accelerator pedal depressed to full kickdown position, adjust the length of the toggle rod so that the nylon bushing fits in the slot at point "F" with approximately ¼" clearance on Lincoln and .100" on Continental.
9. Adjust toggle rod so that it is in a vertical plane when viewed from the front of the vehicle. This is done by loosening jam nut at point "G" and turning the stud with a screw driver in the desired direction. Retighten jam nut after making the adjustment.

Manual Adjustment

1. Referring to Fig. 2, disconnect manual shift rod from selector arm at point "1".
2. Position manual lever at point "1"

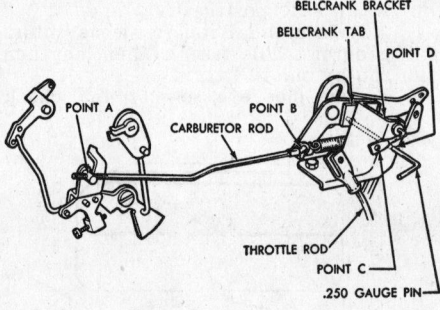

Fig. 4 Carburetor rod adjustment. 1959

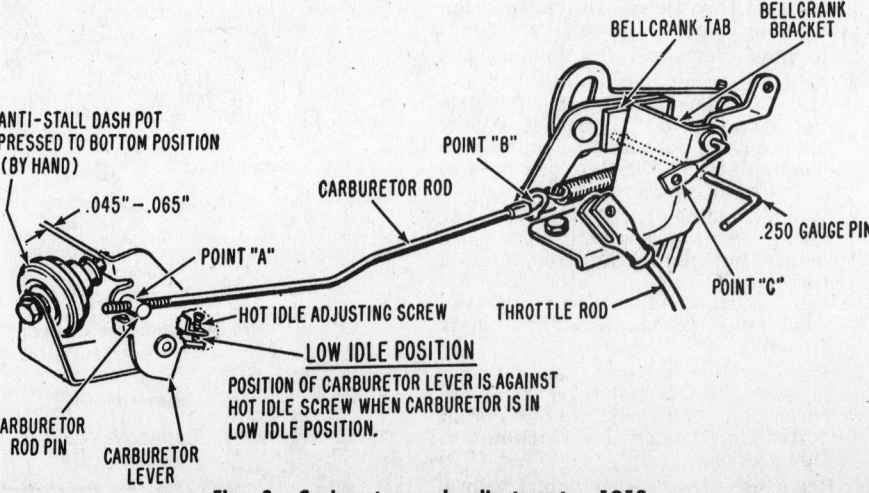

Fig. 3 Carburetor rod adjustment. 1958

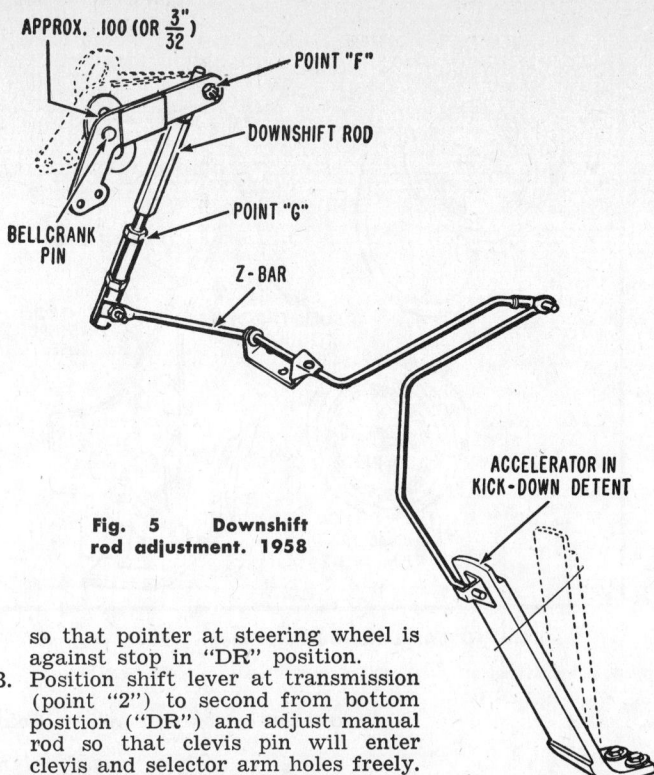

Fig. 5   Downshift rod adjustment. 1958

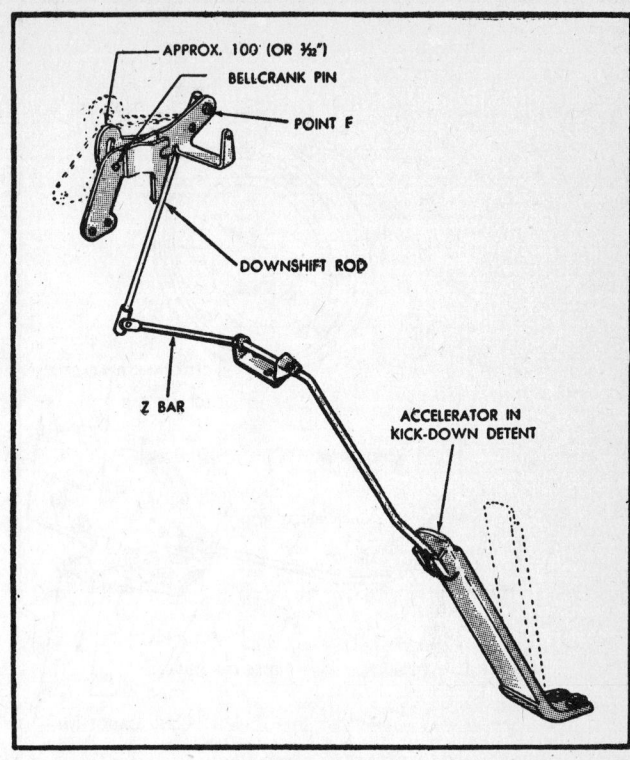

Fig. 6   Downshift rod adjustment, 1959-60

so that pointer at steering wheel is against stop in "DR" position.
3. Position shift lever at transmission (point "2") to second from bottom position ("DR") and adjust manual rod so that clevis pin will enter clevis and selector arm holes freely. Lengthen rod by one full turn.
4. Check position of pointer for all stations on dial.

Transmission Only, Replace

1. Drain transmission fluid.
2. Disconect drive shaft from rear axle and remove drive shaft.
3. Disconnect oil cooler lines from transmission.
4. Disconnect shift linkage at transmission.
5. Disconnect speedometer cable.
6. Remove engine rear support-to-transmission bolts.
7. Raise transmission slightly with jack to take weight off crossmember; then remove crossmember.
8. Unfasten transmission from converter and slide it back and out.

TWIN RANGE TURBO-DRIVE LINKAGE

Carburetor Rod, Adjust

1958—Refer to Fig. 3.
1. Insert ¼" gauge rod through bellcrank bracket and tab.
2. Holding carburetor lever against hot idle screw, adjust carburetor rod between points "A" and "B" so pin enters carburetor lever freely.
3. Lengthen rod pin one full turn and reassemble.
4. Remove ¼" gauge rod.
5. Adjust dashpot clearance to .045" to .065".

1959—Refer to Fig. 4.
1. Insert ¼" gauge rod through bellcrank bracket and tab.
2. Hold primary throttle shaft lever against hot idle screw and adjust carburetor rod between points "A"

and "B" so rod enters primary throttle shaft lever freely.
3. Remove ¼" gauge rod.
4. Check anti-stall dashpot operating lever adjustment. With primary throttle plates in wide open position, there should be a distance of $\frac{7}{16}$" between top surface of bowl and bottom of dashpot arm lever. To adjust, bend dashpot inner arm tang. With primary throttle plates closed to normal idle position, there should be a clearance of $\frac{1}{16}$" to $\frac{3}{32}$" between dashpot plunger operating lever and top surface of air horn. To adjust, bend dashpot lever in area between lever arm base and dashpot plunger.
5. Recheck hot idle rpm.

Downshift Rod, Adjust

1958-59—Refer to Figs. 5 and 6.
1. With engine shut off, depress accelerator to full kickdown position.
2. Check alignment of downshift rod. The rod must be vertical, and the bellcrank pin within $\frac{3}{32}$ from top of bellcrank slot. Release accelerator pedal when making this adjustment.
3. Looking straight down from bellcrank to Z bar, adjust screw and jam nut at point "F" so downshift rod is vertical; if not, free travel of bellcrank will be restricted. Tighten jam nuts after adjustment.
4. With accelerator pedal again depressed, the top of the bellcrank pin must be $\frac{3}{32}$" from top of bellcrank slot. At point "G", loosen lock nut and adjust downshift rod.

Throttle Rod, Adjust

1958-59—Refer to Fig. 7.
1. Install pressure gauge at rear of

transmission.
2. Pull upward on throttle rod firmly but gently. Adjust clevis at point "C" so clevis pin enters freely. Lengthen clevis 3 full turns and reassemble. Total adjustment must not exceed 4 full turns.
3. Start engine and place selector lever in Dr-2 range.
4. Accelerate engine to 1000 rpm. Pressure gauge reading should be 80-95 psi.
5. To adjust pressure, adjust length of throttle rod. Lengthen clevis to increase pressure; shorten to reduce pressure. *Do not operate engine for long period at 1000 rpm as transmission will overheat.*

Manual Linkage, Adjust

1958-59—Refer to Fig. 8.
1. Disconnect manual rod clevis at point "1".
2. Position selector lever at point "2" so pointer is against stop in Dr-1 range. (Hold this position throughout the manual adjustment.)
3. Position detent lever in second position (Dr-1) from bottom.
4. Adjust manual rod clevis so pin enters clevis and detent lever freely. Lengthen clevis one full turn and reassemble.
5. Check position of quadrant pointer in each range. If pointer is off location, adjust the position of the letters. Do not adjust linkage to correct pointer alignment.

1960 Adjustments

Carburetor Rod, Fig. 9:
1. Disconnect throttle rod at point C.

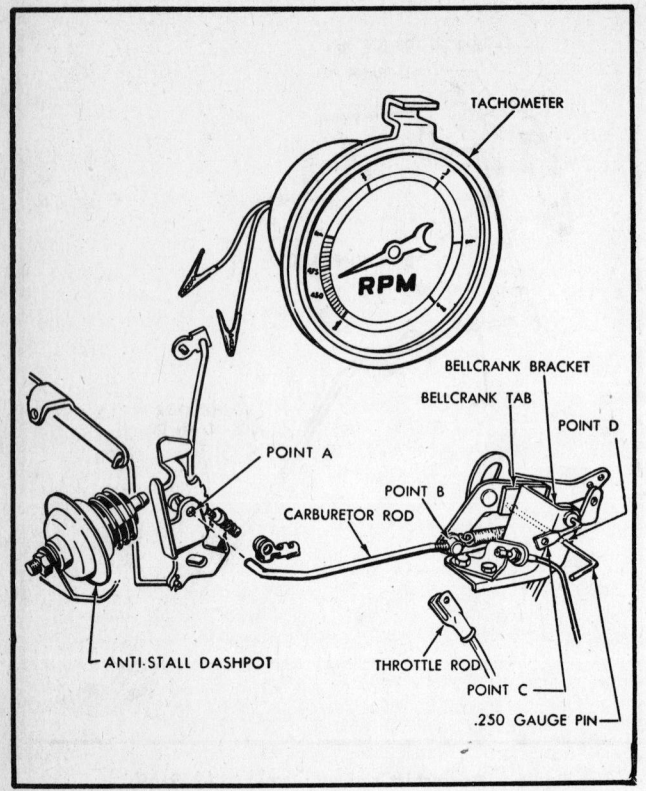

Fig. 9   Carburetor rod adjustment, 1960

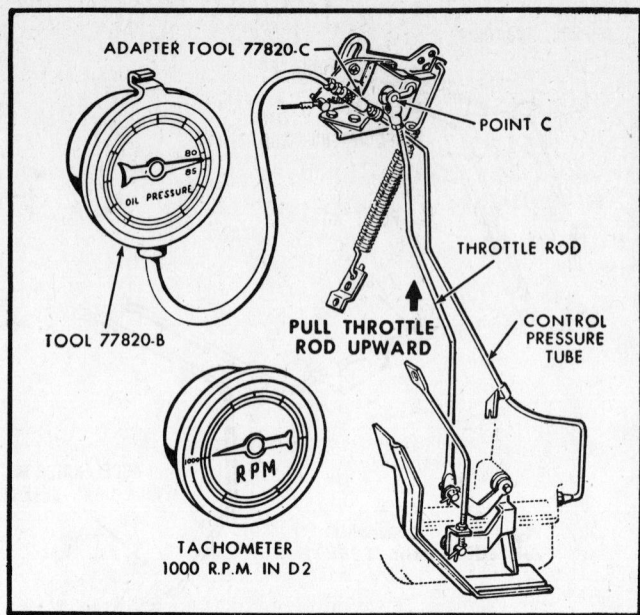

Fig. 10   Throttle rod adjustment, 1960

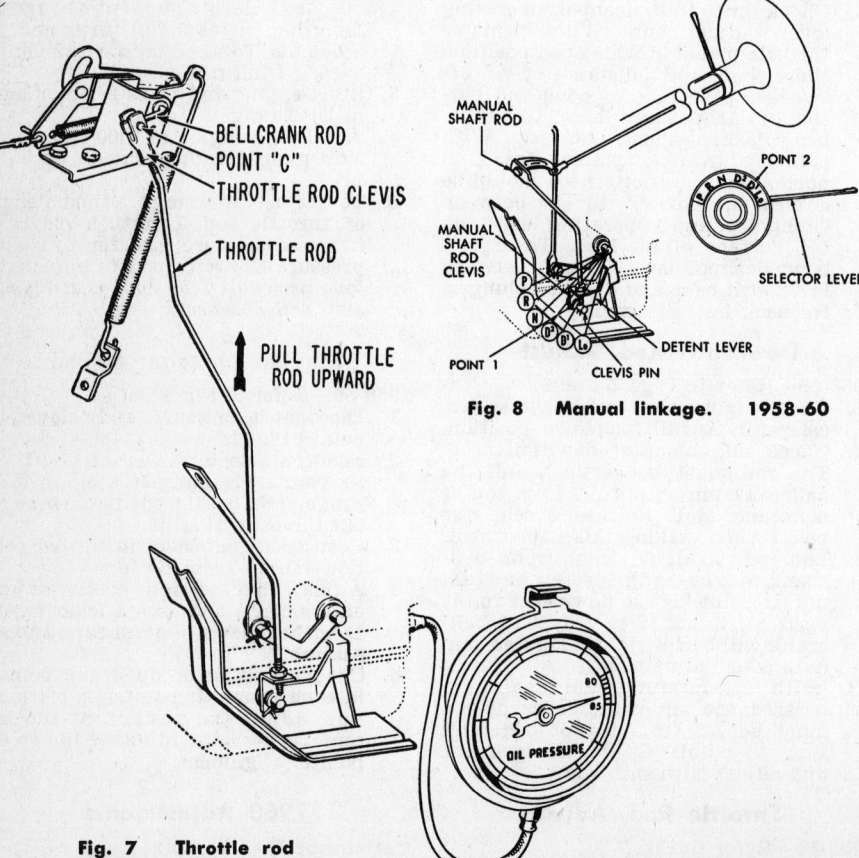

Fig. 8   Manual linkage.   1958-60

Fig. 7   Throttle rod adjustment. 1958-59

2. Disconnect carburetor rod at point A.
3. Insert ¼" gauge pin through alignment holes in bellcrank bracket and tab, point D.
4. While holding carburetor lever against hot idle adjusting screw, adjust length of carburetor rod between points A and B for free fit into carburetor lever. Lengthen rod one turn.
5. Remove gauge pin and connect carburetor rod.

Throttle Rod, Fig. 10:
1. Raise hood and connect pressure gauge as shown.
2. Pull upward on throttle rod firmly but gently. Adjust clevis at point C so clevis pin enters freely. Lengthen clevis 3½ turns and reassemble throttle rod.
3. Start engine and with foot brake set firmly, place selector lever in D2 position.
4. Accelerate engine to a fast idle (1000 rpm). Pressure gauge reading must be 80-85 psi. To correct the pressure, adjust length of throttle rod. Lengthen clevis to increase or shorten to reduce pressure. *To avoid overheating transmission, selector must be returned to neutral position and throttle closed after each check.*

Downshift Rod, Fig. 6:
1. With ignition off, depress accelerator to full kickdown position. Check position of bellcrank rod and pin. Check alignment of downshift rod. Downshift rod must be vertical and the bellcrank pin within $\frac{3}{32}$" from top of bellcrank slot. Release accelerator pedal when making adjustment.
2. Looking straight down from bellcrank to the "Z" bar, adjust screw and jam nut at point F so downshift rod is vertical with relation to sides of car. If downshift rod is

not vertical, free travel of bellcrank will be restricted. After adjustment, tighten jam nuts.

3. With accelerator again depressed, top of bellcrank pin must be within ³⁄₃₂" from top of bellcrank slot. To adjust, snap downshift rod off stud at point F and lengthen or shorten rod as required to obtain correct linkage travel.

Manual Linkage: This adjustment is made as outlined for 1958-59 models.

1961 Linkage, Adjust

Downshift Rod, Fig. 11

1. Loosen locknut on downshift rod. Disconnect rod from ball stud on bellcrank and slide off spring clip. Make sure movable outer bracket on bellcrank is up against stop pin on inner mounting bracket on bellcrank.
2. Pull upward and hold downshift rod against transmission internal stop. Adjust length of rod until hole in rod is aligned with ball stud on bellcrank.
3. Loosen downshift rod one turn and position it on ball stud. Slide spring clip over end of rod to lock rod to stud. Tighten lock nut. *Be sure outer bracket remains against stop pin; if not lengthen downshift rod one additional turn.*

Accelerator Pedal Height, Fig. 11

1. With engine off, measure distance from top of pedal to carpet, which should be approximately 4¾".
2. Depress accelerator pedal and check for detent feel and kickdown action of bellcrank. Be sure carburetor throttle plates are fully closed. Then adjust pedal height at accelerator connecting link to achieve proper operation of downshift rod.

Manual Linkage, Fig. 12

1. With engine shut off, place selector lever against stop in "Dl" position.
2. Raise car and disconnect adjustable link from manual shift lever at transmission.

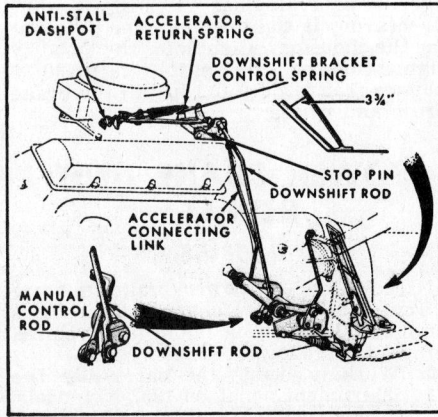

Fig. 11 Accelerator linkage and downshift rod adjustments. 1961

3. Loosen locknut on adjustable link. Pull down on link to hold selector lever against stop. Lengthen or shorten link by rotating its lower end until hole in link aligns with stud on transmission shift lever. Lengthen link one additional turn and connect it to transmission shift lever.
4. Check selector lever through all ranges to assure correct adjustment.

TRANSMISSION, REPLACE

1961

It is necessary to remove the complete transmission and converter housing as a unit as there is one additional attaching bolt located behind the converter where it is not accessible until after the converter has been removed.

1. Drain transmission oil pan. Remove converter access cover from front of converter housing. Remove transmission linkage splash shield.
2. *Mark rear universal joint flange and pinion flange before removing drive shaft so it can be reinstalled in same position, thus maintaining original balance.*
3. Disconnect parking brake cables and equalizer.
4. Disconnect linkage from transmission levers and vacuum hose at vacuum diaphragm. D i s c o n n e c t speedometer cable.
5. Remove three upper converter housing-to-engine bolts. Remove nuts attaching converter to flywheel.
6. Turn front wheels to right and remove starter motor. Raise transmission slightly with a jack. Remove crossmember.
7. Detach vacuum line at converter housing. Remove manual linkage equalizer mounted between transmission and underbody.
8. Remove remaining transmission-to-engine bolts and remove transmission and converter assembly from car.
9. Reverse removal procedure to install. Adjust linkage as outlined previously.

1960

It is necessary to remove the complete transmission and converter housing as a unit as there are two additional attaching bolts located behind the converter where they are not accessible until after the converter has been removed.

1. Disconnect a c c e l e r a t o r linkage (downshift rod) from bellcrank.
2. Remove two upper and one bolt from right side of converter housing-to-engine. Remove one inner upper bolt attaching starter motor to converter housing.
3. Disconnect engine stabilizer bracket from converter housing. Remove converter housing lower plate.
4. Drain converter and transmission.
5. Remove exhaust crossover pipe.
6. Disconnect oil cooler lines.

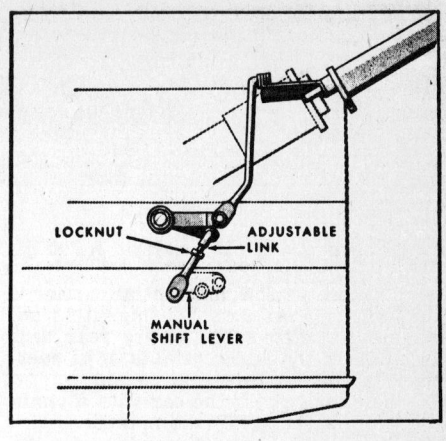

Fig. 12 Manual linkage adjustments. 1961

7. *Before removing drive shaft, mark rear universal joint and axle shaft flange so it can be reinstalled in same position, thus maintaining original balance.*
8. Disconnect parking brake cables from equalizer bar and remove bar.
9. Detach starter and slide it forward over frame crossmember and secure in place.
10. Remove control linkage splash shield. Disconnect linkage from transmission; also speedometer cable.
11. Remove nut from engine rear mount lower stud.
12. Support transmission with jack and remove rear mount from crossmember and remove crossmember by sliding it over left exhaust pipe to rear of left mounting bracket. Lower transmission slightly and remove remaining converter housing-to-engine bolts.
13. Remove transmission from car.
14. Reverse removal procedure to install and adjust linkage as outlined previously.

1958-59

The transmission can be removed from the car, leaving the converter housing attached to engine. The procedure is as follows:

1. Disconnect battery.
2. Drain transmission fluid.
3. Disconnect linkage from transmission.
4. Disconnect speedometer cable.
5. Remove drive shaft.
6. Disconnect parking brake equalizer from its lever.
7. Disconnect parking brake cable from equalizer lever and remove lever.
8. Position jack under transmission. Relieve weight on rear engine mount and remove mount and support member.
9. Lower jack until engine just rests on frame crossmember.
10. Unfasten transmission from converter and slide it back and out.

Rear Axle and Brake Section

Refer To Hydraulic Brakes Chapter For Brake Adjustments

REAR AXLE, REPLACE

Inasmuch as the differential carrier is part of the rear axle housing, it is advisable to remove the entire rear axle assembly if the differential is to be overhauled. The procedure is as follows:
1. Lift the rear of the car with a chain hoist attached to the bumper.
2. Set chassis support stands under the frame side rails ahead of the front spring hangers.
3. Drain the differential housing.
4. Remove axle shafts and propeller shaft.
5. Remove hydraulic brake line clips from axle housing and free brake line from differential housing. Wire hydraulic line to frame.
6. Raise axle housing with a jack until shock absorbers start to compress. Remove nut holding shock absorber to spring seat.
7. Remove U-bolts attaching axle housing to rear springs.
8. Lower axle assembly to floor.

REAR AXLE REPAIRS

In this type axle, Fig. 1, the drive pinion is held in position by shoulders in the differential carrier, upon which the pinion bearing cups seat. The pinion position is maintained by shims located between the rear bearing and the rear shoulder in the differential carrier. Shims between the bearing spacer and the front bearing cone are used to adjust pinion bearings.

The shimmed type of differential bearing adjustment is employed. The procedure for making this adjustment, as well as the assembly of the differential case, replacing the ring gear, checking ring gear and pinion backlash, and other differential case operations, is given in the *Rear Axle* chapter.

The axle tubes are pressed into the differential carrier to form a one-piece housing. To overhaul the unit, therefore, the rear axle assembly must be removed from the chassis.

Pinion & Bearings, Replace—After removing the axle shafts and differential unit, unscrew the pinion flange retaining nut and pull off the flange. The pinion may then be removed from the carrier by driving it out of the front bearing with a brass drift and hammer. After the pinion is free of the front bearing, pull it out through the rear of the carrier.

Mount the pinion in a press and press the pinion shaft out of the bearing. When replacing the bearing select a suitable sleeve or length of pipe of the same diameter as the cone so the rollers or cage will not be damaged when being forced on the shaft.

Drive the front bearing cup and oil seal out of the forward end of the carrier. If the rear bearing cup is to be replaced or if the pinion setting is to be changed, remove the rear bearing cup.

To change the pinion setting, the shims behind the rear bearing cup should be measured with a micrometer. The necessary shims may then be removed or added to obtain the proper pinion setting as indicated when a pinion setting gauge is used (see *Rear Axle* Chapter). After the required shims have been added or subtracted, replace the rear bearing cup.

When making a pinion adjustment, the same thickness of pinion bearing adjusting shims should be added or removed at the rear bearing cup to retain the proper pinion bearing adjustment.

To install the pinion, support it under the head with a wood block while the pinion flange is reinstalled. The pinion oil seal should not be replaced until after the pinion setting has been checked.

Pinion Bearings, Adjust—The only occasion for adjusting the drive pinion bearings is when a new pinion or differential carrier is installed. To make the adjustment, install sufficient shims between the bearing spacer and front bearing so that when the pinion retaining nut is tightened against the pinion flange, all rollers in the bearing are tight, but still permit rotating the pinion by hand.

Pinion, Adjust—After adjusting the pinion bearings, the position of the pinion may be checked. If a pinion setting gauge is available, check the pinion depth as outlined in the *Rear Axle* Chapter. If a correction is necessary, disassemble the pinion and, if it is to be moved toward the center of the axle, add shims between the rear bearing and rear shoulder in the carrier. If the pinion has to be moved away from the center of the axle, remove shims from this point.

If no pinion setting gauge is available, assemble the differential unit in the carrier and check the tooth contact by painting the ring gear teeth as described in the *Rear Axle* Chapter. After satisfactory tooth contact has been established, remove the pinion flange to install the seal.

AXLE SHAFTS

Axle shafts are mounted on sealed ball bearings pressed to a shoulder on the axle shaft, and held in place by a pressed-on bearing retainer ring. The shaft bearings are pre-lubricated and require no additional lubrication. The shafts are held in place in the axle housing by a retainer plate. The wheel hub and brake drum flange are forged integral with the axle shaft. The flange provides the brake drum and wheel mounting and eliminates the need for a keyed hub.

To remove an axle shaft, take off the wheel and unfasten the brake drum from the axle shaft flange. Through the hole provided in the flange, remove the nuts which secure the brake support plate to the axle housing. Then with a suitable puller, pull the shaft out of the housing, using care not to dislodge the brake support plate or damage the oil seal in the housing. Install one nut to hold the brake plate in position.

Axle shaft bearings should be removed only when necessary to install a new bearing. A bearing once removed must be discarded.

If necessary to disassemble, loosen the axle shaft bearing retainer ring and remove the retainer. The bearing may be removed with a bearing puller, after which remove the retainer plate.

To assemble, place the retainer plate on the shaft. Press the bearing up against the shoulder on the shaft. Install the bearing retainer ring and press it firmly against the bearing. Before installing the shaft examine the oil seal and replace it if necessary.

Before installing a new oil seal it should be thoroughly soaked in oil for at least ½ hour to make it soft and pliable. When installing the seal, use a suitable seal driver, driving the seal into the axle housing with the axis of the shaft and tight against the shoulder. After installing the seal, check the outer diameter for tightness in the housing to avoid possible leaks.

To install the shaft, remove the temporary nut holding the brake plate, and lubricate the bearing bore in the housing. Clean the brake plate surface and install new gaskets between the retainer plate and brake plate. Slide the shaft into the housing, using care not to damage the oil seal. Push the shaft in until its bearing is tight against the shoulder in the housing. Complete the job by tightening the axle shaft nuts to 30-35 pounds feet torque, and install the brake drum and wheel.

POWER BRAKE UNIT, REPLACE
1953-55

Repairs on the power brake unit are given in a separate chapter. To remove and install the unit from the vehicle, proceed as follows:
1. Working inside the car under the instrument panel, on 1953-55 models, disengage valve push rod from brake pedal.
2. Working in engine compartment, remove master cylinder outlet fitting bolt from master cylinder. *It is not necessary to remove the stop light switch, wires or hose assembly from the outlet fitting. Do not disturb the outlet fitting.*

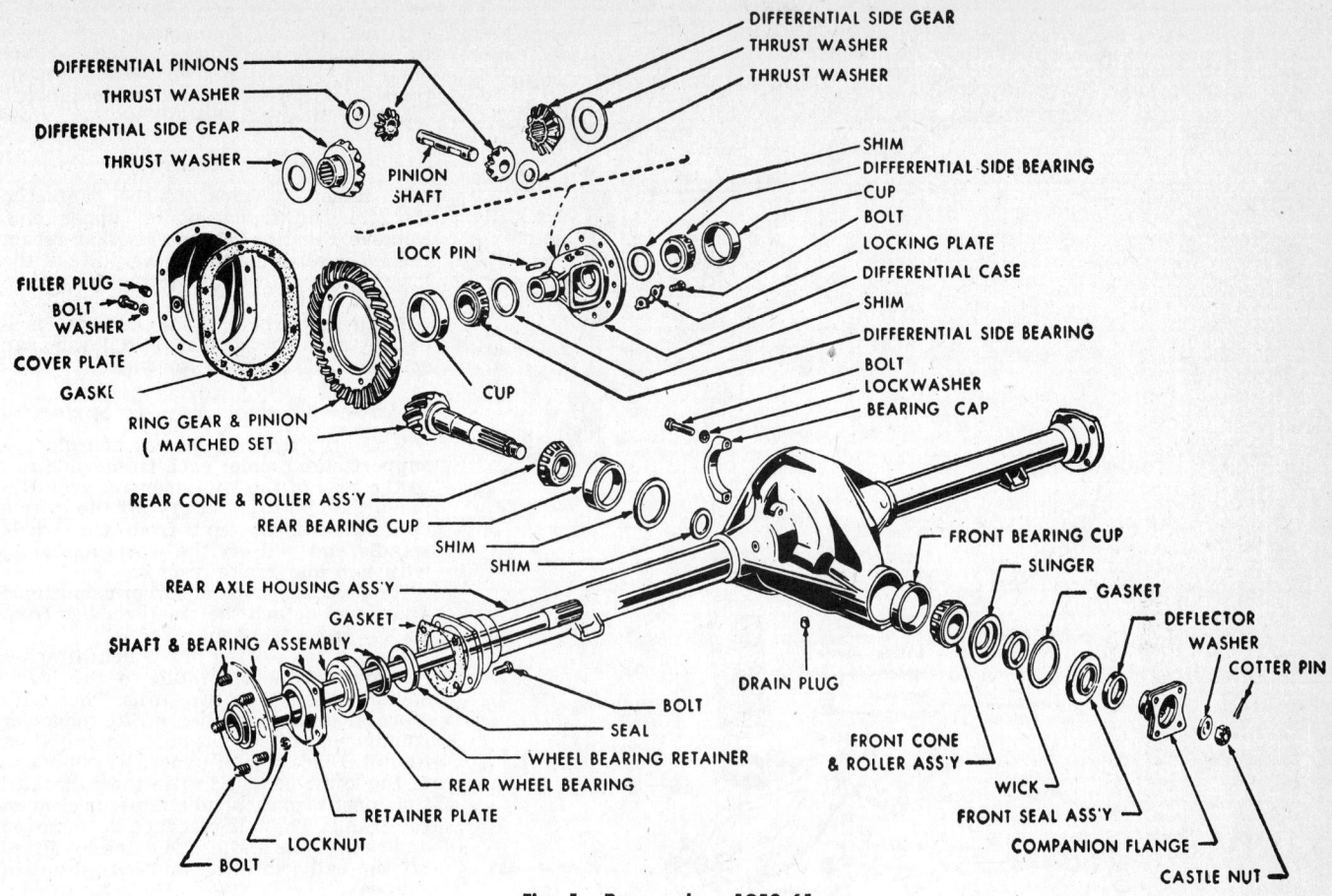

Fig. 1 Rear axle. 1953-61

3. Remove manifold vacuum hose from check valve on power unit.

4. Remove vacuum reserve tank hose from fitting on check valve.

5. Unfasten power brake assembly (4 screws) from bracket on dash panel.

6. To install, reverse foregoing procedure. Then bleed brakes in the usual manner. After bleeding, fill hydraulic brake reservoir to within ¼" of the top of filler cap opening and replace cap.

1956-57

1. Working in engine compartment, remove master cylinder outlet fitting bolt from master cylinder. It is not necessary to remove stop light switch.

2. Remove manifold vacuum hose from check valve on power unit.

3. Remove vacuum reserve tank hose from fitting on check valve.

4. Unfasten and remove power unit from dash panel.

5. To install, reverse foregoing procedure. Then bleed brakes in the usual manner. After bleeding, fill reservoir to within ¼" of the top of the filler cap opening and replace cap.

1958-61

1. From inside car, disengage push rod from lever.

2. From engine compartment, remove master cylinder outlet fitting. It is not necessary to remove stop light switch.

3. Remove manifold vacuum hose from power unit.

4. Remove shoulder bolt retaining booster push rod from pedal linkage.

5. Unfasten and remove power unit from dash panel.

6. To install, reverse foregoing procedure. Bleed brake system in usual manner. Then fill master cylinder to within ¼" of filler cap opening and replace cap.

Front End and Steering Section

WHEEL ALIGNMENT

1961 Caster

1. Raise hood and unsnap clips retaining top of rubber bushing shield to fender apron.

2. Loosen bolts that secure upper control arm shaft to frame and, with a pry bar, move shaft in or out as required. A movement of approxi-

mately $\frac{3}{32}$" at either front or rear bolt location will change caster ½°. Inboard movement of the front bolt, or outboard movement of rear bolt, will change caster in negative direction. Outboard movement of front bolt or inboard movement of rear bolt will change caster in positive direction.

3. When adjustment is correct, torque shaft retaining bolts to 100-125 ft. lbs.

1961 Camber

1. Raise hood and unsnap clips retaining top of bushing rubber shield to fender apron.

2. Loosen bolts that secure upper control arm shaft to frame and, with a pry bar, move shaft in or out as required. A movement of approximately $\frac{3}{64}$" of the entire shaft will change camber ¼°. Inboard move-

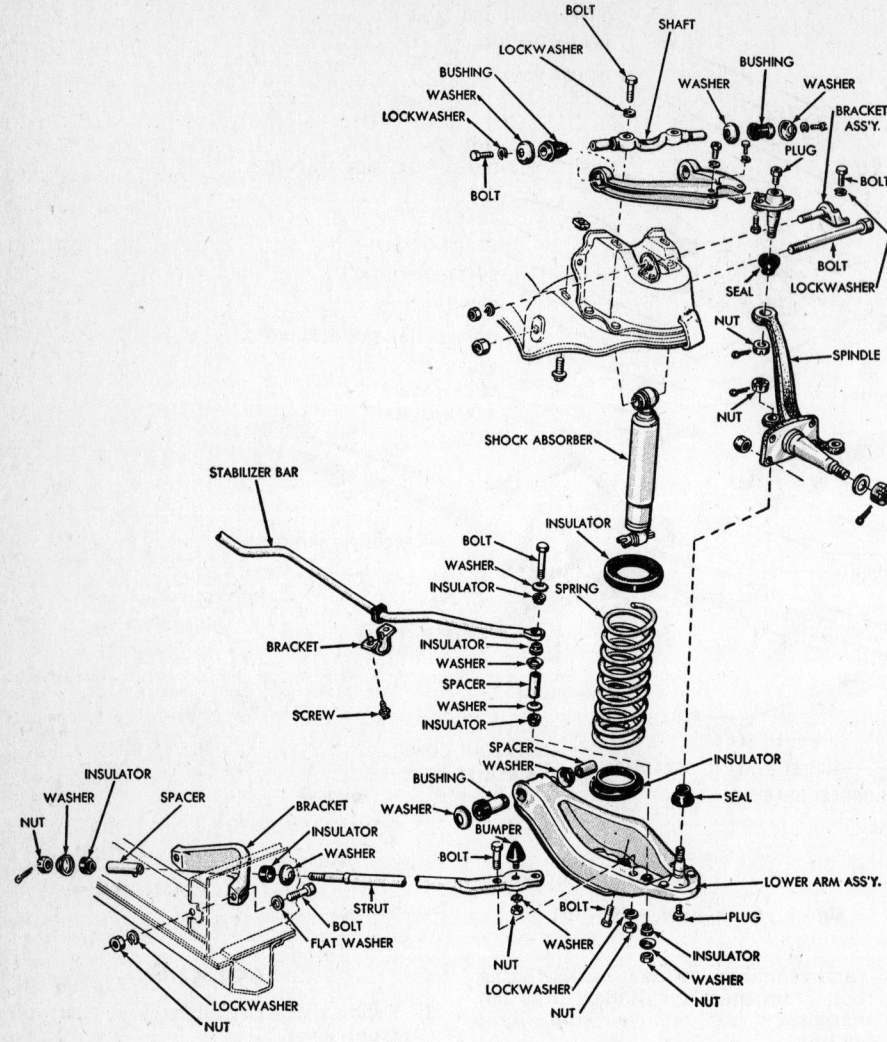

BOLT
LOCKWASHER
SHAFT
BUSHING
WASHER
BUSHING
WASHER
WASHER
LOCKWASHER
BRACKET ASS'Y.
BOLT
PLUG
BOLT
BOLT
LOCKWASHER
SEAL
NUT
SPINDLE
NUT
SHOCK ABSORBER
STABILIZER BAR
INSULATOR
BOLT
WASHER
INSULATOR
SPRING
BRACKET
INSULATOR
WASHER
SPACER
WASHER
INSULATOR
SCREW
SPACER
WASHER
INSULATOR
SEAL
BUSHING
WASHER
INSULATOR
WASHER
NUT
WASHER
SPACER
BRACKET
INSULATOR
BUMPER
WASHER
LOWER ARM ASS'Y.
BOLT
BOLT
STRUT
BOLT
BOLT
PLUG
FLAT WASHER
WASHER
INSULATOR
NUT
WASHER
LOCKWASHER
NUT
LOCKWASHER
NUT
NUT

Fig. 1   Front suspension.   1961

ment will change camber in negative direction. Outboard movement will change camber in positive direction.
3. When adjustment is correct, torque shaft retaining bolts to 100-125 ft. lbs.

1953-60 Caster & Camber

To adjust caster, Fig. 2, loosen the two bolts that secure the upper suspension arm shaft to the frame and insert shims between the shaft and frame. A $\frac{1}{16}$" shim at the front bolt will produce a negative caster of $\frac{1}{2}$ degree. A $\frac{1}{16}$" shim at the rear bolt will produce a positive caster of $\frac{1}{2}$ degree. Shims are available in thicknesses of $\frac{1}{64}$", $\frac{1}{32}$", $\frac{1}{16}$" and $\frac{1}{8}$". When the correct adjustment is obtained, torque the bolts to 75-80 lbs. ft. Caster must be held within $\frac{1}{2}$ degree difference on both sides.

Camber is also adjusted at the upper suspension shaft. To adjust, insert or remove the shims from between the shaft and the frame at both the front and rear bolts. Each $\frac{1}{16}$" shim removed will add $\frac{1}{4}$ degree of positive camber. The camber must be the same on both sides within $\frac{1}{4}$ degree.

1953-61 Toe-In

Position the front wheels in their straight-ahead position. Then turn both tie rod adjusting sleeves an equal amount until the desired toe-in setting is obtained.

WHEEL BEARINGS, ADJUST

1. Tighten spindle nut with a 12" wrench, while rotating wheel back and forth, until there is a noticeable drag or bind. This assures that bearing cones are properly seated.
2. Then back off spindle nut to line up to the nearest cotter pin hole that will allow the hub to rotate freely with no perceptible end play.

FRONT END REPAIRS

1953-61

This suspension, Figs. 1 and 2, is the ball joint type. It differs from other types

of suspension in that the wheel spindle is attached directly to the suspension arms by means of ball joints located at the outer ends of both arms. The conventional steering knuckle, knuckle support and kingpin is eliminated.

Shock Absorber

To remove a shock absorber, unfasten it from the frame at its upper end. Remove the two cap screws that retain the shock absorber mounting plate to the lower conrol arm and lower the shock absorber unit.

To install, reverse the removal procedure and tighten the two lower cap screws to 18-24 lbs. ft. torque.

Lower Control Arm & Spring

Raise the front of the car and place a support stand under each frame side rail to the rear of the lower control arm. Remove the hub cap and pry off the grease cap. Remove the nut from the wheel spindle and pull off the wheel assembly with hub and brake drum.

Remove the shock absorber as outlined above and detach the stabilizer bar from the lower control arm.

Loosen the slotted nut which attaches the lower ball joint stud to the lower spindle boss one or two turns. Then with a brass bar and hammer, strike the lower spindle boss to pop the stud loose against its nut. Place a jack under the outer end of the lower arm and raise the jack until the upper arm rebound bumper is clear of the frame. The nut can then be removed and the spindle and brake assembly lifted off the ball joint stud and moved out of the way.

Lower the jack until the coil spring is free and can be removed. Note the rubber insulators at the upper and lower ends of the spring.

Unfasten the lower control arm from the frame and remove the arm. Inspect the bushings on the inner end of each arm leg and replace if defective.

INSTALL—To install the lower control arm, secure the rearward leg to the frame crossmember tube, running the nut up finger tight. With the arm forced firmly against the tube, install enough shims to fill the space between the forward arm leg bushing and front crossmember. Then install the bolt and washers and run the nut up finger tight. With the arm in curb load position (approximately horizontal) with the outer end slightly lower than the inner, tighten the nuts to 80-100 lbs. ft. torque.

Place the coil spring with the rubber insulators in position on the lower control arm. Then with a jack under the lower arm, compress the coil spring. Care must be taken to see that the upper and lower ends of the spring are properly seated and the rubber insulators are in place. Guide the spindle boss over the ball joint stud. Install the nut and torque it to 100 lbs. ft. Continue to tighten until the cotter pin holes are lined up and install the cotter pin.

Remove the jack from under the arm and install the shock absorber. Secure the stabilizer bar to lower suspension arm.

Ball Joints

Remove the cover and seal from the

ball joint. Inspect the joint and replace if found defective. If the joint is still serviceable, *do not* wash it in solvent as it will be extremely difficult to lubricate it again. Do not hammer the ball joint bodies as binding will result. Inspect the metal seal parts for damage and replace if necessary. Replace the sponge rubber seal, making sure it is stuffed into the metal seal cup before pushing it down over the ball joint stud.

Upper Arm

Remove the shock absorber. Place a jack under the lower control arm spring seat and raise it until some of the tension has been removed from the upper bumper. Remove the wheel and tire assembly.

Wire the spindle to the frame to avoid possible damage to the brake hose from undue tension. Loosen the ball joint stud by backing the nut off one or two turns and striking the spindle boss. Remove the stud nut completely and then remove the two bolts that secure the inner shaft to the frame. Note the number of shims between the shaft and frame at each of the bolt locations. Then take off the upper control arm.

To install, position the arm on the frame crossmember. On models before 1961, use the same number of shims that were originally used between the shaft and frame bracket. Secure the shaft to the bracket with the two bolts and torque the bolts to 75-90 lbs. ft. (100-125 on 1961). Place the ball joint stud in the spindle boss, install the nut and tighten it to 80 lbs. ft. minimum. Continue to tighten until the cotter pin holes are lined up and install a cotter pin.

Install the wheel and hub assembly and remove the jack from under the lower control arm. Finally, check the wheel alignment as previously outlined.

HORN RING

1953-57

Remove the cap and emblem by grasping with the hand and pulling outward from the steering wheel hub. On 1952-53 remove the three screws (beneath the wheel) that secure the horn ring attaching plate to the steering wheel. The horn ring, securing plate, gasket and spring can then be removed.

1958-61

Remove cap and emblem from steering wheel by inserting a flat implement between the steering wheel hub and horn ring and pushing up. Remove steering shaft nut and pull off steering wheel.

The horn ring, horn ring coil spring and/or electrical contact ring or insulator may be removed at this time by removing the three screws from the rear of the steering wheel hub.

STEERING WHEEL

After removing the horn button or emblem from the steering wheel as outlined above, take off the steering wheel nut and use a suitable puller to remove the steering wheel.

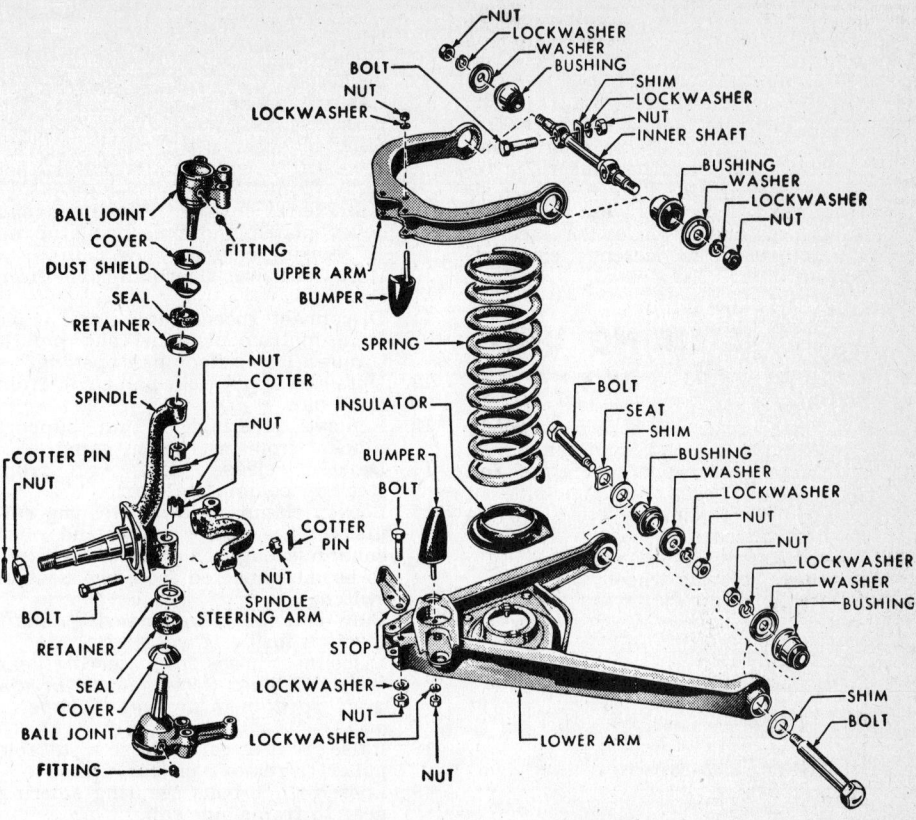

Fig. 2 Front suspension. 1953-60

STEERING GEAR, REPLACE

1953

Remove cap and emblem assembly from the steering wheel hub by grasping with the hand and pulling outward. Remove the nut from the steering shaft and, with a suitable puller, take off the steering wheel. Remove the pitman arm with a puller.

Remove the necessary floor covering and take out the steering column-to-dash cover plate. Disconnect the steering column electrical connections at the junction points. Remove the shift rod from the steering column shift arm. Unfasten the steering column housing from the bracket, secured to the brake pedal support bracket. Loosen the clamp at the lower end of the steering column. Remove the steering shaft nut, spring and sleeve from the upper steering column. Remove the column tube from the steering shaft.

Raise the car and remove the oil filter. Remove the screw that secures the clips holding the heater tube, spark plug cables and oil sending wire to engine block. Unfasten the steering gear housing from the frame. Before removing the steering gear from the vehicle, cover the top of the steering shaft with tape to avoid damage to the instrument panel. Then take the steering gear out from under the car, being careful not to damage the brake line pipes, oil sending unit or radio condenser.

1954-55

1. Remove clamp that secures reservoir

hose to fitting on brake booster cylinder (if equipped).
2. Remove clamp that secures reservoir hose to dash panel. Move hose away from steering column opening in dash panel.
3. Remove front seat cushion.
4. Remove steering wheel.
5. Disconnect steering column electrical connections.
6. Remove accelerator pedal from accelerator push rod. Remove bolt and clevis pin securing brake pedal to brake pedal support and push rod, and remove brake pedal.
7. Remove sheet metal screw, located under accelerator pedal, securing floor carpeting to floor pan and pull carpeting away from dash panel opening.
8. Disconnect speedometer drive cable from instrument panel and pull it through lower floor pan opening cover. Remove insulator and floor pan opening cover plates.
9. Remove two cap screws that secure steering column bracket to instrument panel and pedal support bracket.
10. Release shift rod from steering column shift arm.
11. Loosen clamp on lower steering column at steering gear housing. Raise column sufficiently to disconnect wires at neutral switch on Automatic Transmission equipped models only. Remove steering column tube from steering shaft through inside of vehicle.
12. Raise front of car and remove pitman arm.
13. Loosen three bolts that secure steer-

ing gear to frame. *Remove shims, if any, located between mounting bolts and frame side rail. Mark bolt holes and number of shims required to facilitate assembly. Mark shims for identification with bolt holes.*

14. With one man in the passenger compartment and another under the vehicle, remove the three steering gear mounting bolts that were previously loosened and remove the steering gear through the passenger compartment.

POWER STEERING UNIT, REPLACE, 1953-55

1. Unfasten reservoir hose from power brake fitting on vacuum cylinder.
2. Unfasten reservoir hose from fire wall. Pull hose to engine side of floor pan opening cover to provide working clearance.
3. Remove front seat cushion.
4. Remove steering wheel.

5. Disconnect steering column electrical connections.
6. Detach accelerator pedal from its push rod.
7. Remove brake pedal from its support bracket.
8. Remove sheet metal screw (under accelerator pedal) and pull carpet away from floor pan opening.
9. Unfasten insulator from floor pan cover plates and pull insulator up on steering column.
10. Unfasten lower floor pan cover from floor pan.
11. Disconnect speedometer drive cable from instrument panel and pull it through lower floor pan opening.
12. Unfasten upper floor pan cover from floor pan.
13. Remove steering column support bracket from instrument panel.
14. Detach release shift rod from steering column shift arm.
15. Loosen clamp on lower steering column at the gear housing and raise column enough to permit the wires to be disconnected from the neutral switch.
16. Pull column from steering shaft through inside of vehicle.
17. Disconnect hoses from steering gear valve housing. *Secure hoses in upward position to prevent leakage of oil.*
18. Raise front of car and use a suitable puller to remove pitman arm.
19. Loosen three bolts securing steering gear to frame side rail.

20. Remove shims, if any, located between mounting bolts and frame. *Mark bolt holes and number of shims at each bolt hole to assure correct assembly.*
21. With one man in driver's compartment and another under the car, remove the three previously loosened gear-to-frame bolts and lift the steering gear through the passenger compartment.
22. Install the unit by reversing the foregoing procedure.

1956-57

1. Remove battery ground cable.
2. Remove radio speaker.
3. Remove steering wheel.
4. Disconnect speedometer cable.
5. Disconnect accelerator rod.
6. Remove brake pedal pad.
7. Remove steering column supports.
8. Remove access covers from floor.
9. Remove shift rod from pin on shift arm.
10. Disconnect turn signal wires at junction block. Also neutral switch and back-up light wires attached to terminal block on steering column.
11. Remove steering column from steering shaft.
12. Working through floor pan opening, remove rear manifold cap screw.
13. Raise car and remove pitman arm from steering sector shaft.
14. Unfasten muffler inlet to manifold.
15. Remove two forward screws that secure steering gear to frame side rail. Leave remaining screw in place until remaining operations are accomplished. Mark position of any shims found under screws to insure proper assembly.
16. Lower car to complete operations in engine compartment.
17. Remove manifold, and spark plugs from cylinder Nos. 6, 7 and 8 and on Continental, remove air cleaner and air duct as an assembly.
18. Remove as much fluid as possible from reservoir with suction gun.
19. Place drain pan under car to catch oil drained from system.
20. Disconnect pressure and return lines at power steering gear. Drain steering gear by turning from stop to stop several times.
21. Remove remaining steering gear-to-frame attaching bolt.
22. Place steering shaft with coupling slot in a vertical position to facilitate removal. Remove gear by tilting gear housing down and rearward until sector shaft can be removed first.
23. Reverse the removal procedure to install the steering gear. Fill the pump reservoir to the proper level. Loosen bleed screw in side cover and start engine. Turn steering wheel several times through its entire range to bleed all air from system. Tighten bleed screw and recheck fluid level.

1958-60

1. Remove pressure and return lines from steering gear. Elevate the lines to minimize fluid leakage.
2. Remove power brake unit.

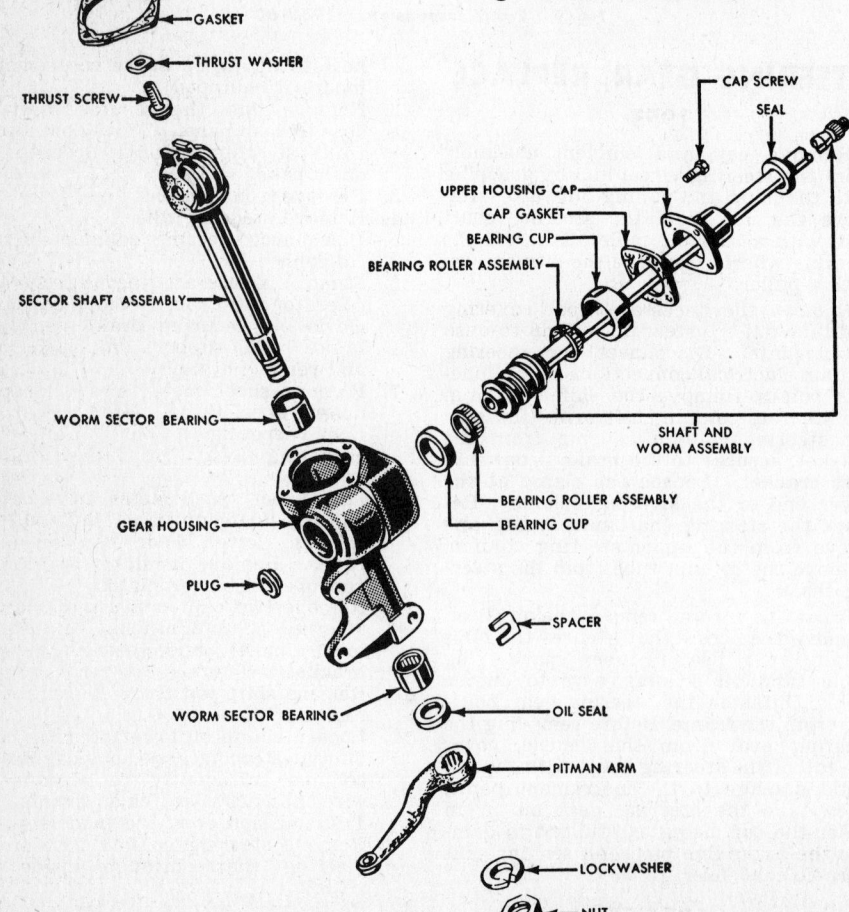

Fig. 3 Exploded view of manual steering gear. Typical of all 1953-55

3. Unfasten steering shaft coupling from steering gear.
4. Remove pitman arm with a suitable puller.
5. Remove 3 bolts securing steering gear to underbody side rail.
6. Remove steering gear from car.
7. Reverse the foregoing procedure to install the gear. Then bleed the brake system and power steering system.

1961

1. Remove splash shield at pitman arm and pull off pitman arm.
2. Disconnect hoses from gear and tie hose ends higher than reservoir to prevent fluid loss.
3. Loosen Allen screw that attaches flexible coupling to steering shaft. Use an Allen socket and a universal joint to loosen screw.
4. Disconnect resonator inlet pipe at exhaust manifold and resonator and remove pipe.
5. Remove transmission linkage rods from equalizer shaft and force shaft outward. This compresses spring within shaft which frees shaft from inner ball joint.
6. Unfasten gear housing from body member and remove gear assembly.
7. Installation is the reverse of removal. Fill reservoir. Before checking fluid level, turn steering wheel from one extreme to the other and operate windshield wipers. This bleeds system of air and assures that it is filled with fluid.

MANUAL STEERING GEAR, ADJUST

1953-55, Fig. 3

Before proceeding with the adjustments, loosen the gear housing from the frame side rail to relieve any possible vertical strain. Loosen the steering column clamp to relieve any possible horizontal strain. Then tighten the mounting and clamp bolts which will relieve any misalignment in the steering gear mounting.

Steering gear adjustments must be made in the order given below to insure satisfactory results.

Worm Bearing Preload

The worm bearing preload is controlled by the shim pack installed between the steering gear housing and the housing upper cap. The shim pack contains shims of various thicknesses; the thinner shims are installed on the top of the pack, and the adjustment is made as follows:

Disconnect the sector shaft arm from the steering linkage. Turn the steering wheel two complete turns from the straight-ahead position. Hook a spring scale to the steering wheel rim. Rotate the wheel at least one turn with the aid of the scale. The pull required to keep the wheel moving should be between $\frac{1}{8}$ and $\frac{5}{8}$ lbs., which is the worm bearing preload. If the reading is high, a shim or shims should be added. If reading is too low, remove a shim or shims.

If an adjustment is required, unfasten the upper cap from the housing and work the cap and column jacket upward to allow clearance for removing or adding shims. For additional working clearance it may be necessary to remove the steering wheel.

To add a shim, split the shim at one point and install the shim with the split in the upward position. Make sure the split ends do not overlap as this could lead to a false adjustment.

To remove a shim separate the first shim from the pack with a knife blade. Pass the blade all around the shim, being careful not to damage the shims.

The steering column and upper housing cap must be assembled on the gear housing each time the preload is checked.

Worm & Roller Mesh

This adjustment is controlled by the adjustment screw mounted on the sector shaft cover. Adjustment is made as follows:

Disconnect the sector shaft arm from the steering linkage. Attach a spring scale to the steering wheel rim. Pull the wheel through the straight-ahead position and note reading on scale. The scale reading should be at least $\frac{1}{2}$ lb. above that of the worm bearing preload previously determined, but the total reading must not exceed $1\frac{5}{8}$ lbs. If the scale reading does not exceed the worm bearing preload by at least $\frac{1}{2}$ lb., the worm and roller mesh should be adjusted.

Place the steering wheel in the straight-ahead position. Remove the adjusting screw cover and lock washer. Rotate the adjusting screw clockwise while moving the steering gear arm back and forth until all backlash is removed.

Install the lock washer and cover and check the preload with the spring scale as previously described. The reading should be between 1 and $1\frac{5}{8}$ lbs. If the reading is too high, turn the adjusting screw slightly counterclockwise. If too low, turn the screw slightly clockwise.

STEERING GEAR REPAIRS

1953-55

Fig. 3, illustrates the conventional steering gear used on 1952-55 models. But inasmuch as it is typical of earlier models the following procedure will mainly apply to these models.

Disassemble

1. Drain lubricant from housing.
2. Remove sector shaft and cover.
3. Remove cover from sector shaft.
4. Unfasten and slide housing cap off steering shaft.
5. Pull shaft out of housing.
6. Slide housing upper cap gaskets (shim pack), bearing cup, and upper worm bearing out of housing.
7. Use suitable puller to remove lower worm bearing cup.
8. Press sector shaft needle bearings and oil seal through steering arm end of housing.

Inspect & Assemble

After cleaning all parts, inspect worm and rollers for scores, cracks or for signs of chipping. Inspect steering shaft bearing cups and bearings for wear, cracks or damage. Check sector shaft for wear at needle bearing locations. Replace all parts that are damaged enough to impair steering gear operation, and assemble the steering gear in the reverse order of disassembly.

Instruments, Radio and Windshield Wiper

INSTRUMENTS

1953-55

To remove the speedometer or any one of the dash instruments, first remove the radio. The instruments or speedometer can then be removed individually by removing the screws from the back edge of each instrument.

1956-57

The speedometer forms part of the instrument cluster assembly, which is removed as follows:
1. Disconnect battery ground cable.

2. Remove radio speaker and radio.
3. Disconnect speedometer cable.
4. Remove odometer cable and knob from lower edge of lower control panel.
5. Unfasten and remove instrument cluster.
6. Remove speedometer from panel.

1958-59

1. Disconnect battery ground cable.
2. Remove instrument cluster top cover plate.
3. Disconnect wiring and socket and bulbs around speedometer area to provide clearance. Note position and color codes of wires to facilitate reassembly.
4. Disconnect speedometer cable.
5. Remove instrument panel left lower cover plate.
6. Remove trip odometer reset cable from lower lip of instrument panel.
7. Unfasten and remove speedometer (6 screws).

1960

The top row of instruments and gauges are grouped in four pod-like assemblies. To service the pod assemblies (one of which contains the speedometer), remove the instrument cluster hood, remove two pod-to-cluster retaining screws and disconnect the wiring and bulbs.

To remove the instrument cluster hood, remove three screws, one at each end of the hood and one in the center. On air conditioned models, it is necessary to remove the left hand instrument panel air conditioner grille upper moulding (3 screws) to gain access to the left hand cluster hood retaining screw.

1961

The instrument panel is composed of two clusters, upper and lower. The upper cluster consists of three housings that can be serviced from the front of the instrument panel. The lower housing is removable in two sections.

All lamps in the upper cluster can be replaced from the front of the cluster. To replace the lamps in the temperature and fuel gauge housing, remove the bezel and gauges and replace the lamps. To replace the lamps in the speedometer housing, it is necessary to remove the speedometer to replace the high beam indicator and/or the two upper background lamps.

To replace the bulbs in the lower cluster, remove the lower speaker and grille assembly. Remove hood release handle and bracket from instrument panel. Remove lower left instrument panel cover and replace lamp bulbs as required.

RADIO REMOVAL

1961

1. Disconnect battery ground cable.
2. Pull off radio control knobs and remove outer bezel.
3. Remove large bezel (4 screws).
4. Unfasten and slide trim panel (2 screws) away from windshield to remove it.
5. Disconnect feed and panel lamp bullet connector and antenna lead-in cable.

6. Unfasten radio (3 screws) and pull radio and support out of instrument panel.

1958-60

Tuning Head—The negative battery cable should be disconnected to eliminate the possibility of shorting while removing the tuning head as the ignition switch is close to the path of removing.

1. Remove instrument panel top cover.
2. Remove instrument panel lower cover panel.
3. Remove power lubricator lines and control assembly from instrument panel.
4. Remove cigar lighter.
5. Remove fuse holders as required.
6. Remove manual selector control knob and speaker control disc.
7. Remove volume control knob and tone control disc.
8. Remove mounting nuts retaining shafts to instrument cluster.
9. Disconnect five wires at left of tuning head, and two fuse holders from fuse panel.
10. Disconnect antenna lead-in cable.
11. Remove right instrument panel lower cover panel.
12. Disconnect tuning head lower coaxial cable from audio chassis plug.
13. Disconnect speaker jacks from top of tuning head.
14. Remove tuning head rear brace.
15. Lower tuning head out of instrument panel.

Audio Chassis—

1. Remove right instrument panel lower cover panel.
2. Disconect coaxial cable at audio chassis.
3. Unfasten chassis (3 screws) and lower it down and out from rear of panel.

4" Speaker—In order to remove this speaker, remove glove compartment and glove compartment cover.

6" x 9" Right Instrument Panel Speaker—Remove instrument panel right lower

cover panel. Unfasten speaker (2 wing nuts) from panel. Lower speaker a few inches, then disconnect lead cable and 4" speaker cable and complete removal.

WINDSHIELD WIPER

1954-57

Wiper Motor—Removal of the wiper motor is fairly obvious. However, when installing be sure the rubber gasket is on the motor shaft end, and is inserted evenly into the auxiliary drive.

Pivot Shaft Housing—When removing the pivot shaft housing it will be necessary to remove the glove compartment box (1956-57) and defroster outlet on right side. Pull the cable tensioner toward the center of the car and lock in this position with a drift pin through the hole provided.

When installing, be sure to rig the cables properly on the pulleys before connecting to the auxiliary drive. Then take the drift pin out of the cable tensioner and allow the pulleys to take up the slack in the cables.

1958-60

The cable tension is secured to the rear of the auxiliary drive. Cable tension can be automatically increased by loosening the wing nut on the tensioner and retightening the wing nut.

To gain access to the auxiliary drive and wiper pivot, it will be necessary to remove the center, right and left lower instrument panel covers, and also the glove box and its cover.

1961

1. Remove washer coordinator hose from bottom of wiper motor.
2. Remove oil return, feed and control lines from wiper motor.
3. Disconnect cable at motor.
4. Remove motor (2 screws) from auxiliary drive mounting plate and remove motor.

MERCURY

INDEX OF SERVICE OPERATIONS

PAGE NO.

ACCESSORIES

Instruments 850
Radio Removal 850
Windshield Wiper 851
Windshield Wiper Troubles.......... 37

BODY

Air Conditioning 177
Automatic Seat Adjuster Troubles...... 36
Automatic Top Troubles............. 36
Automatic Window Lift Troubles....... 36

BRAKES (Mechanical)

Adjustments 112
Brake Cylinder Sizes................809
Hydraulic Brake System.............112
Master Cylinder, Replace...........839
Trouble Shooting 31

BRAKES (Power)

Power Unit Repairs.................128
Power Unit, Replace................838
Trouble Shooting 32

CLUTCH

Clutch Pedal, Adjust...............828
Clutch Service 828
Trouble Shooting 13

COOLING SYSTEM

Radiator, Replace 821
Trouble Shooting 8
Water Pump Repairs................822
Water Pump, Replace...............822

ELECTRIC SYSTEM

Dash Gauge Service................ 85
Distributor, Replace 823
Distributor Service 46
Distributor Specifications.........808
Generator Regulator Service........ 62
Generator Regulator Specifications.... 809
Generator Service 62
Generator Specifications 809
Horn Ring, Replace................843
Ignition System Service............ 46
Ignition Timing 823
Starter, Replace..................824
Starter Switch Service............ 83
Starting Motor Service............ 77
Starting Motor Specifications......809
Trouble Shooting 10
Turn Signal Troubles.............. 12

ENGINE

Camshaft, Replace 818
Camshaft Bearings 818
Crankshaft Oil Seal, Replace........820
Cylinder Head, Replace.............813
Crankshaft & Bearing Specs.........808
Engine, Replace...................811
Main Bearings, Replace............819
Piston Pins, Replace..............819
Piston Rings, Replace.............819
Piston, Pin & Ring Specs..........808
Pistons & Rods, Remove...........818
Piston & Rod, Assemble...........819
Pistons, Replace..................819
Rocker Arms 815
Rod Bearings, Replace............819
Timing Case Cover, Replace........816
Timing Chain, Replace.............817
Timing Gears, Replace.............817
Trouble Shooting 4
Valve Arrangement 814
Valves, Adjust...................814
Valves, Remove 815
Valve Guides 816
Valves, Grind 816
Valve Lifters 816
Valve Specifications..............807
Valve Spring Installed Height.......816
Valve Spring Testing..............816

ENGINE OILING

Oil Pan, Replace..................820
Oil Pump Repairs.................821
Trouble Shooting 9

FRONT SUSPENSION

Camber, Adjust 839
Caster, Adjust 839
Front End Repairs................840
Toe-in, Adjust 840
Trouble Shooting 33
Wheel Alignment Specifications.......810

FUEL & EXHAUST SYSTEM

Carburetors 824
Fuel Pumps 96
Mufflers and Pipes...............824
Trouble Shooting 4

OVERDRIVE 100

Trouble Shooting 14

PAGE NO.

REAR AXLE

Axle Shaft, Replace................838
General Service 102
Non-Slip Differentials 109
Rear Axle Repairs 835
Rear Axle, Replace...............835
Rear Axle Specifications...........809
Trouble Shooting 31

SPECIFICATIONS

Brake Cylinder Sizes..............809
Capacity Data 810
Cooling System 810
Crankshaft & Bearings............808
Carburetors 825
Distributors 808
Engine Tightening 806
Generators & Regulators..........809
Pistons, Pins & Rings............808
Rear Axle 809
Starting Motors 809
Tune Up 807
Valves 807
Valve Timing 818
Wheel Alignment 810

STEERING GEARS (Mechanical)

Horn Ring, Replace...............843
Steering Gear, Adjust.............845
Steering Gear Repairs............845
Steering Gear, Replace...........843
Steering Wheel, Replace..........843
Trouble Shooting 33

STEERING GEARS (Power)

Steering Gear, Repairs............847
Trouble Shooting 34

TRANSMISSIONS (Manual Shift)

Gearshift, Adjust 829
Transmission Repairs.............828
Transmission, Replace............828
Trouble Shooting 14

TRANSMISSIONS (Automatic)

Linkage, Adjust 830
Transmission, Replace............830
Mercomatic Repairs 240
Multi-Drive Repairs 240
Trouble Shooting 24

TUNE UP.........................38

GENERAL SPECIFICATIONS

Year	Model Designation	Wheelbase, Inches	Valve Location	Bore and Stroke	Piston Displacement, Cubic Inches	Compression Ratio (Standard)	Maximum Brake H.P. @ R.P.M.	Maximum Torque Lbs. Ft. @ R.P.M.	Normal Oil Pressure Pounds
1953	V8-255 Engine...............	118	In Block	3.1875 x 4.000	255	7.2	125 @ 3800	218 @ 1700	57
1954	V8-256 Engine...............	118	In Head	3.6250 x 3.100	256	7.5	161 @ 4400	238 @ 2000	40
1955	Custom & Monterey.... V8-292	119	In Head	3.7500 x 3.300	292	7.6	188 @ 4400	272 @ 2500	40
	Montclair.............. V8-292	119	In Head	3.7500 x 3.300	292	8.5	198 @ 4400	282 @ 2500	40
1956	Std. Trans............. V8-312	119	In Head	3.8000 x 3.440	312	8.0	210 @ 4600	312 @ 2600	50
	Automatic Trans....... V8-312	119	In Head	3.8000 x 3.440	312	8.4	215 @ 4600	317 @ 2600	50
	Power Pack.......... V8-312	119	In Head	3.8000 x 3.440	312	9.0	225 @ 4600	324 @ 2600	50
1957	Pass. Cars........... V8-312	119	In Head	3.8000 x 3.440	312	9.7	255 @ 4600	340 @ 2600	50
	Sta. Wagons........ V8-312	122	In Head	3.8000 x 3.440	312	9.7	255 @ 4600	340 @ 2600	50
	Optional.............. V8-368	...	In Head	4.0000 x 3.660	368	10.0	290 @ 4600	405 @ 2600	45
1958	Medalist............. V8-312	122	In Head	3.8000 x 3.440	312	9.7	235 @ 4600	325 @ 2600	35-50
	Monterey............ V8-383	122	In Head	4.3000 x 3.660	383	10.5	312 @ 4600	405 @ 2900	45
	Montclair............ V8-383	122	In Head	4.3000 x 3.660	383	10.5	330 @ 4800	425 @ 3000	35-50
	Park Lane........... V8-430	125	In Head	4.3000 x 3.700	430	10.5	360 @ 4600	480 @ 3000	35-50
	Commutor........... V8-383	122	In Head	4.3000 x 3.660	383	10.5	312 @ 4600	405 @ 2900	35-50
	Colony Park......... V8-383	122	In Head	4.3000 x 3.660	383	10.5	330 @ 4800	425 @ 3000	35-50
	Voyager............. V8-383	122	In Head	4.3000 x 3.660	383	10.5	330 @ 4800	425 @ 3000	35-50
1959	Monterey............ V8-312	126	In Head	3.8000 x 3.440	312	9.6	210 @ 4400	325 @ 2200	35-50
	Montclair............ V8-383	126	In Head	4.3000 x 3.300	383	10.0	322 @ 4600	420 @ 2800	35-50
	Park Lane........... V8-430	128	In Head	4.3000 x 3.700	430	10.0	345 @ 4400	480 @ 2800	35-50
1960	Monterey............ V8-312	126	In Head	3.8000 x 3.440	312	8.9	205 @ 4000	328 @ 2100	35-50
	Montclair............ V8-430	126	In Head	4.3000 x 3.700	430	10.0	310 @ 4100	460 @ 2200	35-50
	Park Lane........... V8-430	126	In Head	4.3000 x 3.700	430	10.0	310 @ 4100	460 @ 2200	35-50
	Optional Monterey..... V8-383	126	In Head	4.3000 x 3.300	383	8.5	280 @ 4200	405 @ 2200	35-50
1961	6-223 Engine①	120	In Head	3.6250 x 3.600	223	8.4	135 @ 4000	196 @ 2000	35-55
	V8-292 Engine②	120	In Head	3.7500 x 3.300	292	8.8	175 @ 4200	279 @ 2200	35-55
	V8-352 Engine②	120	In Head	4.000 x 3.500	352	8.9	220 @ 4400	336 @ 2400	35-55
	V8-390 Engine③	120	In Head	4.050 x 3.784	390	9.6	300 @ 4600	427 @ 2800	35-55

①—Available on Meteor "600" and "800".   ②—Available on all Meteor and Monterey.   ③—Available on Meteor "800" and Monterey.

ENGINE TIGHTENING SPECIFICATIONS★

★Torque specifications are for clean and lightly lubricated threads only. Dry or dirty threads produce increased friction which prevents accurate measurement of tightness.

Year	Engine	Spark Plugs Ft. Lbs.	Cylinder Head Bolts Ft. Lbs.	Intake Manifold Ft. Lbs.	Exhaust Manifold Ft. Lbs.	Rocker Arm Shaft Bracket Ft. Lbs.	Rocker Arm Cover Ft. Lbs.	Connecting Rod Cap Bolts Ft. Lbs.	Main Bearing Cap Bolts Ft. Lbs.	Flywheel to Crankshaft Ft. Lbs.	Vibration Damper or Pulley Ft. Lbs.
1953	All	24-30	65-70	23-28	23-28	None	None	45-50	100	75-85	130-145
1954	All	25-30	55-75	23-28	23-28	12-15	2-2½	45-50	80-90	75-85	85-90
1955	All	15-20	55-75	23-28	23-28	12-15	2-2½	45-50	80-90	75-85	85-90
1956	All	15-20	75	23-28	23-28	12-15	2-2½	45-50	95-105	75-85	85-95
1957	V8-312	15-20	55-75	23-28	23-28	12-15	2-2½	45-50	95-105	75-85	130-145
	V8-368	15-20	①	23-28	23-28	22-23	2-2½	45-50	120-130	75-85	130-145
1958-60	V8-383	15-20	85-105	23-28	23-28	45-50	2-2½	45-50	95-105	75-85	75-90
	V8-430	15-20	85-105	23-28	23-28	45-50	2-2½	45-50	95-105	75-85	75-90
	V8-312	15-20	55-75	23-28	23-28	12-15	2-2½	45-50	95-105	75-85	130-145
1961	6-223	15-20	115	23-28	23-28	45-55	4-7	40-45	95-105	75-85	70-90
	V8-292	15-20	65-75	23-28	23-28	12-15	2-2½	40-45	80-90	75-85	70-90
	V8-352	15-20	80-90	32-35	23-28	40-45	4-7	40-45	95-105	75-85	70-90
	V8-390	15-20	80-90	32-35	23-28	40-45	4-7	40-45	95-105	75-85	70-90

①—"EAD" head 70-90 ft. lbs., "EAM" head 80-110 ft. lbs. (EAD, EAM cast on head).

TUNE UP SPECIFICATIONS

★Disconnect vacuum line when setting timing with timing light.

Year	Model	Ground Polarity and Voltage	Spark Plug		Distributor		Firing Order ②	Ignition Timing ★		Idle Speed RPM In Drive	Compression Pressure @ Cranking Speed Minimum
			Type ①	Gap Inch	Point Gap Inch	Cam Angle Degrees		Mark	Location		
1953	All	P-6	H-10	.030	.015	26–28	15486372	Ball	Pulley	450	105
1954	All	P-6	H-10	.031	.015	26–28	15486372	3°BTDC	Pulley	440	120
1955	All	P-6	870	.034	.015	26–28	15486372	③	Damper	440	130
1956	All	N-12	870	.034	.015	26–28	15486372	③	Damper	440	155
1957	V8-312	N-12	860	.034	.015	26–28	15486372	6°BTDC	Damper	440	160
	V8-368	N-12	860	.034	.015	26–28	15486372	8°BTDC	Damper	440	150
1958	V8-383, 430	N-12	F-11Y	.034	.015	26–28	15426378	9°BTDC	Damper	450	190
	V8-312	N-12	F-14Y	.034	.015	26–28	15486372	③	Damper	450	160
1959	V8-312	N-12	F-14Y	.034	.015	26–28	15486372	③	Damper	450	150
	V8-383, 430	N-12	F-11Y	.034	.015	26–28	15426378	③	Damper	450	190
1960	V8-312	N-12	F-14Y	.034	.015	26–28	15486372	③	Damper	450	140
	V8-383	N-12	F-11Y	.034	.015	26–28	15426378	③	Damper	450	140
	V8-430	N-12	F-11Y	.034	.015	26–28	15426378	6°BTDC	Damper	450	160
1961	6-223	N-12	870	.034	.025	35–38	153624	④	Damper	485	150
	V8-292	N-12	F-14Y	.034	.015	26–28	15486372	⑤	Damper	465	160
	V8-352	N-12	F-11Y	.034	.015	26–28	15426378	③	Damper	465	180
	V8-390	N-12	F-11Y	.034	.015	26–28	15426378	③	Damper	465	180

①—Champion.
②—Engine numbering (front to rear): Right bank 1-2-3-4, left bank 5-6-7-8.
③—Manual shift transmission 3°BTDC, automatic trans. 6°BTDC.
④—Standard trans. 4°BTDC; automatic trans. 10°BTDC.
⑤—Standard trans. 3°BTDC; automatic trans. 10°BTDC.

VALVE SPECIFICATIONS

Year	Model	Valve Lash		Valve Angles		Valve Spring Installed Height	Valve Spring Pressure Lbs. @ In.	Valve Lift		Stem Clearance		Stem Diameter	
		Int.	Exh.	Seat	Face			Int.	Exh.	Intake	Exhaust	Int.	Exh.
1953	All	.014C	.018C	45	45	1⁵⁷⁄₆₄	87 @ 1⁹⁄₁₆	.319	.315	.0015–.0035	.002–.004	.3415	.3410
1954	All	.019H	.019H	45	45	1⁵³⁄₆₄	130 @ 1½	.333	.326	.001–.002	.002–.003	.3420	.3410
1955	All	.019H	.019H	45	45	1⁵³⁄₆₄	130 @ 1½	.377	.375	.001–.002	.002–.003	.3420	.3410
1956	All	.019H	.019H	45	45	1²⁵⁄₃₂	170 @ 1²⁵⁄₆₄	.386	.384	.001–.002	.002–.003	.3420	.3410
1957	V8-312	.019H	.019H	45	45	1²⁵⁄₃₂	170 @ 1²⁵⁄₆₄	.401	.421	.001–.0025	.0025–.0035	.3420	.3407
	V8-368	Zero	Zero	45	45	1⁵¹⁄₆₄	190 @ 1⅜	.417	.417	.001–.0025	.0025–.0035	.3420	.3407
1958	V8-312	.019H	.019H	45	45	1²⁵⁄₃₂	170 @ 1²⁵⁄₆₄	.401	.421	.001–.0025	.0025–.0035	.3420	.3407
	V8-383	Zero	Zero	①	①	1⁵¹⁄₆₄	250 @ 1⅜	.403	.403	.001–.0025	.003–.004	.3715	.3697
	V8-430	Zero	Zero	①	①	1⁵¹⁄₆₄	250 @ 1⅜	.441	.441	.001–.0025	.003–.004	.3715	.3697
1959	V8-312	.019H	.019H	45	45	1²⁵⁄₃₂	170 @ 1²⁵⁄₆₄	.406	.404	.001–.0025	.0025–.0035	.3420	.3402
	V8-383	Zero	Zero	45	45	1⁵³⁄₆₄	250 @ 1⁷⁄₁₆	.408	.408	.001–.0025	.003–.004	.3715	.3697
	V8-430	Zero	Zero	45	45	1⁵³⁄₆₄	250 @ 1⁷⁄₁₆	.408	.408	.001–.0025	.003–.004	.3715	.3697
1960	V8-312	.019H	.019H	45	45	1²⁵⁄₃₂	170 @ 1²⁵⁄₆₄	.358	.356	.001–.0025	.003–.004	.3420	.3402
	V8-382	Zero	Zero	45	45	1⁵³⁄₆₄	250 @ 1⁷⁄₁₆	.408	.408	.001–.0025	.0025–.004	.3715	.3697
	V8-430	Zero	Zero	45	45	1⁵³⁄₆₄	250 @ 1⁷⁄₁₆	.408	.408	.001–.0025	.0025–.004	.3715	.3697
1961	6-223	.019C	.019C	45	45	1¾	170 @ 1²⁵⁄₆₄	.370	.370	.001–.0024	.0028–.0042	.342	.340
	V8-292	.019C	.019C	45	45	1¾	170 @ 1²⁵⁄₆₄	.377	.375	.001–.0024	.0028–.0042	.342	.340
	V8-352	Zero	Zero	45	45	1¹³⁄₁₆	190 @ 1²⁷⁄₆₄	.408	.408	.001–.0024	.0028–.0042	.371	.370
	V8-390	Zero	Zero	45	45	1¹³⁄₁₆	200 @ 1²⁷⁄₆₄	.408	.408	.001–.0024	.0028–.0042	.371	.370

①—Intake 30°, exhaust 45°.

PISTONS, PINS, RINGS, CRANKSHAFT & BEARINGS

Year	Model	Fitting Pistons		Ring End Gap ①		Wrist-pin Diameter	Rod Bearings		Main Bearings			
		Shim To Use	Pounds Pull On Scale	Comp.	Oil		Shaft Diameter	Bearing Clearance	Shaft Diameter	Bearing Clearance	Thrust on Bear. No.	Shaft End Play
1953	All	.002	6–12	.010	.010	.7502	2.138–2.139	.0005–.003	2.498–2.499	.0002–.002	3	.002–.006
1954	All	.002	5–10	.010	.010	.9121	2.188–2.189	.0005–.0025	2.498–2.499	.0005–.0025	3	.002–.006
1955	All	.002	5–10	.010	.010	.9121	2.188–2.189	.001–.003	2.498–2.499	.0005–.0025	3	.002–.006
1956	All	.002	5–10	.012	.015	.9121	2.188–2.189	.001–.003	2.623–2.624	.001–.003	3	.002–.006
1957	312 Engine	.002	5–10	.012	.015	.9121	2.188–2.189	.001–.003	2.623–2.624	.001–.003	3	.002–.006
	368 Engine	.002	6–12	.013	.015	.9121	2.248–2.249	.001–.003	2.623–2.624	.001–.003	3	.002–.006
1958	V8-383, 430	②	②	.015	.015	.9750	2.5992–2.600	.0006–.0026	2.8994–2.9002	.0009–.0029	3	.004–.008
	V8-312	②	②	.012	.015	.9121	2.188–2.189	.0008–.0027	2.6235–2.6243	.0009–.0029	3	.004–.008
1959	V8-312	②	②	.012	.015	.9121	2.188–2.189	.0008–.0027	2.6235–2.6243	.0009–.0029	3	.004–.008
	V8-383	②	②	.015	.015	.9750	2.5992–2.600	.0006–.0026	2.8994–2.9002	.0009–.0029	3	.004–.008
	V8-430	②	②	.015	.015	.9750	2.5992–2.600	.0006–.0026	2.8994–2.9002	.0009–.0029	3	.004–.008
1960	V8-312	②	②	.012	.015	.9121	2.1880–2.1888	.0005–.0024	2.6235–2.6243	.0006–.0032	3	.004–.008
	V8-383	②	②	.013	.015	.9750	2.5992–2.6000	.0006–.0026	2.8994–2.9002	.0009–.0029	3	.004–.008
	V8-430	②	②	.015	.015	.9750	2.5992–2.6000	.0006–.0026	2.8994–2.9002	.0009–.0029	3	.004–.008
1961	6-223	②	②	.010	.015	.912	2.2980–2.2988	.0006–.0025	2.4980–2.4988	.0006–.0028	3	.004–.008
	V8-292	②	②	.010	.015	.912	2.1880–2.1888	.0005–.0024	2.4980–2.4988	.0006–.0032	3	.004–.008
	V8-352	②	②	.015	.015	.975	2.4380–2.4388	.0006–.0026	2.7484–2.7492	.0006–.0031	3	.004–.008
	V8-390	②	②	.015	.015	.975	2.4380–2.4388	.0006–.0026	2.7484–2.7492	.0006–.0031	3	.004–.008

①—Fit rings in tapered bores for clearance listed in tightest portion of ring travel.
②—See Piston Clearance Chart, Fig. 19.

DISTRIBUTOR SPECIFICATIONS

Year and Model	Part No.①	Rotation ②	Cam Angle, Degrees	Breaker Point Opening, Inch	Condenser Capacity, Mfds.③	Breaker Arm Spring Tension, Ounces	Centrifugal Advance Data Degrees @ R.P.M. of Dist.		Vacuum Advance Data		
							Advance Starts	Full Advance	Inches of Vacuum to Start Plunger Movement	Inches of Vacuum for Full Plunger Travel	Maximum Vacuum Advance, Dist. Degrees
1953	7RA-12127C	C	26–28	.015	.21–.25	17–20	None	None	.57④	3.70⑤	7½–8½
1954	FAE-12127C	CC	26–28	.015	.21–.25	17–20	None	None	.24⑥	1.52⑤	15¼–16½
1955	FEC-12127A	CC	26–28	.015	.21–.25	17–20	None	None	.19⑦	1.95⑤	14¼–15½
1956	B6A-12127D	CC	26–28	.015	.21–.25	17–20	None	None	.29⑧	2.19⑤	13–14¼
1957	312 Engine	CC	26–28	.015	.21–.25	17–20	0 @ 400	12½ @ 2000	5	20	11–13
	368 Engine	CC	26–28	.015	.21–.25	17–20	0 @ 300	13½ @ 2000	5	20	7–9
1958	V8-383, 430	CC	26–28	.015	.21–.25	17–20	1 @ 400	13 @ 2000	6	20	11½
	V8-312	CC	26–28	.015	.21–.25	17–20	0 @ 400	13 @ 2000	9½	18	11
1959	V8-312	CC	26–28	.015	.21–.25	17–20	0 @ 400	13 @ 2000	9½	18	11
	V8-383	CC	26–28	.015	.21–.25	17–20	0 @ 350	14 @ 2000	6½	20	11
	V8-430	CC	26–28	.015	.21–.25	17–20	0 @ 350	14 @ 2000	6½	20	11
1960	V8-312	CC	26–28	.015	.21–.25	17–20	1¾ @ 800	11 @ 2000	7	20	12½
	V8-383	CC	26–28	.015	.21–.25	17–20	1¼ @ 525	14 @ 2000	6	16	12½
	V8-430	CC	26–28	.015	.21–.25	17–20	¾ @ 500	15 @ 2000	6½	15	12½
1961	6-223	C	35–38	.025	.21–.25	17–20	None	None			
	V8-292	CC	26–28	.015	.21–.25	17–20					
	V8-352	CC	26–28	.015	.21–.25	17–20					
	V8-390	CC	26–28	.015	.21–.25	17–20					

①—Stamped on plate riveted to housing.
②—As viewed from top. C—Clockwise. CC—Counterclockwise.
③—Microfarads—as indicated on a condenser tester.
④—At 600 RPM. ⑤—At 2000 RPM. ⑥—At 500 RPM. ⑦—At 300 RPM. ⑧—At 400 RPM.

GENERATOR AND REGULATOR SPECIFICATIONS

★ To polarize generator, disconnect field lead from regulator and momentarily flash this wire to regulator battery terminal.

Year	Generator Number	Rotation and Ground Polarity ②	Rated Cap. Amps.	Gen. Field Ground Location ★	Brush Spring Tension, Ounces	Field Current Amperes	Regulator Number	Cutout Relay Voltage to Close Points	Cutout Relay Armature Air, Gap, Inch	Voltage Regulator Setting Volts	Current Regulator Setting Amperes	Current and Voltage Armature Air Gap, Inch
1953	FAA-10002A	C-P	35	Internal	26-34	1.5-2.5③	FAC-10505A	6.3	⑤	7.6	35	⑤
1954-55	B5C-10002A	C-P	40	Internal	24-28	2.5-2.8③	B5A-10505C	6.3	⑤	7.6	40	⑤
1955	FBB-10002A	C-P	50	Internal	26-34	2.5-2.8③	FAJ-10505A	6.3	⑤	7.6	50	⑤
1956	B6A-10002A	C-N	30	Internal	26-34	1.4-1.6①	B6A-10505A	12.4	⑤	15.0	30	⑤
1957	B6A-10002H	C-N	30	Internal	26-34	1.5-1.6①	B6A-10505A	12.4	⑤	15.0	30	⑤
1958	Std. Trans.	C-N	30	Internal	26-34	1.5-1.6①	30 Ampere	12.4	⑤	15.0	30	⑤
	Auto. Trans.	C-N	35	Internal	26-34	1.5-1.6①	35 Ampere	12.8	⑤	15.0	35	⑤
	Air Cond.	C-N	40	Internal	26-34	1.5-1.6④	40 Ampere	12.4	⑤	15.0	40	⑤
1959	Std. Trans.	C-N	30	Internal	32-40	1.45-1.50①	30 Ampere	12.4	⑤	15.0	30	⑤
	Auto. Trans.	C-N	35	Internal	32-40	1.25-1.30①	35 Ampere	12.8	⑤	15.0	35	⑤
	Air Cond.	C-N	40	Internal	32-40	1.20-1.25④	40 Ampere	12.4	⑤	15.0	40	⑤
1960	Std. Trans.	C-N	30	Internal	32-40	1.0-1.1④	30 Ampere	12.4	⑤	15.0	30	⑤
	Auto. Trans.	C-N	35	Internal	32-40	1.0-1.1④	35 Ampere	12.8	⑤	15.0	35	⑤
	Air Cond.	C-N	40	Internal	32-40	1.0-1.1④	40 Ampere	12.4	⑤	15.0	40	⑤
1961	Std. Equip.	C-N	30	Internal	32-40	1.0-1.5④	30 Ampere	12.4	⑤	15.0	30	⑤
	Air Cond.	C-N	35	Internal	32-40	1.0-1.5④	35 Ampere	12.8	⑤	15.0	35	⑤
	Opt. Equip.	C-N	40	Internal	28	2.0-2.5④	40 Ampere	12.9	⑤	15.0	40	⑤

①—At 5 volts.　②—C-Clockwise.　P-Positive.　③—At 6 volts.　④—At 10 volts.　⑤—No adjustment.

STARTING MOTOR SPECIFICATIONS

Year	Model	Part No.	Rotation ①	Brush Spring Tension, Ounces	No Load Test Amperes	No Load Test Volts	No Load Test R.P.M.	Torque Test Amperes	Torque Test Volts	Torque, Lbs. Ft.
1953	Mercomatic	FAJ-11002A	C	48-56	70	6	3200	700	3.5	16
1953	Std. Trans.	FAD-11002A	C	48-56	70	6	3200	700	3.5	16
1954-55	All	FAC-11002G	C	48-56	70	6	5000-6000	700	3.5	14
1956-57	All	B6A-11002A	C	48-56	120	12	4800	550	5.0	15½
1958-59	All	B9S-11002A	C	48-56	80	12	4500	550	5.0	15½
1960	All	FAY-11002A	C	48-56	85	12	4500	550	5.0	15½
1961	All		C	48-56	110	12	Free Run	580	5.0	14.8

①—As viewed from the drive end.　C—Clockwise.

REAR AXLE AND BRAKE CYLINDER SPECIFICATIONS

Year	Model	Ring Gear & Pinion Backlash, Inch	Drive Pinion Adjustment	Drive Pinion Bearing Preload, Inch Lbs.	Drive Pinion Bearing Adjustment	Axle Shaft End Play, Inch	Wheel Cylinder Front	Wheel Cylinder Rear	Master Cylinder
1953	All	.005-.008	Shims	18-20①	Shims	②	1⅛	15⁄16	1
1954-55	All	.003-.008	Shims	18-20①	Shims	②	1⅛	⅞	1
1956	All	.003-.008	Shims	18-20①	Shims	②	1⅛	⅞	1
1957	All	.004-.009	Shims	17-27①	Shims	②	1⅛	⅞	1
1958	All	.004-.009	Shims	17-27①	Shims	②	1⅛	31⁄32	1
1959-61	All	.004-.009	Shims	17-27①	Shims	②	1⅛	31⁄32	1.00

①—For used bearings, 8-12 inch lbs.　②—No adjustment.

COOLING SYSTEM & CAPACITY DATA

Year and Model	Cooling System Data					Fuel Tank Gals.	Engine Oil			Transmissions			Rear Axle Pints
	Quarts No Heater	Quarts With Heater	Rad. Cap Relief Pressure	Thermostat Opening Temp. ①	Thermostat Opening Temp. ②		Refill Qts. ③	Summer Grade	Winter Grade	Std. Pints	With Over-drive Pints	Auto-matic Qts.	
1953	21½	22½	6¼-7¾	180	160	19	4	20	10W	3	4½	9	3½
1954	19	20	12-15	180	160	19	5	20	10W	3	4½	9¾	3½
1955-56 Cars	19	20	12-15	180	160	18	5	20	10W	3½	5	10¼	3½
1955-56 Sta. Wag.	19	20	12-15	180	160	19	5	20	10W	3½	5	10¼	3½
1957	19	20	12-15	180	160	20	5	20	10W	3½	5	9⅔	4½
1958 Cars	20½	21½	12-15	180④	160④	20	5	20	10W	3½	5	9⅔	4½
1958 Sta. Wag.	20½	21½	12-15	180④	160④	19½	5	20	10W	3½	5	9⅔	4½
1959 V8-312	20	21	12-15	180	160	20	5	20	10W	3	None	10	4½
1959 V8-383	21	22	12-15	180④	160④	20	5	20	10W	3	None	11	4½
1959 V8-430	21	22	12-15	180④	160④	20	5	20	10W	None	None	12	4½
1960 V8-312	20	21	12-15	180	160	20	5	20	10W	3	None	10	4½
1960 V8-383	21	22	12-15	180④	160④	20	5	20	10W	None	None	10	4½
1960 V8-430	21	22	12-15	180④	160④	20	5	20	10W	None	None	10½	4½
1961 Six	15	16	12-15	180	160		4	20	10W	3	4		4½
1961 V8-292	19	20	12-15	180	160		5	20	10W	3	4		4½
1961 V8-352	19	20	12-15	180	160		5	20	10W				4½
1961 V8-390	19	20	12-15	180	160		5	20	10W				4½

①—For permanent type anti-freeze.
②—For alcohol type anti-freeze.
③—Add 1 qt. with filter change.
④—Thermostats in block (383, 430 Eng.) 137-142°.

WHEEL ALIGNMENT SPECIFICATIONS

Year	Model	Caster, Degrees③		Camber, Degrees④		Toe-in, Inch	Toe-out on Turns, Degrees①		Kingpin or Steering Axis Inclination②
		Limits	Desired	Limits	Desired		Outer Wheel	Inner Wheel	
1953	All	− 1½ to 0	− ¾	0 to + ¾	+ ⅜	3/32 to 5/32	23½	20	5 @ ¾ Camber
1954-56	All	− 1½ to 0	− ¾	0 to + ¾	+ ⅜	3/32 to 5/32	25	20	7 @ ¾ Camber
1957-58	All	− 1½ to 0	− ¾	0 to + ¾	+ ⅜	3/16 to 5/16	17°6'⑤	20	7 @ ¾ Camber
1959-60	All	0 to − 1½	− ¾	0 to + ¾	+ ⅜	1/16 to 3/16	17°30'⑥	20	7° @ ¾ Camber
1961	All	− ½ to + ½	0	+ ¼ to + 1	+ ⅝	⅛ to ¼	20	24¼	

①—Incorrect toe-out, when other adjustments are correct, generally indicates bent steering arms.
②—Incorrect kingpin or knuckle support angle with correct camber indicates bent suspension arms or knuckle support.
③—Within ½° one side of car to the other. ④—Within ¼° one side of car to the other.
⑤—Power steering 17°20'. ⑥—Power steering 17°18'.

ENGINE & SERIAL NUMBER LOCATION
1953-54: Plate On Right Front Door Pillar.
1955-61: Plate On Left Front Door Pillar.

ENGINE IDENTIFICATION

Year	Engine	Ser. No. Prefix
1953	V8-255	53
1954	V8-256	54
1955	V8-292	55
1956	V8-312	56
1957	V8-312	57
	V8-368④	57
1958	V8-312	L8
	V8-383	M8
	V8-430①	K8
	V8-430②	J8

Year	Engine	Ser. No. Prefix
1959	V8-312	P9
	V8-383③	N9
	V8-383①	M9
	V8-430	L9
1960	V8-312	OP
	V8-383	ON
	V8-430	OM

Year	Engine	Ser. No. Prefix
1961	6-223	IV
	V8-292	IW
	V8-352	IX
	V8-390	IZ

①—Four barrel carburetor.
②—Three 2-barrel carburetors.
③—Two barrel carburetor.
④—Turnpike Cruiser.

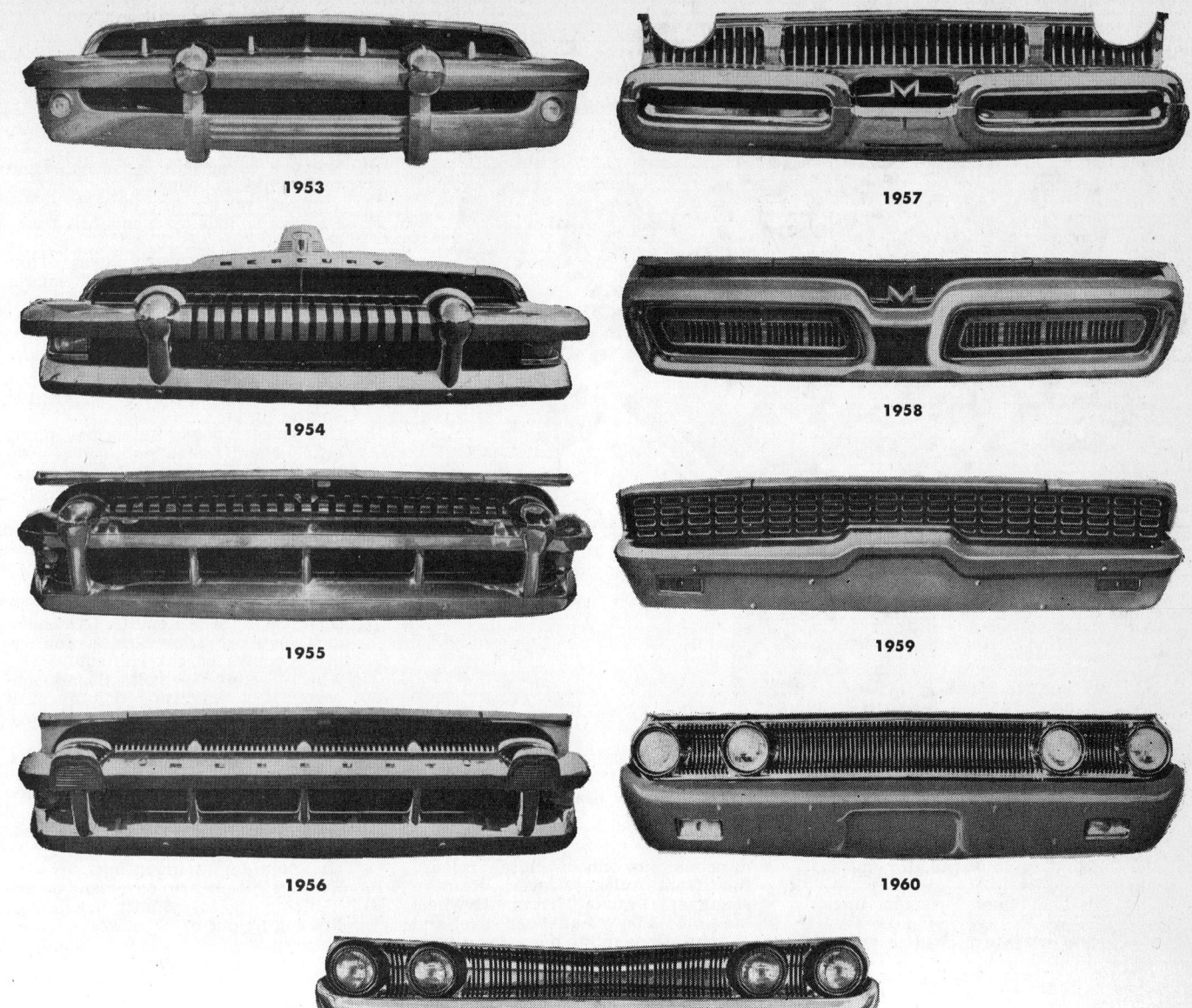

1953

1957

1954

1958

1955

1959

1956

1960

1961

Engine Section

ENGINE, REPLACE

1953

1. To remove engine with transmission attached, remove hood, battery, heater blower motor, air cleaner, generator, fan, radiator and oil filter.
2. Remove fuel lines, vacuum lines, accelerator linkage, hoses and wires attached to engine.
3. Detach shift linkage from transmission and clutch release rod from clutch lever.
4. Remove equalizer bracket from flywheel housing.
5. If equipped with overdrive, remove kickdown switch, solenoid, governor and control wire.
6. Remove drive shaft.
7. Remove engine mounting bolts.
8. Detach exhaust pipe from manifold.
9. Lift engine and transmission from chassis.

1954-1960

1. To remove engine separately from transmission, remove hood, air cleaner, battery, radiator, fan, heater blower and duct, power brake and power steering pump.
2. Remove oil filter and starter. When removing starter on 1954-55, turn wheels to extreme left turn position and pull starter down between tie rods and tubular engine support crossmember.

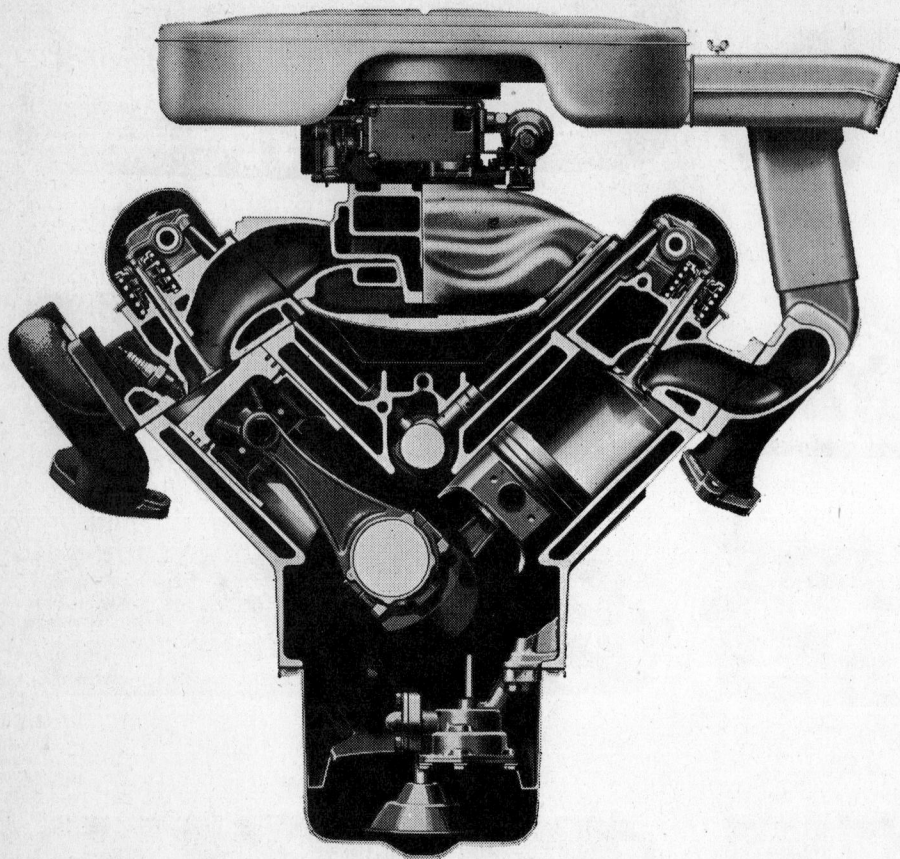

V8-352, 383, 390, 430 engines. Note wedge-shaped combustion chamber formed in block and that underside of cylinder head is flat

linkage from firewall, allowing linkage to stay on engine.
7. Remove converter access covers from bell housing.
8. Detach exhaust pipes from manifolds.
9. On 1954-55 unfasten flex plate from converter.
10. Remove capscrews securing engine to flywheel housing.
11. Support transmission with jack.
12. Remove front engine mounting capscrews.
13. Pull engine forward away from transmission and lift out of chassis.

1961 Six

1. Remove hood and radiator.
2. Remove fuel lines, vacuum lines, hoses, linkage and wires attached to engine units.
3. Disconnect power steering pump bracket and fasten pump in a position that will prevent oil from draining out.
4. Remove starter.
5. Remove automatic transmission fluid filler tube bracket and crankcase ventilation tube.
6. Disconnect exhaust pipe from exhaust manifold.
7. On cars with automatic transmission, support transmission and remove converter cover. Remove flywheel-to-converter bolts. Secure converter within housing to prevent it from being withdrawn as transmission is removed.
8. On standard transmission jobs, disconnect clutch and transmission linkage. Then slide transmission back far enough to clear flywheel housing and wedge it between floor pan and crossmember.
9. Unfasten engine mountings.
10. Remove rocker arm cover and attach a lifting rig to cylinder head. Then lift engine out of chassis.

1961 V8

1. Disconnect exhaust pipes from exhaust manifolds.

3. On 1956-60 remove radiator splash shield.
4. Remove fuel lines, vacuum lines, accelerator linkage as necessary, hoses and wires attached to engine units.
5. On standard and overdrive transmissions, disconnect clutch release rod from release lever. Remove equalizer bracket from flywheel housing. Allow equalizer bar and clutch release rod to hang down from frame.
6. On 1954-55, disconnect accelerator

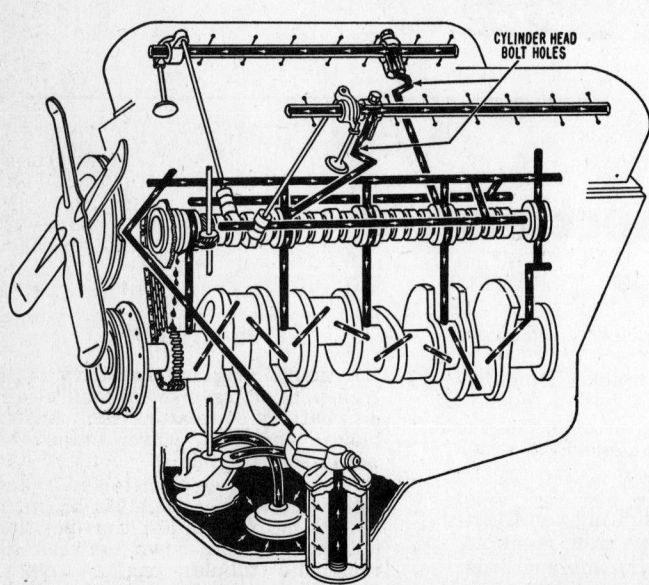

Engine lubrication. V8-352, 383, 390, 430 engines

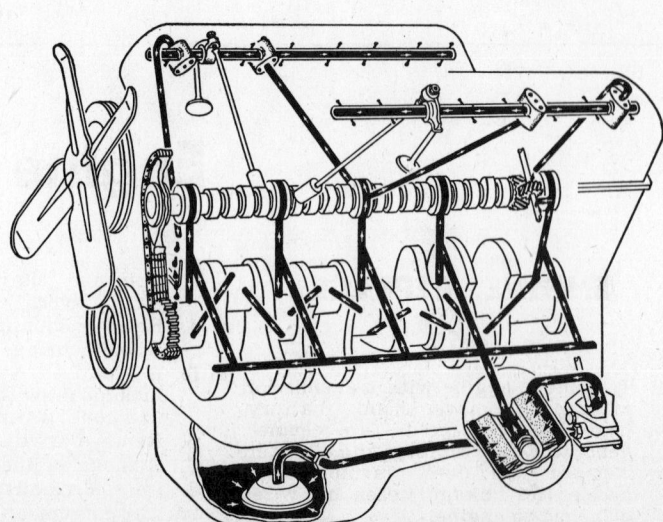

Engine lubrication. V8-292 and 312 engines

2. On standard transmission jobs, slide transmission rearward and support it with a block of wood wedged across frame crossmember.
3. On automatic transmission jobs, remove converter housing access cover. Remove four nuts securing converter to flywheel. Support transmission with a jack. Unfasten converter housing from cylinder block. Remove oil cooler bracket from cylinder block.
4. Remove starter, hood, battery carrier, radiator and power steering pump.
5. Remove fuel lines, vacuum lines, hoses, linkage and wires attached to engine.
6. Unfasten engine mountings. Then attach a lifting rig to engine and remove engine from chassis.

CYLINDER HEADS, REPLACE

1961 Six

1. Disconnect all linkage, wires, fuel and vacuum lines connected to cylinder head.
2. Remove air cleaner and radiator supply tank.
3. Remove rocker arm cover.
4. Remove capscrew and bracket from No. 6 rocker arm support and pull oil inlet line out of support and cylinder block.
5. Remove capscrew from No. 1 rocker arm support and remove oil outlet line and bracket.
6. Loosen all rocker arm adjusting screws to relieve valve spring load from rocker arms then remove rocker arm shaft assembly.
7. Remove valve push rods in sequence and identify them so they can be installed in their original positions.
8. Unfasten and pull manifold away from engine.
9. Unfasten and remove cylinder head.
10. Reverse removal procedure to install the head and tighten head bolts in the sequence shown in Fig 1 in three progressive steps. Make the final tightening to the torque given in the *Engine Tightening Specifications* chart.

1954-61 V8

1. Drain cooling system.
2. Remove rocker arms and push rods.
3. Remove intake manifold.
4. Remove ignition coil from the left cylinder if that particular head is being removed.
5. Unfasten exhaust pipe from manifold.

V8-292 and 312 engines

6. Unfasten and remove cylinder head and exhaust manifold as a unit. *The exhaust manifolds should not be separated from the cylinder heads unless the head is to be replaced or the valves are to be ground.*
7. Reverse removal procedure to install either head and tighten head bolts in the sequence shown in Fig. 2 in three progressive steps. Make the final tightening to the torque given in the *Engine Tightening Specifications* chart.

1953

Always tighten cylinder heads with a torque wrench to the values given in the *Engine Tightening* chart. Make the final tightening after the engine has been warmed up, Fig. 3.

Head gaskets are stamped with the word "Front" and should be so installed. Improper installation of head gaskets will block some of the water passages, causing improper water circulation with consequent overheating of the engine.

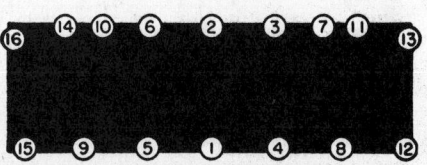

Fig. 1 Cylinder head tightening sequence. 1961 Six

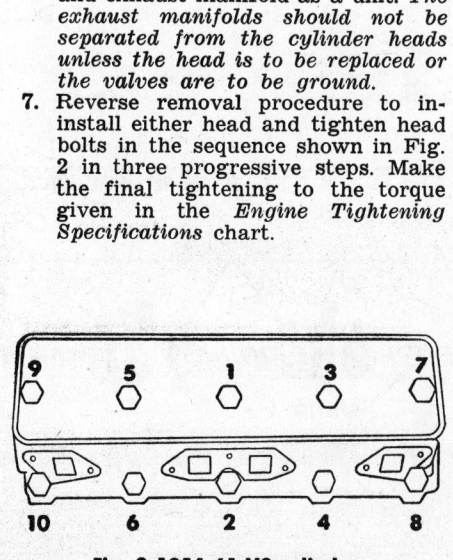

Fig. 2 1954-61 V8 cylinder head tightening sequence

Fig. 3 1953 cylinder head tightening sequence

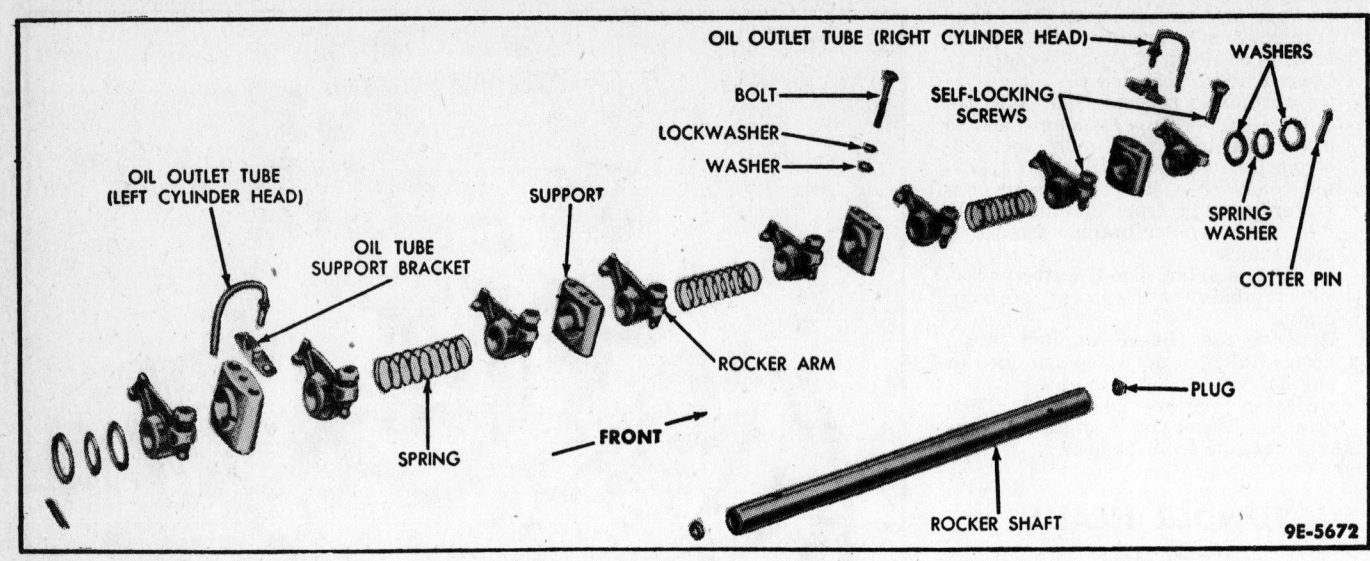

Fig. 4   Rocker arm shaft assembly.   V8-256, 292, 312

9E-5672

VALVE ARRANGEMENT

Front to Rear

1953-57 . . . . E-I-I-E-E-I-I-E
V8-292, 312 . . . . E-I-I-E-E-I-I-E
V8-383, 430:
   Right Bank . . . . I-E-I-E-I-E-I-E
   Left Bank . . . . E-I-E-I-E-I-E-I
   Six Cyl. . . . . . E-I-I-E-I-E-E-I-E-I-I-E
V8-352, 390 . . . . E-I-E-I-I-E-I-E

VALVES, ADJUST

1961 Six Cylinder

Make two chalk marks on the vibration damper. Space the marks approximately 120 degrees apart (⅓ of circumference) so that with the timing mark the damper is divided into three equal parts. Adjust the valves for No. 1 cylinder. Repeat this procedure for the remaining set of valves, turning the crankshaft ⅓ turn at a time in the direction of normal rotation, while adjusting the valves in the firing order sequence, which is 153624.

V8-256, 292, 312

Make three chalk marks on the vibration damper. Space the marks 90 degrees apart (¼ of circumference) so that with the timing mark the damper is divided into four equal parts. Rotate the crankshaft until No. 1 piston is near TDC at the end of the compression stroke and adjust the following valves:
  No. 1 intake and exhaust
  No. 2 exhaust
  No. 4 exhaust
  No. 5 exhaust
  No. 7 intake
Rotate the crankshaft 180 degrees (½ turn) which puts No. 4 piston on TDC. Then adjust the following valves:
  No. 4 intake
  No. 5 intake
  No. 6 exhaust
  No. 8 exhaust
Rotate the crankshaft 270 degrees (¾ turn), which puts No. 3 piston on TDC. Then adjust the following valves:
  No. 2 exhaust
  No. 3 intake and exhaust
  No. 6 intake

  No. 7 exhaust
  No. 8 intake

V8-352, 383, 390, 430

On these engines there is no provision for adjusting valve clearances. However, after a valve job, if the clearance between the rocker arm and valve stem does not have a clearance of .078″ to .218″ with hydraulic valve lifter collapsed .060″ shorter or .060″ longer push rods are available to reestablish the proper clearance. The shorter push rod is daubed with white paint and the longer one is daubed with yellow paint. If the measured clearance with hydraulic lifter collapsed is less than .078″, install a shorter push rod. If the clearance is more than .218″ install the longer push rod.

1953

Since there are no means of adjusting valves when these engines are assembled, this operation must be performed after the valves have been refaced, and before assembling the guides and springs.

To check the clearance, turn over the engine until the valve being checked is

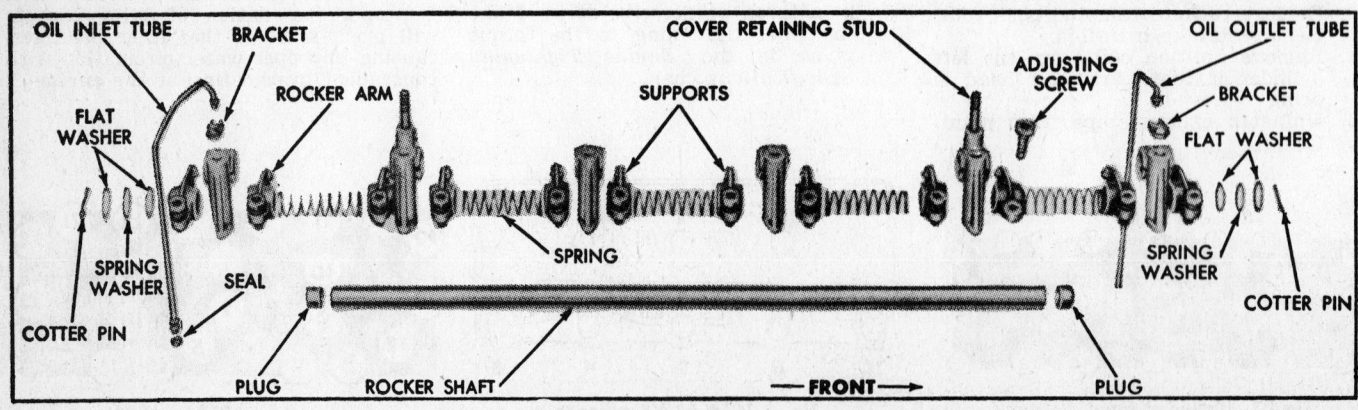

Fig. 5   Rocker arm shaft assembly.   1961 Six

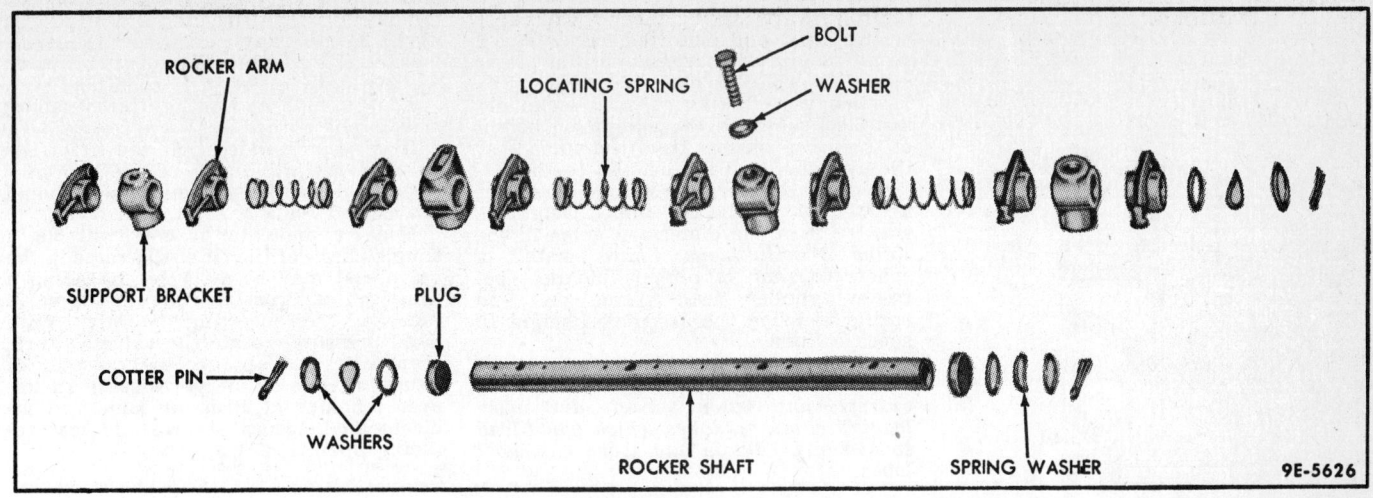

Fig. 6 Rocker arm shaft assembly. V8-352, 383, 390, 430

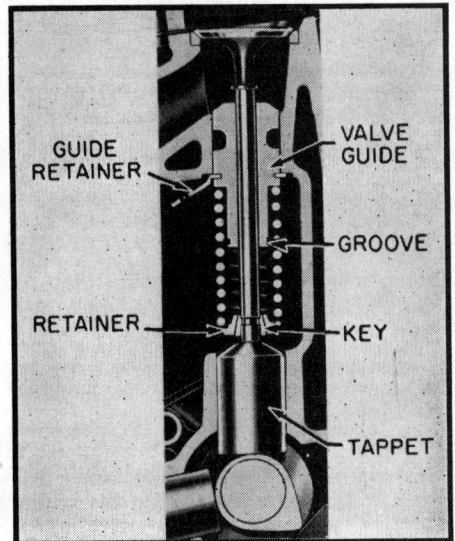

Fig. 7 Valve parts. 1953

fully closed. Slip a feeler gauge of the correct thickness between the valve stem and tappet. If the clearance is less than specifications call for, remove the valve and grind the end of the valve stem, being sure it is ground perfectly square.

ROCKER ARMS

Sludge and gum formation in the rocker arms and shafts, Figs. 4, 5, 6 will restrict the normal flow to the rocker arms and valves. Each time the assemblies are removed (see *Cylinder Heads*), they should be disassembled and thoroughly cleaned.

Remove the support bracket bolts, cotter pins, washers, springs, support brackets and shafts. Clean all gum and sludge formation from the inside and outside of the shafts and rocker arms. Inspect the shafts for wear. Check the fit of the rocker arms on the shafts and the valve end of the rocker arms for excessive wear. If the rocker arm radius is grooved on the valve end, do not attempt grinding; replace the part.

When the assemblies are installed, make sure the rocker arms are correctly positioned to actuate the valves. The oil overflow pipe hole in the shaft should be seen through the center hole of the front support on the right bank and the rear support on the left bank. If the hole cannot be seen, turn the shaft until the holes line up.

Check each push rod for a bent or damaged condition. If bent more than .020", when checked with an indicator, replace the push rod. Do not attempt to straighten a bent rod. If a dial gauge is not available, at least check the rod for straightness by rolling it on a perfectly flat surface plate.

VALVES, REMOVE

1954-61

With the cylinder head removed as outlined previously, use a suitable valve spring compressor to compress each spring. Remove the valve locks and release the pressure on the spring. Remove the spring compressor and lift off the valve retainer, spring and valve. Repeat for the remaining valves. Keep the valves and related parts together so they may be installed in their respective positions if found in satisfactory condition.

1953

The valve, guide, spring and retainer

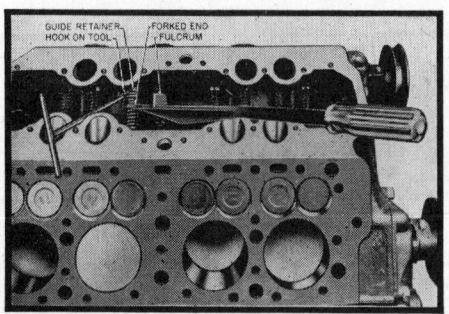

Fig. 8 Removing valve guide retainer. 1953

Fig. 9 Removing stuck valve with puller. 1953

are assembled and installed in the engine as one unit, Fig. 7.

To remove the assembly, insert a bar type valve lifter through the valve spring and to the flange on the lower end of the valve guide, Fig. 8. Using the top of the valve chamber as a fulcrum, pull down on the valve guide and withdraw the guide retainer. Then with the valve lifter tool, push the assembly up and remove it from above.

If the guides are stuck to the extent that they cannot be removed by this method, a puller is available to break them loose, Fig. 9.

When replacing valve and guide assemblies in the block, be sure to have the joint in the valve guide at *right angles* to the camshaft.

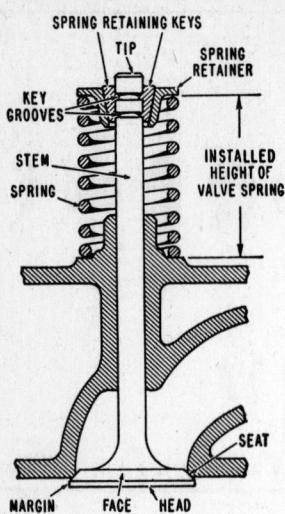

Fig. 10 Checking installed height of valve spring

VALVE GUIDES

1954-61

Valve guides in these engines are an integral part of the cylinder head and, therefore, cannot be removed. For service, guides can be reamed oversize to accomodate one of three service valves with oversize stems (.003", .015", .030").

Check the valve stem clearance of each valve (after cleaning) in its respective guide bore. If the clearance exceeds the service limit of .0045" on the intake or .0055" on the exhaust, ream the valve guides to accomodate the next oversize diameter valve.

1953

See *Valves, Remove* for data on these valve guides.

VALVE SPRING INSTALLED HEIGHT

When valves and seats are reground the position of the valve in the head is changed so as to lessen the valve spring tension. Without proper valve spring tension the valve does not seat long enough or it may not seat completely. Since the valve is cooled by transferring heat from the valve head to the coolant,

improper valve spring tension will cause worn, pitted and distorted valves which result in loss of compression and power as well as poor gasoline mileage.

When valves, springs, and locks are installed, measure the assembled height of the valve springs from the surface of the cylinder head spring pad to the underside of the spring retainer as shown in Fig. 10. If the assembled height is greater than the dimension given in the *Valve Specifications Chart*, install a spacer or shim of proper thickness between cylinder head spring pad and spring to bring the assembled height to specifications.

Do not install spacers unless necessary. Excessive use of spacers will result in overstressing valve springs and overloading camshaft lobes which could lead to spring breakage and worn camshaft lobes.

VALVE SPRING TESTING

After taking out the valves, remove the springs and wash them with gasoline or other suitable solvent. Examine the springs for damage or corrosion due to acid etching, which will develop into surface cracks and cause spring failure.

Check the valve spring tension on a spring testing fixture if one is available. If a fixture is not available, at least check the free length of each spring by standing it alongside a new spring. Any spring that does not conform to the pressure specifications given in the *Valve Specifications* table within 10 per cent should be replaced. Likewise any spring that stands shorter than the new spring used for comparison should be discarded.

VALVES, GRIND

Clean the valves with a wire wheel brush, making sure that all carbon is removed from the top and bottom of the heads as well as the gum which might have accumulated on the stems.

In refacing valves, take off only the minimum of metal required to clean up the valve faces. If the outer edge of the valve becomes too thin or sharp due to excessive grinding, the valve must be replaced. In other words, the valve head margin must be at least $\frac{3}{64}$", otherwise the valve must be replaced. This margin is the area above the contact surface of the valve face.

Inspect the valve seats in the block for

cracks, burns, pitting, ridges or improper angle. During any general engine overhaul it is advisable to reface the valve seats, regardless of their condition.

The valve seat width after refacing should not exceed $\frac{1}{32}$".

It is recommended that the fit of the valve in the valve seat be checked with a dial indicator for run-out, which should not exceed .0005".

If a dial indicator is not available, a simple check of the fit of the valve in the valve seat may be made by spreading a thin film of Prussian Blue on the valve face and then inserting the valve. With hand pressure, rotate the valve ¼ turn, remove it and observe the transfer of Prussian Blue to the valve seat. An uneven transfer of Prussian Blue will indicate an inaccurate valve and seat refacing operation.

VALVE LIFTERS

1957-61 Hydraulic

The internal parts of each hydraulic lifter assembly are a matched set. If these are mixed, improper valve operation may result. Therefore, disassemble, inspect and test each assembly separately to prevent mixing the parts.

Fig. 11 illustrates the type lifter used. See the *Trouble Shooting Chapter* under the heading *Engine Noises* for causes of hydraulic valve lifter noise.

The easiest method of locating a noisy valve lifter is by the use of a piece of garden hose about four feet long. Press one end of the hose near each valve in progression and listen through the other end. In this manner the sound is localized, making it easier to determine which lifter is at fault.

Another method is to place a finger on the valve spring retainer. If the lifter is not functioning properly, a distinct shock will be felt when the valve returns to its seat.

In most cases where noise exists in one or more lifters, all lifter units should be removed and cleaned. If dirt, varnish or carbon is found to exist in one unit, it more than likely exists in all units.

To disassemble, first immerse the lifter in solvent and remove all traces of varnish and carbon. Remove the lock ring from the lifter body and disassemble as shown in Fig. 11. Wash all parts in solvent and wipe dry with lint-free cloth.

To assemble, hold the plunger inverted and assemble the valve disc, small spring, valve disc retainer, and large spring on the plunger. Slip the body over the plunger, then install the push rod cup and lock ring in the body.

TIMING CASE COVER

1961 Six

To remove front cover, remove radiator, radiator supply tank, fan, drive belt, pulley, vibration damper and water pump. Unfasten front cover from cylinder block and oil pan and remove cover. *If oil pan gasket is broken or damaged during front cover removal, drop the oil pan and install a new gasket.*

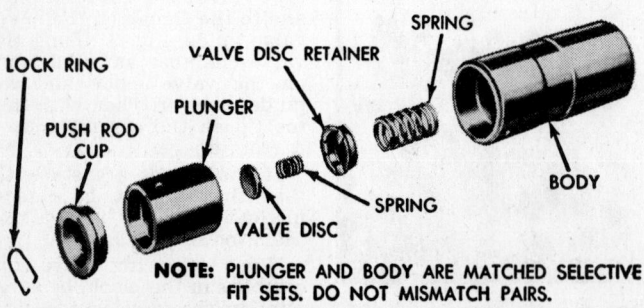

NOTE: PLUNGER AND BODY ARE MATCHED SELECTIVE FIT SETS. DO NOT MISMATCH PAIRS.

Fig. 11 Hydraulic valve lifter disassembled

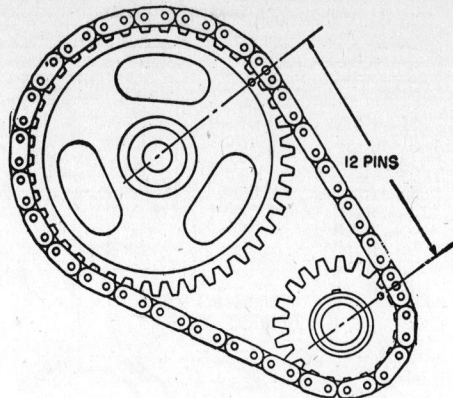

Fig. 12   Valve timing. 1961 Six

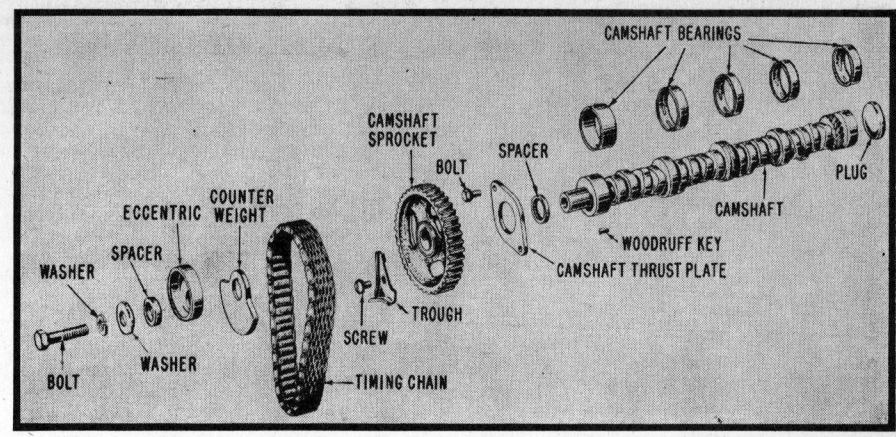

Camshaft and related parts. 1954-57 and 1958-61 V8-292, 312

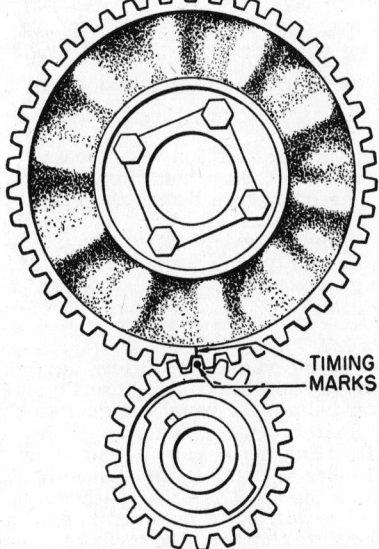

Fig. 13   Valve timing. 1953

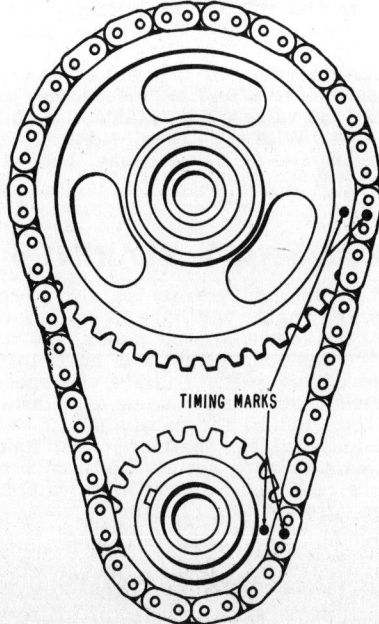

Fig. 14   Timing marks aligned for correct valve timing. V8-256, 292, 312

1954-61 V8-256, 292, 312, 352, 390

1. Remove oil pan.
2. Disconnect battery ground cable.
3. Remove radiator.
4. Remove power steering pump.
5. Remove drive belts.
6. Remove water pump and hoses as a unit.
7. Remove power steering pump pulley.
8. Remove vibration damper.
9. Remove fuel pump.
10. Remove front cover.

1958-60 V8-383, 430

1. Remove oil pan.
2. Drain cooling system and remove radiator.
3. On cars with automatic transmission, disconnect and plug oil cooler lines from radiator.
4. Disconnect battery ground cable.
5. Remove power steering pump (if used) and mounting bracket from engine.
6. Remove generator and fan belt.
7. Remove water pump.
8. Remove fuel pump. Remove cup-type plug from top of cylinder front cover, using a punch and mallet. Then remove fuel pump push rod.
9. Remove vibration damper with suitable puller.
10. Unfasten and remove timing cover.
11. Install a new cover seal and reinstall cover in reverse order of removal.

1953

The timing case cover carries an oil seal which should be renewed every time the cover is removed. Take out the old packing and clean out the groove thoroughly. Soak the new packing in oil for about 30 minutes to swell the fabric so that a good seal will be obtained immediately.

To remove the timing gear cover, drain the cooling system, disconnect the water hose, unfasten the radiator from its mountings and lift it out. Disconnect the generator lead wires, and take off the fan and generator belts.

TIMING GEARS

1953

When installing a camshaft gear, the cap screw holes are unevenly spaced so that the gear can be attached in one position only. Before installing the gear, however, turn over the engine so that the timing mark on the crankshaft gear is facing up. Then turn the camshaft so that when the camshaft gear is installed, the timing marks on both gears will be meshed, Fig. 13. In other words, the mark on the tooth of the crankshaft gear should be meshed between the two teeth on the camshaft gear at the mark.

TIMING CHAIN

V8-256, 292, 312

When replacing a chain on these engines, insert a woodruff key in the keyway of the crankshaft and camshaft. Place the timing chain over the camshaft and crankshaft sprockets, making sure the timing marks are lined up adjacent to marks on timing chain, Fig. 14.

Holding the sprockets and chain in place, install on the camshaft and crankshaft at the same time. Take up the slack on the driving side of the chain by rotating the crankshaft and measure the chain deflection—which should not exceed ½″ slack. Install the camshaft eccentric and counterweight as a unit. Align the keyway of the eccentric and counterweight with the woodruff key on the camshaft. Place the spacer in position and secure with a plain washer, lock washer and cap screw.

V8-352, 383, 390, 430

1. To remove the chain, first take off the timing chain cover as outlined previously.
2. Crank the engine until the timing mark on the camshaft sprocket is adjacent to the timing mark on the crankshaft sprocket, Fig. 15.
3. Remove cap screws, lock plate and fuel pump eccentric from front of camshaft.
4. Place a screwdriver behind the camshaft sprocket and carefully pry the

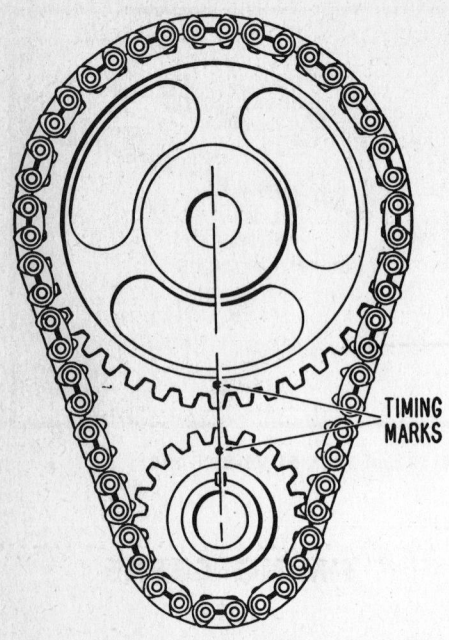

Fig. 15 Timing marks aligned for correct valve timing. V8-352, 383, 390, 430

sprocket and chain off the camshaft.
5. Reverse the foregoing procedure to install the chain, being sure to align the timing marks as shown.

VALVE TIMING DATA

Year	Model	Intake Opens①	Intake Closes②	Exhaust Opens③	Exhaust Closes④
1953	All	5	51	47	9
1954	All	8	44	47	5
1955	All	12	54	58	8
1956	All	12	54	58	8
1957	V8-312	18	58	66	10
	V8-368	18	72	59	31
1958	V8-383	34	68	75	27
	V8-430	27	69	69	27
1959	V8-312	18	58	66	10
	V8-383	22	68	63	27
	V8-430	22	68	63	27
1960	V8-312	12	54	58	8
	V8-383	22	68	63	27
	V8-430	22	68	63	27
1961	Six	23	59	71	10
	V8-292	12	54	58	8
	V8-352	22	68	68	22
	V8-390	26	64	67	23

①—Degrees before top dead center.
②—Degrees after bottom dead center.
③—Degrees before bottom dead center.
④—Degrees after top dead center.

CAMSHAFT, REPLACE

1961 Six

1. To remove camshaft, drain cooling system and oil pan.
2. Remove radiator, supply tank, grille and engine front cover.
3. Remove oil level dipstick, crankcase ventilation tube, stabilizer bar links, flywheel housing inspection cover and oil pan.
4. Remove rocker arm shaft assembly and push rods.
5. Remove distributor cap, valve push rod cover and fuel pump.
6. Remove timing chain and sprockets and distributor.

7. Raise valve lifters and secure them with spring-type clothes pins or window regulator clips.
8. Position crankshaft so that camshaft lobes will clear crankshaft counterweights.
9. Carefully remove camshaft from engine.

1954-61 V8-256, 292, 312

1. Remove hood.
2. On 1957 models, remove parking lamps without disconnecting wires, grille upper mouldings and center grille moulding.
3. Remove rocker arm shaft assemblies, intake manifold and push rod cover.
4. Remove power steering pump.
5. Remove radiator and water pump.
6. Remove vibration damper. If equipped with power steering, its pulley must be removed from damper before removing damper.
7. Remove fuel pump and oil pan.
8. Remove timing chain and sprockets.
9. Raise valve lifters and hold them up with spring-type clothes pins.
10. Slide camshaft out of engine.

1961 V8-352, 390

1. Remove oil level dipstick.
2. Drain cooling system and oil pan.
3. Remove oil pan.
4. Remove center grille lower retaining bolts.
5. Remove radiator.
6. Remove radiator center grille.
7. Remove timing chain and sprockets.
8. Remove intake manifold and valve push rod chamber baffle.
9. Remove valve lifters, being sure to identify them so they can be installed in the original bores.
10. Slide camshaft out of engine.

1958-60 V8-383, 430

1. Remove the timing chain cover and chain as outlined previously.
2. Remove intake manifold.
3. Remove valve lifter cover.
4. Remove the hydraulic valve lifters and place them in a rack so they may be reinstalled in their respec-

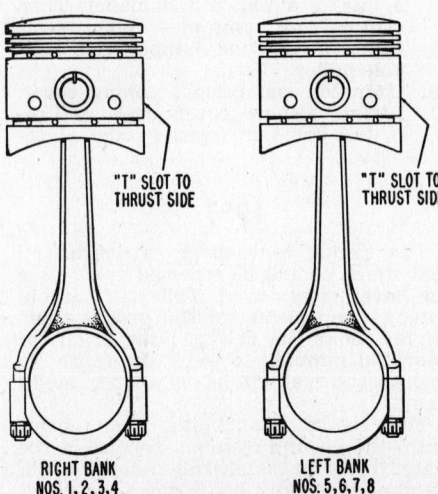

Fig. 16 Correct assembly of pistons and rods. 1953

Fig. 17 Piston and rod assembly. All V8's

tive bores. It may be necessary to remove the carbon from the top of the lifter bore before the lifters can be removed.
5. Remove grille.
6. Carefully slide camshaft out of engine.

1953

After the valves and lifters have been removed from the engine, insert a screwdriver behind the camshaft gear to start the shaft forward. Then pull out the shaft, using great care not to allow the cam lobes to damage the camshaft bearings as the shaft is being withdrawn.

If it is desired to remove the camshaft without taking off the cylinder heads, remove the valve chamber covers and oil baffles. Then use a bar type valve lifter to pull down the valve spring in order to remove the valve guide retainer. Raise the valve assembly enough so that the opening in the side of the valve lifter is across the boss in the valve chamber. Raise all the lifters in this manner and insert the valve guide retainers in these openings. With the lifters held up in this manner, the camshaft may be withdrawn.

CAMSHAFT BEARINGS

When necessary to replace these bearings, the engine will have to be removed from the vehicle and the plug at the rear of the cylinder block will have to be removed in order to utilize the special camshaft bearing removing and installing tools required to do this job. If properly installed, camshaft bearings require no reaming—nor should this type bearing be reamed or altered in any manner in an attempt to fit bearings.

PISTONS & RODS, REMOVE

After removing the cylinder heads and oil pan, use a ridge reamer to remove

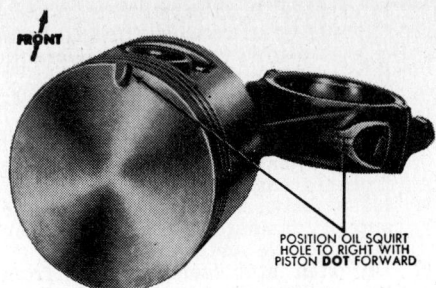

FRONT

POSITION OIL SQUIRT HOLE TO RIGHT WITH PISTON **DOT** FORWARD

Fig. 18 Piston and rod assembly. 1961 Six

any ridge that may have formed on the cylinder wall at the top of the piston ring travel. Cutting the ridge before the piston is removed will avoid damaging rings or cracking ring lands of pistons during removal.

Remove the connecting rod cap and push the piston and rod out through the top of the bore. Use care to prevent the rod from nicking crankshaft journals. Identify the connecting rods (original rods are marked) when removing them so they may be installed in their original cylinder.

PISTON & ROD, ASSEMBLE

Assemble the rod to the piston as shown in Figs. 16, 17 and 18.

PISTONS

Pistons are available for service replacement in standard sizes and oversizes of .005", .020", .030" and .040".

If the pistons are to be re-used with new rings, remove the carbon from the ring grooves. A special tool is available for this work but a satisfactory job can be done by breaking an old piston ring. File the broken end to a sharp, square edge and use it to scrape out the carbon. Soak the piston in cleaning solvent to loosen any carbon residue. Clean out the loosened carbon, being careful not to cut away any piston material. Clean out the oil return holes with a drill just large

enough to fill the holes. Hold the drill in a tap wrench and make sure the drill does not remove any metal from the piston.

Rinse the piston in solvent and wipe off the carbon on the sides of the piston. *Never use a wire brush to clean a piston as the brush will round off the edges of the ring lands.* Pistons showing scuffed or scored skirts should be discarded for new ones. Examine the ring lands carefully for cracks. If in the least bit doubtful, the piston should be scrapped.

New pistons should be fitted according to recommendations given in Fig. 19.

PISTON PINS
All (Except V8-383, 430)

It is recommended procedure to replace piston pins whenever new rings are installed. Pins that have been relatively quiet when the old rings were in service may be noisy after new rings are installed.

Use a suitable reamer to ream the piston for oversize pins. The pins are retained by snap rings, one located at each end of the pin. When installing the retainers, make sure each one enters the groove in the piston pin boss.

V8-383, 430

Pins are a press fit and no snap rings are used to retain them in place.

PISTON RINGS

New rings should be assembled on the piston according to the instructions furnished by the ring manufacturer. Always use standard size rings in cylinder bores that are *standard at the bottom, regardless of the amount of cylinder wear.*

When new rings are installed without reboring cylinders, the glazed cylinder walls should be slightly dulled, but without increasing the bore diameter. This is done with a "Glaze-buster" or with a hone equipped with the finest grade of stones.

New rings must be checked for clearance in piston grooves and for gap in cylinder bores. Cylinder bores and piston grooves must be clean, dry and free of carbon and burrs.

Check the clearance of each ring in its piston groove by installing the ring and then inserting feeler gauges *under* the ring. Any wear that occurs in the piston groove forms a step or ridge at the inner portion of the lower land. If gauges are inserted above the ring, the ring may rest on the step instead of on the worn portion of the lower land, and a false measurement of clearance will result.

If the piston grooves are worn to the extent that relatively high steps or ridges exist on the lower lands, the piston should be replaced because the steps will interfere with the operation of the new rings and the ring clearances will be excessive. Piston rings are not furnished in oversize widths to compensate for ring groove wear.

To check the end gap of rings, place the ring in the cylinder in which it will

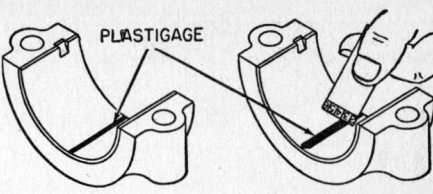

PLASTIGAGE

PLASTIGAGE IN PLACE BEFORE BEARING CAP IS TORQUED

PLASTIGAGE AFTER BEARING CAP IS REMOVED

Fig. 20 Checking bearing clearance with Plastigage

be used. Square it in the bore by tapping with the lower end of the piston. Then measure the gap with feeler gauges. If necessary to increase the gap, file the ends of the rings carefully with a smooth file.

ROD BEARINGS

These bearings are of the insert type, selectively fitted, and available for service replacement in standard and undersizes for use on crankshaft journals that have been reground.

If inspection reveals badly worn or scored bearings, they should be replaced. Bearings may be removed by simply taking off the bearing caps and slipping the old ones out and the new ones in. The installation of new bearings must be closely checked to maintain the proper clearance between the crankshaft and bearing surface. A convenient and accurate method for checking bearing clearance is with the use of Plastigage, which is available at any auto parts jobber.

Place the string-like plastic material so it extends the full width of the bearing, Fig. 20. Install the bearing and cap and tighten the nuts to the recommended torque which is listed in *Engine Torque Specifications* chart. Then loosen the nuts and carefully remove the cap and bearing. The widest portion of the Plastigage is then measured with the scale on the Plastigage envelope, Fig. 20. The graduation on the envelope corresponding to the thickness of the Plastigage gives the bearing clearance in thousandths of an inch.

MAIN BEARINGS

Caution—Main bearing clearance can be checked with Plastigage in the same manner described for rod bearings. If bearings are measured with the engine in the chassis, the crankshaft must be supported in order to take up clearance between the upper bearing insert and crankshaft journal. This can be done by tightening bearing caps of adjacent bearings with .005" to .015" cardboard, (such as a calling card) between lower bearing shell and journal. Use extreme care when this is done to avoid unnecessary strain on the crankshaft or bearings or a false reading may be obtained. Do not rotate crankshaft while Plastigage is installed. *Be sure to remove cardboard.* To install new bearings, proceed as follows:

PISTON CLEARANCE CHART

Minimum Clearance 0.0008		Maximum Clearance 0.0026		Wear Limit Clearance 0.0045	
RIBBON 0.002" THICK AND 0.500" WIDE		RIBBON 0.0025" THICK AND 0.500" WIDE		RIBBON 0.003" THICK AND 0.500" WIDE		RIBBON 0.0045" THICK AND 0.500" WIDE
Ribbon Pull Lbs.	Clear-ance Inches	Ribbon Pull Lbs.	Clear-ance Inches	Ribbon Pull Lbs.	Clear-ance Inches	Ribbon Pull Lbs.	Clear-ance Inches

Ribbon Pull Lbs.	Clearance Inches	Ribbon Pull Lbs.	Clearance Inches	Ribbon Pull Lbs.	Clearance Inches	Ribbon Pull Lbs.	Clearance Inches
12	—	12	—	12	0.0008	12	Use a 0.003" Ribbon
11	—	11	—	11	0.001	11	0.0028
10	—	10	—	10	0.0013	10	0.0031
9	—	9	0.0008	9	0.0014	9	0.0033
8	—	8	0.0012	8	0.0017	8	0.0035
7	0.0007	7	0.0014	7	0.0019	7	0.0037
6	0.001	6	0.0016	6	0.0022	6	0.0038
5	0.0013	5	0.0018	·5	0.0024	5	0.0041
4	0.0015	4	0.0021	4	0.0026	4	0.0043
3	0.0018	3	0.0023	3	0.0028	3	0.0044
2	0.002	2	0.0026	2	0.0031	2	0.0046
1	0.0023	1	0.0028	1	0.0033	1	0.0048
0	0.0025	0	0.003	0	0.0035	0	0.005

Fig. 19

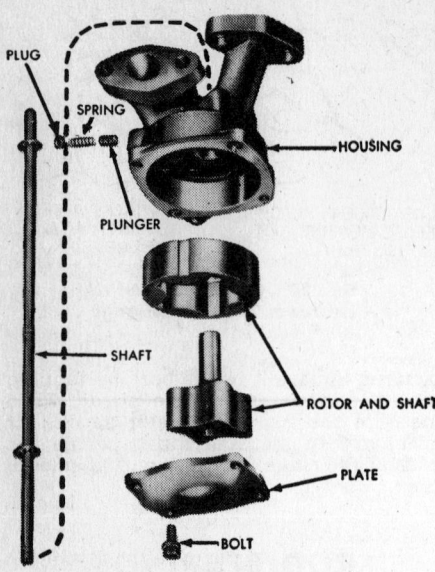

PLUG
SPRING
HOUSING
PLUNGER
SHAFT
ROTOR AND SHAFT
PLATE
BOLT

Fig. 21   Rotor type oil pump

1. Remove bearing cap and worn lower shell.
2. Rotate crankshaft in normal direction to turn upper bearing shell out of crankcase. Use a cotter pin with a flattened head or the special tool made for the purpose in the crankshaft oil hole to contact the bearing and force it out.
3. Place a new upper shell on the crankshaft journal with the locating notch in the correct position and rotate the shaft to turn the bearing in place.
4. Install the lower bearing shell in the cap.
5. Tighten all cap nuts to the torque figures given in the *Engine Torque Data* table.

CRANKSHAFT OIL SEAL

1954-61

A braided oil seal is pressed into the upper and lower grooves behind the rear main bearing. Directly in front of this seal is an oil slinger which deflects the oil back into the oil pan. Should the braided seal require replacement, the installation of the lower half is accomplished as follows:

With the bearing cap and lower bearing half removed, install a new seal so that both ends protrude above the cap. Tap the seal down into position or roll it snugly in its groove with a smooth rounded tool. Then cut off the protruding ends of the seal with a sharp knife or razor blade.

Installing Upper Seal

Although the usual practice is to remove the crankshaft when the upper half of the seal is to be replaced it is possible to do the job without removing the crankshaft as follows:

To remove the seal, use needle-nose pliers to grasp the end of the seal which is most accessible. Pull the seal downward while rotating the crankshaft slowly in the direction that the seal is being removed.

To install the new seal, fasten a length of wire or strong string such as fishing line securely to one end of the new seal. See that the point of fastening is not bulky and that it is not over ⅜″ from the end of the seal. Coat the seal with Lubriplate. Pass the free end of the wire or string up over the crankshaft at the point where the seal is to be installed. Then exert a firm, steady pull on the wire or string and at the same time rotate the crankshaft slowly in the direction of the pull. This will help to move the seal into position. When the installation is completed, trim the ends of the seal flush with the engine block.

1953

Oil sealing is controlled by a two-piece metal retainer having a groove which returns excess oil to the crankcase. These retainers can be replaced without removing the crankshaft by simply taking off the rear main bearing cap. The upper half of the retainer can be pushed around and taken out through the bottom.

OIL PAN

1961 Six

1. Remove oil level dipstick and drain oil pan.
2. Unfasten stabilizer from lower suspension arm.
3. Remove left stabilizer clamp.
4. Loosen bolts securing right stabilizer clamp to frame side member. Pry stabilizer toward right, then pull stabilizer arms downward to allow clearance for removing oil pan.
5. Unfasten and remove oil pan, oil pump inlet tube and screen.

1961 V8's

1. For oil pan and crankshaft clearance purposes, crank engine to place No. 1 piston on top dead center (No. 6 on 292 engine). Remove oil level dipstick.
2. Drain oil pan.
3. Remove ends of stabilizer from mounting studs and pull the ends downward to allow clearance for oil pan removal.
4. On 292 engine, remove inlet tube from oil pump and loosen nut securing inlet tube to oil pan. Then unfasten and remove oil pan.
5. On 352 and 390 engines, unfasten and lower oil pan onto frame crossmember. Then reach into crankcase with a socket wrench and unfasten oil pick-up tube from oil pump. Allow screen and tube to drop into pan. Move pan forward and down to remove it from chassis.

1958-60 V8-383, 430

1. Crank engine to bring No. 1 piston at about 14° BTDC to obtain clearance between crankshaft counterbalances (refer to timing marks on vibration damper).
2. Disconnect battery ground cable.

3. Remove oil level dipstick.
4. On 1959-60 disconnect throttle linkage at plastic bushing at bellcrank.
5. Raise vehicle and drain oil.
6. Remove front engine support attaching nuts.
7. Position jack under front edge of oil pan. Lower vehicle enough to raise front of engine about 2″. Place 1″ block between each front engine support insulator and frame. Then raise vehicle and remove jack.
8. Unfasten stabilizer brackets from frame. Then disconnect either stabilizer link at lower suspension arm. Swing stabilizer down and outward to allow clearance for removal of pan.
9. Unfasten and lower oil pan to frame crossmember.
10. Unfasten oil pump tube and screen and allow to drop into pan.
11. Remove oil pan in a lowering forward motion.

1954-57 & 1958-60 V8-312

1. Bring No. 6 piston up on TDC to allow clearance between oil pan and crankshaft.
2. Remove screws attaching engine splash shield to frame side members.
3. Raise car and drain crankcase.
4. Unfasten and remove engine splash shield from frame crossmember.
5. Disconnect stabilizer and pull it forward to allow clearance for oil pan removal.
6. Remove inlet tube from oil pump and loosen nut securing inlet tube to oil pan.
7. Remove attaching screws and drop pan.

1953

To remove the pan, remove the two bolts holding the steering idler arm support to the frame, and pull down on the steering linkage. Take off the starter motor. Remove the front and bottom flywheel housing cover. This comes straight down after the removal of the necessary nuts and bolts. Remove the oil level indicator tube from the pan, and the bottom section of the road draft tube. Remove the pan attaching screws and lower the pan.

It is not necessary to raise the front end of the engine although the proper combination of standard tools are necessary to reach the two forward screws holding the pan to the block.

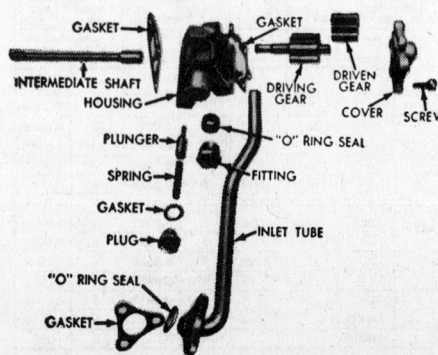

GASKET
GASKET
INTERMEDIATE SHAFT
HOUSING
DRIVING GEAR
DRIVEN GEAR
COVER
SCREW
PLUNGER
"O" RING SEAL
SPRING
FITTING
GASKET
PLUG
INLET TUBE
"O" RING SEAL
GASKET

Fig. 22   Gear type oil pump

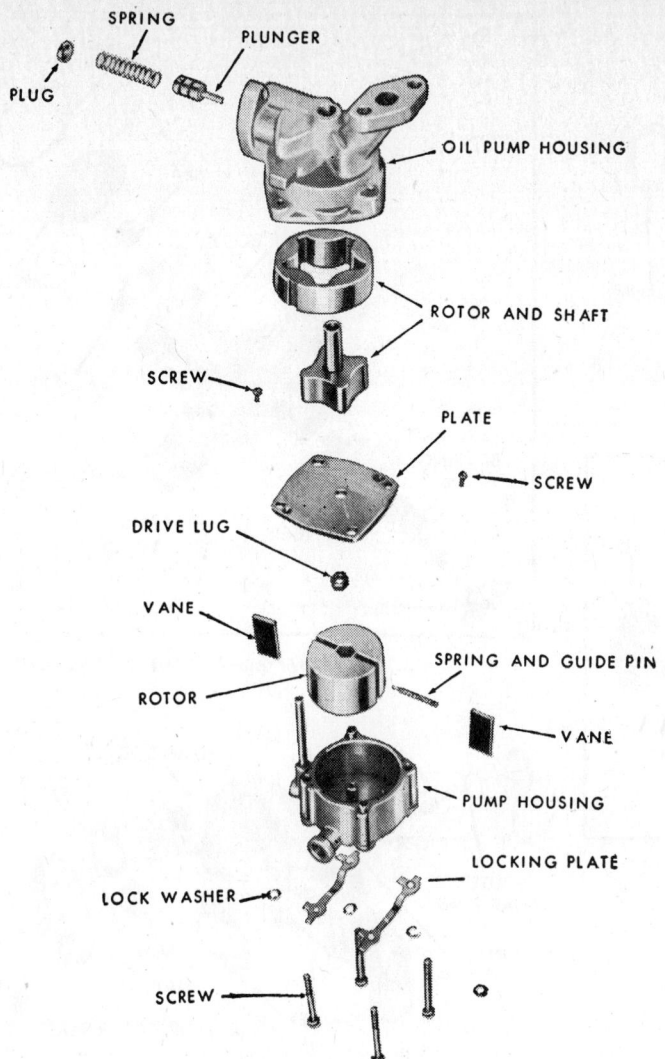

SPRING
PLUG
PLUNGER
OIL PUMP HOUSING
ROTOR AND SHAFT
SCREW
PLATE
SCREW
DRIVE LUG
VANE
SPRING AND GUIDE PIN
ROTOR
VANE
PUMP HOUSING
LOCKING PLATE
LOCK WASHER
SCREW

Fig. 23 Oil and vacuum pump disassembled. 1958

OIL PUMP REPAIRS

Rotor Type Pump, Fig. 21

1. With all parts clean and dry, check the inside of the pump housing and the outer race and rotor for damage or excessive wear.
2. Check the mating surface of the pump cover for wear. If this surface is worn, scored or grooved, replace the cover.
3. Measure the clearance between the outer race and housing. This clearance should be .006-.012".
4. With the rotor assembly installed in the housing, place a straight edge over the rotor assembly and housing. Measure the clearance between the straight edge and the rotor and outer race. Recommended limits are .0011-.0041". *The outer race, shaft and rotor are furnished only as an assembly.*
5. Check the drive shaft-to-housing bearing clearance by measuring the O.D. of the shaft and the I.D. of the housing bearing. The recommended clearance limits are .0015-0029".
6. Inspect the relief valve spring for a collapsed or worn condition.
7. Check the relief valve piston for scores and free operation in the bore. The specified piston clearance is .0015-.0029".

Gear Type Pump, Fig. 22

After all parts are clean and dry, inspect the pump body and gear teeth for damage or wear. Check the gear end clearance with a dial indicator or Plastigage. The Plastigage method is as follows:

Position the gasket on the housing, then place a strip of Plastigage on the gears and install the cover. Remove the cover and check the Plastigage reading. The recommended clearance is .0015-.006".

Check the gears for freedom of rotation. Inspect the relief valve spring for a collapsed or worn condition. Check the relief valve piston for scores and free operation in the bore.

1958 Oil-Vacuum Pump

1. Referring to Fig. 23, remove oil inlet pipe and screen from pump.
2. Disconnect vacuum inlet pipe from pump body.
3. Detach vacuum pump from oil pump.
4. Scribe a mark on cover plate and vacuum pump. Then remove oil pump cover plate and drive lug.
5. Remove vacuum pump eccentric and vanes as a unit, using a wire hook.
6. Remove vanes from rotor, and vane pin and spring.
7. Remove rotor and shaft from oil pump body.
8. Scrape the stake marks that secure the relief valve in the oil pump housing unit until the retainer can be removed together with spring and relief valve.
9. With all parts clean and dry, check the inside of the pump housing and the outer race and rotor for damage or excessive wear.
10. Check the mating surface of the pump cover for wear. If this surface is worn, scored or grooved, replace the cover.
11. Measure the clearance between the outer race and housing. This clearance should be .004-011".
12. With the rotor assembly installed in the housing, place a straight edge over the rotor assembly and housing. Measure the clearance between the straight edge and the rotor and outer race. Recommended limits are .0015-.003". *The outer race, shaft and rotor are furnished only as an assembly.*
13. Check the drive shaft-to-housing bearing clearance by measuring the O.D. of the shaft and the I.D. of the housing bearing. The recommended clearance limits are .0015-.0029".
14. Inspect the relief valve spring for a collapsed or worn condition.
15. Check the relief valve piston for scores and free operation in the bore.

RADIATOR

1954-61

1. To remove the radiator, first drain the cooling system and disconnect upper and lower radiator hoses.
2. On cars equipped with automatic transmission, disconnect oil cooler inlet and outlet lines at the radiator.
3. Remove radiator support bolts and lift out radiator.
4. When installing the radiator on cars with automatic transmission, do not tighten the radiator support bolts until after the cooler lines have been connected.

1953

To remove the radiator, drain the cooling system and remove the hoses from the radiator. Release the strap that secures the generator to the generator bracket. Tilt the generator forward and remove the belt. Remove the two capscrews that secure the fan to the generator, lower the fan and remove the belt. Take the fan off the engine from the left side. Then remove the three screws that secure each side of the radiator to its support and lift out the radiator.

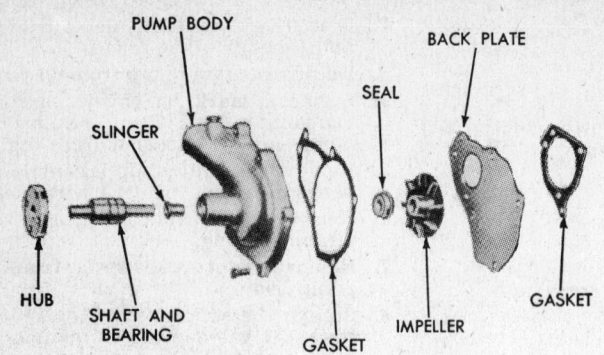

Fig. 24 Water pump. 1961 Six

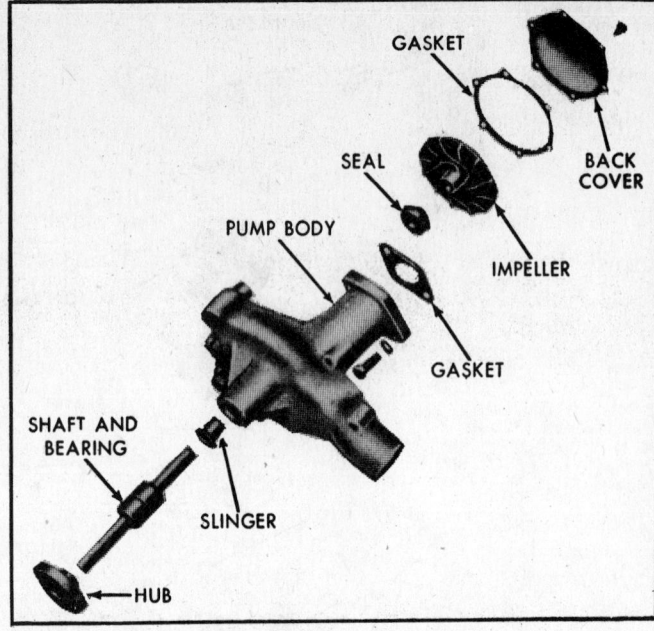

Fig. 25 Water pump. 1961 V8-352, 390

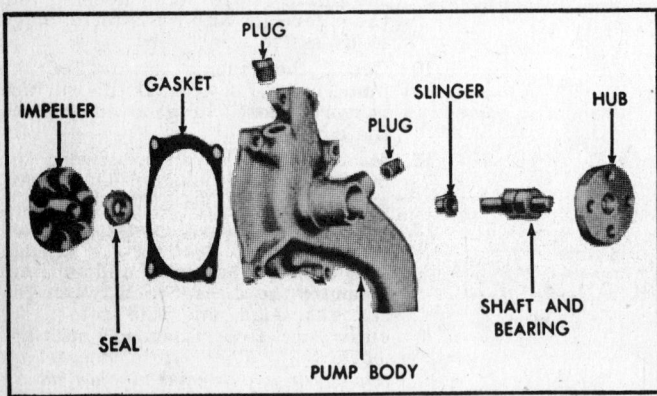

Fig. 26 Water pump. V8-256, 292, 312

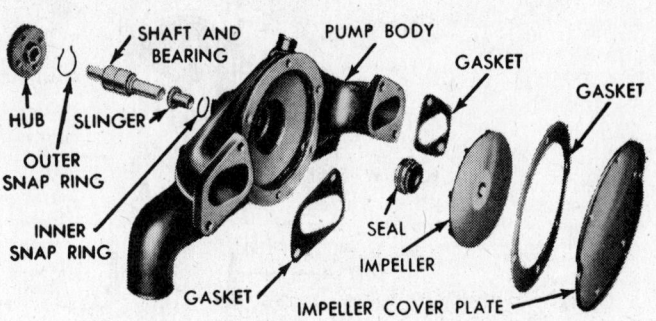

Fig. 27 Water pump. V8-383, 430

WATER PUMP, REPLACE

1961 Six

1. Drain cooling system and disconnect hoses at water pump.
2. Remove fan, pulley and drive belt.
3. On power steering cars, remove power steering pump with hoses attached and place it in a position that will prevent fluid from draining out of reservoir.
4. Unfasten and remove pump from engine along with radiator supply tank.

1961 V8's

1. Drain cooling system and disconnect hoses from water pump.
2. Remove fan belt, fan, spacer (if equipped) and pulley.
3. On power steering jobs, remove power steering pump with hoses attached and place it in a position that will prevent fluid from draining out of reservoir.
4. Unfasten and remove water pump from engine front cover (292) or from cylinder block (352 and 390).

1958-60

1. Disconnect ground cable from battery.
2. Loosen and move generator toward engine to relieve tension on drive belts.
3. On air conditioned cars, loosen and move compressor inward to relieve drive belt tension. Remove power booster fan and take off compressor drive belt and pulleys.
4. On standard cars, remove fan, spacer and water pump.

1954-57

To remove the pump, drain the cooling system and take off the fan blades, drive belt and upper and lower hoses. Unfasten the pump from the engine front cover and lift it off.

1953

To remove the pump, drain the cooling system and remove the upper hoses. On the right-hand pump, remove the heater hose. Remove the generator belt. On the right-hand pump only, remove the fan belt.

To prevent damage when raising the engine, remove the throttle lever rod from the "Z" bar. Remove the nut that secures each water pump housing to the engine front support brackets. Place a jack under the oil pan until the front engine support studs are clear of the water pump housing. Unfasten the water pump from the cylinder block. And remove the cap screw from the inside of the water pump inlet that secures the water pump housing to the cylinder block.

WATER PUMP REPAIRS

1961 Six

1. When servicing the pump, refer to Fig. 24. Clean all gasket material from pump and back plate.
2. Install a new oil slinger on the new bearing and shaft assembly furnished with repair kit.
3. Apply a light film of waterproof sealer on the new seal and press seal into pump housing.
4. Coat bearing outer diameter with grease. Position the shaft assembly and press it into the housing until the outer face of the bearing is even with the outer face of the pump.
5. Position hub on shaft and press hub into place until the distance from the housing mounting face to the front face of the hub is 4 5/16".
6. Coat the impeller-to-seal rubbing surfaces with grease.

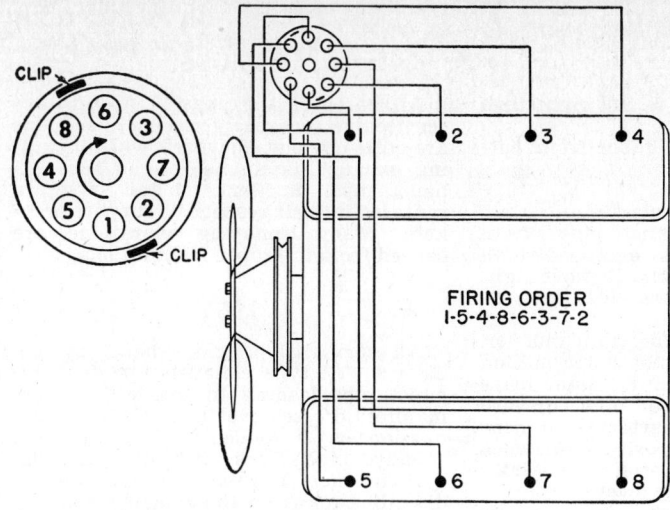

Fig. 28   Ignition details.   1953

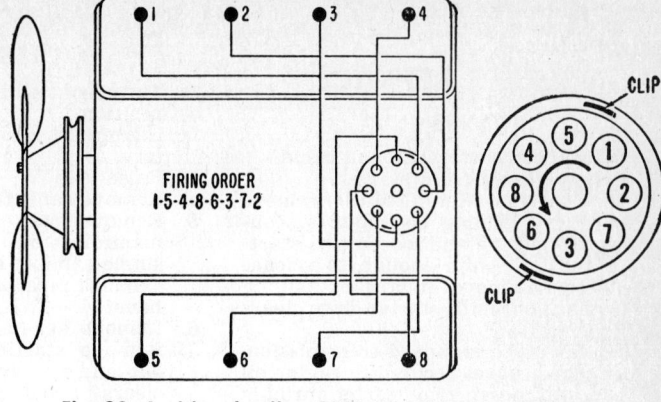

Fig. 29   Ignition details.   1954-57 & 1958-61 292, 312

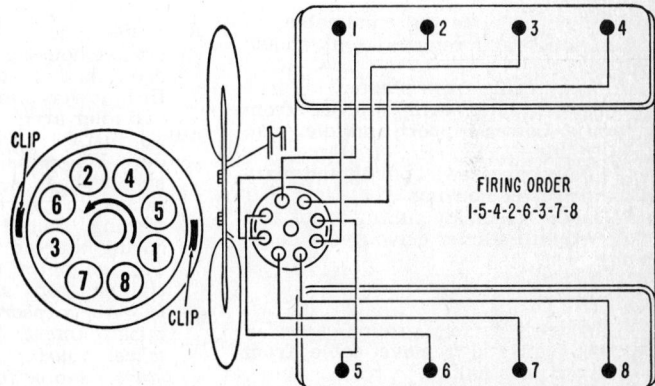

Fig. 30   Ignition details.   1958-61 352, 383, 390, 430

1961 V8-352, 390

1. When servicing this pump, refer to Fig. 25.
2. Position pump on an arbor press with hub end of shaft resting on a steel plate.
3. Press impeller onto shaft until it sets .070-.080" below back cover mounting face of pump housing.
4. Press hub on shaft until it sets 8 $\frac{21}{32}$" from housing mounting face to front face of hub.

V8-256, 292, 312

1. Referring to Fig. 26, coat the impeller seal rubbing surface with grease.
2. Install impeller on shaft and press downward until impeller-to housing clearance is .025-.035".
3. Coat new gasket on both sides with sealer and install on pump housing.

V8-383, 430

1. Referring to Fig. 27, support pump housing on hub end and insert seal with brass covered end down. Press seal into seat. Use sealer around edge of seat.
2. Support pump on arbor press. Position shaft and bearing assembly in pump with slinger facing downward.
3. Press shaft-bearing and slinger into housing until bearing is flush with hub edge of housing.
4. Press hub on shaft until a dimension of 6 $\frac{13}{32}$" is obtained between pulley mounting face of hub and mounting face of water pump legs.
5. Press impeller on shaft until rear flat face of impeller sets $\frac{7}{64}$" below back cover mounting face of pump housing.
6. Coat cover gasket with non-hardening type sealer and install gasket and back cover.

DISTRIBUTOR, REPLACE

1. To remove the distributor, disconnect the primary wire and vacuum control pipe. On some models the work may be made easier if the accelerator pull back spring is disconnected.
2. Remove distributor cap.
3. Scribe a mark on the distributor body indicating the position of the rotor, and scribe another mark on the body and engine block indicating position of distributor body in block. These marks can be used as guides when installing distributor in a correctly timed engine.
4. Remove hold down screw or screws and lift distributor out of block. *Do not crank engine while distributor is removed or the initial timing operation will have to be performed.*

Installation

If the crankshaft has not been disturbed, install the distributor, using the scribed marks previously made on the distributor body and engine block as guides.

If the crankshaft has been rotated while the distributor was removed from the engine, it will be necessary to retime the engine. Crank the engine to bring No. 1 piston on top dead center of its compression stroke. Align the timing mark on the vibration damper or pulley with the timing pointer (see *Tune Up* chart). Install the distributor so that the rotor points to the No. 1 spark plug wire terminal in the distributor cap, Figs. 28, 29, 30.

IGNITION TIMING

Align the distributor rotor with No. 1 spark plug wire terminal in the distributor cap, when No. 1 piston is on the compression stroke and timing marks on the crankshaft pulley and pointer are aligned.

With the timing mark in line with the pointer, the distributor points should just start to open. It may be necessary to rotate the distributor body clockwise slightly and then counter-clockwise until the points just start to open. Tighten the distributor lock plate screw.

Start the engine and check the timing with a timing light.

Using Timing Light

When using a timing light, *be sure to disconnect the distributor vacuum line before checking timing*, otherwise the timing will be affected due to the fact that the vacuum opening is above the throttle plate.

Connect the timing light high tension lead to the No. 1 spark plug and the other two leads to the proper battery terminals. Clean the dirt from the timing mark and if necessary use white chalk to make the mark more visible.

Start the engine and operate at idle speed. Direct the light on the timing mark. It should flash just as the timing mark lines up with the pointer, indicating correct timing. If the pointer and timing mark does not line up as the light flashes, rotate the distributor as required to bring them in alignment.

STARTER REPLACE

1953

1. Disconnect battery ground cable.
2. Remove cable from starter.
3. On cars with Merc-O-Matic, remove capscrew holding end plate to converter housing and loosen two starter through bolts enough to release starter. Remove starter by pulling straight out until starter drive clears housing.
4. On cars with standard transmission, remove bracket secured to engine oil pan and loosen two starter through bolts sufficiently to release starter.

1954-55

1. Disconnect battery ground cable.
2. Raise car and remove front splash pan.
3. Remove cable from starter.
4. Unfasten idler arm support from frame. Lower support and idler arm assembly.
5. Remove capscrews holding end plate to converter housing.
6. Remove starter by pulling it out and down until starter drive clears housing.

1956

1. Disconnect battery ground cable.
2. Raise car and remove cable from starter terminal.
3. Remove capscrews securing starter drive end plate to flywheel housing.
4. Turn front wheels to full right position and remove starter by pulling out and down until starter drive clears housing.

1957

1. Disconnect battery ground cable and cable from starter terminal.
2. Disconnect ignition cable bracket under No. 4 spark plug.
3. Turn wheels full right and, after removing starter attaching screws, remove starter by pulling out and upward until starter drive clears housing. Continue upward movement of starter until it is in near vertical upright position between engine and fender apron with starter drive end facing down. While holding starter drive, rotate starter housing to allow clearance of drive end plate

mounting bosses. Then lower starter between tie rod and idler arm.

1958

1. Turn front wheels to full right turn position.
2. Disconnect ground cable from battery.
3. Raise vehicle.
4. Remove cable from starter.
5. Remove both exhaust pipes from manifolds on cars equipped with single exhaust system. Remove right exhaust pipe on cars with dual exhaust.
6. Remove exhaust pipe from muffler.
7. Remove starting motor by pulling out and upward until starter drive clears housing. Continue upward movement until starter is in near vertical upright position between engine and fender apron with starter drive end facing downward.
8. While holding starter drive, rotate starter housing to allow clearance of drive end plate mounting bosses; then lower starter between tie rod and idler arm.
9. To install, reverse removal procedure. When installing the starter, be sure rubber seal is properly positioned to prevent misalignment or binding. Install three capscrews securing starter to flywheel housing. Tighten outer capscrew first; then tighten top and bottom screws. *If outer capscrew is tightened last, misalignment of starter with flywheel housing may result, causing starter motor failure.*

1959-61

1. Disconnect battery ground cable.
2. Disconnect throttle linkage at bellcrank.
3. Raise vehicle.
4. Remove cable from starter terminal.
5. Remove engine splash shield from front crossmember.
6. Remove front engine support insulator nuts.
7. Place jack under front edge of engine oil pan (protect with wood block) and raise engine about 1″.
8. Unfasten starter from flywheel housing (3 capscrews).
9. Starter can then be removed by lowering it between tie rod and steering idler arm (drive end down).
10. Install in reverse order of removal, being sure rubber seal is properly positioned to prevent misalignment or binding.

MUFFLER & PIPES

1953-56

All parts of the exhaust system are serviceable separately and all operations are quite obvious. However, when installing exhaust assemblies, make sure exhaust pipe, muffler and tail pipe are centered in their respective support brackets. Many annoying vibrations are caused from improper installations.

1957

All cars with single exhaust system have a "Y" type exhaust pipe. The exhaust pipe leading to the left exhaust manifold crosses over beneath the transmission and is welded to the right hand exhaust pipe. Cars with dual exhaust systems have the exhaust pipe leading directly back from the exhaust manifold to the muffler.

All parts of the exhaust system can be serviced separately and the operations are fairly obvious. However, it is not necessary to remove bracket and insulator assemblies attached to frame unless damaged. On tail pipes using a resonator, an additional clamp must be removed holding the tail pipe extension to the resonator.

1958

On power steering jobs, turn front wheels to the right. When removing exhaust pipe, disconnect solenoid-to-starter cable. On dual exhaust jobs, it may be necessary to remove the starter brush cover strap.

1959-60

Service mufflers do not have welded-on extension pipes. Therefore, when replacing a muffler, it is necessary to use separate extension pipes. These can be cut from the muffler that has been removed, providing the extensions are in good condition. New extension pipes are available for service.

1961

Unfasten muffler from frame mounted bracket. Loosen muffler inlet pipe clamp and slide clamp away from muffler. Separate muffler from inlet pipe and remove tail pipe.

Carburetor Section

Performance Complaints

Flooding, stumble on acceleration or other performance complaints are in many instances caused by the presence of dirt, water or other foreign matter in the carburetor. To aid in diagnosing the cause of the complaint, the carburetor should be carefully removed from the engine without draining the fuel

from the bowl. The contents of the fuel bowl may then be examined for contamination as the carburetor is disassembled.

Check the fuel in the bowl for contamination by dirt, water, gum or other foreign matter. A magnet moved through the fuel in the bowl will pick up and identify any iron oxide dust that may have caused intake needle and seat leakage.

Inspect gasketed surfaces between body and air horn. Small nicks or burrs should be smoothed down to eliminate air or fuel leakage. On carburetors having a vacuum piston, be especially particular when inspecting the top surface of the inner wall of the bowl around the vacuum piston passage. A poor seal at this location may contribute to a "cutting-out" on turns complaint.

Fill the carburetor bowl with clean fuel before installing on manifold. This will help prevent dirt trapped in the fuel system from being dislodged by the free flow of fuel as the carburetor is primed. The operation of the floats and intake needle and seats may be checked under pressure if a fuel pump is used at the bench to fill the carburetor bowl. Operate the throttle several times and visually check the discharge from pump jets.

Poor Mileage and Engine Loading Complaints

Cases of poor mileage and engine loading may be due in many instances to sluggish choke valve opening during cold driveaway, caused by insufficient vacuum in choke housing, a plugged or restricted heat pipe or inlet in choke cover. To check for this condition, have engine warm and running at slow idle.

Remove choke heat pipe and hold a finger over the heat inlet hole (hole is on choke housing on some carburetors). If there is little or no vacuum pull on the finger, check the choke housing for gasket leaks or plugged vacuum passages. If these are OK, check choke vacuum passages in carburetor between choke housing and manifold.

Dirty or Rusty Choke Housing

In cases where it is found that the interior of the choke housing is dirty, gummed or rusty while the carburetor itself is comparatively clean, look for a punctured or eroded manifold heat tube (if one is used).

Manifold Heat Control Valve

An engine equipped with a manifold heat control valve can operate with the valve stuck either in the open or closed position. Because of this, an inoperative valve is frequently overlooked at vehicle lubrication or tune-up.

A valve stuck in the "heat-off" position can result in slow warm up, deposits in combustion chamber, carburetor icing, flat spots during acceleration, low gas mileage and spark plug fouling.

A valve stuck in the "heat-on" position can result in power loss, engine knocking, sticking or burned valves and spark plug burning.

To prevent the possibility of a stuck valve, check and lubricate the valve each time the vehicle is lubricated or tuned-up. Check the operation of the valve manually. To lubricate the valve, place a few drops of penetrating oil on the valve shaft where it passes through the manifold. Move the valve up and down a few times to work in the oil. *Do not use engine oil for this purpose as it will leave a residue which hampers valve operation.*

CARTER CARBURETOR ADJUSTMENTS

| Year | Carburetor Model | Idle Adjustments | | | | Float Level | | Float Drop | | Pump Travel Setting | Choke Unloader Setting | Choke Setting |
		Mixture Screws Turns Open	Hot Idle Speed In Drive	Fast Idle Speed	Dashpot Plunger Clearance	Primary	Secondary	Primary	Secondary			
1960	ABD-2965S	1½	450	525④	.075⑩	¼⑥	None	None	None	7/16⑦	⅛⑨	Index
1959	AFB-2853S	1½–2½	450	550④	7/16⑪	3/16①	3/16①	23/32②	23/32②	17/32③	⅛⑤	Index
1957	AFB-2441S-A	½–1½	440	1900⑧	7/16⑪	5/32①	5/32①	23/32②	23/32②	15/32③	.067⑤	1 Rich

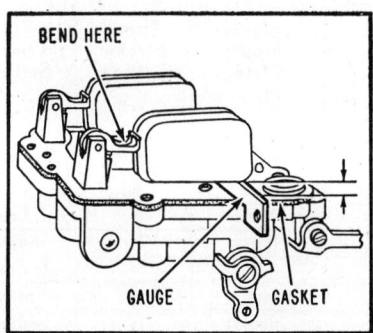

Fig. ①—AFB float level. Adjust by bending float lever.

Fig. ②—AFB float drop. Adjust by bending stop tabs on float brackets.

CARTER NOTES

METERING ROD

WCFB—Metering rod adjustment must be made after pump adjustment. With throttle valves fully closed, loosen metering rod arm clamp screw. With metering rods in place, press down on vacumeter link until metering rods bottom in casting. Holding rods down, revolve metering rod arm until finger on arm contacts lip of vacumeter link. Hold in place and tighten clamp screw.

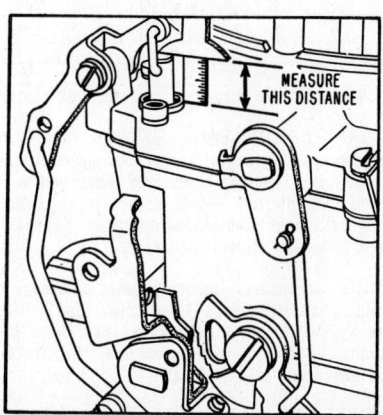

Fig. ③—Measure from top of bowl cover to top of plunger shaft with throttle connector rod in inner hole in pump arm. Adjust by bending throttle connector rod.

④—With engine at normal operating temperature, turn fast idle screw against low step of fast idle cam until specified rpm is obtained.

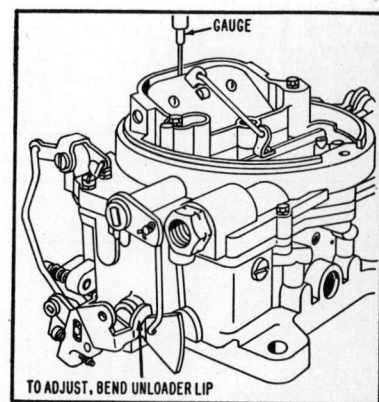

Fig. ⑤—With throttle wide open, clearance between upper edge of choke valve and inner wall of air horn should be as specified. Adjust by bending unloader lip on throttle lever.

(Continued on next page)

CARTER NOTES
continued

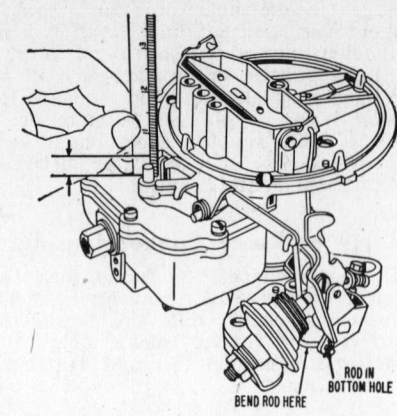

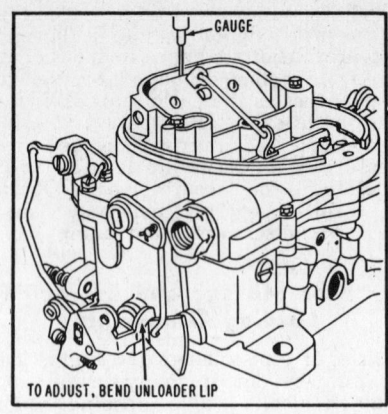

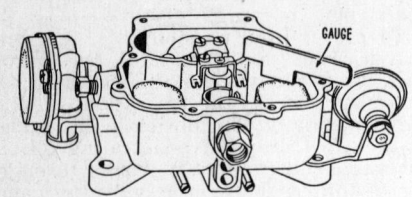

Fig. ⑥—ABD float level. Adjust by bending lip on float arm.

Fig. ⑦—Measured from top of pump plunger to top of bowl cover. Adjust by bending throttle connector rod.

TO ADJUST, BEND UNLOADER LIP

Fig. ⑨—With throttle wide open, there should be the clearance specified between upper edge of choke valve and air horn wall. Adjust by bending tang on choke unloader lever.

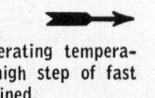

Fig. ⑧—With engine at normal operating temperature, turn fast idle screw against high step of fast idle cam until specified rpm is obtained.

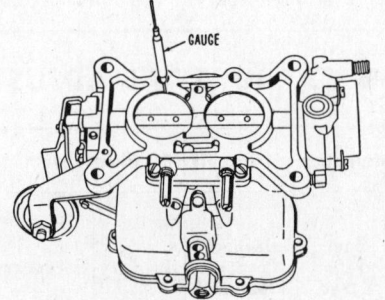

⑩—With throttle closed and hot idle screw against its stop, loosen dashpot locknut. Hold dashpot plunger in to the limit of its travel. There should be the clearance specified between plunger and throttle operating lever. Rotate dashpot in its bracket to obtain desired clearance.

⑪—With primary throttle valves wide open, there should be the clearance specified from top of bowl cover to top of dashpot plunger. Adjust by bending stop lug on flat lever.

FORD CARBURETOR ADJUSTMENTS

Year	Model	Carb. Type	Idle Adjustments				Float Level	Fast Idle Cam	Secondary Throttle Plate	Pump Stroke Setting	Choke Setting
			Mixture Screws Turns Open	Hot Idle R.P.M. In Drive	Cold Idle R.P.M.	Dashpot Setting					
1961	V8-292	2 Barrel	$1\frac{1}{2}$	465②	1700②	.075⑤	$^{29}/_{64}$①	②	None	⑥	⑨
	V8-352	2 Barrel	$1\frac{1}{2}$	465②	1700②	.075⑤	$^{29}/_{64}$①	②	None	⑥	⑨
	V8-390	4 Barrel	$1\frac{1}{2}$	465②	1700②	.075⑤	$^{21}/_{32}$①	②	.009④	⑥	2 Lean
1960	All	2 Barrel	$1-1\frac{1}{2}$	450②	1800②	.067⑤	$^{7}/_{16}-^{15}/_{32}$①	.030③	None	⑥	Index
1959	All	4 Barrel	$1-1\frac{1}{2}$	450②	⑧	.067⑤	$^{7}/_{16}-^{15}/_{32}$①	⑦	.009④	⑥	Index
	All	2 Barrel	$1-1\frac{1}{2}$	450②	⑧	.067⑤	$^{7}/_{16}-^{15}/_{32}$①	⑦	None	⑥	Index
1958	All	4 Barrel	$1-1\frac{1}{2}$	450②	⑧	.067⑤	$^{7}/_{16}-^{15}/_{32}$①	⑦	.005④	⑥	Index

FORD NOTES

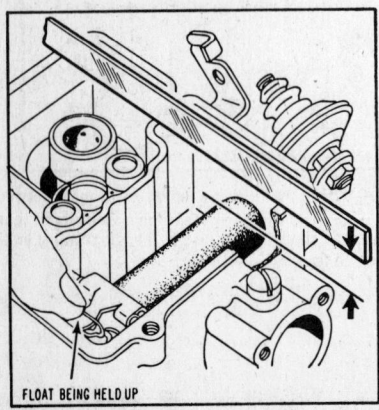

FLOAT BEING HELD UP

②—With fast idle screw on high step of cam.

③—Open throttle plates halfway. Hold choke plate closed by means of choke housing shaft. Clearance between cast stop on back of choke housing and edge of fast idle cam should be as listed. To adjust, loosen bellcrank lever screw and turn lever as required to obtain correct clearance.

④—Hold secondary throttle plates closed. Turn secondary throttle shaft lever screw out until the plates stick in the throttle bores and there is the clearance listed between screw and throttle lever. Then turn screw in one full turn.

⑤—With engine at normal operating temperature

◄ Fig. ①—Float level measured from top surface of main body to top of free end of float with float in uppermost position.

and hot idle speed properly adjusted, loosen dashpot locknut. Hold throttle closed and depress plunger. Clearance between throttle lever and plunger should be as listed. To adjust, turn dashpot in its bracket as required.

⑥—Pump lever has four holes and pump link has two holes to control pump stroke. Install pump rod in top hole for winter operation, and second hole from bottom for summer operation. Install pump operating rod in outside hole in pump link.

⑦—With choke plate fully closed, adjust bellcrank lever so that fast idle stop screw seats on next to highest step on fast idle cam.

⑧—Turn fast idle speed screw in until it just touches the lowest step on the fast idle cam, then back off $\frac{1}{4}$ to $\frac{1}{2}$ turn.

⑨—For standard transmission set on Index; for automatic transmission set 2 notches lean.

HOLLEY CARBURETOR ADJUSTMENTS

Year	Model	Carb. Type	Idle Adjustments					Float Level	Fuel Level	Float Bowl Vent Valve	Pump Override Spring	Choke Unloader	Choke Setting
			Mixture Screws Turns Open	Air Bypass Turns Open	Hot Idle Speed In Drive	Fast Idle Speed	Dashpot Plunger Clearance						
1961	Six	1 Bore	1½	None	485	None	.075⑬	13/64⑭	11/16⑮	None	None	None	None
1960	All	2 Bore	1-1½	None	450	③	.075④	7/8①	⑤	.067⑥	.015⑧	None	2 Rich
1959	V8-312	2 Bore	¾-1¾	None	450	1900⑨	.055④	11/16①	⑤	.067⑥	.015⑧	None	Index
1958	V8-312	2 Bore	¾-1¾	None	450	1800⑨	.055④	¾①	⑤	.067⑥	.015⑧	None	1 Rich
	V8-383	4 Bore	1½	None	450	1800⑨	.055④	⑩	⑤	.067⑥	.015⑧	None	2 Rich
	V8-430	4 Bore	1½	None	450	1800⑨	.055④	⑪	⑤	.067⑥	.015⑧	None	1 Rich
1957	V8-312	4 Bore	1½	None	440	2250⑨	.055④	⑪	⑤	.067⑥	.015⑧	None	Index
1956	All	4 Bore	1¼	None	440	③	.055②	½⑫	½⑦	None	None	None	Index
1955	All	4 Bore	1¼	None	440	③	.055②	¼⑫	½⑦	None	None	None	Index
1954	All	4 Bore	1¼	None	440	③	.055②	¼⑫	½⑦	None	None	None	Index
1953	All	2 Bore	1½-2	None	450	③	.055②	¼⑫	½⑦	None	None	None	Index

HOLLEY NOTES

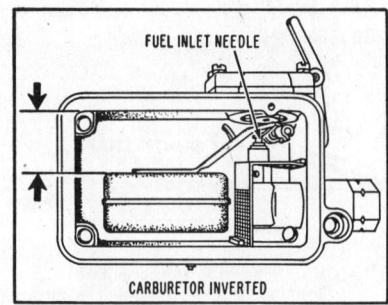

Fig. ①—Float level measured from floor of float bowl to bottom of float with bowl inverted. Adjust as outlined in note ⑤.

②—With throttle fully closed, hold dashpot plunger in to the limit of its travel. Then turn adjusting screw as required to obtain the clearance specified between end of screw and plunger.

③—Turn fast idle adjusting screw in until it just touches lowest step on fast idle cam.

④—With throttle fully closed and dashpot plunger held in to the limit of its travel, there should be the clearance listed between plunger and throttle lever. Adjust by rotating dashpot in its bracket as required.

⑤—With engine running at hot idle speed, remove plug (both plugs on 4-bore units) from sight hole. If fuel just dribbles out of sight hole, fuel level is correct. If not, adjust float level on 1959 and later units by loosening lock screw on top of bowl and rotate adjusting nut as required. On 1957-58 models, adjust float level internally by bending tab on float lever.

⑥—With throttle plates closed, there should be the clearance listed between unseated bowl vent valve and vent valve seat. Adjust by bending vent arm of accelerating pump lever (not valve rod).

⑦—Below machined surface of float bowl.

⑧—With primary throttle plates held wide open, there should be the clearance listed between pump arm and hex nut on accelerating lever with pump held fully depressed. To adjust, hold hex nut and turn adjusting screw as required.

⑨—With fast idle screw on highest step of fast idle cam.

⑩—See Fig. ①. Primary ¾", secondary ½".

⑪—See Fig. ①. Primary 11/16", secondary 9/16".

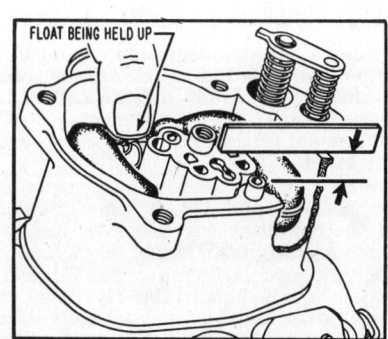

Fig. ⑫—Float level measured from machined surface of float bowl.

⑬—With engine running at hot idle speed, loosen dashpot screw. Hold throttle closed and depress dashpot plunger fully. Turn dashpot in its bracket as required to obtain the specified clearance between plunger and accelerator lever.

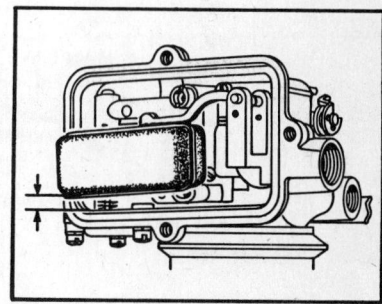

Fig. ⑭—Float level measured from roof of float chamber to lowest point of float with carburetor inverted.

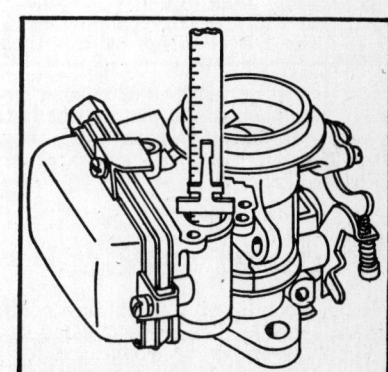

Fig. ⑮—Fuel level measured from power valve mounting surface.

Clutch and Transmission Section

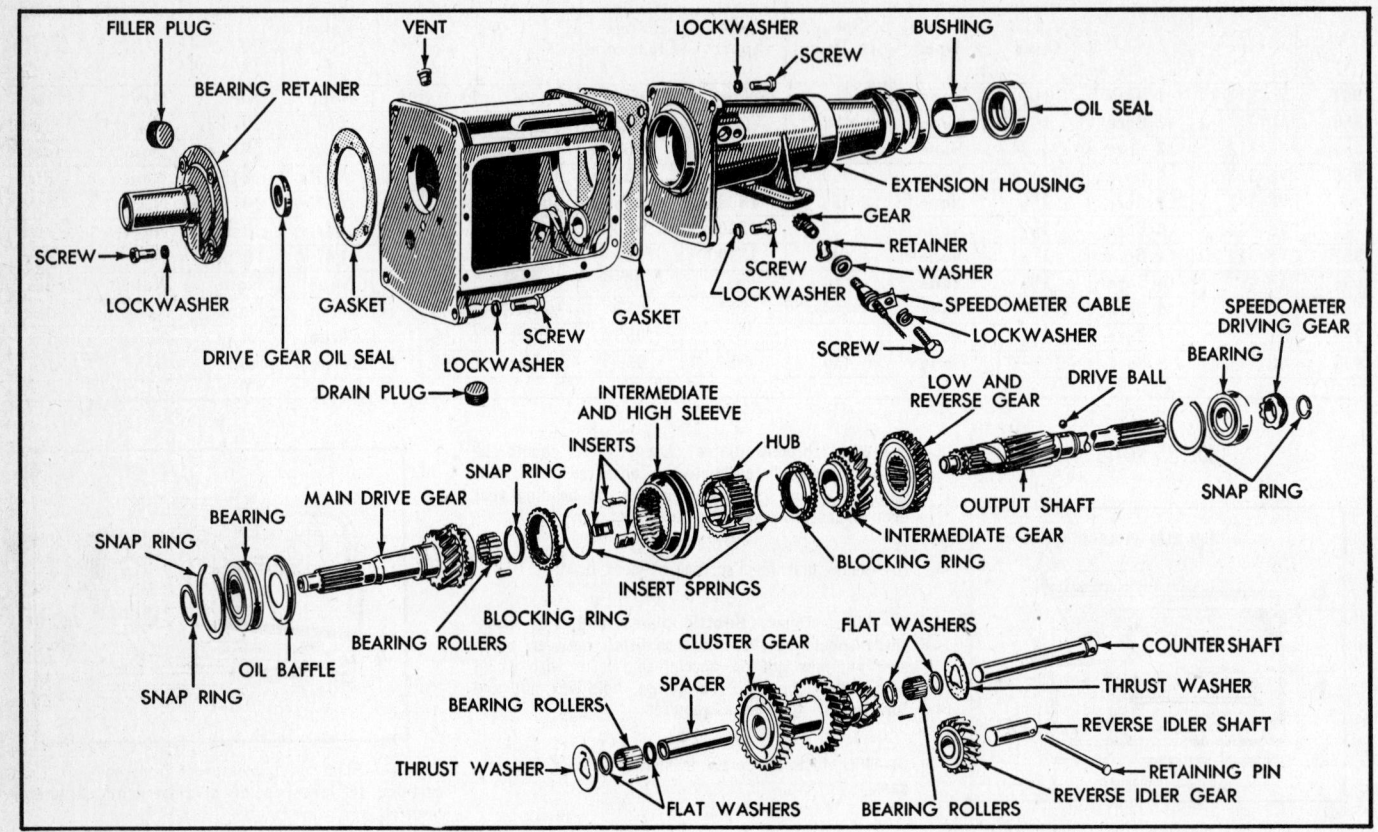

Fig. 1 Disassembled view of synchromesh transmission. 1953-54 and 1959-61

CLUTCH PEDAL, ADJUST

To check the clutch pedal free play, depress the clutch pedal by hand and measure the distance the pedal travels before the beginning of clutch disengagement is felt. The free travel should be ¾" to 1". If the travel is not within these limits, adjust as follows:

Loosen the clutch pedal release rod lock nut and turn the adjusting nut until the free pedal travel is within the above limits. Tighten the lock nut to secure the adjustment.

CLUTCH SERVICE

Unless special clutch rebuilding equipment is available, it is recommended that the clutch assembly be exchanged for a rebuilt unit should the clutch require rebuilding. The driven disc, however, may be replaced without special equipment.

1953-56

If the clutch facings become worn to the extent that clutch pedal free travel cannot be adjusted to the correct limits,

the clutch assembly should be removed and the clutch disc replaced. The clutch or disc may be removed as follows:

Remove the transmission as outlined further on. Slide the clutch release bearing and hub assembly off the end of the clutch release lever. Disconnect the clutch pedal release rod from the release lever assembly.

Remove the clutch release equalizer bar bracket from the flywheel housing and the equalizer bar. Remove the split bronze bushing from the bracket.

On all models, remove the flywheel housing. Prick-punch the flywheel and clutch cover so that at assembly these parts may be installed in their original position. Loosen the clutch-to-flywheel attaching screws a turn or two at a time until clutch pressure spring load is relieved. Then remove the screws and take the clutch from the flywheel.

1957-61

After removing the transmission as outlined further on, disengage clutch pedal retracting spring from clutch release lever. Unfasten equalizer bracket from flywheel housing. Remove flywheel housing cover. Unfasten clutch from flywheel and remove.

TRANSMISSION, REPLACE
1953-61

Drain the transmission. Disconnect gearshift linkage at the transmission. Remove speedometer cable and gear. Remove propeller shaft and necessary exhaust pipes. Unfasten the transmission extension from the engine rear support. Place a jack under the engine to relieve its weight, then remove the frame crossmember and engine rear support.

Unfasten the transmission from the clutch housing. Install two guide pins in the upper holes. Slide the transmission to the rear until the main drive gear clears the clutch housing. Then lower the transmission and pull forward to remove it from the vehicle.

When removing transmissions equipped with overdrive, be sure first to disconnect the overdrive control cable and solenoid and governor wires and remove the governor.

TRANSMISSION REPAIRS

The following describes the procedure for units without overdrive. For detailed service on the overdrive, consult the *Overdrive* chapter. To disassemble the

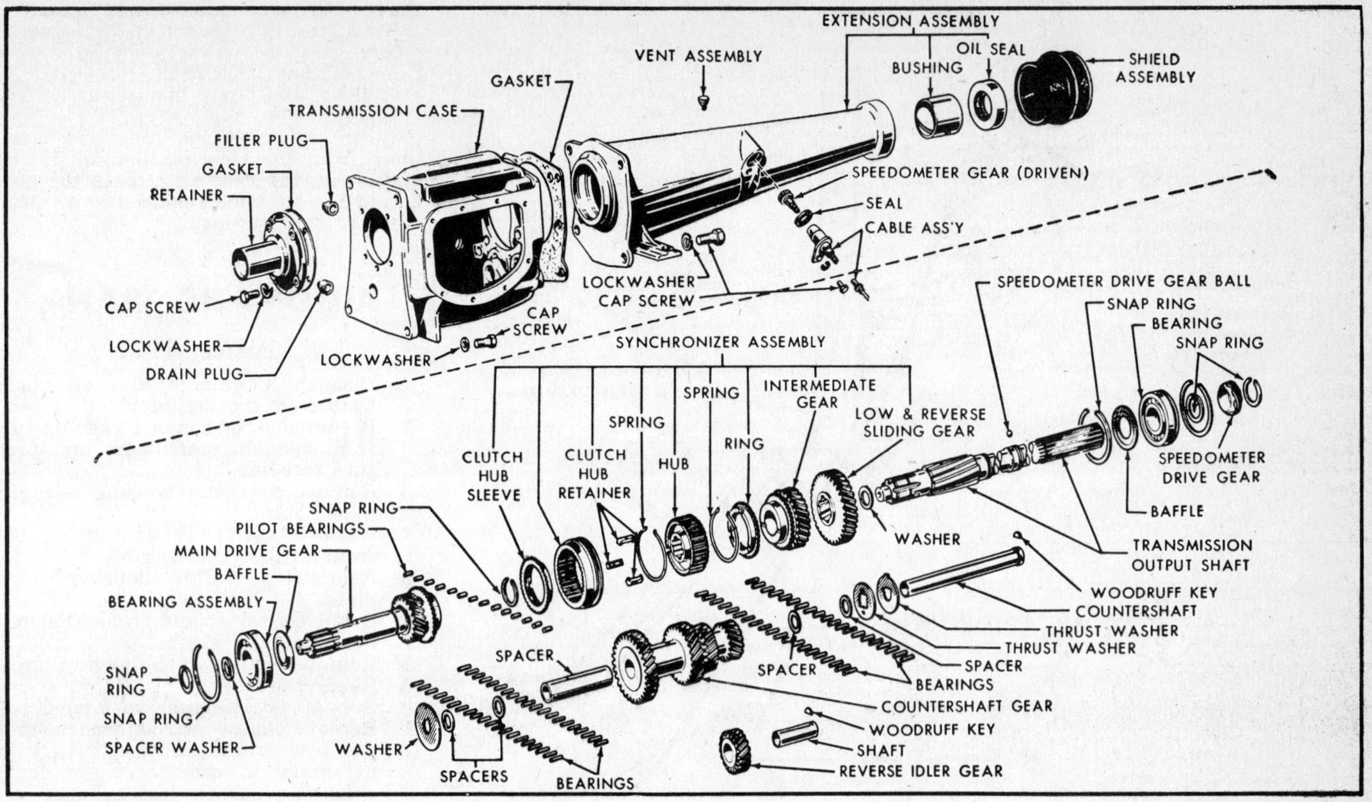

Fig. 2   Disassembled view of synchromesh transmission.   1955-58

transmission, see Figs. 1 and 2 and proceed as follows:

1. Remove gearshift housing.
2. Drive out the pin that retains the countershaft and idler gear shaft to the transmission case (prior to 1955).
3. Unfasten the extension housing and twist it ¼ turn counterclockwise to permit removal of countershaft. Drive countershaft out the rear of case, using a cluster gear roller retainer shaft tool or a spare countershaft cut to the length of the cluster gear. Leave cluster gear and dummy shaft in case until after main drive gear and mainshaft have been removed. Remove extension and mainshaft assembly from case.
4. Drive reverse idler shaft out of case and lift out reverse idler gear.
5. Unfasten and remove main drive gear bearing retainer.
6. Tap main drive gear out through front of case.
7. To disassemble mainshaft, remove snap ring that holds it to the extension housing. Tap mainshaft out of extension. Remove snap ring from in front of synchronizer and strip mainshaft of all parts.
8. After cleaning and inspecting parts, reassemble transmission by reversing the order of the foregoing procedure.

SYNCHROMESH GEARSHIFT, ADJUST
1958-61

The gearshift rods are adjusted so

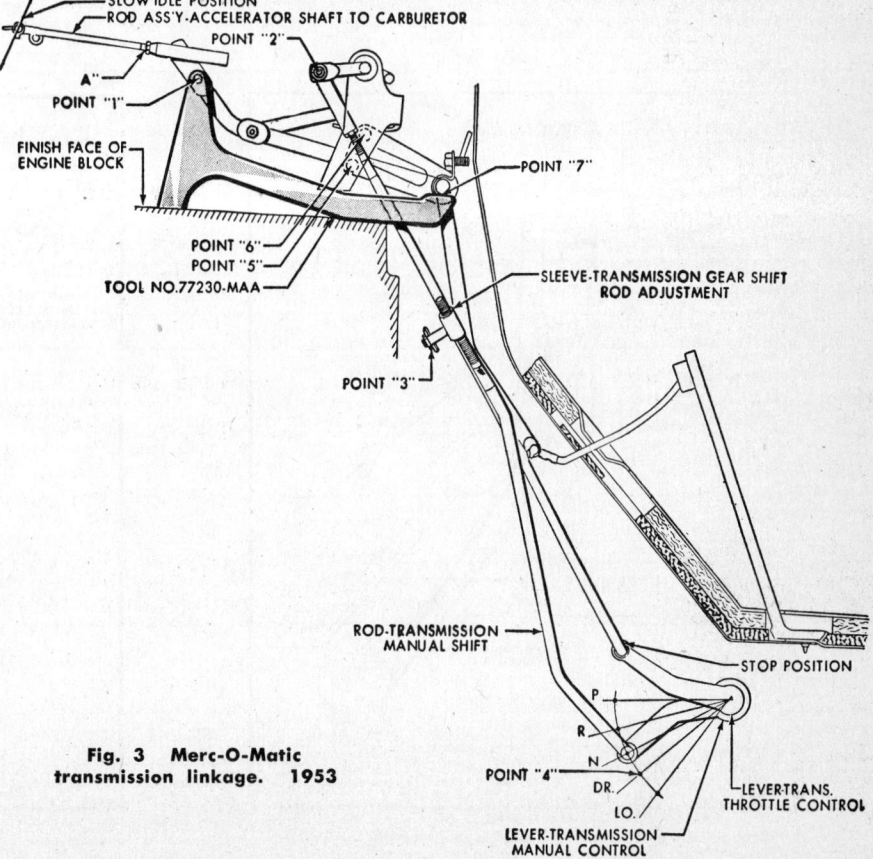

Fig. 3   Merc-O-Matic transmission linkage.   1953

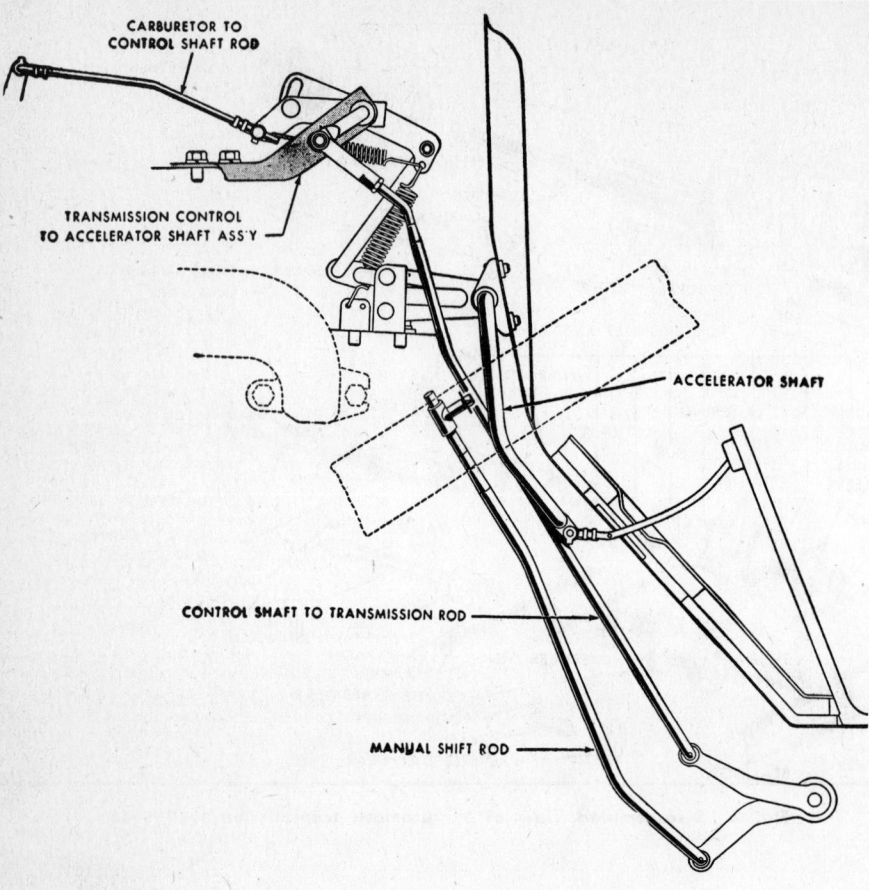

Fig. 4   Merc-O-Matic transmission linkage.   1954

that with the transmission gears in neutral, the two levers on the steering column are in line with each other. In this position, the shift lever can be moved up and down in neutral without binding.

When adjusting the rods, disconnect them from the steering column linkage and loosen the lock nuts. Turn the clevises in the direction required to establish the correct adjustment.

AUTOMATIC TRANS.

Replace, 1961

1. Disconnect linkage and oil cooler lines from transmission.
2. If equipped, disconnect vacuum tube from vacuum diaphragm and pressure test line.
3. Remove converter housing-to-engine upper bolts.
4. Remove starter motor upper bolt from right side of engine.
5. Remove converter housing lower plate.
6. Drain converter and transmission.
7. Remove drive shaft.
8. Remove converter-to-flywheel nuts.
9. Remove starter.
10. Support transmission with jack.
11. Remove engine rear support bolts.
12. Remove crossmember (it may be necessary to disconnect and lower exhaust pipes on dual exhaust jobs to provide clearance).
13. Remove converter housing-to-engine lower bolts and remove transmission and converter.
14. Reverse foregoing procedure to install.

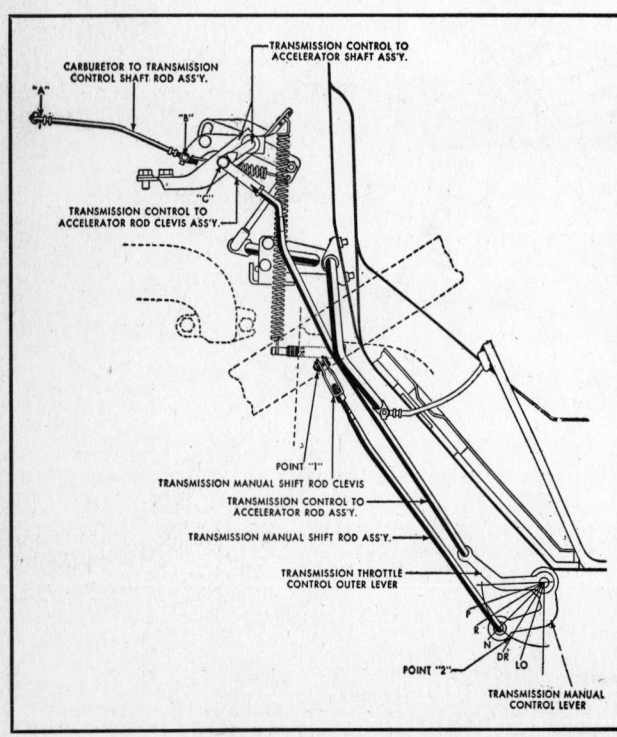

Fig. 5   Throttle control linkage adjustment.   1955

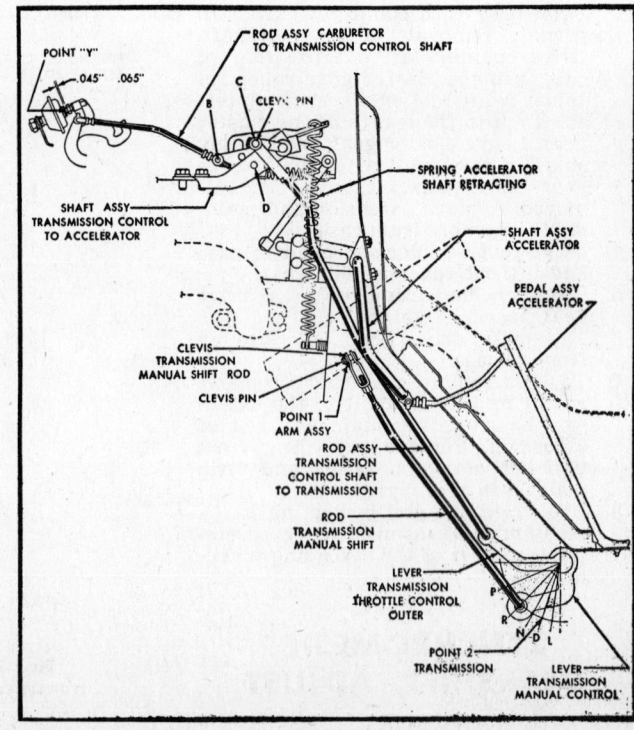

Fig. 6   Throttle linkage adjustments.   1956-57

Replace, 1960

When removing the transmission on cars with V8-312 engine, follow the procedure outlined for previous models. However, on cars equipped with V8-383 and V8-430 engines, the transmission gear box cannot be removed without also removing the torque converter and converter housing. To increase rigidity, two additional bolts are used to attach the converter housing to the case. These additional bolts are located at the rear of the converter and are not accessible in the vehicle.

Replace, 1953-59

1. To remove the transmission only, first drain fluid.
2. Disconnect linkage from transmission.
3. Disconnect speedometer cable from transmission.
4. Remove drive shaft after disconnecting rear universal joint.
5. Unfasten rear engine mount from frame cross member.
6. Support engine and transmission with separate jacks.
7. Remove rear engine mount from transmission.
8. Remove detachable cross member from frame X member.
9. Unfasten transmission from converter housing (4 bolts).
10. Pull transmission straight back and out.
11. Reverse foregoing procedure to install.

1953 Throttle Linkage

To adjust the throttle linkage, see Fig. 3 and proceed as follows:
1. Disconnect clevis pin at point "2" and loosen two bolts, points "5" and "6".

2. With the special tool in place as shown, adjust accelerator shaft so it contacts tool surfaces at point "7", and tighten bolts "5" and "6". With engine at normal operating temperature, carburetor at slow idle, adjust accelerator shaft to carburetor or rod at "A" to enter carburetor throttle arm freely.
3. Holding carburetor at slow idle, pull upward gently but firmly on rod to transmission throttle lever to position throttle lever in "stop" position at transmission. Adjust clevis at point "2" so clevis pin enters clevis and lever on control shaft freely. Remove clevis pin and tighten rod by turning clevis 2½ full turns counterclockwise and assemble in place. If adjustment is unsatisfactory, use 3 full turns. However, do not exceed 3½ full turns from the "stop" position.

1953 Manual Linkage

1. Referring to Fig. 3, disconnect manual shift rod at point "3" from control selector lever.
2. Position selector lever at steering wheel against stop in DR position.
3. Position manual lever at transmission, point "4", to second position from bottom (counting end position as first position).
4. Adjust manual shift rod so gearshift rod adjustment sleeve enters grommet hole freely at point "3". Disengage sleeve and lengthen manual shift rod by turning adjustment sleeve one full turn counterclockwise, and assemble in place.
5. Check position of selector lever in all ranges.

1954 Throttle Linkage

The new linkage, Fig. 4, is designed to accommodate the new overhead valve engine. The adjustment is as follows:
1. Disconnect carburetor-to-control shaft rod at carburetor.
2. Remove clevis pin that secures transmission control rod to transmission control shaft.
3. Insert gauge pin through control rod and shaft bracket.
4. With engine at operating temperature and on slow idle, adjust carburetor-to-control shaft rod so that it enters the hole in the carburetor freely. If rod is too long, shorten one full turn and assemble into hole in carburetor.
5. Remove positioning pin gauge.
6. While holding carburetor throttle in slow idle position, hold control shaft-to-transmission rod against its stop and adjust the length of the rod to allow free entry of the clevis pin in the hole in the transmission control shaft. Then lengthen the rod by turning the clevis three full turns in a counterclockwise direction.
7. Install the clevis pin and tighten the lock nut. *If a clutch or band slip is indicated after completing the adjustment, the rod may be lengthened another complete turn but the complete adjustment must never exceed a total of four turns from the "stop" position.*

1954 Manual Linkage

This adjustment is made in the same manner as outlined for earlier models. Refer to Fig. 3 for adjusting points.

1955 Throttle Linkage

1. Referring to Fig. 5, set the hand brake and adjust the engine idle at 425-450 rpm with transmission in Drive range.
2. Disconnect clevis at point "C" and insert gauge pin through shaft and bracket.
3. Set carburetor at low idle at point "A".
4. Adjust carburetor-to-transmission control shaft rod so that goes in freely at point "A". If too long, shorten one turn and assemble at "A".
5. Remove gauge pin.
6. Holding carburetor arm in low idle

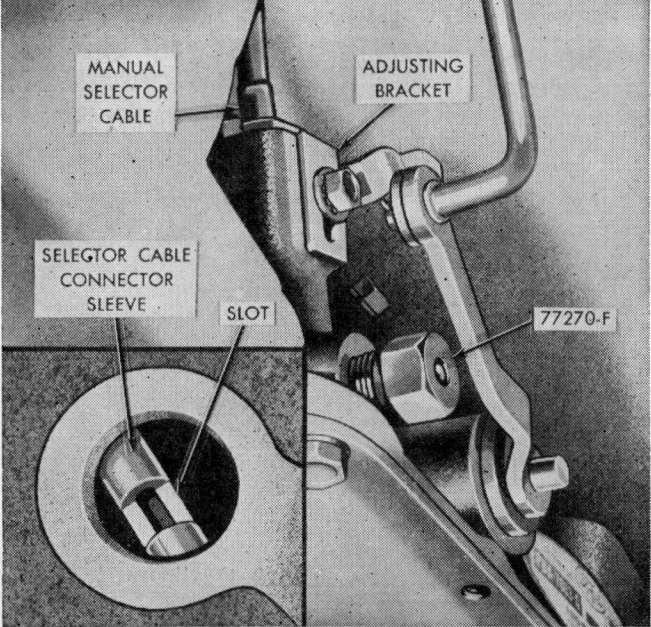

Fig. 7 Manual selector cable adjustment. 1958 automatic transmissions

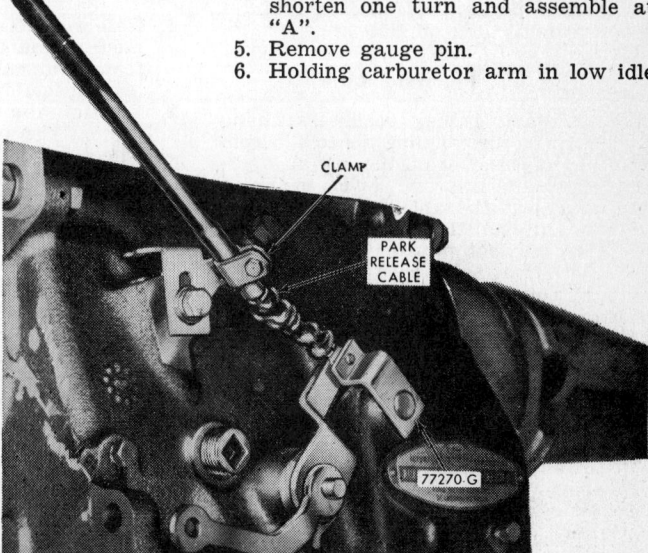

Fig. 8 Park release cable adjustment. 1958 automatic transmissions

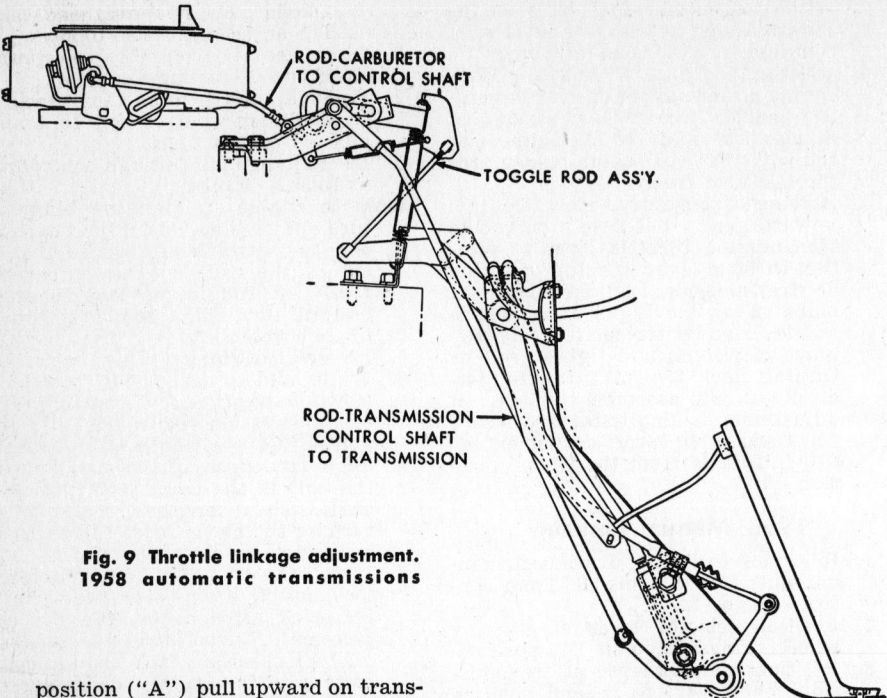

ROD-CARBURETOR TO CONTROL SHAFT

TOGGLE ROD ASS'Y.

ROD-TRANSMISSION CONTROL SHAFT TO TRANSMISSION

Fig. 9 Throttle linkage adjustment. 1958 automatic transmissions

position ("A") pull upward on transmission control-to-accelerator rod. This positions transmission control outer lever in stop position at transmission. Adjust clevis at point "C" so that clevis pin enters clevis and lever freely. Lengthen rod by turning clevis three full turns counterclockwise and assemble in place.

1955 Manual Adjustment

1. Referring to Fig. 5, disconnect clevis at point "1".
2. Position manual lever at point "1" so pointer at steering wheel is against stop in "DR" position.
3. Position manual lever at transmission at point "2".
4. Adjust manual shift rod so that clevis pin enters the hole freely. Then lengthen rod by turning clevis one full turn.
5. Check position of selector pointer at all positions on dial.

1956-57 Throttle Linkage

Before starting this procedure, set hand brake and adjust engine idle to 425 rpm with engine and transmission at operating temperature and lever in Drive range. Adjust the anti-stall dashpot by turning the throttle lever set screw out until the dashpot plunger bottoms, then backing off to give .045" - .065" clearance at point "Y" on Fig. 6. Then proceed as follows:

1. Disconnect clevis at point "C" as shown in Fig. 6.
2. Disconnect carburetor to transmission control shaft rod at carburetor.
3. Insert gauge pin through bellcrank and bracket in transmission control to accelerator shaft assembly at point "D".
4. Set carburetor arm at low idle manually.
5. Adjust carburetor to transmission control shaft rod so that with trunnion pin in place at point "B"

trunnion pin at carburetor end will go in freely.
6. With gauge pin locking bellcrank, pull upward gently on transmission control shaft to transmission rod assembly. This will position the throttle lever in the stop at the transmission.
7. Adjust clevis at point "C" so the clevis pin enters the clevis and lever on transmission control to accelerator shaft assembly.
8. Then, lengthen transmission control shaft to transmission rod assembly by turning clevis 3 full turns counterclockwise and assemble in place.
9. Remove the gauge pin.

1956 Manual Adjustment

1. Referring to Fig. 6, disconnect transmission manual shift rod assembly from transmission control selector arm assembly at point "1".
2. Position the manual lever at point "1" so the pointer at the steering wheel is against the stop in Drive position.
3. Position transmission manual control lever so it is in the second position from the bottom at point "2".
4. Adjust transmission manual shift rod so the clevis pin enters the hole freely, then lengthen the rod by turning the clevis one full turn.
5. Check position of pointer at all stations on the dial.

1957 Manual Linkage

1. Depress L button until it latches.
2. Raise car and attach detent selector cable to transmission by pushing cable downward into selector cable guide hole in transmission case. Selector cable retainer spring is most easily engaged when the low gear

selector button is depressed. Test to find if retainer spring is engaged by pushing upward on cable. The cable cannot be removed if retainer spring has engaged.
3. Attach control cable mounting bracket to groove in cable casing. Install bracket retaining bolt and washer *finger tight*.
4. Move mounting bracket and cable upward to limit of slot travel in mounting bracket. Rotate Park Lever counterclockwise against "LO" stop in case. Hold Park Lever in this position and tighten screw to insure correct position of "LO" detent.
5. Torque bracket bolt 18-22 lb. ft.

1957 Park Release Cable

1. After selector cable has been adjusted, depress N/S button until it latches. *Tape the park slide fully back in the pull out position.*
2. Route the park release cable through retaining clip at transmission, leaving clip retainer screw loose enough so that cable can be adjusted forward or back. Pull cable core lightly toward rear of car to remove slack.
3. With N/S button in latched position, rotate park release lever counterclockwise to its neutral stop position. Hold lever in this position and adjust park release cable so that the hole in the cable aligns with pin in lever. Then attach park release cable to park release lever.
4. Tighten screw and bracket. Attach retracting spring to park lever pin.
5. With engine running and transmission at normal operating temperature, push all of the buttons and note whether the desired ratios are obtained.

1958 Manual Selector Cable

1. Raise car, remove splash shield and pipe plug from left side of transmission case.
2. Remove park release control cable from lever and clamp.
3. Loosen control cable mounting bracket retaining screw and washer leaving it finger-tight).
4. On Merc-O-Matic, hold Drive button on transmission keyboard selector in the fully depressed position. On Multi-Drive, hold Cruising range button in fully depressed position.
5. Move adjusting bracket downward to limit of travel.
6. Install tool shown in place of pipe plug in transmission case, Fig. 7.
7. Pull upward on selector cable and housing assembly until pin in gauge seats in locating slot of selector cable connector sleeve (see insert in Fig. 7).
8. Leaving tool in place, torque control cable mounting screw to 18-22 lb. ft.
9. With gauge installed, pull gauge pin out and hold out so selector cable connector sleeve will clear. Depress the "Neutral Start" button and release the gauge pin so it contacts connector sleeve. Now depress "Drive" button and check to see that gauge pin seats in the locating slot

in the selector cable connector sleeve.
Release the gauge pin and depress
the "Drive" button. If the gauge pin
fails to seat in the slot the selector
cable must be readjusted.

10. Remove gauge and replace pipe plug.

1958 Park Cable, Adjust

A correct park release cable adjustment cannot be obtained until proper
selector cable adjustment is completed.

1. Install park cable on the pin of the
   park release lever and install clamp
   and screw on adjusting bracket.
2. Fully depress park bar on keyboard
   selector.
3. On small transmissions, install
   Gauge 77270-E over torsion lever
   support pin in transmission case and
   the pin on the park release lever as
   shown in Fig. 8. On large transmissions, use Gauge 77270-G.
4. Remove cable slack by pulling cable
   housing toward rear of car.
5. Holding cable in this position, tight-
   en cable clamp screw.
6. Remove gauge tool.
7. Install washer and retaining pin in
   park release lever pin.
8. Check operation of all selector buttons and the park bar.

1958 Throttle Linkage, Adjust

1. Referring to Fig. 9, adjust toggle
   rod for shortest overall length.
2. Attach one end of rod to accelerator
   shaft and other end to transmission
   control shaft.
3. Measure distance between bottom
   surface of accelerator pedal and bare
   floor pan. This distance should be
   4 inches.
4. To raise pedal to required height,
   lengthen the rod; to lower pedal,
   shorten rod.
5. After pedal height is adjusted, have
   someone depress accelerator pedal
   to floor while a check is made to
   see that the "kickdown" mechanism
   is properly adjusted. This is determined by watching for additional
   movement of the transmission control shaft after the throttle is fully
   opened. The added movement of the
   shaft will cause the pin to override
   the full throttle position in the slot

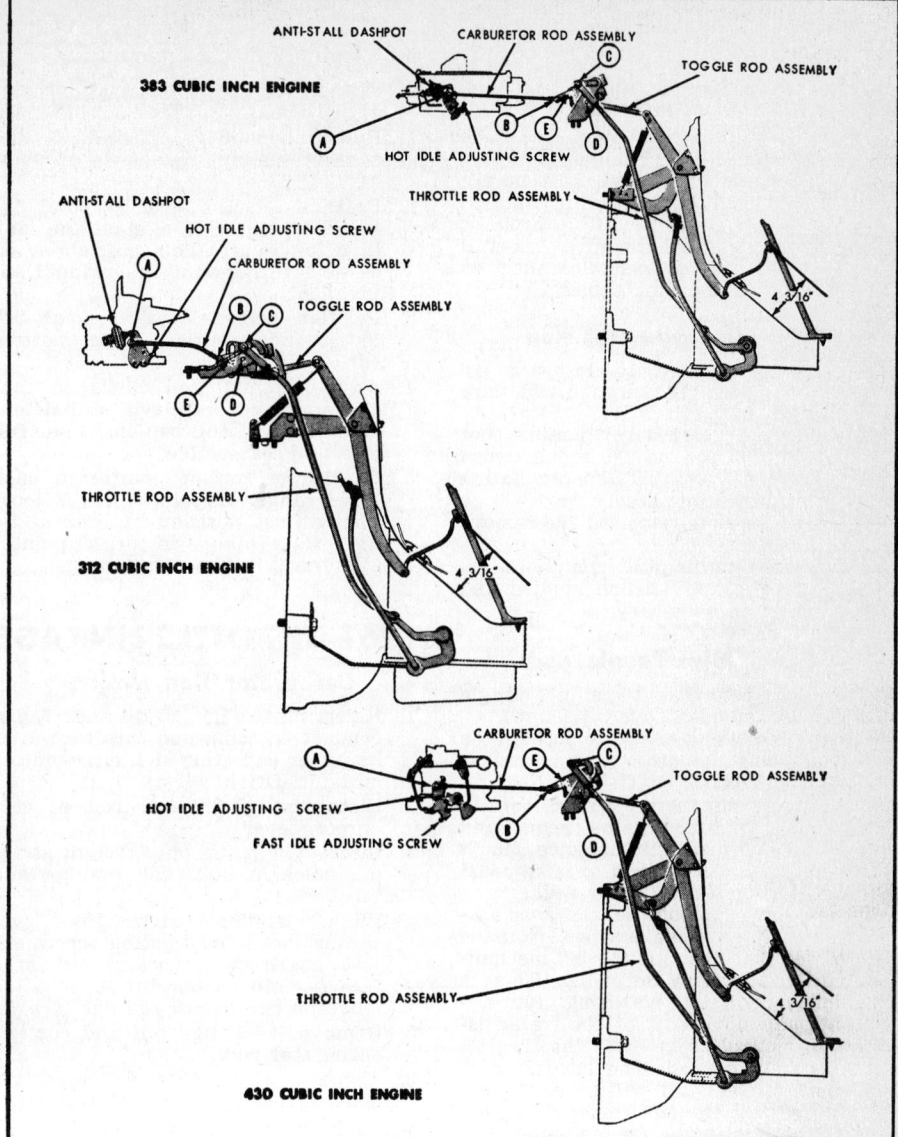

Fig. 10 Throttle linkage adjustments. 1959

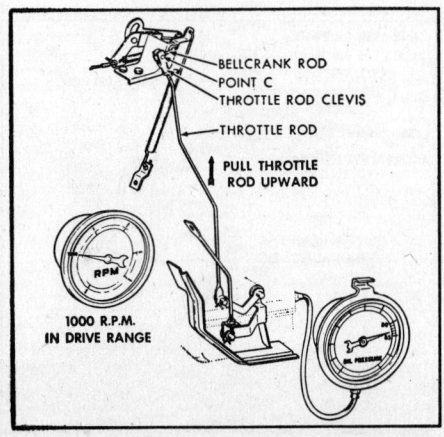

Fig. 11 Throttle rod adjustments. 1959

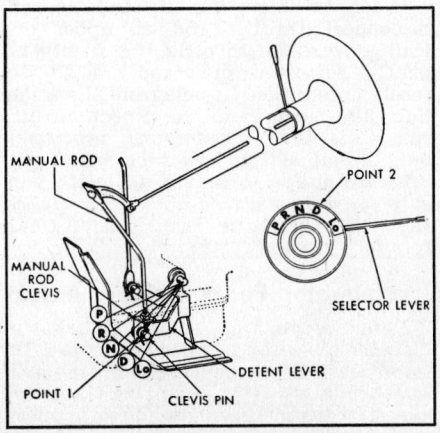

Fig. 12 Mercomatic manual linkage. 1959

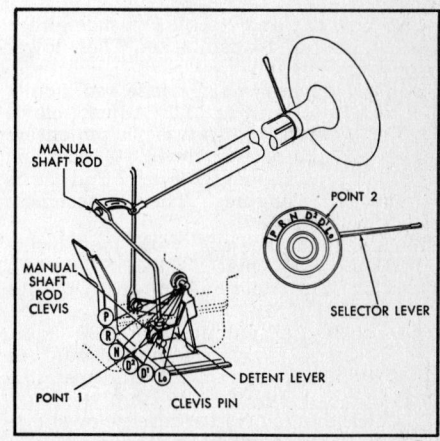

Fig. 13 Multi-drive manual linkage. 1959

in the transmission control-to-accelerator shaft assembly. If kickdown is not obtained, lengthen rod slightly.

1959-60 Linkage

Linkage adjustments must be made in the sequence which follows: First, however, engine idle speed must be adjusted to 450-475 rpm with manual lever in "D" position for Mercomatic or "D2" for Multi-Drive. Be sure anti-stall dashpot has the proper clearance as given in the carburetor tables.

1959-60 Carburetor Rod

1. Referring to Fig. 10, insert a ¼" drill at point "D" through bellcrank bracket and tab.
2. Hold carburetor lever against hot idle screw and adjust rod between points "A" and "B" so pin enters carburetor lever freely.
3. Assemble carburetor rod and remove ¼" drill.
4. Recheck engine idle rpm with retracting spring tension applied and readjust if necessary.

1959 (Only) Toggle Rod

1. Referring to Fig. 10, adjust toggle rod for shortest overall length.
2. Attach one end of rod to accelerator shaft and the other end to transmission control shaft.
3. Measure distance between bottom surface of accelerator pedal and bare floor pan. This distance should be 4 3/16". Lengthen rod to raise pedal or shorten rod to lower pedal.
4. Now have someone depress accelerator to floor while a check is made to see that the "kickdown" mechanism is properly adjusted. This is determined by watching for additional movement of the transmission control shaft after the throttle has fully opened. The added movement of the shaft will cause the pin to override the full throttle position in the slot in the transmission control-to-accelerator shaft (refer to point "E").
5. If kickdown is not obtained, lengthen toggle rod slightly.

1959-60 Throttle Rod

1. Raise car and install pressure gauge at rear of transmission. Then lower car.
2. Pull upward on throttle rod firmly but gently, Fig. 11. Adjust clevis at point "C" so that clevis pin enters freely. Lengthen clevis 3½ turns on 383 and 430 engines or 2 full turns on 312 engines. Then reassemble throttle rod.
3. Start engine and with foot brake firmly set, place selector lever in "D" for Mercomatic or "D2" for Multi-Drive.
4. Accelerate engine to 1000 rpm. Pressure gauge reading should be 80-85 psi. To correct the pressure, adjust length of throttle rod. Lengthen clevis to increase or shorten clevis to decrease pressure. *These checks must be made quickly. The selector must be returned to neutral*

position and the throttle closed after each check to avoid overheating the transmission.
5. Remove pressure gauge.

1959-60 Manual Linkage

1. Referring to Figs. 12 and 13, disconnect manual rod clevis at point "1".
2. Position selector lever at point "2" so that pointer is against the stop in drive range. This position must be held throughout the manual adjustment.
3. Position detent lever at point "1" in second position from bottom (drive detent).
4. Adjust manual rod clevis so that clevis pin enters clevis and detent lever freely. Lengthen clevis one full turn and reassemble.
5. Check position of pointer in each drive range. If pointer is off location, adjust position of letters. *Do not adjust linkage to correct pointer alignment in the other ranges.*

1961 THROTTLE LINKAGE

Carburetor Rod, Adjust

1. Referring to Figs. 15, 16 and 17, disconnect transmission throttle rod at its upper end (this step not required on Multi-Drive).
2. Disconnect carburetor rod at carburetor lever.
3. Insert ¼" gauge pin through gauge pin holes in bellcrank bracket and tab.
4. While holding carburetor lever against hot idle adjusting screw, adjust length of carburetor rod for a free fit into carburetor lever. *Then lengthen carburetor rod one turn.*
5. Remove ¼" gauge pin and connect carburetor rod.
6. Recheck alignment of gauge pin holes in bellcrank and tab. Further adjustment of carburetor rod may be required as the ¼" gauge alignment holes must be in alignment to assure correct carburetor-to-transmission calibration.

Throttle Rod, Adjust

Refer to Figs. 14, 15 and 16, and disconnect throttle rod at upper end. Pull upward on throttle rod firmly but gently. Adjust throttle rod link so stud freely enters hole in bellcrank. Lengthen link 3½ turns and reconnect throttle rod. *This is a preliminary adjustment only. Final setting must be made with pressure gauge to assure adequate pressure for proper clutch and band application. See Automatic Transmission Chapters for pressure testing procedures.*

Accelerator Pedal Height, Adjust

Referring to Figs. 14 and 17, measure distance from top of accelerator pedal to floor mat. This measurement must be approximately 3½". Road test car and check transmission "kickdown" operation. If "kickdown" cannot be obtained or if it occurs too early, shorten or lengthen the accelerator link as required.

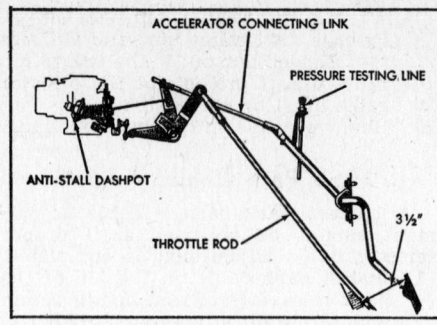

Fig. 14   Throttle linkage for 1961 Six

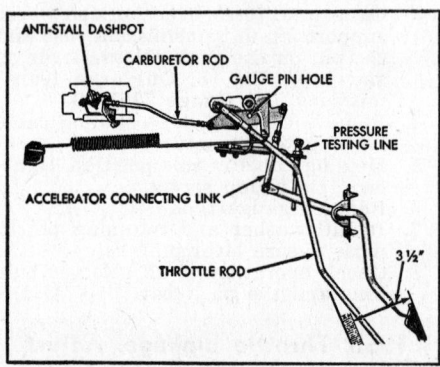

Fig. 15   Throttle linkage for 1961 V8 with two-speed Mercomatic

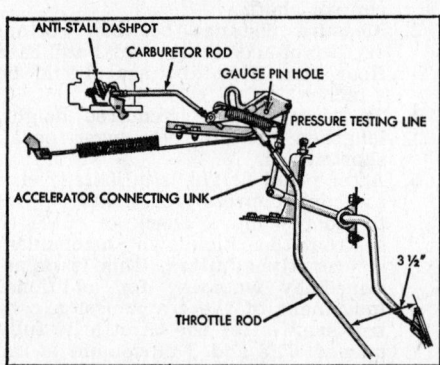

Fig. 16   Throttle linkage for 1961 V8 with three-speed Mercomatic

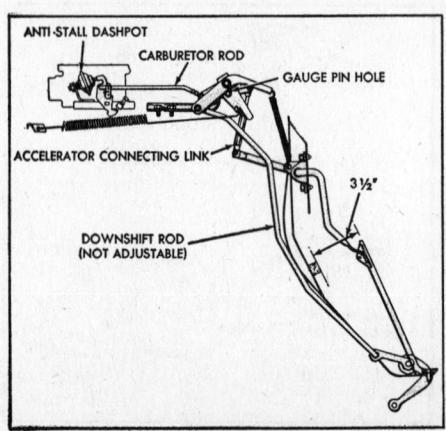

Fig. 17   Throttle linkage for 1961 Multi-Drive

Rear Axle and Brake Section

Refer To Hydraulic Brakes Chapter For Brake Adjustments

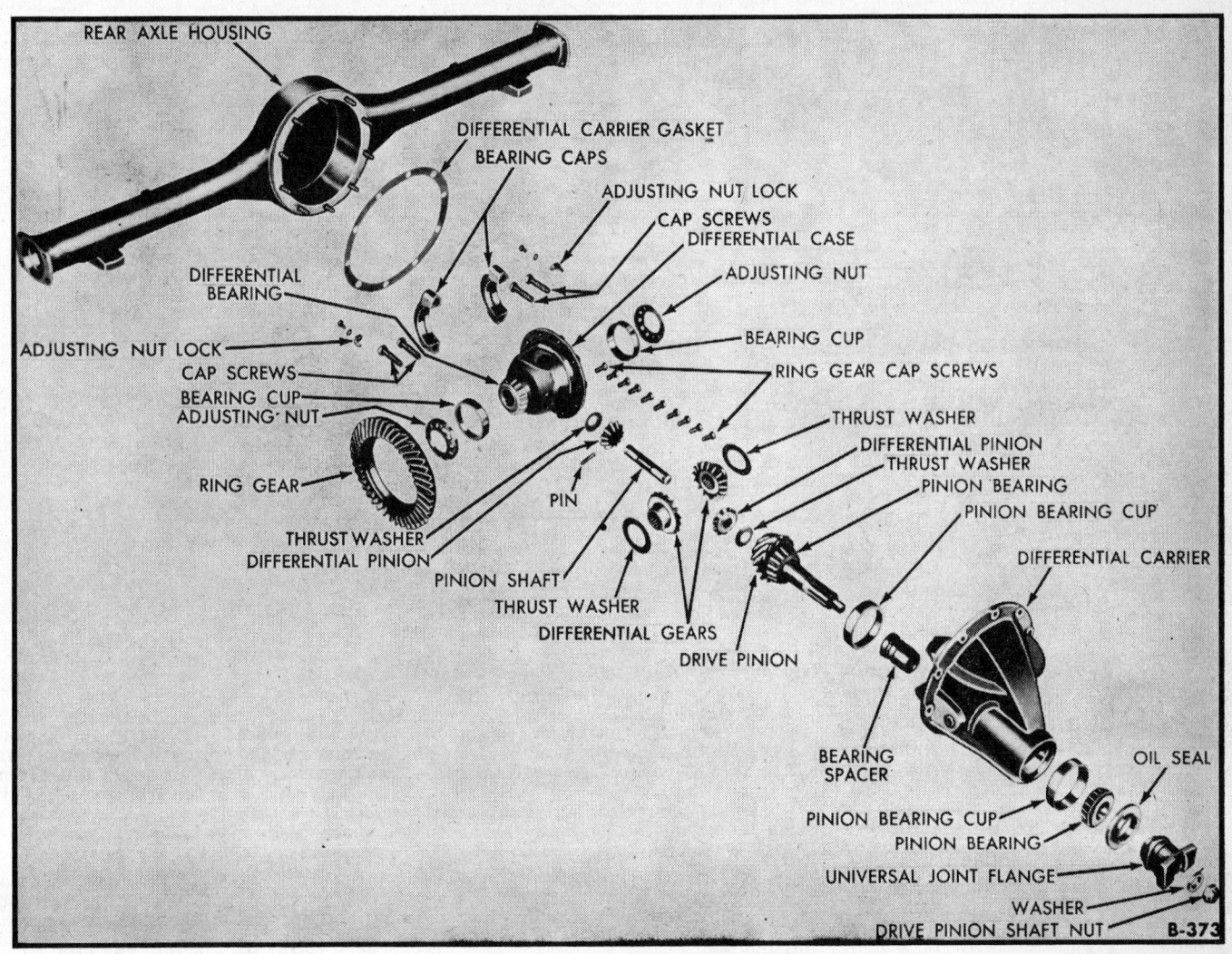

REAR AXLE HOUSING
DIFFERENTIAL CARRIER GASKET
BEARING CAPS
ADJUSTING NUT LOCK
CAP SCREWS
DIFFERENTIAL CASE
DIFFERENTIAL BEARING
ADJUSTING NUT
BEARING CUP
ADJUSTING NUT LOCK
CAP SCREWS
RING GEAR CAP SCREWS
BEARING CUP
ADJUSTING NUT
THRUST WASHER
RING GEAR
DIFFERENTIAL PINION
THRUST WASHER
PINION BEARING
PIN
PINION BEARING CUP
THRUST WASHER
DIFFERENTIAL PINION
DIFFERENTIAL CARRIER
PINION SHAFT
THRUST WASHER
DIFFERENTIAL GEARS
DRIVE PINION
BEARING SPACER
OIL SEAL
PINION BEARING CUP
PINION BEARING
UNIVERSAL JOINT FLANGE
WASHER
DRIVE PINION SHAFT NUT
B-373

Fig. 1   Layout of 1953-54 passenger car rear axle

REAR AXLE, REPLACE

1955-56 Passenger Car,
1953-56 Station Wagon

Inasmuch as the differential carrier is part of the rear axle housing, it is advisable to remove the entire rear axle assembly if the differential is to be overhauled. The procedure is as follows:

1. Lift the rear of the car with a chain hoist attached to the bumper.
2. Set chassis support stands under the frame side rails ahead of the spring front hangers.
3. Drain differential housing.
4. Remove axle shafts and propeller shaft.
5. Remove hydraulic brake line clips from axle housing and free brake line from differential housing. Wire hydraulic line to frame.
6. Raise axle housing with a jack until shock absorbers start to compress. Remove nut holding shock absorber to spring seat.
7. Remove U-bolts attaching axle housing to springs.
8. Lower rear axle assembly to the floor.

1953-54 Passenger Car & All 1957-61

It is not necessary to remove the entire rear axle assembly to service the differential assembly. After removing the axle shafts as described further on, unfasten the differential carrier from the axle housing and lift it out.

REAR AXLE, REPAIRS

1953-54 Passenger Car

Fig. 1. Before the differential carrier assembly can be taken out, the axle shafts must be removed (how this is done is explained further on).

The splined universal joint flange is fastened to the pinion shaft with a nut which seats directly on the counterbore in the flange.

The drive pinion is mounted on taper roller bearings. Adjustment of the pinion along its axis is obtained by shims placed between the rear bearing outer race and

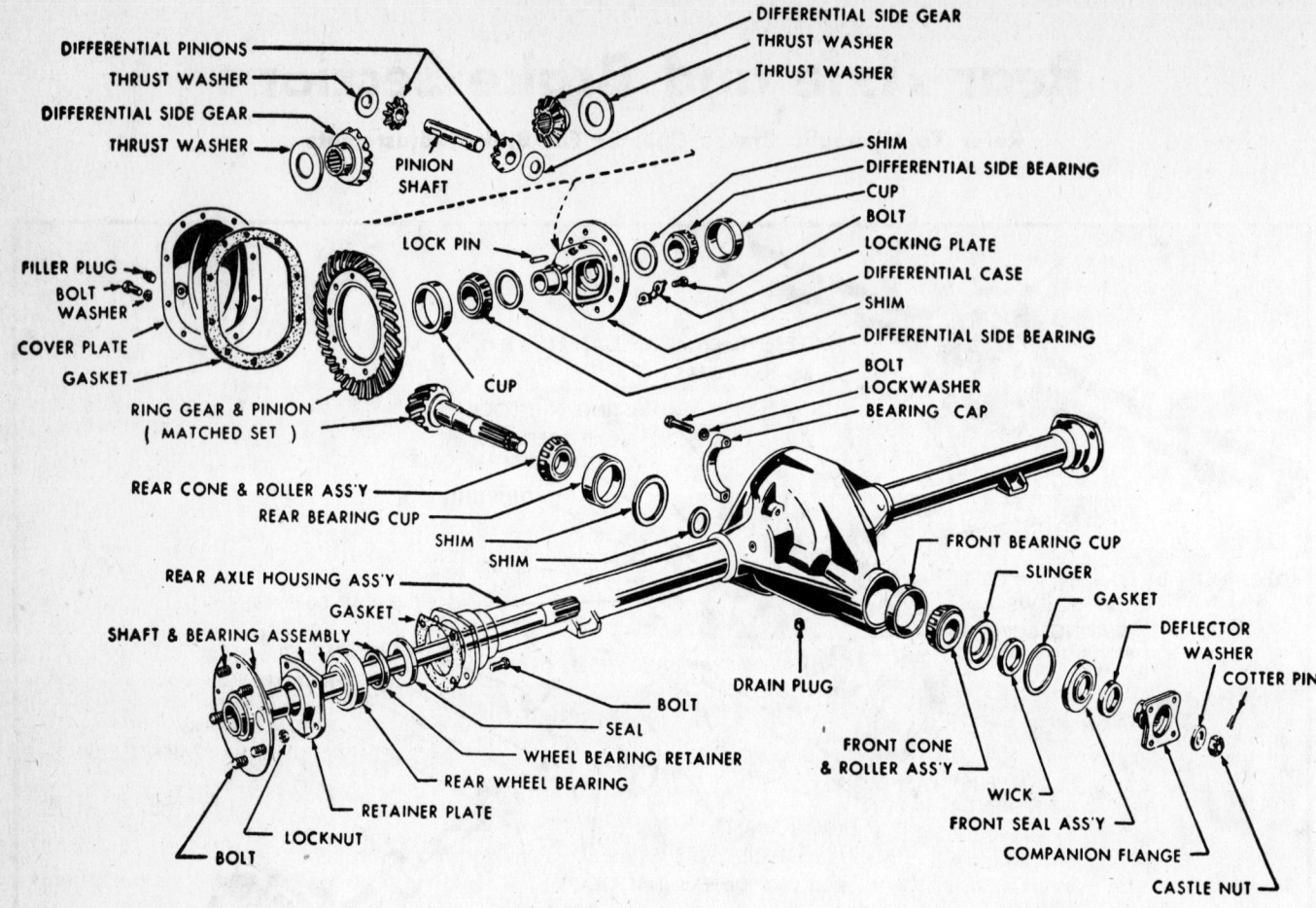

DIFFERENTIAL PINIONS
THRUST WASHER
DIFFERENTIAL SIDE GEAR
THRUST WASHER
PINION SHAFT
DIFFERENTIAL SIDE GEAR
THRUST WASHER
THRUST WASHER
LOCK PIN
SHIM
DIFFERENTIAL SIDE BEARING
CUP
BOLT
LOCKING PLATE
DIFFERENTIAL CASE
SHIM
DIFFERENTIAL SIDE BEARING
BOLT
LOCKWASHER
BEARING CAP
FILLER PLUG
BOLT
WASHER
COVER PLATE
GASKET
RING GEAR & PINION
(MATCHED SET)
CUP
REAR CONE & ROLLER ASS'Y
REAR BEARING CUP
SHIM
SHIM
REAR AXLE HOUSING ASS'Y
GASKET
SHAFT & BEARING ASSEMBLY
FRONT BEARING CUP
SLINGER
GASKET
DEFLECTOR WASHER
COTTER PIN
DRAIN PLUG
FRONT CONE & ROLLER ASS'Y
WICK
FRONT SEAL ASS'Y
COMPANION FLANGE
CASTLE NUT
BOLT
SEAL
WHEEL BEARING RETAINER
REAR WHEEL BEARING
RETAINER PLATE
LOCKNUT
BOLT

Fig. 2   Rear axle.   1953-54 station wagon and all 1955-56

a shoulder in the carrier. Preload of the two bearings is obtained by tightening the universal flange nut which compresses a spacer over the pinion shaft between the bearings. Both bearing outer races are pressed into the carrier, the rear race against pinion adjusting shims, the front race against the shoulder in the carrier. The rear bearing inner race is pressed onto the pinion shaft to a shoulder at the pinion end. The front bearing is a light press fit to a close sliding fit on the pinion shaft.

The threaded nut type of differential bearing adjustment is used. The procedure for making this adjustment, as well as the assembly of the differential case, replacing a ring gear, checking ring gear and pinion backlash, and other differential case operations, is given in the *Rear Axle* chapter.

Pinion & Bearings, Replace

After removing the differential unit from the carrier, unscrew the pinion flange retaining nut and pull off the flange. Press the pinion out of the front bearing and through the rear end of the carrier. The rear bearing cone and bearing spacer will come out with the pinion. The bearings may then be removed and installed with suitable pulling equipment.

Reverse the operations to assemble and, after pressing on the flange, slip on

the washer and nut. Tighten the nut until the bearings have a preload drag of 22 to 28 inch pounds of torque to rotate the pinion shaft.

To adjust the preload, draw up the nut with a torque wrench until the spacer starts to buckle. This adjustment must be made every time the flange nut is removed or loosened. If the adjustment is to be made with the differential in the carrier, the rear wheels must be jacked off the floor.

Drive Pinion Position

The drive pinion position usually does not require adjustment other than the bearing preload unless a new pinion bearing cup is installed. If a new rear bearing cup is installed, check the pinion position by using a micrometer depth gauge as outlined in the *Rear Axle* chapter. If the depth of the pinion measures more than 2.000" (plus or minus .002") it will be necessary to install shims in back of the pinion shaft rear bearing cup. Shims are available in .003, .005, .010, and .020" thicknesses for this purpose.

Note—A new pinion bearing spacer is required when a new ring gear and pinion set is installed, when any part of either pinion bearing is changed, when a new carrier casting is used, or when pinion adjusting shim thickness is increased. When the same universal joint flange is removed and reinstalled (as when an oil

seal is replaced) checking for pinion bearing preload with a torque wrench is not necessary if care is taken to tighten the nut exactly to its previous position. Should a new flange be required, a torque wrench reading should be taken before loosening the nut and the nut tightened to the same torque wrench reading.

1955-56 Passenger Car, 1953-56 Station Wagon

In this type axle, Fig. 2, the drive pinion is held in position by shoulders in the differential carrier, upon which the pinion bearing cups seat. The pinion position is maintained by shims located between the rear bearing and the rear shoulder in the differential carrier. Shims between the bearing spacer and the front bearing cone are used to adjust pinion bearings.

The shimmed type of differential bearing adjustment is employed. The procedure for making this adjustment, as well as the assembly of the differential case, replacing the ring gear, checking ring gear and pinion backlash, and other differential case operations, is given in the *Rear Axle* chapter.

The axle tubes are pressed into the differential carrier to form a one-piece housing. To overhaul the unit, therefore, the rear axle assembly must be removed from the chassis.

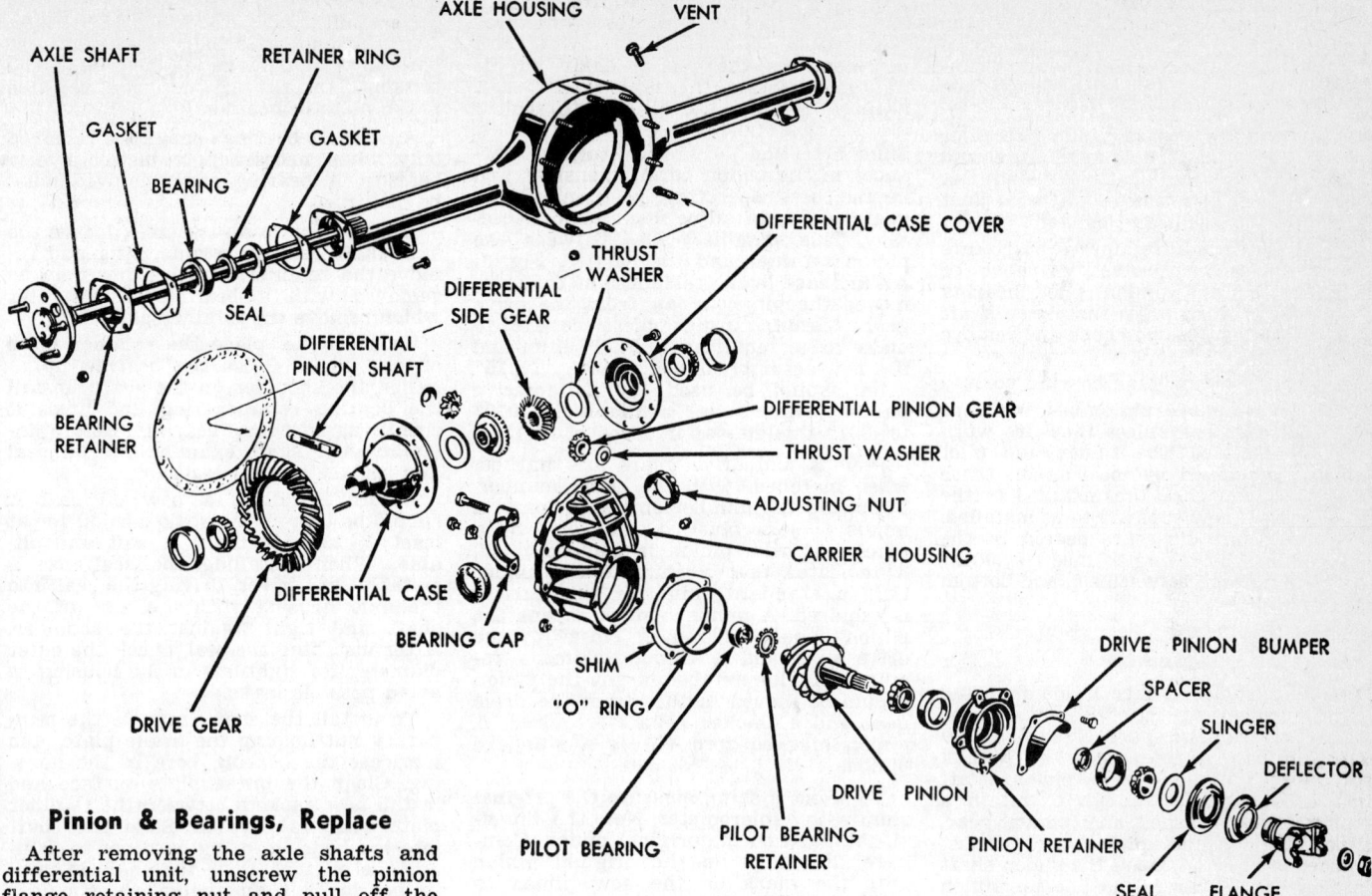

AXLE SHAFT
RETAINER RING
AXLE HOUSING
VENT
GASKET
GASKET
BEARING
SEAL
DIFFERENTIAL CASE COVER
DIFFERENTIAL SIDE GEAR
THRUST WASHER
DIFFERENTIAL PINION SHAFT
BEARING RETAINER
DIFFERENTIAL PINION GEAR
THRUST WASHER
ADJUSTING NUT
CARRIER HOUSING
DIFFERENTIAL CASE
DRIVE GEAR
BEARING CAP
SHIM
"O" RING
PILOT BEARING
PILOT BEARING RETAINER
DRIVE PINION
PINION RETAINER
SEAL
FLANGE
DRIVE PINION BUMPER
SPACER
SLINGER
DEFLECTOR

Fig. 3 Exploded view of 1957-61 rear axle

Pinion & Bearings, Replace

After removing the axle shafts and differential unit, unscrew the pinion flange retaining nut and pull off the flange. The pinion may then be removed from the carrier by driving it out of the front bearing with a brass drift and hammer. After the pinion is free of the front bearing, pull it out through the rear of the carrier.

Mount the pinion in a press and press the pinion shaft out of the bearing. When replacing the bearing select a suitable sleeve or length of pipe of the same diameter as the cone so the rollers or cage will not be damaged when being forced on the shaft.

Drive the front bearing cup and oil seal out of the forward end of the carrier. If the rear bearing cup is to be replaced or if the pinion setting is to be changed, remove the rear bearing cup. To change the pinion setting, the shims behind the rear bearing cup should be measured with a micrometer. The necessary shims may then be removed or added to obtain the proper pinion setting as indicated when a pinion setting gauge is used (see *Rear Axle* Chapter). After the required shims have been added or subtracted, replace the rear bearing cup. When making a pinion adjustment, the same thickness of pinion bearing adjusting shims should be added or removed at the rear bearing cup to retain the proper pinion bearing adjustment.

To install the pinion, support it under the head with a wood block while the pinion flange is reinstalled. The pinion oil seal should not be replaced until after the pinion setting has been checked.

Pinion Bearings, Adjust

The only occasion for adjusting the

drive pinion bearings is when a new pinion or differential carrier is installed. To make the adjustment, install sufficient shims between the bearing spacer and front bearing so that when the pinion retaining nut is tightened against the pinion flange, all rollers in the bearing are tight, but still permit rotating the pinion by hand.

Pinion, Adjust

After adjusting the pinion bearings, the position of the pinion may be checked. If a pinion setting gauge is available, check the pinion depth as outlined in the *Rear Axle* Chapter. If a correction is necessary, disassemble the pinion and, if it is to be moved toward the center of the axle, add shims between the rear bearing and rear shoulder in the carrier. If the pinion has to be moved away from the center of the axle, remove shims from this point.

If no pinion setting gauge is available, assemble the differential unit in the carrier and check the tooth contact by painting the ring gear teeth as described in the *Rear Axle* Chapter. After satisfactory tooth contact has been established, remove the pinion flange to install the seal.

REAR AXLE, 1957-61

This rear axle, Fig. 3, is a banjo-

housing hypoid in which the drive pinion is mounted 2¼" below the centerline of the drive gear. The drive pinion is straddle-mounted in that two opposed tapered roller bearings support the pinion shaft at the front of the pinion gear and a straight roller bearing supports the pinion shaft at the rear of the pinion gear.

The pinion shaft and gear are assembled in the pinion retainer which is bolted to the carrier housing. Two carrier and differential cases are used to accommodate two bearing sizes. The right and left axle shafts are not interchangeable since the left shaft is shorter than the right.

Disassembly

1. Mark one differential bearing cap and bearing support to ensure proper assembly. Remove adjusting nut locks, bearing caps and adjusting nuts. Lift differential out of carrier.
2. Remove drive gear from differential case.
3. Drive out differential pinion shaft retainer and separate the differential pinion shaft and remove gears and thrust washers.
4. Remove drive pinion retainer from carrier. Remove O-ring from retainer.
5. Remove pinion locating shim. Measure shim thickness with micrometer.
6. If the drive pinion pilot bearing is

to be replaced, drive the pilot end and bearing retainer out at the same time. When installing, drive the bearing in until it bottoms. Install a new retainer with the concave side up.

7. Mount the drive pinion retainer assembly in a holding fixture and remove pinion shaft nut and flat washer. Then remove universal joint flange, oil seal and slinger.

8. Remove pinion retainer from fixture and place a protective sleeve or hose on the pinion pilot bearing surface. Then press the pinion shaft out of front bearing cone and remove spacer.

9. Remove pinion rear bearing cone.

10. Do not remove pinion bearing cups from retainer unless they are worn or damaged. The flange and pilot are machined by locating on these cups after they are installed in the bores. If new cups are to be installed, make sure they are seated in the retainer by trying to insert a .0015" feeler gauge between cup and bottom of bore.

Assembly

Differential Case—Place a side gear and thrust washer in the differential case bore. *Lubricate all parts liberally with axle lubricant during assembly.* With a soft-faced hammer, drive pinion shaft into case only far enough to retain a pinion thrust washer and pinion gear. Place the second pinion and thrust washer in position. Drive the pinion shaft into place. Be careful to line up pinion shaft retainer holes. Place second side gear and thrust washer in position and install differential case cover. Install retainer. A pinion or axle shaft spline can be inserted in side gear spline to check for free rotation of differential gears.

Insert two $\frac{7}{16}$" x 2" bolts through differential flange and thread them 3 or 4 turns into the drive gear as a guide in aligning the drive gear bolt holes. Press or tap the drive gear into position. Install and tighten the drive gear bolts evenly and alternately across the gear to 60-65 lb. ft. torque.

If the differential bearings have been removed, use a suitable press to install them.

Pinion and Retainer—Install the pinion rear bearing cone on the pinion shaft and install a new spacer on the shaft. Place the bearing retainer on the pinion shaft, then install the front bearing cone. *As the bearing is pressed into position, rock the pinion retainer. Do not press the bearing on the shaft until all play is removed between retainer and bearings as the spacer may be compressed too much.*

Lubricate both bearings with axle lubricant. Place oil slinger in position. Coat the outside edge of a new oil seal with an oil-resistant sealer and press it into the bearing retainer. New seals need not be soaked before installation. Install the universal joint flange. Place the flat washer over the pinion shaft and start the pinion shaft nut.

Hold the flange and tighten the pinion

shaft nut until a torque required to turn the pinion is 8-12 *inch* lbs. with used bearings or 17-27 *inch* lbs. with new bearings. As the pinion shaft nut is tightened, rotate the pinion shaft frequently to allow the bearing to seat.

Shim Selection — Manufacturing tolerances in the pinion bore dimensions and in the best operating position of the gears make an adjustment shim necessary. This shim is placed between the pinion retainer and the carrier, Fig. 1. An increase in the thickness of the shim moves the pinion *away* from the drive gear. Manufacturing objectives are to make axles requiring a .0015" shim and if a new assembly is being built, a .0015" shim should be used for a tentative build-up. Shims are available in .010" to .021" thicknesses in steps of .001".

Pinions and drive gears are marked, when matched, with the same number. Following the number on the pinion is a minus (—) or plus (+) followed by a number. If the pinion is marked "—1" it indicates that a shim .001" thinner than a standard shim for this carrier is required. A minus number means the pinion should be moved closer to the drive gear and a thinner shim is required. A plus number means the pinion should be moved farther from the drive gear and a thicker shim is required. A pinion marked zero (0) is a standard pinion.

To select a shim, measure the original shim with a micrometer. Note the dimensional mark on the original pinion. Compare the mark on the original pinion with the mark on the new pinion to determine how the original shim should be modified.

For example, if the original shim is .015" and the original pinion is marked "—1", the new pinion requires a +1 shim. Therefore, the new pinion requires a .002" thicker shim, and a .017" shim should be used. If the new pinion is marked the same as the old pinion, no shim change is required.

Backlash Adjustment—The threaded nut type of differential bearing adjustment is used. The procedure for making this adjustment and checking drive gear and pinion backlash is given in the *Rear Axle Service* chapter.

AXLE SHAFT & OIL SEALS

Axle shafts are mounted on sealed ball bearings pressed to a shoulder on the axle shaft, and held in place by a pressed-on bearing retainer ring. The shaft bearings are pre-lubricated and require no additional lubrication. The shafts are held in place in the axle housing by a retainer plate. The wheel hub and brake drum flange are forged integral with the axle shaft. The flange provides the brake drum and wheel mounting and eliminates the need for a keyed hub.

To remove an axle shaft, take off the wheel and unfasten the brake drum from the axle shaft flange. Through the hole provided in the flange, remove the nuts which secure the brake support plate to

the axle housing. Then with a suitable puller, pull the shaft out of the housing, using care not to dislodge the brake support plate or damage the oil seal in the housing. Install one nut to hold the brake plate in position.

Axle shaft bearings should be removed only when necessary to install a new bearing. A bearing once removed must be discarded.

If necessary to disassemble, loosen the axle shaft bearing retainer ring and remove the retainer. The bearing may be removed with a bearing puller, after which remove the retainer plate.

To assemble, place the retainer plate on the shaft. Press the bearing up against the shoulder on the shaft. Install the bearing retainer ring and press it firmly against the bearing. Before installing the shaft examine the oil seal and replace it if necessary.

Before installing a new oil seal it should be thoroughly soaked in oil for at least ½ hour to make it soft and pliable. When installing the seal, use a suitable seal driver, driving the seal into the axle housing with the axis of the shaft and tight against the shoulder. After installing the seal, check the outer diameter for tightness in the housing to avoid possible leaks.

To install the shaft, remove the temporary nut holding the brake plate, and lubricate the bearing bore in the housing. Clean the brake plate surface and install new gaskets between the retainer plate and brake plate. Slide the shaft into the housing, using care not to damage the oil seal. Push the shaft in until its bearing is tight against the shoulder in the housing. Complete the job by tightening the axle shaft nuts to 30-35 pounds feet torque, and install the brake drum and wheel.

POWER BRAKE UNIT, REPLACE

1960-61

Remove master cylinder outlet fitting from cylinder. If only the brake booster is to be removed, support the master cylinder with a prop from the underside. This eliminates the necessity of disconnecting the outlet fitting and consequently bleeding is not required during assembly.

Remove vacuum hoses. Unfasten and remove master cylinder. Remove power brake unit from bracket on dash panel (4 capscrews) and remove power brake.

1959

1. Working in engine compartment, remove master cylinder outlet fitting bolt. *It is not necessary to remove stop light switch, wires or tube from fitting. Do not disturb master cylinder outlet fitting.*

2. Remove vacuum hose from power unit.

3. Remove vacuum reserve tank hose from fitting.

4. Working inside car under instrument

panel, remove capscrew and locknut securing push rod to brake lever.

5. Remove power brake from bracket on dash panel.

6. Install in reverse order of removal and bleed system in the conventional manner.

1953-58

1. Working inside the car under the instrument panel, disengage valve push rod from brake pedal.

2. Working in engine compartment, remove master cylinder outlet fitting bolt from master cylinder. *It is not necessary to remove the stop light switch, wires or hose assembly from the outlet fitting. Do not disturb the outlet fitting.*

3. Remove manifold vacuum hose from check valve on power unit.

4. Remove vacuum reserve tank hose from fitting on check valve.

5. Unfasten power brake assembly (4 screws) from bracket on dash panel.

6. To install, reverse foregoing procedure. Then bleed brakes in the usual manner. After bleeding, fill hydraulic brake reservoir to within ¼" of the top of filler cap opening and replace cap.

BRAKE MASTER CYLINDER, REPLACE

1960-61

1. Working inside passenger compartment, remove eccentric bolt, bushing and lock nut that secures master cylinder push rod to brake pedal. Remove push rod and bushing from pedal.

2. Remove hydraulic outlet fitting.

3. Remove stop light switch.

4. Unfasten master cylinder from dash panel (2 capscrews).

5. Reverse above procedure to install and bleed hydraulic system.

1953-59

To remove the master cylinder, take off the eccentric bolt, bushing and lock nut that secures the master cylinder push rod to the brake pedal from inside the passenger compartment. Remove the hollow bolt attaching the stop light switch and hydraulic line outlet fitting to the master cylinder. Unfasten the master cylinder (4 bolts) from the engine side of the dash panel.

Reverse the order of removal to install the master cylinder and bleed the hydraulic system as directed in the *Brakes* chapter.

Front End and Steering Section

CAMBER & CASTER, ADJUST

1953

Camber adjustment is provided by an eccentric bushing at the top of the kingpin support, Fig. 1. To adjust, loosen the lock bolt through the top of the support and place the tool shown in Fig. 2 on the hex of the bushing and turn until the top end of the support is moved toward or away from the frame to obtain the correct camber angle.

Caster adjustment is accomplished by turning the bushing at the lower end of the kingpin support. Loosen the lock nut

and install the tool shown in Fig. 3 on the hex on the front end of the bushing. Turning the bushing moves the support forward or backward until the correct caster angle is obtained.

Note—The maximum movement of the caster adjusting bushing is ⅛" either way from center. If correct camber and caster angles cannot be obtained by bushing movement, check all the component parts for excessive wear or being bent and replace parts affected.

1954-56

To adjust caster, loosen the two bolts that secure the upper suspension arm shaft to the frame and insert shims be-

Fig. 2 Adjusting camber. 1953

tween the shaft and frame. A $\frac{1}{16}$" shim at the front bolt will produce a *negative* caster of ½ degree. A $\frac{1}{16}$" shim at the rear bolt will produce a positive caster of ½ degree. Shims are available in thicknesses of $\frac{1}{64}$", $\frac{1}{32}$", $\frac{1}{16}$" and ⅛". When the correct adjustment is obtained, torque the bolts to 75-80 lbs. ft. Caster must be held within ½ degree difference on both sides.

Camber is also adjusted at the upper suspension shaft. To adjust, insert or remove the shims from between the shaft and the frame at both the front and rear bolts. Each $\frac{1}{16}$" shim removed will add

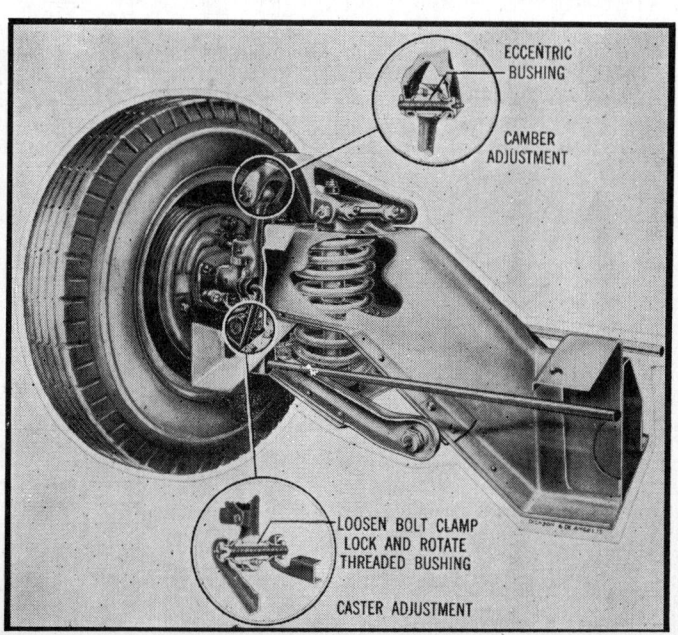

Fig. 1 Caster and camber adjustment. 1953

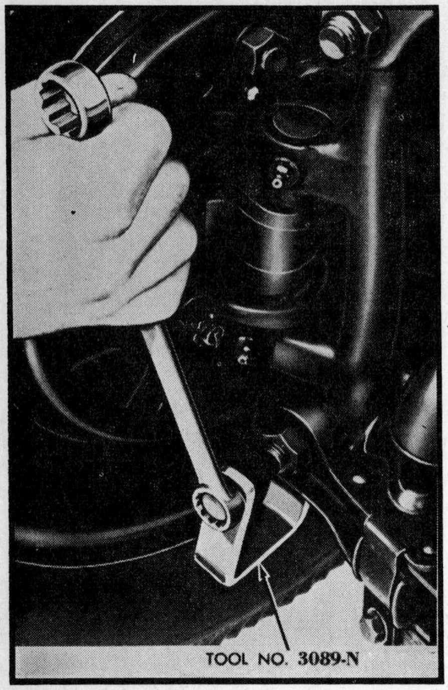
TOOL NO. 3089-N

Fig. 3 Adjusting caster. 1953

¼ degree of positive camber. The camber must be the same on both sides within ¼ degree.

1957-58

While the front suspension is fundamentally the same as 1956 the fact that the upper control arm inner shaft is bolted to the outer surface of the frame bracket affects wheel alignment adjustments.

Loosen the two bolts that secure the upper control arm to the frame and adjust caster and camber as follows:

Caster—A 1/16" shim added at the rear bolt will add a *negative* caster of ½ degree. A 1/16" shim added at the front bolt will add a *positive* caster of ½ degree.

Camber—To adjust camber, insert or remove shims at both the front and rear bolts. Each 1/16" of shim added will give ¼ degree of *positive* camber. Each 1/16" of shim removed will give ¼ degree of *negative* camber.

1959-60

Front wheel alignment is accomplished without the use of shims. Alignment is performed by movement of the upper control arm shaft. The holes in the upper control arm shafts are oversize, permitting them to be moved as required for correct camber and caster adjustment.

To adjust caster and camber, two ¼" x 1½" bolts with nuts are required to be inserted in the frame bracket holes as shown in Fig. 4. The upper control arm shaft nuts are then loosened and the shaft moved to obtain the adjustment. Fig. 4 illustrates the results that can be obtained by moving the shaft. *When the adjustment is correct, torque the control arm shaft bolts to 100-110 lbs. ft. Proper torquing of these bolts is essential to insure that the alignment will not change during vehicle operation.*

1961

Caster—To adjust caster, loosen the two bolts that secure the upper suspension arm shaft to the frame and insert or remove shims as required between shaft and frame.

A 1/16" shim added at the front bolt will change caster ½° in the positive direction. A 1/16" shim removed from the front bolt will change caster ½° in the negative direction. When caster is correct torque bolts to 65-85 ft. lbs.

Camber—To adjust camber, insert or remove an equal number of shims from between the upper suspension arm shaft and frame at both the front and rear bolts. Each 1/16" of shim will change camber ¼°.

TOE-IN, ADJUST

Position the front wheels in the straight-ahead position. Then turn both tie rod adjusting sleeves an equal amount until the desired toe-in setting is obtained.

FRONT SUSPENSION

1961

The front suspension, Figs. 5 and 6, is quite similar to that used in 1958, the chief difference being that threaded metal bushings are used in the upper control arm shaft instead of the rubber type used in 1958. In Fig. 6, note that the front suspension lower arms are at-

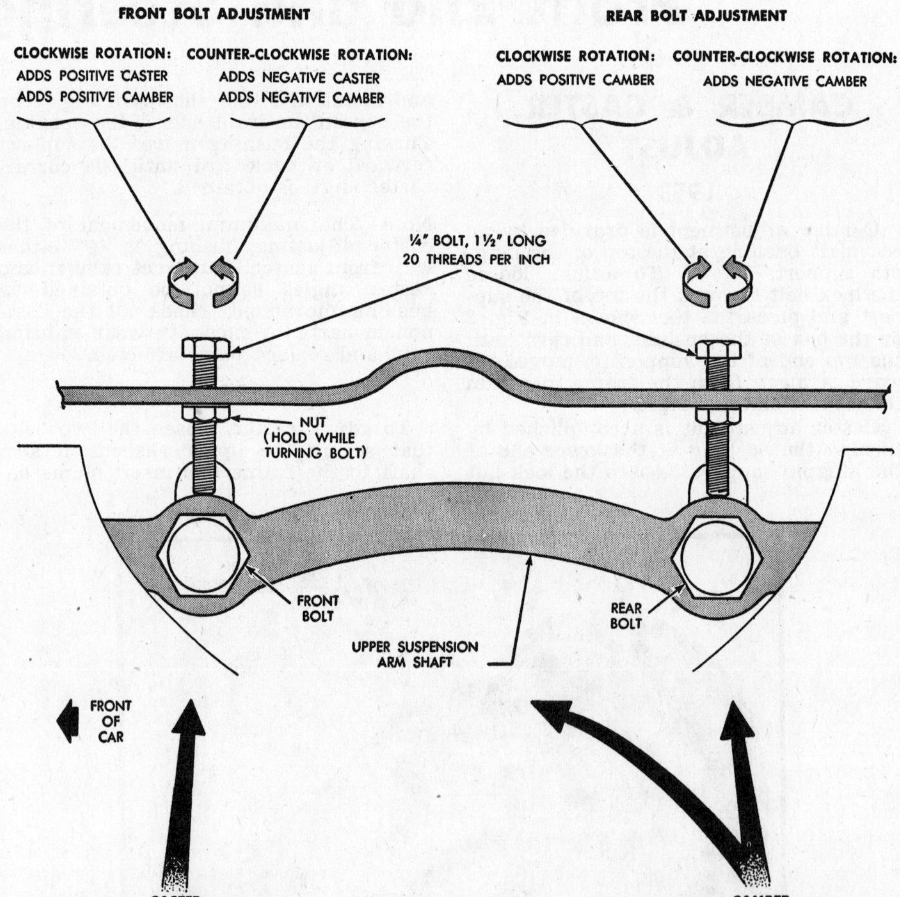
FRONT BOLT ADJUSTMENT
CLOCKWISE ROTATION: ADDS POSITIVE CASTER ADDS POSITIVE CAMBER
COUNTER-CLOCKWISE ROTATION: ADDS NEGATIVE CASTER ADDS NEGATIVE CAMBER
REAR BOLT ADJUSTMENT
CLOCKWISE ROTATION: ADDS POSITIVE CAMBER
COUNTER-CLOCKWISE ROTATION: ADDS NEGATIVE CAMBER
¼" BOLT, 1½" LONG 20 THREADS PER INCH
NUT (HOLD WHILE TURNING BOLT)
FRONT BOLT
REAR BOLT
UPPER SUSPENSION ARM SHAFT
FRONT OF CAR

CASTER

TURNS OF FRONT BOLT	APPROXIMATE CHANGE IN CASTER
⅚	¼°
1⅔	½°
2½	¾°
3⅓	1°
4	1¼°
5	1½°

CAMBER

TURNS OF BOTH BOLTS	APPROXIMATE CHANGE IN CAMBER
1	¼°
2	½°
3	¾°
4	1°
5	1¼°
6	1½°

Fig. 4 Caster and camber adjustments. 1959. For 1960, use 5/16" bolt instead of ¼" indicated

tached to the frame front crossmember through a shackle and rubber bushing arrangement.

1959-60

This suspension, Fig. 7, is similar to 1958 except that a different method of adjusting caster and camber is employed (see Fig. 4). Note that the shim type of caster and camber adjustment has again been adopted in 1961.

1957-58

As shown in Fig. 8, the front suspension is fundamentally the same as 1956. However, the suspension arms are one-piece metal stampings. They are secured to the frame and crossmembers in the same manner as prior models but the upper control arm shaft is secured to the outer surface of the frame bracket in place of the inner surface.

The ball joints are riveted to the control arms. These joints can be replaced by using a ⅜" drill to remove the old rivets. The new ball joints are then secured to the control arm with ⅜-24 x 2" bolts furnished in the ball joint kit.

The control arm bushings are removed and installed in the same manner as in 1956. The shock absorbers are basically the same as prior models but the upper mounting utilizes a one-piece rubber bushing as an insulator between the frame and shock absorber.

All other front suspension operations are performed in a similar manner to that of the 1956 suspension.

1954-56

This suspension, Fig. 9, is the ball joint type. It differs from other types of suspension in that the wheel spindle is attached directly to the suspension arms by means of ball joints located at the outer ends of both arms. The conventional steering knuckle, knuckle support and kingpin is eliminated.

The working parts of this type suspension are assembled directly to the vehicle frame and cannot be removed as an assembly. However, individual parts may be replaced as outlined below.

Shock Absorber

To remove a shock absorber, unfasten it from the frame at its upper end. Remove the two cap screws that retain the shock absorber mounting plate to the lower control arm and lower the shock absorber unit.

To install, reverse the removal procedure and tighten the two lower cap screws to 13-18 lbs. ft. torque.

Lower Arm & Spring, Remove

Raise the front of the car and place a support stand under each frame side rail to the rear of the lower control arm. Remove the hub cap and pry off the grease cap. Remove the nut from the wheel spindle and pull off the wheel assembly with hub and brake drum.

Remove the shock absorber as outlined above and detach the stabilizer (stabilizer) bar from the lower control arm.

Loosen the slotted nut which attaches the lower ball joint stud to the lower

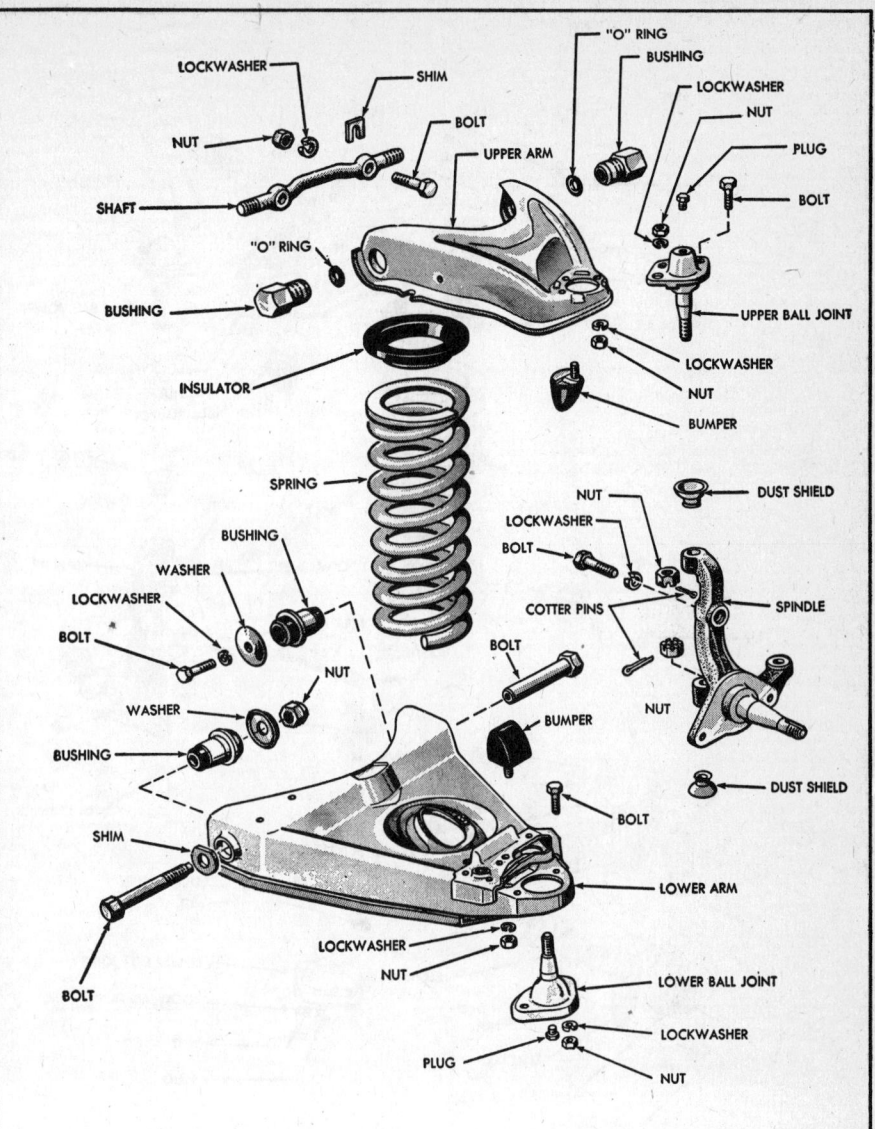

Fig. 5 Front suspension. 1961 "600" Series

spindle boss one or two turns. Then with a brass bar and hammer, strike the lower spindle boss to pop the stud loose against its nut. Place a jack under the outer end of the lower arm and raise the jack until the upper arm rebound bumper is clear of the frame. The nut can then be removed and the spindle and brake assembly lifted off the ball joint stud and moved out of the way.

Lower the jack until the coil spring is free and can be removed. Note the rubber insulators at the upper and lower ends of the spring.

Unfasten the lower control arm from the frame and remove the arm. Inspect the bushings on the inner end of each arm leg and replace if defective.

When installing bushings, do not attempt to press them beyond the edge of the shoulder ribs as severe distortion will result, which will affect the operation of the suspension unit. Under no circumstances should only one bushing be replaced.

Ball Joint Service

Remove the cover and seal from the ball joint. Inspect the joint and replace if found defective. If the joint is still serviceable, *do not* wash it in solvent as it will be extremely difficult to lubricate it again. Do not hammer the ball joint bodies as binding will result. Inspect the metal seal parts for damage and replace if necessary. Replace the sponge rubber seal, making sure it is stuffed into the metal seal cup before pushing it down over the ball joint stud.

Lower Arm & Spring, Install

To install the lower control arm, secure the rearward leg to the frame crossmember tube, running the nut up finger tight. With the arm forced firmly against the tube, install enough shims to fill the space between the forward arm leg bushing and front crossmember. Then install the bolt and washers and run the nut up finger tight. With the arm in curb load

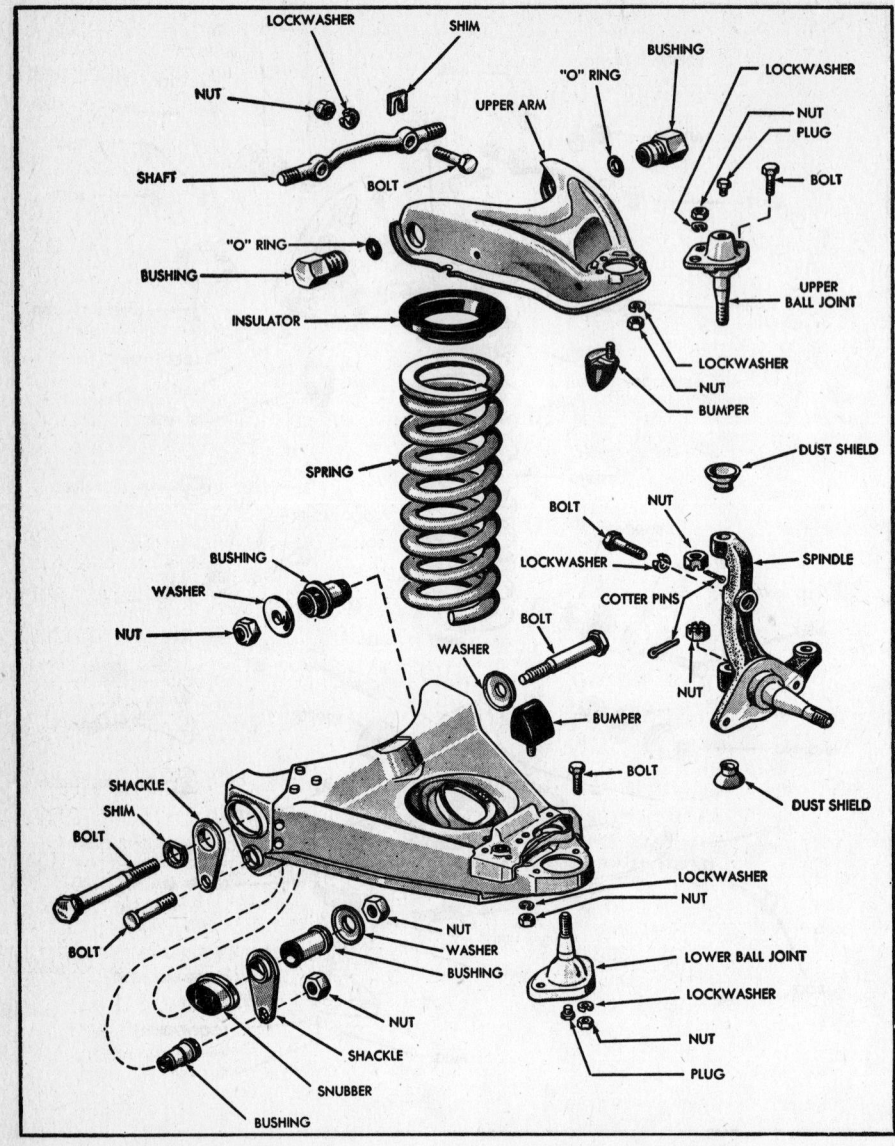

Fig. 6 Front suspension. 1961 "800" and Monterey Series

undue tension. Loosen the ball joint stud by backing the nut off one or two turns and striking the spindle boss. Remove the stud nut completely and then remove the two bolts that secure the inner shaft to the frame. Note the number of shims between the shaft and frame at each of the bolt locations. Then take off the upper control arm.

When installing bushings, be sure to use a spacer tool of the proper dimensions between the arm legs so that the arm will not be distorted or bent. When both bushings are in place, install the nut and washer on each end of the shaft and tighten finger tight. Position the shaft in the arm so that the shaft bolt holes are parallel with the arm. Then tighten the nuts from 80-100 lbs. ft. torque. Under no circumstances should only one bushing be replaced.

Note—The upper ball joint is serviced in exactly the same way as the lower.

Upper Arm, Install

Position the arm on the frame cross-member. Use the same number of shims that were originally used between the shaft and frame bracket. Secure the shaft to the bracket with the two bolts and torque the bolts to 75-80 lbs. ft. Place the ball joint stud in the spindle boss, install the nut and tighten it to 80 lbs. ft. minimum. Continue to tighten until the cotter pin holes are lined up and install a cotter pin.

Install the wheel and hub assembly and remove the jack from under the lower control arm. Finally, check the wheel alignment as previously outlined.

1953 FRONT END REPAIRS

The working parts of the suspension system are assembled directly to the car frame and cannot be removed as an assembly. Fig. 10. Therefore to remove any part for replacement, it is necessary to disassemble the part from the car.

Lower Arm & Spring, Replace

To replace either of these parts, jack up the car until the wheels clear the floor and place a stationary jack under the frame. Remove the shock absorber, and stabilizer end clip. Place a jack under the lower arm pivot shaft and exert enough pressure on the jack to keep the pivot shaft tight to the frame. Unfasten the pivot shaft and lower the jack slowly. When the spring is fully extended, lift it out of the lower arm. Remove the nut from the lower bushing pin and screw out the pin. The lower arm can then be lifted out.

To install, position the lower arm, screw in the bushing pin and tighten the nut. Place the flat end of the spring upward and the lower end in the spring seat in the arm. With the jack in position under the pivot shaft, raise the lower arm to the frame. Use a drift to align the holes in the pivot shaft and cross member for easy installation of bolts. Install the shock absorber, fasten the

position (approximately horizontal) with the outer end slightly lower than the inner, tighten the nuts to 80-100 lbs. ft. torque.

Place the coil spring with the rubber insulators in position on the lower control arm. Then with a jack under the lower arm, compress the coil spring. Care must be taken to see that the upper and lower ends of the spring are properly seated and the rubber insulators are in place. Guide the spindle boss over the ball joint stud. Install the nut and torque it to 100 lbs. ft. Continue to tighten until the cotter pin holes are lined up and install the cotter pin.

Remove the jack from under the arm and install the shock absorber. Secure the stabilizer bar to the lower suspension arm.

Wheel Bearings, Adjust

Pack the wheel bearings with the proper lubricant. Install the wheel, hub

and drum as a unit. Tighten the spindle nut with a 12" wrench, while rotating the wheel back and forth, until there is a noticeable drag or bind. This assures that the bearing cones are properly seated. Then back off the spindle nut to line up to the nearest cotter pin hole which will allow the hub to rotate freely with no perceptible end play. Lock the spindle nut in this position with a cotter pin and install the grease cap and hub cap.

Remove the support stands and check the wheel alignment as previously outlined.

Upper Arm, Remove

Remove the shock absorber. Place a jack under the lower control arm spring seat and raise it until some of the tension has been removed from the upper bumper. Remove the wheel and tire assembly.

Wire the spindle to the frame to avoid possible damage to the brake hose from

stabilizer end with clip on lower arm and remove jacks.

Upper Arm, Replace

To replace the upper control arm, place a jack under the lower spring seat and raise the car. Remove the wheel. Run a strong wire from the kingpin support to the frame to avoid damage to the hydraulic brake hose from undue tension. Unfasten the upper pivot shaft from the frame. Remove the nut and bushing pin at the top of the support, and lift off the upper arm.

When assembling, install the bushing pin before attempting to fasten the pivot shaft to the frame. Install the wheel and remove the jack.

Kingpin Support, Replace

To replace this support, place a jack under the lower arm spring seat and raise the car. Remove the wheel and brake drum. Unfasten the brake support plate and fasten it with wire to the frame to prevent undue strain on the hydraulic brake hose. Drive the kingpin locking pin from the knuckle. Pry out the grease seal plug from the support. Using a soft drift, drive the kingpin from the support and knuckle, forcing out the lower grease seal at the same time. Remove the upper and lower pivot pins and lift out the kingpin support. Loosen the lock bolts at each end of the support and press out the bushings.

Kingpin Bushings, Replace

These bushings can be replaced without removing the kingpin support. After taking off the wheel, drum, brake support plate, steering arm and knuckle, press out the bushings. After pressing in the new bushings, they can be reamed from below.

Pivot Shaft Bushings

It is necessary to remove the upper control arm to replace these bushings. When screwing in the new bushings, insert a hard wood block between the ends of the arm at the pivot shaft to keep the ends in the proper position.

The lower control arm pivot shaft bushings can be replaced without removing the arm from the car.

Pivot Pin or Bushing

To replace either the upper or lower pivot pin or bushing, place a jack under the spring seat of the lower arm and remove the wheel. Remove the pivot pin nut and screw out the pin. To remove the bushing from the support, loosen the lock bolt and press out the bushing. *After replacing any part of the suspension, check and adjust camber and caster.*

HORN RING, REPLACE

1959-61

Remove horn ring emblem by turning counterclockwise. Remove steering shaft nut and, with suitable puller, remove horn ring and steering wheel.

When installing, align mark in steer-

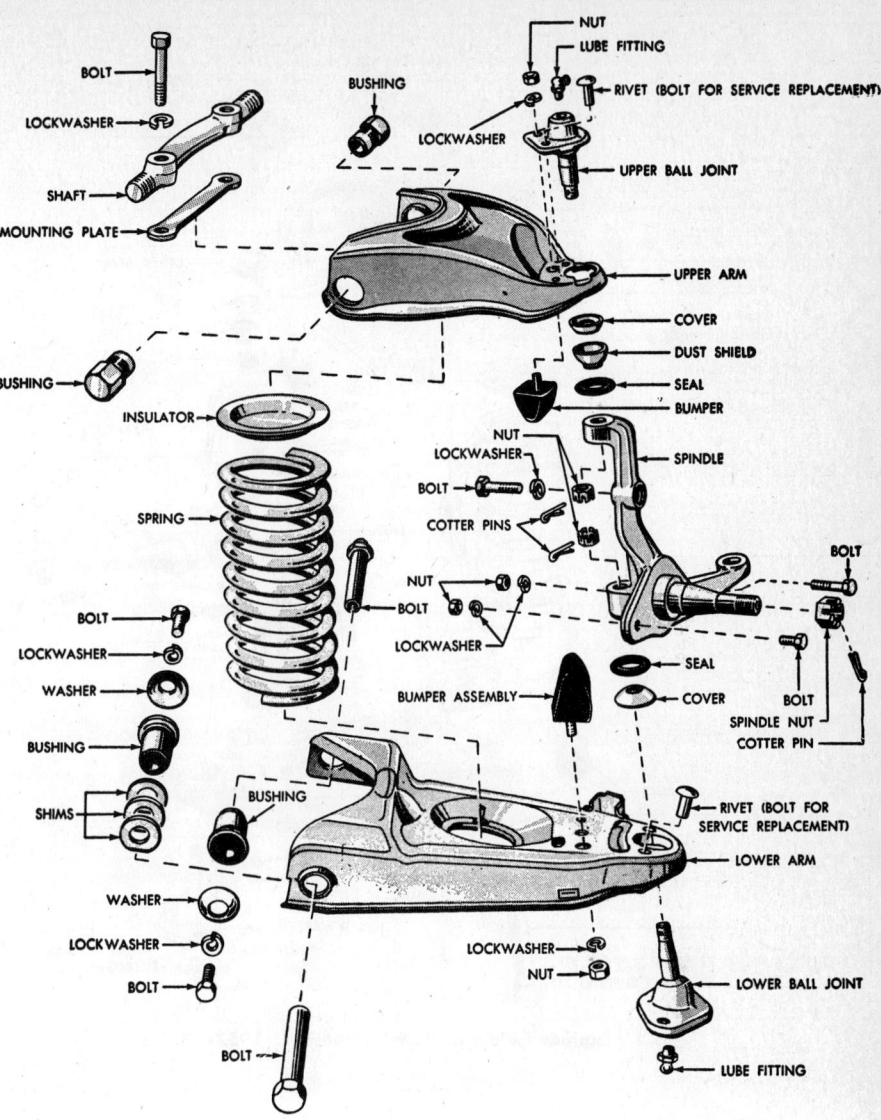

Fig. 7 Front suspension. 1959-60

ing wheel hub with mark on steering gear shaft.

1958

The horn ring is removed in the same manner as outlined for 1959 except that the horn ring emblem is pried from the column head with a screwdriver.

1954-57

Remove the emblem from the steering column head by rotating the emblem counterclockwise with the palm of the hand. Remove the steering shaft nut and, with a suitable puller, remove the steering wheel and horn ring.

Reverse the foregoing operations to install the wheel and ring and torque tighten the wheel nut 60-70 lbs. ft.

1953

Take off the cap and emblem from the steering column head by rotating the cap counterclockwise with the palm of the

hand. Remove the steering shaft nut and, using a suitable puller, pull off the steering wheel.

To remove the horn ring, remove the three screws that secure the horn ring retainer plate to the steering wheel. Then take out the ring, plate and spring.

STEERING WHEEL

After removing the horn button or emblem from the steering column head as outlined above, take off the steering wheel nut and use a suitable puller to remove the wheel.

STEERING GEAR, REPLACE

1959-61

1. Disconnect steering shaft from gear at flexible coupling.
2. Raise car and remove pitman arm.
3. Loosen manifold outlet clamp and

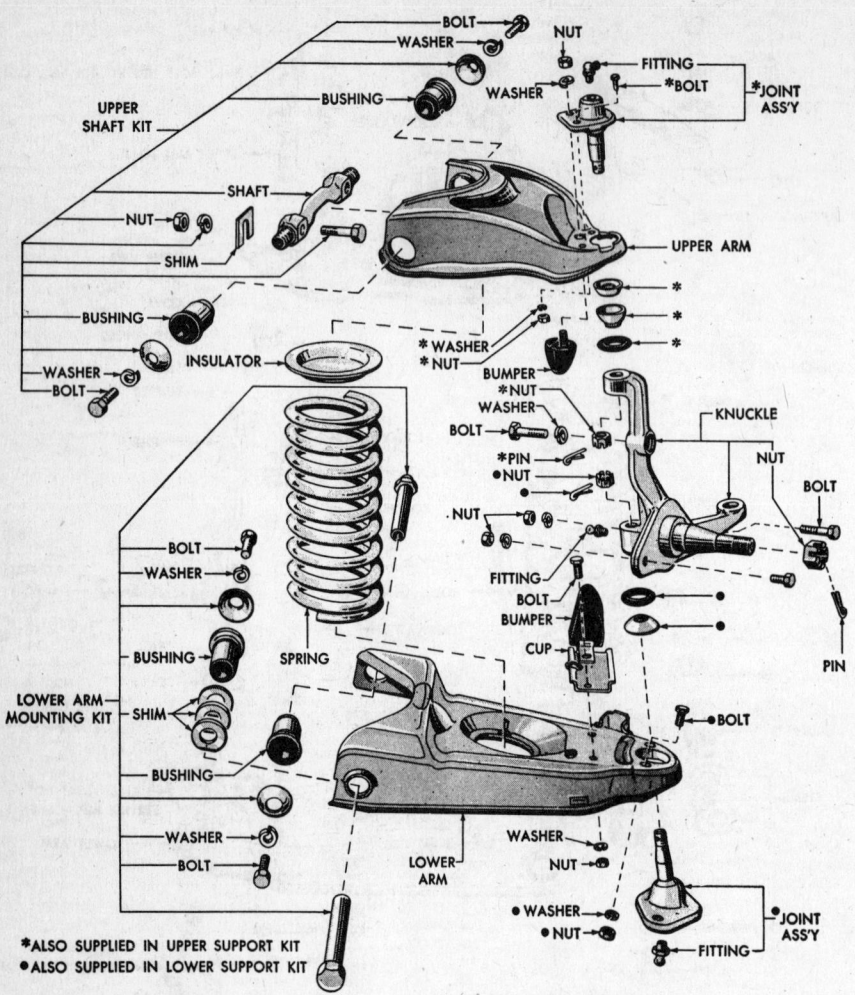

Fig. 8 Exploded view of front suspension. 1957-58

*ALSO SUPPLIED IN UPPER SUPPORT KIT
•ALSO SUPPLIED IN LOWER SUPPORT KIT

car. Also remove back-up light switch.

12. Remove steering column cover plates attaching parts. Remove left plate and slide right plate back along speedometer cable.
13. Remove steering column opening seal.
14. Unfasten steering column bracket.
15. Remove steering gear through opening in dash panel.

1954-57

1. Remove clamp that secures reservoir hose to fitting on brake booster cylinder (if equipped).
2. Remove clamp that secures reservoir hose to dash panel. Move hose away from steering column opening in dash panel.
3. Remove steering wheel.
4. Disconnect steering column electrical connections.
5. Remove accelerator pedal from accelerator push rod.
6. Remove clutch and brake pedals.
7. Pull floor carpeting away from dash panel opening.
8. Remove insulator and floor opening cover plates.
9. Unfasten steering column bracket from instrument panel and pedal support bracket.
10. Disconnect shift rods from steering column shift arms.
11. Loosen clamp on lower steering column at steering gear housing. Raise column sufficiently to disconnect wires at neutral switch on Merc-O-Matic models only. Remove steering column tube from steering shaft through inside of vehicle.

hanger at forward end of muffler.
4. Remove manifold outlet pipe (on dual exhaust jobs, remove crossover pipe and left hand outlet pipe only).
5. Unfasten steering gear from frame and remove.

1958

1. Disconnect battery ground cable.
2. Remove pitman arm.
3. Loosen three bolts securing steering gear to frame. *If shims are used between gear housing and frame, mark bolt holes where these shims are used. Also mark shims in such a manner that they may be returned to the same location.*
4. Unfasten exhaust pipe from manifold.
5. Remove air cleaner and intake duct.
6. Remove exhaust manifold.
7. Remove No. 8 spark plug.
8. Remove steering wheel.
9. Disconnect electrical connections for turn signal and horn.
10. Disengage accelerator pedal from its push rod and pivot pedal toward rear.
11. On cars with manual shift transmission, disengage shift arms from shift rods and push rods toward center of

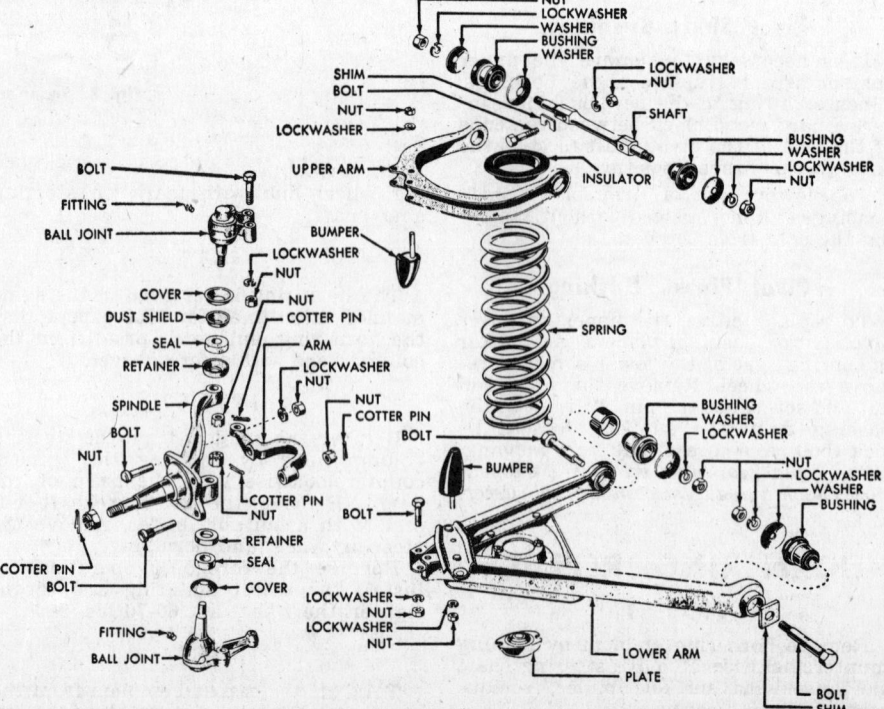

Fig. 9 Ball joint front suspension. 1954-56

12. Raise front end of car and remove nut securing pitman arm to steering gear shaft. Then pull off pitman arm.

13. *Loosen* three bolts that secure steering gear assembly to frame side rails. *Remove shims, if any, located between mounting bolts and frame side rail. Mark bolt holes and number of shims required to facilitate assembly. Mark shims for identification with bolt holes.*

14. With one man in passenger compartment and another under the vehicle, remove the three bolts previously loosened and lift the steering gear out through the passenger compartment.

15. Reverse the order of the foregoing procedure to install the unit.

1953

Take off the horn ring and steering wheel as directed above.

To remove the steering gear, take off the steering column-to-dash cover seal. Disconnect steering column electrical connections at the junction points. Remove shift rods from steering column shift levers. Use a suitable puller to remove the steering gear arm. Remove two bolts that secure steering column housing to the column bracket, which is attached to the brake pedal support bracket.

Loosen the clamp on lower steering column at the gear housing. Loosen (do not remove) the bolts holding the steering gear housing to the frame. Remove the steering shaft nut, spring and sleeve from upper steering column. Remove the column tube from the steering shaft. Remove the bolts attaching the gear housing to the frame and take the gear assembly out through the passenger compartment.

MANUAL STEERING GEAR, ADJUST

1953-55 & Early 1956, Fig. 11

Before proceeding with the adjustments, loosen the gear housing from the frame side rail to relieve any possible vertical strain. Loosen the steering column clamp to relieve any possible horizontal strain. Then tighten the mounting and clamp bolts which will relieve any misalignment in the steering gear mounting.

Steering gear adjustments must be made in the order given below to insure satisfactory results.

Worm Bearing Preload

The worm bearing preload is controlled by the shim pack installed between the steering gear housing and the housing upper cap. The shim pack contains shims of various thicknesses; the thinner shims are installed on the top of the pack, and the adjustment is made as follows:

Disconnect the sector shaft arm from the steering linkage. Turn the steering wheel two complete turns from the straight-ahead position. Hook a spring scale to the steering wheel rim. Rotate

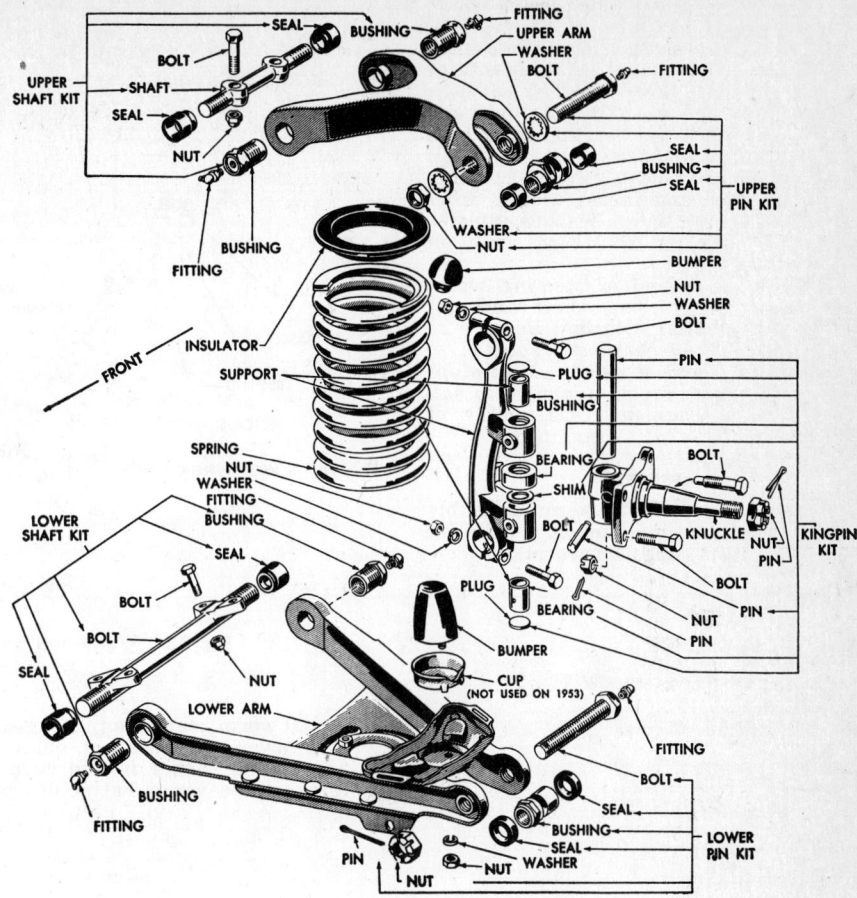

Fig. 10   Front suspension. 1953

the wheel at least one turn with the aid of the scale. The pull required to keep the wheel moving should be between $\frac{1}{8}$ and $\frac{5}{8}$ lbs., which is the worm bearing preload. If the reading is high, a shim or shims should be added. If reading is too low, remove a shim or shims.

If an adjustment is required, unfasten the upper cap from the housing and work the cap and column jacket upward to allow clearance for removing or adding shims. For additional working clearance it may be necessary to remove the steering wheel.

To add a shim, split the shim at one point and install the shim with the split in the upward position. Make sure the split ends do not overlap as this could lead to a false adjustment.

To remove a shim separate the first shim from the pack with a knife blade. Pass the blade all around the shim, being careful not to damage the shims.

The steering column and upper housing cap must be assembled on the gear housing each time the preload is checked.

Worm & Roller Mesh

This adjustment is controlled by the adjustment screw mounted on the sector shaft cover. Adjustment is made as follows:

Disconnect the sector shaft arm from the steering linkage. Attach a spring

scale to the steering wheel rim. Pull the wheel through the straight-ahead position and note reading on scale. The scale reading should be at least $\frac{1}{2}$ lb. above that of the worm bearing preload previously determined, but the total reading must not exceed $1\frac{5}{8}$ lbs. If the scale reading does not exceed the worm bearing preload by at least $\frac{1}{2}$ lb., the worm and roller mesh should be adjusted.

Place the steering wheel in the straight-ahead position. Remove the adjusting screw cover and lock washer. Rotate the adjusting screw clockwise while moving the steering gear arm back and forth until all backlash is removed.

Install the lock washer and cover and check the preload with the spring scale as previously described. The reading should be between 1 and $1\frac{5}{8}$ lbs. If the reading is too high, turn the adjusting screw slightly counterclockwise. If too low, turn the screw slightly clockwise.

STEERING GEAR REPAIRS
Worm & Ball Nut Type

1. Rotate steering worm until nut is in center of travel, Fig. 12.
2. Remove sector shaft nut.
3. Use puller to remove pitman arm.
4. Remove side cover screws and re-

move side cover and sector shaft from housing.

5. To remove side cover from sector shaft, turn adjuster screw in end of sector shaft down through cover.
6. Remove screws and take out end cover with worm bearing, outer race and thrust washer.
7. To remove lower worm bearing, outer race and thrust washer from cover, loosen worm bearing adjuster screw lock nut and turn screw in through cover.
8. Grasp lower end of steering worm and draw steering shaft and nut out of steering housing. *Be sure to keep shaft in horizontal position so that nut does not move against stops at any time, causing damage to ball return mechanism.* Disassembly of worm nut is not recommended.

Assemble

1. Install worm shaft and nut assembly in gear housing, keeping ball nut away from stops on worm.

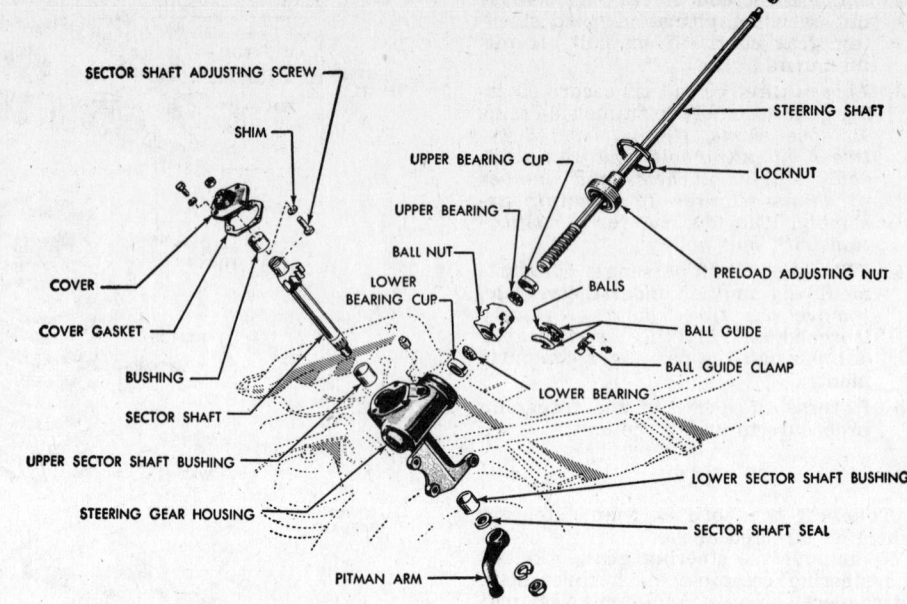

Fig. 12 Worm and ball nut type steering gear. 1956-61

2. Install worm bearing adjusting screw with lower worm bearing, outer race and thrust washer in end cover.
3. Install end cover and attaching parts on gear housing, making sure bearings seat properly.
4. Tighten worm bearing adjusting screw until a slight drag is felt on bearings. Do not tighten lock nut.
5. Install pitman arm.
6. Install sector shaft and adjusting screw inside cover.
7. Rotate steering column until ball nut is in center of travel so that center tooth on sector shaft will enter center space on nut.
8. Install side cover and sector shaft in gear housing.
9. Tighten sector shaft adjusting screw until a slight drag is felt on bearing but do not tighten lock nut.
10. After steering gear is installed in car, adjust as outlined below:

Adjustments

1. Disconnect steering relay rod from pitman arm.
2. Loosen sector shaft lash adjuster screw a few turns to relieve load from bearings.
3. Turn steering wheel in one direction until stopped by gear, then back away about one turn.
4. With a spring scale hooked to rim of steering wheel, measure pull required to keep wheel in motion; this should be ¼ to ¾ lbs. on a 9" radius. If not within these limits, adjust worm bearings as follows:
5. Loosen worm bearing adjuster lock nut and turn adjuster until there is no perceptible end play in worm. Check pull at wheel rim, readjusting as required to obtain proper pull. Tighten lock nut and recheck pull.
6. After worm bearing adjustment is completed and all mounting bolts tightened, adjust sector shaft end play.
7. With steering wheel in straight-ahead position, turn lash adjuster screw clockwise to remove all lash

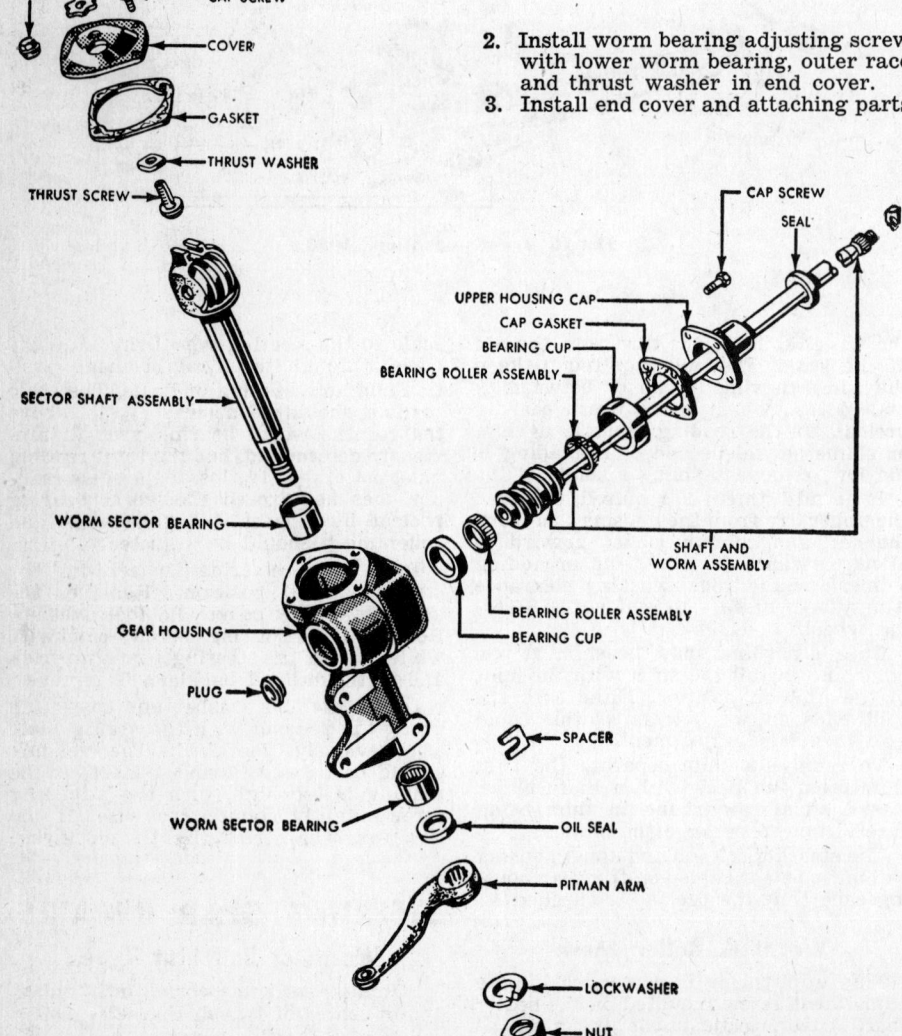

Fig. 11 Exploded view of steering gear. Worm and roller type, 1953-56

and tighten lock nut.

8. Check pull at rim of steering wheel, taking highest reading on scale as wheel is turned through the central or straight-ahead position. This should be between ⅞ and 1½ lbs. *If more than 1½ lb., turn lash adjuster screw counterclockwise, then come up on the adjustment in a clockwise motion.*

9. Tighten lock nut and recheck pull.

Worm & Roller Type Disassemble, Fig. 11.

1. Drain lubricant from housing.
2. Remove sector shaft and cover.
3. Remove cover from sector shaft.
4. Unfasten and slide housing cap off steering shaft.
5. Pull shaft out of housing.
6. Slide housing upper cap gaskets (shim pack), bearing cup, and upper worm bearing out of housing.
7. Use suitable puller to remove lower worm bearing cup.
8. Press sector shaft needle bearings and oil seal through steering arm end of housing.

Inspect & Assemble

After cleaning all parts, inspect worm and rollers for scores, cracks or for signs of chipping. Inspect steering shaft bearing cups and bearings for wear, cracks or damage. Check sector shaft for wear at needle bearing locations. Replace all parts that are damaged enough to impair steering gear operation, and assemble the steering gear in the reverse order of disassembly.

POWER STEERING,
1954-61

There are two items in the power steering system which require periodic maintenance. First, the oil level in the

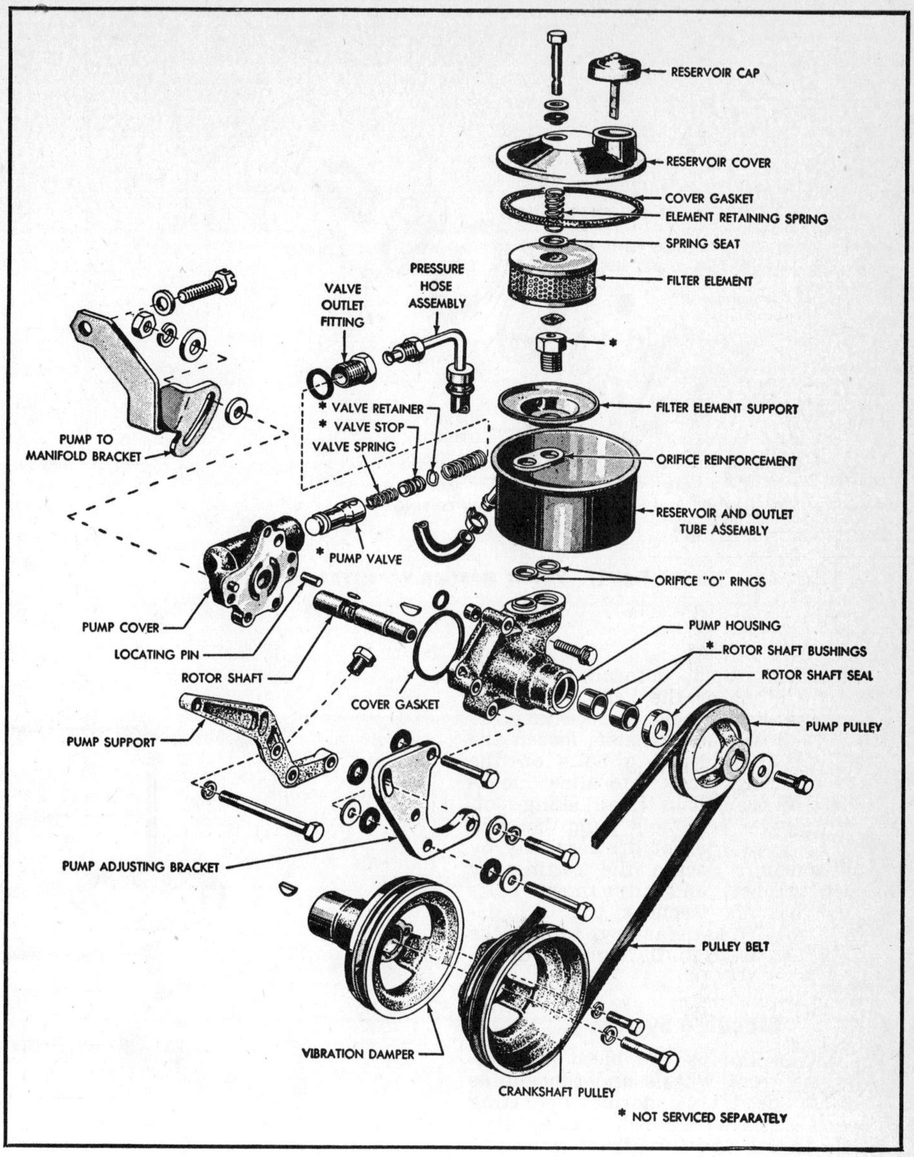

Fig. 14   Power steering rotor type pump

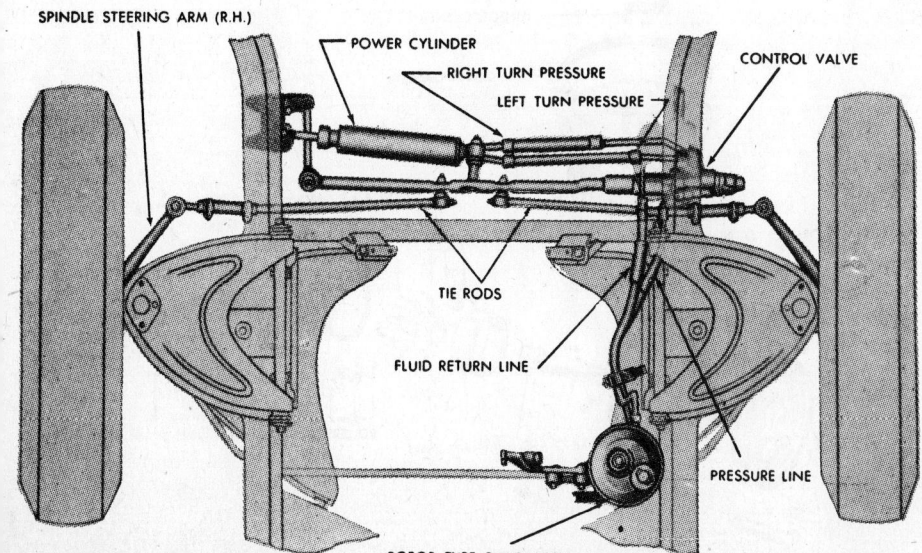

SPINDLE STEERING ARM (R.H.)
POWER CYLINDER
RIGHT TURN PRESSURE
LEFT TURN PRESSURE
CONTROL VALVE
TIE RODS
FLUID RETURN LINE
PRESSURE LINE
ROTOR TYPE PUMP ASS'Y

Fig. 13   Power steering system. 1954-61

reservoir should be checked at 2000-mile intervals. If fluid is below the oil level mark on the reservoir, add automatic transmission fluid as required. Second, check belt tension periodically. If any adjustment is made, turn wheels full right and left several times. Then, with the engine at idle check the fluid level. Before installing the cover on the reservoir, be sure there are no air bubbles in the fluid.

On Car Adjustments

Adjustment of belt tension and bleeding of the system are the only two "on the car" adjustments which can be made.

Belt Tension

There are two methods by which belt tension can be checked: Using a hook gauge, apply 5 to 7 lbs. upward force. Measure deflection of belt. If the deflection is ¼", adjustment is unnecessary. In the absence of a gauge, the wheels may be turned full right or left

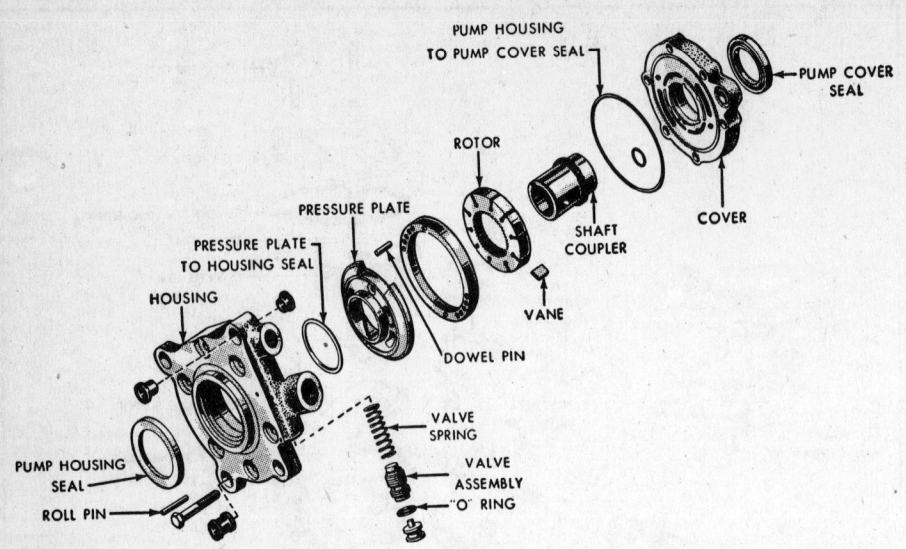

Fig. 15 Power steering vane type pump

as a unit. If the pump is to be serviced, refer to Fig. 14.

5. Reverse removal procedure to install the pump and adjust belt tension as outlined previously.

6. Fill reservoir to proper level and bleed the system as outlined above.

1958-60 Removal V8-383, 430

1. To remove the pump, take off hood.
2. Remove radiator and hoses.
3. If so equipped, remove air conditioning condenser, condenser inlet lines and receiver.
4. Loosen generator adjusting strap and belts.
5. Drain power steering system and disconnect hydraulic fittings.
6. Remove vibration damper.
7. Unfasten and slide pump from front end of crankshaft. If pump does not slide easily off shaft, use a suitable puller, utilizing the two tapped holes in the pump cover.
8. If the pump is to be disassembled, refer to Figs. 15, 16.

to the wheel stop to determine whether the pump stops or the belt squeals. In either case, adjustment is necessary.

To adjust the belt tension, loosen the belt pivot and adjusting bolts on the pump mounting bracket to allow movement of the bracket in its adjusting slot. To tighten the belt, hold pump body in hand and raise (do not lift assembly by the reservoir). Secure the setting by tightening pivot and adjustment bolts enough to hold. Recheck the belt deflection and, if satisfactory, torque the pivot bolt to 20-25 lb. ft. Tighten adjusting bolt.

Bleeding System

Belt Driven Pumps—To bleed the system, raise front wheels and run engine at idling speed until normal operating temperatures are obtained. Then accelerate the engine and turn front wheels to right and left several times until bubbles in reservoir disappear. *Do not hold wheels against stops.* Always recheck and replenish fluid in reservoir after bleeding.

Crankshaft Driven Pump—Fill reservoir and bleed system as follows: Run engine at idling speed. *Do not steer the wheels.* When all foam is free from reservoir (inspect with light), rotate steering wheel from stop to stop to remove air from steering gear. Refill reservoir to full mark, replace cover and check system for leaks.

PUMP, REPLACE
1954-57

1. Remove cover and drain reservoir with a suction gun.
2. Disconnect hose at fitting on pump and tube on reservoir. Secure hose and tube in raised position to prevent further drainage from system.
3. Remove pump drive belt.
4. Remove pump, reservoir and bracket

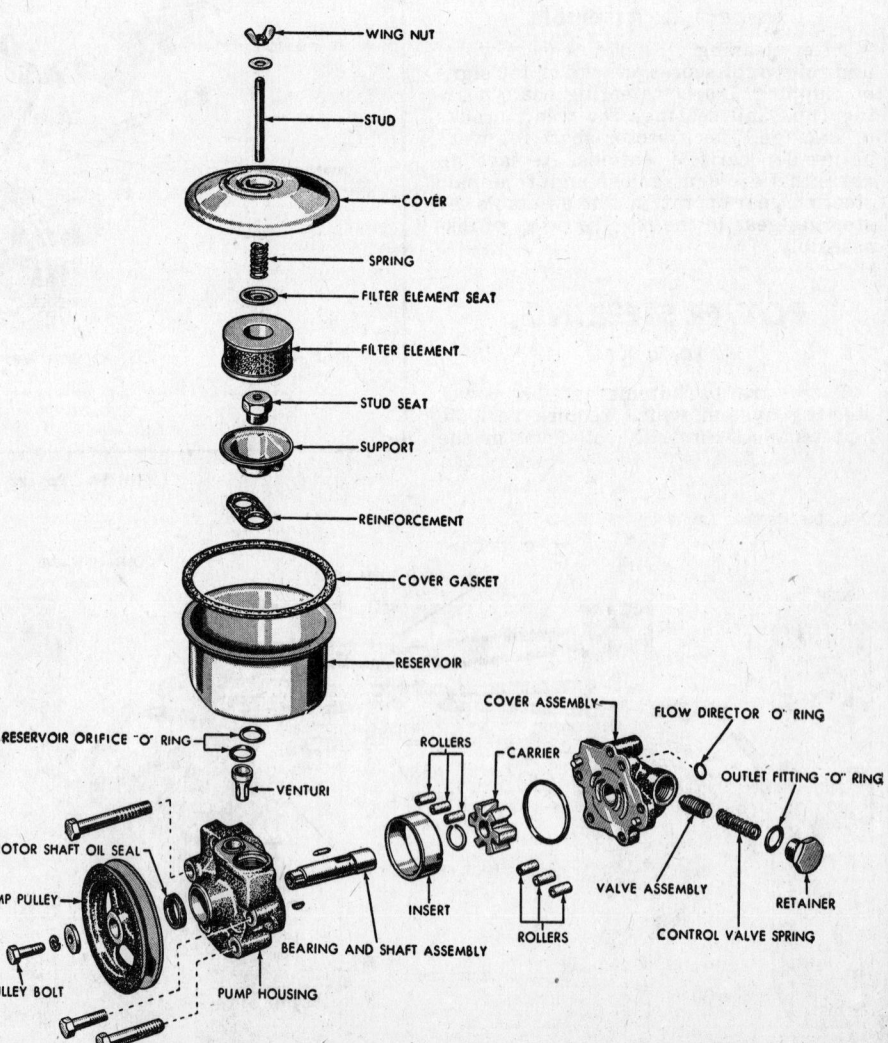

Fig. 16 Roller type power steering pump

1958-60 Installation V8-383, 430

1. Wipe crankshaft clean of any foreign matter. Replace key if damaged or worn.
2. Install rubber grommets in pump housing. All holes except bottom left rear accommodate one-piece grommets. Bottom left hole uses a two-piece grommet.
3. Slide pump on shaft. Inspect pressure and return hoses for cleanliness and for condition of flares and threads. Install hose ends in pump and torque nuts to 20-25 lb. ft. Pressure hose should not touch body sheet metal because of sound transmission.
4. Tighten pump mounting bolts to 10-13 lb. ft.
5. Insert woodruff key in shaft, place pulley on shaft and secure with washer and bolt. Torque to 80-100 lb. ft.
6. Tighten generator adjusting strap and belt.
7. Install radiator and hoses. On cars with air conditioning, install condenser inlet line, receiver and condenser.
8. Install hood.
9. Fill reservoir and bleed system as outlined previously.

CONTROL VALVE, REPLACE

1. Remove reservoir cover and drain fluid with a suction gun.
2. Raise car and drain remaining oil in system by disconnecting valve-to-cylinder lines at valve. Turn wheels to right and left several times to insure complete drainage.
3. Disconnect lines from cylinder. Then remove index pin from steering arm rod.
4. Loosen sleeve clamp bolt.
5. Remove pitman arm from control valve ball stud.
6. Lift control valve and ball stud clear of pitman arm and turn pitman arm out of the way.
7. Twist control valve off connecting link.

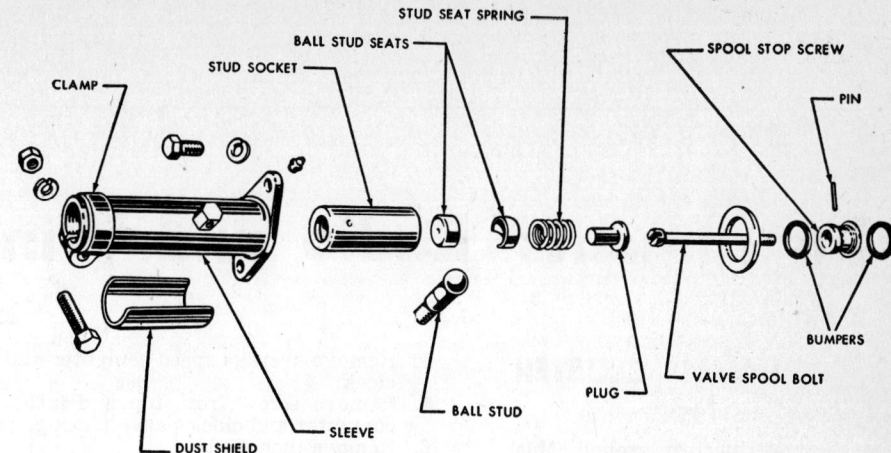

Fig. 18 Power steering control valve sleeve assembly

8. If the control valve is to be disassembled, refer to Figs. 17 and 18.
   Upon reassembly of control valve, be sure to install the valve spool with the large diameter end toward the small end of the valve housing.

Installation

1. Screw control valve onto connecting link until approximately four threads are showing on link rod.
2. Install ball stud in pitman arm.
3. Before installing the ball stud nut on models prior to 1961, measure the distance from the center of the ball stud to the center of the tie rod ball stud (on 1961, measurement is taken from center of tie rod ball stud to center of lubrication fitting plug in the control valve sleeve). The distances are as follows:

1954-56	9"
1957-58	11¼"
1959-60	9⅜"
1961	11¹⁵⁄₁₆"

4. Align slot in sleeve with hole in connecting link and install indexing pin.

5. Torque sleeve clamp bolt to 22-28 lb. ft.
6. Install and torque ball stud nut to 40-50 lb. ft.
7. Install hydraulic line. Torque all fittings except inlet pressure line to 20-30 lb. ft.
8. Check centering of steering wheel and make any necessary adjustment of tie rods to properly center wheel.
9. Check toe-in and adjust if necessary.
10. Fill pump reservoir and bleed system.
11. Verify wheel pull with 15 pound scale. If the installation is satisfactory, 7 to 12 lbs. pull will be required to activate the system, assuming that the car is on dry concrete and engine is running at idling speed.

POWER CYLINDER

Removal

1. Drain fluid from reservoir with a suction gun.
2. Raise car and drain remaining fluid by disconnecting valve-to-cylinder hoses at cylinder. To insure complete drainage, move wheels to left and right several times.
3. Remove nut which secures piston rod to mounting bracket on frame. Remove cup washer and rubber bushing.
4. Remove palnut and nut which secures cylinder to stud on connecting link. Remove cup washer, rubber bushing and cylinder.
5. Remove rubber bushings and cup washers from end of piston rod and from connecting link stud.
6. Inspect all bushings and washers for wear and replace those parts which are worn or damaged.

Installation

1. Place cup washer and rubber bushing on piston rod. Insert rod of piston through hole in frame bracket, then place cup washer and bushing on connecting link stud. Install end of cylinder on connecting link stud.
2. Place second bushing and cup wash-

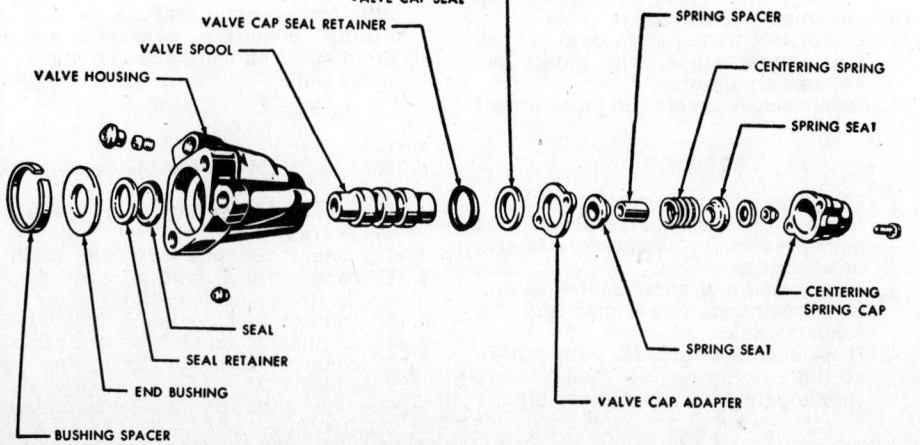

Fig. 17 Power steering control valve assembly

er on connecting link stud. Install nut and torque to 50-65 lb. ft. Install palnut finger tight plus ⅓ turn. *Be sure nut is tightened until it bottoms.*

3. Place second rubber bushing and cup washer on piston rod end of frame, torque attaching nut to 40-50 lb. ft.

4. Install valve-to-cylinder lines. Short line in forward hole in cylinder, and long line in rear hole of cylinder.
5. Fill reservoir and bleed system.

Instruments, Radio and Windshield Wiper

INSTRUMENT CLUSTER

1954

1. Disconnect battery ground cable.
2. Remove heater control lever knobs.
3. Remove instrument control panel upper housing.
4. Unfasten heater control levers (3 screws) and move levers to right of cap screw on instrument cluster.
5. Unfasten instrument cluster from lower control panel (2 screws).
6. Unfasten instrument panel from lower control panel (4 screws). This is done so that cluster may be removed; the lower control panel need not be removed completely.
7. Disconnect speedometer cable and pull instrument cluster forward as far as wires will allow.
8. Disconnect wire which runs through metal loop on back of charge indicator at circuit breaker.
9. Remove wires from other instruments.
10. Remove instrument cluster.
11. Remove speedometer from cluster.

1955-56

1. Disconnect battery cable to prevent accidental short circuit.
2. Unfasten steering column from instrument panel and pull steering column down as far as possible to provide clearance for cluster removal.
3. Remove four nuts from back of instrument cluster and two Phillips screws from front of cluster (at the top).
4. Pull cluster forward, disconnect wires from gauges and remove speedometer (or any other instrument as required).

1957 Except Turnpike Cruiser

1. Disconnect battery ground cable.
2. Remove two screws at top rear of cluster.
3. Remove two screws in right and left instrument cluster.
4. Lift cluster straight up from instrument panel. Disconnect speedometer cable and remove all lamps from rear of cluster.

1957 Turnpike Cruiser

1. Disconnect battery ground cable.
2. Remove three screws at top rear of speedometer cluster.
3. Remove four screws just ahead of heater controls.

4. Remove average speed computer and clock.
5. Remove screw from top and inside computer and clock panel housing.
6. Remove tachometer.
7. Remove screw at top and inside tachometer panel housing.
8. Remove turn signal sockets and bulbs.
9. Pull speedometer cluster out far enough to enable removal of generator and oil pressure indicator lamp socket and bulb.
10. Remove other sockets and bulbs.
11. Disconnect computer drive cable and speedometer cable.
12. Remove speedometer and instrument cluster.

1958

1. Disconnect battery ground cable.
2. Remove steering wheel.
3. Mask steering column tube and area around speedometer and instrument cluster to avoid scratching the finish.
4. Unfasten speedometer and instrument cluster hood (4 screws) from dash panel.
5. Remove instrument cluster hood.
6. Remove windshield wiper knob and shaft.
7. Unscrew wiper control retaining nut.
8. Pull speedometer and instrument cluster out slightly to facilitate removal of both turn signal sockets and bulbs, high beam indicator socket and bulb, generator indicator and oil pressure indicator sockets and bulbs, and instrument lamp socket and bulb.
9. Remove light switch shaft and knob by pushing switch shaft straight in and releasing shaft spring pin retainer; remove lock nut and switch.
10. Disconnect speedometer cable.
11. Disconnect wiring from terminals on fuel gauge, temperature gauge and voltage regulator.
12. Remove speedometer and instrument cluster.

1959-60

1. Disconnect battery ground cable.
2. Remove two screws securing hood and speedometer assembly to instrument cluster.
3. Raise hood and speedometer assembly upward off dowel pins and disconnect cable.
4. Disconnect speedometer lamp wiring at four-way connector and remove speedometer and hood assembly.

1961

In order to remove the speedometer,

the upper instrument cluster must be taken out after which the speedometer can be removed. To remove the upper instrument cluster, proceed as follows:
1. Disconnect battery ground cable.
2. Disconnect speedometer cable.
3. Remove wires from clip at right hand clock retaining nut.
4. Release instrument cluster wire loom from two clips.
5. Protect upper cluster and steering column from damage with cloth.
6. Remove automatic transmission quadrant dial cover moulding.
7. Place transmission selector lever in low gear position.
8. Remove ten upper cluster-to-instrument panel retaining screws. Four long screws at top, four screws at bottom and two screws just above steering column.
9. Turn automatic transmission indicator to one side.
10. Carefully pull upper cluster outward and lay it on protective cloth on steering column.
11. Remove wiring harness and clips. Disconnect gauge wires, remove sockets and lamps and remove cluster.

RADIO REMOVAL

1957

1. Disconnect battery ground cable.
2. Disconnect speaker and antenna leads from radio.
3. Disconnect pilot light.
4. Disconnect radio and battery wire at fuse block.
5. Remove nuts on each side of radio.
6. Remove control knobs and mounting nuts from control shafts.
7. Spring mounting brackets away from studs on sides of radio and remove radio.

1958

1. Disconnect ground cable from battery.
2. Disconnect front and rear speaker plugs from radio.
3. Disconnect antenna lead from radio.
4. Disconnect dial light wire at connector (left side of radio).
5. Disconnect foot control switch lead (if equipped) from left side of radio.
6. Disconnect radio-to-battery wire at fuse block.
7. Remove nuts from radio mounting studs.
8. Remove radio control knobs.
9. Remove two shaft housing nuts.

10. Spring two mounting brackets away from studs on sides of radio and remove radio. It is not necessary to remove electric antenna control switch (if equipped).

1959-60

1. Disconnect battery ground cable.
2. Remove glove box.
3. Remove glove box light and switch.
4. Remove air conditioning "Spot Cooler" (1959) or register (1960) if equipped.
5. Disconnect pilot light and "A" lead at two-way connector.
6. Disconnect foot control switch lead if equipped (orange wire).
7. Remove front speaker plug and rear speaker plug (if equipped) from bottom of receiver.
8. Disconnect audio power lead from audio unit (if equipped) which is located at brake pedal support.
9. Disconnect antenna lead.
10. Remove control knobs from receiver.
11. Remove two control shaft nuts, and two screws from right edge of trim plate.
12. Remove trim plate.
13. Unfasten receiver from instrument panel (2 nuts).
14. Push receiver inward from instrument panel and remove it through glove box opening.

1961

1. Disconnect battery ground cable.
2. On air conditioned cars, remove glove box liner.
3. Disconnect antenna lead in cable and speaker plug from radio.
4. On air conditioned cars, remove speaker grille and speaker. If rear speaker is employed, unplug speaker from speaker harness.
5. Disconnect dial lamp lead at bullet connector and power lead at main lighting junction block.
6. Remove control knobs and two nuts and washers from front of radio.
7. Remove bracket retaining nut from left side of radio and bracket attaching screw from right side. On air conditioned cars, remove right radio support bracket.
8. Remove radio from car. On air conditioned cars, remove radio through speaker grille opening with push buttons facing down.

WINDSHIELD WIPER

1954-56

1. To remove wiper motor on 1954-55 first remove heater plenum chamber and radio; on 1956, remove radio only.
2. Remove retainer that holds pivot shaft arm to wiper motor pivot. Remove arms from pivot.
3. Remove motor from mounting bracket (2 screws). Lower motor until set screw that retains control cable to slide valve becomes accessible. Loosen set screw and remove cable from valve.
4. Remove vacuum hose from motor.

1957-58

The wiper motor is secured to the cowl top panel with a spacer and nut. When installing the motor, be sure the gasket is on the motor shaft end and is inserted evenly into the auxiliary drive.

To remove the wiper pivot and cable assembly, it is necessary to remove the fresh air intake grille, rubber plugs from tensioner access holes, and (on 1957) right hand fresh air duct to gain access to the auxiliary drive drum.

To install wiper pivot and cable assembly, hold tensioner in a vise and release leaf spring tension lock. Then turn tensioner enough to align the two small holes and insert a cotter pin to temporarily maintain slack. Install cables on pulleys and bend cable guide tabs to original position so they barely clear pulleys. After cables are installed on auxiliary drive drum, install tensioner assembly into cowl panel and tighten securely. Then, using a hooked tool, pull locking cotter pin out of tensioner assembly.

1959

To remove the windshield wiper cable and pivot assembly, *it is necessary to remove the glove box, radio and cowl vent grille.*

On cars with manual shift transmission, the cable end of the pivot housing must be installed from the right side of the clutch mounting bracket. Then the assembly must be rotated and at the same time entered into the mounting hole to provide clearance for the assembly.

On all models, when the tension lug on the auxiliary drive is locked in the compressed position, install the cables on the auxiliary drive. After the cables are installed, move the spring clip on the "up" position, then compress the prongs to release the tension lugs.

To locate the wiper pivots, turn ignition key to "ACC" position. Turn wiper control knob to operate wiper momentarily. Install wiper arms and blades so that they point toward right side of windshield and just contact belt moulding. Check wiper operation and make any necessary adjustments.

1960

Do not operate or test the wiper motor unless all wire connections are made. The motor may be checked for operation when it is disconnected from the cowl only when the wiring quick disconnect is connected and the motor assembly is grounded. *Under no circumstances should the motor be operated by connecting a hot lead to the motor and grounding the individual leads as damage may result.*

When removing or replacing the relay and cover assembly, care should be taken not to bend or damage the full sweep switch as the relay is adjusted and riveted to the cover.

Before attaching the motor assembly to the cowl, check its operation by connecting the wiring quick disconnect in the engine compartment to the motor wiring, turning the motor control switch and grounding the motor. *This test should be concluded by turning wiper control switch to the "off" position. This positions the motor in "park" position.*

To remove the wiper motor if the car is equipped with air conditioning, take off the glove box liner, radio speaker assembly, radio and the brace from the right defroster nozzle to the instrument panel. Remove the attaching parts and take the motor out through the speaker opening.

OLDSMOBILE

INDEX OF SERVICE OPERATIONS

PAGE NO.

ACCESSORIES
Radio Removal 879
Speedometer Removal 879
Windshield Wiper 880
Windshield Wiper Troubles............ 37

BODY
Air Conditioning 177
Automatic Seat Adjuster Troubles...... 36
Automatic Top Troubles.............. 36
Automatic Window Lift Troubles....... 36

BRAKES (Mechanical)
Adjustments 112
Brake Cylinder Sizes................856
Hydraulic Brake System..............112
Master Cylinder, Replace............874
Trouble Shooting 31

BRAKES (Power)
Power Unit Repairs..................128
Power Unit, Replace 873
Trouble Shooting 32

CLUTCH
Clutch Pedal, Adjust................868
Clutch, Replace 868
Trouble Shooting 13

COOLING SYSTEM
Radiator, Replace 863
Trouble Shooting 8
Water Pump Repairs.................863
Water Pump, Replace................863

ELECTRIC SYSTEM
Dash Gauge Service 85
Distributor, Replace 863
Distributor Service 46
Distributor Specifications...........855
Generator Regulator Service........ 62
Generator Regulator Specifications.... 855
Generator Service 62
Generator Specifications............855
Horn Button or Ring, Replace........877
Ignition System Service.............. 46
Ignition Timing 864
Starter, Replace 864
Starter Switch Service.............. 83
Starting Motor Service.............. 77
Starting Motor Specifications........855
Trouble Shooting 10
Turn Signal Troubles................ 12

ENGINE
Camshaft, Replace 861
Crankshaft & Bearing Specs..........854
Crankshaft Oil Seal, Replace........862
Cylinder Head, Replace 859
Engine, Replace 858
Main Bearings, Replace 862
Piston Pins, Replace................862
Piston Rings, Replace..............862
Piston, Pin & Ring Specs............854
Pistons & Rods, Remove.............861
Piston & Rod, Assemble.............861
Pistons, Replace 861
Rocker Arm, Replace 859
Raising Engine 857
Rod Bearings, Replace..............862
Timing Case Cover, Replace.........861
Timing Chain, Replace..............861
Trouble Shooting 4
Valve Arrangement 859
Valve Guides, Replace.............859
Valves, Grind 860
Valves Lifters 860
Valves, Remove 859
Valve Specifications...............854
Valve Spring Installed Height........859
Valve Spring Testing...............860

ENGINE OILING
Oil Pan, Replace...................863
Oil Pump Repairs..................863
Trouble Shooting 9

FRONT SUSPENSION
Camber, Adjust 875
Caster, Adjust 875
Front End Repairs.................875
Toe-in, Adjust 875
Trouble Shooting 33
Wheel Alignment Specifications........856
Wheel Bearings, Adjust.............875

FUEL & EXHAUST SYSTEMS
Carburetors 864
Fuel Pumps 96
Mufflers and Pipes................864
Trouble Shooting 4

PAGE NO.

REAR AXLE
Axle Shaft, Replace....'............873
General Service 102
Non-Slip Differentials..............109
Rear Axle Repairs.................872
Rear Axle Specifications............856
Trouble Shooting 31

SPECIFICATIONS
Brake Cylinder Sizes...............856
Capacity Data 854
Carburetors 865
Cooling System 854
Crankshaft & Bearings..............854
Distributors 855
Engie Tightening 856
Generator & Regulators.............855
Pistons, Pin & Rings...............854
Rear Axle 856
Starting Motors 855
Tune Up 853
Valves 854
Valve Timing 861
Wheel Alignment 856

STEERING GEARS (Mechanical)
Horn Button or Ring, Replace........877
Steering Gear Repairs..............878
Steering Gear, Replace.............877
Steering Wheel, Replace............877
Trouble Shooting 33

STEERING GEARS (Power)
Steering Gear, Repairs.............145
Steering Gear, Replace.............878
Trouble Shooting 34

TRANSMISSIONS (Manual Shift)
Gearshift, Adjust 870
Transmission Repairs 869
Transmission, Replace 868
Trouble Shooting 14

TRANSMISSIONS (Automatic)
Hydra-Matic Linkage, Adjust.........871
Hydra-Matic, Replace 870
Hydra-Matic Repairs (Single Coupling) .283
Hydra-Matic Repairs (Two Couplings) .263
Hydra-Matic Repairs, Three Speed....1132
Trouble Shooting, Three Speed.......1144
Trouble Shooting, Four Speed.......25, 28

TUNE UP 38

Year	Model Designation	Wheelbase, Inches	Valve Location	Bore and Stroke	Piston Displacement, Cubic Inches	Compression Ratio (Standard)	Maximum Brake H.P. @ R.P.M.	Maximum Torque Lbs. Ft. @ R.P.M.	Normal Oil Pressure Pounds
1953	V8............De Luxe 88	120	In Head	3.7500 x 3.437	303	8.00	150 @ 3600	280 @ 1800	35–45
	V8............Super 88	120	In Head	3.7500 x 3.437	303	8.00	165 @ 3600	284 @ 1800	35–45
	V8............98	124	In Head	3.7500 x 3.437	303	8.00	165 @ 3600	284 @ 1800	35–45
1954	V8............88	122	In Head	3.8750 x 3.437	324	8.25	170 @ 4000	300 @ 2000	35–45
	V8............Super 88	122	In Head	3.8750 x 3.437	324	8.25	185 @ 4000	300 @ 2000	35–45
	V8............98	126	In Head	3.8750 x 3.437	324	8.25	185 @ 4000	300 @ 2000	35–45
1955	V8............88	122	In Head	3.8750 x 3.437	324	8.50	185 @ 4000	320 @ 2000	35–45
	V8............Super 88	122	In Head	3.8750 x 3.437	324	8.50	202 @ 4000	332 @ 2400	35–45
	V8............98	126	In Head	3.8750 x 3.437	324	8.50	202 @ 4000	332 @ 2400	35–45
1956	V8............88	122	In Head	3.8750 x 3.437	324	9.25	230 @ 4400①	340 @ 2400②	35–45
	V8............Super 88	122	In Head	3.8750 x 3.437	324	9.25	240 @ 4400	350 @ 2800	35–45
	V8............98	126	In Head	3.8750 x 3.437	324	9.25	240 @ 4400	350 @ 2800	35–45
1957	V8............88	122	In Head	4.0000 x 3.688	371	9.50	277 @ 4400	400 @ 2800	35–45
	V8............Super 88	122	In Head	4.0000 x 3.688	371	9.50	277 @ 4400	400 @ 2800	35–45
	V8............98	126	In Head	4.0000 x 3.688	371	9.50	277 @ 4400	400 @ 2800	35–45
1958	V8............Dynamic 88	122½	In Head	4.0000 x 3.688	371	10.0	265 @ 4400	390 @ 2400	35–45
	V8............Super 88	122½	In Head	4.0000 x 3.688	371	10.0	305 @ 4600	410 @ 2800	35–45
	V8............98	126½	In Head	4.0000 x 3.688	371	10.0	305 @ 4600	410 @ 2800	35–45
	J-2 Engine............	...	In Head	4.0000 x 3.688	371	10.0	312 @ 4600	415 @ 2800	35–45
1959	V8............Dynamic 88	123	In Head	4.0000 x 3.688	371	9.75	270 @ 4600	390 @ 2400	35–45
	V8............Super 88	123	In Head	4.1250 x 3.688	394	9.75	315 @ 4600	435 @ 2800	35–45
	V8............98	126.3	In Head	4.1250 x 3.688	394	9.75	315 @ 4600	435 @ 2800	35–45
1960	V8............Dynamic 88	123	In Head	4.0000 x 3.688	371	8.75	240 @ 4600	375 @ 2400	35–45
	V8............Super 88	123	In Head	4.0000 x 3.688	371	9.75	315 @ 4600	435 @ 2800	35–45
	V8............98	126.3	In Head	4.1250 x 3.688	394	9.75	315 @ 4600	435 @ 2800	35–45
1961	88, Super 88............V8③	123	In Head	4.1250 x 3.688	394	8.75	250 @ 4200	405 @ 2400	35–45
	88, Super 88............V8④	123	In Head	4.1250 x 3.688	394	10.0	325 @ 4600	435 @ 2800	35–45
	98............V8③	126	In Head	4.1250 x 3.688	394	8.75	250 @ 4200	405 @ 2400	35–45
	98............V8④	126	In Head	4.1250 x 3.688	394	10.0	325 @ 4600	435 @ 2800	35–45

①—With 4-barrel carburetor 240 @ 4400 R.P.M.   ②—With 4-barrel carburetor 350 @ 2800 R.P.M.
③—Regular fuel.   ④—Premium fuel.

TUNE UP SPECIFICATIONS

★ Disconnect vacuum line when using timing light to set timing.

Year	Model	Ground Polarity and Voltage	Spark Plug Type	Spark Plug Gap Inch	Distributor Point Gap Inch	Distributor Cam Angle Degrees	Firing Order ①	Ignition Timing★ Mark	Ignition Timing★ Location	Idle Speed RPM In Drive	Compression Pressure @ Cranking Speed Minimum
1953	All	N-12	AC-46-5	.030	.016	26–33	18736542	⑤	Pulley	375	120
1954	All	N-12	AC-46-5	.030	.016	26–33	18736542	⑤	Pulley	400	120
1955	All	N-12	AC-44-5	.030	.016	26–33	18736542	⑤	Pulley	400	120
1956	All	N-12	AC-44	.030	④	30	18736542	⑤	Pulley	400	150
1957	All	N-12	AC-44	.030	④	30	18736542	⑤	Damper	425	160
1958	All	N-12	AC-44	.030	④	30	18736542	⑥	Damper	460	160
1959	All	N-12	AC-44	.030	④	30	18736542	⑥	Damper	460	155
1960	Dynamic 88	N-12	AC-45	.030	④	30	18736542	②	Damper	460	150
	Super 88, 98	N-12	AC-44	.030	④	30	18736542	②	Damper	425	155
1961	Reg. Fuel	N-12	AC-45	.030	④	30	18736542	②	Damper	500	150
	Prem. Fuel	N-12	AC-44	.030	④	30	18736542	③	Damper	500	160

①—V8 cylinder numbering (front to rear): Left bank 1-3-5-7, right bank 2-4-6-8.
②—Center line on vibration damper which is 5°BTDC (see Fig. 15).
③—Between center line and right-hand line (viewed from front) which is 7½°BTDC (see Fig. 15).
④—Turn adjusting screw in (clockwise) until engine misfires. Then turn screw out ½ turn.
⑤—Cars with one notch set at leading edge of notch. On cars with 3, set at center slot.
⑥—Two slots. Set timing to first slot which is 5°BTDC.

VALVE SPECIFICATIONS

Year	Model	Valve Lash		Valve Angles		Valve Spring Installed Height	Valve Spring Pressure Lbs. @ In.	Valve Lift		Stem Clearance		Stem Diameter	
		Int.	Exh.	Seat	Face			Int.	Exh.	Intake	Exhaust	Int.	Exh.
1953	All	Zero	Zero	45	45	1⁵³⁄₆₄	156 @ 1¹⁵⁄₃₂	.366	.366	.0022–.0042	.0027–.0045	.3421	.3934
1954	All	Zero	Zero	45	45	1⁵³⁄₆₄	156 @ 1¹⁵⁄₃₂	.366	.366	.0022–.0042	.0027–.0045	.3421	.3934
1955	All	Zero	Zero	45	45	1⁵³⁄₆₄	156 @ 1¹⁵⁄₃₂	.403	.403	.0022–.0042	.0027–.0045	.3421	.3934
1956	All	Zero	Zero	45	45	1⁷⁄₈	190 @ 1³¹⁄₆₄	.418	.418	.0017–.004	.0022–.0045	.3421	.3934
1957	All	Zero	Zero	45	45	1⁷⁄₈	190 @ 1³¹⁄₆₄	.419	.435	.0017–.0035	.0022–.004	.3421	.3934
1958	All	Zero	Zero	45	45	1⁵³⁄₆₄	227 @ 1⁷⁄₁₆	.435	.437	.0017–.0035	.0022–.004	.3421	.3934
1959	All	Zero	Zero	45	45	1⁵³⁄₆₄	175 @ 1⁷⁄₁₆	.419	.435	.0017–.0035	.0022–.004	.3421	.3934
1960–61	All	Zero	Zero	45	45	1⁵³⁄₆₄	182 @ 1⁷⁄₁₆	.435	.437	.001–.0025	.0015–.003	.3430	.3943

PISTONS, PINS, RINGS, CRANKSHAFT & BEARINGS

Year	Model	Fitting Pistons		Ring End Gap ①		Wrist-pin Diameter	Rod Bearings		Main Bearings			
		Shim To Use	Pounds Pull On Scale	Comp.	Oil		Shaft Diameter	Bearing Clearance	Shaft Diameter	Bearing Clearance	Thrust on Bear. No.	Shaft End Play
1953–54	V8	.0015	10–18	.010	.010	.9805	2.249–2.250	.001–.003	②	③	5	.004–.008
1955	V8	.0015	10–18	.010	.010	.9805	2.249–2.250	.001–.003	②	④	5	.004–.008
1956	V8	.0015	5–12	.010	.013	.9805	2.249–2.250	.001–.003	②	④	5	.004–.008
1957–58	V8	.0015	1–6	.013	.015	.9805	2.249–2.250	.001–.003	2.748–2.749	④	5	.004–.008
1959–60	Dynamic 88	.0015	2–6	.013	.015	.9805	2.4992–2.5002	.0005–.0026	2.999–3.000	⑤	5	.004–.008
	Others	.0015	3–12	.013	.015	.9805	2.4992–2.5002	.0005–.0026	2.999–3.000	⑤	5	.004–.008
1961	All	.0015	3–12	.013	.015	.9805	2.4992–2.5002	.0005–.0026	2.999–3.000	⑤	5	.004–.008

①—Fit rings in tapered bores for clearance listed in tightest portion of ring travel.
②—Rear bearing 2.623–2.624, all others 2.498–2.499.
③—Rear bearing .002–.0035″, all others .0005–.003″.
④—Front .0005–.002″, rear .002–.0035″, others .0005–.003″.
⑤—No. 1 and 2 .0005″, No. 3 and 4 .0008–.0024″, rear .002–.0034″.

COOLING SYSTEM & CAPACITY DATA

Year & Model	Cooling System Data			Thermostat Opening Temp.		Fuel Tank Gals.	Engine Oil			Transmissions			Rear Axle Pints
	Quarts No Heater	Quarts With Heater	Rad. Cap Relief Pressure	①	②		Refill Qts.③	Summer Grade	Winter Grade	Std. Pints	With Over-drive Pints	Auto-matic Qts.	
1953	21½	22½	7	180	160	18	5	20	10W	2	None	10½	4¾
1954	20½	21½	7	180	160	20	5	20	10W	2½	None	10	4¾
1955	20½	21½	7	180	160	20	5	20	10W	2½	None	11	4¾
1956	20½	21½	7	180	160	20	5	20	10W	2½	None	11	4¾
1957	19½	21	12–15	180	160	20	5	20	10W	2½	None	11	5¼
1958	20	21	13④	180	160	20	4	20	10W	2½	None	11	5¼
1959	20	21	13④	180	160	20	4	20	10W	2½	None	11	5⅓
1960	20	21	13④	170	—	20	4	20	10W	2½	None	9½	5⅓
1961	19¼	20¼	14	170	—	20	4	20	10W	2½	None	5½	5⅓

①—For permanent type anti-freeze. ②—For alcohol type anti-freeze. ③—Add one quart with filter change.
④—With air conditioning 15 lbs.

Year	Model	Part No. [1]	Rotation [2]	Cam Angle, Degrees	Breaker Point Opening, Inch	Condenser Capacity, Mfds.[3]	Breaker Arm Spring Tension, Ounces	Centrifugal Advance Data Degrees @ R.P.M. of Dist.		Vacuum Advance Data		
								Advance Starts	Full Advance	Inches of Vacuum to Start Plunger Movement	Inches of Vacuum for Full Plunger Travel	Maximum Vacuum Advance, Dist. Degrees
1953	V8	1110824	CC	26–33	.016	.18–.23	19–23	1 @ 400	15 @ 1850	4½–6½	15–16	10
1953–54	V8	1110843	CC	26–33	.016	.18–.23	19–23	1 @ 400	14 @ 1725	4½–6½	15–16	10
1954–55	V8	1110850	CC	26–33	.016	.18–.23	19–23	1 @ 400	14 @ 1725	4½–6½	15–16	10
1956	V8	1110857	CC	30	[4]	.18–.23	19–23	1 @ 575	10 @ 1950	4½–6½	15½–16	10¾
1957	V8	1110883	CC	30	[4]	.18–.23	19–23	1 @ 400	12 @ 2200	4½–6½	15¼–16	10
1958	All	1110929	CC	30	[4]	.18–.23	19–23	1 @ 400	12 @ 2200	8–10	13–16	12
1959	All	1110931	CC	30	[4]	.18–.23	19–23	1 @ 400	12 @ 2200	8–10	19–21	10–12
1960–61	All	1110968	CC	30	[4]	.18–.23	19–23	2 @ 400	12 @ 2200	8–10	19–21	11

[1]—Stamped on plate riveted to side of distributor housing.
[2]—As viewed from the top.   CC—Counter clockwise.
[3]—Microfarads—as indicated on a condenser tester.

[4]—Turn adjusting screw in (clockwise) until engine begins to misfire. Then turn screw ½ turn in opposite direction.

GENERATOR AND REGULATOR SPECIFICATIONS

★To polarize generator, reconnect the leads to the regulator; then momentarily connect a jumper wire from the "Gen" to the "Bat" terminals of the regulator.

Year	Generator						Regulator					
	Generator Number	Rotation and Ground Polarity [1]	Rated Cap. Amps.	Gen. Field Ground Location★	Brush Spring Tension, Ounces	Field Current Amperes	Regulator Number	Cutout Relay		Voltage Regulator Setting Volts	Current Regulator Setting Amperes	Current and Voltage Armature Air Gap, Inch
								Voltage to Close Points	Armature Air Gap, Inch			
1953–55	1102003	C-N	30	External	28	1.48–1.62[8]	1118825	12.6	.020	14.3	30	.075
1956	1102003	C-N	30	External	28	1.48–1.62[8]	1119003	12.6	.020	14.3	30	.075
1956	1102021	C-N	30	External	28	1.48–1.62[8]	1119003	12.6	.020	14.3	30	.075
1957	1102063	C-N	30	External	28	1.48–1.62[8]	1119001	12.6	.020	14.3	30	.075
1957	1102067	C-N	35	External	28	1.62–1.83[8]	1119002	12.6	.020	14.3	35	.075
1958–59	1102092	C-N	35	External	28	1.62–1.82[8]	1119002	12.6	.020	14.3	35	.075
	1102093	C-N	45	External	28	2.66–2.86[8]	1119600	12.4	.020	14.2[4]	41	.075[5]
1960	1102166	C-N	35	External	28	1.62–1.82[8]	1119253	12.6	.020	14.3	35	.075
1960–61	1102187	C-N	45	External	28	2.66–2.86[8]	1119600	12.4	.020	14.2[4]	45	.075[5]
1961	1102217	C-N	35	External	28	1.62–1.82[8]	1119253	12.8	.020	14-3	35	.075

[1]—C-Clockwise.   N-Negative.
[8]—At 12 volts.

[4]—Lower contact setting .1 to .3 volt lower.
[5]—Voltage regulator contact air gap: Upper .016″, lower .067″.

STARTING MOTOR SPECIFICATIONS

Year	Model	Part No.	Rotation [1]	Brush Spring Tension, Ounces	No Load Test			Torque Test		
					Amperes	Volts	R.P.M.	Amperes	Volts	Torque, Lbs. Ft.
1953	V8	1107603	C	24 Min.	75	10.3	6500	520	4.9	11
1954–55	V8	1107623	C	35 Min.	95	10.1	3500	470	5.4	10½
1956	V8	1107638	C	35 Min.	95	10.1	3500	470	5.4	10½
1957–61	V8	1107665	C	35 Min.	65–100	10.6	3600–5100	300–360	3.5	...
1959–60	S-88, 98	1107716	C	35 Min.	80–120	10.6	4700–5400	290–370	2.0	...
1961	All	1107776	C	35 Min.	80–120	10.6	3900–5400	[2]	[2]	[2]

[1]—As viewed from the drive end.   C—Clockwise.   [2]—Not specified.

OLDSMOBILE

REAR AXLE AND BRAKE CYLINDER SPECIFICATIONS

Year	Model	Ring Gear & Pinion Backlash, Inch	Drive Pinion Adjustment	Drive Pinion Bearing Preload, Inch Lbs.	Drive Pinion Bearing Adjustment	Axle Shaft End Play, Inch	Hydraulic Cylinder Bore Sizes, Inch		Master Cylinder
							Wheel Cylinder		
							Front	Rear	
1953	All	.004–.006	Shims	24–32①	Spacer	....	1³⁄₃₂	1⁵⁄₁₆	1
1954–55	All	.004–.006	Shims	24–32①	Spacer	....	1³⁄₃₂	3¹⁄₃₂	1
1956–58	All	.004–.008	Shims	24–32①	Spacer	....	1³⁄₃₂	3¹⁄₃₂	1
1959–61	All	.007–.008	Shims	24–32①	Spacer	....	1¹⁄₈	1	1

①—For used bearings, 10-15 inch lbs.

WHEEL ALIGNMENT SPECIFICATIONS

Year	Model	Caster, Degrees		Camber, Degrees		Toe-in, Inches	Toe-out on Turns, Degrees①		Kingpin or Steering Axis Inclination②
		Limits	Desired	Limits	Desired		Outer Wheel	Inner Wheel	
1953	All	−³⁄₄ to 0	−³⁄₈	−³⁄₄ to +³⁄₄	0	¹⁄₁₆ to ¹⁄₈	23	20	5
1954–56	All	−³⁄₄ to 0	−³⁄₈③	−³⁄₄ to +³⁄₄	0	¹⁄₁₆ to ¹⁄₈	23	20	6
1957	All	0 to +³⁄₄	+³⁄₈	−³⁄₄ to +³⁄₄	0	¹⁄₁₆ to ¹⁄₈	23	20	7 @ 0 Camber
1958	All	−1 to 0	−¹⁄₂	−¹⁄₄ to +³⁄₄	+¹⁄₄	0 to ¹⁄₈	23	20	7 @ 0 Camber
1959	All	0 to +1	+¹⁄₂	−¹⁄₄ to +¹⁄₂	+¹⁄₈	0 to ¹⁄₁₆	23	20	10 @ 0 Camber
1960–61	All	0 to −1	−¹⁄₂	−¹⁄₄ to +³⁄₄	+¹⁄₄	0 to ¹⁄₈	23	20	10 @ 0 Camber

①—Incorrect toe-out, when other adjustments are correct, indicates bent steering arms.
②—Incorrect angle with correct camber indicates bent suspension arms or steering knuckle support.
③—Maximum variation between the two sides of the car should not exceed ½ degree.

ENGINE TIGHTENING SPECIFICATIONS★

★Torque specifications are for clean and lightly lubricated threads only. Dry or dirty threads produce increased friction which prevents accurate measurement of tightness.

Year	Spark Plugs Ft. Lbs.	Cylinder Head Bolts Ft. Lbs.	Intake Manifold Ft. Lbs.	Exhaust Manifold Ft. Lbs.	Rocker Arm Shaft Bracket Ft. Lbs.	Rocker Arm Cover Ft. Lbs.	Connecting Rod Cap Bolts Ft. Lbs.	Main Bearing Cap Bolts Ft. Lbs.	Flywheel to Crankshaft Ft. Lbs.	Vibration Damper or Pulley Ft. Lbs.
1953–54	25	65–70	22–26	18–22	14–17	2–3	45–50	①	85–95	45–50
1955–56	23–28	60–70	22–26	22–26	14–17	2–3	40–50	①	85–95	45–50
1957	23–28	60–70	25–35	19–25	14–17	1–2	45–50	①	85–95	100
1958	23–28	60–70	22–34	19–25	14–17	5–6	35–50	①	85–95	100
1959–61	18–34	60–80	22–34	19–25	14–22	2–4	38–48	②	85–95	100

①—Rear 140 ft. lbs., others 100 ft. lbs.
②—Rear 130-160 ft. lbs., others 90-120 ft. lbs.

SERIAL NUMBER LOCATION
Left Front Door Pillar

ENGINE NUMBER LOCATION
1953-57: Left Bank Of Cylinder Block
1958-61: Top Of Center Exhaust Port Of Left Cylinder Head

1953

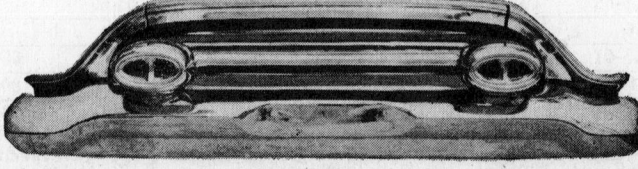

1954

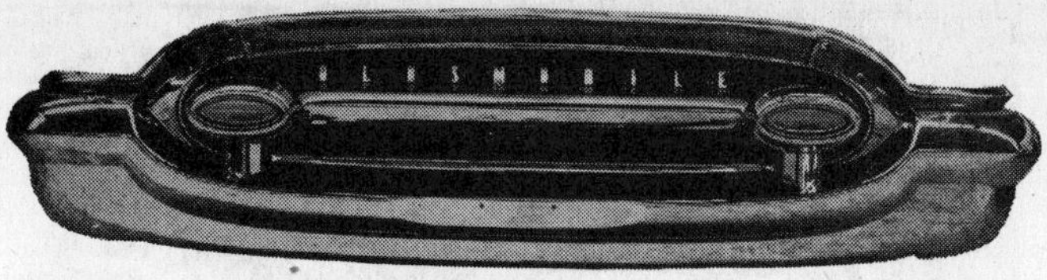

1955

1959

1956

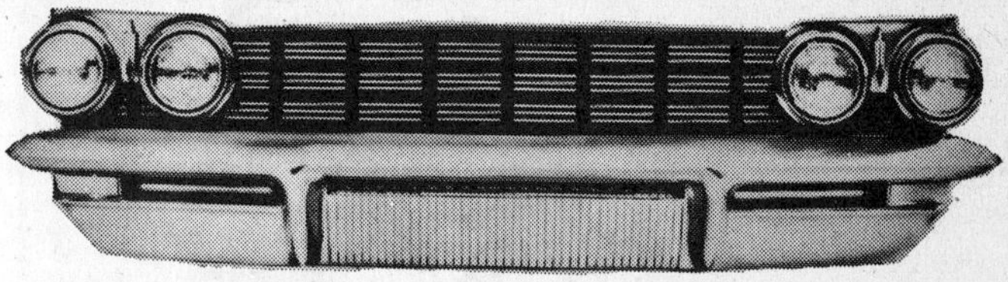

1960

1957

1961 "88"

1958

1961 "98"

Engine Section

RAISING ENGINE

1961 Service Note

When removing the exhaust manifold, oil pan, timing case cover or the engine front mount, the front of the engine must be raised to provide clearance. This is accomplished as follows, referring to Fig. 1A.

1. Remove engine front mount-to-front crossmember attaching nuts. On air conditioned cars, disconnect fan ring.
2. Remove threaded bolt of tool (shown in illustration) from support plate. Feed support plate through large opening in underside of front cross-member. Align hole in support plate with center hole in crossmember.
3. Attach a chain 18 to 24″ long to the tool to aid in positioning the tool in and out of the crossmember.
4. Insert the threaded bolt into the support plate. Rotate the threaded bolt until it contacts the engine front mount. Raise engine until proper clearance is obtained. *When raising*

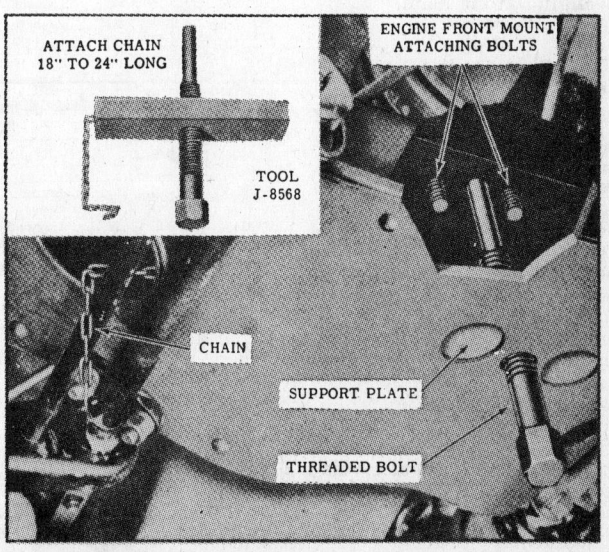

ATTACH CHAIN 18″ TO 24″ LONG

ENGINE FRONT MOUNT ATTACHING BOLTS

TOOL J-8568

CHAIN

SUPPORT PLATE

THREADED BOLT

Fig. 1A Raising front of engine. 1961

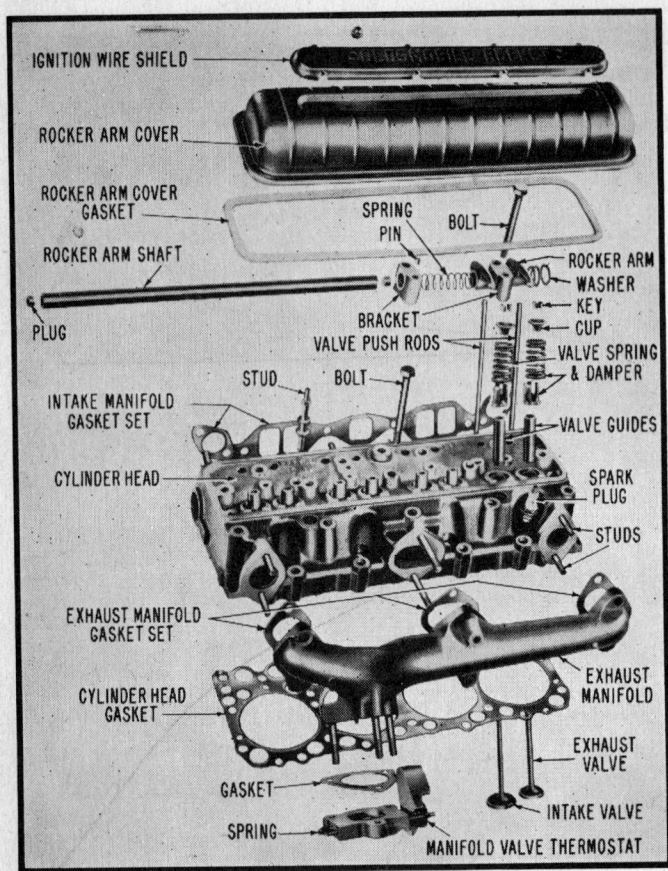

IGNITION WIRE SHIELD
ROCKER ARM COVER
ROCKER ARM COVER GASKET
SPRING PIN
BOLT
ROCKER ARM SHAFT
ROCKER ARM
WASHER
KEY
CUP
PLUG
BRACKET
VALVE PUSH RODS
VALVE SPRING & DAMPER
STUD
BOLT
INTAKE MANIFOLD GASKET SET
VALVE GUIDES
CYLINDER HEAD
SPARK PLUG
STUDS
EXHAUST MANIFOLD GASKET SET
CYLINDER HEAD GASKET
EXHAUST MANIFOLD
EXHAUST VALVE
GASKET
INTAKE VALVE
SPRING
MANIFOLD VALVE THERMOSTAT

CYLINDER BLOCK
BAFFLE
GASKET
GASKET
FLANGE
VENTILATOR TUBE
FLYWHEEL HOUSING (UPPER REAR)
CAMSHAFT THRUST PLATE (1949 ONLY)
DRAIN COCK
OIL DIPSTICK
STUD
BAFFLE
ENGINE MOUNTING (REAR)
OIL PUMP SHAFT
OUTER TUBE
FLYWHEEL HOUSING PAN
FLYWHEEL LOWER HOUSING
COVER
INNER TUBE
OIL PUMP ASSY
OIL PAN GASKET SET
OIL PUMP SCREEN
OIL PAN
PLUG
GASKET

Cylinder head and related parts

Cylinder block and related parts

engine, do not allow rear of engine or engine components to contact cowl.

5. When removing the timing case cover or the engine front mount, raise the engine to the desired height, then insert wood blocks between exhaust manifolds and front crossmember. Lower engine until supported on the blocks. The threaded bolt can now be lowered away from the engine front plate.

ENGINE, REPLACE

Due to variations in equipment, no attempt is made to itemize every step for an engine replacement procedure. The following recommendations are given as a guide.

1. Drain cooling system.
2. Disconnect battery cables.
3. Disconnect radiator hoses.
4. Disconnect transmission oil cooler lines (if used).
5. Disconnect exhaust pipe at front flange.
6. Remove radiator.
7. Remove hood assembly.
8. On conventional models, disconnect clutch control linkage.
9. If equipped with Hydra-Matic, disconnect transmission control linkage.
10. Disconnect accelerator control.
11. Disconnect windshield wiper vacuum line.
12. Disconnect wiring from engine units

including generator, starter distributor and coil.
13. Remove cable from starter terminal.
14. Disconnect flexible line from fuel pump.
15. Disconnect oil pressure gauge line at filter.
16. Disconnect propeller shaft at rear of transmission.

17. Remove two bolts attaching engine front support mounting to engine bracket.
18. Attach a lifting sling to raise power plant from above.
19. Remove rear mounting bolts and lower mounting.
20. Raise power plant to permit removal of support member.
21. Move power plant forward, raising as necessary to clear frame.
22. Reverse the foregoing procedure to install power plant.

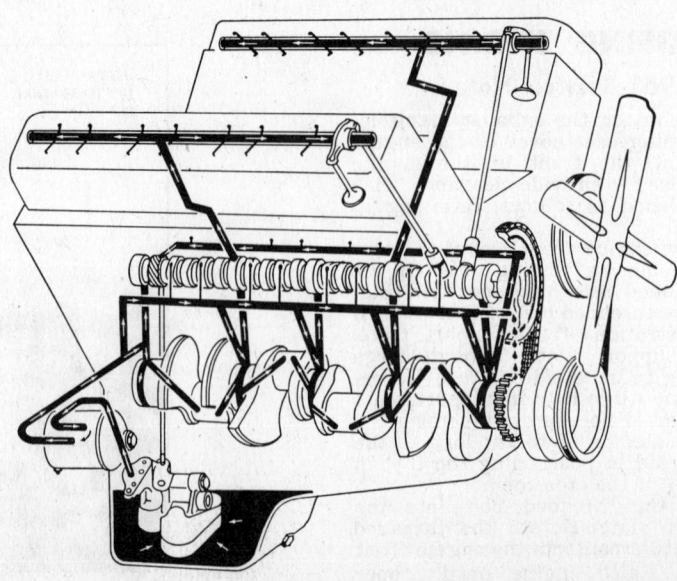

Engine lubrication. V-8 engines

Fig. 1 Head tightening. 1958-61 Tighten numbered bolts first, then lettered bolts

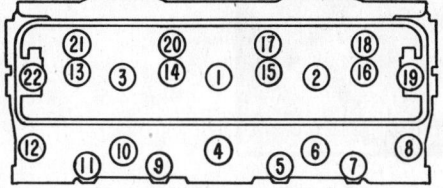

Fig. 2 Head tightening. 1957

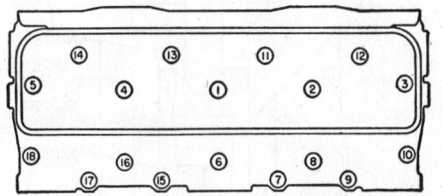

Fig. 3 Head tightening. 1953-56

Service Note

On V8 engines, whenever installation of a front engine mounting becomes necessary, the cap screws fastening the mounting to the frame or bracket should first be screwed finger tight, then tightened alternately, one at a time. *Do not tighten one cap screw in position independently of the other.* This is extremely important since the lower portion of the assembly would not seat evenly in the upper portion. The front mounting must be properly positioned and tightened, otherwise the mounting will not properly function as an insulator.

CYLINDER HEAD, REPLACE

1. Drain radiator and cylinder block.
2. Remove intake manifold.
3. Remove generator.
4. Disconnect exhaust pipes.
5. Remove valve cover.
6. Remove rocker arm assembly.
7. Remove push rods. Keep rods in proper sequence or otherwise tag them to be sure they will be installed in their original locations. On 1957-58 models, it will be necessary to remove the heater blower motor and core from the dash to remove the No. 8 cylinder push rods. Before removing push rods on all models, rock the rods to break the oil seal between rod and valve lifter to avoid pulling lifter from bore.
8. Remove remaining head bolts and lift off head with exhaust manifold attached.

Installation Notes—Coat a new gasket on both sides with No. 3 gasket sealer and install the gasket with the crimped side up.

After cylinder heads have been placed in position, the push rods and rocker arm assemblies should be installed and care taken to see that the push rods are properly seated in the rocker arms and valve lifters.

Cylinder head bolts should be tightened in the sequence shown in Figs. 1, 2 and 3.

On 1957 heads, tighten the bolts the first time around to 50-60 lb. ft. *except bolts 13, 14, 15 and 16 which should be tightened to 14-17 lb. ft.* Retighten the bolts in the same sequence to 60-70 lb. ft. except bolts 13, 14, 15 and 16.

On 1958-61 heads, tighten the numbered bolts in the sequence shown the first time around to 50-60 lb. ft. Tighten the lettered bolts to 14-22 lb. ft. Retighten the numbered bolts in sequence shown to 60-80 lb. ft. Then retighten the lettered bolts to 14-22 lb. ft.

VALVE ARRANGEMENT

Front to Rear

All Models . . . . E-I-I-E-E-I-I-E

ROCKER ARMS

Sludge and gum formation in the rocker arms and shafts, Fig. 4, will restrict the normal flow of oil to the rocker arms and valves. Therefore each time the assemblies are removed, they should be disassembled and cleaned.

Clean all gum and sludge formation from the inside and outside of the shafts and rocker arms. Check the fit of the rocker arms on the shafts and the valve end of the rocker arms for excessive wear. If the rocker arm radius is grooved on the valve end, do not attempt grinding; replace the part.

When assemblies are installed, make sure the rocker arms are correctly positioned to actuate the valves.

Check each push rod for a bent condition. If bent more than .020" when checked with a dial idicator, replace the push rod. If a dial gauge is not available, at least check the rod for straightness by rolling it on a perfectly flat surface plate.

Fig. 5 Special tool for replacing valves and springs

VALVES, REMOVE

With cylinder head removed as outlined previously, use a suitable valve spring compressor to compress the springs in order to take out the valve locks, Fig. 5. Then remove spring retainers, valve stem seals and valve springs. Remove burrs from valve stem lock grooves to prevent damage to valve guides, and slide valves from heads.

Place valves in a board with numbered holes to identify their location so that, if re-used, they can be returned to the original guide holes.

VALVE GUIDES

Check valve stem-to-guide clearance, using a $\frac{1}{16}$" wide strip of .005" brass shim stock on a "no-go" basis. Bend the end of the shim and hang it in the end of the valve guide. Shim should not extend more than $\frac{1}{4}$" into the guide. If valve stem will enter guide, clearance is excessive and valve and guide should be replaced to prevent excessive oil consumption and improper seating of valves.

Unless a special installing tool is available for guides, before removing a guide, measure the distance it sticks out of the valve port with a steel scale. Then drive out the old guide and install the new one to the measured depth.

VALVE SPRING INSTALLED HEIGHT

When valves and seats are reground the position of the valve in the head is

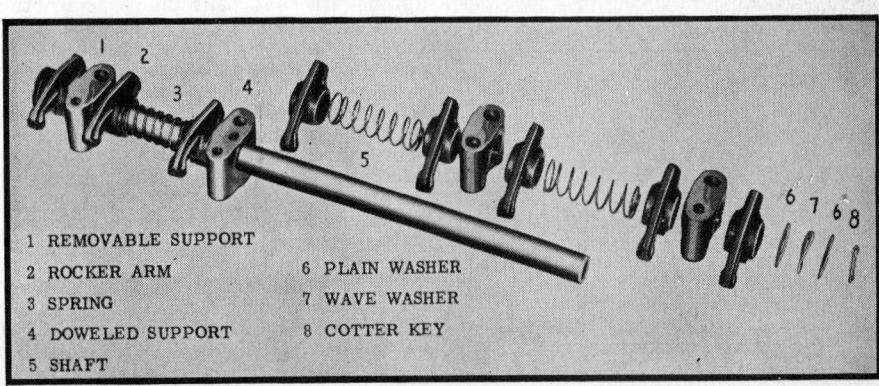

1 REMOVABLE SUPPORT	
2 ROCKER ARM	6 PLAIN WASHER
3 SPRING	7 WAVE WASHER
4 DOWELED SUPPORT	8 COTTER KEY
5 SHAFT	

Fig. 4 Layout of rocker arm parts. 1953-56

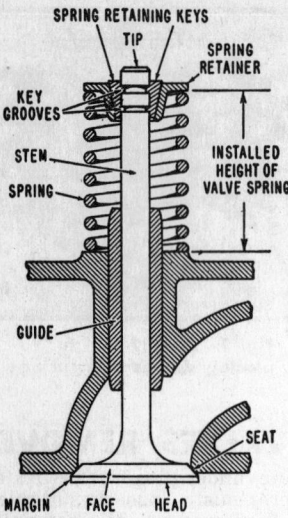

Fig. 5A   Checking installed height of valve spring

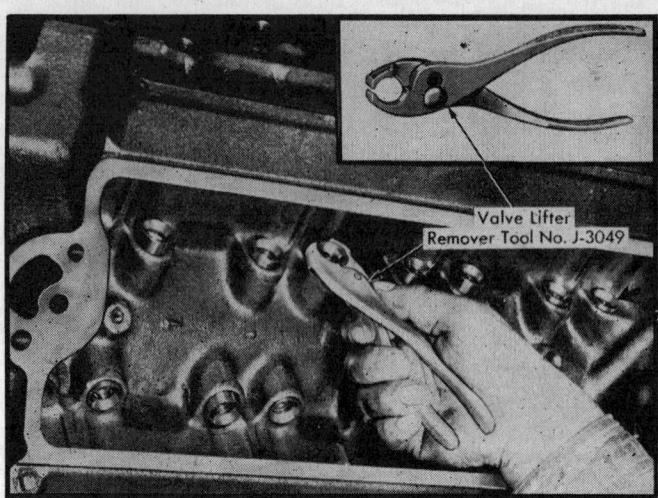

Fig. 7   Tool for removing stuck valve lifter

changed so as to lessen the valve spring tension. Without proper valve spring tension the valve does not seat long enough or it may not seat completely. Since the valve is cooled by transferring heat from the valve head to the seat and thence to the coolant, improper valve spring tension will cause worn, pitted and distorted valves which result in loss of compression and power as well as poor gasoline mileage.

When valves, springs, retainers and locks are installed, measure the assembled height of the valve springs from the surface of the cylinder head spring pad to the underside of the spring retainer as shown in Fig. 5A. If the assembled height is greater than the dimension given in the *Valve Specifications Chart*, install a spacer or shim of proper thickness between cylinder head spring pad and spring to bring the assembled height to specifications.

Do not install spacers unless necessary. Excessive use of spacers will result in overstressing valve springs and overloading camshaft lobes which could lead to spring breakage and worn camshaft lobes.

VALVE SPRING TESTING

After taking out the valve springs, wash them with gasoline or other suit-

able solvent. Examine the springs for damage or corrosion due to acid etching, which will develop into surface cracks and cause spring failure.

Check the valve spring tension on a spring testing fixture, Fig. 6, if one is available, and according to the specifications given in the *Valve Specifications* chart.

If a spring tester is not available, at least check the free length of each spring by standing it alongside a new spring. Any spring that does not conform to the pressure specifications with 10% should be replaced. Likewise, any spring that stands shorter than the new spring used for comparison should be discarded. Of course, cocked springs should also be scrapped.

VALVES, GRIND

Valve seats should be cut so there is $\frac{1}{32}$" from the outer edge of the seat to the edge of the flange on the valve head to allow heat to escape and to provide maximum life for newly ground valves.

Cars operated at moderate or slow speeds in city driving should have a valve seat width of $\frac{3}{64}$" to $\frac{1}{16}$". For cars driven a great deal at high speeds the seat width should be $\frac{1}{16}$" to $\frac{3}{32}$" to assure adequate cooling.

Test valves for concentricity with seats and for tight seating. Valves can be tested by lightly coating the valve face with prussian blue and turning the valve against its seat. This indicates whether the seat is concentric with the valve guide *but does not prove that the valve face is concentric with the valve stem, or that the valve is seating all around.* After making this test, wash all blue from the surfaces, lightly coat the *valve seat* with blue and repeat the test to see whether a full mark is obtained on the valve. Both tests are necessary to prove that a proper seat is being obtained.

VALVE LIFTERS

See the *Trouble Shooting Chapter* under the heading *Engine Noises* for causes of hydraulic valve lifter noise.

The easiest method for locating a noisy valve lifter is by the use of a piece of gar-

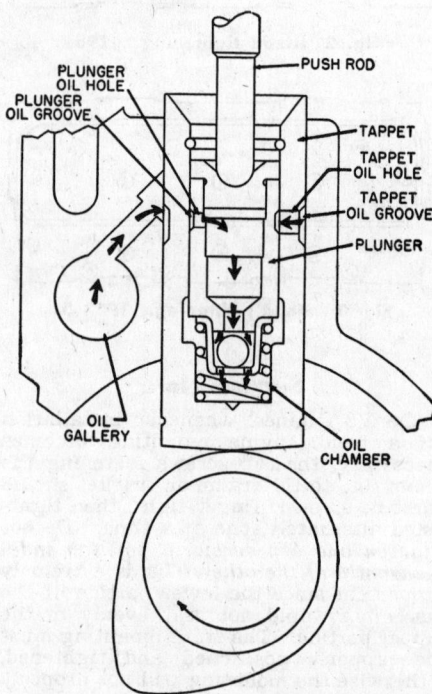

Fig. 9   Valve timing for No. 6 cylinder

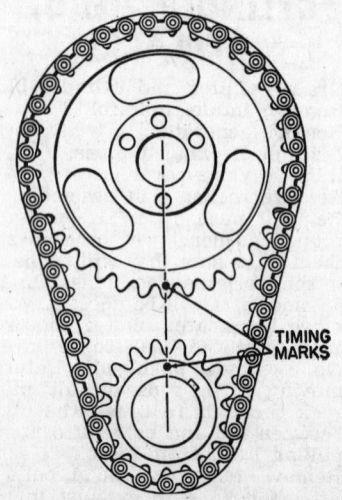

Fig. 8   Hydraulic valve lifter

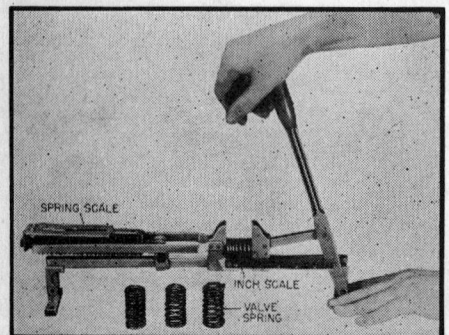

Fig. 6   Valve spring testing fixture

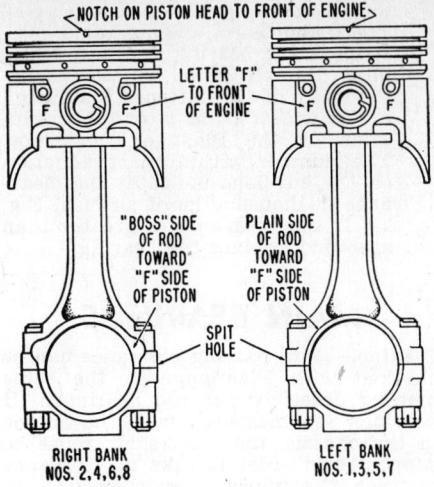

Fig. 10 Correct assembly of pistons and rods. 1953-56 V8

den hose about 4 feet long. Place one end of the hose near each valve in progression and listen through the other end. In this manner the sound is localized, making it easier to determine which lifter is at fault.

Another method is to place a finger on the valve spring retainer. If the lifter is not functioning properly, a distinct shock will be felt when the valve returns to its seat.

In most cases where noise exists in one or more lifters, all lifter units should be removed and cleaned. If dirt, varnish or carbon is found to exist in one unit, it more than likely exists in all the units.

To remove valve lifters, take off successively the intake manifold, engine push rod cover, valve cover, rocker arm shaft assembly, push rods and remove valve lifters, Fig. 7.

Valve lifters in production engines may be one of four sizes: standard, .001, .002 or .003 in. oversize. It is important when replacing one or more lifters that the proper size lifter be ordered. An identification numeral is etched on all lifter bodies except standard. The cylinder block is marked for lifter size on the rail under the push rod cover. Valve lifters .005 in. oversize are available for service replacement.

When a lifter has been in service for a long time, the body bore above the plunger may be caked with hard carbon so that the plunger cannot be removed easily. When this condition exists, submerge the lifter in a suitable carbon softener for a time and then remove the carbon with a stiff bristle brush.

When the lifter is disassembled, use extreme care to avoid nicking or otherwise damaging the body and plunger through contact with other parts. Keep the parts of one lifter separate from all others so that parts will not be interchanged during assembly.

Plungers are not interchangeable because they are selectively fitted to the bodies at the factory, Fig. 8.

If plunger and body appear satisfactory blow off with air to remove all particles of dirt. Install the plunger in the body without other parts and check for free movement. A simple test is to

be sure that the plunger will drop of its own weight in the body.

TIMING CASE COVER

1961 Service Note

See procedure for raising front of engine as described at the beginning of the engine text matter.

1. To remove front cover, drain cooling system and disconnect lower radiator hose and heater hose from front cover.
2. Disconnect generator link at generator.
3. Remove oil pan.
4. Remove two bolts attaching front engine mount to frame.
5. Support engine so that engine mount will clear frame cross member.
6. Remove radiator.
7. Remove fan blades and pulley.
8. Remove crankshaft pulley.
9. Crank engine until distributor rotor points to No. 3 or No. 7 firing position; then remove fuel pump.
10. Unfasten and remove front cover.
11. Reverse the operations to install the cover. However, always install a new front oil seal. The front cover attaching bolts should be dipped in a suitable sealer and torqued to 24-40 lb. ft. One side of the fuel pump gasket should be coated with gasket cement to hold it in place during its installation.

TIMING CHAIN

Place the chain over the sprockets so that when the camshaft sprocket and fuel pump eccentric are bolted to the camshaft hub, the timing marks on both sprockets are facing each other in line with the center of both the camshaft and crankshaft, Fig. 9. The fuel pump eccentric must be assembled with the cupped side out.

VALVE TIMING DATA

Year	Model	Intake Opens①	Intake Closes②	Exhaust Opens③	Exhaust Closes④
1953	All	14	50	50	14
1954	All	13½	50½	49½	14½
1955	All	13½	50½	49½	14½
1956	All	11½	52½	51	13
1957	All	13½	54½	51½	20½
1958	All	16	45	64	20
1959	All	16	45	64	20
1960	All	16	45	64	20
1961	⑤	14	50	54	16
	⑥	11	59	59	20

① —Degrees before top dead center.
② —Degrees after bottom dead center.
③ —Degrees before bottom dead center.
④ —Degrees after top dead center.
⑤ —Regular fuel.
⑥ —Premium fuel.

CAMSHAFT, REPLACE

1. To remove the camshaft, remove valve lifters.
2. Remove distributor.
3. Remove engine front cover.
4. Remove camshaft thrust plunger, fuel pump eccentric, camshaft sprocket and timing chain.
5. Remove camshaft by carefully sliding it out from front of engine.

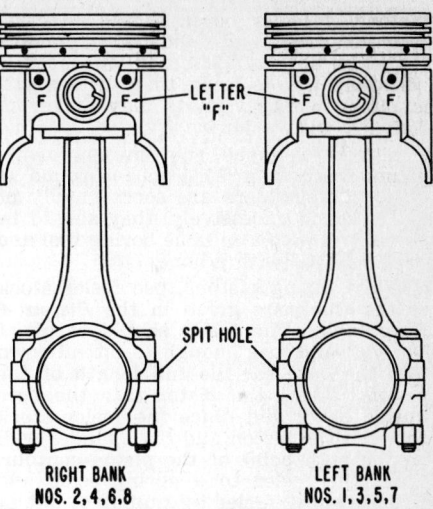

Fig. 11 Assembly of piston to rod. 1957-61

6. To install, reverse the above sequence of operations. Lubricate the end of the camshaft thrust plunger with suitable seal lubricant. Set valve timing, ignition timing, adjust carburetor idle and check throttle linkage.

PISTONS & RODS, REMOVE

After removing the connecting rod cap, push the rod and piston out through the cylinder bore, being careful to keep the rod in alignment to clear the crankshaft. The internal crankcase clearances are very limited and extreme care must be taken not to damage parts. After removing the piston assembly, reinstall the bearing cap. Remove seven other pistons in the same manner.

PISTON & ROD, ASSEMBLE

1953-56

On 1, 3, 5, 7 pistons, assemble the connecting rod with the machined surface of the bearing face on the same side as the "F" marks, Fig. 10. On 2, 4, 6, 8 pistons, assemble rods with machined surface having two bosses placed on same side as letter "F."

1957-61

Lubricate the piston pin hole and piston pin to facilitate installation of pin, then position the connecting rod with its respective piston as shown in Fig. 11.

PISTONS

For checking sizes of stock pistons, measurements should be taken with micrometer calipers across the high point of the piston skirt contour, which is across the piston pin support ribs on the piston skirt.

Before any attempt is made to fit new

pistons, cylinder bores should be carefully measured, and refinished. Cylinders that are not badly scored but need a "cleaning up" to bring them within satisfactory working limits may be reconditioned with a hone.

A good job should show measurements of not more than .0005" out-of-round or taper. If cylinders are scored badly or out-of-round excessively, they should be bored first with a reliable boring tool and then polished with a hone.

When fitting pistons, use feeler stock of the thickness given in the *Piston & Ring* table. The feeler should be about ½" wide and long enough to extend down into the bore for the full length of the piston. Insert the piston into the bore upside down and place the feeler stock between the piston and the cylinder wall on the high point of the piston contour. Hook the feeler to a spring scale and withdraw the feeler by pulling it out of the cylinder with the scale. The piston is fitted properly if the amount of pounds pull registered on the scale comes within the limits given in the *Piston & Ring* table.

PISTON RINGS

Piston rings are available in standard sizes and the following inch oversizes: .010, .020 and .030.

When installing a new set of rings without reconditioning the cylinder bores, always remove the top ridge of the bore with a reliable ridge reamer. Care must be taken not to cut below the top of the upper ring position in the bore. Always cut the ridge before removing the piston assemblies, keeping the tops of the pistons covered to prevent cuttings from reaching bearings, crankshaft, timing case, etc.

New rings must be fitted with end gaps and groove clearances according to the specifications given in the *Piston & Ring* table. Ring grooves must be clean and free from carbon and must show no perceptible wear.

Install rings according to the instructions which are usually contained in the ring package. When assembled on the pistons, the gaps should be staggered around the circumference of the piston but with no gaps over the piston pin.

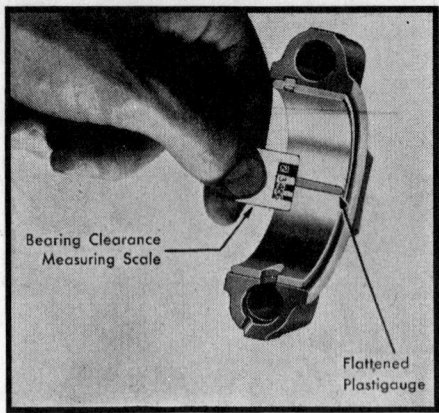

Fig. 12   Checking bearing clearance with Plastigage

Bearing Clearance Measuring Scale

Flattened Plastigauge

PISTON PINS

Piston pins are available in standard, .001" and .003" oversizes. If necessary, reaming and honing of the piston pin hole for the installation of oversize pins are satisfactory. The fit of the pin in the piston should be a tight hand push. If considerable hand pressure is required, the pin may be tapped in place with a hammer and brass drift.

It is very important that both the pin and piston pin hole be clean and free from oil. When assembling the rods to the pistons, follow directions shown in Figs. 10 and 11.

ROD BEARINGS

Connecting rod bearings can be replaced without removing the rod assembly by removing the cap and replacing the upper and lower halves. The clearance between the rod bearing and crankshaft can be measured with Plastigage gauge as follows:

1. Remove bearing cap and wipe oil from crankshaft journal and bearing insert.
2. With crankpin at approximately bottom dead center, place a piece of Plastigage in the center of the cap.
3. Reinstall the cap and tighten to the

torque value given in the *Engine Tightening Specifications* table.

4. Remove the bearing cap and determine the clearance by comparing the width of the flattened Plastigage at its widest point with the graduation on the Plastigage envelope. The number within the graduation on the envelope indicates the clearance in thousandths of an inch, Fig. 12. If this clearance is greater than specified, replace the bearing.

MAIN BEARINGS

Caution—Main bearing clearance can be checked with Plastigage in the same manner described for rod bearings. If bearings are measured with the engine in the chassis, the crankshaft must be supported in order to take up clearance between the upper bearing insert and crankshaft journal. This can be done by tightening bearing caps of adjacent bearings with .005" to .015" cardboard, (such as a calling card) between lower bearing shell and journal. Use extreme care when this is done to avoid unnecessary strain on the crankshaft or bearings or a false reading may be obtained. Do not rotate crankshaft while Plastigage is installed.

Be sure to remove cardboard. To install new bearings, proceed as follows:

1. Remove bearing cap and worn lower shell.
2. Rotate crankshaft in normal direction to turn upper bearing shell out of crankcase. Use a cotter pin with a flattened head or the special tool made for the purpose in the crankshaft oil hole to contact the bearing and force it out.
3. Place a new upper shell on the crankshaft journal with the locating notch in the correct position and rotate the shaft to turn the bearing in place.
4. Install the lower bearing shell in the cap.
5. Tighten all cap nuts to the torque value given in the *Engine Tightening Data* table.

CRANKSHAFT OIL SEAL

A braided oil seal is pressed into the upper and lower grooves behind the rear

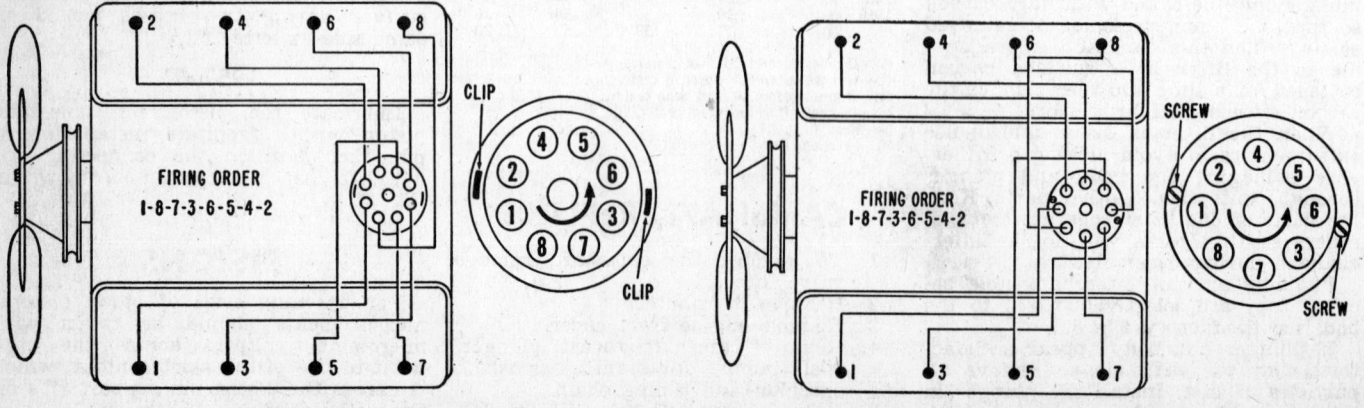

Fig. 13   Ignition details.   1953-55 V8s

FIRING ORDER 1-8-7-3-6-5-4-2

CLIP

CLIP

Fig. 14   Ignition details   1956-61

FIRING ORDER 1-8-7-3-6-5-4-2

SCREW

SCREW

main bearing. Directly in front of this seal is an oil slinger which deflects the oil back into the oil pan. Should the braided seal require replacement, the installation of the lower half is accomplished as follows:

With the bearing cap and lower bearing half removed, install a new seal so that both ends protrude above the cap. Tap the seal down into position or roll it snugly in its groove with a smooth rounded tool. Then cut off the protruding ends of the seal with a sharp knife or razor blade.

Installing Upper Seal

Although the usual practice is to remove the crankshaft when the upper half of the seal is to be replaced it is possible to do the job without removing the crankshaft as follows:

To remove the seal, use needle-nose pliers to grasp the end of the seal which is most accessible. Pull the seal downward while rotating the crankshaft slowly in the direction that the seal is being removed.

To install the new seal, fasten a length of wire or strong string such as fishing line securely to one end of the new seal. See that the point of fastening is not bulky and that it is not over 3/8" from the end of the seal. Coat the seal with Lubriplate. Pass the free end of the wire or string up over the crankshaft at the point where the seal is to be installed. Then exert a firm, steady pull on the wire or string and at the same time rotate the crankshaft slowly in the direction of the pull. This will help to move the seal into position. When the installation is completed, trim the ends of the seal flush with the engine block.

OIL PAN

1953-58

To remove the oil pan, remove the starting motor on engines up to 1955 or merely loosen it on 1956-58 models.

Disconnect exhaust crossover pipe. Disconnect idler arm support from frame. Unfasten and remove pan.

1959-60

1. Position No. 1 piston on bottom of stroke. This moves crankshaft counterweight out of the way to aid in the pan's removal.
2. Disconnect battery cable.
3. If equipped with single exhaust system, remove exhaust crossover pipe.
4. Disconnect idler arm support from frame.
5. Remove starter and lower flywheel housing.
6. Drain and remove oil pan. *Holes are provided in the frame crossmember for access to the four front oil pan bolts.*

1961

The oil pan is removed in the same manner as outlined for 1960 models. However, it is necessary to raise the engine, the procedure for which is described at the beginning of the engine text matter.

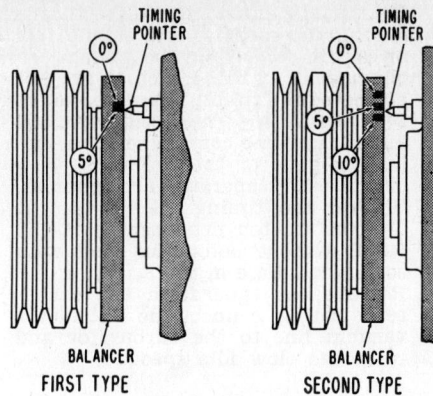

Fig. 15 Ignition timing marks. Left view is for 1953-56 and first 15,000 cars for 1957. Right view is used on later 1957 and 1960-61 models.

OIL PUMP

The positive gear type oil pump is attached to the rear main bearing cap by three bolts and can be removed without disturbing any of the drive mechanism.

To disassemble the pump, release lock wire and remove screen. Take off the oil screen shroud and remove the snap ring from the extension shaft coupling. Remove the oil pump cover and take out the gears. Remove oil pressure regulator nut. spring and valve.

RADIATOR, REPLACE

1953-58

To remove the radiator, drain the complete cooling system. Disconnect upper and lower radiator hoses. Disconnect horn wires and remove horns.

If car is equipped with Jetaway transmission, disconnect and cap oil cooler lines. Disconnect radiator shroud and position away from radiator.

Remove upper radiator baffle. Remove screws from radiator flange (both sides). Position fan blades to clear radiator lower outlet and remove radiator.

1959-61

1. Drain cooling system and disconnect upper and lower hoses. If equipped with Hydra-Matic, disconnect and cap oil cooler lines.
2. Remove fan upper support.
3. Unfasten radiator from flange (6 screws). If equipped with air conditioning, position fan ring away from radiator.
4. Position fan blades to clear radiator lower outlet and remove radiator.

WATER PUMP, REPLACE

Remove fan and fan pulley. Remove six water pump attaching bolts and lift off pump.

When reinstalling the pump, one side of the pump bearing housing gasket should be coated with gasket cement. The four bearing housing bolt threads should be dipped in a suitable sealer.

WATER PUMP REPAIRS

The water pump double row bearing has one large groove in the center and two smaller grooves toward one end. The end with the two smaller grooves must always be assembled into the pump housing first. This end of the bearing shaft will then be at the impeller end of the pump.

To assemble the pump, press the seal into the housing. Press the bearing into the housing until the bearing seats on shoulder in housing. Install the bearing retainer spring at the front end of the housing. Press the bearing shaft through the impeller until the bottom edge of the vanes are 1 3/8" from the machined face at edge of housing. If the fan hub was removed, press the hub on the shaft.

DISTRIBUTOR, REPLACE

1. Disconnect primary wire from distributor and disconnect pipe from vacuum control unit.
2. Remove distributor cap.
3. Crank engine until distributor rotor is in position to fire No. 1 cylinder and the timing mark (see *Tune Up Chart*) is aligned with the timing indicator.
4. Remove distributor clamp and lift the distributor out of the crankcase.

Installation, All Models

Before installation of either a new or repaired distributor apply a few drops of engine oil to the drain hole near the lower and of the housing and apply oil to the oiler on the housing. Rotate the distributor shaft several times by hand to distribute the oil and to make sure that the shaft turns freely.

1. Check to make sure that the timing mark is aligned with the timing indicator with No. 1 piston on the compression stroke in position to fire.
2. Place a new seal or gasket on distributor housing.
3. Rotate distributor cam until rotor is in position to fire No. 1 cylinder, Figs. 13 and 14.
4. Rotate oil pump shaft with screwdriver to align slot in shaft with tongue on lower end of distributor shaft.
5. Install distributor in crankcase.
6. Install distributor clamp and bolt with lockwasher, leaving bolt just loose enough to permit movement of distributor.
7. Rotate distributor housing until breaker points just start to open and tighten clamp bolt. This will permit starting engine for setting timing.
8. Connect pipe to vacuum control and primary wire to terminal stud.
9. Install distributor cap. If spark plug wires are disconnected from cap make certain that wires are connected in accordance with firing order, Figs. 13 and 14.
10. Check and set ignition timing as given below.

IGNITION TIMING

The timing marks are located on the rim of the crankshaft pulley in the form of a slot on 1953-56 and the first 15,000 cars on 1957 models. As shown in Fig. 15, later 1957 and 1960-61 models have three slots.

For 1958-59 there are two slots, the first to come under the pointer is 5° before top dead center and the second slot is T.D.C.

The slow idle method of setting ignition timing, formerly recommended, should not be used. The correct method of setting the timing is as follows:

1. *Disconnect distributor vacuum advance line at the carburetor and close the carburetor fitting with a piece of tape.*
2. Connect a tachometer and set the carburetor throttle adjustment so the engine runs at 850 RPM.
3. Set the timing at 5° before top dead center. This is the normal setting.

If a tuned engine detonates with this setting the cause is low octane fuel or carbon build-up in the combustion chambers. If these factors are not corrected the timing should be set at 2½° before top dead center at 850 RPM. In some cases where fuel octane is good or the engine is clean or the car is operated at higher altitudes, the timing can be set at 7½° before top dead center at 850 RPM without detonation and with some advantage in performance.

4. Remove the tape from the carburetor fitting, connect the distributor vacuum line to the carburetor and reset the slow idle speed.

STARTER, REPLACE

1956-61

Disconnect battery cable at junction block and solenoid wire (purple) from chassis wiring harness. Raise car and re-move engine filler plate (if used). On cars with dual exhaust, disconnect exhaust pipe at manifold. Unfasten starter from flywheel housing and remove motor while sliding battery cable loom through sleeve.

MUFFLER & PIPES

To remove any component of the exhaust system is a fairly obvious operation. However, on 1956 models with dual exhaust system, to remove the left exhaust pipe, disconnect the pitman arm from the steering shaft. To remove the left tail pipe on 98's, disconnect the lower end of the left shock absorber. Install the pipe with 1¾" clearance at the rear axle housing.

On all models, before tightening any part of the exhaust system, align the exhaust and tail pipes to provide adequate clearance between body and frame. It is also advisable to run the engine until it reaches operating temperature before tightening the attaching nuts.

Carburetor Section

Performance Complaints

Flooding, stumble on acceleration or other performance complaints are in many instances caused by the presence of dirt, water or other foreign matter in the carburetor. To aid in diagnosing the cause of the complaint, the carburetor should be carefully removed from the engine without draining the fuel from the bowl. The contents of the fuel bowl may then be examined for contamination as the carburetor is disassembled.

Check the fuel in the bowl for contamination by dirt, water, gum or other foreign matter. A magnet moved through the fuel in the bowl will pick up and identify any iron oxide dust that may have caused intake needle and seat leakage.

Inspect gasketed surfaces between body and air horn. Small nicks or burrs should be smoothed down to eliminate air or fuel leakage. On carburetors having a vacuum piston, be especially particular when inspecting the top surface of the inner wall of the bowl around the vacuum piston passage. A poor seal at this location may contribute to a "cutting-out" on turns complaint.

Fill the carburetor bowl with clean fuel before installing on manifold. This will help prevent dirt trapped in the fuel system from being dislodged by the free flow of fuel as the carburetor is primed. The operation of the floats and intake needle and seats may be checked under pressure if a fuel pump is used at the bench to fill the carburetor bowl. Operate the throttle several times and visually check the discharge from pump jets.

Poor Mileage and Engine Loading Complaints

Cases of poor mileage and engine loading may be due in many instances to sluggish choke valve opening during cold driveaway, caused by insufficient vacuum in choke housing, a plugged or restricted heat pipe or inlet in choke cover. To check for this condition, have engine warm and running at slow idle. Remove choke heat pipe and hold a finger over the heat inlet hole (hole is on choke housing on some carburetors). If there is little or no vacuum pull on the finger, check the choke housing for gasket leaks or plugged vacuum passages. If these are OK, check choke vacuum passages in carburetor between choke housing and manifold.

Dirty or Rusty Choke Housing

In cases where it is found that the interior of the choke housing is dirty, gummed or rusty while the carburetor itself is comparatively clean, look for a punctured or eroded manifold heat tube (if one is used).

Manifold Heat Control Valve

An engine equipped with a manifold heat control valve can operate with the valve stuck either in the open or closed position. Because of this, an inoperative valve is frequently overlooked at vehicle lubrication or tune-up.

A valve stuck in the "heat-off" position can result in slow warm up, deposits in combustion chamber, carburetor icing, flat spots during acceleration, low gas mileage and spark plug fouling.

A valve stuck in the "heat-on" position can result in power loss, engine knocking, sticking or burned valves and spark plug burning.

To prevent the possibility of a stuck valve, check and lubricate the valve each time the vehicle is lubricated or tuned-up. Check the operation of the valve manually. To lubricate the valve place a few drops of penetrating oil on the valve shaft where it passes through the manifold. Move the valve up and down a few times to work in the oil. *Never use engine oil for this purpose as it will leave a residue which hampers valve operation.*

CARTER CARBURETOR ADJUSTMENTS

Year	Carburetor Model	Idle Adjustments				Float Level		Float Drop		Pump Travel Setting	Choke Unloader Setting	Choke Setting
		Mixture Screws Turns Open	Hot Idle Speed In Drive	Fast Idle Speed	Dashpot Plunger Clearance	Primary	Secondary	Primary	Secondary			
1955	WCFB-2246S	1-2	400	.015④	None	3/16①	3/16①	11/16②	11/16②	③	3/16⑤	Index
1954	WCFB-2059S	1-2	400	.015④	None	1/4①	1/4①	3/4②	3/4②	③	3/16⑤	Index
	WGD-2058S	1½-2½	400	.020⑧	None	1/4⑥	None	None	None	⑦	7/32⑨	Index
1953	WCFB-2016S	1¾-2¾	375	.018④	None	3/16①	3/16①	1/2②	1/2②	③	3/16⑤	Index
	WCFB-2080S	1¾-2¾	375	.018④	None	3/16①	3/16①	11/16②	11/16②	③	3/16⑤	Index
	WGD-851S-A	3/4-1¼	375	.020⑪	None	1/4⑥	None	None	None	⑩	1/4⑫	Index
	WGD-2015S	3/4-1¼	375	.020⑪	None	1/4⑥	None	None	None	⑩	1/4⑫	Index

CARTER NOTES

METERING RODS

WCFB and WGD—Metering rod adjustment must be made after pump adjustment. With throttle valves fully closed, loosen metering rod arm clamp screw. With metering rods in place, press down on vacumeter link until metering rods bottom in casting. Holding rods down, revolve metering rod arm until finger on arm contacts lip of vacumeter link. Hold in place and tighten clamp screw.

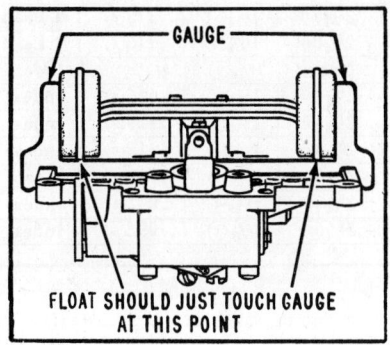

Fig. ①—WCFB float level. Adjust by bending float lever.

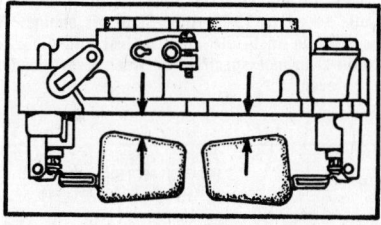

Fig. ③—With pump connector link in outer hole of pump arm, and straightedge placed across top of dust cover boss, flat on pump arm should be parallel with straightedge. Adjust by bending throttle connector rod.

④—With choke valve closed, tighten fast idle screw on high step of fast idle cam until there is the clearance specified between throttle valve and carburetor bore (side opposite idle port).

⑤—With throttle valve wide open, there should be the clearance specified between upper edge of choke valve and inner wall of air horn. Adjust by bending unloader lip on throttle shaft lever.

Fig. ②—WCFB float drop. Adjust by bending stop tabs on float bracket.

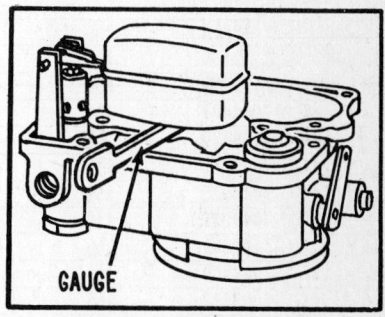

Fig. ⑥—WGD float level. Adjust by bending float lever.

⑦—Same as ③. Adjust by bending pump arm.

⑧—With choke valve closed there should be the clearance specified between throttle valve and carburetor bore (side opposite idle port.) Adjust by bending choke connector rod.

⑨—With throttle wide open there should be the clearance specified between lower edge of choke valve (vent tube side) and inner wall of air horn. Adjust by bending choke shaft unloader arm.

⑩—Same as ⑦ except pump connector link goes in outer hole in pump arm.

⑪—With choke valve closed and slight tension on throttle lever, loosen locknut on choke rod and turn adjusting sleeve until there is the clearance specified between throttle valve and carburetor bore (side opposite idle port.) Hold sleeve in position and tighten locknut.

⑫—With throttle wide open there should be the clearance specified between upper edge of choke valve and inner wall of air horn. Adjust by bending arm on choke trip lever.

ROCHESTER CARBURETOR ADJUSTMENTS

Year	Carburetor Model	Mixture Screws Turns Open	Hot Idle Speed In Drive	Fast Idle Speed	Dashpot Plunger Clearance	Float Level Primary	Float Level Secondary	Float Drop Primary	Float Drop Secondary	Pump Rod Setting	Choke Unloader Setting	Choke Setting
1961	2GC-7016106	1½	500	1900[3]	.050[5]	11/16[7]	None	1 29/32[8]	None	1 7/16[9]	.150[10]	Index
	4GC-7016107	1½	500	1600[3]	.020[5]	9/32[1]	1 3/8[1]	1½[2]	1 5/16[2]	1 1/64[9]	.115[6]	Index
1960	2GC-7015052	2	460	1900[3]	.050[5]	11/16[7]	None	1 29/32[8]	None	1 7/16[9]	.163[10]	1 Rich
	2GC-7015058	2	460	1900[3]	.050[5]	11/16[7]	None	1 29/32[8]	None	1 7/16[9]	.163[10]	1 Rich
1959-60	4GC-7013950	1¾	460	1600[3]	.020[5]	9/32[1]	1 3/8[1]	1½[2]	1 5/16[2]	1 1/64[1]	.115[6]	Index
	4GC-7013952	1¾	460	1600[3]	.020[5]	9/32[1]	1 3/8[1]	1½[2]	1 5/16[2]	1 1/64[1]	.115[6]	Index
1959	4GC-7013050	1¾	460	1600[3]	.020[5]	9/32[1]	1 3/8[1]	1½[2]	1 5/16[2]	1 1/64[1]	.115[6]	Index
	4GC-7013150	1¾	460	1600[3]	.020[5]	9/32[1]	1 3/8[1]	1½[2]	1 5/16[2]	1 1/64[1]	.115[6]	Index
	2GC-7013052	2	460	1900[3]	.050[5]	11/16[7]	None	1 29/32[8]	None	1 7/16[9]	.163[10]	1 Rich
	2GC-7015915	2	460	1900[3]	.050[5]	11/16[7]	None	1 29/32[8]	None	1 7/16[9]	.163[10]	1 Rich
1958	2GC-7012450	1½	460	1500[3]	.050[5]	1 25/64[11]	None	1 29/32[8]	None	15/16[9]	.140[10]	1 Lean
	4GC-7012400	1½	460	1550[3]	.020[5]	3/4[12]	1 3/8[12]	1½[2]	1 5/16[2]	1 3/64[9]	.115[6]	Index
	4GC-7012401	1½	460	1550[3]	None	3/4[12]	1 3/8[12]	1½[2]	1 5/16[2]	1 3/64[9]	.115[6]	Index
1957	4GC-7009470	1½	425	1550[3]	.020[5]	1 5/8[13]	1 5/8[13]	2¼[14]	2¼[14]	1 3/64[9]	.092[6]	Index
	4GC-7009471	1½	425	1550[3]	None	1 5/8[13]	1 5/8[13]	2¼[14]	2¼[14]	1 3/64[9]	.092[6]	Index
	4GC-7010925	1½	425	1550[3]	.020[5]	1 5/8[13]	1 5/8[13]	2¼[14]	2¼[14]	1 3/64[9]	.092[6]	Index
	4GC-7010926	1½	425	1550[3]	None	1 5/8[13]	1 5/8[13]	2¼[14]	2¼[14]	1 3/64[9]	.092[6]	Index
1956	2GC-7007223	1½	400	1500[3]	.028[5]	1 7/16[15]	None	2[16]	None	5/16[9]	.155[10]	1 Rich
	2GC-7008800	1½	400	1500[3]	.028[5]	1 7/16[15]	None	2[16]	None	5/16[9]	.155[10]	1 Rich
	4GC-7007222	1½	400	1500[3]	None	1 5/8[13]	1 5/8[13]	2¼[14]	2¼[14]	1 1/16[4]	.115[6]	1 Lean
	4GC-7007221	1½	400	1500[3]	.028[5]	1 5/8[13]	1 5/8[13]	2¼[14]	2¼[14]	1 1/16[4]	.115[6]	1 Lean
1955	2GC-7006970	1½	400	1500[3]	.028[5]	1 9/32[15]	None	1 29/32[16]	None	15/16[9]	9/64[10]	Index
	4GC-7007000	1½	400	1500[3]	.028[5]	1 5/8[13]	1 5/8[13]	2¼[14]	2¼[14]	1 1/16[6]	.115[6]	Index
1954-55	4GC-7006000	1½	400	1500[3]	None	1 5/8[13]	1 5/8[13]	2¼[14]	2¼[14]	1 1/16[6]	.115[6]	Index
1954	4GC-7005900	1½	400	1500[3]	.028[5]	1 5/8[13]	1 5/8[13]	2¼[14]	2¼[14]	1 1/16[6]	.115[6]	Index
1953	4GC-7005600	1½	375	1450[3]	.028[5]	1 9/16[13]	1 9/16[13]	2¼[14]	2¼[14]	1 1/16[4]	.092[6]	Index
	4GC-7005700	1½	375	1450[3]	None	1 9/16[13]	1 9/16[13]	2¼[14]	2¼[14]	1 1/16[4]	.092[6]	Index
	4GC-7006250	1½	375	1450[3]	.028[5]	1 9/16[13]	1 9/16[13]	2¼[14]	2¼[14]	1 1/16[4]	.092[6]	Index

ROCHESTER NOTES

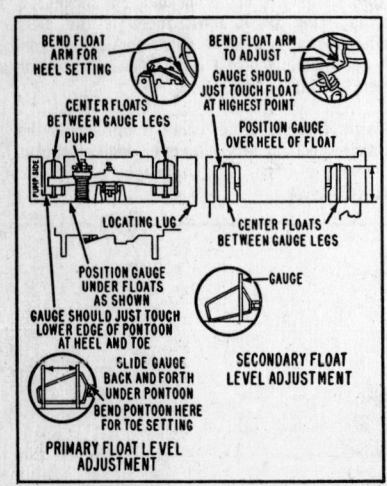

Fig. ①—4GC float level.

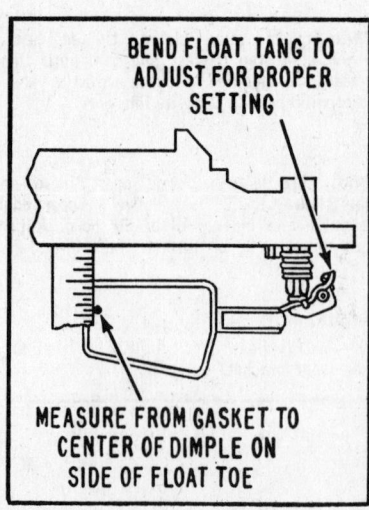

Fig. ②—4GC float drop.

③—With engine at normal operating temperature, turn fast idle screw against highest step of fast idle cam until specified rpm is obtained.

④—With throttle valves closed, measure from top of air horn casting to bottom of plunger shaft (with pump rod in inner hole of pump arm on 1959-61). Adjust by bending pump rod.

⑤—With engine running in neutral, and with fast idle screw on highest step of fast idle cam, adjust fast idle speed to 1500 rpm. Shut off engine. With screw still on fast idle cam, adjust plunger screw to obtain clearance specified between screw head and throttle lever.

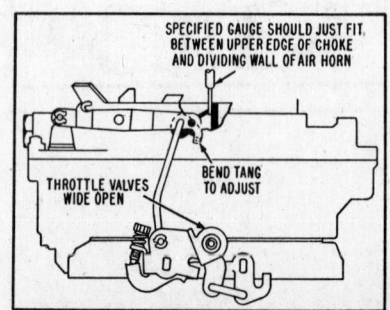

Fig. ⑥—Bend unloader tang on fast idle cam to obtain clearance specified between choke valve edge and dividing wall of air horn with throttle valves wide open.

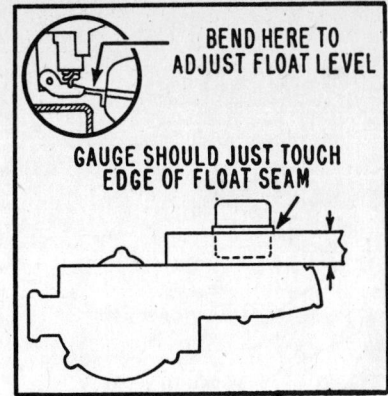

Fig. ⑦—2GC float level.

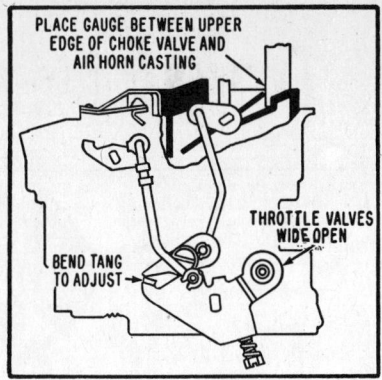

Fig. ⑩—Bend unloader tang on throttle lever to obtain clearance specified between upper edge of choke valve and inner wall of air horn with throttle valves wide open.

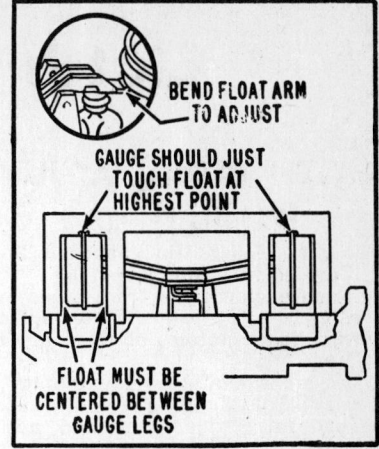

Fig. ⑬—4GC float level.

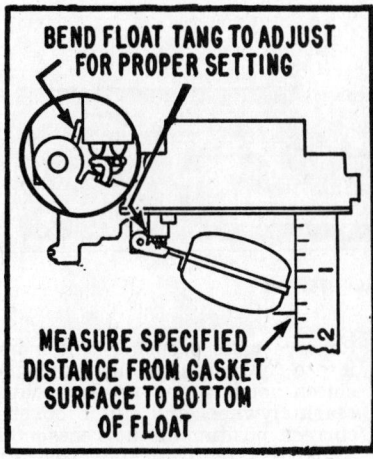

Fig. ⑧—2GC float drop.

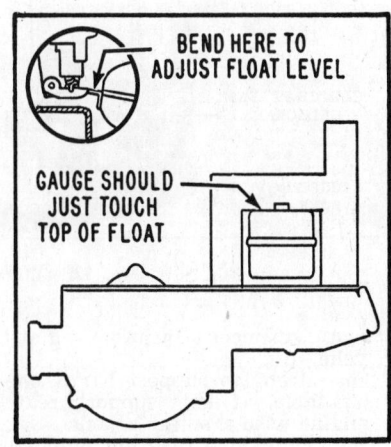

Fig. ⑪—2GC float level.

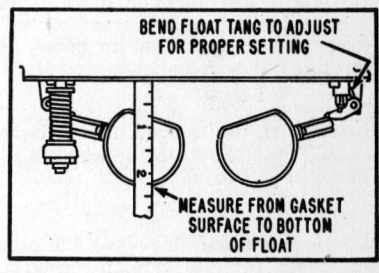

Fig. ⑭—4GC float drop.

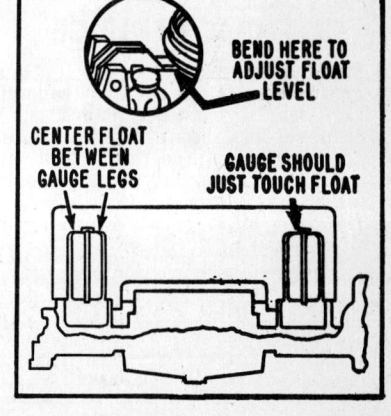

Fig. ⑮—2GC float level.

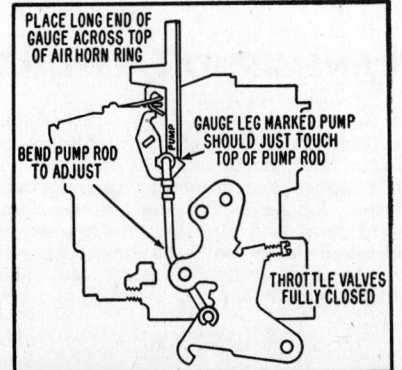

Fig. ⑨—With throttle valves fully closed, bend pump rod as necessary to obtain dimension specified from top of pump housing to top of pump rod.

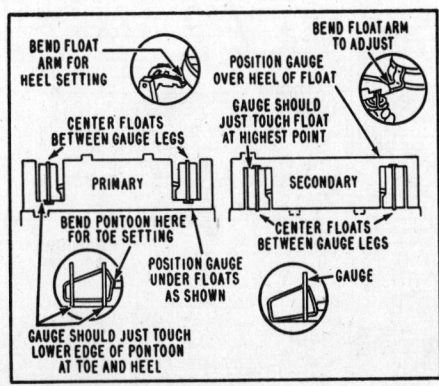

Fig. ⑫—4GC float level.

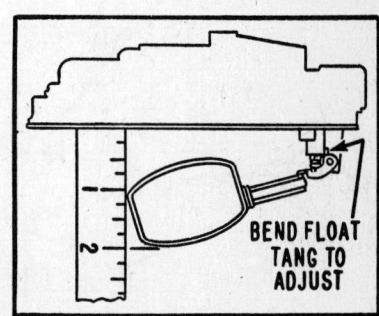

Fig. ⑯—2GC float drop.

Clutch and Transmission Section

CLUTCH PEDAL, ADJUST

1959-61, Fig. 1A

1. Insert a ¼" rod in gauge pin holes provided in frame side rail.
2. Remove clevis pin from upper end of rod "A". The overcenter springs will hold bottom of rod against gauge pin.
3. Loosen lock and adjusting nuts on rod "B" until rod is free of tension.
4. Turn back floor mat and adjust pedal stop screw until top of pedal pad is 8" from floor pan. After linkage is connected, pedal height should be 8¼" with spring load applied.
5. Adjust upper clevis on rod "A" until gauge pin is free in frame hole, after rod "A" is connected to pedal bellcrank. Install clevis pin and tighten lock nut.
6. Adjust rod "B" until 1 to 1¼" free pedal travel is obtained. Tighten lock nut and remove gauge pin.

1953-58

To adjust the free travel of the clutch pedal, loosen the lock nut on the adjustable rod and turn the adjusting nut in the desired direction to obtain from 1 to 1¼ inches free travel.

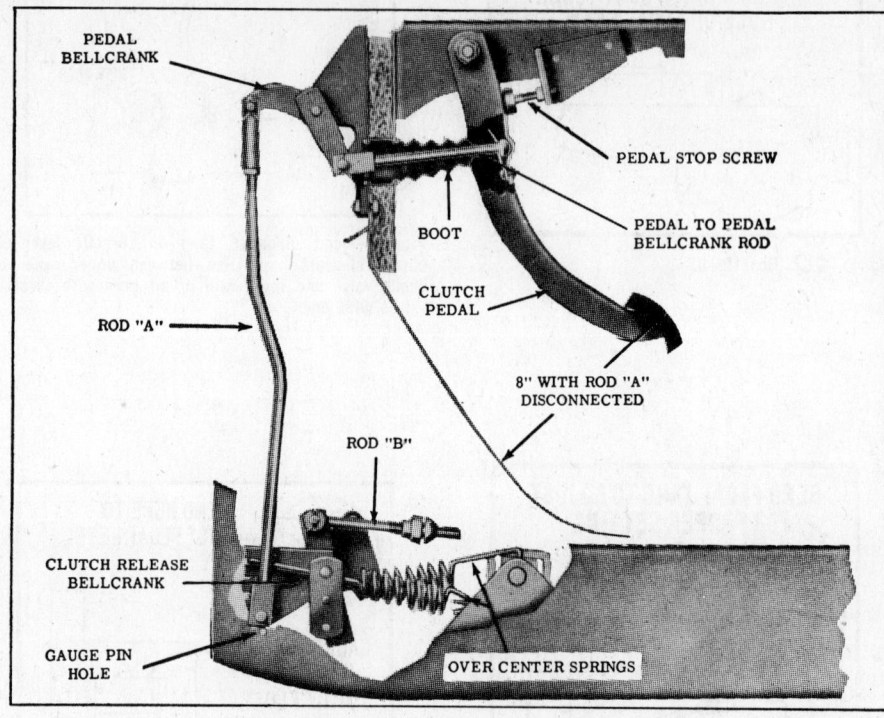

Fig. 1A Clutch linkage. 1959-61

CLUTCH, REPLACE

1. Remove transmission as outlined further on. Then remove transmission bearing retainer sleeve.
2. Remove left engine filler plate, engine breather pipe, and right and left rear lower flywheel housing bolts.
3. Remove clutch pedal return spring and disconnect adjustable rod at the yoke.
4. Install engine support bar if one is available. If not, support rear of engine with a suitable jack.
5. Remove engine rear mount bolts at clutch housing and remove frame crossmember by removing three bolts at each end.
6. Remove bolts securing clutch housing to flywheel housing, and remove clutch housing and release yoke.
7. Mark flywheel and clutch cover for correct positioning at reassembly.
8. Remove clutch from flywheel, Fig. 1.
9. To install, reverse sequence of removal operations. Use an old transmission mainshaft to align clutch disc while tightening clutch to flywheel. Lubricate clutch shaft pilot bearing and bearing surface of release levers. Adjust transmission shaft linkage and adjust clutch pedal free travel. Lubricate clutch release bearing.

TRANSMISSION, REPLACE

1953-56

After raising the car, drain the transmission and disconnect the manual control rods and speedometer cable at transmission. Detach drive shaft at rear universal joint and slide shaft from transmission. Remove bolts holding transmission to the clutch housing and slide transmission out.

1957-61

1. Drain transmission and disconnect control rods and speedometer cable at transmission.
2. Remove propeller shaft.
3. Remove transmission-to-clutch housing bolts and slide the transmission

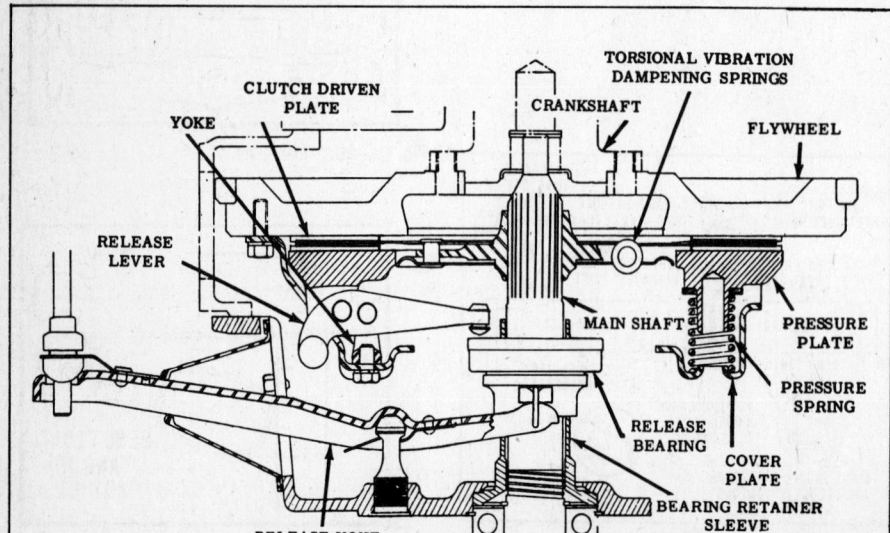

Fig. 1 Section through clutch. Typical of all 1953-61

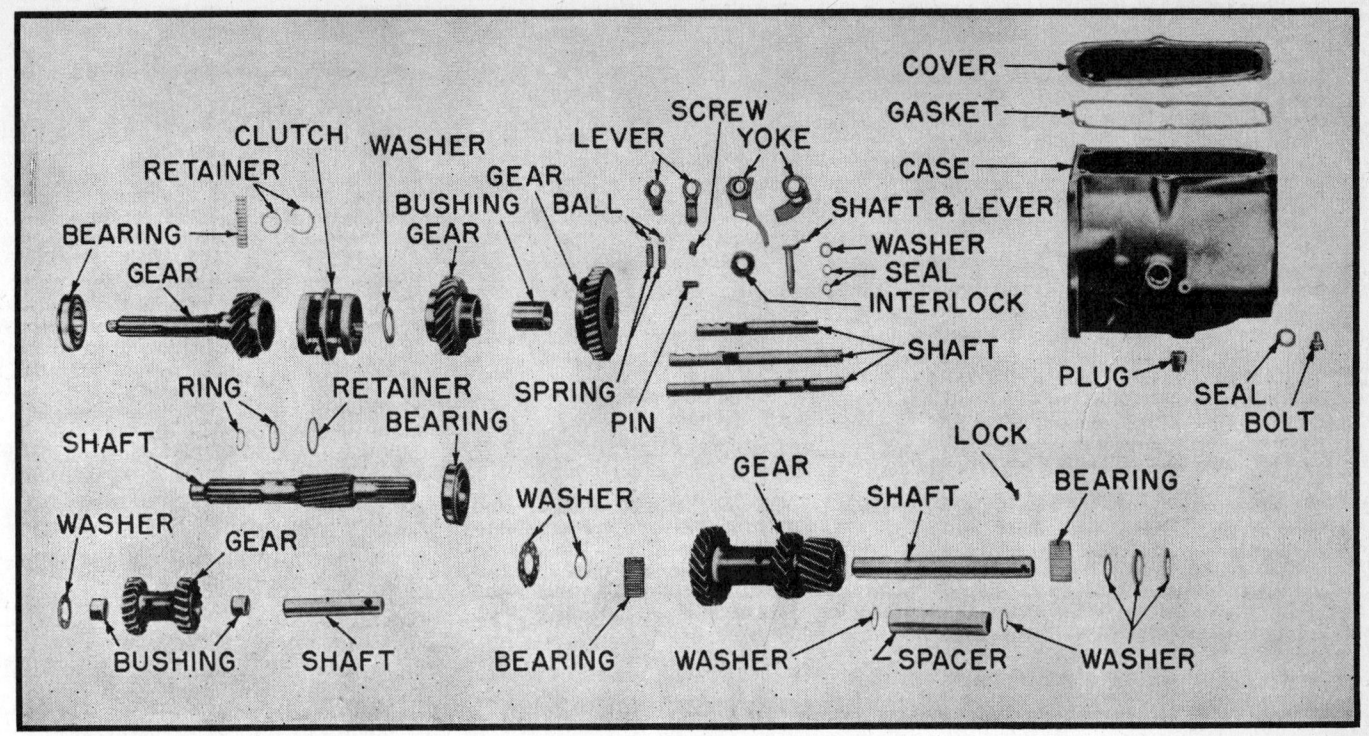

Fig. 2 Synchromesh transmission. 1953-61

rearward until the main drive shaft clears the clutch housing. Lower the transmission.

4. To install the transmission, apply Lubriplate to the pilot and the first 1″ of splines on the main drive shaft. Reverse the sequence of removal operations, align the propeller shaft, and adjust transmission shift linkage.

TRANSMISSION REPAIRS

1. Thoroughly clean all dirt from exterior of transmission to avoid getting dirt into bearings when transmission is opened, Figs. 2, 3.
2. Remove transmission cover and gasket, toggle spring, spring clip and spring extension.
3. Remove speedometer driven gear, then remove rear bearing retainer and gasket.
4. Place transmission in second gear, move mainshaft back until rear bearing is clear of case, and disengage shift yoke from synchronizer. Then lift front end of mainshaft enough to remove synchronizer from shaft. Note that the counterbored end of the synchronizer must face the second speed gear when replaced.
5. Remove snap ring holding second speed gear to mainshaft. Remove thrust washer after lining up small wire spacer ring installed in bottom of snap ring groove with thrust washer key, then remove second speed gear from mainshaft.
6. Remove snap ring holding low and reverse gear to mainshaft.
7. Slide low and reverse gear off mainshaft while pulling shaft out through rear of transmission case.

8. Place transmission levers in neutral and remove set screws holding shifter yokes and levers to their respective shafts. NOTE: Each yoke shaft is in neutral position when the notch for the shifter lever is directly above the selector shaft.
9. Slide shift lever and interlock away from second and high yoke shaft, then remove interlock retainer from

notch for the shifter lever is directly above the selector shaft.
9. Slide shift lever and interlock away from second and high yoke shaft, then remove interlock retainer from

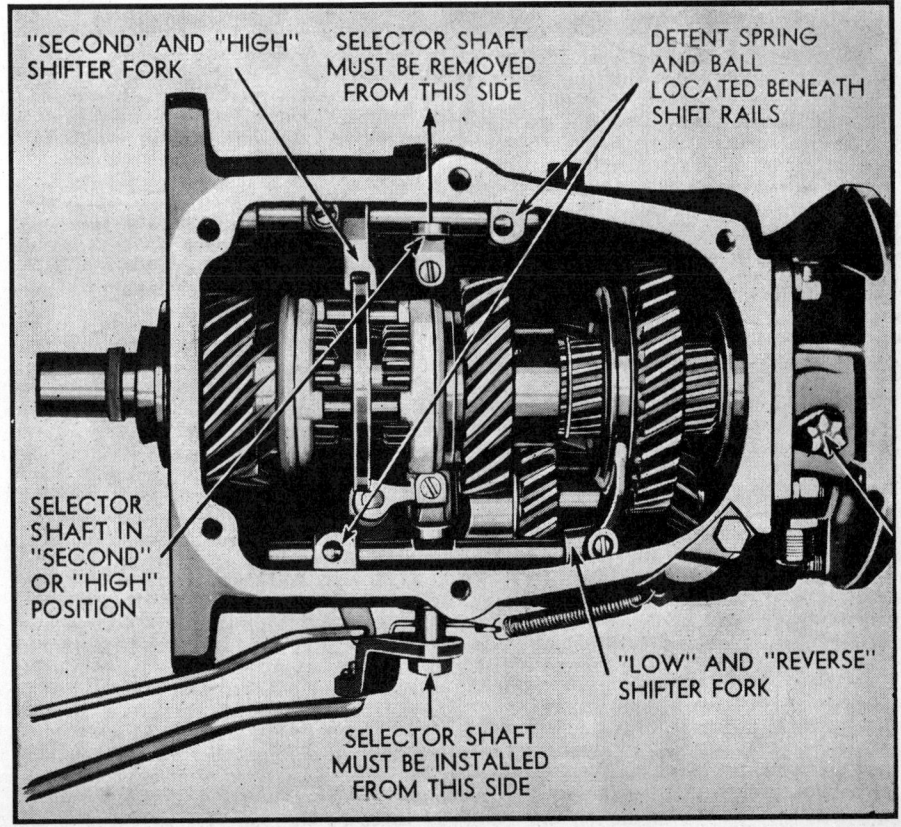

Fig. 3 1953-61 synchromesh transmission

10. Remove outer shift lever and lock washer from left end of selector shaft and, after making sure transmission is still in neutral, depress inner selector lever and drive the shaft out through the right side of the transmission, using a soft hammer. NOTE: The welch plug in right side of case will be driven out by the shaft. Do not allow shift levers and interlock to drop into case.
11. Push second and high speed yoke shaft out through front of case, taking care to prevent poppet ball and spring from flying out. Remove shift yoke, ball and spring.
12. Taking care to prevent poppet ball and spring from flying out, push low and reverse yoke shaft out through rear of case. Remove poppet ball, spring and low and reverse interlock pin.
13. Drive countershaft lock pin into the shaft, then drive shaft out through rear end of case, using a suitable tool to hold needle bearings and washers in place. Allow cluster gear to rest on bottom of case.
14. Remove snap ring from main drive gear bearing and tap drive gear and bearing toward rear of transmission to remove.
15. Carefully raise cluster gear out of case so that related parts remain in gear.
16. Remove transmission outer selector lever, lock washer and nut; then remove inner lever and shaft, spring washer, flat washer, and oil seal from case.
17. Drive reverse idler gear shaft lock pin into the shaft, then remove shaft, gear and thrust washers.

Assembly Notes — Reverse the order of the foregoing procedure to assemble the transmission, observing the following:

Install the reverse idler gear so that the chamfered teeth is at the rear of the case. The idler gear shaft is ground slightly larger at one end in order to form a positive seal at the rear end of the transmission case. Make sure that this end of the shaft is at the rear when replaced and that the small hole in the opposite end lines up with the lock pin hole in the case. Install a new lock pin coated with white lead or other sealing compound to prevent leaks. Drive lock pin 1" below surface of boss on case.

When installing the cluster gear and related parts, note that a small diameter bronze washer and a steel washer are used at the rear of the gear (bronze washer next to gear) and a larger bronze washer (only) is used at the front. When countershaft is installed, install a new lock pin coated with white lead or other suitable sealing compound to prevent leaks. Drive pin flush with surface of transmission case.

After shift yoke shafts are installed, install a new welch plug coated with white lead or other sealing compound in right side of transmission case.

After installing second speed gear on mainshaft and, after lining up the small wire spacer ring in bottom of mainshaft snap ring groove with spline which is machined *part way* onto the ground second speed gear bearing surface, install

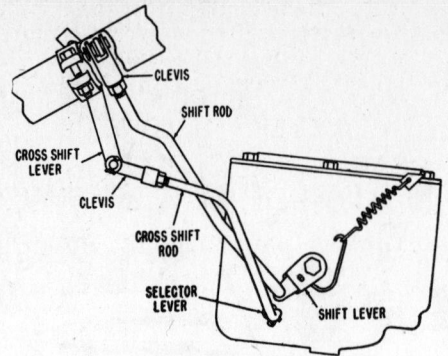

Fig. 4 Synchromesh transmission linkage. 1957-61

second speed gear thrust washer and snap ring. Note that one spline is machined the entire length of the second speed gear bearing surface on the mainshaft. This full spline is for lubrication purposes and should not be obstructed by the thrust washer key.

GEARSHIFT, ADJUST

1953-56

Two adjustments are required to properly position the hand control lever with respect to the steering wheel. The procedure is as follows:

Set the transmission outer shift lever in neutral. Adjust the clevis to obtain a dimension of 1¼" on 1953, 2" on 1954, and 2¹¹⁄₁₆" on 1955-56 (horizontal) between the steering wheel centerline to the centerline of the shift lever knob. With transmission outer selector lever against rear stop, and hand control lever knob resting in neutral position, adjust the clevis on this rod so that the clevis pin will easily enter the hole in the lever.

Remove the clevis pin connecting the outer selector lever to the cross shift lever, lengthen the clevis by 3 full turns and replace the pin. This gives the proper vertical adjustment between the steering wheel and shift lever knob.

1957-61, Fig. 4

To adjust the shift lever position, set the transmission shift lever in second gear position. Disconnect shift rod from steering column lower shift lever at the clevis. Hold the steering column lower shift lever against its stop in the mast jacket. Adjust the shift rod clevis so the pin enters freely the clevis and lever. Then remove the clevis pin and shorten the rod by 3 full turns (5½ on 1959-61) of the clevis. Secure the adjustment.

To adjust the cross shift linkage, disconnect the cross shift rod from the cross shift lever. With the transmission selector held rearward against its stop, adjust the cross shift rod clevis so that its pin will freely enter the hole in the lever while holding the cross shift lever rearward to take up the lash. Then remove the clevis pin and lengthen the rod by three (5 on 1959-61) full turns of the clevis. Secure the adjustment.

HYDRA-MATIC DRIVE

Hydramatic, Replace, 1953-55

1. To remove the hydramatic, raise the car off the floor and drain the oil from the transmission.
2. Disconnect side pan at rear and drop out of place in order to remove starter. Starter wires should be identified so that they can be reinstalled properly.
3. Remove the exhaust pipe and crankcase ventilator brackets from the lower flywheel housing and then remove housing (attached by 8 cap screws).
4. Remove flywheel housing pan.
5. Remove ⅛ in. hex head plug from torus cover to drain oil.
6. Disconnect propeller shaft at rear universal joint and slide rearward away from transmission.
7. Disconnect speedometer cable at transmission.
8. Remove transmission fluid filler tube from transmission oil pan.
9. Disconnect manual rod from transmission lever.
10. Remove throttle rod lever.
11. Remove 30 torus cover-to-flywheel attaching screws and lockwashers.
12. Support the engine at the rear with a suitable support bar or other available means.
13. Remove two bolts, engine mount-to-frame cross member (left side only). Remove two cap screws from engine mount-to-flywheel housing (right side only).
14. Remove three bolts from each end of cross member-to-frame.
15. Lift engine approximately ½ in. and remove frame cross member.
16. Lower engine just enough to remove transmission-to-bell housing upper screws (approximately 1½ in.). *Do not lower engine more than 1½ in. to remove upper cap screws unless upper radiator hose and exhaust pipe-to-manifold connection are loosened.*
17. Remove the two remaining transmission-to-bell housing cap screws.
18. Remove transmission assembly by moving it toward the rear of the car, and at the same time lowering assembly to floor. *To prevent the end of the mainshaft from striking the flywheel-to-crankshaft bolts when lowering the transmission, be sure to turn the flywheel so the end of the mainshaft passes between the two bolts.*
19. Reverse the foregoing procedure to install the transmission and adjust the control linkage as outlined below.

Hydramatic, Replace, 1956-60

1. Disconnect battery.
2. Remove trans. oil filler tube.
3. Drain transmission.
4. Disconnect speedometer cable.
5. Remove linkage from transmission levers. *Remove throttle lever.*
6. Remove crankcase breather tube.
7. On 1956 models, remove propeller shaft. On 1957-60 models, scribe a line from one of the propeller shaft center bearing support-to-frame bolts on the frame member for later

center bearing support alignment. Remove propeller shaft center bearing support bolts and shims. *Identify shims so the same total thickness of shims can be reinstalled.* Disconnect the two "U" bolts at transmission companion flange. Raise center bearing so it will clear frame member and slide front propeller shaft and bearing approximately 2" to rear of slip joint (the bearing mounting plate will rest on frame and keep propeller shaft from dropping down).

8. Disconnect left-hand exhaust pipe (if dual exhaust equipped).
9. Remove starter.
10. Support transmission with jack.
11. Raise engine enough to relieve weight from rear engine mounts. Unfasten engine mount from cross member.
12. Remove cross member.
13. Remove lower flywheel housing.
14. Drain torus.
15. Lower engine not more than 1½" to permit removal of the two upper flywheel housing to block bolts.
16. Disconnect oil cooler hoses from lines and *cap lines immediately.*
17. Remove four flex plate-to-flywheel attaching bolts.
18. Remove remaining flywheel housing-to-block bolts.
19. Move transmission rearward approximately ¾" to clear dowels and lower transmission from car.
20. Reverse above procedure to install. Torque flex plate-to-flywheel attaching nuts 20-25 lb. ft. Torque oil pan drain plug 35-45 lb. ft. Torque throttle lever 10-12 lb. ft.

1961

1. Disconnect transmission vent pipe from rear of right-hand exhaust manifold.
2. Raise car and remove oil filler pipe from transmission and drain fluid.
3. Disconnect speedometer cable and shift levers from transmission.
4. Remove propeller shaft.
5. Disconnect exhaust pipe bracket from transmission rear housing.
6. Support rear of engine.
7. Support transmission with transmission lift.
8. Raise engine enough to relieve weight from rear engine mounts and remove bolts attaching mounts to crossmember.
9. Remove crossmember.
10. Lower engine enough to gain access to upper transmission attaching bolts.
11. Disconnect oil cooler lines and cap lines immediately.
12. Pry vent pipe from transmission case.
13. Remove remaining transmission attaching bolts.
14. Position exhaust pipe bracket to clear transmission output shaft, then move transmission rearward about 1½" to disengage input shaft from damper hub.

15. Lower transmission from car.
16. Reverse removal operations to install transmission and adjust shift linkage.

Manual Linkage, Adjust
1953

1. Place selector lever in "S" range by pulling down on the shift rod until stop is felt.
2. Loosen jam nut on shift rod clevis.
3. Remove clevis pin from shift rod.
4. Move manual control lever at side of transmission all the way forward into "N" position. Then move manual lever back again to the second detent "S" position.
5. Hold lower shift lever in "S" position (manual control against stop) while making the following adjustment.
6. Adjust shift rod clevis so the clevis pin will just slide freely in the hole through clevis and steering column lower shift lever.
7. Remove pin and lengthen rod by turning clevis one full turn from this position.
8. Assemble clevis pin and cotter pin and tighten jam nut.

Note—The foregoing adjustment properly positions the selector lever in relation to the "S" range stop and the manual valve in the valve body, assuring correct pointer positioning in all selector lever positions on the sector below the steering wheel.

1954

1. Loosen jam nut on shift rod clevis and neutral safety switch.
2. Remove clevis pin from shift rod and move manual control lever at side of transmission all the way forward to the Neutral position.
3. Raise and hold shift lever beyond Neutral position against side of opening in jacket.
4. Adjust shift rod clevis so end of clevis contacts outside diameter of bushing in lower shift lever.
5. Return lower shift lever to Neutral position and insert pin through clevis and bushing, fastening with cotter pin.

1955-60

Set the transmission manual lever in neutral detent position. Disconnect manual rod from lower shift lever. Hold lower shift lever upward so selector lever is positioned against stop in upper steering column. Adjust manual rod end so pin will enter approximately ⅛" into lower shift lever bushing with selector lever against stop. On 1959-60 models, lengthen clevis 2½ turns. Tighten clevis lock nut and connect manual rod to lower shift lever.

Throttle Linkage, Adjust
1953-61

Before making any checks or adjust-

ments of the linkage, check the performance of the engine. The transmission is often blamed for poor operation of the vehicle when the engine is not tuned to deliver maximum power.

There are so many linkage variations and intricate hook-ups that it is impractical to illustrate and go into specific procedures for each one. However, there are only two things to remember when it becomes necessary to adjust the throttle linkage.

1. Throttle linkage must be adjusted so that when the carburetor throttle valves are fully closed (hot idle) the transmission throttle valve lever must be all the way toward the rear of the transmission against the internal stop.
2. In order to assure kickdown operation, the accelerator pedal linkage must be adjusted so that when it is fully depressed, the carburetor throttle valves are in wide open position.

The most obvious symptom of misadjusted throttle linkage is either the absence of a 4-3 (3-2 on 1961) kickdown or a kickdown which takes place before full throttle is reached. Lengthening or shortening the lower throttle rod to the transmission controls kickdown to a great extent. Before adjusting the lower throttle rod, however, the proper functioning of the upper or carburetor throttle rod must be ascertained. In general, the following procedure should be followed:

When There is No Kickdown:

1. Disconnect lower throttle rod at transmission.
2. With engine shut off, depress the accelerator pedal down to the floor. With the pedal in this position, the carburetor throttle valves should be wide open. If not, check for obstructions such as a lumpy floor mat under the pedal or misaligned linkage. It may be that the length of the upper throttle rods have to be changed through adjustment to obtain wide open throttle at the carburetor.
3. While holding the fast idle cam (of carburetor) in the "off" position, release the accelerator pedal slowly. The pedal return spring should bring the throttle back to the hot idle position. If it doesn't, make the necessary corrections.
4. Reconnect the throttle rod at the transmission and adjust by shortening a turn at a time between road tests until kickdown is obtained.

Kickdown Occurs Before Wide Open Throttle Is Reached:

1. Follow Steps 1, 2 and 3 as outlined above.
2. Reconnect lower throttle rod at transmission and adjust by lengthening a turn at a time between road tests until the transmission kicks down at the desired throttle position.

Rear Axle and Brake Section

Refer To Hydraulic Brakes Chapter For Brake Adjustments

REAR AXLE, 1953-56

In these axles, the splined companion flange is fastened to the pinion stem with a special nut which seats directly on a counterbore in the flange. The nut is retained by staking the end of the pinion stem into two slots milled on top of the nut.

The drive pinion is mounted on preloaded taper roller bearings. Adjustment of the pinion along its axis is obtained by shims placed between the rear bearing outer race and a shoulder in the carrier. Adjustment of preload of the two bearings is obtained by tightening the companion flange nut which compresses a sleeve over the pinion stem between the bearings. Both bearing outer races are pressed into the carrier, the rear race against pinion adjusting shims, the front race against the shoulder in the carrier. The rear bearing inner race is pressed onto the pinion stem to a shoulder at the pinion end. The front bearing is a light press to a close sliding fit on the pinion stem.

The threaded nut type of differential bearing adjustment is used. The procedure for making this adjustment, as well as the assembly of the differential case, replacing a ring gear, checking ring gear and pinion backlash and other differential case operations, is given in the *Rear Axle Chapter*.

Pinion & Bearings, Replace

After removing the differential unit from the carrier, unscrew the pinion flange retaining nut and pull off the flange. Press the pinion out of the front bearing and through the rear end of the carrier. The rear bearing cone and bearing spacer will come out with the pinion. The bearings may then be removed and installed with suitable pulling equipment.

Reverse the operations to assemble and, after pressing on the pinion flange, slip on the washer and nut. Tighten the nut until the bearings have a preload drag of 24 to 32 inch pounds on new bearings or 10 to 15 inch pounds on used bearings to rotate the pinion shaft.

To adjust the preload, draw up the nut until the spacer starts to buckle. Check the pull as shown in Figs. 2 or 3, depending upon the equipment available. This adjustment must be made every time the flange nut is removed or loosened. If the adjustment is to be made with the differential unit in the carrier, the rear wheels must be jacked off the floor.

The pinion can be moved in toward the center of the axle by removing the required thickness of shims from between the spacer and the carrier. If it is to be moved away from the center of the axle, add shims.

Note — A new spacer is required between the pinion bearings when a new ring gear and pinion set is installed, either outer or inner members of either pinion bearing is changed, a new carrier casting used, or pinion adjusting shim thickness is increased. When the same pinion flange is removed and reinstalled as when an oil seal is replaced, checking for pinion bearing preload with a torque wrench is not necessary if care is taken to tighten the nut to exactly its previous position. Should a new pinion flange be required, a torque wrench reading should be taken before loosening the nut and the nut tightened to the same torque wrench reading.

The side bearing adjustment of the pedestal cap spread must be determined.

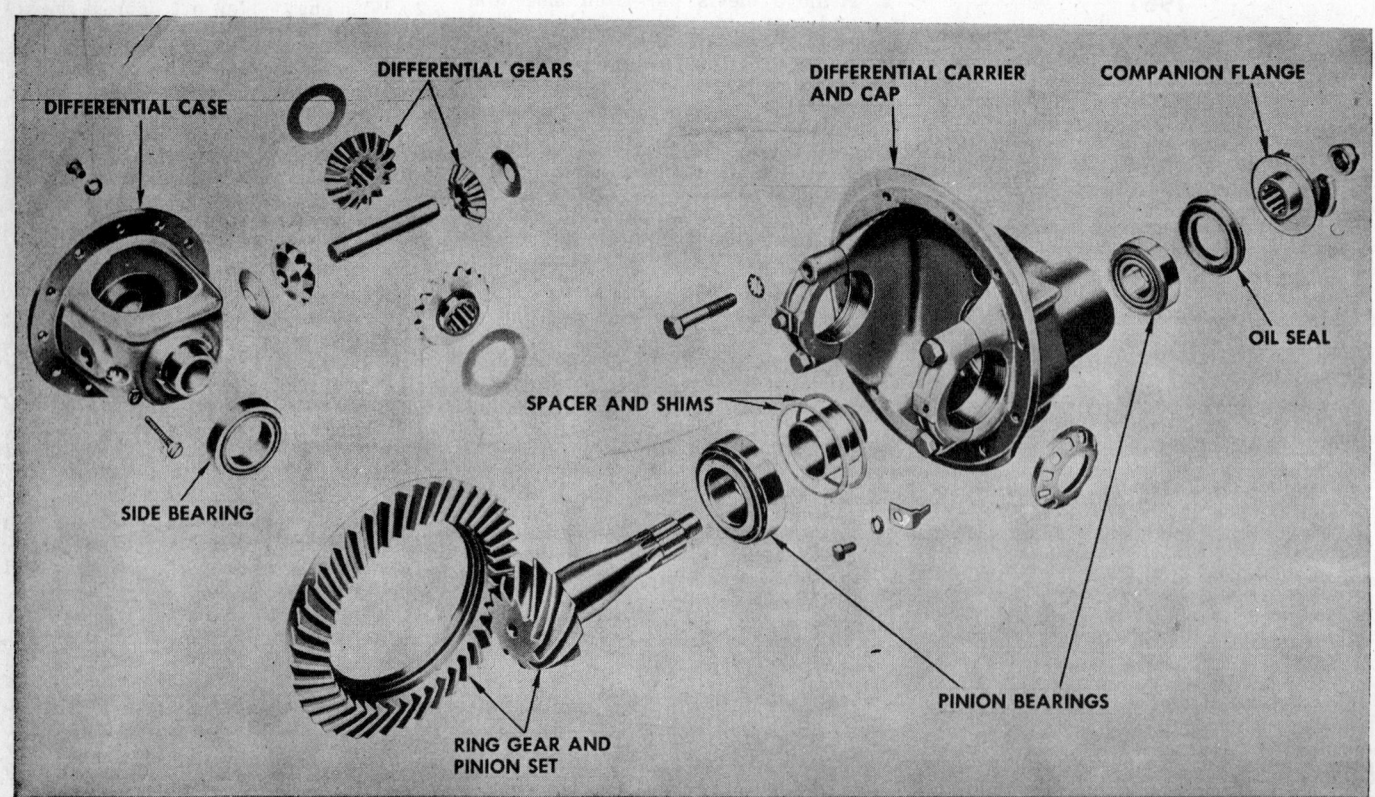

Fig. 1   Rear axle, 1953

Fig. 2 Measuring pinion bearing preload with a torque wrench

Fig. 3 Measuring pinion bearing preload with a spring scale

With the differential case assembled in the carrier, adjusting nuts in place, and pedestal caps tightened just snug, proceed as follows:

1. Back off the right adjusting nut (one opposite ring gear) four turns.

2. Tighten the left hand adjusting nut against the bearing race, removing all lash between the ring gear and pinion. Then back off four notches, leaving slot in adjusting nut in line with lock cap screw hole in bearing cap.

3. Tighten right hand adjusting nut, watching race of bearing. When bearing race starts to turn, continue to tighten two to three notches, align slot in nut.

4. Tighten cap bolts 70 to 75 lbs. ft. with hole in bearing cap.

5. Clamp an indicator to differential carrier and check backlash. This should not be less than .004" nor more than .008".

6. If necessary, adjust by turning the nuts in the required direction to obtain the correct lash; always moving both nuts an equal number of notches.

7. Again tighten pedestal caps 70 to 75 lbs. ft. and check lash. After the correct backlash has been obtained, proceed as follows:

8. With the special gauge positioned as shown in Fig. 4, check the clearance between the gauge and the machined surface of the pedestal cap—which should be .005". If the clearance is incorrect, loosen the right hand bearing cap bolts and adjust the nut as required (one notch at a time) to obtain .005" clearance. Be sure bearing cap bolts are tight each time clearance is checked. Do not tighten adjusting nut more than 4 notches nor less than 2 notches.

9. Recheck backlash. If necessary, move adjusting nuts an equal number of notches to obtain .004" to .008" backlash.

Note — On eight-cylinder models, the differential carrier is a press fit in the axle housing. When installing the carrier it must be held so the pedestal caps are in line with the supports in the housing before the assembly can be drawn into the axle housing.

To perform this operation, position the gasket and install 3 special pilot studs into the housing as shown in Fig. 5. Assemble the carrier over the pilot studs. Then temporarily use four 1½" long bolts, two each side as shown, and tighten the bolts evenly to draw the carrier into the housing. Remove the pilot studs and install 6 of the regular carrier bolts in the vacant holes. Remove the four temporary bolts, install the regular ones and tighten all 40 to 45 lbs. ft.

1957-61 REAR AXLE

The differential carrier is larger and heavier than previous models to withstand the increased engine torque without excessive deflecting or twisting, Fig. 6. The number of splines have been increased on side gears, axle shafts and drive pinion. The drive pinion and ring gear, pinion bearings, side bearings, side gears and differential case are larger. The pinion adjusting shims are located between the pinion head and the inner bearing race instead of in front of the outer bearing race on 1956. The differential pinion cross shaft is locked in the case by means of a screw and washer instead of a roll pin used in 1956. The carrier attaching screws are pressed into the axel housing and the carrier is attached to the housing screws by means of nuts and lockwashers.

Service Procedures

All service procedures are the same as in 1956. Due to the new construction, however, a new set of pinion adjusting shims is required. Shims are available in thicknesses of .004", .005" .006", .007"

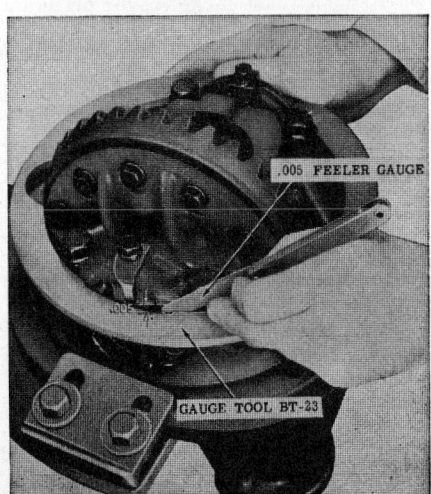

Fig. 4 Adjusting differential carrier pedestal spread

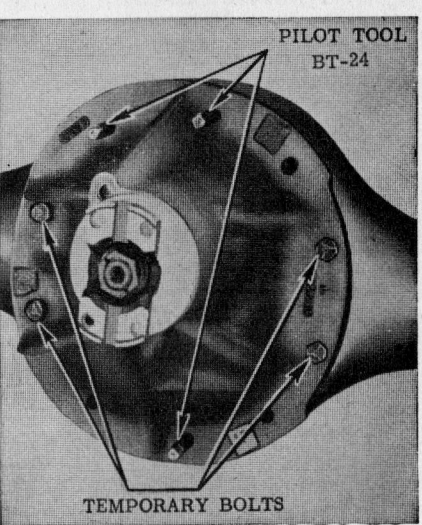

Fig. 5 Installing machined carrier into axle housing

and .010". The pinion rear bearing must be removed from the pinion to change the shim pack. The thickness of the shim pack must be established by the red (or white) lead test as outlined in the *Rear Axles* chapter.

AXLE SHAFT

These axle shafts are supplied with the wheel studs pressed into the flange. Studs on the left-hand axle have left-hand threads.

To remove a shaft, unfasten the brake drum from the flange and the brake support plate from the axle housing. Pull the bearing retainer plate away from the brake plate, using care not to dislodge the brake plate as the brake line might be damaged. Remove the shaft with a puller.

POWER BRAKE UNIT, REPLACE

1960-61

1. Disconnect hydraulic line. Plug or tape line to prevent dirt from entering hydraulic system.
2. Disconnect vacuum lines from vacuum cylinder.
3. Disconnect operating rod from brake pedal.
4. Unfasten vacuum cylinder from cowl (4 nuts).
5. Reverse sequence of operations to install and torque attaching nuts 8-16 ft. lbs.

1959

1. Disconnect hydraulic line. Plug line with rubber stopper to prevent dirt entering the hydraulic system.
2. Disconnect wires from stop light switch.
3. Remove brake pedal and bracket.
4. Slide steering column grommet and retainer up mast jacket.
5. Remove floor cover plate screws.

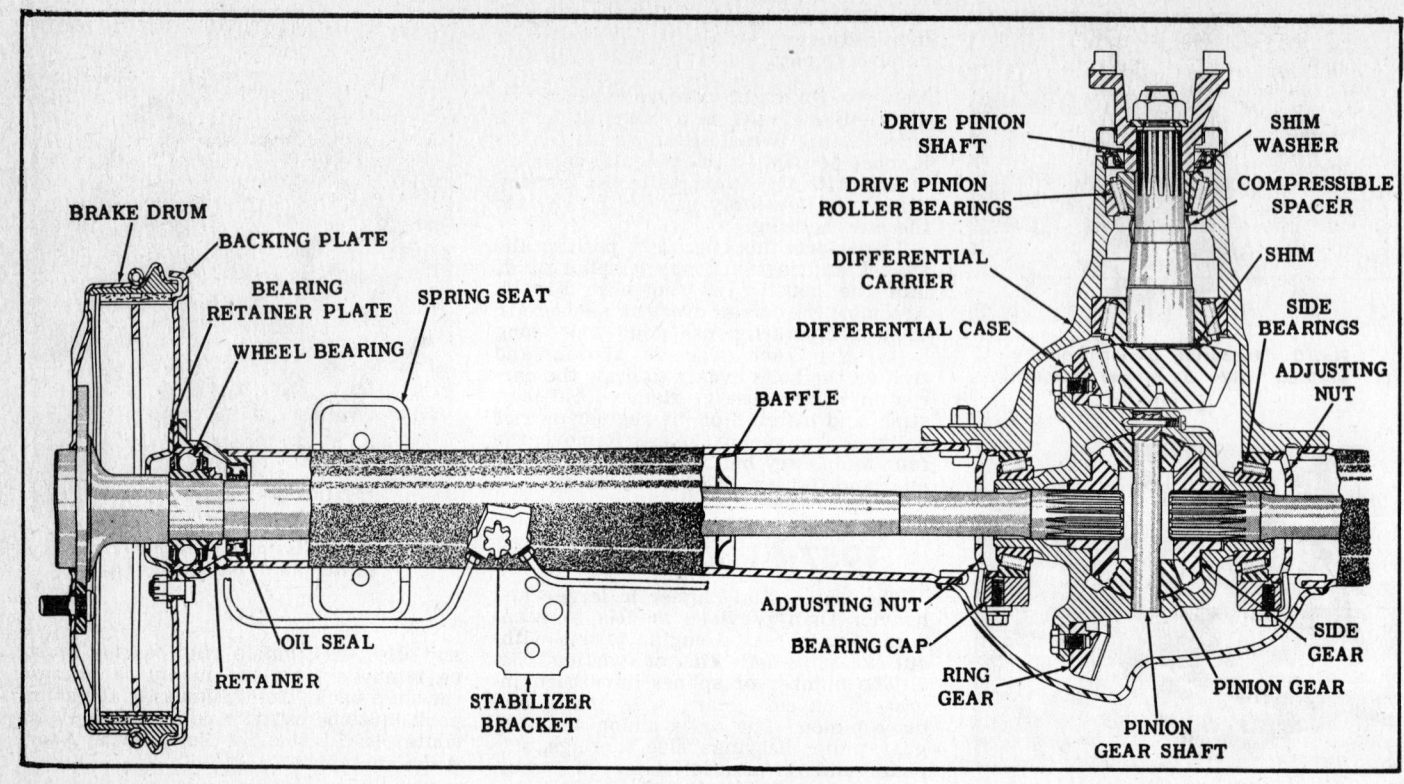

Fig. 6 Rear axle, 1957-61

6. Remove cover plate-to-power cylinder bolt and remove cover plate.
7. Disconnect vacuum hose and remove power brake unit through toe pan opening.
8. Reverse removal operations to install.
9. Fill master cylinder and bleed system.

1956-58

1. Disconnect positive battery cable at junction block on right fender filler plate. Disconnect solenoid lead wire (purple) from wiring harness, then pull cable through sleeve on power brake.
2. Disconnect brake line at junction block at frame. Use care to prevent dirt from entering the hydraulic line. Plug brake line with a rubber stopper.
3. Disconnect wires from stop light switch and fold back floor mat.
4. Remove three brake pedal attaching bolts and remove bracket and pedal assembly.
5. Remove mast jacket grommet and retainer clamp and slide grommet and retainer up mast jacket.
6. Remove floor cover attaching screws.
7. Remove speedometer cable from clips.
8. Remove two cover plate-to-power cylinder bolts and remove cover plate while positioning power brake unit so it rests on edge of opening in toe pan.
9. Disconnect vacuum hose and remove power brake unit through toe pan opening. *When reinstalling hose, position clamp so screw head may*

be reached from below car.

10. Reverse foregoing procedure to install, fill master cylinder and bleed system.

1954-55

1. Disconnect the hydraulic line at the power brake master cylinder.
2. Disconnect vacuum hoses at power cylinder, and remove dipstick.
3. Disconnect leads from stop light switch and fold back floor mat.
4. Remove three bolts and take off brake pedal and bracket assembly.
5. Slide mast jacket grommet up on mast jacket.
6. Remove mast jacket cover plate and power cylinder assembly.
7. Remove cover plate from power cylinder.
8. Install in the reverse order, fill master cylinder with brake fluid and bleed system.

1953

1. To remove the power brake unit, disconnect the hydraulic line at the power brake master cylinder.
2. Disconnect vacuum hose at power cylinder, and remove dipstick.
3. Remove brake pedal pivot pin and tip upper end of pedal back to expose push rod pivot pin under pedal pad.
4. Remove push rod pivot pin retainer and pin, and remove brake pedal.
5. Remove accelerator pedal and fold back carpet.
6. Remove steering column grommet retainers and slide grommet up on steering column.
7. Remove steering column cover plate-

to-toe pan screws, and remove cover plate and Power Brake as a unit.
8. Remove Four cover plate-to-power cylinder bolts and remove cover plate.

Installation Notes—Reverse the sequence of operations to install the unit. The master cylinder may be filled before reinstallation. Avoid depressing the push rod until the flex line is connected. Always use washers at the outlet fitting. Fill the master cylinder with approved brake fluid and bleed the hydraulic system.

BRAKE MASTER CYLINDER, REPLACE

1960-61

The standard brake master cylinder can be removed without disconnecting the push rod and clevis. The master cylinder on cars with power brakes can be removed without removing the vacuum cylinder from the car. Power cylinders can be identified by the bronze Moraine cylinder and the black Bendix cylinder.

1. Disconnect hydraulic line at master cylinder and plug or tape end to prevent dirt entering the system.
2. If equipped with standard transmission, install a gauge pin in the holes provided in the frame side rail and "X" member to hold clutch linkage in position; then disconnect clutch linkage from clutch pedal bellcrank and remove bellcrank.
3. Remove master cylinder (4 nuts). On Moraine units, remove and record number of any shims found be-

tween master and power cylinders. *On Moraine units, the master cylinder piston will remain attached to the vacuum unit. If piston is to be serviced, the vacuum unit must be removed and disassembled.*

1959

1. Disconnect junction block-to-master cylinder hydraulic line at master

cylinder. Plug line with rubber stopper.
2. Unfasten and remove master cylinder (with boot) from dash panel. Push rod and clevis need not be removed.
3. Install in reverse order of removal and bleed hydraulic system as outlined in the *Hydraulic Brake System* chapter.

1953-58

To remove the master cylinder, disconnect the push rod from the brake pedal. Disconnect the brake pipe from the master cylinder and tape its end to prevent dirt from entering. Unfasten the cylinder from the frame bracket and remove it from the car.

Install in the reverse order and bleed the hydraulic system as directed in the *Hydraulic Brake* chapter.

Front End and Steering Section

CAMBER & CASTER

1957-61, Fig. 1

Camber and caster are adjusted by shims placed between the upper pivot shafts and the frame. In order to remove or install shims, raise the car to remove weight from the front wheels, then loosen the pivot shaft-to-frame bolts.

To *decrease* positive caster, *remove* shim at front bolt. To *increase* positive caster, *add* shim at front bolt.

To *increase* camber, *add* shims at both the front and rear bolts. To *decrease* camber, *remove* shims at both the front and rear bolts.

By adding or subtracting an equal amount of shims from both the front and rear bolts, camber will change without affecting caster adjustment. Refer to shim chart when changing shims as follows:

Shim Thickness	Camber Change	Caster Change
.020"	$\frac{1}{8}$°	$\frac{3}{8}$°
.060"	$\frac{3}{8}$°	$1\frac{3}{8}$°
.120"	$\frac{3}{4}$°	$2\frac{1}{4}$°

1955-56

Caster—Loosen the clamp bolt at the upper end of the steering knuckle support. Turn the eccentric bushing to obtain desired adjustment. Turning the bushing in a clockwise direction will increase caster; turning it counterclockwise decreases caster.

Camber—Since the camber adjustment is controlled by the eccentric action of the bushing, ½ turn of the bushing gives the maximum adjustment and is all that should be required. Moreover, changing camber will change caster angle slightly but it will usually be within proper limits.

1953-54

To adjust caster, loosen the clamp bolt at the upper end of the steering knuckle support. Remove the lubrication fitting from the front bushing of the eccentric pin at the outer end of the upper control arms. Insert an Allen wrench through the hole from which the lubrication fitting was removed and turn the threaded eccentric pin until the

desired caster angle is obtained. Turn the threaded pin on each side of the car clockwise to increase caster and counterclockwise to decrease caster. Always turn the pin in multiples of one turn so that the camber will not be disturbed. After completing the adjustment, tighten the knuckle support clamp bolts and install the lubrication fittings. This procedure should only be used to change the caster less than 3 degrees.

To adjust camber, insert an Allen wrench as described for making a caster adjustment. The camber angle is controlled by the eccentric action of the threaded pin and a half turn gives the maximum adjustment. Changing the camber will change the caster angle slightly but if the pin is not turned more than a half turn the caster angle will still be within its limits.

TOE-IN, ADJUST

To adjust the toe-in, loosen the clamps at both ends of the adjustable tubes at each tie rod. Then turn the tubes an equal amount until the toein is correct. Turning the tubes in the direction the wheels revolve when the car moves forward decreases the toe-in and vice-versa. When the adjustment is complete, tighten all clamp screws.

WHEEL BEARINGS, ADJUST

Tighten the spindle nut with a torque wrench to approximately 17 lb. ft. to insure that all parts are properly seated and threads are free. Back off nut and retighten to 4 lb. ft. If cotter pin hole in spindle and slot in nut line up, insert cotter pin; if not, back off spindle nut to the nearest line-up of slot and hole and insert cotter pin.

When installing front wheel hub and drum, the complete inner bearing, including the cone, should always be assembled to the hub, and the assembly then installed on the spindle.

1957-61 FRONT END REPAIRS

This suspension, Fig. 2, utilizes ball

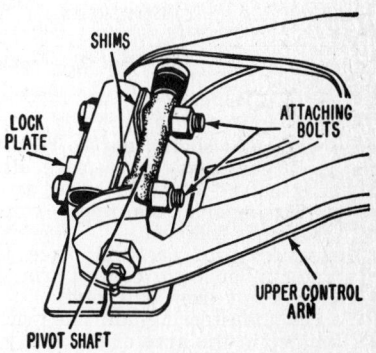

Fig. 1 Upper control arm mounting showing location of caster and camber shims. 1957-61

joints instead of knuckle supports, kingpins and thrust bearings.

Shock Absorber, Replace

Remove the pivot bolt from the upper end of the shock absorber. Unfasten the shock absorber from the lower control arm and remove the unit out through the lower control arm spring seat.

To install the shock absorber, reverse the sequence of removal. Torque the pivot bolt 60-70 lb. ft. and the cap screws 15-25 lb. ft.

Stabilizer, Replace

Disconnect each side of stabilizer linkage by removing nut from top of link bolt. Pull out bolt from bottom of linkage and remove retainers, grommets and spacer. Unfasten stabilizer bracket from frame and remove bar, rubber bushings and brackets.

To install, reverse sequence of removal operations. The rubber bushings should be positioned squarely in the brackets. Torque stabilizer link nut 8-18 lb. ft. and bracket bolts 25-35 lb. ft.

NOTE—Never lubricate stabilizer bar rubber bushings as they are dependent upon a bonding of the rubber to the bar for proper stabilizing action.

Upper Control Arm and Ball Joint, Replace

NOTE—The ball joint is riveted to the

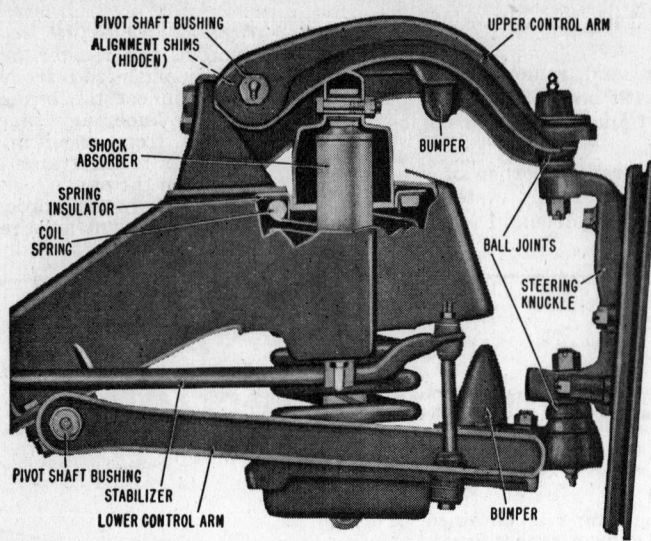

PIVOT SHAFT BUSHING
ALIGNMENT SHIMS
(HIDDEN)

UPPER CONTROL ARM

SHOCK
ABSORBER

BUMPER

SPRING
INSULATOR

COIL
SPRING

BALL JOINTS

STEERING
KNUCKLE

PIVOT SHAFT BUSHING
STABILIZER
LOWER CONTROL ARM

BUMPER

Fig. 2   Front suspension. 1957-61

control arm and should not be removed from it. If necessary to replace either part, they should be replaced as an assembly. To remove the upper control arm, proceed as follows:

1. Raise front of car and place jack stands under lower control arm.
2. Remove nut from ball joint.
3. Strike the steering knuckle with a hammer in the area of the ball joint stud to loosen the joint.
4. Support hub and drum to prevent their weight from damaging brake hose.
5. If necessary to remove pivot shaft from control arm, loosen pivot shaft bushings at this time.
6. Unfasten pivot shaft from frame, being sure to locate wheel alignment shims so they can be reinstalled in their original location during re-assembly.
7. Remove control arm and pivot shaft from car.

Lower Control Arm, Ball Joint and/or Spring, Replace

NOTE—The ball joint is riveted to the control arm and should not be removed from it. If either part is to be replaced, both should be replaced as an assembly. If a worn ball joint is suspected, check by attempting to chuck the top of the wheel in and out with the weight of the car on the wheel. Under any other condition the lower ball joint will appear to be worn regardless of its actual condition.

1. Raise and support of car with stand jacks.
2. Remove wheel assembly.
3. Disconnect stabilizer link from lower control arm.
4. Remove shock absorber.
5. Place jack under control arm to be removed.
6. Remove nut from lower ball joint.
7. Strike steering arm with a hammer in the area of the ball joint stud to break the joint loose.
8. Slowly lower hydraulic jack until spring is fully extended and remove spring. *Important*—Left and right springs are not interchangeable.

Spring part number is stamped on outer side of end coil.

9. If necessary to remove lower control arm, unfasten pivot shaft from frame crossmember.

1955-56 FRONT END REPAIRS

NOTE—Except for the new type shock absorber which necessitates the use of a new upper control arm, service on the front suspension is the same as for previous models. Therefore, follow the procedure given for *Front Wheel Bearings* and *Kingpins and Bushings*. Service on the *Front Spring* and *Lower Control Arm* is also the same except that the shock absorber must be removed—the procedure for which is given below.

Shock Absorber, Replace

1. To remove a shock absorber, hold the shock absorber mounting stem with a wrench while removing the pal-nut and retaining nut. Then remove retainer and rubber grommet.
2. Remove bolts and lockwashers attaching lower mounting brackets to the spring seats on the lower control arm and pull the shock absorber and bracket down through the opening in the spring seat.
3. Clamp lower mounting bracket in a vise and remove the pivot bolt and nut, rubber grommet and spacer.
4. Inspect all grommets and replace if not in good condition. If shock absorber operation is faulty, it should be replaced as it cannot be repaired.
5. Reverse the foregoing procedure to install the shock absorber, being certain that the unit being installed is correct for the car model as indicated by the code and part number stamped on the outer tube.

Upper Control Arm

If the control arm is bent or broken, use a new arm assembly which includes

the shaft, bushings and dirt seals. If only the shaft and bushings require replacement, proceed as follows:

1. Remove generator and engine front mounting nuts and raise the engine just enough to allow removal of the upper arm shaft bolts.
2. Remove pivot pin and bushings and shaft attaching bolts and remove the arm assembly from the car.
3. Unscrew the shaft bushings and remove shaft and seals from upper arm.
4. Before installing any new parts, check the distance between the inner ends of the upper arm.
5. Install rubber seal over each end of upper arm shaft, with the large (or bell) end of seals outward.
6. Insert one end of shaft with the seal in one end of the upper arm and force the opposite end of the shaft into the other end of the arm.
7. Fasten the upper arm securely in a vise (close to one end to avoid springing or distortion).
8. Apply a liberal amount of white lead or Lubriplate to both bushings before installation.
9. Start the first bushing on the shaft and into the upper arm at the same time. Turn the bushing until the head is tight against the arm. Then tighten to a minimum of 100 lbs. ft. torque.
10. Center the shaft between the ends of the arm and install the second bushing in the same manner, turning the shaft as required to thread into the bushing so that no binding exists.
11. Before installing the upper arm and shaft assembly, turn the shaft to locate the bolt holes equally distant from ends of arm and bolt the shaft securely to the frame crossmember.
12. Lower engine and tighten front mounting nuts. Reinstall generator.
13. Reinstall upper pivot pin, bushings and seals. Then check front wheel alignment.

FRONT END, 1953-54

Upper Pivot Pin

To remove the pin, unscrew the clamp bolt and the two bushings and remove the rubber seals. Loosen the clamp bolt in the knuckle support and unscrew the pivot pin.

To replace, hold the knuckle support in line with the hole through the control arm and screw the pivot pin into the support, having the wrench hole in the pin toward the front of the car. Screw in the pin until it is centralized and tighten the clamp bolt. Assemble the seals over the pin. Centralize the knuckle support in the control arm yoke and start the rear bushing on the pin and into the control arm. Start the front bushing on the pin before locking the rear bushing up tight. After tightening the rear bushing, screw up the front bushing until there is $\frac{1}{32}$ inch clearance between the bushing and arm. Replace and lock the control arm clamp bolt, and set the caster, camber and toe-in.

Lower Pivot Pin

To remove, unscrew lock nut and remove the pin. To install, centralize the knuckle support between the control arm yoke and screw the pin through the front control arm and into the knuckle support bushing. After screwing the pin into the rear control arm, install the lock nut and washer and set the camber, caster and toe-in. When properly spaced, there will be about ⅛ inch clearance.

Lower Arm or Spring

To remove, disconnect the outer end of the tie rod and stabilizer link. Remove the lower pivot pin. Remove the jack from under the spring seat, allowing the lower arm to drop out of position. Take out the spring. Unfasten the pivot shaft from the frame crossmember. Unscrew the bushings and remove the pivot shaft from the lower control arm.

To prevent the arms from moving inward while the bushings are being installed, a special spreader tool should be used. To install the shaft and bushings into the lower control arm, place the tool in position and set the shaft in the control arm. Start a bushing on the shaft and into the arm at the same time and tighten the bushing. Center the shaft between the control arms and install the other bushing, being sure the threads index so there is no bind. Remove the tool and check the distance between the center of the pivot shaft bolt holes and the inside face of the arm. The dimension should be the same on both sides. Install the control arm assembly, replace the spring and lower pivot pin. Then set the caster, camber and toe-in.

Kingpins & Bushings

After removing the wheel and brake support plate, drive out the kingpin lock and the kingpin. Press out the bushings.

With the oil hole in the new bushings in line with the hole for the oil fitting, press the bushings into the knuckle. Then burnish the bushings in place and line-ream to size. Install the kingpin and complete the assembly in the reverse order of removal.

HORN BUTTON & RING

1953-57 Standard Wheel

The horn button may be removed by inserting a sharp instrument underneath the edge of the horn button and prying upward. Removal of the steering wheel nut will permit removal of the contact assembly.

1953-56 Deluxe Wheel

The deluxe horn button is held in place by two spring clips on the ends of the horn button which engage the horn ring hub. They are accessible from the underside of the steering wheel.

To remove the button, use a small screwdriver to relieve the spring tension on one end and lift the button from its seat. The steering wheel nut will have to be removed in order to remove the horn contact plate, horn ring or steering wheel.

1957 Deluxe

The deluxe horn ring cap is retained to the horn ring hub by a screw which is accessible from the underside of the cap. The steering wheel nut will have to be removed in order to remove the horn contact assembly or steering wheel.

1958 Deluxe

To remove the horn button, insert a sharp instrument underneath the edge at the center of the button housing and pry upward. Disconnect wires from horn button.

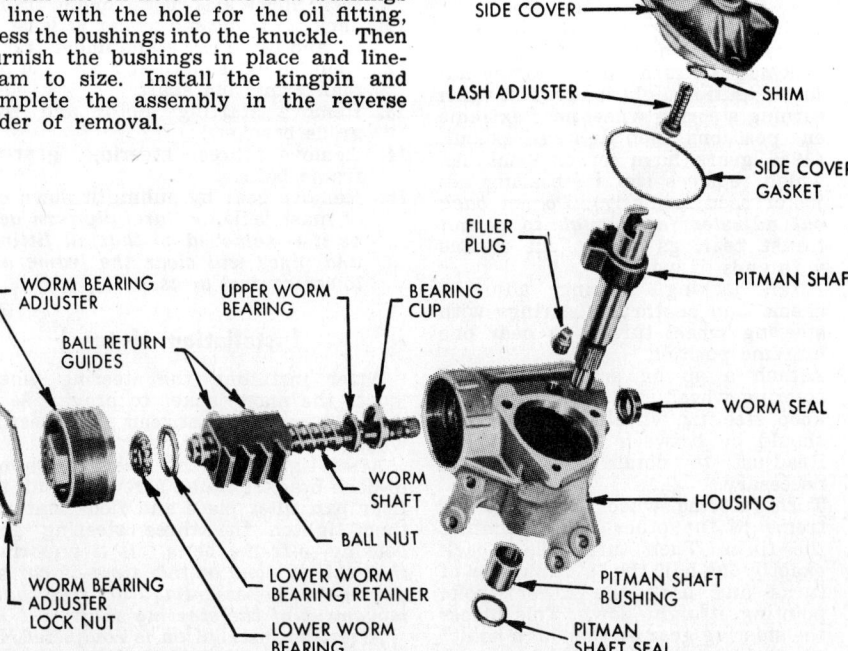

Fig. 3 Exploded view of manual steering gear

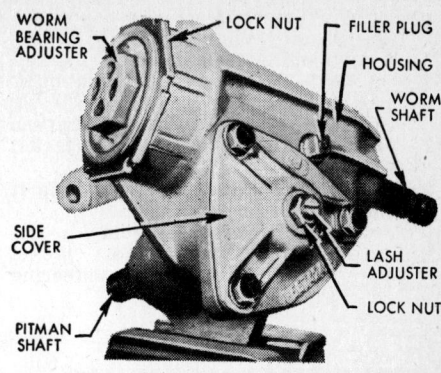

Fig. 4 Manual steering gear adjustments

1959-61

1. Disconnect horn wire from harness.
2. On Standard wheels, remove cap-to-steering wheel attaching screw, pull cap from wheel and disconnect horn switch wire from contact assembly lead.
3. On Deluxe wheels, pry cap and emblem from shroud.

STEERING WHEEL

After removing the horn button and/or horn ring as outlined above, use a suitable puller to remove the steering wheel. When installing the wheel, be sure it is positioned so the mark on the wheel hub and steering shaft are aligned.

STEERING GEAR, REPLACE

1953-54 Standard Gear

1. Disconnect horn wire at horn relay.
2. Remove steering wheel.
3. Remove floor mat, and mast jacket cover attaching screws.
4. Loosen upper and lower mast jacket clamps.
5. Hoist car and remove engine filler plate.
6. Remove pitman arm.
7. Unfasten steering gear from frame.
8. Remove gear by pulling it down out of mast jacket.
9. Reverse the above sequence to install the gear.

1955-61 Standard Gear

1. Remove steering wheel, upper bearing spring and seat.
2. Turn back floor mat and remove mast jacket cover plate attaching screws. *On 1960-61 models, disconnect horn wire and turn signal wire, and neutral safety switch and back-up light wires on cars with Hydra-Matic from switches on mast jacket and horn wire connector.*
3. On 1957-61, remove upper mast jacket clamps, and disconnect shift linkage from lower end of mast jacket.
4. On 1955-56, loosen upper and lower mast jacket clamps. Hoist car and remove engine filler plate.
5. Remove pitman arm from pitman shaft.

6. Unfasten steering gear from frame.
7. On 1955-56, remove gear by pulling it down out of mast jacket.
8. On 1957-60, remove gear and mast jacket assembly by pulling it up through opening in floor. Loosen lower clamp and remove mast jacket from gear.
9. On 1961, remove gear by pulling it out from under car.
10. To install, reverse foregoing procedure. Tighten upper mast jacket clamp before tightening steering gear frame.

MANUAL STEERING GEAR REPAIRS

Disassemble, Figs. 3, 4

1. Loosen adjusting screw lock nut and remove housing side cover by unscrewing adjusting screw.
2. Loosen lock nut and back off worm bearing adjuster several turns, then remove housing end cover and gasket.
3. Remove lower thrust bearing, steering shaft and upper bearing from housing.
4. Remove ball return guide clamps and guides from ball nut, turn ball nut over to remove balls and remove ball nut from steering shaft worm.

Inspection of Parts

1. Clean and inspect all ball and roller bearings and races, including race in housing.
2. Inspect pitman shaft bushings in gear housing and end cover. Replace bushings in housing and replace end cover if bushings are worn excessively.
3. It is advisable to replace pitman shaft grease seal in housing to avoid possible leakage of lubricant. Seal must be installed with feather edge toward inside of housing.
4. Inspect steering shaft for wear or pits in bearing races, which would require replacement of shafts.
5. Check shaft for straightness.
6. Inspect teeth of ball nut and pitman shaft. If scored or excessively worn it is advisable to replace both parts to insure proper mating of teeth.
7. Check serrations of pitman shaft; if twisted, replace shaft.
8. Check fit of pitman shaft adjusting screw and shim in slot in end of pitman shaft. *With shim in place, screw head must be free to turn in slot with zero to .002" end play.* If end play is excessive, selectively fit a new shim, which are furnished in four different thicknesses.
9. Inspect steering column jacket for distortion. A ripple or wavy feeling of jacket surface, particularly at lower end, will usually indicate a sprung jacket. Replace jacket if sprung or otherwise damaged.
10. Inspect control shaft bearing in tube of gear housing, and steering shaft upper bearing in control lever housing support. Replace worn or damaged parts.

Assemble

To assemble the steering gear, reverse the order of procedure given for disassembly. In addition, observe the following instructions.
1. Lubricate bearings and gears with steering gear lubricant.
2. Use all new gaskets to avoid oil leaks.
3. When assembling ball nut on worm, be sure to place 30 balls in each circuit, making a total of 60 balls.
4. When installing pitman shaft, avoid damaging or turning the feather edge of leather seal in gear housing.
5. Temporarily install steering wheel and adjust worm shaft thrust bearing for proper load and pitman shaft for proper gear lash as described below.

Adjustments

1. Disconnect steering linkage from pitman arm.
2. Turn steering wheel gently in one direction until it stops, then turn it back one revolution. *Never turn steering gear hard against stopping point as damage to ball nut assembly may result.*
3. Check lash between ball nut and pitman shaft by working pitman arm. If a perceptible lash *does not* exist, loosen lock nut and turn pitman shaft adjusting screw counterclockwise until lash can be felt when working pitman arm.
4. Turn steering wheel slowly from one extreme to the other. Wheel should turn freely and smoothly through entire range. Roughness indicates faulty worm thrust bearings or pitted races. Hard pull or binding indicates misalignment of steering gear in its mountings, or an excessively tight adjustment of worm thrust bearings. Any misalignment must be corrected before steering gear can be properly adjusted.
5. Tighten housing and cover bolts.
6. Loosen worm thrust bearing adjuster lock nut and turn thrust bearing adjuster until a slight load is felt when turning steering wheel near extreme end positions, then tighten lock nut. (1956 gears have an external hex which replaces slot on bearing adjuster used formerly). *Do not back out adjuster far enough to* permit thrust bearings to get out of line with ends of worm.
7. After locking bearing adjuster, check load on thrust bearings with steering wheel turned to near one extreme position.
8. Attach a spring scale to rim of steering wheel. The pull required to keep steering wheel turning slowly should be between ½ and ⅞ lbs. Readjust to obtain this load if necessary.
9. Turn steering wheel from one extreme to the other while counting the turns. Then turn wheel back exactly one-half the total number of turns and have the lower spoke pointing straight down. This places the steering gear on the "high point" at which no lash should exist between ball nut and pitman shaft teeth.
10. Tighten housing side cover bolts. Loosen lock nut and turn pitman shaft adjusting screw clockwise until lash is just removed.
11. After "tightening" adjusting screw lock nut, rotate wheel back and forth to check for tight spots. Also recheck pull at wheel rim as given above.
12. The pull required to keep the wheel moving through the "high point" should be between 1½ to 2 lbs. Readjust if necessary to remove tight spots.

POWER STEERING UNIT, REPLACE

Removal, 1953-55

The following procedure leaves the mast jacket in the car, thereby eliminating the possibility of scratching the finish on the jacket. It also eliminates disconnecting the shifter linkage and the wiring housed in the mast jacket.
1. Disconnect battery.
2. Drain fluid reservoir on hydraulic steering pump.
3. Disconnect hydraulic hoses at gear and pump. *Use plastic plugs or tape to cover openings against dirt entering.*
4. Loosen mast jacket-to-steering gear housing clamp.
5. Remove steering wheel.
6. Mask the steering column for about 2 in. above the instrument panel bracket.
7. Loosen the steering column in the bracket.
8. Remove floor mat and floor pan plate attaching screws.
9. Pull mast jacket up. *The upward travel will be limited by the shifter linkage striking lower side of toe pan.*
10. Place a 2 in. block between left front shock absorber arm and frame.
11. Jack up front end of car at least 10 in. and place car stand under frame.
12. Remove left side filler plate, and pitman arm from shaft.
13. Remove starting motor and wire guide bracket.
14. Remove three steering gear-to-frame bolts.
15. Remove gear by pulling it down out of mast jacket. *Carefully turn gear as it is removed so that all fittings and pipes will clear the frame and lower control arms.*

Installation Notes

After installing the steering wheel, locate the mast jacket to provide ⅛ to ¹⁄₁₆ in. clearance between the steering wheel and collar.

After tightening the steering column-to-dash bracket clamp screws, install the floor pan filler plate and floor mat and then tighten the three steering gear housing-to-frame bolts. *It is important that this is done at this time as correct alignment is essential for free axial movement of the steering shaft.*

After the installation is completed, fill the fluid reservoir and bleed the lines as outlined in the *Power Steering* chapter.

Removal, 1956-61

1. Scribe marks on coupling flange and steering shaft flange.
2. Disconnect hoses from pump and cap pump and hose fittings.
3. Hoist car and on 1956-58 remove engine filler plate. Remove pitman arm from pitman shaft.
4. Separate coupling from coupling flange.
5. Unfasten steering gear from frame and remove gear with hoses attached.

Installation Notes

When installing the gear assembly, align the coupling flange and steering shaft flange alignment marks so that the steering wheel will be positioned properly. Make sure that gear housing alignment pin enters hole in frame before tightening mounting bolts.

Bleeding System

After gear is installed and hoses connected to pump, add Hydra-Matic Fluid to the reservoir to the Full mark. With engine running, loosen bleed screw in pitman shaft side cover, turn steering wheel through its full travel 2 or 3 times to bleed all air from the system, and tighten bleed screw. Recheck oil level and add if necessary.

Speedometer, Radio & Windshield Wiper

SPEEDOMETER REMOVAL

1961

1. Disconnect parking brake from instrument panel and loosen it at cowl. Disconnect left-hand instrument panel brace, headlamp switch and ventilation or air conditioning control assembly from panel.
2. Remove light sockets, wiring harness and safety sentinel buzzer from speedometer.
3. Remove two speedometer mounting nuts and rotate assembly downward, *being careful not to damage printed circuit*.
4. Disconnect speedometer cable and withdraw assembly from left side of steering column from under instrument panel.

1960

To remove the speedometer or any other instrument, the instrument cluster must be removed. The procedure is as follows:
1. Remove air conditioning, heater or ventilation controls if car is so equipped.
2. Remove two instrument panel-to-cowl braces.
3. Remove headlamp switch and ignition switch from instrument panel.
4. Disconnect wiring harness, clock, safety sentinal and speedometer cable at cluster.
5. Remove cluster-to-instrument panel attaching nuts; then remove cluster from rear of instrument panel and out to left of steering column.

1959

To remove the speedometer or any other instrument, the instrument cluster must be removed. The procedure is as follows:
1. Remove the two left hand instrument panel molding-to-instrument cluster bracket nuts.
2. Remove air conditioning, heater or ventilation controls if car is so equipped.
3. Remove two instrument panel-to-cowl braces.
4. Disconnect wiring harness and speedometer cable from cluster.
5. Remove cluster-to-instrument panel attaching nuts and remove cluster from rear of panel.
6. Remove speedometer from cluster.

1957-58

To remove the speedometer or any other instrument the instrument cluster must be removed. The procedure is as follows:
1. Remove right-hand instrument panel molding screw and position molding away from cluster. Windshield wiper cables and hoses *do not* have to be disconnected.
2. Remove headlamp switch, parking brake light, ignition-starter switch and cigar lighter.
3. Remove air conditioning, heater or ventilation controls if so equipped.
4. Remove radio knobs and panel.
5. Remove upper clamp from steering column bracket.
6. Remove H-M indicator needle.
7. Remove lower clamp from steering column bracket. On manual steering equipped cars, loosen gear-to-frame bolts. Pull mast jacket away from bracket.
8. Remove steering column bracket from instrument panel.
9. Disconnect wiring harness and speedometer cable from cluster.
10. Remove cluster-to-instrument panel nuts; then remove cluster from front of dash.
11. The speedometer, or any other instrument, may now be removed from cluster.

1956

All the instruments except the speedometer can be removed from the back of the cluster without removing the cluster assembly. To remove the speedometer, first remove the cluster assembly as follows:
1. Disconnect battery and all electrical connections and lights from cluster.
2. Disconnect speedometer cable.
3. Remove H-M indicator needle.
4. Remove cluster-to-adapter nuts and pull cluster free from adapter studs.
5. Guide cluster through opening in center molding.

1953-55

The speedometer may be removed from the instrument cluster without removing the cluster from the instrument panel.

RADIO REMOVAL

1960-61

1. Remove glove box on 1960.
2. Disconnect radio lead from wiring harness.
3. Disconnect rear seat speaker lead (if equipped).
4. Disconnect antenna lead-in from radio. On 1961, access is through opening in top of glove box.
5. On Super Deluxe models, disconnect foot selector plug-in connector from right side of radio.
6. Remove control knobs and nuts from front of instrument panel.
7. Disconnect bracket from radio side support while supporting radio to prevent it from falling.
8. Remove radio.

1959

To remove the Deluxe, Super Deluxe or Transportable radio, proceed as follows:
1. Remove glove box.
2. Disconnect radio lead from wiring harness.
3. On cars equipped with rear seat speaker, disconnect speaker lead.
4. Disconnect antenna lead-in from radio.
5. On Super Deluxe models, disconnect foot selector plug-in connector from right side of radio.
6. On Transportable models, remove radio. Remove rack from bottom of push button unit and let rack rest on bottom flange of glove box opening.
7. Remove radio panel nuts from rear of instrument panel.
8. Disconnect radio from side supports while supporting radio to prevent it from falling. Remove radio.
9. On Transportables, feed rack unit through radio opening as dictated by wire attachments.

1958 Transportable

Open glove box door. Unlock padlock from lock release and remove. Pull down handle on face of radio. Push down on lock release and remove radio.

1957-58 Standard Radio

Remove speaker and glove box. Disconnect radio lead (green) from wiring harness and antenna lead from radio. Remove knobs, nuts and washers from control shafts. Disconnect radio from side supports and remove.

WINDSHIELD WIPER
1960

1. To remove wiper motor, first make sure motor is in parked position.
2. Remove cowl vent grille.
3. Disconnect electrical connectors from motor.

4. Remove windshield washer hoses (if equipped).
5. Remove retainer (2 speed) or nut (1 speed) securing drive linkage to motor and disengage drive linkages from motor. *Hold crank arm on single speed motor with a wrench when removing or tightening linkage-to-crank nut.*
6. Unfasten motor and lower motor from cowl.
7. Reverse procedure to install. *The linkage for right transmission overlaps linkage for left transmission. Apply medium bodied sealer to motor attaching screws.*

1961

1. To remove wiper motor, first make certain motor is in parked position.
2. Remove cowl vent grille.
3. Remove screw securing ground strap to cowl, and disconnect electrical connectors from motor. Remove windshield washer hoses (if equipped).
4. Detach transmission linkage from motor. Hold crank arm on the overlap two-speed motor with a wrench when removing or tightening linkage-to-crank nut.
5. Remove attaching screws and lower wiper motor from cowl.

OLDSMOBILE F-85

INDEX OF SERVICE OPERATIONS

PAGE NO.

ACCESSORIES
Radio Removal 911
Instruments 911
Windshield Wiper 911
Windshield Wiper Troubles........ 37

BRAKES
Adjustments 112
Brake Cylinder Sizes.............882
Hydraulic Brake System...........112
Master Cylinder, Replace.........908
Trouble Shooting 31

CLUTCH
Clutch Pedal, Adjust.............890
Clutch, Replace 890
Trouble Shooting 13

COOLING SYSTEM
Radiator, Replace 888
Trouble Shooting 8
Water Pump 888

ELECTRIC SYSTEM
Dash Gauge Service............... 85
Distributor, Replace 888
Distributor Service.............. 46
Distributor Specifications.......881
Generator & Regulator Specs...... 62
Horn Button or Ring, Replace.....910
Ignition System Service.......... 46
Ignition Timing 889
Starter, Replace 889
Starter Switch Service........... 83
Starting Motor Service........... 77
Starting Motor Specifications....881
Trouble Shooting 10
Turn Signal Troubles............. 12

ENGINE
Camshaft & Bearings..............886
Crankshaft & Bearing Specs.......881
Crankshaft Oil Seal, Replace.....888
Cylinder Head, Replace...........883

PAGE NO.

Engine, Replace 883
Main Bearings, Replace...........887
Piston Pins, Replace.............887
Piston Rings, Replace............887
Piston, Pin & Ring Specs.........881
Pistons & Rods, Remove...........886
Piston & Rod, Assemble...........886
Pistons, Replace 887
Rocker Arms 885
Rod Bearings, Replace............887
Timing Case Cover................886
Timing Chain, Replace............886
Trouble Shooting 4
Valve Arrangement................884
Valve Guides 884
Valves, Grind 884
Valves Lifters 885
Valves, Remove 884
Valve Spring Installed Height....885
Valve Spring Testing.............885
Valve Specifications.............882

ENGINE OILING
Oil Pan, Replace.................888
Oil Pump Repairs.................888
Trouble Shooting 9

FRONT SUSPENSION
Front End Repairs................909
Trouble Shooting 33
Wheel Bearings, Adjust...........908
Wheel Alignment 908
Wheel Alignment Specifications...882

FUEL & EXHAUST SYSTEM
Carburetors 889
Fuel Pumps 96
Mufflers and Pipes...............889
Trouble Shooting 4

REAR AXLE
Axle Shaft, Replace..............906
General Service 102
Non-Slip Differentials...........109
Rear Axle Repairs................907
Rear Axle Specifications.........882
Trouble Shooting 31

PAGE NO.

SPECIFICATIONS
Brake Cylinder Sizes.............882
Capacity Data 883
Carburetors 889
Cooling System 883
Crankshaft & Bearings............881
Distributors 881
Engine Tightening 882
Generator & Regulators...........882
Pistons, Pin & Rings.............881
Rear Axle 882
Starting Motors 881
Tune Up 881
Valve Timing 886
Valves 882
Wheel Alignment 882

STEER GEARS (Mechanical)
Horn Button or Ring, Replace.........910
Steering Gear Repairs............909
Steering Gear, Replace...........910
Steering Wheel, Replace..........910
Trouble Shooting 33

STEERING GEARS (Power)
Steering Gear, Repairs...........145
Steering Gear, Replace...........911
Trouble Shooting 34

TRANSMISSIONS (Manual Shift)
Gearshift, Adjust 890
Transmission Repairs.............891
Transmission, Replace............891
Trouble Shooting 14

TRANSMISSIONS (Automatic)
Linkage, Adjust 892
Repairs 893
Trouble Shooting 906

TUNE UP 38

GENERAL SPECIFICATIONS

Year	Model Designation	Wheel-base, Inches	Valve Location	Bore and Stroke	Piston Dis-place-ment, Cubic Inches	Com-pres-sion Ratio (Stand-ard)	Maximum Brake H.P. @ R.P.M.	Maximum Torque Lbs. Ft. @ R.P.M.	Normal Oil Pressure Pounds
1961	F-85 . . . . V8	112	In Head	3.500 x 2.80	215	8.75	155 @ 4800	210 @ 3200	30

TUNE UP SPECIFICATIONS

★Disconnect vacuum line when setting timing with timing light.

Year	Model	Ground Polarity and Voltage	Spark Plug Type	Gap Inch	Distributor Point Gap Inch	Cam Angle Degrees	Firing Order ①	Ignition Timing★ Mark	Location	Idle Speed RPM In Drive	Com-pression Pressure @ Cranking Speed Minimum
1961	All	N-12	AC-46FF	.040	②	30	18436572	5°BTDC	Damper	500	160

①—Cylinder numbering, front to rear: Left bank 1–3–5–7, right bank 2–4–6–8.

②—Turn adjusting screw in (clockwise) until engine misfires. Then turn screw out ½ turn.

STARTING MOTOR SPECIFICATIONS

Year	Model	Part No.	Rota-tion	Brush Spring Tension, Ounces	No Load Test Amperes	Volts	R.P.M.	Torque Test Amperes	Volts	Torque, Lbs. Ft.
1961	All	1108303	C	35 Min.	70	10.6	7675	①	①	①

①—Not specified.

PISTONS, PINS, RINGS, CRANKSHAFT & BEARINGS

Year	Model	Fitting Pistons Shim To Use	Pounds Pull On Scale	Ring End Gap① Comp.	Oil	Wrist-pin Diam-eter	Rod Bearings Shaft Diameter	Bearing Clearance	Main Bearings Shaft Diameter	Bearing Clearance	Thrust on Bear. No.	Shaft End Play
1961	All	.0015	3–8	.010	.015	.875	2.000	.0002–.0022	2.2986	.0005–.0021	3	.004–.008

①—Fit rings in tapered bores for clearance listed in tightest portion of ring travel.

DISTRIBUTOR SPECIFICATIONS

Year	Part No.	Rota-tion	Cam Angle, Degrees	Breaker Point Open-ing, Inch	Con-denser Capac-ity, Mfds.	Breaker Arm Spring Tension, Ounces	Centrifugal Advance Data Degrees @ R.P.M. of Dist. Advance Starts	Full Advance	Vacuum Advance Data Inches of Vacuum to Start Plunger Move-ment	Inches of Vacuum for Full Plunger Travel	Maximum Vacuum Advance, Dist. Degrees
1961	1110975	C	30	.016	.18–.23	19–23	1 @ 535	12 @ 2100	5–7	16	13

VALVE SPECIFICATIONS

Year	Model	Valve Lash		Valve Angles		Valve Spring Installed Height	Valve Spring Pressure Lbs. @ In.	Valve Lift		Stem Clearance		Stem Diameter	
		Int.	Exh.	Seat	Face			Int.	Exh.	Intake	Exhaust	Int.	Exh.
1961	All	Zero	Zero	45	45	1¾	167 @ 1¹¹⁄₃₂	.384	.384	.001-.0025	①	.3430	②

① — Top .001-.003″, bottom .0025-.004″.　② — Top .3425″, bottom .3415″.

GENERATOR AND REGULATOR SPECIFICATIONS

★To polarize generator, reconnect the leads to the regulator; then momentarily connect a jumper wire from the "Gen" to the "Bat" terminals of the regulator.

Year	Generator					Regulator							
	Generator Number	Rotation and Ground Polarity	Rated Cap. Amps.	Gen. Field Ground Location★	Brush Spring Tension, Ounces	Field Current Amperes	Regulator Number	Cutout Relay		Voltage Regulator Setting Volts	Current Regulator Setting Amperes	Current and Voltage Armature Air Gap, Inch
								Voltage to Close Points	Armature Air, Gap, Inch			
1961	1102236	C-N	35	External	28	1.69-1.79	1119253	12.8	.020	14.3	35	.075

ENGINE TIGHTENING SPECIFICATIONS★

★Torque specifications are for clean and lightly lubricated threads only. Dry or dirty threads produce increased friction which prevents accurate measurement of tightness.

Year	Engine	Spark Plugs Ft. Lbs.	Cylinder Head Bolts Ft. Lbs.	Intake Manifold Ft. Lbs.	Exhaust Manifold Ft. Lbs.	Rocker Arm Shaft Bracket Ft. Lbs.	Rocker Arm Cover Ft. Lbs.	Connecting Rod Cap Bolts Ft. Lbs.	Main Bearing Cap Bolts Ft. Lbs.	Flywheel to Crankshaft Ft. Lbs.	Vibration Damper or Pulley Ft. Lbs.
1961	All	12-17	45-55	25-30	18-24	45-55	3-5	30-35	50-60①	85-95	140-160

① — Rear bearing cap 70 ft. lbs.

WHEEL ALIGNMENT SPECIFICATIONS

Year	Model	Caster, Degrees		Camber, Degrees		Toe-in, Inch	Toe-out on Turns, Degrees①		Steering Axis Inclination②
		Limits	Desired	Limits	Desired		Outer Wheel	Inner Wheel	
1961	All	— ½ to — 1½	— 1	0 to + ¾	+ ⅜	¹⁄₁₆	17¾	20	7½ @ 0 Camber

① — Incorrect toe-out, when other adjustments are correct, indicates bent steering arms.
② — Incorrect angle with correct camber indicates bent suspension arms or steering knuckle support.

REAR AXLE AND BRAKE CYLINDER SPECIFICATIONS

Year	Model	Ring Gear & Pinion Backlash, Inch	Drive Pinion Adjustment	Drive Pinion Bearing Preload, Inch Lbs.	Drive Pinion Bearing Adjustment	Axle Shaft End Play, Inch	Hydraulic Cylinder Bore Sizes, Inch		Master Cylinder
							Wheel Cylinder		
							Front	Rear	
1961	All	.007-.009	Shim	24-35①	Shim	None	1	⅞	1

① — For used bearings 15 to 25 inch lbs.

COOLING SYSTEM & CAPACITY DATA

Year	Model	Cooling System Data					Fuel Tank Gals.	Engine Oil			Transmissions			Rear Axle Pints
		Quarts No Heater	Quarts With Heater	Rad. Cap Relief Pressure	Thermostat Opening Temp. ①	②		Refill Qts.③	Summer Grade	Winter Grade	Std. Pints	With Over-drive Pints	Auto-matic Qts.	
1961	All	11	12½	15	170	...	16	4	20	10W	2.1	None	6	2.1

①—For permanent type anti-freeze.   ②—For alcohol type anti-freeze.   ③—Add one quart with filter change.

SERIAL NUMBER LOCATION
Left Front Door Pillar

ENGINE NUMBER LOCATION
Front of Right Cylinder Head

1961

Engine Section

ENGINE, REPLACE

When necessary to remove the engine from the car, disconnect the following items and raise the body off the engine and front suspension.
1. Front exhaust pipe from rear exhaust pipe.
2. Speedometer cable, front of propeller shaft and shift linkage from transmission.
3. Clutch and clutch equalizer on manual shift cars.
4. Wires, pipes, linkage, hoses, etc.
5. Stabilizer brackets from frame rail.
6. Front brake hoses.
7. Steering column from gear and raise up into steering column.
8. Remove air cleaner and carburetor cover.
9. Place a block of wood between front cross bar and front of engine oil pan. Remove rear transmission mount cross support and support rear of transmission with stand.
10. With front wheels on floor, remove the three isolation mount bolts and carefully raise body off engine and transmission, using care not to let suspension tip.
11. Reverse removal procedure to install.

CYLINDER READ, REPLACE

1. Drain cooling system.
2. Remove intake manifold.
3. Disconnect exhaust pipe.
4. Remove rocker arm cover.
5. When removing right cylinder head, remove generator rear mounting bracket bolt. Also remove ground straps at front and rear of head.
6. To remove left head, remove power

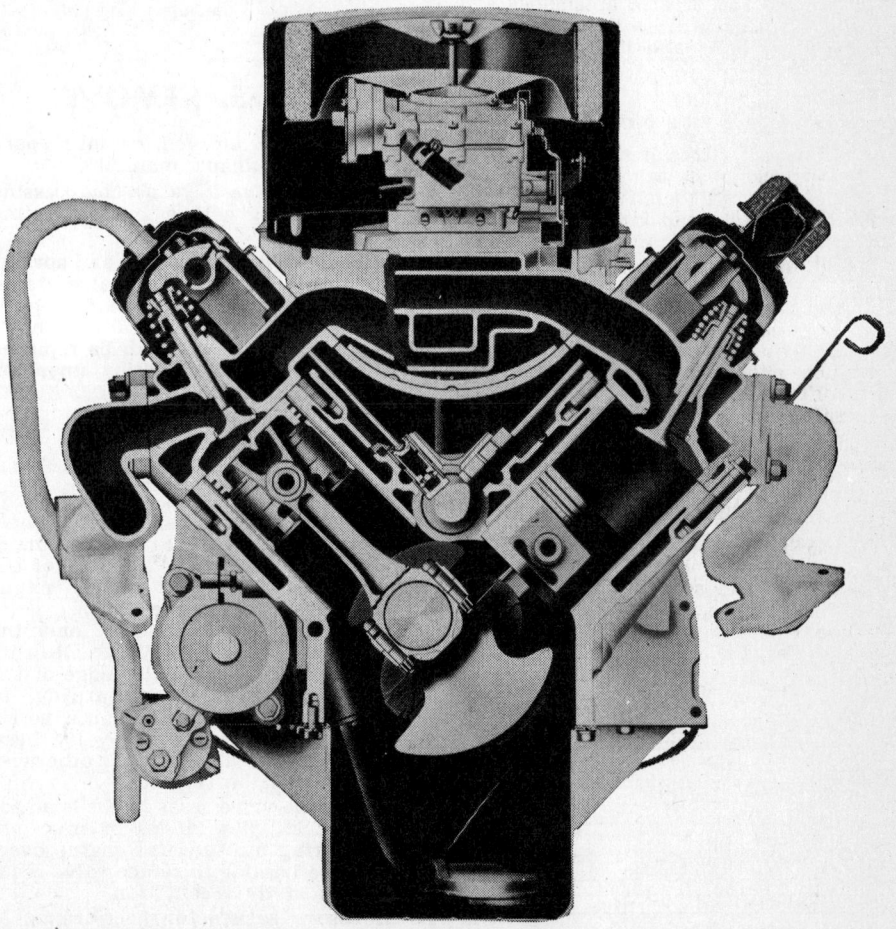

Cross section of engine

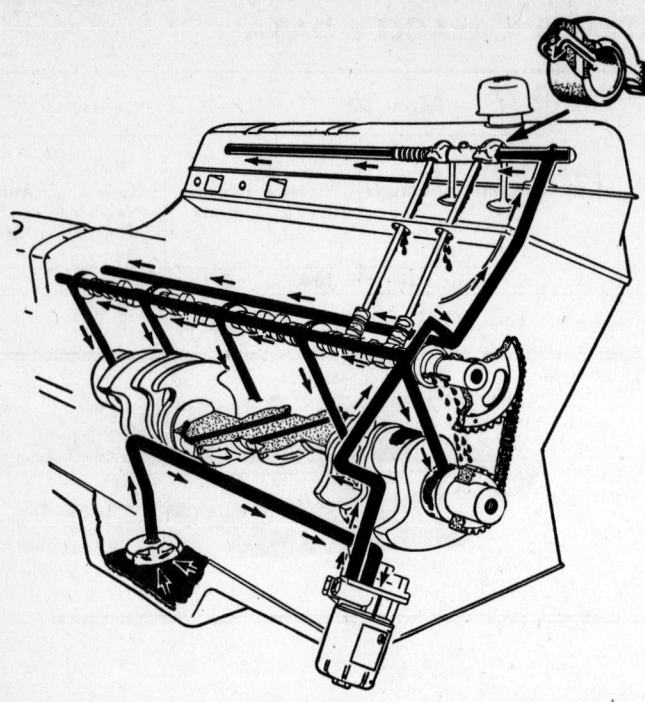

Engine lubrication

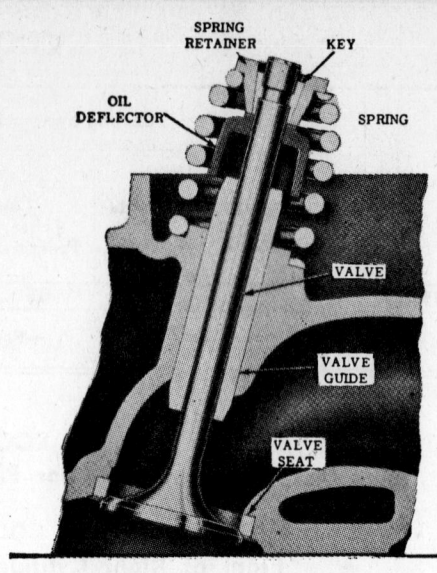

Fig. 2 Valve assembly

steering belt and two pump bracket bolts from head.

7. Remove rocker arm assemblies and push rods.
8. Remove bolts and lift off cylinder heads.

Service Note

If equipped with a heater, the following steps should be taken when removing the right cylinder head:

1. Remove all head bolts except rear rocker arm shaft bracket bolt (blower motor prevents).
2. Loosen rear rocker arm bracket bolt and raise shaft assembly from head and remove push rods except No. 16.
3. Lift No. 16 push rod to within one inch of blower case and tape to rocker shaft.
4. Lift head, rocker shaft and exhaust manifold off dowel pins and move forward to clear blower case.

Installation

All cylinder head bolt threads must be coated with a suitable sealer. Torque head bolts in the sequence shown in Fig. 1 and to the specifications listed in the *Engine Tightening Chart*. Head gaskets should also be coated with a suitable sealer.

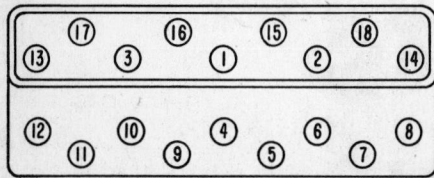

Fig. 1 Cylinder head tightening sequence

VALVE ARRANGEMENT

Front to rear . . . . . E-I-E-I-I-E-I-E

VALVES, REMOVE

1. With head removed, remove spark plugs and exhaust manifold.
2. Remove valve keys by compressing valve spring with a suitable spring compressor.
3. Remove spring retainers and springs and oil deflectors from valve stems. Remove valves from head, Fig. 2. Keep valves in a board with numbered holes so they can be replaced in their original position upon reassembly.

VALVES, GRIND

Clean the valve with a wire wheel brush, making sure that all carbon is removed from the top and bottom of the heads as well as the gum which might have accumulated on the stems.

In refacing valves, take off only the minimum of metal required to clean up the valve faces. If the outer edge of the valve becomes too thin or sharp due to excessive grinding, the valve must be replaced. In other words, the valve head margin must be at least $\frac{1}{32}$", otherwise the valve must be replaced.

Inspect the valve seats in the head for burns, cracks, pits, ridges or improper angle. During any general engine overhaul, it is advisable to reface valve seats regardless of their condition.

To assure satisfactory service, it is necessary that the valve seat widths be maintained at $\frac{1}{16}$".

VALVE GUIDES

Clean the valve guides with a wire guide brush and check the clearance between valve stems and guides carefully. The standard clearances are given in the *Valve Specifications* table.

Excessive clearance between valve stems and guides will cause improper seating and burned valves. When there is too much clearance between intake valve stems and guides, there is a tendency to draw oil vapor through the guide on the suction stroke, causing excessive oil consumption, fouled spark plugs and poor low speed performance.

To check valve stem-to-guide clearance, take a new valve and place it in each valve guide and feel the clearance by moving the valve stem from side to side. If this check shows excessive clearance, it will be necessary to replace the valve guide.

If the clearance is not excessive when checking with a new valve but is excessive when checked with the old valve, the old valve stem is worn and a new valve must be installed.

If it is necessary to replace valve guides, use a suitable driver to drive them out of the cylinder head. If suitable tools are not available, guides can be pulled out by using a piece of pipe together with a long bolt and washers.

Before removing guides, carefully measure the portion of the guide that protrudes from the cylinder head and install the new guides accordingly.

After the new guides have been installed, they should be reamed to provide the clearance given in the *Valve Specifications* table.

Valve guides are identified as follows:

Standard . . . . . . No Groove
.001" oversize . . 2 Grooves
.010" oversize . . . .1 Groove
.011" oversize . . 3 Grooves

Standard guides should be replaced with .001" oversize guides and .010" guides should be replaced with .011" oversize.

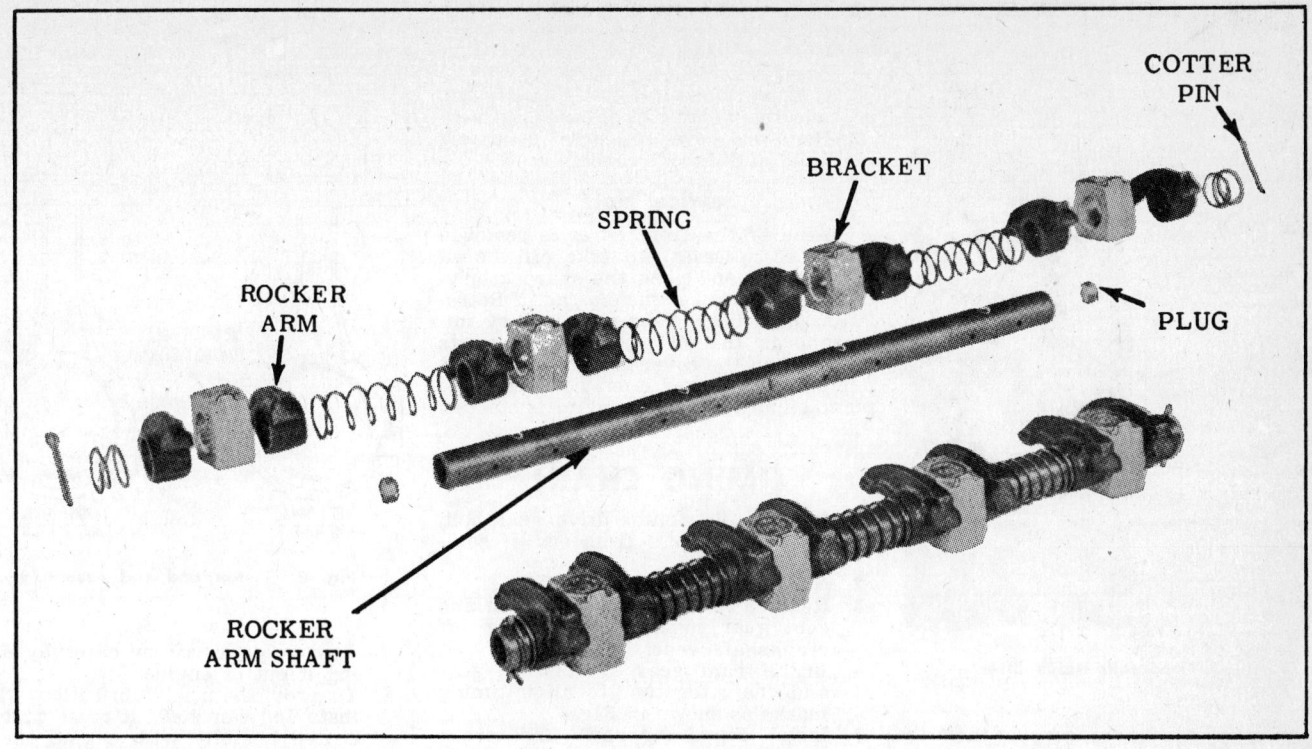

Fig. 3   Rocker arm shaft assembly

ROCKER ARMS

1. With rocker arm shaft assembly removed from head, remove cotter pins from ends of shaft.
2. Remove springs, arms and brackets from shaft.
3. If necessary to remove shaft end plug, punch hole in plug, then pry plug from end of shaft.
4. When assembling, refer to Fig. 3 and lubricate frictional surfaces of rocker arms and shaft with engine oil.
5. When installing, be sure to position rocker arm shaft over dowel in head.

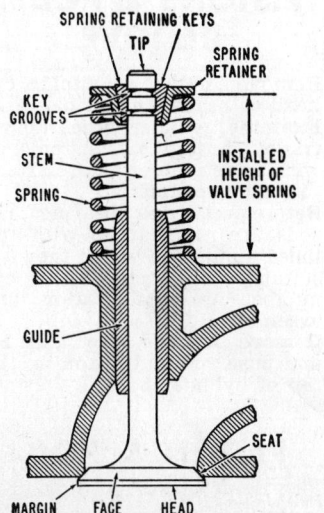

Fig. 4   Checking valve spring installed height

VALVE SPRING INSTALLED HEIGHT

When valves and seats are reground the position of the valve in the head is changed so as to lessen the valve spring tension. Without proper valve spring tension the valve does not seat long enough or it may not seat completely. Since the valve is cooled by transferring heat from the valve head to the seat and thence to the coolant, improper valve spring tension will cause worn, pitted and distorted valves which result in loss of compression and power as well as poor gasoline mileage.

When valves, springs, retainers and locks are installed, measure the assembled height of the valve springs from the surface of the cylinder head spring pad to the underside of the spring retainer as shown in Fig. 4. If the assembled height is greater than the dimension given in the *Valve Specifications Chart*, install a spacer or shim of proper thickness between cylinder head spring pad and spring to bring the assembled height to specifications.

Do not install spacers unless necessary. Excessive use of spacers will result in overstressing valve springs and overloading camshaft lobes which could lead to spring breakage and worn camshaft lobes.

VALVE SPRING TESTING

Check valve spring tension on a suitable spring testing fixture if one is available. Fig. 5. If a fixture is not available, at least check the free length of each spring by standing it alongside a new spring. Any spring that does not conform to the pressure specifications in the *Valve Specifications* table within 10 percent should be replaced. Likewise any spring that stands shorter than the new spring used for comparison should be discarded.

HYDRAULIC VALVE LIFTERS

Failure of an hydraulic valve lifter is generally caused by an inadequate oil supply or dirt. An air leak at the intake side of the oil pump or too much oil in the engine will cause air bubbles in the

Fig. 5   Testing valve spring pressure

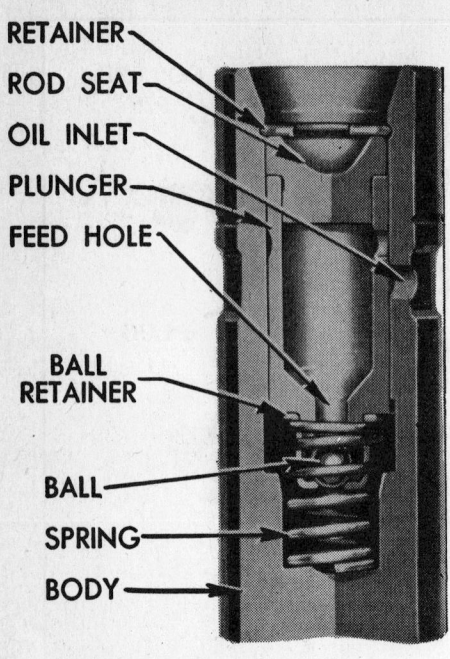

RETAINER
ROD SEAT
OIL INLET
PLUNGER
FEED HOLE

BALL RETAINER

BALL
SPRING
BODY

Fig. 6 Hydraulic valve lifter

oil supply to the lifters, causing them to collapse. This is a probable cause of trouble if several lifters fail to function, but air in the oil is an unlikely cause of failure of a single unit.

The valve lifters may be lifted out of their bores after removing the rocker arms and push rods. Adjustable pliers with taped jaws may be used to remove lifters that are stuck due to varnish, carbon, etc.

To disassemble, press down on the center of the push rod cup. Using a pointed tool, remove lock wire from the groove while holding cup down. Invert lifter and slide out push rod cup, plunger, ball retainer and spring.

To assemble, place the ball on its seat in the lower end of the plunger while holding the plunger upside down. Position the ball retainer and spring over ball and end of plunger. Lower the body over the plunger. Turn the assembly right side up and fill the plunger with clean engine oil. Jiggle the ball with a small piece of wire until oil drains out of plunger into the body and trapped air is released from the body. Refill the plunger with oil, place the push rod cup on the plunger and position the lock wire over the cup, locking it in its groove, Fig. 6.

VALVE TIMING DATA

Year	Model	Intake Opens①	Intake Closes②	Exhaust Opens③	Exhaust Closes④
1961	All	22	58	60	20

① —Degrees before top dead center.
② —Degrees after bottom dead center.
③ —Degrees before bottom dead center.
④ —Degrees after top dead center.

TIMING CASE COVER

1. To remove cover, drain cooling system and disconnect water hoses and oil pressure switch wire.

2. Remove all belts, crankshaft and fan pulleys.
3. Remove distributor cap, vacuum hose, generator and bracket.
4. Remove fuel pump hoses, fuel pump and two front oil pan bolts.
5. Remove cover-to-block attaching bolts and remove cover.

Service Note

Whenever the front cover is removed it will be necessary to take off the oil pump cover and pack the space around the pump gears *completely full* of Petrolatum (vaseline). This step is very important as the oil pump may lose its prime when the cover is removed. If the pump is not packed it may not begin to pump oil as soon as the engine is started.

TIMING CHAIN

1. Remove distributor drive gear bolt, washer and gear from end of camshaft.
2. Remove fuel pump eccentric.
3. Remove crankshaft gear, chain and cam gear together by prying off crankshaft gear.
4. Install cam gear, crankshaft gear and chain together to align timing marks as shown in Fig. 7.
5. Install remaining parts and torque distributor drive gear bolt to 40-45 ft. lbs. Then install oil slinger and cover.

CAMSHAFT

1. To remove camshaft, remove grille, radiator, front cover, timing chain and gears, and intake manifold.
2. Remove rocker arm assembly, push rods and valve lifters.

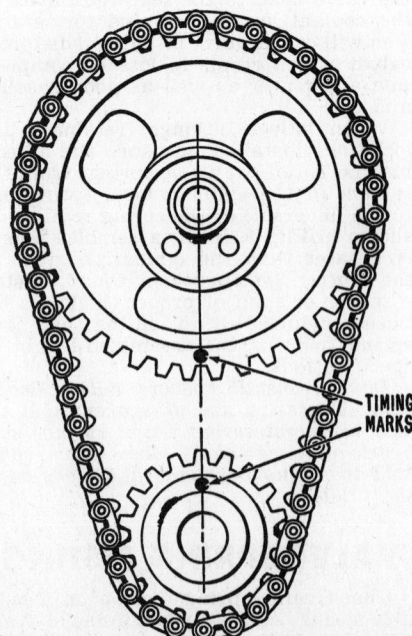

TIMING MARKS

Fig. 7 Timing marks aligned for correct valve timing

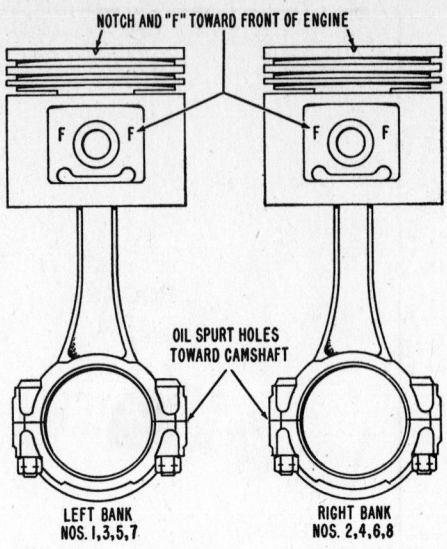

NOTCH AND "F" TOWARD FRONT OF ENGINE

OIL SPURT HOLES TOWARD CAMSHAFT

LEFT BANK NOS. 1,3,5,7

RIGHT BANK NOS. 2,4,6,8

Fig. 8 Piston and rod assembly

3. Remove camshaft by carefully sliding it out of engine.
4. To provide initial lubrication when installing camshaft, it must first be coated liberally with engine oil.

CAMSHAFT BEARINGS

The camshaft bearings must be replaced in complete sets. All bearings must be removed before any can be installed. The bearings may be removed by driving them rearward out of their bores with the exception of No. 5. This bearing must be removed by drilling a $\frac{3}{16}$" hole in the block at the bearing bore. Do not drill through the bearing. With a small punch, dent the bearing enough to allow it to be removed out the front of the bore.

When installing the bearings, install No. 5 first, then 4, 3, 2 and 1. Make sure that all oil passages are aligned.

PISTONS & RODS, REMOVE

1. Remove intake manifold, cylinder head or heads, and oil pan.
2. Examine cylinder bores above ring travel. If ridge exists, remove ridge with ridge reamer before attempting to remove pistons.
3. Before removing bearing caps, if rods are not marked with the cylinder number in which they operate, suitably mark them with the cylinder number for identification upon reassembly.
4. Remove bearing cap and bearing and push rod and piston up through top of cylinder bore.

PISTON & ROD, ASSEMBLE

Assemble pistons and rods as indicated in Fig. 8.

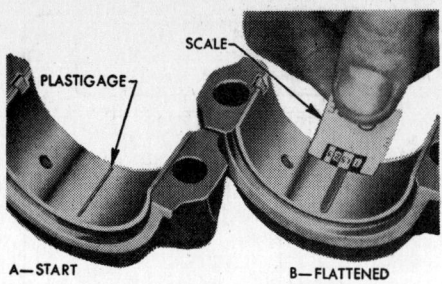

Fig. 9 Checking bearing clearance with Plastigage

PISTONS

New pistons are furnished in standard size and .010" oversize. Since these are nominal or basic sizes it is important that new pistons be measured to insure proper fit. All new pistons are provided with selectively fitted piston pins, therefore, it is important to check the fit of the pin in connecting rod.

If the equipment required to measure fit of pistons in cylinder is not available, a fit can be satsfactorily checked by using a ½" x .0015" feeler ribbon and spring scale. When fitting pistons to cylinders by this method, the fit should be checked with the piston in the lower half of the cylinder, and both cylinder wall and piston clean and dry. The feeler ribbon should require a pull (in pounds listed in the chart) when drawn from between the piston (without rings) and cylinder wall.

If the pistons are to be reused with new rings, remove the carbon from the ring grooves. A special tool is available for this work but a satisfactory job can be done by breaking an old piston ring, filing the broken end to a sharp, square edge and using it to scrape out the carbon. Soak the piston in cleaning solvent to loosen any carbon residue. Clean out the loosened carbon, being careful not to cut away any piston material.

Clean out the oil return holes with a drill just large enough to fill the holes. Hold the drill in a tap wrench and make sure the drill does not remove any metal from the piston.

Rinse the piston in solvent and wipe off the carbon on the sides of the piston. *Never use a wire brush to clean a piston* as the brush will round off the edges of the ring lands. Pistons showing scuffed or scored skirts should be scrapped. Examine the ring lands carefully for cracks. If the piston is in the least bit doubtful, it should be discarded.

PISTON PINS

The correct piston pin fit in the piston is .0003" to .0005" loose. If the pin-to-piston clearance is to the high limit (.0005") the pin can be inserted in the piston with very little hand pressure. The pin will fall through the piston by its own weight. The pin is a press fit in the connecting rod.

PISTON RINGS

When new piston rings are installed without reboring cylinders, the glazed cylinder walls should be slightly dulled, but without increasing the bore diameter. This is done with a "Glazebuster" or with a hone equipped with the finest grade of stones.

New piston rings must be checked for clearance in piston grooves and for gap in cylinder bores. Cylinder bores and piston grooves must be clean, dry and free of carbon and burrs.

Check the clearance of each ring in its piston groove by installing the ring and then inserting feeler gauges *under* the ring. Any wear that occurs in the piston groove forms a step or ridge at the inner portion of the lower land. If gauges are inserted above the ring, the ring may rest on the step instead of on the worn portion of the lower land, and a false measurement of clearance will result.

If the piston grooves have worn to the extent that relatively high steps or ridges exist on the lower lands, the piston should be replaced because the steps will interfere with the operation of new rings and the ring clearances will be excessive. Piston rings are not furnished in oversize widths to compensate for ring groove wear.

To check the end gaps of rings, place the ring in the cylinder in which it will be used. Square it in the bore by tapping with the lower end of the piston, then measure the gap with feeler gauges. If necessary to increase the gap, file the ends of rings carefully with a smooth file.

ROD BEARINGS

Connecting rod bearings can be replaced without removing the rod assembly by removing the cap and replacing the upper and lower bearing halves. The clearance between the bearing and crankshaft can be measured with Plastigage as follows:

1. Remove bearing cap and wipe oil from crankshaft and bearing.
2. With crankpin at approximately bottom dead center, place a piece of Plastigage in the center of the cap.
3. Reinstall cap and tighten to the torque value given in the *Engine*

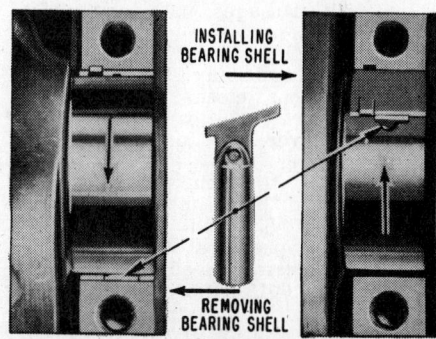

Fig. 10 Tool for removing upper main bearing shells

INSTALLING BEARING SHELL

REMOVING BEARING SHELL

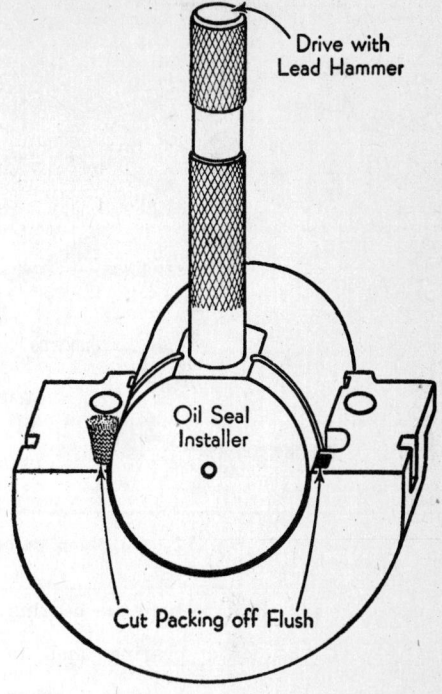

Drive with Lead Hammer

Oil Seal Installer

Cut Packing off Flush

Fig. 11 Install rear main bearing oil seal

Tightening Specifications table.
4. Remove the bearing cap and determine bearing clearance by comparing the width of the flattened Plastigage with the graduation on the Plastigage envelope, Fig. 9. The number withing the graduation on the envelope indicates the clearance in thousandths of an inch. If clearance is excessive, replace the bearing.

MAIN BEARINGS

Caution—Main bearing clearance can be checked with Plastigage in the same manner described for rod bearings. If bearings are measured with the engine in the chassis, the crankshaft must be supported in order to take up clearance between the upper bearing insert and crankshaft journal. This can be done by tightening bearing caps of adjacent bearings with .005" to .015" cardboard, (such as a calling card) between lower bearing shell and journal. Use extreme care when this is done to avoid unnecessary strain on the crankshaft or bearings or a false reading may be obtained. Do not rotate crankshaft while Plastigage is installed. *Be sure to remove cardboard.* To Install new bearings, proceed as follows:

1. Remove bearing cap and worn lower shell.
2. Rotate crankshaft in normal direction to turn upper bearing shell out of crankcase. Use a cotter pin with a flattened head or the special tool made for the purpose in the crankshaft oil hole to contact the bearing and force it out, Fig. 10.
3. Place a new upper shell on the crankshaft journal with the locating notch in the correct position and

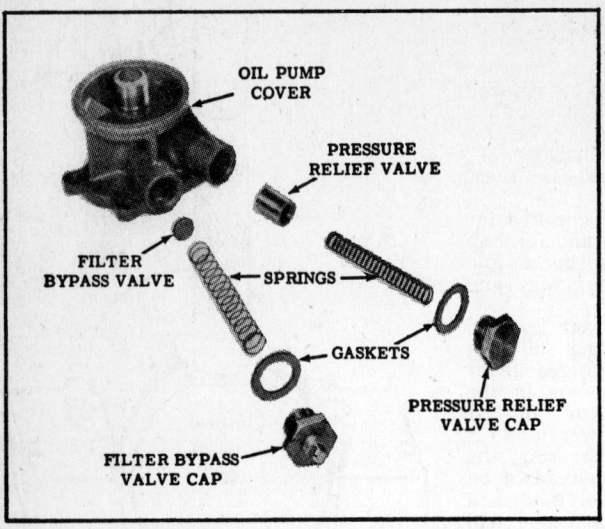

Fig. 12   Oil pump assembly

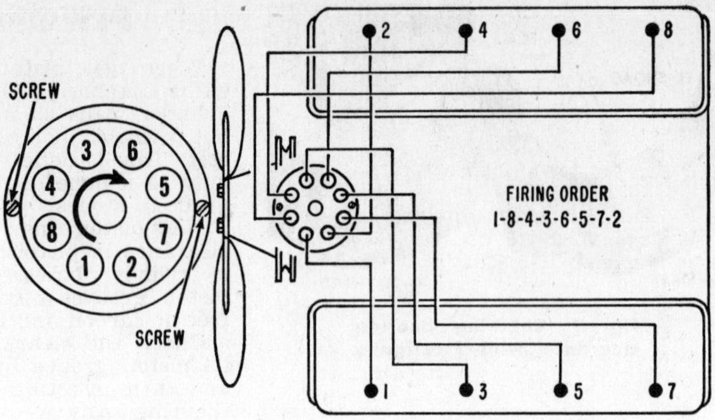

Fig. 13   Ignition details

rotate the shaft to turn the bearing in place.

4. Install the lower bearing shell in the cap.
5. Tighten all cap nuts to the torque value given in the *Engine Tightening Specifications* table.

CRANKSHAFT OIL SEAL

A braided oil seal is pressed into the upper and lower grooves behind the rear main bearing. Directly in front of this seal is an oil slinger which deflects the oil back into the oil pan. Should the braided seal require replacement, the installation of the lower half is accomplished as follows:

With the bearing cap and lower bearing half removed, install a new seal so that both ends protrude above the cap. Tap the seal down into position or roll it snugly in its groove with a smooth rounded tool, Fig. 11. Then cut off the protruding ends of the seal with a sharp knife or razor blade.

Installing Upper Seal

Although the usual practice is to remove the crankshaft when the upper half of the seal is to be replaced it is possible to do the job without removing the crankshaft as follows:

To remove the seal, use needle-nose pliers to grasp the end of the seal which is most accessible. Pull the seal downward while rotating the crankshaft slowly in the direction that the seal is being removed.

To install the new seal, fasten a length of wire or strong string such as fishing line securely to one end of the new seal. See that the point of fastening is not bulky and that it is not over ⅜″ from the end of the seal. Coat the seal with Lubriplate. Pass the free end of the wire or string up over the crankshaft at the point where the seal is to be installed. Then exert a firm, steady pull on the wire or string and at the same time rotate the crankshaft slowly in the direction of the pull. This will

help to move the seal into position. When the installation is completed, trim the ends of the seal flush with the engine block.

OIL PAN, REPLACE

1. Remove dipstick and drain oil.
2. Disconnect steering idler arm from relay rod.
3. Remove cover on front of lower flywheel housing and remove pan bolts.
4. On some types of lifts, it may be necessary to drop the oil intake into the pan before removing pan. The crankshaft should be positioned so the counterweights do not interfere with the pan's removal.

OIL PUMP REPAIRS

1. To remove pump, disconnect oil pressure switch.
2. Clean all dirt from pump-to-front cover joint; also around oil filter joint.
3. Remove oil filter and six pump cover-to-front cover screws.
4. Remove pump cover carefully as idler gear may fall out. Slide out idler and pump drive gears.

Inspection

1. Disassemble pump as indicated in Fig. 12. Wash all parts and blow out all passages with compressed air.
2. Inspect all parts for scoring. Small imperfections may be cleaned up with crocus cloth. *Do not break edges of valve.*
3. Check cover bore for cracks, nicks or warping.
4. Clearance between pressure relief valve and bore should be .0015-.0035″. Too much clearance can affect oil pressure at idle.
5. Check clearance of gears which shoud be .0015-.0075″.

Assembly

1. Install filter by-pass valve into output passage bore (passage with in-

side diameter ribs) seating squarely in bottom of passage.
2. Install remaining parts as shown in illustration. Tighten caps to 30-35 ft. lbs.
3. When assembled, fill gear pocket completely with petrolatum and force into every cavity of gear pocket; also between teeth of gears. *This step is very important. To assist in instant priming when engine is started, unless pump is packed as directed, it may not prime itself when engine is started.*

RADIATOR

1. Drain cooling system and remove upper radiator bracket.
2. Remove upper and lower hoses.
3. If equipped with Hydramatic, disconnect and cap cooler lines.
4. If equipped with air conditioning, loosen fan shroud and move rearward.
5. Loosen lower radiator support bolts and move supports rearward to allow radiator to be removed.

WATER PUMP

1. Drain cooling system and remove heater and lower hose from pump.
2. Loosen pulley belts and remove fan and pulley.
3. Remove nine pump-to-front cover bolts and take off pump. *Water pump is serviced only as an assembly.*

DISTRIBUTOR, REPLACE

1. Disconnect primary wire from coil and remove distributor cap. If necessary to remove wires from cap, mark the position for No. 1 cylinder on the cap tower and reassemble as shown in Fig. 13.
2. Remove vacuum hose line from vacuum advance unit.
3. Remove hex head bolt and holddown clamp.
4. Mark position of rotor; then pull distributor up until rotor just stops turning clockwise and note the position of the rotor at this point.
5. Remove distributor from front cover.

Installation

1. If engine was not disturbed while distributor was off, rotate rotor to same position as that at removal.
2. Install distributor into block and align distributor drive gear with oil pump drive shaft and camshaft gear. This can be done by rotating distributor drive shaft to first pick up oil pump drive shaft and then engage cam gear and distributor drive gear so that rotor is positioned as it was before removal after gear is engaged.
3. Complete the installation and check ignition timing.

IGNITION TIMING

Correct ignition timing exists when the timing mark on the vibration damper *(see Tune Up Chart)* is aligned with the timing indicator with engine running and with No. 1 piston up on its compression stroke.

STARTER, REPLACE

1. Disconnect battery positive cable.
2. Disconnect positive cable and starter cable from junction block and solenoid switch wire from chassis wiring harness.
3. Unfasten and remove starter from engine while sliding battery cable loom through cable support tube.

MUFFLERS & PIPES

Replacing any of the exhaust system components is a fairly obvious operation. However, before tightening any part of the system, align for adequate clearance between the body.

Carburetor Section

Performance Complaints

Flooding, stumble on acceleration or other performance complaints are in many instances caused by the presence of dirt, water or other foreign matter in the carburetor. To aid in diagnosing the cause of the complaint, the carburetor should be carefully removed from the engine without draining the fuel from the bowl. The contents of the fuel bowl may then be examined for contamination as the carburetor is disassembled.

Check the fuel in the bowl for contamination by dirt, water, gum or other foreign matter. A magnet moved through the fuel in the bowl will pick up and identify any iron oxide dust that may have caused intake needle and seat leakage.

Inspect gasketed surfaces between body and air horn. Small nicks or burrs should be smoothed down to eliminate air or fuel leakage. On carburetors having a vacuum piston, be especially particular when inspecting the top surface of the inner wall of the bowl around the vacuum piston passage. A poor seal at this location may contribute to a "cutting-out" on turns complaint.

Fill the carburetor bowl with clean fuel before installing on manifold. This will help prevent dirt trapped in the fuel system from being dislodged by the free flow of fuel as the carburetor is primed. The operation of the floats and intake needle and seats may be checked under pressure if a fuel pump is used at the bench to fill the carburetor bowl. Operate the throttle several times and visually check the discharge from pump jets.

Poor Mileage and Engine Loading Complaints

Cases of poor mileage and engine loading may be due in many instances to sluggish choke valve opening during cold driveaway, caused by insufficient vacuum in choke housing, a plugged or restricted heat pipe or inlet in choke cover. To check for this condition, have engine warm and running at slow idle. Remove choke heat pipe and hold a finger over the heat inlet hole (hole is on choke housing on some carburetors). If there is little or no vacuum pull on the finger, check the choke housing for gasket leaks or plugged vacuum passages. If these are OK, check choke vacuum passages in carburetor between choke housing and manifold.

Dirty or Rusty Choke Housing

In cases where it is found that the interior of the choke housing is dirty, gummed or rusty while the carburetor itself is comparatively clean, look for a punctured or eroded manifold heat tube (if one is used).

Manifold Heat Control Valve

An engine equipped with a manifold heat control valve can operate with the valve struck in either the open or closed position. Because of this, an inoperative valve is frequently overlooked at vehicle lubrication or tune-up.

A valve stuck in the "heat-off" position can result in slow warm up, deposits in combustion chamber, carburetor icing, flat spots during acceleration, low gas mileage and spark plug fouling.

A valve stuck in the "heat-on" position can result in power loss, engine knocking, sticking or burned valves and spark plug burning.

To prevent the possibility of a stuck valve, check and lubricate the valve each time the vehicle is lubricated or tuned-up. Check the operation of the valve manually. To lubricate the valve, place a few drops of penetrating oil on the valve shaft where it passes through the manifold. Then move the valve up and down a few times to work the oil in. *Do not use engine oil to lubricate the valve as it will leave a residue which hampers valve operation.*

ROCHESTER CARBURETOR ADJUSTMENTS

| Year | Carburetor Model | Idle Adjustments | | | | Float Level | | Float Drop | | Pump Rod Setting | Choke Unloader Setting | Choke Setting |
		Mixture Screws Turns Open	Hot Idle Speed In Drive	Fast Idle Speed	Dashpot Plunger Clearance	Primary	Secondary	Primary	Secondary			
1961	2GC-7016114	1½	500	①	None	③	None	④	None	⑤	⑥	Index
	2GC-7016115	1½	500	①	.020②	③	None	④	None	⑤	⑥	Index

ROCHESTER NOTES

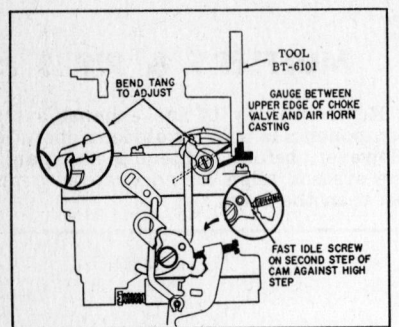

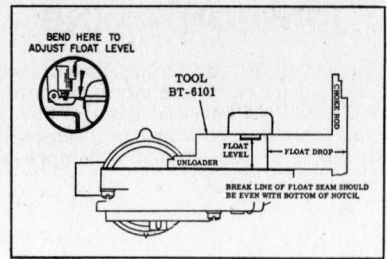

Fig. ③—2GC float level.

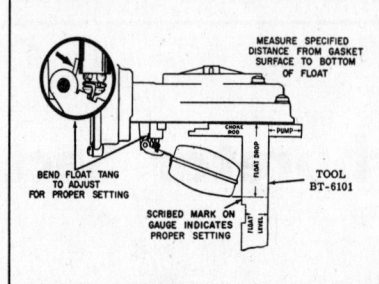

Fig. ④—2GC float drop.

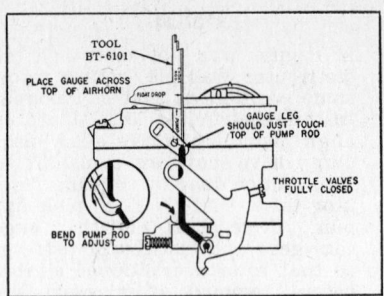

Fig. ⑤—Place pump rod in outer hole. With throttle valves completely closed, place gauge across top of air horn casting with leg of gauge pointing downward toward top of pump rod. Bend pump rod until top of pump rod just touches edge of gauge leg.

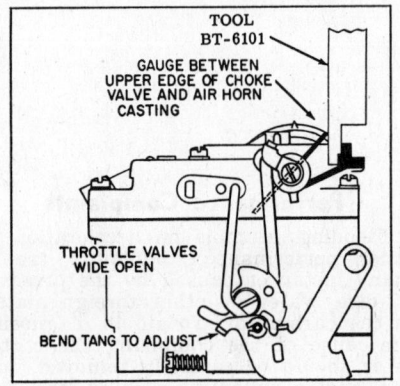

Fig. ①—Fast idle adjustment is not required if hot idle speed is correctly set and choke rod properly adjusted. To adjust choke rod, turn idle screw in until it just contacts second step of fast idle cam. With screw resting on second step and against high step, bend choke lever tang as necessary to admit small end of gauge between upper edge of choke valve and air horn wall.

②—Rotate fast idle cam so that idle screw rests on top of highest step of cam. Clearance between plunger and stop screw should be as specified. Turn stop screw in or out as required.

Fig. ⑥—With throttle valves wide open, large end of gauge should just go between upper edge of choke valve and inner wall of air horn. To adjust, bend tang on throttle lever.

Clutch Transmission Section

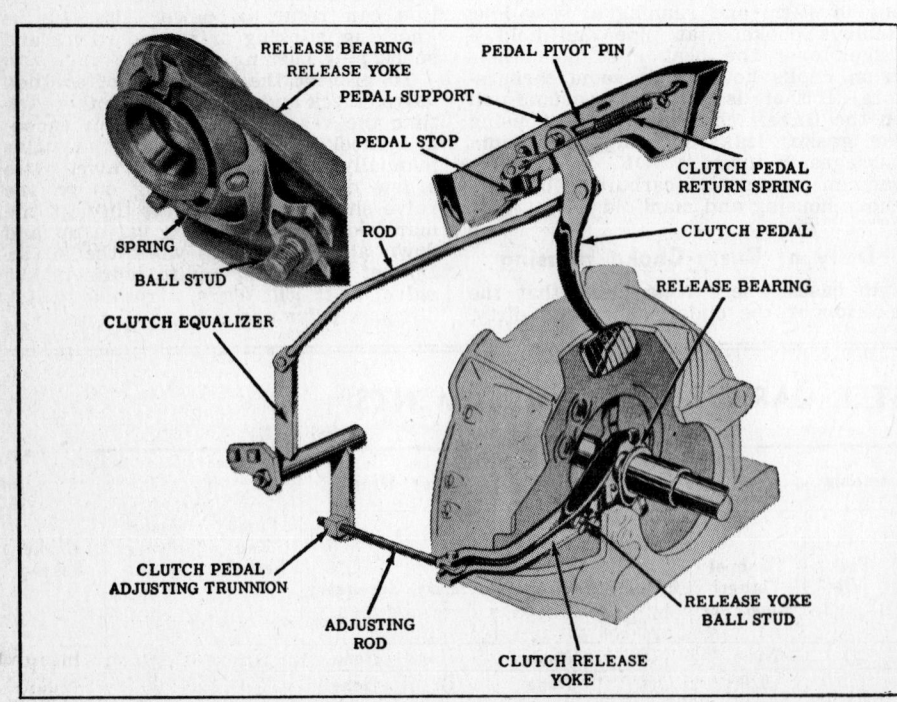

Fig. 1 Clutch mechanism

CLUTCH PEDAL, ADJUST

1. Disconnect lower clutch control rod from equalizer, Fig. 1.
2. Adjust lower clutch control rod in or out of the trunnion nut to obtain ⅞" to 1" free travel of the clutch pedal.
3. Check free travel at the clutch pedal pad with the lower clutch control rod connected to the release yoke.

CLUTCH, REPLACE

1. Remove transmission.
2. Remove lower flywheel housing and release bearing.
3. Mark flywheel and clutch cover for reassembly and alternately loosen the six clutch cover attaching bolts two turns at a time to prevent distortion of the cover.
4. Install the clutch in the reverse order of removal and adjust clutch pedal free play.

SHIFT LINKAGE, ADJUST

1. Loosen trunnion nuts at bottom of steering column-to-equalizer and shift lever rods.

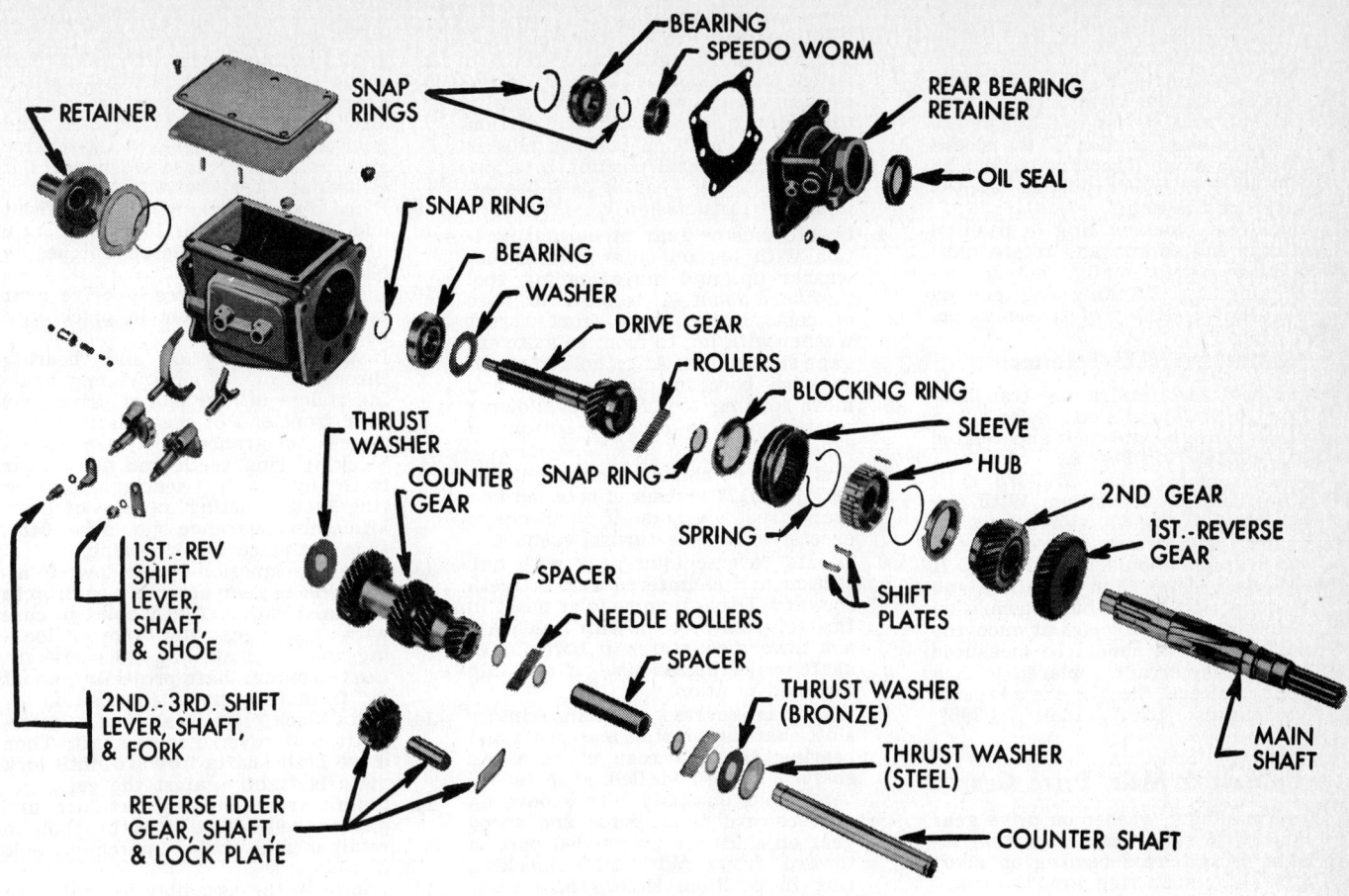

Fig. 2   Exploded view of manual shift transmission

2. Place hand selector lever and shift levers on transmission in neutral.
3. Position shift levers in steering column in alignment with each other as well as horizontal, and tighten trunnion nuts.

TRANSMISSION, REPLACE

1. Disconnect shift rods from levers.
2. Disconnect speedometer cable.
3. Disconnect propeller shaft from transmission companion flange. *Do not let front section of propeller shaft fall loose; move it to one side and tie it to exhaust pipe to avoid damage to center joint ball and seat.*
4. Support rear of engine with high floor stand.
5. Remove rear transmission mount and support bar.
6. Remove four transmission-to-clutch housing bolts.
7. Slide transmission straight back until main drive gear is free of splines in clutch disc.
8. Install transmission in reverse order of removal and adjust shift linkage.

TRANSMISSION REPAIRS

Disassembly

1. Referring to Fig. 2, remove top cover.

2. Remove front bearing retainer.
3. Remove retainer holding speedometer sleeve in rear bearing retainer, and remove driven gear and sleeve.
4. Remove companion flange from rear of transmission.
5. Remove rear bearing retainer.
6. Remove speedometer drive gear.
7. Drive countershaft-idler shaft lock plate from ends of shafts.
8. Drive countershaft rearward with a brass drift until shaft is just free in front shaft bore of case.
9. Using a suitable dummy shaft to hold bearings and thrust washers intact, allow countershaft to drop to bottom of case.
10. Remove main drive gear and bearing, and 14 pilot rollers from rear end of shaft.
11. Remove front bronze blocking ring from synchronizer. Remove snap ring from front of mainshaft.
12. Move mainshaft rearward until rear bearing is free of case. Then move mainshaft to extreme right of case, which will permit the 2nd-3rd shift fork to be removed.
13. Remove mainshaft by sliding shaft rearward through rear of case, at the same time stripping mainshaft as shaft is being withdrawn.
14. Remove 1st-reverse shift shoe from shift shaft. Drive reverse idler shaft

out of case using a brass drift. Lift out reverse idler gear.
15. Lift cluster gear assembly from case.

Reassembly

During reassembly, apply a thin film of transmission lube to all parts. Always use new seals and gaskets. Refer to Fig. 2 and assemble the transmission in the following sequence:

Countershaft Assembly

1. Install dummy shaft or Loading Tool J-8965 in cluster gear.
2. Insert tubular spacer.
3. Hold cluster gear in vertical position and while supporting loading tool from below, insert inner bearing spacer (washer) and place 22 rollers around loading tool, using heavy grease to hold them in place. Insert rollers on opposite end.
4. Install inner rear bronze thrust washer so that lugs engage notches in cluster gear. Install outer rear steel thrust washer. Large front thrust washer should not be installed at this time.

Synchronizer Assembly

1. Install springs solidly in recesses on both ends of synchronizer hub. One end of both springs should be located in same shift plate slot so that

springs will extend in opposite directions from each other. Install shift plate directly over these ends.

2. While holding shift plates in their grooves, slide synchronizer sleeve over hub until detent is felt. The extended tapered portion of the sleeve faces the same direction (front) as the long extended portion at the center of the hub.

3. Place rear blocking ring in position at rear end of hub and rotate until shifting plates match notches in blocking ring. Blocking ring remains free until assembly of transmission.

Shift Levers & Interlock

Insert new seals and apply transmission lube in seals and shaft holes. Then install shift levers, interlock and related parts as indicated in Fig. 2.

When assembled, shift 2nd-3rd shift lever into 2nd speed position. With one end of interlock sleeve against 1st-reverse cam, the clearance between sleeve and 2nd-3rd cam should be .001-.007". If clearance is greater than specified, and if it seems possible that the transmission can be forced into two gears at once, the old interlock sleeve should be measured with a micrometer and replaced with a new, longer sleeve. Sleeves are available in five lengths: 1.287", 1.291", 1.295", 1.299" and 1.303".

Mainshaft & Main Drive Gear

1. Locate slinger washer on drive gear shaft with raised center portion toward front. Press bearing on shaft with outer snap ring groove toward front. Install bearing outer snap ring and thickest shaft snap ring that will properly seat in snap ring groove (three thicknesses are available).

2. Press bearing on rear of mainshaft with outer snap ring groove toward rear. Install bearing outer snap ring

and shaft snap ring.

3. With bearing loading tool in place, and with cluster gear parts in place except front thrust washer, lower cluster gear assembly vertically through top of case with rear section of gear down. Then position cluster gear in horizontal position to allow front of cluster gear to pass projections in transmission case.

4. Locate cluster gear in normal position with lug on outer rear thrust washer up, and move loading tool rearward about ¼" to pass into bore of case. Insert large front thrust washer with lug to front so as to engage slot in case. Align hole in washer with bore in cluster gear and move loading tool forward allowing cluster gear to drop to bottom of case.

5. End play of cluster gear should be .005" to .017" measured between two rear thrust washers. If clearance is excessive, replace thrust washers.

6. Locate reverse idler gear with hub section and chamfered side of teeth forward. Drive reverse idler shaft in through rear of case with lock plate slot toward countershaft bore. Leave shaft projecting about $\frac{1}{16}$" from fully installed position.

7. Insert 1st-reverse shift shoe in its shift shaft and install mainshaft and bearing through rear of case. As shaft is being installed, slide 1st-reverse gear on shaft with groove on gear toward front. Slide 2nd speed gear on shaft with extended portion toward front. With rear blocking ring in position, slide synchronizer on shaft with extended portion of sleeve toward front. Install mainshaft snap ring. Insert 2nd-3rd shift fork in its shaft and engage fork in groove in synchronizer sleeve. With 1st-reverse shoe offset toward front, engage shift shoe in groove on its gear. Move complete mainshaft as-

sembly forward until rear bearing is fully installed in case bore.

8. With synchronizer hub and 2nd speed gear pressed forward against snap ring, there shoud be .003" to .016" end clearance between 2nd gear and front facing of 1st-reverse gear splines. Replace worn parts if clearance is excessive.

9. Place front blocking ring at front end of synchronizer hub and rotate until shift plates match notches in blocking ring.

10. Insert 14 pilot rollers in drive gear pocket, holding them in place with heavy grease.

11. Install drive gear and bearing through front of case, sliding bearing rollers in rear end of drive gear over front end of mainshaft.

12. Check clearance between front blocking ring teeth and drive gear teeth by lightly seating blocking ring on contacting surface of gear. Minimum clearance should be .045". If less replace blocking ring.

13. Turn transmission upside down to allow cluster gear assembly to drop to normal position. Align holes in case with cluster gear and drive out loading tool by installing countershaft. Leave countershaft projecting about $\frac{1}{16}$" from fully installed position.

14. Install lock plate in slots of countershaft and reverse idler shaft. Then drive both shafts forward until lock plate is tight against the case.

14. Install front bearing retainer and gasket, being sure oil return hole in retainer and gasket match oil hole in case.

15. Complete the assembly by installing rear bearing retainer seal, speedometer drive gear, companion flange, speedometer driven gear and sleeve with new O-ring, and driven gear retainer.

16. Install top cover with new gasket and check transmission in all shift positions.

Oldsmobile F-85 Hydra-matic

DESCRIPTION

This transmission, Fig. 1, consists of a fluid coupling combined with a hydraulically controlled automatic transmission having three speeds forward and one reverse. The fluid coupling incorporates a torque multiplier. The coupling also dumps and fills to act as a clutch.

In first speed the fluid coupling and torque multiplier provide an increase of 1.3 times engine torque to the rear unit, thus increasing the overall gear ratio.

In second speed the coupling is emptied and not used. The drive through the transmission is purely mechanical.

In third speed all three members of the fluid coupling are turning at approximately the same speed and, therefore, the torque multiplier is no longer effective. Because of the overall transmission design, the coupling is required to carry only 40% of the engine torque.

During reverse operation the coupling and torque multiplier is again capable of increasing torque output from the engine by 1.3.

MAINTENANCE

Fluid Level

Fluid level in the transmission should be checked every 2000 miles and changed every 26,000 miles. Check the level with the selector lever in "Park" and with engine running at hot idle speed.

Approximately 4 quarts of oil are required to fill the transmission after it has been drained; 5 quarts if the oil pan has been removed; and 7 quarts if the transmission has been overhauled.

When changing the oil, add 4 quarts, start the engine and add oil to bring the level up to the "Full" mark on the dipstick. Use only approved automatic

transmission oil and do not overfill as this causes areation and foaming.

T.V. Lever, Adjust

Referring to Fig. 1A, remove lower T.V. rod from T.V. lever. Place pin of gauge tool indicated in threaded hole in case, ahead of T.V. lever. If hole in lever does not align *within* the hole in gauge, bend T.V. lever as necessary to center the hole within the gauge hole.

Manual Linkage, Adjust

Place selector lever in "N" position. Loosen front and rear lock units on manual lever on transmission. Hold manual rod and shift lever upward so selector lever is positioned against neutral stop. Tighten rear lock nut until it just contacts swivel, then tighten it two additional turns. Tighten front lock nut.

BAND, ADJUST

Every 26,000 miles remove the oil pan and screen and adjust the band. Use an inch-pound torque wrench and an Allen wrench extension to torque the adjusting screw to 20 inch lbs.; then back off screw two turns. Tighten adjusting screw lock nut to 18-20 ft. lbs.

IN CAR REPAIRS

Units that may be removed from an installed transmission are as follows: Limit valve, pressure regulator valve, companion flange, rear oil seal, oil filler pipe, oil pan, and rear bearing retainer.

Units that can be removed after oil pan removal are: Control valve assembly, parking linkage, control valve channel plate, band adjusting screw and nut, accumulator, servo, throttle and manual control levers and related parts, oil cleaner, oil pump intake pipe and "O" ring seals.

Units that can be serviced after extension housing removal are: Speedometer drive gear, governor, reverse blocker valve, and rear bearing.

Hydramatic, Replace

1. Support engine.
2. Remove oil filler tube and breather tube.
3. Disconnect propeller shaft, shift and throttle linkage, cooler lines and speedometer cable.
4. Remove exhaust pipe and transmission rear cross support bar.

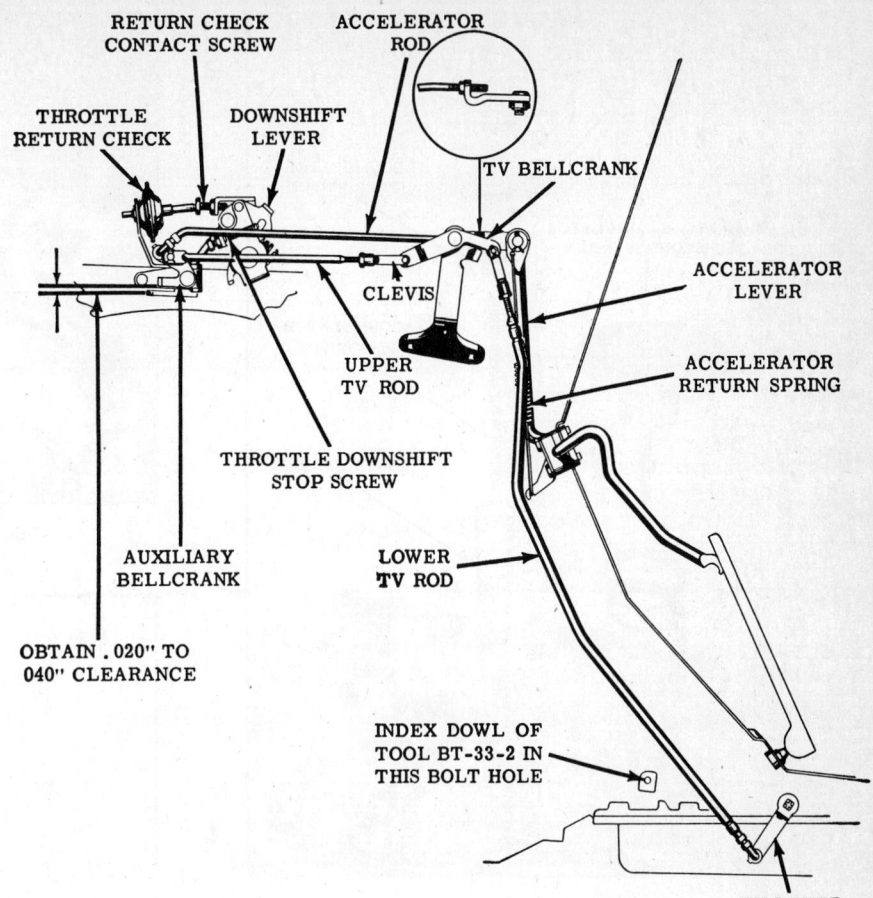

Fig. 1A   Throttle linkage

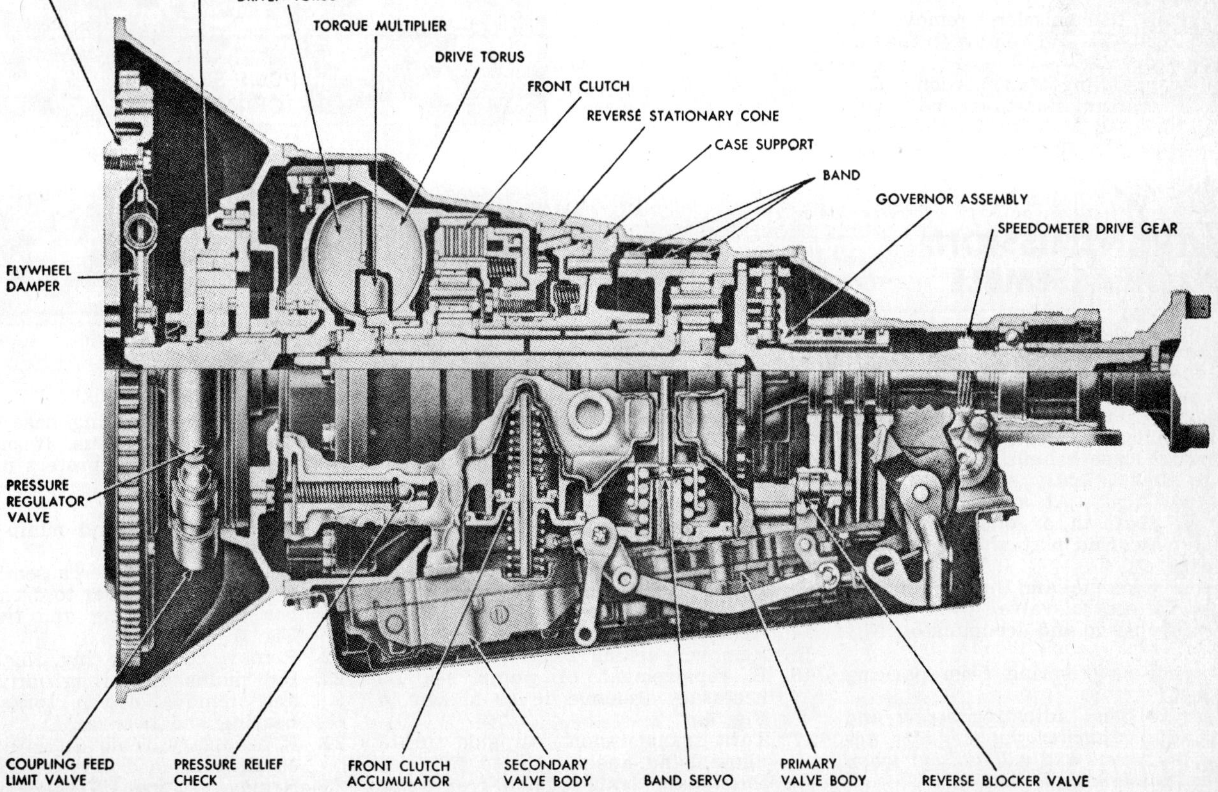

Fig. 1   Cross section of transmission

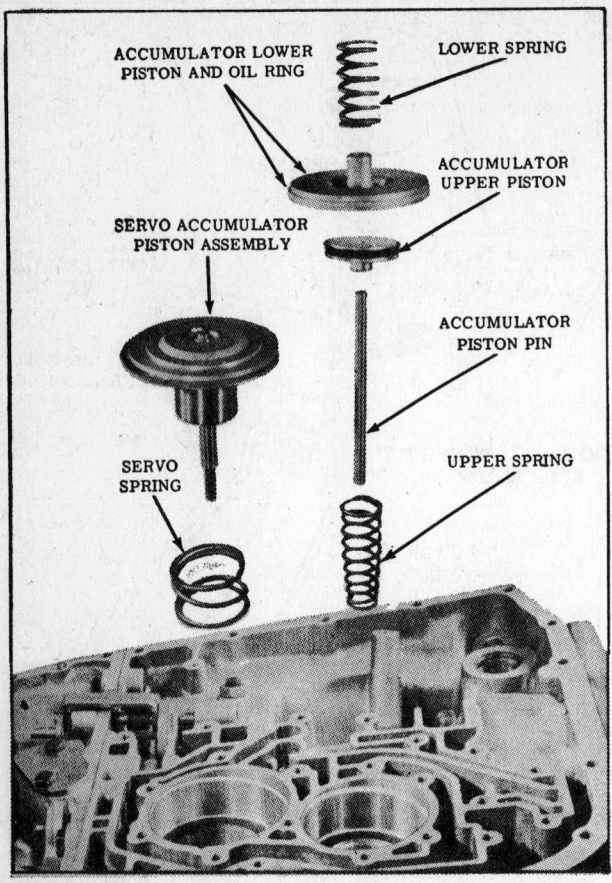

Fig. 2 Servo and accumulator

Fig. 3 Case center support seals

Fig. 4 Pump seal

5. Support transmission, remove attaching bolts and remove transmission from car.
6. When installing transmission, lubricate transmission-to-engine bolts and torque to 30-35 ft. lbs. Fill transmission with fluid and adjust linkage.

TRANSMISSION, DISASSEMBLE

1. Remove filler pipe "O" ring seal from side of case.
2. Remove oil pan and gasket.
3. Remove oil cleaner.
4. Check front unit end play with a dial indicator. Position screwdriver through case behind flange on output shaft. Gently pry forward on output shaft. At same time move input shaft in or out to measure end play. End play should be .006-.018".
5. Remove manual and throttle linkage.
6. Remove control valve.
7. Remove servo and accumulator, Fig. 2.
8. Unhook pawl spring from parking lever.
9. Remove band adjusting screw and nut. *Band anchor pin is under adjusting screw and will fall out when transmission is turned over.*
10. Remove two case center support seal spring retainers, springs and seals, Fig. 3.
11. Remove rear bearing retainer.
12. Remove rear bearing snap ring and, with parking pawl engaged, remove speedometer drive gear and governor.
13. Scribe mark on dowel of carrier and lug of output shaft for alignment on reassembly.
14. Remove output shaft.
15. Remove parking pawl.
16. If replacement of pump seal is necessary, remove it as shown in Fig. 4.
17. Turn transmission pan side up to allow band anchor pin to fall out, then place transmission front side up.
18. Remove 8 remaining case cover-to-case attaching bolts. If pump seal was not removed protect it by sliding a suitable sleeve over input shaft.
19. Lift case cover and pump straight up.
20. Remove torus cover assembly.
21. Remove torus cover-to-driven member thrust bearing and two races, Fig. 5.
22. Remove retaining ring, Fig. 6.
23. Pull mainshaft through driven torus and remove driven torus, thrust bearing and two races.
24. If necessary, remove two hook type oil rings from driven torus.
25. Remove mainshaft sun gear and thrust washer, Fig. 7.

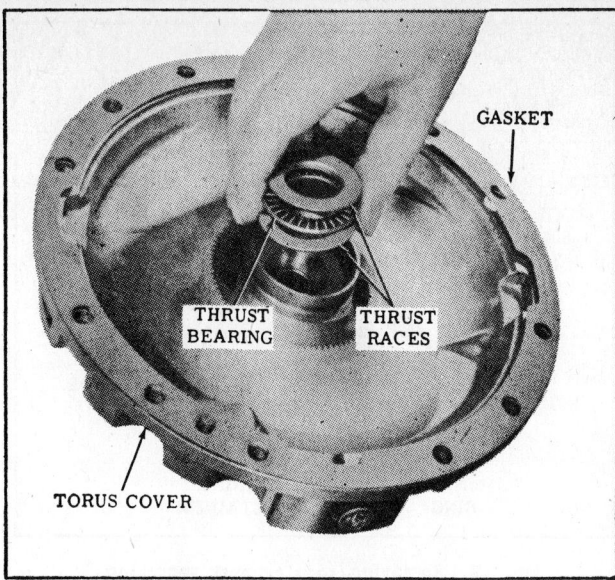

Fig. 5   Torus cover bearing

Fig. 7   Mainshaft sun gear

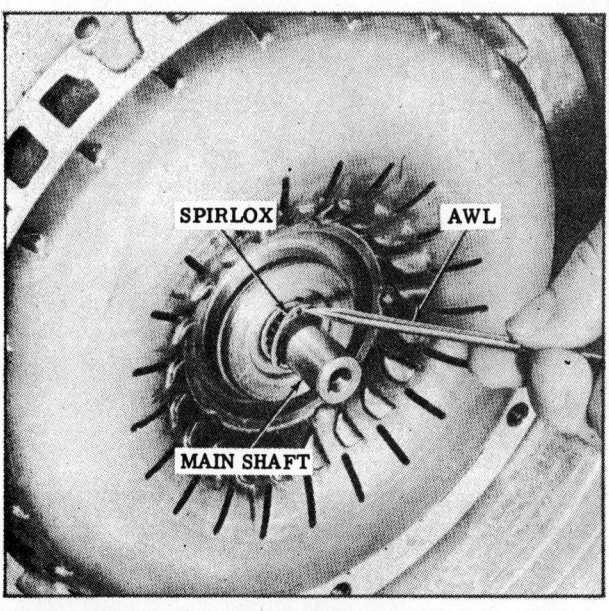

Fig. 6   Removing spirlox retaining ring

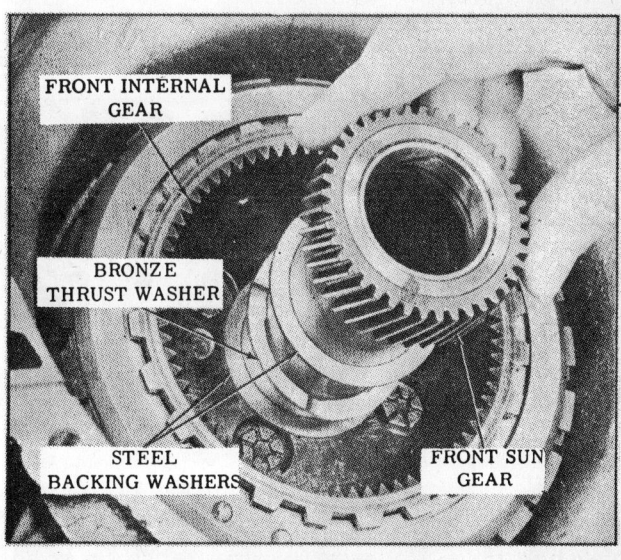

Fig. 8   Front sun gear and washers

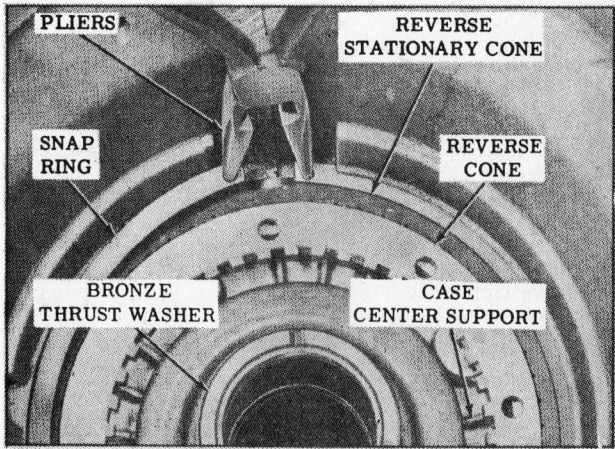

Fig. 9   Case center support and related parts

26. Remove rear sun gear from mainshaft.
27. Remove drive torus and torque multiplier as a unit.
28. If necessary, remove hook-type oil ring from torque multiplier.
29. Remove front carrier-to-rear carrier shaft snap ring.
30. Remove front planet carrier, bronze thrust washer and front unit sun gear.
31. Remove rear unit carrier and internal gear bronze thrust washer from rear of case.
32. Remove rear internal gear.
33. With transmission front end up, remove front sun gear and related parts, Fig. 8.

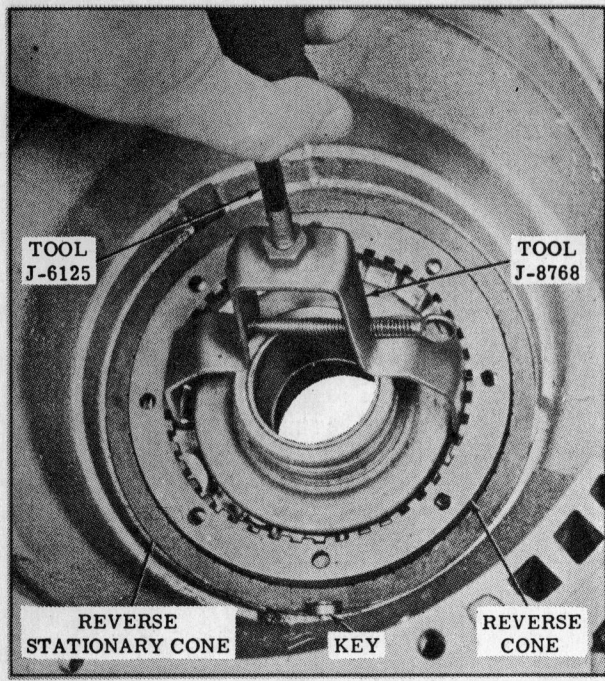

Fig. 10 Removing reverse cone

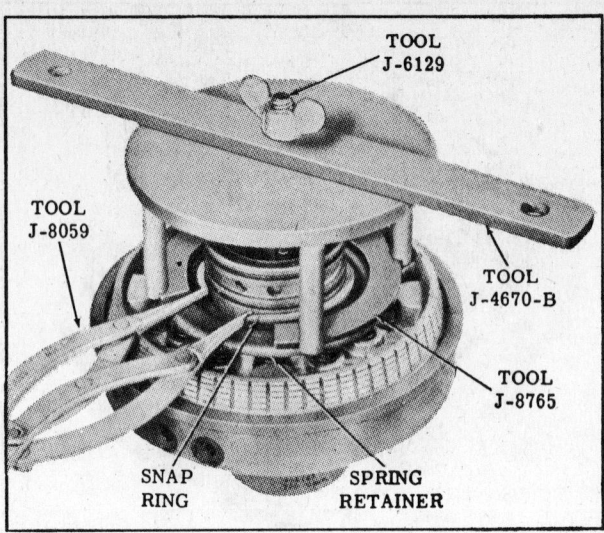

Fig. 12 Removing case support snap ring

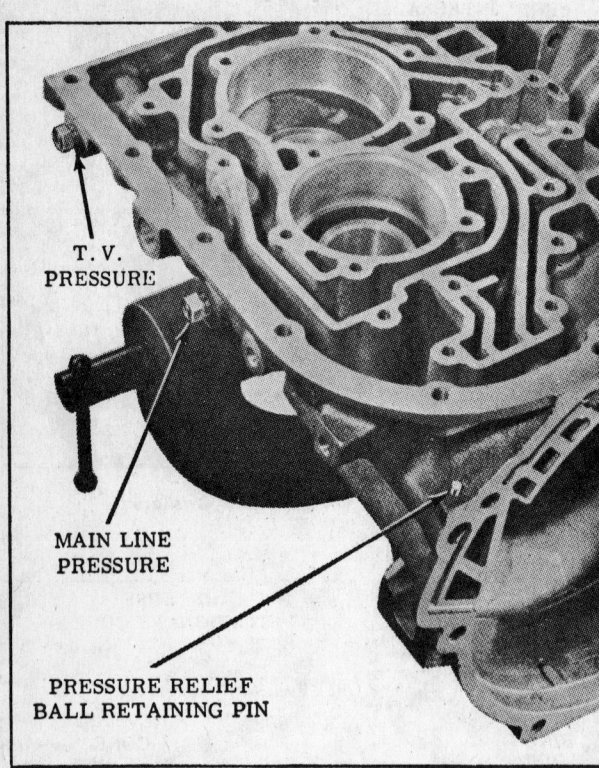

Fig. 11 Transmission case

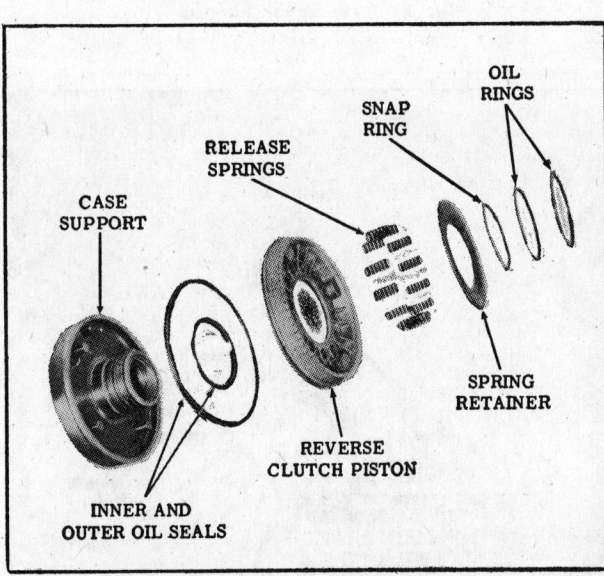

Fig. 13 Reverse clutch assembly

34. Remove front unit internal gear and clutch housing by lifting straight up.
35. Remove bronze thrust washer, Fig. 9.
36. Remove reverse and stationary cones, Fig. 10. Remove cone key from case by pressing from bottom of case.
37. Remove case center support.

UNIT REPAIRS

Transmission Case

If pressure leak is indicated, replacement of pressure relief ball or spring may be necessary. Pull tapered pin and remove spring and ball check valve, Fig. 11. *The spring is under considerable pressure so extreme care should be exercised during disassembly.* Use a new pin on each assembly.

Case Support

Remove two lock-type oil rings from case support. With tools shown in Fig. 12, remove snap ring. Remove spring retainer and disassemble parts as shown in Fig. 13. Remove and discard inner and outer reverse piston seals.

Assemble

1. Install new inner and outer reverse piston seals so lip of seals face case support.
2. Install a seal protector over oil delivery sleeve. Then install reverse piston into case center support guiding outer piston seal into support with small screwdriver. Piston will go on only two ways because of offset dowels.
3. Remove seal protector and install 12 release springs and spring re-

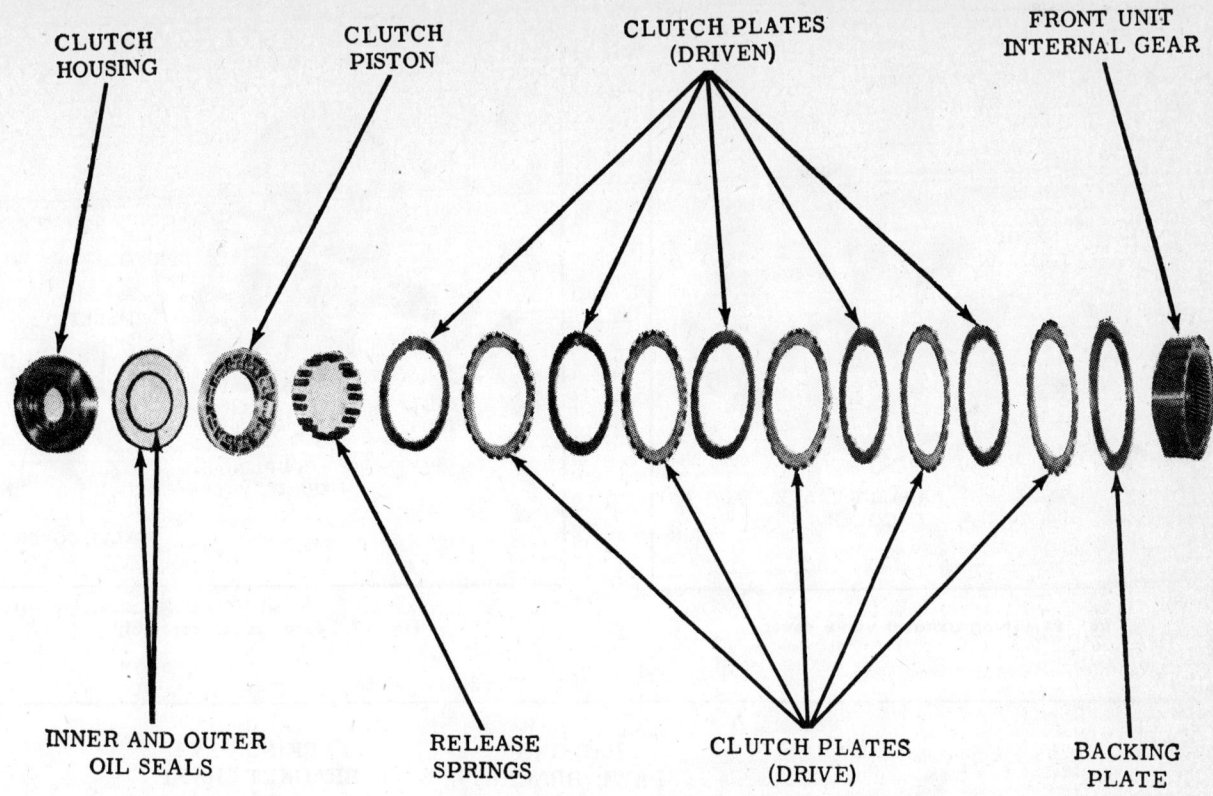

CLUTCH HOUSING · CLUTCH PISTON · CLUTCH PLATES (DRIVEN) · FRONT UNIT INTERNAL GEAR

INNER AND OUTER OIL SEALS · RELEASE SPRINGS · CLUTCH PLATES (DRIVE) · BACKING PLATE

Fig. 14   Front unit clutch assembly

tainer. Be sure all release springs are seated in their pockets.

4. Place snap ring on case support and attach spring compressing tools, Fig. 12. Install snap ring and remove tools. Install two new oil rings.

Front Internal Gear and Clutch Housing

1. Install two guide studs in dowel pin holes in clutch housing and secure in vise.
2. Remove four internal gear-to-clutch housing bolts. Remove assembly from vise and separate internal gear clutch drum by tapping to free internal gear from dowel pins.
3. Remove internal gear, backing plate and discs, Fig. 14.

Assemble

1. Install new inner piston seal on clutch housing with lip of seal facing down.
2. Install new outer piston seal on clutch piston with lip of seal facing flat side of piston.
3. Install piston into clutch housing using small screwdriver to guide outer seal into bore. Install 20 springs into clutch piston pockets.
4. Install backing plate with counter-bore facing tooth flange on internal gear.
5. Install five composition drive and five steel plates alternately, nesting them as follows:
6. Place composition plate over internal gear. Place a steel plate over internal gear and notice the position

NEST CLUTCH PLATES WITH NOTCHES AS SHOWN

Fig. 15   Clutch plates assembled

of the slight half moon notch in edge of steel plate.

7. Continue to install composition and steel plates alternately so that all steel plates have their notches one above the other, Fig. 15.
8. Place backing plate and clutch plates over clutch housing, aligning dowel pins and holes.
9. Install four attaching bolts. Tighten bolts lightly and evenly, using care so as not to pinch bottom steel plate between internal gear and clutch piston.

10. Install guide studs in dowel pin holes in clutch housing and secure in vise. Torque bolts to 22-27 ft. lbs.

Torus Cover

Install exhaust valve retainer tools and remove valves as shown in Fig. 16.

If necessary, remove two lock-type rings from input shaft.

Assemble in reverse order of disassembly, referring to Figs. 16 and 17, and torque screws to 20-25 ft. lbs.

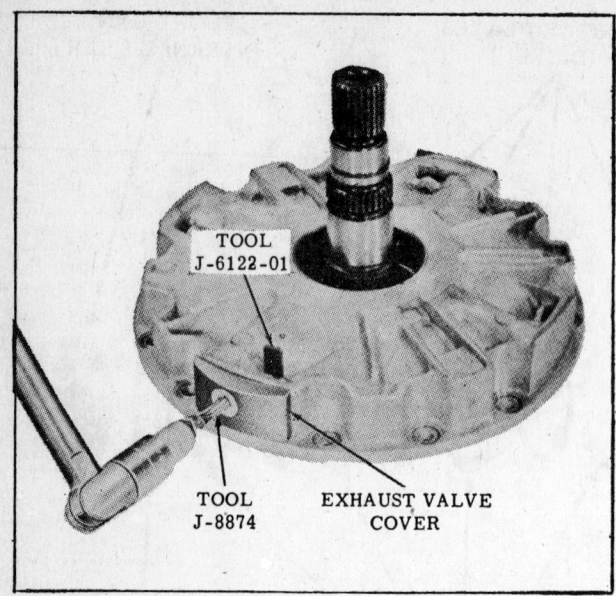

Fig. 16   Removing exhaust valve covers

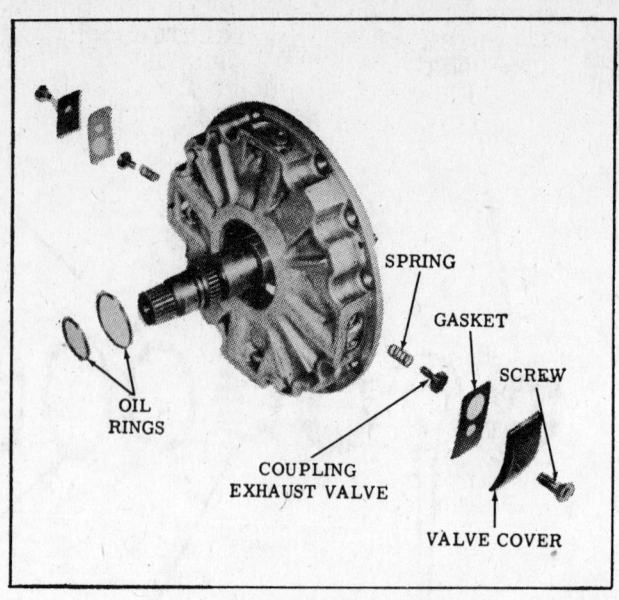

Fig. 17   Torus cover assembly

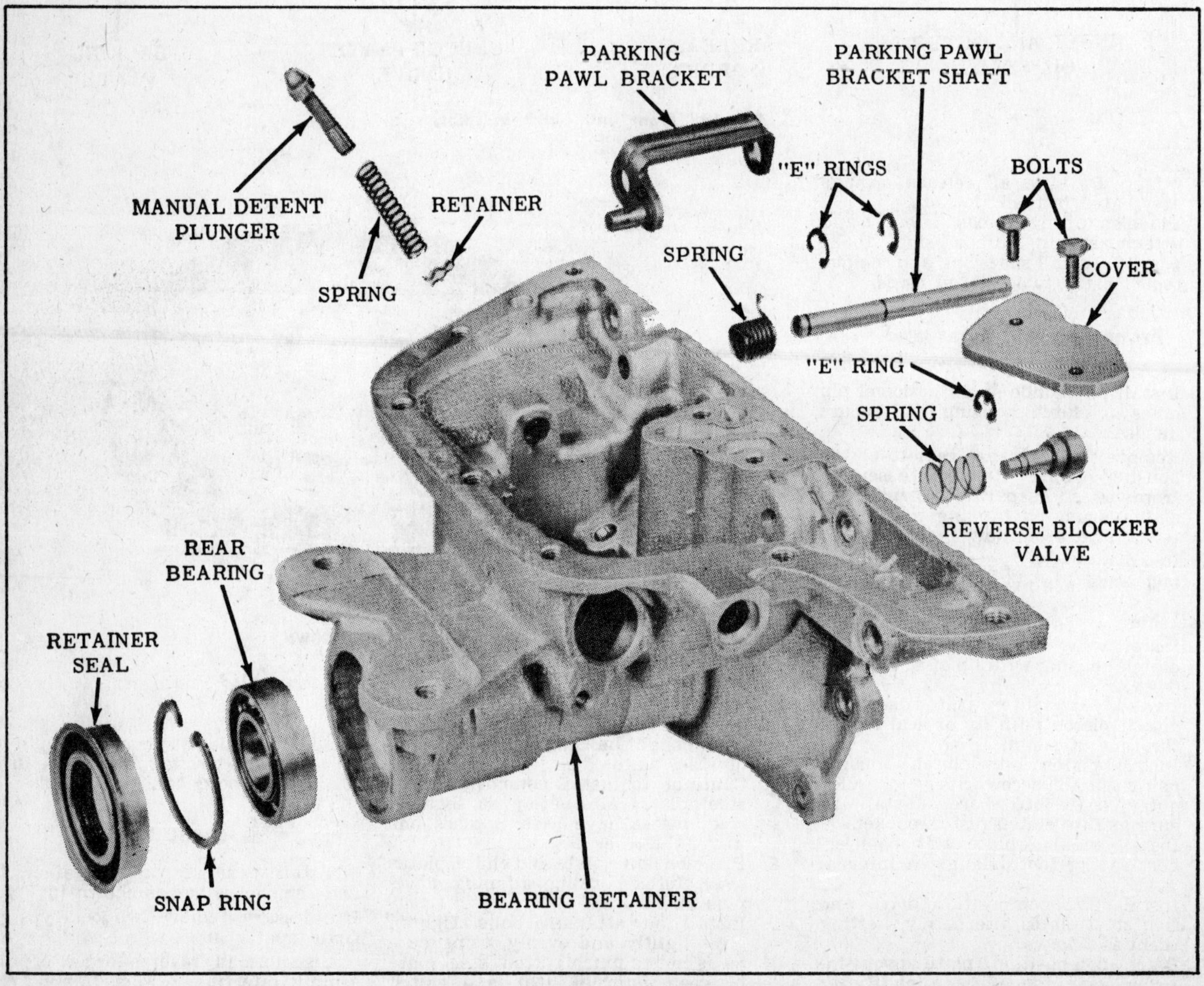

Fig. 18   Rear bearing retainer

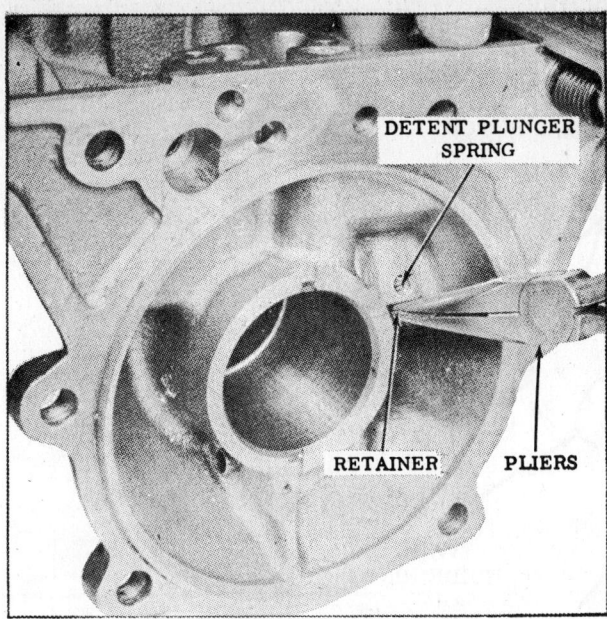

Fig. 19   Removing detent plunger

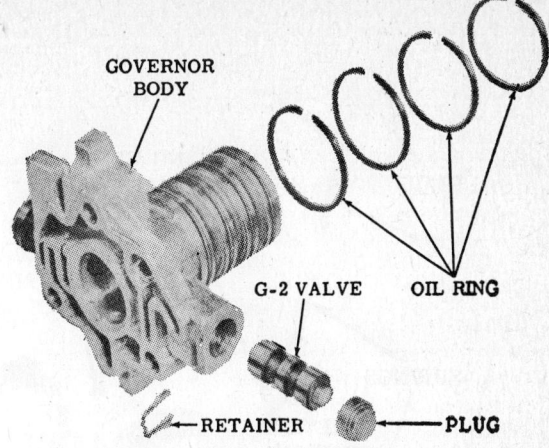

Fig. 20   Governor

Rear Bearing Retainer

1. Remove reverse blocker valve and spring by removing "E" ring, Fig. 18.
2. Remove detent plunger and spring by holding plunger against spring tension while removing retainer, Fig. 19.
3. Remove snap ring and rear bearing.
4. If necessary to remove parking pawl bracket shaft, remove two bracket shaft "E" rings.

Assemble

1. Install rear bearing and snap ring.
2. Install detent plunger and spring, compressing plunger and spring and install retainer.
3. Install reverse blocker valve and spring into rear bearing retainer and secure with "E" ring.
4. Apply a coating of sealer to outer rim of rear oil seal and install seal.
5. Install parking pawl bracket, shaft and spring into bearing retainer and install two "E" rings on shaft.

Governor

If necessary, remove four lock-type oil rings, Fig. 20. Remove remaining parts shown. Reassemble in reverse order.

Servo Piston

To disassemble, place tool shown in Fig. 21 and piston in vise to remove retaining ring and washer. Carefully remove assembly from vise and disassemble as suggested by Fig. 22. Reassemble in reverse order.

Accumulator Piston

To disassemble, remove and discard lip seal from upper accumulator piston, if necessary. Inspect seal ring on lower piston and replace if necessary.

To assemble, install a new piston seal on upper accumulator piston, lip facing flat side of piston, and new ring on lower piston if removed.

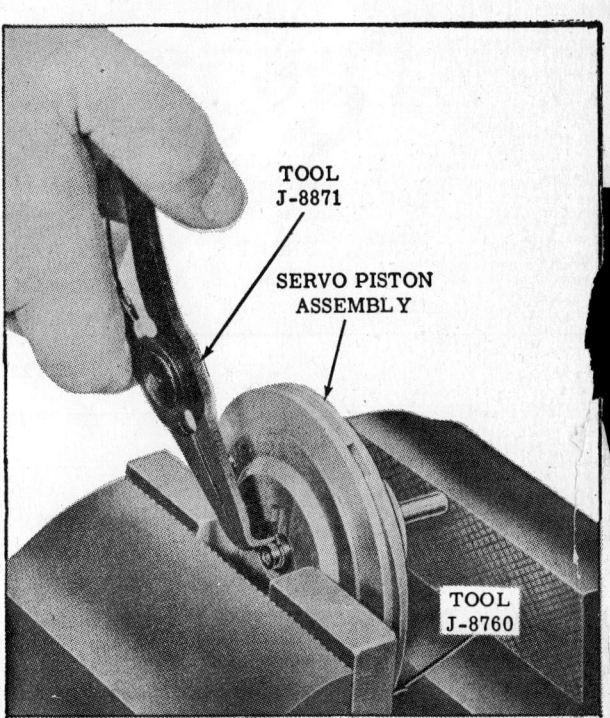

Fig. 21   Servo piston retaining ring

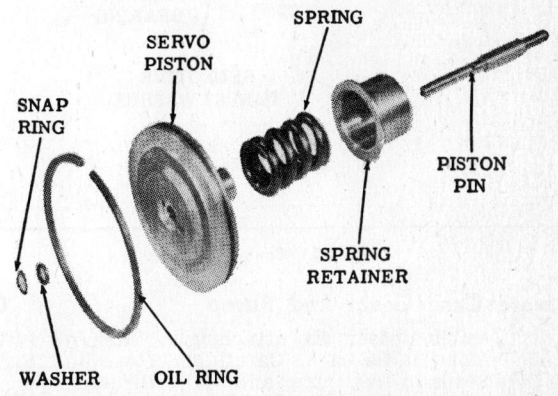

Fig. 22   Servo piston

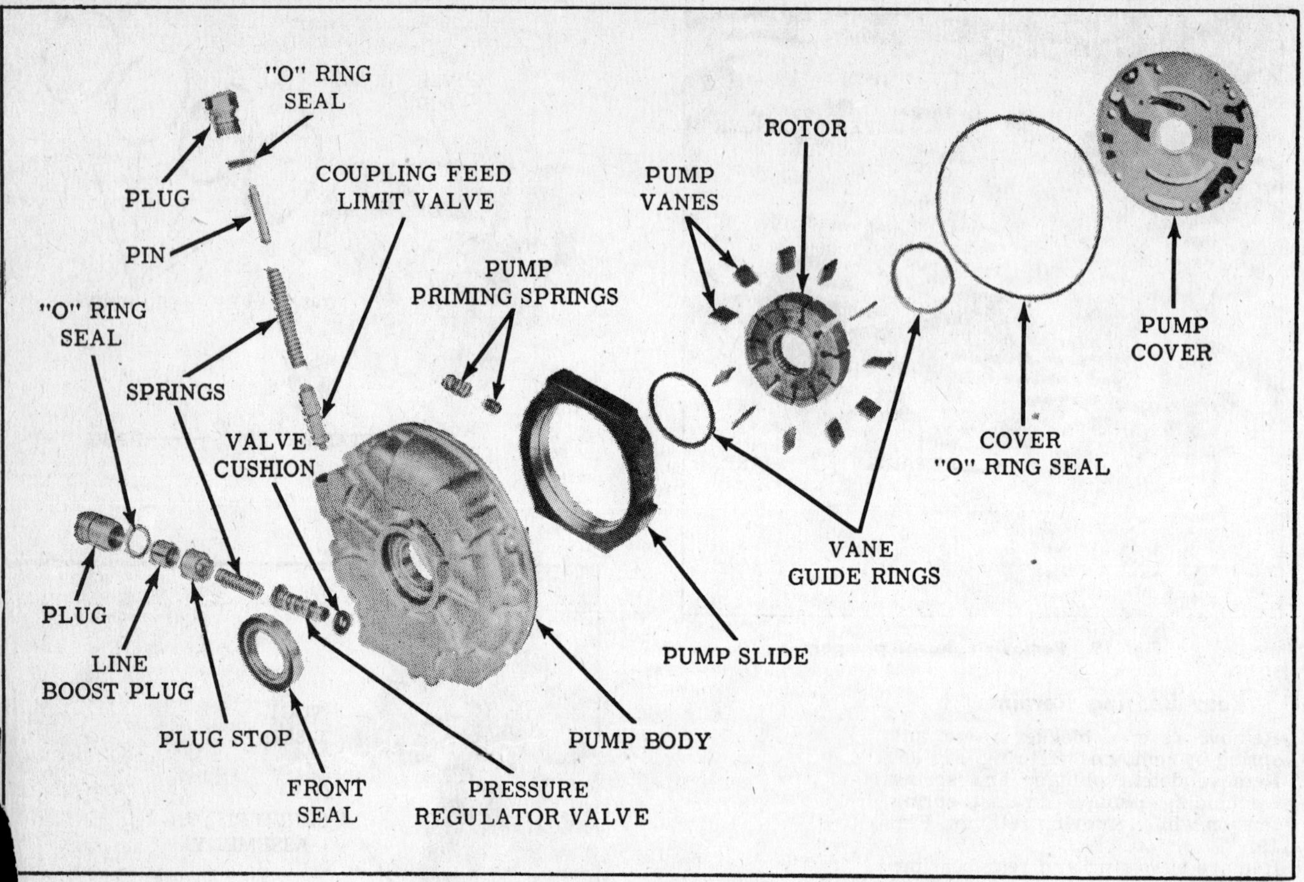

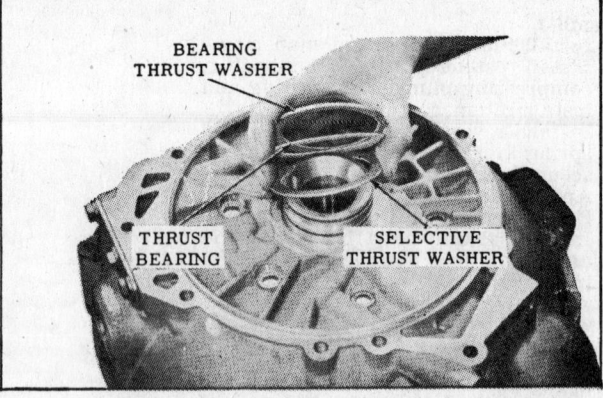

Fig. 25 Pump assembly

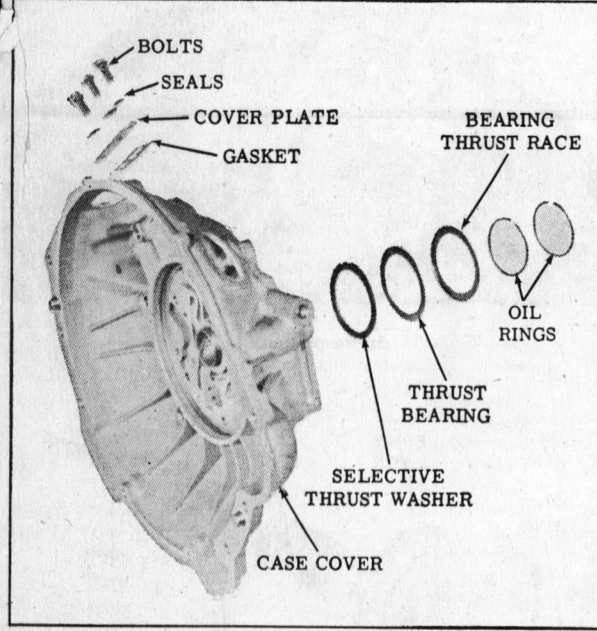

Fig. 23 Case cover

Fig. 24 Case cover bearing

Separate Case Cover and Pump

To disassemble, loosen six attaching bolts about four turns each. Carefully tap on bolt heads to free pump and "O" ring seal from case cover. Remove case cover-to-pump bolts and remove pump.

Case Cover

Remove two lock-type oil seals from cover hub, Fig. 23. Remove cupped race, thrust bearing and selective washer, Fig. 24. Remove three bolts and remove case cover plate and gasket.

Install case cover plate and gasket, using three attaching bolts and bolt head washer seals, and torque to 18-20 ft. lbs. Install predetermined selective washer over hub of case cover. Install thrust bearing and cupped race with cover over bearing and two lock-type oil rings.

Pump

Disassemble pump as suggested by Fig. 25. If condition of pump-to-case cover "O" ring seal indicates replacement, remove and discard seal.

Assemble

1. Install pressure regulator valve cushion. Install pressure regulator

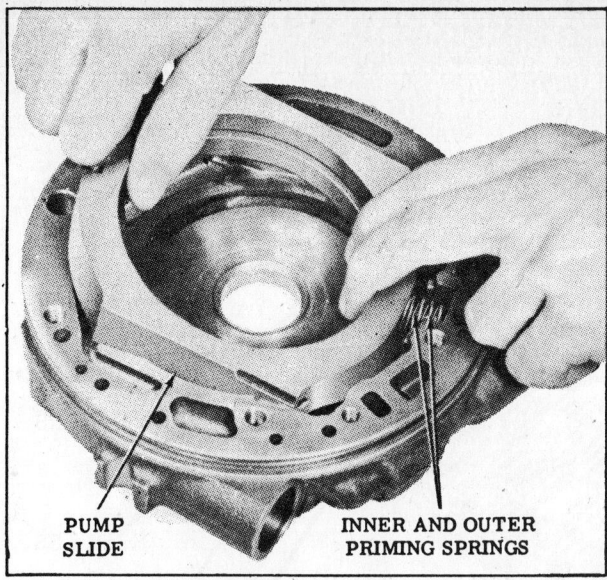

PUMP SLIDE

INNER AND OUTER PRIMING SPRINGS

Fig. 26   Installing pump slide

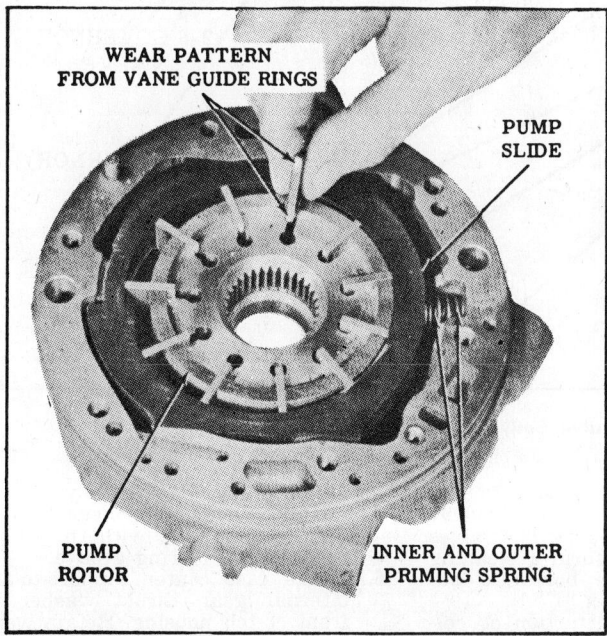

WEAR PATTERN FROM VANE GUIDE RINGS

PUMP SLIDE

PUMP ROTOR

INNER AND OUTER PRIMING SPRING

Fig. 27   Installing pump vanes

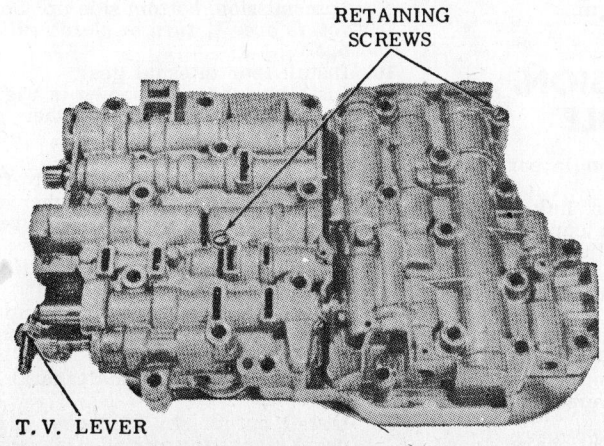

RETAINING SCREWS

T.V. LEVER

Fig. 28   Control valve assembly

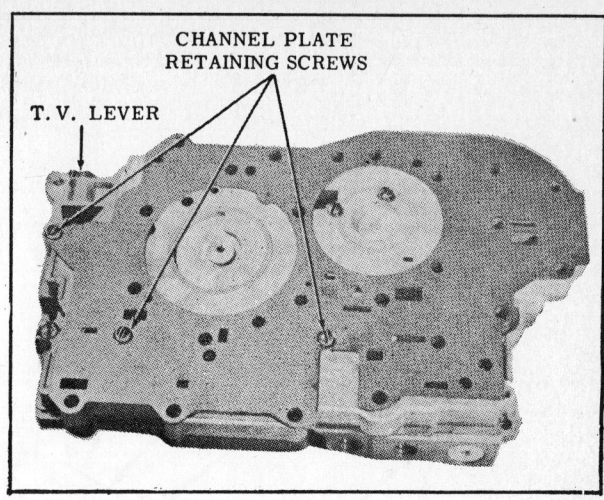

CHANNEL PLATE RETAINING SCREWS

T.V. LEVER

Fig. 29   Channel plate screws

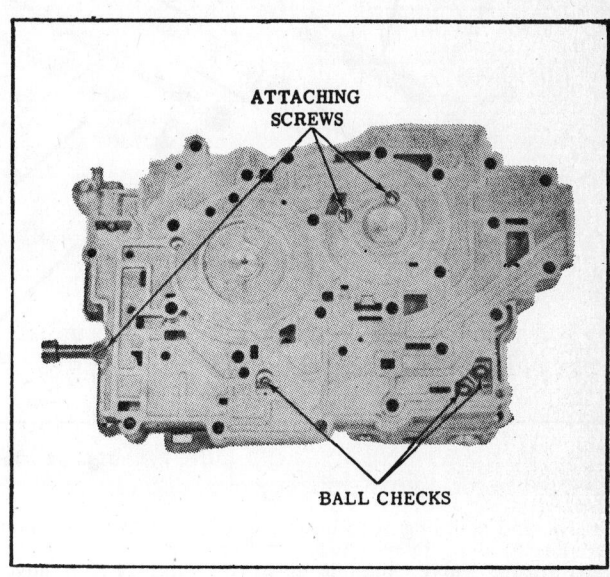

ATTACHING SCREWS

BALL CHECKS

Fig. 30   Channel plate ball checks

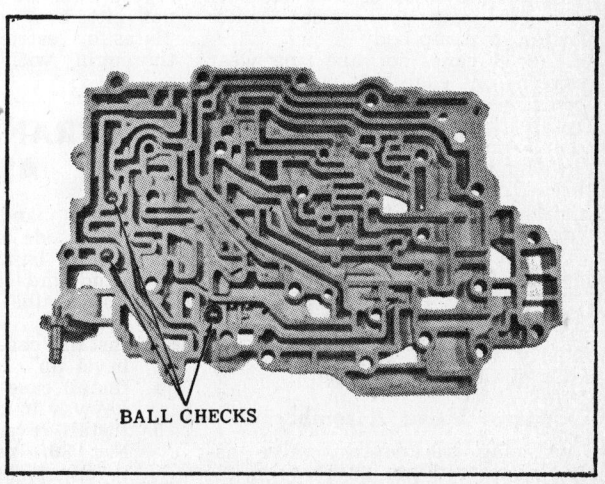

BALL CHECKS

Fig. 31   Channel plate ball checks

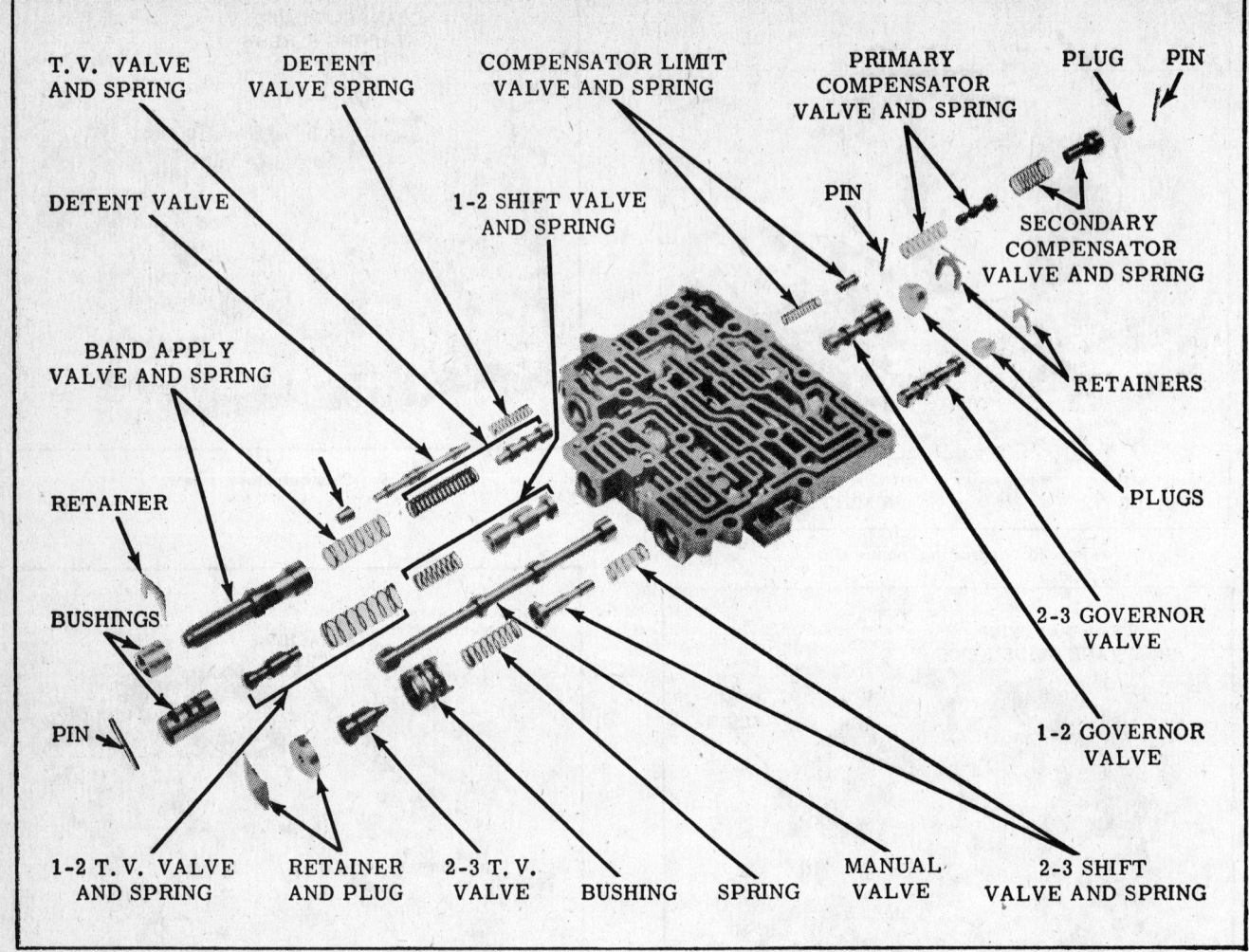

T. V. VALVE AND SPRING — **DETENT VALVE SPRING** — **COMPENSATOR LIMIT VALVE AND SPRING** — **PRIMARY COMPENSATOR VALVE AND SPRING** — **PLUG** — **PIN**

DETENT VALVE — **1-2 SHIFT VALVE AND SPRING** — **PIN** — **SECONDARY COMPENSATOR VALVE AND SPRING**

BAND APPLY VALVE AND SPRING

RETAINER — **RETAINERS**

BUSHINGS — **PLUGS**

PIN — **2-3 GOVERNOR VALVE**

1-2 GOVERNOR VALVE

1-2 T. V. VALVE AND SPRING — **RETAINER AND PLUG** — **2-3 T. V. VALVE** — **BUSHING** — **SPRING** — **MANUAL VALVE** — **2-3 SHIFT VALVE AND SPRING**

Fig. 32 Primary valve body

valve and coupling feed limit valves and related parts as shown in Fig. 25. Torque valve plugs to 15-20 ft. lbs.
2. Install inner and outer priming springs and slide, Fig. 26.
3. Install lower vane guide ring.
4. Install pump rotor so that shoulder on rotor seats over raised center portion of pump body.
5. Install 11 vanes so vane ring wear pattern on edge of vanes faces toward vane rings, Fig. 27.
6. Install upper vane guide ring.
7. Install pump cover by locating on pin and secure with one attaching screw, torquing to 6-8 ft. lbs.
8. Install pump body-to-case cover "O" ring seal.

Assemble Case Cover and Pump

Align case cover to pump bolt holes and install bolts. Draw bolts up evenly to properly seat "O" ring seal in case cover. Torque to 20-25 ft. lbs.

Control Valve Assembly

In servicing the control valve assembly, refer to Figs. 28 through 35. When disassembled, inspect each valve

for free movement in valve bore. It may be necessary to stone lands of valve lightly to remove small burrs. The valves have sharp edges to perform a cleaning action within the valve bore. Do not remove these sharp edges.

Inspect springs for distortion or collapsed coils. Be sure check ball seats are not pitted or chipped. Inspect spacer plates for restrictions. Clean valve bodies thoroughly with an air gun.

TRANSMISSION, ASSEMBLE

1. Install band with single ear facing servo side of case.
2. Install band anchor link between band and case with cupped end of link against band adjusting stop pin hole.
3. Install case center support key, bevel up.
4. Install case center support, aligning keyway in support with key.
5. Install reverse stationary cone key, Fig. 36. Install reverse cone over reverse piston.
6. Install reverse stationary cone,

aligning key slot with key.
7. Install reverse stationary cone retaining snap ring with ring gap at open section of ring groove.
8. Install case center support-to-front internal gear thrust washer into front clutch housing. Retain washer with petrolatum (see Fig. 9).
9. Install front internal gear and clutch over splines of reverse cone. Rotate transmission, bottom side up. *Do not rotate over 1/4 turn or clutch will fall out.*
10. Install rear internal gear.
11. Install washers as shown in Fig. 37.
12. Install bronze thrust washer over rear carrier shaft.
13. Install rear carrier.
14. Install front sun gear-to-front carrier bronze thrust washer over carrier shaft and retain with petrolatum.
15. Install front carrier and retain with snap ring.
16. Rotate transmission rear end up and install rear sun gear on mainshaft.
17. Install thrust washer into rear carrier and install mainshaft, Fig. 38.
18. Install output shaft on rear carrier using marks for proper alignment.

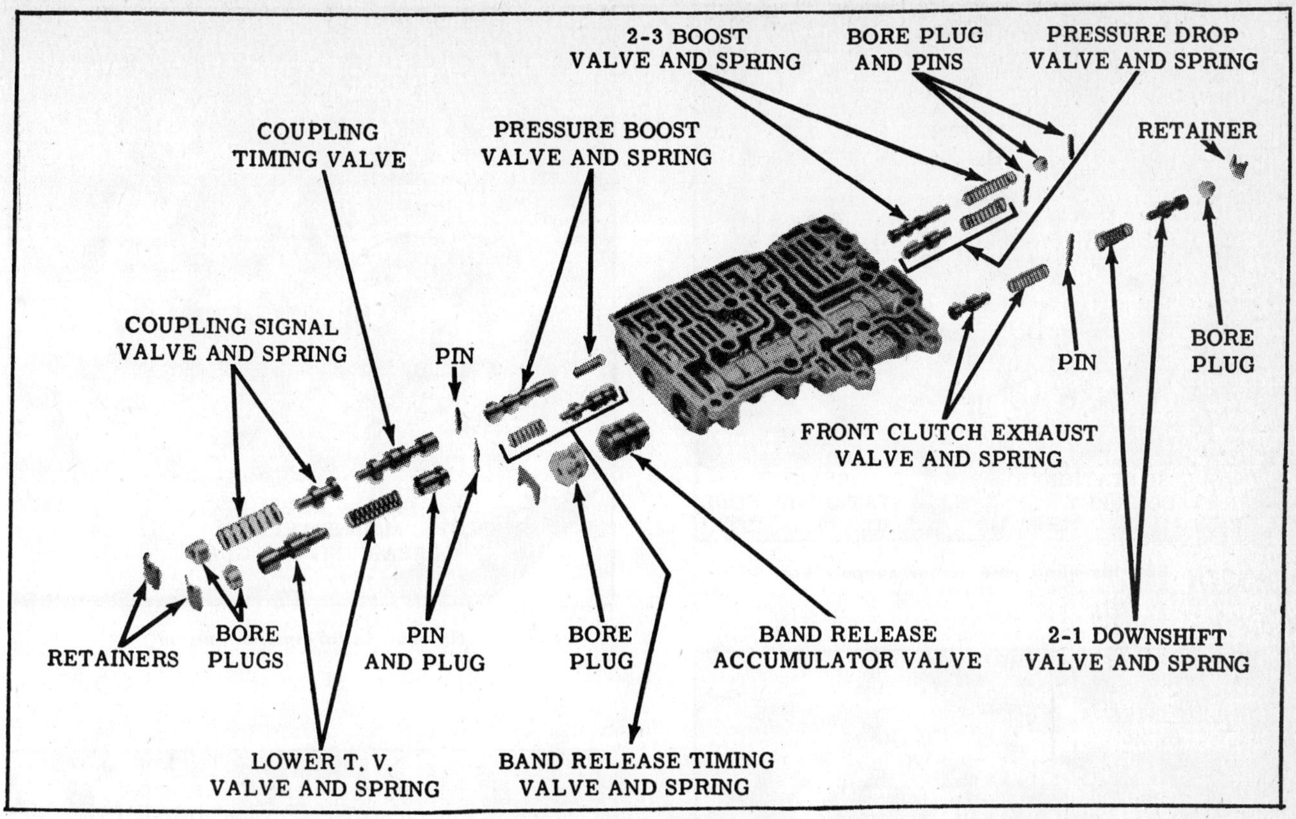

2-3 BOOST
VALVE AND SPRING

BORE PLUG
AND PINS

PRESSURE DROP
VALVE AND SPRING

COUPLING
TIMING VALVE

PRESSURE BOOST
VALVE AND SPRING

RETAINER

COUPLING SIGNAL
VALVE AND SPRING

PIN

PIN

BORE
PLUG

FRONT CLUTCH EXHAUST
VALVE AND SPRING

RETAINERS

BORE
PLUGS

PIN
AND PLUG

BORE
PLUG

BAND RELEASE
ACCUMULATOR VALVE

2-1 DOWNSHIFT
VALVE AND SPRING

LOWER T. V.
VALVE AND SPRING

BAND RELEASE TIMING
VALVE AND SPRING

Fig. 33 Secondary valve body

19. Install parking pawl spacer into counterbore in case, Fig. 39. Install parking pawl and linkage against spacer so that tooth of pawl faces

flange on output shaft. Install parking pawl pivot shaft. Engage pawl with output shaft.

20. Install governor. Torque bolts to 22-

27 ft. lbs. Install speedometer drive gear ½" past snap ring groove on output shaft. Install snap ring.

21. Install rear bearing retainer with new gasket, guiding parking pawl shaft into parking pawl, Fig. 40. Use care when guiding retainer over governor rings.

22. Install one long bearing retainer attaching bolt in lower left hand corner of retainer. Install breather pipe clip over upper right bolt.

23. Install seven remaining rear bearing

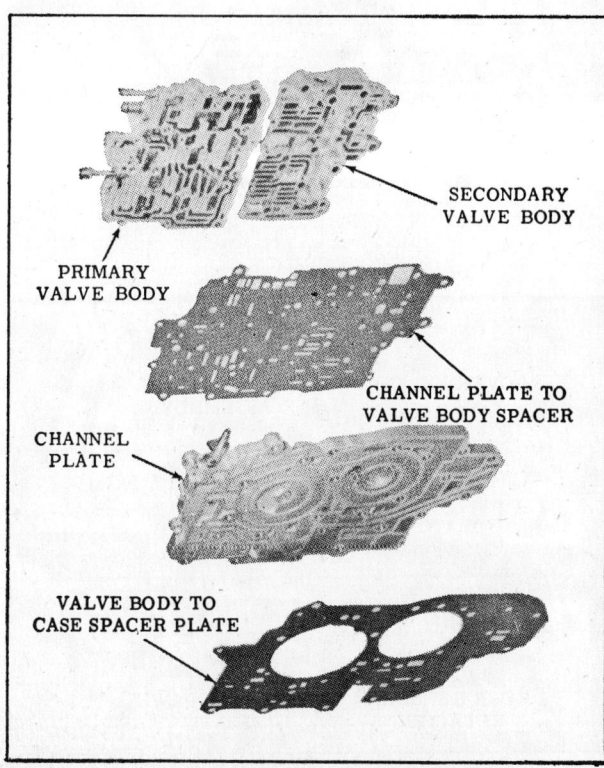

SECONDARY
VALVE BODY

PRIMARY
VALVE BODY

CHANNEL PLATE TO
VALVE BODY SPACER

CHANNEL
PLATE

VALVE BODY TO
CASE SPACER PLATE

Fig. 34 Complete control valve

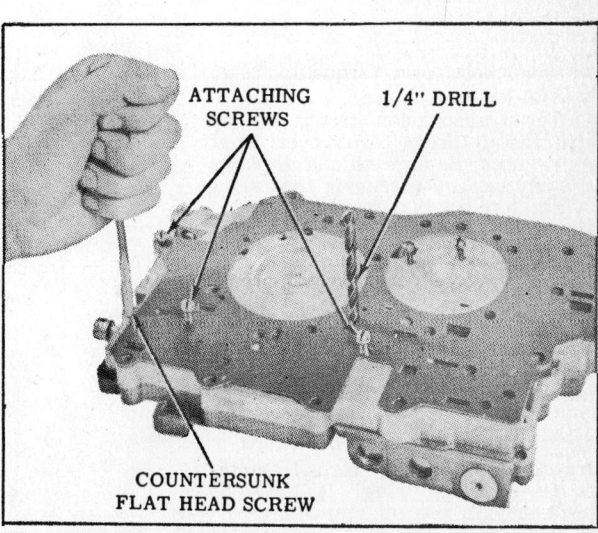

ATTACHING
SCREWS

1/4" DRILL

COUNTERSUNK
FLAT HEAD SCREW

Fig. 35 Assembling valve bodies. Drill is used to align primary valve to channel plate

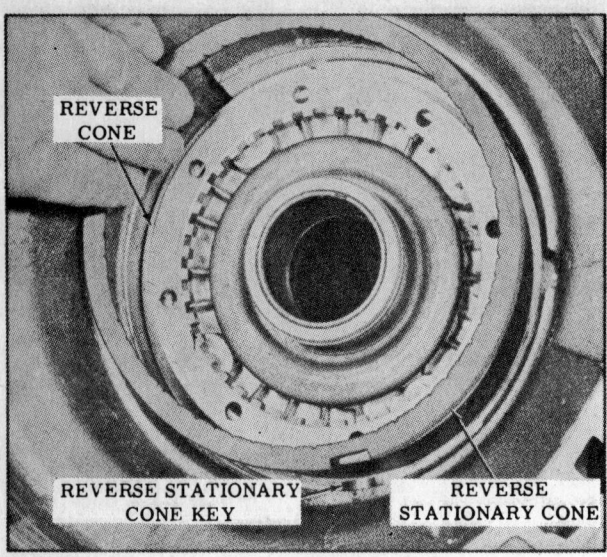

Fig. 36   Installing case center support key

REVERSE CONE

REVERSE STATIONARY CONE KEY

REVERSE STATIONARY CONE

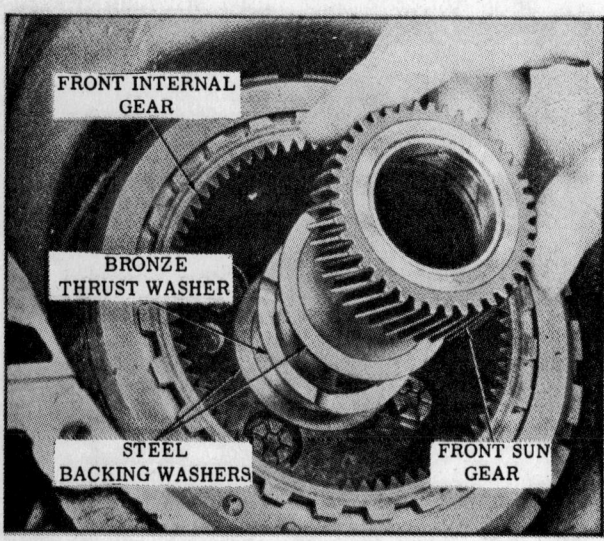

Fig. 37   Sun gear washers

FRONT INTERNAL GEAR

BRONZE THRUST WASHER

STEEL BACKING WASHERS

FRONT SUN GEAR

Fig. 38   Installing rear carrier

THRUST WASHER

MAIN SHAFT AND REAR UNIT SUN GEAR

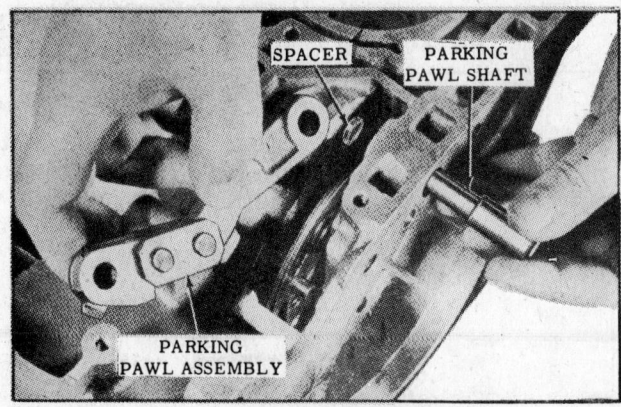

Fig. 39   Installing parking pawl

SPACER

PARKING PAWL SHAFT

PARKING PAWL ASSEMBLY

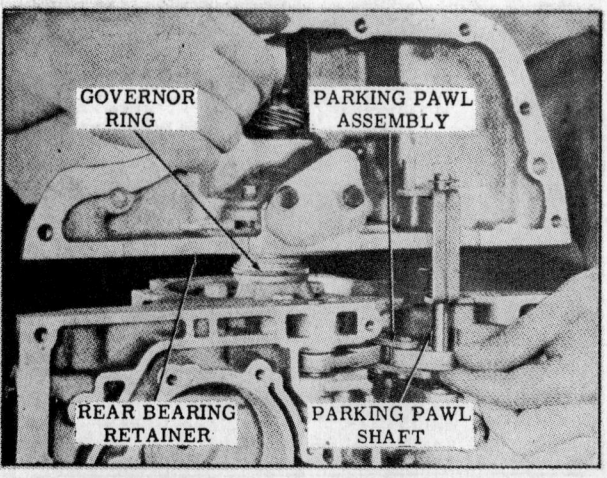

Fig. 40   Installing rear bearing retainer

GOVERNOR RING

PARKING PAWL ASSEMBLY

REAR BEARING RETAINER

PARKING PAWL SHAFT

retainer bolts and torque to 20-25 ft. lbs.

24. Rotate transmission front end up and install drive torus over front unit clutch. *Be sure all clutch plates are engaged by observing that drive torus rests against front carrier.*

25. Install lock-type oil ring on torque multiplier. Install multiplier.

26. Install two lock-type oil rings on driven torus.

27. Install flat bearing race into torque multiplier. Install cupped race and bearing into driven torus with bearing out. Retain with petrolatum, Fig. 41.

28. Install driven torus on mainshaft.

29. Install new driven torus-to-mainshaft retaining ring. It may be necessary to lift up mainshaft.

30. Install flat bearing race, bearing and cupped race (cup facing torus cover)

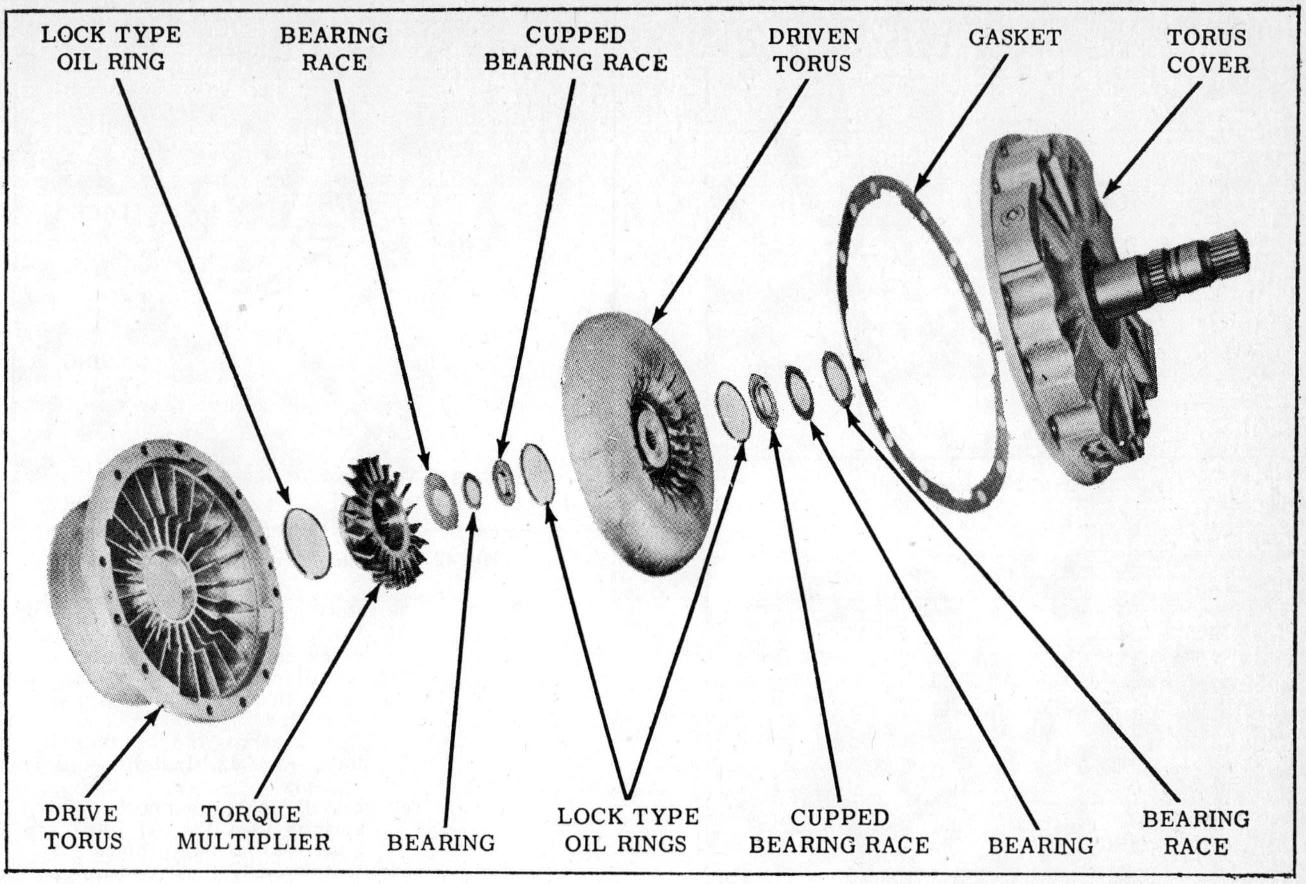

LOCK TYPE OIL RING   BEARING RACE   CUPPED BEARING RACE   DRIVEN TORUS   GASKET   TORUS COVER

DRIVE TORUS   TORQUE MULTIPLIER   BEARING   LOCK TYPE OIL RINGS   CUPPED BEARING RACE   BEARING   BEARING RACE

Fig. 41 Front unit assembly

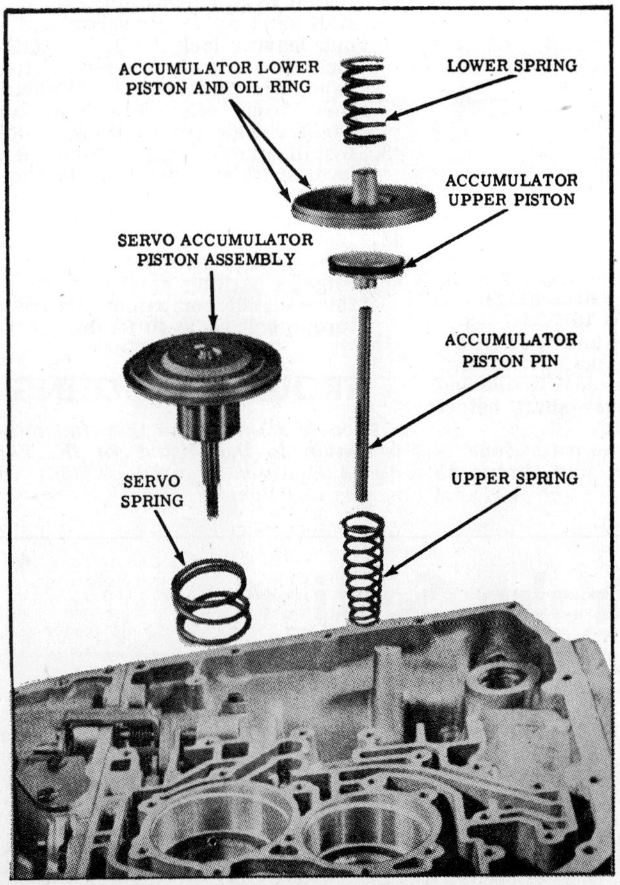

Fig. 42 Installing accumulator

ACCUMULATOR LOWER PISTON AND OIL RING   LOWER SPRING

ACCUMULATOR UPPER PISTON

SERVO ACCUMULATOR PISTON ASSEMBLY

ACCUMULATOR PISTON PIN

SERVO SPRING   UPPER SPRING

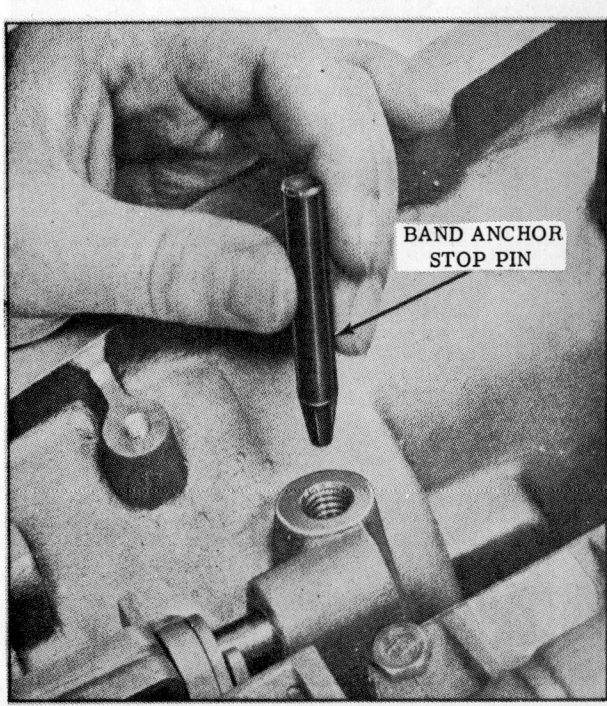

BAND ANCHOR STOP PIN

Fig. 43 Installing band anchor pin

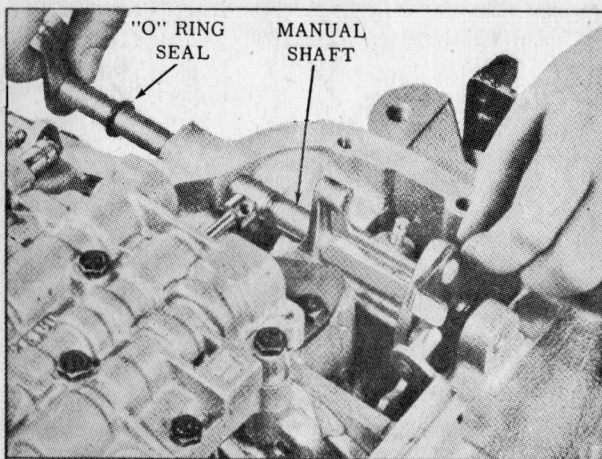

Fig. 44 Installing manual shaft

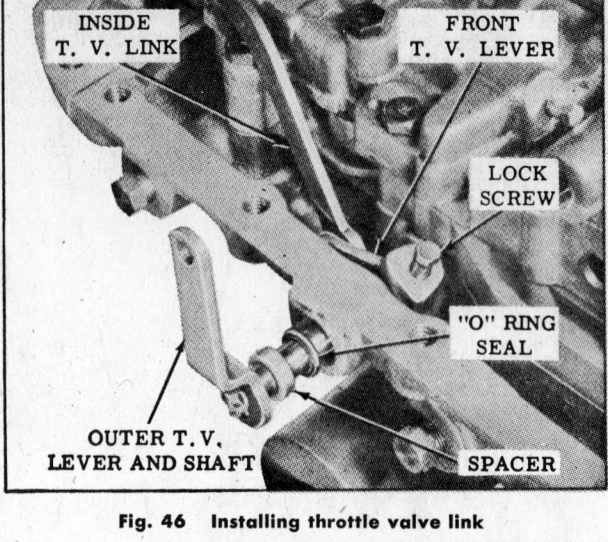

Fig. 46 Installing throttle valve link

36. Rotate transmission pan side up.
37. Hook curved end of spring into notch on parking lever.
38. Install rear bearing retainer cover, using two bolts, and torque to 20-25 ft. lbs.
39. Install servo and accumulator pistons, Fig. 42. Install servo spring and piston.
40. Install case support seals and springs (see Fig. 3) into case and push retainers into place.
41. Install control valve, torquing bolts to 6-8 ft. lbs.
42. Install band anchor pin, Fig. 43. Install band adjusting screw and lock nut, leaving lock nut loose. With an inch pound torque wrench, torque band adjusting screw to 20 inch lbs., then back off screw two turns. Tighten lock nut to 18-20 ft. lbs.
43. Install an "O" ring seal on manual lever shaft and install shaft, Fig. 44.
44. Install manual link and T.V. link as shown in Figs. 45 and 46.
45. Install oil cleaner and oil pan (torque to 12-15 ft. lbs.)
46. Engage parking pawl in park position. Install companion flange and torque bolt to 30-40 ft. lbs.

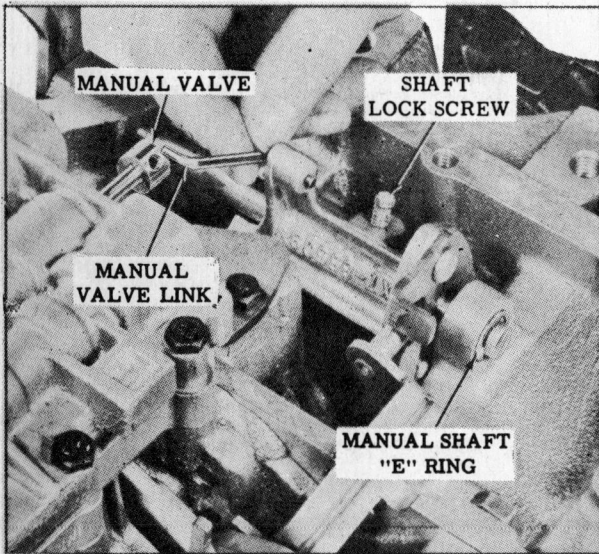

Fig. 45 Installing manual link

TROUBLE SHOOTING

Trouble diagnosis on this transmission is similar to that listed for the Three-Speed Hydramatic used on 1961 Oldsmobile and Pontiac.

into torus cover and retain with petrolatum.
31. Install new gasket on torus cover, aligning dowel pin holes. Retain with petrolatum.
32. Install torus cover on drive torus, aligning dowel pins with holes. *Dowel pins are slightly offset and must be aligned with holes to prevent damage to cover.*

33. Install 12 torus cover attaching bolts and cross tighten to 10-12 ft. lbs.
34. Install case cover and pump assembly, with new gasket. If seal was not removed, protect seal by placing a suitable sleeve over shaft before installing cover.
35. Install 9 case cover bolts (one is longer than others) and torque to 20-25 ft. lbs.

Rear Axle & Brake Section

Refer To Hydraulic Brakes Chapter For Brake Adjustments

AXLE SHAFT

1. To remove the axle shafts, Fig. 1, take off the wheels. *Note that the left side wheel bolts have left hand threads and the nuts are marked "LH".*

2. Remove brake drums.
3. Remove nuts holding retainer plates to brake backing plates. Pull retainers clear of bolts and reinstall two lower nuts finger tight to hold brake backing plate in position.
4. Pull out axle shafts using a puller

and adapter with a slide hammer. *While pulling axle shaft out through oil seal, support shaft carefully in center of seal to avoid cutting seal lip.*
5. Reverse removal procedure to install axle shafts. Note that the left shaft

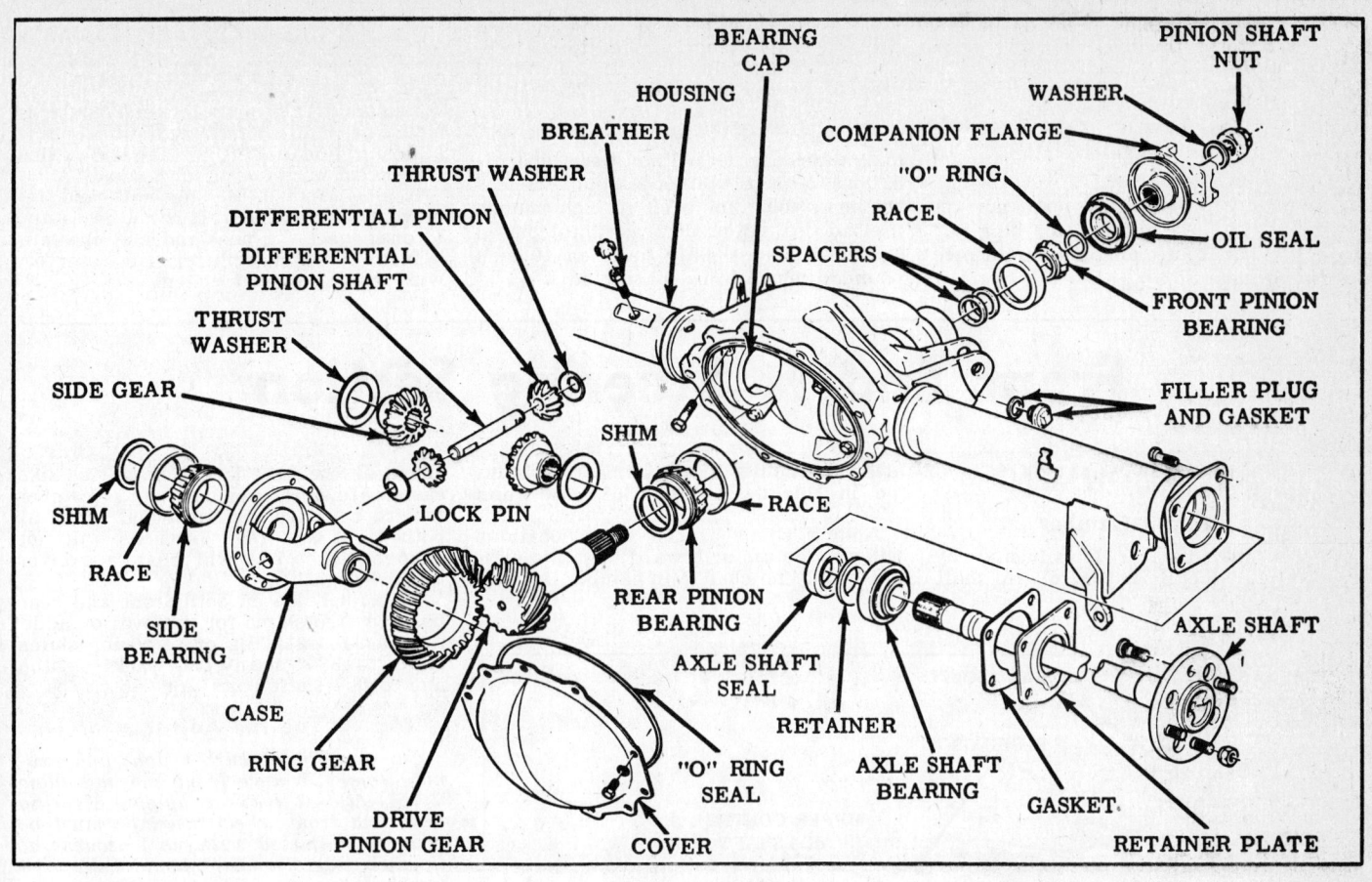

Fig. 1   Rear axle assembly

is shorter than the right shaft. Apply wheel bearing grease in the bearing recesses of the housing. Install new outer retainer gaskets. Insert axle shaft carefully until shaft splines engage in differential to avoid damage to seals. Torque retainer stud nuts to 60 ft. lbs.

Axle Shaft Bearing

1. With axle shaft removed, nick bearing retainer in three or four places with a chisel deep enough to spread ring. Retainer will then slip off.
2. Press bearing off shaft. An arbor press may be used.
3. Press new axle shaft bearing against shoulder on axle shaft. *Retainer plate which retains bearing in housing must be on axle shaft before bearing is installed; retainer gasket can be installed after bearing.*
4. Press new retainer ring against bearing.

Axle Shaft Seal

1. Insert axle shaft so that splined end is just through seal.
2. Using axle shaft as a lever, push down on shaft until seal is pried from housing.
3. Apply sealer to O.D. of new seal.
4. Position seal over a suitable installer and drive seal straight into axle housing until fully seated.

REAR AXLE

As shown in Fig. 1, the drive pinion is mounted on two tapered roller bearings that are preloaded by two selected spacers. The drive pinion is positioned by shims located between a shoulder on the pinion and the rear bearing. The front bearing is held in place by a large nut.

The differential is supported in the carrier by two tapered roller side bearings. These are preloaded by inserting shims between the bearings and the pedestals. The differential assembly is positioned for ring gear and pinion backlash by varying these shims.

Rear Axle Repairs

Disassembly and assembly of the differential case, replacing the ring gear, checking ring gear and pinion backlash and other differential case operations are given in the *Rear Axles Chapter*. The following operations are significant for this type rear axle.

Side Bearing Preload

After the differential case has been assembled, differential side bearing preload is adjusted by changing the thickness of both the right and left shim by an equal amount. By changing the thickness of both shims equally, the original backlash will be maintained. Differential adjustment shims are available in thicknesses ranging from .040″ to .082″ in .002″ increments.

In order to adjust side bearing preload accurately, adjustment should be made before the pinion is installed. This allows the ring gear and case assembly to be rotated freely.

Place differential case and bearing assembly in carrier. If new side bearings are installed, use original adjusting shims; if same bearings are to be reused, select new right and left adjusting shims each .002″ thicker than the original shim. Slip right shim in position at right bearing, then drive left shim carefully into position using a soft hammer.

Rotate differential case several complete turns to seat bearings. Check bearing preload with an inch-pound torque wrench applied to a ring gear attaching bolt. With torque wrench projecting approximately straight out, bearing preload should read 20-30 inch lbs. with new bearings and 10-20 inch lbs. with reused bearings. If preload is not within these limits, increase shim thickness .002″ on each side for each added 10 inch lbs. preload desired, or decrease shim thickness .002″ on each side for each 10 inch lbs. preload to be subtracted.

When adjustment is satisfactory, remove differential, keeping bearing caps and shims together so that they may be reinstalled properly after the drive pinion has been installed.

Drive Pinion Preload

If new pinion bearings are installed, use the original pinion preload spacers. If the same bearings are being reused, select a pair of pinion preload spacers having a total thickness of .002″ less than the original spacers. Install spacers on pinion and position pinion in carrier. Pinion preload spacers are furnished to be used in pairs so that the possible combined thickness range from .400″ to .470″.

Install pinion and bearings and new oil seal. Install flange and nut, torquing nut to 200 ft. lbs. Rotate pinion several times to seat bearings.

Check bearing preload using an inch pound torque wrench applied to the pinion nut. The preload reading including drag of new seal should be 25-35 inch pounds with new bearings or 15 to 25 inch pounds for reused bearings. If preload torque is not within these specifications, reduce the total pinion spacer thickness .001″ for each 10 inch pounds preload desired, or decrease total pinion spacer thickness .001″ for each 10 inch pounds preload to be subtracted.

MASTER CYLINDER, REPLACE

Be sure area around master cylinder is clean, then disconnect hydraulic line at master cylinder. Plug or tape end of line to prevent entrance of dirt.

Remove four attaching nuts and remove master cylinder. It is not necessary to disconnect the push rod and clevis.

Install master cylinder, fill reservoir with fluid and bleed system.

Front End & Steering Section

WHEEL ALIGNMENT

Caster & Camber

Caster and camber is adjusted by shimming at the upper control arm shaft attaching points. These shims are available in thicknesses of .030″, .060″ and .120″.

Adding shims at the front locations will change caster toward negative with practically no change in camber. Adding shims at the rear locations will change caster toward positive and camber toward negative. Adding equal shims at both front and rear locations will not change caster but will change camber toward negative.

To adjust, loosen both front and rear bolts to free shims for removal or addition. After installing or removing shims (limit to .380″ in any one stack) tighten and torque shaft bolts to 60-85 ft. lbs.

Toe-In, Adjust

Car must be at curb weight and running height; bounce front end and allow it to settle at running height. Steering gear and front wheel bearings must be properly adjusted with no looseness at tie rod ends. The car should be moved forward one complete revolution of the wheels before the toe-in check and adjustment is started and the car should never be moved backward while making the check and adjustment.

With front wheels in the straight ahead position, toe-in is adjusted by turning the tie rod adjusting sleeves as required. Left and right adjusting sleeves must be turned exactly the same amount but in opposite directions in order to maintain front wheels in straight ahead position when steering wheel is in straight ahead position.

The steering knuckle and steering arm "rock" or tilt as front wheel rises and falls. Therefore, it is vitally important to position the bottom face of the tie rod end parallel with the machined surface at the outer end of the steering arm when tie rod length is adjusted. Severe damage and possible failure can result unless this precaution is taken. The tie rod sleeve clamps must be straight down to provide clearance.

WHEEL BEARINGS, ADJUST

1. Tighten spindle nut to 10-15 ft. lbs. torque and rotate hub to seat bearings.
2. Back off 1/6 turn minimum to ¼ turn maximum to allow installation of cotter pin.
3. Before installation of grease cap in hub, make sure end of spindle and inside of cap are free of grease so that radio static collector makes good contact. Make sure that static

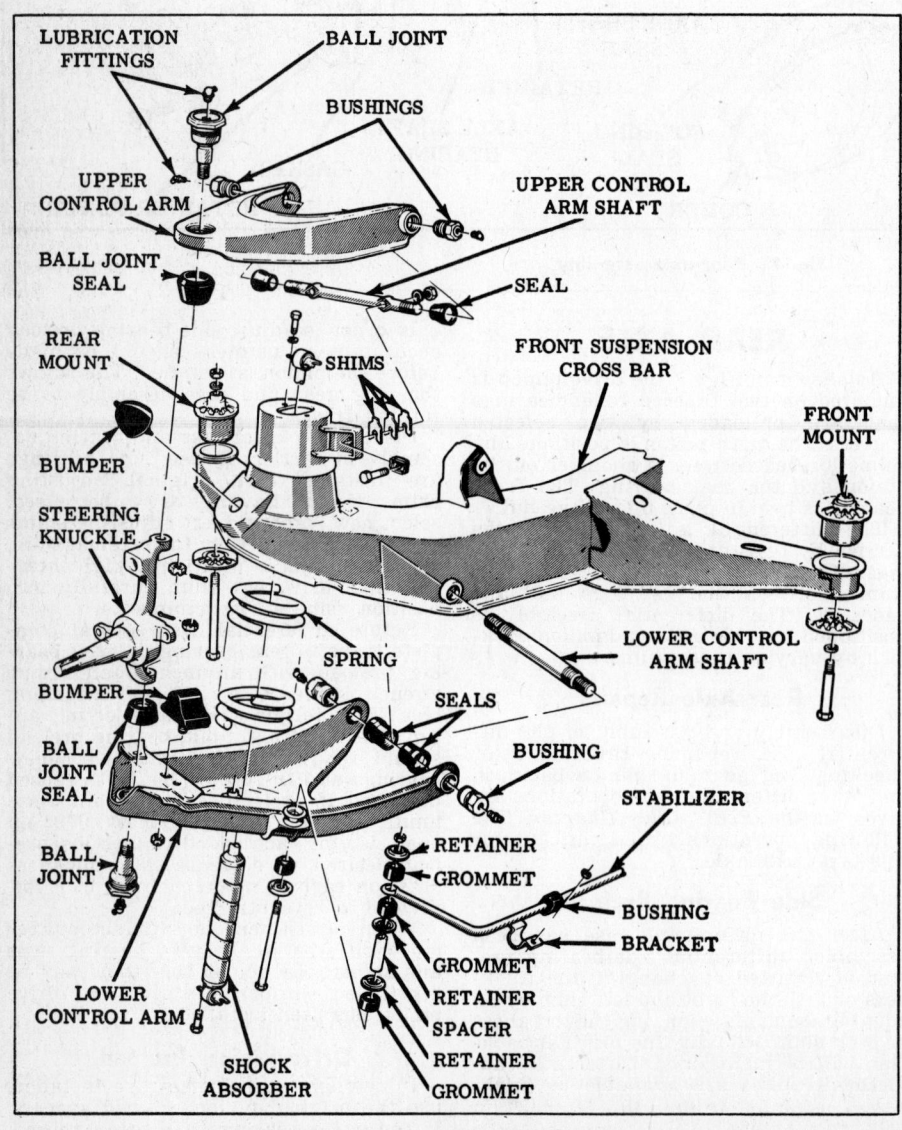

LUBRICATION FITTINGS
BALL JOINT
BUSHINGS
UPPER CONTROL ARM
UPPER CONTROL ARM SHAFT
BALL JOINT SEAL
SEAL
REAR MOUNT
FRONT SUSPENSION CROSS BAR
SHIMS
FRONT MOUNT
BUMPER
STEERING KNUCKLE
LOWER CONTROL ARM SHAFT
BUMPER
SPRING
SEALS
BALL JOINT SEAL
BUSHING
STABILIZER
BALL JOINT
RETAINER
GROMMET
BUSHING
BRACKET
GROMMET
RETAINER
SPACER
RETAINER
GROMMET
LOWER CONTROL ARM
SHOCK ABSORBER

Fig. 1 Front suspension assembly

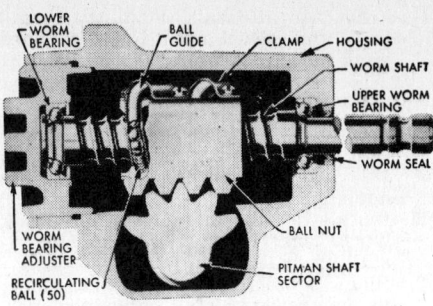

Fig. 2 Steering gear worm and ball nut

collector is properly shaped to provide good contact between end of spindle and grease cap.

FRONT END REPAIRS

Ball Joints, Replace, Fig. 1

Upper and lower ball joints are similar in appearance but are not interchangeable. Upper ball joints are spring-loaded to prevent looseness while the force of the chassis spring keeps the lower ball loaded.

If the upper stud has any perceptible shake, or if it can be twisted in its socket with the fingers, it should be replaced.

1. Loosen (do not remove) stud nut.
2. Rap knuckle sharply in area of stud to disengage stud from knuckle.
3. Support lower control arm with jack and remove (loosened) nut from stud. Raise upper control arm to remove stud from knuckle.
4. Tie brake backing plate and steering knuckle out of the way.
5. Remove ball joint from control arm.
6. Install new ball joint into control arm and tighten until hex section of ball joint seats firmly into arms.
7. Turn tapered stud until cotter pin hole is fore and aft and assemble rubber dust shield over stud.

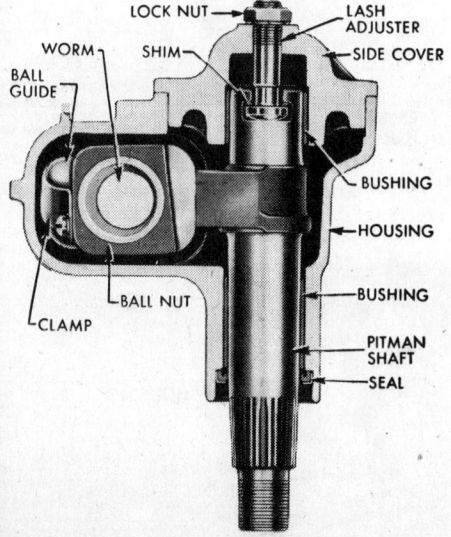

Fig. 3 Steering gear pitman shaft and ball nut

8. Assemble knuckle and backing plate and torque castellated nut to 35-60 ft. lbs.

Shock Absorber, Replace

Unfasten shock absorber top and bottom and remove it through the spring seat. Check shock absorber for obvious physical damage or oil leakage. Push and pull shock absorber in an upright position. If smooth hydraulic resistance is not present in both directions, replace shock absorber.

Spring, Replace

1. Remove wheel with hub and drum.
2. Disconnect stabilizer link from lower control arm and remove shock absorber.
3. Disconnect lower control arm ball joint from steering knuckle.
4. Lower floor jack under spring until spring is fully extended and remove spring.
5. To install spring, tape spring insulator to top of spring (identified by a ground flat coil). Rotate spring so end of bottom coil will index with edge of hole in lower control arm spring seat. Complete the installation in the reverse order of removal.

Upper Control Arm

1. Disconnect upper ball joint from steering knuckle.
2. Remove control arm, carefully noting number, location and thickness of adjusting shims between shaft and frame bracket.
3. If shaft and bushings only are to be replaced, clamp control arm in vise and remove shaft and bushings.
4. Assemble new grease seals on shaft. Apply light coating of grease to shaft threads and position shaft in arm. Start new bushing in arm and thread shaft into bushing to aid in alignment. Tighten bushing into arm until hex section of bushing seats firmly into arm.
5. Start second bushing into threads of arm with shaft threaded into opposite bushing.
6. After bushing has been threaded part way into arm, rotate shaft to engage threads of second bushing as and aid in piloting bushing squarely into position.
7. Tighten bushing into arm until hex section of bushing seats firmly into arm. Shaft should be free enough to turn by hand. Install grease fittings and lubricate bushings.
8. Rotate shaft to make distance between shaft bolt holes and arm equal on both sides as nearly as possible.
9. Assemble upper control arm assembly, making certain the wheel alignment shims are correct. Torque shaft-to-bracket bolts to 60-85 ft lbs.
10. Assemble ball joint.
11. Check and adjust wheel alignment if necessary.

Lower Control Arm

1. Remove coil spring.
2. Remove threaded bushings from control arm and remove arm from shaft.
3. Lightly coat shaft threads with

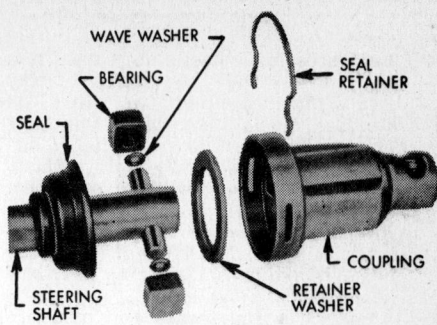

Fig. 4 Steering shaft coupling

grease and install rubber seals on shaft.
4. Position control arm on shaft and start front bushing onto shaft threads. Place a suitable spacer between control arm and crossmember to maintain control arm spread.
5. Thread front bushing into control arm. Tighten bushing until hex of bushing seats firmly into arm.
6. Remove spacer and install rear bushing as above.
7. Install coil spring.

MANUAL STEERING GEAR

The steering gear is the recirculating ball worm and nut type, Fig. 2. The teeth on the pitman shaft sector are slightly tapered so that a proper lash may be obtained by moving the pitman shaft endways by means of a lash adjuster screw which extends through the gear housing side cover, Fig. 3. The outer race or cup of the lower worm bearing is pressed into the worm bearing adjuster which screws into the housing and is locked by a nut, Fig. 2. The upper steering shaft is connected to the steering worm shaft through a universal joint type coupling, Fig. 4.

Steering Gear, Adjust

Never attempt to adjust the steering gear while it is connected to the intermediate rod. The steering gear must be free of all outside load to properly make any steering gear adjustments.

1. Torque steering gear-to-frame bolts to 45-60 ft. lbs.

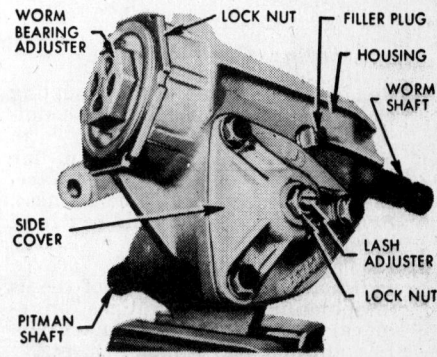

Fig. 5 Steering gear adjusters

2. Disconnect relay rod from pitman arm.

3. Turn steering wheel slowly from one extreme to the other. *Never turn wheel hard against end stops as damage to ball nut may result. If gear is hard pulling or binding it indicates an excessively tight adjustment of worm bearings or excessive misalignment of steering shaft. Roughness of gear indicates faulty internal parts. These conditions must be corrected before steering gear can be properly adjusted.*

4. Attach a spring scale and measure pull at wheel rim required to keep wheel in motion at about one turn of wheel from either extreme position. Pull required should be ¼ to ¾ lb. If not within these limits, adjust worm bearing preload as follows:

5. Loosen worm bearing adjuster lock nut, Fig. 5. Turn bearing adjuster as required to bring wheel pull between ¼ to ¾ pounds. Tighten lock nut and recheck adjustment.

6. To check pitman shaft overcenter preload, turn steering wheel from one extreme to the other while counting the total turns; then turn wheel back ½ the number of turns. This positions gear on the high point where a preload should exist between ball nut and pitman shaft teeth.

7. A pull of ⅞ to 1½ lbs. should be required to turn the wheel through the high point. Loosen the lock nut and turn the pitman shaft lash adjuster, Fig. 5, as required to obtain ⅞ to 1½ lbs.

8. After tightening lock nut, rotate steering wheel back and forth through the high point and through the entire range to check for tight spots. *If lash cannot be removed at high point or if gear load varies greatly and feels rough, the gear should be removed for inspection of internal parts.*

Steering Wheel & Horn Button, Replace

1. To remove standard wheel cap, loosen attaching screw by inserting screwdriver through access hole in side of cap. With screw loosened, cap can slide off steering wheel. The deluxe cap is held in place by spring steel clips. To remove the cap, gently pry it from the wheel.

2. Disconnect horn wire.

3. Remove nut and use puller to remove wheel.

Steering Gear, Replace

1. Remove steering shaft coupling clamp bolt and slide clamp off coupling housing onto steering gear worm shaft. Mark steering shaft in line with slot at coupling clamp surface.

2. Disconnect horn wire from harness. Remove horn shroud from center of steering wheel.

3. Pull off steering wheel.

4. Pull horn contact plate out of recess in actuator to give clearance for removal of upper bearing retainer clip. Pry clip out of actuator housing.

5. Pull steering shaft out of steering

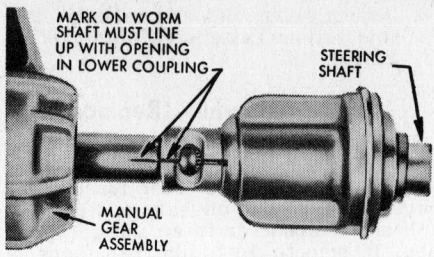

MARK ON WORM SHAFT MUST LINE UP WITH OPENING IN LOWER COUPLING

STEERING SHAFT

MANUAL GEAR ASSEMBLY

Fig. 6 Correct worm to lower coupling attachment

column and block shaft up about two inches.

6. Remove left-hand end plug from relay rod and pull relay rod off pitman arm.

7. Remove four bolts attaching gear to suspension cross bar and remove gear from car.

8. Reverse removal procedure to install gear (see Fig. 6). Torque pitman shaft nut to 100-125 ft. lbs. Torque gear attaching bolts to 45-50 ft. lbs.

Steering Gear Repairs

Using Fig. 7 as a guide, disassemble the steering gear, observing the following:

1. The lower worm bearing cup is not replaced separately but is serviced with the worm bearing adjuster.

2. If the side cover bushing is worn, the side cover must be replaced as the bushing is not furnished separately.

4. Inspect teeth of ball nut and pitman shaft for pitting or scoring which would require replacement of nut or pitman shaft.

5. Check pitman shaft surface for wear or scoring, then check fit of lash adjuster and shim in the slot in end of pitman shaft by inserting a feeler gauge between head of screw and bottom of slot. Adjuster must be free to turn and end play should not exceed .002". If end play exceeds .002", install proper shim. Shims are available in thicknesses of .063", .065", .067", and .069".

6. Lubricate all seals, bushings, bearings and gears with multi-purpose gear lube just before assembling.

Steering Gear, Assemble

1. Position ball nut over worm shaft so that deep side of teeth will be toward side cover when installed in gear housing.

2. Install 19 balls in each circuit. Rock worm shaft slightly to aid in installing balls.

3. Place 6 balls in each return guide, using grease to hold balls in place.

4. Install return guides, clamp and screws.

5. Rotate worm through its complete travel several times to insure balls are installed correctly and rotate freely.

6. Place upper bearing on worm shaft into housing.

7. Place lower bearing in worm bearing adjuster and install bearing retainer.

8. Install adjuster with lock nut in housing. Tighten adjuster only enough to hold worm bearings in place.

9. Turn worm shaft until center groove in ball nut lines up with center of pitman shaft bushing. Install pitman shaft and lash adjuster with shim so that center tooth meshes with center groove in ball nut.

10. Install side cover with new gasket on lash adjuster by turning adjuster counterclockwise. Install and torque side cover bolts to 30 ft. lbs.

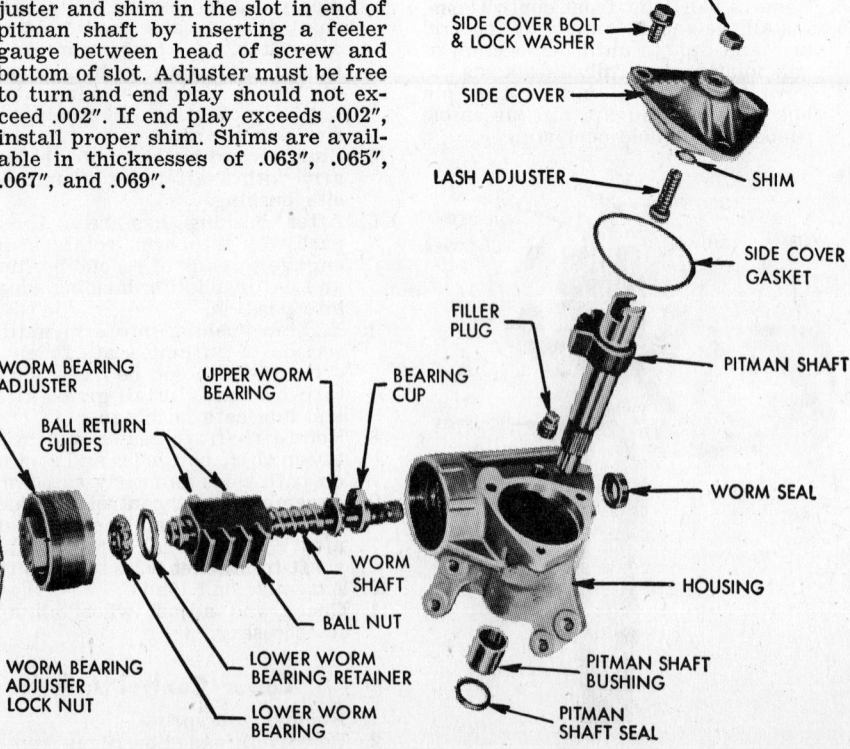

LASH ADJUSTER LOCK NUT

SIDE COVER BOLT & LOCK WASHER

SIDE COVER

LASH ADJUSTER

SHIM

SIDE COVER GASKET

FILLER PLUG

PITMAN SHAFT

WORM BEARING ADJUSTER

BALL RETURN GUIDES

UPPER WORM BEARING

BEARING CUP

WORM SEAL

HOUSING

WORM SHAFT

BALL NUT

WORM BEARING ADJUSTER LOCK NUT

LOWER WORM BEARING RETAINER

LOWER WORM BEARING

PITMAN SHAFT BUSHING

PITMAN SHAFT SEAL

Fig. 7 Exploded view of manual steering gear

11. Turn lash adjuster so that teeth on shaft and ball nut engage but do not bind. Install lash adjuster lock nut loosely.

12. To protect pitman shaft seal from damage, cover shaft splines with masking tape. Slide new seal into place and seat against shoulder in housing.

13. Install new worm shaft seal flush with surface of housing.

14. Fill gear with multi-purpose lubricant, install on car and adjust as previously described.

POWER STEERING

Service procedures on the power steering gear are given in the *Power Steering* chapter. To remove the gear from the car, proceed as follows:

1. Remove coupling flange nuts, and ground wire from flange attaching bolt.

2. Disconnect hoses from pump and gear. Cap pump, hose fittings and gear connectors.

3. Disconnect horn wire from harness. Remove horn shroud from center of steering wheel. Pull off wheel. Pull horn contact out of recess in actuator to give clearance for removal of upper bearing retainer clip. Pry clip out of actuator housing.

4. Pull steering shaft out of steering column and block shaft up about two inches.

5. Disconnect relay rod from pitman arm. Remove four bolts attaching gear to front suspension cross bar and remove coupling from gear.

6. Reverse removal procedure to install, tightening gear attaching nuts to 45-60 ft. lbs.

Instruments, Radio & Windshield Wiper

INSTRUMENT CLUSTER

All instruments and speedometer can be serviced after the instrument cluster has been removed. The procedure is as follows:

1. Disconnect battery positive cable.

2. Remove cluster attaching screws.

3. Disconnect wiring harness, clock and speedometer cable at cluster.

4. Remove four attaching nuts from under instrument panel and remove cluster from top of instrument panel.

RADIO REMOVAL

1. Disconnect radio lead from wiring harness.

2. Disconnect antenna lead-in and speaker wire.

3. Remove control knobs, escutcheons and nuts from front of instrument panel.

4. While supporting radio to prevent it from falling, disconnect radio rear bracket from radio and remove radio.

WINDSHIELD WIPER

1. To remove wiper motor, disconnect drive link from crank arm under instrument panel by removing retaining clip.

2. Disconnect harness connector from motor terminals.

3. If equipped with windshield washers, note location of hoses, then remove hoses from washer pump.

4. Remove three attaching screws and lift motor from cowl, guiding crank arm out of hole in cowl panel.

PLYMOUTH

INDEX OF SERVICE OPERATIONS

PAGE NO.

ACCESSORIES

Radio Removal 961
Speedometer Removal 961
Windshield Wiper 962
Windshield Wiper Troubles............ 37

BODY

Air Conditioning 177
Automatic Seat Adjuster Troubles...... 36
Automatic Top Troubles.............. 36
Automatic Window Lift Troubles........ 36

BRAKES (Mechanical)

Adjustments 112
Brake Cylinder Sizes..................917
Emergency Brake 112
Hydraulic Brake System 112
Master Cylinder, Replace............955
Trouble Shooting 31

BRAKES (Power)

Power Unit Repairs...................128
Power Unit, Replace.................955
Trouble Shooting 32

CLUTCH

Clutch Pedal, Adjust.................942
Clutch Service 943
Trouble Shooting 13

COOLING SYSTEM

Radiator, Replace 935
Trouble Shooting 8
Water Distributor Tube, Replace......936
Water Pump Repairs 935
Water Pump, Replace................935

ELECTRIC SYSTEM

Alternator, Replace 937
Alternator Service 57
Alternator Specs. 914
Dash Gauge Service.................. 85
Distributor, Replace..................936
Distributor Service 46
Distributor Specifications............917
Generator & Regulator Service...... 62
Generator & Regulator Specs......918
Horn Button or Ring, Replace......959
Ignition System Service.............. 46
Ignition Timing 937
Starter, Replace 937
Starter Switch Service............... 83
Starting Motor Service............... 77
Starting Motor Specifications......916
Trouble Shooting 10
Turn Signal Troubles................. 12

ENGINE

Camshaft, Replace 929
Crankshaft & Bearing Specs........916
Crankshaft Oil Seal, Replace........931
Cylinder Head, Replace 921
Engine, Replace 920
Main Bearings, Replace 931
Piston Pins, Replace..................930
Piston Rings, Replace................930
Piston, Pin & Ring Specs............916
Pistons & Rods, Remove............930
Piston & Rod, Assemble.............930
Pistons, Replace 930
Rocker Arms 923
Rod Bearings, Replace...............931
Timing Cover, Replace...............928
Timing Chain, Replace...............928
Trouble Shooting 4
Valve Arrangement 923
Valves, Adjust 923
Valves, Grind 926
Valve Guides 926
Valve Lifters (Mechanical)...........927
Valve Lifters (Hydraulic)............927
Valves, Remove 924
Valve Seat Inserts, Replace.........927
Valve Spring Installed Height 925
Valve Spring Testing 925
Valve Specifications 915

ENGINE OILING

Oil Pan, Replace 932
Oil Pressure Regulator 934
Oil Pump Repairs....................933
Oil Pump, Replace...................933
Trouble Shooting 9

FRONT SUSPENSION

Front End Repairs....................956
Trouble Shooting 33
Wheel Alignment 955
Wheel Alignment Specifications.......918
Wheel Bearings, Adjust..............956

FUEL & EXHAUST SYSTEMS

Carburetors 937
Fuel Pumps 96
Mufflers and Pipes....................937
Trouble Shooting 4

OVERDRIVE....................100

Trouble Shooting 14

REAR AXLE

Axle Shaft, Replace...................953
General Service 102
Non-Slip Differentials 109
Rear Axle Repairs....................954
Rear Axle Specifications............917
Trouble Shooting 31

SPECIFICATIONS

Alternators 914
Brake & Cylinder Sizes..............917
Capacity Data 919
Carburetors 938
Cooling System 919
Crankshaft & Bearings..............916
Distributors 917
Engine Tightening 915
Generator & Regulators.............918
Pistons, Pins & Rings...............916
Rear Axle 917
Starting Motors 916
Tune Up 914
Valves 915
Valve Timing 929
Wheel Alignment 918

STEERING GEARS (Mechanical)

Horn Button or Ring, Replace.........959
Steering Gear Repairs................961
Steering Gear, Replace..............959
Steering Wheel, Replace............959
Trouble Shooting 33

STEERING GEARS (Power)

Steering Gear Repairs................145
Steering Gear, Replace..............960
Trouble Shooting 34

TRANSMISSION (Manual Shift)

Gearshift, Adjust 949
Transmission Repairs 943
Transmission, Replace................943
Trouble Shooting 14

TRANSMISSION (Automatic)

Hy-Drive 945
Powerflite Controls 950
  Replace 950
  Repairs 297
  Trouble Shooting 21
Torqueflite Controls 952
  Replace 951
  Repairs, 6 331
  Repairs, V8 341
  Trouble Shooting 23

TUNE UP....................... 38

GENERAL SPECIFICATIONS

Year	Model Designation	Wheelbase, Inches	Valve Location	Bore and Stroke	Piston Displacement, Cubic Inches	Compression Ratio (Standard)	Maximum Brake H.P. @ R.P.M.	Maximum Torque Lbs. Ft. @ R.P.M.	Normal Oil Pressure Pounds
1953	Cambridge 6..........P24-1	114	In Block	3.2500 x 4.375	217.8	7.10	100 @ 3600	177 @ 1200	40–45
	Cranbrook 6..........P24-2	114	In Block	3.2500 x 4.375	217.8	7.10	100 @ 3600	177 @ 1200	40–45
1954 Early	Plaza 6..........P25-1	114	In Block	3.2500 x 4.375	217.8	7.10	100 @ 3600	177 @ 1600	40–45
	Savoy 6..........P25-2	114	In Block	3.2500 x 4.375	217.8	7.10	100 @ 3600	177 @ 1600	40–45
	Belvedere 6..........P25-3	114	In Block	3.2500 x 4.375	217.8	7.10	100 @ 3600	177 @ 1600	40–45
1954 Late	Plaza 6..........P25-1	114	In Block	3.2500 x 4.625	230	7.25	110 @ 3600	190 @ 1600	40–45
	Savoy 6..........P25-2	114	In Block	3.2500 x 4.625	230	7.25	110 @ 3600	190 @ 1600	40–45
	Belvedere 6..........P25-3	114	In Block	3.2500 x 4.625	230	7.25	110 @ 3600	190 @ 1600	40–45
1955	Six [1]..........P26	115	In Block	3.2500 x 4.625	230	7.40	117 @ 3600	177 @ 1200	40–45
	V8 [1]..........P27	115	In Head	3.4375 x 3.250	241.3	7.6	157 @ 4400	217 @ 2400	50–65
	V8 [1] (2-Bar. Carb.)..........P27	115	In Head	3.5625 x 3.250	259	7.6	167 @ 4400	231 @ 2400	50–65
	V8 [1] (4-Bar. Carb.)..........P27	115	In Head	3.5625 x 3.250	259	7.6	177 @ 4400	231 @ 2800	50–65
1956	Six [1] (1-Bar. Carb.)..........P28	115	In Block	3.2500 x 4.625	230	7.6	125 @ 3600	200 @ 1600	40–45
	Six [1] (2-Bar. Carb.)..........P28	115	In Block	3.2500 x 4.625	230	7.6	131 @ 3600	203 @ 2000	40–45
	V8 [1] (2-Bar. Carb.)..........P29	115	In Head	3.6250 x 3.250	270	8.0	180 @ 4400	260 @ 2400	50–65
	V8 [1] (2-Bar. Carb.)..........P29	115	In Head	3.7500 x 3.125	277	8.0	187 @ 4400	265 @ 2400	50–65
	V8 [1] (4-Bar. Carb.)..........P29	115	In Head	3.7500 x 3.125	277	8.0	200 @ 4400	272 @ 2400	50–65
	Fury V8..........P29	115	In Head	3.8125 x 3.312	303	9.25	240 @ 4800	310 @ 2800	50–65
1957	Six [1]..........P30	118	In Block	3.2500 x 4.625	230	8.0	132 @ 3600	205 @ 1600	40–45
	V8 [1] (2-Bar. Carb.)..........P31	118	In Head	3.7500 x 3.125	277	8.0	197 @ 4400	270 @ 2400	50–65
	V8 [1] (2-Bar. Carb.)..........P31	118	In Head	3.9062 x 3.125	301	8.5	215 @ 4400	285 @ 2800	50–65
	V8 [1] (4-Bar. Carb.)..........P31	118	In Head	3.9062 x 3.125	301	8.5	235 @ 4400	305 @ 2800	50–65
	V8 [1] (4-Bar. Carb.)..........P31	118	In Head	3.9062 x 3.312	318	9.25	290 @ 5400	325 @ 4000	50–65
1958	Six [1]..........LP1	118 [2]	In Block	3.2500 x 4.625	230	8.0	132 @ 3600	205 @ 1200	40–45
	V8 [1] (2-Bar. Carb.)..........LP2	118 [2]	In Head	3.9062 x 3.312	318	9.0	225 @ 4400	330 @ 2800	50–65
	V8 [1] (4-Bar. Carb.)..........LP2	118 [2]	In Head	3.9062 x 3.312	318	9.0	250 @ 4490	340 @ 2400	50–65
	Fury V8..........LP2	118	In Head	3.9062 x 3.312	318	9.25	290 @ 5200	330 @ 3600	50–65
	Golden Commando [3]..........	...	In Head	4.0625 x 3.375	350	10.0	305 @ 5000	370 @ 3600	50–65
1959	Six [1]..........MP1	118 [2]	In Block	3.2500 x 4.625	230	8.0	132 @ 3600	205 @ 1200	40–45
	Standard V8 [1]..........MP2	118 [2]	In Head	3.9062 x 3.312	318	9.0	230 @ 4400	340 @ 2400	45–65
	Golden Commando [1]..........	118 [2]	In Head	4.1250 x 3.375	361	10.0	305 @ 4600	395 @ 3000	45–65
1960	Six [1]..........PP1	118 [2]	In Head	3.4000 x 4.125	225	8.5	145 @ 4000	215 @ 2800	40–65
	Standard V8 [1]..........PP2	118 [2]	In Head	3.9062 x 3.312	318	9.0	230 @ 4000	340 @ 2400	45–65
	Golden Commando [1]..........	118 [2]	In Head	4.1250 x 3.375	361	10.0	305 @ 4800	395 @ 3000	45–65
	Sonoramic Commando [1]......	118 [2]	In Head	4.1250 x 3.375	361	10.0	310 @ 4800	435 @ 2800	45–65
1961	Six [1]..........RP1	118 [2]	In Head	3.4000 x 4.125	225	8.2	145 @ 4000	215 @ 2800	40–65
	Standard V8 [1]..........RP2	118 [2]	In Head	3.9062 x 3.312	318	9.0	230 @ 4400	340 @ 2400	45–65
	Golden Commando [1]..........	118 [2]	In Head	4.1250 x 3.375	361	9.0	305 @ 4800	395 @ 3000	45–65
	Sonoramic Commando [1]......	118 [2]	In Head	4.2500 x 3.375	383	10.0	330 @ 4800	460 @ 2800	45–65

[1]—All models are available with any of the engines listed.
[2]—Suburbans 122".

TUNE UP SPECIFICATIONS

★When using a timing light disconnect vacuum line to prevent vacuum advance mechanism from operating.

Year	Model	Ground Polarity and Voltage	Spark Plug Type ①	Spark Plug Gap Inch	Distributor Point Gap Inch	Distributor Cam Angle Degrees	Firing Order ②	Ignition Timing★ Mark	Ignition Timing★ Location	Idle Speed RPM In Neutral	Compression Pressure @ Cranking Speed Minimum
1953	All	P-6	4S-140	.035	.020	39	153624	2°BTDC	Pulley	475	105
1954	All	P-6	4S-140	.035	.020	39	153624	2°BTDC	Damper	475	105
1955	Six	P-6	4S-140	.035	.020	39	153624	2°BTDC	Damper	500	120
	V8	P-6	4S-165	.035	.017	⑥	18436572	4°BTDC	Pulley	500	125
1956	Six	N-12	AR-80	.035	.020	39	153624	2°BTDC	Damper	500	120
	V8	N-12	AR-52	.035	.017	31	18436572	4°BTDC③	Pulley	500	125
	Fury	N-12	4S-250	.035	.017	31	18436572	4°BTDC	Damper	500	130
1957	Six	N-12	AR-51	.035	.020	39	153624	2°BTDC	Damper	500	120
	V8-277	N-12	AR-52	.035	.017	29	18436572	④	Pulley	500	125
	V8-301	N-12	AR-52	.035	.017	29	18436572	⑤	Pulley	500	130
	V8-318	N-12	AR-32	.035	.017	⑦	18436572	8°BTDC	Damper	500	130
1958	Six	N-12	AR-51	.035	.020	39	153624	2°BTDC	Damper	500	125
	V8-318	N-12	AR-42	.035	.017	29	18436572	10°BTDC	Pulley	500	130
	V8-350	N-12	AR-32	.035	.017	⑦	18436572	8°BTDC	Damper	500⑨	150
1959	MP1	N-12	AR-51	.035	.020	39	153624	2½°BTDC	Damper	500	125
	MP2 Std.	N-12	AR-42	.035	.017	29	18436572	10°BTDC	Pulley	500	130
	MP2 Power Pak.	N-12	AR-42	.035	.017	29	18436572	10°BTDC	Damper	500	150
	MP2 Gold. Com.	N-12	A-32	.035	.017	⑧	18436572	7½°BTDC	Damper	500	150
1960	PP1	N-12	AG-52	.035	.020	36–42	153624	⑩	Damper	500	125
	PP2 Std. Tr.	N-12	A-42	.035	.017	27–32	18436572	5°BTDC	Pulley	500	130
	PP2 Auto. Tr.	N-12	A-42	.035	.017	27–32	18436572	10°BTDC	Damper	500	150
	V8-318 Pow. Pak.	N-12	A-42	.035	.017	27–32	18436572	10°BTDC	Damper	500	135–165
	V8-361 Gold. Com.	N-12	A-32	.035	.017	⑧	18436572	10°BTDC	Damper	500	135–165
	Sonoramic Eng.	N-12	A-32	.035	.017	⑧	18436572	5°BTDC	Damper	500	150–180
1961	Six	N-12	AG-52	.035	.020	36–42	153624	⑩	⑩	550	130–160
	V8-318 Auto. Tr.	N-12	A-42	.035	.017	27–32	18436572	10°BTDC	Damper	500	135–165
	V8-318 Std. Tr.	N-12	A-42	.035	.017	27–32	18436572	5°BTDC	Pulley	500	135–165
	V8-361	N-12	A-32	.035	.017	27–32	18436572	10°BTDC	Damper	500	135–165
	V8-383	N-12	A-32	.035	.017	27–32	18436572	7½°BTDC	Damper	500	150–180

①—Auto-Lite.
②—V8 cylinder numbering (front to rear): Left bank 1-3-5-7, right bank 2-4-6-8.
③—TDC on 277 engine with 4-barrel carburetor.
④—With 1BJ distributor, TDC. With 1BP distributor 4°BTDC.
⑤—With 1BP-4003A, 4°BTDC. With 1BP-4003, 10°BTDC.

⑥—Each set 26–28, total dwell both sets 32–36.
⑦—Each set 29–32, total dwell both sets 36–39.
⑧—Each set 27–32, total dwell both sets 34–40.
⑨—Two carburetor jobs 650 RPM.
⑩—Automatic trans. 5° BTDC, manual shift trans. 2½° BTDC.

ALTERNATOR & REGULATOR SPECIFICATIONS

Year	Unit Number	Ground Polarity and Rotation	Field Coil Draw Amperes	Current Output Engine R.P.M.	Current Output Amperes	Current Output Volts	Operating Voltage Engine R.P.M.	Operating Voltage Amperes	Operating Voltage Voltage @ 120° ①	Voltage Regulator Point Gap	Regulator Armature Air Gap
1961	2095060	Neg.-C	2.38-2.75②	1250	28③	14.6	1250	15	13.48-14.08④	.015	.048-.052

①—For each 10° rise in temperature subtract .04 volt; for each 10° drop in temperature add .04 volt. Temperature is checked with a thermometer 2 inches from installed voltage regulator cover.
②—Current draw at 12 volts while turning rotor shaft by hand.
③—If output is low, stator or rectifier is shorted.
④—At 2200 R.P.M. there should be a voltage increase of .2 to .7 volt.

VALVE SPECIFICATIONS

Year	Model	Valve Lash		Valve Angles		Valve Spring Installed Height	Valve Spring Pressure Lbs. @ In.	Valve Lift		Stem Clearance		Stem Diameter	
		Int.	Exh.	Seat	Face			Int.	Exh.	Intake	Exhaust	Int.	Exh.

PLYMOUTH

Year	Model	Int.	Exh.	Seat	Face	Installed Height	Pressure	Int.	Exh.	Intake	Exhaust	Int.	Exh.
1953	All	.010H	.010H	45	45	1¾	115 @ 1⅜	.365	.365	.001–.003	.002–.005	.3405	.3405
1954	All	.010H	.010H	45	45	1¾	115 @ 1⅜	.365	.365	.001–.003	.002–.005	.3405	.3405
1955	Six	.010H	.010H	45	45	1¾	115 @ 1⅜	.365	.365	.001–.003	.003–.005	.3405	.3405
	V8	Zero	Zero	45	45	1¹¹⁄₁₆	140 @ 1⁵⁄₁₆	.360	.360	.001–.003	.002–.004	.3725	.3715
1956	Six	.010H	.012H	45	45	1¾	115 @ 1⅜	.365	.365	.001–.003	.003–.005	.3405	.3405
	V8-277	.012H	.020H	45	45	1¹¹⁄₁₆	166 @ 1⁵⁄₁₆	.374	.380	.001–.003	.002–.004	.3725	.3715
	V8-270	Zero	Zero	45	45	1¹¹⁄₁₆	140 @ 1⁵⁄₁₆	.360	.360	.001–.003	.002–.004	.3725	.3715
	V8-318	.010H	.018H	45	45	1¹¹⁄₁₆	166 @ 1⁵⁄₁₆	.379	.376	.001–.003	.002–.004	.3725	.3715
1957	Six	.010H	.010H	45	45	1¾	115 @ 1⅜	.365	.365	.001–.003	.002–.004	.3405	.3405
	V8-277	.008H	.018H	45	45	1¹¹⁄₁₆	166 @ 1⁵⁄₁₆	.387	.387	.001–.003	.002–.004	.3725	.3715
	V8-301	.008H	.018H	45	45	1¹¹⁄₁₆	166 @ 1⁵⁄₁₆	.387	.387	.001–.003	.002–.004	.3725	.3715
	V8-318	.008H	.018H	45	45	1²¹⁄₃₂	185 @ 1⁹⁄₃₂	.405	.405	.001–.003	.002–.004	.3725	.3715
1958	Six	.010H	.010H	45	45	1¾	115 @ 1⅜	.365	.365	.001–.003	.003–.005	.3405	.3405
	V8-318	.010H	.018H	45	45	1¹¹⁄₁₆	166 @ 1⁵⁄₁₆	.405	.405	.001–.003	.002–.004	.3725	.3715
	V8-350	Zero	Zero	45	45	1⁵⁵⁄₆₄	195 @ 1¹³⁄₃₂	.390	.390	.001–.003	.002–.004	.3725	.3715
1959	Six	.010H	.010H	45	45	1¾	115 @ 1⅜	.365	.365	.001–.003	.002–.004	.3405	.3405
	V8-318	.010H	.018H	45	45	1¹¹⁄₁₆	166 @ 1⁵⁄₁₆	.390	.386	.001–.003	.002–.004	.3725	.3715
	V8-361	Zero	Zero	45	45	1⁵⁵⁄₆₄	195 @ 1¹⁵⁄₃₂	.390	.390	.001–.003	.002–.004	.3725	.3715
1960	Six	.010H	.020H	①	①	1¹¹⁄₁₆	177 @ 1⁵⁄₁₆	.375	.360	.001–.003	.002–.004	.3725	.3715
	V8-318	.010H	.018H	45	45	1¹¹⁄₁₆	177 @ 1⁵⁄₁₆	.389	.389	.001–.003	.002–.004	.3725	.3715
	V8-361	Zero	Zero	45	45	1⁵⁵⁄₆₄	205 @ 1⁷⁄₁₆	.430	.430	.001–.003	.002–.004	.3725	.3715
1961	Six	.010H	.020H	①	①	1¹¹⁄₁₆	165 @ 1⁵⁄₁₆	.375	.360	.001–.003	.002–.004	.3725	.3715
	V8-318	.010H	.018H	45	45	1¹¹⁄₁₆	175 @ 1⁵⁄₁₆	.370	.368	.001–.003	.002–.004	.3725	.3715
	V8-361	Zero	Zero	45	45	1⁵⁵⁄₆₄	195 @ 1¹⁵⁄₃₂	.389	.389	.001–.003	.002–.004	.3725	.3715
	V8-383	Zero	Zero	45	45	1⁵⁵⁄₆₄	195 @ 1¹⁵⁄₃₂	.389	.389	.001–.003	.002–.004	.3725	.3715

①—Intake face and seat 45°, exhaust seat 45°, exhaust face 47°.

ENGINE TIGHTENING SPECIFICATIONS★

★Torque specifications are for clean and lightly lubricated threads only. Dry or dirty threads produce increased friction which prevents accurate measurement of tightness.

Year	Spark Plugs Ft. Lbs.	Cylinder Head Bolts Ft. Lbs.	Intake Manifold Ft. Lbs.	Exhaust Manifold Ft. Lbs.	Rocker Arm Shaft Bracket Ft. Lbs.	Rocker Arm Cover Ft. Lbs.	Connecting Rod Cap Bolts Ft. Lbs.	Main Bearing Cap Bolts Ft. Lbs.	Flywheel to Crankshaft Ft. Lbs.	Vibration Damper or Pulley Ft. Lbs.
1953–56 Six	30	60–70	15–20	15–20	—	—	40–50	80–85	55–60	108
1955–56 V8	30	85	30	25	30	②	45	85	60	135
1957–59 Six	32	70	30	25	—	—	45	85	60	135
1957 V8	32	85	30	25	85	③	45	85	60	135
1958–59 V8-318	32	85	30	25	85	③	45	85	60	135
1958 V8-350	32	70	30	30	—	③	45	85	60	135
1959 V8-361	30	70	30	30	30	③	45	85	60	135
1960–61 Six	30	65	①	10	30	③	45	85	60	④
1960–61 V8-318	30	85	30	25	85	⑤	45	85	60	135
1960–61 361, 383	30	70	40	30	30	③	45	85	...	135

①—200 inch lbs.　②—20–25 inch lbs.　③—40 inch lbs.　④—Press fit.　⑤—36 inch lbs.

PISTONS, PINS, RINGS, CRANKSHAFT & BEARINGS

Year	Model	Fitting Pistons		Ring End Gap ①		Wrist-pin Diameter	Rod Bearings		Main Bearings			
		Shim To Use	Pounds Pull On Scale	Comp.	Oil		Shaft Diameter	Bearing Clearance	Shaft Diameter	Bearing Clearance	Thrust on Bear. No.	Shaft End Play
1953-54	Six	.002	5-10	.010	.010	.8592	2.061-2.062	.0005-.0015	2.499-2.500	.0005-.0015	5	.002-.007
1955	Six	.002	5-10	.010	.010	.8592	2.061-2.062	.0005-.0015	2.499-2.500	.0005-.0015	5	.002-.007
	V8	.0015	5-10	.010	.010	.8592	1.9375	.0005-.0015	2.374-2.375	.0005-.0015	3	.002-.007
1956	Six	.002	5-10	.010	.010	.8592	2.061-2.062	.0005-.0015	2.499-2.500	.0005-.0015	5	.002-.007
	V8-277	.0015	5-10	.010	.010	.9842	2.124-2.125	.0005-.002	2.499-2.500	.0005-.0023	3	.002-.007
	V8-270	.0015	5-10	.010	.010	.8592	1.9375	.0005-.0015	2.375-2.375	.0005-.0015	3	.002-.007
	V8-Fury	.0015	5-10	.010	.010	.9842	2.124-2.125	.0005-.002	2.499-2.500	.0005-.0023	3	.002-.007
1957	Six	.002	5-10	.010	.010	.8592	2.061-2.062	.0005-.0015	2.499-2.500	.0005-.0015	5	.002-.007
	V8	.0015	5-10	.010	.010	.9842	2.124-2.125	.0005-.002	2.499-2.500	.0005-.0023	3	.002-.007
1958	Six	.002	5-10	.010	.010	.8592	2.061-2.062	.0005-.0015	2.499-2.500	.0005-.0015	5	.002-.007
	V8-318	.0015	5-10	.010	.010	.9842	2.124-2.125	.0002-.0022	2.499-2.500	.0005-.0015	3	.002-.007
	V8-350	.0015	5-10	.013	.013	1.094	2.379-2.380	.0005-.0015	2.629-2.630	.0005-.0015	3	.002-.007
1959	MP1	.002	5-10	.010	.010	.859	2.061-2.062	.0005-.0015	2.499-2.500	.0005-.0015	5	.002-.007
	MP2	.0015	5-10	.010	.010	.984	2.124-2.125	.0002-.0022	2.499-2.500	.0005-.0015	3	.002-.007
	Gold. Com.	.0015	5-10	.013	.013	1.093	2.379-2.380	.0005-.0015	2.629-2.630	.0005-.0015	3	.002-.007
1960	6-255	.0015	5-10	.010	.015	.9008	2.1865-2.1875	.0005-.0015	2.7495-2.7505	.0005-.0015	3	.003-.008
	V8-318	.0015	5-10	.010	.010	.984	2.124-2.125	.0005-.0015	2.4995-2.5005	.0005-.0015	3	.002-.007
	V8-361	.001	5-10	.013	.013	1.0936	2.374-2.375	.0005-.0015	2.6245-2.6255	.0005-.0015	3	.002-.007
1961	Six	.0015	5-10	.010	.015	.9008	2.1865-2.1875	.0005-.0015	2.7495-2.7505	.0005-.0015	3	.003-.008
	V8-318	.0015	5-10	.010	.010	.9842	2.124-2.125	.0005-.0015	2.4995-2.5005	.0005-.0015	3	.002-.007
	V8-361	.001	5-10	.013	.013	1.0936	2.374-2.375	.0005-.0015	2.6245-2.6255	.0005-.0015	3	.002-.007
	V8-383	.001	5-10	.013	.013	1.0936	2.374-2.375	.0005-.0015	2.6245-2.6255	.0005-.0015	3	.002-.007

①—Fit rings in tapered bores for clearance listed in tightest portion of ring travel.

STARTING MOTOR SPECIFICATIONS

Year and Model	Part No.	Rotation ①	Brush Spring Tension, Ounces	No Load Test			Torque Test		
				Amperes	Volts	R.P.M.	Amperes	Volts	Torque, Lbs. Ft.
1953-54	MCH-6205	C	42-53	65	5.0	4300	335	2.0	6
1954-55 Six	MCH-6305	C	42-53	65	5.0	4300	335	2.0	6
1955 V8	MCH-6206	C	42-53	65	5.0	4300	335	2.0	6
1956 Six	MDF-6002	C	42-53	60	10.0	3200	240	4.0	6½
1956 V8	MDF-6007	C	42-53	60	10.0	3200	240	4.0	6½
1956 Six	MDG-6001	C	42-53	50	10.0	4400	210	4.0	5
1956 V8	MDG-6002	C	42-53	50	10.0	4400	210	4.0	5
1957-58	MDM-6001	C	31-47	60	10.0	3200	225	4.0	6
1957 Six	MDM-6004	C	31-47	60	10.0	3200	225	4.0	6
1957 V8	MDM-6002	C	31-47	50	10.0	4400	210	4.0	5
1958	MDL-6004	C	31-47	60	10.0	3200	225	4.0	6
1958-59	MDT-6001	C	31-47	58	11.0	3800	350	4.0	8½
1959	MDU-6003	C	31-47	50	11	5500	355	4.0	9
1960	MDT-7002	C	31-47	58	11	3800	350	4	8½
	MDU-7001	C	31-47	50	11	5500	355	4	9
	MDT-7001	C	31-47	58	11	3800	350	4	8½
1961	MDT-7002	C	31-47	58	11	3800	350	4	8½
	1889100	C	32-48	78	11	3800	350	4	8½
	1889200	C	32-48	78	11	3800	350	4	8½

①—As viewed from the drive end. C—Clockwise.

DISTRIBUTOR SPECIFICATIONS

Year and Model	Part No. ①	Rotation ②	Cam Angle, Degrees	Breaker Point Opening, Inch	Condenser Capacity, Mfds. ③	Breaker Arm Spring Tension, Ounces	Centrifugal Advance Data Degrees @ R.P.M. of Dist.		Vacuum Advance Data		
							Advance Starts	Full Advance	Inches of Vacuum to Start Plunger Movement	Inches of Vacuum for Full Plunger Travel	Maximum Vacuum Advance Dist. Degrees
1953–54	1AT-4101	C	39	.020	.25–.28	17–20	1 @ 450	10 @ 1425	4¼	14	8
1954	1AT-4101C	C	39	.020	.25–.28	17–20	1 @ 440	9 @ 1300	4¼	14	8
1954–57 Six	1AT-4101B	C	39	.020	.25–.28	17–20	1 @ 525	8 @ 1350	4¾	14	8
1955 V8	1AZ-4003C	C	④	.017	.25–.28	17–20	1 @ 375	18 @ 1900	5¼	17	11½
1955 V8	1AZ-4003E	C	④	.017	.25–.28	17–20	1 @ 375	18 @ 1900	5¼	11¼	7
1955 V8	1AZ-4003G	C	④	.017	.25–.28	17–20	1 @ 375	16 @ 1650	5¼	8½	4
1955 V8	1AZ-4003H	C	④	.017	.25–.28	17–20	1 @ 375	16 @ 1650	5¼	17	11½
1956 V8	1BJ-4301A	C	31	.017	.25–.28	17–20	1 @ 400	15 @ 2150	5½	15	12½
1956–57 V8	1BJ-4301B	C	31	.017	.25–.28	17–20	1 @ 385	16 @ 2000	5½	15	11½
1957–58 Six	1BR-4001	C	39	.020	.25–.28	17–20	1 @ 460	8½ @ 1800	6	16	9½
1957 V8	1BP-4003	C	29	.017	.25–.28	17–20	1 @ 575	9½ @ 2200	7⅛	18	13
1957 V8	1BP-4003A	C	29	.017	.25–.28	17–20	1 @ 370	11 @ 950	7⅛	13½	9½
1957 V8	1BP-4003C	C	29	.017	.25–.28	17–20	1 @ 400	15 @ 2150	6	15½	12½
1957–58 V8	1BS-4003	C	⑤	.017	.25–.28	17–20	1 @ 375	8 @ 1000	9⅛	18	10¼
1958	1BP-4003F	C	29	.017	.25–.28	17–20	1 @ 565	9 @ 2300	6¾	14	13½
	1BP-4003D	C	29	.017	.25–.28	17–20	1 @ 425	11 @ 2400	6¾	16	13½
	1BS-4006B	C	⑤	.017	.25–.28	17–20	1 @ 425	10 @ 2000	7⅛	16½	13
	1BS-4009	C	⑤	.017	.25–.28	17–20	1 @ 425	10 @ 2000	7⅛	16½	13
1959	1BR-4001	C	39	.020	.25–.28	17–20	0 @ 350	8.5 @ 1800	6	16	9.5
	1BP-4003F	C	29	.017	.25–.28	17–20	0 @ 450	9 @ 2300	6¾	16	13
	1BS-4006C	CC	⑥	.017	.25–.28	17–20	0 @ 450	9.5 @ 2000	8⅜	18⅛	13
	1838505-P	C	29	.017	.25–.28	17–20	0 @ 450	9 @ 2300	6¾	16	13
	1BP-4005B	CC	27–32	.017	.25–.28	17–20	1 @ 450	9½ @ 2150	9	16½	12½
1960	2095270	C	36–42	.020	.25–.28	17–21	1 @ 450	11½ @ 2200	5.9	12	10.3
	1BP-4003T	C	27–32	.017	.25–.28	17–21	1 @ 430	11½ @ 2300	8	17	14.8
	1BP-4003L	C	27–32	.017	.25–.28	17–21	1 @ 565	9 @ 2300	8	17	14.8
	1BS-4006D	CC	⑥	.017	.25–.28	17–21	0 @ 450	9½ @ 2400	7½	16	11
	1BS-4006E	CC	⑥	.017	.25–.28	17–21	0 @ 400	10 @ 2400	7½	14½	9
1961	2095270	C	36–42	.020	.25–.28	17–21	1 @ 450	11½ @ 2200	5.9	12	10.3
	1838505	C	27–32	.017	.25–.28	17–21	1 @ 565	10 @ 2300	6.8–9.2	17	15
	1889710	C	27–32	.017	.25–.28	17–21	1 @ 405	9½ @ 2200	4.5–6.6	13.2	11½
	2095647	C	27–32	.017	.25–.28	17–21	1 @ 430	12½ @ 2300	6.8–9.2	17	15
	1BS-4006F	CC	27–32	.017	.25–.28	17–21	2 @ 425	13 @ 2050	7.5–9.2	16	12½

①—Stamped on plate riveted to side of distributor housing.
②—As viewed from the top. C—Clockwise. CC—Counterclockwise.
③—Microfarads—as indicated on a condenser tester.
④—Each set 26–28, total dwell both sets 32–36.
⑤—Each set 29–32, total dwell both sets 36–39.
⑥—Each set 27–32, total dwell both sets 34–40.

REAR AXLE AND BRAKE CYLINDER SPECIFICATIONS

Year	Model	Ring Gear & Pinion Backlash, Inch	Drive Pinion Adjustment	Drive Pinion Bearing Preload, Inch, Lbs.	Drive Pinion Bearing Adjustment	Axle Shaft End Play, Inch	Hydraulic Cylinder Bore Sizes, Inch		Master Cylinder
							Wheel Cylinder		
							Front	Rear	
1953–54	All	.006–.010	Washer	15–25①	Shims	.003–.008	1⅛	1⅛	1⅛
1955–56	All	.006–.010	Washer	20–30①	Shims	.003–.008	1⅛	1⅛	1⅛
1957–61	All	.006–.008	Washer	20–30①	Shims	.013–.023②	1⅛	1⅛	1⅛

①—For used bearings, drag should be zero to one-half that specified but with no end play of the drive pinion.
②—Adjust to .018″.

PLYMOUTH

GENERATOR AND REGULATOR SPECIFICATIONS

★To polarize generator, reconnect the leads to the regulator; then momentarily connect a jumper wire from the "Arm" to the "Bat" terminals of the regulator.

Year	Generator Number	Rotation and Ground Polarity ②	Rated Cap. Amps.	Gen. Field Ground Location★	Brush Spring Tension, Ounces	Field Current Amperes	Regulator Number	Cutout Relay Voltage to Close Points	Cutout Relay Armature Air Gap, Inch	Voltage Regulator Setting Volts	Current Regulator Setting Amperes	Current and Voltage Armature Air Gap, Inch
1953–55	GGW-6001K	C-P	45	External	35–53	1.4–1.5③	VBE-6201A	6.5	.032	7.2	45	.050
1953–55	GGW-6001J	C-P	45	External	35–53	1.4–1.5③	VBE-6201A	6.5	.032	7.2	45	.050
1954	GGW-6008F	C-P	45	External	35–53	1.4–1.5③	VBE-6201A	6.5	.032	7.2	45	.050
1955	GGW-6012B	C-P	45	External	35–53	1.4–1.5③	VBE-6201A	6.5	.032	7.2	45	.050
1955	GGW-6016A	C-P	45	External	35–53	1.4–1.5③	VBE-6201A	6.5	.032	7.2	45	.050
1956	GJC-7001A	C-N	30	External	18–36	1.2–1.3①	VRX-6201A	13.1	.032	14.3	30	.050
1956	GJC-7002A	C-N	30	External	18–36	1.2–1.3①	VRX-6201A	13.1	.032	14.3	30	.050
1956–57	GJC-7003B	C-N	30	External	18–36	1.2–1.3①	VRX-6201A	13.1	.032	14.3	30	.050
1957–58	GJC-7012A	C-N	30	External	18–36	1.2–1.3①	VRX-6201A	13.1	.032	14.3	30	.050
1959	GJM-8001A	C-N	35	External	34–41	1.6–1.7①	VRX-6301A	13.1	.032	14.3	35	.050
	GGA-6001AC	C-N	40	External	18–36	1.1–1.3①	VAT-6201A	13.1	.032	14.3	40	.050
1960	GJM-8201A	C-N	35	External	18–36	1.6–1.7①	VBO-4202BC	13.1	.032	14.6	35	.050
1961	GJM-8203A	C-N	35	External	18–36	1.6–1.7①	VBO-4202BC	13.1	.032	14.6	35	.050
	GGA-6003	C-N	40	External	34–41	1.2–1.3①	VBO-4202BC	13.1	.032	14.6	40	.050

①—At 10 volts.
②—C-Clockwise. P-Positive. N-Negative. ③—At 5 volts.

WHEEL ALIGNMENT SPECIFICATIONS

Year	Model	Caster, Degrees Limits	Caster, Degrees Desired	Camber, Degrees Limits	Camber, Degrees Desired	Toe-In, Inches	Toe-out on Turns, Degrees① Outer Wheel	Toe-out on Turns, Degrees① Inner Wheel	Kingpin or Steering Axis Inclination②
1953–54	All	− 1 to + 1	0	− ⅜ to + ⅜	0	0 to 1/16	20	20½ to 22½	5 to 6½
1955–56	All	− 2 to 0	− 1	− ⅛ to + ⅝	③	⅛	20	20½ to 22½	5 to 6½
1957–58	Manual Steering	0 to − 1½	− ¾	④	④	3/32 to 5/32	18°46′	20	6½ @ 0 Camber
	Power Steering	0 to + 1½	+ ¾	④	④	3/32 to 5/32	18°46′	20	6½ @ 0 Camber
1959	Manual Steering	0 to − 1½	− ¾	④	④	⅛	18°46′	20	6½ @ 0 Camber
	Power Steering	0 to + 1½	+ ¾	④	④	⅛	18°46′	20	6½ @ 0 Camber
1960	Manual Steering	0 to − 1	− ½	⑤	⑤	⅛	18°42′	20	6½ @ 0 Camber
	Power Steering	+ ¼ to + 1¼	+ ¾	⑤	⑤	⅛	18°42′	20	6½ @ 0 Camber
1961	Manual Steering	0 to − 1	− ½	⑥	⑥	⅛	20	21½	5½ to 7½
	Power Steering	+ ¼ to + 1¼	+ ¾	⑥	⑥	⅛	20	21½	5½ to 7½

①—Incorrect toe out, when other adjustments are correct, indicates bent steering arms.
②—Incorrect kingpin angle with correct camber indicates bent suspension arms or steering knuckle support.
③—Desired camber is + ½° on left side and 0° on right side.
④—Left side preferred + ⅜°, right side zero.
⑤—Left side preferred + ⅜°, right side + ⅛°.
⑥—Left side preferred ½°, right side ¼°.

COOLING SYSTEM & CAPACITY DATA

Year	Model	Cooling System Data					Fuel Tank Gals.	Engine Oil			Transmissions			
		Quarts No Heater	Quarts With Heater	Rad. Cap Relief Pressure	Thermostat Opening Temp. (1)	(2)		Refill Qts. (3)	Summer Grade	Winter Grade	Std. Pints	With Over-drive Pints	Automatic Quarts	Rear Axle Pints
1953–54	All	13	14	7	180	160	17	5	30	10W	2¾	3½	10 (4)	3¼
1955	Six	13	14	7	180	160	17	5	30	10W	2¾	3½	10	3¼
	V8	19	20	7 (8)	180	160	17	5	30	10W	2¾	3½	10	3¼
1956	Six	13	14	7	180	160	17	5	30	10W	2¾	3½	10	3¼
	V8-277	20	21	7 (8)	180	160	17	5	30	10W	2¾	3½	10	3¼
	V8-270	19	20	7 (8)	180	160	17	5	30	10W	2¾	3½	10	3¼
	Fury	20	21	7 (8)	180	160	17	5	30	10W	2¾	3½	10	3¼
1957	Six	13	14	14	180	160	(6)	5	30	10W	2¾	3½	10	3¼
	V8	20	21	14	180	160	(6)	5	30	10W	2¾	3½	(5)	3½
1958	Six	13	14	14	180	160	20 (7)	5	30	10W	2¾	3½	(5)	3¼
	V8-318	20	21	14	180	160	20 (7)	5	30	10W	2¾	3½	(5)	3½
	V8-350	16	17	14	180	160	20 (7)	4	30	10W	2¾	None	(5)	3½
1959	Six	13	14	14	180	160	20 (7)	5	30	10W	2¾	3½	(5)	3¼
	V8-318	20	21	14	180	160	20 (7)	5	30	10W	2¾	3½	(5)	3½
	V8-361	16	17	14	180	160	20 (7)	5	30	10W	2¾	None	(5)	3½
1960	Six	14	15	14	180	160	20 (9)	4	30	10W	5	None	6½	3¼
	V8-318	20	21	14 (10)	180	160	20 (9)	5	30	10W	2¾ (11)	None	(5)	3½
	V8-361	16	17	14 (10)	180	160	20	5	30	10W	5	None	11½	3½
1961	Six	13	14	14	180	160	20	4	30	10W	5	None	7	3¼
	V8-318	20	21	14 (10)	180	160	20	5	30	10W	5	None	9	3½
	V8-361	16	17	14 (10)	180	160	20	5	30	10W	4¼	None	10½	3½
	V8-383	16	17	14 (10)	180	160	20	5	30	10W	4¼	None	10½	3½

①—For permanent type anti-freeze.
②—For alcohol type anti-freeze.
③—Add one quart with filter change.
④—With Hy-Drive engine and converter have a combined oiling system and requires 10 quarts of oil. An additional quart is necessary when replacing oil filter element.
⑤—Powerflite 10 quarts. Torqueflite 9 quarts.

⑥—Station wagons, 22; all others, 20.
⑦—Suburban 22 gals.
⑧—14 lbs. with air conditioning.
⑨—Suburbans 21 gallons.
⑩—16 lbs. with air conditioning.
⑪—Golden Comando 3¼ pints.

SERIAL NUMBER LOCATION
Left Front Door Pillar

ENGINE NUMBER LOCATION
Sixes: Left Front Side of Block
V8-318: Left Front Face of Block
V8-350: Righ Side of Block Below Distributor
V8-361: Right Side of Block Next To Water Pump

ENGINE IDENTIFICATION

Year	Engine	Eng. No. Prefix	Year	Engine	Eng. No. Prefix
1958	V8-318	LD2	1960	V8-318	P318
	V8-350	LD3		V8-361	P36
1959	V8-318	MD2	1961	V8-318	R318
	V8-361	MD3		V8-361	R36

1953

1954

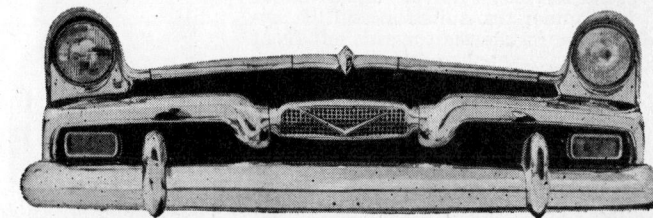

1955

1956

1957

1959

1958

1960

1961

Engine Section

ENGINE, REPLACE

In addition to the usual items such as fuel lines, linkage, propeller shaft, etc., the following operations must be performed:

1. Remove hood and battery.
2. Remove radiator.
3. Remove exhaust pipes.
4. On 1953-59 Six, remove transmission as outlined further on. Then remove crankcase breather pipe and front and rear engine support bolts. Raise engine, remove front engine support and lift out engine. When installing engine, before tightening engine support bolts, loosen exhaust pipe support brackets and allow engine to run a few seconds so it will align itself and then complete tightening.
5. On 1955 V8, if transmission is to be removed, place a jack under transmission and remove engine rear crossmember. Lower and remove jack under transmission and lift engine out of chassis towards left front fender.
6. On 1956-61 V8 except Commando, remove crossmember-to-transmission bolts. Place a jack under transmission and remove crossmember rear engine support. Remove engine front support and lift engine out of chassis.
7. On 1958-61 Commando engines, sup-

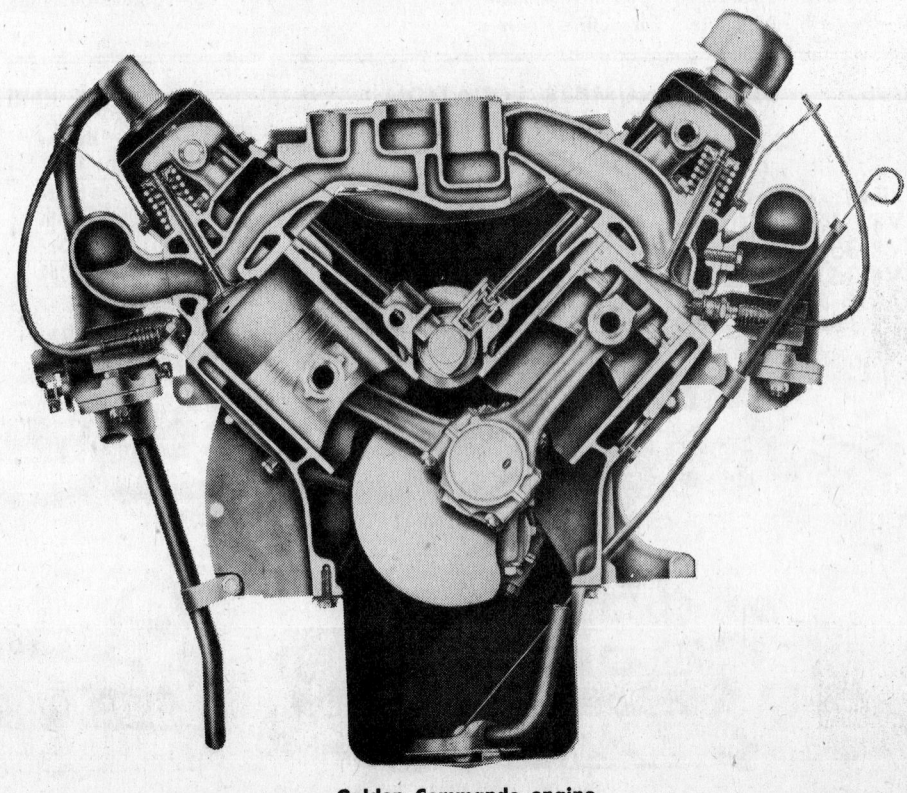

Golden Commando engine

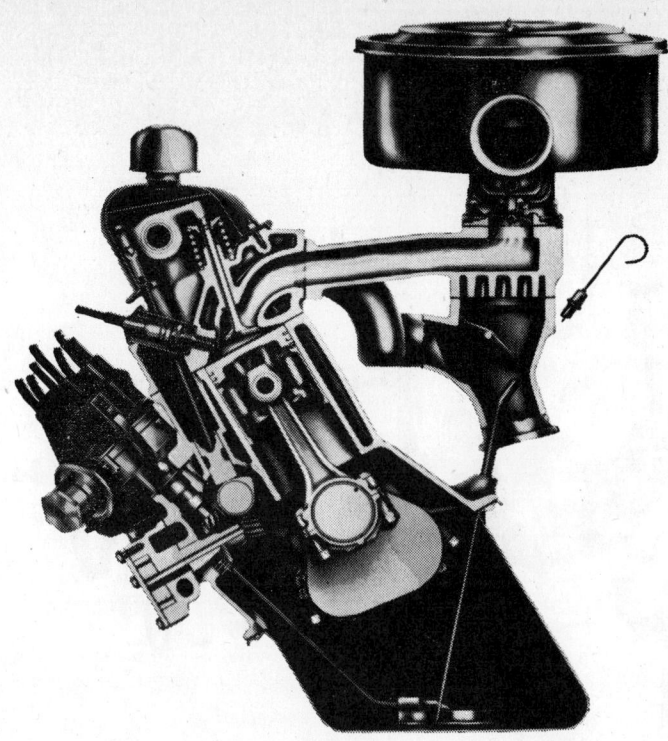

1960-61 Six cylinder engine

Engine lubrication. V8-277, 301, 318
(oil filler cap in rocker arm cover)

port rear of engine and remove engine rear support crossmember. Then remove transmission and lift engine out of chassis.

8. On 1960-61 Six, support rear of engine and remove engine rear support crossmember. Disconnect converter from flex plate and remove transmission and converter assembly. Remove engine support and front engine mounting bolts and lift engine out of chassis.

CYLINDER HEAD
1960-61 Six

1. To remove head, drain cooling system.

2. Remove carburetor air cleaner and fuel line.

3. Disconnect accelerator linkage.

4. Remove vacuum control tube at carburetor and distributor.

5. Disconnect spark plug wires, heater hose and clamp holding by-pass hose.

6. Disconnect heat indicator sending unit wire.

7. Disconnect exhaust pipe at manifold.

8. Remove intake and exhaust manifold and carburetor as a unit.

9. Remove outlet vent tube and rocker arm cover.

10. Remove thermostat housing and thermostat.

11. Remove rocker arms and push rods.

12. Remove head bolts and lift off head.

13. Install head in reverse order of removal and tighten bolts in the sequence shown in Fig. 1A, and to the torque listed in the *Engine Tightening table. When installing the manifolds, loosen the three bolts holding the intake manifold to the exhaust manifold. This is required to maintain proper alignment. Install intake and exhaust manifold and carburetor as a unit and with cup side of conical washers against the manifolds. Tighten the nuts to 10 ft. lbs. Then tighten the three bolts holding the intake manifold to the exhaust manifold to 15 ft. lbs.*

1958-61 Commando

Rocker arm assemblies can be removed without disturbing the cylinder heads or cooling system. To remove the heads, proceed as follows:

1. Drain cooling system, remove air cleaner, fuel line from pump to car-

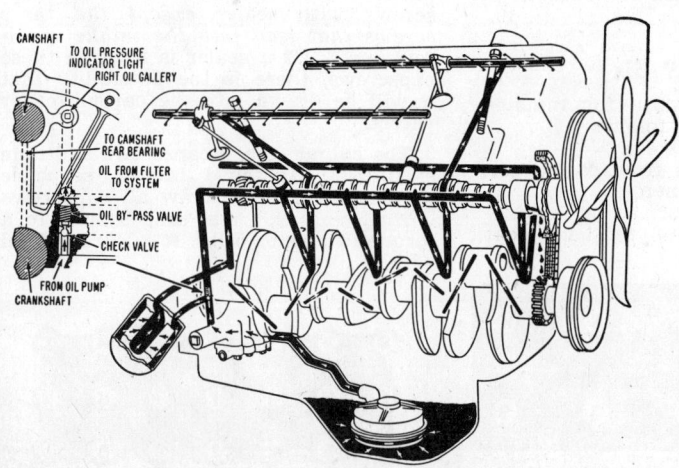

Engine lubrication. 1955-56 V8-241, 260, 270 (oil filler cap in block)

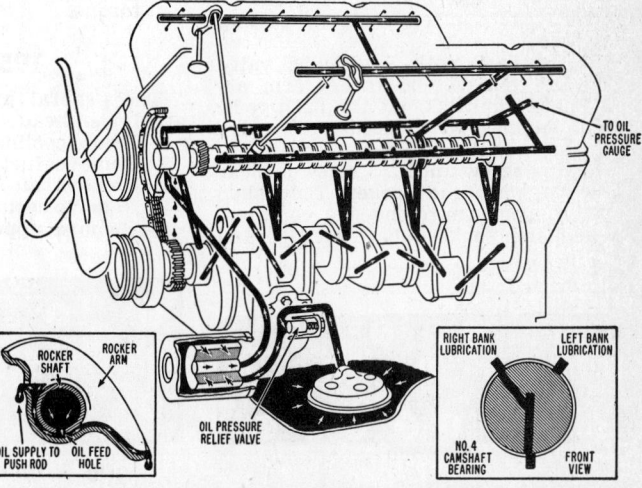

Engine lubrication. V8-350, 361, 383

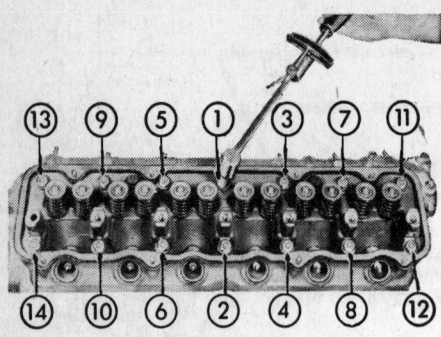

Fig. 1A Cylinder head tightening sequence. 1960-61 Six

Internal parts of engine. 1960-61 Six

buretor, distributor vacuum tube and generator.
2. Disconnect throttle linkage at carburetor, distributor cap, coil wires, heat indicator sending unit wire and heater hoses at engine.
3. Remove spark plugs and cables, and engine ventilating outlet pipe.
4. Remove intake manifold, carburetor and coil as an assembly.
5. Remove exhaust manifolds.
6. Remove cylinder head covers and spark plug cable support brackets.
7. Remove rocker shaft assemblies; *do not remove bolts from end brackets.*
8. Remove push rods and valve lifter chamber cover.
9. Remove attaching bolts and lift off heads.
10. Reverse foregoing procedure to install the heads and tighten the bolts in the sequence shown in Fig. 1 to a torque of 70 lb. ft. Tighten intake and exhaust manifold bolts to a torque of 30 lb. ft.

Note—Be sure to install the small end (¼" diameter) of push rods so it contacts the rocker arms. If the rods are installed in the opposite manner, the larger push rod end will not seat in the tappet, thereby increasing the effective length of the push rod by ⅛" and hold the valve partially open.

1955-61 V8 Except Commando

1. Remove intake manifold and rocker arm covers after draining cooling system.
2. On engines with hydraulic valve lifters, remove the rocker arm assemblies and lift out the push rods.
3. On engines with mechanical valve lifters, back out each tappet adjusting screw until the screw is clear of the push rod socket. Then slide the rocker arm to one side, compressing the rocker shaft spring, and

lift out the push rod. Repeat this procedure for all other push rods. *Place push rods in a suitable rack in order that each rod can be reinstalled in its original position.*
4. Remove cylinder head bolts and lift off cylinder head.
5. When installing the heads, tighten all bolts evenly the first time around to a torque of 35 lb. ft. Then repeat the tightening procedure in the sequence shown in Fig. 2 to the specified torque of 85 lb. ft. Run the engine until normal operating temperature is reached and recheck the torque.

1953-59 Six

The general procedure for removing a cylinder head is as follows:
1. Drain cooling system.
2. Remove fuel line from carburetor.
3. Remove air cleaner.
4. Remove carburetor.
5. Remove upper radiator hose, spark

plugs, engine heat indicator unit and cylinder head nuts and capscrews.
6. Lift cylinder head from block, using lifting hooks in two of the spark plug holes. Do not use a screwdriver, chisel or other sharp instrument to drive between the head and block in an attempt to loosen the head as damage may result.

When installing a cylinder head, always use a new gasket. Coat both sides of the gasket with approved sealing compound. Coat the threads of the capscrews with sealer *except the three screws that lead into the intake manifold ports.* If a sealer is used on these capscrews, there is the possibility that it will be drawn into the carburetor or valves.

The cylinder head capscrews and nuts should be tightened in the sequence shown in Fig. 3. Draw all capscrews down evenly the first time around to a torque of about 35 lbs. ft. During final

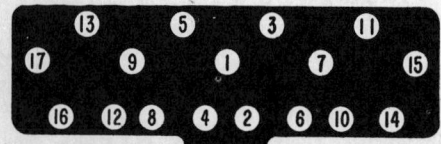

Fig. 1 Cylinder head tightening V8-350, 361, 383 engines

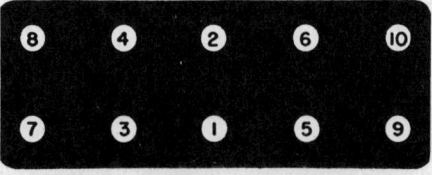

Fig. 2 Cylinder head tightening. V8-241, 259, 270, 277, 301, 303, 318

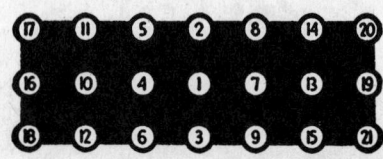

Fig. 3 Cylinder head tightening sequence. 1953-59 Six

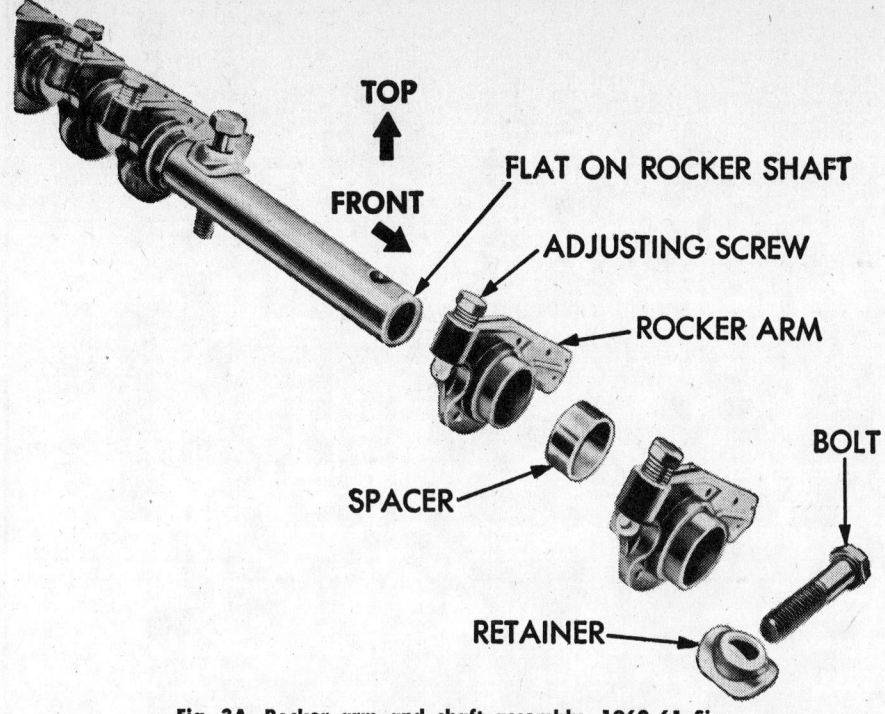

Fig. 3A Rocker arm and shaft assembly. 1960-61 Six

V8s With Mechanical Lifters

Engines with mechanical valve lifters can be identified by the rocker arm adjusting screws. These screws are self-locking and when turning them during the process of adjustment they should indicate some resistance to turning (a minimum of 3 lb. ft. tension). If any screw turns too easily it should be replaced and, if necessary, the rocker arm as well.

Valve clearances should be set up after the engine is warmed up to operating temperature and to the clearances listed in the *Valve Specifications* table.

ROCKER ARMS

1960-61 Six

To remove rocker arms, take off outlet tube, rocker arm cover, rocker shaft bolts and retainers and lift off rocker arms and shaft.

Clean all parts, being sure the inside of the shaft is clean and the oil holes are open. The drilled oil hole in the bore of the rocker arm must be open to the trough and valve end of the arms. The trough also feeds oil to the adjusting screw and push rod. Assemble the arms and shaft as follows:

1. Referring to Fig. 3A, note flat on forward end of rocker shaft which denotes upper side of shaft. Rocker arms must be put on the shaft with the adjusting screw to the right side of the engine. Place one of the small retainers on the one long bolt and install the bolt in the rear hole in the shaft from the top side.
2. Install one rocker arm and one spacer; then two rocker arms and a spacer. Continue in same sequence until all rocker arms and spacers are on the shaft.
3. Place a bolt and small retainer in front hole in shaft.
4. Place a bolt and the one *wide* retainer through the center hole in the shaft with six rocker arms on each side of center.
5. Install remaining bolts and retainers, separating the four pairs of rocker arms.
6. Locate assembly on cylinder head and position rocker arm adjusting screws in push rods.
7. Tighten bolts finger tight, bringing retainers in contact with the shaft *between rocker arms*. Tighten bolts to 30 ft. lbs.

---

tightening, the capscrews should be tightened to the torque given in the *Engine Tightening Chart* with the engine at normal operating temperature.

VALVE ARRANGEMENT

Front to Rear

1960-61 Six . . . . E-I-E-I-E-I-E-I-E
1958-61 Commando . . . . . E-I-I-E-E-I-I-E
1955-61 V8 Except Commando
I-E-I-E-I-E-I-E
1953-59 Six. . . . E-I-I-E-E-I-I-E-E-I-I-E

VALVES, ADJUST

1953-57 Six

Valve tappets should be adjusted with the engine running and at normal operating temperature. It is important that the clearances given in *Valve Chart* be maintained to insure satisfactory engine performance. If the car is driven at continuous high speeds, an additional .002" clearance for exhaust tappets is desirable.

If the car being serviced is one wherein the valves are not accessible when the hood is raised, proceed as follows:

1. Raise right front end of car and support it with a stand.
2. Remove right front wheel and splash shield access cover if one is provided.
3. Remove valve chamber covers.
4. With engine idling and warmed up to operating temperature, adjust the intake valves and then follow through by adjusting all exhaust valves.

1958-59 Six

The procedure for adjusting the valves is the same as prior models. However, the right front fender shield must be removed to gain access to the tappets. After removing all the shield attaching bolts, pull the lower corner of the fender outward to gain clearance for removing shield. Support fender on a 9" block of wood.

When installing the shield, first partially install the bolt used to secure the fender shield to the frame.

1960-61 Six

Before the final valve lash is made, operate the engine for 30 minutes at a fast idle to stabilize engine temperatures.

Before startng the adjustment procedure, make two chalk marks on the vibration damper. Space the marks approximately 120 degrees apart (⅓ of circumference) so that with the timing mark the damper is divided into three equal parts. Adjust the valves for No. 1 cylinder. Repeat the procedure for the remaining valves, turning the crankshaft ⅓ turn in the direction of normal rotation while adjusting the valves in the firing order sequence of 153624.

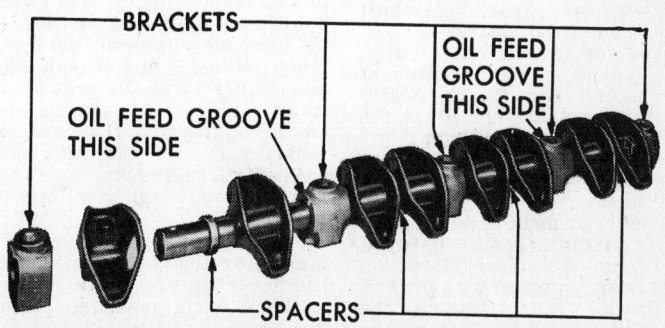

Fig. 4 Rocker arm shaft assembly. 1958-61 Golden Commando engine

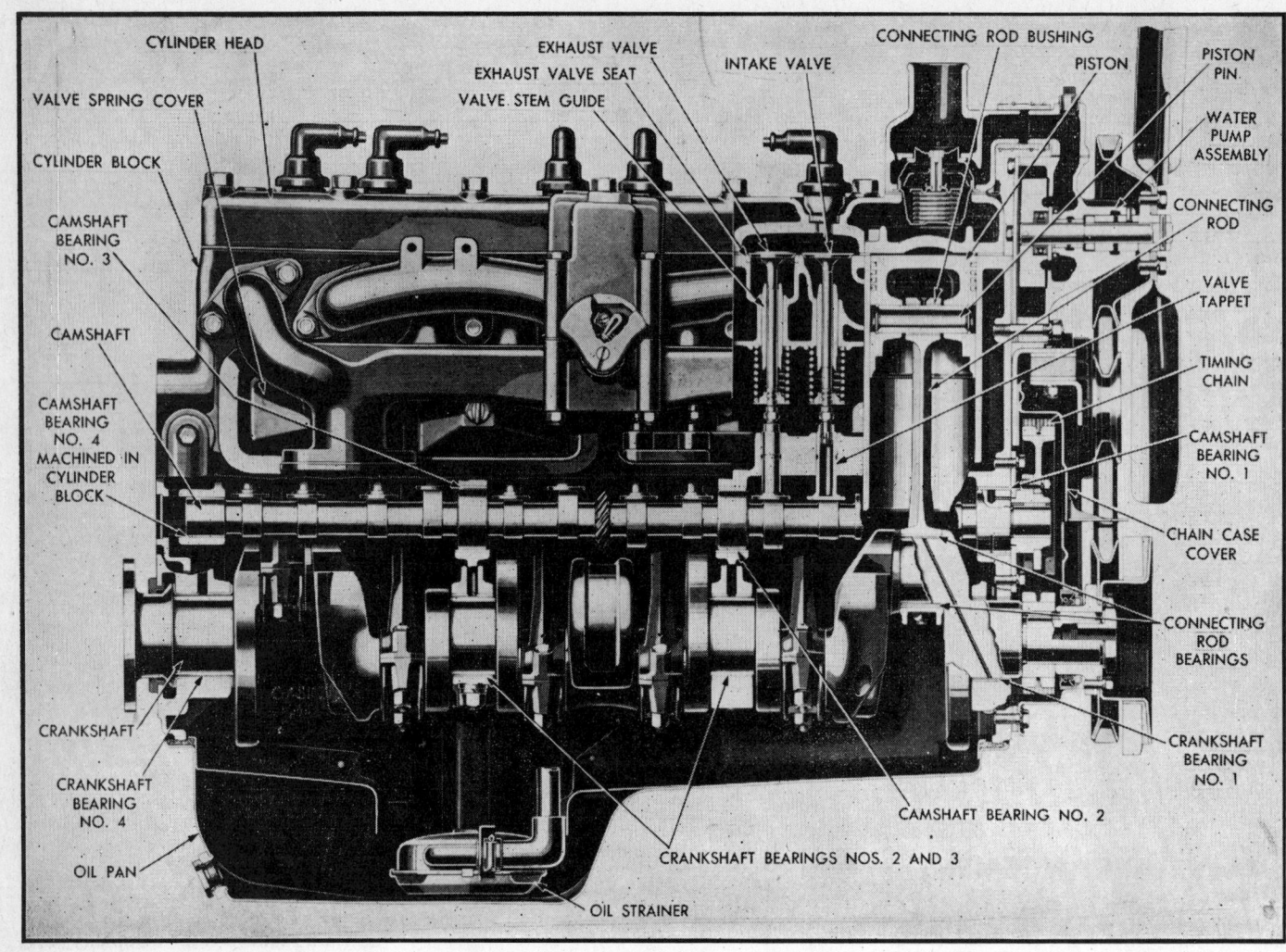

CYLINDER HEAD — VALVE SPRING COVER — CYLINDER BLOCK — CAMSHAFT BEARING NO. 3 — CAMSHAFT — CAMSHAFT BEARING NO. 4 MACHINED IN CYLINDER BLOCK — CRANKSHAFT — CRANKSHAFT BEARING NO. 4 — OIL PAN — OIL STRAINER — CRANKSHAFT BEARINGS NOS. 2 AND 3 — EXHAUST VALVE — EXHAUST VALVE SEAT — VALVE STEM GUIDE — INTAKE VALVE — CONNECTING ROD BUSHING — PISTON — PISTON PIN — WATER PUMP ASSEMBLY — CONNECTING ROD — VALVE TAPPET — TIMING CHAIN — CAMSHAFT BEARING NO. 1 — CHAIN CASE COVER — CONNECTING ROD BEARINGS — CRANKSHAFT BEARING NO. 1 — CAMSHAFT BEARING NO. 2

Sectional view of 1953-59 Six engine

8. After running engine to normal operating temperature, adjust valve lash to specifications.
9. Complete the job by installing the remaining parts removed.

1958-61 Commando

Disassemble rocker shaft assemblies by removing bolts from support brackets and sliding brackets, rocker arms and spacers from the shaft, Fig. 4. Clean all parts *except the oilite spacers* in a suitable solvent. Keep oilite spacers soaked in engine oil until reassembled. Inspect all parts for excessive wear. Test shaft end plugs for evidence of leaks.

When assembling, rocker shaft outlet holes must face away from center of engine. The second and fourth (wide) support brackets must be placed on the shaft with the oil passages facing the center of the engine. This is necessary to provide proper lubrication to the rocker assemblies.

Assemble rocker arms in pairs between brackets with an oil spacer between the arms and the push rod socket section of each arm close together rather than far apart. Install bolts through the brackets to hold the assembly together until ready to install on cylinder heads.

NOTE—When installing push rods be sure the larger ends are in contact with the rocker arms. If rods are installed in the opposite manner, the larger push rod end will not seat in the tappet, thereby increasing the effective length of the push rod by ⅛" and hold the valve partially open.

1955-61 V8 Except Commando

Sludge and gum formation in the rocker arms and shafts, Fig. 5, will restrict the normal flow to the rocker arms and valves. Each time the assemblies are removed (see *Cylinder Heads*), they should be disassembled and thoroughly cleaned.

Clean all gum and sludge formation from the inside and outside of the shafts and rocker arms. Inspect the shafts for wear. Check the fit of the rocker arms on the shafts and the valve end of the rocker arms for excessive wear. If the rocker arm radius is grooved on the valve end, do not attempt grinding; replace the part.

When the assemblies are installed, make sure the rocker arms are correctly positioned to actuate the valves.

Check each push rod for a bent or damaged condition. If bent more than .020", when checked with an indicator, replace the push rod. Do not attempt to straighten a bent rod. If a dial gauge is not available, at least check the rod for straightness by rolling it on a perfectly flat surface plate.

VALVES, REMOVE
V8 & 1960-61 Six

With the cylinder head removed as outlined previously, use a suitable valve spring compressor to compress each spring, Fig. 6. Remove the valve locks. Remove the spring compressor and lift off the valve retainer, spring and valve. Repeat for the remaining valves. Keep the valves and related parts together so they may be installed in their respective positions if found in satisfactory condition.

1953-59 Six

Fig. 7. After taking off the cylinder head as outlined previously, take off the valve chamber covers and use cloth to block off the holes in the valve chamber to prevent the valve locks from falling into the crankcase.

With a suitable valve spring compres-

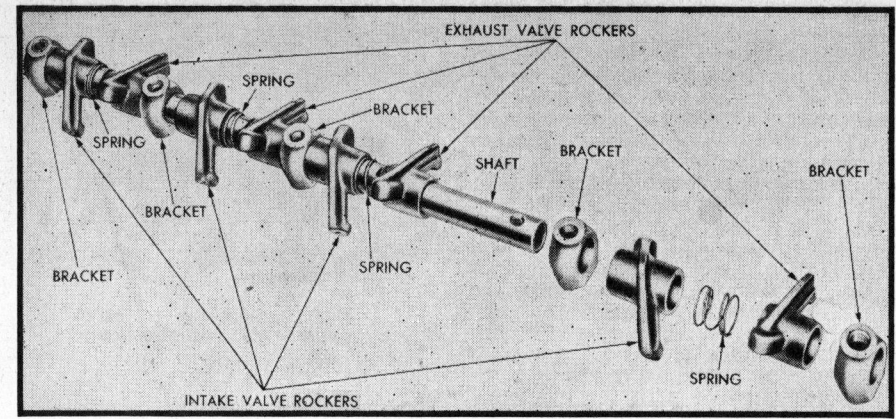

Fig. 5   Layout of rocker arm parts.   V8-241, 259, 270

sor, raise the springs on those valves which are closed and remove the valve locks. Then turn the crankshaft until those valves which are open are closed and remove the remaining valve locks.

Remove all valves and place them in a board with numbered holes so that they can be identified as to the valve port from which they were removed.

VALVE SPRING INSTALLED HEIGHT

When valves and seats are reground the position of the valve in the head is changed so as to lessen the valve spring tension. Without proper valve spring tension the valve does not seat long enough or it may not seat completely. Since the valve is cooled by transferring heat from the valve head to the seat and thence to the coolant, improper valve spring tension will cause worn, pitted and distorted valves which result in loss of compression and power as well as poor gasoline mileage.

When valves, springs, retainers and locks are installed, measure the assembled height of the valve springs from the surface of the cylinder head spring pad to the underside of the spring retainer as shown in Fig. 7A. If the assembled height is greater than the dimension given in the *Valve Specifications Chart*, install a spacer or shim of proper thickness between cylinder head spring pad and spring to bring the assembled height to specifications.

Do not install spacers unless necessary. Excessive use of spacers will result in overstressing valve springs and overloading camshaft lobes which could lead to spring breakage and worn camshaft lobes.

VALVE SPRING TESTING

After taking out the valve springs, wash them with gasoline or other suitable solvent. Examine the springs for damage or corrosion due to acid etching, which will develop into surface cracks and cause spring failure.

Check the valve spring tension on a spring testing fixture, if one is available,

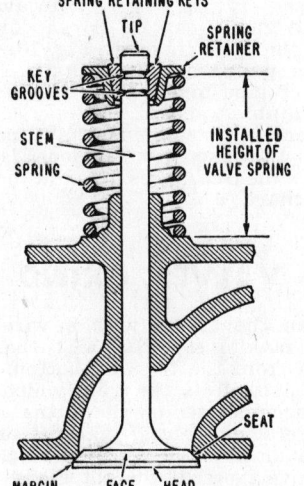

Fig. 7A   Checking installed height of valve springs

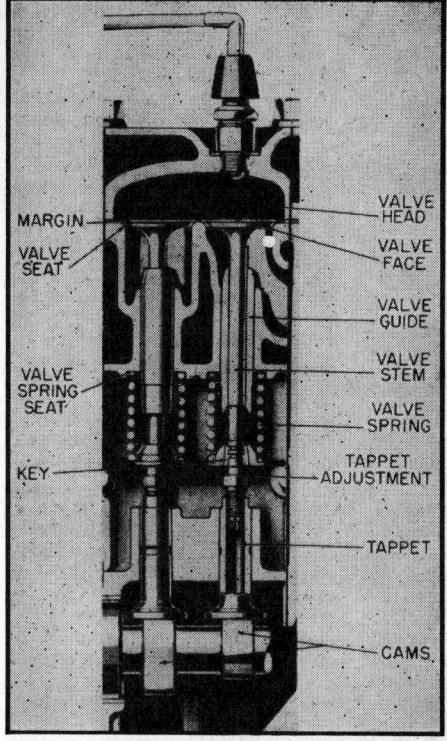

Fig. 7   Details of valve mechanism. 1953-59 Six

and according to the specifications given in the *Valve Data Chart*. If a fixture, Fig. 8, is not available, at least check the free length of each spring by standing it alongside a new spring. Any spring that does not conform to the pressure specifications within 10% should be replaced. Likewise any spring that stands shorter

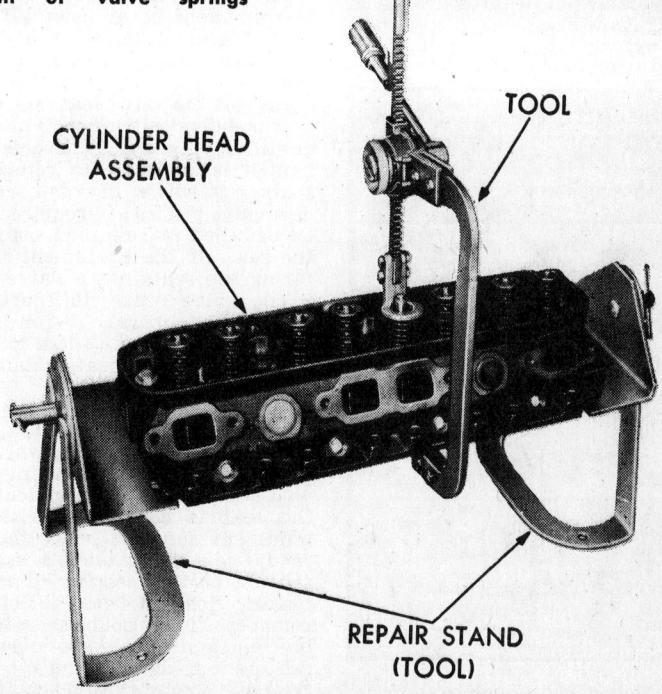

Fig. 6   Compressing valve spring.   V8 engines

than the new spring used for comparison should be discarded. Of course, cocked springs should also be scrapped.

1960-61 Six

To check the length of the valve spring when installed, install the valve, spring retainer and locks (without the spring). With the locks seated in the retainer and the valve seated, the space between the spring seat on the cylinder head and the underside of the retainer should be $1\frac{5}{8}$" to $1\frac{11}{16}$". If more than $1\frac{11}{16}$", use a $\frac{1}{16}$" spacer under the spring when assembling.

VALVE GUIDES

All V8's & 1960-61 Six

Valve guides in these engines are an integral part of the cylinder heads and, therefore, cannot be removed. For service guide holes can be reamed oversize to accommodate one of three service valves with oversize stems (.005", .015" and .030").

Test the valve guides for wear as shown in Fig. 9. Install a suitable sleeve over the valve stem to hold the valve at working height in the head. Attach a dial indicator having a stem at right angle with edge of valve. Move valve to and from indicator. Total movement should not exceed .010" on intake valves and .014" on exhaust valves. If tolerance is excessive, ream guide holes and install valves with oversize stems. Always use a .005" reamer first, then (if necessary) a .015" reamer and finally a .030" reamer so the guides remain true in relation to the seat.

1953-59 Six

Clean the valve guides with a wire guide brush and check the clearance between valve stems and guides carefully. The standard clearances are given in the *Valve Data* chart.

Fig. 8 Fixture and torque wrench for checking valve spring pressure

ARM
VALVE SPRING
COMPRESSED LENGTH OF SPRING
HAND WHEEL NUT
STATIONARY SCREW

Excessive clearance between valve stems and guides will cause improper seating and burned valves. When there is too much clearance between intake valve stems and guides, there is a tendency to draw oil vapor through the guide on the suction stroke, causing excessive oil consumption, fouled spark plugs and poor low speed performance.

To check valve stem-to-guide clearance, take a new valve and place it in each valve guide and feel the clearance by moving the valve stem back and forth. If this check shows excessive clearance, it will be necessary to replace the valve guide.

If the clearance is not excessive when checking with a new valve but is excessive when checked with the old valve, the old valve stem is worn and a new valve must be installed.

If it is necessary to replace valve guides, they may be removed and installed with special tools made for the purpose. If they are not available, the old guides can be driven down and out of the valve chamber, Fig. 10, or they can be pulled out by using a suitable piece of pipe together with a long bolt and suitable washers.

After the new guides have been installed, they should be reamed, Fig. 11, to provide the clearances given in the *Valve Data* chart.

VALVES, GRIND

Clean the valves with a wire wheel brush, making sure that all carbon is removed from the top and bottom of the heads as well as the gum which might have accumulated on the stems.

In refacing valves, take off only the minimum of metal required to clean up the valve faces. If the outer edge of the valve becomes too thin or sharp due to excessive grinding, the valve must be replaced. In other words, the valve head margin must be at least $\frac{3}{64}$", otherwise the valve must be replaced. This margin is the area above the contact surface of the valve face, Fig. 12.

Inspect the valve seats in the block for cracks, burns, pitting, ridges or improper angle. During any general engine overhaul it is advisable to reface the valve seats regardless of their condition. If new valve guides are required, they must be installed and reamed before refacing the seats if the equipment used for refacing the seats has a valve guide pilot.

The valve seat width after refacing should be a liberal $\frac{1}{16}$" for intake seats but not more than $\frac{3}{32}$" in any case. The width of exhaust seats should be $\frac{3}{64}$" to a liberal $\frac{1}{16}$".

Test valves for concentricity with seats and for tight seating. Valves can be tested by lightly coating the valve face with prussian blue and turning the valve against its seat. This indicates whether the seat is concentric with the valve guide *but does not prove that the valve face is concentric with the valve stem, or that the valve is seating all around.* After making this test, wash all blue from the surfaces, lightly coat the *valve seat* with blue and repeat the test to see whether a full mark is obtained on the valve. *Both tests are necessary to prove that a proper seat is being obtained.*

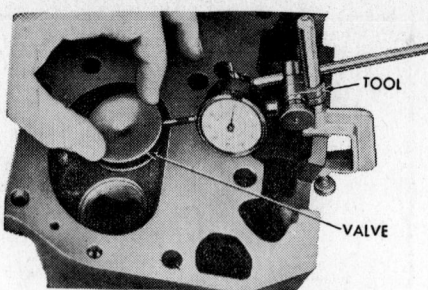

Fig. 9 Measuring valve guide wear with dial gauge

TOOL
VALVE

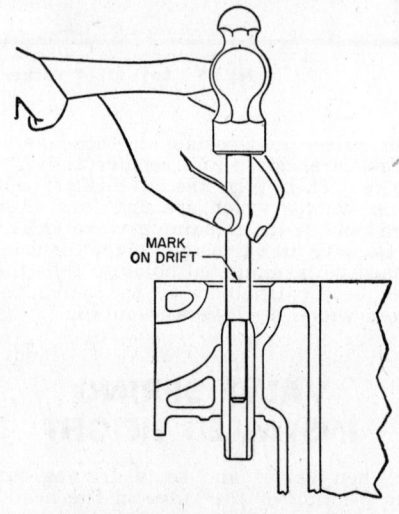

MARK ON DRIFT

Fig. 10 Showing drift with pilot extending into valve guide for removing and installing guides. Mark drift as shown to indicate the depth to which the guide must be driven in. 1953-59 Six

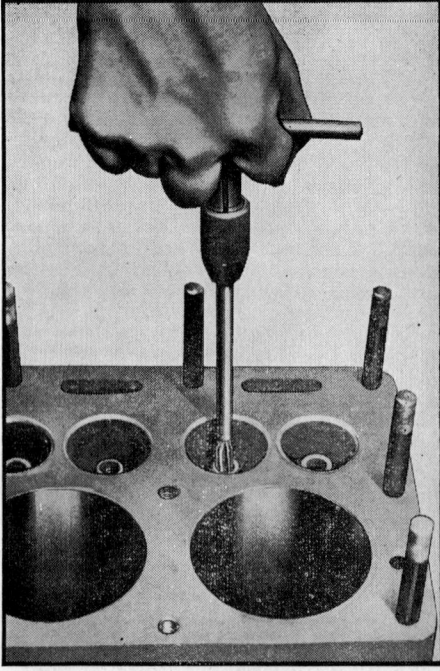

Fig. 11 Reaming valve guides. 1953-59 Six

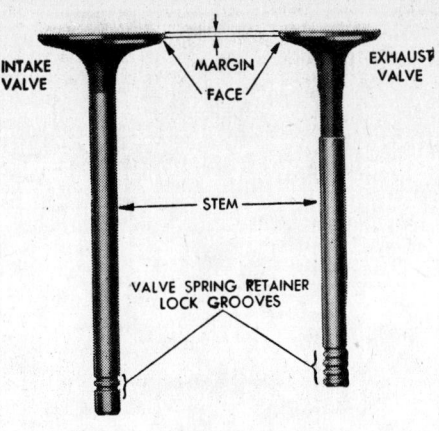

Fig. 12 Valve nomenclature

VALVE SEAT INSERTS

1953-59 Six

Since these inserts are too hard to reface by hand valve grinding methods, a high speed grinder or special lapping equipment should be used to perform this operation. When using this equipment, be sure valve guides are clean and the valve guide pilot is a snug fit in order to assure a concentric finish. Finished seats should be checked with a dial indicator and runout should not exceed .001".

To remove an insert (if a suitable puller is not available, Fig. 14) drill two holes at opposite sides of the insert, but not all the way through. Then cut through the undrilled portion with a sharp chisel and remove the two pieces.

To install a new insert, first remove all burrs and sharp edges from the seat recess. Then chill the new insert with dry ice to obtain maximum contraction and place it in the recess.

If a standard insert is too loose (less than .002" press fit) a .010" oversize seat

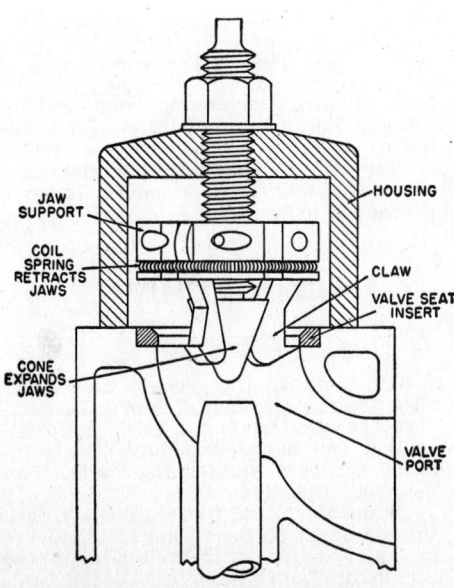

Fig. 14 Typical valve seat insert puller. 1953-59 Six

is available. Before it can be installed, however, the recess in the block must be machined to fit the seat.

MECHANICAL VALVE LIFTERS

V8 Engines

To remove mechanical type valve lifters, take off the rocker arm covers and intake manifold. Back off each rocker arm adjusting screw until the screw is clear of the push rod socket. Then slide each rocker arm to one side, compressing the rocker shaft spring, and lift out the push rod. The lifter may then be lifted out of its bore.

1953-59 Six

Since these valve lifters (or tappets) are of the mushroom type, Fig. 7, operating in guide holes bored in the cylinder block, it is necessary to take out the camshaft before the lifters can be removed.

Remove the oil pan and raise the lifters away from the camshaft lobes. The lifters can be held up with spring type clothes pins or other types of holders, Fig. 15. Then remove the camshaft, rotating it to clear the lifters.

If new lifters fit too loosely in the block, ream the guide holes oversize (special tool C-265 is available for this operation). Oversize lifters are furnished in .001", .008" and .030". If a reaming tool is used, remove the cylinder head, the valves and springs so that the reamer pilot can be installed.

Check the mushroom faces of the lifters for pitting or scratches that might damage the cams. Make sure the lifters have been rotating in operation. Before installing a new lifter, check the cam lobe for roughness.

1960-61 Six

After taking off rocker arm and shaft assembly, lift out push rods. The valve lifters may then be removed with a suitably long magnet rod. If the lifters cannot be removed with the magnet rod, a special tool (C-3661) may be used. Insert the tool through the push rod opening in the cylinder head and into the lifter. Turn the handle to expand the tool in the lifter, then with a twisting motion remove the lifter from its bore. Place lifters in a board or rack with numbered holes since each lifter must be installed in its original location.

Inspect the lifters for scores and the lower ends for pits and rough surfaces. Check crowned faces of lifters with a straightedge. If any negative crown (dish) is observed, the lifter should be replaced.

HYDRAULIC LIFTERS

Engines with these lifters may be identified by the absence of rocker arm adjusting screws. They are used in all 1955 engines as well as the 1956 270 cu. in. engine and the Golden Commando.

Figs. 16 and 17 illustrate the types of

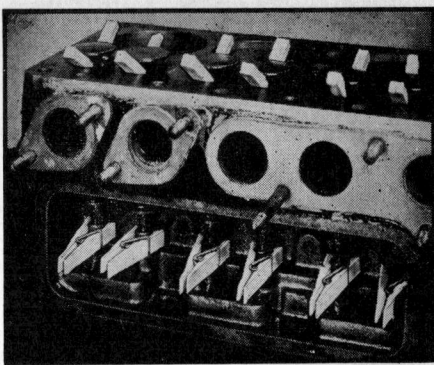

Fig. 15 One method of holding up valves and tappets for camshaft removal. 1953-59 Six

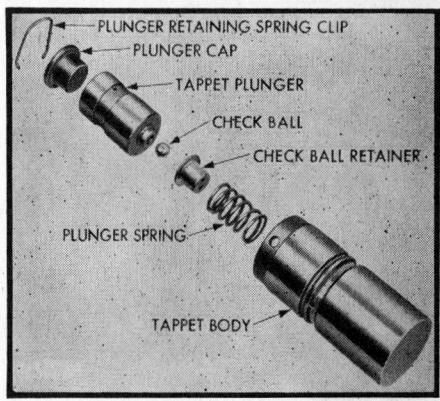

Fig. 16 Layout of hydraulic valve lifter parts. 1955

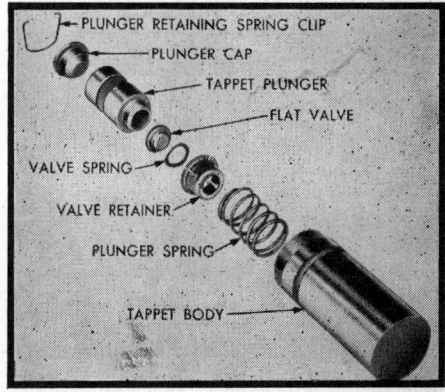

Fig. 17 Hydraulic valve lifter. 1956-60

hydraulic valve lifters used. See the *Trouble Shooting Chapter* under the heading *Engine Noises* for cause of hydraulic valve lifter noise.

The easiest method for locating a noisy valve lifter is by the use of a piece of garden hose about 4 feet long. Place one end of the hose near each valve in progression and listen through the other end. In this manner the sound is localized, making it easier to determine which lifter is at fault.

Another method is to place a finger on the valve spring retainer. If the lifter is not functioning properly, a distinct shock will be felt when the valve returns to its seat.

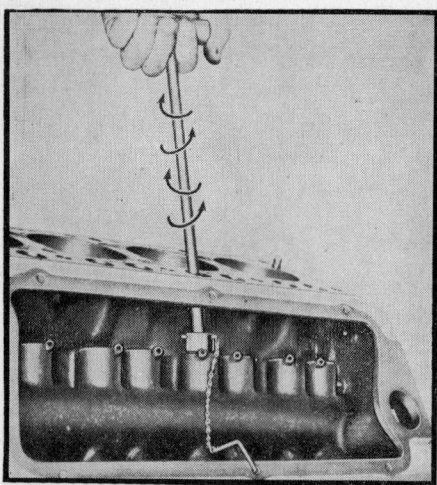

Fig. 18 Tool for removing valve lifters

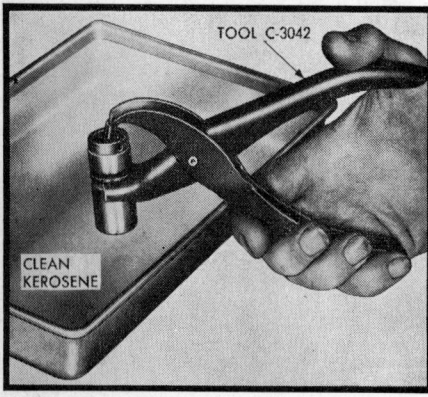

Fig. 19 Testing hydraulic valve lifter

In most cases where noise exists in one or more lifters, all lifter units should be removed and cleaned. If dirt, varnish or carbon is found to exist in one unit, it more than likely exists in all the units.

These valve lifters can be removed after the intake manifold, rocker arm assemblies and push rods have been removed.

Removing Lifters

On the Golden Commando engine the valve lifters can be removed through the push rod holes in the cylinder heads by the use of a tool of the type shown in Fig. 18, after removing the rocker shaft assemblies and push rods.

On all engines except the Golden Commando, the lifters may be removed after taking off the intake manifold. If the lifters are stuck in the bores due to carbon or varnish build-up, use a tool of the type shown in Fig. 18 and use a twisting motion to pull the lifter out of the bore. The sharp edge at the bottom of the lifter bore will shave the varnish and carbon deposits off the lifter as it is being withdrawn.

Servicing Lifters

Hydraulic plungers and bodies are not interchangeable. Therefore, it is advisable to work on one lifter at a time to avoid mixing parts. *Mixed parts will not function.*

In testing a lifter, secure a container deep enough to completely immerse the lifter assembly. Fill the container with clean kerosene. Remove the cap from the plunger and submerge the lifter. Allow the cylinder to fill with kerosene. Then remove the lifter and replace the cap.

Holding the lifter upright, insert the lower jaw of the pliers shown in Fig. 19 in a groove of the lifter body. Engage the upper jaw of the pliers with the top of the plunger cap as shown. Check the leakdown by compressing the pliers. If the plunger collapses almost instantly, disassemble the unit, clean it again and retest. If the lifter still does not function satisfactorily, install a new unit, being sure to test the new one before installing it in the engine.

TIMING CHAIN COVER

1955 V8

To remove the chain case cover, support the engine with a suitable chain hoist fastened to the intake manifold. Then remove engine front support "U" bolts. Remove the crankshaft pulley and water pump housing. Loosen oil pan bolts sufficiently until pan clears chain case cover. Unfasten and remove cover.

1956-61 V8 Except Commando

To remove the cover, take off the crankshaft pulley and water pump housing. Loosen oil pan bolts sufficiently until pan clears chain case cover. Unfasten and remove cover.

1958-61 Commando

1. Drain cooling system.
2. Remove radiator, fan and belt.
3. Remove water pump and housing as an assembly.
4. Remove crankshaft bolt and pulley from vibration damper and remove damper with a puller.
5. Remove key from crankshaft.
6. Remove chain case cover and gasket. *Use extreme caution to avoid damaging the oil pan gasket; if damaged it will be necessary to remove the oil pan to install a new gasket.*

Fig. 20 Arrows point to special centering tool for chain case cover oil seal. 1953-59 Six

---

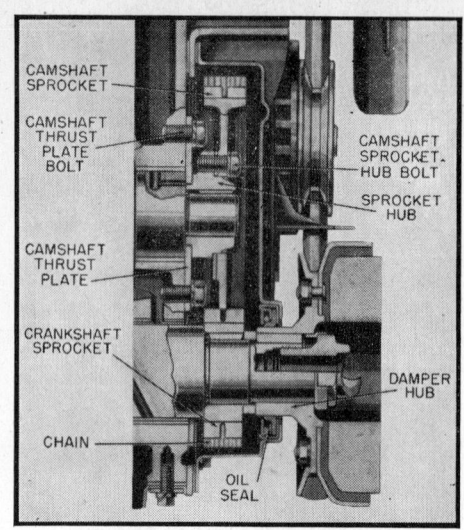

Fig. 21 Details of front end of engine. 1953-59 Six

1953-59 Six

When installing the chain case cover oil seal, place a new gasket in the cover. Drive the seal into position, using a drift or a piece of flat metal. This will insure a tight, even contact between seal gasket and cover flange.

When installing the chain case cover, tighten the screws only enough to hold the cover in place and, if possible, use special tool C-522 to center the seal on the crankshaft, Fig. 20.

Install the tool, holding it in place with the crankshaft nut. Tighten the nut with the fingers only. Then tighten the chain case cover screws securely, remove the tool and install the crankshaft nut.

Inspect the surface of the crankshaft (or damper) hub, Fig. 21, for worn spots or roughness which could damage the seal. If there is any evidence of the above conditions, the hub should be replaced.

1960-61 Six

To remove the cover, drain cooling system and remove radiator and fan. Remove vibration damper with a puller. Loosen oil pan bolts to allow clearance and remove chain case cover. Reverse procedure to install.

TIMING CHAIN

1955 V8

After removing the chain case cover as outlined previously, remove the camshaft sprocket hub nut, fuel pump eccentric and dowel assembly. The camshaft sprocket and timing chain may now be taken off.

To install, rotate the crankshaft until the zero mark on the crankshaft sprocket is exactly in line with the center of the camshaft. Temporarily install the camshaft sprocket (less chain) and line up the hub dowel pin hole with the sprocket

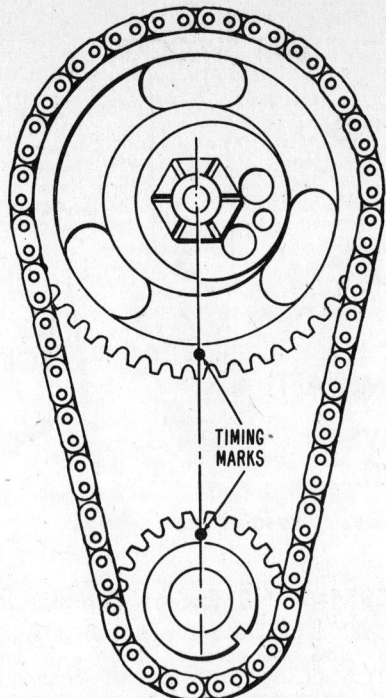

Fig. 22 Timing marks aligned for correct valve timing. All V8's.

dowel pin hole, while at the same time positioning the camshaft sprocket zero mark exactly in line with the center of the crankshaft. A straight edge should be used to check the accuracy of this alignment, Fig. 22.

Remove the camshaft sprocket again and position it in the timing chain. Then place the chain on the crankshaft sprocket. Install the camshaft sprocket, being sure both zero timing marks are facing each other and in line with the center of both the camshaft and crankshaft.

1956-61 V8

To install chain and sprockets, lay both the camshaft and crankshaft sprockets on the bench. Position the sprockets so that the timing marks are next to each other. Place the chain on both sprockets, then push the gears apart as far as the chain will permit. Use a straightedge to form a line through the exact centers of both gears. The timing marks must be on this line, Fig. 22.

This is the same procedure as in previous models, except that now the alignment is done on the bench rather than on the engine.

Slide the chain with both sprockets on the camshaft and crankshaft at the same time; then recheck the alignment.

Install the fuel pump eccentric on the camshaft and install cup washer and bolt. Tighten bolt to a torque of 35 lb. ft.

1953-59 Six

The timing chain is not adjustable for wear. If the slack in the chain is more than ½", Fig. 23, install a new chain.

To remove the chain, take off the chain case cover, chain and camshaft sprocket. To assemble, place the chain

over the sprockets so that when the camshaft sprocket is bolted to its hub, the timing marks on both sprockets are opposite each other as shown in Fig. 23. Be sure the oil tube is located so as to direct oil onto the crankshaft sprocket.

The crankshaft sprocket and hub should never be driven off with a hammer, nor pried off with a pry bar, otherwise the chain, hub or sprocket will be damaged. A special puller (C-355) is available for this operation. Remove by loosening the front engine mount and raising the front end of the engine.

1960-61 Six

1. After removing the timing chain cover as outlined above, take off camshaft sprocket attaching bolt.
2. Remove chain with camshaft sprocket.
3. Clean all parts and dry with compressed air.
4. Inspect chain for broken or damaged links. Inspect sprockets for cracks and chipped, worn or damaged teeth.

Fig. 23 For correct valve timing, marks on sprockets should line up as shown. If there is more than ½" slack in the chain, it should be replaced. 1953-59 Six

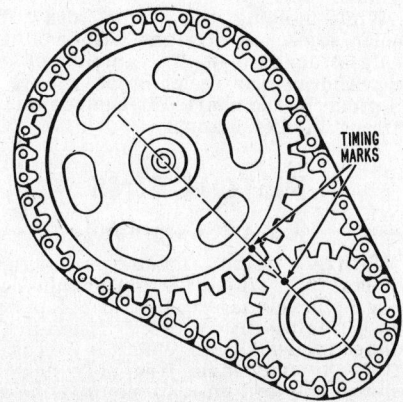

Fig. 23A Timing marks aligned for correct valve timing. 1960-61 Six

Installation

1. Turn crankshaft so sprocket timing mark is toward and directly in line with centerline of camshaft.
2. Temporarily install camshaft sprocket. Rotate camshaft to position sprocket timing mark toward and directly in line with centerline of crankshaft; then remove camshaft sprocket.
3. Place chain on crankshaft sprocket and position camshaft sprocket in chain so sprocket can be installed with timing marks aligned without moving camshaft, Fig. 23A.
4. Install parts removed in reverse order of removal.

VALVE TIMING DATA

Year	Model	Intake Opens①	Intake Closes②	Exhaust Opens③	Exhaust Closes④
1953	All	12	44	50	6
1954	All	12	44	50	6
1955	Six	12	44	50	6
	V8	14	47	55	9
1956	Six	12	44	50	6
	V8-270	14	47	55	9
	V8-277	14	47	52	12
	V8-303	9	55	47	17
1957	Six	12	44	50	6
	V8	8	52	52	8
1958	Six	12	44	50	6
	V8-318	8	52	52	8
	V8-350	15	57	57	15
	Fury	17	47	55	19
1959	Six	12	44	50	6
	V8-318	17	47	55	9
	V8-361	20	60	58	22
1960-61	Six	⑤	52	40	80
	V8-318⑥	17	47	55	9
	V8-318⑦	13	55	51	17
	Golden Com.	24	64	64	24
	Sono Ramic	20	68	60	28

①—Degrees before top dead center.
②—Degrees after bottom dead center.
③—Degrees before bottom dead center.
④—Degrees after top dead center.
⑤—Top dead center.
⑥—Two barrel carburetor.
⑦—Four barrel carburetor.

CAMSHAFT

V8 Engines

To remove the camshaft, remove all valve lifters, timing chain and sprockets. Remove distributor and oil pump-distributor drive gear. Remove fuel pump and see that push rod has moved away from eccentric drive cam. Withdraw the camshaft from the engine, using care to see that the cam lobes do not damage the camshaft bearings.

If camshaft bearings are to be replaced, it is recommended that the engine be removed from the chassis and the crankshaft taken out in order that any chips or foreign matter may be removed from the oil passages.

1960-61 Six

The camshaft, Fig. 23B, can be removed after removing the grille, radiator and timing chain. To remove the camshaft bearings, the engine must be removed.

1. Remove valve lifters, oil pump and distributor and fuel pump.
2. Slide camshaft out of engine.
3. Remove welch plug from back of rear camshaft bearing.
4. Remove bearings with suitable

5. Install new bearings, being sure oil holes in bearings line up with corresponding holes in crankcase.

1953-59 Six

Remove the hood, wheel, splash shield and radiator core. Remove the fuel pump, oil pump and valve compartment covers. Take off the chain case cover and chain. If the valves are not being removed hold them up by inserting two wooden wedges under each valve head as shown in Fig. 15. Raise the valve lifters and hold them up with spring type clothes pins as shown. Then withdraw the camshaft by rotating it to clear the lifters.

If valve lifters are to be replaced, remove the oil pan and clothes pins and take the lifters out from below.

Before installing the camshaft, check the end play between the sprocket hub and thrust plate. If end play exceeds .006", press off the thrust plate and install a new one.

When installing the camshaft, use new gaskets, reset the ignition timing and check the valve clearance with the engine hot.

PISTONS, REMOVE

After removing the cylinder heads and oil pan, examine the cylinder bores above the ring travel area. If the bores are worn so that a shoulder or ridge exists at this point, remove the ridge with a ridge reamer to avoid damaging rings or cracking ring lands of pistons during removal.

Remove the connecting rod caps and push the pistons and rods out of the cylinders, using care to prevent rod bolts from nicking crankshaft journals. Make sure rods and pistons are properly numbered so they can be reinstalled in their proper cylinders. It is advisable to install the caps on the rods as they are removed to avoid mixing parts.

PISTONS & RODS, ASSEMBLE

V8 Engines

When installing piston and rod assemblies in the cylinders, the compression ring gaps should be diametrically opposite one another and not in line with the oil ring gap. The oil ring expander gap should be toward the outside of the "V" of the engine. The oil ring gap should be turned toward the inside of the engine "V".

Immerse the piston head and rings in clean engine oil and, with a suitable piston ring compressor, insert the piston and rod assembly into the bore. Tap the piston down into the bore, using the handle of a hammer.

Assemble the pistons to the rods as shown in Fig. 24.

1953-59 Six

When assembling the piston to the connecting rod, assemble aluminum pistons so that the slotted side of the piston is opposite the metered oil hole in the connecting rod.

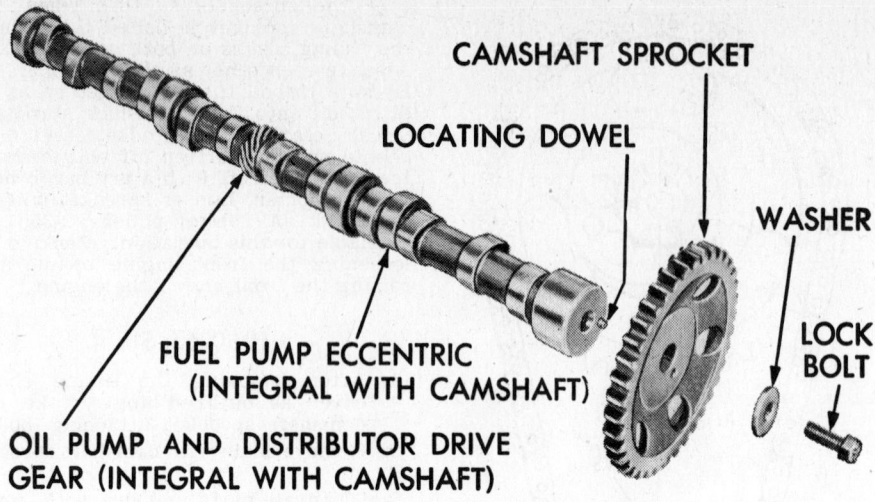

CAMSHAFT SPROCKET

LOCATING DOWEL

WASHER

LOCK BOLT

FUEL PUMP ECCENTRIC (INTEGRAL WITH CAMSHAFT)

OIL PUMP AND DISTRIBUTOR DRIVE GEAR (INTEGRAL WITH CAMSHAFT)

Fig. 23B Camshaft and sprocket. 1960-61 Six

When installing piston and rod in the engine, be sure the metered oil hole in the rod is *toward the camshaft side of the engine.*

1960-61 Six

Piston and rod assemblies must be installed with the notch on the piston head toward the front of the engine, and the oil hole in the connecting rod toward the manifold side of the engine.

PISTONS

Due to the necessity of maintaining piston balance, all pistons are machined to the same weight in grams, regardless of oversize. Only finished pistons are available in service and are supplied in standard and the following oversizes: .010, .020, .030, .040, .050, .060 inch.

The recommended clearance between the thrust face of the piston and cylinder wall is .00075" to .00175" when measured with a micrometer and a dial indicator. Or the clearance can be checked with a 1/2" wide feeler .0015" thick.

Starting with the No. 1 cylinder, coat the bore very lightly with a light engine oil (10W). Insert the piston in the bore upside down with the feeler stock between the thrust face of the piston and cylinder wall.

While holding the piston, draw the feeler stock out straight with a spring scale attached to it. The amount of pull to withdraw the feeler stock should be as given in the chart. Fit the remaining pistons in like manner.

PISTON PINS

1958-61 Commando

With new pistons and new pins at room temperature (70°), the pin should be a very light thumb press fit in the piston. The pin is tightly (pressed) fitted in the connecting rod. Replacement is necessary after any noticeable free play has developed between pin and piston. Pins are available through Chrysler only with new pistons. New pistons are supplied with pins properly fitted.

1955-61 V8 Except Commando

Piston pins are supplied in standard size and oversizes of .003" and .008". The fit of the pin in both the connecting rod and piston should be a tight thumb press fit with the parts at normal room temperature.

When using an expansion reamer to fit piston pins, start off by taking a very light cut. Try the fit. Then ream and try the fit again until the pin can be pushed into the rod and piston as described above.

1953-59 Six

To remove a piston pin, take off the lock rings and heat the piston in a container of hot water. Push the pin out with hand pressure. If it cannot be removed with hand pressure, use a suitable drift to drive it out.

When removing the pin with a drift, hold the piston in one hand, insert the drift and tap lightly with a hammer. Do not hold the connecting rod during this operation, otherwise misalignment of the rod may occur.

If the new pin cannot be installed in the piston with thumb pressure, enlarge the holes with an expansion reamer. Take only a light cut with the reamer. Ream the holes until the pin can be pushed into the piston with the pressure of both thumbs.

The fit of the pin in the connecting rod should be a tight thumb press fit with the parts at normal room temperature of 70°F.

1960-61 Six

Piston pins should be a very light thumb press fit in the piston with the parts at room temperature (70°). Piston pins are supplied in standard size only. If excessive clearance is noted, both piston and pin should be replaced.

PISTON RINGS

When new rings are to be installed without reboring cylinders, the glazed

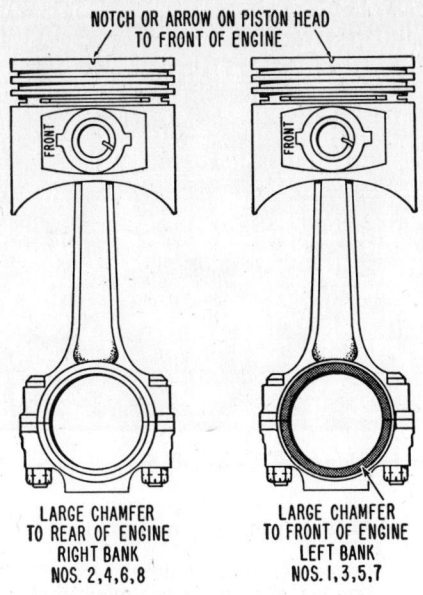

NOTCH OR ARROW ON PISTON HEAD TO FRONT OF ENGINE

LARGE CHAMFER TO REAR OF ENGINE RIGHT BANK NOS. 2,4,6,8

LARGE CHAMFER TO FRONT OF ENGINE LEFT BANK NOS. 1,3,5,7

Fig. 24   Correct assembly of pistons and rods. V8 engines

cylinder wall should be slightly dulled, but without increasing the bore diameter. This is done with a "Glazebuster" or with a hone equipped with the finest grade of stones.

New piston rings must be checked for clearance in piston grooves and for gap in cylinder bores. The latter operation must be measured with the ring about two inches from the bottom of the cylinder bore to which it is fitted. An inverted piston can be used to push the rings down to this position. Cylinder bores and piston grooves must be clean, dry and free from carbon and burrs.

Check the clearance of each ring in its piston groove by installing the ring and then inserting feeler gauges *under* the ring. Any wear that occurs in the piston groove forms a step or ridge at the inner portion of the lower land. If the feeler gauge is inserted above the ring, the ring may rest on the step instead of on the worn portion of the lower land, and a false measurement of clearance may result.

If the piston grooves have worn to the extent that relatively high steps or ridges exist on the lower lands, the piston should be replaced because the steps will interfere with the operation of the new rings and ring clearances will be excessive. Piston rings are not furnished in oversize widths to compensate for ring groove wear.

ROD BEARINGS

Connecting rod bearings can be replaced without removing the piston and rod assemblies merely by taking off the rod cap and replacing the upper and lower bearing halves.

The clearance between the bearings and crankshaft can be measured with Plastigage as follows:

1. Remove bearing cap and wipe oil from crankshaft journal and bearing.
2. With crankpin at approximately bot-

tom dead center, place a piece of Plastigage in the center of the bearing, Fig. 25.
3. Reinstall the bearing cap and tighten the bolts to the torque value given in the *Engine Tightening Data* table.
4. Remove the bearing cap again and check the bearing clearance by measuring the width of the flattened Plastigage, Fig. 25. The measuring strip is supplied in the same envelope which contains the Plastigage.

MAIN BEARINGS
V8's & 1960-61 Six

Caution—Main bearing clearance can be checked with Plastigage in the same manner described for rod bearings. If bearings are measured with the engine in the chassis, the crankshaft must be supported in order to take up clearance between the upper bearing insert and crankshaft journal. This can be done by tightening bearing caps of adjacent bearings with .005" to .015" cardboard, (such as a calling card) between lower bearing shell and journal. Use extreme care when this is done to avoid unnecessary strain on the crankshaft or bearings or a false reading may be obtained. Do not rotate crankshaft while Plastigage is installed. *Be sure to remove cardboard.* To install new bearings, proceed as follows:

1. Remove bearing cap and worn lower shell.
2. Rotate crankshaft in normal direction to turn upper bearing shell out of crankcase. Use a cotter pin with a flattened head or the special tool made for the purpose in the crankshaft oil hole to contact the bearing and force it out, Fig. 26.
3. Place a new upper shell on the crankshaft journal with the locating notch in the correct position and rotate the shaft to turn the bearing in place.
4. Install the lower bearing shell in the cap.
5. Tighten all cap nuts to the torque value given in the *Engine Tightening Data* table.

1953-59 Six

Main bearings can be replaced after removal of the oil pan. Both standard and undersize bearings are available for service replacement.

1. Remove oil pan and oil suction pipe.
2. Disconnect chain case cover from

Fig. 26   Using special tool (1) in crankshaft oil hole to turn upper main bearing in place

the oil pan seal and remove oil pan gasket seal plate, Fig. 27.
3. Remove clutch housing pan.
4. Loosen bearing caps slightly, Fig. 28.
5. Remove one cap at a time and replace both upper and lower bearing shells.
6. Before installing bearings, be sure crankshaft is not nicked or scored.
7. Measure clearance between bearing and crankshaft when installing either old or new bearings.
8. Plastigage may be used to measure clearance as shown in Fig. 25. Lacking Plastigage, however, coat a piece of .0015" brass shim stock (1/2" wide and 1" long) with oil and place it between the bearing and crankshaft.
9. Install the bearing cap and draw it up tight.
10. If the clearance is not excessive, there will be a slight drag when the crankshaft is turned. The desired clearance is given in the *Engine Bearing Data* chart.
11. Tighten caps to the recommended torque.

Note—The tool shown in Fig. 26 or a flattened cotter pin head may be used in the crankshaft oil hole to contact the upper bearing half and force it out.

Service Note

In case of warpage or other damage to main bearing caps, replacement caps are available which have stud holes 1/64" larger than the original caps and 1/16" shorter. This permits shimming or filing to adjust for variations between original and replacement caps. Never file, dress down or shim original bearing caps.

CRANKSHAFT REAR OIL SEAL
V8's & 1960-61 Six

A braided oil seal is pressed into the upper and lower grooves behind the rear main bearing. Directly in front of this seal is an oil slinger which deflects the oil back into the oil pan. Should the braided seal require replacement, the installation of the lower half is accomplished as follows:

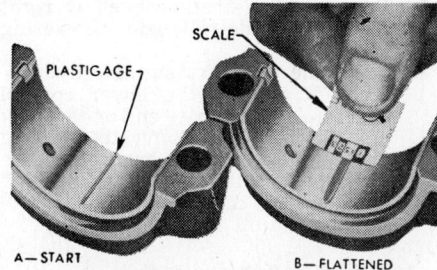

Fig. 25   Bearing clearance is determined by measuring width of flattened Plastigage

With the bearing cap and lower bearing half removed, install a new seal so that both ends protrude above the cap. Tap the seal down into position or roll it snugly in its groove with a smooth rounded tool. Then cut off the protruding ends of the seal with a sharp knife or razor blade.

Installing Upper Seal

Although the usual practice is to remove the crankshaft when the upper half of the seal is to be replaced it is possible to do the job without removing the crankshaft as follows:

To remove the seal, use needle-nose pliers to grasp the end of the seal which is most accessible. Pull the seal downward while rotating the crankshaft slowly in the direction that the seal is being removed.

To install the new seal, fasten a length of wire or strong string such as fishing line securely to one end of the new seal. See that the point of fastening is not bulky and that it is not over ⅜″ from the end of the seal. Coat the seal with Lubriplate. Pass the free end of the wire or string up over the crankshaft at the point where the seal is to be installed. Then exert a firm, steady pull on the wire or string and at the same time rotate the crankshaft slowly in the direction of the pull. This will help to move the seal into position. When the installation is completed, trim the ends of the seal flush with the engine block.

1953-59 Six

A neoprene rear main bearing oil seal is incorporated on all engines. The new seal is a lip type with a steel channel insert.

To remove the lower seal, take off the oil pan, clutch housing pan, and rear main bearing cap. Remove the seal from the cap. Thoroughly clean and inspect the bearing cap and bearing.

To remove the upper seal, use a screw driver, or similar tool, push one corner of the seal until the opposite end protrudes about ⅜ of an inch from the block. Pull the seal out from around the crankshaft with a pair of long nose pliers.

Fig. 27 The two screws marked (1) must be removed from chain case cover before front main bearing cap can be taken off. 1953-59 Six

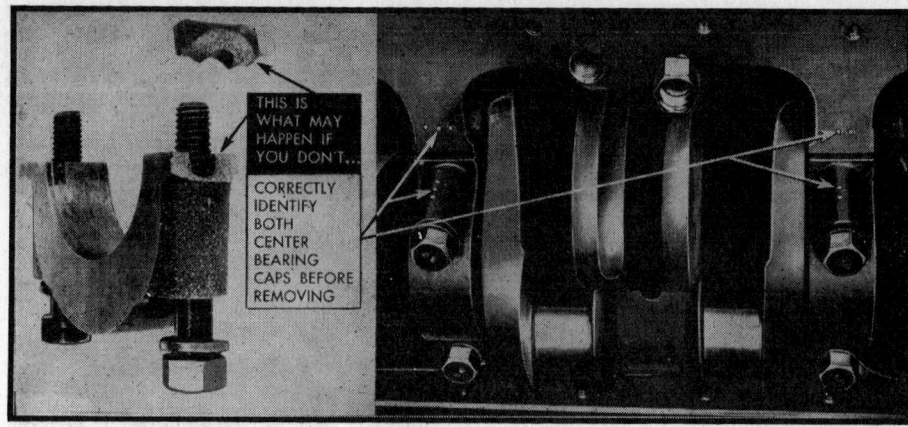

Fig. 28 Method of identifying main bearing caps. 1953-59 Six

Remove all traces of oil from the oil slinger groove in the block. This can be done by feeding a strip of cloth into the groove with a suitable length of wire. Work the cloth back and forth until the groove is cleaned.

When installing the Neoprene seal, apply a little Lubriplate to the contacting lip and be sure that the lip is pointed toward the front of the engine. Carefully insert the lower half of the seal into the bearing cap and position the cap gaskets in place. *Install the gaskets absolutely dry.* Be sure that the tabs of the parting line seals fit in the cap seat channel.

Place one end of the upper seal into the block and push it into place with a rolling motion. Turn the crankshaft at the same time as pressure is applied if the seal is difficult to install. Tighten the main bearing cap bolts to the recommended torque.

OIL PAN

1955 V8

Drain the oil and remove the oil level dipstick. Disconnect the steering linkage at the idler arm support bracket and allow the linkage to drop. Unfasten the pan and slide it out and down away from the engine.

1956 V8

1. Remove starting motor.
2. Remove clutch housing cover.
3. Remove front and rear engine mounting bolts.
4. Remove oil pan cap screws.
5. Remove idler arm bracket at right frame sub side-rail before lowering tie rods.
6. Place the base of a suitable hydraulic jack against the lower control arm and the opposite end of the jack against the torque converter housing at the starter motor location.
7. Move the engine approximately ¾″ to 1″ toward the rear of the car and remove the oil pan.

1957-59 V8 Except Commando

1. Remove distributor cap and rotor.
2. Raise car and drain engine oil.
3. Disconnect pitman arm from cross

shaft and idler arm from idler arm bracket.
4. Remove starting motor.
5. Remove exhaust cross-over pipe.
6. Remove dust shield.
7. Disconnect front engine mounts and raise front of engine approximately 2 inches. Install small blocks under mounts to support engine.
8. Remove oil pan bolts and pan.

1958-59 V8 Commando

1. Remove oil level dipstick.
2. Drain oil (leave plug out).
3. Disconnect steering linkage from steering arm.
4. On single exhaust system, remove crossover exhaust pipe.
5. Remove attaching screws and lower rear of pan, turning it sideways to clear crossmember.
6. Before installing the pan, clean the oil strainer and check it for alignment. The bottom of the strainer must be parallel with the lower, machined surface of the engine block.

1960-61 V8-318

1. Remove dipstick and drain oil.
2. Disconnect steering linkage from steering arm.
3. Remove starting motor.
4. On single exhaust system, remove crossover pipe.
5. Remove converter dust shield. Raise engine 1¼″ and disconnect front engine mounts.
6. Remove oil pan bolts and lower rear of pan, turning it sideways to clear crossmember.

1960-61 V8-361, 383

1. Disconnect battery cable.

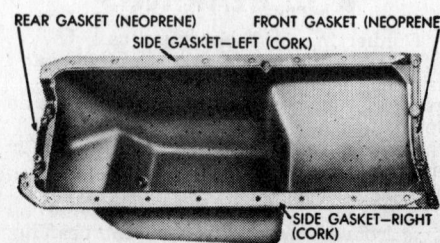

Fig. 28A Oil pan gaskets. 1960-61 Six

Fig. 29 Correct position of oil strainer on 1953-59 Six. This is important to prevent interference between strainer and oil pan baffles

2. Disconnect steering linkage from idler arm and steering arm.
3. Remove outlet vent pipe and disconnect exhaust pipes from manifolds.
4. Remove clamp attaching exhaust pipe to extension and remove exhaust pipe.
5. Drain crankcase oil and remove converter dust shield.
6. Remove oil pan bolts and lower pan, turning counterclockwise to clear oil pick up assembly as it is lowered.

1960-61 Six

1. Remove tie rod at steering and idler arms.
2. Remove front engine mounting bolts.
3. Remove left side support, connecting converter housing and cylinder block.
4. Raise engine about 2" and drain oil.
5. Remove pan bolts and lower pan down to the rear. *Do not turn oil pick up out of position.*
6. Reverse removal procedure to install noting location of pan gaskets as shown in Fig. 28A.

1953-56 Six

To remove the oil pan, remove the clutch housing lower pan to prevent damaging the oil pan gaskets on the housing. Lower the pan part way, lift up the oil strainer and take down the pan.

When installing the oil strainer, position the elbow so that the strainer will be located as shown in Fig. 29. Proper installation is important to prevent interference between the strainer and oil pan baffles.

Before installing the oil pan, clean the pan and the pan rail of the block thoroughly and install new gaskets. Four gaskets are used as a seal between the pan and block, Fig. 30. The gaskets are fitted into the fold-over slots of the oil pan ends to allow a more secure fit.

The right and left oil pan side gaskets may be installed with sealing compound applied on both sides. The end gaskets should be installed so that the ends of the gaskets stick out above the oil pan at least ⅛". Do not cut off the gasket ends as they will compress against the block and form a better seal as the oil pan is tightened against the block.

1957-59 Six

1. Raise car on hoist and drain engine oil.
2. Disconnect pitman arm from steering gear and idler arm from idler arm bracket.
3. Remove dust shield.
4. Remove starter motor.
5. Disconnect front engine mounts and raise front of engine approximately 2 inches. Install small blocks under engine mounts to support engine.
6. Remove pan bolts and oil pan.

OIL PUMP, REPLACE

1958-61 Commando

The oil pump and filter assembly, Fig. 17, is removed from underneath the engine by removing the three short and one long attaching bolts. Clean the assembly before disassembling. The filter can usually be removed by hand. However, a strap wrench can be used to unscrew it if necessary.

1955-61 V8 Except Commando

After removing the oil pan as outlined previously, unfasten the pump mounting bolts and drop the pump straight down and away from the engine.

When installing the pump, be sure to align the drive slot in the pump shaft with the distributor drive shaft. Install new seal rings and tighten the bolts with a torque wrench 30 to 35 lbs. ft.

1960-61 Six

Remove oil pump attaching bolts and remove pump and filter assembly from side of engine. When installing the pump tighten the attaching bolts to 200 inch lbs.

1953-59 Six

Before removing the oil pump, rotate the crankshaft and make sure the "DC" mark on the crankshaft pulley lines up with the pointer on the chain case cover

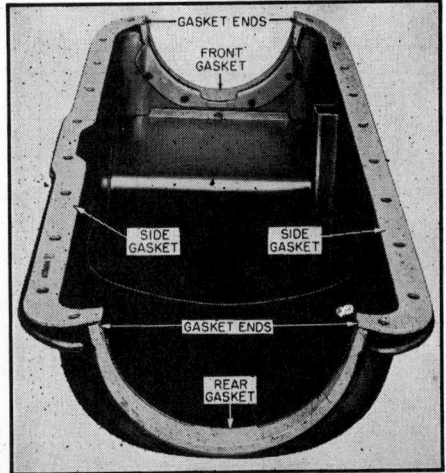

Fig. 30 Oil pan gaskets installed. 1953-59 Six. Be sure side gasket ends rest on top of end gaskets

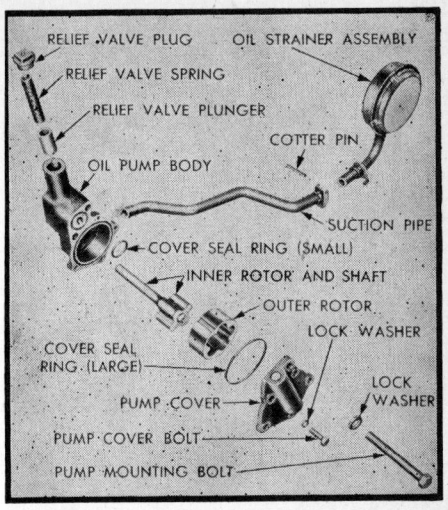

Fig. 31 Layout of oil pump parts. 1955-61 V8 (Except Gold. Com.)

and that the distributor rotor is ready to fire No. 1 spark plug. After the pump is removed, do not bump the starter or let the engine turn as this will change the ignition timing.

On some models, it is necessary to remove the two upper capscrews of the oil pump cover to provide sufficient clearance to remove the pump.

Use a new gasket when installing the oil pump. Line up the slots on the end of the pump shaft with the mounting holes in the pump flange. Turn the drive gear counter-clockwise one tooth and slip the oil pump into position. Check the position of the distributor rotor. It should be ready to fire No. 1 spark plug (rotor in seven o'clock position).

If the position of No. 1 piston was accidentally changed while the oil pump was removed, take out the spark plug. Rotate the crankshaft and check the compression of No. 1 cylinder. Do this by holding the thumb tightly over the spark plug hole. When the compression is felt by the thumb, turn the crankshaft until the piston is at top dead center, as indicated when the pointer lines up with the DC mark on the crankshaft pulley.

Turn the pump drive shaft until the slot in its end lines up with the cap screws holes in the mouting flange. Then turn the drive gear one tooth counter-clockwise, and carefully install the pump. Do not turn the drive gear while installing the pump.

OIL PUMP REPAIRS

1953-59 Six & 1955-61 V8

After removing the pump from the engine it should be disassembled, cleaned and inspected for wear or damage, Figs. 31, 32, 33.

1. Remove the cotter pin holding the oil strainer to the oil suction pipe. Then remove the pipe from the pump body.
2. Remove the pump cover and discard the oil seal ring.
3. Remove pump rotor and shaft and lift out rotor body.

4. Remove oil pressure relief valve plug and lift out the spring and plunger.

5. Wash all parts in cleaning solvent and inspect carefully for damage or wear.

6. The mating face of the oil pump cover should be smooth. If it is scratched or grooved, the cover should be replaced with a new one.

7. Check for excessive cover-to-rotor wear by laying a straight edge across the cover surface. If a .0015" feeler gauge can be inserted between cover and straight edge, the cover should be discarded and a new one installed.

8. Slide rotor body and rotor into pump body and then place a straight edge across the face of the pump body between the bolt holes. If a feeler gauge of less than .003" or more than .006" can be inserted between the rotors and straight edge, install a new pump body.

9. Remove the pump rotor and shaft, leaving rotor body in pump cavity. Press rotor body to one side with the fingers and measure the clearance between rotor and pump bodies. If it is more than .012", install a new pump body.

10. Check the clearance between the pump rotor and rotor body. If the measurement is more than .012", install a new pump rotor and rotor body.

11. Check the oil pump relief valve plunger for scoring and free operation in its bore. If the plunger is scored, install a new one.

Refer to Fig. 33A and remove the pump cover seal ring. Press off the drive gear, supporting the gear to keep load off aluminum body. Remove rotor and shaft and lift out outer pump rotor. Remove oil pressure relief valve plug and lift out spring and plunger.

Inspection

1. The rotor contact area and the bores for the shaft and valve in the pump body should be smooth, free from scratches, scoring or excessive wear.

2. The pump cover should be smooth, flat and free from scoring or ridges. Lay a straightedge across the cover. If a .0015" feeler gauge can be in-

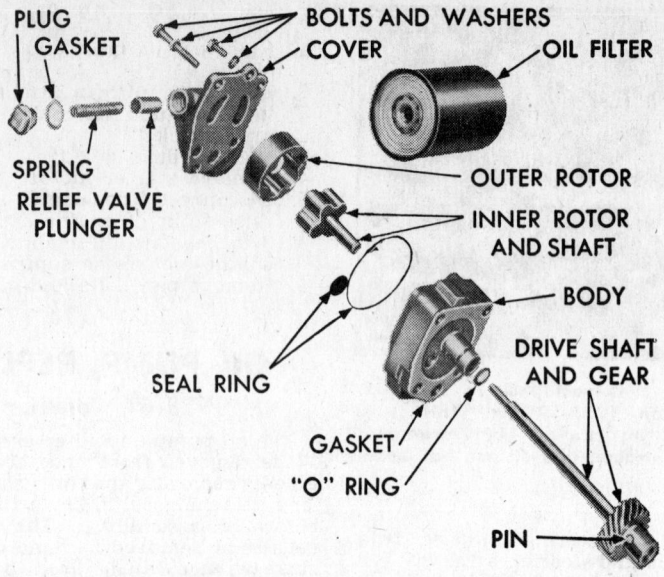

Fig. 32 Oil pump disassembled. 1958-61 Golden Commando engine

serted under the straightedge, the cover should be replaced.

3. All surfaces of the outer rotor should be smooth and uniform, free from ridges, scratches or uneven wear. Discard a rotor less than .649" thick and/or less than 2.469" in diameter.

4. The inner rotor and shaft assembly should be smooth, free from scoring and uneven wear. Discard rotors less than .649" thick.

5. Place outer rotor in pump body and measure clearance between rotor and body. Discard pump body if clearance is more than .012".

6. Install inner rotor and shaft in pump body. Shaft should turn freely but without side play. If clearance between rotor teeth is more than .010", replace both rotors.

7. Measure rotor end clearance. If feeler gauge of more than .004" can be inserted between straightedge and rotors, install a new pump body.

8. The oil pressure relief valve should be smooth, free from scratches or scoring, and should be a free fit in its bore.

9. Relief valve springs are painted either gray, red or brown to denote free lengths of $2\frac{3}{16}$, $2\frac{19}{32}$ and $2\frac{23}{32}$ inches, respectively. Rather than change the length, replace a spring with one of the same color.

OIL PRESSURE REGULATOR

1953-59 Six

Oil pressure is controlled by a relief valve located on the left side of the engine.

Inspect the relief valve plunger and spring after removing the valve cap and gasket. If the plunger is scratched, remove the scratches by polishing, or install a new plunger. If the old plunger is to be reinstalled, clean it and flush out the bore with engine oil by cranking the

engine with the starter.

If the spring is to be replaced, use a new one of the same type. Do not use a heavier spring or a steel ball or washers behind the spring to raise the oil pressure. If oil pressure is low, check the fit of crankshaft bearings or look for other causes of possible loss of oil pressure.

Different colored springs are used in the relief valve. The medium spring is unpainted; the light spring is red, and the heavy spring is green. If it is necessary to replace a spring, install a spring of the same color.

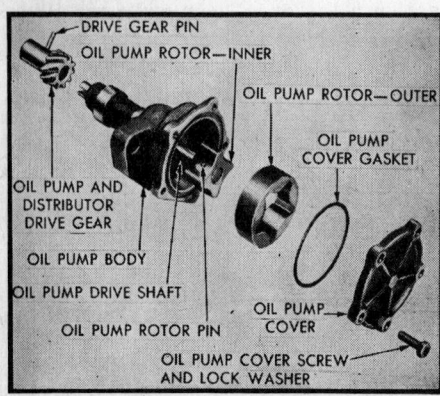

Fig. 33 Oil pump. 1953-59 Six

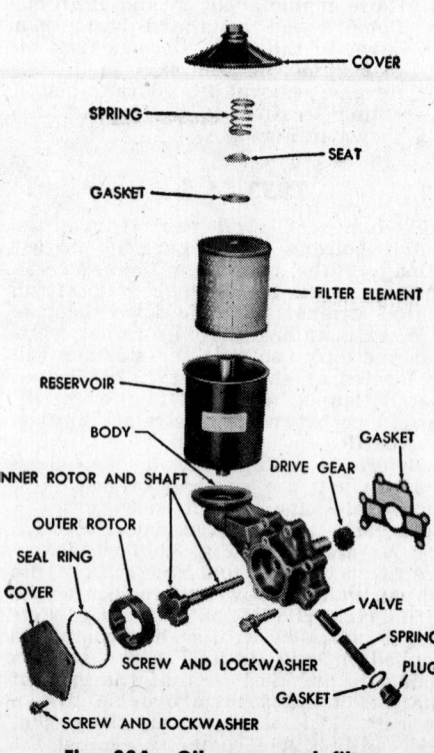

Fig. 33A Oil pump and filter disassembled. 1960-61 Six

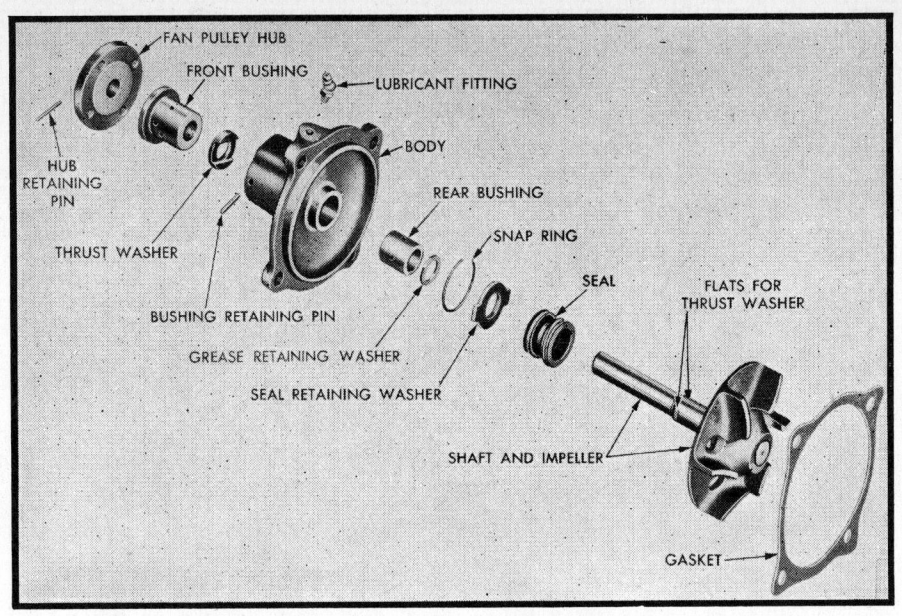

Fig. 34 Bushing type water pump. 1955-56 V8

RADIATOR, REPLACE

V8 Engines

To remove radiator, drain cooling system and disconnect hoses. Remove fan shroud (if equipped). Unfasten radiator from its support and lift it out.

Six Cylinder Engines

Drain cooling system and disconnect hoses. Remove fan blades only if additional clearance is necessary. Remove fan shroud (if equipped). Unfasten radiator from its support and lift it out.

WATER PUMP, REPLACE

1958-61

Drain cooling system and then remove fan shroud (if equipped). Loosen fan belt and remove fan, spacer and pulley. Remove the water pump to housing retaining bolts and remove the pump.

1955-57 V8

Remove the fan and belt and disconnect water pump hose. Unfasten the water pump from the engine and lift it off.

1953-57 Six

Remove the fan belt and disconnect water pump hose. Unfasten the water pump from the engine and lift out the pump and fan blade assembly.

When installing the pump, make sure all mating surfaces are clean, and use new gaskets.

WATER PUMP REPAIRS

Bushing Type Pump, 1955-56 V8

To disassemble, Fig. 34, first drive the fan pulley hub retaining pin out of the

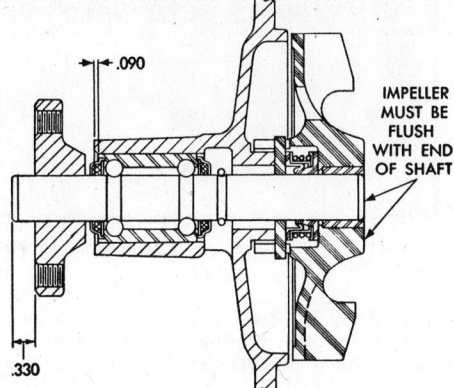

Fig. 36 Water pump assembly details. 1956-61 V8

hub. Remove hub with puller. Remove shaft and impeller. Drive front bushing retaining pin into shaft hole. Remove front and rear bushings and thrust washer.

Assembly

When installing the rear bushing, press it into the bore .130-.155" beyond seat surface. Press in front bushing far enough to seat the shoulder. Install a suitable flat washer so as not to damage the bearing surface as the bushing is pressed into position.

Drill a hole in the front bushing (No. 13 drill) and install the retaining pin. Drive the pin flush with the pump body surface.

The bushings should be burnished if a burnisher is available. If not, line ream the rear bushing .6704-.6714" and the front bushing .595-.596". When using the reamer, be careful not to engage the thrust washer between the bushings as damage to the washer and bushings may result. Use a suitable tool to reface the seal seat.

When inserting the shaft and impeller, be certain that the flats on the shaft interlock with the lugs on the thrust washer.

When installed, the clearance between the pulley hub and front bushing should be .0005-.005". Measure with feeler gauge.

Drill a hole through the fan pulley hub and shaft (No. 22 drill) and insert a new pin.

Lubricate the pump with water pump grease and install on the engine, using a new gasket. Torque tighten attaching bolts 25-30 lbs. ft.

Ball Bearing Pump, 1955 V8

This pump uses a cast iron impeller which is a press fit on the end of the shaft. Whenever the seal or bearing and shaft assembly is to be replaced, the impeller must be removed. First remove the set screw or lock wire which retains the bearing and shaft assembly. Place the

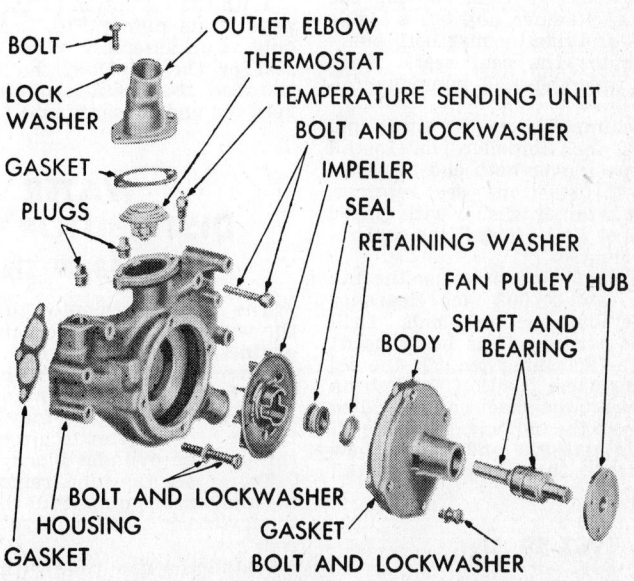

Fig. 35 Water pump disassembled. 1958-61 Golden Commando

pump in a press and press on the impeller end of the shaft to remove the impeller. Continue pressing until bearing and shaft assembly is out of pump body.

When reassembling the pump, a new seal and seal washer should be used. It is also advisable to replace the bearing and shaft since damage to this assembly usually results during its removal. The hub and impeller must fit tightly on the shaft; a hub that has been used previously usually does not fit tight enough.

Ball Bearing Pump, 1956-61 V8

This pump does not use a lock pin to hold the fan pulley hub in place. To disassemble, use a suitable puller to pull the hub off the shaft. Remove the impeller by breaking the plastic away from the metal insert. Remove impeller insert and press the shaft and bearing assembly out of the housing from the impeller end, Fig. 35.

When assembled the impeller should be flush with the end of the shaft. And when installing the fan pulley hub, press it on until there is .330" between the end of the shaft and the front face of the hub, Fig. 36.

1953-56 Six

To disassemble the pump, see Fig. 37 and proceed as follows:

Drive pin out of fan pulley hub and use a puller to pull hub off the shaft. Remove cover and pull impeller and shaft out of body. If either impeller or shaft is to be replaced, drive out the pin holding these parts together. Drive the front bushing pin into the shaft hole of the bushing to permit removal of the bushings. Pull the bushings from the body, pulling them out toward the front. Remove the seal, spring and retainer washers from the shaft.

If new bushings are to be installed, insert the thrust washer in the body with flat side facing out. Press the front bushing in with the oil groove on top and grooved end out. Press in the rear bushing, allowing $\frac{3}{32}$ inch clearance between the rear end of the bushing and the impeller housing. Drill and pin the front bushing. Remove any burrs inside the bushings and line burnish both bushings and reface the seal seat. Then continue to assemble the pump as follows:

Install the impeller on the shaft and drill for a $\frac{1}{8}$ inch impeller pin. Install the pin and peen over both ends. Assemble the seal thrust spring, seal retainer, seal and seat retainer washer with glazed surface against seal. Install the seal retainer lock ring.

Insert the shaft and press on the fan pulley hub, leaving .003 inch clearance between the bushing and hub. Drill the shaft (if a new one is being used) and install the retaining pin. If the old shaft is being used, position the hub on the shaft so that the shaft can be drilled 90 degrees from the old hole. Remove all traces of old gaskets and install new ones. Lubricate the pump and install on the engine.

1957-59 Six

A sealed ball bearing type water pump

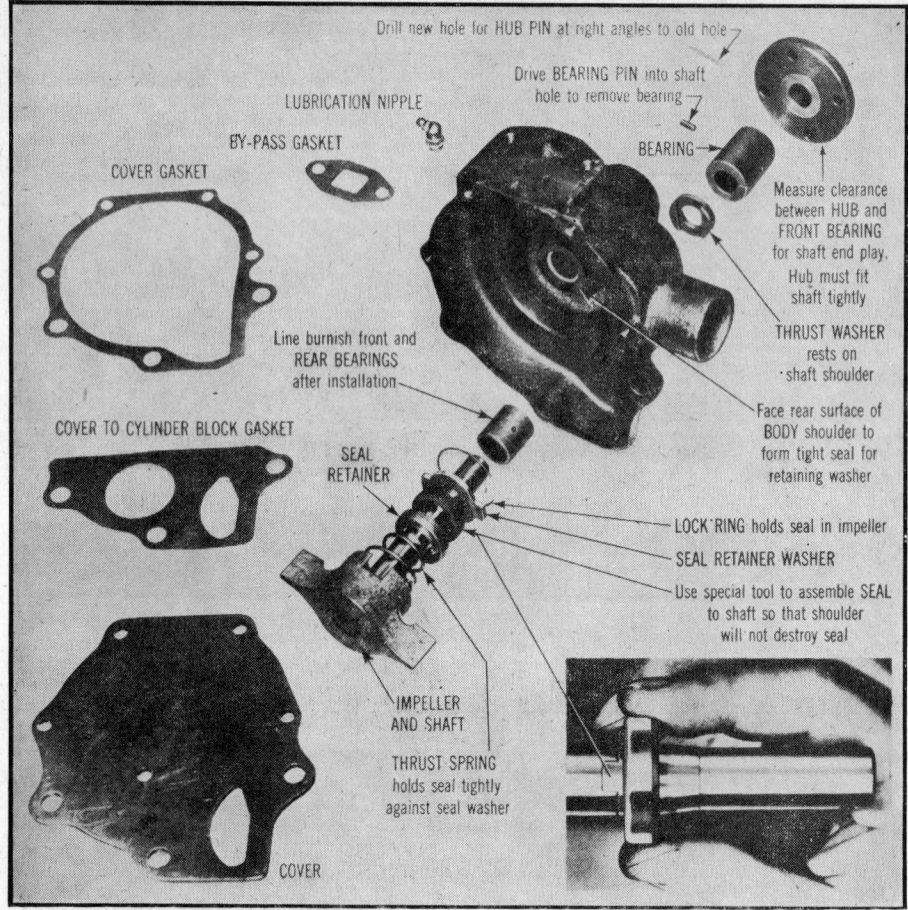

Fig. 37 Disassembled view of water pump. 1953-56

is used. It is similar to the pump employed on V8 engines and, therefore, follow the same procedure given for V8 water pumps with exception that the hub must be installed flush with end of shaft.

1960-61 Six

With the exception of the seal and impeller, this pump, Fig. 37A, is serviced only as an assembly. When replacing the seal or the impeller, the hub must be installed to obtain a dimension of .41" between end of shaft and face of hub.

WATER DISTRIBUTOR TUBE

1953-59 Six

The water distributor tube, located in the water jacket on the valve side of the engine, should be replaced whenever the engine is completely overhauled. If the tube becomes rusted or corroded, overheating of the engine may occur due to failure of the water to circulate properly through the cylinder block.

To replace the tube, remove the radiator and water pump. Pull the tube out of the cylinder block with a stiff hooked rod.

Install the new tube with the slots up and be sure it is inserted far enough into

the block so that the water pump will seat properly against the block.

DISTRIBUTOR, REPLACE

To remove the distributor, disconnect the vacuum control line and low tension wire and remove the cap and lock plate hold-down screw.

When installing the distributor, make sure that No. 1 piston is on top dead center on compression stroke and that the distributor rotor is in No. 1 firing position, Figs. 38, 39.

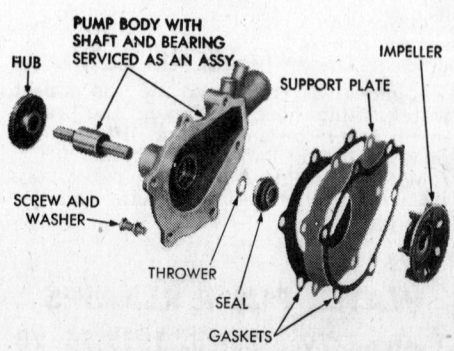

Fig. 37A Water pump disassembled. 1960-61 Six

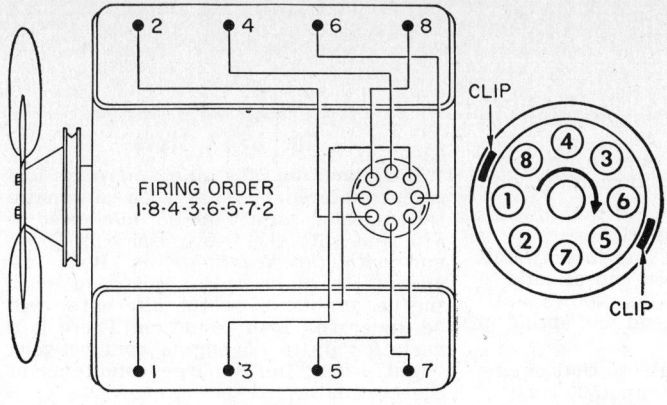

Fig. 38 Ignition details. 1955-61 V8 except Golden Commando

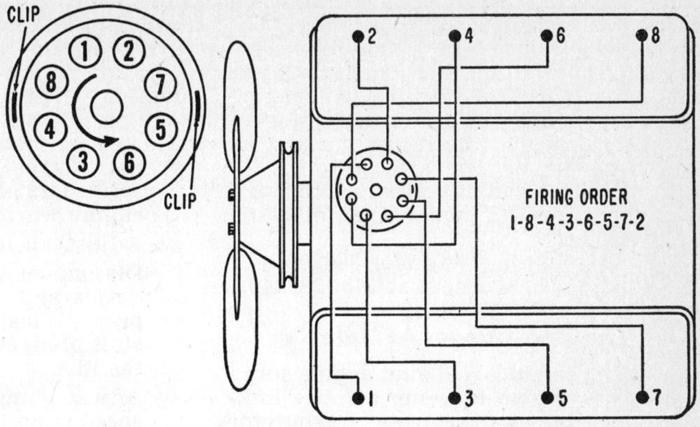

Fig. 39 Ignition details. 1958-61 Golden Commando engine

IGNITION
TIMING

With the distributor properly installed on the engine as outlined below, set the ignition timing with a timing light so that with the engine idling, the timing light will flash when the pointer on the engine is opposite the timing mark on the vibration damper. Chalk-mark the spot on the vibration damper so that it stands out when the light flashes.

ALTERNATOR, REPLACE

Disconnect battery ground cable and wires from alternator. Unfasten and remove alternator from engine.

STARTER, REPLACE

Disconnect battery ground cable, and wires from starter. Unfasten starter from flywheel housing and remove from car.

MUFFLER & PIPES

The exhaust pipe and muffler are welded together, forming a complete assembly. To replace the muffler, the exhaust pipe should be cut off as close to the front of the muffler as possible. Then loosen the tail pipe clamps and slide the tail pipe to the rear.

When any part of the exhaust system has been replaced, leave the attaching bolts and clamps loose and run the engine to allow all parts of the system to align themselves. Then, tighten all bolts and clamps securely, making sure there is no interference.

Carburetor Section

Performance Complaints

Flooding, stumble on acceleration or other performance complaints are in many instances caused by the presence of dirt, water or other foreign matter in the carburetor. To aid in diagnosing the cause of the complaint, the carburetor should be carefully removed from the engine without draining the fuel from the bowl. The contents of the fuel bowl may be examined for contamination as the carburetor is disassembled.

Check the fuel in the bowl for contamination by dirt, water, gum or other foreign matter. A magnet moved through the fuel in the bowl will pick up and identify any iron oxide dust that may have caused intake needle and seat leakage.

Inspect gasketed surfaces between body and air horn. Small nicks or burrs should be smoothed down to eliminate air or fuel leakage. On carburetors having a vacuum piston, be especially particular when inspecting the top surface of the inner wall of the bowl around the vacuum piston passage. A poor seal at this location may contribute to a "cutting-out" on turns complaint.

Fill the carburetor bowl with clean fuel before installing on manifold. This will help prevent dirt trapped in the fuel system from being dislodged by the free flow of fuel as the carburetor is primed.

The operation of the floats and intake needle and seats may be checked under pressure if a fuel pump is used at the bench to fill the carburetor bowl. Operate the throttle several times and visually check the discharge from pump jets.

Poor Mileage and Engine Loading Complaints

Cases of poor mileage and engine loading may be due in many instances to sluggish choke valve opening during cold driveaway, caused by insufficient vacuum in choke housing, a plugged or restricted heat pipe or inlet in choke cover. To check for this condition, have engine warm and running at slow idle. Remove choke heat pipe and hold a finger over the heat inlet hole (hole is on choke housing on some carburetors). If there is little or no vacuum pull on the finger, check the choke housing for gasket leaks or plugged vacuum passages. If these are OK, check choke vacuum passages in carburetor between choke housing and manifold.

Dirty or Rusty Choke Housing

In cases where it is found that the interior of the choke housing is dirty, gummed or rusty while the carburetor itself is comparatively clean, look for a punctured or eroded manifold heat tube (if one is used).

Manifold Heat Control Valve

An engine equipped with a manifold heat control valve can operate with the valve stuck either in the open or closed position. Because of this, an inoperative valve is frequently overlooked at vehicle lubrication or tune-up.

A valve stuck in the "heat-off" position can result in slow warm up, deposits in combustion chamber, carburetor icing, flat spots during acceleration, low gas mileage and spark plug fouling.

A valve stuck in the "heat-on" position can result in power loss, engine knocking, sticking or burned valves and spark plug burning.

To prevent the possibility of a stuck valve, check and lubricate the valve each time vehicle is lubricated or tuned-up. Check the operation of the valve manually. To lubricate the valve, place a few drops of penetrating oil on the valve shaft where it passes through the manifold. Move the valve up and down a few times to work in the oil. *Never use engine oil for this purpose as it will leave a residue which hampers valve operation.*

Carburetor Stumble

Stromberg WW15-42—If a hesitation or

PLYMOUTH

stumble occurs upon light acceleration, particularly before the engine is thoroughly warmed up, is may be necessary to replace the main metering jets and main discharge nozzles. An engine tune up should be performed prior to changing jets and discharge nozzles, as fuel economy may be affected.

These parts can be obtained through Stromberg outlets under the following part numbers:

2 Main metering jets No. 386208.
2 Main discharge nozzles No. 386949.

Engine Surge At Idle

Sonoramic Engines—Should engine surge at idle, an engine tune-up, throttle linkage adjustment, accurate carburetor adjustment and balance should be performed. Exhaust manifold heat control valves should be examined for proper operation and for the correct five-coil manifold heat control valve spring. In addition, the anti-stall dashpot should be adjusted as follows:

1. Set normal curb idle to the prescribed 725-750 rpm in neutral with engine warmed up.
2. Adjust all linkage properly.
3. Disconnect vacuum line to anti-stall device and tape open end of tube to prevent leakage. This allows anti-stall plunger to extend and speed up the idle.
4. Adjust plunger length so that engine speed is no higher than 1500 rpm.
5. Connect vacuum line to anti-stall device. The plunger should retract and engine speed should drop to normal curb idle speed.

Adjusting Idle Speed On 1961 Sixes

If a condition of stalling or rough idle is encountered on cars with automatic transmission, adjust the hot idle speed to 500 rpm with the transmission in Drive and *with the headlights on.* It is important to make this adjustment with the headlights on so the alternator will be under full load condition. There is a variation up to 65 engine rpm between "light" and "full" charge conditions of the alternator.

CARTER CARBURETOR ADJUSTMENTS

Year	Carburetor Model	Idle Adjustments				Float Level		Float Drop		Pump Travel Setting	Choke Unloader Setting	Choke Setting
		Mixture Screws Turns Open	Hot Idle Speed Neutral	Fast Idle Speed	Dashpot Plunger Clearance	Primary	Secondary	Primary	Secondary			
1961	BBS-3098S	1	550	1800(10)	None	7/32(1)	None	None	None	27/32(2)	3/16(4)	Index
	BBS-3099S	1	550	1600(10)	None	7/32(1)	None	None	None	27/32(2)	3/16(4)	Index
	BBS-3097S	1	550	(25)	None	7/32(1)	None	None	None	3/4(2)	3/16(4)	Index
	BBS-3128S	1	550	(25)	None	7/32(1)	None	None	None	27/32(2)	3/16(4)	Index
	BBS-3129S	1	550	(25)	None	7/32(1)	None	None	None	3/4(2)	3/16(4)	Index
	BBD-2921S	1	500	1400(10)	None	9/32(1)	None	None	None	5/64(26)	1/4(4)	Index
	BBD-2922S	1	500	1400(10)	None	9/32(1)	None	None	None	5/64(26)	1/4(4)	Index
	AFB-3103S	1½	500	1800(10)	None	7/32(18)	7/32(18)	9/16(19)	9/16(19)	7/16(20)	1/4(21)	Index
	AFB-3131S	1½	500	1800(10)	None	7/32(18)	7/32(18)	9/16(19)	9/16(19)	7/16(20)	1/4(21)	Index
	AFB-3105S	1½	500	1700(10)	None	7/32(18)	7/32(18)	9/16(19)	9/16(19)	7/16(20)	1/4(21)	Index
	AFB-3106S	1½	500	1800(10)	None	7/32(18)	7/32(18)	9/16(19)	9/16(19)	7/16(20)	1/4(21)	Index
	AFB-3140S	1½	500	1700(10)	None	7/32(18)	7/32(18)	9/16(19)	9/16(19)	7/16(20)	1/4(21)	Index
	AFB-2968S	1½	500	1800(10)	None	7/32(18)	7/32(18)	9/16(19)	9/16(19)	7/16(20)	1/4(21)	2 Rich
	AFB-3133S	1½	500	1800(10)	None	7/32(18)	7/32(18)	9/16(19)	9/16(19)	7/16(20)	1/4(21)	2 Rich
	AFB-2903S	1½	750	1500(10)	(16)	9/32(18)	9/32(18)	9/16(19)	9/16(19)	1/4(20)	1/4(21)	1 Rich
1960	BBS-2985S	1/8-1	500	1300(10)	None	7/32(1)	None	None	None	27/32(2)	11/64(4)	Index
	BBS-2986S	1/2-1½	500	1300(10)	None	7/32(1)	None	None	None	27/32(2)	11/64(4)	Index
	BBD-2921S	1/4-1½	500	1400(10)	None	9/32(1)	None	None	None	1⅛(2)	1/4(4)	Index
	BBD-2922S	1/4-1½	500	1400(10)	None	9/32(1)	None	None	None	1⅛(2)	1/4(4)	Index
	BBD-2983S	1/4-1½	500	1400(10)	None	9/32(1)	None	None	None	1⅛(2)	1/4(4)	Index
	AFB-2903S	1/8-1½	750	1500(10)	(16)	9/32(18)	9/32(18)	23/32(19)	23/32(19)	27/64(20)	1/4(21)	1 Rich
	AFB-2925S	1¼-2¾	500	2100(10)	None	7/32(18)	7/32(18)	23/32(19)	23/32(19)	7/16(20)	1/4(21)	Index
	AFB-2969S	1/4-1¾	500	1800(10)	None	7/32(18)	7/32(18)	23/32(19)	23/32(19)	7/16(20)	1/4(21)	Index
	AFB-2970S	1/4-1¾	500	1800(10)	None	7/32(18)	7/32(18)	23/32(19)	23/32(19)	7/16(20)	1/4(21)	Index
1959	BBD-2775S	1/4-1½	500	1400(10)	None	9/32(1)	None	None	None	1⅛(2)	1/4(4)	Index
	BBD-2776S	1/4-1½	500	1400(10)	None	9/32(1)	None	None	None	1⅛(2)	1/4(4)	Index
	BBD-2777S	1/4-1½	500	1400(10)	None	9/32(1)	None	None	None	1⅛(2)	1/4(4)	Index
	BBD-2864S	1/4-1½	500	1400(10)	None	9/32(1)	None	None	None	1⅛(2)	1/4(4)	Index
	BBD-2865S	1/4-1½	500	1400(10)	None	9/32(1)	None	None	None	1⅛(2)	1/4(4)	Index
	BBD-2866S	1/4-1½	500	1400(10)	None	9/32(1)	None	None	None	1⅛(2)	1/4(4)	Index
	BBD-2896S	1/4-1½	500	1400(10)	None	9/32(1)	None	None	None	1⅛(2)	1/4(4)	Index
1958	AFB-2812S	1/4-1¾	500	1400(10)	None	7/32(18)	7/32(18)	23/32(19)	23/32(19)	7/16(20)	1/4(21)	Index
	AFB-2813S	1/4-1¾	500	1400(10)	None	7/32(18)	7/32(18)	23/32(19)	23/32(19)	7/16(20)	1/4(21)	2 Rich
	AFB-2652S	1/4-1½	650	None	None	(22)	(22)	23/32(19)	23/32(19)	7/16(20)	None	None
	AFB-2653S	1/4-1½	650	1450(10)	None	(23)	(23)	23/32(19)	23/32(19)	7/16(20)	1/4(21)	1 Rich
	AFB-2641S	1/4-1¾	500	1400(10)	None	(23)	(23)	23/32(19)	23/32(19)	7/16(20)	1/4(21)	2 Rich
	AFB-2744S	1/4-1¾	500	1400(10)	None	(24)	(24)	23/32(19)	23/32(19)	7/16(20)	1/4(21)	2 Rich
	BBD-2644S	1/4-1¼	500	1400(10)	None	9/32(1)	None	None	None	1 1/32(2)	1/4(4)	Index
	BBD-2645S	1/4-1¼	500	1400(10)	None	9/32(1)	None	None	None	1 1/32(2)	1/4(4)	Index
	BBD-2646S	1/4-1¼	500	1400(10)	None	9/32(1)	None	None	None	1 1/32(2)	1/4(4)	Index

CARTER CARBURETOR ADJUSTMENTS continued

Year	Carburetor Model	Idle Adjustments				Float Level		Float Drop		Pump Travel Setting	Choke Unloader Setting	Choke Setting
		Mixture Screws Turns Open	Hot Idle Speed Neutral	Fast Idle Speed	Dashpot Plunger Clearance	Primary	Secondary	Primary	Secondary			
1957	BBD-2512S-A	¼-1¼	500	1475(10)	None	9/32(1)	None	None	None	1 1/32(2)	¼(4)	Index
	BBD-2512SB-C	¼-1¼	500	1475(10)	None	9/32(1)	None	None	None	1 1/32(2)	¼(4)	Index
	BBD-2513S-A	¼-1¼	500	1475(10)	None	9/32(1)	None	None	None	1 1/32(2)	¼(4)	Index
	BBD-2513SB-C	¼-1¼	500	1475(10)	None	9/32(1)	None	None	None	1 1/32(2)	¼(4)	Index
	BBD-2514S-A	¼-1¼	500	1475(10)	None	9/32(1)	None	None	None	1 1/32(2)	¼(4)	Index
	BBD-2514SB-C	¼-1¼	500	1475(10)	None	9/32(1)	None	None	None	1 1/32(2)	¼(4)	Index
	BBD-2567S	½-1¾	500	1650(11)	None	7/32(1)	None	None	None	27/32(2)	9/64(6)	Index
	BBD-2568S	½-1¾	500	1650(11)	None	7/32(1)	None	None	None	27/32(2)	9/64(6)	Index
	BBD-2569S	½-1¾	500	1650(11)	1/16(15)	7/32(1)	None	None	None	27/32(2)	9/64(6)	Index
	BBD-2604S	½-1¾	500	1650(11)	None	7/32(1)	None	None	None	27/32(2)	9/64(6)	Index
1956	WCFB-2442S	1-2	500	1375(10)	None	7/32(7)	9/32(7)	23/32(8)	25/32(8)	(9)	11/64(4)	Index
	BBS-2410S	1-2	500	.018(5)	None	9/32(1)	None	None	None	27/32(2)	9/64(6)	Index
	BBS-2293S	½-1¾	500	.018(5)	None	7/32(1)	None	None	None	27/32(2)	9/64(6)	Index
	BBS-2294S	½-1¾	500	.018(5)	None	7/32(1)	None	None	None	27/32(2)	9/64(6)	Index
	BBS-2295S	½-1¾	500	.018(5)	3/32(15)	7/32(1)	None	None	None	27/32(2)	9/64(6)	Index
	BBS-2380S	½-1¾	500	.018(5)	None	7/32(1)	None	None	None	27/32(2)	9/64(6)	Index
	BBD-2407S	½-1½	500	1375(10)	None	¼(1)	None	None	None	1 1/32(2)	3/16(4)	Index
	BBD-2408S	½-1½	500	1375(10)	None	¼(1)	None	None	None	1 1/32(2)	3/16(4)	Index
	BBD-2409S-A	½-1½	500	1375(10)	1/16(15)	¼(1)	None	None	None	1 1/32(2)	3/16(4)	Index
	BBD-2299S	½-1½	500	1375(10)	None	¼(1)	None	None	None	1 1/32(2)	3/16(4)	Index
	BBD-2300S	½-1½	500	1375(10)	None	¼(1)	None	None	None	1 1/32(2)	3/16(4)	Index
	BBD-2301S	½-1½	500	1375(10)	1/16(15)	¼(1)	None	None	None	1 1/32(2)	3/16(4)	Index
	BBD-2422S	½-1½	500	.018(5)	None	7/32(1)	None	None	None	1(2)	¼(4)	Index
	BBD-2423S	½-1½	500	.018(5)	None	7/32(1)	None	None	None	1(2)	¼(4)	Index
	BBD-2424S	½-1½	500	.018(5)	1/16(15)	7/32(1)	None	None	None	1(2)	¼(4)	Index
1955	WCFB-2253S	½-1½	500	.012(3)	None	⅛(7)	3/16(7)	⅝(8)	11/16(8)	(9)	3/16(4)	Index
	BBD-2141S	½-1½	500	.011(3)	None	7/32(1)	None	None	None	29/32(2)	¼(4)	Index
	BBD-2154S	½-1½	500	.011(3)	None	7/32(1)	None	None	None	29/32(2)	¼(4)	Index
	BBD-2155S	½-1½	500	.011(3)	1/16(15)	7/32(1)	None	None	None	29/32(2)	¼(4)	Index
	BBD-2262S	½-1½	500	.011(3)	None	7/32(1)	None	None	None	29/32(2)	¼(4)	Index
1954-55	BBS-2203S	½-1½	475	.021(5)	None	7/32(1)	None	None	None	51/64(12)	9/64(6)	Index
	BBS-2215S	½-1½	475	.021(5)	None	7/32(1)	None	None	None	49/64(2)	9/64(6)	Index
	BBS-2062S-A	½-1½	475	.024(5)	None	7/32(1)	None	None	None	27/32(2)	9/64(6)	Index
	BBS-2063S-A	½-1½	475	.024(5)	None	7/32(1)	None	None	None	27/32(2)	9/64(6)	Index
	BBS-2116S-A	½-1½	475	.024(5)	3/32(15)	7/32(1)	None	None	None	27/32(2)	9/64(6)	Index
	BBS-2249S	½-1½	475	.024(5)	None	7/32(1)	None	None	None	27/32(2)	9/64(6)	Index
1954	BBS-920S-A	½-1½	475	.021(5)	None	7/32(1)	None	None	None	27/32(2)	9/64(6)	Index
	BBS-993S-A	½-1½	475	.021(5)	None	7/32(1)	None	None	None	27/32(2)	9/64(6)	Index
	BBS-994S-A	½-1½	475	.021(5)	3/32(15)	7/32(1)	None	None	None	27/32(2)	9/64(6)	Index
	BBS-2248S	½-1½	475	.021(5)	None	7/32(1)	None	None	None	29/32(2)	9/64(6)	Index
1953	BB-D6P1, 2	½-1½	475	None	3/32(15)	5/64(13)	None	None	None	11/32(14)	None	None
	BB-D6R1	½-1½	475	None	None	5/64(13)	None	None	None	11/32(14)	None	None
	BB-D6U1	½-1½	475	None	None	5/64(13)	None	None	None	11/32(14)	None	None
	BB-D6N1, 2	½-1½	475	None	None	5/64(13)	None	None	None	11/32(14)	None	None

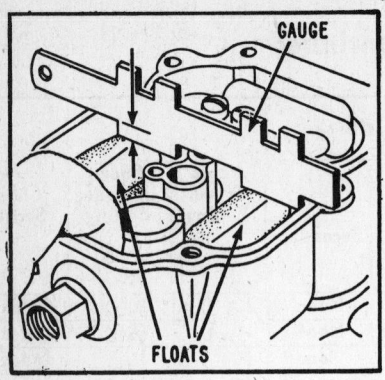

Fig. ①—BBD and BBS float level. Adjust by bending lip on float arm.

CARTER NOTES

METERING RODS

WCFB—This adjustment must be made after pump setting. Seat throttle valves in bores of carburetor and loosen metering rod arm clamp screw. With metering rods in place, press down on vacumeter link until metering rods bottom in casting. Holding rods down, revolve metering rod arm until finger on arm contacts vacumeter link. Hold in place and tighten clamp screw.

OVERDRIVE KICKDOWN SWITCH

BBD and BBS—With throttle valves wide open, there should be $\frac{1}{64}''$ to $\frac{3}{64}''$ clearance between kickdown lever and switch stem guide. Adjust by loosening lock nuts and adjust switch as required.

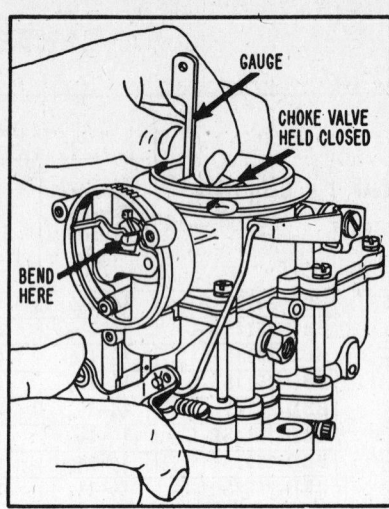

Fig. ⑥—With throttle valve wide open, there should be the clearance specified between upper edge of choke valve and inner wall of air horn. Adjust by bending arm on choke trip lever.

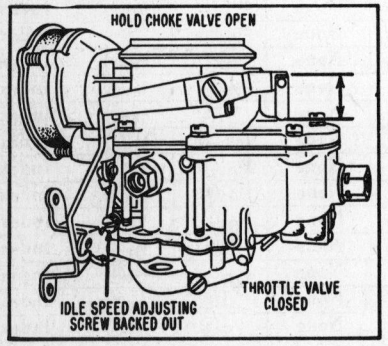

Fig. ②—Measure from top of bowl cover to top of plunger shaft with throttle connector rod in center hole of throttle lever and inner hole of pump arm. Adjust by bending throttle connector rod.

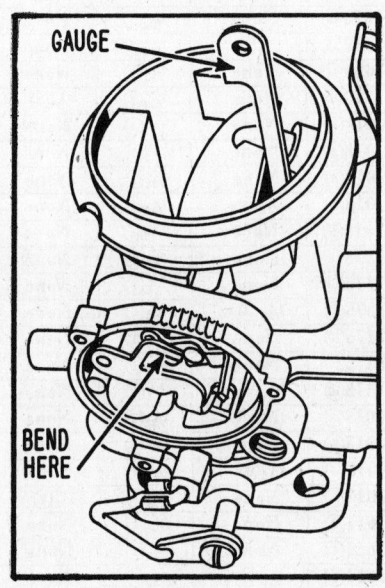

Fig. ④—With throttle valves wide open, clearance between upper edge of choke valve and inner wall of air horn should be as specified. Adjust by bending unloader arm on throttle lever.

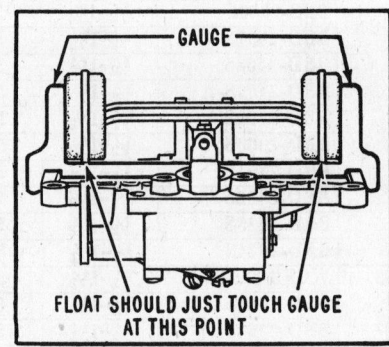

Fig. ⑦—WCFB float level. Adjust by bending float lever.

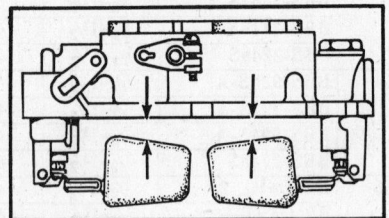

Fig. ⑧—WCFB float drop. Adjust by bending stop tabs on float bracket.

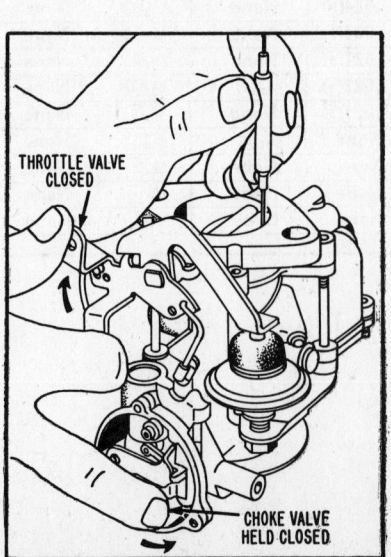

Fig. ③—With choke valve closed, tighten fast idle adjusting screw on high step of fast idle cam until the clearance between throttle valve and carburetor bore is as specified.

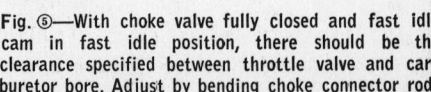

Fig. ⑤—With choke valve fully closed and fast idle cam in fast idle position, there should be the clearance specified between throttle valve and carburetor bore. Adjust by bending choke connector rod.

CARTER NOTES
continued

Fig. ⑨—With pump connector link in outer hole of pump arm, flat on pump arm should be parallel with a straightedge across dust cover boss. Adjust by bending throttle connector rod.

⑩—With engine at normal operating temperature, turn fast idle screw against high step on fast idle cam or on index mark until specified rpm is obtained.

⑪—With engine at normal operating temperature and choke trip lever on high step of cam.

⑫—Same as ⑨ except connector rod goes in upper hole in pump arm.

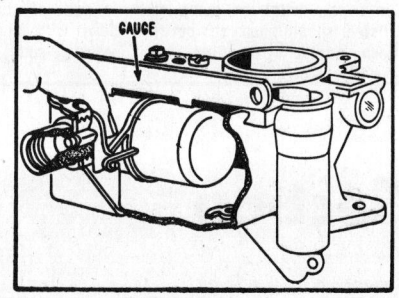

Fig. ⑬—BB float level.

⑭—Pump plunger should travel distance specified. Adjust by bending pump lifter link.

⑮—Maximum dashpot action is obtained by loosening locknut and turning dashpot unit in or out so that its plunger shaft can be moved the dimension specified with throttle valve tightly closed.

⑯—See service note "Engine Surge At Idle".

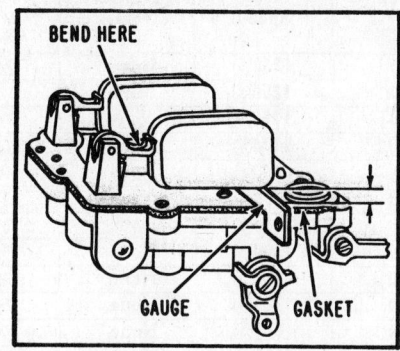

Fig. ⑱—AFB float level. Adjust by bending float lever.

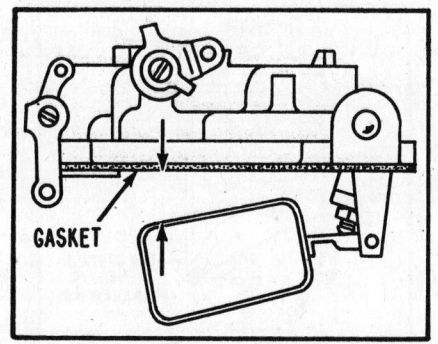

Fig. ⑲—AFB float drop. Adjust by bending stop tabs on float bracket.

⑫—See ⑱. Smooth floats ⅜", ribbed floats $\frac{9}{32}$".

㉓—See ⑱. Smooth floats $\frac{5}{16}$", ribbed floats $\frac{7}{32}$".

㉔—See ⑱. Smooth floats ¼", ribbed floats $\frac{7}{32}$".

㉕—See Note ⑩. Std. trans. 1800, auto. trans. 1600.

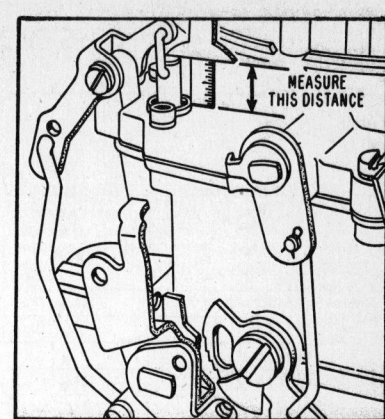

Fig. ⑳—Measure from top of bowl cover to top of plunger shaft with throttle connector rod in center hole of pump arm. Adjust by bending throttle connector rod.

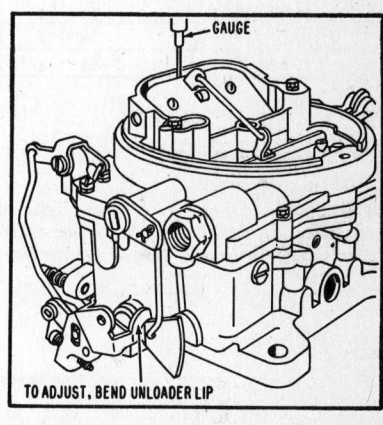

Fig. ㉑—With throttle valves wide open, clearance between upper edge of choke valve and inner wall of air horn should be as specified. Adjust by bending unloader lip on throttle lever.

㉖—Pump travel is automatically taken care of when bowl vent is properly adjusted. To adjust bowl vent, open choke valve and close throttle valves. With pump rod in medium stroke hole and bowl vent clip in center notch on pump stem, a drill of the size listed should just fit between bowl vent and air horn. Adjust by bending pump operating rod.

STROMBERG NOTES

CARBURETOR BALL CHECKS

Whenever it becomes necessary to dismantle a carburetor be sure to account for the ball check valves that may be found under pump plungers and compensating or power valves.

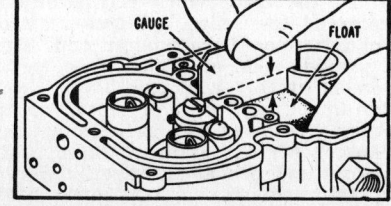

Fig. ①—WW float level. Adjust by bending float lever.

Fig. ②—With choke valve held open, pump travel from fully closed to fully open position should be as specified. Adjust by bending pump rod.

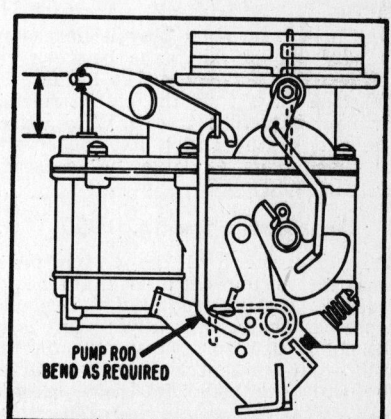

STROMBERG CARBURETOR ADJUSTMENTS

Year	Carburetor Model	Idle Adjustments				Float Level	Pump Travel	Choke Unloader	Choke Setting
		Mixture Screws Turns Open	Hot Idle Speed Neutral	Fast Idle Speed	Dashpot Plunger Clearance				
1961	WW15-43	$1\frac{1}{4}$	500	1250⑤	None	$\frac{7}{32}$①	$\frac{5}{64}$⑥	$\frac{15}{64}$④	Index
	WW15-44	$1\frac{1}{4}$	500	1250⑤	None	$\frac{7}{32}$①	$\frac{5}{64}$⑥	$\frac{15}{64}$④	Index
	WW15-45	$1\frac{1}{4}$	500	1250⑤	None	$\frac{7}{32}$①	$\frac{5}{64}$⑥	$\frac{15}{64}$④	Index
1960	WW15-41A	$1\frac{1}{4}$	500	1400⑤	None	$\frac{7}{32}$①	$\frac{19}{64}$②	$\frac{15}{64}$④	Index
	WW15-42	$1\frac{1}{4}$	500	1400⑤	None	$\frac{7}{32}$①	$\frac{19}{64}$②	$\frac{15}{64}$④	Index
1959	WW15-38	$1\frac{1}{8}$	500	1300⑥	None	$\frac{7}{32}$①	$\frac{1}{4}$②	$\frac{15}{64}$④	Index
	WW15-39	$1\frac{1}{8}$	500	1300⑥	None	$\frac{7}{32}$①	$\frac{1}{4}$②	$\frac{15}{64}$④	Index
	WW15-40	$1\frac{1}{8}$	500	1300⑥	None	$\frac{7}{32}$①	$\frac{1}{4}$②	$\frac{15}{64}$④	Index
1957-58	WW15-26	$1\frac{1}{8}$	500	$7\frac{1}{2}$③	None	$\frac{7}{32}$①	$\frac{1}{4}$②	$\frac{1}{4}$④	Index
	WW15-27	$1\frac{1}{8}$	500	$7\frac{1}{2}$③	None	$\frac{7}{32}$①	$\frac{1}{4}$②	$\frac{1}{4}$④	Index
	WW15-28	$1\frac{1}{8}$	500	$7\frac{1}{2}$③	None	$\frac{7}{32}$①	$\frac{1}{4}$②	$\frac{1}{4}$④	Index
1956	WW-124	$\frac{3}{4}$-$1\frac{1}{4}$	500	$5\frac{1}{8}$③	None	$\frac{3}{16}$①	$\frac{13}{64}$②	.166④	Index
	WW-125	$\frac{3}{4}$-$1\frac{1}{4}$	500	$5\frac{1}{8}$③	None	$\frac{3}{16}$①	$\frac{13}{64}$②	.166④	Index
	WW-126	$\frac{3}{4}$-$1\frac{1}{4}$	500	$5\frac{1}{8}$③	None	$\frac{3}{16}$①	$\frac{13}{64}$②	.166④	Index

STROMBERG NOTES
continued

③—With throttle valves closed, turn fast idle adjusting screw out until it rests on the highest step of fast idle cam. Then turn screw in the number of turns specified.

Fig. ④—With throttle valves wide open, choke valve should be open the dimension listed between edge of choke valve and air horn wall. Adjust by bending tang on throttle lever.

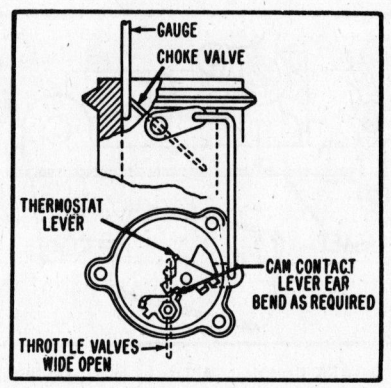

⑤—With engine running at normal operating temperature, turn fast idle screw against lighest step on fast idle cam until the rpm specified is obtained.

⑥—Pump travel is automatically taken care of when bowl vent is properly adjusted. To adjust bowl vent, open choke valve and close throttle valves. With pump rod in medium stroke hole and bowl vent clip in center notch on pump stem, a drill of the size listed should just fit between bowl vent and air horn. Adjust by bending pump operating rod.

Clutch and Transmission Section

CLUTCH PEDAL, ADJUST
1957-60

One inch free pedal play is necessary to insure proper clearance between release bearing and levers. To adjust the pedal free play, turn the clutch release fork rod adjusting nut until $\frac{5}{32}$" free movement of the clutch fork outer end is obtained. This will give the necessary one inch pedal play.

Overcenter Spring, 1957

The adjustment of the clutch pedal overcenter spring controls the amount of pedal pressure required to release the clutch. The correct adjustment is to tighten the eye bolt sleeve nut on the clutch pedal overcenter spring bolt finger tight with the pedal in the depressed position, then tighten four complete turns.

Overcenter Spring, 1958-59

When adjusting the overcenter spring, disconnect the clutch pedal rod at the upper end. Move the clutch pedal to the floor and then loosen the overcenter spring adjusting nut until it is free; then tighten finger tight. After this is done, tighten the adjusting nut 5 complete turns for 6-cyl. cars and 7 complete turns for 8-cyl. Reinstall clutch pedal rod and clip.

If heavier pedal action is desired, loosen the nut one turn; if lighter action is desired, tighten the nut one turn.

Overcenter Spring, 1960-61

The procedure for adjusting the over-center spring is the same as that outlined previously for 1958-59 with the following exception. After tightening the adjusting nut finger tight it should be turned up five turns more on 10, $10\frac{1}{2}$ and 11" clutches and three turns more on $9\frac{1}{4}$" clutches.

1955-56

Adjust the clutch fork rod in or out as required to secure $\frac{3}{16}$" free play of the clutch release fork outer end. This will provide the one inch free pedal movement at the pedal pad.

The upper end of the clutch pedal pivots in the lower end of the mounting bracket on needle bearings. These bearings require no periodic lubrication. However, they should be lubricated with wheel bearing grease if the pedal is removed for any reason.

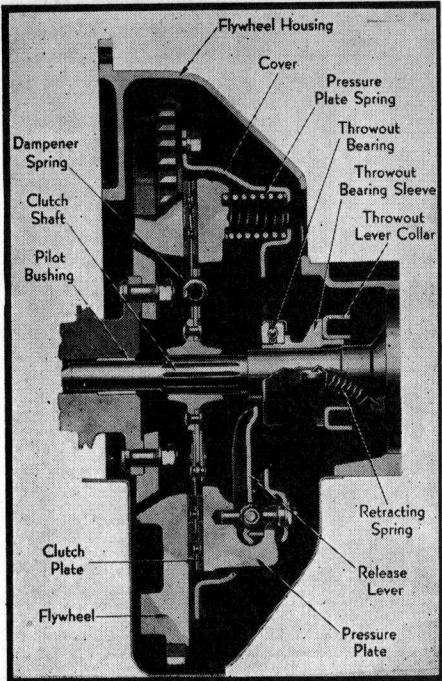

Fig. 2   Cross section of typical Borg and Beck clutch

1953-54

To adjust pedal free play, turn the clutch release fork rod adjusting nut until ⅛ to ³⁄₃₂" free play in the clutch fork is obtained. This adjustment, if correctly set, with give the necessary one inch free pedal play.

CLUTCH SERVICE

Unless special clutch rebuilding equipment is available, it is recommended that the clutch assembly be exchanged for a rebuilt unit should the clutch require rebuilding. The driven disc, however, may be replaced without special equipment. If clutch rebuilding equipment is available, follow the equipment manufacturer's instructions, Figs. 2, 3.

Removal

1. Remove transmission and clutch pan.
2. Pull out clutch release bearing and sleeve.
3. Mark clutch cover and flywheel so they may be assembled in the same relative position and thus maintain original balance.
4. Remove capscrews which retain clutch cover to flywheel. Loosen each screw a few turns in succession until cover is free.
5. Clutch assembly and driven disc may now be removed from the clutch housing.

Installation

1. Coat the pilot bearing in crankshaft with wheel bearing grease.
2. Clean surfaces of flywheel and pressure plate, making certain no oil or grease remains on these parts.

3. Hold cover plate and disc in place and insert a special clutch aligning tool or a spare clutch shaft through the hub of the disc and into the crankshaft pilot bearing.
4. Bolt clutch cover loosely to flywheel, being sure marks previously made are lined up.
5. To avoid distortion of clutch cover, tighten cover bolts a few turns each in progression until all are tight. The final tightening should be 15-20 lb. ft. torque.
6. Install transmission by guiding it into place with guide studs inserted in the two top holes of the clutch housing.
7. Adjust clutch pedal free travel.

Service Note

The clutch on 1952-53 cars with fluid drive or torque converter is removed in the same manner as outlined for models without this equipment but the installation of the driven disc differs slightly as follows:

1. Clean surface of clutch driving plate and clutch pressure plate, making sure no oil remains on these parts.
2. Hold clutch disc in place and bolt clutch cover loosely to clutch driving plate with marks on cover and drive plate lined up.
3. Insert special clutch aligning tool or a spare clutch shaft through the hub of the driving plate and into the fluid drive runner inner bearings in the runner hub.
4. Clutch cover bolts should then be tightened a few turns at a time each in progression until they are all tight.
5. Install transmission.

TRANSMISSION, REPLACE

Remove the propeller shaft. If the transmission is to be disassembled, loosen the mainshaft flange nut. Disconnect the speedometer cable. Disconnect the hand brake cable at the brake. Disconnect the gearshift control rod and selector rod at the transmission. Remove the capscrews or nuts which hold the transmission to the clutch housing. Handle the transmission carefully to avoid springing the clutch disc as the transmission is being withdrawn from the clutch housing. On 1960-61 models, it is necessary to support engine and remove crossmember.

Reverse the order of the above procedure to install the transmission. Use a suitable aligning arbor or a spare main drive gear to align the clutch plate before installing the transmission. When installing the unit, handle the transmission carefully to avoid springing the clutch disc. Check the pedal adjustment after the transmission is installed.

TRANSMISSION REPAIRS
1953-59

For detailed service on the overdrive, see the *Overdrive* chapter. To disassemble the standard transmission, see Fig. 4 and proceed as follows:

1. Remove speedometer drive pinion.
2. Take off the transmission cover and gear selector.
3. Roll the transmission over and remove the selector balls and springs.
4. Use a suitable puller to remove the mainshaft flange and hand brake drum.

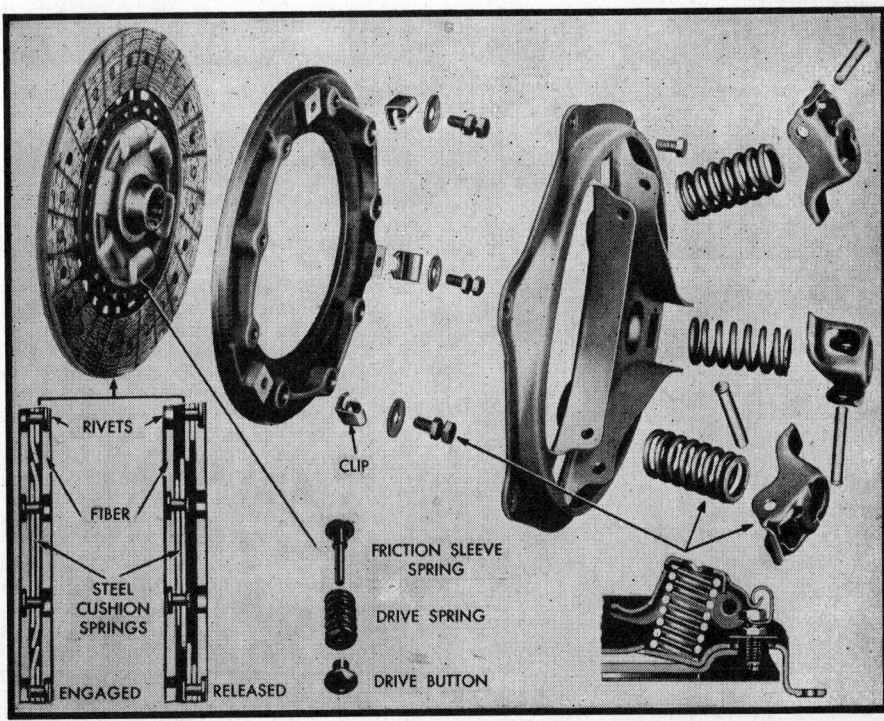

Fig. 3   Layout of Auburn clutch parts

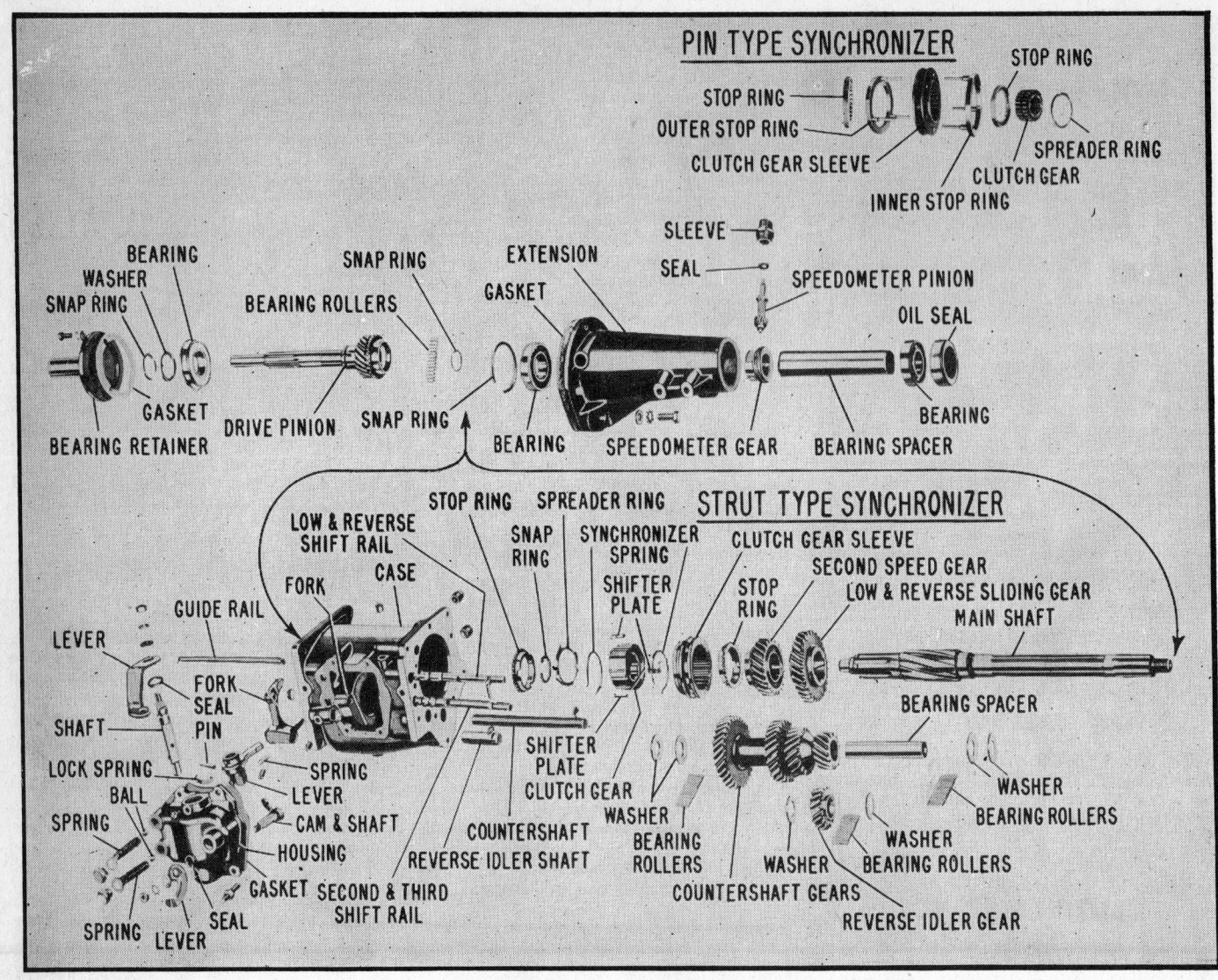

Fig. 4 Manual shift transmission. 1953-59

5. Remove shifter fork guide rail.
6. With gears in neutral, remove shift fork lock screws.
7. Remove plug for lower shift rail.
8. Slide shift rails out through front of case.
9. Lift out shift forks.
10. Remove extension housing and mainshaft, being careful not to allow the synchronizer to become disassembled.
11. Strip the mainshaft of synchronizer, second speed gear and sliding gear.
12. Release snap ring and pull mainshaft out of extension housing.
13. Remove mainshaft bearing, spacer and speedometer drive gear.
14. Pull bearing and oil seal from extension housing.
15. Drive countershaft through rear of case, allowing cluster gear to lie in bottom of case.
16. Remove main drive gear and bearing and disassemble, if necessary.
17. The cluster gear and related parts may now be lifted out of the case.
18. Drive reverse idler shaft out rear-

ward and lift out the gear.

Assembly Notes—Reverse the order of the above procedure to assemble the transmission, taking note of the following:

1. Use new gaskets, oil seals and snap rings, being sure snap rings fit firmly in their grooves.
2. When assembling the cluster gear, place the steel washer plates next to the gear and bronze washers next to the case. Select the proper thickness bronze washers to provide end play of .002″ to .008″.
3. If a special oil seal drift is not available, be sure that the oil seal protrudes $\frac{7}{32}$″ out of the mainshaft extension housing.

Note—On some transmissions, a synchronizer spreader spring is used, Fig. 6. This spring helps reduce gear clash due to gears spinning after the clutch is released. The spreader spring is assembled between the high gear synchronizer stop ring and the clutch gear. The fingers point toward the front of the

transmission. *After 1955, a pin-type synchronizer is used.*

4. Assemble synchronizer unit on mainshaft as shown in Fig. 7.
5. If the second speed gear end play is not within .003″ and .008″, use a snap ring of different thickness to establish the correct end play.
6. Install the low and reverse shifter rail on top, Fig. 8, other rail on bottom.
7. Install gearshift housing as shown in Figs. 9 and 10.

Pin Type Synchronizer

Found on some standard, overdrive and Hy-Drive transmissions is a new pin-type synchronizer. It does the same job as its counterpart but is different in construction and appearance. Transmissions with this pin-type synchronizer can be identified by the letters "PT" on the date line of the transmission case.

The clutch gear and sleeve are selectively fitted. With the mainshaft on end and the front end up, index the etched mark on the clutch gear with the mark

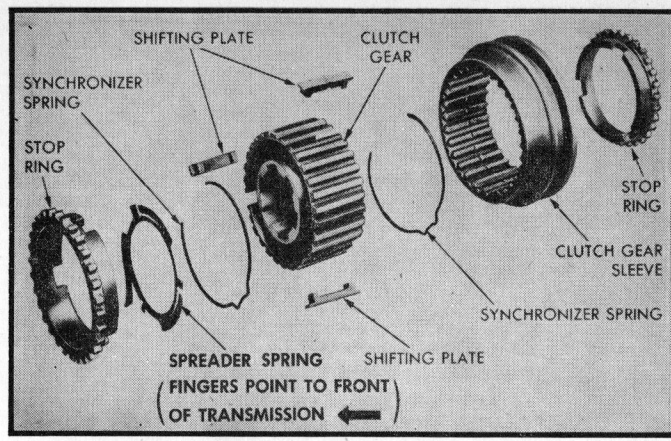

Fig. 6 Details of 1953-54 synchronizer. On 1955 and later units, a pin-type synchronizer is used

Fig. 7 Details of mainshaft and extension assembly

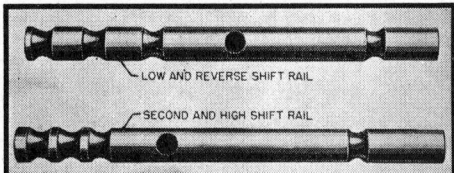

Fig. 8 Transmission gearshift rails

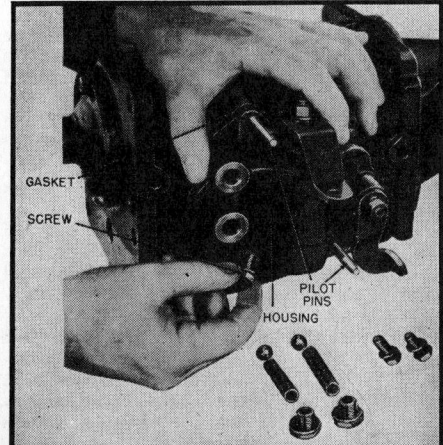

Fig. 10 Showing use of pilot pins to line up cover for installation. 1953-56

Fig. 9 Details of transmission shifter mechanism. 1953-56

on the sleeve. Use a piece of chalk or grease pencil to make index marks on other side of the gear and sleeve so that they can be seen after the parts are installed.

One face of the clutch gear has a slightly raised surface. The opposite face is flat. Install the clutch gear on the mainshaft with the raised surface up.

Be sure to inspect the cone face of the two stop ring assemblies. Nicks or burrs may pick up small particles of dirt or metal which would interfere with proper synchronizing action.

1960-61

1. Referring to Fig. 10A, remove transmission flange.
2. Remove extension housing.
3. Remove transmission cover.
4. Remove clutch shaft bearing retainer.
5. Grasp clutch shaft with hand and pull assembly out of case. *Be careful not to bind inner synchronizer ring on clutch teeth.*
6. With transmission in reverse, remove outer center bearing snap ring, using a hook or a flat blade, then partially remove mainshaft.
7. Cock mainshaft; then remove synchronizer sleeve, rings and 2-3 shift fork.
8. Remove clutch gear snap ring, using snap ring pliers. Slide clutch gear off end of mainshaft.
9. Slide second speed gear, stop ring and synchronizer spring off mainshaft.
10. Remove low-reverse sliding gear and shift fork as mainshaft is withdrawn from case.
11. Using a feeler gauge, check end play of cluster gear, which should be .004-.012″ on Standard units and .007-.012″ on Heavy Duty units. This measurement will determine if new thrust washers are to be installed at reassembly.
12. Drive countershaft rearward and out of case. Remove key from end of shaft.

13. Lift cluster gear and thrust washers out of case. Disassemble cluster gear by removing needle bearings (22 each end) and spacer.
14. Using a suitable drift, drive reverse idler gear shaft towards rear and out of case. Remove key fom shaft.
15. Lift out reverse idler gear, thrust washers and needle bearings (22) out of case. Remove needle bearings from gear.
16. To remove gearshift mechanism, remove operating levers from their shafts.
17. Drive out tapered retaining pin from either of the two lever shafts, then withdraw lever shaft from inside transmission case. *As the shaft is being withdrawn, detent balls will drop to bottom of case.*
18. Remove interlock sleeve, spring, pin and both balls from case. Drive out remaining tapered pin, then slide lever shaft out of transmission.

Assembly Notes

Reassembling the transmission is accomplished by reversing the disassembly procedure. However, observe the following:

1. When installing the reverse idler gear, have the bevelled ends of the gear teeth forward. Raise the idler gear slightly to align with shaft; then drive shaft into case, through thrust washer and gear, until end of shaft is approximately $\frac{1}{64}$″ below surface of case.
2. On Standard Duty units, cluster gear thrust washers are available in two sizes marked "A" and "B". Make a selection to give .004″ to .012″ total end play of cluster gear. Make sure tabs on thrust washers slide into grooves in case. Countershaft should be installed until approximately $\frac{1}{64}$″ below surface of case.
3. When installing mainshaft, have offset of low-reverse fork to rear. Engage fork in low-reverse gear, then position in case by shifting into reverse.

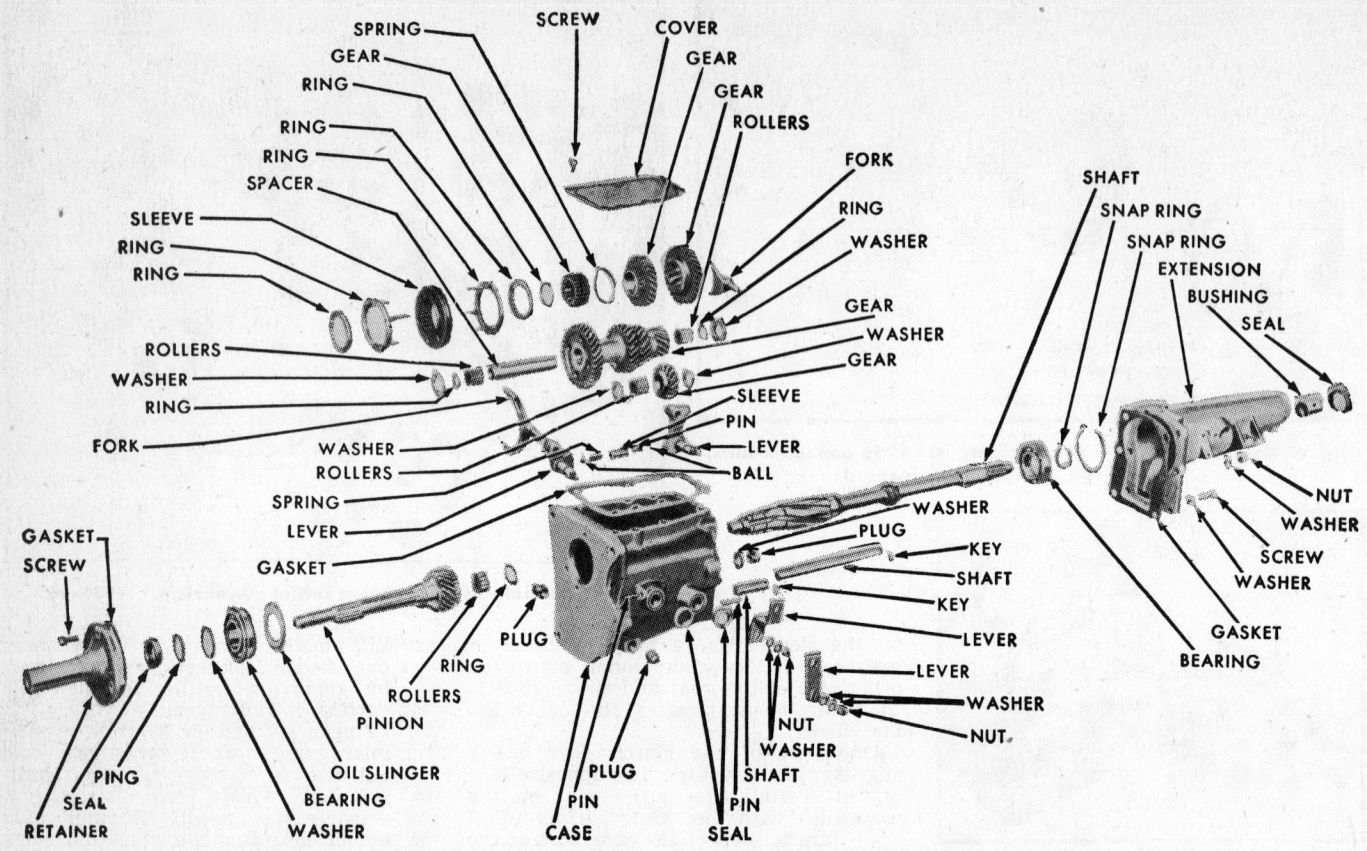

SPRING
GEAR
RING
RING
RING
SPACER
SLEEVE
RING
RING
ROLLERS
WASHER
RING
FORK
WASHER
ROLLERS
SPRING
LEVER
GASKET
GASKET
SCREW
PING
SEAL
RETAINER
RING
ROLLERS
PINION
OIL SLINGER
BEARING
WASHER
PLUG
PLUG
PIN
CASE
SCREW
COVER
GEAR
GEAR
ROLLERS
FORK
RING
WASHER
GEAR
WASHER
GEAR
SLEEVE
PIN
LEVER
BALL
WASHER
PLUG
KEY
SHAFT
KEY
LEVER
LEVER
WASHER
NUT
NUT
WASHER
SHAFT
PIN
SEAL
SHAFT
SNAP RING
SNAP RING
EXTENSION
BUSHING
SEAL
NUT
WASHER
SCREW
WASHER
GASKET
BEARING

Fig. 10A   Standard manual shift transmission for 1960-61. The 1960 heavy duty unit is similar except that it has a removable side cover. The 1961 heavy duty model is also similar the chief difference being the cut of the mainshaft splines

4. After sliding the synchronizer clutch gear on mainshaft and down against second speed gear, select a snap ring of the correct thickness and install. *Snap ring should eliminate end play and must be a snug fit.*

5. Check clearance between clutch gear and second speed gear, which should be .003-.008″ on Standard Duty units and .004-.011″ on Heavy Duty units. *End play in excess of these limits will permit gear "jump out."*

6. After mainshaft is properly positioned, select a snap ring that will be a snug fit at the rear bearing.

HY-DRIVE

1953-54

Hy-Drive consists chiefly of a four-element torque converter capable of producing an engine torque multiplication of 2.6 to 1. The unit is used in combination with an 8½″ clutch and a synchromesh transmission modified to absorb the added Hy-Drive torque.

General Description

The torque converter, Fig. 11, is known as the engine-fed type. This means that oil for the converter is supplied by the engine oiling system. The engine oil pump supplies the required oil under pressure for both the converter and engine.

The torque converter unit is bolted to and supported by the crankshaft flange. It consists of four basic parts: an impeller, a turbine, a primary stator and a secondary stator.

The impeller, which forms the outer shell of the converter unit, is driven by the engine. The turbine is driven by the force of the oil from the impeller vanes. The turbine is splined to the turbine shaft, which is bolted to the clutch driving plate.

The two stators, located between the impeller and turbine, serve to redirect the flow of oil in the unit, thus multiplying engine torque. The stators are mounted on overrunning clutches, which permit them to rotate only in the direction of the impeller and turbine.

Since the torque converter is a welded unit, it can be serviced only as a complete assembly. Other parts of the Hy-Drive, however, can be removed for servicing.

The adapter plate is located between the converter housing and rear face of the engine block. Two O-ring seals are used between the adapter plate and the rear face of the cylinder block, Fig. 15.

Oil passages, located in the adapter plate and the converter housing, allow engine oil to circulate under pressure to the torque converter unit and return to the engine oil pan, Figs. 12 and 13.

The converter housing is bolted to the adapter plate. Located in the housing are the reaction shaft, turbine shaft, oil seals, bearing, two O-ring seal sleeves and neoprene oil seal O-rings. These parts can be serviced.

Draining and Refilling

When changing oil, both the engine and converter must be drained. Remove the drain plug from the engine oil pan and allow the oil to drain. To drain the converter, remove the cover plate from the bottom of the converter housing and rotate the converter until the drain plug is accessible. Remove the plug and drain the converter.

After draining, replace both drain plugs, using new gaskets. Torque tighten the converter plug to 45-50 lbs. ft. and the oil pan drain plug 30-40 lbs. ft. Replace converter housing cover plate.

Pour 10 qts. of the proper viscosity oil into the crankcase (11 if the filter element is changed). Start the engine and run at a fast idle for five minutes to bring the engine oil pressure above 20 lbs. to properly circulate the oil and fill the torque converter. Check the oil level at the end of the running period; it should be at the "Full" mark on the dipstick.

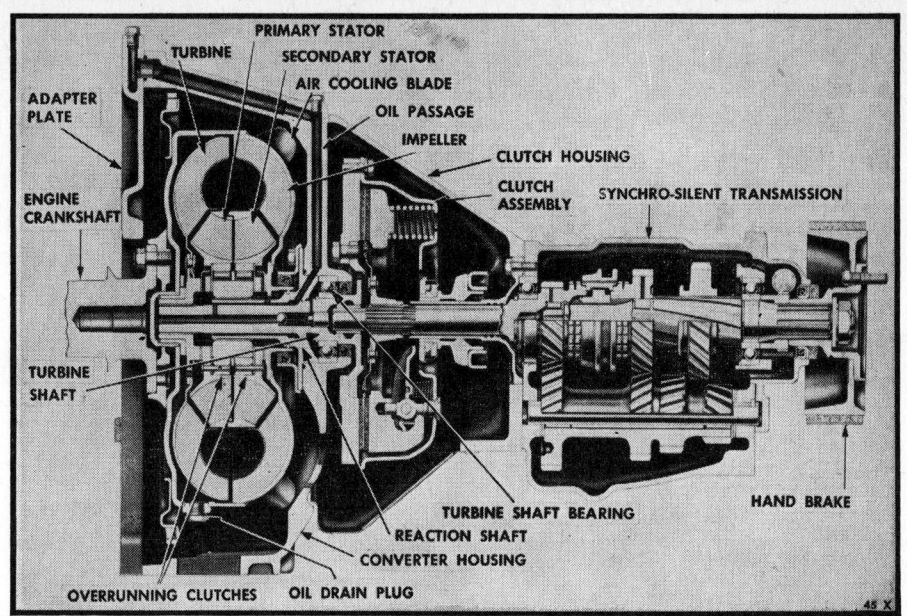

Fig. 11 Hy-Drive consists of a four-element torque converter, a conventional clutch and a standard three-speed transmission modified to absorb the added Hy-Drive torque

Torque Converter, Remove

First drain the oil from both the engine and torque converter as outlined above. Then disconnect the battery cables and the two wires leading to the transmission neutral safety switch. Remove the transmission as outlined under *Transmission, Remove.*

Clutch Linkage

Remove the clutch release fork, pull back spring, and disconnect the rear end of the clutch fork rod assembly. Remove the pivot bracket from the clutch housing and then remove the shaft.

After removing the clutch fork rod, push the clutch pedal down. The overcenter spring will hold the pedal against the floor board and prevent accidental movement of the pedal and possible personal injury.

Clutch Housing

The engine is supported at the two legs of the clutch housing. Remove the rear engine-to-cross member bolts and install an engine support fixture (tool C-3162 is available for this work). Lacking a fixture, support the engine with a jack and block of wood under the oil pan. Adjust the fixture or jack so that it will support the engine while removing the rear engine crossmember.

After removing the engine rear crossmember, lower the engine 3 or 4 inches to gain access to the upper clutch housing-to-converter housing bolts. Remove the bolts and carefully remove the clutch housing from underneath the car.

Do not pry between the housing flanges or pound the housing to loosen it since this would distort the housing and result in misalignment. Both the converter housing and clutch housing are machined as an assembly. If either housing requires replacement, replace both housings.

Clutch Assembly

Punchmark the clutch cover and driving plate so that they can be assembled in their original position in order to maintain balance. Then remove the clutch cover and pressure plate assembly and the clutch disc from the driving plate, Fig. 14.

Torque Converter Housing

Remove the torque converter housing-to-adapter plate bolts. Three bolts are located on the engine side of the adapter plate. The housing is doweled to the adapter plate and care should be exercised when removing the housing.

Do not hammer or pry between the flanges to loosen it since this will distort the metal and result in misalignment. Carefully move the housing straight back to avoid damage to the torque converter impeller hub oil seal ring. Remove the seal rings between the converter housing and adapter plate.

The oil outlet and inlet ports in the converter housing contain thin wall aligning sleeves. These sleeves are a press fit in the housing, and care must be taken to prevent damaging them.

Inspect the mating surfaces of the adapter plate and converter housing and remove any burrs or rough spots with emery cloth.

Torque Converter Unit

Remove the six bolts that hold the metal dust shield to the adapter plate and lift the shield out. Remove the eight nuts and washers that hold the converter unit to the crankshaft (special wrench No. C-811 is available for this work). Take off the unit.

Adapter Plate

Unfasten the adapter plate from the engine block and lift off the plate. Do not pound or pry on the adapter plate to loosen it. Remove the oil rings and inspect the mating surfaces of the plate and engine block. Remove any burrs or rough spots with emery cloth.

Converter Housing, Disassemble

Remove the eight seal retainer bolts and lift the retainer off the reaction shaft. Using a blunt drift, drive the seal out of the retainer and discard it. Inspect the retainer for burrs or rough spots and remove them with emery cloth.

To remove the reaction shaft, turn two of the seal retainer bolts into the two threaded holes in the reaction shaft.

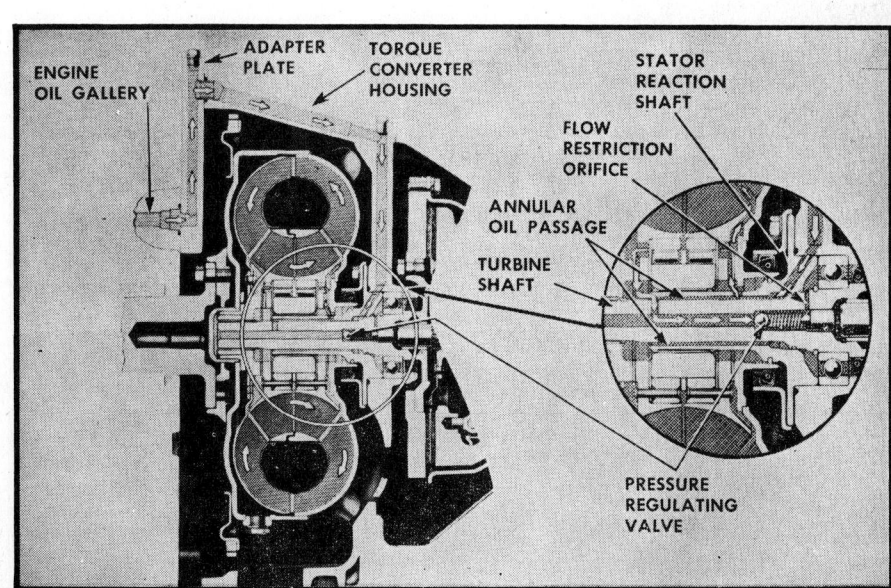

Fig. 12 Oil flow from engine to torque converter. Hy-Drive

Tighten the bolts evenly until the shaft is pulled free of the housing. Make certain that the reaction shaft is pulled straight out to prevent binding in the torque converter housing.

After removing the snap ring from the turbine shaft, use a suitable puller (or tool C-3182) to remove the turbine shaft from the bearing. The bearing may then be pulled from the housing with special puller C-3184.

To remove the turbine shaft oil seal, use a blunt drift to drive it from the housing. Inspect the recess for burrs or rough spots and remove with emery cloth.

To remove the regulator valve spring plug from the turbine shaft, a special puller (C-3179) should be used. After removing the plug, invert the shaft and take out the spring and ball. Special driver C-3178 must be used to install the plug as the use of any other method or tool may cause the plug to be driven in too deeply. *This would result in excessive torque converter oil pressure due to a too tightly compressed valve spring.*

Make a thorough inspection of all parts for wear or damage. New seals and gaskets should always be used to insure proper sealing. Clear all oil passages with compressed air. If new oil rings are to be used on the turbine shaft and reaction shaft, make certain that the ends are interlocked.

The pinion shaft pilot bushing may be removed with special puller C-3185. When installing the new bushing, insert enough short fiber grease to fill the annular groove inside the turbine shaft, and apply a light film of grease on the inside surface of the bushing. Special tool C-3181 and spacer washer SP-1615 is used to install the new bushing.

Converter Housing, Assemble

The turbine shaft bearing should be installed so it bottoms in the recess of the converter housing. Tool C-3186 is

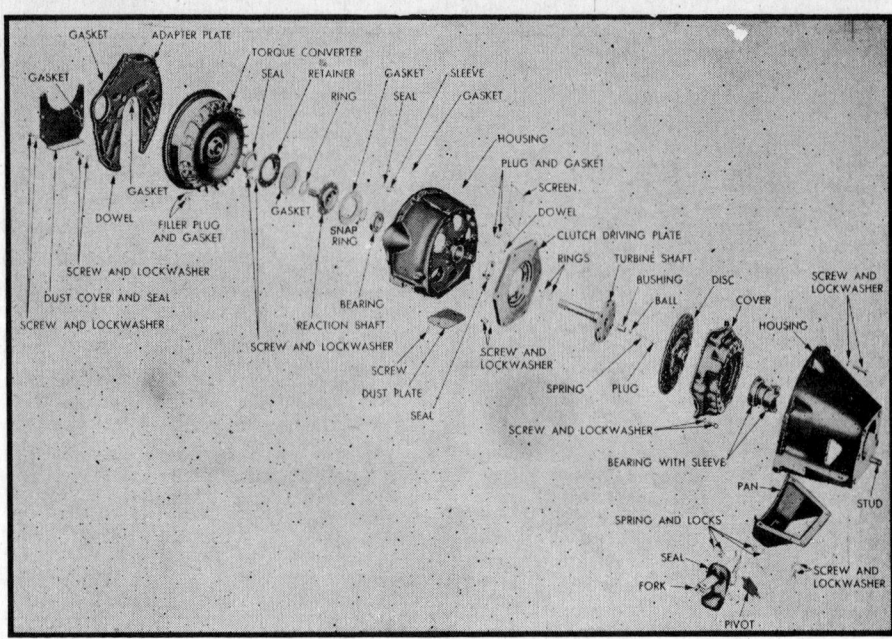

Fig. 14 Hy-Drive disassembled

designed for this operation.

The turbine shaft oil seal should be installed with special driver C-3187. Extreme care should be used during installation to avoid damage to the O-ring seal sleeves on the front face of the the housing.

Place the converter housing over the end of the turbine shaft. Make certain that the shaft enters the bearing inner race squarely. Then, using drift C-3183, drive against the bearing inner race until the shaft bottoms against the bearing.

With the turbine shaft in place, install the bearing snap ring. The snap ring is selectively fitted to control end play of the turbine shaft. Four sizes of snap rings are available: .086-.088″, .089-.091″,

.092-.094″ and .095-.097″. Make sure that the snap ring selected is a tight fit against the bearing inner race so that no end play exists.

If a new seal is to be installed in the impeller hub, position it in the seal retainer with the lip of the seal entered first. Then, using drift C-3180, drive the seal into position until the drift bottoms on the seal retainer.

Place a new gasket between the reaction shaft and converter housing. The bolt holes are positioned so that the reaction shaft and gaskets and retainer can be installed in one position.

Install the reaction shaft on the gasket so that all holes are properly aligned. Install two bolts to serve as guides and, using drift C-3192, drive the reaction shaft down until it is sealed in the converter housing. Remove the guide bolts and install a new gasket and oil seal retainer. Thread the seal retainer bolts in position and tighten to a torque of 20 lbs. ft.

Adapter Plate, Install

Make certain that the rear face of the engine block and the forward face of the adapter plate are free of dirt, burrs and rough spots.

Clean the recesses for the O-ring seals in the rear face of the cylinder block. Install new O-rings and apply a light coat of grease to hold them in place.

Install the adapter plate to the cylinder block, being sure the plate is seated evenly on the locating dowels. Install the bolts and washers. Torque the $\frac{7}{16}$″ bolts to 45-50 lbs. ft., and the $\frac{3}{8}$″ bolts to 25-30 lbs. ft.

Converter Unit, Install

Attach the converter unit to the crankshaft flange, tightening the nuts to 55-60 lbs. ft. torque. The mating surfaces of the crankshaft flange and

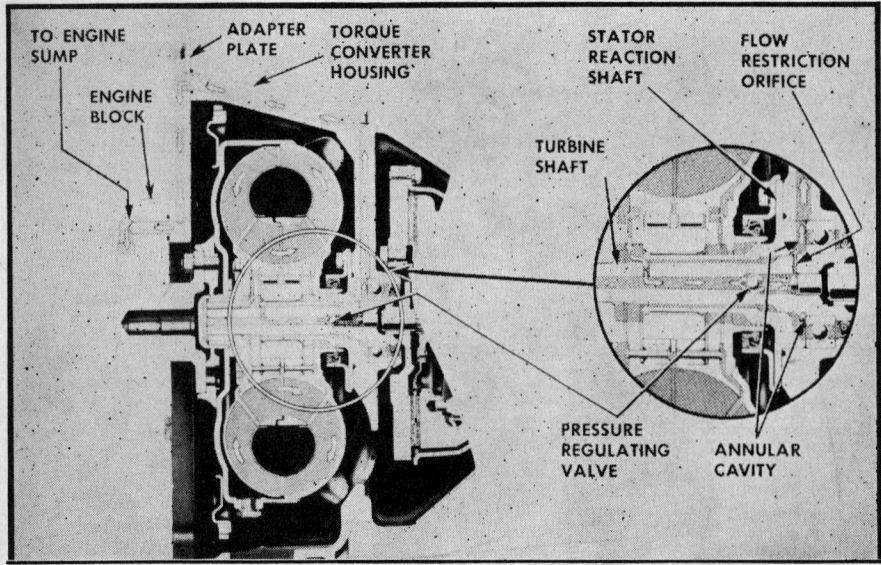

Fig. 13 Oil flow from torque converter to engine. Hy-Drive

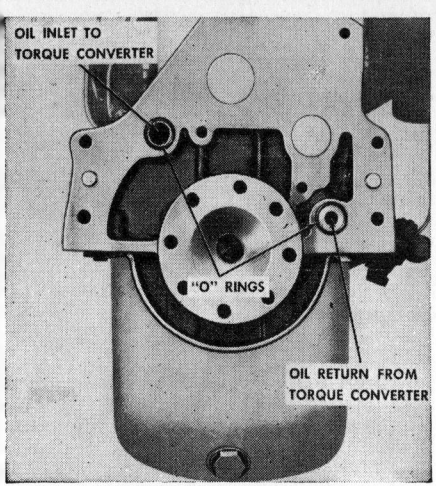

Fig. 15 Main oil galley and oil return at rear of Hy-Drive engine block

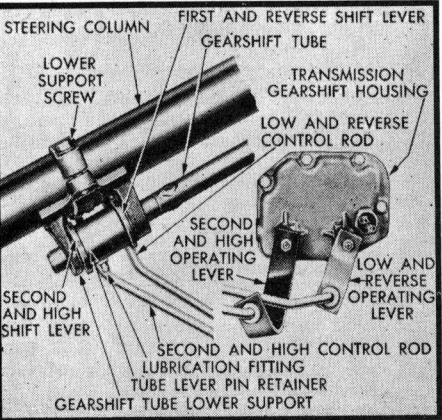

Fig. 16 Manual transmission shift linkage. 1957-61

torque converter must be clean and free of rough spots or burrs, otherwise excessive converter runout will result.

To check the converter hub runout, mount a dial indicator on the adapter plate in such a manner so as to bring the dial indicator stem to bear against the hub ¼″ forward of the rear edge. Runout should not exceed .008″.

Converter Housing, Install

Clean the O-ring seal recesses in the housing and make certain that the aligning sleeves are undamaged. Coat the new O-rings with a light film of grease to hold them in place when installed. Install the housing in position on the adapter plate.

Examine the O-ring seals to be sure they are correctly positioned as the aligning dowels enter the converter housing. Then install the lockwashers and bolts, tightening the bolts to 25-30 lbs. ft. torque.

Clutch, Install

Install the clutch disc, clutch cover and pressure plate assembly. Align the punchmarks made during disassembly and make certain that the clutch disc,

pressure plate and clutch driving plate are free of grease or oil.

Clutch Housing, Install

Make certain that the mating surfaces of the converter housing and clutch housing are free of dirt, burrs or rough spots. Carefully position the clutch housing on the locating dowels in the converter housing. Install the bolts and lockwashers and tighten to a torque of 25 lbs. ft.

Raise the engine a little above its normal position and install the frame crossmember. Install the engine support insulator and bolts. Lower the engine and install the washers and nuts on the bolts and tighten. Install the transmission and propeller shaft and connect the clutch and parking brake linkage.

GEARSHIFT, ADJUST
1953-56

Shift Control Rod—Loosen the lock bolt at the upper lever of the lower end of the steering column. Set the transmission gears in neutral and the hand control lever in the horizontal position and tighten the lock bolt.

Shift Selector—Set the transmission gears in neutral and loosen the lock nut on the selector rod at the transmission end. Tighten the nut until all play is removed and back off ½ turn for clearance and tighten.

1957-61 Manual Transmission

This transmission incorporates an individual rod shifting mechanism, Fig. 16, which simplifies maintenance, improves shift quality and decreases shifting effort.

Cross-over adjustments and gearshift operating lever positions are adjusted by threads on the upper ends of the shift rods. Movement of the shift lever should be smooth when moving through the cross-over position.

If an up and down motion at the hand lever is experienced during cross-over, the shift rod length should be adjusted by turning the adjusting nuts on one rod to vary the trunnion position on the rod. This will raise or lower the lever at the lower end of the steering column and thus align the cross-over. The hand lever knob must be in a horizontal position following cross-over adjustments.

If the lever binds when moving into a

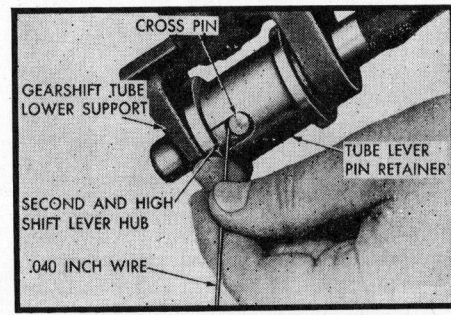

Fig. 17 Checking gearshift lever shaft in Neutral position. 1957-61

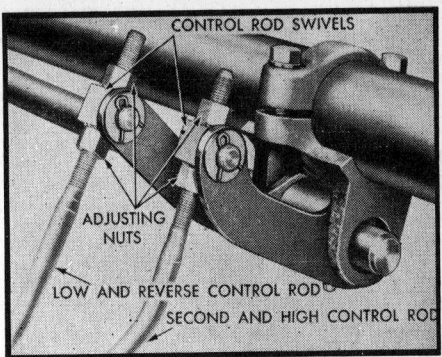

Fig. 18 Gearshift control rod adjustments. 1957-61

gear position after cross-over, check the position of the gearshift tube support at the lower end of the steering column. The support should be moved up to relieve binding on the second-to-high side and down for the low-to-reverse side.

Cross-Over Adjustments

Before making the cross-over adjustments, Fig. 17, the levers on the transmission must be positioned in the middle detents (neutral).

1. Remove grease fitting from tube lever pin retainer. Rotate retainer until gearshift tube cross pin is exposed.
2. If a .040″ round feeler cannot be inserted between pin and bottom of slot as shown in Fig. 17, an adjustment at the gearshift tube lower support must be made as follows:
3. Loosen lower support screws slightly. Move support by tapping lightly with a plastic hammer. On cars with power steering, do not attempt to separate lower support after loosening.
4. Adjust support up or down as required to secure the necessary .040″ clearance.
5. Tighten support clamping screws to 150 *inch* lb. torque (90 *inch* lb. for power steering equipped cars).
6. Rotate tube-lever pin retainer to original position and install grease fitting securely. (Loss of fitting will result in loss of cross pin.)

Control Rod Adjustments

1. Position the upper second and high control rod swivel adjusting nut so that it is secured 1 3/16″ from the threaded end of the rod, Fig. 18. This is a basic adjustment and is most important in obtaining complete low gear disengagement when the transmission is fast-shifted, or complete clutch disengagement when the shift is made.
2. Adjust low and reverse control rod swivel so that an entirely free up-and-down movement of the gearshift lever is obtained.
3. When this point of complete free movement for the cross pin has been determined, tighten the low and reverse control rod swivel nuts slightly and then turn both the upper and lower adjusting nuts clockwise approximately two turns.
4. Make certain all control rod swivel adjusting nuts are securely tightened

to eliminate any future change in the linkage adjustments.

POWERFLITE

A detailed service procedure on this transmission is given in the *Automatic Transmission Section* of this manual.

Transmission, Replace

1. Drain transmission and converter.
2. Disconnect front universal and secure propeller shaft to frame.
3. Remove hand brake linkage.
4. Disconnect speedometer cable, neutral starter and back-up light wires from switches.
5. Disconnect throttle linkage from lever at transmission.
6. Remove push button control cable (if equipped).
7. Remove oil cooler lines (if equipped).
8. Remove nuts from rear engine mount and support engine with a suitable jack.
9. Remove crossmember, leaving engine rear support adapter attached to transmission.
10. Unfasten transmission from converter housing and slide it straight back and out of car.
11. Reverse foregoing procedure to install.

POWERFLITE LINKAGE

Selector Linkage, 1955

There should be $\frac{1}{32}$" clearance between the selector lever and the gate at the instrument panel with the lever in neutral. Adjustment is made at the end of the gearshift lever rod on the engine side of the firewall.

Loosen the adjusting nuts and place the transmission shift lever in neutral position. Tighten the front adjusting nut to provide clearance on the instrument panel, then tighten the rear nut. Check for full detent engagement at the transmission.

Throttle Linkage, 1954-58 V8

The throttle linkage adjustment is made on the throttle control rod. Loosen the clamp nut on the throttle control rod

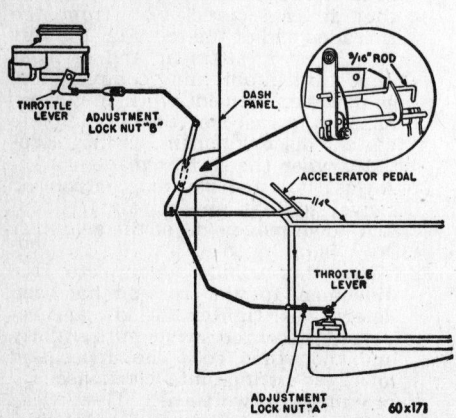

Fig. 18A Throttle linkage. 1960-61 V8

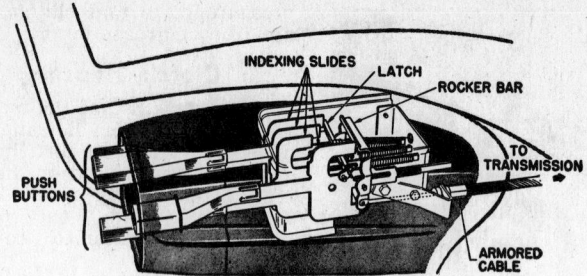

Fig. 19 Powerflite push button control

and slide the rear part of the rod toward the rear of the car to take up all slack. Then tighten the clamp nut. *Be sure carburetor is "off" the fast idle when making the adjustment.*

Throttle Linkage, 1954-58 Six

Loosen the vertical clamp rod and adjust the carburetor lever rod to provide $5\frac{7}{16}$" distance between the anchor points of the throttle return spring. Then with engine idling (off fast idle) take up the slack at the vertical rod and tighten the clamp nut.

Throttle Linkage, 1959 V8

1. With engine shut off and carburetor off fast idle, disconnect throttle rod at carburetor.
2. With rod held to the limit of its travel rearward the distance from the dash to the bellcrank should be $\frac{1}{2}$" to $\frac{9}{16}$". If measurement is correct the balance of the linkage is properly adjusted and all that is necessary is to adjust the throttle rod length to fit between the bellcrank (held to rear) and the carburetor lever. If distance is incorrect, adjust as follows:
3. Connect transmission throttle rod to carburetor.
4. With engine running at operating temperature, and carburetor off fast idle, adjust speed to 475-500 rpm.
5. Loosen adjusting lock nuts on transmission throttle rod and the rod at the transmission.
6. Adjust throttle rod to correct length by holding bellcrank $\frac{1}{2}$" to $\frac{9}{16}$" from dash while tightening lock nut on rod.
7. Accelerator pedal should be 115 degrees from the horizontal, measured from rear of pedal. If necessary, adjust pedal rod under slanting toeboard.
8. Adjust length of rod at transmission by holding transmission lever forward against internal stop while tightening lock nut on rod.

Throttle Linkage, 1959 Six

1. With carburetor choke valve fully open and throttle off fast idle, the distance from heater housing to the center of the bellcrank ball stud should be approximately $2\frac{1}{4}$". Length of linkage spring should be $8\frac{1}{4}$".
2. Only when heater housing to ball stud distance is correct can the

throttle rod be adjusted to produce the $8\frac{1}{4}$" spring length. If the distance is incorrect, adjust as follows:
3. With engine at operating temperature and carburetor off fast idle, adjust idling speed to 475-500 rpm.
4. Loosen lock nuts on throttle rod above cylinder head and the rod at the transmission.
5. While holding heater housing-to-bellcrank ball stud distance at $2\frac{1}{4}$", adjust throttle rod to produce $8\frac{1}{4}$" spring length.
6. Adjust accelerator pedal-to-bellcrank rod to hold the pedal 115 degrees from horizontal.
7. Adjust length of rod at transmission by holding transmission lever forward against internal stop while tightening lock nut on rod.

Throttle Linkage, All 1960 & 1961 Six

1. With engine at operating temperature, carburetor off fast idle cam and transmission in neutral, adjust idle speed to 475-500 rpm.
2. Loosen throttle adjusting lock nuts on both carburetor rod and the transmission throttle rod.
3. Insert a $\frac{3}{16}$" rod in the hole and open slot of accelerator shaft bracket end into the elongated hole of the throttle lever.
4. With rod in position, hold transmission throttle valve lever all the way forward and tighten transmission to accelerator lever assembly rod adjusting lock nut "A", Fig. 18A.
5. Remove rod from accelerator lever,

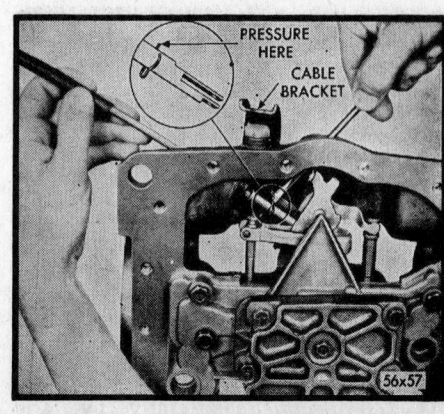

Fig. 20 Remove Powerflite control cable from transmission (oil pan removed to show operation)

Fig. 21 Adjusting Power-flite control cable backlash

shaft and bracket assembly.

6. With carburetor throttle lever off fast idle cam and against the idle stop screw, move the rear half of the carburetor rod rearward until the stop in the transmission is felt, tighten lock nut "B", Fig. 18A.

7. The accelerator pedal should be at an angle of 114° to the horizontal. If necessary to adjust, remove accelerator pedal end of the bell crank to pedal rod, and shorten or lengthen the rod by loosening lock nut at the swivel end and rotate the swivel. Reinstall the rod and tighten the lock nut. *Be sure the rod is properly aligned to prevent binding. Poor engine performance due to carburetor throttle not opening fully or lack of kickdown may result if pedal angle is incorrect.*

Throttle Linkage, 1961 V8

1. With lock nuts loose in carburetor and transmission rods, insert a $\frac{3}{16}$" rod approximately 10" long into the holes provided in the accelerator shaft bracket and lever.

2. Move transmission throttle lever forward against stop and tighten transmission rod lock nut.

3. Disconnect one end of accelerator pedal rod and adjust its length to provide a pedal angle of 113° to 115°.

4. Remove $\frac{3}{16}$" rod.

5. Open choke valve and open throttle slightly to release fast idle cam, then return throttle to hot idle position.

6. Move rear of carburetor rod rearward until stop is contacted and tighten carburetor rod lock nut.

POWERFLITE PUSH BUTTONS

1956-61

Mechanical connection between the push button unit, Fig. 19, and the manual control valve is obtained through the use of a single push-pull cable. One end of the wire cable is secured to the cable actuator in the speed range selector unit on the instrument panel. The other end enters the transmission case to engage the manual control valve assembly.

Cable Remove, Push Button End

Remove bezel attaching screws, then remove the bezel and push buttons. Remove nuts holding the push button unit to the instrument panel and remove push button unit from rear of panel. The cable bracket is held by two screws to the push button unit. A hairpin clip secures the cable to the actuator bar.

Cable Remove, Trans. End

Remove throttle adjustment hole plug and allow transmission fluid to drain off to the level of the hole. Remove neutral starter switch to provide access to the cable lock spring. Remove cable bracket. On star wheel type, push "R" button in to place cable adapter near switch hole. Insert screwdriver through neutral switch hole. Push gently on projecting portion of cable lock spring and pull outward on cable, Fig. 20.

Cable Install, Trans. End

Push in "L" button. Place transmission manual valve lever in reverse detent by moving neutral switch contact part of lever full travel towards rear of car manually, by using a screwdriver in neutral switch hole. With "L" button held tightly in, insert cable into transmission case engaging cable ferrule groove with lock spring in cable adapter. Push and pull the cable, using pressure, to be sure groove in ferrule has engaged lock spring. Replace mounting bracket and tighten cap screw finger tight.

Cable Adjustment, 1960-61

Loosen and move cable bracket assembly manually at the transmission as required to position the manual valve lever into neutral. Hold "N" button tightly in at full travel. The neutral starting switch cam should then be practically centered in its mounting hole. Use a free fitting flat nosed rod, inserted through the neutral switch mounting hole, and then apply light pressure against the manual valve lever to maintain the neutral detent position of the manual lever. Carefully move cable assembly in and out, without moving the manual lever, to determine total free-play of cable. Locate the cable in mid-position of the free-play, Fig. 21, release the pressure against the manual lever and tighten the mounting bracket securely. *Do not allow the cable to move when tightening the bracket or backlash will be disturbed.* Replace neutral starting switch and check fluid level.

V8 TORQUEFLITE

A detailed service procedure on this transmission is given in the *Automatic Transmission Section* of this manual.

Transmission, Replace

1. Disconnect battery.
2. Place push button in "1" position ("R" position on 1960-61) so as to be able to remove cable from adapter housing on transmission.
3. Drain transmission and converter.
4. Disconnect front universal joint.
5. Disconnect hand brake linkage.

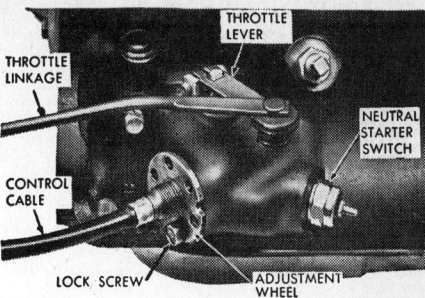

Fig. 21A Wheel-type push button control cable adjustment. 1959-61 V8 Torqueflite

6. Disconnect speedometer cable.
7. Disconnect neutral starter switch wire.
8. Disconnect throttle control linkage at transmission.
9. Loosen push button control cable adjustable mounting bracket or adjustment wheel locking screw.
10. Remove control cable adapter housing plug, insert screwdriver through hole, release cable spring lock and remove cable from adapter housing.
11. Using same screwdriver, insert through cable opening in housing and push lever rearward to last detent. Then reinstall housing plug and tighten.
12. Remove oil cooler lines from transmission (if equipped).
13. Unfasten rear engine support from crossmember.
14. Remove starting motor.
15. Support engine with suitable jack.
16. Raise engine slightly and remove crossmember.
17. Unfasten and remove transmission from converter.
18. Reverse foregoing procedure to install transmission.

TORQUEFLITE SIX

A detailed service procedure on this transmission is given in the *Automatic Transmission Section* of this manual. The following outlines the procedure for replacing the unit and adjusting the linkage.

TRANS. & CONV., REPLACE

Service Note

The transmission and converter must be removed and installed as an assembly; otherwise the converter drive plate, front pump bushing and oil seal will be damaged. The drive plate will not support the load; therefore, none of the weight of the transmission should be allowed to rest on the plate during removal or installation.

1. Disconnect high tension wire from distributor cap.
2. Drain transmission and converter.
3. *Mark converter and drive plate to aid in reassembly. The crankshaft flange bolt circle, the inner and outer circle of holes in the drive plate and the four tapped holes in the front face*

of the converter all have one hole offset so these parts will be installed in the original position. This maintains the balance of the engine and converter.

4. Rotate engine to locate two converter-to-drive plate bolts at "4 and 7 o'clock" positions. Remove the two bolts, rotate engine and remove the other two bolts.
5. Depress the "L" push button to position control cable for removal.
6. Disconnect ground cable from battery.
7. Remove starting motor.
8. Remove neutral starting switch.
9. Remove push button control cable from transmission.
10. Remove throttle link and lever from transmission.
11. Disconnect oil cooler lines at transmission and remove oil filler tube.
12. Remove speedometer pinion and sleeve.
13. Disengage ball end of parking brake cable from operating lever and remove cable from brake support.
14. Remove drive shaft.
15. Remove nut securing extension housing insulator to crossmember.
16. Raise engine slightly.
17. Remove crossmember.
18. Support transmission with jack.
19. Attach small "C" clamp to edge of converter housing to hold converter in place during transmission removal.
20. Remove converter housing retaining bolts and carefully work transmission off engine block dowels and disengage converter hub from end of crankshaft.
21. Lower transmission jack and remove transmission and converter.
22. Reverse removal procedure to install the assembly and adjust cable and linkage as outlined below.

TORQUEFLITE PUSH BUTTONS

Wheel-Type Cable, 1959-61

1. To remove the cable, drain approximately three quarts of oil from the transmission.
2. Engage "1" push button.
3. Remove adjusting wheel lock screw, Fig. 21A.
4. Remove neutral starter switch, cupped washer and seal.
5. With a screwdriver inserted through neutral starter switch opening, push

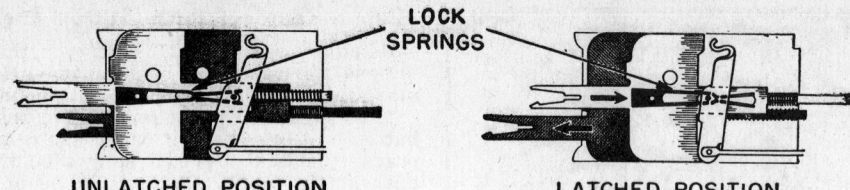

UNLATCHED POSITION   LATCHED POSITION

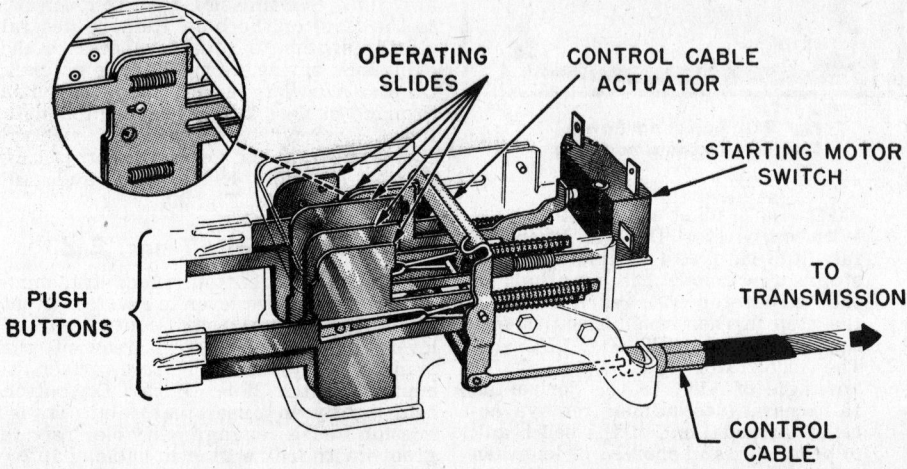

Fig. 22 Torqueflite gearshift control unit

gently against the upward projecting portion of the control cable adapter lock spring and pull outward on cable to remove cable assembly from case.

Install and Adjust

1. Engage "R" push button. *Have an assistant hold this button firmly until the transmission end of the cable has been adjusted and locked.*
2. Back off the cable adjustment wheel (turn counter-clockwise) on cable housing until only two or three threads are showing. *Caution: do not back the wheel entirely off the guide threads because it serves as a stop to prevent the "O" ring from going too far into the case and becoming caught inside the case when the cable is installed.*
3. Push cable control housing into the transmission case with just enough force to overcome the "O" ring friction and to bottom the assembly. While holding the cable firmly into

the bottomed position, rotate adjusting wheel clockwise *to just contact the transmission case.*

4. Release the inward pressure on the cable and then turn the adjusting wheel until the next adjustment hole in the wheel lines up with the lock screw hole in the case. Counting this hole as number one, continue turning the wheel clockwise until the fifth hole lines up with the screw hole in the case. Check cable adjustment to be sure of full detent in all shift ranges.
5. Install neutral starter switch and refill transmission with oil.

Non-Wheel Type Cable Adjust, 1959

1. Drain approximately two quarts of fluid from transmission.
2. Engage "L" button. Then remove control cable lock clip. Remove plug and adjustment locking screw.
3. With a screwdriver inserted through the plug hole, push gently against upward projecting portion of cable adapter spring and pull outward on cable to remove it from adapter housing.
4. Insert screwdriver through cable entrance hole in adapted housing and push adapter to limit of travel to reverse detent position.
5. Withdraw screwdriver. Reinstall plug and locking screw.
6. Turn locking screw with screwdriver counterclockwise (left-hand thread) until locking screw contacts adapter. Tighten screw firmly against adapter to cause adapter to bind against its housing during ad-

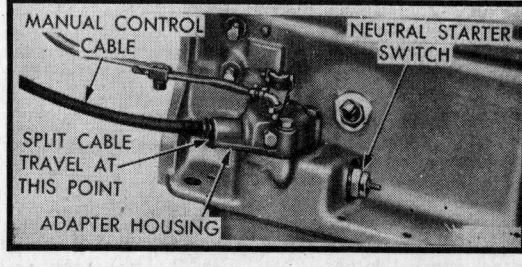

Fig. 23 Torqueflite manual control cable adjustment

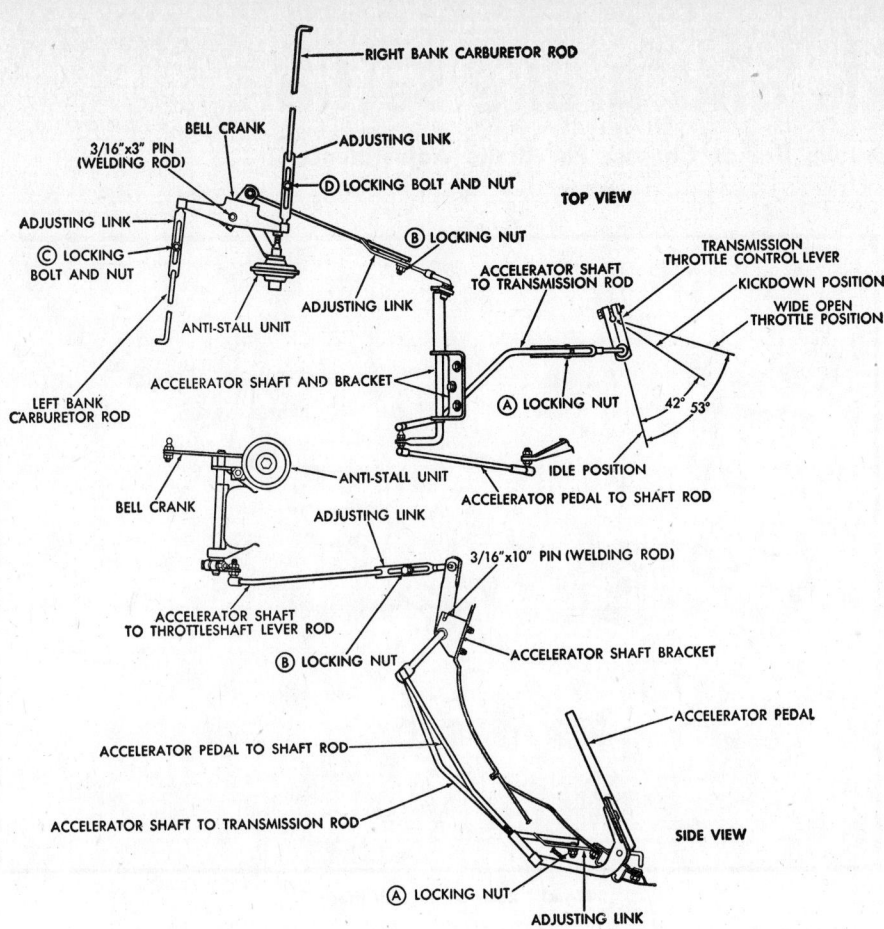

RIGHT BANK CARBURETOR ROD

BELL CRANK

3/16"x3" PIN (WELDING ROD)

ADJUSTING LINK

Ⓓ LOCKING BOLT AND NUT

TOP VIEW

ADJUSTING LINK

Ⓒ LOCKING BOLT AND NUT

Ⓑ LOCKING NUT

ACCELERATOR SHAFT TO TRANSMISSION ROD

TRANSMISSION THROTTLE CONTROL LEVER

KICKDOWN POSITION

WIDE OPEN THROTTLE POSITION

ANTI-STALL UNIT

ADJUSTING LINK

ACCELERATOR SHAFT AND BRACKET

LEFT BANK CARBURETOR ROD

Ⓐ LOCKING NUT

42° 53°

ANTI-STALL UNIT

BELL CRANK

ADJUSTING LINK

IDLE POSITION

ACCELERATOR PEDAL TO SHAFT ROD

3/16"x10" PIN (WELDING ROD)

ACCELERATOR SHAFT TO THROTTLESHAFT LEVER ROD

Ⓑ LOCKING NUT

ACCELERATOR SHAFT BRACKET

ACCELERATOR PEDAL

ACCELERATOR PEDAL TO SHAFT ROD

ACCELERATOR SHAFT TO TRANSMISSION ROD

SIDE VIEW

Ⓐ LOCKING NUT

ADJUSTING LINK

Fig. 24 Throttle linkage. 1960-61 Ram manifold engine

justment. *Do not overtighten screw as adapter housing may be damaged.*

7. Engage "R" button. Then hold cable in alignment with hole in adapter housing. Push cable into adapter housing until adapter spring engages groove in cable end.

8. With an assistant firmly holding R button "in" at full travel position, carefully position cable housing at midpoint of cable backlash.

9. While continuing to hold "R" button firmly, tighten cable adjusting clip screw, being careful not to move cable during tightening process.

10. With adjustment completed, turn adapter locking screw clockwise (to right) to limit of travel. Tighten to 10-16 *inch* pounds. In this position, locking screw seats against inner end of plug and prevents oil leakage at this point.

Cable Adjust, 1957-58

1. Reverse button must be depressed and held all the way in during adjustment, Figs. 22, 23.

2. Loosen cable lock clip screw at transmission.

3. Push cable in until it stops; then release cable.

4. Tighten cable clip screw, making sure cable housing is not forced in or out during adjustment.

5. To check for proper operation, push the various buttons, return to Neutral (N) each time while checking starter operation. Engine should start only when Neutral button is depressed.

THROTTLE LINKAGE

1957-59 4 Bar. Carb.

1. With engine at operating temperature and idle speed adjusted to 475-500 rpm with transmission in neutral, loosen throttle linkage adjusting nut on bell crank-to-intermediate throttle control.

2. Hold light pre-load rearward on rod so that throttle valve lever is against stop in transmission.

3. Tighten throttle adjusting nut.

4. Adjust accelerator pedal rod by moving pedal-to-accelerator shaft rod at pedal arm. Loosen lock nut and turn ball and socket end of rod in the direction required to adjust the pedal so that wide open throttle is obtained when the pedal is depressed just down to the floor mat but not compressing it.

1957-59 2 Bar. Carb.

All operations are the same as the four barrel carburetor except that since there is no intermediate throttle control assembly, adjustment is made on the bell crank-to-carburetor rod.

1960-61 Six

1. With engine at operating temperature and carburetor off fast idle cam, adjust idle speed to 500 rpm.

2. Loosen lock nut and move transmission throttle control lever forward until it stops. Tighten lock nut.

3. Check accelerator pedal angle. It should be 115°. To adjust, disconnect pedal and adjust rod length. When correct, reconnect pedal.

1960-61 V8

The procedure is the same as that outlined previously for the 1960 Powerflite.

1960-61 Ram Manifold

Refer to Fig. 24 and perform the following operations to properly adjust the linkage:

1. Loosen adjusting nuts "A" and "B".

2. Insert a $\frac{3}{16}$" drill rod, 10" long into the accelerator shaft bracket and through the hole in the lever.

3. Move transmission throttle control lever forward until it stops and tighten locknut "A" securely. This positions accelerator shaft.

4. Unsnap accelerator pedal to shaft rod.

5. Turn threaded end of rod in or out to obtain 114° angle between floor of car and flat face of accelerator pedal and connect rod.

6. Remove drill rod from accelerator shaft bracket.

7. Inspect carburetors to be sure that choke valves are open, fast idle cams are released and throttle valves are closed.

8. Loosen locknuts "C" and "D" and back off anti-stall plunger far enough to allow bellcrank to be pivoted.

9. Pivot bellcrank until a $\frac{3}{16}$" drill rod, 3" long can be inserted through bell-crank hole and down into intake manifold.

10. Tighten locknuts "C" and "D" and remove the drill rod from the bell-crank.

11. Push rearward on the accelerating shaft to throttle shaft lever rod adjusting link until stop is reached and tighten locknut "B" securely.

Rear Axle and Brake Section

Refer To Hydraulic Brakes Chapter For Brake Adjustments

REAR AXLE REPAIRS

Referring to Figs. 1 and 2 the drive pinion is held in position by the shoulders in the differential carrier upon which the pinion bearing cups seat. The pinion position is maintained by a washer or shims located between the pinion head and the rear bearing cone. Shims between the bearing spacer and the front bearing cone are used to adjust pinion bearings.

The threaded nut type of differential bearing adjustment is used. The procedure for making this adjustment, as well as the assembly of the differential case, replacing a ring gear, checking ring gear and pinion backlash, and other differential case operations, is given in the *Rear Axle* chapter.

Pinion & Bearings, Replace — The differential unit must be removed before the drive pinion can be taken out, but it is not necessary to remove the drive pinion or differential unit if only the drive pinion bearing oil seal is to be replaced.

To remove the oil seal, take off the pinion flange retaining nut and use a

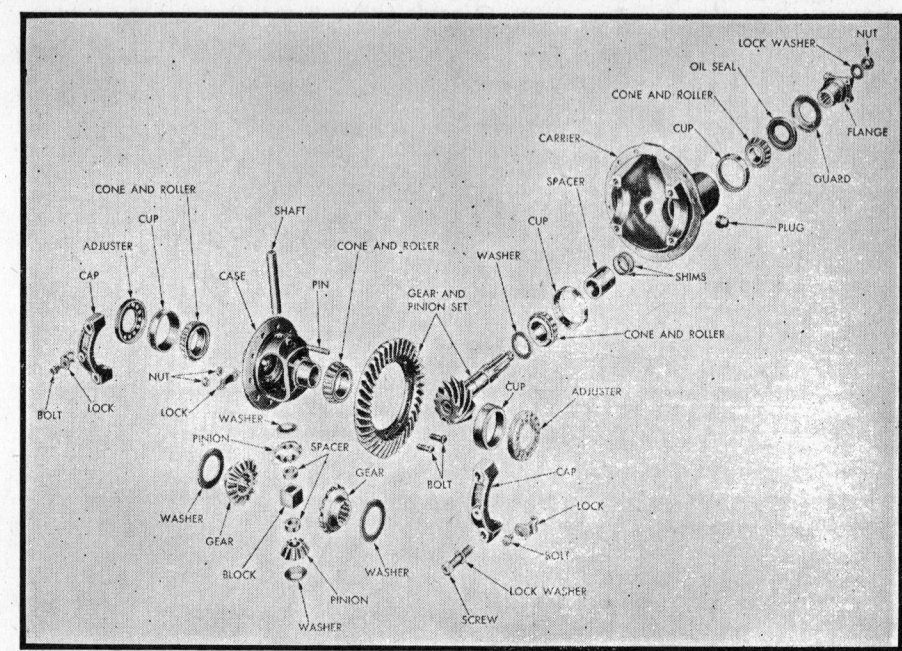

Fig. 1   Rear axle.   All models

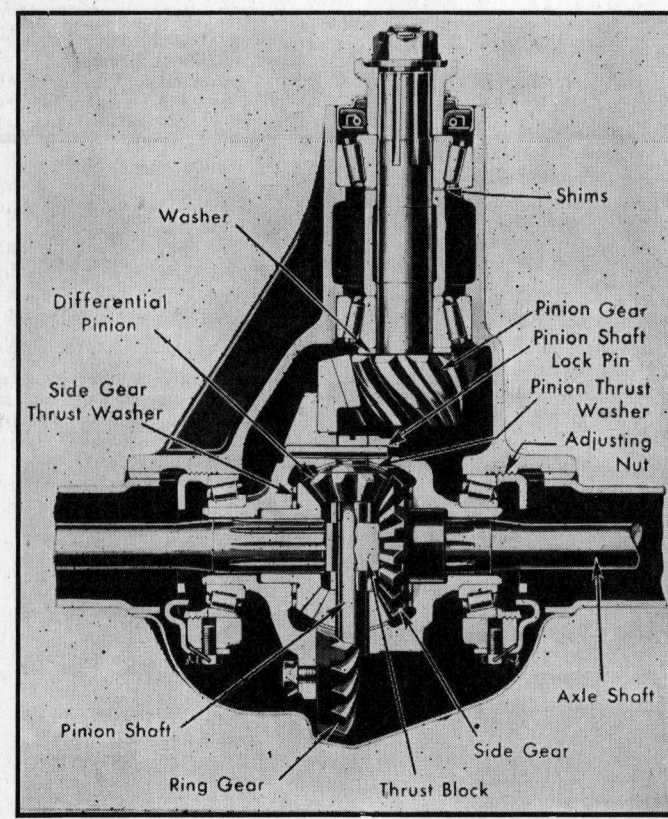

Fig. 2   Sectional view of rear axle.   All models

suitable tool to remove the flange. The oil seal may then be pulled out of the carrier.

Pull the drive pinion through the gear end of the differential carrier. The bearing spacer, front bearing and shims may then be taken out. Using a bearing puller, remove the rear bearing cone from the pinion shaft and, unless the ring gear and pinion are to be replaced with new parts, use care not to allow the front and rear shim packs to become mixed.

If the differential unit was satisfactory from the standpoint of noise before the unit was dismantled, the drive pinion may be assembled with the original shims (or washer) behind the rear bearing. If new parts are used or if an adjustment was necessary, change the shims until the correct combination is obtained to locate the pinion properly.

To assemble, place the front bearing in its cup and install the pinion shaft oil seal, using a suitable tool. Place the washer or shims on the pinion shaft against the pinion head and press on the rear bearing. Slip the bearing spacer against the rear bearing, then place the front bearing shims ahead of the spacer. Install the pinion and assembled parts in the carrier, passing the forward end of the pinion through the front bearing. Replace the pinion flange, slip on the washer, screw on the retaining nut and tighten it securely.

Pinion Bearings, Adjust — The only occasion for adjusting the drive

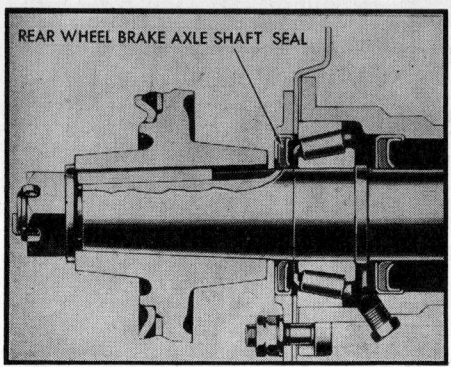

Fig. 3 Details of axle shaft, bearing and oil seals

AXLE SHAFT & OIL SEALS

Fig. 3 shows the details of the new type outer oil seal employed on these models. To remove, take off the wheel, hub and drum. Then disconnect the brake tube at the wheel cylinder, and remove the brake support. Drive out the old seal and remove the burrs from the support plate to prevent damaging the new seal. With the brake support removed, install the new seal from the outer side of the brake support plate. Then stake the plate in three places with a center punch to hold the seal in position. Install the special tool, Fig. 4, in the seal or use other suitable means to protect the leather portion of the seal from being damaged by the axle shaft keyway and install the brake support as shown. Remove the tool and complete the installation of the brake support, hub and drum and wheel.

To remove the axle shaft and inner oil seal, disconnect the brake line and remove the wheel hub and drum assembly. *Do not use a knock-out type puller or strike the ends of the axle shafts to loosen wheel hubs as this may damage the bearings.* Remove the axle shaft keys and install the special sleeve shown in Fig. 4 to protect the seal while removing brake supports, seals and bearing shims. Keep each set of shims separate to assure proper assembly. Use a suitable puller to remove the axle shaft and bearing from the housing. Then pull the inner oil seal from the housing.

To adjust axle shaft end play, add or remove shims to obtain the desired end play of .003"-.008". When adjusting bearings, remove or install an equal thickness of shims on the right and left sides of the axle housing to maintain central position of thrust block.

BRAKE MASTER CYLINDER, REPLACE

1953-54

The master cylinder is combined with the pedal bracket into a single assembly. To remove the cylinder, take out the floor mat and floor pan. Disconnect the brake line tubes at the cylinder fitting. Disconnect the clutch pedal rod at the clutch pedal and unhook the brake pedal return spring. Remove the three bolts from the master cylinder body. The cylinder with pedals, shaft and bracket can

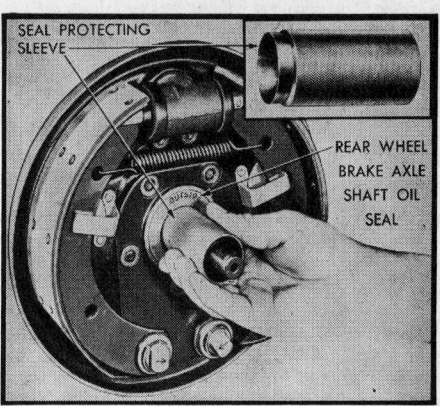

Fig. 4 Installing axle shaft oil seal with special sleeve

then be lifted off the frame bracket. Install in the reverse order of removal.

1955-61

To remove the master cylinder, remove pedal return spring. Disconnect push rod and brake line tube at master cylinder. Unfasten cylinder from its mounting and remove from dash panel.

POWER BRAKE UNIT

1957-61 Bellows Type

1. To remove the unit, insert a wooden wedge or block between the power lever and bracket (this will prevent damage to the ramp of the trigger arm).
2. Scratch alignment marks across power unit adjacent to the vacuum test port and across the mounting bracket.
3. Disconnect vacuum hose from end of power unit.
4. Remove master cylinder push rod eye bolt from pedal.
5. Remove stop light switch wires and master cylinder brake tube from master cylinder.
6. Remove master cylinder.
7. Unfasten power unit from dash panel and slide the unit and bracket straight out.
8. Reverse above procedure to install the power unit, being sure to align the scribe marks made before removal.

pinion bearings is when a new pinion or differential carrier is installed. To make the adjustment, install sufficient shims between the bearing spacer and front bearing so that when the pinion retaining nut is tightened against the pinion flange, all rollers in the bearings are tight, but still permit rotating the pinion by hand.

The bearing pre-load should be .0015 to .0025 inch. To check and adjust this pre-load (tension) mount a dial indicator on the carrier with the stem of the indicator contacting the pinion flange. Then if the indicator, for example, shows .004 inch end play, remove the parts including .006 inch of shimming to give the necessary .002 inch draw tension or pre-load on the bearings.

Pinion, Adjust — After adjusting the pinion bearings, the position of the pinion should be checked. If a pinion setting gauge is available, check the pinion depth as outlined in the *Rear Axle* chapter. If a correction is necessary, disassemble the parts and, if the pinion is to be moved toward the center of the axle, add shims or install a thicker washer (whichever is used) between the pinion head and the rear bearing cone. If the pinion has to be moved away from the center of the axle, remove shims or install a thinner washer.

If no pinion setting gauge is available, assemble the differential unit in the carrier and check the tooth contact by painting the ring gear teeth as described in the *Rear Axle* chapter. When the adjustment is correct, install a new cotter pin in the pinion retaining nut.

Front End and Steering Section

CASTER & CAMBER, ADJUST

1959-61

Caster and camber adjustments are accomplished by means of the upper control arm attaching bolt and cam assemblies, Fig. 1.

To adjust caster and camber, carefully loosen the upper control arm adjusting bolt nuts while holding the bolts to prevent turning. Record caster and camber readings.

Adjustment of caster through camber readings is possible because of the consistent relation between caster change and camber change when either the front or rear cam bolt at each control arm is individually rotated.

Turning one bolt affects caster more than camber. Turning both bolts an equal amount in the same direction affects camber directly, and caster indirectly. Turning the cams an equal amount in opposite directions will change caster with little change in camber, depending on the relative position of the cams.

By bringing caster within specifications by turning one bolt at a time, then by turning both bolts an equal amount to bring camber to the preferred reading, the caster will usually be brought close to the preferred setting.

After both caster and camber readings are correct, tighten the nuts to a torque of 65 lbs. ft. while holding the bolts from turning.

Always recheck the settings after tightening the nuts since the bolts may have turned slightly during the tightening process.

1957-58

Adjustments are performed by installing $\frac{1}{16}''$ and $\frac{1}{32}''$ shims between the upper control arm support brackets and the frame sub-side rails. Installing or removing shims at either the front or rear bracket changes the *caster* setting. Installing or removing shims equally at both brackets changes the *camber*.

Raise the car from the floor and loosen the upper control arm support bracket bolts. Add or remove shims as required and tighten bolts. *Adding shims equally at both front and rear support brackets will decrease positive camber.* One shim $\frac{1}{16}''$ thick at each bracket will change camber $\frac{5}{16}$ degree.

Addition of shims to the front bracket or removal of shims at the rear bracket will decrease positive caster. One shim $\frac{1}{16}''$ thick will change caster approximately ½ degree. Total thickness of each shim pack should *not* exceed $\frac{9}{16}''$.

After lowering car, jounce front end up and down a few times before rechecking wheel alignment to allow suspension to assume normal position.

1953-56

Fig. 2. Caster is not adjustable but the proper setting is obtained when assembling the camber eccentric bushing. To adjust camber, loosen the clamp screw and turn the bushing to obtain the correct setting within a half revolution where the correct caster setting is obtained. Do not turn the bushing until it binds against the upper control arm. Keep the steering knuckle support as nearly central as possible.

TOE-IN, ADJUST

With the steering wheel in mid-position, loosen the clamps on the end of both tie rods and turn both ends until the wheels are straight ahead. Then, without disturbing the steering wheel, turn both tie rods and turn both ends until the toe-in is correct and equal at each wheel.

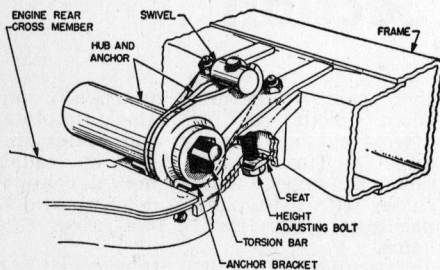

Fig. 3 Torsion bar spring cam and height adjustment. 1957-59

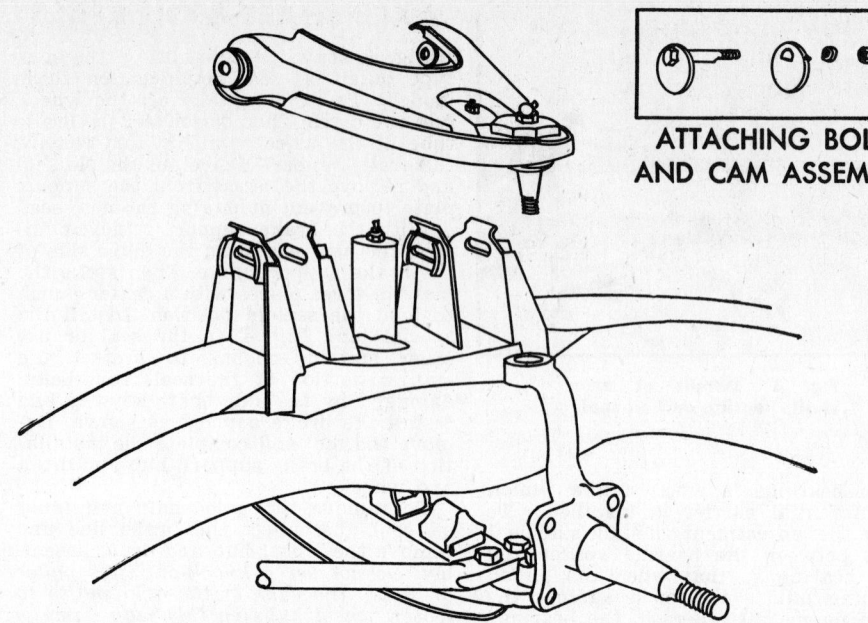

Fig. 1 Upper control arm and frame brackets. 1959-61

WHEEL BEARINGS, ADJUST

1. Tighten wheel bearing adjusting nut to 90 inch pounds torque while rotating wheel.
2. Position nut lock on nut with one pair of slots in line with cotter pin hole.
3. Back off lock and adjusting nut to next slot.
4. Install cotter pin. The resulting adjustment should be zero to .003" end play.
5. Clean grease cap, coat inside with wheel bearing grease (do not fill) and install cap.

TORSION BAR SUSPENSION

Service Note 1957-61

When new torsion bars are to be installed, special emphasis must be placed on the following:

1. Remove all accumulated dirt, scale and moisture from inside the torsion bar rear anchor, (see Figs. 3 to 6).
2. Do not apply heat to the anchor assembly in order to remove a torsion bar. Use an arbor press to remove the bar from the anchor whenever necessary.

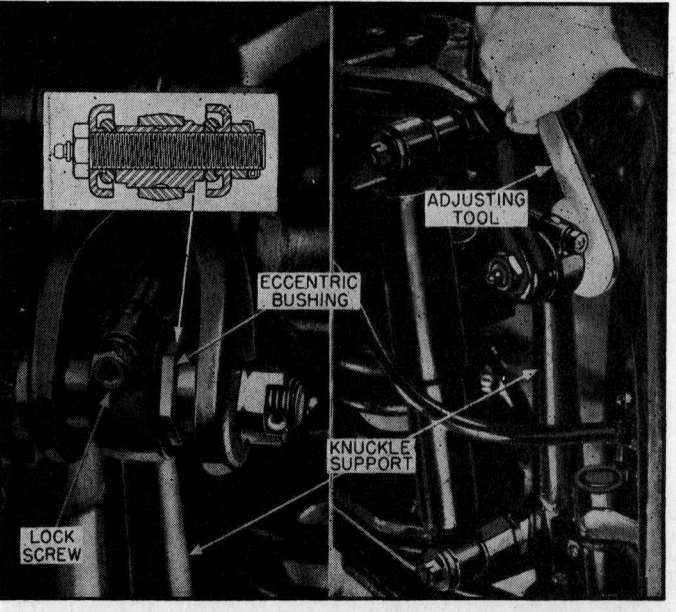

Fig. 2 Caster and camber adjustment. 1953-56

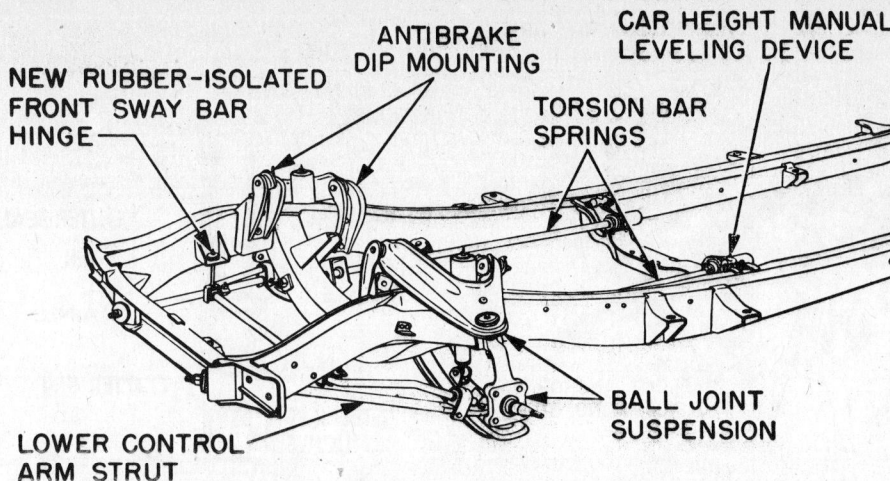

NEW RUBBER-ISOLATED FRONT SWAY BAR HINGE

ANTIBRAKE DIP MOUNTING

CAR HEIGHT MANUAL LEVELING DEVICE

TORSION BAR SPRINGS

LOWER CONTROL ARM STRUT

BALL JOINT SUSPENSION

Fig. 3 Torsion bar suspension

3. Coat the inside of the anchor with multi-purpose grease.

4. The torsion bars have a pre-set loading for right and left side usage. Therefore, it is important that the left side bar be installed on the left side and the right side bar installed on the right side. The bars can be identified by the letter "R" and "L" stamped on one end of the bar. This letter is not visible when the bar is installed. However, the last three digits of the part number can be seen from the anchor end of the bar. The left bar is stamped with the odd number. The right bar has an even number.

5. Always use a new torsion bar anchor seal.

6. In every case where a torsion bar is being replaced for breakage, apparently as a result of corrosion within the torsion bar rear anchor, it should be assumed that the other bar would be in a similar condition, and both bars should be replaced.

1961 Torsion Bars

When installing the torsion bar, be sure the rear anchor is positioned approximately 60° down from the horizontal (at 4 o'clock position). Then engage the front end of the bar in the hex opening of lower control arm until full contact of torsion bar and lower control arm shaft is made. Install lock ring in rear of rear anchor, then move torsion bar rearward until it contacts lock ring. After installing adjusting bolts, adjust front suspension height as necessary.

1957-60 Torsion Bars

Install the torsion bar and position the seal on the anchor so it indexes in the groove. Turn the torsion bar until the anchor cam is positioned approximately 120° down from the frame. Engage front end of bar in hex opening of lower control arm. *If the cam is not in the position just described when installing the bar, it will be impossible to adjust the front suspension to the correct height.*

Before installing the lock ring, center the bar so that contact is obtained at anchor and arm shaft. Install lock ring, making sure it is seated in its groove.

Slide the adjusting swivel bolt in position on the frame. Hold in place while installing bolt and seat. Tighten bolt into swivel until approximately one inch of threads are showing out of the swivel. This is an approximate setting and is to be used only as a starting point when adjusting for correct height. This setting is also necessary to place a load on the torsion bar before lowering the vehicle to the floor.

Checking Front Suspension Height

Jounce the car to settle the suspension and measure from the bottom of the lower ball joint to the floor and from the lower control arm bushing housing to the floor. Subtract the outer measurement from the inner measurement. The difference between the two measurements should be as follows:

1957-58 Sedans and Coupes	$2\frac{3}{16}$"
Suburbans	$2\frac{11}{16}$"
Fury	$1\frac{11}{16}$"
1959 Sedans and Coupes	$2\frac{1}{8}$"
Suburbans	$2\frac{1}{2}$"
1960-61 Sedans and Coupes	2"
Suburbans	$2\frac{1}{2}$"

If these measurements differ more than $\frac{1}{8}$" or if one or both of them are outside the specified limits, the suspension height of both sides must be adjusted. To adjust, turn the anchor bolt clockwise to raise the height and counterclockwise to lower it, Figs. 4, 5, 6.

BALL JOINT SERVICE

1. To replace ball joints, Fig. 7, raise car by jacking under lower control arm and remove wheel assembly.

2. Remove upper and lower ball stud nuts and slide tool shown in Figs. 8 and 9 down over lower stud until it rests on steering knuckle.

3. Turn threaded portion of tool, locking it against ball joint being removed. Spread tool enough to place ball stud under pressure, then strike steering knuckle sharply with a hammer to loosen the stud. *Do not attempt to force stud out of knuckle with tool alone.*

4. Remove tool, then disengage ball joint from knuckle.

5. Remove dust seal and grease seal.

6. Remove grease fitting and unscrew ball joint from control arm.

7. When installing ball joints, it is important that the threads engage those of the control arms squarely. Torque ball joints to control arms to 125 ft. lbs., the lower stud nut to 135 ft. lbs., and the upper stud nut to 100 ft. lbs.

FRONT END REPAIRS

Service Note, 1955-56

The front end of these models is basically the same as 1954 models except that the shock absorber is mounted within the coil spring. To remove a front shock absorber, proceed as follows, Fig. 10.

1. Raise hood and clean the area around the upper mounting.

2. Slide a wrench over the flats on top of the shock absorber piston rod to keep the rod from turning. Then remove the nut and cup washer.

3. Remove the two lower mounting bolts and withdraw the shock absorber through the opening in the spring seat. Lower cup washer may remain in place or drop through when shock absorber is removed.

4. Using a suitable drift, force the inner steel sleeve out of the bushing and remove the bushing from the frame opening.

5. Before installing a new bushing, dip it in soapy water and insert it in the frame with a twisting motion. When installed properly, the groove in bushing with index the frame.

6. Force steel sleeve through opening in bushing and down into position.

Note—In servicing the balance of the front end, follow the procedure given for 1954 models, disregarding any items which obviously do not apply to 1955-56 models.

1953-54

Kingpins & Bushings—Remove the wheel and hub and block the brake pedal

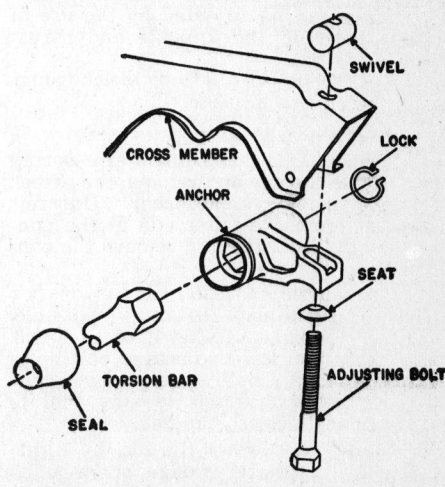

SWIVEL

CROSS MEMBER

LOCK

ANCHOR

SEAT

TORSION BAR

ADJUSTING BOLT

SEAL

Fig. 4 Torsion bar rear support. 1960

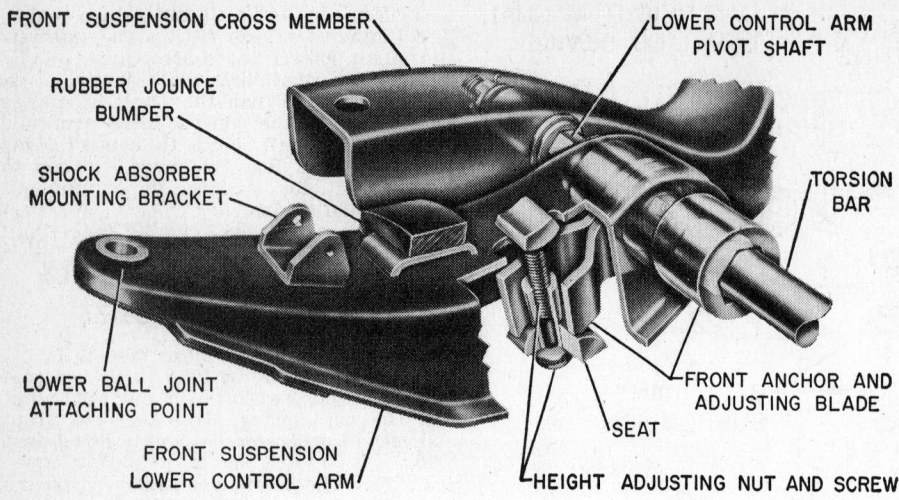

FRONT SUSPENSION CROSS MEMBER

LOWER CONTROL ARM PIVOT SHAFT

RUBBER JOUNCE BUMPER

SHOCK ABSORBER MOUNTING BRACKET

TORSION BAR

LOWER BALL JOINT ATTACHING POINT

FRONT SUSPENSION LOWER CONTROL ARM

FRONT ANCHOR AND ADJUSTING BLADE

SEAT

HEIGHT ADJUSTING NUT AND SCREW

Fig. 6 Front suspension height adjustment. 1961

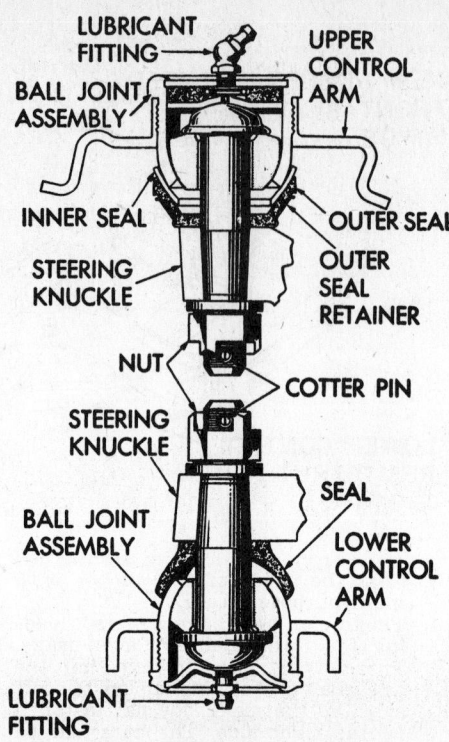

LUBRICANT FITTING

UPPER CONTROL ARM

BALL JOINT ASSEMBLY

INNER SEAL

OUTER SEAL

STEERING KNUCKLE

OUTER SEAL RETAINER

NUT

COTTER PIN

STEERING KNUCKLE

SEAL

BALL JOINT ASSEMBLY

LOWER CONTROL ARM

LUBRICANT FITTING

Fig. 7 Sectional view of upper and lower ball joints

so it cannot be depressed, which would separate the hydraulic wheel cylinder parts. Unfasten the brake support plate from the steering knuckle. Remove the steering arm from the knuckle. Remove brake hose and connection and lift off brake support. Drive out the kingpin lock pin. Drive a punch into the upper steering knuckle welch plug and pry out the plug. Drive the kingpin down, forcing out the lower welch plug. Use a soft brass drift in driving against the top of the kingpin.

If needle bearings are used in the knuckle, they should be removed with a suitable puller. A puller should also be used when pressed-in bushings are employed.

When installing needle bearings they must be replaced from the top of the knuckle with the trade mark on top and the oil hole lined up with the oil hole in the knuckle.

Pressed-in type bushings must be line-reamed.

After installing the steering knuckle, make sure it is free in the support as binding at this point may cause sensitive steering and car wander. There should be .008″ clearance between the knuckle and knuckle support. This clearance can be adjusted by the use of shims between the knuckle and thrust bearing.

After their installation, welch plugs must be staked in place.

Upper Control Arm—Fig. 11. With a jack under the lower control arm spring seat, raise the car and remove the wheel. Remove the shock absorber. Unscrew the bolt from the outer end of the control arm. Unfasten and remove the control arm pivot bar.

To assemble, position the pivot bar with the seals installed and, if possible, use the tool shown in Fig. 12 on the pivot bar. This tool has two sets of bolt holes to accommodate both sizes of upper control arm pivot bars. Be sure tool is securely fastened to the bar.

Expand the jaws of the tool by tightening the expander wedge screw until the jaws of the tool are just snug against

the inside web of the control arm. Do not bring the screw down more than is necessary to place jaws firmly against the control arm. If the tool is properly fastened to the pivot bar, the jaws will make proper contact on the inside faces.

Lay a scale across the base of the expander, noting the distance between the two lines, Fig. 12. Tighten the expander wedge screw until the control arm has been spread $\frac{1}{16}$″ from its original "at rest" position.

Start the bushings on both ends of the pivot bar. Lubricate them with light engine oil or cutting oil to allow them to cut their own threads in the control arm without scoring.

Thread the bushings into the control arm until shoulders of bushings contact surface of control arm. Use a torque wrench to tighten the bushings to at least 120-140 lbs. ft.

Remove the tool and check the operation of the pivot bar for freedom of movement. Only a moderate grip should be required to turn the pivot bar. The pivot bar should not be rotated as this would throw it off center with the control arm and affect the caster adjustment.

Grease the control arm bushings with chassis lubricant before installing on the car.

Lower Control Arm

Lower Control Arm—To remove the lower control arm, raise the front end of the car off the floor and place a support under the frame side member behind the suspension unit. After removing the wheel, disconnect the shock absorber and the sway eliminator at the lower shock absorber mounting stud. Place a jack under the control arm pivot bar where it is attached to the frame cross member. Use a block of wood, cut to receive the lower control arm bar between the jack and the bar, which will prevent the jack from slipping. Now raise the jack just enough to relieve the pressure on the pivot bar fastening bolts. Remove the bolts, placing tapered drifts in each hole, to prevent binding of the last bolt removed. Lower

BALL JOINT

STEERING KNUCKLE

TOOL

57x72

Fig. 8 Removing upper ball joint from steering knuckle

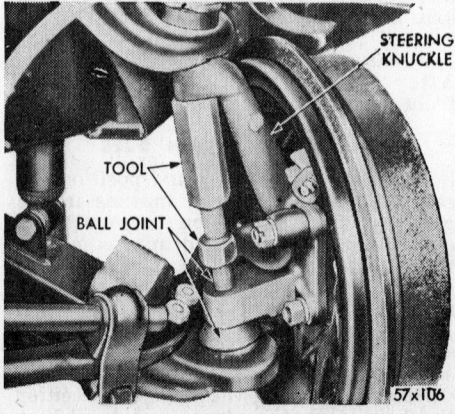

STEERING KNUCKLE

TOOL

BALL JOINT

57x106

Fig. 9 Removing lower ball joint from steering knuckle

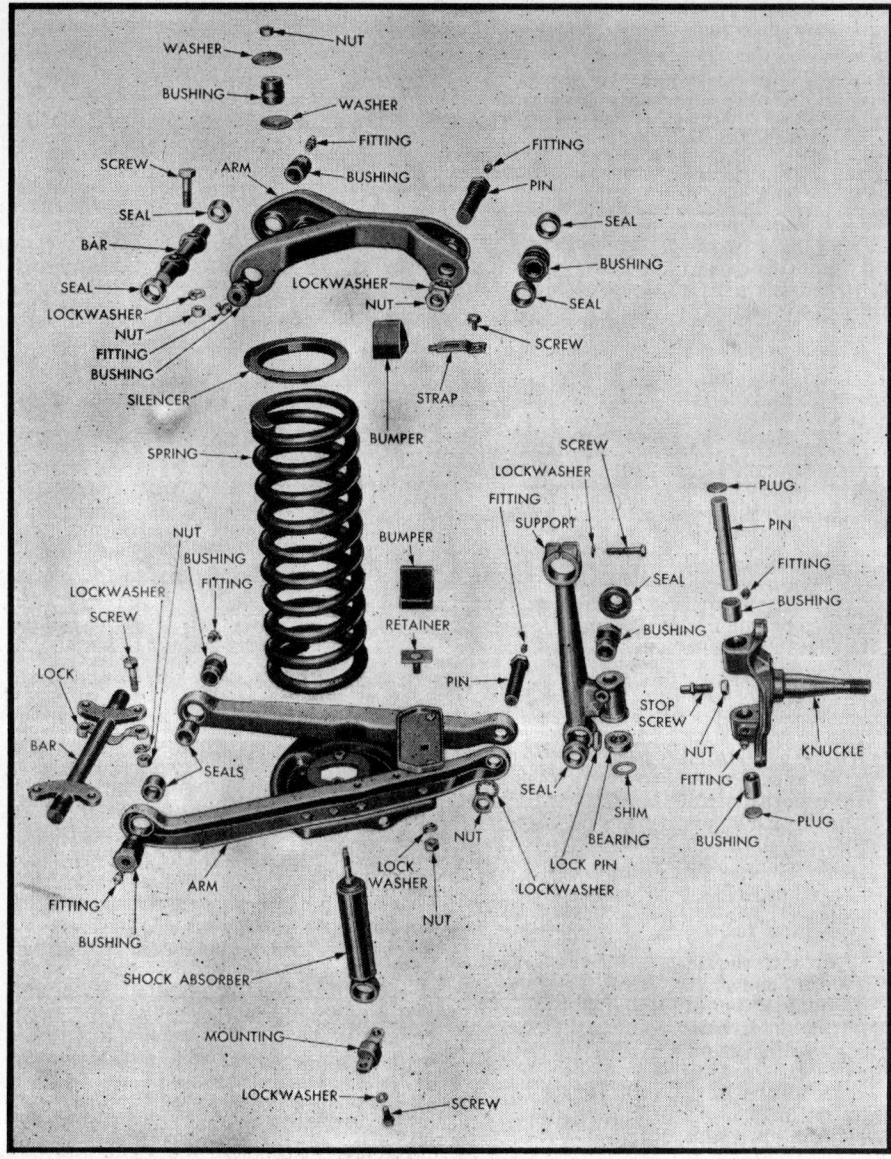

Fig. 10 Front suspension. 1955-56

the jack slowly, allowing the lower control arm to come down, then lift out the spring. Remove the lower control arm pin from the knuckle support and take out the lower control arm assembly.

HORN BUTTON

1953-54

Remove the four screws which fasten the horn button retainer to the steering wheel spokes. Then lift off the retainer, button cover, button and related parts.

HORN RING

1953-56

Depress the center ornament carefully and rotate it counter-clockwise. Remove the ornament, spring and rubber grommet. Remove the three retainer screws and lift off the ring.

1957-60

Disconnect battery. Remove the two screws on the underside of the medallion

and remove the medallion. Disconnect the horn wire from terminal on travel plate and insulator. Remove horn ring, travel plate and insulator, contact spring plate and ground plate.

1961

Disconnect battery ground cable. Remove two screws from the underside of steering wheel and remove horn ring, retainer and screws.

STEERING WHEEL

Remove the horn button or horn ring and related parts as outlined above.

Install a suitable puller and pull the steering wheel off the tube. If the horn wire has been left in the tube, push it down into the end of the tube to avoid damage when the puller is used.

MANUAL STEERING GEAR, REPLACE

1953-54

The following data applies to all models unless otherwise indicated.
1. Disconnect battery.
2. Disconnect horn wire at connector between steering gear and horn.
3. Remove four screws from underside of steering wheel and lift off cover and horn ring.
4. Remove attaching screws from horn contact plate and spring retainer.
5. Pull horn wire from steering tube.
6. Use puller to remove steering wheel.
7. Disconnect direction signal control wires at instrument panel; two wires connected through connectors, the third to flasher unit terminal.
8. Remove screws at bracket holding column to instrument panel.
9. Unfasten rubber draft pad.
10. Remove foot accelerator and toe board plate.
11. Unfasten gear from frame.
12. Remove gearshift rods.
13. Lift steering gear through toe board opening.
14. Reverse the order of the foregoing procedure to install the gear.

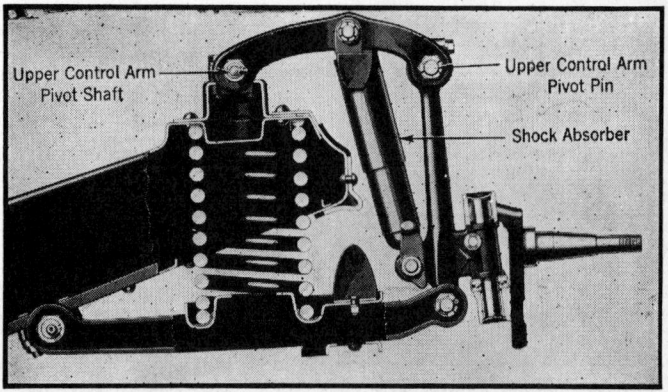

Fig. 11 Front suspension. 1953-54. 1955-56 is similar except the shock absorber is mounted within the coil spring

1955-56

To remove the steering gear assembly, take off the steering wheel. Remove the lower half of the instrument panel bracket and loosen the steering column jacket clamp. Disconnect the pitman arm and remove the housing bolts at the frame. Hold the steering column jacket and slide the gear assembly out from below, leaving the jacket and gearshift controls inside the car.

1957-59

To remove the steering gear, jack up the car and remove the left front wheel. Remove front seat cushion and floor mat after sliding draft pad up the column. Then remove steering column opening cover.

Disconnect directional signal control wires (if equipped). Attach a length of wire to the loose ends of control wires before withdrawing through the jacket tube. This will enable all wires to be drawn back through the tube at reassembly. *Be sure to disconnect battery before tying wires together.*

Remove transmission shifting mechanism at steering column (if equipped). Remove bolts which hold steering gear housing to frame. Then disconnect pitman arm from steering gear.

Remove steering post bracket cap at the instrument panel. Then remove the gear assembly by withdrawing it up through the opening in the floor pan and out of the car.

1960

1. Disconnect ground cable at battery.
2. Remove steering wheel and horn ring.
3. Remove turn signal lever.
4. Unfasten steering jacket tube from instrument panel and loosen jacket tube clamp at steering gear housing.
5. Pull off Pitman arm.
6. Remove brake line at master cylinder.
7. Slide jacket tube out through driver's compartment.
8. Disconnect transmission linkage at steering gear and move out of the way.
9. Unfasten gear housing from frame and remove the gear out through the engine compartment.

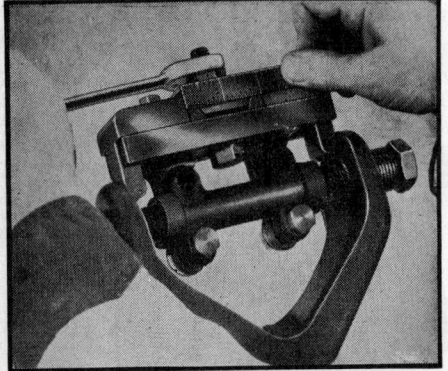

Fig. 12 Spreading upper control arm with special tool when installing upper control arm bushings. 1953-54

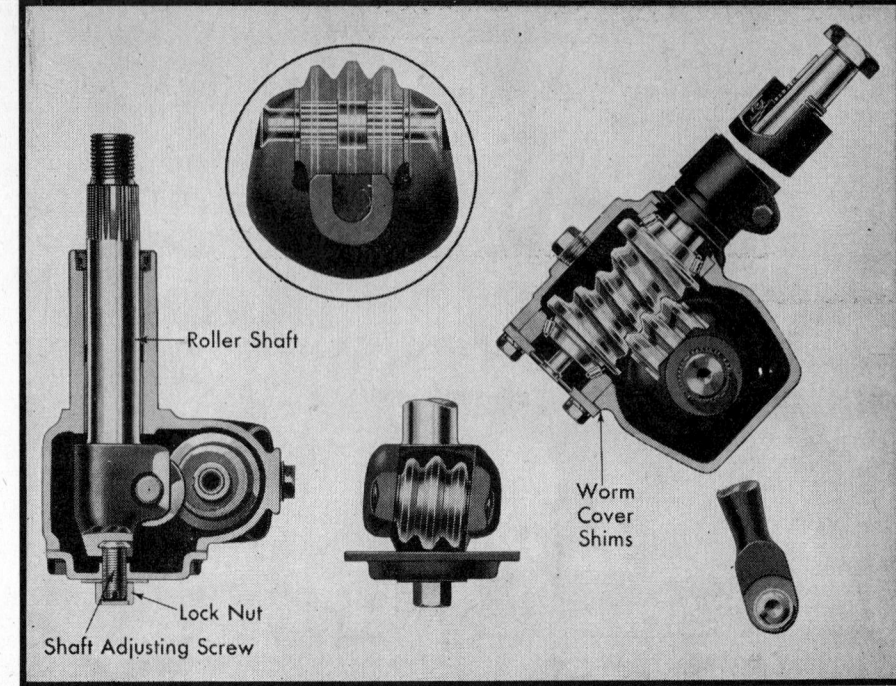

Fig. 13   Manual steering gear adjustments

Labels: Roller Shaft, Lock Nut, Shaft Adjusting Screw, Worm Cover Shims

1961

1. Disconnect ground cable at battery.
2. Pull off Pitman arm.
3. Remove bolt attaching lower coupling to steering gear worm shaft.
4. Unfasten gear housing from frame and slide gear toward front of car to disengage the column tube flexible coupling from the worm shaft.
5. Remove gear through engine compartment.

POWER STEERING
1955-56

1. Remove steering wheel.
2. Remove steering column-to-instrument bracket and shroud.
3. Disconnect drag link from pitman arm, and pitman arm from steering gear.
4. Loosen gear housing-to-frame attaching bolts.
5. Pull jacket from steering shaft.
6. Remove floor mat retaining plate and dust pad.
7. Disconnect pressure and return hoses and drain gear assembly by turning steering wheel back and forth.
8. Fasten disconnected end of hoses above oil level in reservoir to prevent further loss of oil and cap ends to prevent any foreign matter from entering.
9. Remove gear housing-to-frame attaching bolts and alignment wedge.
10. Remove steering gear from underside of car.

1957-58 Coaxial Type

1. Remove steering wheel.
2. Remove turn signal lever.

3. Remove steering column-to-instrument panel bracket and shroud.
4. Loosen steering column jacket clamp screw.
5. Disconnect drag link from pitman arm and pitman arm from steering gear.
6. Loosen gear housing-to-frame attaching bolts.
7. Pull jacket from steering shaft and remove floor mat retaining plate, rubber dust pad and access plate.
8. Disconnect pressure and return hoses and drain gear assembly by turning steering gear back and forth.
9. Fasten disconnected end of hoses above oil level in reservoir and cap open end of hoses to prevent dirt from entering.
10. Remove steering gear attaching bolts and remove gear assembly up through opening in floor pan.

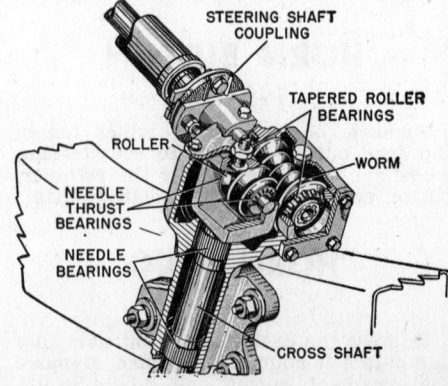

Fig. 14   Manual steering gear.   1961

Labels: STEERING SHAFT COUPLING, TAPERED ROLLER BEARINGS, WORM, ROLLER, NEEDLE THRUST BEARINGS, NEEDLE BEARINGS, CROSS SHAFT

1958-61 Constant Control Type

1. To remove the unit, disconnect battery ground cable.
2. Disconnect horn wire.
3. Remove horn button, horn ring and horn wire.
4. Remove steering wheel.
5. Disconnect turn signal wires at connectors. On 1960-61, remove turn signal switch and also remove retainer snap ring from groove in steering tube at top of bearing.
6. Remove jacket tube support bracket at instrument panel.
7. Loosen two bolts attaching jacket tube to steering housing, push jacket tube upward to expose steering coupling pin and remove pin.
8. Remove nut at drag link-to-steering arm ball joint.
9. Disconnect pressure and return hoses at steering gear. Fasten disconnected end of hoses above oil level in reservoir. Cap hose ends and fittings on steering gear to prevent entrance of dirt.
10. Remove steering arm with puller.
11. Unfasten gear housing from frame and remove steering gear at engine compartment.
12. On cars with Ram Manifold, remove left front wheel and fender opening panel. Raise lower end of gear housing in a clockwise motion towards cowl panel until the gear shaft end of the housing and shaft will clear the "A" frame of front suspension. Then tilt gear assembly towards engine slightly to allow swinging the gear downward through opening at fender side panel.
13. Reverse foregoing procedure to install steering gear.

MANUAL STEERING GEAR REPAIRS

In this type steering gear, Figs. 13, 14, worm is integral with the steering shaft and is supported on each end by opposed tapered roller bearings. The triple tooth roller is attached to the roller shaft by means of a steel shaft. Two needle bearing assemblies are installed between this shaft and the roller. (Some light duty models have a two tooth roller shaft).

The roller shaft is mounted in the steering gear housing on two needle bearing assemblies which are pressed into the housing. The housing cover is attached to the housing by four cap screws. An adjustment screw, mounted in the cover, controls roller shaft end play and worm and roller mesh adjustment.

The steering wheel and roller shaft arm (pitman arm) are splined to the steering shaft and roller shaft respectively. Both the pitman arm and steering wheel have master splines to insure correct installation.

Worm End Play, Adjust

1. Free the steering gear of all load by disconnecting the drag link and loosening the steering column braces.
2. Loosen the four cover screws about 1/8".
3. Use a knife to separate the top shim, passing the blade all the way around between the shims, being careful not to damage the remaining shims.
4. Remove one shim at a time between inspections to remove the end play.
5. The adjustment is correct when there is no end play and no stiffness in the steering gear throughout the complete range of its travel.

Roller Shaft End Play, Adjust

1. Turn the steering gear to either extreme and back off 1/8 of a turn.
2. Gripping the pitman arm at the hub, the roller shaft should rotate freely without a particle of end play.
3. If end play exists, adjust as required by means of the roller shaft adjusting screw in the side cover.
4. Be sure to tighten the lock nut securely and inspect for end play and free rotation throughout the entire range of steering gear travel.

Worm & Roller Mesh, Adjust

1. Loosen the roller shaft adjusting screw lock nut.
2. With the steering gear in its central position (drag link disconnected) tighten the roller shaft adjusting screw just enough to remove play between the roller shaft roller tooth and worm.
3. Check this by the amount of play felt at the pitman arm. It is better to leave a slight amount of play at this point than to tighten too much.
4. If tightened beyond the point where the lash is removed, serious results will occur which will cause poor steering operation.
5. Tighten the adjusting screw lock nut.

Speedometer, Radio and Windshield Wiper

SPEEDOMETER
1953-58

1. Disconnect battery cable.
2. Disconnect speedometer cable housing.
3. Remove four speedometer to panel attaching screws in back of panel.
4. Remove speedometer assembly from behind the dash.

1959

1. Disconnect battery.
2. Disconnect speedometer cable housing.
3. Remove two screws from the top of the instrument cluster which are accessible from the outside.
4. Remove two nuts from the bottom of the instrument cluster behind the dash panel.
5. Move instrument cluster toward steering post and disconnect all wiring.
6. Disassemble speedometer from instrument cluster.

1960

1. Disconnect battery ground strap.
2. Remove screws securing bezel to pod and remove pod.
3. Remove screws located at each end of lower nacelle.
4. Gently pull upper nacellé toward rear of car to release two spring-type retainers located at rear of upper nacelle. When spring retainers clear cavity in lower nacelle lift upper nacelle clear.
5. Disconnect all electrical connections.
6. Remove screws at bottom center of lower nacelle. This screw prevents "rocking" of speedometer in its supports that are integral with lower nacelle.
7. Loosen two nuts on studs located on back of speedometer housing and gently lift speedometer until sufficient clearance is obtained to release drive cable.
8. Reverse above procedure to install.

1961

1. Disconnect battery ground strap.
2. Remove four screws attaching speedometer and instrument panel cover to the base.
3. Remove panel cover by raising front edge slightly to clear instrument cluster and carefully pushing panel toward windshield to disengage retaining spring clips from speedometer and instrument panel base.
4. Disconnect wires and bulb sockets from instrument panel.
5. Remove four screws attaching speedometer and instrument cluster and bezel to speedometer and instrument panel base. Remove clusters and bezel as an assembly.
6. Disconnect speedometer cable and lamp connectors at speedometer head.
7. Remove speedometer from panel base.

RADIO REMOVAL
1953-54

Models 602 and 812—Disconnect antenna lead, and battery lead wire at fuse holder.

Remove four screws from face of grille and two bolts at bottom of grille. Remove bolt from mounting bracket on cowl vent brace at rear of radio. Pull radio out of fr nt of panel.

Models 608 and 819—Disconnect antenna lead, and battery lead wire at fuse holder. Pull power cable out of back of speaker unit. Remove nuts from side of speaker and screw at bottom of speaker. Remove speaker. Remove control unit mounting bracket screw and control knobs and nuts. Move radio forward and to the right. Then remove control unit from underneath panel.

1955-56

1. Disconnect antenna lead at radio and battery wire at fuse holder.
2. Disconnect dial light and speaker at radio.
3. Remove two lower grille attaching screws (inside glove box).
4. Remove four upper molding screws.
5. Remove two screws in upper part of radio panel.
6. Remove radio bracket screw inside glove box at top.
7. Pull radio out of panel.

1957-58

1. Disconnect antenna lead at radio and battery lead at fuse holder.
2. Disconnect pilot light and speaker at radio.

3. Remove four screws from front of radio panel.
4. Loosen radio bracket screw under radio and pull radio out of panel.

1959

1. Disconnect radio antenna lead-in wire at radio and disconnect battery wire at fuse holder.
2. Disconnect speaker leads.
3. Remove manual tuning knob, on-off control knob and mounting nuts.
4. Remove mounting screw located behind ash tray. Loosen attaching nut on radio mounting bracket at instrument panel. Remove radio from rear of instrument panel.

1960-61

1. Disconnect battery, antenna "A" lead, light lead and speaker leads.
2. Remove control knobs and shaft mounting nuts.
3. Remove bracket-to-receiver attaching bolt.
4. Remove speaker grille from top side of instrument panel by lifting up the left corner and sliding the grille out.
5. Remove speaker mounting screws and remove speaker.
6. Remove heater push button assembly.
7. Remove radio through speaker opening of instrument panel.

WINDSHIELD WIPER

1953-59

The wiper is held in position by studs which attach the mounting brackets on the motor to the windshield belt bar reinforcement. Remove the radio to facilitate removal of wiper motor. Use care so as not to damage the linkage when removing. When installing motor be sure not to tighten the attaching studs too tightly as the rubber mounting will be distorted resulting in wiper motor noise.

1960-61

1. Remove glove compartment door and remove glove compartment.
2. Remove bolts attaching wiper motor bracket to cowl panel to instrument panel brace.
3. Disconnect wires at wiper motor.
4. Disconnect links at pivot cranks. Clips are removed by lifting the top tab and sliding it sideways out of engagement with the groove in the pivot crank pin.
5. Remove the spacing washer and remove link from the pivot crank.
6. Slide the wiper motor and links far enough towards the left so that right hand link will clear glove compartment opening and remove using care not to bend the links.

PONTIAC

INDEX OF SERVICE OPERATIONS

PAGE NO.

ACCESSORIES

Radio, Replace 1007
Speedometer, Replace 1007
Windshield Wiper.................. 1008
Windshield Wiper Troubles........... 37

BODY

Air Conditioning 177
Automatic Seat Adjuster Troubles..... 36
Automatic Top Troubles.............. 36
Automatic Window Lift Troubles...... 36

BRAKES (Mechanical)

Adjustments 112
Brake Cylinder Sizes 968
Hydraulic Brake System 112
Master Cylinder, Replace........... 1001
Trouble Shooting 31

BRAKES (Power)

Power Unit Repairs.................. 128
Power Unit, Replace................ 1000
Trouble Shooting 32

CLUTCH

Clutch Pedal, Adjust................ 986
Clutch Service 987
Trouble Shooting 13

COOLING SYSTEM

Radiator, Replace 980
Trouble Shooting 8
Water Distributor Tube, Replace...... 981
Water Pump Repairs 981
Water Pump, Replace............... 981

ELECTRIC SYSTEM

Dash Gauge Service................. 85
Distributor, Replace 981
Distributor Service 46
Distributor Specifications 966
Generator & Regulator Service........ 62
Generator & Regulator Specs........ 967
Horn Button or Ring, Replace........ 1004
Ignition System Service.............. 46
Ignition Timing 981
Starter, Replace.................. 982
Starter Switch Service.............. 83
Starting Motor Service............. 77
Starting Motor Specifications....... 967
Trouble Shooting 10
Turn Signal Troubles................ 12

PAGE NO.

ENGINE

Camshaft, Replace 976
Crankshaft & Bearing Specs. 966
Crankshaft Oil Seal, Replace......... 979
Cylinder Head, Replace............. 970
Engine, Replace................... 970
Main Bearings, Replace............. 978
Piston Pins, Replace............... 978
Piston Rings, Replace.............. 978
Piston, Pin, & Ring Specs........... 966
Pistons & Rods, Remove............ 977
Piston & Rod, Assemble............ 977
Pistons, Replace.................. 977
Rocker Arm Stud, Replace........... 972
Rod Bearings, Replace.............. 978
Timing Case Cover, Replace......... 976
Timing Chain, Replace............. 976
Trouble Shooting 4
Valves, Adjust 971
Valve Arrangement 971
Valves, Grind 974
Valve Guides 972
Valve Lifters 975
Valves, Remove 972
Valve Spring Installed Height........ 974
Valve Spring Testing............... 974
Valve Specifications 965

ENGINE OILING

Oil Pan. Replace 979
Oil Pump Repairs.................. 980
Trouble Shooting 9

FRONT SUSPENSION

Front End Repairs.................. 1002
Trouble Shooting 33
Wheel Alignment 1001
Wheel Alignment Specifications 968
Wheel Bearings, Adjust............. 1001

FUEL & EXHAUST SYSTEMS

Carburetors 982
Fuel Pumps 96
Mufflers and Pipes................. 982
Trouble Shooting 4

OVERDRIVE 100

Trouble Shooting 14

PAGE NO.

REAR AXLE

Axle Shaft, Replace................. 1000
General Service 102
Non-Slip Differentials 109
Rear Axle Repairs 999
Rear Axle Specifications............ 968
Trouble Shooting 31

SPECIFICATIONS

Brake Cylinder Sizes 968
Capacity Data 968
Carburetors 983
Cooling System 968
Crankshaft & Bearings 966
Distributors 966
Engine Tightening 969
Generator & Regulators 967
Pistons, Pins & Rings 966
Rear Axle 968
Starting Motors 967
Tune Up 965
Valve Timing 976
Valves 965
Wheel Alignment 968

STEERING GEARS (Mechanical)

Horn Button or Ring, Replace........ 1004
Steering Gear Repairs.............. 1005
Steering Gear, Replace............. 1004
Steering Wheel, Replace............ 1004
Trouble Shooting 33

STEERING GEARS (Power)

Steering Gear, Repairs............. 145
Steering Gear, Replace............. 1005
Trouble Shooting 34

TRANSMISSIONS (Manual Shift)

Gearshift, Adjust 993
Transmission Repairs 987
Transmission, Replace 987
Trouble Shooting 14

TRANSMISSIONS (Automatic)

Hydra-Matic Linkage, Adjust 994
Hydra-Matic, Replace 997
Repairs, 3 Speed Type............. 1132
   Single Coupling Type........ 283
   Dual Coupling Type........ 263
Trouble Shooting, 3 Speed......... 1144
   Single Coupling Type........ 25
   Dual Coupling Type........ 28

TUNE UP 38

GENERAL SPECIFICATIONS

Year	Model Designation	Wheelbase, Inches	Valve Location	Bore and Stroke	Piston Displacement, Cubic Inches	Compression Ratio (Standard)	Maximum Brake H.P. @ R.P.M.	Maximum Torque Lbs. Ft. @ R.P.M.	Normal Oil Pressure Pounds
1953	Six (Std. Trans.)........53–25	122	In Block	3.5625 x 4.000	239.2	7.0	115 @ 3800	193 @ 2000	35
	Six (Hydramatic).......53–25	122	In Block	3.5625 x 4.000	239.2	7.7	118 @ 3800	197 @ 2000	35
	Eight (Std. Trans.)......53–27	122	In Block	3.3750 x 3.750	268.4	6.8	118 @ 3600	222 @ 2200	35
	Eight (Hydramatic)......53–27	122	In Block	3.3750 x 3.750	268.4	7.7	122 @ 3600	222 @ 2200	35
1954	Chieftian 6 (Std. Tr.) 54–25	122	In Block	3.5625 x 4.000	239.2	7.0	115 @ 3800	193 @ 2000	35
	Chieftian 6 (Hydra.) 54–25	122	In Block	3.5625 x 4.000	239.2	7.7	118 @ 3800	197 @ 2000	35
	Chieftian 8 (Std. Tr.) 54–27	122	In Block	3.3750 x 3.750	268.4	6.8	122 @ 3800	226 @ 2200	35
	Chieftian 8 (Hydra.) 54–27	122	In Block	3.3750 x 3.750	268.4	7.7	127 @ 3800	234 @ 2200	35
	Star Chief 8 (Std. Tr.)....54–28	124	In Block	3.3750 x 3.750	268.4	6.8	122 @ 3800	226 @ 2200	35
	Star Chief 8 (Hydra.)....54–28	124	In Block	3.3750 x 3.750	268.4	7.7	127 @ 3800	234 @ 2200	35
1955	V8.................55–27	122	In Head	3.7500 x 3.250	287.2	8.0	180 @ 4600	264 @ 2400	40
	V8.................55–28	124	In Head	3.7500 x 3.250	287.2	8.0	180 @ 4600	264 @ 2400	40
1956	V8 Std. Tr. 2-Bar. Carb.④.....	①	In Head	3.9375 x 3.250	316.6	7.9②	192 @ 4400	297 @ 2400	35–45
	V8 Std. Tr. 2-Bar. Carb.④.....	①	In Head	3.9375 x 3.250	316.6	8.9	192 @ 4400	297 @ 2400	35–45
	V8 Std. Tr. 4-Bar. Carb.④.....	①	In Head	3.9375 x 3.250	316.6	8.9	216 @ 4800	315 @ 2800	35–45
	V8 Hydra. 4-Bar. Carb.④......	①	In Head	3.9375 x 3.250	316.6	8.9	227 @ 4800	312 @ 3000	35–45
	V8 Hydra. 2-Bar. Carb.④......	①	In Head	3.9375 x 3.250	316.6	8.9	205 @ 4600	294 @ 2600	35–45
	V8 Two 4-Bar Carbs.④.......	①	In Head	3.9375 x 3.250	316.6	10.0	285 @ 5100	330 @ 2600	35–45
1957	V8 Std. Tr. 2-Bar. Carb.⑤.....	①	In Head	3.9375 x 3.562	347	8.5③	227 @ 4600	333 @ 2300	35–45
	V8 Hydra. 2-Bar. Carb.⑤.....	①	In Head	3.9375 x 3.562	347	10.0	252 @ 4600	354 @ 2400	35–45
	V8 Hydra. 4-Bar. Carb.⑤.....	①	In Head	3.9375 x 3.562	347	10.0	270 @ 4800	359 @ 2800	35–45
1958	V8 Std. Tr. 2-Bar. Carb.⑥.....	①	In Head	4.0625 x 3.562	370	8.6	240 @ 4500	354 @ 2600	35–45
	V8 Std. Tr. 4-Bar. Carb.⑥.....	①	In Head	4.0625 x 3.562	370	8.6	255 @ 4500	360 @ 2600	35–45
	V8 Std. Tr. 4-Bar. Carb.⑥.....	①	In Head	4.0625 x 3.562	370	10.0	285 @ 4600	395 @ 2800	35–45
	V8 Hydra. 2-Bar. Carb.⑥.....	①	In Head	4.0625 x 3.562	370	10.0	270 @ 4600	388 @ 2800	35–45
	V8 Hydra. 4-Bar. Carb.⑥.....	①	In Head	4.0625 x 3.562	370	10.0	285 @ 4600	395 @ 2800	35–45
	V8 Three 2-Bar. Carbs.⑥.....	①	In Head	4.0625 x 3.562	370	10.5	300 @ 4600	400 @ 3000	35–45
	V8 Fuel Injection⑥...........	①	In Head	4.0625 x 3.562	370	10.5	310 @ 4800	400 @ 3400	35–45
1959	Catalina V8.........59–21	122	In Head	4.0625 x 3.750	389	8.6⑦	245 @ 4200	392 @ 2000	35–40
	Star Chief V8........59–24	124	In Head	4.0625 x 3.750	389	8.6⑦	245 @ 4200	392 @ 2000	35–40
	Bonneville Sta. Wagon V8 59–27	122	In Head	4.0625 x 3.750	389	8.6⑦	260 @ 4200	400 @ 2800	35–40
	Bonneville V8........59–28	124	In Head	4.0625 x 3.750	389	8.6⑦	260 @ 4200	400 @ 2800	35–40
1960	Catalina V8.........60–21	122	In Head	4.0625 x 3.750	389	8.6⑦	215 @ 3600	390 @ 2000	35–40
	Ventura V8.........60–23	122	In Head	4.0625 x 3.750	389	8.6⑦	215 @ 3600	390 @ 2000	35–40
	Star Chief V8........60–24	124	In Head	4.0625 x 3.750	389	8.6⑦	215 @ 3600	390 @ 2000	35–40
	Bonneville V8 Sta. Wag. 60–27	124	In Head	4.0625 x 3.750	389	8.6⑦	281 @ 4400	407 @ 2800	35–40
	Bonneville V8........60–28	124	In Head	4.0625 x 3.750	389	8.6⑦	281 @ 4400	407 @ 2800	35–40
1961	Catalina V8.............	119	In Head	4.0625 x 3.750	389	8.6	215 @ 3600	390 @ 2000	30–40
	Ventura V8.............	119	In Head	4.0625 x 3.750	389	8.6	215 @ 3600	390 @ 2000	30–40
	Star Chief V8...........	123	In Head	4.0625 x 3.750	389	8.6	215 @ 3600	390 @ 2000	30–40
	Bonneville V8..........	123	In Head	4.0625 x 3.750	389	8.6	235 @ 3600	402 @ 2000	30–40

① —122″ on 25 and 27 models and 124″ on 28 models.
② —Special engine for use with regular fuels, identified by an L with a circle around it stamped on serial number pad.
③ —Engines with 8.5 to 1 compression ratio are identified by an L with a circle around it stamped on serial number pad.
④ —Star Chief and Chieftain available with any of the engines listed.
⑤ —Super Chief, Star Chief and Chieftain available with any of the engines listed.
⑥ —Bonneville, Super Chief, Star Chief and Chieftain available with any of the engines listed.
⑦ —Standard engine.   Many options are available.

TUNE UP SPECIFICATIONS

★Disconnect vacuum line when using timing light to set timing.

Year	Model	Ground Polarity and Voltage	Spark Plug		Distributor		Firing Order ①	Ignition Timing ★		Idle Speed RPM In Drive	Compression Pressure @ Cranking Speed Minimum
			Type	Gap Inch	Point Gap Inch	Cam Angle Degrees		Mark	Location		
1953	Six	N-6	AC-44-5	.025	.022	31-37	153624	③	Damper	375	⑤
	Eight	N-6	AC-44-5	.025	.016	21-30	16258374	②	Damper	375	⑤
1954	Six	N-6	AC-44-5	.025	.016	38-45	153624	③	Damper	375	⑤
	Eight	N-6	AC-44-5	.025	.016	21-30	16258374	②	Damper	375	⑤
1955	All	N-12	AC-44-5	.035	.016	26-33	18436572	④	Damper	400	120
1956	V8	N-12	AC-46	.035	.016	26-33	18436572	④	Damper	440	⑥
	⑨	N-12	AC-44	.035	.016	26-33	18436572	10°BTDC	Damper	650	⑥
1957	All	N-12	AC-45	.035	⑦	30	18436572	④	Damper	440	140
1958	All	N-12	AC-45	.035	⑦	30	18436572	④	Pulley	490	145
1959	All	N-12	AC-45	.035	⑦	30	18436572	6°BTDC⑧	Pulley	490	145
1960	All	N-12	AC-45S	.035	⑦	30	18436572	6°BTDC	Pulley	490	145
1961	All	N-12	AC-45S	.035	⑦	30	18436572	6°BTDC	Pulley	490	145

①—V8 cylinder numbering (front to rear): Left bank 1-3-5-7, right bank 2-4-6-8.
②—When cranking engine first line to come under pointer is for standard head and second line for high compression head.
③—When cranking engine second line to come under pointer.
④—When cranking engine first line to come under pointer.
⑤—With Hydramatic 139, with standard trans. 123.
⑥—With standard head 120, with H. C. head 145.
⑦—Turn adjusting screw in (clockwise) until engine begins to misfire. Then turn screw out ½ turn.
⑧—4°BTDC for Tempest 420-E engine only.
⑨—Two 4-barrel carburetors.

VALVE SPECIFICATIONS

Year	Model	Valve Lash		Valve Angles		Valve Spring Installed Height	Valve Spring Pressure Lbs. @ In.	Valve Lift		Stem Clearance		Stem Diameter	
		Int.	Exh.	Seat	Face			Int.	Exh.	Intake	Exhaust	Int.	Exh.
1953	Six	.012H	.012H	①	②	$1\frac{29}{32}$	100 @ $1\frac{19}{32}$	.319	.318	③	③	.3105	.3105
	Eight	.012H	.012H	①	②	$1\frac{23}{32}$	105 @ $1\frac{13}{32}$	.300	.300	③	③	.3105	.3105
1954	Six	.012H	.012H	①	②	$1\frac{29}{32}$	100 @ $1\frac{19}{32}$	.319	.318	③	③	.3105	.3105
	Eight	.012H	.012H	①	②	$1\frac{23}{32}$	105 @ $1\frac{13}{32}$	.300	.300	③	③	.3105	.3105
1955	All	Zero	Zero	①	②	$1\frac{17}{32}$④	102 @ $1\frac{13}{64}$	.370	.370	③	③	.3412	.3412
1956	Auto. Tr.	Zero	Zero	①	②	$1\frac{17}{32}$④	112 @ $1\frac{1}{8}$④	.403	.403	③	③	.3412	.3412
	Std. Tr.	Zero	Zero	①	②	$1\frac{17}{32}$④	108 @ $1\frac{5}{32}$④	.373	.373	③	③	.3412	.3412
1957	Auto. Tr.	Zero	Zero	①	②	$1\frac{17}{32}$④	112 @ $1\frac{1}{8}$④	.403	.403	.001-.0027	.0015-.0032	.3419	.3414
	Std. Tr.	Zero	Zero	①	②	$1\frac{17}{32}$④	108 @ $1\frac{5}{32}$④	.373	.373	.001-.0027	.0015-.0032	.3419	.3414
1958	Auto. Tr.	Zero	Zero	①	②	$1\frac{33}{64}$④	114 @ $1\frac{1}{8}$④	.400	.400	.0016-.0033	.0021-.0038	.3416	.3411
	Std. Tr.	Zero	Zero	①	②	$1\frac{33}{64}$④	109 @ $1\frac{5}{32}$④	.370	.370	.0016-.0033	.0021-.0038	.3416	.3411
1959	Auto. Tr.	Zero	Zero	①	②	$1\frac{33}{64}$④	114 @ $1\frac{1}{8}$④	.400	.400	.0016-.0033	.0021-.0038	.3411	.3406
	Std. Tr.	Zero	Zero	①	②	$1\frac{33}{64}$④	109 @ $1\frac{5}{32}$④	.370	.370	.0016-.0033	.0021-.0038	.3411	.3406
	420A Eng.	Zero	Zero	①	②	$1\frac{33}{64}$④	131 @ $1\frac{1}{8}$④	.400	.400	.0016-.0033	.0021-.0038	.3411	.3406
	420E Eng.	Zero	Zero	①	②	$1\frac{33}{64}$④	104 @ $1\frac{3}{16}$④	.330	.330	.0016-.0033	.0021-.0038	.3411	.3406
1960-61	21, 23, 24	Zero	Zero	①	②	$1\frac{17}{32}$④	171 @ $1\frac{13}{64}$	.330	.330	.0021-.0038	.0026-.0043	.3411	.3406
	26, 27, 28	Zero	Zero	①	②	$1\frac{33}{64}$④	114 @ $1\frac{1}{8}$④	.400	.400	.0021-.0038	.0026-.0043	.3411	.3406
	425A Eng.	Zero	Zero	①	②	$1\frac{33}{64}$④	131 @ $1\frac{1}{8}$④	.400	.400	.0021-.0038	.0026-.0043	.3411	.3406

①—Intake 30°, exhaust 45°. ②—Intake 29°, exhaust 44°.
③—Guides taper .0015" (.001" on 1953-54) to the inch and when started in guide the valve should fall through of its own weight.
④—Outer spring.

DISTRIBUTOR SPECIFICATIONS

Year	Model	Part No. ①	Rotation ②	Cam Angle, Degrees	Breaker Point Opening, Inch	Condenser Capacity, Mfds.③	Breaker Arm Spring Tension Ounces	Centrifugal Advance Data Degrees @ R.P.M. of Dist.		Vacuum Advance Data		
								Advance Starts	Full Advance	Inches of Vacuum to Start Plunger Movement	Inches of Vacuum for Full Plunger Travel	Maximum Vacuum Advance, Dist. Degrees
1953–54	Eight	1110831	CC	21–30	.016	.18–.23	19–23	1 @ 400	11 @ 1950	7–9	20½	10
1953	Six	1110232	CC	31–37	.022	.18–.23	17–21	1 @ 450	11 @ 1950	4–6	20½	11
1953	Six	1110233	CC	31–37	.022	.18–.23	17–21	1 @ 500	11½ @ 1800	4–6	20½	11
1954	Six	1110234	CC	38–45	.016	.18–.23	19–23	1 @ 450	11 @ 1950	4–6	19–20½	11
1954	Six	1110235	CC	38–45	.016	.18–.23	19–23	1 @ 500	11½ @ 1800	4–6	19–20½	11
1955	All	1110828	CC	26–33	.016	.18–.23	19–23	1 @ 325	15 @ 1700	4–6	12½–13½	8
1956	All	1110862	CC	26–33	.016	.18–.23	19–23	1 @ 525	10 @ 1800	4–6	12½–13½	8
1957	All	1110871	CC	30	④	.18–.23	19–23	1 @ 400	13 @ 2125	6–8	15¾–17¼	11
1958	Std. Tr.	1110924	CC	30	④	.18–.23	19–23	1 @ 375	14 @ 2300	6–8	13–15	10
1958	Hydra.	1110913	CC	30	④	.18–.23	19–23	1½ @ 450	11 @ 2300	6–8	13–15	10
1958	Fuel Inj.	1110925	CC	⑤	⑤	.18–.23	19–23	1½ @ 450	11 @ 2300	6–8	13–15	10
1959	All	1110941	CC	30	④	.18–.23	19–23	1½ @ 450	9 @ 2200	7–9	13–15	10
1960	Standard	1110964	CC	30	④	.18–.23	19–23	2 @ 400	9 @ 1450	10–12	16¾–18¾	10
	Standard	1110970	CC	30	④	.18–.23	19–23	2 @ 400	9 @ 1450	10–12	16¾–18¾	10
	Economy	1110965	CC	30	④	.18–.23	19–23	2 @ 450	10 @ 1800	6–8	13–15	10
	Economy	1110971	CC	30	④	.18–.23	19–23	2 @ 450	10 @ 1800	6–8	13–15	10
1961	⑨	1110971	CC	30	④	.18–.23	19–23	1 @ 350	14 @ 1050	6–8	14	10
	⑩	1110970	CC	30	④	.18–.23	19–23	1 @ 325	16 @ 1000	8–10	16	10

①—Stamped on plate riveted to side of distributor housing.

②—As viewed from the top.   CC—Counter Clockwise.

③—Microfarads—as indicated on a condenser tester.

④—Turn adjusting screw in (clockwise) until engine begins to misfire.   Then turn screw ½ turn in opposite direction.

⑤—Adjust cam angle for each breaker individually to 29° which should give a point opening of about .016″. Cam angle for both breakers operating must be 33–35°.

⑨—With regular fuel engines.

⑩—With premium fuel engines.

PISTONS, PINS, RINGS, CRANKSHAFT & BEARINGS

Year	Model	Fitting Pistons		Ring End Gap ①		Wrist-pin Diameter	Rod Bearings		Main Bearings			
		Shim To Use	Pounds Pull On Scale	Comp.	Oil		Shaft Diameter	Bearing Clearance	Shaft Diameter	Bearing Clearance	Thrust on Bear. No.	Shaft End Play
1953	Six	.0015	8–15	.008	②	.9372	2.1237–2.1247	.0001–.002	④	.0003–.0023	3	.003–.008
	Eight	.0015	10–20	.008	.008	.9372	1.9987–1.9997	.0001–.002	⑤	.0003–.0023	4	.003–.008
1954	Six	.0015	8–15	.008	.005	.9372	2.1237–2.1247	.0001–.002	④	.0003–.0023	3	.003–.008
	Eight	.0015	10–20	.008	.008	.9372	1.9987–1.9997	.0001–.002	⑤	.0003–.0023	4	.003–.008
1955–56	All	.0015	8–15	③	.015	.9805	2.2488–2.2498	.001–.003	2.498–2.499	⑥	4	.003–.008
1957	All	.0015	8–15	③	.015	.9805	2.2488–2.2498	.001–.003	2.623–2.624	⑥	4	.003–.008
1958	All	.0015	8–15	⑦	.025	.9802	2.2488–2.2498	.001–.003	2.623–2.624	⑧	4	.003–.008
1959–61	All	.0015	8–15	⑦	.025	.9802	2.2488–2.2498	.0005–.0025	2.998–2.999	⑧	4	.003–.008

①—Fit rings in tapered bores for clearance listed in tightest portion of ring travel.

②—Early .012″, late .005″.

③—Top ring .010″, second ring .008″.

④—No. 1, 2.4982–2.4992, No. 2, 2.5294–2.5304, No. 3, 2.5919–2.5929, No. 4, 2.6232–2.6242.

⑤—No. 1, 2.3732–2.3742, No. 2, 2.4044–2.4054, No. 3, 2.4357–2.4367 No. 4, 2.4669–2.4679, No. 5, 2.4982–2.4992.

⑥—Front .0005–.0025″, rear .0008–.0033″, others .0005–.003″.

⑦—Top ring .021″, second ring .019″.

⑧—Front .0025″ maximum, others .0005–.003″.

Year	Model	Part No.	Rotation ①	Brush Spring Tension, Ounces	No Load Test			Torque Test		
					Amperes	Volts	R.P.M.	Amperes	Volts	Torque, Lbs. Ft.
1953	Six	1107994	C	24 Min.	70	5.65	5500	570	3.15	13½
1953–54	Eight	1107107	C	24 Min.	70	5.65	5500	550	3.25	11
1953	Six②	1107144	C	24 Min.	70	5.65	5500	550	3.25	11
1953	Eight②	1108031	C	24 Min.	80	5.67	5500	600	3.0	14
1954	Eight	1107957	C	24 Min.	80	5.67	5500	600	3.0	14
1955	All	1107631	C	35 Min.	95	10.1	3500	470	5.4	10½
1955	All③	1107632	C	35 Min.	95	10.1	3500	470	5.4	10½
1956	All	1107641	C	35 Min.	95	10.1	3500	470	5.4	10½
1957	All	1107661	C	35 Min.	100	10.6	5100	300	3.5	④
1958	Std. Tr.	1107697	C	35 Min.	65–100	10.6	3600–5100	300–360	3.5	④
1958	Hydra.	1107700	C	35 Min.	80–120	10.6	4700–5400	290–370	2.0	④
1959	Hydra.	1107735	C	35 Min.	80–120	10.6	4700–5400	290–370	2.0	④
1959–60	Std. Tr.	1107661	C	35 Min.	65–100	10.6	3600–5100	300–360	3.5	④
1960	Hydra.	1107777	C	35 Min.	80–120	10.6	3900–5400	290–370	2.0	④
1961	Reg. Fuel	1107791	C	35 Min.	65–100	10.6	3600–5100	300–360	3.5	④
	Prem. Fuel	1107781	C	35 Min.	80–120	10.6	4700–5400	290–370	2.0	④

①—As viewed from the drive end. C—Clockwise. ②—Power Glide transmission. ③—Power steering. ④—Armature locked.

GENERATOR AND REGULATOR SPECIFICATIONS

★To polarize generator, reconnect the leads to the regulator; then momentarily connect a jumper wire from the "Gen" to the "Bat" terminals of the regulator.

Year	Generator						Regulator					
	Generator Number	Rotation and Ground Polarity ③	Rated Cap. Amps.	Gen. Field Ground Location★	Brush Spring Tension, Ounces	Field Current Amperes	Regulator Number	Cutout Relay		Voltage Regulator Setting Volts	Current Regulator Setting Amperes	Current and Voltage Armature Air Gap, Inch
								Voltage to Close Points	Armature Air Gap, Inch			
1953–54	1102794	C-N	45	External	28	1.87–2.0④	1118827	6.3	.020	7.1	44	.075
1955	1100304	C-N	25	External	28	1.5–1.62①	1118945	12.6	.020	14.3	25	.075
1956	1100304	C-N	25	External	28	1.5–1.62①	1119000	12.6	.020	14.3	25	.075
1956	1102052	C-N	35	External	28	1.62–1.82①	1119002	12.6	.020	14.3	34	.075
1956	1102054	C-N	35	External	28	1.62–1.82①	1119002	12.6	.020	14.3	34	.075
1957	1100304	C-N	25	External	28	1.5–1.62①	1119000	12.6	.020	14.3	25	.075
1957	1102070	C-N	35	External	28	1.69–1.79①	1119002	12.6	.020	14.3	35	.075
1957	1102074	C-N	40	External	28	3.50–3.70①	1119163	12.6	.020	14.3	40	②
1958	1102107	C-N	30	External	28	1.69–1.79①	1119001	12.6	.020	14.3	30	.075
1958	1102104	C-N	45	External	28	2.66–2.86①	1119602	12.4	.020	14.2⑤	40	.075⑥
1958	1102108	C-N	30	External	28	1.69–1.79①	1119001	12.6	.020	14.3	30	.075
1958	1102106	C-N	45	External	28	2.66–2.86①	1119602	12.4	.020	14.2⑤	40	.075⑥
1958	1102105	C-N	45	External	28	2.66–2.86①	1119602	12.4	.020	14.2⑤	40	.075⑥
1959	1102142	C-N	30	External	28	1.69–1.79①	1119001	12.6	.020	14.3	30	.075
1959	1102143	C-N	45	External	28	2.66–2.86①	1119601	12.4	.020	14.4⑤	45	.075⑥
1960	1102203	C-N	30	External	28	1.69–1.79①	1119001	12.6	.020	14.3	30	.075
	1102200	C-N	35	External	28	1.69–1.79①	1119002	12.6	.020	14.3	35	.075
	1102143	C-N	45	External	28	2.66–2.86①	1119623	12.4	.020	14.4⑤	45	.075⑥
1961	1102204	C-N	30	External	28	1.69–1.70	1119263	12.6	.020	14.3	30	.075
	1102199	C-N	35	External	28	1.69–1.70	1119264	12.6	.020	14.3	35	.075
	1102220	C-N	45	External	28	2.66–2.86	1119623	12.4	.020	14.4	45	.075⑥
	1102143	C-N	45	External	28	2.66–2.86	1119623	12.4	.020	14.4	45	.075⑥

①—At 12 volts.

②—Voltage regulator air gap .080″, current regulator air gap .075″.

③—C-Clockwise. N-Negative. ④—At 6 volts. ⑤—Lower contact setting .1 to .3 volt lower.

⑥—Voltage regulator contact air gap: upper .016″, lower .067″.

REAR AXLE AND BRAKE CYLINDER SPECIFICATIONS

Year	Model	Ring Gear & Pinion Backlash, Inch	Drive Pinion Adjustment	Drive Pinion Bearing Preload, Inch Lbs.	Drive Pinion Bearing Adjustment	Axle Shaft End Play, Inch	Hydraulic Cylinder Bore Sizes, Inch		
							Wheel Cylinder		Master Cylinder
							Front	Rear	
1953–54	All	.003–.012	Shim	27–37①	Spacer	None	1 1/16	7/8	1
1955–57	All	.003–.012	Shim	24–32②	Spacer	None	1 1/16	15/16	1
1958	All	.003–.012	Shim	24–32②	Spacer	None	1 1/8	1	1
1959–61	All	.005–.009	Shim	24–32②	Spacer	None	1 3/16	1	1

①—For used bearings, 10–12 inch lbs.

②—For used bearings, 12–15 inch lbs.

WHEEL ALIGNMENT SPECIFICATIONS

Year	Model	Caster, Degrees		Camber, Degrees		Toe-in, Inches	Toe-out on Turns, Degrees①		Kingpin Angle, Degrees②
		Limits	Desired	Limits	Desired		Outer Wheel	Inner Wheel	
1953–54	All	− 1/2 to + 1/2	0	0 to + 1	+ 1/2	0 to 1/16	18 1/2	20	4 1/2 @ 1/2 Camber
1955–57	All	− 1/2 to − 1 1/2	− 1	0 to + 1	+ 1/2	0 to 1/16	19	20	4 1/3 @ 0 Camber
1958	All	− 1 to 0	− 1/2	0 to + 1	+ 1/2	0 to 1/16	19	20	4 1/2 @ 0 Camber
1959–60	All	− 1 to − 2	− 1 1/2	− 1/4 to + 3/4	+ 1/4	0 to 1/16	19	20	4 1/2 @ 0 Camber
1961	All	− 1 to − 2	− 1 1/2	− 1/4 to + 3/4	+ 1/4	0 to 1/8	19	20	4 5/6 @ 0 Camber

①—Incorrect toe-out, when other adjustments are correct, indicates bent steering arms.

②—Incorrect kingpin angle with correct camber indicates bent suspension arms or steering knuckle support.

COOLING SYSTEM & CAPACITY DATA

Year	Model	Cooling System Data					Fuel Tank Gals.	Engine Oil			Transmissions			Rear Axle Pints
		Quarts No Heater	Quarts With Heater	Rad. Cap Relief Pressure	Thermostat Opening Temp.			Refill Qts.⑧	Summer Grade	Winter Grade	Std. Pints	With Over-drive Pints	Auto-matic Qts.	
					①	②								
1953–54	Six	18 1/4	20	6 1/2–7 1/2	170	151	20	5	20	10 W	1 3/4	None	11	3 1/4
1953–54	Eight	18 3/4	20 1/2	6 1/2–7 1/2	170	151	20	5	20	10 W	1 3/4	None	11	3 1/4
1955	All	22 3/4	24 1/3	7	180	151	20	5	④	④	1 3/4	None	9 1/2	3 1/4
1956	All	22 3/4	24 1/3	7⑥	180	160	20	5	④	④	2 1/2	None	9 1/2	3 1/4
1957	All	21 1/2	23	13⑦	180	170	⑤	5	④	④	3 1/4	None	9 1/4	3 1/4
1958	All	21.2	23.3	12–15⑧	180	170	20	5	④	④	2	None	9	5 1/2
1959	All	21.4	22.4	13⑦	180	170	21.5	5	④	④	2	None	9 1/4	5 1/2
1960	All	21.2	22.2	12–15	180	170	23	5	④	④	2	None	8 1/4	5 1/2
1961	3 Sp. H.D.	18 1/2	19 1/2	14	170	...	25	4	④	④	1.8⑨	None	6	5 3/4
	4 Sp. H.D.	18 1/2	19 1/2	14	170	...	25	4	④	④	2.8⑩	None	9	5 3/4

①—For permanent type anti-freeze.

②—For alcohol type anti-freeze.

③—Add one quart with filter change.

④—Use 20 W for 10° to 110° temp. Use 10 W for 10° below zero to 95° above.

⑤—Safari 2 seat model, 17; Safari 3 seat model, 16; all others 20.

⑥—13 lbs. with air conditioning.

⑦—15 lbs. with air conditioning.

⑧—14–17 lbs. with air conditioning.

⑨—Three speed transmission.

⑩—Four speed transmission.

ENGINE TIGHTENING SPECIFICATIONS★

★Torque specifications are for clean and lightly lubricated threads only. Dry or dirty threads produce increased friction which prevents accurate measurement of tightness.

Year	Spark Plugs Ft. Lbs.	Cylinder Head Bolts Ft. Lbs.	Intake Manifold Ft. Lbs.	Exhaust Manifold Ft. Lbs.	Rocker Arm Shaft Bracket Ft. Lbs.	Rocker Arm Cover Ft. Lbs.	Connecting Rod Cap Bolts Ft. Lbs.	Main Bearing Cap Bolts Ft. Lbs.	Flywheel to Crankshaft Ft. Lbs.	Vibration Damper or Pulley Ft. Lbs.
1953–54	25	60	—	—	—	—	45	95①	105	95
1955	25	95	40	25	15	3	45	95①	95	160
1956	25	95	40	25	15	3	45	95①	95	160
1957	25	95	40	25	15	5	45	95①	95	160
1958–61	25	95	40	30	15	5	45	95①	95	160

①—Rear 120.

SERIAL NUMBER LOCATION
Left Front Hinge Pillar

ENGINE NUMBER LOCATION
1953-54: Front of Left Side of Block
1955-61: Front of Right Bank of Block

1957

1953

1958

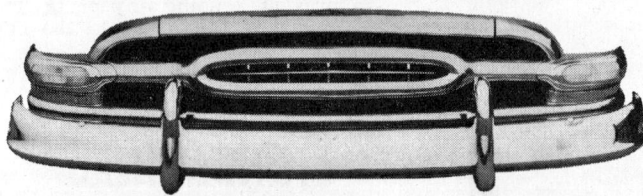

1954

1959

1955

1960

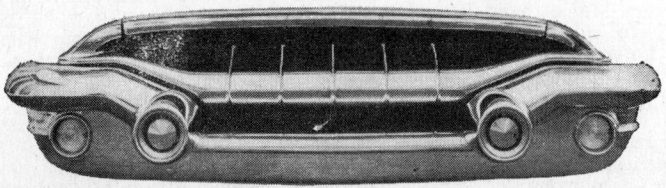

1956

1961

Engine Section

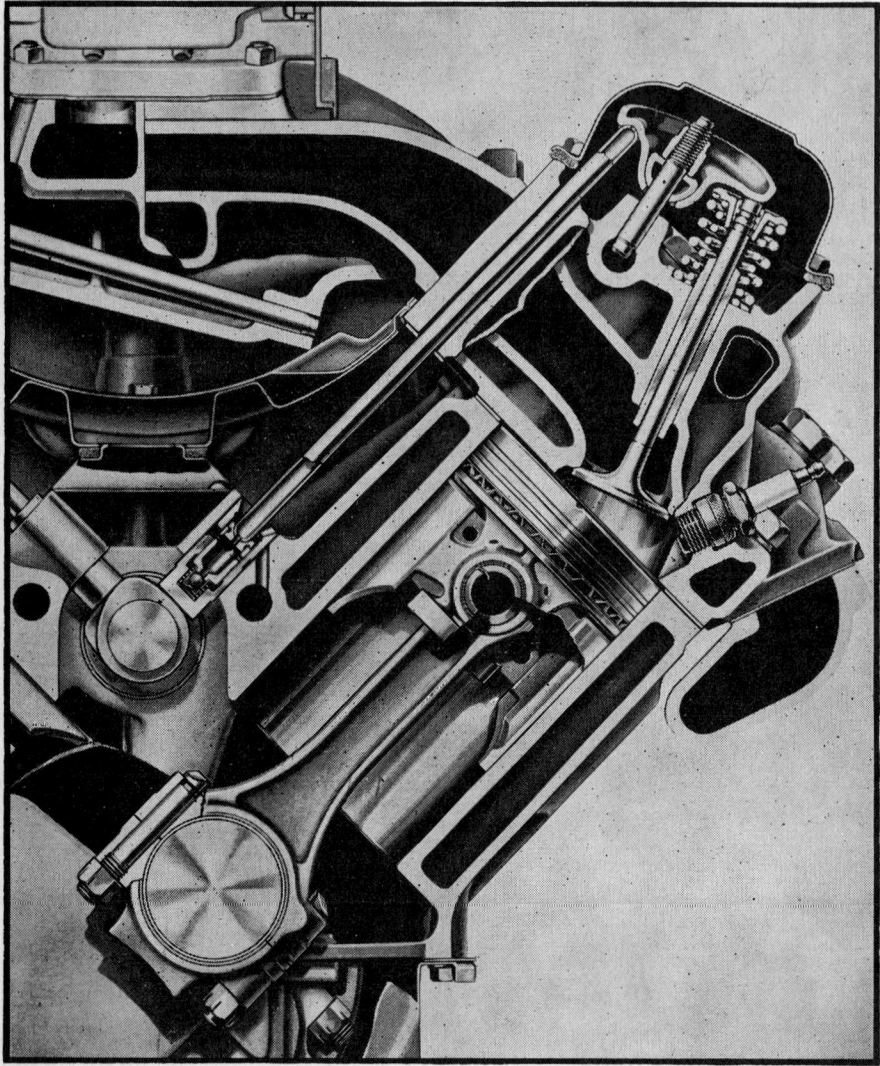

Engine cross section (one block). 1955 V8.
After 1955 removable valve guides are not used

ENGINE, REPLACE

V8 Engines

In addition to the usual items such as radiator, hood, battery, propeller shaft, lines and linkage, it will be necessary to perform the following operations:

1. On 1955-56, remove engine right side apron.
2. Disconnect exhaust pipe from cross-over pipe.
3. On manual shift cars, disconnect linkage from clutch and remove clutch control countershaft bracket from flywheel housing.
4. Thread a chain through openings in intake manifold behind carburetor. Attach chain to a hoist and raise engine just enough to take weight off mounts.
5. Unfasten mountings from cross-members.
6. On Hydra-Matic cars, support transmission with a jack and remove frame crossmember to which rear engine mounts are fastened.
7. Hoist engine and transmission as a unit.
8. Reverse above procedure to install. However, on Hydra-Matic cars it will be necessary to raise rear of engine to install the crossmember.

L-Head Engines

The engine may be removed from the chassis with the transmission attached. However, if it is desired to remove the transmission before removing the engine, the procedure given below will still generally apply. In addition to the usual items such as radiator, hood, battery, propeller shaft, fuel lines and linkage, it will be necessary to perform the following operations:

1. On power steering cars, remove pump, belt and mounting bracket leaving hose connected.
2. Disconnect exhaust pipe from manifold and exhaust pipe bracket from flywheel housing.
3. Remove thermo-gauge unit from head and disconnect coil primary lead at coil.
4. Disconnect wiring from generator and starter solenoid.
5. Disconnect linkage from clutch and remove clutch control bracket from flywheel housing.
6. If a hoisting bar fastened to the head is used the engine may be removed without further removal of fuel and electrical units.
7. Attach hoisting equipment to engine and remove bolts holding front insulator to frame. Take weight off engine rear insulators with a jack under rear of engine and remove bolts holding rear insulators to frame crossmember.
8. On Hydra-Matic cars, remove frame crossmember to which engine rear insulators were fastened. *Use care to prevent the transmission from swinging down as crossmember is removed or damage to transmission or personal injury may result.*
9. Carefully hoist engine and transmission out of car, checking frequently to see that sufficient clearance exists to prevent bending any parts. This is especially important in the case of Hydramatic linkage.
10. Installation is accomplished by reversing the above procedure.

CYLINDER HEAD

V8 Engines

1. Remove intake manifold.
2. Remove push rod cover.
3. Remove rocker arm cover.
4. Remove battery ground strap from left head or engine ground strap from right head.
5. Remove Hydra-Matic oil level indicator tube bracket and engine oil level indicator and tube from right head (1955-57 and 1961).
6. Loosen all rocker arm adjusting nuts and move rocker arms off push rods.
7. Remove push rods and place in a suitable stand so they can be replaced in exact position from which they were removed. *No. 7 exhaust valve push rod (rearmost on left bank) cannot be removed on 1955-57 cars with defroster. In this case withdraw rod part way and fasten it to head.*
8. Remove screws attaching exhaust crossover pipe to manifold.
9. Remove screws from cylinder head water inlet fitting.

10. Remove cylinder head screws and remove head with exhaust manifold attached. *If left head is being removed, it will be necessary to raise head off dowel pins, move it forward and shift it in order to clear the defroster, power steering and power brake equipment.*

Installation

Right and left heads are the same except for the location of the water passage plug in end of water passage. Therefore, only one head is provided for service replacement. New heads are complete with valve guides, rocker arm studs and all plugs except the one water passage plug.

When installing a new head, ream the valve guides and check the concentricity of valve seats. Transfer all serviceable parts to the new head, using new seals on the intake valve stems and new exhaust manifold gasket. Install new water passage plug using gasket cement, and install new intake manifold mounting studs.

Install the head in the reverse order of removal. The head screws are three different lengths. When inserted in the proper holes all screws will project an equal distance from the head. Do not use sealer of any kind on the threads. Tighten screws evenly to 90-95 lb. ft. torque.

Use four thin (.075") gaskets or two thick (.135") gaskets when installing the exhaust crossover pipe to the exhaust manifold.

L-Head Engines

1. To remove the cylinder head, drain the radiator.
2. Remove upper radiator hose from water outlet elbow.
3. Remove air cleaner and brace.
4. Remove accelerator linkage on cylinder head.
5. Remove thermo-gauge unit from head.
6. Disconnect heater hose from head.
7. Remove water outlet elbow and thermostat if the elbow gasket is to be replaced.
8. On cars with power steering, remove pump belt and pump with mounting bracket from head. Leave hose connected and lay pump on top of battery cover and fender skirt.
9. Remove bolts and lift off head.
10. When installing the head, install the head bolts finger tight after coating bolt threads with white lead and oil. Clean bolt threads before applying sealer to threads.
11. Using a torque wrench, tighten the head bolts to 60 lbs. ft., in the sequence shown in Figs. 1 and 2.

Fig. 1   Head tightening.   In-Line Sixes

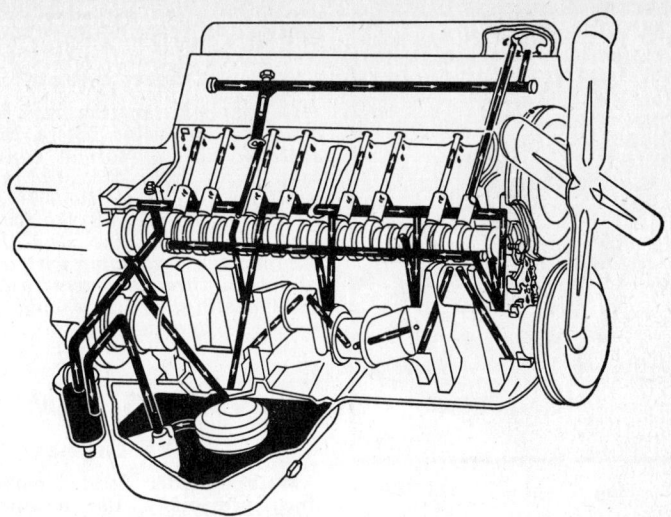

Engine lubrication.   V8 engines

VALVE ARRANGEMENT

Front to Rear

V8's . . . . E-I-I-E-E-I-I-E

VALVES, ADJUST

1955

Whenever rocker arms, push rods and valve lifters are removed, an initial setting of the rocker arm nuts must be made to establish the correct operation of the valve train.

Install the lifters in the bores from which they were removed. Install push rods and rocker arms with balls and start rocker arm nuts. *Push rods should be installed in same places they were originally installed and with same end contacting rocker arm.*

The self-locking rocker arm nuts should be adjusted as follows to properly position the plungers within the lifters. Each rocker arm nut must be adjusted when the corresponding valve is completely closed. The simplest and most accurate way to make this adjustment is to adjust one cylinder at a time while it is in the firing position.

With distributor rotor pointing to firing position for No. 1 cylinder, tighten No. 1 intake and exhaust rocker arm ball nuts, one at a time, just until there is no up and down movement of the push rod (do not depress lifter plunger). When rocker arm movement has just been eliminated, tighten rocker arm ball nut *one complete turn.* This will depress the plunger the proper amount within the lifter.

Turn the crankshaft and adjust each set of rocker arm nuts according to the firing order of the engine in the same manner as outlined above.

Service Note

To be sure that the valves and lifters function perfectly, it is strongly recommended that a vacuum gauge be used when tightening rocker arm nuts. With vacuum gauge connected and engine idling, tighten each rocker arm nut until the *highest and steadiest vacuum reading is indicated on the gauge.*

1956-61

No valve adjustment is required on these engines due to the new valve train. This was accomplished by moving the valve lifter oil supply hole nearer to the top of the lifter body to insure ample oil reserve, along with the new design of the rocker arm ball retaining nut and rocker arm mounting stud.

L-Head Engines

Run the engine until normal operating temperature is reached. Then remove the valve covers and, with engine idling, adjust the valves to the clearances given in the *Valve Data* chart.

If desired, valves may be initially adjusted with the engine cold (not running and at room temperature). If this procedure is followed, adjust the valves to .012-.014 in. and use care to see that the lifter of the valve being adjusted is on the low point of the cam.

It is recommended that any valves adjusted cold should be rechecked for proper clearance (.011-.013 in.) when engine has reached normal operating temperature and readjusted if necessary.

The importance of uniform correct valve adjustment cannot be over-emphasized. Non-uniform settings, even if only slightly outside of limits, will result in poor idle or excessive valve noise.

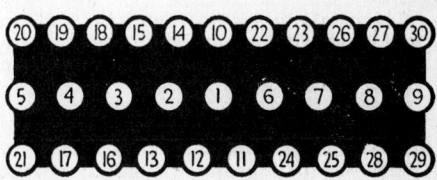

Fig. 2   Head tightening.   In-Line Eights

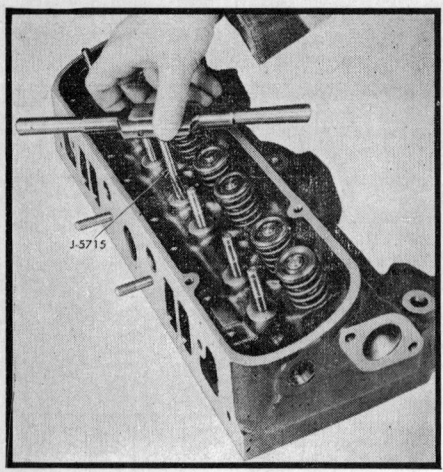

Fig. 3   Reaming rocker arm stud hole

ROCKER ARM STUD

V8 Engines

Rocker arm studs are replaceable providing a press of two tons capacity or more is available.
1. Remove cylinder head.
2. Remove rocker arm.
3. Pull out rocker arm stud by using washers or other suitable shims under the nut.

Installation, 1955

1. Ream out hole, Fig. 3. *Service replacement studs are .003″ oversize.*
2. Remove plugs from ends of cylinder head oil gallery and thoroughly clean out metal deposits and foreign matter from oil gallery.
3. Position rocker arm on new stud and place Stud Installer J-5716, Fig. 4, on stud in place of rocker arm ball.
4. Coat stud with white lead and oil, and with cylinder head mounted in press on Tool No. J-5712 so studs are vertical, position new stud with rocker arm and stud installer over hole in head.
5. Press stud into head until it is in about halfway ($\frac{7}{16}″$).
6. Position Valve Train Gauge J-5710, Fig. 5, in push rod hole so that it seats properly in rocker arm.
7. With valve seated, slowly press stud into cylinder head until the gauge is positioned as shown in Fig. 5.
8. Blow air through hole in stud to be sure passage is not restricted.
9. Reinstall parts removed and install head.

Installation, 1956-61

To install a new rocker arm stud in the cylinder head, a special Rocker Arm Stud Installer and a special Valve Train Gauge should be used, following the procedure outlined for 1955 models.

When the valve rocker arm ball retaining nut is tightened to a torque of 15-25 ft. lbs., proper location of the rocker arm with respect to the push rod and valve lifter is automatically assured.

The need for adjusting rocker arm position as in 1955 is thereby eliminated.

Service Note

In the event that the nut can be turned down to the point where the required 15-25 ft. lbs. of torque cannot be obtained, probably the stud has worked itself up out of position. If such is the case, run the nut all the way up flush with the top of the stud threads and hammer the stud down with a brass drift to get the threads nearer to the cylinder head casting, which should permit the proper torque to be obtained.

VALVES, REMOVE

V8 Engines

With cylinder head removed as outlined previously, use a suitable valve spring compressor to compress the spring in order to take out the valve locks. Then remove spring retainers, valve stem cup seals (intake valves only) and valve springs. Remove burrs from valve stem lock grooves to prevent damage to valve guide holes and slide valves from heads.

Place the valves in a board with numbered holes to identify their location so that, if re-used, they can be returned to their original guide holes.

L-Head Engines

To remove the valves, drain the radiator and remove the cylinder head and gasket. Take off the valve cover plates and plug the holes in the valve chamber around the valve lifters so that the valve locks will not fall into the oil pan when the locks are removed. Then, with a suitable valve spring compressor, compress the valve spring, remove the valve locks and lift out the valve.

VALVE GUIDES

1955 V8's

1. Drive out old guide, Fig. 6.
2. Drive new valve guide into place from combustion side of cylinder head as follows:
3. Coat outside of valve guide with white lead or oil.
4. Start chamfered end of guide into its

Fig. 4   Pressing in new rocker arm stud

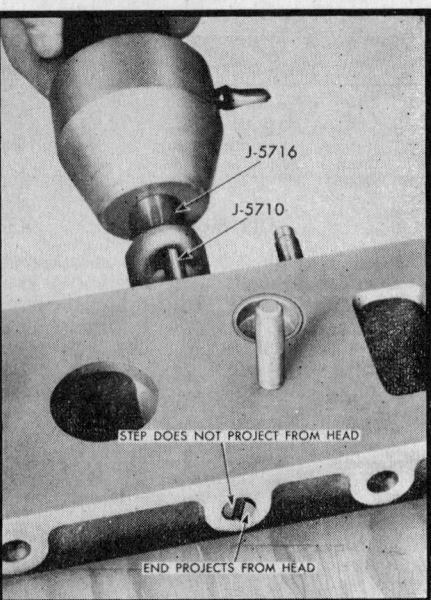

Fig. 5   Gauge should be positioned as shown when stud is properly installed

hole and drive into cylinder head with the tool shown in Fig. 6 until the end of the guide is positioned as shown in Fig. 7. Use the depth gauge shown in Fig. 8 to measure this distance.

1956 V8's

Valve guides are cast integral with the cylinder head and are tapered as in the past. Some cylinder heads may be equipped with one or more 1955 removable type valve guides. These valve guides are installed in production if the integral valve guides are reamed oversize in the machining operation.

If necessary to service a guide to accommodate either the .001″ or .003″ oversize valve stem, use the proper reamer, Fig. 10. If replacement of a removable type guide is necessary, use the procedure outlined for 1955 models.

Since valve guides taper .0015″ to the inch, a tapered reamer, Fig. 9, must be used to ream the guides to provide the correct taper and correct valve fit. Correct fit of valve stem in guide is such that when valve is started in guide it will just drop through of its own weight, but will have no perceptible side play.

Since this is a tapered reamer, the hole in the valve guide will become larger as the reamer is turned down. To avoid reaming oversize, when using the type reamer shown in Fig. 9, set the sliding stop to 3″ from the end and ream until the sliding stop bottoms. Then move the stop back to 3¼″ from the end and carefully continue reaming a little at a time, alternately reaming and testing the valve stem fit until the exact fit is obtained.

1957-61 V8's

Unlike previous models the valve guides are straight (not tapered). Valves with oversize stems are available in .001″, .003″ and .005″. Valve stem clearance is given in the *Valve Specifications* chart.

Fig. 6   Driving out valve guide.   1955 V8

Fig. 7   Correct installation
of valve guide.   1955 V8

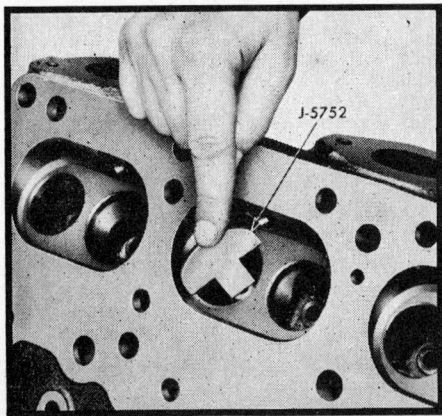

Fig. 8   Checking position of valve
guide with depth gauge. 1955 V8

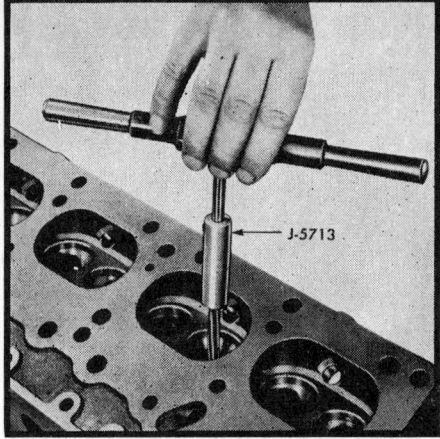

Fig. 9   Reaming valve guide with
tapered reamer, 1955-56. After
1956, valve guides are straight

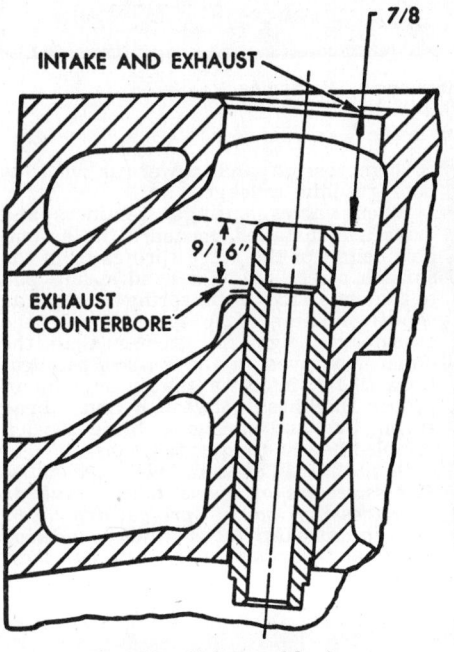

Fig. 10   Valve guide installation.   L-head 8's

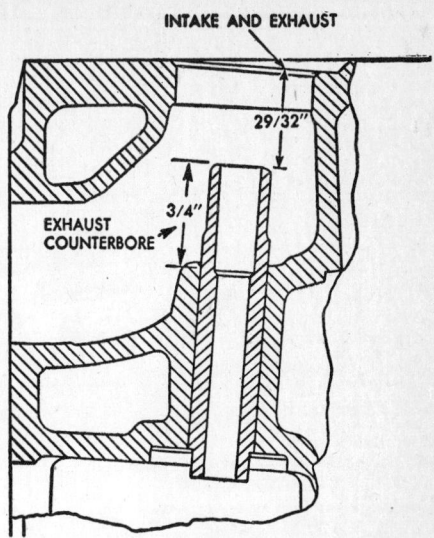

Fig. 11   Six-cyl. valve guide installation

Fig. 12   Valve guide removal.
L-head engines

The same clearance applies for oversize stems. Oversize reamers are required to enlarge the valve guide holes to fit the oversize valve stems. When the reamer is turned through the valve guide it will size the hole to fit the valve stem according to the clearance specifications. The tolerance for the oversize valve stem is controlled so that they will automatically fit properly in the hole after it is reamed. For best results when installing .005" oversize valve stems, use a .003" oversize reamer first and then ream to .005" oversize. *Always reface the valve and valve seat after reaming valve guide.*

L-Head Engines

Clean the valve guides thoroughly with a wire guide brush, being sure to clean the counterbore in exhaust valve guides to proper depth, Figs. 10 and 11.

Clean the valves thoroughly to remove head and stem deposits.

Try the fit of each valve stem in the valve guide. Valves should have from a free fit to .0006 in. maximum clearance at the bottom end of the guide.   In other words, when started in the guide the valve should just fall through by its own weight. If clearance is excessive, defective valve guide should be driven out, Fig. 12, and a new guide installed.

Coat the outside surface of the new valve guide with white lead and oil. Using a suitable driver, drive the guide into the block (with counterbored end of guide up toward valve head) until end of guide is the proper distance from the top edge of the valve seat (not from top of block), Figs. 10 and 11.

Since service replacement guides have straight holes it is necessary to ream them to the required taper, using a suitable taper reamer (.001 in. taper per inch), after installation in the block. The

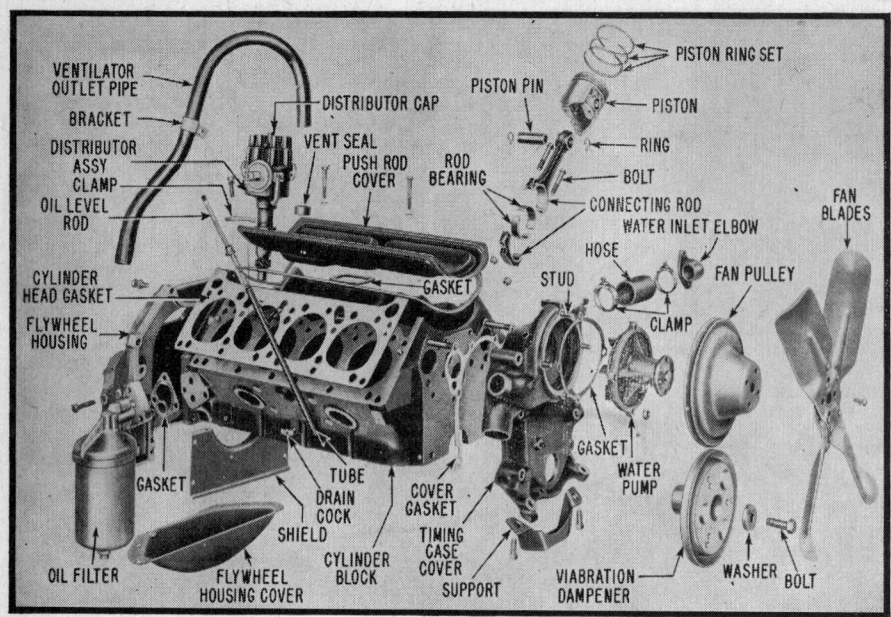

VENTILATOR OUTLET PIPE — BRACKET — DISTRIBUTOR ASSY — CLAMP — OIL LEVEL ROD — CYLINDER HEAD GASKET — FLYWHEEL HOUSING — GASKET — TUBE — DRAIN COCK — SHIELD — OIL FILTER — FLYWHEEL HOUSING COVER — CYLINDER BLOCK — COVER GASKET — TIMING CASE COVER — SUPPORT — DISTRIBUTOR CAP — VENT SEAL — PUSH ROD COVER — ROD BEARING — GASKET — STUD — VIABRATION DAMPENER — WATER PUMP — GASKET — CLAMP — HOSE — WATER INLET ELBOW — CONNECTING ROD — BOLT — RING — PISTON — PISTON PIN — PISTON RING SET — FAN BLADES — FAN PULLEY — WASHER — BOLT

Cylinder block and related parts. V8 engine

counterbore in exhaust valves should be deepened if necessary after exhaust guides are installed in block.

VALVE SPRING INSTALLED HEIGHT

When valves and seats are reground the position of the valve in the head is changed so as to lessen the valve spring tension. Without proper valve spring tension the valve does not seat long enough or it may not seat completely. Since the valve is cooled by transferring heat from the valve head to the seat and thence to the coolant, improper valve spring tension will cause worn, pitted and distorted valves which result in loss

of compression and power as well as poor gasoline mileage.

When valves, springs, retainers and locks are installed, measure the assembled height of the valve springs from the surface of the cylinder head spring pad to the underside of the spring retainer as shown in Figs. 12A and 12B. If the assembled height is greater than the dimension given in the *Valve Specifications Chart,* install a spacer or shim of proper thickness between cylinder head spring pad and spring to bring the assembled height to specifications.

Do not install spacers unless necessary. Excessive use of spacers will result in overstressing valve springs and overloading camshaft lobes which could lead to spring breakage and worn camshaft lobes.

VALVE SPRING TESTING

After taking out the valve springs, wash them in suitable solvent or gasoline. Examine the springs for damage or corrosion due to acid etching, which will develop into surface cracks and cause spring failure.

Check the valve spring tension on a spring testing fixture if one is available, and according to the specifications given in the *Valve Specifications* chart. If a fixture is not available, at least check the free length of each spring by standing it alongside a new spring. Any spring that does not conform to the pressure specifications within 10% should be replaced. Likewise, any spring that stands shorter than the new spring used for comparison should be discarded. Of course, cocked springs should also be scrapped.

VALVES, GRIND

V8 Engines

Clean the valves with a wire wheel brush, making sure that all carbon is removed from the top and bottom of the valve heads as well as the gum which might have accumulated on the stems.

In refacing valves, take off only the minimum of metal required to clean up the valve faces. If the outer edge of the valve becomes too thin or sharp due to excessive grinding, the valve must be replaced. This condition leads to premature breakage, burning or pre-ignition due to heat localizing on this knife edge. If the edge of the valve head is less than $\frac{1}{32}''$ thick after grinding, replace the valve.

Reface valves to 44 degrees for exhaust and 29 degrees on the intake valve; true up valve seats to 45 degrees on the exhaust and 30 degrees on the intakes. Cutting a valve seat results in lowering valve spring pressure and increases the width of the seat. The normal width of a valve seat is $\frac{3}{64}''$ to $\frac{1}{16}''$.

Test valves for concentricity with seats and for tight seating. Valves can be tested by lightly coating the valve face with prussian blue and turning the valve against its seat. This indicates whether the seat is concentric with the valve guide *but does not prove that the valve face is concentric with the valve stem, or that the valve is seating all around.* After making this test, wash all blue from the surfaces, lightly coat the *valve seat* with blue and repeat the test to see whether a full mark is obtained on the valve. *Both tests are necessary to prove that a proper seat is being obtained.* If a dial gauge is used to check the concentricity of valve seats, the concentricity should be held within .002″.

When valves and seats are reground, the position of the valve in the head is changed so as to shorten the operating length of the hydraulic lifter. This means that the plunger is operating closer to its bottom position, and less clearance is available for the thermal expansion of the valve mechanism during high speed driving.

To check and correct the length of the valve stem after grinding valves, position the rocker arm on the stud and hold in

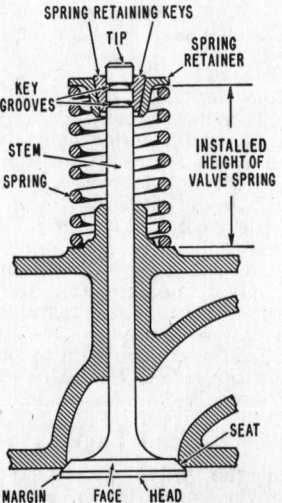

SPRING RETAINING KEYS — TIP — SPRING RETAINER — KEY GROOVES — STEM — SPRING — GUIDE — SEAT — MARGIN — FACE — HEAD — INSTALLED HEIGHT OF VALVE SPRING

Fig. 12A Checking installed height of valve springs. Engines with removable guides

SPRING RETAINING KEYS — TIP — SPRING RETAINER — KEY GROOVES — STEM — SPRING — SEAT — MARGIN — FACE — HEAD — INSTALLED HEIGHT OF VALVE SPRING

Fig. 12B Checking installed height of valve springs. Engines with integral guides

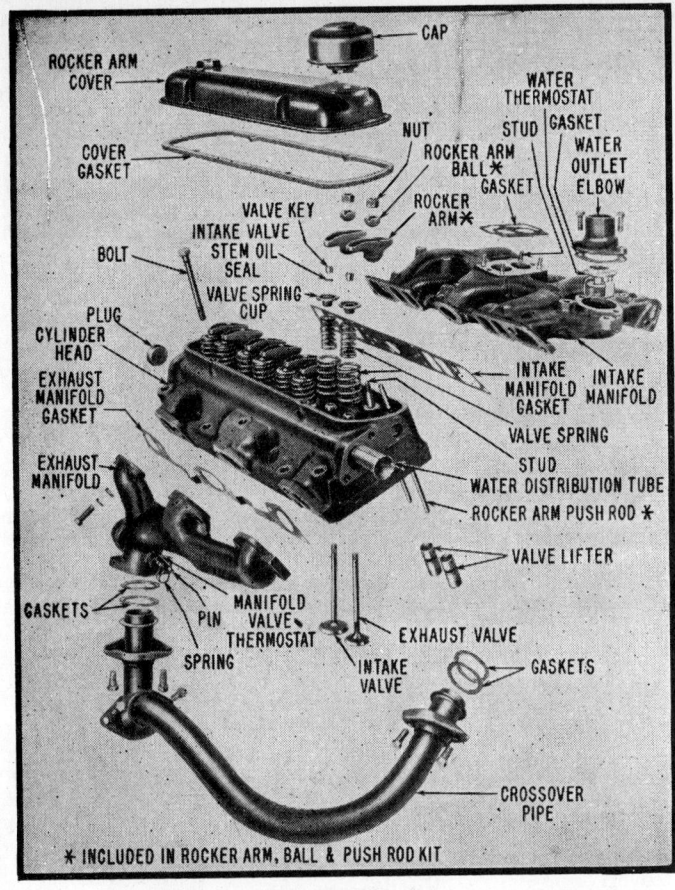

Cylinder head and related parts. V8 engine

Crankshaft and related parts. V8 engine

place with Special Rocker Arm Stud Installer, Fig. 13. Slip the valve into place and hold it against the valve seat. While holding the rocker arm and valve in position securely, insert Special Valve Train Gauge, Fig. 13, through push rod hole and seat snugly in push rod of rocker arm. With all parts seated, step end of gauge should be at least flush with gasket face of head but should not project

past the step on the gauge, as shown.

If the gauge projects too far, indicating that the valve stem is too long, grind the tip of the valve stem as necessary to make the gauge index properly. *Do not overheat the valve stem when grinding as excessive heat will soften the hardened stem, causing rapid wear.*

L-Head Engines

In refacing valves take off only the minimum of metal required to clean up the valve faces. If the outer edge of the valve becomes too thin or sharp due to excessive grinding, the valve must be replaced.

Inspect the valve seats in the block for cracks, burns, pitting, or improper angle. During any general engine overhaul it is advisable to reface the valve seats regardless of their condition. If new valve guides are required, they must be installed before refacing the seats if the equipment used has a valve guide pilot.

The valve seat width after refacing should be $\frac{1}{16}$ in. The width may be checked by placing a scale across the face of the seat.

A simple check can be made to prove the fit of the valve in the valve seat by spreading a thin film of prussian blue on the valve face and then inserting the valve into the valve seat. With hand pressure, rotate the valve ¼ turn and then remove it to observe the transfer of prussian blue to the valve seat. An uneven transfer of prussian blue will in-

dicate an inaccurate valve and valve seat refacing operation.

VALVE LIFTERS

V8 Engines

See the *Trouble Shooting Chapter* under the heading *Engine Noises* for causes of hydraulic valve lifter noise.

The easiest method for locating a noisy valve lifter is by the use of a piece of garden hose about 4 feet long. Place one end of the hose near each valve in progression and listen through the other end. In this manner the sound is localized, making it easier to determine which lifter is at fault.

Another method is to place a finger on the valve spring retainer. If the lifter is not functioning properly, a distinct shock will be felt when the valve returns to its seat.

In most cases where noise exists in one or more lifters, all lifter units should be removed and cleaned. If dirt, varnish or carbon is found to exist in one unit, it more than likely exists in all the units.

Removal

Remove intake manifold, push rod cover and rocker arm cover. Loosen rocker arm ball nut and move rocker arm off push rod.

Remove push rod. *The rearmost push rod in the left bank cannot be removed on 1955-57 with defroster unit. In this case the push rod can be moved off the valve lifter seat and tied or otherwise held away from lifter.*

END OF GAUGE PROJECTS BUT STEP IS WITHIN HEAD

Fig. 13 Checking length of valve stem

Remove lifter or lifters. If more than one lifter is to be replaced, be sure to identify them (push rods as well) so they will be installed in the same position.

Disassemble

With a suitable tool, pry out the plunger retainer ring, Fig. 14. Clean varnish deposits from inside the lifter body above the push rod seat. Then invert the lifter body and drop out the parts.

Assemble & Install

Rinse all parts in clean kerosene and assemble without drying. This will avoid the adherence of dust or lint if they are blown off or wiped with cloth.

Place the parts in the body in the order shown in Fig. 14. The plunger must slide freely in the body. Place the push rod seat on the plunger and depress these parts and install the plunger retainer in the groove in the body.

Install lifters in the reverse order of removal and on 1955 engines be sure to adjust the rocker arm nuts as directed under Valve Clearance, Adjust.

L-Head Engines

Valve lifters are assembled directly to the block and are furnished in standard size and .005 in. oversize. When installation of an oversize lifter is required, a specially designed reamer for finishing valve lifter holes should be used as follows:

1. Remove the cylinder head and valves and pick the lifters out of the guides.
2. Drive out the valve guides above the lifters to be replaced. This is necessary so the pilot on the reamer can enter the valve guide hole in the block.
3. Insert the pilot of the special reamer in the valve guide hole in the block after oiling thoroughly.
4. Ream the lifter hole using plenty of lard oil on the reamer.
5. Clean out all chips thoroughly and install new oversize lifter in block. A new lifter should be selected to give as close a fit as possible in the reamed hole, allowing the lifter to be moved freely with the fingers.
6. Install new valve guide and ream to size.

TIMING CHAIN COVER

1959-61

1. Drain cooling system.
2. Remove generator adjusting strap.
3. Remove fan and accessory drive belts.
4. Remove fan and pulley.
5. Disconnect radiator hoses.
6. Remove water inlet elbows from cylinder heads (leave attached to hose).
7. Remove fuel pump.
8. Remove vibration damper.
9. Remove front four oil pan-to-timing chain cover screws.

10. Remove cover-to-block screws and nuts.
11. Pull cover forward to clear studs and remove.

1955-58

1. Drain radiator.
2. On cars with power steering, remove pump with mounting bracket from pad on top of timing chain cover and lay back on fender skirt where it will be out of the way. Before doing so, however, disconnect battery ground strap to prevent pump from grounding "BAT" terminal of regulator.
3. Remove generator.
4. Remove fan belt and power steering pump belt.
5. Remove fan and pulley.
6. Disconnect upper radiator hose from radiator and remove fan shroud (1955-57).
7. Disconnect lower radiator hose and heater hose and take off radiator.
8. Remove water inlet elbows from cylinder heads (leave attached to hose).
9. Remove fuel pump.
10. Remove harmonic balancer.
11. Take weight off engine front insulator, using suitable engine lifting equipment. *Do not use jack under engine oil pan.*
12. Unfasten front engine support from timing chain cover.
13. Remove front four oil pan to timing chain cover screws.
14. Unfasten timing chain cover from block and remove cover.

L-Head Engines

To remove the cover, remove the radiator and use a puller to pull off the vibration damper. Support the engine with a jack and wood block under the oil pan and remove the front engine support retaining bolts. Remove the engine support and insulator by removing the insulator-to-frame bolts. Remove oil pan front screws and timing cover bar. Then unfasten the cover from the block and lift it off.

Install the cover in the reverse order of its removal. Apply gasket cement to the gasket surface of the cover and install the cover and gasket on the engine so the hole in the cover is centered on the crankshaft, and cover oil seal bears evenly on cover with equal area all the way around. Be sure to coat the cover seal with graphite lubricant.

TIMING CHAIN

V8 Engines

Take off radiator and timing chain cover as outlined above. Remove fuel pump eccentric and cover oil seal, Fig. 15. Align timing marks, Fig. 16, to simplify proper positioning of sprockets during reassembly. Slide chain and sprockets off ends of camshaft and crankshaft.

Install timing chain and/or sprockets, making sure timing marks on sprockets are aligned exactly on a straight line passing through the shaft centers. Then replace other parts removed.

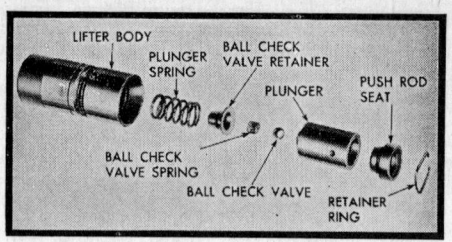

Fig. 14 Exploded view of valve lifter

L-Head Engines

The timing chain has no adjustment for wear. To remove the chain or sprockets, follow the procedure given above under *Timing Case Cover,* then take off the timing chain and sprockets, as required.

To assemble, Fig. 17, place the chain over the sprockets so that when the camshaft sprocket is bolted to its hub, the timing marks on both sprockets are opposite each other and in line with the centers of both the camshaft and crankshaft.

VALVE TIMING DATA

Year	Model	Intake Opens[1]	Intake Closes[2]	Exhaust Opens[3]	Exhaust Closes[4]
1953	Six	12½	52½	52½	12½
	Eight	5	39	45	5
1954	Six	12½	52½	52½	12½
	Eight	5	39	45	5
1955	All	22	67	63	27
1956	Synchro. Tr.	22	67	63	27
	Hydramatic	27	73	69	31
	[5]	34	75	81	37
1957	Synchro. Tr.	22	67	63	27
	Hydramatic	22	67	69	31
1958	Synchro. Tr.	22	67	63	27
	Hydramatic	30	63	77	25
1959	Synchro. Tr.	22	67	63	27
	Hydramatic	30	63	77	25
1960	21, 23, 24[6]	14	58	48	24
	425E Eng.	14	58	48	24
	27, 28[6]	30	63	77	25
	425 Eng.	30	63	77	25
	425A Eng.	29	74	82	31
1961	Std. Eng.	14	58	48	24
	425E Eng.	22	67	63	27
	425A Eng.	29	74	82	31

[1]—Degrees before top dead center.
[2]—Degrees after bottom dead center.
[3]—Degrees before bottom dead center.
[4]—Degrees after top dead center.
[5]—285 horsepower engine with two 4-barrel carburetors.
[6]—Manual shift transmission.

CAMSHAFT

V8 Engines

1. Drain radiator.
2. Remove intake manifold.
3. Remove crankcase ventilator outlet pipe.
4. Remove push rod cover.
5. Disconnect spark plug wires from plugs. Remove distributor.
6. Remove rocker arm covers.
7. Loosen rocker arm ball nuts so that rocker arms can be disengaged from push rods and turned sideways.
8. Remove push rods and hydraulic lifters. The rearmost rocker arm on the left bank cannot be removed if car is equipped with defroster unit (1955-57). Block it up with a spring-type clothes pin so it will not interfere with the camshaft as it is being withdrawn.

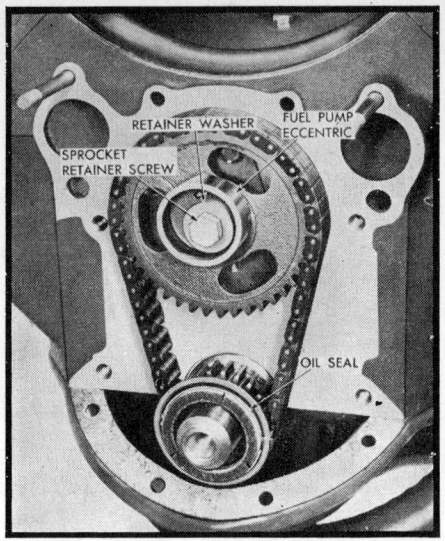

Fig. 15 Front of engine with timing chain cover removed. V8's

9. Remove radiator and timing chain cover, chain, sprockets and related parts.
10. Unfasten and remove camshaft thrust plate.
11. Slide camshaft out of engine carefully, making sure not to damage bearings in block. *The front of the engine should be raised as necessary to permit shaft to slide between the grill and hood catch plate support.*

Reverse the removal procedure to install the camshaft. Line up the timing marks on the sprockets and install the chain as shown in Fig. 16. Be sure to adjust the rocker arm ball nuts as outlined under Valve Clearance, Adjust.

L-Head Engines

To remove the camshaft and thrust plate, follow the procedure given under *Timing Case Cover,* then remove the cylinder head, valve covers, oil pump, fuel pump and distributor, after which block up the valves and lifters with clamps or rubber bands and withdraw the camshaft.

If the end play between the sprocket hub and the thrust plate is in excess of .005", install a new thrust plate.

To install the camshaft, reverse the foregoing operations, using new gaskets. Reset the ignition timing and check the valve clearance with the engine at normal operating temperature.

PISTONS & RODS, REMOVE

V8 Engines

1. Drain radiator and engine oil.
2. Remove intake manifold and cylinder head on bank from which piston is to be removed.
3. Remove oil pan and if 5, 6, 7 or 8 rod and piston is to be removed, remove oil baffle and oil pump screen.
4. Rotate crankshaft so crank pin carrying assembly to be replaced projects straight downward.

5. Remove bearing cap and push assembly up and out of block, using extreme care to see that crankshaft journal is not nicked during the process.

L-Head Engines

After removing the cylinder head and oil pan, examine the cylinder bores above the ring travel area. If the bores are worn so that a ridge exists at this point, remove the ridge with a ridge reamer to avoid damaging rings or cracking ring lands of pistons during removal.

Remove connecting rod caps and push pistons and up rods out of cylinders, using care to prevent rod bolts from nicking crankshaft journals.

Make sure the rods and pistons are properly numbered so that they can be reinstalled in original locations. It is advisable to install caps on rods to avoid mixing parts.

PISTON & ROD, ASSEMBLE

V8 Engines

Assemble pistons and rods as indicated in Figs. 18 and 19.

L-Head Engines

Connecting rods on all 8-cylinder models can be installed with either side toward the front of the engine.

When assembling connecting rod and aluminum pistons on 1953-54 Sixes, the oil spit hole in the side of the rod must be on the same side as the offset of the piston pin. Piston and rod assembly must be installed with the notch in the

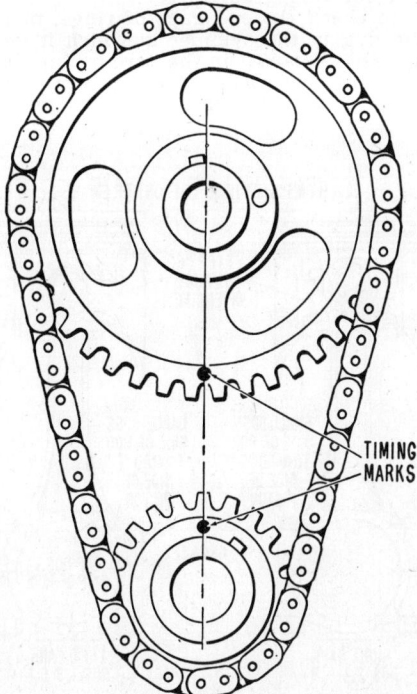

Fig. 16 Valve timing marks. V8 engines

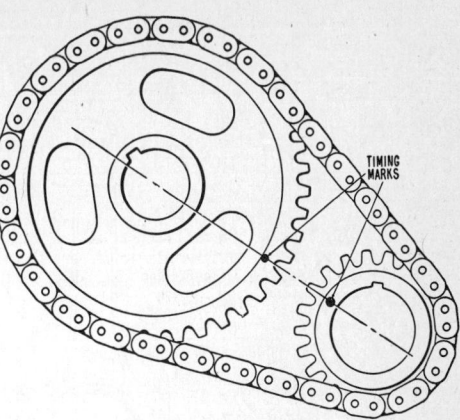

Fig. 17 Valve timing marks. L-head engines

top of the piston and the "F" on front of piston toward front of engine. When assembled as above, the oil hole in the rod will direct a stream of oil against the thrust (camshaft) side of the cylinder bore.

PISTONS

New pistons are furnished in standard size and .005", .010", .020" and .030" oversizes. Since these are nominal or basic sizes it is important that new pistons be measured to insure proper fit. All new pistons are provided with selectively fitted piston pins, therefore, it is important to check the fit of the pin in connecting rod bushings.

If the equipment required to measure fit of pistons in cylinder is not available, a fit can be satisfactorily checked by using a ½" x .0015" feeler ribbon and spring scale. When fitting pistons to cylinders by this method, the fit should be checked with the piston in the lower half of the cylinder, and both cylinder wall and piston clean and dry. The feeler ribbon should require a pull (in pounds listed in the chart) when drawn from between the piston (without rings) and cylinder wall.

If the pistons are to be reused with new rings, remove the carbon from the ring grooves. A special tool is available for this work but a satisfactory job can be done by breaking an old piston ring, filing the broken end to a sharp, square edge and using it to scrape out the carbon. Soak the piston in cleaning solvent to loosen any carbon residue. Clean out the loosened carbon, being careful not to cut away any piston material.

Clean out the oil return holes with a drill just large enough to fill the holes. Hold the drill in a tap wrench and make sure the drill does not remove any metal from the piston.

Rinse the piston in solvent and wipe off the carbon on the sides of the piston. *Never use a wire brush to clean a piston* as the brush will round off the edges of the ring lands. Pistons showing scuffed or scored skirts should be scrapped. Examine the ring lands carefully for cracks. If the piston is in the least bit doubtful, it should be discarded.

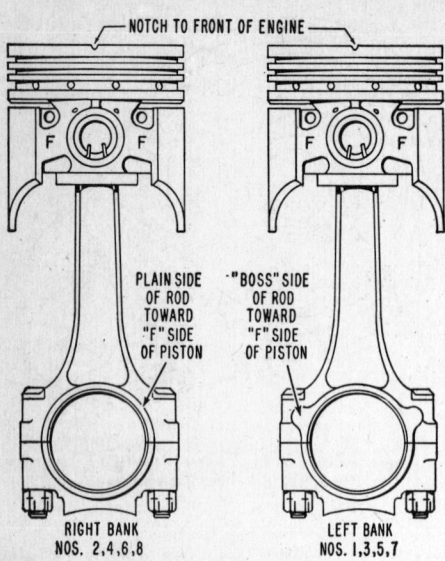

NOTCH TO FRONT OF ENGINE

F F   F F

PLAIN SIDE OF ROD TOWARD "F" SIDE OF PISTON

"BOSS" SIDE OF ROD TOWARD "F" SIDE OF PISTON

RIGHT BANK NOS. 2,4,6,8   LEFT BANK NOS. 1,3,5,7

Fig. 18 Piston and rod assembly. 1955-56 V8's

PISTON PINS

1958-61 V8's

Piston pins are pressed into the connecting rods instead of being retained by snap rings as in the past. Therefore, when necessary to install new pins suitable press equipment should be used. Fitting the pin in the piston is the same as outlined for earlier models.

1954-57 V8's

The fit of piston pin should be checked in the piston and also in the rod bushing. When new pistons (with pins), oversize pins, or new rod bushings are installed, honing of bushing or piston pin bosses, or both, may be necessary to effect a proper fit.

The fit of the piston pin in the rod bushing should be .0003" to .0005" loose (.0001" to .0006" on 1956-57). Pin and bushing should be dry when checking this fit. If clearance is excessive, as determined by micrometer measurement of inside diameter of bushing and outside diameter of pin, new bushing or oversize pin should be installed.

The piston fit in the piston is zero to .0002" loose (zero to .0004" on 1956-57) with pin and piston bosses clean and dry. When clearance is toward the high limit pin can be inserted by light hand pressure (pin should not fall through by its own weight).

When clearance is toward the low limit (zero) considerable hand pressure will be required to insert the pin. By using a brass drift, pin can be tapped into place with light pressure. Piston and pin must be at room temperature when checking fit.

L-Head Engines

Pins are furnished in standard size and oversizes of .001, .003 and .005 in.

On cast iron pistons, piston pins are fitted to the piston so that a 150-250 lb. force is required to press the pin into the piston. This force is a press load required to move the pin through one piston boss before the end of the pin enters the other boss. With this fit the pin will not remain permanently tight in the engine, and in high mileage engines pistons may be found in which the pins are free.

In aluminum pistons (1953-54 Six), the fit of the pin will be correct if the pin can be pushed into place with the thumb. Clearance is excessive if the pin will slide through due to its own weight.

PISTON RINGS

When new piston rings are installed without reboring cylinders, the glazed cylinder walls should be slightly dulled, but without increasing the bore diameter. This is done with a "Glazebuster" or with a hone equipped with the finest grade of stones.

New piston rings must be checked for clearance in piston grooves and for gap in cylinder bores. Cylinder bores and piston grooves must be clean, dry and free of carbon and burrs.

Check the clearance of each ring in its piston groove by installing the ring and then inserting feeler gauges *under* the ring. Any wear that occurs in the piston groove forms a step or ridge at the inner portion of the lower land. If gauges are inserted above the ring, the ring may rest on the step instead of on the worn portion of the lower land, and a false measurement of clearance will result.

If the piston grooves have worn to the extent that relatively high steps or ridges exist on the lower lands, the piston should be replaced because the steps will interfere with the operation of new rings and the ring clearances will be excessive. Piston rings are not furnished in oversize widths to compensate for ring groove wear.

To check the end gaps of rings, place the ring in the cylinder in which it will be used. Square it in the bore by tapping with the lower end of the piston, then measure the gap with feeler gauges. If

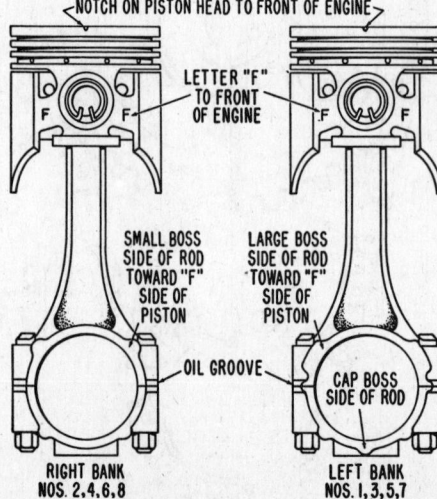

NOTCH ON PISTON HEAD TO FRONT OF ENGINE

LETTER "F" TO FRONT OF ENGINE

F F   F F

SMALL BOSS SIDE OF ROD TOWARD "F" SIDE OF PISTON

LARGE BOSS SIDE OF ROD TOWARD "F" SIDE OF PISTON

OIL GROOVE

CAP BOSS SIDE OF ROD

RIGHT BANK NOS. 2,4,6,8   LEFT BANK NOS. 1,3,5,7

Fig. 19 Piston and rod assembly. 1957-61 V8's

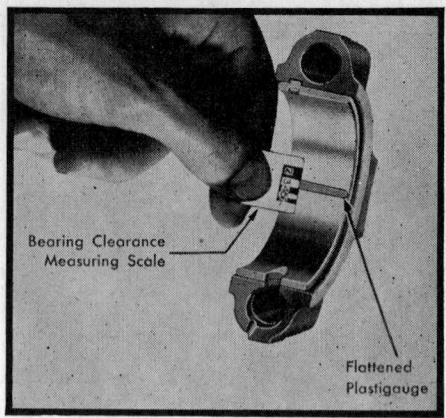

Bearing Clearance Measuring Scale

Flattened Plastigauge

Fig. 20 Checking bearing clearance with Plastigage

necessary to increase the gap, file the ends of rings carefully with a smooth file.

ROD BEARINGS

Connecting rod bearings can be replaced without removing the rod assembly by removing the cap and replacing the upper and lower bearing halves. The clearance between the bearing and crankshaft can be measured with Plastigage as follows:

1. Remove bearing cap and wipe oil from crankshaft and bearing.
2. With crankpin at approximately bottom dead center, place a piece of Plastigage in the center of the cap.
3. Reinstall cap and tighten to the torque value given in the *Engine Tightening Specifications* table.
4. Remove the bearing cap and determine bearing clearance by comparing the width of the flattened Plastigage with the graduation on the Plastigage envelope, Fig. 20. The number within the graduation on the envelope indicates the clearance in thousandths of an inch. If clearance is excessive, replace the bearing.

MAIN BEARINGS

Caution—Main bearing clearance can be checked with Plastigage in the same manner described for rod bearings. If bearings are measured with the engine in the chassis, the crankshaft must be supported in order to take up clearance between the upper bearing insert and crankshaft journal. This can be done by tightening the bearing caps of adjacent bearings with .005" to .015" cardboard, (such as a calling card) between lower bearing shell and journal. Use extreme care when this is done to avoid unnecessary strain on the crankshaft or bearings or a false reading may be obtained. Do not rotate crankshaft while Plastigage is installed. *Be sure to remove cardboard.* To Install new bearings, proceed as follows:

1. Remove bearing cap and worn lower shell.
2. Rotate crankshaft in normal direc-

tion to turn upper bearing shell out of crankcase. Use a cotter pin with a flattened head or the special tool made for the purpose in the crankshaft oil hole to contact the bearing and force it out.

3. Place a new upper shell on the crankshaft journal with the locating notch in the correct position and rotate the shaft to turn the bearing in place.
4. Install the lower bearing shell in the cap.
5. Tighten all cap nuts to the torque value given in the *Torque Specifications* table.

CRANKSHAFT OIL SEAL

A braided oil seal is pressed into the upper and lower grooves behind the rear main bearing. Directly in front of this seal is an oil slinger which deflects the oil back into the oil pan. Should the braided seal require replacement, the installation of the lower half is accomplished as follows:

With the bearing cap and lower bearing half removed, install a new seal so that both ends protrude above the cap. Tap the seal down into position or roll it snugly in its groove with a smooth rounded tool, Fig. 21. Then cut off the protruding ends of the seal with a sharp knife or razor blade.

Installing Upper Seal

Although the usual practice is to remove the crankshaft when the upper half of the seal is to be replaced it is possible to do the job without removing the crankshaft as follows:

To remove the seal, use needle-nose

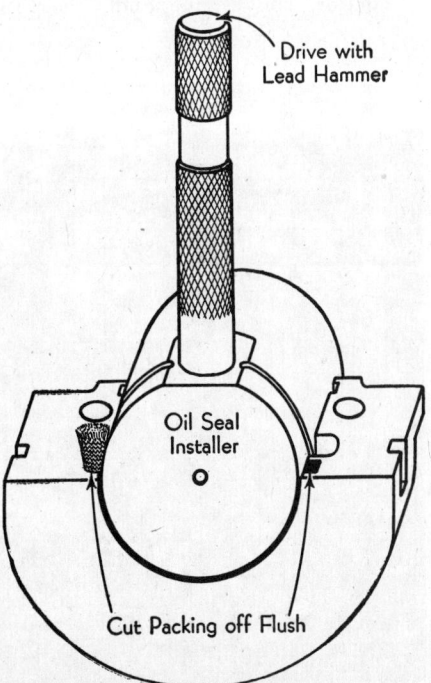

Fig. 21 Installing rear main bearing oil seal

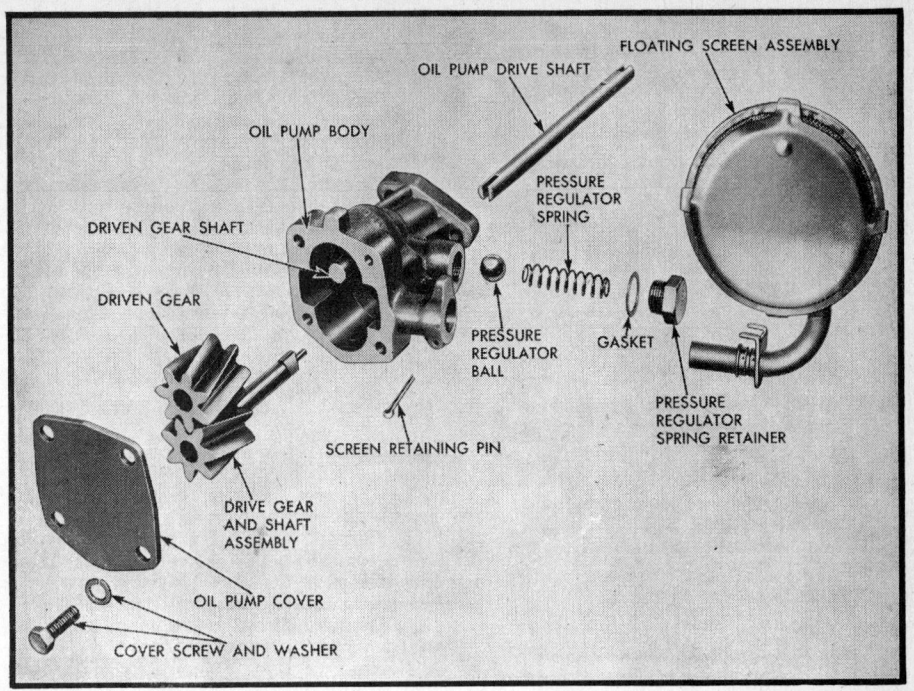

Fig. 22 Exploded view of oil pump. V8's

pliers to grasp the end of the seal which is most accessible. Pull the seal downward while rotating the crankshaft slowly in the direction that the seal is being removed.

To install the new seal, fasten a length of wire or strong string such as fishing line securely to one end of the new seal. See that the point of fastening is not bulky and that it is not over ⅜" from the end of the seal. Coat the seal with Lubriplate. Pass the free end of the wire or string up over the crankshaft at the point where the seal is to be installed. Then exert a firm, steady pull on the wire or string and at the same time rotate the crankshaft slowly in the direction of the pull. This will help to move the seal into position. When the installation is completed, trim the ends of the seal flush with the engine block.

OIL PAN REPLACE

1961

1. Drain radiator and oil pan.
2. Remove hood and air cleaner.
3. Disconnect battery ground cable.
4. Remove upper radiator support and fan guard.
5. Unfasten and move coil away from body.
6. Remove crossover and exhaust pipe-to-exhaust manifold retaining nuts.
7. Unfasten and lower idler arm and tie rod.
8. Remove front engine mount bolts.
9. Unfasten and lower starter motor.
10. Remove oil pan bolts.
11. Remove clutch housing lower cover.
12. Hook chain fall under front of intake manifold and lift engine as high as possible.
13. Let oil pan drop.

14. Remove front main bearing cap and move crankshaft to No. 1 "up" position.
15. Holding crossover pipe and tie rod down, remove oil pan.
16. Reverse removal procedure to install pan.

1960

1. Remove engine fan.
2. Drain radiator just enough to allow removal of upper and lower radiator hoses.
3. Raise front of car and place on jack stands.
4. Drain oil from crankcase.
5. Disconnect crossover pipe at left hand exhaust manifold and at right hand exhaust connector. Remove crossover pipe. Disconnect exhaust pipe from right hand exhaust manifold. If equipped with dual exhausts, disconnect both exhaust pipes from exhaust manifolds.
6. Remove two rear oil pan screws which retain flywheel housing front shield-to-cylinder block. Remove two screws which retain shield to flywheel housing and remove shield.
7. Remove flywheel housing lower cover.
8. Disconnect clutch linkage (if equipped).
9. Remove frame bolts from right hand idler arm bracket.
10. *Remove* front engine mount-to-frame bolts and *loosen* rear engine mount-to-frame bolts.
11. Disconnect oil cooler lines at timing cover.
12. Loosen Hydramatic oil filler tube bracket to allow clearance between tube and floor pan.
13. Jack up front of engine until sufficient clearance is obtained between oil pan and rear upper edge of en-

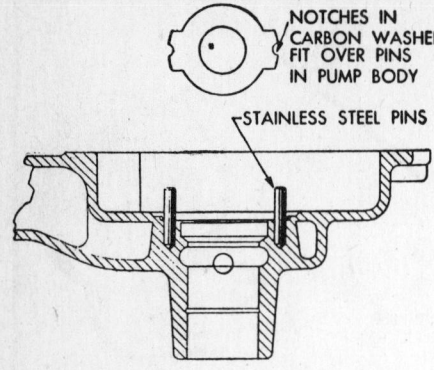

NOTCHES IN CARBON WASHER FIT OVER PINS IN PUMP BODY

STAINLESS STEEL PINS

Fig. 23 1953 water pump. Pins keep carbon washer from turning

gine support cross member.
14. Remove screws and oil pan.
15. Reverse above procedure to install pan.

1959

1. Remove air cleaner and fan.
2. Drain radiator to allow removal of upper radiator hose on cars with air suspension.
3. Remove exhaust crossover pipe.
4. Disconnect exhaust pipe from right-hand exhaust manifold.
5. If equipped with dual exhaust system, disconnect exhaust pipes from manifolds.
6. Remove flywheel housing front shield (6 screws).
7. Remove crankcase outlet ventilator pipe (or cleaner if equipped).
8. Remove flywheel housing lower cover.
9. Disconnect clutch linkage (if equipped).
10. Remove frame bolts from right-hand idler arm bracket.
11. Remove front and rear engine mount bolts.
12. Loosen Hydra-Matic oil filler tube bracket to allow for clearance between tube and floor pan.
13. Place jacks beneath bell housing and raise engine until about 4″ clearance is obtained between oil pan and rear upper edge of engine support cross-member.
14. Remove oil pan.
15. Reverse above procedure to install pan. Be sure no distortion is injected into engine mounts during installation.

1955-58

1. Drain oil from crankcase.
2. Remove engine side pans.
3. Remove two idler lever support attaching screws and lower the steering linkage as far as possible (1955-57).
4. Disconnect exhaust crossover pipe from both manifolds and from exhaust pipe. (Universal socket must be used at left manifold connection.) Remove pipe by shifting it around to a position where it will come out without forcing.
5. Remove two rear oil pan screws which retain flywheel housing front

shield to cylinder block. Remove four screws which retain shield to flywheel housing and remove shield.
6. Remove flywheel housing lower cover.
7. Loosen crankcase ventilator outlet pipe brace clamp and swing brace out of the way.
8. Remove oil pan screws and drop pan. Reverse the removal procedure to install the pan and related parts. However, the rear main bearing cap gasket should be removed from its groove in the cap, the groove cleaned thoroughly and a new gasket installed. Apply gasket cement to the groove before installing the gasket.

1953-54

After draining crankcase and radiator, proceed as follows:
1. Remove radiator hose from water pump and cylinder head.
2. Remove two bolts holding steering idler arm support to frame so as to allow steering linkage to drop down for clearance in removing oil pan.
3. Remove front cross member to radiator cross member apron.
4. Remove two self-locking nuts holding front engine insulator to engine support.
5. Place wooden block on floor jack pad and position under oil pan.
6. Raise engine about one inch above insulator and then remove insulator and clamp. It is not absolutely necessary to remove the mount from the frame but by so doing slightly more clearance is obtained for reaching the front pan capscrews.
7. Place a block approximately 2½ in. high between frame and engine support (if insulator was left on frame, use a one inch block between insulator and engine support) and lower engine so it rests securely on wood block at front.
8. Remove flywheel housing lower cover.
9. Remove oil pan. In some cases it may be necessary to remove one of the engine side aprons to give sufficient clearance for removing oil pan.

OIL PUMP REPAIRS

V8 Engines

Remove oil pan. While holding pump in place, remove attaching screws. Lower the pump away from the block with one hand while removing the oil pump drive shaft with the other.
Remove oil screen and pressure regulator parts. Detach cover from pump body and take out gears, Fig. 22. Examine all parts for damage and assemble. Do not attempt to change oil pressure by varying length of pressure regulator spring.
Position drive shaft in distributor and oil pump drive gear. Place pump in position in the block, indexing the drive shaft with pump drive gear shaft. Install attaching screws with lock washers and tighten securely.
Removal and installation of pump does not affect distributor timing since the oil pump and distributor drive gear are mounted on the distributor shaft.

L-Head Engines

To remove the pump, lift off the distributor cap and rotate the crankshaft until the distributor rotor is in the position to fire No. 1 cylinder. Keep the engine in this position while the pump is off.
Continue on all models by removing the cap screws in the pump body, drop the pump, remove the pump cover and oil pump idler gear. Drive out the pin from the oil pump and distributor drive gear, pull the shaft out of the housing and press the drive gear from the shaft.

Note—Reverse the operations to assemble and install the pump. If, for any reason, the crankshaft has been moved while the pump was off, rotate the crankshaft to bring No. 1 cylinder on the firing position. Set the distributor rotor on No. 1 and install the oil pump, being sure that the prick-punch mark is down when the gear is meshed with the camshaft gear and the distributor rotor is not moved from the No. 1 firing position. Finally, replace the engine side pan and reset the ignition.

RADIATOR

V8 Engines

1. To remove radiator, remove attaching screws which fasten fan shroud (if equipped) to radiator and move shroud out of the way.
2. Disconnect hoses from radiator.
3. Unfasten radiator from support.
4. Lift radiator out of support. *If removing Hydra-Matic transmission radiator, disconnect inlet and outlet hose and plug openings with cork or similar plug.*
5. Install radiator by reversing removal steps and, after refilling radiator, run engine and check for

Fig. 24 Showing how water is sprayed through holes in distributor tube to cool exhaust valve seats. L-head engines

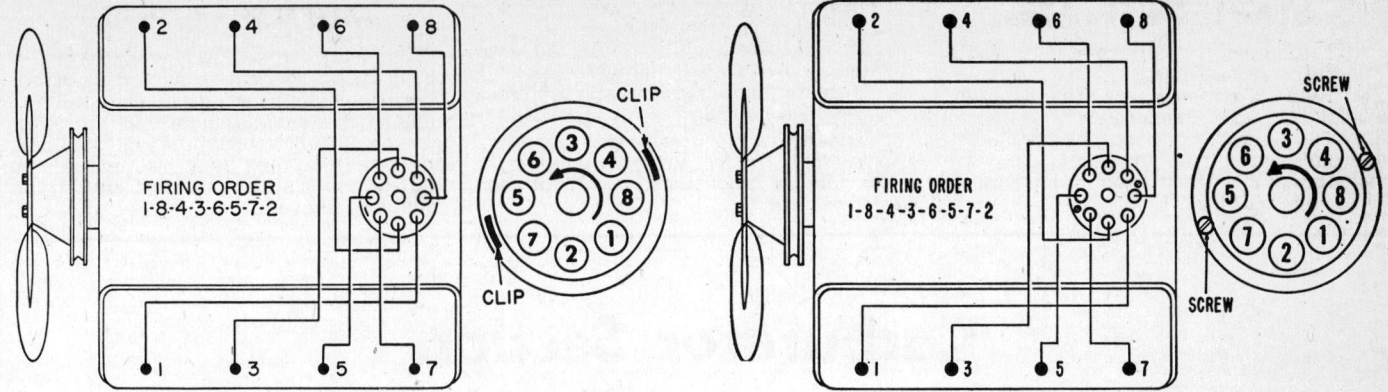

Fig. 25 Ignition details. 1955-56   **Fig. 26 Ignition details. 1957-61**

leaks. *If Hydra-Matic radiator, re-check transmission oil level.*

L-Head Engines

Drain radiator and cylinder block. Remove fan belt, upper and lower hoses from radiator and also heater return from lower tank. Disconnect headlight wiring from right junction block and wire loom from top of fan shroud. Unfasten fan shroud from radiator and radiator from its support. Turn fan so blades will miss hose outlet connection on radiator lower tank and remove radiator from support.

WATER PUMP, REPLACE

V8 Engines

Water pump is serviced only as an assembly. To remove, drain radiator and engine block. Remove fan belt, fan and pulley. Unfasten pump from block and lift off.

Install the pump in the reverse order. When pump is installed, drain hole will be at the bottom.

L-Head Engines

To remove the water pump, drain radiator and remove fan belt. Unfasten pulley from fan hub. Work fan blade assembly to lower right of fan shroud by passing end of pump shaft along groove of fan blade. With fan resting on shroud, slip fan pulley off water pump shaft, then lift fan blade from shroud. Remove radiator hose from water pump and remove pump from engine.

WATER PUMP REPAIRS

L-Head Engines

After removing water pump, proceed as follows:

1. Remove cover plate from pump.
2. On early 1952 models, remove shaft retainer wire.
3. Press shaft and bearing through impeller.
4. Revolve bearing by hand. If bearing is smooth and does not feel rough, it is serviceable and should be reinstalled. If rough, install a new shaft and bearing assembly.

5. Check seals at both ends of bearing outer race. If steel seals are loose in outer race so they can be turned with the fingers, replace the bearing.
6. Rust on shaft and outer surface of bearing is not harmful. If water has entered the bearing to any extent it will naturally be rough.
7. If the shaft bearing must be replaced, press it from the fan hub, being sure not to apply pressure to the outer race of the bearing.
8. Remove carbon washer and seal assembly from pump body, being sure to note the arrangement of the parts so they may be reinstalled correctly.
9. Clean the face of the counterbore in the pump body against which the spring-loaded seal seats, using a suitable water pump seat reamer.
10. Reassemble the pump, and engage the notches in the carbon washer with the two pins in the pump body, Fig. 23. When installing the shaft into the impeller, press on the impeller so its rear face is $\frac{3}{64}$ in. below a straight edge laid across the face of rear of pump body.

WATER DISTRIBUTOR TUBE

V8 Engines

A water distributor tube (inlet tube) is located in each cylinder head. Whenever a valve job is being done, these tubes should be pulled out and examined. If damage or corroded, install new tubes.

L-Head Engines

The tube, Fig. 24, is located between the cylinders and valve ports near the top of the cylinder block, and is used to direct water against the valve ports. One end of the tube is closed and the other is open. The closed end goes to the rear of the block.

Note — When over-heating is experienced on cars with high mileages, remove the tube and check for rust or corrosion. It is good practice to replace the tube whenever the engine has had a complete overhaul.

DISTRIBUTOR, REPLACE

1. Disconnect distributor-to-coil primary wire.
2. Remove distributor cap.
3. Crank engine so rotor is in position to fire No. 1 cylinder and timing mark on vibration damper is indexed with pointer.
4. Remove vacuum line from distributor.
5. Remove distributor clamp.
6. Lift distributor from engine.

Installation

1. Check to see that engine is at firing position for No. 1 cylinder.
2. Install new gasket on block.
3. Install distributor so vacuum unit faces right side of engine and rotor points toward contact in cap for No. 1 cylinder.
4. Install distributor clamp, leaving screw loose enough to allow distributor to be turned for adjustment.
5. Attach vacuum line to distributor.
6. Install wires in distributor cap, Figs. 25 and 26.
7. Attach distributor primary wire.
8. Adjust point gap, replace cap and set ignition timing.

IGNITION TIMING

With the breaker gap set to the proper clearance, crank the engine to bring No. 1 piston up on its compression stroke and stop when the ignition mark on the vibration damper is in line with the pointer.

Locate No. 1 spark plug wire on the distributor cap, Figs. 25 and 26, place the cap in position on the distributor and mark the housing opposite No. 1 terminal so that its relative position will be known when the cap is removed.

Loosen the distributor body clamp and rotate the distributor until the points close. Then rotate the distributor in the opposite direction until the points just begin to open, after which tighten the clamp bolt.

For best results, use a timing light to check the timing, and be sure to disconnect the vacuum line to prevent the advance mechanism from functioning.

STARTER REPLACE

1. Disconnect battery-to-starter cable from battery post.
2. Remove rubber cover from junction block on left fender skirt.
3. Disconnect junction block-to-solenoid wires from junction block.
4. Remove battery cable from clip on junction block.

5. Remove engine side apron from below starter.
6. Pull battery cable and solenoid wire loom down so they hang free.
7. Unfasten and remove starter from flywheel housing.

If clearance is insufficient to drop starter, look for worn engine mounts. If worn, remove transmission crossmember to get out starter.

MUFFLER & PIPES

Replacing any of the components of the exhaust system is a fairly obvious operation. However, when necessary to replace the exhaust manifold crossover pipe on 1955-56 models the right and left engine side aprons must be removed; on 1957-58 models only the left side apron must be removed.

Carburetor Section

Performance Complaints

Flooding, stumble on acceleration or other performance complaints are in many instances caused by the presence of dirt, water or other foreign matter in the carburetor. To aid in diagnosing the cause of the complaint, the carburetor should be carefully removed from the engine without draining the fuel from the bowl. The contents of the fuel bowl may then be examined for contamination as the carburetor is disassembled.

Check the fuel in the bowl for contamination by dirt, water, gum or other foreign matter. A magnet moved through the fuel in the bowl will pick up and identify any iron oxide dust that may have caused intake needle and seat leakage.

Inspect gasketed surfaces between body and air horn. Small nicks or burrs should be smoothed down to eliminate air or fuel leakage. On carburetors having a vacuum piston, be especially particular when inspecting the top surface of the inner wall of the bowl around the vacuum piston passage. A poor seal at this location may contribute to a "cutting-out" on turns complaint.

Fill the carburetor bowl with clean fuel before installing on manifold. This will help prevent dirt trapped in the fuel system from being dislodged by the free flow of fuel as the carburetor is primed. The operation of the floats and intake needle and seats may be checked under pressure if a fuel pump is used at the bench to fill the carburetor bowl. Operate the throttle several times and visually check the discharge from pump jets.

Poor Mileage and Engine Loading Complaints

Cases of poor mileage and engine loading may be due in many instances to sluggish choke valve opening during cold driveaway, caused by insufficient vacuum in choke housing, a plugged or restricted heat pipe or inlet in choke cover. To check for this condition, have engine warm and running at slow idle. Remove choke heat pipe and hold a finger over the heat inlet hole (hole is on choke housing on some carburetors). If there is little or no vacuum pull on the finger, check the choke housing for gasket leaks or plugged vacuum passages. If these are OK, check choke vacuum passages in carburetor between choke housing and manifold.

Dirty or Rusty Choke Housing

In cases where it is found that the interior of the choke housing is dirty, gummed or rusty while the carburetor itself is comparatively clean, look for a punctured or eroded manifold heat tube (if one is used).

Manifold Heat Control Valve

An engine equipped with a manifold heat control valve can operate with the valve stuck either in the open or closed position. Because of this, an inoperative valve is frequently overlooked at vehicle lubrication or tune-up.

A valve stuck in the "heat-off" position can result in slow warm up, deposits in combustion chamber, carburetor icing, flat spots during acceleration, low gas mileage and spark plug fouling.

A valve stuck in the "heat-on" position can result in power loss, engine knocking, sticking or burned valves and spark plug burning.

To prevent the possibility of a stuck valve, check and lubricate the valve each time the vehicle is lubricated or tuned-up. Check the operation of the valve manually. To lubricate the valve, place a few drops of penetrating oil on the valve shaft where it passes through the manifold. Move the valve up and down a few times to work in the oil. *Never use engine oil for this purpose as it will leave a residue which hampers valve operation.*

Engine Stumble On Acceleration

1959-60 Carter AFB Carbs.—This condition is caused by a collapsed accelerator pump "S" link which connects the pump lever and pump plunger. This collapse, caused by improper hardening of the part, shortens the pump stroke, resulting in this condition. A new link should be installed with particular caution that the lower end of the link points toward the carburetor air horn. If installed incorrectly, it will contact the bowl cover casting during operation.

1960 Two-Barrel Carbs.—This condition is caused by improper positioning of the air cleaner assembly. Position the air cleaner inlet tube 30° to 40° to the right of the engine centerline, except on air conditioned cars where the generator limits the amount of rotation.

Choke Sticking

1960 Rochester 2GC—In most instances this condition is caused by a burr at the upper end of the fast idle link. This condition may be aggravated by a burr around the pierced hole for the link in the fast idle lever. In a few cases the condition has also been caused by a roughness or out-of-round condition at the lower end of the link causing a bind at the fast idle cam.

Corrective measures are to remove the fast idle link and lever and smooth out the areas mentioned, using a small flat file.

CARTER CARBURETOR ADJUSTMENTS

Year	Carburetor Model	Idle Adjustments				Float Level		Float Drop		Pump Travel Setting	Choke Unloader Setting	Choke Setting
		Mixture Screws Turns Open	Hot Idle Speed In Drive	Fast Idle Speed	Dashpot Plunger Clearance	Primary	Secondary	Primary	Secondary			
1961	AFB-3123S	$\frac{1}{2}$-2	490	2200④	$\frac{15}{16}$⑫	$\frac{21}{64}$①	$\frac{21}{64}$①	$\frac{23}{32}$②	$\frac{23}{32}$②	$\frac{5}{16}$⑧	$\frac{5}{32}$⑤	1 Rich
	AFB-3124S	$\frac{1}{2}$-2	490	2200④	$\frac{15}{16}$⑫	$\frac{21}{64}$①	$\frac{21}{64}$①	$\frac{23}{32}$②	$\frac{23}{32}$②	$\frac{5}{16}$⑧	$\frac{5}{32}$⑤	1 Rich
	AFB-3125S	$\frac{1}{2}$-2	490	2200④	$\frac{15}{16}$⑫	$\frac{21}{64}$①	$\frac{21}{64}$①	$\frac{23}{32}$②	$\frac{23}{32}$②	$\frac{5}{16}$⑧	$\frac{5}{32}$⑤	1 Rich
1960	AFB-2975S	$\frac{1}{2}$-2	490	2200④	None	$\frac{21}{64}$①	$\frac{21}{64}$①	$\frac{23}{32}$②	$\frac{23}{32}$②	$\frac{33}{64}$⑧	$\frac{5}{32}$⑤	1 Rich
	AFB-2976S	$\frac{1}{2}$-2	490	2200④	$\frac{3}{32}$⑫	$\frac{21}{64}$①	$\frac{21}{64}$①	$\frac{23}{32}$②	$\frac{23}{32}$②	$\frac{33}{64}$⑧	$\frac{5}{32}$⑤	1 Rich
1959	AFB-2819S	$\frac{1}{2}$-2	490	2200④	$\frac{3}{32}$⑫	$\frac{21}{64}$①	$\frac{21}{64}$①	$\frac{23}{32}$②	$\frac{23}{32}$②	$\frac{33}{64}$⑧	$\frac{5}{32}$⑤	1 Rich
	AFB-2820S	$\frac{1}{2}$-2	490	2200④	None	$\frac{9}{32}$①	$\frac{9}{32}$①	$\frac{23}{32}$②	$\frac{23}{32}$②	$\frac{33}{64}$⑧	$\frac{5}{32}$⑤	1 Rich
1958	AFB-2767S-A	$\frac{1}{2}$-2	490	2200④	$\frac{1}{8}$⑫	$\frac{21}{64}$①	$\frac{21}{64}$①	$\frac{23}{32}$②	$\frac{23}{32}$②	$\frac{33}{64}$⑧	$\frac{1}{8}$⑤	1 Rich
	AFB-2768S-A	$\frac{1}{2}$-2	490	2200④	None	$\frac{9}{32}$①	$\frac{9}{32}$①	$\frac{23}{32}$②	$\frac{23}{32}$②	$\frac{33}{64}$⑧	$\frac{1}{8}$⑤	1 Rich
	AFB-2740S	$\frac{1}{2}$-2	490	1900④	$\frac{1}{8}$⑫	$\frac{21}{64}$①	$\frac{21}{64}$①	$\frac{23}{32}$②	$\frac{23}{32}$②	$\frac{33}{64}$⑧	$\frac{1}{8}$⑤	1 Rich
	AFB-2751S	$\frac{1}{2}$-2	490	1900④	None	$\frac{9}{32}$①	$\frac{9}{32}$①	$\frac{23}{32}$②	$\frac{23}{32}$②	$\frac{33}{64}$⑧	$\frac{1}{8}$⑤	Index
1957	AFB-2506S	1-2	440	1900④	None	$\frac{17}{64}$①	$\frac{17}{64}$①	$\frac{3}{4}$②	$\frac{3}{4}$②	$\frac{33}{64}$⑧	$\frac{1}{8}$⑤	Index
1956	WCFB-2364S-A	$1\frac{1}{4}$-$2\frac{1}{4}$	440	1900④	None	$\frac{3}{16}$⑥	$\frac{3}{16}$⑥	$\frac{11}{16}$⑦	$\frac{11}{16}$⑦	⑩	$\frac{1}{8}$⑤	1 Rich
	WGD-2359S	$1\frac{1}{4}$-$2\frac{1}{4}$	440	1900④	None	$\frac{15}{64}$⑨	None	None	None	⑩	$\frac{1}{8}$⑤	Index
1955	WCFB-2268S	$\frac{3}{4}$-$1\frac{3}{4}$	400	1900④	None	$\frac{3}{16}$⑥	$\frac{3}{16}$⑥	$\frac{11}{16}$⑦	$\frac{11}{16}$⑦	⑩	$\frac{1}{8}$⑤	Index
	WCFB-2283S	$\frac{3}{4}$-$1\frac{3}{4}$	400	1900④	None	$\frac{3}{16}$⑥	$\frac{3}{16}$⑥	$\frac{11}{16}$⑦	$\frac{11}{16}$⑦	⑩	$\frac{1}{8}$⑤	Index
	WGD-2182S-A-B	$1\frac{1}{4}$-$2\frac{1}{4}$	400	1900④	None	$\frac{7}{32}$⑨	None	None	None	⑪	$\frac{5}{32}$⑬	1 Rich
	WGD-2207S-B	$\frac{1}{2}$-$1\frac{1}{2}$	400	1900④	None	$\frac{7}{32}$⑨	None	None	None	⑪	$\frac{5}{32}$⑬	1 Lean
1954	WCD-2122S	$\frac{3}{4}$-$1\frac{3}{4}$	375	1300⑧	None	$\frac{3}{16}$⑥	None	None	None	$\frac{5}{16}$⑭	$\frac{1}{8}$⑤	Index
1953	WCD-2010S	$\frac{1}{2}$-$1\frac{1}{2}$	375	1300⑧	None	$\frac{5}{32}$⑥	None	None	None	⑮	$\frac{9}{64}$⑤	Index

CARTER NOTES

IDLE SPEED SETTING

1958-61 4-barrel carburetors do not have a conventional throttle speed screw but instead use an air adjustment screw. The idle air screw is located in the throttle body and can be identified by it being larger than the idle mixture screws. Turning the air screw outward increases engine speeds but also leans the mixture. This must be compensated for by adjusting the idle mixture screws.

METERING ROD

WCFB, WCD and WGD—Metering rod adjustment must be made after pump adjustment. With throttle valves seated, loosen metering rod arm clamp screw. With metering rods in place, press down on vacumeter link until rods bottom in casting. Holding rods down, revolve metering rod arm until finger on arm contacts lip of vacumeter link. Hold in place and tighten clamp screw.

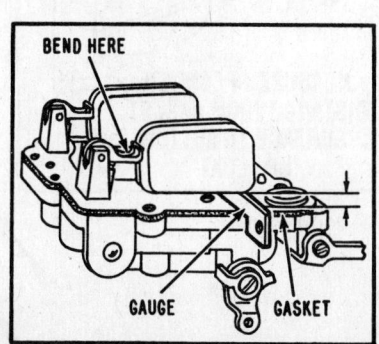

Fig. ①—AFB float level. Adjust by bending float lever.

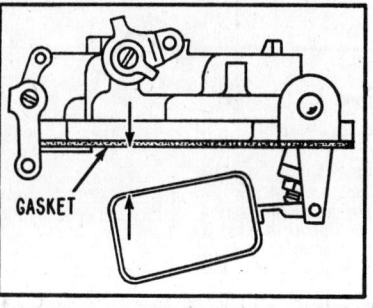

Fig. ②—AFB float drop. Adjust by bending stop tabs on float brackets.

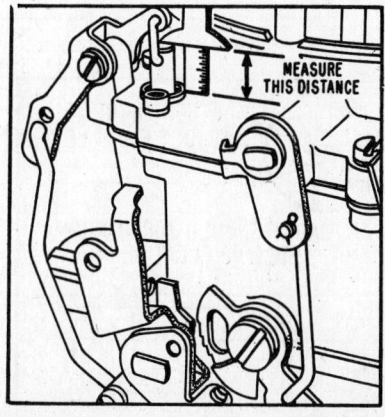

Fig. ③—With pump connector link installed with offset toward pump lever, there should be the dimension specified from top of bowl cover to top of plunger shaft. Adjust by bending throttle connector rod.

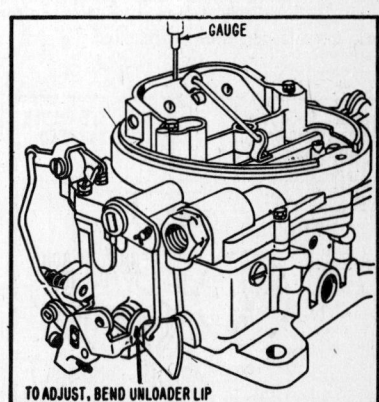

Fig. ⑤—With throttle valve wide open there should be the clearance specified between upper edge of choke valve and inner wall of air horn. Adjust by bending unloader lip on throttle shaft lever.

④—With engine at normal operating temperature and with fast idle screw on highest step on fast idle cam, turn screw to obtain the specified rpm.

CARTER NOTES
continued

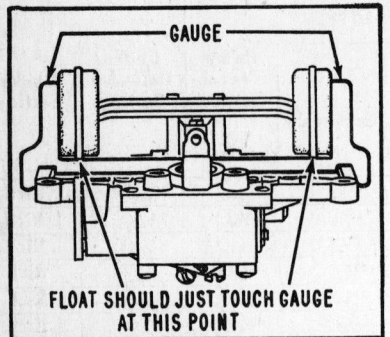

Fig. ⑥—WCFB and WCD float level. Adjust by bending float lever.

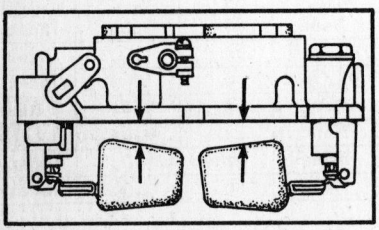

Fig. ⑦—WCFB float drop. Adjust by bending stop tabs on float bracket.

⑧—With engine at normal operating temperature, move fast idle cam so first full serration below highest step is under end of fast idle screw. Then turn screw to obtain specified rpm.

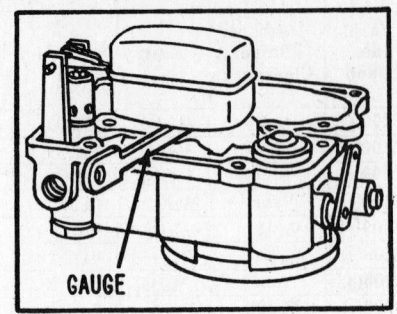

Fig. ⑧—WGD float lever. Adjust by bending float lever.

⑪—See ⑩. With throttle valve closed, flat on pump arm should be parallel with a straightedge placed across dust cover boss. Adjust by bending pump arm.

⑫—After adjusting fast idle speed, shut off engine. Then with fast idle screw resting on highest step of fast idle cam, clearance between dashpot plunger screw and throttle lever should be as specified. Adjust plunger screw as required.

Fig. ⑩—with pump connector link in outer hole of pump arm, flat on pump arm should be parallel with a straightedge placed across dust cover boss. Adjust by bending throttle connector rod.

⑬—With throttle valve wide open, there should be the clearance specified between upper edge of choke valve and inner wall of air horn. Adjust by bending choke shaft unloader arm.

⑭—With throttle valves closed, distance from top of plunger shaft to top of dust cover boss should be as specified. Adjust by bending throttle connector rod.

⑮—With throttle valves closed, flat on pump arm should be parallel with a straightedge placed across dust cover boss. Adjust by bending throttle connector rod.

ROCHESTER NOTES
IDLE SPEED SETTING

Some late model carburetors do not have a conventional throttle speed screw but instead use an air adjustment screw. The idle air screw is located in the throttle body and can be identified by it being larger than the idle mixture screws. Turning the air screw outward increases engine speeds but also leans the mixture. This must be compensated for by adjusting the idle mixture screws.

①—After adjusting fast idle speed, shut off engine. Then with fast idle screw resting on highest step of fast idle cam, clearance between dashpot plunger screw and throttle lever should be as specified. Adjust plunger screw as required.

③—Bend unloader tang on fast idle cam to obtain clearance specified between choke valve edge and dividing wall of air horn with throttle valves wide open.

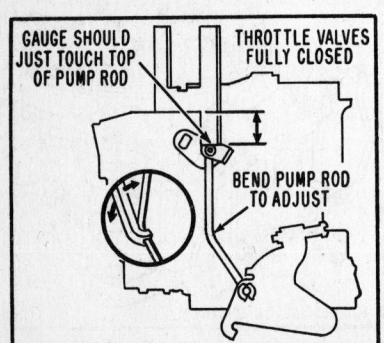

Fig. ②—With throttle valves closed, bend pump arm as necessary to obtain specified measurement from top of air horn casting to top of pump rod.

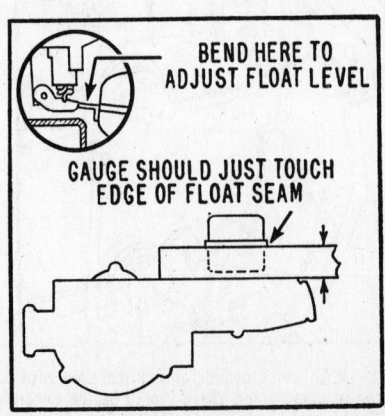

Fig. ④—2GC float level.

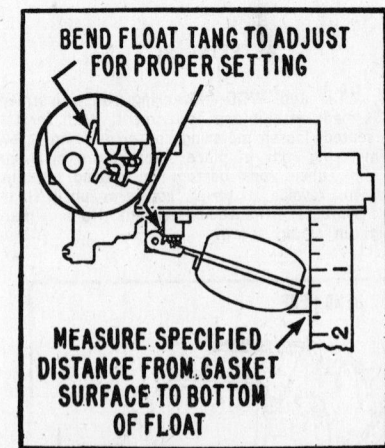

Fig. ⑤—2GC float drop.

ROCHESTER CARBURETOR ADJUSTMENTS

Year	Carburetor Model	Idle Adjustments				Float Level		Float Drop		Pump Rod Setting	Choke Unloader Setting	Choke Setting
		Mixture Screws Turns Open	Hot Idle Speed In Drive	Fast Idle Speed	Dashpot Plunger Clearance	Primary	Secondary	Primary	Secondary			
1961	2GC-7019070	$1\frac{1}{2}$	490[17]	None	None	$\frac{5}{8}$[4]	None	$1\frac{3}{4}$[5]	None	$1\frac{21}{64}$[6]	.163[8]	Index
	2GC-7019071	$1\frac{1}{2}$	490[17]	None	.064[16]	$\frac{5}{8}$[4]	None	$1\frac{3}{4}$[5]	None	$1\frac{21}{64}$[6]	.163[8]	Index
	2GC-7019072	$1\frac{1}{2}$	490[17]	None	None	$\frac{5}{8}$[4]	None	$1\frac{3}{4}$[5]	None	$1\frac{21}{64}$[6]	.163[8]	Index
	2GC-7019073	$1\frac{1}{2}$	490[17]	None	.064[16]	$\frac{5}{8}$[4]	None	$1\frac{3}{4}$[5]	None	$1\frac{21}{64}$[6]	.163[8]	Index
	2GC-7019060	$1\frac{1}{2}$	490[17]	None	None	$\frac{11}{16}$[4]	None	$1\frac{3}{4}$[5]	None	$1\frac{1}{8}$[6]	.163[8]	Index
1960	2GC-7015070	$1\frac{3}{4}$	490[17]	2700[11]	None	$\frac{5}{8}$[4]	None	$1\frac{3}{4}$[5]	None	$1\frac{21}{64}$[6]	.163[8]	Index
	2GC-7015062	$2\frac{3}{4}$	490[17]	None	None	$\frac{11}{16}$[4]	None	$1\frac{3}{4}$[5]	None	$1\frac{5}{8}$[6]	.163[8]	Index
	2GC-7015073	$2\frac{3}{4}$	490[17]	None	None	$\frac{11}{16}$[4]	None	$1\frac{3}{4}$[5]	None	$1\frac{5}{8}$[6]	.163[8]	Index
1959	2GC-7013060	$1\frac{3}{4}$	490[17]	2700[11]	None	$\frac{5}{8}$[4]	None	$1\frac{29}{32}$[5]	None	$1\frac{5}{16}$[6]	.163[8]	Index
	2GC-7013061	$2\frac{3}{4}$	490[17]	2700[11]	None	$\frac{5}{8}$[4]	None	$1\frac{29}{32}$[5]	None	$1\frac{5}{16}$[6]	.163[8]	Index
	2GC-7013069	$2\frac{1}{2}$	490[17]	None	None	$\frac{11}{16}$[4]	None	$1\frac{29}{32}$[5]	None	$1\frac{3}{16}$[6]	.163[8]	Index
	2GC-7013075	$2\frac{3}{4}$	490[17]	None	None	$\frac{11}{16}$[4]	None	$1\frac{29}{32}$[5]	None	$1\frac{3}{16}$[6]	.163[8]	Index
1958	4GC-7011701	2	490[17]	2300[11]	$\frac{1}{8}$[1]	$\frac{9}{32}$[9]	$1\frac{3}{8}$[9]	$1\frac{1}{2}$[10]	$1\frac{5}{16}$[10]	$\frac{15}{16}$[12]	.115[3]	Index
	2GC-7011702	$1\frac{1}{2}$	490[17]	None	None	$\frac{11}{16}$[4]	None	$1\frac{29}{32}$[5]	None	$1\frac{23}{64}$[6]	.163[8]	Index
	2GC-7011703	$1\frac{1}{2}$	490[17]	None	None	$\frac{11}{16}$[4]	None	$1\frac{29}{32}$[5]	None	$1\frac{23}{64}$[6]	.163[8]	Index
	2GC-7012702	2	490[17]	None	None	$\frac{11}{16}$[4]	None	$1\frac{29}{32}$[5]	None.	$1\frac{23}{64}$[6]	.163[8]	Index
	2GC-7012703	2	490[17]	None	None	$\frac{11}{16}$[4]	None	$1\frac{29}{32}$[5]	None	$1\frac{23}{64}$[6]	.163[8]	Index
1957	4GC-7009829	$1\frac{1}{2}$	440	None	None	$1\frac{3}{8}$[14]	$1\frac{3}{8}$[14]	$1\frac{13}{16}$[15]	$1\frac{13}{16}$[15]	$\frac{15}{16}$[12]	.115[3]	Index
	4GC-7009830	$1\frac{1}{2}$	440	None	None	$1\frac{3}{8}$[14]	$1\frac{3}{8}$[14]	$1\frac{13}{16}$[15]	$1\frac{13}{16}$[15]	$\frac{15}{16}$[12]	.115[3]	Index
	2GC-7009831	$1\frac{1}{2}$	440	None	None	$1\frac{15}{64}$[7]	None	$1\frac{29}{32}$[5]	None	$\frac{53}{64}$[2]	.163[8]	Index
	2GC-7009832	$1\frac{1}{2}$	440	None	None	$1\frac{15}{64}$[7]	None	$1\frac{29}{32}$[5]	None	$\frac{53}{64}$[2]	.163[8]	Index
1956	4GC-7007900	$1\frac{1}{2}$	440	1700[11]	None	$1\frac{19}{32}$[14]	$1\frac{19}{32}$[14]	$2\frac{1}{4}$[13]	$2\frac{1}{4}$[16]	$\frac{61}{64}$[12]	.115[3]	Index
	4GC-7008697	$1\frac{1}{2}$	440	1700[11]	None	$1\frac{19}{32}$[14]	$1\frac{19}{32}$[14]	$2\frac{1}{4}$[13]	$2\frac{1}{4}$[16]	$\frac{61}{64}$[12]	.115[3]	Index
	2GC-7008695	$1\frac{1}{2}$	440	None	None	$1\frac{15}{64}$[7]	None	$1\frac{29}{32}$[5]	None	$\frac{57}{64}$[2]	.163[8]	Index
	2GC-7008696	$1\frac{1}{2}$	440	None	None	$1\frac{15}{64}$[7]	None	$1\frac{29}{32}$[5]	None	$\frac{57}{64}$[2]	.163[8]	Index
1955	4GC-7007800	$1\frac{1}{2}$	400	1700[11]	None	$1\frac{19}{32}$[14]	$1\frac{19}{32}$[14]	$2\frac{1}{4}$[13]	$2\frac{1}{4}$[16]	$1\frac{1}{16}$[12]	.115[3]	Index
	2GC-7006100	$1\frac{1}{2}$	400	None	None	$1\frac{15}{64}$[7]	None	$1\frac{29}{32}$[5]	None	$\frac{15}{16}$[2]	.163[8]	Index

ROCHESTER NOTES

continued

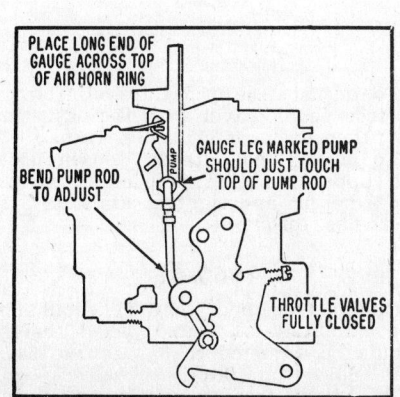

Fig. ⑥—With throttle valves fully closed, bend pump rod as necessary to obtain measurement specified from top of pump housing to top of pump rod.

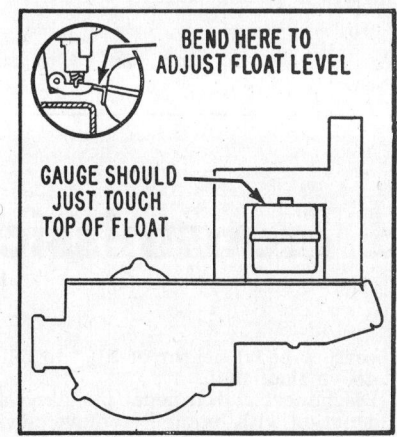

BEND HERE TO ADJUST FLOAT LEVEL

GAUGE SHOULD JUST TOUCH TOP OF FLOAT

Fig. ⑦—2GC float level.

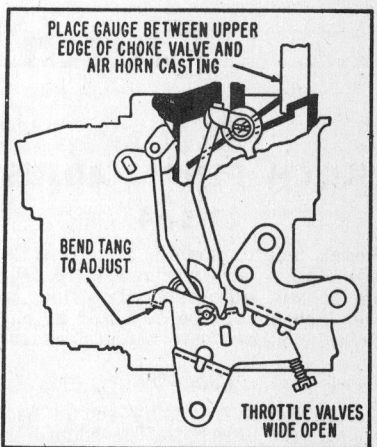

PLACE GAUGE BETWEEN UPPER EDGE OF CHOKE VALVE AND AIR HORN CASTING

BEND TANG TO ADJUST

THROTTLE VALVES WIDE OPEN

Fig. ⑧—Bend unloader tang on throttle lever to obtain clearance specified between upper edge of choke valve and inner wall of air horn with throttle valves wide open.

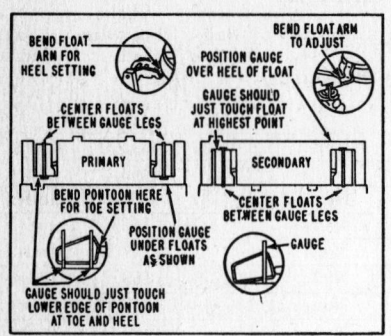

Fig. ⑨—4GC float level.

⑪—With engine at normal operating temperature, turn fast idle screw against highest step on fast idle cam until the specified rpm is obtained.

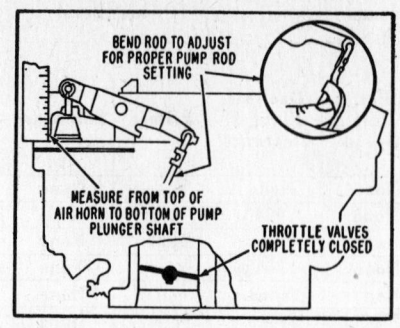

Fig. ⑫—With throttle valves closed, bend pump rod as necessary to obtain specified measurement from top of air horn casting to bottom of pump plunger shaft.

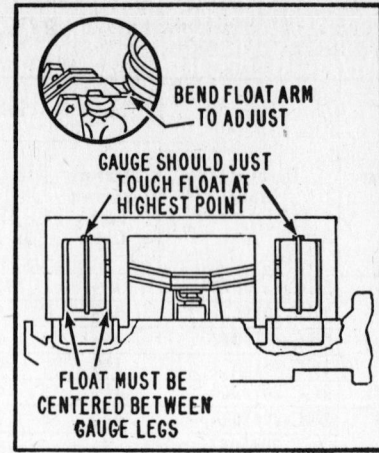

Fig. ⑭—4GC float level.

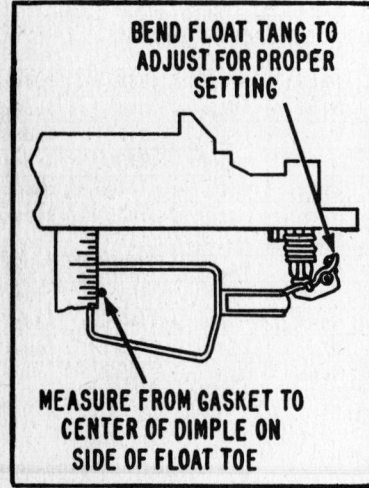

Fig. ⑩—4GC float drop.

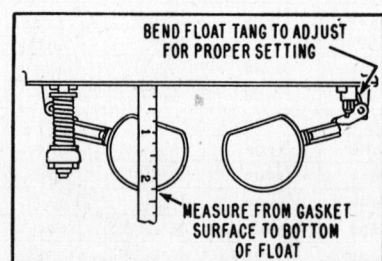

Fig. ⑬—4GC float drop.

⑯—Rotate fast idle cam so that speed screw rests on next to highest step of fast idle cam. Adjust clearance between contact screw and contact on throttle lever to dimension listed.

⑰—550 RPM with air conditioning off on cars so equipped.

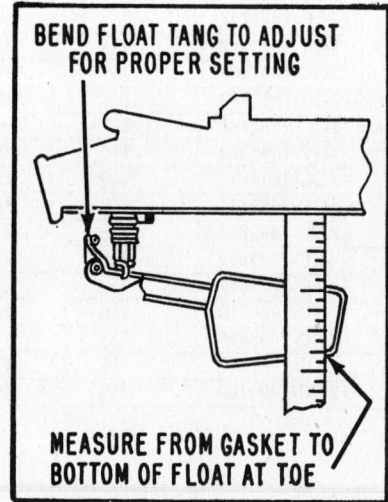

Fig. ⑮—4GC float drop.

Clutch and Transmission Section

CLUTCH PEDAL, ADJUST

1953-54

Pedal height should be adjusted at pedal stop screw to give 4⅜ to 4⅝ in. from bottom side of pedal to floor mat. Pedal lash should be adjusted at clutch fork link to give ⅞ to 1⅛ in. free travel.

1955-57

Clutch pedal free play should be adjusted at the clutch fork-to-countershaft rod from ¾" to 1⅛".

1958

1. Set clutch pedal stop bracket (under instrument panel) to provide the correct pedal height of 5½" to 5¾" above floor mat.
2. Disconnect clutch pedal push rod at junction with linkage (remove clevis pin).
3. With pedal held up tight against stop bracket, adjust clevis at lower end of pedal push rod until clevis pin will enter freely.
4. Then adjust the clutch fork rod until ½" to ⅝" free pedal play is obtained.

1959

Clutch pedal free travel should be approximately ⅝" and pedal height should be adjusted to 6¾" to 7" above the floor mat.

To adjust free pedal travel, remove all free pedal travel with the adjusting nut; then back off 3½ to 3¾ turns.

To adjust pedal height, loosen pedal rod upper trunnion jam nuts. Adjust pedal height and tighten jam nuts 5 to 10 ft. lbs. torque.

1960-61

Clutch free pedal travel should be approximately ¾" and pedal height should be adjusted to 6½" above floor mat (6-6¼" on 1961).

To adjust free travel, loosen clutch fork rod adjusting lock nut. Remove all free travel with adjusting nut, then back off 3½ turns.

To adjust pedal height, loosen pedal

rod upper trunnion jam nuts and adjust pedal height.

CLUTCH SERVICE

1958-61

1. To remove the clutch, remove transmission as outlined further on.
2. Remove clutch housing bottom cover.
3. Disconnect clutch fork return spring and remove clutch fork ball support and fork from housing.
4. Remove clutch release bearing.
5. Mark clutch pressure plate cover and flywheel so they can be reassembled in the same position as balanced at factory.
6. Loosen bolts holding cover to flywheel one turn at a time until tension is relieved.
7. When bolts are removed, move clutch away from flywheel at bottom so as to permit removal of clutch driven plate.
8. Lower cover and pressure plate through bottom of clutch housing.

Service Note

Unless special clutch rebuilding equipment is available, it is recommended that the clutch assembly be exchanged for a rebuilt unit should the clutch require rebuilding. The driven disc, however, may be replaced without special equipment. If clutch rebuilding equipment is available, follow the equipment manufacturer's instructions.

Installation

1. Position clutch disc so long end of hub is in flywheel and install clutch assembly to flywheel *but do not tighten bolts.* See that marks placed on flywheel and cover are lined up.
2. Use a spare transmission main drive gear inserted in spline of clutch disc to move disc into correct alignment so pilot on end of drive gear will enter clutch pilot bearing.
3. Tighten clutch cover-to-flywheel bolts one turn at a time until tight, then tighten to 30 lb. ft. torque. Remove spare main drive gear used to align clutch disc.
4. Install clutch release bearing.
5. Lubricate surface of release fork fingers, which contact release bearring, and the release fork ball fulcrum and install release fork. See that lock washer is used under screw fastening fork ball fulcrum to clutch housing.
6. Apply a light coating of grease to outer diameter of transmission release bearing support (retainer). Also grease the inner diameter of the release bearing and fill to recess in inner diameter of bearing.
7. Install transmission, connect linkage to release fork and adjust clutch pedal free play.

1953-57

1. Remove transmission as outlined further on.
2. Remove clutch release bearing from release fork.

3. Remove clutch fork tension spring from fork.
4. Disconnect clutch fork push rod.
5. Remove clutch fork by forcing it forward and toward center of vehicle.
6. Install a suitable clutch pilot tool or a spare clutch shaft to support clutch assembly during removal.
7. Loosen clutch attaching bolts one turn at a time until diaphragm spring is released.
8. Remove clutch pilot tool and take clutch assembly from vehicle.

Disassemble

1. Remove three drive strap-to-pressure plate bolts and retracting springs and remove pressure plate from clutch cover. *When disassembling, note position of grooves on edge of pressure plate and cover. These marks must be aligned at assembly to maintain balance.*
2. The diaphragm spring and two pivot rings are riveted to the clutch cover. Spring, rings and cover should be inspected for excessive wear or damage and if there is a defect, it is necessary to replace the complete cover assembly.

Inspection

1. Wash all parts except the release bearing in cleaning solvent. *The release bearing is permanently packed with lubricant and should not be soaked in cleaning solvent as this may dissolve the lubricant.*
2. Inspect pressure plate and flywheel for scores on contact surfaces.
3. Check drive-straps for looseness at the clutch cover rivets and evidence of looseness at pressure plate bolt holes.
4. Check release bearing for roughness and free fit on sleeve of clutch shaft bearing retainer.
5. Inspect clutch disc for worn, loose or oil soaked facings, broken springs, loose rivets or riding.
6. Examine splines in hub and make sure they slide freely on splines of clutch shaft. If splines are worn, clutch disc or clutch shaft should be replaced as necessary.

Assemble

1. Install pressure plate in cover, lining up groove on edge of pressure plate with groove on edge of cover.
2. Install pressure plate retracting springs and drive strap-to-pressure plate bolts and lockwashers. Tighten to 11 lb. ft. torque. The clutch is now ready to be installed.

Installation

1. Install clutch disc, pressure plate and cover assembly, and support them with clutch pilot tool or spare clutch shaft.
2. Turn clutch assembly until mark on cover flange lines up with mark on flywheel. Align nearest bolt holes in clutch and in flywheel.
3. Install attaching bolts and tighten each one a turn at a time to prevent distorting the cover as the spring pressure is taken up.

4. Remove clutch pilot tool.
5. Pack clutch fork ball seat with a small amount of high melting point grease.
6. Install fork on ball in clutch housing.
7. Lubricate recess on inside of release bearing collar and coat release fork groove with a small amount of graphite grease.
8. Install release bearing assembly to the fork and hook up linkage.
9. Install transmission.

TRANSMISSION, REPLACE

1958-61

1. Remove propeller shaft assembly.
2. Disconnect speedometer cable.
3. Disconnect gearshift linkage.
4. On 1961, support rear of engine with jack. Then remove two transmission bracket-to-crossmember retaining nuts.
5. Remove upper transmission-to-clutch housing bolts and install aligning studs in these holes.
6. Remove lower bolts and remove transmission.
7. Reverse removal procedure to install transmission.

1953-57

Before removing the transmission on 1955-57 models, the back-up lamp switch wires must be disconnected.

1. Disconnect speedometer cable, gearshift selector rod and control rod from transmission.
2. Disconnect rear universal joint, using a wire or rubber band to prevent trunnions from slipping off universal joint spider.
3. Remove propeller shaft by sliding it to the rear off the transmission mainshaft spline.
4. Remove transmission shifter lever spring yoke and extension to obtain working clearance when removing upper capscrew holding transmission to clutch housing. To avoid damage to shifter levers on shaft inside of transmission, remove shifter lever screw while holding shifter lever in neutral (center position). Then take off the shift lever.
5. Remove the transmission upper capscrews and install two transmission guide pins. These pins can be made by cutting the heads off two transmission capscrews and sawing a screwdriver slot in the ends.
6. Remove lower capscrews and move transmission to the rear.
7. Bring the rear bearing extension into the intersection of the frame "X" members until main drive gear is free.
8. Lower transmission to floor.

TRANSMISSION REPAIRS

1953-55, Fig. 1

1. Remove external shift parts and take off cover.
2. Unfasten rear bearing retainer and withdraw mainshaft assembly.
3. Remove internal shifter parts.

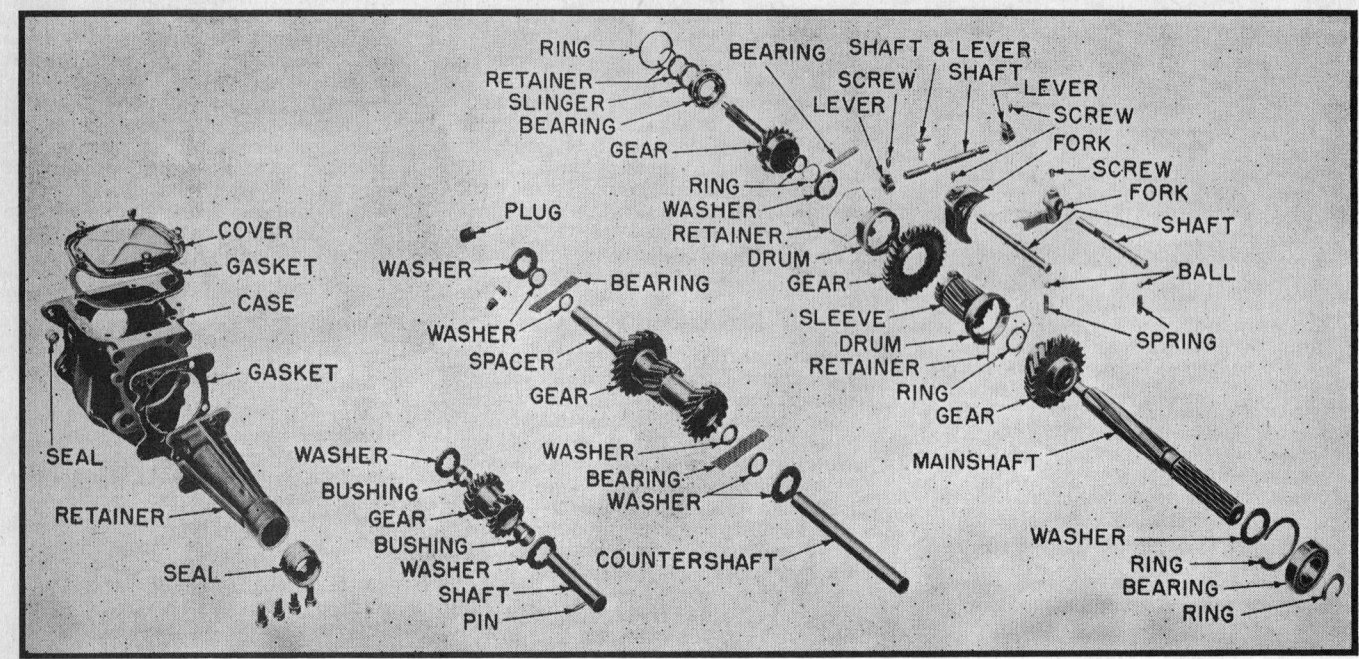

Fig. 1 Exploded view of 1953-55 synchromesh transmission

4. Drive countershaft out through rear, allowing cluster gear to lie in case.

5. Release snap ring and push main drive gear into case and lift out.

6. Remove cluster gear, Fig. 2.

7. Drive in the retaining pin, push out reverse idler shaft and lift out gear.

8. To disassemble mainshaft, expand wire retainer and slide second speed drum from shaft. Release snap ring and thrust washer and slide off second speed gear.

9. To disassemble the main drive gear, expand wire retainer and remove synchronizing drum. Release snap ring and washer and bump the shaft of a wooden block to remove bearing.

NOTE—The main drive gear shaft, Fig. 3, is undercut to accommodate the main drive gear oil seal. An oil slinger is installed next to the transmission front bearing and held in place by a spring washer and snap ring. When the transmission is installed, the oil slinger extends over the flared end of the clutch release bearing support.

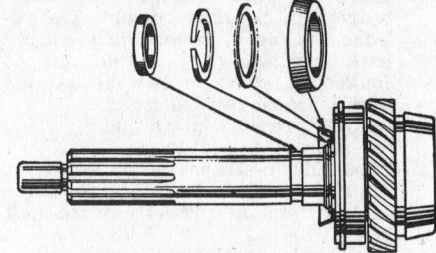

Fig. 3 Oil seal and slinger on synchromesh transmission main drive gear, 1953-55

Assembly Notes — When replacing the main drive gear bearing, make sure that the shielded side is placed toward the gear. Press the bearing firmly in place, using a tube placed over the gear shaft and pressing on the inner race of the bearing.

Make sure that the high and second speed clutch slides freely on the mainshaft. The synchronizing drums must be smooth and free from scores. They must also show the heaviest contact on their large diameters for best results when synchronizing. Make sure that the oil grooves are cleaned.

To assemble the countergear, insert a dummy shaft in place of the regular countershaft and insert 25 needle rollers at each end of the gear, Fig. 4, after using a liberal supply of vaseline or lubriplate to hold them in position. Coat the bearing retainers and thrust washers with lubricant and position them at each end of the cluster.

Lay the countergear assembly in the bottom of the case until the main drive gear is installed. When this has been done, position the cluster gear assembly and install the countershaft from the rear of the case, pushing the dummy shaft out through the front. Align the

slots in the case and the shaft and insert the lock ball before driving the countershaft to its final position.

On models prior to 1955 installing the idler shaft pin, its outer end should be ¾" from the outside of the transmission case. On 1955, the reverse idler gear shaft is retained by a set screw which also acts as a support for the selector shaft shift lever spring support.

1956-57, Fig. 5

1. Thoroughly clean all dirt from exterior of transmission to avoid getting dirt into bearings when transmission is opened.

2. Remove transmission cover and gasket, toggle spring, spring clip and spring extension.

3. Remove speedometer driven gear, then remove rear bearing retainer and gasket.

4. Place transmission in second gear, move mainshaft back until rear bearing is clear of case, and disengage shift yoke from synchronizer.

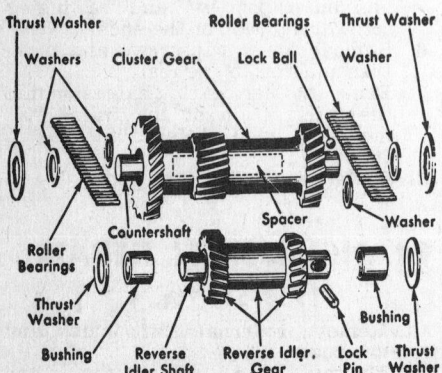

Fig. 2 Synchromesh transmission cluster gear and reverse idler gear details, 1953-55

Fig. 4 Assembling countershaft rollers on synchromesh transmission, 1953-55

Then lift front end of mainshaft enough to remove synchronizer from shaft. Note that the counterbored end of the synchronizer must face the second speed gear when replaced.

5. Remove snap ring holding second speed gear to mainshaft. Remove thrust washer after lining up small wire spacer installed in bottom of snap ring groove with thrust washer key, then remove second speed gear from mainshaft.

6. Remove snap ring holding low and reverse gear to mainshaft.

7. Slide low and reverse gear off mainshaft while pulling shaft out through rear of transmission case.

8. Place transmission levers in neutral and remove set screws holding shifter yokes and levers to their respective shafts. *Each yoke shaft is in neutral position when the notch for the shifter lever is directly above the selector shaft.*

9. Slide shift lever and interlock away from second and high yoke shaft, then remove interlock retainer from groove in right end of selector shaft.

10. Remove outer shift lever and lock washer from left end of selector shaft and, after making sure transmission is still in neutral, depress inner selector lever and drive the shaft out through the right side of the transmission, using a soft hammer. *The welch plug in right side of case will be driven out by the shaft. Do not allow shift levers and interlock to drop into case.*

11. Push second and high speed yoke shaft out through front of case, taking care to prevent poppet ball and spring from flying out. Remove shift yoke, ball and spring.

12. Taking care to prevent poppet ball and spring from flying out, push low and reverse yoke shaft out through rear of case. Remove poppet ball, spring and low and reverse interlock pin.

13. Drive countershaft lock pin into the shaft, then drive shaft out through rear end of case, using a suitable tool to hold needle bearings and washers in place. Allow cluster gear to rest on bottom of case.

14. Remove snap ring from main drive gear bearing and tap drive gear and bearing toward rear of transmission to remove.

15. Carefully raise cluster gear out of case so that related parts remain in gear.

16. Remove transmission outer selector lever, lock washer and nut; then remove inner lever and shaft, spring washer, flat washer, and oil seal from case.

17. Drive reverse idler gear shaft lock pin into the shaft, then remove shaft, gear and thrust washers.

Assembly Notes

Reverse the order of the foregoing procedure to assemble the transmission, observing the following:

Install the reverse idler gear so that the chamfered teeth are at the rear of the case. The idler gear shaft is ground slightly larger at one end in order to form a positive seal at the rear end of

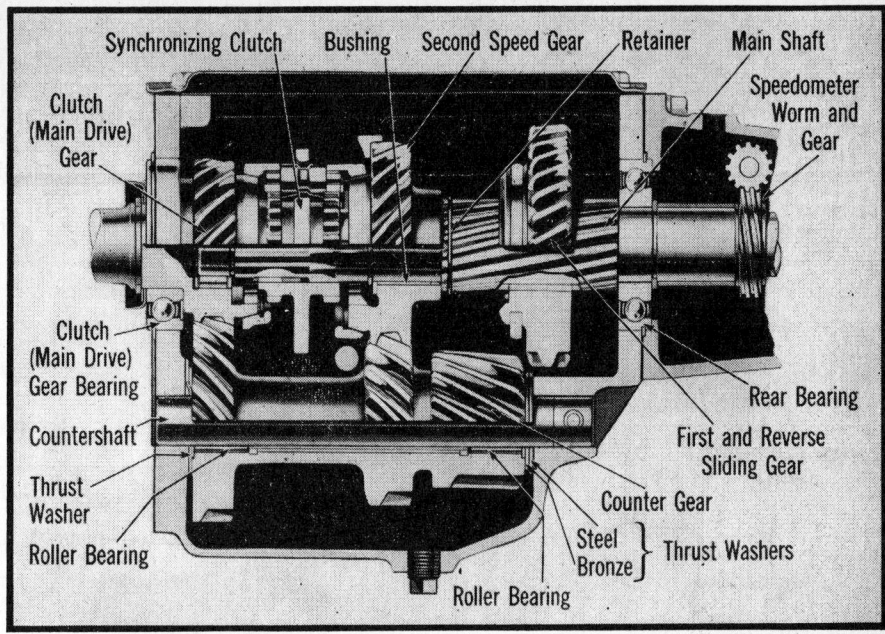

Fig. 5 Section through 1956 transmission. The 1957 transmission is similar but a steel thrust washer has been added to the rear of the mainshaft second speed gear and is retained by a snap ring

the transmission case. Make sure that this end of the shaft is at the rear when replaced and that the small hole in the opposite end lines up with the lock pin hole in the case. Install a new lock pin coated with white lead or other sealing compound to prevent leaks. Drive lock pin 1″ below surface of boss on case.

When installing the cluster gear and related parts, note that a small diameter bronze washer and a steel washer are used at the rear of the gear (bronze washer next to gear) and a larger bronze washer (only) is used at the front. When countershaft is installed, install a new lock pin coated with white lead or other suitable sealing compound to prevent leaks. Drive pin flush with surface of transmission case.

After shift yoke shafts are installed, install a new welch plug coated with white lead or other sealing compound in right side of transmission case.

After installing second speed gear on mainshaft and, after lining up the small wire spacer ring in bottom of mainshaft snap ring groove with spline which is machined *part way* onto the ground second speed gear bearing surface, install second speed gear thrust washer and snap ring. Note that one spline is machined the entire length of the second speed gear bearing surface on the mainshaft. This full spline is for lubrication purposes and should not be obstructed by the thrust washer key.

the main drive gear and bearing.

3. Remove 24 roller rear pilot bearings, 2 washers and 14 roller front bearings.

4. Unfasten extension housing from transmission case and pull extension and mainshaft out of transmission case, leaving the synchronizer and first and reverse gear in case.

5. Remove synchronizer clutch sleeve and first and reverse gear through side opening in case.

6. Remove countershaft by driving it from front to rear of case, using a soft steel drift. Remove the countergear rollers and thrust washers.

7. Remove the countergear.

8. Drive the idler shaft lock pin into the shaft. This pin is shorter than the diameter of the shaft so the shaft may be slipped out when the pin is driven in.

9. Using a drift pin, tap rear of idler shaft to drive out plug ahead of shaft. Do not turn the shaft while removing as the lock pin may drop down between the idler gear bushings.

10. Remove reverse idler gear and thrust washers.

11. To remove the mainshaft from the extension, expand the bearing snap ring and tap the rear of the shaft with a soft hammer to bring the shaft, speedometer drive gear, second speed gear and bearing out of the extension as an assembly.

Mainshaft, Disassemble

1. Press speedometer gear off mainshaft, using suitable split plates in an arbor press.

2. Remove bearing-to-mainshaft snap ring and press bearing off shaft.

3. Remove second speed gear thrust washer, pull drive pin out of shaft and remove second speed gear.

3 SPEED STD. TRANS.

1958-61

Disassemble, Fig. 6

1. Remove side cover and gasket.

2. Remove main drive gear bearing retainer and, with the puller remove

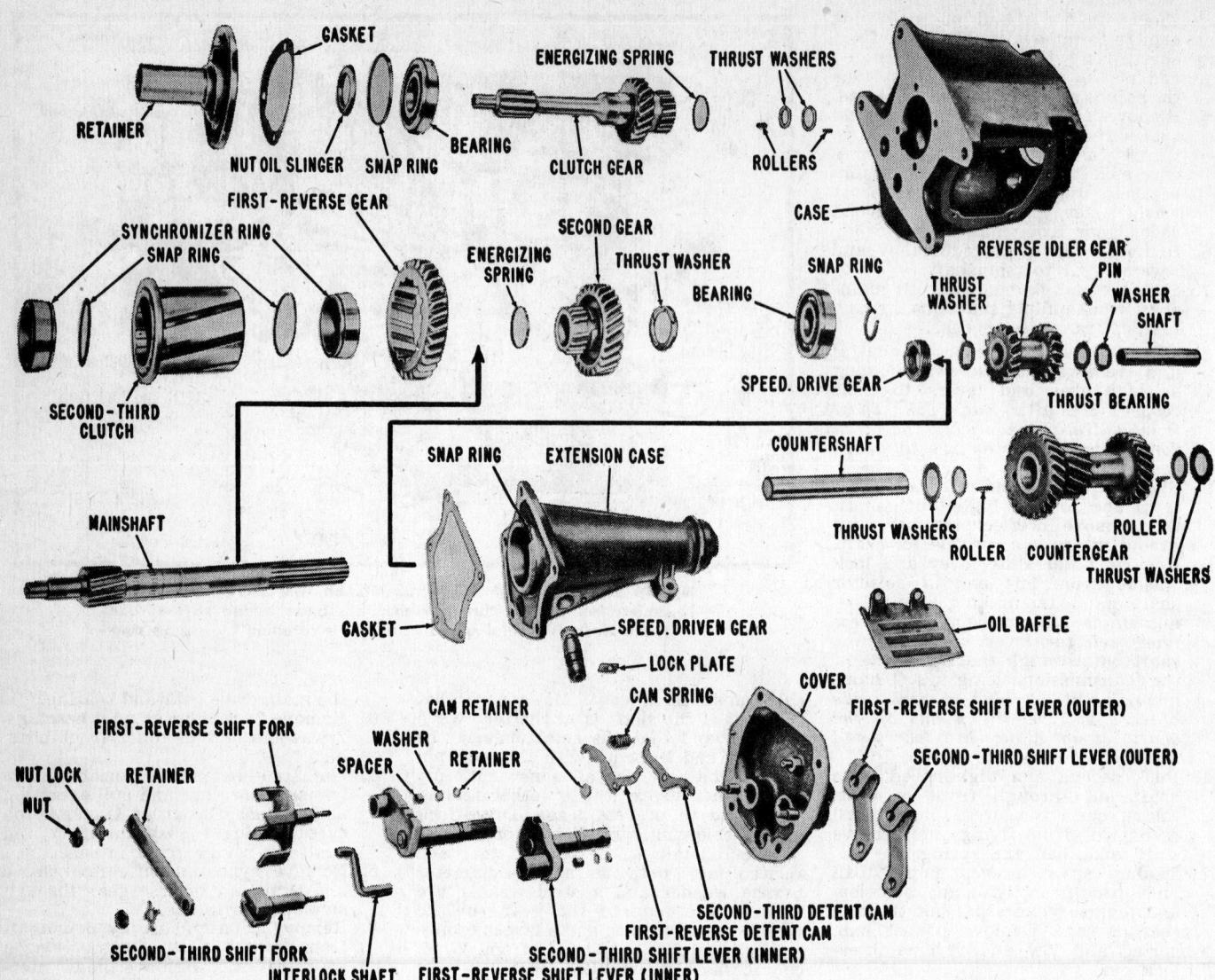

Fig. 6   Three speed standard manual shift transmission.   1958-61

Mainshaft, Assemble

1. Slide second speed gear on mainshaft, insert drive pin in shaft and install thrust washer against gear.
2. Install new bearing with groove in outside diameter of bearing toward second speed gear.
3. Select one of four available snap rings so end play of bearing on shaft is a maximum of .004". This may be determined by installing successively larger rings. Use the thickest ring that will enter snap ring groove on shaft.
4. Start speedometer drive gear on shaft with chamfered inside diameter of gear toward bearing. Press gear on shaft so forward face of gear is ⅞" from rear face of bearing.

Assembly Details

Inspect all gears for wear or damage, and see that the first and reverse sliding gear and the clutch sleeve slide freely on the mainshaft. See that the synchronizing cones are not loose in the clutch sleeve. If the cones are damaged, it will be necessary to replace the clutch sleeve assembly and both synchronizing rings.

See that the synchronizer rings are smooth and that they do not rock in the cones. Excessive rocking affects proper synchronizing of the gears during shifting.

Normally, it should not be necessary to replace the energizing springs. However, should this be necessary, the spring is assembled in its groove with its offset end between the fourth and fifth clutch teeth of either bank of teeth. This will prevent the spring from turning in its groove.

Check the countershaft bushings for excessive wear by using a narrow feeler gauge between the shaft and the bushings. The proper clearance should be from .002" to .004".

When installing the reverse idler, the chamfered teeth should be placed to the rear of the case. Install the idler shaft, making sure that the lock pin hole in the shaft lines up with the hole in the case at the same angle. It is well to line up these holes with a punch before installing the lock pin. Use a new lock pin and drive it in about 1/16" beyond flush with the case, and peen the hole slightly.

When installing the countershaft, the step on the forward end should be flush with the front face of the case, or about 1/64" below the face, to maintain proper transmission alignment.

When installing the mainshaft, the proper seating of the shoulder on the shaft against the inner race of the mainshaft rear bearing should permit .010" end play of the second speed gear.

When the assembly has been completed, check the transmission in all gears to be sure that there is no indication of binding in any position.

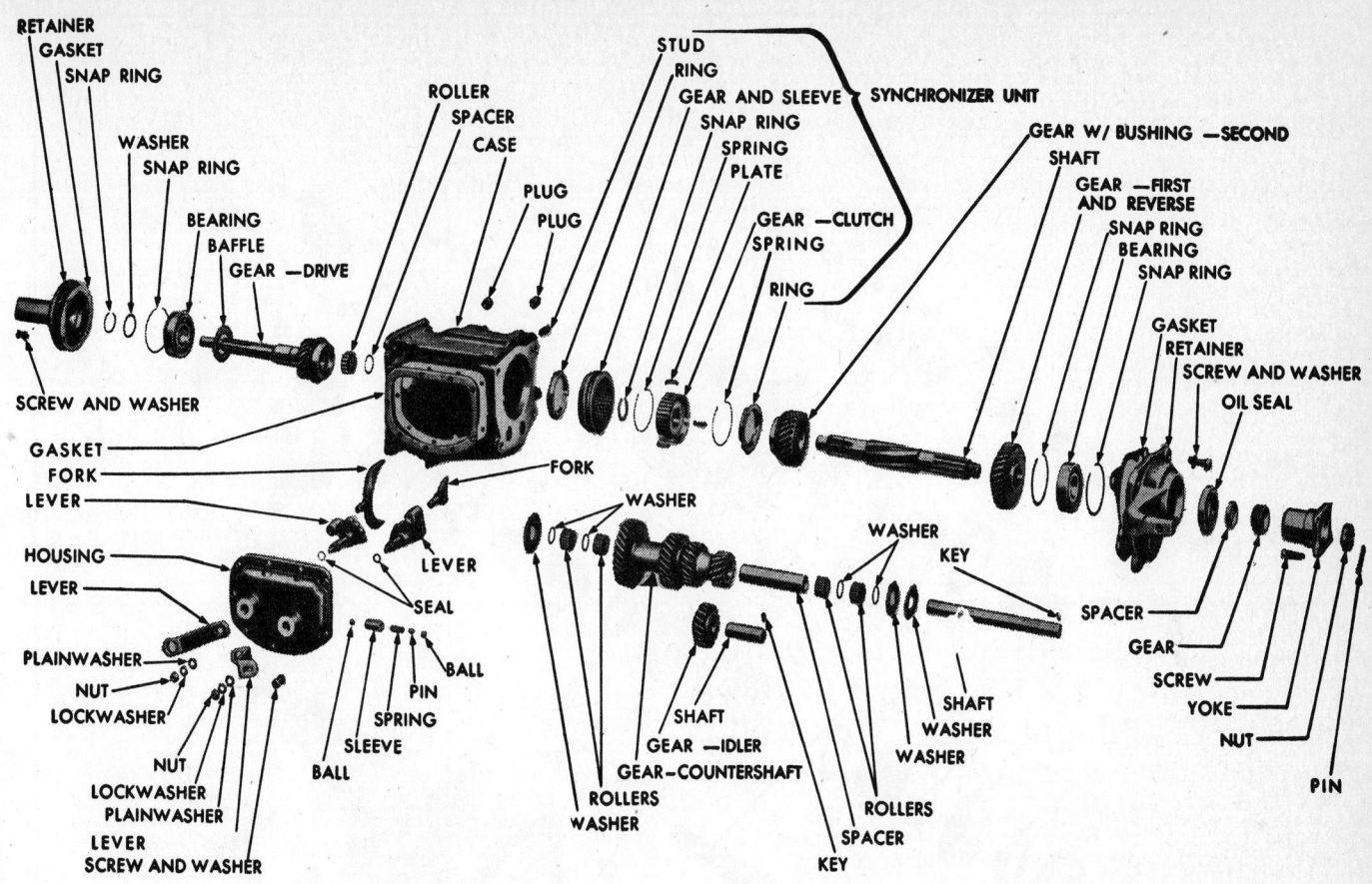

Fig. 7 Three speed heavy duty transmission, 1958-60. For 1961 a long extension housing is used at rear of transmission case

3 SPEED HEAVY DUTY TRANS.

1958-61, Fig. 7

1. To disassemble, remove side cover.
2. On 1961, remove clamp, bracket and insulator from rear extension. Unfasten and move extension away from case about ½" to expose countershaft and lock key.
3. On 1958-60, remove mainshaft nut, yoke, speedometer drive gear and spacer. Unfasten and move rear bearing retainer away from transmission about ½" to expose countershaft and lock key.
4. On all models, from front of case, drive countershaft to rear. When lock key in countershaft clears case, remove key to permit countershaft to clear rear bearing retainer. Drive countershaft all the way out.
5. Allow countershaft gear to drop into case and then remove rear bearing retainer or extension housing, and mainshaft assembly from case.
6. Remove pilot rollers from inside main drive gear and bearing spacing washer from front end of mainshaft.
7. Remove main drive gear bearing retainer. Remove bearing snap ring and washer from main drive gear. Drive main drive gear out of bearing. Then tap main drive gear out through front of case.
8. Remove reverse idler gear.
9. Lift out countershaft gear and related parts.
10. Remove synchronizer from mainshaft and strip parts from mainshaft.

Assemble

1. Position reverse idler gear in case with chamfered teeth ends toward front and install shaft from rear of case, aligning keyway for installation.
2. Assemble parts in countershaft gear. Place small amount of grease on thrust washers to hold them in place during installation. Install tang on front thrust washer to fit into slot in case thrust face. The tab on rear steel washer must be up.
3. Install main drive gear bearing and snap ring in case from front until snap ring bottoms on case.
4. Install drive gear retainer without a gasket and finger tighten retainer bolts. Install oil slinger on drive gear shaft with small amount of grease with dished side away from pinion bearing.
5. Install main drive gear with oil slinger in case and drive shaft into bearing.
6. Remove drive gear bearing retainer and install spacer washer and thickest snap ring that will fit.
7. Tap pinion shaft and bearing forward out of case as far as gear will allow. Install pilot rollers in drive gear pocket, using grease to hold rollers in place.
8. Install synchronizer stop ring on rear end of drive pinion shaft. Coat inside of stop ring with grease.
9. Press rear bearing on mainshaft. Install snap ring into rear bearing retainer or extension housing and tap mainshaft and bearing into retainer.
10. Assemble parts on mainshaft and install assembly in case.
11. Tap main drive gear to rear until snap ring seats on case.
12. Turn transmission to help align countershaft and install countershaft. When countershaft end is close to case, install lock key and drive into case.
13. Turn rear bearing retainer into position and bolt securely.
14. Check clearance between main drive gear bearing retainer and case. Then select gasket or gaskets that will seal lubricant and prevent end play between bearing snap ring and retainer.
15. Complete assembly and shift transmission into neutral and install side cover.

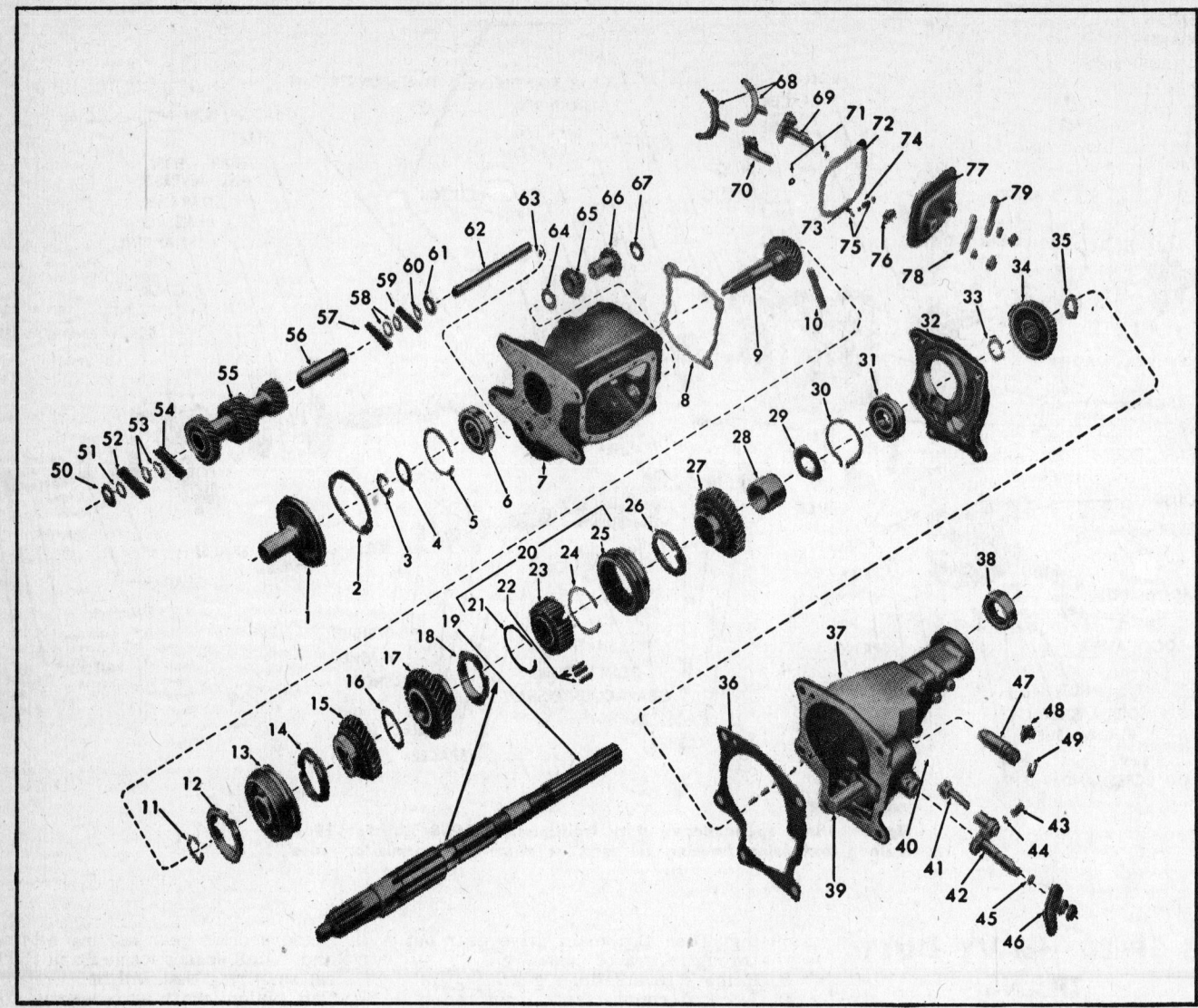

Fig. 8 Four speed manual shift transmission. 1960-61

1. Bearing Retainer
2. Gasket
3. Selective Fit Snap Ring
4. Spacer Washer
5. Bearing Snap Ring
6. Main Drive Gear Bearing
7. Transmission Case
8. Rear Bearing Retainer Gasket
9. Main Drive Gear
10. Bearing Rollers (14)
11. Snap Ring (.086" to .088")
12. Fourth Speed Gear Synchronizing Ring
13. Third and Fourth Speed Clutch Sliding Sleeve
14. Third Speed Synchronizing Ring
15. Third Speed Gear
16. Second and Third Speed Gear Thrust Washer (Needle Roller Bearing)
17. Second Speed Gear
18. Second Speed Gear Synchronizing Ring
19. Mainshaft

20. First and Second Speed Clutch Assembly
21. Clutch Key Spring
22. Clutch Keyes
23. Clutch Hub
24. Clutch Key Spring
25. First and Second Speed Clutch Sliding Sleeve
26. First Speed Gear Synchronizing Ring
27. First Speed Gear
28. First Speed Gear Bushing
29. First Speed Gear Thrust Washer
30. Rear Bearing Snap Ring
31. Rear Bearing
32. Rear Bearing Retainer
33. Selective Fit Snap Ring
34. Reverse Gear
35. Speedometer Drive Gear
36. Rear Bearing Retainer to Case Extension Gasket
37. Case Extension
38. Rear Oil Seal
39. Reverse Idler Shaft
40. Reverse Shifter Shaft Lock Pin

41. Reverse Shift Fork
42. Reverse Shifter Shaft and Detent Plate
43. Reverse Shifter Shaft Ball Detent Spring
44. Reverse Shifter Shaft Detent Ball
45. Reverse Shifter Shaft "O" Ring Seal
46. Reverse Shifter Lever
47. Speedometer Driven Gear and Fitting
48. Retainer and Bolt
49. "O" Ring Seal
50. Tanged Washer
51. Spacer (.050")
52. Bearing Rollers (20)
53. Spacers (2—.050")
54. Bearing Rollers (20)
55. Countergear
56. Countergear Roller Spacer
57. Bearing Rollers (20)
58. Spacers (2—.050")
59. Bearing Rollers (20)
60. Spacer (.050")
61. Tanged Washer
62. Countershaft

63. Countershaft Woodruff Key
64. Reverse Idler Front Thrust Washer (Flat)
65. Reverse Idler Gear (Front)
66. Reverse Idler Gear (Rear)
67. Tanged Thrust Washer
68. Forward Speed Shift Forks
69. First and Second Speed Gear Shifter Shaft and Detent Plate
70. Third and Fourth Speed Gear Shifter Shaft and Detent Plate
71. "O" Ring Seals
72. Gasket
73. Interlock Pin
74. Poppet Spring
75. Detent Balls
76. Interlock Sleeve
77. Transmission Side Cover
78. Third and Fourth Speed Shifter Lever
79. First and Second Speed Shifter Lever

FOUR SPEED TRANS.

1960-61, Fig. 8

1. To disassemble, remove side cover.
2. Remove front bearing retainer.
3. Drive lock pin from bottom side of reverse shifter lever boss and pull shifter out about ⅛". This disengages reverse shift fork from reverse gear.
4. Unfasten case extension from rear bearing retainer (5 bolts). Tap extension to rear. When reverse idler shaft is out as far as it will go, move extension to left so reverse fork clears reverse gear and remove extension.
5. Remove snap ring from end of mainshaft. Remove speedometer gear, reverse idler gear, tanged thrust washer and reverse gear.
6. Remove self-locking bolt attaching rear bearing retainer to case. Then remove mainshaft assembly.
7. Lift front reverse idler gear and thrust washer fom case.
8. Remove pilot rollers from main drive gear and 4th speed synchronizing ring.
9. Remove main drive gear snap ring and spacer washer. Tap drive gear from front bearing. From inside case, tap out front bearing and snap ring.
10. From front of case, tap out countershaft and remove countershaft gear and thrust washers.
11. Strip mainshaft of all parts.

Assemble

Mainshaft

1. From rear of mainshaft, assemble 1st-2nd clutch to mainshaft with sleeve taper toward rear and hub to front. Press 1st gear bushing on shaft.
2. Install 1st gear synchronizing ring so notches in ring correspond to keys in hub.
3. Install 1st gear with hub to front, and thrust washer. Make sure that grooves in washer are facing 1st gear.
4. Press rear bearing with snap ring groove toward front, making certain bearing is firmly seated against shoulder on mainshaft.
5. Choose correct selective fit snap ring and install it in mainshaft groove behind rear bearing. Snap rings are available in three thicknesses; use ring that will produce from zero to .005" clearance between rear face of bearing and front face of snap ring.
6. From front of mainshaft, install 2nd gear synchronizing ring so notches in ring correspond to keys in hub. Install 2nd speed gear with hub toward rear, and install 2nd-3rd gear thrust (bearing) washer.
7. Install 3rd gear with hub to front and 3rd gear synchronizing ring with notches to front.
8. Install 3rd-4th gear clutch (hub and sliding sleeve) with taper toward front, making sure that keys in hub correspond to notches in 3rd gear synchronizing ring. Install snap ring in mainshaft groove in front of clutch.

9. Install rear bearing retainer plate. Spread snap ring on plate to allow it to drop around rear bearing and press on end of mainshaft until snap ring engages groove in rear bearing.
10. Install reverse gear with shift collar to rear.
12. Press speedometer gear on mainshaft so it is 4½" from center of gear to flat surface of rear bearing retainer. Install snap ring in groove at rear of mainshaft.

Countershaft Gear

1. Install spacer in countergear.
2. Using grease to retain rollers, install 20 rollers in each end of gear, two .050" spacers, 20 more rollers, then one .050" spacer. Insert dummy shaft to hold parts in place during installation.

Transmission, Assemble

1. Place countershaft tanged thrust washers in place, retaining them with grease and being sure that tangs are resting in notches in case. Set counter gear in bottom of case.
2. Press bearing onto main drive gear with snap ring groove to front and firmly seat bearing against shoulder of main drive gear.
3. Install spacer washer and selective fit snap ring in groove on gear stem. Use ring that will provide zero to .005" clearance between rear face of snap ring and front face of spacer washer.
4. Install main drive gear through side cover opening. Place snap ring in groove in front bearing.
5. With transmission resting on its front face, move countergear into mesh with main drive gear, being sure thrust washers are in place. Install key in end of countershaft and, from front of case, tap shaft until its end is flush with rear of case and dummy shaft is displaced. End play of countergear should be not more than .025".
6. Install 14 pilot rollers in main drive gear pocket, using grease to hold them in place.
7. Place a greased gasket on front face of rear bearing retainer.
8. Install 4th gear synchronizing ring on main drive gear with clutch key notches toward rear.
9. Position reverse idler gear thrust washer (untanged) on machined face of ear cast in case for reverse idler shaft. Position front reverse idler gear on top of thrust washer with hub facing rear of case.
10. Lower mainshaft assembly into case, making certain that notches on 4th gear synchronizing ring correspond to keys in clutch assembly.
11. Install self-locking bolt attaching rear bearing retainer to case, tightening it to 20-30 ft. lbs.
12. From rear of case, insert rear reverse idler gear, engaging splines with portion of gear within case.
13. Place greased gasket on rear face of rear bearing retainer.
14. Install remaining tanged thrust washer on reverse idler shaft, being sure tang is in notch in idler thrust face of extension case.
15. Place two clutches in neutral.
16. Full reverse shifter shaft to left side

of extension and rotate shaft to bring reverse shift fork to extreme forward position in extension. Line up forward and rear reverse idler gears, being sure front thrust washer is in place.
17. Start extension into transmission case by carefully inserting reverse idler shaft through reverse idler gears. Slowly push it on shifter shaft until shift fork engages reverse gear shift collar. When fork engages, rotate shifter shaft to move reverse gear rearward, permitting extension to slide onto case.
18. Install 3 extension-to-case bolts, tightening to 35-45 ft. lbs. and 2 extension-to-retainer bolts, tightening to 20-30 ft. lbs. Use suitable sealer on lower right attaching bolt (viewed from rear).
19. Adjust reverse shifter shaft so that groove in shaft lines up with hole in boss and drive in lock pin from top of boss.
20. Install main drive gear bearing retainer and gasket, making certain oil well lines up with oil outlet hole. Install bolts with suitable sealer and tighten to 15-20 ft. lbs.
21. Install a shift fork in each clutch sleeve. With both clutches in neutral, install side cover and gasket. Tighten cover bolts evenly to 10-20 ft. lbs. torque. Use suitable sealer when installing lower right bolt. Install shift levers.

GEARSHIFT, ADJUST

For Standard Trans.

1953-57

Proper position of the gearshift lever is obtained by means of the clevis pin and trunnion which connect the gearshift control rod and selector rod, respectively, to levers at the lower end of the steering column.

When the gearshift lever is in neutral position, clearance between the lever and steering wheel should be approximately 3 7/16" (3½" on 1955, 3¼" on 1956-57). To adjust, hold the transmission selector rod in its rearmost position (normal position for 2nd and 3rd) and adjust the selector rod trunnion for proper gearshift lever position. Lengthen selector rod to move lever closer to steering wheel.

Neutral position of the gearshift lever should be approximately 9 degrees above horizontal (13 degrees on 1956-57). To raise or lower the lever, adjust the length of the control rod by adjusting the clevis.

1958

Proper gearshift lever position is obtained by means of the shifter levers which connect respectively to the gearshift control rods.

1. Set both lower steering column shifter levers in the neutral position and both transmission shifter levers in neutral detent position.
2. Adjust shifter rods by adjustment provided at shifter rod swivels until the shift lever at the steering wheel is approximately 13 degrees above the horizontal.

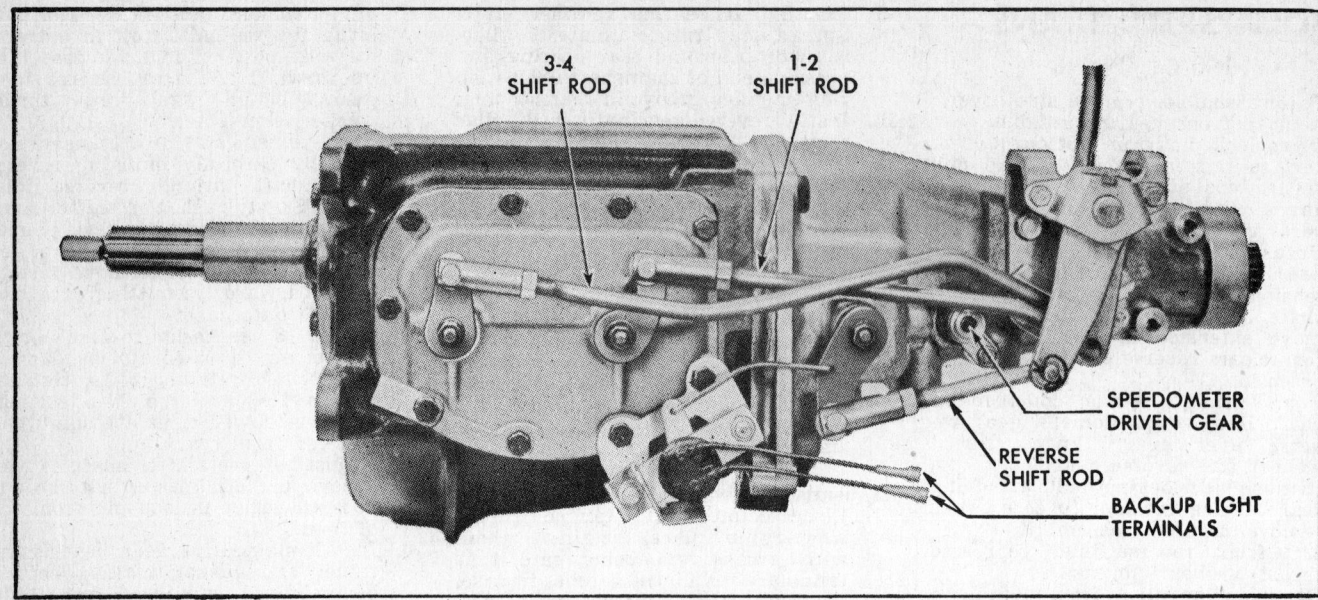

Fig. 9 Four speed manual shift transmission gearshift linkage. 1960-61

1959

With shifter levers in neutral position and transmission shifter levers in neutral detent, adjust rods by adjusting nuts as required at both sides of trunnion.

Check movement of gearshift lever in neutral. A slight readjustment may be necessary due to the weight of the upper gearshift rotating the gearshift tube through the clearances in the linkage.

1960

This adjustment must be made so that both levers are located in the true neutral position in the window of the mast jacket. A special gauge (J-8638) is available to make the adjustment properly.

Insert the gauge between 2-3 shift lever and key to place tangs of both 2-3 and 1-Rev. levers in key slots and locate both levers in neutral position in window of mast jacket. With gauge in place and transmission levers in full neutral detent, adjust 2-3 shifter rod trunnion at idler lever and 1-Rev. trunnion at transmission lever.

1961 Three Speed Trans.

1. Position selector lever in neutral.

2. Disconnect shift rods at transmission.
3. Line up 2nd-3rd and 1st-reverse levers at lower end of steering column so they move freely back and forth (this is neutral position).
4. Attach shift rods to transmission levers and, with transmission levers in full neutral detent, adjust 2nd-3rd shifter rod trunnion at idler lever and 1st-reverse trunnion at transmission lever. Tighten lock nuts to 5-10 inch lbs.

1960-61 Four Speed Trans.

As shown in Fig. 10, a simple gauge block, locally made to the specifications indicated, will aid in making the proper adjustments. The adjustments can be made without the gauge block by having an assistant hold the manual shift lever in neutral position.

1. Referring to Figs. 9 and 10, remove move gearshift lever seal from floor pan.
2. Place transmission in neutral and, if gauge block is used, position in slot.
3. Remove clevis pin at each shift lever.
4. On each shift rod, adjust threaded clevis to permit free entry of pin into hole in transmission shift lever.
5. Connect clevises to levers.
6. Remove gauge block and check shifts. If any roughness exists, one of the clevises may require adjustment of about ½ turn. Determine the rod and clevis requiring adjustment by sighting along the slot where the gauge block was used. *If transmission is removed from car, shift linkage should be adjusted before transmission is reinstalled.*

HYDRA-MATIC DRIVE

A step-by-step pictorial service procedure is given in the *Automatic Transmission Section.* The following material

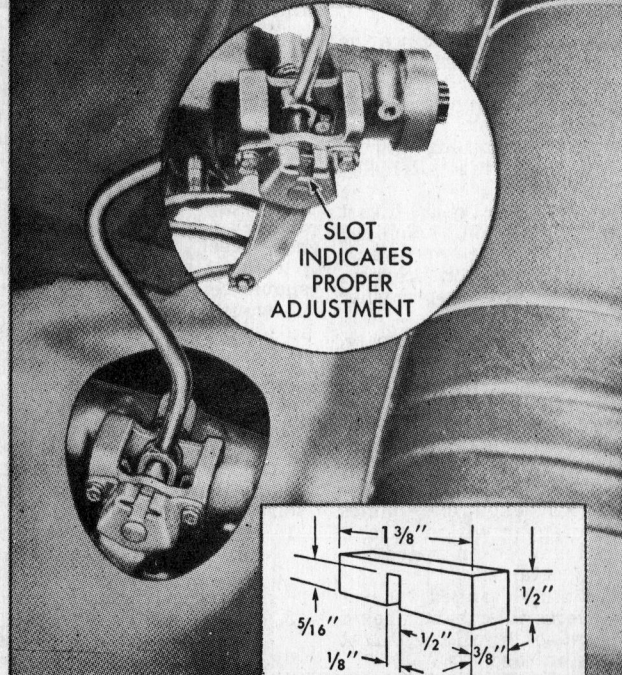

Fig. 10 Four speed manual shift transmission gearshift linkage adjustments. 1960-61

**Fig. 11 Adjusting pin installed at "A".
1953-54 Six Hydramatic**

covers external adjustments and removing and installing the unit.

1953-54 ADJUSTMENTS

Throttle Control Linkage

Linkage operations will not be satisfactory if binding or excessive wear exists. Take corrective measures and then adjust as follows:

1. Remove cotter pin and washers from trunnion on transmission throttle (rear) rod at transmission throttle control outer lever.
2. Adjust engine idle speed to 365-385 RPM with engine temperature 150-160 degrees, transmission warm and control lever in neutral.
3. Install linkage adjustment gauge pin through holes in lever and bracket at "A", Figs. 11 and 12.
4. With idle screw seated against its stop, adjust length of carburetor throttle rod (at carburetor rod lock nuts) so that adjustment gauge pin is free in hole "A". Leave pin installed. Tighten lock nuts securely.
5. Install second linkage adjustment gauge pin through transmission throttle rod idler lever and bracket in hole marked "B", Fig. 13.
6. If pin does not enter hole "B" freely, adjust transmission front rod at trunnion. Tighten lock nuts securely.
7. Check the position of the transmission throttle lever to see if it is bent. If necessary, bend the lever to establish the correct location of the lever as outlined in the Hydra-Matic chapter.
8. With transmission throttle lever toward rear, lightly against stop in transmission, adjust rear transmission throttle rod to length by moving check nuts. Shorten rod length by turning check nuts one full forward. Lock check nuts securely.

9. Install spring washer, flat washer, and cotter key in transmission rear throttle rod trunnion.

Selector Lever Linkage

1. If the gearshift control shaft upper bracket is loose, tighten the clamp screw while holding the selector lever firmly against the stop between the right hand drive position and LO.
2. Place selector lever in right hand drive position (DR▲) which prevents accidental shift to LO.
3. Back off both gearshift control rod trunnion lock nuts.
4. See that transmission outer shift lever is in the three-speed drive position (third position from front or rear).
5. Turn lower trunnion nut against trunnion (finger tight) to remove clearance in linkage. Then lengthen rod by turning rear trunnion one full turn. Tighten upper lock nut securely.

Neutral Safety Switch

Place manual control lever in DR (left arrow) position. Loosen switch bracket clamp screw and adjust bracket to a position where the starter will not operate when the starter button is pressed. Then place manual lever in N and tighten clamp screw.

1955-57 ADJUSTMENTS

1957 Service Note

A new throttle linkage to the carburetor and transmission improves accelerator pedal feel by the use of a throttle control cross shaft. One end of the cross shaft is mounted to a bracket on the rear

**Fig. 12 Adjusting pin installed at "A".
1953-54 Eight Hydramatic**

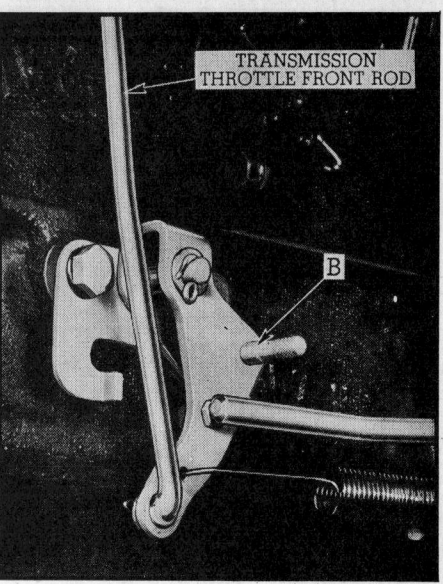

**Fig. 13 Adjusting pin installed at "B".
1953-54 Hydramatic**

of the engine and the other end is mounted to a bracket attached to the dash.

Adjustment of the throttle linkage is basically the same as in 1956. The carburetor throttle rod should be adjusted so that a gauge pin fits freely through the lever and bracket at the rear of the engine.

The accelerator pedal height is set by adjusting the intermediate rod to give not more than $\frac{1}{4}$" clearance between the end of the accelerator pedal lever and the underside of the pedal bellows.

Throttle Control Linkage

1. Loosen both nuts on throttle control transmission rod trunnion.
2. Adjust engine idle speed to the recommended rpm with engine at normal operating temperature.
3. Shut off engine and install a suitable linkage adjustment pin in lever and bracket at "A", Fig. 14.
4. With idle adjusting screw seated, adjust length of carburetor throttle rod at lock nuts so that gauge pin is free in hole "A". Leave pin installed and tighten lock nuts securely. Recheck freeness of gauge pin in holes.
5. Push throttle control transmission rod downward until the throttle control outer lever is felt to touch end of travel. *Make sure when lever is in this position that top lock nut is not touching trunnion.*
6. While holding throttle control transmission rod in this position, tighten upper and lower trunnion lock nuts. Shorten throttle control transmission rod by backing off trunnion rear nut two full turns. Tighten front trunnion nut securely.
7. Remove gauge pin from "A".
8. Loosen lock nuts on throttle control intermediate rod trunnion.
9. With carburetor in "Full Open" position, and downshift return spring fully extended, adjust throttle con-

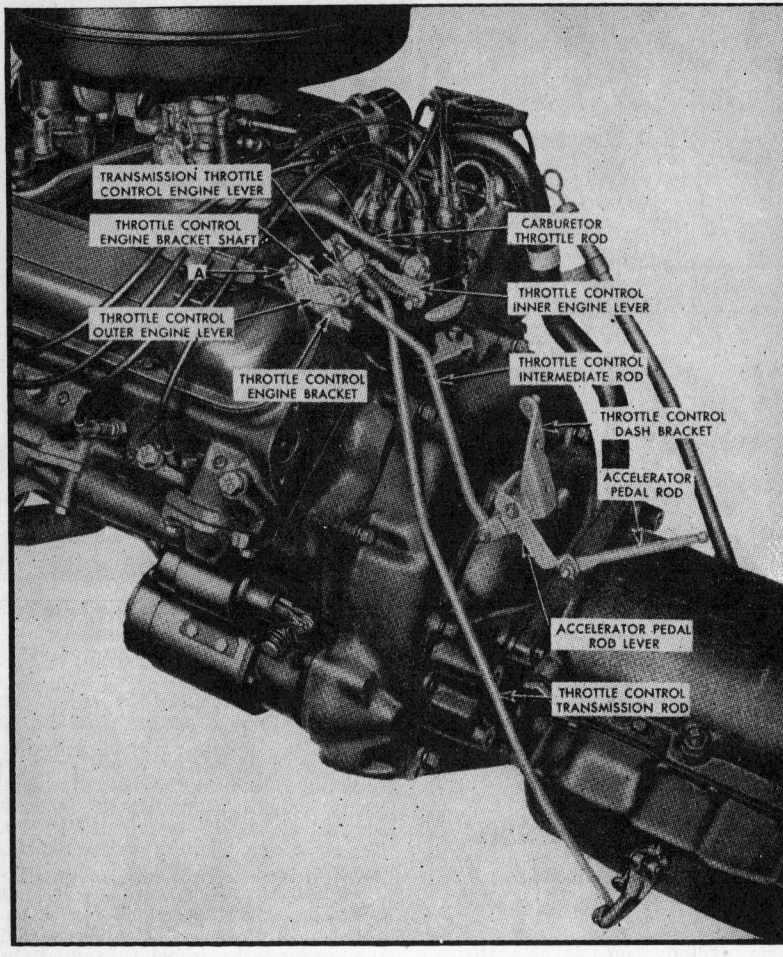

TRANSMISSION THROTTLE CONTROL ENGINE LEVER

THROTTLE CONTROL ENGINE BRACKET SHAFT

THROTTLE CONTROL OUTER ENGINE LEVER

THROTTLE CONTROL ENGINE BRACKET

CARBURETOR THROTTLE ROD

THROTTLE CONTROL INNER ENGINE LEVER

THROTTLE CONTROL INTERMEDIATE ROD

THROTTLE CONTROL DASH BRACKET

ACCELERATOR PEDAL ROD

ACCELERATOR PEDAL ROD LEVER

THROTTLE CONTROL TRANSMISSION ROD

Fig. 14 Hydra-Matic control linkage. 1955-56

trol intermediate rod trunnion so that accelerator pedal clears floor mat by approximately ¼" at closest point. Tighten trunnion lock nuts.

Selector Lever Linkage

1. Place gearshift indicator in "Drive Right" position against stop which prohibits accidental shift into low range.
2. Loosen both trunnion lock nuts and remove trunnion from outer shift lever at transmission.
3. Make sure transmission outer shift lever is in "Drive Right" position (second detent from front). On Strato-Flight Hydramatic, "Drive Right" position is third detent from the front.
4. Install trunnion (with lock nuts loose) in outer shift lever, tighten front lock nut against trunnion finger tight to remove clearance in linkage and then tighten front lock nut one complete turn to lengthen rod.
5. Tighten rear nut against trunnion.

Neutral Safety Switch

1. Place selector lever in "Drive Left".
2. Loosen switch mounting screw.
3. Adjust switch bracket to a position where starter will not operate when ignition key is turned to the start

position.
4. Make certain that switch arm does not touch stop on switch bracket. Then tighten switch mounting screw.

1958 ADJUSTMENTS

Throttle Control Linkage

1. Loosen both nuts at transmission control rod trunnion.
2. After adjusting engine idle speed, shut off engine and install a suitable gauge pin through holes in throttle control lever and bracket.
3. With idle adjusting screw seated against its stop, adjust length of carburetor throttle rod at trunnion so that gauge pin is free in hole. Leave pin installed and tighten check nut securely. Recheck freeness of gauge pin in holes.
4. Push transmission throttle control rod downward until the throttle control outer lever is felt to touch end of travel. Make sure that when lever is in this position, top lock nut is not touching trunnion.
5. While holding throttle control transmission rod in this position, tighten upper and lower trunnion lock nuts. Shorten rod by turning upper nut 1½ turns against trunnion. Tighten both nuts and remove gauge pin.

Selector Lever Linkage

1. Place shift control lever and transmission lever at P (park) position and, with outer transmission shift lever trunnion nuts backed clear of trunnion, pull shift rod down toward transmission as far as possible. While holding in this position, run trunnion upper nut down to just contact trunnion.
2. Holding shift rod, shift transmission into reverse, using upper shift lever, and observe the position of upper trunnion nut.
3. If upper nut is short of trunnion, screw upper nut down to just contact trunnion and then screw it down two additional turns to assure necessary reserve. Tighten lower nut.
4. If upper nut is contacting trunnion, count number of turns nut can be backed off and still contact trunnion. If less than two turns, turn nut down two turns against trunnion from the "just contact" position and lock lower nut. If more than two turns, turn upper nut down against trunnion from the "just contact" position to the original or starting position and lock lower nut.
5. After completing above adjustments, check transmission parking lock with car on ramp or grade for positive lock.
6. The shift indicator must not be off index more than .080" after linkage is properly adjusted.

Neutral Safety Switch

1. Place selector lever in neutral.
2. Loosen switch mounting screws.
3. Adjust neutralizer switch to index with selector lever. Starter must not operate when ignition key is turned to start position with selector lever in "Drive Left" position.
4. Test to see that engine starts when lever is in P or N position.
5. Tighten switch mounting screws.

1959-60 ADJUSTMENTS

1. Remove air cleaner.
2. Loosen both nuts at transmission throttle control rod trunnion.
3. Adjust engine idle speed to 480-500 in drive range (540-560 with air conditioning).
4. Shut off engine and install a suitable gauge pin through holes in throttle control lever and bracket. *Four-barrel units are equipped with a throttle return check. Before installing pin, it will be necessary to either remove throttle return check or install a suitable tool (J-6342-01) over return check so that it will not interfere with linkage adjustment.*
5. With throttle valves fully closed, loosen lock nut and adjust length of transmission throttle control rod so that gauge pin is free in hole. Leave pin installed and tighten lock nut securely. Recheck freeness of gauge pin in hole.
6. Push throttle control rod to transmission (T.V. rod) downward until the throttle control outer lever is felt to touch end of travel. *Make*

sure upper lock nut is not touching trunnion.

7. While holding rod in this position, tighten upper and lower trunnion lock nuts finger tight. Then shorten throttle control-to-transmission rod by backing off lower trunnion nut 2½ turns and tighten upper nut securely.
8. Remove gauge pin.
9. Loosen lock nut on carburetor throttle rod.
10. Adjust carburetor throttle rod to obtain 4⅞" (5⅔⁄₆₄" on 1960) clearance from spherical end of pedal rod to body toe pan.
11. Tighten lock nut on carburetor throttle rod securely.
12. Install air cleaner.

1961 ADJUSTMENTS

Throttle Linkage

1. Refer to Figs. 15 and 16. Remove air cleaner.
2. Loosen two throttle control rod trunnion nuts.
3. Adjust engine idle speed to 480-500 rpm in Drive (540-560 with air conditioning).
4. Shut off engine and install a suitable pin through holes in throttle control lever and bracket. *Four barrel carburetors are equipped with an anti-stall dashpot (throttle return check). Before installing pin, either remove dashpot or install tool J-6324-01 over dashpot so that it will not interfere with linkage adjustment.*
5. With throttle valves fully closed, loosen lock nut and adjust length of transmission control rod to carburetor so that gauge pin is free in holes. Leave pin installed and tighten lock nut securely. Recheck freeness of pin in holes.
6. Push throttle valve upper control rod downward until outer throttle valve lever is felt to touch end of travel. Make sure that when lever is in this

position, upper lock nut is not touching trunnion.
7. While holding throttle valve upper control in this position, tighten upper and lower trunnion lock nuts finger tight. Shorten upper control rod by backing off lower trunnion nut 2½ turns and tighten upper lock nut securely. Remove gauge pin.
8. Loosen lock nut on carburetor throttle rod. Then adjust this rod to obtain 4.55" clearance from underside of attaching boss on pedal-to-body toe pan, Figs. 15 and 16. (approximately 3¾" to carpet).
9. Tighten lock nut on carburetor throttle rod securely.

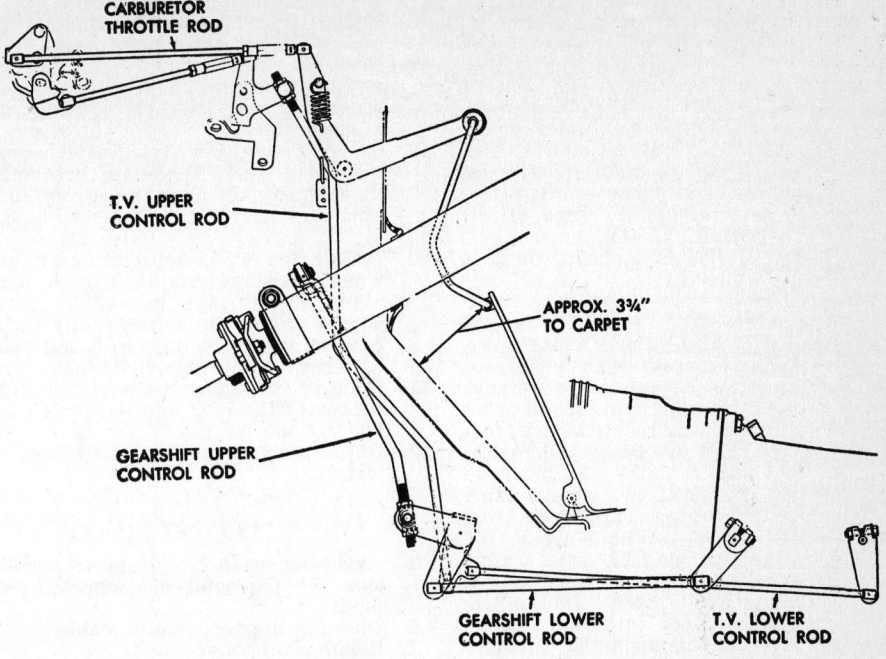

Fig. 15   Three speed Hydra-Matic linkage. 1961

CARBURETOR THROTTLE ROD
T.V. UPPER CONTROL ROD
APPROX. 3¾" TO CARPET
GEARSHIFT UPPER CONTROL ROD
GEARSHIFT LOWER CONTROL ROD
T.V. LOWER CONTROL ROD

Selector Linkage

1. Place upper shift lever and transmission lever in Park position and, with transmission outer shift lever trunnion nuts backed clear of trunnion, pull shift rod down toward transmission as far as possible. While holding rod in this position, run trunnion upper nut down to just contact trunnion. Run lower nut up to contact trunnion and lock nuts securely.
2. After completing above adjustments, check transmission parking lock with car on ramp or grade for positive lock.
3. Place upper shift lever in Drive Right position and check indicator pointer index. If necessary to adjust, loosen check nut above ball stud, adjust index by rotating rod and lock check nut securely.

Neutralizer Switch

1. Place selector lever in Neutral.
2. Loosen switch mounting screw.
3. Adjust switch to index with selector lever. Starter must not operate when ignition key is turned to start position with selector lever in Drive Left position.
4. Test to see that engine starts when selector is in P or N position.
5. Tighten switch mounting screw securely.

HYDRAMATIC, REPLACE

1953-54

The transmission, rear flywheel housing, torus cover, and torus members are removed as an assembly. The procedure is as follows:

1. Raise car on hoist and drain transmission oil pan.

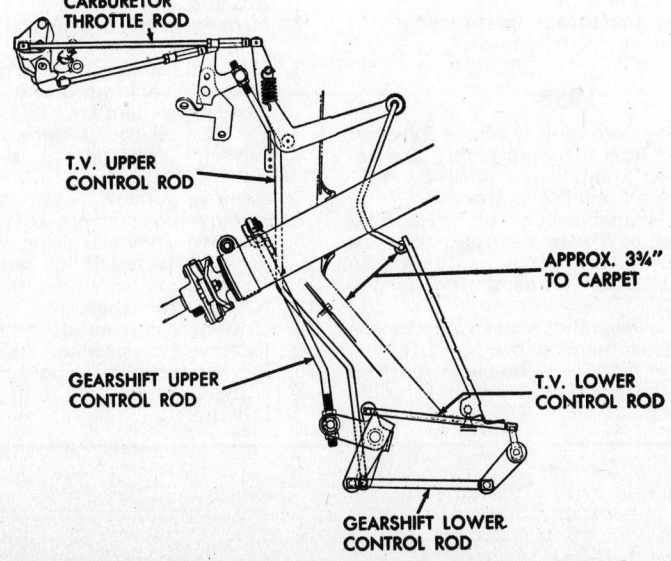

CARBURETOR THROTTLE ROD
T.V. UPPER CONTROL ROD
APPROX. 3¾" TO CARPET
GEARSHIFT UPPER CONTROL ROD
T.V. LOWER CONTROL ROD
GEARSHIFT LOWER CONTROL ROD

Fig. 16   Four speed Hydra-Matic linkage. 1961

PONTIAC

2. Disconnect speedometer cable and housing at transmission.
3. Disconnect propeller shaft at differential flange and slide propeller shaft from transmission output shaft.
4. Remove crankcase ventilator outlet pipe and loosen exhaust pipe bracket on exhaust pipe to facilitate removal of flywheel housing bottom cover.
5. Loosen exhaust pipe flange at exhaust manifold.
6. Remove flywheel housing bottom cover.
7. Drain oil from torus cover.
8. Disconnect hand brake cables at cross lever and remove cross lever.
9. On cars equipped with underseat heater it is necessary to remove heater-to-radiator rear tube in order to remove engine rear support cross member. Remove heater tube without draining radiator and block as follows: (a) Make two clamps using two rear engine support-to-cross member plates, two bolts about 1½" long, and two nuts for each clamp. (b) Install clamp on rubber hose below heater and tighten clamp to prevent flow of coolant from heater. (c) Remove clamp in X member holding heater to radiator rear tube, and defroster-to-heater tube. (d) Loosen heater hose clamp at front of heater to radiator rear tube. (e) Slip heater-to-radiator rear tube backward far enough to permit installation of the second clamp. Tighten clamp. (f) Remove heater-to-radiator rear tube.
10. Remove throttle control lever (outer) from shaft at side of transmission.
11. Disconnect gearshift control rod assembly from shift lever at side of transmission. (Hand brake cable may be wrapped around lower control rods to hold them clear when transmission is lowered.)
12. Remove 30 torus cover-to-flywheel attaching bolts.
13. Disconnect two rear engine mountings and reinforcing plates from cross member.
14. With a 4" x 4" x 10" wood block held on hydraulic jack pad and placed in center of engine oil pan, raise rear of engine until rear engine mountings are approximately ½" above cross member. *Do not raise engine any more than necessary to remove cross member.*
15. Remove six cross member-to-frame bolts and remove reinforcing plates from inside of side rails.
16. Remove cross member by tapping both ends of cross member down until right end is resting on exhaust pipe. Then tap left end down until it clears frame left side rail. Lift right end over exhaust pipe and remove. *Mark cross member so left side can be distinguished from right when reinstalling.*

17. Lower engine below its normal position so rear flywheel housing upper attaching bolts are accessible.
18. Position jack under transmission and lift transmission slightly to take strain off rear flywheel housing attaching bolts.
19. Remove six rear flywheel housing attaching bolts. The lower two bolts on each side of the rear housing also hold rear engine mountings to housing.
20. Install two 9⁄16"-12 bolts into rear flywheel housing (one each side) just above dowel pins to act as jack screws. Thread bolts evenly into housing until housing and dowel pins are free. Then remove bolts.
21. Remove the transmission by sliding it toward the rear and lower assembly to floor.
22. Reverse the foregoing procedure to install.

1955-57

1. Raise car on hoist, drain transmission oil pan and disconnect filler pipe.
2. Disconnect speedometer cable.
3. Remove propeller shaft.
4. Loosen exhaust pipe at crossover pipe flange. On Strato-Flight models with dual exhausts, it is necessary to remove the right hand exhaust pipe.
5. Remove flywheel housing bottom cover and on Strato-Flight, remove crankcase ventilator outlet filter.
6. Drain oil from torus cover.
7. Remove linkage from transmission.
8. Remove torus cover bolts.
9. Disconnect rear engine mounting insulators from cross member.
10. Raise engine so that rear mountings are about ½" above cross member and remove cross member.
11. Lower engine below its normal position so rear flywheel housing upper attaching bolts are accessible.
12. Support weight of transmission on a suitable jack, remove rear housing-to-front flywheel housing attaching bolts.
13. Move transmission toward rear of car and lower it to the floor.
14. Reverse the foregoing procedure to install.

1958

1. The transmission, rear flywheel housing and torus assembly are removed as a unit.
2. Remove oil level indicator.
3. Drain transmission by removing filler pipe. Torus assembly can be drained at this time or it can be drained after transmission is removed.
4. Remove propeller shaft and disconnect speedometer cable.
5. Remove flywheel housing bottom cover and crankcase ventilator outlet filter.

6. If equipped with dual exhaust, right-hand exhaust pipe must be removed.
7. Disconnect rear engine insulators from engine rear support cross member.
8. Raise rear of engine until insulators are about ½" above cross member.
9. Loosen transmission filler pipe to cylinder head clamp.
10. Remove shift levers from transmission.
11. Remove engine rear support cross member.
12. Remove nuts from six torus cover-to-flywheel plate bolts.
13. Lower engine about 1½" below its normal position.
14. Disconnect cooler lines from transmission. Plug holes in transmission with corks to stop oil flow.
15. Raise transmission slightly to take weight off flywheel housing screws.
16. Remove flywheel housing screws and work transmission rearward and down out of car.

1959-60

1. Remove oil level dipstick and drain transmission.
2. Disconnect oil cooler adapter with lines and plug in adapter and transmission with corks to stop oil flow.
3. On single exhaust cars, remove exhaust cross-over pipe.
4. Remove propeller shaft and disconnect speedometer cable.
5. Remove flywheel housing bottom cover and crankcase ventilator outlet filter.
6. Disconnect shift levers at transmission.
7. Support rear end of engine and remove nuts from torus cover-to-flywheel plate bolts.
8. Support transmission with jack and remove transmission cross member and insulator assembly from frame.
9. Raise transmission slightly and remove flywheel housing bolts.
10. Work transmission rearward and out of chassis.

1961 3 and 4 Speed Units

1. Remove filler tube and drain transmission.
2. Remove propeller shaft and disconnect speedometer cable.
3. Remove linkage from transmission.
4. Remove parking brake guide hook from crossmember.
5. Remove oil cooler lines.
6. Loosen exhaust pipe-to-manifold nuts about ¼".
7. Remove starter motor.
8. Remove cover from bottom of case.
9. Remove flywheel front cover plate.
10. Support transmission with jack.
11. Remove crossmember.
12. Remove breather pipe.
13. Unfasten transmission from engine.
14. Remove transmission from car.
15. Reverse removal procedure to install transmission. Add fluid and adjust linkage.

Rear Axle and Brake Section
Refer To Hydraulic Brakes Chapter For Brake Adjustments

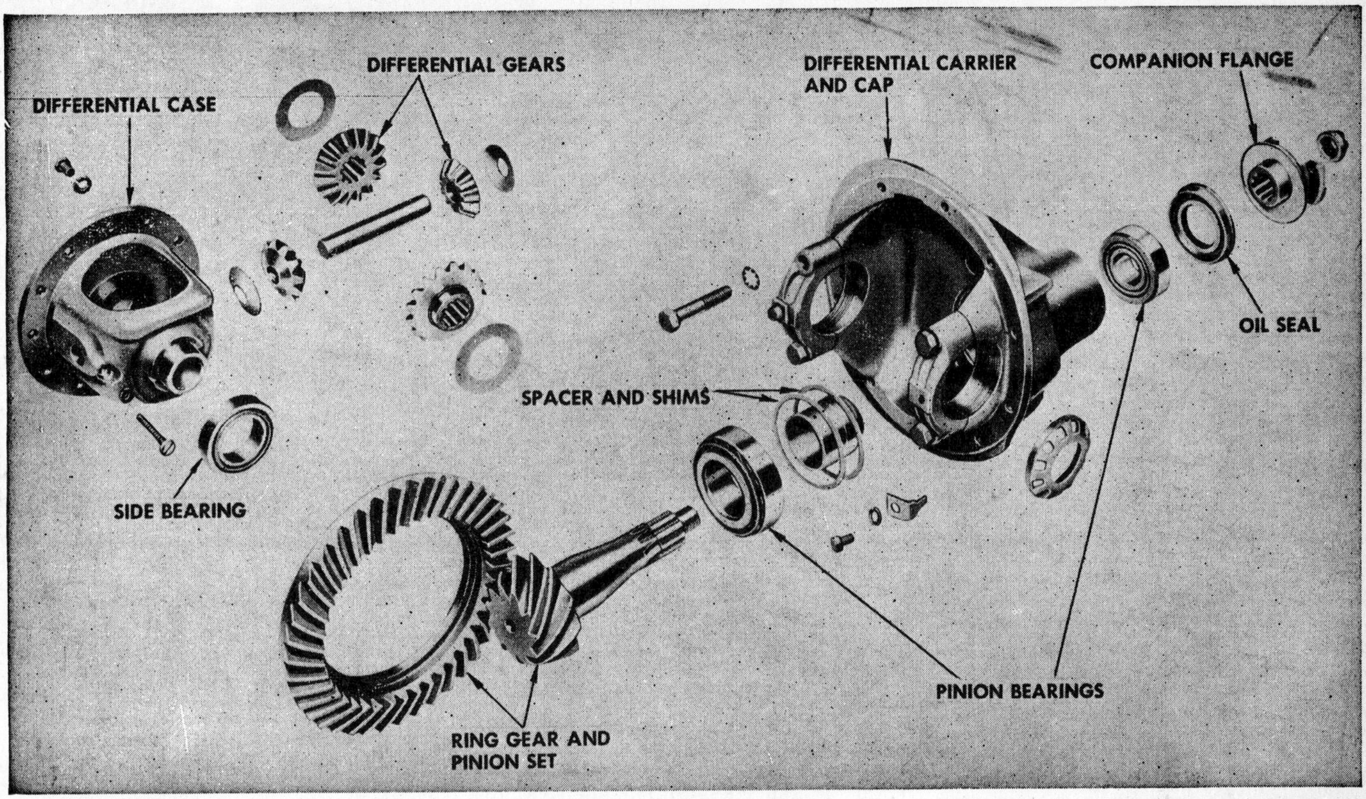

DIFFERENTIAL GEARS

DIFFERENTIAL CASE

DIFFERENTIAL CARRIER AND CAP

COMPANION FLANGE

OIL SEAL

SPACER AND SHIMS

SIDE BEARING

PINION BEARINGS

RING GEAR AND PINION SET

Fig. 1   Rear axle, 1953-56

REAR AXLE, 1953-56

In this axle, Fig. 1, the splined companion flange is fastened to the pinion stem with a special nut which seats directly on a counterbore in the flange. The nut is retained by staking the end of the pinion stem into two slots milled on top of the nut.

The drive pinion is mounted on preloaded taper roller bearings. Adjustment of the pinion along its axis is obtained by shims placed between the rear bearing outer race and a shoulder in the carrier. Adjustment of preload of the two bearings is obtained by tightening the companion flange nut which compresses a sleeve over the pinion stem between the bearings. Both bearing outer races are pressed into the carrier, the rear race against pinion adjusting shims, the front race against the shoulder in the carrier. The rear bearing inner race is pressed onto the pinion stem to a shoulder at the pinion end. The front bearing is a light press to a close sliding fit on the pinion stem.

The threaded nut type of differential bearing adjustment is used. The procedure for making this adjustment, as well as the assembly of the differential case, replacing a ring gear, checking ring gear and pinion backlash and other differential case operations, is given in the *Rear Axle Chapter*.

Pinion & Bearings, Replace—After removing the differential unit from the carrier, unscrew the pinion flange retaining nut and pull off the flange. Press the pinion out of the front bearing and through the rear end of the carrier. The rear bearing cone and bearing spacer will come out with the pinion. The bearings may then be removed and installed with suitable pulling equipment.

Reverse the operations to assemble and, after pressing on the pinion flange, slip on the washer and nut. Tighten the nut until the bearings have a preload drag of 27 to 37 inch pounds on new bearings or 10 to 12 inch pounds on used bearings to rotate the pinion shaft.

To adjust the preload, draw up the nut until the spacer starts to buckle. Check the pull as shown in Figs. 2 and 3, depending upon the equipment available. This adjustment must be made every time the flange nut is removed or loosened. If the adjustment is to be made with the differential unit in the carrier, the rear wheels must be jacked off the floor.

Fig. 2   Measuring pinion bearing preload with torque wrench, 1953-56

Fig. 3   Measuring pinion bearing preload with spring scale, 1953-56

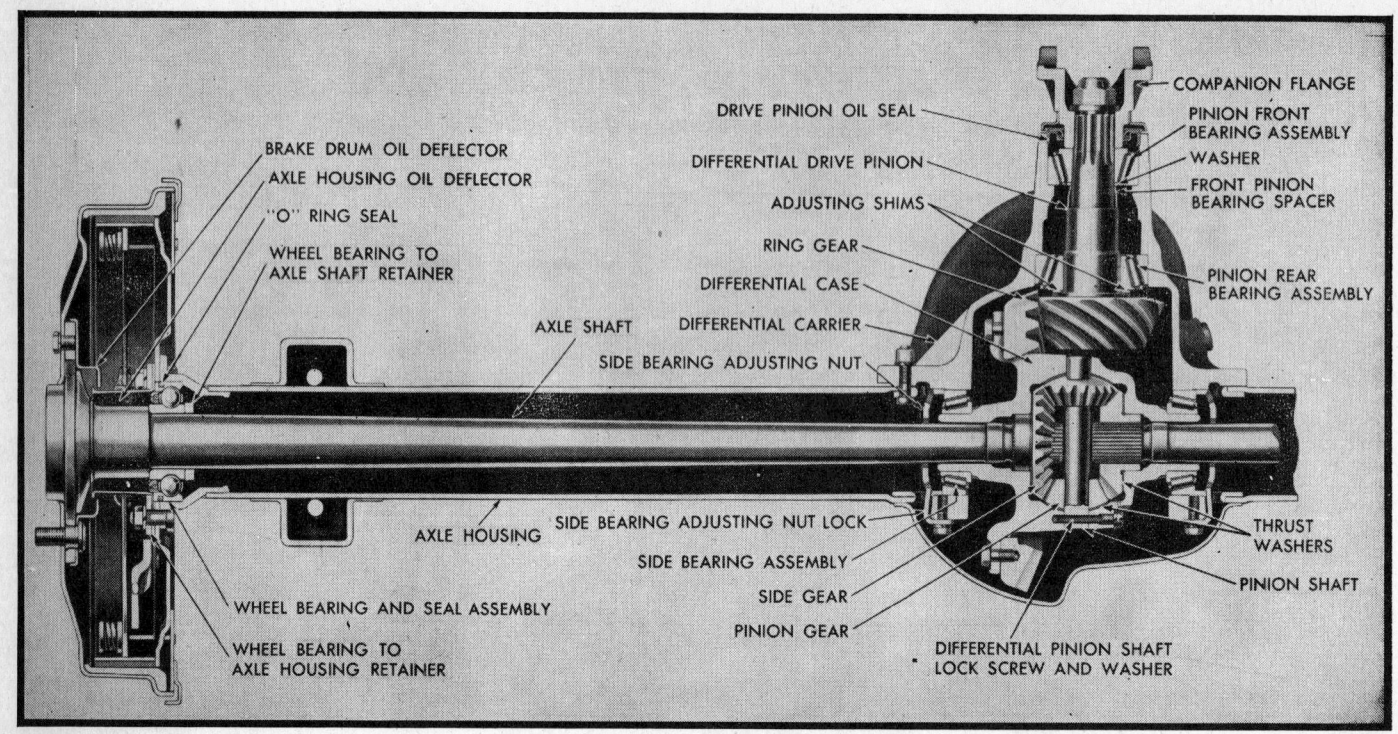

Fig. 4   Rear axle assembly.   1957-61

The pinion can be moved in toward the center of the axle by removing the required thickness of shims from between the spacer and the carrier. If it is to be moved away from the center of the axle, add shims.

Note—A new spacer is required between the pinion bearings when a new ring gear and pinion set is installed, either outer or inner members of either pinion bearing is changed, a new carrier casting used, or pinion adjusting shim thickness is increased. When the same pinion flange is removed and reinstalled as when an oil seal is replaced, checking for pinion bearing preload with a torque wrench is not necessary if care is taken to tighten the nut exactly its previous position. Should a new pinion flange be required, a torque wrench reading should be taken before loosening the nut and the nut tightened to the same torque wrench reading.

1957-61 REAR AXLE

In this type axle, Fig. 4, the differential carrier is larger and heavier to withstand the increased engine torque without excessive deflecting or twisting. The number of splines have been increased on side gears, axle shafts and drive pinion. The drive pinion and ring gear, pinion bearings, side bearings, side gears and differential case are larger. The pinion adjusting shims are located between the pinion head and the inner bearing race instead of in front of the outer bearing race on 1956. The differential pinion cross shaft is locked in the case by means of a screw and washer instead of a roll pin used in 1956. The carrier attaching screws are pressed into the axle housing and the carrier is attached to the housing

screws by means of nuts and lock-washers.

Service Procedures

All service procedures are the same as in 1956. Due to the new construction, however, a new set of pinion adjusting shims is required. Shims are available in thicknesses of .004″, .005″, .006″, .007″ and .010″. The pinion rear bearing must be removed from the pinion to change the shim pack. The thickness of the shim pack must be established by the red (or white) lead test as outlined in the *Rear Axles* chapter.

AXLE SHAFTS

Remove wheel and brake drum. Remove nuts from the four bolts attaching the brake backing plates to the housing. Withdraw the shaft. Before replacing, examine the oil seals and renew if damaged. Slide the shaft into place and take care not to injure the oil seals. The shaft with the left hand wheel studs goes to the left side of the car. Enter the splines of the shaft into the splines in the differential side gear and slide the shaft home, seating the shaft bearing to the shoulder in the housing. Clean the surfaces at the backing plate and oil guard and coat these surfaces with liquid seal and install a new gasket. Install the static ground brush. Tighten the bearing retainer bolt nuts. Replace the brake drum and wheel.

POWER BRAKE UNIT, REPLACE
1954

1. To remove the power brake unit,

disconnect upper end of vacuum hose which is attached to the inlet tube on the vacuum cylinder.
2. Disconnect hydraulic line at the connector on the hydraulic cylinder.
3. Remove stop light switch wires.
4. Disconnect push rod from brake pedal and remove pedal from pivot bracket.
5. Remove clutch pedal and steering column seals.
6. Remove vacuum cylinder mounting plate screws while holding the power unit by the push rod.
7. Remove the mounting plate, working it over the clutch pedal while holding the power unit in position.
8. Remove power unit from car.
9. Install in the reverse order and bleed the system in the conventional manner.

1955-58

1. Disconnect vacuum hose from pipe running from tee connector.
2. On 1956 models, raise car and remove engine side apron from left side.
3. Disconnect hydraulic pipe from outlet fitting on hydraulic cylinder.
4. Disconnect push rod from pedal, and wires from stop light switch.
5. Remove nuts from U-bolt which retains pedal pivot bracket to steering column. Then remove pedal and bracket, with stop light switch attached.
6. Remove accelerator pedal on 1956 models.
7. Remove clutch pedal seal retainer (synchromesh cars) and steering column seal retainer and remove seals.
8. On Hydra-Matic cars, remove mounting plate and power brake unit as

9. On synchromesh cars, remove screws which retain power brake unit to mounting plate (brake unit will rest on frame). Remove mounting plate from floor pan. Remove power brake unit. *Do not support or carry brake unit by push rod since push rod may be pulled out of plunger.*

10. Install in the reverse order and bleed the system in the usual manner.

1959-61

1. Remove lock nut or clevis from auxiliary push rod inside car.

2. Disconnect vacuum hose from vacuum exhaust tube and cover to prevent entrance of dirt.

3. Disconnect pipe from master cylinder hydraulic port and cover opening and pipe end to prevent entrance of dirt.

4. Remove power brake unit (4 nuts).

5. Remove nut and auxiliary push rod grommet from push rod.

6. Install in reverse order of removal and bleed system in usual manner.

BRAKE MASTER CYLINDER, REPLACE

1953-61

To remove the master cylinder, disconnect the wires from the stop light switch and the brake tubes at the master cylinder connector. Remove the brake pedal-to-push rod clevis pin and disconnect the brake pedal retracting spring. Unfasten the master cylinder from its mounting and lift it off the car. Install in the reverse order.

Front End and Steering Section

CASTER & CAMBER

1958-61

Caster and camber are adjusted by shims placed between the upper pivot shafts and the frame. Both caster and camber adjustments can be made at the same time after the wheel alignment checks have been completed. In order to remove or install shim, raise car to remove weight from front wheel and loosen the pivot shaft-to-frame bolts. In changing caster and camber, the following general rules apply:

1. To decrease positive caster, add shim to front pivot shaft bolt.
2. To increase positive caster, remove shims from front pivot shaft bolt.
3. To increase camber, remove shims from front and rear bolts.
4. To decrease camber, add shims to both front and rear bolts.

By adding or subtracting an equal amount of shims from front and rear bolts, camber will be changed without affecting caster. After the correct number of shims have been installed, torque the pivot shaft bolts to 50-65 lb. ft. on 1958 and 80-95 on 1959-61.

On 1958 models, shims are available in thicknesses of .020″, .060″ and .120″. One .020″ shim change at both bolts will change camber 1/8°, a .060″ shim 3/8°, and a .120″ shim 3/4°. One .020″ shim change at the front bolt only will change caster 1/4°, a .060″ shim 3/4°, and a .120″ shim 1½°.

On 1959-61 models, shims are available in thicknesses of .030″, .060″ and .164″. One .030″ shim change at both bolts will change camber 1/6°, a .060″ shim 1/3°, and a .164″ shim 1°. One .030″ shim at the front or rear bolt will change caster 1/3°, a .060″ shim 3/4°, and a .164″ shim about 7/8°.

1953-57

Caster adjustment must always be made before camber adjustment. To set caster, loosen the eccentric bushing clap bolt and turn eccentric bushing to give the correct caster setting at each wheel.

When correct caster setting has been obtained, tighten the clamp bolt only enough to prevent changing the adjustment and proceed with camber adjustment.

To adjust camber, again loosen the clamp bolt and turn the eccentric bushing to get the correct camber setting at each wheel. It is never necessary to turn the eccentric bushing more than ½ turn to obtain the maximum adjustment possible on the eccentric bushing.

Tighten eccentric bushing clamp bolt to 35-40 lbs. ft. torque.

TOE-IN, ADJUST

To increase toe-in, turn the right adjusting tube in the direction of wheel rotation forward and the left adjusting tube in the direction the wheels revolve when the car is going rearward. Be sure to turn both tubes an equal amount in order to maintain the correct position of the steering wheel. When the adjustment is complete, tighten all clamp screws.

WHEEL BEARINGS, ADJUST

Torque Wrench Method: With wheel raised off ground, tighten spindle nut to a torque of 27 ft. lbs on 1960-61 (17 on 1953-59) to be sure all parts are properly seated. Then back off nut until it is finger loose and retighten 25-35 inch lbs. on 1960-61 (45-50 inch lbs. on 1953-59). If cotter pin cannot be inserted, tighten nut only enough to permit insertion of cotter pin.

Hand Feel Method: With wheel off ground, tighten nut with an 8″ or 10″ wrench using enough arm length leverage to ensure parts are properly seated. Back off nut until finger loose; then tighten finger tight. Tighten nut just far

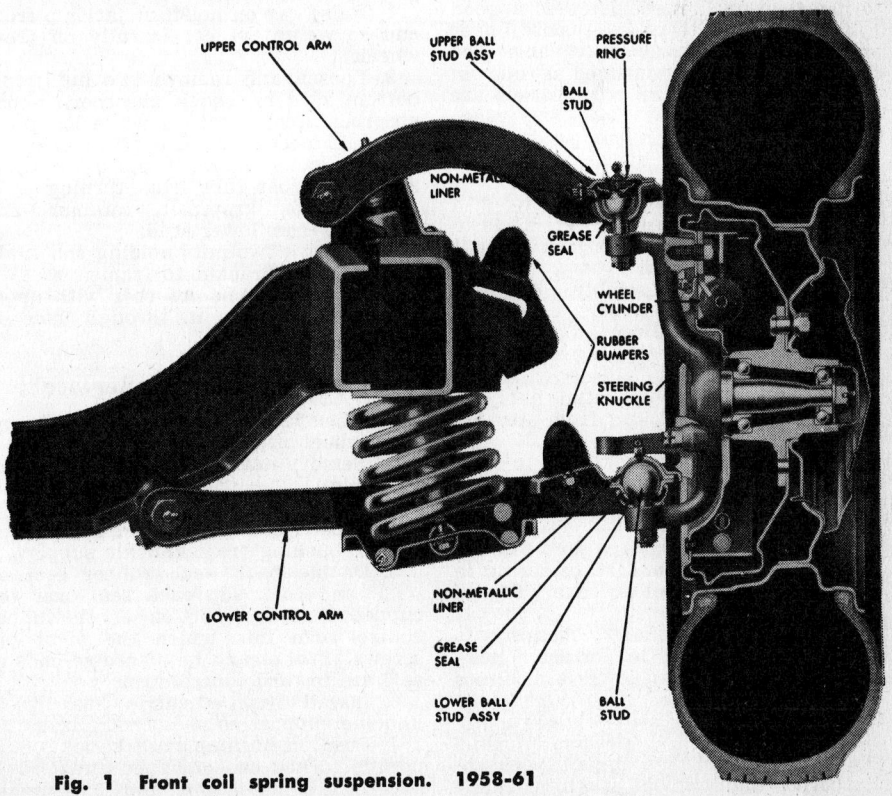

UPPER CONTROL ARM

UPPER BALL STUD ASSY

PRESSURE RING

BALL STUD

NON-METALLIC LINER

GREASE SEAL

WHEEL CYLINDER

RUBBER BUMPERS

STEERING KNUCKLE

NON-METALLIC LINER

LOWER CONTROL ARM

GREASE SEAL

LOWER BALL STUD ASSY

BALL STUD

Fig. 1 Front coil spring suspension. 1958-61

enough to permit cotter pin to be inserted.

1958-61 FRONT END

A ball joint front suspension is used in which both suspension and steering action are combined. The system, Fig. 1, is comprised of an upper and lower ball joint located at the outer ends of the upper and lower control arms. These joints serve as pivot points for both the vertical motion of the wheel and the rotation of the steering knuckle. Construction of both ball joints is similar except that tension is maintained on the upper joint by an integral pressure ring while the lower joint acquires tension from the front coil spring.

Shock Absorber, Replace

1. Raise car on hoist or jack up front end so weight of car is fully off front wheels.
2. Unfasten upper end of shock absorber from frame. *Shock absorber piston rod must not turn while loosening nuts. If necessary, use pliers or wrench to hold top of shock absorber stud mounting while removing nuts.*
3. Unfasten shock absorber at bottom and remove unit through lower control arm.
4. Install new shock absorber by reversing the above procedure. Be sure all grommets and retainers are correctly installed.

Front Spring, Replace

Front spring replacement may be accomplished by the chain hoist method or the floor jack method. Do not attempt to use floor jack method unless a good hydraulic jack with positive control over lowering a load slowly is available. The floor jack method is outlined as follows:

1. Raise front of car until wheels are about 10" above floor and place stand jacks under frame side members on each side of the car forward of radiator.
2. Place jack under lower control arm spring seat from which spring is to be removed and raise jack until it touches spring seat.
3. Remove wheel assembly.
4. Remove shock absorber.
5. Disconnect stabilizer link at lower control arm and steering arm at the rod.
6. Remove lower ball stud nut and press lower ball stud from steering knuckle.
7. Tilting steering knuckle out to clear control arm, lower jack slowly until spring is fully extended and remove spring.
8. To install spring, have jack pad under spring seat and place spring in seat on lower control arm. Top of spring is flat.
9. Raise jack gradually, checking to see that spring is correctly positioned. Raise until lower arm clears steering knuckle.
10. Lower jack slightly while guiding ball joint stud into steering knuckle.
11. Install nut on stud, install shock absorber and connect stabilizer link.

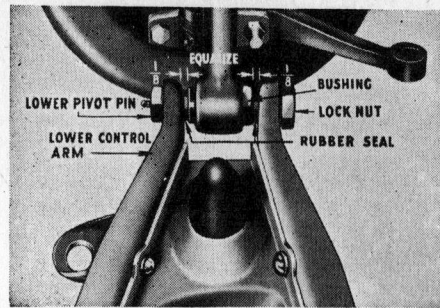

Fig. 2   Lower pivot details, 1953-57

Control Arms and Bushings, Replace

The procedure for replacing these parts is the same as outlined for earlier models.

Ball Joint, Replace

With the control arm removed, chisel or drill heads of rivets retaining the ball joint to the control arm and drive out the rivets. Remove ball joint assembly. Install new ball joint, securing it with special bolts, nuts and washers supplied with new joints. Tighten nuts to 10-12 lb. ft. torque.

1953-57 FRONT END

Shock Absorber, Replace

Front shock absorbers may be removed from the top or bottom on 1949-52 models and from the top only on 1953-57 models. To remove from the top, proceed as follows:

1. Raise car on hoist, or jack up front end so weight of car is fully off front wheels.
2. Loosen and remove two nuts from bottom stud on shock absorber. Shock absorber must not turn while loosening nuts. If necessary, use pliers inserted through coils of front spring to hold shock absorber tube from turning.
3. Remove grommet retainer and grommet from lower stud.
4. Remove two nuts holding shock absorber upper bracket to frame.
5. Remove shock absorber with upper bracket upward out through hole in frame.

Upper Pivot Pin, Replace

1. Place jack under lower control arm, raise wheel off floor and remove wheel.
2. Remove nut from rear end of upper pivot pin.
3. Remove threaded pivot pin.
4. Loosen clamp bolt and remove eccentric bushing from knuckle support.
5. Double back each rubber seal on itself and then slip each seal over the cupped threaded portion of the upper control arm into which the pivot pin screws. Seal should be placed so ends of seal are toward control arm.
6. Install new eccentric bushing in knuckle support so it is centralized.
7. Position bushing with knuckle support in forked end of upper control arm and install pivot pin and lockwasher

after coating threads of pin with chassis lubricant.
8. See that pivot pin bolt head is turned up tightly against surface of control arm and tighten to 40 lbs. ft. torque.
9. Install pivot pin nut and lockwasher and tighten nut securely against surface of control arm with 40 lbs. ft. torque. Make visual inspection to see that bolt head and nut are turned up securely against metal of control arm to insure firm seating. If not, apply additional torque to seat parts properly.
10. Strip back rubber seals so threaded portion of pivot pin is covered.
11. Install front wheel, lower car, lubricate pivot pin and check front wheel alignment.

Lower Pivot Pin, Replace

1. Place jack under lower control arm, raise wheel off floor and remove wheel and brake drum assembly.
2. If knuckle support lower bushing is to be replaced, remove brake backing plate from knuckle. Omit this operation if only the pin is to be replaced.
3. Remove nut from pivot pin and remove pin.
4. If knuckle support lower bushing is to be replaced, remove upper pivot pin. Omit this operation if lower pivot pin only is to be replaced.
5. If lower bushing is to be replaced, clamp knuckle support in vise, remove old bushing and install new one. Bushing must be firmly tightened in knuckle support so there is no clearance between bushing shoulder and knuckle support.
6. If upper pivot pin was removed, reinstall it as previously outlined.
7. Position rubber seals at lower pivot pin bushing. Hold bushing with knuckle support in a central position in lower control arm and install lower pivot pin and lockwasher after coating threads on it with chassis lubricant. Lower pin must be installed with clearances shown in Fig. 2.
8. With hex head of pivot pin firmly tightened against control arm, install nut and lockwasher and tighten until securely seated against metal of control arm.
9. Reinstall brake backing plate if it was removed. Then install wheel and brake drum.
10. Lower car, lubricate pivot pins, and check wheel alignment.

Spring, Replace

This operation requires use of a chain hoist and a car stand. If a chain hoist is not available the operation can be performed by using three car stands and a hydraulic floor jack. The latter method should not be attended unless the hydraulic jack has a positive control over slowly lowering a load.

Using Chain Hoist—
1. Lift car with hoist so wheels are 8 in. off floor and place a car stand under inner side of lower control arm spring pad from which spring is to be removed.
2. Lower car until it touches top of car stand. Remove wheel.
3. Remove shock absorber.
4. Disconnect stabilizer link at lower control arm.
5. Remove lower pivot pin from bushing.

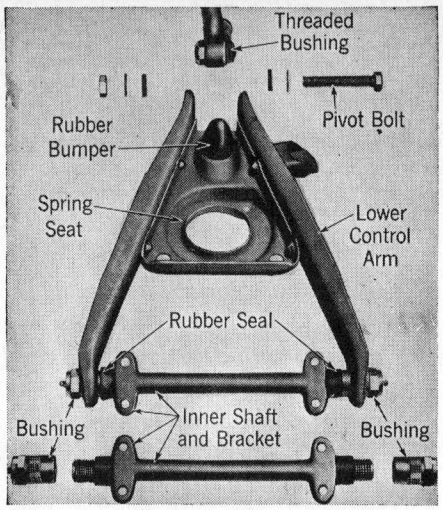

Fig. 3   Lower control arm details, 1953-55. 1956-57 is 3-piece construction

6. Raise car slowly with chain hoist and remove spring.

7. When installing spring, have car elevated on chain hoist and place bottom of spring in seat on lower control arm. Top of spring may be identified since it is flattened and bottom end is not. End of coil at bottom of spring must index with hole provided in spring seat in lower control arm.

8. Lower chain hoist gradually, checking to see that spring is correctly seated top and bottom.

9. Install lower pivot pin and connect stabilizer link.

10. Install shock absorber and front wheel. Lower car, lubricate pivot pin and check wheel alignment.

Using Floor Jack—

1. Raise front end of car until wheels are about 10 in. above floor and place a car stand under frame side member on each side forward of front door hinge pillar so car will be firmly supported.

2. Place a car stand under the lower control arm of the spring which is *not* to be replaced.

3. Place floor jack under lower control arm spring seat from which spring is to be removed and raise jack until it touches spring seat.

4. Remove wheel on side of car from which spring is to be removed.

5. Remove shock absorber and disconnect stabilizer link at lower control arm.

6. Remove lower pivot pin.

7. Slowly lower jack until spring is fully extended and remove spring.

8. To install spring, have jack pad under spring seat and place spring in seat on lower control arm with end of coil at bottom of spring indexing with hole in spring seat.

9. Raise jack gradually, checking to see that spring is correctly seated top and bottom.

10. Install lower pivot pin and connect stabilizer to lower control arm.

11. Install shock absorber and front wheel. Lower car, lubricate pivot pin and check wheel alignment.

Lower Arm, Replace

1. Remove front spring.

2. Unfasten lower control arm shaft from frame cross member and remove control arm and shaft.

3. When installing a new lower control arm, it is necessary to cut a thread for the bushing in the arm. The shaft bushing has threads on the inside and outside so that as the bushing threads onto the pivot shaft, the outside thread on the bushing cuts its own thread in the control arm. The distance between the inside face of the inner ends of the lower control arms when assembled must be 11½ in. (plus or minus $\frac{3}{32}$ in.) so it is necessary to use a steel block, wood or the special tool shown in Fig. 4 to prevent the arms from being forced together while the bushing is forming a thread during installation.

4. To install the pivot shaft in a new arm, place the spreader tool in position and expand it until distance between inner faces of arms is 11½ in.

5. Place pivot shaft with rubber seals in position in control arm, Fig. 3.

6. After lubricating pivot shaft threads with chassis lubricant, start bushing on pivot shaft and into arm at same time. Tighten until bushing flange is firmly seated against metal of control arm.

7. Center pivot shaft in control arm and install other bushing being sure threads index so there is no bind. Tighten until bushing flange is firmly seated against metal of control arm.

8. Check to see that distance between inner faces of shaft ends of control arm are 11½ in. (plus or minus $\frac{3}{32}$ in.). Also check to see that distances from center of pivot shaft bolt holes to inside faces of arm are equal at each end. Turn pivot shaft in arm to centralize if distance is not equal.

9. Fasten pivot shaft to frame cross member and tighten nuts to 50-55 lbs. ft. torque (70-80 on 1955-57).

10. Complete installation by following procedure for installing spring.

11. Lower car, lubricate control arm shaft and lower pivot pin and check wheel alignment.

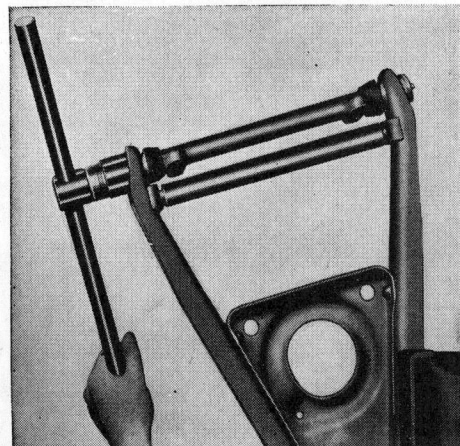

Fig. 4   Using spreader tool to prevent lower control arms from moving inward while installing bushings, 1953-57

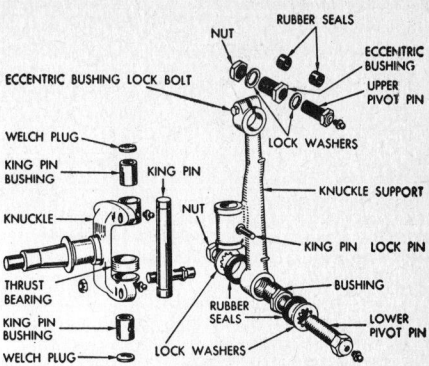

Fig. 5   Steering knuckle and related parts. 1953-55. For 1956-57 kingpin bushings are a press fit

Upper Arm, Replace

1. Place jack under lower control arm, raise wheel off floor and remove wheel.

2. Remove shock absorber and upper bracket.

3. Remove upper pivot pin.

4. Unfasten and remove upper control arm shaft from frame. Note position of notch in shaft with respect to frame bolts so shaft can be installed in same position on frame. Normal position of shaft is with notch toward center of car. Turning shaft over will result in changing centerline of shaft ⅛ in. with resultant change in camber of approximately ⅔ degree.

5. Remove shaft from control arm by removing front and rear threaded bushings.

6. Install the pivot shaft in the new arm, following the procedure outlined for the lower control arm shaft. A suitable spreader should be used between the legs of the arm to keep them spread 7½" (6 9/16" on 1956-57). After installing the bushings so they are tight against the metal surface of the arms, check to see that the distance remains at 7½" (6 9/16" on 1956-57) (plus or minus 1/16 in.). Also check to see that the pivot shaft is equalized in the arm. If not, turn the shaft in the arm to centralize if distance from each bolt hole to arm are not equal.

7. After completing the installation, lower car, lubricate control arm shaft and upper pivot pin, and check wheel alignment.

Kingpins & Bushings, 1953-55

1. Jack up wheel under lower control arm and remove wheel and brake drum assembly.

2. Remove brake backing plate without disconnecting brake hose. Place backing plate out of way to avoid any strain on brake hose.

3. Remove kingpin lock pin, Fig. 5.

4. Remove lower welch plug under kingpin by driving a punch through upper welch plug. If necessary, the kingpin can then be driven up to remove upper welch plug.

5. Drive out kingpin.

6. Bushings are the floating type and may be lifted out.

7. Use a suitable reamer to clean up recesses for welch plugs in knuckle.

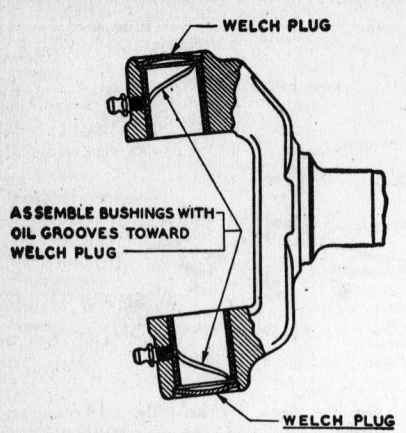

Fig. 6 Correct assembly of bushings in knuckle. 1953-54. Bushings for 1955 have inner and outer groove encircling bushing at its midpoint, thereby requiring no special alignment.

8. Install new bushings as shown in Fig. 6. No reaming or burnishing is required.

9. Position the steering knuckle on the knuckle support and install new kingpin. Make sure thrust bearing is correctly installed below knuckle support.

10. Drive in kingpin lock pin.

11. Install welch plugs in both ends of knuckle, staking them securely in place.

12. Complete the installation and lubricate kingpin.

Kingpins & Bushings, 1956-57

Procedure for removing and installing kingpins and bushings is the same as previous models except that, being a press fit, the bushings will have to be pressed in and out of the knuckle.

When installing bushings, align grease hole in bushing with similar hole in steering knuckle. Press new bushing into place with a suitable tool. After installing, line-ream bushings to size.

HORN BUTTON OR RING

1960-61

Twist steering wheel ornament, pry up on end and lift it out. Remove two nuts and washers from shaft. Remove screws and spacer bushing. Remove horn ring and related parts.

1958-59

Standard Wheel—Press down on one side of horn button, insert a screwdriver underneath opposite edge of button and pry upward.

Deluxe Wheel—Remove wheel ornament by prying up on end. Remove plate and insulator (2 nuts) and remove horn ring.

1957

Standard Wheel—Same as 1958.

Deluxe Wheel—Remove four screws which retain covers to bottom of horn ring. Then remove horn ring side plates, horn ring and related parts.

1953-56

Standard Wheel—Same as 1958.

Deluxe Wheel—Remove horn ring button by turning counterclockwise. Remove retaining nuts and lift out horn ring, insulator and contact assembly.

STEERING WHEEL

All Models —After removing the horn button and/or ring, use a suitable puller to remove the steering wheel from the steering column shaft.

STEERING GEAR, REPLACE

1953-57 Standard Gear

1. If car is equipped with power brakes, remove the power unit as outlined previously.
2. Remove horn button and steering wheel.
3. Disconnect turn signal wiring harness at connector under instrument panel and remove turn signal lever.
4. Remove column lower finish plate.
5. Roll back floor mat and remove steering column pedal plates, felts, and felt retainer plate.
6. Disconnect horn and neutral switch wires.
7. Remove gearshift lever.
8. Disconnect gearshift and selector rods from steering column levers.
9. Raise car on hoist, if available, otherwise on high car stands *under both lower control arms* so as to provide clearance for removing steering gear.
10. Remove engine left side apron.
11. Pull pitman arm from gear shaft.
12. Loosen three bolts holding steering gear housing to frame. Then remove two bolts, leaving the front upper bolt to support the steering gear.
13. Remove bolts holding steering column lower bracket to upper bracket on instrument panel.
14. Remove remaining gear-to-frame bolt and remove the steering gear by bringing it down through the floorboard and over steering linkage toward right front wheel. *Be sure to save any shims found between*

gear housing and frame so they can be reinstalled. If the car is equipped with NO-ROL the steering gear will have to be removed by way of the driver's compartment, passing the pitman shaft between the pedals.

15. Reverse the foregoing procedure to install the gear.

1958-59

1. Remove steering wheel.
2. Disconnect turn signal wiring harness at connector under instrument panel.
3. Remove turn signal lever.
4. Remove steering column lower finish plate.
5. Roll back floor mat and remove steering felt and felt retainer plate.
6. Disconnect horn wire and neutral safety switch wire.
7. Remove gearshift levers.
8. Disconnect gearshift selector rods from steering column.
9. Remove splash apron.
10. Remove starter motor (1958 only).
11. Remove turn signal wires.
12. Remove pitman shaft arm.
13. Remove bolts holding steering column lower bracket to upper bracket on instrument panel.
14. Unfasten steering gear housing from frame. *Make sure shims found between gear housing and frame are installed in the same position.*
15. On 1958 models, the gear is removed or replaced from the front of the car with the lower control arm disconnected and the coil spring or air spring removed.

1960

1. Remove steering wheel.
2. Disconnect turn signal wiring harness at connector under instrument panel.
3. Remove turn signal lever.
4. Remove column lower finish plate.
5. Roll back floor mat and remove steering felt and felt retainer plate.
6. Disconnect horn wire and neutral switch wire.
7. Disconnect gearshift selector rods from steering column.
8. Remove floor pan cover.
9. Remove backup lamp and switch wires.
10. Remove turn signal wires.
11. Remove pitman shaft arm.

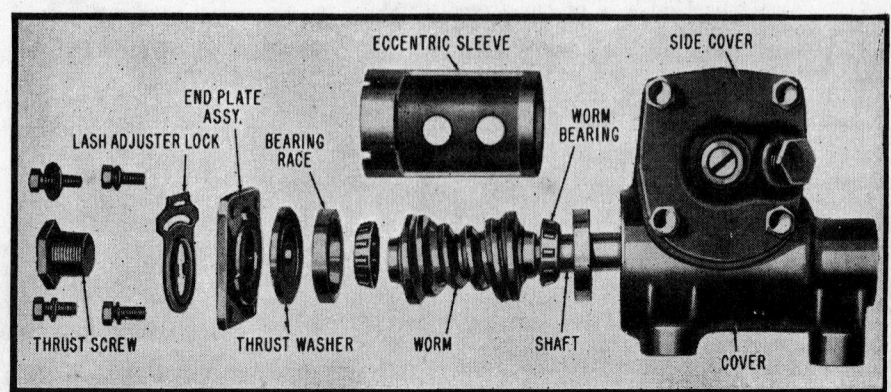

Fig. 7 Manual steering gear. 1953-54

12. Unfasten steering gear from frame (3 bolts). Make sure shims found between gear housing and frame are installed in same position when gear is installed.

1961

1. Use puller to remove pitman arm from steering gear shaft.
2. Scribe a mark on worm shaft flange and steering shaft and disconnect lower flange from steering shaft.
3. Unfasten gear housing from frame (3 bolts) and remove from car.

POWER STEERING UNIT, REPLACE

1953-55

1. If equipped with power brakes, remove the power brake unit as outlined below.
2. Hold down the front suspension by compressing the front springs and use a suitable hook with one end in the hole in the cross member and the other end under the lower control arm support.
3. Remove steering wheel.
4. Remove turn signal switch handle and gearshift lever.
5. Remove steering column-to-instrument panel bracket cap.
6. Slide rubber grommet up on steering column jacket.
7. Roll back floor mat and remove pedal plates from floor.
8. Remove back-up light and neutral switch on Hydramatic cars.
9. Disconnect gearshift and selector rods.
10. Disconnect turn signal wires.
11. Disconnect power steering oil lines at gear and secure lines so ends are higher than reservoir to prevent fluid leakage. Install plastic plugs or tape to cover gear and line openings and prevent entry of dirt.
12. Protect all finished surfaces on steering column with masking tape.
13. Raise car on hoist.
14. Remove pitman arm.
15. Remove idler lever support attaching bolts.
16. Remove engine left side apron.
17. Remove brake pedal hairpin spring retainer and slide pedal to right as far as it will go.
18. If car is on a twin post hoist it will be necessary to place stands under both front frame ends and lower the front post approximately 3 feet to allow steering gear assembly to clear hoist.
19. Push steering connecting linkage down and toward rear of car.
20. Unfasten steering gear from frame, removing front upper bolt last.
21. Lower assembly between lower control arm and steering linkage. *Be sure to save any shims found between gear housing and frame so they can be reinstalled.*
22. Reinstall in the reverse order.

1956

1. Remove power brake unit.
2. Remove steering wheel.

3. Remove turn signal switch handle and gearshift lever.
4. Remove steering column-to-instrument panel bracket cap.
5. Slide rubber grommet up column jacket.
6. Remove pedal plates from floor.
7. Remove neutral and back-up light switch wires on Hydra-Matic cars.
8. Disconnect gearshift and selector rods.
9. Disconnect turn signal and horn wires.
10. Disconnect power steering oil lines at gear and secure lines so ends are higher than reservoir to prevent fluid leaking. Install plastic plugs or tape to cover gear and line openings and prevent entry of dirt.
11. Protect all finished surfaces on steering colunm with masking tape.
12. Raise car on hoist.
13. Remove starter motor.
14. Remove pitman arm.
15. Remove left side tie rod end and drop steering linkage.
16. Remove engine left side apron.
17. Remove spring retainer and slide brake pedal to right as far as possible.
18. Push steering connecting linkage down and toward rear of car.
19. Unfasten steering gear from frame, removing front upper bolt last. Then lower steering gear between lower control arm and steering linkage. *Check and keep intact shims that may be present between gear and frame for reassembly.*
20. Reverse the removal procedure to install the steering gear. Then, after filling the reservoir to the proper level with fluid, turn the wheels from stop to stop several times to bleed all air from the system. Replenish the reservoir and install the cap.

1957-58

1. Scribe alignment marks on the steering shaft and worm shaft flanges.
2. Remove two flange attaching nuts and washers.
3. Disconnect pressure and return hoses from valve body.
4. Remove pitman arm.
5. Unfasten gear housing from frame and lift gear out of car.

1959-61

1. Scribe two coupling flanges just above gear and remove flange attaching nuts.
2. Disconnect pressure and return hoses from gear housing.
3. Disconnect pitman arm.
4. Unfasten gear from frame and remove.

MANUAL STEERING GEAR REPAIRS

1953-54, Fig. 7

Before any adjustments are made to the steering gear in an attempt to correct such conditions as shimmy, hard or loose steering and road shocks, a careful check should be made to determine that

front end alignment, shock absorbers, wheel balance and tire pressure are correct.

There are three adjustments on the steering gear and it is very important that they be made in the sequence given below, otherwise damage to the steering gear will result.

Pitman Shaft End Play

1. Disconnect steering connecting rod from pitman arm.
2. Tighten pitman arm nut to 110-125 lb. ft. torque.
3. Loosen steering column bracket to make certain it is not sprung due to misalignment. If misaligned, shim at steering gear housing-to-frame bolts and tighten bracket.
4. Tighten four side cover-to-housing bolts.
5. Loosen pitman shaft lock nut.
6. Turn steering gear to end position, near but not against stop, and tighten pitman shaft adjusting screw securely. Back off screw until it is free and again turn it in until it can just be felt to be bearing against shaft. Holding screw from turning, tighten lock nut.
7. Test for end play. No end play should be felt when attempting to move pitman arm in and out. The arm should be free without any bind when moved through backlash which is present in steering direction of movement.

Worm Bearing Preload

1. Tighten three screws holding end plate to housing. Do not tighten the bolt which is in the slot of the lash adjuster lock.
2. Loosen worm thrust screw lock nut.
3. With steering gear turned to its end position, near but not against stop, tighten worm thrust screw so as to obtain a pull of $\frac{3}{8}$ to $\frac{5}{8}$ lb. at steering wheel rim when measured with a spring scale.
4. While holding screw from turning, tighten lock nut.

Worm & Roller Backlash

1. Loosen bolt in slot of lash adjuster lock $\frac{1}{2}$ turn.
2. Center steering gear so wheel is in straight-ahead driving position.
3. Tap lash adjuster in direction of arrow until a pull of $1\frac{1}{4}$ to $1\frac{3}{4}$ lbs. is secured at steering wheel rim when measured with spring scale. *Lash adjuster plate should not be moved more than $\frac{1}{16}$" at a time in relation to lock bolt, and in no case should a tighter adjustment than $1\frac{3}{4}$ lbs. be allowed or damage to gear will result.*
4. *Tighten lash adjuster lock bolt.*

MANUAL STEERING GEAR REPAIRS, 1955-61

Disassemble, Figs. 8 and 9

1. Loosen adjusting screw lock nut and remove housing side cover by unscrewing adjusting screw.
2. Loosen lock nut and back off worm

bearing adjuster several turns, then remove housing end cover and gasket.

3. Remove adjusting screw from slot in end of pitman shaft making sure shim found on adjusting screw is kept with screw.

4. Remove pitman shaft from housing using care that threads do not damage seal in housing.

5. Loosen worm bearing adjuster lock nut and remove adjuster and lower bearing.

6. Push worm and shaft, with ball nut, through bottom of housing and remove upper bearing.

7. Remove ball return guide clamps and guides from ball nut, turn ball nut over to remove balls and remove ball nut from steering shaft worm.

Inspection of Parts

1. Clean and inspect all ball and roller bearings and races, including race in housing.

2. Inspect pitman shaft bushings in gear housing and end cover. Replace bushings in housing and replace end cover if bushings are worn excessively.

3. It is advisable to replace pitman shaft grease seal in housing to avoid possible leakage of lubricant. Seal must be installed with feather edge toward inside of housing.

4. Inspect steering shaft for wear or pits in bearing races, which would require replacement of shafts.

5. Check shaft for straightness.

6. Inspect teeth of ball nut and pitman shaft. If scored or excessively worn it is advisable to replace both parts to insure proper mating of teeth.

7. Check serrations of pitman shaft; if twisted, replace shaft.

8. Check fit of pitman shaft adjusting screw and shim in slot in end of pitman shaft. *With shim in place, screw head must be free to turn in slot with zero to .002" end play. If end play is excessive, selectively fit a new shim, which is furnished in four different thicknesses.*

9. Inspect steering column jacket for distortion. A ripple or wavy feeling

of jacket surface, particularly at lower end, will usually indicate a sprung jacket. Replace jacket if sprung or otherwise damaged.

10. Inspect control shaft bearing in tube of gear housing, and steering shaft upper bearing in control lever housing support. Replace worn or damaged parts.

Assemble

To assemble the steering gear, reverse the order of procedure given for disassembly. In addition, observe the following instructions.

1. Lubricate bearings and gears with steering gear lubricant.

2. Use all new gaskets to avoid oil leaks.

3. When assembling ball nut on worm, be sure to place 18 balls in each circuit, making a total of 36 balls.

4. When installing pitman shaft, avoid damaging or turning the feather edge of leather seal in gear housing.

5. Temporarily install steering wheel and adjust worm shaft thrust bearing for proper load and pitman shaft for proper gear lash as described below.

Adjustments

1. Disconnect steering linkage from pitman arm.

2. Turn steering wheel gently in one direction until it stops, then turn it back one revolution. *Never turn steering gear hard against stopping*

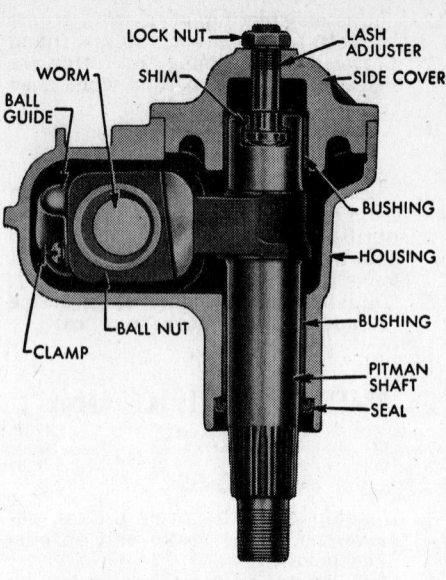

Fig. 9 Manual steering gear adjustments. 1955-61

point as damage to ball nut assembly may result.

3. Check lash between ball nut and pitman shaft by working pitman arm. If a perceptible lash *does not* exist, loosen lock nut and turn pitman shaft adjusting screw counter-clockwise until lash can be felt when working pitman arm.

4. Turn steering wheel slowly from one extreme to the other. Wheel should turn freely and smoothly through entire range. Roughness indicates faulty worm thrust bearings or pitted races. Hard pull or binding indicates misalignment of steering gear in its mountings, or an excessively tight adjustment of worm thrust bearings. Any misalignment must be corrected before steering gear can be properly adjusted.

5. Tighten housing and cover bolts.

6. Loosen worm thrust bearing adjuster lock nut and turn thrust bearing adjuster until a slight load is felt when turning steering wheel near extreme end positions, then tighten lock nut. (1956 gears have an external hex which replaces slot on bearing adjuster used formerly). *Do not back out adjuster far enough to* permit thrust bearings to get out of line with ends of worm.

7. After locking bearing adjuster, check load on thrust bearings with steering wheel turned to near one extreme position.

8. Attach a spring scale to rim of steering wheel. The pull required to keep steering wheel turning slowly should be between ⅜ and ⅞ lbs. Readjust to obtain this load if necessary.

9. Turn steering wheel from one extreme to the other while counting the turns. Then turn wheel back exactly one-half the total number of turns and have the lower spoke pointing straight down. This places the steering gear on the "high point" at which no lash should exist be-

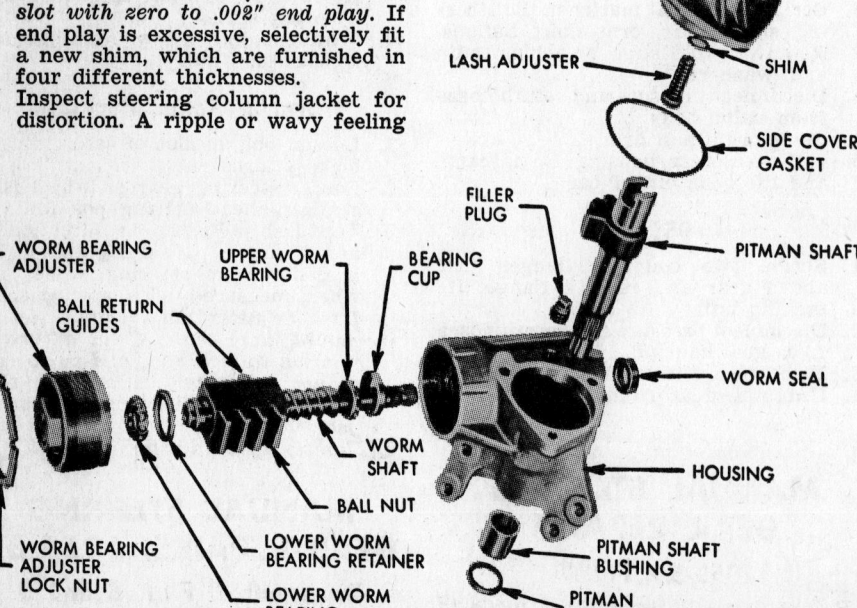

Fig. 8 Manual steering gear. 1955-60 models have a one-piece worm shaft extending up to steering wheel. 1961 is a two-piece shaft fastened together by a flange

10. Tighten housing side cover bolts. Loosen lock nut and turn pitman shaft adjusting screw clockwise until lash is just removed.

tween ball nut and pitman shaft teeth.

11. After tightening adjusting screw lock nut, rotate wheel back and forth to check for tight spots. Also recheck pull at wheel rim as given above.

12. The pull required to keep the wheel moving through the "high point" should be between 1 to 2 lbs. Readjust if necessary to remove tight spots.

Speedometer, Radio and Windshield Wiper

SPEEDOMETER REPLACE

1953-54

Disconnect the speedometer cable and remove two screws from face of cluster and pull cluster out of panel. Then remove lamps and five screws which hold speedometer housing to cluster.

1955-56

Disconnect speedometer cable and remove lamp sockets from back of speedometer. Remove lamp socket wire harness from clip on left hand side of speedometer. Remove three screws from face of speedometer. Remove speedometer by tipping top out of panel, then lifting out. Now remove three screws which fasten speedometer to assembly.

1957

1. Remove gauge cluster simply by disconnecting wires and remove three attaching nuts from the back.
2. Remove radio knobs and radio trim plate attaching nuts.
3. Remove instrument panel trim plate (6 screws).
4. Disconnect speedometer cable, wiring and oil pressure gauge line.
5. From face of instrument panel, remove two screws which retain speedometer to instrument panel.
6. Pull speedometer out of panel.
7. Detach lamp sockets from speedometer and remove unit.

1958

1. Disconnect speedometer cable and wiring.
2. Remove three nuts from back of speedometer case.
3. Pull speedometer out of panel through rear.

1959 Safeguard Speedometer

1. Disconnect electric wire located at rear top of speedometer case.
2. Remove lamp sockets and speedometer cable from speedometer unit.
3. Remove instrument cluster from panel.
4. Remove two nuts and clamps holding speedometer in cluster housing.
5. Lift speedometer and case from cluster housing.

1959 Standard Speedometer

1. Remove instrument cluster from below.
2. Remove two nuts and retainers and lift speedometer from cluster.

1960

1. Remove 8 screws.
2. Remove clock or dummy plate (remove safeguard knob if equipped).
3. Remove back of cluster housing (remove clip on safeguard point and remove wire).
4. Remove speedometer (2 screws).
5. Reverse above procedure to install.

1961

1. Disconnect Safeguard control cable on cars so equipped (pull straight out).
2. Remove speedometer cluster.
3. Remove cluster face plate and lens by unsnapping face plate from housing.
4. Remove three screws on back of cluster at cable area.
5. Remove speedometer and instruments. If equipped with Safeguard speedometer, disconnect ground wire at clip terminal and also wire retainer clip. Carefully note routing of wires before removing ground wire.
6. Remove two screws retaining numeral plate and remove speedometer.

RADIO REPLACE

1953-54

1. On Convertibles and models with lighted ash tray, remove ash tray and its bracket.
2. Disconnect power lead and pilot light from fuse block on firewall.
3. Disconnect antenna lead and unplug power supply cable and speaker plugs at speaker power supply unit (directly behind clock).
4. Remove two hex bolts, one at each side of radio.
5. Remove control knobs.
6. While supporting radio from below, remove nuts from control bushings and remove radio from panel.
7. Remove speaker-power supply unit from front of panel.

1955-56

Tuner—

1. Disconnect power lead and dial light lead from fuse block and remove wires from clips.
2. Remove connecting cable from audio power unit.
3. Remove antenna lead at connector between tuner unit and audio power unit.
4. Remove nuts from stud at right rear side of tuner unit.

5. Remove control knobs, nuts and finish plate.
6. Remove screw on either side of tuner and remove tuner by pulling outward.

Audio Power Unit—

1. After removal of tuner unit, remove antenna lead.
2. Remove screw at top left side of audio power unit.
3. Support unit and remove retaining screws from bottom of instrument panel and remove unit.

1957

De Luxe Radio—It is first necessary to remove the glove box. Then take off control knobs and nuts from shafts. Remove nut from brace fastened to left side of radio and lift out.

Electramatic Model—It is first necessary to remove the glove box. The tuner is retained by nuts behind the control knobs and by a brace attached to the left side. The audio power unit is retained at the front by two screws through the flange of the instrument panel and at the rear by a bracket attached to the underside of the cowl.

1958

1. Remove control knobs and wing knobs by lining up hole in bottom of chrome escutcheon and hole in winged knob and loosen. Allen set screw.
2. Remove two hex nuts.
3. Remove screw from bracket retaining radio to instrument panel. If car is Air Conditioned, it will be necessary to remove the center air outlet before the radio bracket screw can be removed.
4. Remove radio from panel and disconnect radio-to-fuse block wire antenna and speaker leads.

1959-60 Non-Portable Type

1. Remove glove compartment.
2. Remove control knobs.
3. Remove large hex nuts.
4. Remove screw from radio support bracket at rear of receiver.
5. Remove radio through glove compartment opening.

1961

1. Remove glove compartment, control knobs and large hex nuts.
2. Remove nut and washer from radio support bracket on left side of radio.
3. Remove radio-to-fuse block wire, antenna lead in wire and speaker leads.

PONTIAC

4. Remove radio through glove compartment door.

WINDSHIELD WIPER
1953-58

The removal and servicing of the windshield wiper motor and transmission mechanism are fairly obvious operations.

The only differences in the complete wiper assembly between vacuum and electrically-operated, are in the wiper motor, wiper arms and blades. The transmission, cable drives and cable tensioners are exactly the same on either installation.

1959-61
1. To remove wiper motor, remove

arms and blades.
2. Remove both retaining nuts, cam parts, washers and escutcheons.
3. Remove ventilator grille.
4. Remove link retainer.
5. Disconnect all electrical connections and washer hoses.
6. Unfasten and remove motor and gear box assembly (4 screws).

PONTIAC TEMPEST

Specifications for the optional V8 engine are tabulated on the pages immediately following this index. For service procedure see the Buick Special Chapter

INDEX OF SERVICE OPERATIONS

PAGE NO.

ACCESSORIES
Radio, Replace 1040
Instruments, Replace 1040
Windshield Wiper 1040
Windshield Wiper Troubles .. 37

BRAKES
Adjustments 112
Brake Cylinder Sizes 1010
Hydraulic Brake System 112
Master Cylinder, Replace ... 1034
Trouble Shooting 31

CLUTCH
Clutch Pedal, Adjust 1018
Clutch, Replace 1018
Trouble Shooting 13

COOLING SYSTEM
Radiator, Replace 1016
Trouble Shooting 8
Water Pump 1016

ELECTRIC SYSTEM
Dash Gauge Service 85
Distributor, Replace 1016
Distributor Service 46
Distributor Specifications ... 1010
Generator & Regulator Service ... 62
Generator & Regulator Specifications 1011

PAGE NO.

Horn Button or Ring, Replace 1037
Ignition System Service 46
Ignition Timing 1016
Starter, Replace 1016
Starter Switch Service 83
Starting Motor Service 77
Starting Motor Specifications 1010
Trouble Shooting 10
Turn Signal Troubles 12

ENGINE
Camshaft & Bearings 1014
Crankshaft & Bearing Specs. 1011
Crankshaft Oil Seal, Replace 1015
Cylinder Head, Replace 1011
Engine, Replace 1011
Main Bearings, Replace 1015
Piston Pins, Replace 1015
Piston Rings, Replace 1014
Piston, Pin, & Ring Specs.... 1011
Pistons & Rods, Remove 1014
Piston & Rod, Assemble 1014
Pistons, Replace 1014
Rocker Arm Stud, Replace .. 1012
Rod Bearings, Replace 1015
Timing Case Cover, Replace. 1014
Timing Chain, Replace 1014
Trouble Shooting 4
Valve Arrangement 1013
Valves, Grind 1013
Valve Guides 1013
Valve Lifters 1013
Valve Spring Installed Height 1013
Valve Spring Testing 1013
Valve Specifications 1009

PAGE NO.

ENGINE OILING
Oil Pan, Replace 1015
Oil Pump 1015
Trouble Shooting 9

FUEL & EXHAUST SYSTEMS
Carburetors 1016
Fuel Pumps 96
Mufflers and Pipes 1016
Trouble Shooting 4

REAR AXLE
Axle Shaft, Replace 1030
General Service 102
Rear Axle Repairs 1029
Rear Axle Specifications 1010
Trouble Shooting 31

SPECIFICATIONS
Brake Cylinder Sizes 1010
Capacity Data 1010
Carburetors 1017
Cooling System 1010
Crankshaft & Bearings 1011
Distributors 1010
Engine Tightening 1009
Generator & Regulators 1011
Pistons, Pins & Rings 1011
Rear Axle 1010
Starting Motors 1010
Tune Up 1009
Valves 1009
Wheel Alignment 1010

PAGE NO.

STEERING GEARS (Mechanical)
Horn Button or Ring, Replace 1037
Steering Gear Repairs 1038
Steering Gear, Replace 1038
Steering Wheel, Replace.... 1037
Trouble Shooting 33

STEERING GEARS (Power)
Steering Gear, Repairs 1039
Trouble Shooting 34

SUSPENSION, Front & Rear
Adjustments 1034
Front End Repairs 1036
Trouble Shooting 33
Wheel Alignment 1034
Wheel Alignment Specs. 1010

TRANSMISSIONS (Manual Shift)
Gearshift, Adjust 1019
Transmission Repairs 1020
Transmission, Replace 1020
Trouble Shooting 14

TRANSMISSIONS (Automatic)
Linkage, Adjust 1022
Replace 1026
Repairs 1021
Trouble Shooting 1024

TUNE UP 38

GENERAL SPECIFICATIONS

Year	Model Designation	Wheel-base Inches	Valve Location	Bore and Stroke	Piston Displacement, Cubic Inches	Compression Ratio (Standard)	Maximum Brake H.P. @ R.P.M.	Maximum Torque Lbs. Ft. @ R.P.M.	Normal Oil Pressure Pounds
1961	Std. 4 Cyl., Std. Trans.	112	In Head	4.0625 x 3.75	194.5	8.6	110 @ 3800	190 @ 2000	30-40
	Opt. 4 Cyl., Auto. Trans.	112	In Head	4.0625 x 3.75	194.5	8.6	130 @ 4400	195 @ 2200	30-40
	Opt. 4 Cyl., Std. Trans.	112	In Head	4.0625 x 3.75	194.5	10.25	120 @ 3800	202 @ 2000	30-40
	Opt. 4 Cyl., Auto. Trans.	112	In Head	4.0625 x 3.75	194.5	10.25	140 @ 4400	207 @ 2200	30-40
	Opt. 4 Cyl., 4 Bar. Carb.	112	In Head	4.0625 x 3.75	194.5	10.25	155 @ 4800	215 @ 2800	30-40
	Opt. V8①	112	In Head	3.5000 x 2.80	215	8.8	155 @ 4600	220 @ 2400	30-40

①—See Buick Special chapter for service procedures.

TUNE UP SPECIFICATIONS

★ When using timing light, disconnect vacuum line to prevent advance mechanism from operating.

Year	Model	Ground Polarity and Voltage	Spark Plug Type	Spark Plug Gap Inch	Distributor Point Gap Inch	Distributor Cam Angle Degrees	Firing Order	★ Ignition Timing Mark	★ Ignition Timing Location	Idle Speed RPM In Drive	Compression Pressure @ Cranking Speed Minimum
1961	4 Cyl.	N-12	AC45S	.035	.016①	75	1342	③	Damper	590	140
	V8	N-12	AC45FFS	.032	.016①	30	18436572②	④	Damper	590	140

①—Turn adjusting screw in (clockwise) until engine begins to misfire; then turn screw ½ turn in opposite direction.
②—Engine numbering (front to rear): Left bank 1-3-5-7, right bank 2-4-6-8.
③—Viewed from front, first line to align with pointer as engine is cranked.
④—Mark on damper to line up with 5° mark cast in block.

VALVE SPECIFICATIONS

Year	Model	Valve Lash Int.	Valve Lash Exh.	Valve Angles Seat	Valve Angles Face	Valve Spring Installed Height	Valve Spring Pressure Lbs. @ In.	Valve Lift Int.	Valve Lift Exh.	Stem Clearance Intake	Stem Clearance Exhaust	Stem Diameter Int.	Stem Diameter Exh.
1961	4 Cyl.①	Zero	Zero	⑧	⑧	1 17/32④	171 @ 1⅕	.330	.330	.0021-.0038	.0026-.0043	.3411	.3406
	4 Cyl.②	Zero	Zero	⑧	⑧	1 17/32④	102 @ 1⅕	.400	.400	.0021-.0038	.0026-.0043	.3411	.3406
	V8⑦	Zero	Zero	45	45	1 41/64	148 @ 1 17/64	.380	.380	.0005-.003	.0015-.0045	⑤	⑥

①—Manual transmission.
②—Automatic transmission.
⑦—See Buick Special chapter for service procedures.
③—Intake 30°, exhaust 45°.
④—Outer spring.
⑤—Tapers from .3412" top to .3407".
⑥—Tapers from .3407" top to .3397".
⑧—Intake 29°, exhaust 44°.

ENGINE TIGHTENING SPECIFICATIONS★

★ Torque specifications are for clean and lightly lubricated threads only. Dry or dirty threads produce increased friction which prevents accurate measurement of tightness.

Year	Model	Spark Plugs Ft. Lbs.	Cylinder Head Bolts Ft. Lbs.	Intake Manifold Ft. Lbs.	Exhaust Manifold Ft. Lbs.	Rocker Arm Shaft Bracket Ft. Lbs.	Rocker Arm Cover Ft. Lbs.	Connecting Rod Cap Bolts Ft. Lbs.	Main Bearing Cap Bolts Ft. Lbs.	Flywheel to Crankshaft Ft. Lbs.	Vibration Damper or Pulley Ft. Lbs.
1961	4 Cyl.	25	95	40	30	None	...	45	95②	...	160
	V8①	15-20	50-55	25-30	10-15	25-30	3-5	30-35	50-55	50-60	140-160

①—See Buick Special chapter for service procedures.   ②—Rear bearing 120 ft. lbs.

STARTING MOTOR SPECIFICATIONS

Year	Model	Part No.	Rotation	Brush Spring Tension, Ounces	No Load Test			Torque Test		
					Amperes	Volts	R.P.M.	Amperes	Volts	Torque, Lbs. Ft.
1961	4 Cyl.	1107796		35	49–76	10.6	6200–9400	270–310	4.25	①
	V8	1108303		35	58–80	10.6	6750–8600	280–320	4.00	①

①—Armature locked.

DISTRIBUTOR SPECIFICATIONS

Year	Model	Part No.	Rotation	Cam Angle, Degrees	Breaker Point Opening, Inch	Condenser Capacity, Mfds.	Breaker Arm Spring Tension, Ounces	Centrifugal Advance Data Degrees @ R.P.M. of Dist.		Vacuum Advance Data		
								Advance Starts	Full Advance	Inches of Vacuum to Start Plunger Movement	Inches of Vacuum for Full Plunger Travel	Maximum Vacuum Advance, Dist. Degrees
1961	4 Cyl.	1110254	CC	75	.016①	.18–.23	19–23	1 @ 410	10 @ 2200	6–8	13–15	10
	4 Cyl.	1110261	CC	75	.016①	.18–.23	19–23	1 @ 410	10 @ 2200	6–8	13–15	10
	V8	1110977	C	30	.016①	.18–.23	19–23	1 @ 350	13 @ 1850	6–8	13–15	10

①—Turn adjusting screw in (clockwise) until engine begins to misfire; then turn screw ½ turn in opposite direction.

REAR AXLE AND BRAKE CYLINDER SPECIFICATIONS

Year	Model	Ring Gear & Pinion Backlash, Inch	Side Bearing Preload, Inch Lbs.	Drive Pinion Adjustment	Drive Pinion Bearing Preload, Inch Lbs.	Drive Pinion Bearing Adjustment	Axle Shaft End Play, Inch	Hydraulic Cylinder Bore Sizes, Inch		Master Cylinder
								Wheel Cylinder		
								Front	Rear	
1961	All	.004–.009	10–20	Shim	10–16	Nut	None	1	1	1

COOLING SYSTEM & CAPACITY DATA

Year	Model	Cooling System Data				Fuel Tank Gals.	Engine Oil			Transmissions			Rear Axle Pints
		Quarts No Heater	Quarts With Heater	Rad. Cap Relief Pressure	Thermostat Opening Temp.		Refill Qts.③	Summer Grade	Winter Grade	Std. Pints	With Overdrive Pints	Automatic Qts.	
1961	All	11.6	12.6	12–15	170	...	15.5	4	20W	10W	3	None	①	3

①—Dry capacity of transmission, including converter, is 6 quarts. Refill capacity of transmission only is 3 quarts.

WHEEL ALIGNMENT SPECIFICATIONS

Year	Model	Caster, Degrees		Camber, Degrees		Front Wheel Toe-In, Inches	Rear Wheel Toe-In, Inches	Toe-out on Turns, Degrees①		Kingpin or Steering Axis Inclination Degrees
		Limits	Desired	Limits	Desired			Outer Wheel	Inner Wheel	
1961	All	− 1⅔①	− 1⅔	− ⅓ to + ⅔	+ ⅙	0 to ⅛	0 to ⅛	18–19	20	6⅚° @ 0 Camber

①—Plus or minus ½ degree.

GENERATOR AND REGULATOR SPECIFICATIONS

★To polarize generator, reconnect the leads to the regulator; then momentarily connect a jumper wire from the "Gen" to the "Bat" terminals of the regulator.

Car & Model	Generator				Brush Spring Tension, Ounces	Field Current Amperes	Regulator Number	Regulator				
	Generator Number	Ground Polarity	Rated Cap. Amps.	Gen. Field Ground Location★				Cutout Relay		Voltage Regulator Setting Volts	Current Regulator Setting Amperes	Current and Voltage Armature Air Gap, Inch
								Voltage to Close Points	Armature Air Gap, Inch			
1961 Four	1102224	N	30	External	28	1.69–1.79	1119263	12.6	.020	14.3	30	.075
1961 V8	1102237	N	30	External	28	1.69–1.79	1119263	12.6	.020	14.3	30	.075

PISTON, PINS, RINGS, CRANKSHAFT & BEARINGS

Year	Model	Fitting Pistons		Ring End Gap①		Wrist-pin Diameter	Rod Bearings		Main Bearings②			
		Shim To Use	Pounds Pull On Scale	Comp.	Oil		Shaft Diameter	Bearing Clearance	Shaft Diameter	Bearing Clearance	Thrust on Bear. No.	Shaft End Play
1961	4 Cyl.	②	②	③	.015	.9802	2.250	.0005–.0025	3.000	.0005–.003	4	.0035–.0085
	V8①	④	④	.010	.015	.8748	2.200	.0002–.0022	2.300	.0005–.0021	3	.004–.008

①—See Buick Special chapter for service procedures.
②—Piston clearance .0007–.0013".
③—Top .016", second .013".
④—Piston clearance .0005–.0011.

SERIAL & ENGINE NUMBER LOCATION
On Machined Pad On Front Right Side Of Block

Tempest 1961

Engine Section

See Buick Special Chapter for Service Procedures on V8 Engine

ENGINE, REPLACE

1. Remove hood, radiator and heater hoses at engine.
2. Disconnect wiring harness at engine units, engine ground straps, fuel line at fuel pump, vacuum modulator line at transmission hose connection, accelerator rod at engine lever and exhaust pipe at manifold.
3. Remove front fender cross brace and fan and pulley.
4. Raise front of car and place wood block at rear of engine to prevent damage to distributor if engine rocks to rear.
5. Disconnect propeller shaft and torque tube from rear of engine and remove engine support at crossmember.
6. Raise engine and move forward to clear firewall and heater.
7. Reverse removal procedure to install the engine. *However, be sure to follow instructions for installing the propeller shaft as outlined in the Propeller Shaft Section. Failure to follow procedure may result in damage to drive line.*

CYLINDER HEAD

1. Remove intake manifold.
2. Disconnect breather pipe and remove push rod cover.
3. Remove bolts attaching exhaust manifold to head.
4. Remove rocker arm cover.
5. Loosen rocker arm nuts and rotate rocker arms so push rods can be removed.
6. Lift out push rods and tag them so they can be reinstalled in original locations.

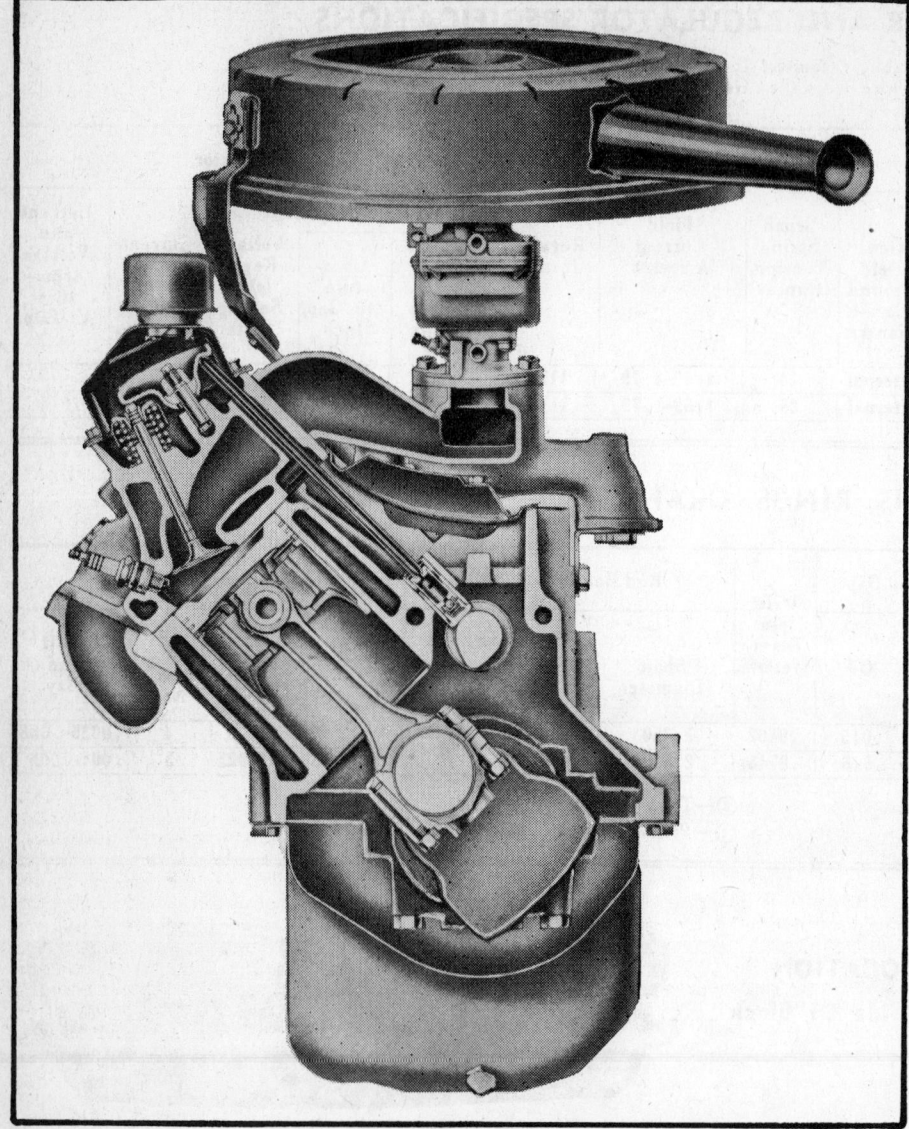

Cross section of four cylinder engine

Fig. 1 Slots filed in rocker arm stud

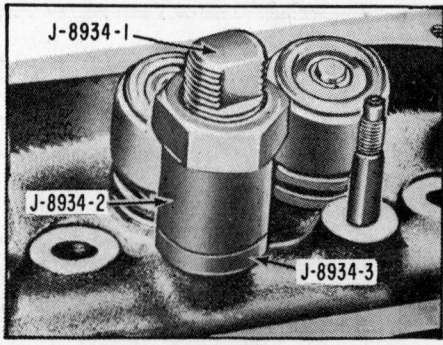

Fig. 2 Tools positioned to remove rocker arm stud

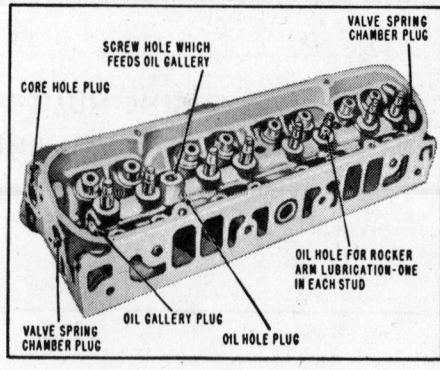

Fig. 3 Location of cylinder head oil gallery plugs

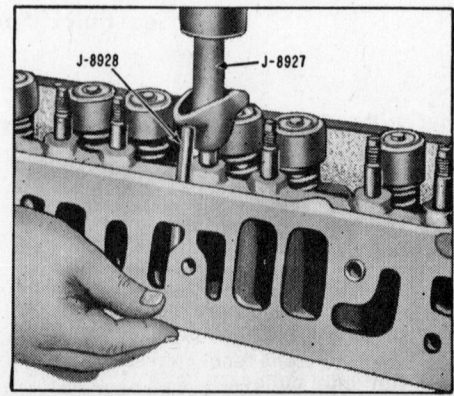

Fig. 4 Positioning rocker arm stud for installation

7. Remove head bolts and lift off head.

8. Note that there are three different length bolts used. When installed properly, they will project an equal amount from their bosses. Do not use sealer on bolt threads. When installed, tighten rocker arm nuts to 15-25 ft. lbs. torque.

ROCKER ARM STUDS

Rocker arm studs are replaceable providing a press of at least two tons capacity is available. Both standard and .003" oversize studs are available. If replacing a loose stud, measure stud diameter with a micrometer. Standard size studs should measure .4340" to .4345". If stud is loose because it is undersize, replace with standard stud. If loose because hole is oversize, replace with .003" oversize stud. No reaming operation is necessary.

1. Remove cylinder head.

2. With rocker arm removed, file two slots $\frac{3}{32}$" to $\frac{1}{8}$" deep on opposite sides of stud, Fig. 1. Top of slots should be $\frac{1}{4}$" to $\frac{3}{8}$" below thread travel.

3. Place special washer (J-8934-3) at bottom of stud, Fig. 2. Position stud remover (J-8934-1) on stud and tighten screws securely with $\frac{5}{32}$" Allen wrench. Place spacer (J-8934-2) over stud remover.

4. Thread $\frac{7}{8}$" standard nut on stud remover and turn nut until stud is out of cylinder head.

5. Remove plugs, Fig. 3, from ends of cylinder head oil gallery and clean out metal deposits and foreign matter.

6. Position rocker arm on new stud and place installer (J-8927) on stud in place of rocker arm ball.

7. Coat stud with white lead and oil and, with cylinder head mounted on press so studs are vertical, position new stud with rocker arm stud installer over hole in head, Fig. 4.

8. Press stud in head until it is in about halfway ($\frac{7}{16}$").
9. Position valve train gauge (J-8928) in push rod hole so that it seats properly in rocker arm.
10. With valve seated, slowly press stud into head until gauge projects about midway between end of gauge and the step with respect to the gasket surface of the head, Fig. 5.
11. Remove stud installer, rocker arm and ball. Blow air through hole in new stud to insure that passage is not restricted. Blow air through oil gallery to remove any foreign matter. Replace plugs in ends of oil gallery.
12. Check oil passages from oil gallery to all studs. Install rocker arm and ball and install nut loosely.
13. Install cylinder head and tighten to specified torque. Tighten rocker arm nuts to a torque of 15-25 ft lbs.

VALVE ARRANGEMENT

Front to Rear.........E-I-I-E-E-I-I-E

VALVES, GRIND

After removing valves and springs from cylinder head, scrape all carbon from combustion chambers and valves. If wire brushes are used for cleaning carbon, use care to avoid scratching valve seats and valve faces. Clean all carbon and gum deposits from valve guides.

In refacing valves, take off only the minimum of metal required to clean up the valve faces. If the outer edge of the valve becomes too thin or sharp due to excessive grinding the valve must be replaced. In other words the valve head margin must be at least $\frac{3}{64}$", otherwise the valve must be replaced. This margin is the area above the contact surface of the valve face.

Inspect the valve seats in the head for cracks, burns, pitting, ridges or improper angle. During any general engine overhaul it is advisable to reface the valve seats regardless of their condition.

Reface valves and true up seats to the angles listed in the *Valve Specifications* chart. Cutting a valve seat results in lowering the valve spring pressure and

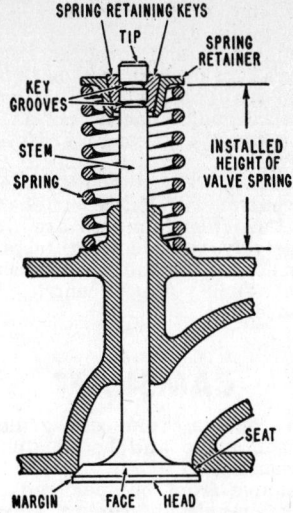

Fig. 6 Valve nomenclature. Tempest engine has an inner and outer spring for each valve

increases the width of the seat. The nominal width of a valve seat is $\frac{1}{16}$". If valve seat is over $\frac{5}{64}$" after truing up, it should be narrowed to specified width by using a flat stone.

Improper hydraulic valve lifter operation may result if valve and seat have been refinished enough to allow the end of the valve stem to raise approximately .050" above normal position. In this case it will be necessary to grind off the end of the valve stem or replace parts.

Test valves for concentricity with seats and for tight seating. Valves can be tested by lightly coating the valve face with Prussian blue and turning the valve against its seat. This indicates whether the seat is concentric with the valve guide *but does not prove that the valve face is concentric with the valve stem, or that the valve is seating all around.* After making this test, wash all blue from the surfaces, lightly coat the *valve seat* with blue and repeat the test to see whether a full mark is obtained on the valve. *Both tests are necessary to prove that a proper seat is being obtained.*

VALVE SPRING INSTALLED HEIGHT

When valves and seats are reground the position of the valve in the head is changed so as to lessen the valve spring tension. Without proper valve spring tension the valve does not seat long enough or it may not seat completely. Since the valve is cooled by transferring heat from the valve head to the seat and thence to the coolant, improper valve spring tension will cause worn, pitted and distorted valves which result in loss of compression and power as well as poor gasoline mileage.

When valves, springs, retainers and locks are installed, measure the assembled height of the valve springs from the surface of the cylinder head spring pad to the underside of the spring

retainer as shown in Fig. 6. If the assembled height is greater than the dimension given in the *Valve Specifications Chart*, install a spacer or shim of proper thickness between cylinder head spring pad and spring to bring the assembled height to specifications.

Do not install spacers unless necessary. Excessive use of spacers will result in overstressing valve springs and overloading camshaft lobes which could lead to spring breakage and worn camshaft lobes.

VALVE SPRING TESTING

Wash all valve springs with a suitable solvent. Examine the springs for damage or corrosion due to acid etching, which will develop into surface cracks and cause spring failure.

Check the valve spring tension on a spring testing fixture if one is available. If a fixture is not available, at least check the free length of each spring by standing it alongside a new spring. Any spring that does not conform to the pressure specifications in the *Valve Specifications* table within 10 per cent should be replaced. Likewise any spring that stands shorter than the new spring used for comparison should be discarded.

VALVE GUIDES

Valve guides are cast integral with the cylinder head. Valves with oversize stems are available in .001", .003" and .005" larger than standard.

Oversize reamers are required to enlarge valve guide holes to fit the oversize stems. For best results when installing .005" oversize valve stem use a .003" oversize reamer first and then ream to .005" oversize. Always reface the valve and valve seat after reaming valve guide. Valves are marked .001, .003 or .005 with colored ink.

HYDRAULIC VALVE LIFTERS

Failure of an hydraulic valve lifter, Fig. 7, is generally caused by an inadequate oil supply or dirt. An air leak at the intake side of the oil pump or too much oil in the engine will cause air bubbles in the oil supply to the lifters, causing them to collapse. This is a probable cause of trouble if several lifters fail to function, but air in the oil is an unlikely cause of failure of a single unit.

The valve lifters may be lifted out of their bores after removing the rocker

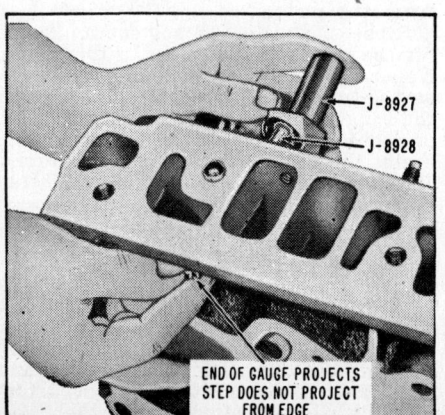

Fig. 5 Checking stud height

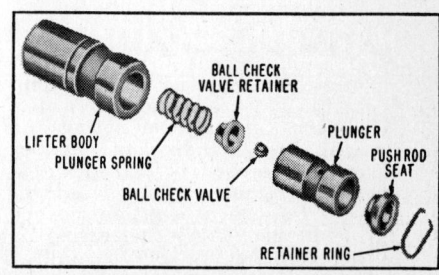

Fig. 7 Hydraulic valve lifter parts

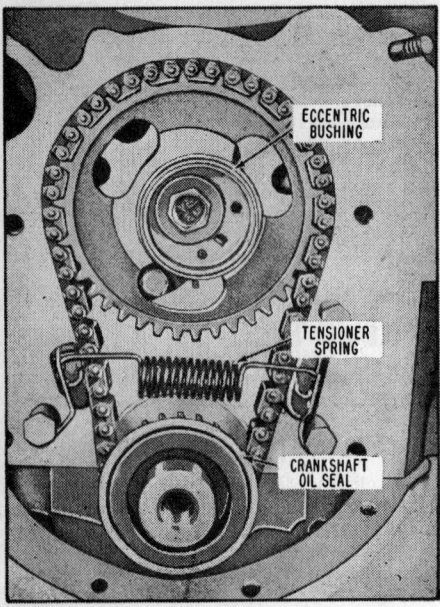

Fig. 8 Front of engine with cover removed

simplify proper positioning on reassembly, Fig. 9.
4. Slide chain and sprockets off shafts.
5. Install new chain and/or sprockets, making sure marks on sprockets are aligned exactly on a straight line passing through shaft centers. Camshaft should extend through sprocket so that hole in fuel pump eccentric will locate on shaft.
6. If tensioner bumpers are worn excessively, replace them. Install chain tensioner assembly, crankshaft oil seal, fuel pump eccentric, bushing and cover.

CAMSHAFT

1. To remove, take off grille lower panel, grille and hood latch as an assembly.
2. Remove front bumper, radiator, intake manifold, timing cover, distributor chain and sprockets, valve lifters and camshaft thrust plate.
3. Pull out camshaft using care not to damage bearings.
4. Reverse removal procedure to install, being sure to install camshaft thrust plate, indexing slot in plate with slot in block.

CAMSHAFT BEARINGS

Camshaft bearings can be replaced while the engine is disassembled for overhaul or without completely disassembling the engine after removing the camshaft.

Special removing and installing equipment is required to replace the bearings. The notch in the edge of the bearing is used to properly position the bearing, with respect to the oil holes, when installed. When bearings are installed at the factory, the notches all face the front except the one in the rear bearing. In the field it is necessary to install bearings with the notch facing the rear.

Coat inner diameters of all bearings with oil and install camshaft. Rotate camshaft through several revolutions to make sure it is completely free. If any tight spots are found, remove camshaft and carefully polish down the center journal slightly. If still not free, polish the front and rear journals slightly. If any particular bearing causes binding in the camshaft, replace that bearing also.

PISTONS & RODS, REMOVE

After removing the cylinder head, examine the cylinder bores above the ring travel area. If bores are worn so that a shoulder or ridge exists at this point, remove the ridge with a ridge reamer to avoid damaging rings or cracking ring lands of piston during removal.

Remove connecting rod caps and push pistons and rods out of cylinders, using care to prevent rod bolts from contacting and nicking crankshaft journals.

Make sure the rods and pistons are properly numbered so that they can be reinstalled in original locations. It is advisable to install caps on rods to avoid mixing parts.

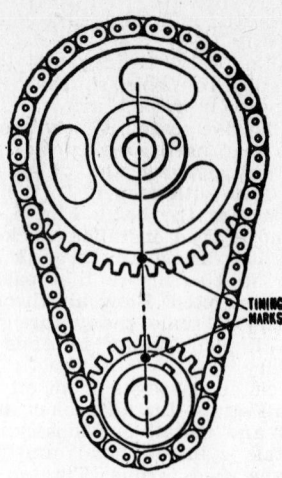

Fig. 9 Valve timing marks

PISTON & ROD, ASSEMBLE

All pistons have an "F" cast on the front side. There is also a notch cast in top of the high compression piston head and two notches cast in the standard compression piston head at the front to facilitate proper installation.

One side of the connecting rod has large machined bosses. This side of the rod should be installed toward the front of the engine. In other words, the large boss on the rod and the "F" side of the piston should be installed toward the front of the engine.

PISTONS

If the pistons are to be reused with new rings, remove the carbon from the ring grooves. A special tool is available for this work but a satisfactory job can be done by breaking an old piston ring, filing the broken end to a sharp, square edge and using it to scrape out the carbon. Soak the piston in cleaning solvent to loosen any carbon residue. Clean out the loosened carbon, being careful not to cut away any piston material.

Clean out the oil return holes with a drill just large enough to fill the holes. Hold the drill in a tap wrench and make sure the drill does not remove any metal from the piston.

Rinse the piston in solvent and wipe off the carbon on the sides of the piston. *Never use a wire brush to clean a piston* as the brush will round off the edges of the ring lands. Pistons showing scuffed or scored skirts should be scrapped. Examine the ring lands carefully for cracks. If the piston is in the least bit doubtful, it should be discarded.

PISTON RINGS

When new piston rings are installed without reboring cylinders, the glazed cylinder walls should be slightly dulled, but without increasing the bore diameter. This is done with a "Glazebuster" or with a hone equipped with the finest grade of stones.

arms and push rods. Adjustable pliers with taped jaws may be used to remove lifters that are stuck due to varnish, carbon, etc.

To disassemble, press down on the center of the push rod cup. Using a pointed tool, remove lock wire from the groove while holding cup down. Invert lifter and slide out push rod cup, plunger, ball, retainer and spring.

To assemble, place the ball on its seat in the lower end of the plunger while holding the plunger upside down. Position the ball retainer and spring over ball and end of plunger. Lower the body over the plunger. Turn the assembly right side up and fill the plunger with clean engine oil. Jiggle the ball with a small piece of wire until oil drains out of plunger into the body and trapped air is released from the body. Refill the plunger with oil, place the push rod cup on the plunger and position the lock wire over the cup, locking it in its groove.

TIMING COVER

1. To remove cover, drain radiator.
2. Remove generator and fuel pump.
3. Disconnect hose from cover.
4. Remove cover attaching bolts and cover.
5. When installing, tighten oil pan-to-cover screws to 15 ft. lbs.

TIMING CHAIN

1. To remove, take off cover, fuel pump eccentric and crankshaft oil seal.
2. Remove chain tensioner spring and bumper, Fig. 8. *Right hand bumper must be removed before spring is removed because of hook in end of spring. Do not attempt to remove spring by stretching or twisting as spring may be damaged.*
3. Align timing marks on sprockets to

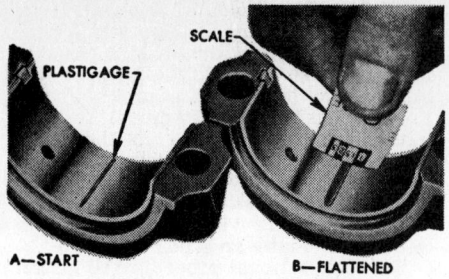

Fig. 10 Checking bearing clearance with Plastigage

New piston rings must be checked for clearance in piston grooves and for gap in cylinder bores. Cylinder bores and piston grooves must be clean, dry and free of carbon and burrs.

Check the clearance of each ring in its piston groove by installing the ring and then inserting feeler gauges *under* the ring. Any wear that occurs in the piston groove forms a step or ridge at the inner portion of the lower land. If gauges are inserted above the ring, the ring may rest on the step instead of on the worn portion of the lower land, and a false measurement of clearance will result.

If the piston grooves have worn to the extent that relatively high steps or ridges exist on the lower lands, the piston should be replaced because the steps will interfere with the operation of new rings and the ring clearances will be excessive. Piston rings are not furnished in oversize widths to compensate for ring groove wear.

To check the end gaps of rings, place the ring in the cylinder in which it will be used. Square it in the body by tapping with the lower end of the piston, then measure the gap with feeler gauges. If necessary to increase the gap, file the ends of rings carefully with a smooth file.

PISTON PINS

Piston pins are a pressed fit in the upper end of the connecting rod and a slide fit in the piston bosses.

ROD BEARINGS

Connecting rod bearings are of the precision insert type and if worn can be replaced without removing the rod assembly by removing the cap and replacing the upper and lower halves. The clearance between the rod bearing and the crankshaft can be measured by the use of Plastigage as follows:

1. Remove bearing cap and wipe oil from crankshaft journal and bearing insert.
2. With crankpin at approximately bottom dead center, place a piece of Plastigage in the center of the cap.
3. Reinstall cap and tighten the bolts to the torque listed on the *Engine Tightening Data* table.
4. Remove bearing cap and determine bearing clearance by comparing the width of the flattened Plastigage at its widest point with the graduation on the Plastigage envelope. The

number within the graduation on the envelope indicates the clearance in thousandths of an inch, Fig. 10.

MAIN BEARINGS

Caution—Main bearing clearance can be checked with Plastigage in the same manner described for rod bearings. If bearings are measured with the engine in the chassis, the crankshaft must be supported in order to take up clearance between the upper bearing insert and crankshaft journal. This can be done by tightening bearing caps of adjacent bearing with .005" to .015" cardboard (such as a calling card) between lower bearing shell and journal. Use extreme care when this is done to avoid unnecessary strain on the crankshaft or bearings or a false reading may be obtained. Do not rotate crankshaft while Plastigage is installed. *Be sure to remove cardboard.* To install new bearings, proceed as follows:

1. Remove bearing cap and worn lower shell.
2. Rotate crankshaft in normal direction to turn upper bearing shell out of crankcase. Use a cotter pin with a flattened head or the special tool made for the purpose in the crankshaft oil hole to contact the bearing and force it out, Fig. 11.
3. Place a new upper shell on the crankshft journal with the locating notch in the correct position and rotate the shaft to turn the bearing in place.
4. Install the lower bearing shell in the cap.
5. Tighten all cap nuts to the torque value given in the *Engine Tightening Data* table.

CRANKSHAFT OIL SEAL

A braided oil seal is pressed into the upper and lower grooves behind the rear main bearing. Should the braided seal require replacement, the installation of the lower half is accomplished as follows:

With the bearing cap and lower bearing half removed, install a new seal so that both ends protrude above the cap. Tap the seal down into position or roll it snugly in its groove with a smooth rounded tool, Fig. 12. Then cut off the protruding ends of the seal with a sharp knife or razor blade.

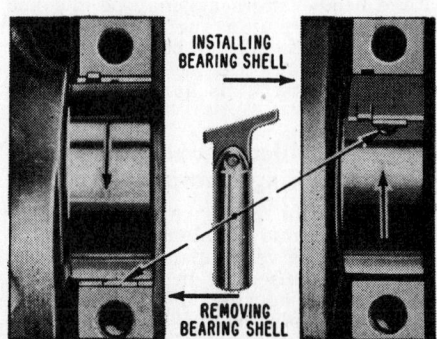

Fig. 11 Tool for removing upper main bearing shells

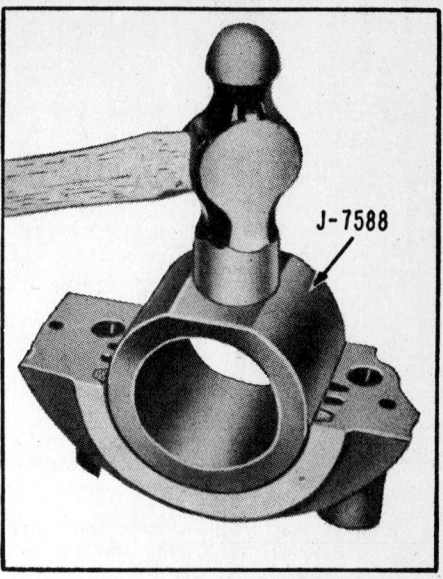

Fig. 12 Installing rear main bearing oil seal

Installing Upper Seal

Although the usual practice is to remove the crankshaft when the upper half of the seal is to be replaced it is possible to do the job without removing the crankshaft as follows:

To remove the seal, use needle-nose pliers to grasp the end of the seal which is most accessible. Pull the seal downward while rotating the crankshaft slowly in the direction that the seal is being removed.

To install the new seal, fasten a length of wire or strong string such as fishing line securely to one end of the new seal. See that the point of fastening is not bulky and that it is not over ⅜" from the end of the seal. Coat the seal with Lubriplate. Pass the free end of the wire or string up over the crankshaft at the point where the seal is to be installed. Then exert a firm, steady pull on the wire or string and at the sme time rotate the crankshaft slowly in the direction of the pull. This will help to move the seal into position. When the installation is completed, trim the ends of the seal flush with the engine block.

OIL PAN

1. To remove, drain oil and remove exhaust crossover pipe.
2. Support engine and remove front crossmember.
3. Remove flywheel housing front shield and lower cover.
4. Unfasten and remove oil pan.

OIL PUMP

To remove pump, take off oil pan. Remove pump attaching screws and carefully lower pump away from block with one hand while removing pump drive shaft with the other hand.

When disassembling the pump, mark gears before removing them so they have

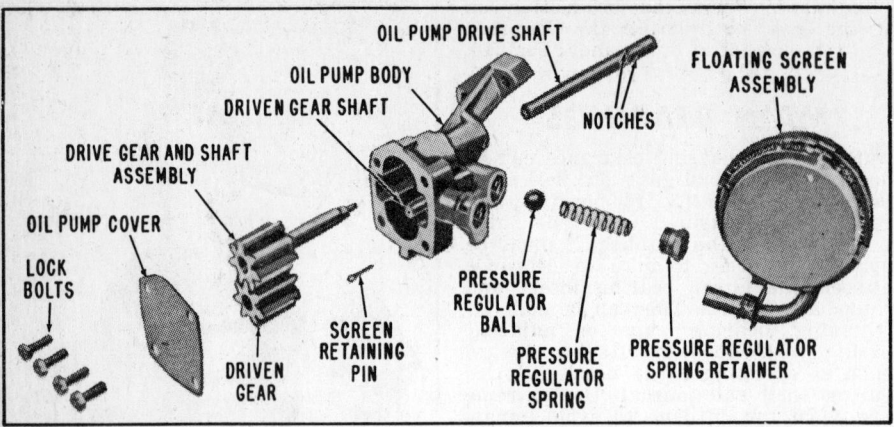

Fig. 13 Exploded view of oil pump

the same relationship when they are reinstalled, Fig. 13. Clean and inspect all parts, discarding any that are worn or otherwise damaged.

To assemble, install drive and driven gear as marked before disassembly. Install cover and turn drive shaft by hand to insure that it turns freely and has a slight amount of end play. Torque cover bolts to 10-20 ft. lbs. Install pressure regulator ball, spring and retainer, tightening retainer to 8-18 ft. lbs. *Do not attempt to change oil pressure by varying the length of the pressure regulator valve spring.* Install pump to engine and torque bolts to 20-35 ft. lbs.

RADIATOR

To remove radiator, drain system and disconnect hoses. Remove radiator fan shield and radiator.

WATER PUMP

To remove water pump, which is *serviced only as an assembly*, drain cooling system. Remove fan belt, fan and pulley. Unfasten and remove pump from engine.

When pump is installed on engine, drain hole will be at bottom. Tighten pump attaching nuts to 15 ft. lbs.

DISTRIBUTOR, REPLACE

1. To remove, disconnect distributor-to-coil primary wire.
2. Remove distributor cap and crank engine so rotor is in position to fire No. 1 cylinder and timing mark on vibration damper is indexed with pointer.
3. Remove vacuum line, distributor

clamp screw and hold-down clamp.
4. When removing distributor, note that the rotor will rotate as the distributor is pulled out of the block. Note the relationship of the rotor and housing after removal so that the rotor can be set in the same position when the distributor is being installed. Always set distributor in an upright position so oil from distributor shaft will not run out onto breaker plate and points.
5. Reverse removal procedure to install distributor, being sure that No. 1 piston is up on its compression stroke and that the rotor is in the position to fire No. 1 spark plug. Then check and adjust ignition timing.

IGNITION TIMING

With distributor vacuum line disconnected and car operating at normal idle speed or below, set ignition timing. See *Tune Up Chart.*

STARTER, REPLACE

To remove starter, disconnect cable from battery and cable and solenoid wire from starter solenoid. Unfasten and remove starter from engine.

MUFFLER & PIPES

Replacing any part of the exhaust system is an obvious operation. Always use new gaskets and torque bolts to 15-25 ft. lbs. except U-bolt nuts which are tightened to 10-15 ft. lbs.

Carburetor Section

Performance Complaints

Flooding, stumble on acceleration or other performance complaints are in many instances caused by the presence of dirt, water or other foreign matter in the carburetor. To aid in diagnosing the cause of the complaint, the carburetor should be carefully removed from the engine without draining the fuel from the bowl. The contents of the fuel bowl may then be examined for contamination as the carburetor is disassembled.

Check the fuel in the bowl for contamination by dirt, water, gum or other foreign matter. A magnet moved through the fuel in the bowl will pick up and identify any iron oxide dust that may have caused intake needle and seat leakage.

Inspect gasketed surfaces between body and air horn. Small nicks or burrs should be smoothed down to eliminate air or fuel leakage. On carburetors having a vacuum piston, be especially particular when inspecting the top surface of the inner wall of the bowl around

the vacuum piston passage. A poor seal at this location may contribute to a "cutting-out" on turns complaint.

Fill the carburetor bowl with clean fuel before installing on manifold. This will help prevent dirt trapped in the fuel system from being dislodged by the free flow of fuel as the carburetor is primed. The operation of the floats and intake needle and seats may be checked under pressure if a fuel pump is used at the bench to fill the carburetor bowl. Operate the throttle several times and visually check the discharge from pump jets.

Poor Mileage and Engine Loading Complaints

Cases of poor mileage and engine loading may be due in many instances to sluggish choke valve opening during cold driveaway, caused by insufficient vacuum in choke housing, a plugged or restricted heat pipe or inlet in choke cover. To check for this condition, have engine warm and running at slow idle. Remove choke heat pipe and hold a finger over

the heat inlet hole (hole is on choke housing on some carburetors). If there is little or no vacuum pull on the finger, check the choke housing for gasket leaks or plugged vacuum passages. If these are OK, check choke vacuum passages in carburetor between choke housing and manifold.

Dirty or Rusty Choke Housing

In cases where it is found that the interior of the choke housing is dirty, gummed or rusty while the carburetor itself is comparatively clean, look for a punctured or eroded manifold heat tube (if one is used).

Manifold Heat Control Valve

An engine equipped with a manifold heat control valve can operate with the valve stuck in either the open or closed position. Because of this, an inoperative valve is frequently overlooked at vehicle lubrication or tune-up.

A valve stuck in the "heat-off" position can result in slow warm up, deposits in combustion chamber, carburetor icing, flat spots during acceleration, low gas mileage and spark plug fouling.

A valve stuck in the "heat-on" position can result in power loss, engine knocking, sticking or burned valves and spark plug burning.

To prevent the possibility of a stuck valve, check and lubricate the valve each time the vehicle is lubricated or tuned-up. Check the operation of the valve manually. To lubricate the valve, place a few drops of penetrating oil on the valve shaft where it passes through the manifold. Then move the valve up and down a few times to work the oil in. *Do not use engine oil to lubricate the valve as it will leave a residue which hampers valve operation.*

ROCHESTER CARBURETOR ADJUSTMENTS

| Year | Carburetor Model | Idle Adjustments | | | | Float Level | | Float Drop | | Pump Rod Setting | Choke Unloader Setting | Choke Setting |
		Mixture Screws Turns Open	Hot Idle Speed In Drive	Fast Idle Speed	Dashpot Plunger Clearance	Primary	Secondary	Primary	Secondary			
1961	B-7019061	1½	690	None	None	1 9/32 ①	None	1 3/4 ②	None	None	None	None
	BC-7019062	1½	590	None	.064 ④	1 9/32 ①	None	1 3/4 ②	None	None	.161 ③	Index
	2GC-7019090	1½	590	None	None	1 17/64 ⑤	None	1 29/32 ⑥	None	1 3/32 ⑦	.157 ⑧	Index
	2GC-7019093	1½	590	None	None	1 17/64 ⑤	None	1 29/32 ⑥	None	1 3/32 ⑦	.157 ⑧	Index
	4GC-7019079	1½	590	3000 ⑬	.085 ④	1 21/64 ⑩	1 21/64 ⑩	1 3/4 ⑪	1 3/4 ⑪	15/16 ⑨	.152 ⑫	Index
	4GC-7019066	1½	590	2500 ⑬	.085 ④	1 21/64 ⑩	1 21/64 ⑩	1 3/4 ⑪	1 3/4 ⑪	15/16 ⑨	.152 ⑫	Index

ROCHESTER NOTES

Choke Rod. Adjust

With idle speed screw on second step and against high step of cam, bend choke rod as necessary to obtain the proper clearance between lower edge of choke valve and inner wall of air horn. Clearance is .081" on BC, .052" on 2GC and .055" on 4GC.

Idle Vent, Adjust

4GC UNITS—Open primary throttle valve to a point where idle vent valve just closes. With a 55/64" gauge, measure between top of air horn casting and bottom of pump plunger rod. To adjust, bend tang on pump lever.

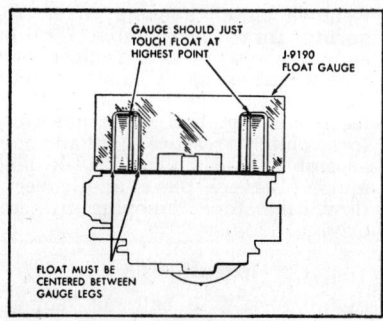

Fig. ①—B and BC float level.

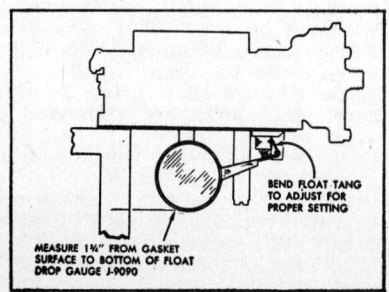

Fig. ②—B and BC float drop.

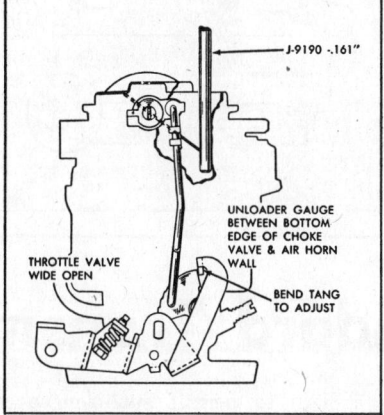

Fig. ③—With throttle valve wide open, bend tang on throttle lever to obtain specified clearance between choke valve and inner wall of air horn.

④—With fast idle on 4GC and hot idle on BC properly adjusted, shut off engine. Rotate fast idle cam so that fast idle screw rests on second step of fast idle cam with screw resting against top step. Clearance between contact screw and contact on throttle lever should be as specified. To adjust, turn contact screw as required.

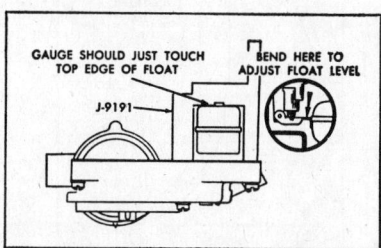

Fig. ⑤—2GC float level.

➤ Fig. ⑧—With throttle valves wide open, clearance between upper edge of choke valve and inner wall of air horn should be as specified. To adjust, bend tang on throttle lever.

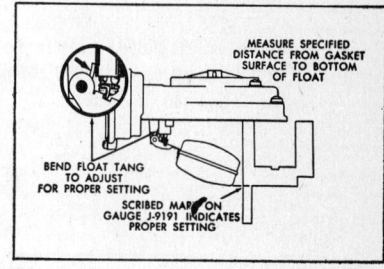

Fig. ⑥—2GC float drop.

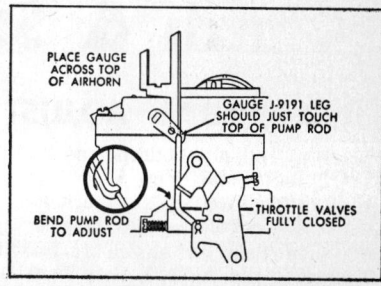

Fig. ⑦—With pump rod in outer hole of lever, back out idle screw until throttle valves are fully closed. Measure distance between top of air horn to top of pump rod. If dimension is not as specified, bend pump rod as required.

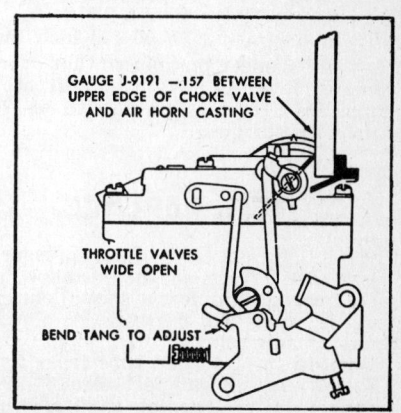

ROCHESTER NOTES

continued

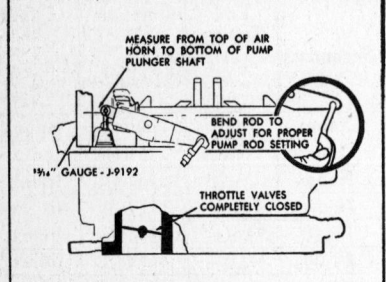

Fig. ⑨—With throttle valves closed, measure from top of air horn casting to bottom of pump plunger rod. To adjust, bend pump rod as required.

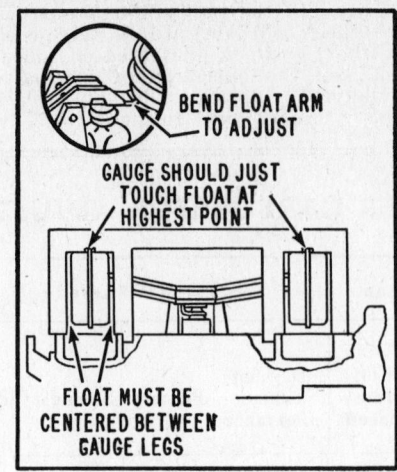

Fig. ⑩—4GC float level.

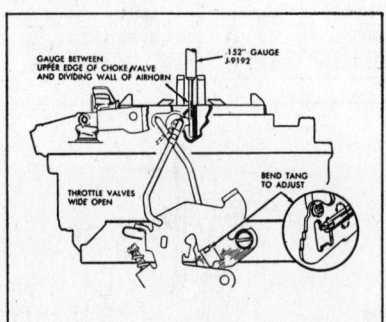

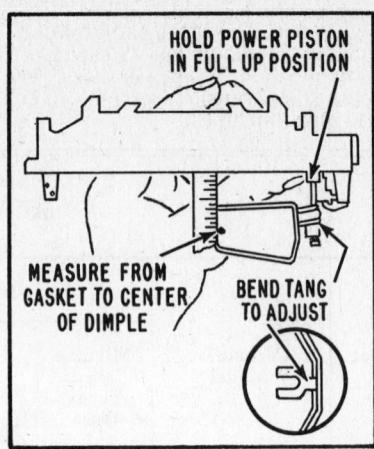

Fig. ⑪—4GC float drop.

Fig. ⑫—With throttle valves fully open, bend tang on fast idle cam to obtain the dimension specified between top of choke valve and inner wall of air horn.

⑬—With fast idle screw resting on top step of cam, adjust fast idle screw to obtain the engine rpm specified.

Clutch & Standard Transmission Section

CLUTCH PEDAL, ADJUST

1. Back off silencer bumper so it does not touch pedal, Fig. 1.
2. Adjust position of stop bracket to establish correct pedal height.
3. Remove lash at clutch fork with adjusting nut on rod, then back off as follows:
   4 Cylinder Engine
   4¼ turns for new driven plate.
   3½ turns for used driven plate.
   V8 Engine
   4¼ turns for new driven plate.
   3 turns for used driven plate.
4. Tighten jam nut to 60-120 inch lbs.
5. Adjust silencer bumper so that over-center lever is just lifted off stop pin. Then tighten jam nuts to 60-120 inch lbs. torque.

CLUTCH, REPLACE

Do not attempt to adjust pressure plate release levers as they cannot be adjusted correctly unless a special clutch fixture is used. To remove the clutch proceed as follows:

1. Remove front torque tube from flywheel housing. Support torque tube at front after dropping front of tube enough to permit sufficient access to clutch.
2. Disconnect accelerator linkage.
3. Remove clutch rod from lever and clutch fork.

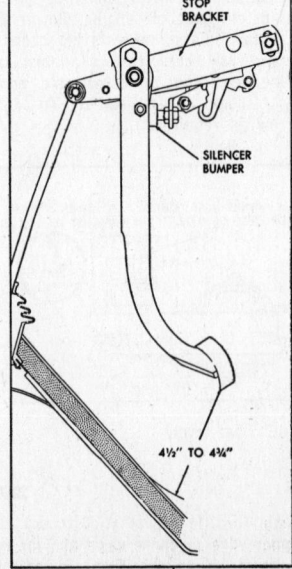

Fig. 1 Clutch pedal clearance

4. Remove clutch housing cover, fork spring, fork cover plates, fork ball support bolt, retaining plate bolts, clutch drive shaft and retaining plate, release bearing support, release bearing, ball nut from clutch fork, clutch pressure plate and cover assembly, and clutch driven plate.
5. Mark pressure plate and cover to flywheel before removing to retain original balance.

Installation

1. Install fork with ball nut facing to rear of car.
2. Install driven plate with longer flange toward engine.
3. Install pressure plate and cover, making sure index marks line up with one on flywheel if old assembly is being installed. Use clutch drive shaft to align clutch driven plate. Remove shaft after all pressure plate bolts are tightened to 20-35 ft. lbs.
4. Coat ball nut with wheel bearing grease and install in fork.
5. Install clutch release bearing and bearing support, having greased lightly the surface of support.
6. Hook clutch fork in groove in release bearing.
7. Coat splines lightly with wheel bearing grease and install drive

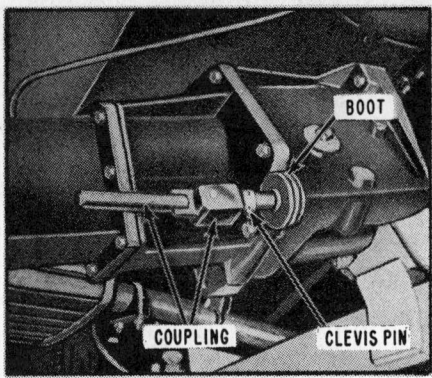

Fig. 2 Gearshift control rod coupling

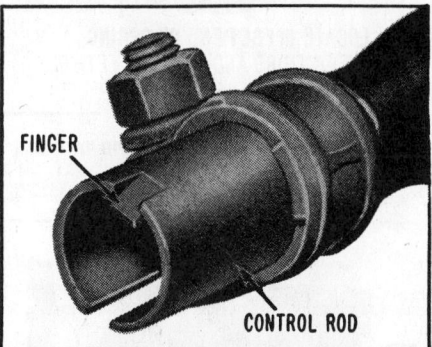

Fig. 3 Gearshift control rod coupling finger

shaft and retaining plate and tighten bolts to 10-25 ft. lbs.

8. Install dust shields together with a light coat of grease between them.
9. Install clutch ball nut bolt and tighten to 30-45 ft. lbs.
10. Install fork spring.
11. Install and tighten clutch housing cover to 10-20 ft. lbs.
12. Coat both ends with grease and install clutch rod in lever and fork. Secure with C-shaped retainer and washer.
13. Hook anti-rattle spring to clutch rod.
14. Install spring, washer and cotter pin at fork end.
15. Adjust clutch pedal as outlined above.

GEARSHIFT CONTROL

Removal

1. Loosen clamp nut securing control rod to coupling.
2. Remove bolts securing gearshift lever and housing to torque tube.
3. Move gearshift lever and housing toward front of car, removing control rod from coupling.
4. Remove cotter and clevis pins securing coupling to manual shift shaft, Fig. 2.
5. Remove coupling and boot from shaft.

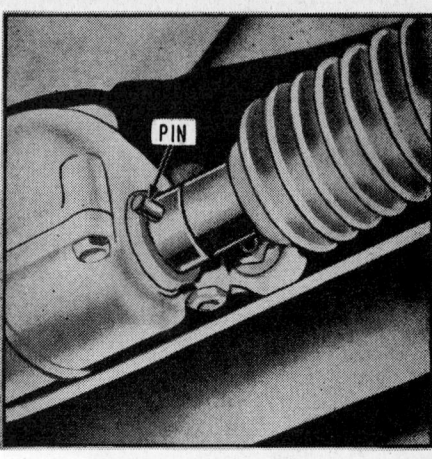

Fig. 4 Gearshift control rod alignment pin

Installation

1. Position manual shift shaft in 1st gear position. To locate 1st gear position in transmission, place shift shaft in neutral, turn counterclockwise, and pull shaft to forward position.
2. Install shift shaft and coupling boot, Fig. 2. Install coupling on shaft and secure with clevis and cotter pins.

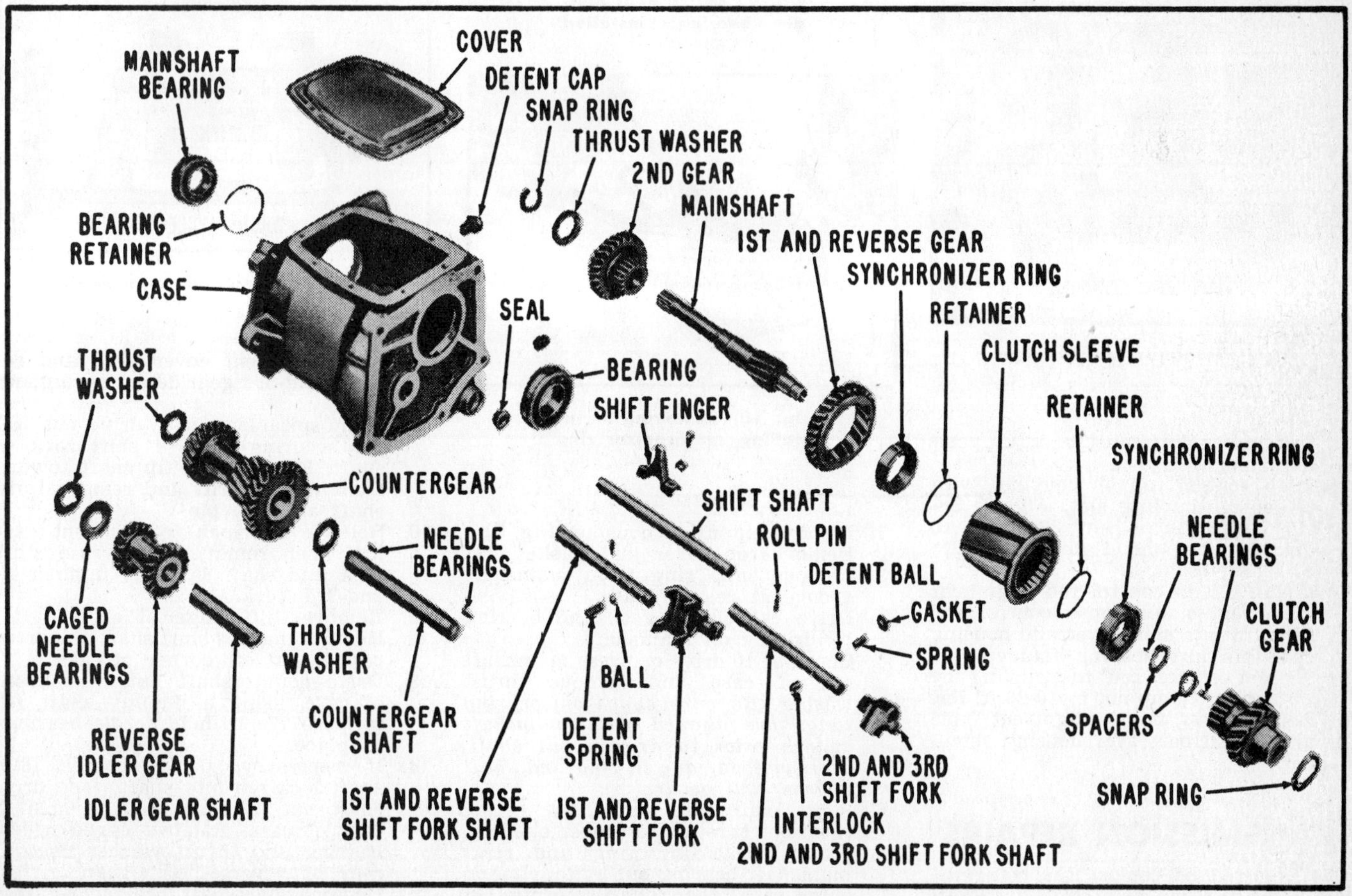

Fig. 5 Manual shift transmission

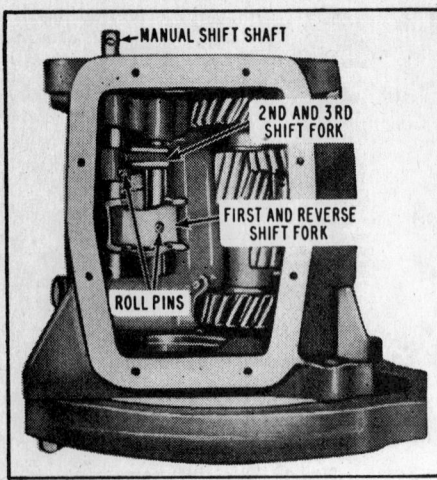

Fig. 6 Transmission shift forks

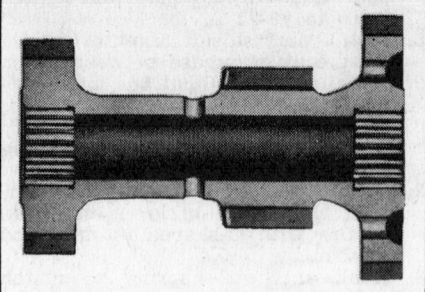

Fig. 8 Countergear needle bearings installed

LOCATE OFFSET END OF SPRING BETWEEN THIRD AND FOURTH TEETH OF EITHER BANK OF TEETH

Fig. 11 Position of energizing spring

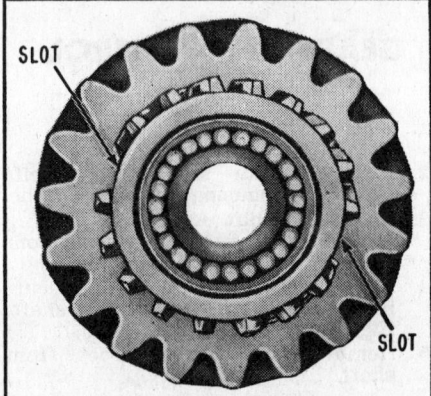

Fig. 9 Clutch gear needle bearings installed

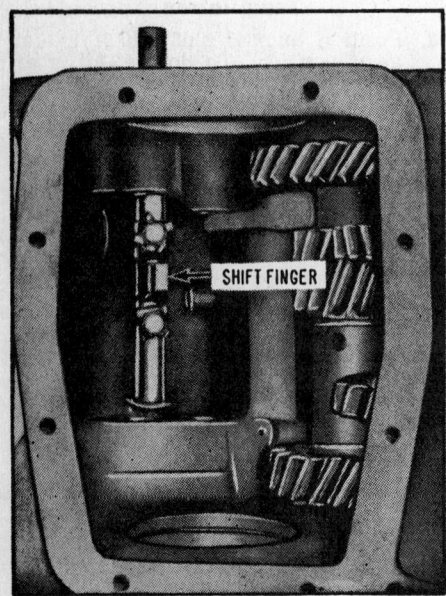

Fig. 7 Transmission shift finger

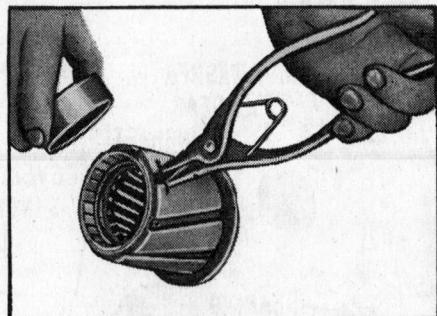

Fig. 10 Removing or installing synchronizer ring

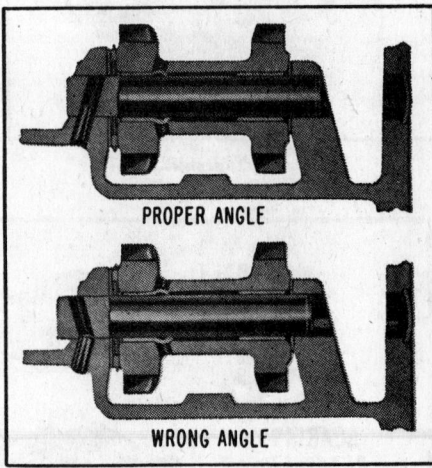

Fig. 12 Reverse idler gear lock pin

Slot in coupling must be in up position.

3. Slide control rod on coupling with finger in coupling slot, Fig. 3. Secure shift lever and housing to torque tube and tighten bolts to 10-15 ft. lbs.
4. Install pin in control rod alignment hole, Fig. 4, and push control rod forward into shift lever and housing until pin hits housing flange.
5. Secure control rod to coupling by tightening clamp nut to 10-20 ft. lbs.
6. Remove pin from alignment hole and install boot over housing shoulder.

TRANSMISSION REPAIRS

To remove and replace the transmission, refer to Rear Axle, Propeller Shaft and Torque Tube Section.

Disassemble

1. Remove extension housing, Fig. 5.
2. Remove top cover and gasket.
3. Remove snap ring from mainshaft groove at rear of case.
4. Drive out clutch gear and bearing by driving on mainshaft.
5. Continue to drive or press mainshaft out of case and remove thrust washer. *Be sure synchronizer ring tangs are aligned with mainshaft splines prior to driving out shaft, otherwise damage to ring and shaft splines will occur.*
6. Strip mainshaft parts by lifting them out through top cover opening.
7. Expand retaining ring and start mainshaft bearing out by tapping on outer race; then drive bearing out of case.

8. Remove detent cover plug and remove 2nd-3rd gear detent spring and ball.
9. With suitable punch, drive out roll pin securing 2nd-3rd shift fork to shaft, Fig. 6, then tap shaft toward front with a drift and remove fork, shaft and roll pin.
10. Remove interlock from detent cavity. Then remove 1st-reverse shift fork and shaft in same manner as 2nd-3rd fork.
11. Remove shift finger, Fig. 7.
12. Remove manual shift shaft seal from rear lower left corner of case.
13. Drive countershaft out from front of case, using a dummy shaft (or tool J-5777) to hold needle bearings in place.
14. If necessary, drive reverse idler shaft lock pin into shaft, then drive shaft out of case through hole at rear of case. Remove caged needle bearing and thrust washer used at rear of reverse idler gear.
15. Remove mainshaft bearing retaining from case.

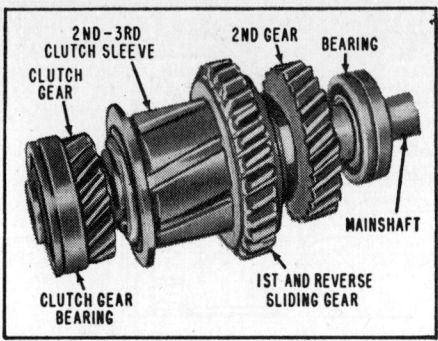

Fig. 13 Mainshaft components assembled

Assemble

Refer to Figs. 8 to 13 for assembly details of several components and use Fig. 5 as a guide when assembling the transmission.

1. Install manual shaft seal.
2. Install assembled countergear, Fig. 8.
3. Install reverse idler gear, Fig. 12.
4. Insert manual shift shaft through seal in case. Position actuating finger and secure to shaft (see Fig. 7) with two lock tabs and capscrews, tightening to 5-7 ft. lbs. Bend lock tabs over screw heads. Install detent ball and spring (in that order) through hole in side of case. Tap ball and spring to be sure spring is resting on bottom of cavity.
5. Start roll pin into 1st-reverse fork. Insert fork shaft through lower hole at front of case with three detents facing detent ball and slip fork on shaft. Depressing ball, press shaft over ball to the center detent position. Secure fork to shaft with roll pin. Coat interlock with oil and install in detent cavity. *Be sure* shift finger is engaged with 1st-reverse shift fork prior to installing 2nd-3rd shift fork, Fig. 6.
6. Start roll pin into fork. Insert 2nd-3rd fork shaft through front of case with three detents facing away from interlock and slip fork onto shaft. Secure with roll pin.
7. Insert detent ball and spring (in that order) for 2nd-3rd shift fork and install detent cavity cover and gasket. Torque cover bolts to 25-35 ft. lbs. After installing detent plug, check for free movement of manual shift shaft in all gear positions.
8. Place assembled clutch sleeve, 1st-reverse sliding gear and 2nd gear in case, Fig. 13. Make sure 1st-reverse gear and shoulder on clutch sleeve are in proper forks.
9. Place mainshaft in clutch gear and, from front of case, insert mainshaft through clutch sleeve and 2nd speed gear. *Be sure tangs of synchronizer ring are aligned with mainshaft splines before installing mainshaft and that clutch gear slots, Fig. 9, are properly aligned with larger tangs on synchronizer ring.*
10. Drive clutch gear bearing into place.
11. Install thrust washer on mainshaft with its oil grooves toward 2nd gear. Install mainshaft bearing retainer ring. Install mainshaft bearing with ring groove toward case and, with retainer ring expanded, drive bearing onto mainshaft.
12. Install a ½" deep socket in clutch gear and continue to drive on mainshaft bearing until snap ring groove is accessible. Install snap ring.
13. Check end play of mainshaft by inserting feeler gauge between snap ring and bearing inner race. Final end clearance must be .004" maximum. Use a snap ring of a size that will establish this clearance. Snap rings are available in four thicknesses ranging from .086" to .097". After making this check, drive mainshaft forward into case until snap ring contacts inner bearing race.
14. Check for free movement of shift shaft to be sure each gear position may be easily obtained. Install top cover, filler plug and extension housing.

Automatic Transmission Section

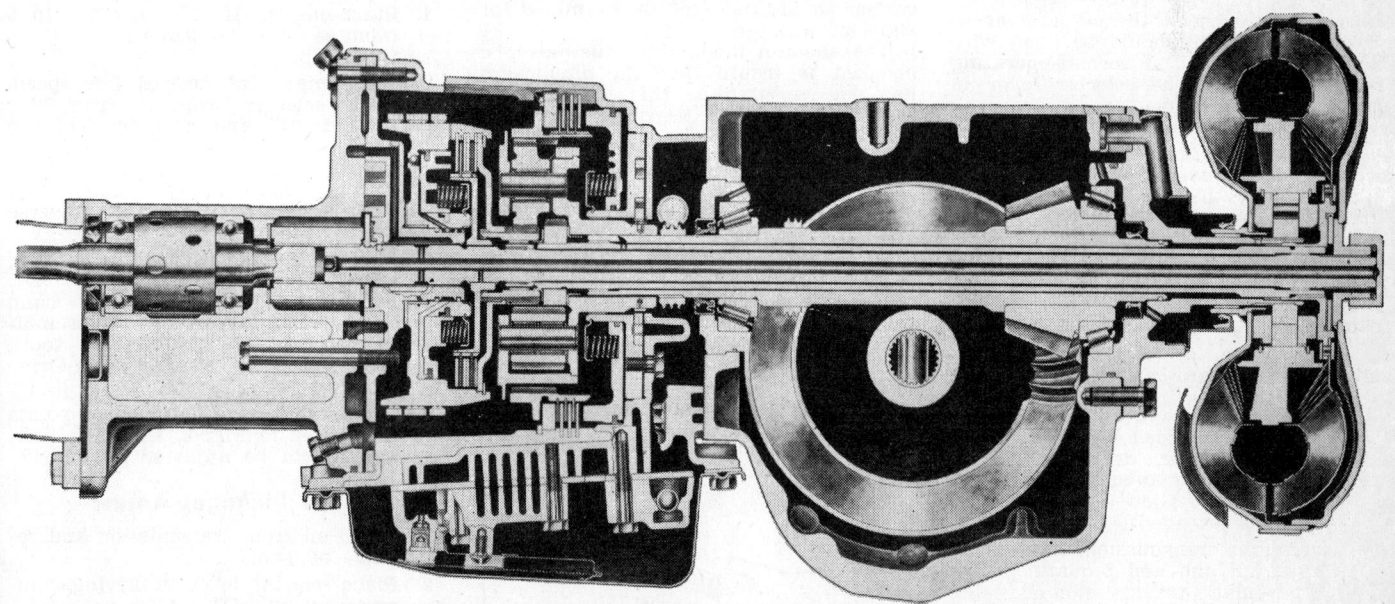

Fig. 1 Automatic transmission and differential carrier (transaxle)

DESCRIPTION

This transmission, Fig. 1, consists of an air cooled, three element torque converter and a two speed planetary transmission. The transmission is attached to the differential carrier to form a transmission-axle (transaxle) assembly. As a result the converter is mounted on the opposite side of the carrier from the transmission. Two shafts run axially (one inside the other) through the differential pinion shaft, transmitting torque from the engine to the converter and back to the transmission. Fig. 2 shows a schematic drawing of the transaxle components.

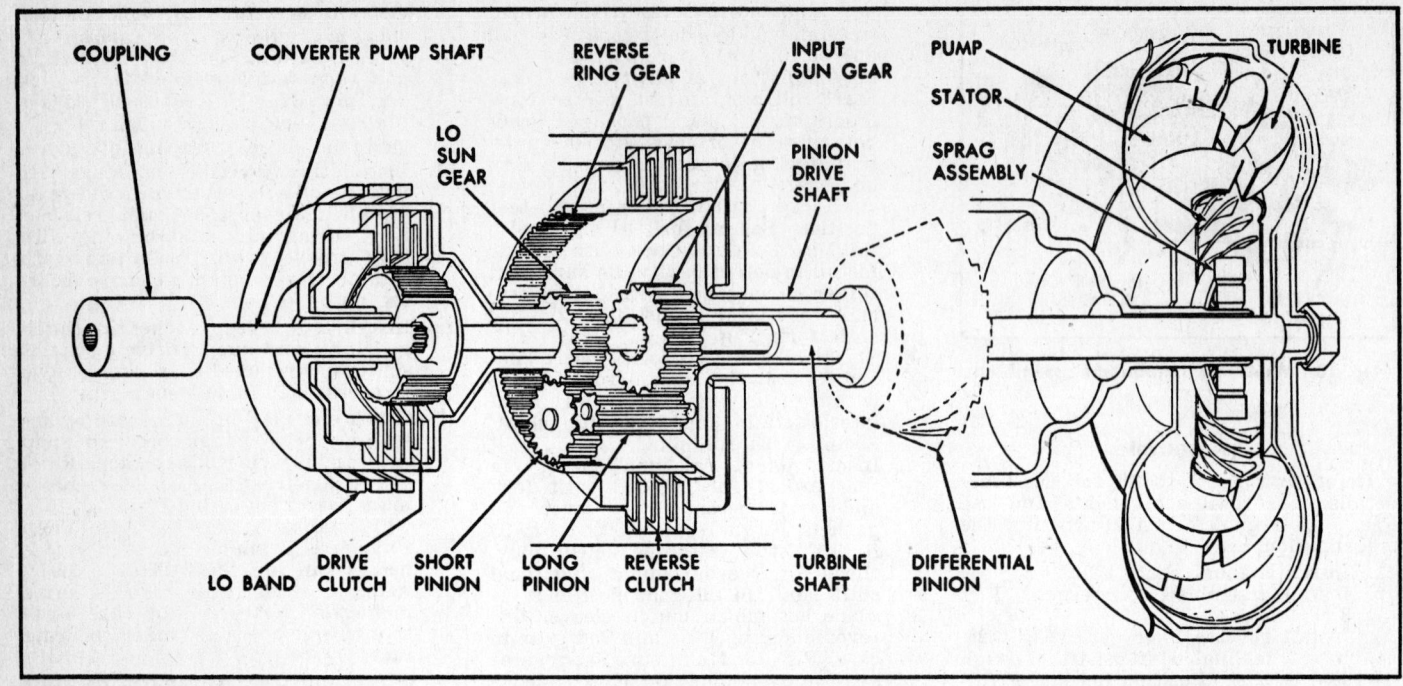

Fig. 2 Schematic drawing of transaxle

MAINTENANCE

Adding Oil

Oil should be added only when the level is near the "ADD" mark on the dipstick with oil at normal operating temperature. The difference in oil level between "FULL" and "ADD" is one pint.

In order to check the oil level accurately, the engine should be idled with the transmission oil at normal operating temperature and the selector lever in neutral (N) position.

It is important that the oil level be maintained no higher than the "FULL" mark. Do not overfill. If oil is added which brings the level above the full mark, the planetary unit will run in the oil, foaming and aerating the oil. This will cause malfunction of the transmission due to improper application of the band or clutches and excessive temperature.

Changing Oil

No periodic draining of the transmission oil is recommended. When transmission requires repair, drain the oil by loosening the filler tube attaching nut in the oil pan and allow oil to drain (no drain plug is provided).

To refill the transmission, tighten the filler tube nut and add 2 quarts of approved automatic transmission oil, using filler tube and funnel. Start engine and allow it to idle in neutral 3 to 5 minutes to warm the oil. Then check the level and add as required to raise the level to the "FULL" mark. Assuming that the converter is not drained (since it is welded) and allowing for nominal spillage or draindown, approximately 3 quarts of oil will be required for refill.

EXTERNAL LEAK CHECK

If the transmission is found to be consistently low on oil, a thorough inspection should be made to find and correct all external oil leaks.

All mating surfaces, such as the front pump, oil pan rail, filler tube, governor, and the attachment to the differential carrier should be carefully examined for signs of leakage.

The vacuum modulator must also be checked to insure that the diaphragm has not ruptured as this would allow transmission oil to be drawn into the intake manifold of the engine. Usually, the exhaust will be excessively smoky if the diaphragm ruptures. Check level in the differential to be certain oil is not leaking from the transmission to the differential carrier.

ADJUSTMENTS

Neutral Switch

The starter neutral switch is located on the rear of the gearshift control and

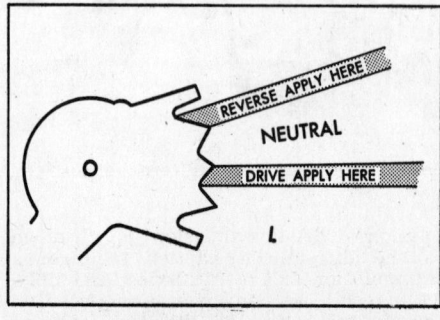

Fig. 3 Shift linkage check diagram

indicator assembly. Properly adjusted, the switch should prevent engine cranking in any position other than "N". If engine cranks in any other position, adjust by loosening the two switch mounting screws and moving switch as required.

Shift Linkage Check

1. Start engine. If cold, allow 2 to 3 minutes for transmission oil to warm up.
2. With engine at normal idle speed, move selector lever up from "N" toward "R" and note by feel the point at which reverse clutch applies. Properly adjusted, reverse clutch should apply within band from tooth peak to full Reverse detent, Fig. 3.
3. Make same check while moving selector lever from "N" to "D". Properly adjusted, the low band should apply as selector lever indicator is felt to be between tooth peak separating Neutral from Drive and full Drive Detent.
4. Unless shifts are obtained at points illustrated in Fig. 3, the shift linkage should be adjusted as follows:

Shift Linkage, Adjust

1. Drain oil from transmission and remove oil pan.
2. Place selector lever in driving compartment in "D".
3. Insert gauge (J-8365), Fig. 4, into manual valve bore with tab of gauge upward so it engages forward part of valve body.
4. With gauge in place, push forward on manual valve levers. Properly adjusted, the gauge will be held in place horizontally without being supported.

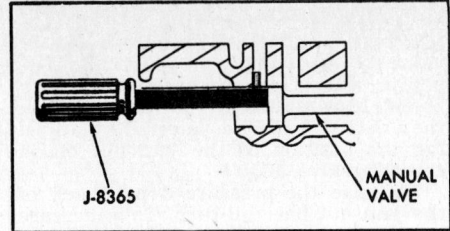

Fig. 4 Gauging manual valve

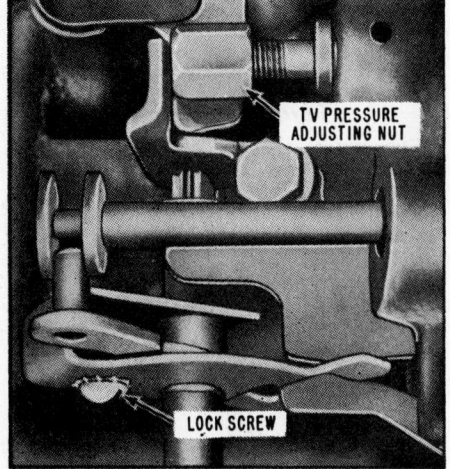

Fig. 5 Throttle valve pressure adjusting nut and manual valve lever lock screw

5. If readjustment is required, loosen lock screw, Fig. 5, push manual valve levers forward so that gauge is held in position. Retighten lock screw.

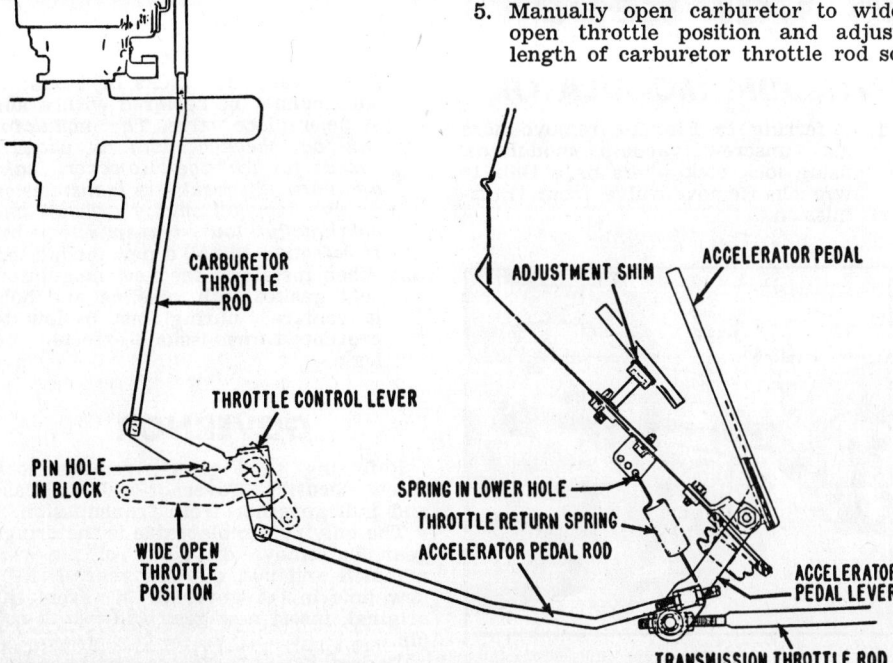

Fig. 6 Throttle linkage (4 cylinder)

Throttle Linkage, Adjust

Incorrect linkage adjustment will cause poorly timed shifts and other out of line operating conditions.

Four Cylinder Engine—

1. If height of accelerator pedal stop is not $1\frac{11}{16}''$, loosen lock nut and reset to correct height.
2. Place .060″ shim over top of accelerator pedal stop, Fig. 6.
3. Disconnect throttle rod at carburetor, and accelerator rod and throttle valve rod at accelerator pedal lever beneath car.
4. Rotate throttle control lever to wide open throttle position. Retain in this position by inserting a suitable pin in hole in block so that flat on throttle lever rests against pin.
5. Manually open carburetor to wide open throttle position and adjust length of carburetor throttle rod so

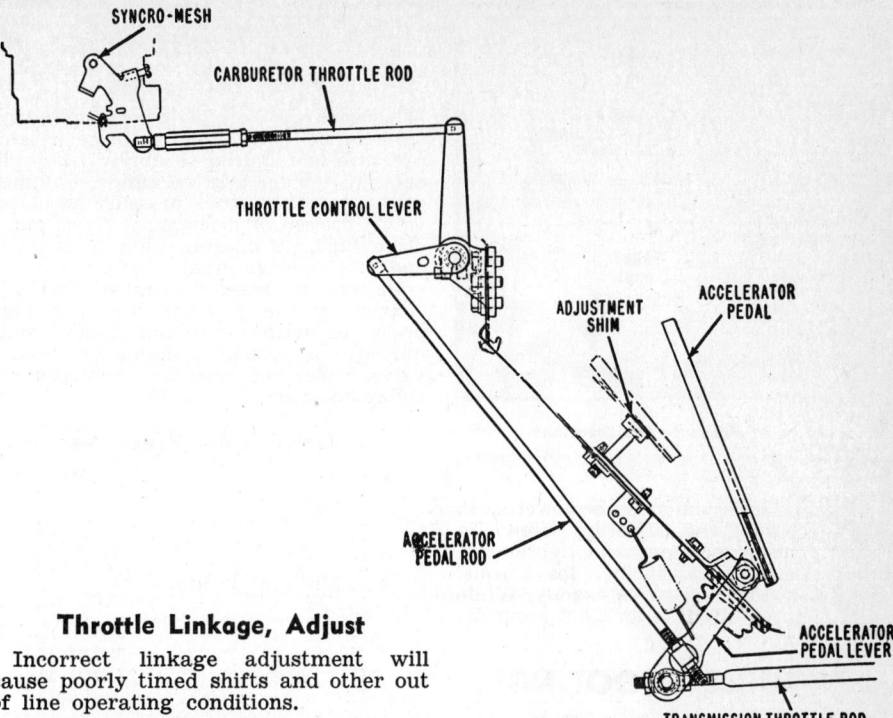

Fig. 7 Throttle linkage (V8 engine)

that it freely engages with carburetor throttle lever.
6. From beneath car pull accelerator pedal to wide open throttle position against shim. Adjust trunnion so it will slip into upper hole of accelerator pedal lever. Tighten securely.
7. With accelerator pedal still held against stop, push rearward on throttle valve rod until TV lever in transmission bottoms solidly. Adjust trunnion to slip into lower hole of pedal lever. Tighten securely. Remove shim and linkage pin.

V8 Engines—Perform Steps 1, 2 and 3 as outlined for 4 cylinder engines and proceed as follows, referring to Fig. 7.
1. Rotate throttle control lever to wide open position and hold in this position.
2. Manually open carburetor to wide open throttle position and adjust length of carburetor throttle rod so that it freely engages with carburetor throttle lever.
3. From beneath car, pull accelerator pedal to wide open throttle position against shim. Adjust trunnion so it will slip into upper hole of accelerator pedal lever. Tighten securely.
4. With accelerator pedal still held against stop, push rearward on throttle valve rod until TV lever in transmission bottoms solidly. Adjust trunnion to slip into lower hole of accelerator pedal lever. Tighten securely. Remove shim from pedal stop.

Low Band, Adjust

No periodic adjustment of the band is recommended. However, if necessary it may be adjusted as follows:

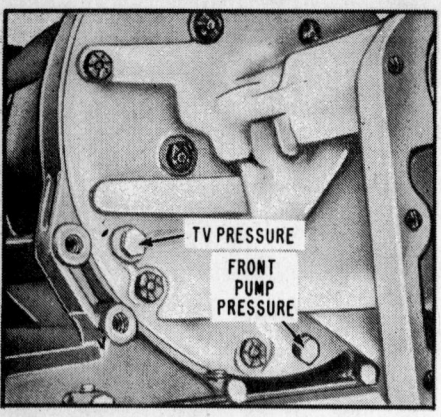

Fig. 8 Pressure tap locations

The transmission must be lowered to gain access to the adjusting screw. To adjust, loosen lock nut and tighten adjusting screw to 35-45 inch lbs. torque, then back off 4 full turns exactly. While holding screw, tighten lock nut securely.

TROUBLE SHOOTING

Hydraulic Pressure Tests

Two pressure tap plugs in the extension housing are shown in Fig. 8. All tests can be made without driving the vehicle by simply raising the wheels 3 to 5 inches from the floor on jack stands. With pressure gauges installed, perform the following preliminary steps:

1. Pressure gauge needles should be at zero pressure.
2. Thoroughly warm up transmission.

3. Check transmission oil level.
4. Check linkage adjustment.

Front Pump Check

Absence of front pump pressures results in no drive in any range as this pressure is required to apply the applicable clutch for a given range. Common causes would be stuck pressure regulator valve, broken or disengaged front pump drive lugs, or missing plug from front end of converter pump shaft.

Failure of pressure to raise when disconnecting the vacuum hose (or high pressures with hose connected) would indicate a stuck vacuum modulator valve, defective vacuum modulator, or collapsed hose.

Front Pump Pressures

Range	PSI*
R	106-130
N	55-67
D	55-67
L	124-137

*At idle (16″ vacuum)

Range	PSI°
R	198-222
N	101-114
D	101-114
L	124-137

°At idle with hose disconnected from vacuum modulator.

Rear Pump Checks

With wheels raised, place selector lever in "D" and accelerate engine. Front pump pressure should drop to 0 to 5 psi at about 20 mph. If pressure does not drop, rear pump is disengaged or clogged, or rear pump ball check is not seating.

Throttle Valve (TV) Pressure

Throttle valve pressure tests are of value in cases where the shift points are not in accordance with the data listed below. If pressures are not as prescribed, they may be raised or lowered by adjusting the position of the jam nut on the throttle valve, Fig. 5.

To raise the pressure 3 psi, back off the jam nut one full turn. This increases the dimension from the jam nut to the throttle valve stop. Conversely, tightening the jam nut one full turn lowers the pressure 3 psi. Smaller pressure adjustments can be made by partial turns on the jam nut. The end of the TV adjusting screw has an Allen head so the screw may be held stationary while the jam nut is moved.

Throttle Pressures

Disconnect throttle valve rod at carburetor and hose at vacuum modulator. Depress accelerator pedal to wide open position. By disconnecting rod engine remains at idle speed throughout test.

Range	PSI
R	0
N	0
D	50-52
L	118-132

Shift Points

Upshifts*	MPH
Minimum throttle	12-15
Full throttle	43-50
Part throttle+	35-45

Downshifts*	MPH
Closed throttle	9-15
Full throttle	39-46
Part throttle+	21-33

*With 3.55:1 axle ratio
+Detent touch

In Car Repairs

EXTENSION OIL SEAL

1. Remove torque tube and propeller shaft as outlined in the *Rear Axle Section*.
2. Pry out old oil seal and tap new seal into position.
3. Install torque tube and propeller shaft.

EXTENSION BEARINGS

1. Remove torque tube and propeller shaft as directed in *Rear Axle Section*.
2. Remove oil seal and bearing snap ring.
3. Insert tool in extension housing, Fig. 9, so that it picks up inner race of bearing.
4. Using slide hammer as shown, tap out front bearing, spacer sleeve and rear bearing.
5. Using suitable socket, tap new rear bearing into position. Install spacer sleeve and tap in new front bearing.
6. Install new oil seal, torque tube and propeller shaft.

VACUUM MODULATOR

1. Referring to Fig. 10, remove hose and unscrew vacuum modulator, using lock pick pliers or a thin 1″ wrench. Remove valve from transmission.

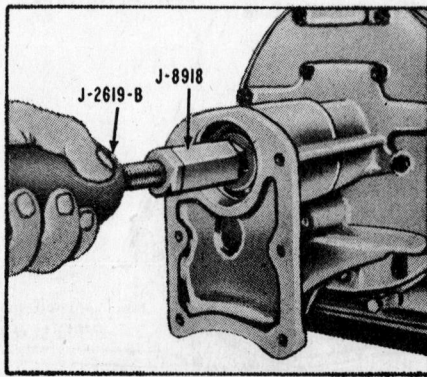

Fig. 9 Removing extension housing bearings

2. Check valve for nicks or burrs; if such cannot be repaired with a slip stone, replace valve. *The modulator can be checked with a vacuum source for leakage. However, leakage normally results in transmission oil pull-over, oil smoky exhaust and continually low transmission oil.* If defective, install a new modulator.
3. When installing the new modulator, coat gasket with vaseline and hold it centered during installation to prevent transmission external oil leak.

GOVERNOR

Referring to Fig. 11, remove lock screw securing governor tab to case and pull governor from transmission. The only part replaceable is the driven gear. To remove, drive out roll pin with a punch and pull out old gear. Drill a new hole in the governor 90° from the original, insert new gear and install roll pin.

To install, use O-ring on governor and install governor into transmission with a

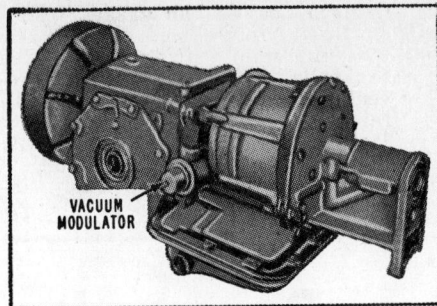

Fig. 10 Location of vacuum modulator

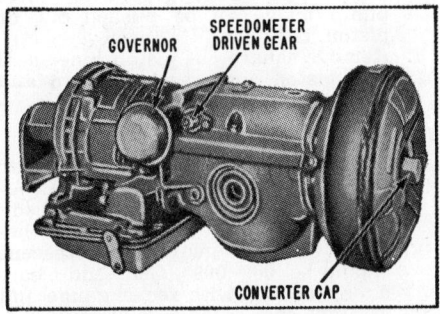

Fig. 11 Transaxle assembly

Fig. 12 Servo piston retainer, downshift timing valve

Fig. 13 Front pump air bleed ball

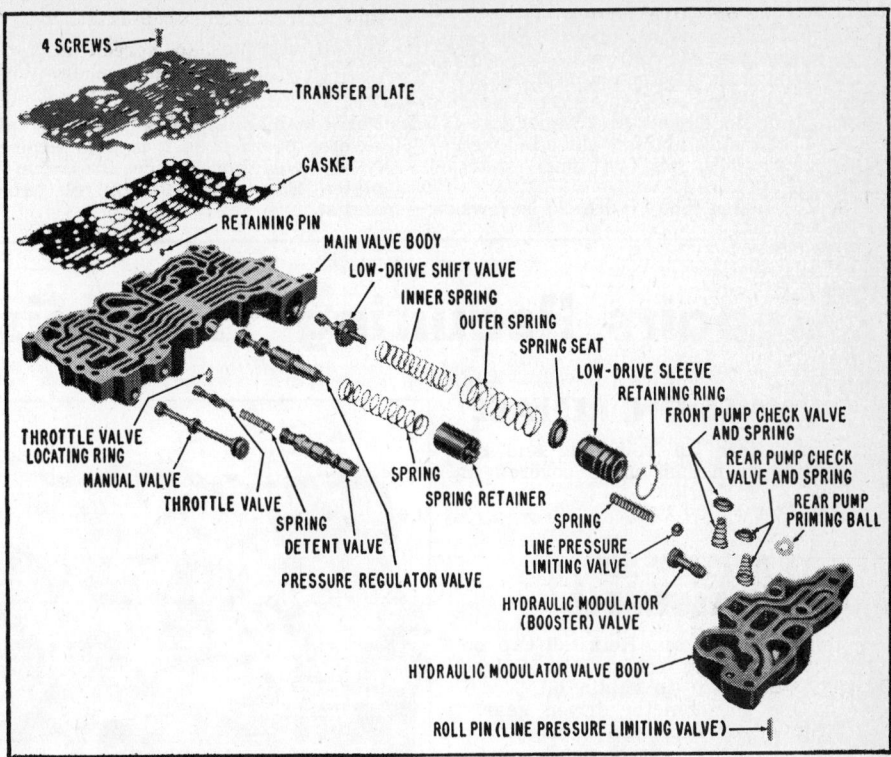

Fig. 14 Valve body parts layout

slight twist to engage gear teeth. Secure with lock bolt.

VALVE BODY & LOW SERVO

1. To remove valve body, loosen oil filler nut in order to drain transmission oil and remove filler pipe.
2. Disconnect throttle valve rods from transmission levers.
3. Remove oil pan and gasket.
4. Remove retainer screw, oil screen and O-ring.
5. Loosely install retainer, Fig. 12, in pan screw hole. Retainer can be made from a piece of sheet metal.
6. Remove valve body attaching screws and tap valve body lightly to loosen from its dowels; then carefully lower body about $\frac{1}{16}$". Rotate retainer into place so it secures servo piston hub and tighten with oil pan screw. This eliminates the possibility of servo piston slipping out of its bore and loss of low band engagement with its apply components.
7. Remove valve body and gasket.
8. If necessary, remove downshift timing valve and install a new one, Fig. 12.
9. If necessary to remove low servo, tighten low band adjusting screw fully. Remove retainer and pull downward on piston shaft with screwdriver.
10. If necessary, replace front pump air bleed valve as shown in Fig. 13.
11. When disassembling the valve body the modulator body should be held during removal of screws as it is under spring pressure from pressure regulator valve spring.

Valve Body, Inspect & Assemble

As most valve body failures are initially caused by dirt or other foreign matter preventing a valve from functioning properly, a thorough cleaning of all parts in clean solvent is mandatory. Check all valves and their operating bores for burrs or other deformities which could result in valve "hang-up".

Assemble the valve body in reverse order of disassembly, referring to Fig. 14 as a guide.

Low Servo Repairs

To disassemble the low servo piston, remove the hairpin retainer securing the piston to the piston rod and separate parts. The cushion spring tension on this piston is relatively light; no press is required.

Remove ring from piston and install it in the low servo bore and measure the ring gap. If within limits ring gap will be .002" to .012".

Assemble ring to piston. Measure clearance between ring and one wall of piston groove. Clearance should be .0005" to .005".

To assemble low servo, place spring seat on piston shaft. Install cushion spring. Complete assembly by compressing cushion spring slightly with piston and secure piston to shaft with hairpin retainer.

Valve Body & Low Servo, Install

1. Install low servo piston and return spring in transmission bore and engage notch in piston shaft with low band apply strut, loosening low band screw slightly to permit piston ring to seat in case bore and allow in-

stallation of valve body.

2. Install retainer to hold servo piston in bore (see Fig. 12).
3. Position new gasket on valve body.
4. Position valve body in transmission, indexing on dowels and remove retainer. Be sure manual valve indexes properly with pin on inner shaft lever.
5. Secure valve body with 20 screws and tighten them to 9-11 ft. lbs.
6. Install oil pick-up screen and O-ring in valve body and secure with screw.
7. Position manual valve lever in full reverse position so it is held securely by wedging device in transfer plate. Engage shift control cable and secure.
8. Using a new oil pan gasket, install oil pan and torque bolts to 3-4 ft lbs. It is important that an even torque be applied to the pan bolts to prevent leakage between pan and pan rail.
9. Tighten filler tube attaching nut; then refill transmission with oil.
10. Readjust band as previously directed.

Repairs Requiring Transmission Removal

TRANSMISSION, REPLACE

The procedure for removing and replacing the transmission is covered in the *Rear Axle Section*.

TRANSMISSION, DISASSEMBLE

1. Remove converter. Reinstall cap on converter after removal and place cap side down to retain oil.
2. Remove speedometer driven gear.
3. Remove governor and O-ring.
4. Remove turbine drive shaft.
5. Unfasten and separate transmission from differential carrier.
6. Remove vacuum modulator and valve.
7. Loosen low band adjusting screw jam nut and fully tighten adjusting screw.
8. Remove 12 housing attaching screws.
9. Tap off extension housing.
10. Remove thrust washer and coupling, Fig. 15. Remove converter pump drive shaft, Fig. 16. It is not necessary to remove drive key unless it is to be replaced.
11. Remove thrust washer from pump body.
12. Remove pump gears. Stack so they may be reassembled with same face up.
13. Remove pump body and gasket.

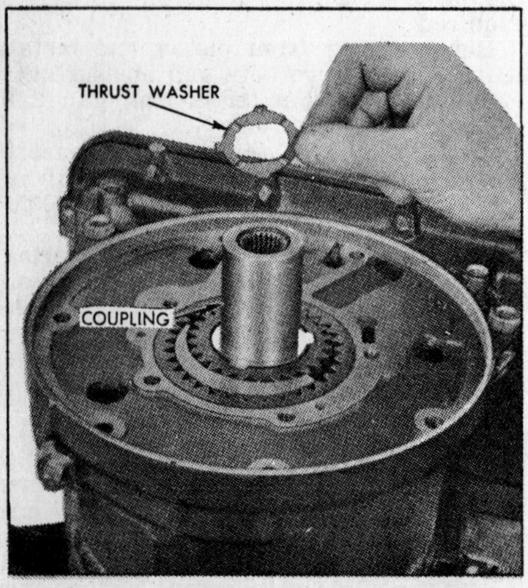

Fig. 16 Converter pump shaft

14. Remove pump body-to-clutch drum thrust washer.
15. Loosen low band adjusting screw and remove low band, apply strut and reaction strut, Fig. 17.
16. Remove clutch drum assembly.
17. Remove clutch drum-to-sun gear thrust washer, Fig. 18.
18. Remove planet carrier from ring gear.
19. Remove ring gear from engagement with reverse clutch plates.
20. Remove clip mounted on thick reverse reaction plate between ends of reverse clutch snap ring and remove snap ring, Fig. 19.
21. Remove thick reverse reaction plate, three drive plates (faced) and three reaction plates (steel).
22. Remove rear pump and reverse piston mounting bolts at rear of case.
23. Remove rear pump and reverse piston assembly.
24. Remove rear pump wear plate.

UNIT REPAIRS

Rear Pump & Reverse Piston

1. To disassemble, remove drive and driven gears. Stack so they may be reasembled with same face up.
2. Compress spring retainer, Fig. 20. With retainer compressed until springs bottom, remove snap ring. Carefully release pressure and remove retainer and springs.
3. In order to remove reverse piston, it is necessary to fill snap ring groove in hub of body with string, a small rubber band or a similar size O-ring. Once groove is filled, pump body can be pushed out of piston bore.
4. Remove square cut piston inner seal and piston outer seal. Discard and install new seals at reassembly.

Inspection

1. With all parts clean and dry, check fit of pump gears. Clearance between OD of driven gear and body should be .0025-.005". Clearance between driven gear and crescent should be .003-.009". Gear end clearance, checked with feeler gauge and straight edge, should be .0005-.0015".
2. Inspect pump body for leaks and scoring. Check hub of pump body for smoothness. *Any burrs on this surface would cause leakage and could result in a jammed reverse piston.*
3. Check for broken piston return springs and make a comparative check of spring heights by standing all springs in a row. If appreciable variance in spring height is noticed, replace springs.
4. If pump body bushing is scored or worn, replace bushing.

Fig. 17 Location of apply and reaction struts

Fig. 15 Thrust washer tend coupling

Fig. 18 Sun gear thrust washer

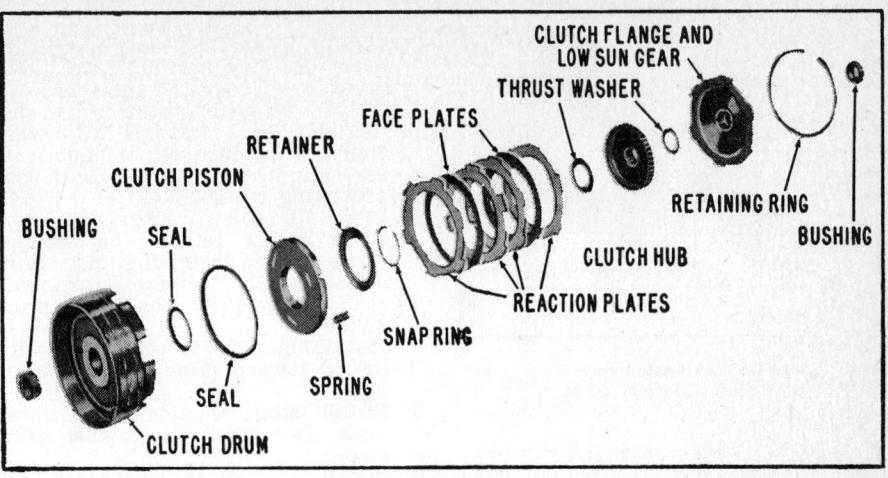

Fig. 23 Clutch drum components

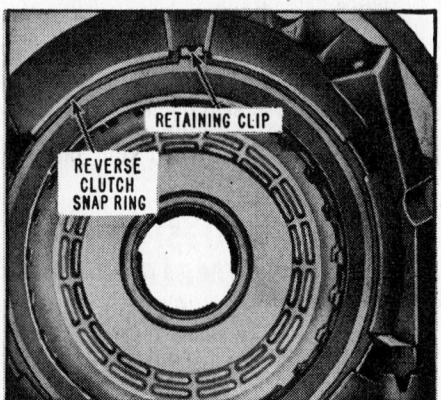

Fig. 19 Reverse snap ring retaining clip installed

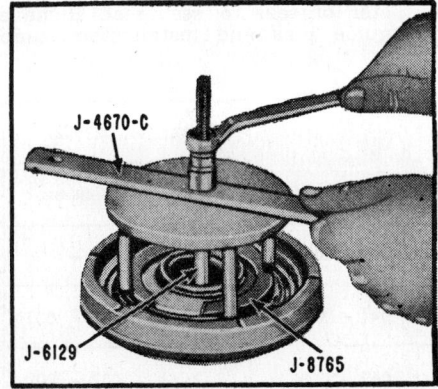

Fig. 20 Compressing reverse piston springs

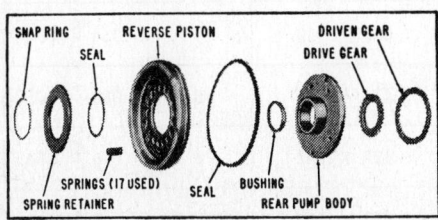

Fig. 21 Rear pump and reverse piston components

Assemble

1. Install piston inner seal in reverse piston, Fig. 21.
2. Install piston outer seal in piston with lip of seal toward pump body.
3. Install piston on pump body.
4. Position 17 return springs in their seats on piston, then replace spring retainer on springs.
5. Compress springs as shown in Fig. 20. With springs fully depressed, install snap ring in groove in pump body.
6. Complete assembly by installing drive and driven gears in body. It is advisable to apply a small amount of vaseline to gears to prevent their being dropped from pump body.

Clutch Drum

1. To disassemble, remove retainer ring securing low sun gear and clutch flange to clutch drum. Remove thrust washer.
2. Lift out clutch hub, then remove drive and driven plates and hub thrust washer.
3. To remove spring retainer, compress springs, Fig. 22, and remove snap ring.
4. Carefully release pressure and remove retainer and springs.
5. To remove clutch piston, pull upward with a twisting motion on

center. Then remove piston seal.
6. Remove piston inner seal from hub of clutch drum.

Inspection

1. Wash and air dry parts, Fig. 23.
2. Inspect drum band surface for excessive scoring or burning. Also check and, if necessary, replace drum bushing if scored or worn.
3. Check steel ball in drum that acts as a relief valve, Fig. 24. Be sure that it is free to move in hole and that orifice leading to front of drum is open. If clutch relief valve check ball in drum is loose enough to come out or not loose enough to rattle, replace drum as an assembly. *Replacement or staking of ball should not be attempted.*
4. Check fit of clutch flange in drum slots. There should be no appreciable radial play between these two parts. Also check low sun gear for nicks or burrs and bushing for wear.
5. Check clutch plates for burning, pitting or metal pick up. Also check to see that faced plates are a free fit over clutch hub and that steel plates are a free fit in clutch flange. Check for excessive wear on friction facing of drive plate teeth. Check condition of clutch hub splines and mating splines on faced plates.

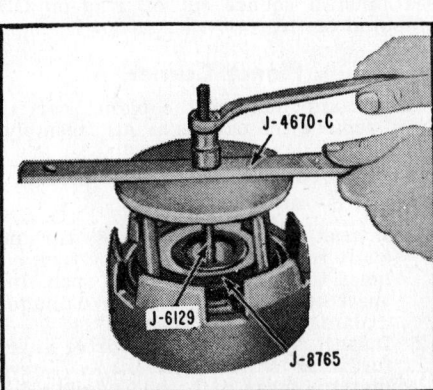

Fig. 22 Compressing clutch springs

Fig. 24 Relief check ball

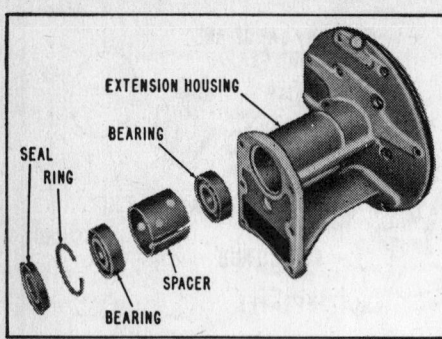

Fig. 25 Extension housing and related parts

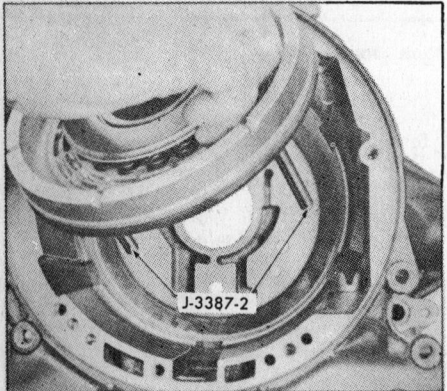

Fig. 26 Rear pump and reverse piston

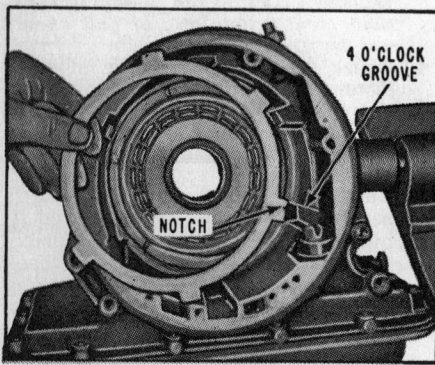

Fig. 27 Reverse clutch reaction plates

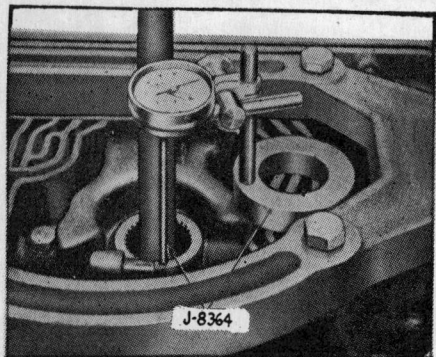

Fig. 28 Zeroing dial indicator on planet carrier hub

Assemble

1. Install piston inner seal in hub of drum. Be sure seal lips are downward (toward front of transmission).
2. Install new piston seal in clutch piston, being sure seal lips are toward front of transmission. Lubricate seals and install piston in drum with a twisting motion.
3. Place 15 return springs on piston. Place spring retainer on springs. Compress springs, Fig. 22. With springs fully compressed, install snap ring in groove on clutch drum hub.
4. Install hub front thrust washer with its lip toward drum. Install clutch hub.
5. Install steel reaction plate, faced plate, two steel plates, then steel plate.
6. Install hub rear thrust washer with its flange toward low sun gear, then install sun gear and clutch flange and secure with retainer ring. Openings of retainer ring should be adjacent to one of the lands of clutch drum.
7. Check assembly by turning clutch hub to insure it is free to rotate.

Front Pump & Extension Housing

1. To disassemble, pry out oil seal and remove bearing retainer ring, Fig. 25.
2. Invert extension housing. Using a suitable socket as a driver, tap out front bearing, spacer sleeve and rear bearing.

Inspection

1. Wash all parts and blow out oil passages.
2. Inspect pump gears, cover face and body for nicks or scoring.
3. Check oil control rings on body.
4. Check condition of bushing in body and replace if necessary.
5. Install pump gear and check clearance between OD of driven gear and body which should be .0025-.005″. Clearance between driven gear and crescent should be .0025-.005″. With scale and feeler gauge, check clearance between gears and cover face which should be .0005-0015″.

Assemble Install parts in extension housing as shown in Fig. 25. Use suitable socket to install bearings. Do not tap on inner races. Install snap ring and oil seal. Install square cut oil ring on OD of pump cover.

Planet Carrier

If a component of the planet carrier fails, replace the carrier as an assembly.

Turbine and Pump Drive Shafts and Converter

1. Inspect splined areas of turbine shaft for wear or damage. Check oil holes to be sure they are open. Inspect bushings for wear or damage; if damaged, replace.
2. Inspect splines of pump drive shaft for wear or damage. Inspect drive lugs for wear or peened edges.
3. It is unnecessary to drain converter as it is welded and no internal re-

Fig. 29 Measuring for shim determination

pairs can be made. Check converter seams for stress or breaks and either replace converter or repair welds as required. If welds are repaired, keep added material to a minimum by chipping off scale and filing away excess weld to retain converter balance. Check converter hub bushing for wear or damage.

TRANSMISSION, ASSEMBLE

1. Install two guide pins in rear pump bolt holes, then install rear pump wear plate on guide pins, using small amount of vaseline to hold wear plate in place.
2. Insert rear pump and reverse piston with guide pins into case, Fig. 26. Insert a length of .010-.015″ shim stock between piston outer seal and case. Run shim around entire diameter of seal to seat seal. Remove guide pins and install five pump

Spacer No. 6256827		
Indicator Reading	Number	Thickness
.025 - .046	None	—
.047 - .062	1	.016 ± .001
.063 - .078	2	.032 ± .002
.079 - .094	3	.048 ± .003
.095 - 110	4	.064 ± .004
.111 - .126	5	.080 ± .005
.127 - .142	6	.096 ± .006
143 - .155	7	.112 ± .007

Fig. 30 Spacer chart

mounting bolts and tighten to 9-11 ft. lbs. Check rear pump for freeness before proceeding.

3. Install reverse clutch drive and re-action plates alternately starting with a steel plate and finishing with a faced plate. Notched lug in each steel plate is installed so it is at top of groove at 4 o'clock position in case, Fig. 27. Install thick reaction plate. It has rectangular "dimple" on its lug which engages 4 o'clock case groove.

4. Install reverse clutch plate retainer ring in such a manner that open ends of ring are at 12 o'clock position, then install retainer ring clip on thick reaction plate between ends of snap ring.

5. With rear of case downward, align internal lands and grooves of reverse face plates.

6. Engage ring gear to reverse drive plates. Engagement must be made by "feel" while moving drive plates laterally.

7. Install planetary unit with a slight twist to engage planet gears with ring gear. Be sure to engage two rear pump drive lugs on planet hub with grooves in rear pump drive gear.

8. Install thrust washer on captive in-put sun gear in planetary gear set with flange of thrust washer toward front of transmission. If necessary, apply a small amount of vaseline to keep washer centered.

9. Install clutch drum assembly, using a slight twist to engage low sun gear to planet gears in planetary gear set.

10. Turn transmission to a horizontal position, then install low band, apply strut and reaction strut. When low band linkage is installed, tighten low band adjusting screw to prevent struts from falling out of place. Then shake clutch drum slightly to center band and linkage.

11. Replace original thrust washer or new washer of same size if original is damaged. Final end play adjust-ment will be performed at governor drive gear prior to assembly of transmission to differential carrier.

12. Install new front pump gasket. Then install pump body, being careful not to break cast iron oil rings on pump body hub when they are indexed to clutch drum.

13. Install inner and outer pump gears with drive notches on inner gear

Fig. 31 Installing spacers

facing up, and outer gear with same face up as removed.

14. Install thrust washer in pump body.

15. Install converter pump drive shaft. Use care when inserting pump shaft not to damage bushings of transmission components already installed.

16. Position coupling on end of pump drive shaft.

17. Position coupling thrust washer in extension housing. Washer is re-tained by light press fit.

18. Install a new square cut seal ring in extension housing. Position ex-tension housing. Dip bolt heads in oil impervious sealer and install bolts loosely. Tighten outer bolts in criss-cross pattern to 15-20 ft. lbs. Then tighten inner bolts to the same torque. By using this sequence, chance of cocking front pump, which would bind pump, is virtually elim-inated. Check pump for freeness be-fore proceeding.

19. Adjust low band by first tightening adjusting screw to 40 inch lbs., then back off four full turns exactly. Hold adjusting screw and tighten lock nut.

TRANS. TO DIFF. CARRIER, ASSEMBLE

1. Prior to reassembly of carrier and transmission it is necessary to deter-mine required thickness of shim pack to be installed at front face of governor drive gear.

2. To do this, mount a dial indicator as shown in Fig. 28. Without gasket, place support on rear pump cavity surface as shown so that dial indi-cator tip rests on planet carrier hub. Adjust indicator to permit maximum indicator travel and set indicator dial to zero. Front end of transmis-sion must face downward when in-dicator is zeroed.

3. Slowly lift support and indicator off rear pump cavity and note its range of needle deflection from zero posi-tion. Properly positioned on support, indicator should not deflect more than .050" (one-half turn) when re-moved; otherwise raise or lower in-dicator on support post as required and again zero gauge.

4. Place gauge and support on gover-nor gear without spacers on differ-ential pinion shaft as shown in Fig. 29, and lower slowly so that revolu-tions of needle can be counted. Measurement starts once indicator needle again reaches zero. Fully de-press support on governor gear, note reading and refer to chart, Fig. 30, for spacers to be installed on governor gear.

5. Install spacers selected on governor gear, Fig. 31, then check that proper total thickness has been installed by again measuring. If shim stack is correct, dial reading will now be .025-.038"; otherwise add or remove spacers until reading is within this range.

6. Apply a new gasket to transmission or carrier face. Align carrier and transmission on a flat surface and carefully guide pump shaft through differential carrier so as not to dam-age bushing in pinion. Then engage splines of pinion shaft with planet carrier internal splines in transmis-sion.

7. Install governor and O-ring seal and secure transmission to carrier with four screws. Drive two screws from carrier side first to minimize chance of cocking mating surfaces. Tighten screws to 30-35 ft. lbs.

8. Install turbine shaft into converter and then install converter and tur-bine shaft, using care not to damage turbine shaft bushings when sliding over converter pump shaft. It is nec-essary to use caution in engaging splines in converter and at end of turbine shaft. Do not force.

Rear Axle, Propeller Shaft & Brake Section

Refer To Hydraulic Brakes Chapter For Brake Adjustments

DESCRIPTION

The differential and carrier assembly is a component of the transmission and differential assembly, Fig. 1. This design combines the two and is commonly re-ferred to as a transaxle. The differential and carrier design utilizes a hypoid ring and drive pinion set with the pinion shaft above the center of the ring gear. The remaining components of the unit are conventional. The assembly is mounted on the rear suspension cross-member and is sprung with the body weight.

Each axle shaft is independently sus-pended and is free to move in a vertical plane in an arc. The axle shaft is at-tached to universal joints which in turn are splined into the differential side gears. The driving force is transmitted by the lower control arm and lateral forces are absorbed by self-aligning wheel bearings and rubber bushings at the lower control arm attachment to the rear crossmember.

The differential and carrier assembly

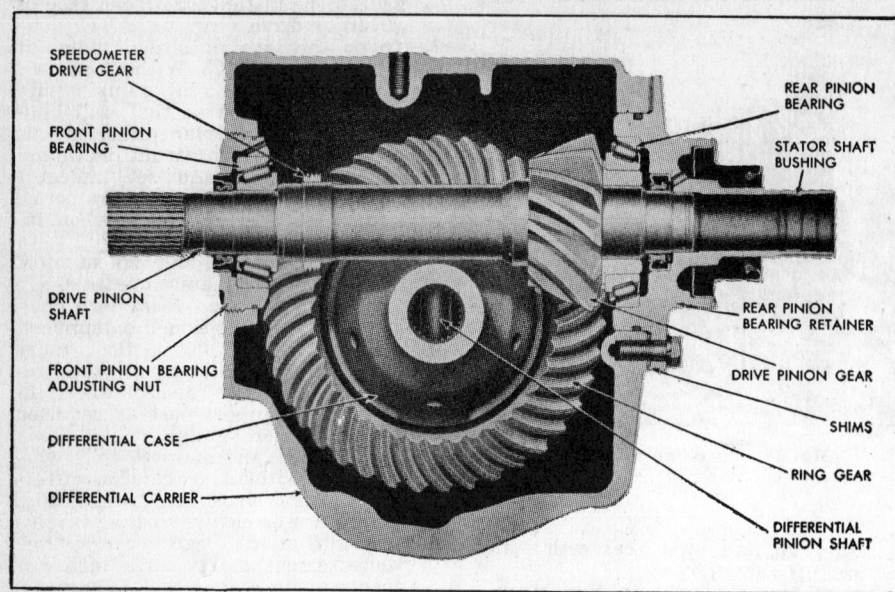

SPEEDOMETER DRIVE GEAR

FRONT PINION BEARING

DRIVE PINION SHAFT

FRONT PINION BEARING ADJUSTING NUT

DIFFERENTIAL CASE

DIFFERENTIAL CARRIER

REAR PINION BEARING

STATOR SHAFT BUSHING

REAR PINION BEARING RETAINER

DRIVE PINION GEAR

SHIMS

RING GEAR

DIFFERENTIAL PINION SHAFT

Fig. 1 Differential and carrier assembly

used with both the manual shift and automatic transmissions are identical except for the drive pinion shaft, front pinion bearing adjustment nut, rear pinion bearing retainer, and oil seals.

The manual shift transmission drive pinion shaft is hollow and is splined internally to receive the transmission mainshaft. The drive pinion shaft used with the automatic transmission is also hollow but is splined externally so that the drive pinion shaft may be inserted in the transmission planet carrier hub. With automatic transmission, the turbine shaft passes through the drive pinion shaft to connect the turbine to the transmission. Details of the propeller shaft and torque tube are shown in Fig. 2.

AXLE SHAFT

Removal
1. Remove wheel and brake drum.
2. Through hole in axle shaft flange, remove four nuts securing axle bearing retainer to brake backing plate.
3. Pull brake backing plate outward slightly, then push it back on the control arm studs to break backing plate away from bearing retainer.
4. Remove four nuts and lock tabs from U-bolts attaching universal to axle flange.
5. Pull axle shaft outward enough to separate flange from U-bolts.
6. Remove flange from shaft.
7. Remove axle shaft from lower control arm. Replace bearing if necessary.

Replace
1. Insert shaft through lower control arm. Install flange on axle shaft splines. It may be necessary to tap flange onto splines if original parts are being installed.
2. Attach universal to flange on axle shaft. *Tighten U-bolts to 14-20 ft. lbs. Also be sure universal joint snap rings are properly installed.*

3. With bearing retainer and brake backing plate holes aligned with control arm studs, insert universal splined yoke through seal at side bearing and index with splines of side gears. Coat lip of seal and splines with hypoid oil to help prevent damage to seal from splines of universal yoke.
4. Secure bearing retainer to backing plate and torque nuts to 30-45 ft. lbs.
5. Install brake drum and wheel.

PROP. SHAFT & TORQUE TUBE
Manual Shift Transmission
Removal
1. Remove propeller shaft damper bearing bolts, Fig. 3.
2. Remove parking brake cable from torque tube.
3. Remove exhaust crossover pipe (V8 engines).
4. Disconnect transmission control rod from transmission.
5. Remove gearshift housing and control rod.
6. Remove flywheel housing bottom cover.
7. Support rear of engine with jack stand.
8. Remove torque tube access hole cover.
9. Remove propeller shaft flange bolts.
10. Place a rag between propeller shaft and torque tube to prevent damage

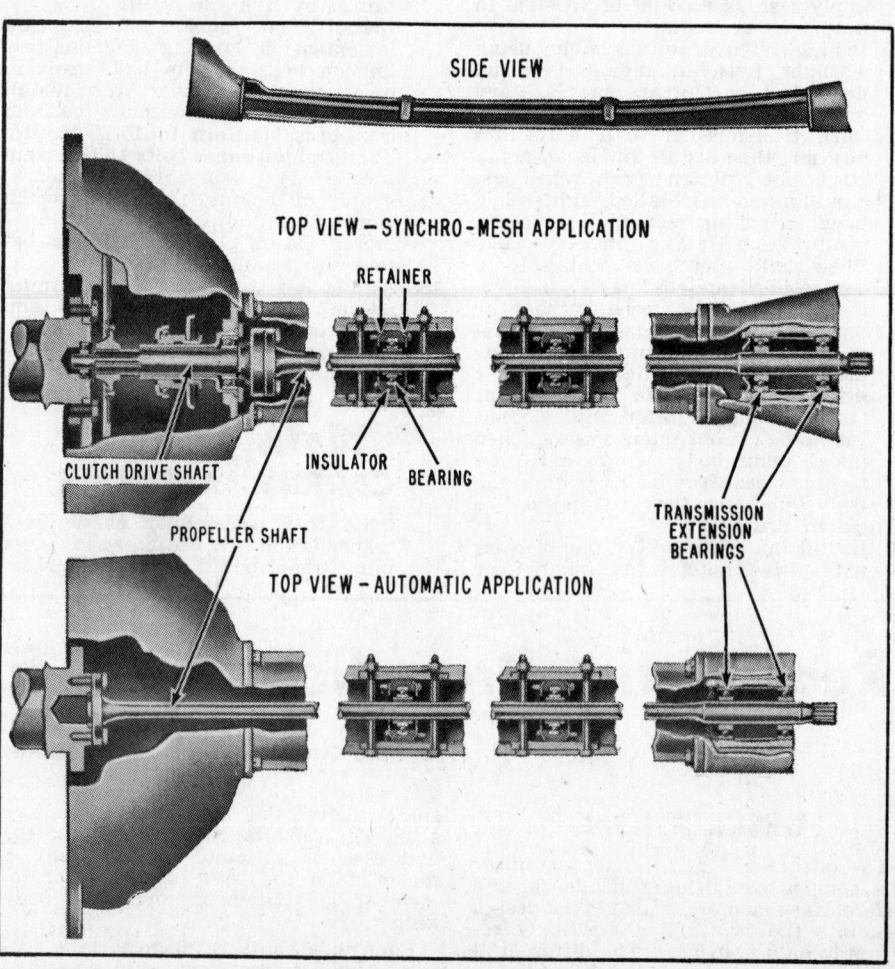

SIDE VIEW

TOP VIEW — SYNCHRO-MESH APPLICATION

RETAINER

INSULATOR   BEARING

CLUTCH DRIVE SHAFT

PROPELLER SHAFT

TOP VIEW — AUTOMATIC APPLICATION

TRANSMISSION EXTENSION BEARINGS

Fig. 2 Propeller shaft and torque tube

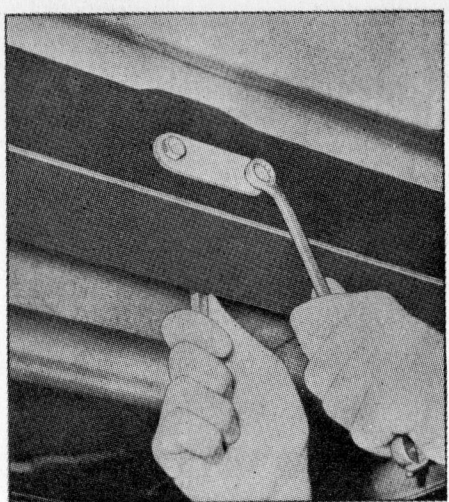

Fig. 3 Removing propeller shaft damper bearing bolts

to coating on drive line.
11. Loosen torque tube-to-flywheel housing bolts.
12. Support torque tube so it won't fall.
13. Remove flywheel housing-to-torque tube bolts.
14. Pry torque tube and propeller shaft away and down from flywheel housing.
15. Place block of wood (3″ square) between transmission extension and floor of car to position transmission for reassembly. Support torque tube with stand.
16. Separate torque tube from transmission.
17. Remove propeller shaft and torque tube as a unit by pulling on propeller shaft flange. *Pull propeller shaft straight out of transmission so that shaft will not bind in transmission or extension housing.*
18. Remove propeller shaft from torque tube, Fig. 4.
19. Bearing insulators may be removed after removing retainer (2 screws). *No attempt should be made to remove bearings from propeller shaft as shaft and bearings are serviced as an assembly.*

Replace
1. Assemble propeller shaft into torque tube and be sure to place a rag between front of propeller shaft and torque tube so that coating on shaft will not be damaged.
2. Install propeller shaft into transmission. Care must be used to engage spline of shaft into transmission and journal diameter into extension bearings so as not to damage journal surface. Visual check of propeller shaft alignment into extension is required and if absolutely necessary, tap front flange lightly with a rubber mallet. *Be sure splines are completely engaged in transmission.*
3. Fasten torque tube to transmission and tighten the six bolts to 30-45 ft. lbs.
4. Remove wood block from between transmission and floor.
5. Insert propeller shaft in place and

tighten bolts finger tight.
6. Remove rag from inside torque tube.
7. Secure torque tube to flywheel housing; tighten bolts finger tight.
8. Tighten loose bolts to 30-45 ft. lbs.
9. Install torque tube cover screws to 40-80 inch lbs.
10. Install and adjust gearshift housing and transmission control rod as outlined in transmission section.
11. Idle engine for about a minute to position propeller shaft bearings and install and tighten damper bearing retainer bolts to 3-12 ft. lbs.

Automatic Transmission

Remove
1. Remove propeller shaft damper bearing bolts, Fig. 3.
2. Remove parking brake cable and vacuum line from torque tube.
3. Remove TV linkage from transmission.
4. On V8's, remove exhaust crossover pipe.
5. Remove flywheel bottom cover.
6. Support rear of engine with stand.
7. Unfasten propeller shaft flange from flywheel.
8. Back out halfway torque tube-to-flywheel housing bolts.
9. Place a rag between propeller shaft and torque tube to prevent damage to coating on drive line.
10. Pry propeller shaft flange to rear far enough for pilot to clear recess in flywheel.
11. Unfasten torque tube from flywheel housing.
12. Pull torque tube and propeller shaft away and down from flywheel housing.
13. Place wood block (3″ square) between transmission extension and floor of car to position extension for reassembly.
14. Support torque tube and remove 6 bolts connecting torque tube to transmission.
15. Remove propeller shaft and torque tube as a unit by pulling on propeller shaft flange. *Pull shaft straight out of transmission so it will not bind in transmission or extension housing.*
16. With assembly on bench, pull propeller shaft out of torque tube (see Fig. 4).
No attempt should be made to remove propeller shaft bearings as shaft and bearings are serviced as an assembly.
17. If necessary to replace bearing insulators, start with bearing toward flange first.

Replace
1. Install shaft into torque tube and place a rag bteween front of shaft and tube to prevent damage to coating on drive line.
2. Install propeller shaft into transmission. Care must be used to engage spline into transmission and journal diameter into extension bearings so as not to damage journal surfaces. Visual check of propeller shaft alignment is required and, if absolutely necessary, use a soft rubber hammer to apply additional force to front flange of propeller shaft. Be sure splines are complete-

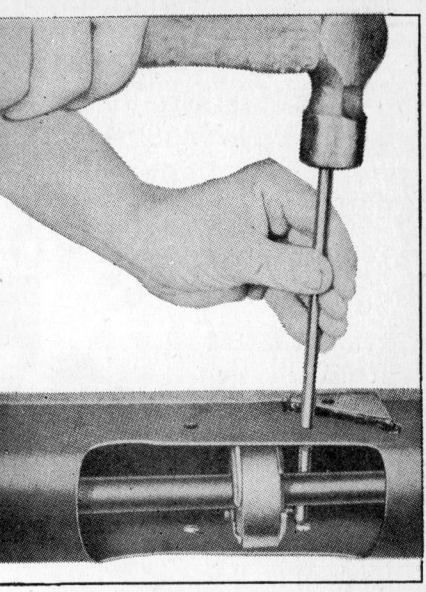

Fig. 4 Spreading torque tube with flat drift if propeller shaft will not come out of torque tube easily

ly engaged in transmission.
3. Fasten torque tube to transmission housing, tightening bolts to 30-45 ft. lbs.
4. Remove wood block from top of transmission.
5. Install propeller shaft to flywheel and tighten attaching bolts finger tight.
6. Remove rag from inside torque tube.
7. Secure torque tube to flywheel housing, tightening bolts finger tight.
8. Tighten all loose bolts to 30-45 ft. lbs.
9. Install flywheel cover.
10. Install and adjust TV linkage as outlined in transmission section.
11. Remove support from rear of engine.
12. On V8's, install exhaust crossover pipe.
13. Idle engine for about a minute to position propeller shaft bearings. Install and tighten bearing bolts to 8-12 ft. lbs.
14. Install parking brake cable and vacuum line and adjust parking brake.

TRANSAXLE, REPLACE

1. Raise car and support transaxle.
2. Drain lubricant from differential and manual shift transmission, or fluid from automatic transmission.
3. Support rear of engine with stand.
4. Remove wheels and brake drums.
5. Unfasten bearing retainer from backing plate.
6. Pull axle shafts out far enough to remove universal from differential carrier.
7. Remove propeller shaft damper bearing bolts, Fig. 3.
8. Remove speedometer driven gear.
9. On manual transmission, disconnect control rod from transmission and parking brake cable from torque tube. Remove gearshift lever hous-

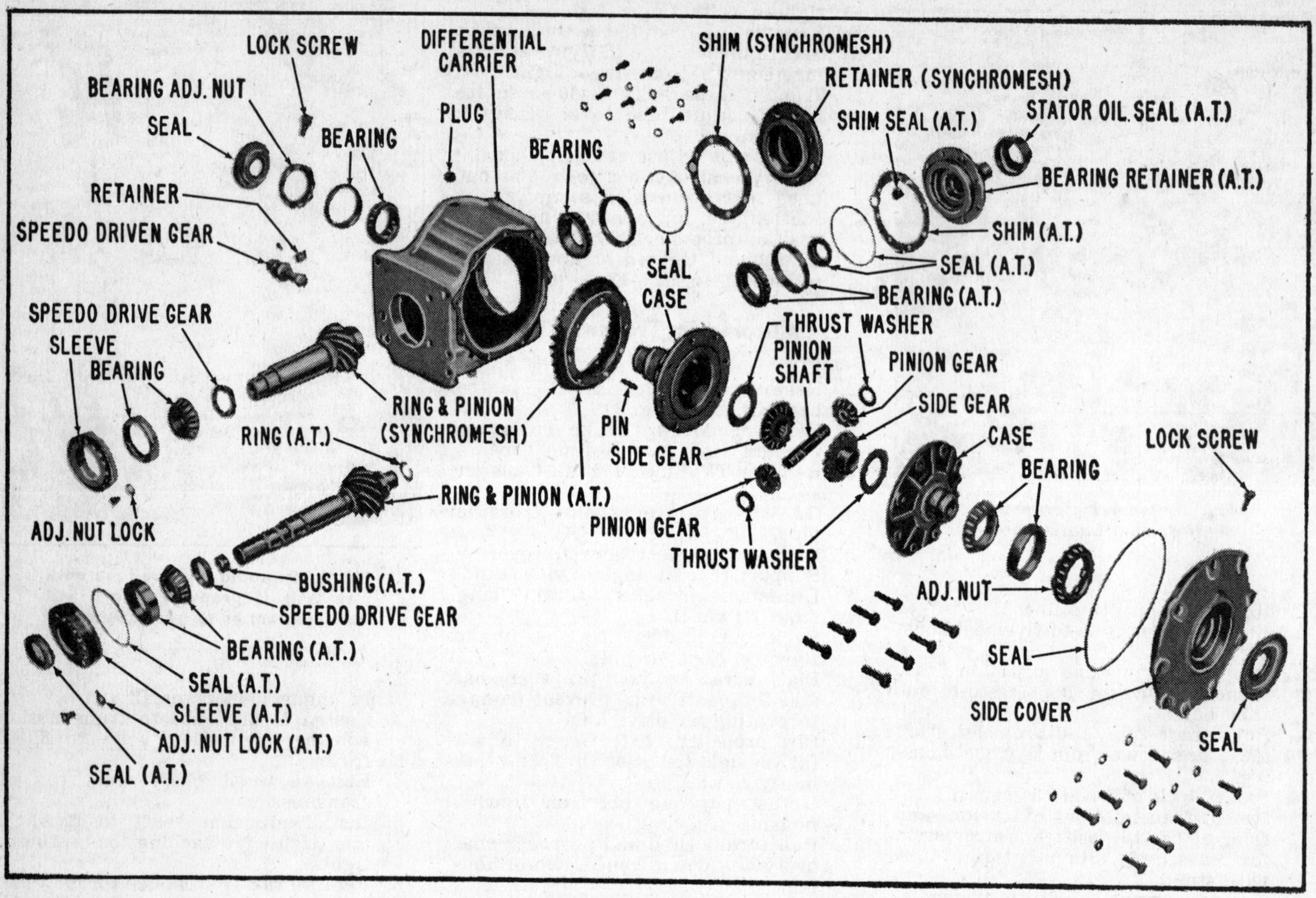

Fig. 5 Differential and carrier components

Diagram labels:

LOCK SCREW
BEARING ADJ. NUT
SEAL
RETAINER
SPEEDO DRIVEN GEAR
BEARING
PLUG
DIFFERENTIAL CARRIER
BEARING
SHIM (SYNCHROMESH)
RETAINER (SYNCHROMESH)
SHIM SEAL (A.T.)
STATOR OIL SEAL (A.T.)
BEARING RETAINER (A.T.)
SHIM (A.T.)
SEAL (A.T.)
BEARING (A.T.)
SEAL CASE
THRUST WASHER
PINION SHAFT
PINION GEAR
SIDE GEAR
SPEEDO DRIVE GEAR
SLEEVE
BEARING
RING (A.T.)
ADJ. NUT LOCK
RING & PINION (SYNCHROMESH)
PIN
SIDE GEAR
RING & PINION (A.T.)
PINION GEAR
THRUST WASHER
CASE
BEARING
LOCK SCREW
BUSHING (A.T.)
SPEEDO DRIVE GEAR
BEARING (A.T.)
SEAL (A.T.)
SLEEVE (A.T.)
ADJ. NUT LOCK (A.T.)
SEAL (A.T.)
ADJ. NUT
SEAL
SIDE COVER
SEAL

10. On automatic transmission, disconnect TV rod and manual valve cable from transmission. Remove vacuum line and parking brake cable from torque tube.
11. On V8's, remove exhaust crossover pipe.
12. Remove flywheel cover from engine.
13. On manual shift jobs, remove torque tube access cover.
14. Unfasten propeller shaft flange from clutch drive extension (manual shift) or flywheel (automatic). Place a rag between front of propeller shaft and torque tube to prevent damage to coating on propeller shaft.
15. Unfasten torque tube from flywheel housing.

16. Through access holes in trunk floor or from under car, remove two bolts securing transaxle to rear crossmember. Remove bolts from bracket.
17. Lower complete transaxle and torque tube from car.
18. Reverse removal procedure to install the assembly, observing the precautions mentioned in the procedure under *Propeller Shaft and Torque Tube.*

DIFF. CARRIER

Disassemble, Fig. 5.
1. Separate differential and transmission.
2. On A.T. jobs, pull off governor drive gear and spacers.
3. Remove differential side bearing oil seals (if the occasion arises, these seals may be replaced without taking assembly for car).
4. Remove side cover and lift out differential case and ring gear.
5. In order to provide complete diagnosis, check tooth pattern with red or white lead as outlined in *Rear Axle* chapter.
6. Remove pinion rear bearing retainer and shim pack. On A.T. jobs only, remove rubber oil passage seal. Tap retainer out from front of case if necessary.

7. Remove front pinion bearing adjusting nut lock and nut.
8. Remove drive pinion.
9. Remove side bearing adjusting nut lock screw and nut.
10. Remove side bearing race. If difficult to remove, screw in adjusting nut until race is pushed out into carrier housing. Remove adjusting nut.
11. Remove drain and filler plugs.
12. Remove adjusting nut lock screw, nut, bearing race and O-ring seal from side cover.

Diff. Case and Ring Gear

1. If side bearings or case is to be replaced, remove bearings.
2. A mark is scribed across parting line of case and cover to aid in alignment on reassembly.
3. Remove 8 ring gear bolts.
4. Reinstall two bolts partially in ring gear and tap ring gear off case.
5. Separate cover and case. Remove side gear and thrust washer from cover half. Drive out roll pin which retains cross shaft and drive out cross shaft.
6. Remove pinions, thrust washers and side gear from case.
7. Reassemble in reverse order and tighten ring gear bolts to 55-65 ft. lbs.

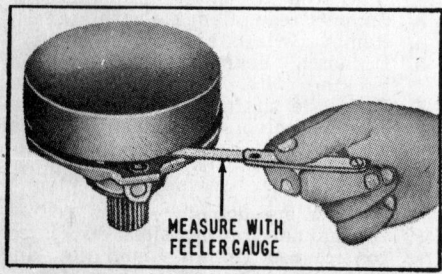

MEASURE WITH FEELER GAUGE

Fig. 6 Determining drive pinion shim thickness required

Dimension Determined With Feeler Gauge	MARK ON CARRIER						
	4.583	4.582	4.581	4.580	4.579	4.578	4.577
	-3	-2	-1	NO MARK	+1	+2	+3
.038	.030	.031	.032	.033	.034	.035	.036
.037	.029	.030	.031	.032	.033	.034	.035
.036	.028	.029	.030	.031	.032	.033	.034
.035	.027	.028	.029	.030	.031	.032	.033
.034	.026	.027	.028	.029	.030	.031	.032
.033	.025	.026	.027	.028	.029	.030	.031
.032	.024	.025	.026	.027	.028	.029	.030
.031	.023	.024	.025	.026	.027	.028	.029
.030	.022	.023	.024	.025	.026	.027	.028
.029	.021	.022	.023	.024	.025	.026	.027
.028	.020	.021	.022	.023	.024	.025	.026
.027	.019	.020	.021	.022	.023	.024	.025
.026	.018	.019	.020	.021	.022	.023	.024
.025	.017	.018	.019	.020	.021	.022	.023
.024	.016	.017	.018	.019	.020	.021	.022
.023	.015	.016	.017	.018	.019	.020	.021
.022	.014	.015	.016	.017	.018	.019	.020
.021	.013	.014	.015	.016	.017	.018	.019
.020	.012	.013	.014	.015	.016	.017	.018

Fig. 7   Drive pinion shim chart

Drive Pinion

1. On A.T. jobs, remove oil ring from pinion shaft.
2. Remove front pinion bearing.
3. Press off speedometer gear.
4. Press off rear bearing.
5. Place rear pinion bearing in its retainer. Place tool (J-8919) on retainer as shown, Fig. 6. Use feeler gauge as shown to determine correct shim thickness required on reassembly. Use chart, Fig. 7, to convert feeler gauge readings to shim specifications. If pinion shaft is marked, use chart, Fig. 8, for correction. *If*

PINION CORRECTION CHART	
MARK	**CORRECTION TO BE APPLIED TO SHIM STACK WHEN PINION IS MARKED**
-4	ADD .004 TO SHIM STACK
-3	ADD .003 TO SHIM STACK
-2	ADD .002 TO SHIM STACK
-1	ADD .001 TO SHIM STACK
NO MARK	MAKE NO CORRECTION
+1	SUBTRACT .001 FROM SHIM STACK
+2	SUBTRACT .002 FROM SHIM STACK
+3	SUBTRACT .003 FROM SHIM STACK
+4	SUBTRACT .004 FROM SHIM STACK

Fig. 8   Drive pinion correction chart

Fig. 9   Checking side bearing preload

bearing race is to be replaced, do so before determining shim requirements.

6. Press on rear bearing, speedometer drive gear and front bearing. On A.T. jobs, replace oil ring.

Assemble and Adjust Differential and Carrier

1. Install side bearing race in carrier casting.
2. Start side bearing adjusting nut.
3. Position side bearing race in side cover and start side bearing adjusting nut.
4. Position ring gear and differential case in carrier.
5. With oil seal removed, place side cover on case with four bolts. Be sure two aligning bolts are in correct holes.
6. Turn side bearing nut in cover finger tight.
7. Install tool, Fig. 9, in end of differential cross shaft through side cover.
8. Adjust side bearing preload to 10-20 inch lbs. by turning adjusting nut in

Fig. 10   Tool installed in pinion shaft

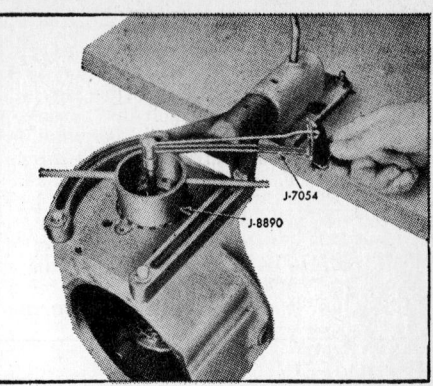

Fig. 11   Adjusting pinion bearing preload

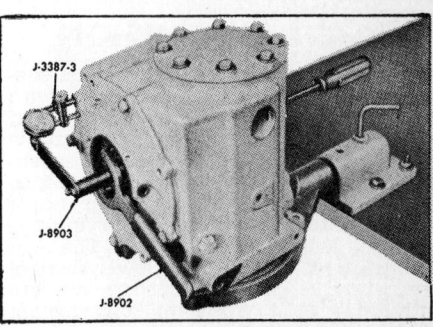

Fig. 12   Tools in position for adjusting backlash

carrier. Check preload as shown.
9. Install adjusting nut lock screws and washers.
10. Remove tool, Fig. 9, from shaft and remove side cover from carrier, and case and ring gear from carrier housing.
11. Install shim pack as already determined. Install new rubber oil passage seal (A.T. only). Install new O-ring seal on rear pinion bearing retainer. Install retainer on housing (8 bolts).
12. Invert carrier and position pinion shaft in carrier. Install pinion adjusting nut (also O-ring seal on A.T. jobs). Tighten nut until play of pinion shaft is eliminated.
13. Install tool, Fig. 10, inside pinion shaft and tighten nut.
14. Adjust pinion bearing preload to 10-16 inch lbs., Fig. 11.
15. Check tooth pattern as described in *Rear Axle* chapter.
16. Place ring gear and differential in carrier. Install side cover without O-ring seal and retain with four bolts. Remove side bearing adjusting nut lock screws.
17. Install tools as shown in Fig. 12. Dial indicator should rest squarely on line scribed on handle of J-8903.
18. Insert large screwdriver in other end of differential shaft.
19. Adjust ring gear and pinion backlash to .004-.009″ by loosening one adjusting nut and tightening the other one notch at a time (do not rotate pinion). Move ring gear toward pinion to decrease backlash

and away from pinion to increase backlash. Remove tools except J-8903.

20. Reinstall side bearing adjusting nut lock screws (10-20 inch lbs. torque).
21. Rotate pinion shaft clockwise 4 turns and counterclockwise 4 turns while creating a drag on tool J-8903, Fig. 12.
22. Remove side cover and ring gear.
23. Analyze tooth patterns and make necessary corrections. *Any change in shim pack will require new pinion bearing preload and side bearing backlash adjustments.* If no corrections are necessary proceed with reassembly.
24. Reinstall ring gear and differential. Install side cover, using new O-ring seal. Tighten side cover bolts to 10-20 ft. lbs. Apply bead of sealer and install new side bearing oil seals. Install drain and filler plugs.
25. Install governor drive gear and spacers on A.T. jobs as outlined in Transmission Section.
26. Assemble transmission and differential carrier.

MASTER CYLINDER

1. To remove, disconnect brake pedal return spring. Disconnect master cylinder push rod from brake pedal.
2. Remove hydraulic line from master cylinder. Unfasten cylinder from cowl and lift off.
3. Reverse removal procedure to install master cylinder. Bleed brake system as outlined in *Hydraulic Brakes* chapter.

Suspension & Steering Section

FRONT SUSPENSION

As shown in Fig. 1, stamped steel suspension control arms are used with rubber bushed mounting shafts. A strut bolted to the lower control arm is mounted at the rear with rubber bushings while the inner end is threaded so that the front suspension caster angle may be readily adjusted by varying the effective length of the strut. The coil springs are seated on the lower control arm and the shock absorbers operate within the coils. To completely isolate the body from road noise, the tops of the springs are seated against rubber insulators. Half ball joints with phenolic seats and anti-dive suspension geometry are also features of this system.

REAR SUSPENSION

As shown in Fig. 2, the swing axle independent rear suspension provides independent action of each rear wheel and reduced unsprung weight as well as positive control of suspension geometry. In this system a rear crossmember is attached to the integral body in four positions. Attached to the rear crossmember is the transaxle support mounted in rubber for noise and vibration isolation. This is in turn affixed to the differential in a manner to provide fore and aft shimming for toe adjustment.

The swing axle suspension gets its name from the fact that suspension travel is provided by allowing each wheel to swing through arcs of radius equal to the axle shaft length. Because the rear wheels are independently suspended, new geometry factors must be considered. Wheel camber, for example, is designed to change as the suspension moves up or down from the design height position. Since the outside wheels carry the greatest weight in a turn, camber characteristics of the rear suspension create desirable understeer geometry.

SUPENSION ADJUSTMENTS

Front Wheel Bearings

1. Remove dust cap.
2. Check for slip fit of bearing cones on spindles. Bores of bearing cones should have a light coat of wheel bearing lubricant to allow cones to creep on spindle.
3. If nuts turn hard on spindle, check for and remove any burrs from spindle threads.
4. With tire off ground, and while rotating it in both directions, tighten nut with torque wrench to 10-20 ft. lbs. to be sure all parts are properly seated.
5. Back off nut one flat (1/6 turn). If locking holes line up insert cotter pin. If not continue to back off nut to nearest locking hole. Final adjustment should be 1 to 1½ flats turn, backed off from initial tightened position. This should result in the desired limits of .001-.010" end play.
6. Install cotter pin, dust cap and wheel.

Checking Curb Height

The suspension parts must be at normal curb height position when checking wheel alignment. This can be obtained by jouncing front and rear of car up and down, decreasing the amount of move-

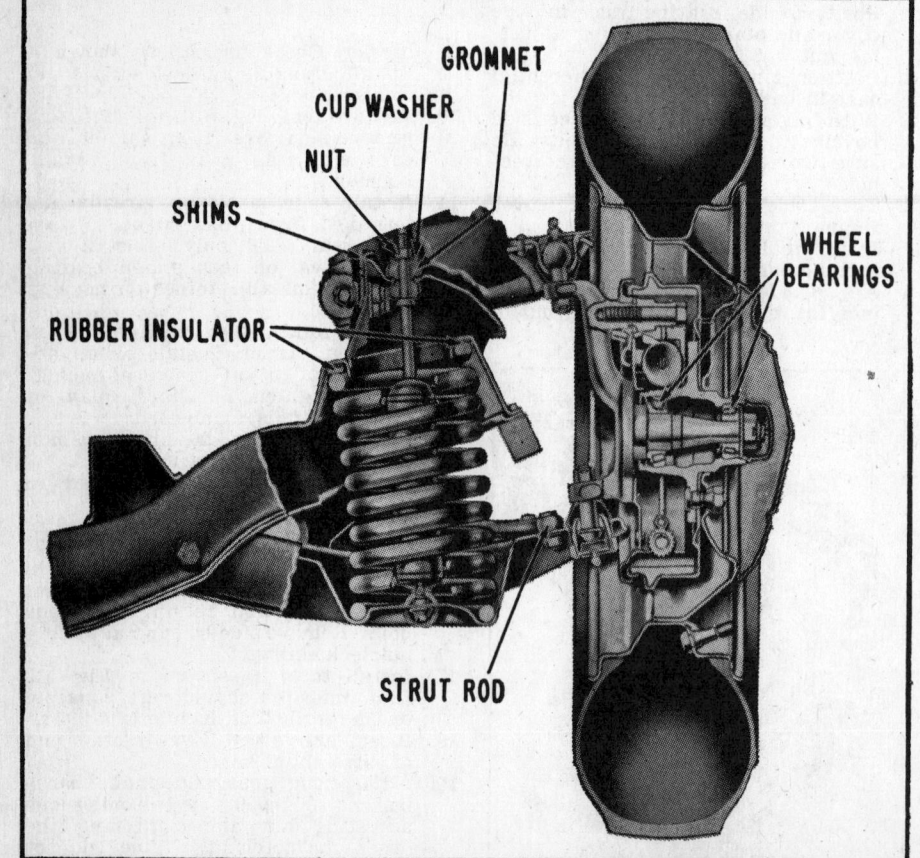

GROMMET
CUP WASHER
NUT
SHIMS
RUBBER INSULATOR
WHEEL BEARINGS
STRUT ROD

Fig. 1   Front suspension.   Note location of camber and caster adjusting shims

ment until parts reach normal curb height position.

To determine whether front and rear suspension height is normal, compare measurement on car with others of the same body type and having comparable equipment. Measurements should be taken as shown in Figs. 3 and 4.

The tendency to remain upward and downward will be more noticeable on new cars on which suspension joints have not yet become burnished and completely free. For this reason, checking of caster and camber on new cars should not be done unless the height is set to correspond with the height of the front end of a similar model that has freed up after usage. Blocks or spacers made of rod or tubing will be useful in positioning parts.

Caster, Adjust

Caster adjustment is made by shimming front and rear on upper control arm. If sufficient adjustment cannot be obtained by shimming, it will be necessary to adjust the length of the strut rod. Lengthening this rod, Fig. 1, by turning the nut increases caster; shortening the rod by turning the nut decreases caster.

Proper strut rod adjustment is necessary to prevent misalignment of lower control arm and bushing in front crossmember. Proper caster adjustment with equal shims at upper arm is given in the *Wheel Alignment* chart.

After adjustment, tighten nut at rear of strut rod to 70-85 ft. lbs. and bend overlocking tab on two sides of nut. Be sure all strut nuts are tight before taking final adjustment reading.

Camber, Adjust

Camber adjustment is made by means of shims between upper control arm inner shaft and front crossmember, Fig. 1. Although shims can be changed at either the front or rear attachment, it is important that the shimming be done equally so as to have no effect on caster. Adding shims at both front and rear of support shaft bolts will decrease positive camber.

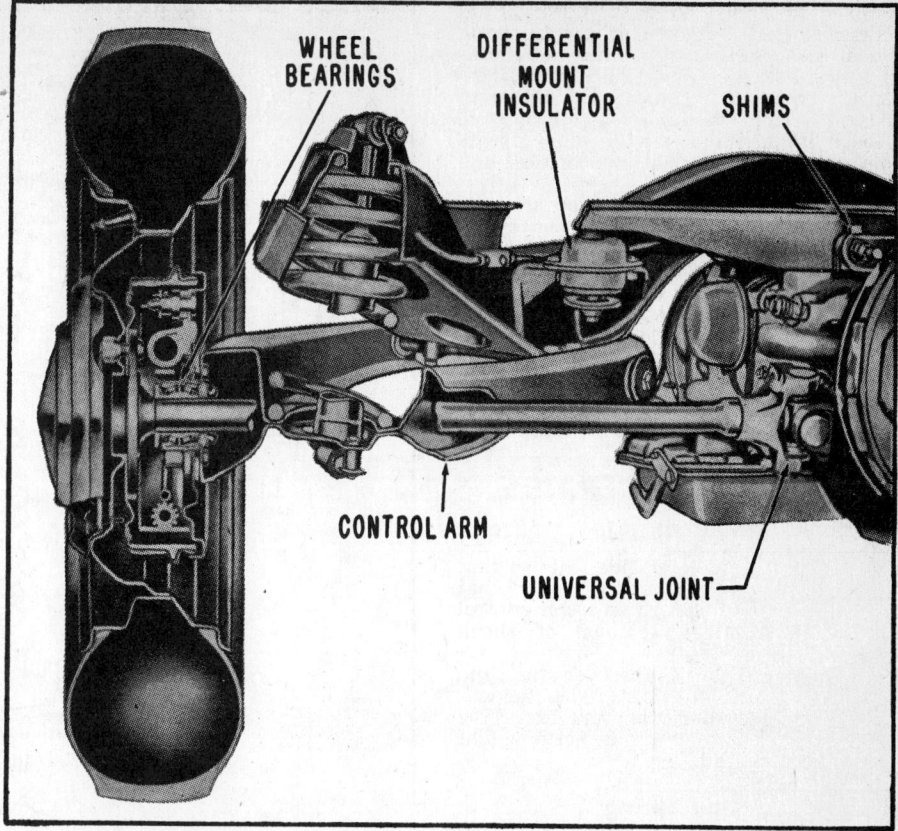

Fig. 2 Rear suspension. Note location of shims for rear wheel toe-in adjustment

Loosen the upper shaft bolts and add or remove shims equally as required and tighten bolts. It may be necessary to remove the wheel to secure these bolts to a torque of 55-70 ft. lbs.

To compensate for drift to the right, induced by road surface camber, it is desirable that the left camber be set $\frac{1}{4}°$ greater than the right camber.

Toe-In, Adjust

1. Remove horn button and set gear on high point of worm by turning steering wheel until mark on shaft is exactly at top. This mark locates center of gear travel or straight ahead position.

2. Loosen tie rod end clamp bolts and turn tie rod tubes an equal amount until toe-in is correct. Turn right tie rod in direction of forward rotation of wheels to increase toe-in; turn left tie rod in opposite direction to increase toe-in.

3. If straight ahead position of front wheels are not equal, turn both tie rod tubes in same direction (so as not to change toe-in) until both wheels are equally facing straight ahead. Re-check toe-in.

4. Tighten tie rod adjuster sleeve bolts to 14-20 ft. lbs., making sure bolts are to lower side of tie rod and at a 25° angle to vertical with head of bolts toward rear of car.

Rear Suspension Toe-In

If the rear wheels are notably tilted just after car has been lowered to floor,

roll car back and forth a few feet to bring wheels back to normal position.

If drive on type equipment is used, reverse car and back it into position. *Toe-in (overall) will be read as toe-out when car is backwards, because readings will be taken from rear of tires rather than front.*

Since the wheels are adjusted by adding or removing shims at the front edge of the differential, Fig. 2, both wheels are adjusted at the same time. With the design of this suspension, it is impossible to adjust one wheel at a time as shims must be added or taken away equally from each side.

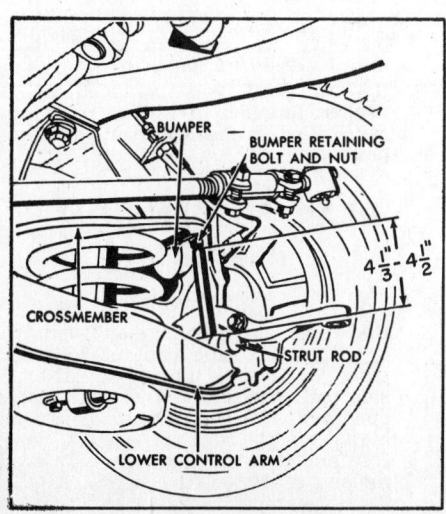

Fig. 3 Measuring front suspension curb height

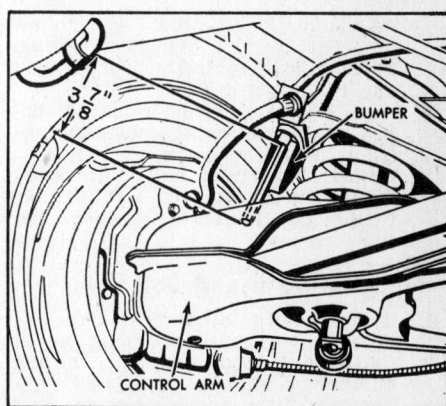

Fig. 4 Measuring rear suspension curb height

A shim added to each side will increase toe-in. Removal of a shim from each side will decrease toe-in. Shims must be added or removed in pairs. Toe-in is listed in the *Wheel Alignment* chart. After shimming is completed, loosen engine mount bolts, run engine to permit it to seek its natural position, and retighten bolts.

Due to manufacturing tolerance and parts stack up, it is possible to have toe-out on one wheel and toe-in on the other wheel. In this instance, adjust the suspension to bring the wheel with the toe-out as close to specifications as possible, but not letting the opposite wheel go out of specifications. For example, if one wheel toes out by ¼″ then opposite wheel must toe-in enough to give 0 to ⅛″ overall toe-in.

FRONT END REPAIRS

Shock Absorber

1. Support vehicle at side rails so that suspension hangs free and that clearance is enough on lower control arms to allow removal of shock absorber, Fig. 5.
2. Unfasten shock absorber top and bottom and withdraw from below.
3. When installed, be sure that the upper grommet nut is bottomed at end of thread.

Coil Spring

1. Support vehicle at frame side rails to allow control arms to swing free and positioned so the arms may be raised or lowered with a hoist.
2. Remove shock absorber.
3. Remove two strut rods-to-control arm nuts. Place stand under lower control arm and take up slightly on spring compression.
4. Remove lower ball stud from knuckle. Carefully raise hoist until spring is free and withdraw spring. *A bar placed through control arm and into spring tower will retain spring and keep it from slipping until free.*
5. Reverse removal procedure to install spring, being sure rubber insulator is in place in crossmember spring tower.

Lower Arm and Ball Joint

1. To remove lower control arm, follow procedure for removing coil spring. Then remove control arm inner bolt and remove arm.
2. If ball joint is to be replaced, unscrew the ball joint (self-tapping) from control arm.
3. To install the new ball joint, screw it into the control arm. Install lube fitting and lubricate. Place rubber cap over stud.

Upper Arm and Ball Joint

1. Remove ball joint from knuckle.
2. Remove two nuts retaining upper control arm to crossmember, noting number of shims at each bolt.
3. Remove sheet metal access hole plugs opposite control arm retaining bolts and remove bolts through these holes.

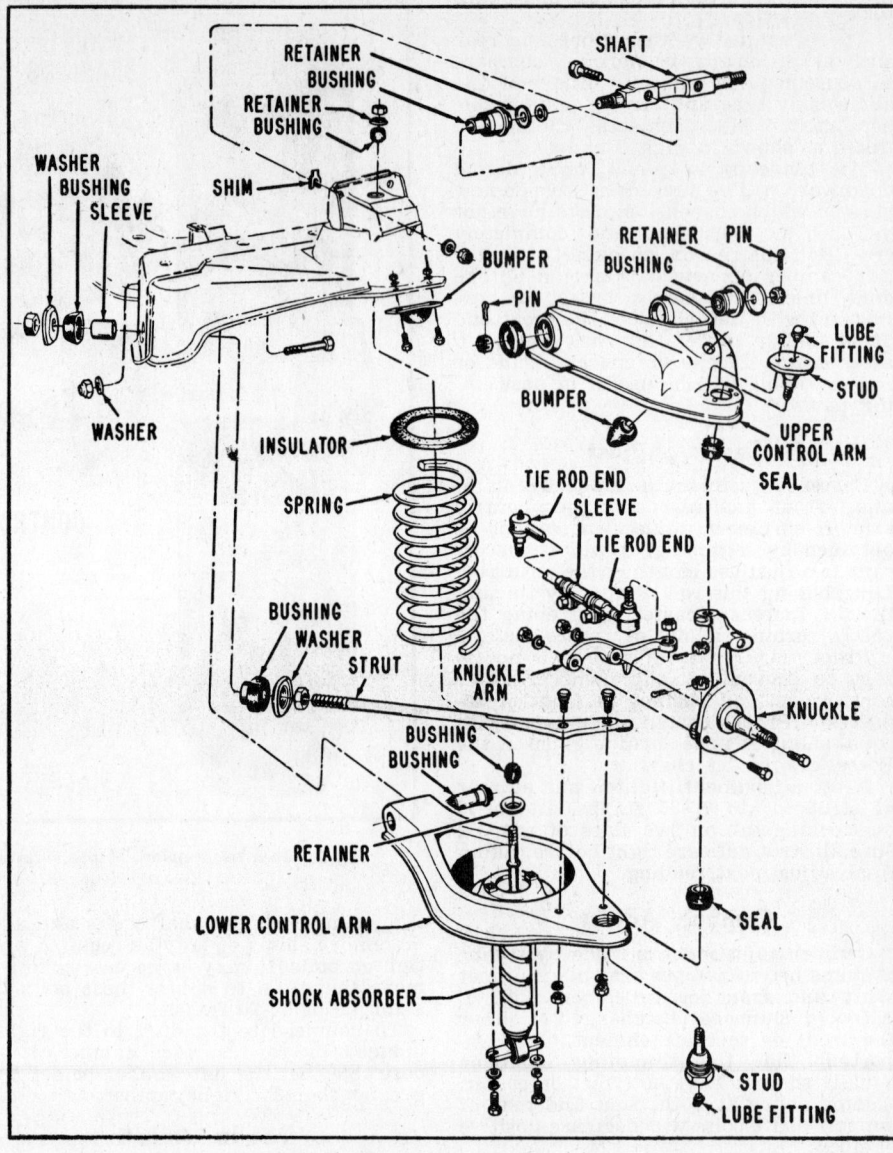

Fig. 5   Front suspension components

4. To remove ball joint from control arm, drill through heads of rivets and cut off rivet heads with a chisel, being careful not to enlarge holes in control arm. Tap rivets out with a punch and remove from control arm.
5. Install new ball joint against top side of control arm. Secure joint to arm with four special alloy nuts and bolts furnished with replacement ball joint. Tighten nuts to 10-12 ft. lbs.
6. Install control arm, being sure to install same number of shims as removed at each bolt. Tighten nuts and bolts to 55-70 ft. lbs. Replace access hole plugs.
7. Install new rubber seal on ball joint stud and lubricate ball. Install ball joint through knuckle and tighten nut to 55-70 ft. lbs. Do not back off nut when aligning holes to install cotter pin.
8. When assembly is completed, bounce front end of vehicle to centralize

bushings and tighten cross shaft nuts to 35-40 ft. lbs.
9. If ball joint was replaced or if proper number of shims were not reinstalled, recheck caster and camber.

REAR SUSPENSION REPAIRS

Shock Absorber

1. Place car on a "drive-on" (ramp) type hoist, frame contact hoist or place jack stands under body at each side rail just forward of rear wheel openings. The body should be raised high enough so that wheels hang free and a floor jack can be placed under tire. Raise tire so that it is in its normal position. This will allow shock absorber to be removed without interfering with the floor.
2. Remove attaching bolts, upper and

lower, and withdraw shock absorber.
3. To install, pull out shock absorber shaft to extend it to its full length.
4. Install shock absorber through lower control arm and spring. Install lower attaching spacers, lockwashers and tighten bolts to 15-25 ft. lbs.
5. Install upper bolt and lockwasher and tighten nut to 45-60 ft. lbs.

Coil Spring

1. Raise vehicle by body side rails so that control arms may swing free. Vehicle must be raised high enough so that a rolling floor jack may be placed under brake drum.
2. Loosen control arm cross shaft bolts (in ends of shaft). Disconnect brake hose from line at junction. Remove wheel and replace nuts on studs to hold drum in place.
3. Remove exhaust system.
4. Position U-Joint as shown in Fig. 6. *This must be done to allow axle shaft and control arm to swing down far enough to remove spring. It also will keep yoke on U-Joint from hitting axle case or side bearing adjustment nut.*
5. Place a rolling jack under drum and brake flange. Raise jack slightly to place a slight load on spring.
6. Remove shock absorber. Mark position of spring with relation to spring seat, Fig. 7, for reassembly.
7. Lower floor jack until spring can be pried out. *Do not remove or lower jack too far as this places too much strain on axle shaft. If both springs are removed, be sure to mark which side each spring goes on.*

Installation

1. Set spring into spring tower and pry into place in lower control arm. *Be sure that index marks line up.*
2. Extend shock absorber shaft and install, tightening lower bolt to 15-25 ft. lbs. Raise lower control arm and attach shock absorber at top, tightening bolt to 45-60 ft. lbs.
3. Connect brake line, remove floor jack and install wheel.
4. Lower vehicle to floor, jounce rear end of car several times and, with full weight on control arms, tighten cross shaft bolts to 45-55 ft. lbs.
5. Bleed and adjust brakes.

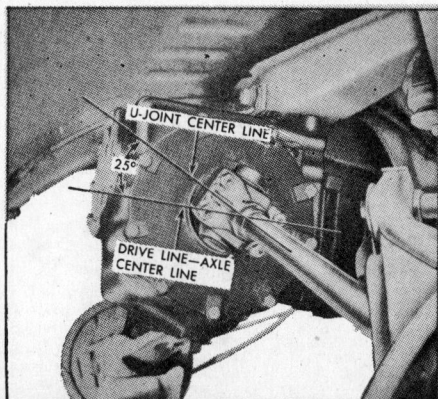

Fig. 6 Position of universal joint for rear spring removal

Fig. 7 Marking spring and spring seat for reassembly

Lower Control Arm

1. Remove spring and shock absorber.
2. Before removing floor jack under drum, support control arm with jack stand.
3. Remove brake drum. Line up hole in axle shaft flange with backing plate nuts and remove nuts.
4. Pull backing plate outward slightly, then push it back onto control arm studs to loosen backing plate from bearing retainer.
5. Remove nuts from universal joint U-Bolts. Pull axle shaft out enough to separate yoke and remove U-Bolts.
6. Remove universal yoke and withdraw axle shaft.
7. Remove backing plate from control arm studs and tie backing plate up to crossmember with wire.
8. Unfasten control arm from crossmember.

Installation

1. Set control arm in place, install and tighten four nuts to 40-55 ft. lbs. *Be sure to attach parking brake bracket and tail pipe support to front two attaching bolts before installing nuts.*
2. Place jack stand under control arm.
3. Install backing plate onto control arm studs and temporarily install two nuts on studs.
4. Install axle shaft, yoke and U-Bolts. Remove two loose nuts from control arm studs and line up holes in axle bearing flange plate with control arm studs and push axle shaft inward until yoke is fully attached to U-Bolts. Install and tighten U-Bolt nuts to 14-20 ft. lbs. Tighten axle shaft flange nuts to 30-45 ft. lbs.
5. Install drum, making certain that holes in drum *do not* line up with hole in axle flange or dirt may get into brake assembly.
6. Install shock absorber and spring. Then bleed and adjust brakes.

STEERING GEAR

Horn Button & Steering Wheel

1. Lift out horn button or ornament.
2. Remove two nuts and spacer from steering shaft.
3. Remove horn ring (Deluxe) or receiver cup.
4. Remove pivot ring (Deluxe) and bellville spring.
5. Remove contact assembly.
6. Use puller to remove wheel.
7. To replace, reverse removal operations, making sure wheel is in straight ahead position. Tighten wheel nut to 25-30 ft. lbs.

Steering Gear Adjustments

There are two adjustments on the steering gear, Fig. 8. They are worm bearing preload and sector and ball nut backlash. It is important that adjustments be made in the sequence mentioned. Failure to do so will result in damage to steering gear.

Worm Bearing Preload

1. Disconnect steering linkage from pitman arm. Tighten pitman arm nut to 100-125 ft. lbs.
2. Loosen steering column bracket to make certain it is not sprung due to misalignment. If misaligned, shim at steering gear housing-to-frame bolts and tighten bracket.
3. Loosen side cover lock nut and back off adjusting screw a few turns.
4. With spring scale hooked to rim of steering wheel, measure pull required to keep wheel in motion when off high point, at least 30° off center. Pull required should be between $\frac{1}{4}$ and $\frac{3}{4}$ lb. (manual gear) or $\frac{1}{4}$ to $\frac{5}{8}$ lb. (power assist). To correct, loosen worm adjuster lock nut with brass drift and turn adjuster to bring adjustment within limits.
5. Retighten lock nut to 18-27 ft. lbs. and worm adjuster lock nut 70-100 ft. lbs. Recheck adjustment.

Sector and Ball Nut Backlash

1. When worm bearing preload has been adjusted, side cover adjusting screw should be turned clockwise until a pull of $\frac{7}{8}$ to $1\frac{1}{2}$ lbs (manual gear) or $\frac{3}{4}$ to 1 lb. (power assist) at steering wheel rim is required to turn wheel through high point.
2. Tighten side cover adjusting screw and worm bearing adjuster lock nuts and recheck adjustments.

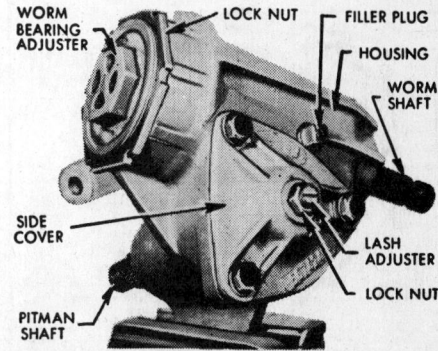

Fig. 8 Steering gear adjustments

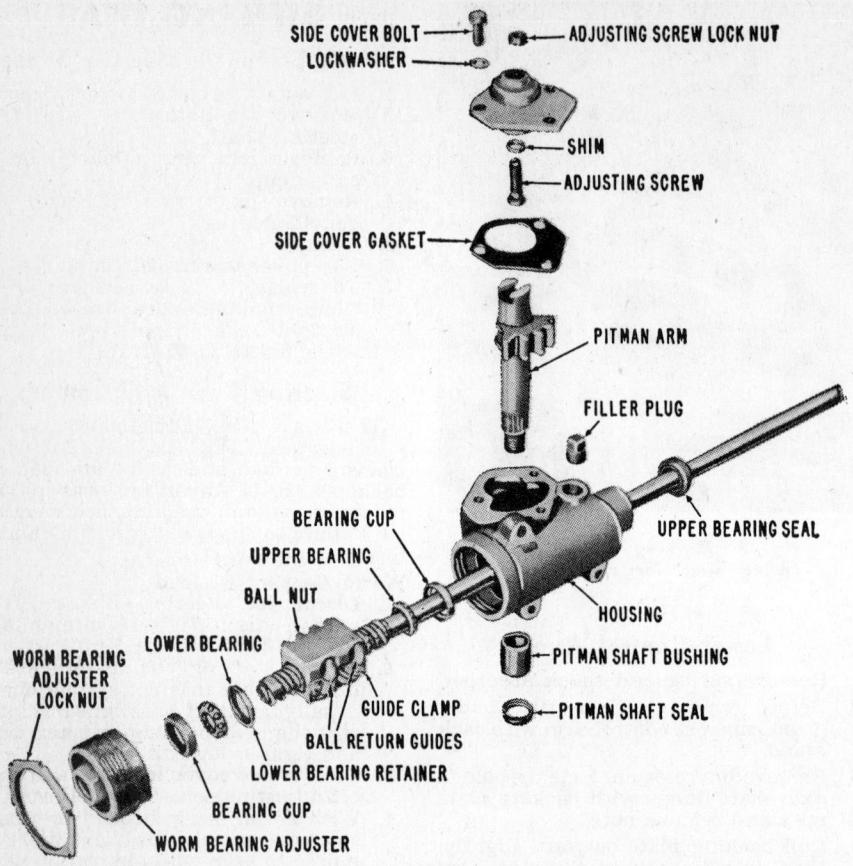

SIDE COVER BOLT
LOCKWASHER
ADJUSTING SCREW LOCK NUT
SHIM
ADJUSTING SCREW
SIDE COVER GASKET
PITMAN ARM
FILLER PLUG
BEARING CUP
UPPER BEARING
BALL NUT
UPPER BEARING SEAL
LOWER BEARING
HOUSING
WORM BEARING ADJUSTER LOCK NUT
PITMAN SHAFT BUSHING
PITMAN SHAFT SEAL
GUIDE CLAMP
BALL RETURN GUIDES
LOWER BEARING RETAINER
BEARING CUP
WORM BEARING ADJUSTER

Fig. 9 Steering gear components

Steering Gear, Replace

1. Remove steering wheel.
2. Unfasten gear from frame and remove gear and shaft from car.
3. Remove plastic collar and felt seal from column.
4. Reverse removal procedure to install gear and tighten attaching bolts to 70-90 ft. lbs.
5. On power steering cars, be sure to secure booster cylinder shaft bracket with two lower steering gear attaching bolts.

Steering Gear Repairs

Disassemble

1. Referring to Fig. 9, turn steering gear to center of travel and remove side cover adjusting screw lock nut. Remove side cover and gasket by turning adjusting screw clockwise through cover.
2. Remove adjusting screw from slot in end of pitman shaft. Make sure shim found on adjusting screw remains with screw.
3. Remove pitman shaft from housing.
4. Remove worm bearing adjuster lock nut and remove adjuster and lower bearing.
5. Push worm and shaft with ball nut through bottom of housing and remove upper bearing.
6. Remove ball nut from return guide clamp, remove guides. turn nut over and remove balls. Rotating shaft slowly from side to side will aid in removing balls.
7. Remove ball nut from worm. Unless

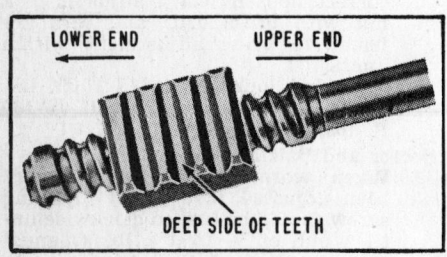

LOWER END   UPPER END

DEEP SIDE OF TEETH

Fig. 10 Ball nut properly installed on shaft

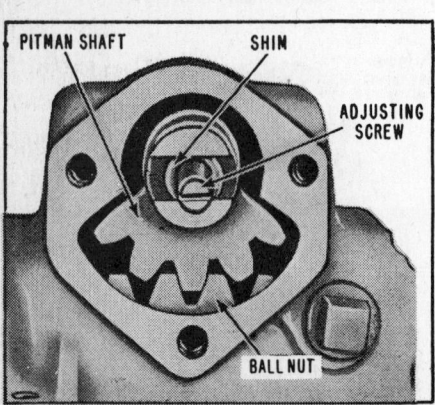

PITMAN SHAFT   SHIM
ADJUSTING SCREW
BALL NUT

Fig. 11 Adjusting worm bearing preload

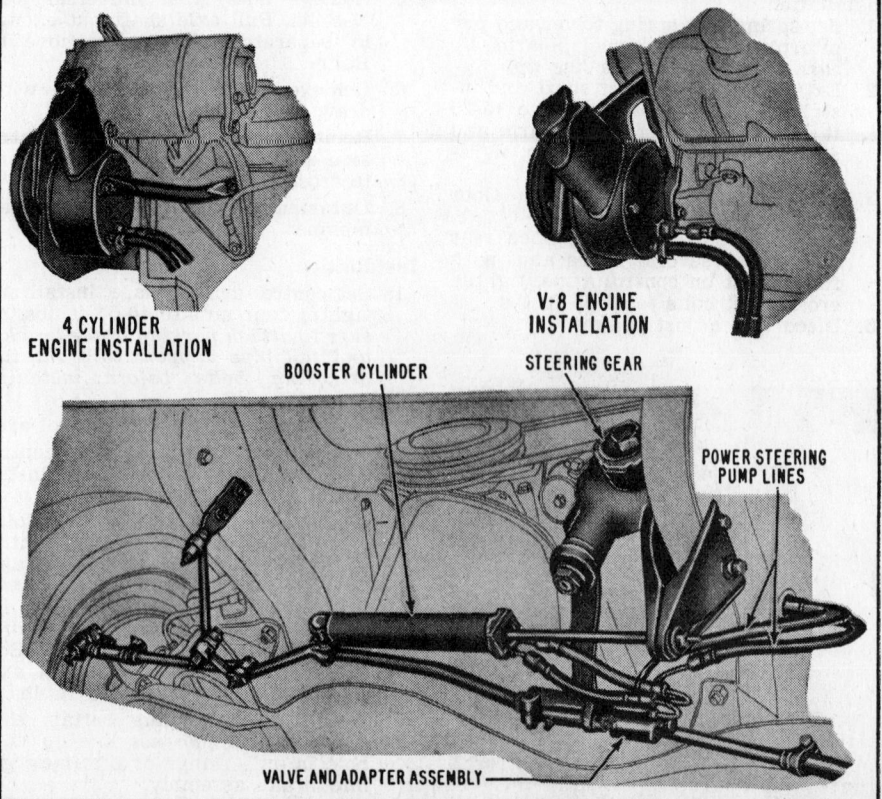

4 CYLINDER ENGINE INSTALLATION

V-8 ENGINE INSTALLATION

STEERING GEAR
BOOSTER CYLINDER
POWER STEERING PUMP LINES
VALVE AND ADAPTER ASSEMBLY

Fig. 12 Power steering installation

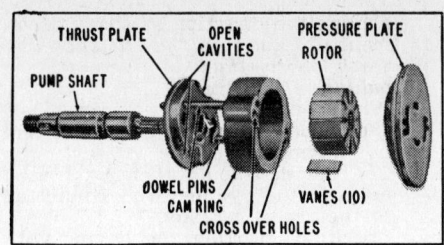

Fig. 13 Power steering pump components

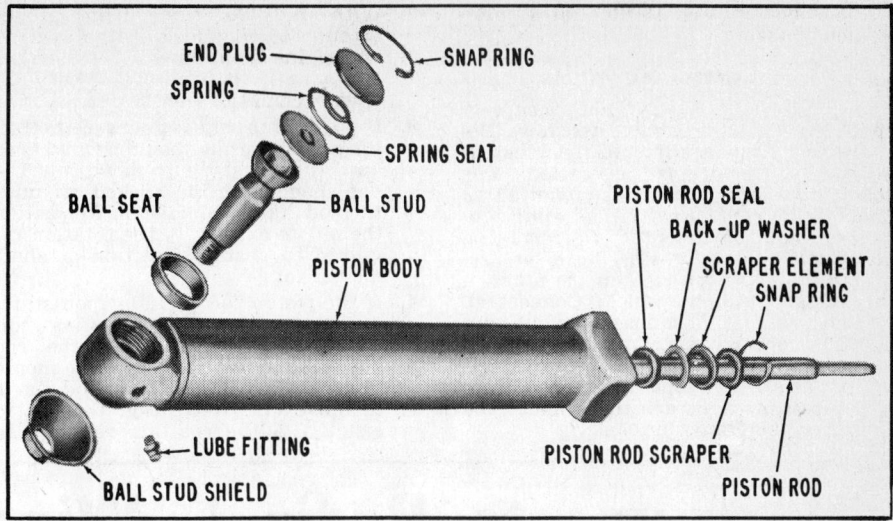

Fig. 15 Booster cylinder components

all balls are removed nut cannot be removed.

Assemble

1. All seals, bushings and bearings should be lubricated before assembly.
2. Place ball nut on worm so deep side of teeth are located as shown in Fig. 10.
3. Install 20 balls in each circuit (one circuit at a time) of ball nut, rotating steering shaft slightly to aid in installing balls.
4. Insert 5 balls in each return guide using vaseline to hold balls in place. Install guide clamp and screw. *Be careful that rotation of shaft does not cause balls to enter crossover passage between circuits as this will cause improper operation of ball nut.*
5. Place upper bearing on shaft. Center ball nut on worm, then slide steering shaft, bearing and nut into housing.
6. Install worm adjuster in housing just tight enough to hold bearing races in place. Final adjustment will be made later.
7. Install pitman shaft adjuster screw and selective shim in pitman shaft slot. *Screw must be free to turn but have no more than .002" end play. If too tight or too loose, select new shim to give proper clearance. Shims*

are furnished in several thicknesses, ranging from .063" to .069".

8. Install pitman shaft as shown in Fig. 11. Install side cover and gasket on adjusting screw, turning screw counterclockwise until it projects through cover ⅝" to ¾".
9. Install cover screws and tighten to 25-35 ft. lbs. Tighten pitman shaft adjusting screw so that teeth engage but do not bind. Final adjustment will be made later.
10. Fill steering gear with proper lubricant and adjust as outlined previously.

POWER STEERING

The power steering system consists of a pulley driven vane type pump, an oil reservoir which is part of the pump assembly, a double-acting power booster cylinder, and a hydraulic control valve, Fig. 12.

Pump, Replace

1. Drain system by removing inlet hose. Disconnect outlet hose and connector.
2. Loosen pump bracket bolt, remove drive belt and pump assembly from car.
3. Install in reverse order of removal. Fill reservoir with Hydra-Matic fluid and run engine at a fast idle speed for 30 seconds. Refill pump and bleed system by running engine and turning steering wheel through entire range of travel to expel air. Check oil level and for leaks through-

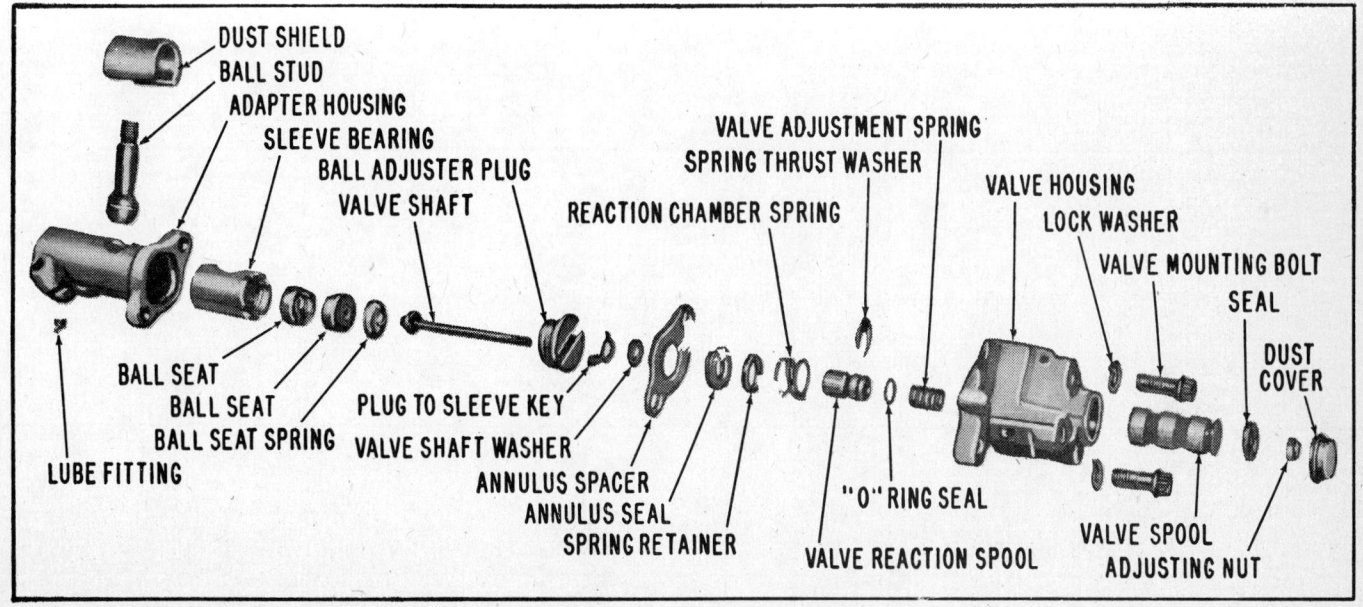

Fig. 14 Hydraulic control valve components

out system. Fig. 13 illustrates pump components.

Control Valve

Fig. 14 illustrates the components of the hydraulic control valve assembly. Because this valve is adjustable, it must be adjusted after being assembled. *The following steps should be followed in balancing a control valve. The same procedure may be followed to correct a complaint of harder steering effort required in one direction than the other.*

1. Install valve in vehicle. Connect all hoses and fill pump reservoir with oil. Do not connect the cylinder rod to the frame bracket. If the vehicle is already in operation, it will be necessary to detach the cylinder rod from the frame bracket.
2. With all hoses attached and proper amount of oil added to the system, the engine should be started with the car on a hoist. One of the two following conditions will exist.
3. If the piston rod remains retracted, the adjusting nut should be advanced until the rod starts to move out. The nut should then be backed off until the rod starts to move in. Reposition the nut to exactly ½ the rotation required to change direction of shaft movement.
4. If the piston rod extends upon starting the pump, the adjusting nut should be retarded until the rod starts to move in. The nut should then be advanced until the rod starts to move out. Reposition the nut to exactly ½ the rotation required to change the direction of shaft movement. *Do not turn the nut back and forth more than is necessary to balance the valve.*
5. When valve is balanced, piston rod should be able to be moved in and out manually.
6. The engine should then be turned off and the cylinder rod connected to the frame bracket.
7. Check by starting the engine with car on a hoist. If front wheels do not turn in either direction from center, valve action is correct. Install dust cap on end of valve.

Booster Cylinder

If repairs are to be made to the booster cylinder, refer to Fig. 15 for proper location of components.

Instruments, Radio & Windshield Wiper

INSTRUMENT CLUSTER

1. To remove cluster, disconnect battery.
2. Remove two ¼″ nuts, and four screws at lower edge of cluster housing.
3. Remove two screws from lower steering column bezel.
4. Remove speedometer cable.
5. Pull cluster and housing out of panel opening to gain access to wiring.
6. Starting at top, remove bulbs and wiring.
7. Remove four screws retaining cluster to housing. When cluster is removed, all instruments will be accessible for servicing.

RADIO, REPLACE

1. Disconnect battery ground cable.
2. Loosen hex screws and remove knobs.
3. Remove retaining nuts and escutcheon.
4. Remove screw securing radio to instrument bracket.
5. Disconnect antenna and power leads from radio and remove radio. *On air conditioned cars the glove box and left hand evaporator support must be removed and radio removed through this opening.*

WINDSHIELD WIPER

1. To remove wiper motor, remove hoses and wire terminals connected to motor.
2. Remove clip securing wiper crank to transmission arm. This connects inside car at fire wall under instrument panel.
3. Remove attaching screws and remove wiper from fire wall.

RAMBLER · NASH · HUDSON

INDEX OF SERVICE OPERATIONS

PAGE NO.

ACCESSORIES

Radio, Replace 1074
Speedometer, Replace 1073
Windshield Wiper 1074
Windshield Wiper Troubles 37

BODY

Air Conditioning 177
Automatic Seat Adjuster Troubles 36
Automatic Top Troubles 36
Automatic Window Lift Troubles 36

BRAKES (Mechanical)

Adjustments 112
Brake Cylinder Sizes 1046
Hydraulic Brake System 112
Master Cylinder, Replace 1070
Trouble Shooting 31

BRAKES (Power)

Power Unit Repairs 128
Trouble Shooting 32

CLUTCH

Clutch Pedal, Adjust 1064
Clutch Repairs 1064
Clutch, Replace 1064
Trouble Shooting 13

COOLING SYSTEM

Radiator, Replace 1060
Trouble Shooting 8
Water Pump Repairs 1060

ELECTRIC SYSTEM

Dash Gauge Service 85
Distributor, Replace 1060
Distributor Service 46
Distributor Specifications 1048
Generator & Regulator Service 62
Generator & Regulator Specs. 1047
Horn Button or Ring, Replace 1071
Ignition System Service 46
Ignition Timing 1061
Starter Switch Service 83
Starting Motor Service 77
Starting Motor Specifications 1049
Trouble Shooting 10
Turn Signal Troubles 12

PAGE NO.

ENGINE

Camshaft 1057
Crankshaft & Bearing Specs. 1045
Crankshaft End Play, Adjust 1059
Crankshaft Oil Seal, Replace 1059
Cylinder Head, Replace 1055
Engine, Replace 1054
Main Bearings, Replace 1059
Piston Pins, Replace 1059
Piston Rings, Replace 1058
Piston, Pin & Ring Specs. 1045
Pistons & Rods, Remove 1057
Piston & Rod, Assemble 1058
Pistons, Replace 1058
Rocker Arms 1056
Rod Bearings, Replace 1059
Timing Case Cover, Replace 1057
Timing Chain, Replace 1057
Trouble Shooting 4
Valves, Adjust 1056
Valve Arrangement 1056
Valve Guides 1056
Valve Lifters 1057
Valves, Remove 1056
Valve Spring Installed Height 1056
Valve Spring Testing 1056
Valve Specifications 1044

ENGINE OILING

Oil Pan, Replace 1060
Oil Pump Repairs 1060
Trouble Shooting 9

FRONT SUSPENSION

Camber, Adjust 1070
Caster, Adjust 1070
Front End Repairs 1070
Toe-in, Adjust 1070
Trouble Shooting 33
Wheel Alignment Specifications 1051

FUEL SYSTEM

Carburetors 1061
Fuel Pumps 46
Trouble Shooting 4

OVERDRIVE 100

Trouble Shooting 14

REAR AXLE

Axle Shaft, Replace 1069
General Service 102
Non-Slip Differentials 109
Rear Axle Repairs 1068
Rear Axle, Replace 1068
Rear Axle Specifications 1046
Trouble Shooting 31

PAGE NO.

SPECIFICATIONS

Brake Cylinder Sizes 1046
Capacity Data 1050
Carburetors 1062
Cooling System 1050
Crankshaft & Bearings 1045
Distributors 1048
Engine Tightening 1045
Generator & Regulators 1047
Pistons, Pins & Rings 1045
Rear Axle 1046
Starting Motors 1049
Tune Up 1043
Valve Timing 1057
Valves 1044
Wheel Alignment 1051

STEERING GEARS (Mechanical)

Horn Button or Ring, Replace 1071
Steering Gear Repairs 1071
Steering Gear, Replace 1071
Trouble Shooting 33

STEERING GEARS (Power)

Steering Gear Repairs 1073
Trouble Shooting 34

TRANSMISSIONS (Manual Shift)

Gearshift, Adjust 1066
Transmission Repairs 1065
Transmission, Replace 1065
Trouble Shooting 14

TRANSMISSIONS (Automatic)

Flashomatic Controls 1067
    Replace 1068
    Repairs 233
    Trouble Shooting 30
Hydramatic Linkage 1067
    Replace 1067
    Repairs 283
    Trouble Shooting 25

TUNE UP 38

RAMBLER · NASH · HUDSON

GENERAL SPECIFICATIONS

Year	Model Designation	Wheelbase, Inches	Valve Location	Bore and Stroke	Piston Displacement, Cubic Inches	Compression Ratio (Standard)	Maximum Brake H.P. @ R.P.M.	Maximum Torque Lbs. Ft. @ R.P.M.	Normal Oil Pressure Pounds
RAMBLER									
1953	Six............①5310	100	In Block	3.1250 x 4.250	196	7.30	90 @ 3800	150 @ 1600	50
	Six............②5310	100	In Block	3.1250 x 4.000	184	7.25	85 @ 3800	150 @ 1600	50
1954	Six............②5410	③	In Block	3.1250 x 4.000	184	7.25	85 @ 3800	150 @ 1600	50
	Six............①5410	③	In Block	3.1250 x 4.250	196	7.30	90 @ 3800	150 @ 1600	50
1955	Six............5510	③	In Block	3.1250 x 4.250	196	7.30	90 @ 3800	150 @ 1600	50
1956	Six............5610	108	In Head	3.1250 x 4.250	196	7.47	120 @ 4200	170 @ 1600	50
1957	Six............5710	108	In Head	3.1250 x 4.250	196	8.25	125 @ 4200	175 @ 1600	50
	V8............5720	108	In Head	3.5000 x 3.250	250	8.00	190 @ 4900	240 @ 2500	55
	Rebel V8............5730	108	In Head	4.0000 x 3.250	327	9.50	255 @ 4700	345 @ 2600	55
1958	American 6............5801	100	In Block	3.1250 x 4.250	196	8.00	90 @ 3800	150 @ 1600	50
	Rambler 6............5810	108	In Head	3.1250 x 4.250	196	8.70	127 @ 4200	180 @ 1600	50
	Rebel V8............5820	108	In Head	3.5000 x 3.250	250	8.70	215 @ 4900	260 @ 2500	55
	Ambassador V8............5880	117	In Head	4.0000 x 3.250	327	9.70	279 @ 4700	360 @ 2600	55
1959	American 6............5901	100	In Block	3.1250 x 4.250	196	8.00	90 @ 3800	150 @ 1600	50
	Rambler 6............5910	108	In Head	3.1250 x 4.250	196	8.70	127 @ 4200	180 @ 1600	50
	Rebel V8............5920	108	In Head	3.5000 x 3.250	250	8.70	215 @ 4900	260 @ 2500	55
	Ambassador V8............5980	117	In Head	4.0000 x 3.250	327	9.70	270 @ 4700	360 @ 2600	55
1960	American 6............6001	100	In Block	3.1250 x 4.250	196	8.00	90 @ 3800	150 @ 1600	50
	American Custom 6......6001	100	In Head	3.1250 x 4.250	196	8.70	125 @ 4200	180 @ 1600	50
	Rambler 6............6010	108	In Head	3.1250 x 4.250	196	8.70	127 @ 4200	180 @ 1600	50
	Rebel V8............6020	108	In Head	3.5000 x 3.250	250	8.70	200 @ 4900	245 @ 2500	55
	Ambassador V8............6080	117	In Head	4.0000 x 3.250	327	8.70	250 @ 4700	340 @ 2600	55
1961	American Deluxe & Super..6101	100	In Block	3.1250 x 4.250	196	8.00	90 @ 3800	160 @ 1600	50
	American Custom......6101	100	In Head	3.1250 x 4.250	196	8.70	125 @ 4200	180 @ 1600	50
	Classic 6............6110	108	In Head	3.1250 x 4.250	196	8.70	127 @ 4200	180 @ 1600	50
	Classic V8............6120	108	In Head	3.5000 x 3.250	250	8.70	200 @ 4900	245 @ 2500	55
	Ambassador V8............6180	117	In Head	4.0000 x 3.250	327	8.70	250 @ 4700	340 @ 2600	55

①—With automatic trans.　②—With synchromesh trans.　③—Two-door 100″, four-door 108″.

Year	Model Designation	Wheelbase, Inches	Valve Location	Bore and Stroke	Piston Displacement, Cubic Inches	Compression Ratio (Standard)	Maximum Brake H.P. @ R.P.M.	Maximum Torque Lbs. Ft. @ R.P.M.	Normal Oil Pressure Pounds
NASH									
1955	Statesman 6............5540	114¼	In Block	3.1250 x 4.250	196	8.50	100 @ 3800	155 @ 1600	50
	Ambassador 6............5560	121¼	In Head	3.5000 x 4.375	253	7.60	130 @ 3700	220 @ 1600	60
	Ambassador V8............5580	121¼	In Head	3.8125 x 3.500	320	8.25	208 @ 4200	300 @ 2000	45
1956	Statesman 6............5640	114¼	In Head	3.1250 x 4.250	196	7.47	130 @ 4500	175 @ 1800	50
	Ambassador Special V8...5650	114¼	In Head	3.5000 x 3.250	250	8.00	190 @ 4900	240 @ 2500	55
	Ambassador 6............5660	121¼	In Head	3.5000 x 4.375	253	7.60	135 @ 3700	220 @ 1600	60
	Ambassador V8............5680	121¼	In Head	4.0000 x 3.500	352	9.55	220 @ 4800	320 @ 2200	45
1957	Ambassador V8............5780	121¼	In Head	4.0000 x 3.250	327	9.00	255 @ 4700	345 @ 2600	55

Year	Model Designation	Wheelbase, Inches	Valve Location	Bore and Stroke	Piston Displacement, Cubic Inches	Compression Ratio (Standard)	Maximum Brake H.P. @ R.P.M.	Maximum Torque Lbs. Ft. @ R.P.M.	Normal Oil Pressure Pounds
HUDSON									
1955	Wasp 6............35540	114¼	In Block	3.0000 x 4.750	202	7.50	115 @ 4000	158 @ 1400	40
	Hornet 6............35560	121¼	In Block	3.8125 x 4.500	308	7.50	160 @ 3800	264 @ 1800	40
	Hornet V8............35580	121¼	In Head	3.8125 x 3.500	320	7.80	208 @ 4200	300 @ 2000	45
1956	Wasp 6............35640	114¼	In Block	3.0000 x 4.750	202	7.50	120 @ 4000	158 @ 1400	40
	Special V8............35650	114¼	In Head	3.5000 x 3.250	250	8.00	190 @ 4900	240 @ 2500	55
	Hornet 6............35660	121¼	In Block	3.8125 x 4.500	308	7.50	165 @ 3800	264 @ 1800	40
	Hornet V8............35680	121¼	In Head	4.0000 x 3.500	352	9.55	220 @ 4600	320 @ 2200	45
1957	Hornet V8............35780	121¼	In Head	4.0000 x 3.250	327	9.00	255 @ 4700	345 @ 2600	55

TUNE UP SPECIFICATIONS

★Disconnect vacuum line at carburetor when using timing light to set timing.

Year	Model	Ground Polarity and Voltage	Spark Plug Type ①	Spark Plug Gap Inch	Distributor Point Gap Inch	Distributor Cam Angle Degrees	Firing Order ③	Ignition Timing★ Mark	Ignition Timing★ Location	Idle Speed RPM In Neutral	Compression Pressure @ Cranking Speed Minimum
RAMBLER											
1953	5310	P-6	A7	.030	.022	31–37	153624	TDC	Damper	375	120
1954	184″ Engine	P-6	A7	.030	.022	31–37	153624	TDC	Damper	450	120
	196″ Engine	P-6	A7	.030	.022	31–37	153624	4°ATDC	Damper	450	120
1955	5510	P-6	A7	.030	.022	31–37	153624	4°ATDC	Damper	475	120
1956	5610	N-12	AL7	.030	.016	28–35	153624	TDC	Damper	475	120
1957	Six	N-12	7J	.035	.016	28–35	153624	TDC	Damper	475	120
	V8	N-12	7J	.035	③	30	18436572②	5°BTDC	Damper	475	140
1958–59	American	N-12	AL7	.035	.016	28–35	153624	3°BTDC	Damper	475	140
	Rambler 6	N-12	7J	.035	.016	28–35	153624	5°BTDC	Damper	475	130
	Rebel V8	N-12	7J	.035	.016	28–32	18436572②	5°BTDC	Damper	475	130
	Amb. V8	N-12	7J	.035	.016	28–32	18436572②	5°BTDC	Damper	475	150
1960	American	N-12	⑦	.035	.020	37–41	153624	3°BTDC	Damper	475	140
	Am. Custom	N-12	⑦	.035	.016	28–35	153624	⑧	Damper	475	130
	Rambler 6	N-12	⑦	.035	.016	28–35	153624	5°BTDC	Damper	475	130
	Rebel V8	N-12	⑦	.035	.016	28–32	18436572②	⑨	Damper	475	130
	Amb. V8	N-12	⑦	.035	.016	28–32	18436572②	⑨	Damper	475	150
1961	6101 L-Head 6	N-12	⑦	.035	.020	37–41	153624	3°BTDC	Damper	475	140
	6101 OHV 6⑩	N-12	⑦	.035	.016	28–35	153624	8°BTDC	Damper	475	130
	6101 OHV 6⑪	N-12	⑦	.035	.016	28–35	153624	10°BTDC	Damper	475	130
	6110	N-12	⑦	.035	.016	28–35	153624	8°BTDC	Damper	475	130
	6120⑩	N-12	⑦	.035	.016	28–32	18436572②	TDC	Damper	475	130
	6120⑪	N-12	⑦	.035	.016	28–32	18436572②	5°BTDC	Damper	475	130
	6180⑩	N-12	⑦	.035	.016	28–32	18436572②	TDC	Damper	475	150
	6180⑪	N-12	⑦	.035	.016	28–32	18436572②	5°BTDC	Damper	475	150
NASH											
1955	5540	P-6	A7	.030	⑤	⑥	153624	4°ATDC	Damper	475	120
	5560	P-6	A7	.030	.016	38–45	153624	4°ATDC	Damper	475	120
	5580	P-6	AG5	.035	.017	38	18436572②	5°BTDC	Damper	475	140
1956	5640	N-12	AL7	.030	.016	28–35	153624	4°ATDC	Damper	475	120
	5650	N-12	AL7	.035	.016	26–33	18436572②	5°BTDC	Damper	475	140
	5660	N-12	A7	.030	.020	39	153624	4°ATDC	Damper	475	120
	5680	N-12	AG5	.035	.017	④	18436572②	5°BTDC	Damper	475	140
1957	5720, 30	N-12	7J	.035	③	30	18436572②	5°BTDC	Damper	475	140
	5780	N-12	7J	.035	③	30	18436572②	5°BTDC	Damper	475	140
HUDSON											
1955	Wasp	P-6	H10	.032	.020	39	153624	Line	Damper	500	100
	Hornet 6	P-6	H11	.032	.020	39	153624	UDC 1-6	Flywheel	500	100
	Hornet V8	P-6	AG5	.035	.017	38	18436572②	5°BTDC	Damper	475	140
1956	Wasp	N-12	H10	.032	.020	39	153624	Line	Damper	500	100
	Hornet 6	N-12	H11	.030	.020	39	153624	UDC 1-6	Flywheel	500	100
	Hornet V8	N-12	AG5	.035	.017	④	18436572②	5°BTDC	Damper	475	140
	Special	N-12	AL7	.035	.016	26–33	18436572②	5°BTDC	Damper	475	140
1957	V8	N-12	AL7J	.035	.016	28–32	18436572②	5°BTDC	Damper	475	140

①—A, AL, AG: Auto-Lite. H, J: Champion.

②—Cylinder numbering (front to rear): Left bank 1-3-5-7, right bank 2-4-6-8.

③—Turn adjusting screw in (clockwise) until engine misfires. Then turn screw ½ turn in opposite direction.

④—Dual breaker units 38°, single breaker 31°.

⑤—Twin carbs. .016″, single carb. .022″.

⑥—Twin carbs. 38–45°, single carb. 31–37°.

⑦—Auto-Lite AL-7 or ARL-82. Champion H-10 or H-18Y.

⑧—8°BTDC with standard trans., 10°BTDC with automatic trans.

⑨—TDC with standard trans., 5°BTDC with automatic trans.

⑩—Manual shift transmission.

⑪—Automatic transmission.

VALVE SPECIFICATIONS

Year	Model	Valve Lash Int.	Valve Lash Exh.	Valve Angles Seat	Valve Angles Face	Valve Spring Installed Height	Valve Spring Pressure Lbs. @ In.	Valve Lift Int.	Valve Lift Exh.	Stem Clearance Intake	Stem Clearance Exhaust	Stem Diameter Int.	Stem Diameter Exh.
RAMBLER													
1953	5310	.016C	.018C	45	44	$1\frac{3}{4}$	79 @ $1\frac{7}{16}$	.340	.300	.0028-.0033	.0028-.0033	.3409	.3409
1954	5410	.016C	.018C	45	44	$1\frac{3}{4}$	79 @ $1\frac{7}{16}$	.325	.325	.0028-.0033	.0028-.0033	.3409	.3409
1955	5510	.016C	.018C	45	44	$1\frac{3}{4}$	79 @ $1\frac{7}{16}$	.340	.340	.0013-.0033	.0013-.0033	.3409	.3409
1956	5610	.012H	.016H	45	44	$1\frac{13}{16}$	120 @ $1\frac{7}{16}$	.3658	.3614	.0013-.0028	.0018-.0033	.3414	.3409
1957	5710	.012H	.016H	45	44	$1\frac{13}{16}$	120 @ $1\frac{7}{16}$	.3658	.3614	.0018-.0033	.0023-.0038	.3414	.3409
	5720, 30	.012H	.014H	①	②	$1\frac{13}{16}$	155 @ $1\frac{7}{16}$	.375	.375	.0013-.0028	.0018-.0033	.3414	.3409
1958	5801	.016C	.018C	45	44	$1\frac{3}{4}$	79 @ $1\frac{7}{16}$	.324	.322	.0013-.0033	.0013-.0033	.3409	.3409
	5810	.012H	.016H	45	44	$1\frac{13}{16}$	120 @ $1\frac{7}{16}$	.3658	.3614	.0018-.0033	.0023-.0038	.3414	.3409
	5820	.012H	.014H	①	②	$1\frac{13}{16}$	155 @ $1\frac{7}{16}$	.375	.375	.0013-.0028	.0018-.0033	.3414	.3409
	5880	Zero	Zero	①	②	$1\frac{13}{16}$	155 @ $1\frac{7}{16}$	.375	.375	.0013-.0028	.0018-.0033	.3414	.3409
1959	5901	.016C	.018C	45	44	$1\frac{3}{4}$	79 @ $1\frac{7}{16}$	.324	.322	.0013-.0033	.0013-.0033	.3409	.3409
	5910	.012H	.016H	45	44	$1\frac{13}{16}$	120 @ $1\frac{7}{16}$	.366	.361	.0018-.0033	.0023-.0038	.3414	.3409
	5920	.012H	.014H	①	②	$1\frac{13}{16}$	155 @ $1\frac{7}{16}$	.375	.375	.0015-.0025	.0015-.0025	.3720	.3720
	5980	Zero	Zero	①	②	$1\frac{13}{16}$	155 @ $1\frac{7}{16}$	.375	.375	.0015-.0025	.0015-.0025	.3720	.3720
1960	6001③	.016C	.018C	45	44	$1\frac{3}{4}$	79 @ $1\frac{7}{16}$	.324	.322	.0018-.0033	.0018-.0033	.3409	.3409
	6001④	.012H	.016H	45	44	$1\frac{13}{16}$	120 @ $1\frac{7}{16}$	.366	.361	.0018-.0033	.0023-.0038	.3414	.3409
	6010	.012H	.016H	45	44	$1\frac{13}{16}$	120 @ $1\frac{7}{16}$	.366	.361	.0018-.0033	.0023-.0038	.3414	.3409
	6020	.012H	.014H	①	②	$1\frac{13}{16}$	155 @ $1\frac{7}{16}$	.375	.375	.0015-.0025	.0015-.0025	.3720	.3720
	6080	Zero	Zero	①	②	$1\frac{13}{16}$	155 @ $1\frac{7}{16}$	.375	.375	.0015-.0025	.0015-.0025	.3720	.3720
1961	6101 L-Head 6	.016C	.018C	45	44	$1\frac{3}{4}$	79 @ $1\frac{7}{16}$	.324	.322	.0018-.0033	.0018-.0033	.3409	.3409
	6101 OHV 6	.012H	.016H	45	44	$1\frac{13}{16}$	120 @ $1\frac{7}{16}$	.366	.361	.0015-.0035	.0020-.0040	.3415	.3410
	6110 Iron Head	.012H	.016H	45	44	$1\frac{13}{16}$	120 @ $1\frac{7}{16}$	.366	.361	.0015-.0035	.0020-.0040	.3415	.3410
	6110 Alum. Head	Zero	Zero	45	44	$1\frac{13}{16}$	120 @ $1\frac{7}{16}$	.388	.388	.0015-.0035	.0020-.0040	.3415	.3410
	6120	.012H	.014H	①	②	$1\frac{13}{16}$	155 @ $1\frac{7}{16}$	.375	.375	.0015-.0025	.0015-.0025	.3720	.3720
	6180	Zero	Zero	①	②	$1\frac{13}{16}$	155 @ $1\frac{7}{16}$	.375	.375	.0015-.0025	.0015-.0025	.3720	.3720
NASH													
1955	5540	.016C	.018C	45	44	$1\frac{3}{4}$	79 @ $1\frac{7}{16}$	.340	.340	.0013-.0028	.0018-.0033	.3409	.3409
	5560	.012H	.016H	①	②	$1\frac{13}{16}$	155 @ $1\frac{7}{16}$	.382	.378	.002-.004	.002-.004	.3730	.3725
	5580	Zero	Zero	①	②	$1\frac{13}{16}$	165 @ $1\frac{3}{8}$	.374	.374	.001-.002	.002-.004	.3725	.3715
1956	5640	.012H	.016H	45	44	$1\frac{13}{16}$	120 @ $1\frac{7}{16}$	.3834	.3834	.0015-.0035	.002-.004	.3414	.3409
	5650	Zero	Zero	①	②	$1\frac{13}{16}$	155 @ $1\frac{7}{16}$	.375	.375	.0013-.0028	.0018-.0033	.3414	.3409
	5660	.012H	.016H	①	②	$1\frac{13}{16}$	155 @ $1\frac{7}{16}$	.382	.378	.002-.004	.002-.004	.3730	.3725
	5680	Zero	Zero	①	②	$1\frac{13}{16}$	165 @ $1\frac{3}{8}$	.374	.374	.001-.002	.002-.003	.3725	.3715
1957	5780	Zero	Zero	①	②	$1\frac{13}{16}$	155 @ $1\frac{7}{16}$	.375	.375	.0013-.0028	.0018-.0033	.3414	.3409
HUDSON													
1955	35540	.010C	.014C	⑤	⑤		120 @ $1\frac{19}{32}$	.346	.346	.001-.003	.002-.004	.3417	.3407
	35560	.010C	.014C	45	44		160 @ $1\frac{27}{32}$	.346	.346	.0015-.003	.002-.004	.3417	.3407
	35580	Zero	Zero	①	②	$1\frac{13}{16}$	165 @ $1\frac{3}{8}$	.374	.374	.001-.002	.002-.003	.3725	.3715
1956	35640	.010C	.014C	⑤	⑤		120 @ $1\frac{19}{32}$	.346	.346	.001-.003	.002-.004	.3417	.3407
	35650	Zero	Zero	45	44		160 @ $1\frac{27}{32}$	.346	.346	.0015-.003	.002-.004	.3417	.3407
	35660	Zero	Zero	①	②	$1\frac{13}{16}$	165 @ $1\frac{3}{8}$	.388	.378	.001-.002	.002-.003	.3725	.3715
	35680	Zero	Zero	①	②	$1\frac{13}{16}$	155 @ $1\frac{7}{16}$	.375	.375	.0013-.0028	.0018-.0033	.3414	.3409
1957	35780	Zero	Zero	①	②	$1\frac{13}{16}$	155 @ $1\frac{7}{16}$	.375	.375	.0013-.0028	.0018-.0033	.3414	.3409

①—Intake 30°, exhaust 45°.
②—Intake 29°, exhaust 44°.
③—De Luxe and Super.
④—Custom.
⑤—Intake 45°, exhaust 46°.

ENGINE TIGHTENING SPECIFICATIONS★

★Torque specifications are for clean and lightly lubricated threads only. Dry or dirty threads produce increased friction which prevents accurate measurement of tightness.

Year	Spark Plugs Ft. Lbs.	Cylinder Head Bolts Ft. Lbs.	Intake Manifold Ft. Lbs.	Exhaust Manifold Ft. Lbs.	Rocker Arm Shaft Bracket Ft. Lbs.	Rocker Arm Cover Ft. Lbs.	Connecting Rod Cap Bolts Ft. Lbs.	Main Bearing Cap Bolts Ft. Lbs.	Flywheel to Crankshaft Ft. Lbs.	Vibration Damper or Pulley Ft. Lbs.
RAMBLER										
1953–55	30	57–60	None	10–15	None	None	27–30	66–70	50–55	65–70
1956	30	60–65	None	20–25	25–30	④	27–30	66–70	50–55	70–80
1957 Six	30	60–65	None	10–15	25–30	④	27–30	66–70	50–55	70–80
1957 V8	30	60–65	15–20	15–20	60–65	④	46–50	①	55–60	130–150
1958–61 Ser. 01⑤	30	57–60	None	20–25	None	None	27–30	66–60	100–110	70–80
1958–61 Ser. 10	30	60–65	None	②	25–30	④	27–30	66–70	100–110	70–80
1958–61 V8	30	60–65	20–25	20–25	60–65	④	46–50	①	100–110	70–80
1960–61 Ser. 01⑥	30	60–65	None	②	25–30	④	27–30	66–70	100–110	70–80
1961 Alum. 6	25–30	50–53	⑦	②	. . .	3–5	27–30	55–58	100–110	70–80
HUDSON										
1955–56 Ser. 40	30	③	12–15	20–30	None	None	40–50	75–80	40–45	80–90
1955–56 Ser. 60	30	③	12–15	20–30	None	None	40–50	75–80	40–45	100–120
1955–56 Ser. 80	30	55–60	25–30	25–30	55–60	15–18	40–45	90–95	55–60	130–150
1956 Ser. 50	30	60–65	10–15	10–15	60–65	④	52–56	80–85	100–110	70–80
1957 Ser. 80	30	60–65	15–20	15–20	60–65	④	46–50	①	100–110	70–80
NASH										
1955 Ser. 40	30	57–60	None	10–15	None	None	27–30	66–70	50–55	65–70
1955–56 Ser. 60	30	65–70	None	25–30	30–35	④	52–56	66–70	100–110	90–100
1955–56 Ser. 80	30	55–60	25–30	25–30	55–60	15–18	40–45	90–95	55–60	130–150
1956 Ser. 40	30	60–65	None	10–15	25–30	④	27–30	66–70	50–55	65–70
1956 Ser. 50	30	60–65	15–20	15–20	60–65	④	52–56	80–85	100–110	70–80
1957 Ser. 80	30	60–65	15–20	15–20	60–65	④	46–50	①	100–110	70–80

①—Rear 50–55, others 80–85.
②—End nuts 8–10; center flange nuts 20–25.
③—Ser. 40:60–65 at operating temperature. Ser. 60:70–80 cold.
④—Hand tight.
⑤—Deluxe and Super.
⑥—Custom.
⑦—Cover screw 15–20 (5/16″), 8–11 (1/4″).

PISTONS, PINS, RINGS, CRANKSHAFT & BEARINGS

Year	Model	Fitting Pistons		Ring End Gap ①		Wrist-pin Diameter	Rod Bearings		Main Bearings			
		Shim To Use	Pounds Pull On Scale	Comp.	Oil		Shaft Diameter	Bearing Clearance	Shaft Diameter	Bearing Clearance	Thrust on Bear. No.	Shaft End Play
RAMBLER												
1953–54	All	②	②	.010	.010	.8594	2.0948–2.0955	.001–.0025	2.4785–2.4795	.001–.002	1	.003–.007
1955–56	All	②	②	.010	.010	.8596	2.0948–2.0955	.001–.0015	2.4791–2.4798	.001–.0015	1	.003–.007
1957	Six	②	②	.010	.015	.8596	2.0948–2.0955	.001–.0015	2.4791–2.4798	.0006–.002	1	.003–.007
	V8	②	②	.010	.015	.9306	2.2483–2.2490	.001–.003	2.4983–2.4990	.0006–.003	1	.003–.007
1958–60	American	②	②	.010	.015	.8596	2.0948–2.0955	.001–.0015	2.4791–2.4798	.0006–.0018	1	.003–.007
	Rambler 6	②	②	.010	.015	.8596	2.0948–2.0955	.001–.0015	2.4791–2.4798	.0006–.0018	1	.003–.007
	Rebel V8	②	②	.010	.015	.9306	2.2483–2.2490	.0007–.0028	2.4983–2.4990	.0006–.0032	1	.003–.007
	Amb. V8	②	②	.015	.015	.9306	2.2483–2.2490	.0007–.0028	2.4983–2.4990	.0006–.0032	1	.003–.007
1961	Series 6101	②	②	.010	.015	.8596	2.0948–2.0955	.001–.0015	2.4791–2.4798	.001–.0015	1	.003–.008
	Series 6110	②	②	.010	.015	.8596	2.0948–2.0955	.001–.0015	2.4791–2.4798	.001–.0015	1	.003–.008
	Series 6120	②	②	.010	.015	.9306	2.2483–2.2490	.0007–.0028	2.4988–2.4995	.0006–.0032	1	.003–.007
	Series 6180	②	②	.010	.015	.9306	2.2483–2.2490	.0007–.0028	2.4988–2.4995	.0006–.0032	1	.003–.007

PISTON, PINS, RINGS, CRANKSHAFT & BEARINGS (continued)

Year	Model	Fitting Pistons		Ring End Gap ①		Wrist-pin Diameter	Rod Bearings		Main Bearings			
		Shim To Use	Pounds Pull On Scale	Comp.	Oil		Shaft Diameter	Bearing Clearance	Shaft Diameter	Bearing Clearance	Thrust on Bear. No.	Shaft End Play
NASH												
1955–56	Statesman	②	②	.010	.010③	.8596	2.0948–2.0955	.001–.0015	2.4791–2.4798	.001–.0015	1	.003–.007
	Amb. 6	②	②	.007	.007③	.9375	2.0003–2.0010	.001–.0015	2.4791–2.4798	.001–.0015	1	.003–.007
	Special V8	②	②	.010	.015	.9306	2.2483–2.2490	.001–.003	2.4983–2.4990	.0006–.003	1	.003–.007
	Amb. V8	.0015	12–18	.010	.010	.9803	2.2490–2.2500	.0005–.0025	2.4990–2.5000	.0005–.0025	1	.003–.007
1957	V8	②	②	.010	.015	.9306	2.2483–2.2490	.001–.003	2.4983–2.4990	.0006–.003	1	.003–.007
HUDSON												
1955–56	Wasp	.002	3–4	.004	.004	.7498	1.937–1.938	.0005–.002	2.499–2.500	.0005–.002	3	.003–.008
	Hornet 6	.002	3–4	.006	.006	.9685	2.124–2.125	.0005–.002	2.499–2.500	.0005–.002	3	.003–.008
	Hornet V8	.0015	12–18	.019	.015	.9803	2.249–2.250	.0005–.003	2.499–2.500	.0005–.003	1	.003–.008
	Special V8	.0015	12–18	.010	.015	.9306	2.248–2.249	.001–.003	2.498–2.499	.001–.003	1	.003–.008
1957	Hornet V8	.0015	12–18	.010	.015	.9306	2.248–2.249	.001–.003	2.498–2.499	.001–.003	1	.003–.008

①—Fit rings in tapered bores for clearance listed in tightest portion of ring travel.

②—Piston should support its own weight in cylinder with all parts clean and dry.

③—No end gap on U-Flex oil rings.

REAR AXLE AND BRAKE CYLINDER SPECIFICATIONS

Year	Model	Ring Gear & Pinion Backlash, Inch	Drive Pinion Adjustment	Drive Pinion Bearing Preload, Inch Lbs.	Drive Pinion Bearing Adjustment	Axle Shaft End Play, Inch	Hydraulic Cylinder Bore Sizes, Inch		Master Cylinder
							Wheel Cylinder		
							Front	Rear	
RAMBLER									
1953–54	All	.002–.006	Washer	12–14	Shims	.002–.004	1	1 3/16	1
1955	5510	.002–.006	Washer	12–14	Shims	.002–.004	1	1 3/16	1
1956	5610	.002–.006	Washer	12–14	Shims	.002–.004	1 1/16	7/8	1
1957	Six	.002–.006	Shims	12–14	Shims	.001–.004	1 1/16	7/8	1
	V8	.002–.006	Shims	15–18	Shims	.001–.004	1	1 3/16	1
1958–61	Six	.002–.006	Shims	12–14	Shims	.001–.004	1	1 3/16	1
	V8	.002–.006	Shims	15–18	Shims	.001–.004	1 1/8	7/8	1
NASH									
1955	All	.002–.006	Washer	①	Shims	.002–.004	1 1/8	15/16	1
1956	Special V8	.002–.006	Shims	15–18	Shims	.001–.004	1 1/8	7/8	1
	Others	.002–.006	Washer	12–14	Shims	.002–.004	1 1/8	7/8	1
1957	V8	.002–.006	Shims	15–18	Shims	.001–.004	1 1/8	7/8	1
HUDSON									
1955	All	.002–.006	Shims	②	Shims	.002–.004	1 1/8	15/16	1
1956	Special V8	.002–.006	Shims	15–18	Shims	.002–.004	1 1/8	7/8	1
	Others	.002–.006	Shims	12–14	Shims	.002–.004	1 1/8	15/16	1
1957	V8	.002–.006	Shims	15–18	Shims	.002–.004	1 1/8	7/8	1

①—Ambassador, 15–18 inch lbs., Statesman, 12–14 inch lbs.

②—Hornet, 15–18 inch lbs., Wasp, 12–14 inch lbs.

GENERATOR AND REGULATOR SPECIFICATIONS

★To Polarize Generator: For internally grounded systems, disconnect field lead from regulator and momentarily flash this lead to the regulator battery terminal.   For externally grounded systems, reconnect the leads to the regulator; then momentarily connect a jumper wire from the "Gen" (Delco-Remy) or "Arm" (Auto-Lite) to the "Bat" terminals of the regulator.

		Generator						Regulator					
									Cutout Relay				
Year	Generator Number ⑥	Rotation and Ground Polarity ①	Rated Cap. Amps.	Gen. Field Ground Location★	Brush Spring Tension, Ounces	Field Current Amperes	Regulator Number	Voltage to Close Points	Armature Air Gap, Inch	Voltage Regulator Setting Volts	Current Regulator Setting Amperes	Current and Voltage Armature Air Gap, Inch
AUTO-LITE													
1955	GGW-4801F	C-P	45	External	35–53	1.4–1.5②	VBE-6101A	6.5	.031	7.3	45	.048
1955	GGW-4802C	C-P	45	External	35–53	1.6–1.7②	VBE-6101A	6.5	.031	7.3	45	.048
1955	GGW-4802B	C-P	45	External	35–53	1.4–1.5②	VBE-6101A	6.5	.031	7.3	45	.048
1956	GJC-7002F	C-N	30	External	18–36	1.2–1.3③	VRX-6008A	13.3	.031	14.5	30	.048
1956	GJC-7007A	C-N	30	External	18–36	1.2–1.3③	VRX-6008A	13.3	.031	14.5	30	.048
1956	GJC-7007B	C-N	30	External	18–36	1.2–1.3③	VRX-6008A	13.3	.031	14.5	30	.048
1956	GJC-7008A	C-N	30	External	18–36	1.2–1.3③	VRX-6008A	13.3	.031	14.5	30	.048
1956	GJC-7008B	C-N	30	External	18–36	1.2–1.3③	VRX-6008A	13.3	.031	14.5	30	.048
1960–61	GJO-7101A	C-N	25	Internal	18–36	1.6–1.7③	VBO-6221C	13.0	.026	14.5	37	.050
1960–61	GJP-7101A	C-N	35	Internal	18–36	1.6–1.7③	VBO-6221A	13.0	.026	14.5	44	.050
DELCO-REMY													
1953–55	1100021	C-P	35	External	28	1.85–2.03④	1118841	6.3	.020	7.1	35	.075
1957–60	1100304	C-N	25	External	28	1.50–1.62⑤	1119122	12.6	.020	14.3	25	.075
1956	1100323	C-N	25	External	28	1.50–1.62⑤	1119122	12.6	.020	14.3	25	.075
1956–61	1100324	C-N	25	External	28	1.50–1.62⑤	1119122	12.6	.020	14.3	25	.075
1957–60	1102018	C-N	30	External	28	1.48–1.62⑤	1119003	12.6	.020	14.3	30	.075
1956	1102049	C-N	30	External	28	1.48–1.62⑤	1119003	12.6	.020	14.3	30	.075
1957–60	1102070	C-N	35	External	28	1.69–1.79⑤	1119168	12.6	.020	14.3	35	.075
1961	1102113	C-N	30	External	28	1.69–1.79	1119003	12.6	.020	14.7	30	.075
1959–61	1102123	C-N	45	External	28	2.66–2.86⑤	1119600	12.4	.020	14.4	45	⑦
1955	1102777	C-P	45	External	28	1.87–2.00④	1118828	6.3	.020	7.1	45	.075
1955	1102815	C-P	45	External	28	1.87–2.00④	1118828	6.3	.020	7.1	45	.075
1956	1103011	C-N	30	External	28	1.48–1.62⑤	1119003	12.6	.020	14.3	30	.075

①—C-Clockwise. P-Positive. N-Negative.   ②—At 5 volts.   ③—At 10 volts.   ④—At 6 volts.   ⑤—At 12 volts.
⑥—Stamped on plate riveted to side of housing.   ⑦—Voltage regulator gap .067", current regulator .075".

RAMBLER · NASH · HUDSON

DISTRIBUTOR SPECIFICATIONS

Year	Part No. ③	Rotation ①	Cam Angle, Degrees	Breaker Points Opening, Inch	Condenser Capacity, Mfds.	Breaker Arm Spring Tension, Ounces	Centrifugal Advance Data Degrees @ R.P.M. of Dist.		Vacuum Advance Data		
							Advance Starts	Full Advance	Inches of Vacuum to Start Plunger Movement	Inches of Vacuum for Full Plunger Travel	Maximum Vacuum Advance, Dist. Degrees
AUTO-LITE											
1955–56	1AT-4202	C	39	.020	.21–.25	17–20	1 @ 300	13 @ 1500	5¼	9½	7½
1955–56	1AT-4203A	C	39	.020	.21–.25	17–20	1 @ 500	9 @ 2000	9½	11¼	3.7
1956	1AT-4301	C	39	.020	.21–.25	17–20	1 @ 300	14 @ 1350	5	14	6
1960	1AT-4402	C	37–41	.020	.25–.28	17–20	1 @ 425	14 @ 2000	5	11	11
1956	1BJ-4001D	CC	31	.017	.25–.28	17–20	1 @ 300	14 @ 1700	6	12½	12
1956	1BJ-4001E	CC	31	.017	.25–.28	17–20	1 @ 375	14 @ 2550	8	16	10
1955	1BK-4001	CC	38	.017	.25–.28	17–20	1 @ 300	20 @ 1200	6	10	5½
1955–56	1BK-4001B	CC	38	.017	.25–.28	17–20	1 @ 300	16 @ 1750	6¼	13	12
1960	1PB-4104	CC	28–32	.016	.18–.23	17–21	1 @ 300	18 @ 1900	6	15	10
1960	1PB-4104A	CC	28–32	.016	.18–.23	17–21	1 @ 315	18 @ 2000	6½	14	12
1961	1AT-4402-1	C	37–41	.020	.18–.23	17–21	1 @ 425	14 @ 2000	5	11	11
1961	1PB-4107	CC	28–32	.016	.18–.23	17–21	1 @ 300	18 @ 1900	6	15	10
DELCO-REMY											
1955	1110241	C	38–45	.016	.18–.23	17–21	1 @ 350	14 @ 1350	4–6	14–16	6
1956	1110242	CC	28–35	.016	.18–.23	17–21	1 @ 350	16 @ 1600	6–8	11–12	5
1957	1110244	CC	28–35	.016	.18–.23	17–21	1 @ 425	13 @ 1700	6–8	16–17	7½
1958–59	1110246	CC	28–35	.016	.18–.23	17–21	1½ @ 600	10½ @ 2100	6–8	16–17	7½
1956	1110863	CC	26–33	.016	.18–.23	17–21	1 @ 375	19 @ 1700	5–7	11½–13½	10
1957	1110884	CC	30	②	.18–.23	17–21	1 @ 375	19 @ 1700	5½–7½	13¼–15¾	12
1958–59	1110887	CC	30	②	.18–.23	17–21	1 @ 350	18 @ 1900	5–7	14¼–15¾	10
1959	1110923	CC	30	②	.18–.23	17–21	1½ @ 375	18 @ 2000	6½	13¼–15¾	12
1953–55	1112382	CC	31–37	.022	.18–.23	17–21	1 @ 325	11 @ 1400	4–6	11	5½
1955	1112409	CC	38–45	.016	.18–.23	17–21	1 @ 375	11 @ 1800	4–6	11	5½
1958–59	1112426	CC	28–35	.016	.18–.23	19–23	1 @ 525	7 @ 2100	5	11	5½
1960–61	1112434	CC	28–35	.016	.18–.23	17–21	1 @ 600	11 @ 2100	6½	16½	11

①—As viewed from the top.   C-Clockwise.   CC-Counterclockwise.
②—Turn adjusting screw in (clockwise) until engine misfires.   Then turn screw ½ turn in opposite direction.
③—Stamped on plate riveted to side of housing.

STARTING MOTOR SPECIFICATIONS

Year	Part No. ②	Rotation ①	Brush Spring Tension, Ounces	No Load Test			Torque Test		
				Amperes	Volts	R.P.M.	Amperes	Volts	Torque, Lbs. Ft.
AUTO-LITE									
1956	MBG-4101	C	42–53	55	10.0	5200	235	4.0	5.2
1956	MBG-4102	C	42–53	55	10.0	5200	235	4.0	5.2
1955	MCH-6109	C	42–53	65	5.0	4300	335	2.0	6.0
1955	MCH-6306	C	42–53	65	5.0	4300	335	2.0	6.0
1955	MCL-6132	C	42–53	65	5.0	4900	410	2.0	8.0
1956	MDF-6008	C	42–53	60	10.0	3200	240	4.0	6.5
1956	MDF-6009	C	42–53	60	10.0	3200	240	4.0	6.5
1956	MDF-6010	C	42–53	60	10.0	3200	240	4.0	6.5
1956	MDF-6011	C	42–53	60	10.0	3200	240	4.0	6.5
1956	MDF-6012	C	42–53	60	10.0	3200	240	4.0	6.5
1960	MDY-6002	C	42–53	80	10	4000	405	4	9.0
1961	MDY-6009	C	42–53	60	10	4200	405	4	9
1960	MEC-6001	C	42–53	70	10	5300	285	4	6.5
1960–61	MEC-6002	C	42–53	48	10	5300	285	4	6.5
1961	MEC-6003	C	42–53	48	10	5300	285	4	6.5
1955	MZ-4167	C	42–53	68	5	4000	280	2	4.4
1955	MZ-4172	C	42–53	68	5	4000	280	2	4.4
DELCO-REMY									
1955	1107119	C	24 Min.	70	5.65	5500	550	3.25	11
1955	1107136	C	24 Min.	70	5.65	5500	550	3.25	11
1961	1107201	C	35 Min.	112	10.6	3240	385	3.5	10.5
1956–57	1107647	C	35 Min.	75	10.30	6900	435	5.80	10.5
1956–57	1107648	C	35 Min.	75	10.30	6900	435	5.80	10.5
1958–59	1107704	C	35 Min.	49	10.6	6200	270	4.25	10.5
1958	1107714	C	35 Min.	112	10.6	3240	320	3.5	10.5
1958–59	1107717	C	35 Min.	65	10.6	3600	300	3.5	10.5
1959–60	1107731	C	35 Min.	64	10.6	7800	290	4.25	10.5
1955	1107950	C	24 Min.	70	5.65	5500	570	3.15	13.5
1955	1108029	C	24 Min.	80	5.67	5500	600	3.00	14

①—As viewed from drive end.　C—Clockwise.　②—Stamped on plate riveted to side of housing.

COOLING SYSTEM & CAPACITY DATA

Year	Model	Cooling System Data					Fuel Tank Gals.	Engine Oil			Transmissions			Rear Axle Pints
		Quarts No Heater	Quarts With Heater	Rad. Cap Relief Pressure	Thermostat Opening Temp. ①	②		Refill Qts. ③	Summer Grade	Winter Grade	Std. Pints	With Over-drive Pints	Auto-matic Qts.	
RAMBLER														
1953	All	11	12	7	180	170	20	4	20	10W	1½	2¾	None	3
1954	All	11	12	7	180	170	20	4	20	10W	1½	2¾	8½	3
1955	All	11	12	7	180	170	20	4	20	10W	1½	2¾	8½	3
1956	All	10	11	7④	180	170	20	4	20	10W	2¼	3½	8½	3
1957	Series 10	10	11	7④	180	170	20	4	20	10W	2¼	3½	8½	3
	Series 20	20	21	7④	180	170	20	5	20	10W	2¼	3½	11½	4
	Series 30	20	21	7④	180	170	20	5	20	10W	4	4	11½	4
1958-60	Series 01⑥	11	12	13	180	170	20⑤	4	20	10W	1½	2¾	10	3
	Series 10	10	11	13	180	170	20⑤	4	20	10W	1½	2¾	10	3
	Series 20	20	21	13	180	170	20⑤	4	20	10W	2¼	3½	10	4
	Series 80	19	20	13	180	170	20⑤	4	20	10W	4	4	11	4
1960	Series 01⑦	10	11	13	195	...	22	4	20	10W	1½	2¾	10	3
1961	Series 01⑥	11	12	13	180	...	20	4	20	10W	1½	2¾	10	3
	Series 01⑦	10	11	13	195	...	20	4	20	10W	1½	2¾	10	3
	Series 10⑧	10	11	13	195	...	20	4	20	10W	1½	2¾	10	3
	Series 10⑨	9½	10½	13	195	...	20	4	20	10W	1½	2¾	10	3
	Series 20	19	20	13	180	...	20	4	20	10W	2¼	3½	10	3
	Series 80	18	19	13	180	...	20	4	20	10W	4	4	11	4
NASH														
1955 5540		14	15	7	180	170	20	4	20	10W	2¼	3½	8½	3
1955 5560		17	18	7	180	170	20	6	20	10W	2¼	3½	11	4
1955 5580		27	28	7	180	170	20	5	20	10W	None	None	11	4
1956 5640		11	12	7④	180	170	20	4	20	10W	2¼	3½	8½	3
1956 5650		21	22	7④	180	170	20	5	20	10W	2¼	3½	11½	3½
1956 5660		17	18	7④	180	170	20	6	20	10W	2¼	3½	11	4
1956 5680		27	28	7④	180	170	20	5	20	10W	None	None	11	4
1957 5780		19	20	7④	180	170	20	5	20	10W	4	4	11½	4
HUDSON														
1955 Wasp		13	14	7	180	170	20	5	20	10W	2¼	3½	8½	3
1955 Hornet 6		18½	19½	7	180	170	20	7	20	10W	2¼	3½	11	4
1955 Hornet V8		27	28	7	180	170	20	5	20	10W	None	None	11	4
1956 Wasp		13	14	13	180	170	20	5	20	10W	2¼	3½	8½	3
1956 Hornet 6		18½	19½	13	180	170	20	7	20	10W	2¼	3½	11	4
1956 Hornet V8		27	28	13	180	170	20	5	20	10W	None	None	11	4
1956 Special V8		21	22	7④	180	170	20	5	20	10W	2¼	3½	11½	3½
1957 V8		19	20	7④	180	170	20	5	20	10W	4	4	11½	4

① —For permanent type anti-freeze.
② —For alcohol type anti-freeze.
③ —Add one quart with filter change.
④ —With air conditioning 13 lbs.
⑤ —For 1960, 22 gallons.
⑥ —Deluxe and Super.
⑦ —Custom.
⑧ —Cast iron cylinder head.
⑨ —Aluminum cylinder head.

WHEEL ALIGNMENT SPECIFICATIONS

Year	Model	Caster, Degrees Limits	Desired	Camber, Degrees Limits	Desired	Toe-In, Inch	Toe-out on Turns, Degrees① Outer Wheel	Inner Wheel	Kingpin or Steering Axis Inclination② Degrees
RAMBLER									
1953–54	All	+ ¼ to + 1¼	+ 1	+ ¼ to + ¾	+ ½	⅛ to ¼	20	21½	8
1955	5510	+ ¼ to + 1¼	+ 1	+ ¼ to + ¾	+ ½	1/16 to ⅛	20	21	8
1956–57	Manual Steer.	0 to + ½	+ ½	− ¼ to + ¼	0	1/16 to 3/16	20	22° 20′	6° 11′
	Power Steer.	+ ½ to + 1	+ ¾	− ¼ to + ¼	0	1/16 to 3/16	20	22° 20′	6° 11′
1958	American	− ¼ to + ¼	0	0 to + ½	+ ¼	1/16 to 3/16	17° 40′	20	8
1959–60	American—Man. Steer.	0 to + ½	+ ½	− ¼ to + ¼	0	1/16 to 3/16	17° 40′	20	8
	American—Power Steer.	+ ½ to + 1③	+ 1③	− ¼ to + ¼	0	1/16 to 3/16	17° 40′	20	8
	Rambler 6—Man. Steer.	0 to + ½	+ ¼	− ¼ to + ¼	0	1/16 to 3/16	17° 17′	20	6° 11′
	Rambler 6—Power Steer.	+ ½ to + 1	+ ¾	− ¼ to + ¼	0	1/16 to 3/16	17° 17′	20	6° 11′
	Rebel—Man. Steer.	0 to + ½	+ ½	− ¼ to + ¼	0	1/16 to 3/16	17° 14′	20	6° 11′
	Rebel—Power Steer.	+ ½ to + 1	+ ¾	− ¼ to + ¼	0	1/16 to 3/16	17° 14′	20	6° 11′
	Amb.—Man. Steer.	0 to + ½	+ ½	− ¼ to + ¼	0	1/16 to 3/16	17° 28′	20	6° 11′
	Amb.—Power Steer.	+ ½ to + 1	+ ¾	− ¼ to + ¼	0	1/16 to 3/16	17° 28′	20	6° 11′
1961	American—Man. Steer.	0 to + ½	+ ½	− ¼ to + ¼	0	1/16 to 3/16	17⅔	20	8
	American—Power Steer.	+ 1½ to + 2	+ 2	− ¼ to + ¼	0	1/16 to 3/16	17⅔	20	8
	Others—Man. Steer.	0 to + ½	+ ½	− ¼ to + ¼	0	1/16 to 3/16	22	25	6½
	Others—Power Steer.	+ ½ to + 1	+ 1	− ¼ to + ¼	0	1/16 to 3/16	22	25	6½
NASH									
1955–56	40, 50—Man. Steer.	0 to + ½	+ ½	− ¼ to + ¼	0	1/16 to 3/16	20	23	6½
	40, 50—Power Steer.	+ ½ to + 1	+ ¾	− ¼ to + ¼	0	1/16 to 3/16	20	23	6½
	60, 80—Man. Steer.	0 to + ½	+ ½	− ¼ to + ¼	0	1/16 to 3/16	20	25	6½
	60, 80—Power Steer.	+ ½ to + 1	+ ¾	− ¼ to + ¼	0	1/16 to 3/16	20	25	6½
1957	Man. Steer.	0 to + ½	+ ½	− ¼ to + ¼	0	1/16 to 3/16	20	23° 18′	6½
	Power Steer.	+ ½ to + 1	+ ¾	− ¼ to + ¼	0	1/16 to 3/16	20	23° 18′	6½
HUDSON									
1955–56	Wasp.—Man. Steer.	0 to + ½	+ ½	− ¼ to + ¼	0	1/16 to 3/16	20	24	3° 36′
	Wasp.—Power Steer.	+ ½ to + 1	+ 1	− ¼ to + ¼	0	1/16 to 3/16	20	24	3° 36′
	Hornet—Man. Steer.	0 to + ½	+ ½	− ¼ to + ¼	0	1/16 to 3/16	20	26	3° 36′
	Hornet—Power Steer.	+ ½ to + 1	+ 1	− ¼ to + ¼	0	1/16 to 3/16	20	26	3° 36′
1957	Man. Steer.	0 to + ½	+ ½	− ¼ to + ¼	0	1/16 to 3/16	20¼	25	6½
	Power Steer.	+ ½ to + 1	+ 1	− ¼ to + ¼	0	1/16 to 3/16	21¾	25	6½

①—Incorrect toe-out, when other adjustments are correct, indicates bent steering arms.
②—Incorrect inclination with correct camber indicates bent suspension arms or steering knuckle support.
③—For 1960, + 1½° to + 2° with + 2° desired.

SERIAL NUMBER LOCATION
Dash Panel Under Hood

ENGINE NUMBER LOCATION
Sixes: Upper Left Corner Of Block
1957 V8: Left Front Lower Side Of Block
1958-61 V8: Front Upper Right Corner Of Block

RAMBLER GRILLE IDENTIFICATION

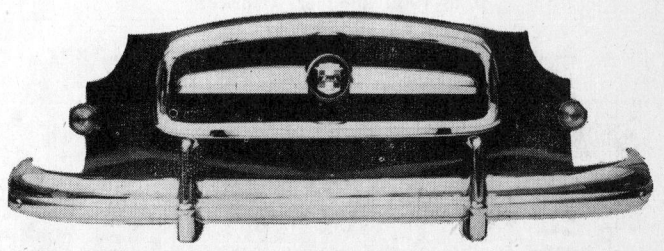

1953-54 Rambler

RAMBLER
GRILLE IDENTIFICATION
continued

1958 Rambler

1955 Rambler

1959 Rambler

1956 Rambler

1959 Rambler Ambassador

1957 Rambler

1960 Ambassador

1958-1960 Rambler American

1960 Rambler

1958 Rambler Ambassador

1961 Classic

1961 American

1961 Ambassador

NASH
GRILLE IDENTIFICATION

1956 Nash

1955 Nash

1957 Nash

HUDSON
GRILLE IDENTIFICATION

1956 Hudson

1955 Hudson

1957 Hudson

Engine Section

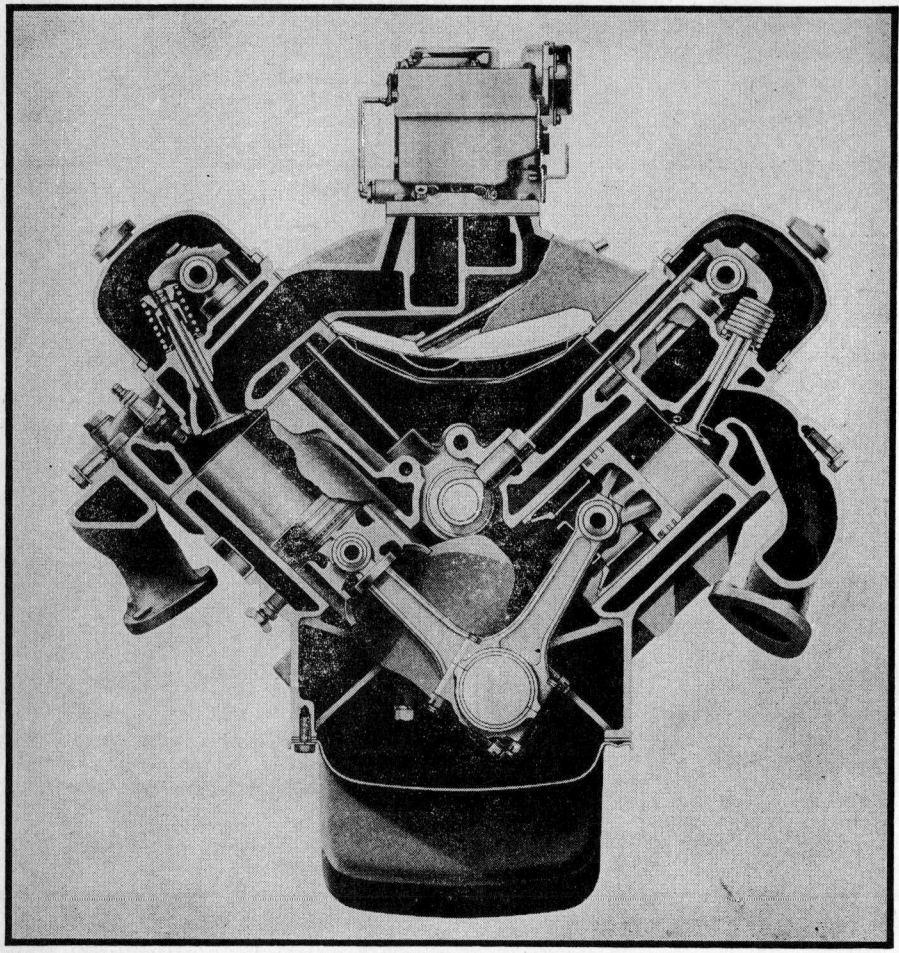

American Motors V8 engine

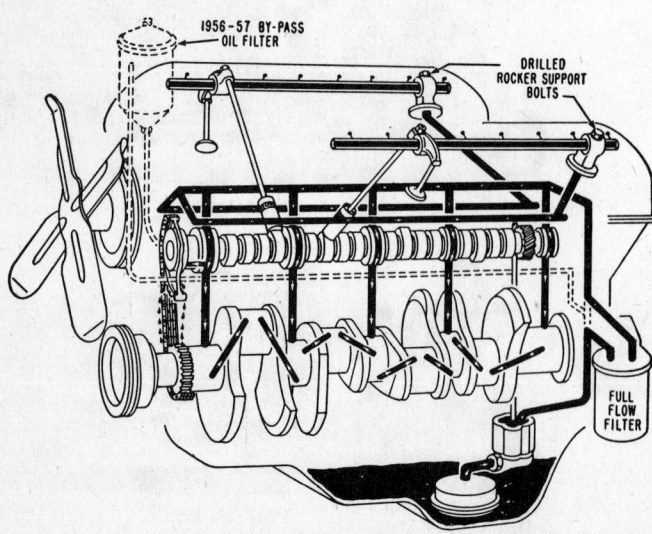

American Motors V8 engine lubrication

ENGINE REPLACE

1961 Classic 6

1. To remove, mark hood hinge location on hood panel to aid in reassembly before removing hood.
2. Drain cooling system and engine oil.
3. Remove starting motor and radiator.
4. Disconnect exhaust pipe from manifold.
5. Remove flywheel housing-to-engine screws.
6. Remove flywheel mud pan.
7. On automatic transmission cars, drain converter and transmission and remove six screws from flywheel drive plate-to-converter.
8. Remove front engine support upper nuts.
9. Disconnect all wiring, lines and hoses from engine, and power steering (if equipped).
10. On air conditioned cars, remove compressor and bracket (system need not be discharged).
11. Attach lifting rig to engine and lift out forward and upward to clear clutch shaft pilot bushing through hood opening.

1961 V8

1. Remove battery and hood.
2. Drain oil and cooling system. On automatic transmission cars, drain transmission and disconnect transmission cooler lines at radiator and straps on engine oil pan.
3. On air conditioned cars, unfasten and move compressor and hoses to one side.
4. Remove radiator and exhaust manifolds.
5. Disconnect all wiring, lines and tubes from engine.
6. Remove starting motor and flywheel housing mud pan.
7. On automatic transmission cars, drain converter and loosen flywheel drive plate from converter.
8. Attach lifting rig to engine.
9. After supporting transmission and torque tube, remove transmission crossmember.
10. Loosen front engine mounting cushions and remove engine from car.

1956-60 V8

1. To remove the engine separately from the transmission, drain cooling system and oil pan.
2. Remove hood, radiator, air cleaner, battery and starter.
3. Remove fuel lines, vacuum lines, accelerator linkage as necessary, hoses and wires attached to engine units.
4. On cars with Standard or Overdrive transmissions, remove the transmission.
5. On cars with Flash-O-Matic transmission, unfasten torque converter

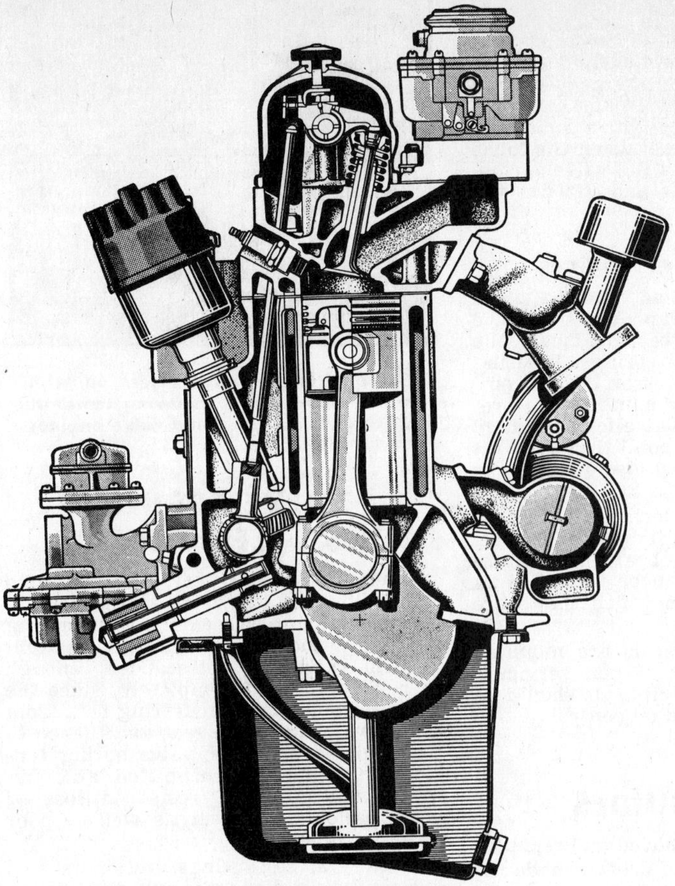

American Motors 6-cyl. overhead valve engine

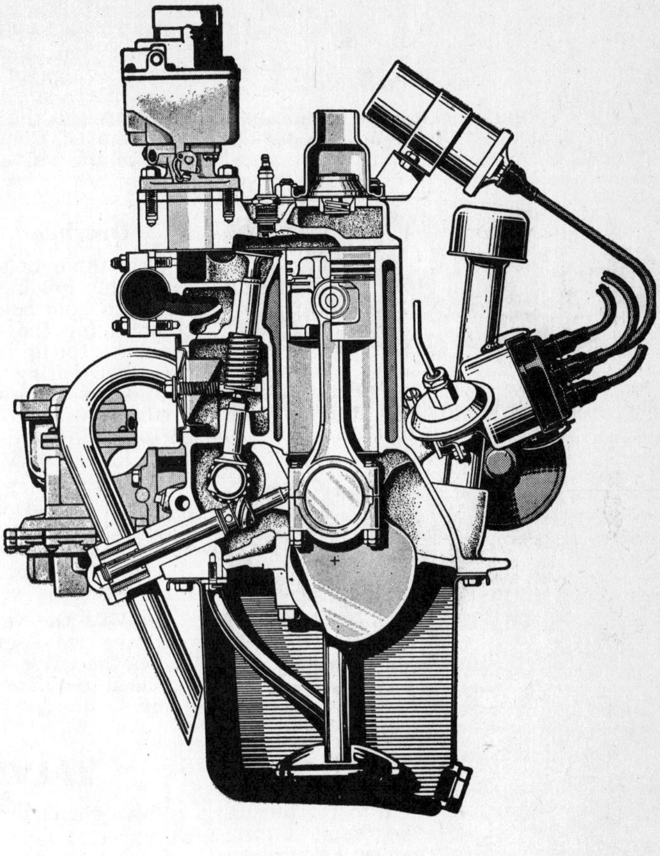

American Motors side valve engine

housing from flywheel housing.

6. Remove engine mounting bolts, and support automatic transmission with a jack.

7. Attach a lifting rig to the engine and raise it out of the chassis.

Nash 1953-55 Six-Cyl.

Engine removal from these cars is simplified by first removing the front bumper assembly. Then take off the front sheet metal including the radiator as a unit. The engine, with or without the transmission attached, can be removed from its mounting after removing the "K" brace which extends behind the fan.

1953-55 Rambler and 1958-60 American

1. On these models the engine is removed from below the car. Remove hood and radiator and disconnect fuel lines, vacuum lines, accelerator linkage as necessary, hoses and wires attached to engine units.

2. Remove exhaust pipe from engine and wire it upward and clear of exhaust pipe mounting studs.

3. Attach lifting rig to cylinder head and raise car on a hoist (twin-post type preferably). If a lift is not available, support front of car with high jacks located under body side sills just behind the rear engine support crossmember.

4. Disconnect cross tie rod from steering linkage, shift rods from transmission and clutch linkage to clutch beam.

5. Drain engine and transmission oil.

6. Disconnect speedometer cable.

7. Attach block and tackle or crane to lifting fixture and adjust to support engine's weight.

8. Remove four bolts holding front support cross member to body side sills.

9. Remove rear engine mounting diagonal braces, and the four bolts which attach the rear engine support cross member to the body side sills.

10. Lower engine slightly and a little forward and slip universal joint from transmission shaft.

11. The engine can be lowered to the floor with cross members attached.

1956-61 Six-Cyl. (Except American)

The general procedure for removing

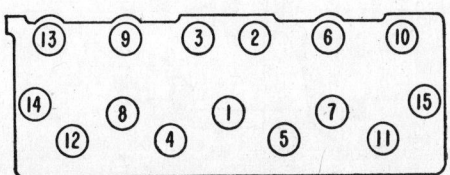

**Fig. 1   Cylinder head tightening.
V8 engines**

the engine is to raise or remove hood, drain cooling system and remove battery and radiator. Disconnect fuel pump, exhaust pipe at manifold, accelerator linkage, and wires attached to engine units. Remove engine support bolts and hoist engine out of chassis.

CYLINDER HEAD

V8 Engines

The cylinder head block surface has two locating dowels to assist in lining up and holding the position of the head and gasket during installation and removal.

After installing push rods, rocker arms and cylinder head cap screws, tighten the cap screws in the sequence shown in Fig. 1, and to the torque values given in the *Engine Tightening Chart*.

The cylinder head and rocker arm cap screws are of various lengths and design, among which are two special tapped heads to accommodate the retaining screws that hold the rocker arm cover; three long plain cap screws to retain rocker arms and cylinder head, and one special bolt to index with oil holes for rocker arm lubrication. *This special 6⅜" long drilled bolt is part of the lubrication system and must be installed in the rear position to index with oil passages in the tappet area.*

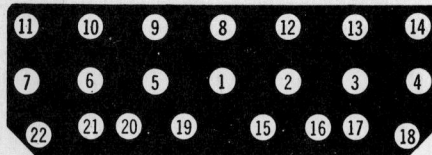

Fig. 2 Cylinder head tightening. Rambler and Nash 6-cyl. side valve engine

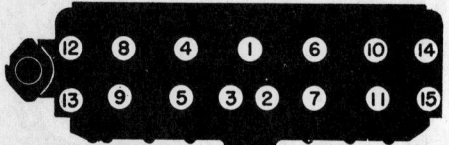

Fig. 3 Cylinder head tightening. Rambler and Nash 6-cyl. overhead valve engine

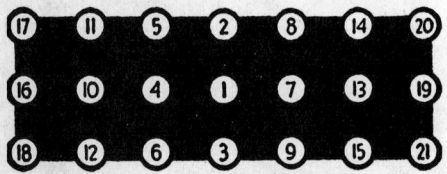

Fig. 4 Cylinder head tightening sequence. Hudson 6-cyl. engines

Six-Cylinder Engines

Tighten cylinder heads in the order shown in Figs. 2, 3, 4 and to the torque given in the *Engine Tightening Chart*. On overhead valve engines be sure to adjust the valves after the tightening operation.

VALVE ARRANGEMENT

Front to Rear

V8 Engines .... E-I-I-E-E-I-I-E
6-Cylinder ..... I-E-E-I-I-E-E-I-I-E-E-I

VALVES ADUST

Mechanical Lifters

Overhead valve engines should always be adjusted whenever the cylinder head has been removed or tightened. The clearances given in the *Valve Specifications* chart should be maintained at all times for normal driving conditions. Check the clearance when the engine is at normal operating temperature and at idling speed.

ROCKER ARMS

To remove the rocker arms, take off rocker arm cover, unfasten rocker arm shafts, support bolts and oil fittings and lift off the assembly.

When disassembling, place all parts on the work bench in their proper relationship to insure correct assembly. And to prevent the possibility of bending or twisting push rods, they should always be removed before taking off the cylinder head, and replaced after the head is installed.

VALVES, REMOVE

Side Valve Engines

Drain the cooling system and remove cylinder head. Take off valve covers and plug openings in cylinder block around valve lifters so that the valve locks will not drop into the oil pan when the locks are removed. Compress the valve spring, remove the valve lock and lift out the valve.

Overhead Valve Engines

With the cylinder head removed, place a suitable holding strap over the valve heads to hold the valves in place while compressing the valve springs. In using the valve spring compressor, do not compress the springs any more than is required to remove the valve locks. If they are compressed to the point that the coils bottom, the spring may lose as much as 10 to 15 lbs. tension.

After removing all locks and springs, invert the head and lift out the valves. Place the valves in a board with numbered holes so they can be identified as to the valve port from which they were removed.

On V8's the valve seals are mounted onto the valve guides. When servicing valves the valve stem oil seals should be replaced to insure good oil control at this point.

VALVE GUIDES

Valve guides are removed and replaced with special pullers and drivers made for the purpose. If this equipment is not available, carefully measure with a steel scale the amount each guide projects from the valve port before removing it so that the position of the new guide will be properly located when it is driven in. After the new guides are installed, they should be reamed to provide the clearance within the limits given in the *Valve Specifications* chart.

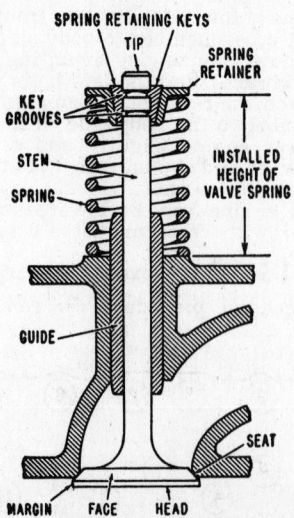

Fig. 5 Checking valve spring installed height

SPRING RETAINING KEYS
TIP
SPRING RETAINER
KEY GROOVES
STEM
SPRING
INSTALLED HEIGHT OF VALVE SPRING
GUIDE
SEAT
MARGIN   FACE   HEAD

Fig. 6 Holding valve lifters up with rubber bands while removing camshaft on six-cylinder overhead valve engines

VALVE SPRING INSTALLED HEIGHT

When valves and seats are reground the position of the valve in the head is changed so as to lessen the valve spring tension. Without proper valve spring tension the valve does not seat long enough or it may not seat completely. Since the valve is cooled by transferring heat from the valve head to the seat and thence to the coolant, improper valve spring tension will cause worn, pitted and distorted valves which result in loss of compression and power as well as poor gasoline mileage.

When valves, springs, retainers and locks are installed, measure the assembled height of the valve springs from the surface of the cylinder head spring pad to the underside of the spring retainer as shown in Fig. 5. If the assembled height is greater than the dimension given in the *Valve Specifications Chart*, install a spacer or shim of proper thickness between cylinder head spring pad and spring to bring the assembled height to specifications.

Do not install spacers unless necessary. Excessive use of spacers will result in overstressing valve springs and overloading camshaft lobes which could lead to spring breakage and worn camshaft lobes.

VALVE SPRING TESTING

Wash all valve springs in a suitable solvent. Examine the springs for damage or corrosion due to acid etching which will develop into surface cracks and cause spring failure.

Check the valve spring tension on a spring testing fixture if one is available. If not available, at least check the free length of each spring by standing it alongside a new spring. Any spring that does not conform to the pressure specifications given in the *Valve Specifications* table within 10% should be replaced. Likewise any spring that stands shorter than the new spring used for comparison should be discarded. Of course, cocked springs should also be scrapped.

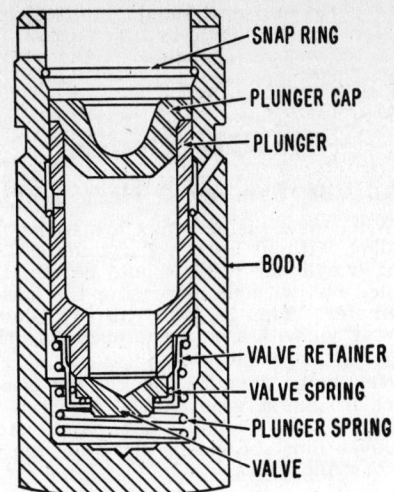

Fig. 7 V8 engine hydraulic valve lifters

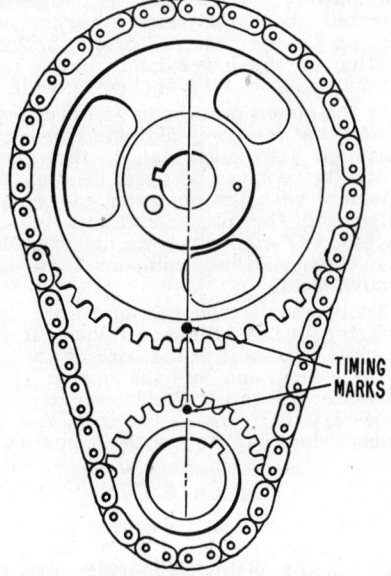

Fig. 8 Valve timing for V8 engines

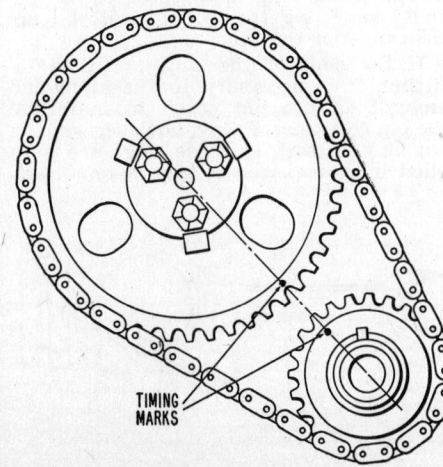

Fig. 9 Valve timing for Rambler and Nash 6-cyl. engines

VALVE LIFTERS

Six-Cylinder Engines

Since these lifters are of the mushroom type and the guides are cast integral with the cylinder block, it is necessary to remove the camshaft before the lifters can be taken out. Follow the instructions for removing the camshaft under that heading; then remove the oil pan and take the lifters out through the bottom.

To make removal of the camshaft easier, hold up the lifters with rubber bands on overhead valve engines, Fig. 6.

V8 Engines

The hydraulic valve lifters used are simple in design, readjustments are not necessary and servicing them requires that care and cleanliness be exercised in the handling of parts, Fig. 7.

The easiest method for locating a noisy valve lifter is by the use of a piece of garden hose approximately 4 feet in length. Place the end of the hose near the end of each intake and exhaust valve with the other end of the hose near the ear. In this manner, the sound is localized, making it easy to determine which lifter is at fault.

Another method is to place a finger on the face of the valve spring retainer. If the lifter is not functioning properly, a distinct shock will be felt when the valve returns to its seat.

In most cases where noise exists in one or more lifters, all lifter units should be removed and cleaned. If dirt, varnish, carbon, etc. is found to exist in one unit, it more than likely exists in all the units.

Plungers are not interchangeable as they are selectively fitted at the factory. Should a plunger or lifter body become damaged, it is necessary to replace the entire unit.

The plunger must be free in the lifter body. A simple test for this is to be sure the plunger will drop of its own weight in the body. There must be no excessive leakdown and there must be no ball check valve leakage.

When removed, valve lifters should be placed in a rack in their proper sequence so they can be installed in the original locations in the block. To service lifters, proceed as follows:

1. Hold plunger down with push rod and, using a small screw driver or awl, remove plunger retainer, Fig. 7.
2. Remove parts from lifter body.
3. Clean all parts and inspect for damage. If any parts are damaged, the entire lifter assembly should be replaced.
4. When assembled, compress plunger to open oil holes and fill plunger with SAE 10 oil. Work plunger up and down and refill.

TIMING CHAIN COVER

When installing the cover it is important that the cover be properly aligned when installing the vibration damper to prevent damage to the oil seal. This is accomplished by leaving the cover-to-block cap screws loose until the vibration damper has been partially installed. Then tighten the cover screws.

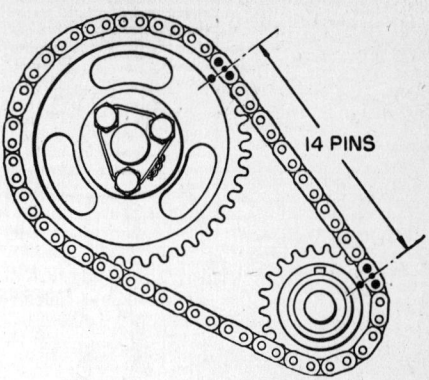

Fig. 10 Valve timing. Hudson six-cyl. engines

TIMING CHAIN

When installing a timing chain, see that the timing marks on the sprockets are in line as shown in Figs. 8, 9, 10.

VALVE TIMING DATA

Rambler

Year	Model	Intake Opens①	Intake Closes②	Exhaust Opens③	Exhaust Closes④
1953	All	10	58	46	10
1954	All	10	58	49	19
1955	All	10	58	49	19
1956	All	12½	51½	53½	10½
1957	All	12½	51½	53½	10½
1958	All	12½	51½	53½	10½
1959	Six	10	58	49	19
	V8	12½	51½	53½	10½
1960	American	10	58	49	19
	Six	12½	51½	53½	10½
	V8	12½	51½	53½	10½
1961	L-Head 6	10	58	49	19
	O.H.V. 6 ⑤	15	55	55	15
	O.H.V. 6 ⑥	12½	51½	53½	10½
	V8	12½	51½	53½	10½

①—Degrees before top dead center.
②—Degrees after bottom dead center.
③—Degrees before bottom dead center.
④—Degrees after top dead center.
⑤—Aluminum engine.
⑥—Cast iron engine.

CAMSHAFT

To remove camshaft, remove all valve lifters on V8's, or prop them up as shown in Fig. 6 on six-cylinder engines. Take off timing chain and sprockets. Remove fuel pump, distributor and distributor-oil pump drive gear. When withdrawing camshaft from engine, use care to avoid damage to the camshaft bearings.

When installing the timing chain, be sure to align the timing marks as shown in Figs. 8, 9, 10.

PISTONS & RODS, REMOVE

After removing cylinder heads and oil pan, examine the cylinder bores above the ring travel area. If the bores are worn so that a shoulder or ridge exists at this point, remove the ridge with a ridge reamer to avoid damaging rings or cracking ring lands of pistons during removal.

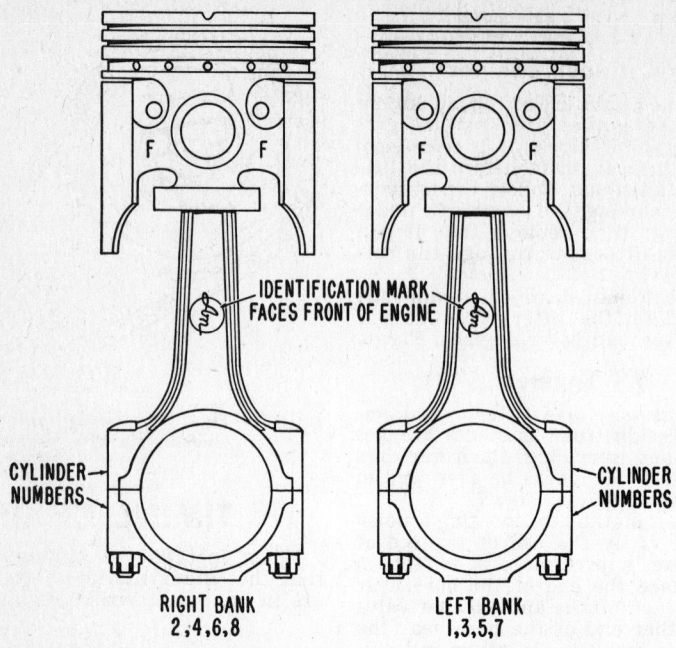

Fig. 11 Piston and rod assembly. V8 engines

Remove connecting rod caps and push the pistons and rods out through the top of the cylinders, using care to prevent the big end of the rods from damaging the crankshaft or cylinder bores. Make sure the rods and pistons are properly numbered so they can be reinstalled in their original bores. It is advisable to install caps on rods as they are removed to avoid mixing parts.

PISTONS & RODS, ASSEMBLE

V8 Engines

To insure proper installation of the piston in the bore, a notch is cast in the piston top and the letters "F" cast in the pin boss structure at the front, Fig. 11.

Overhead Valve 6-Cyl.

Pistons are marked with a depression notch on the top perimeter, Fig. 12. When installed in the engine this notch must be toward the front of the engine. Always assemble rods and caps with the cylinder numbers facing the camshaft side of engine.

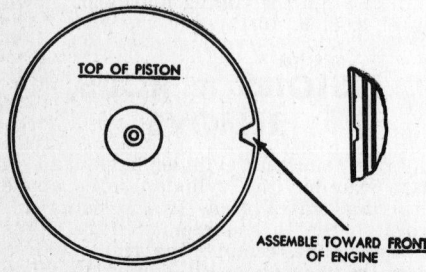

Fig. 12 Piston location reference notch. Rambler and Nash engines

Rambler Side Valve 6-Cyl. 1953-55

When installed, the heavy or offset side of the rod must be placed opposite the camshaft side, and the identification marks on the rod must be toward the front of the engine, Fig. 13.

1958-61

When installed, the identification knob on the connecting rod and the notch on the top of the piston must face front of the engine.

Hudson 6-Cyl.

When installed in the cylinder, the oil squirt hole in the connecting rod should be toward the camshaft side of the engine.

PISTONS

If the pistons are to be reused with new rings, remove the carbon from the ring grooves. A special tool is available for this work but a satisfactory job can be done by breaking an old piston ring, filing the broken end to a sharp, square edge and using it to scrape the carbon. Soak the piston in solvent to loosen any carbon residue. Clean out the loosened carbon, being careful not to cut away any piston material. Clean out the oil return holes with a drill just large enough to fill the holes. Hold the drill in a tap wrench and make sure the drill does not remove any metal from the piston.

Rinse the piston in solvent and wipe off the carbon on the sides of the piston. Never use a wire brush to clean a piston as the brush will round off the edges of the ring lands. Pistons showing scuffed or score marks on the skirt should be scrapped. Examine the ring lands carefully for cracks. If the piston is in the

least bit doubtful, it should be discarded. New pistons should be fitted according to recommendations given in the *Piston Specification* chart.

PISTON RINGS

All V8s, Rambler & Nash 6-Cyl.

When new piston rings are to be installed without reboring cylinders, the glazed cylinder walls should be slightly dulled but without increasing the bore's diameter. This is done with a "Glaze-buster" or with a hone equipped with the finest grade of stones.

New rings must be checked for clearance in piston grooves and for gap in cylinder bores. Cylinder bores and piston grooves must be clean, dry and free of carbon and burrs.

Check the clearance of each ring in its piston groove by installing the ring and then inserting feeler gauges *under* the ring. Any wear that occurs in the piston groove forms a step or ridge at the inner portion of the lower land. If gauges are inserted above the ring, the ring may rest on the step instead of on the worn portion of the lower land, and a false measurement of clearance will result.

If the piston grooves have worn to the extent that relatively high steps or ridges exist on the lower lands, the piston should be replaced because the steps will interfere with the operation of the new rings and the ring clearances will be excessive. Piston rings are not furnished in oversize widths to compensate for ring groove wear.

To check the end gap of rings, place the ring in the cylinder in which it will be used. Square it in the bore by tapping with either end of the piston, then measure the gap with feeler gauges. If necessary to increase the gap, file the ends of rings carefully with a smooth file.

Hudson 6-Cyl.

These rings are the square end type, Fig. 14, and are pinned to prevent rotation on the piston. The rings are cut and notched to fit this pin so that the clearance on the pin is equal to the gap between the ends of the ring. In other words, if the ring is compressed so the ends come together, there will be no clearance on the pin.

If the ends of the ring are filed in fitting, it is necessary to file an equal amount in the pin notch to maintain the pin clearance. Filing, however, should not be necessary as these rings are supplied in exact sizes to give a minimum

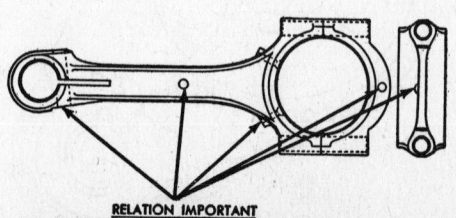

Fig. 13 Connecting rod identification. Rambler side valve engine

gap of .005″ when the ring is compressed.

With this type of ring, there is always a portion of the cylinder wall which is not worn. Therefore, if new rings are fitted, extreme care must be used to see that the gap ends do not rest on the unworn portion of the cylinder otherwise the rings will be lifted off the worn portions of the cylinder. It is advisable to hone these cylinders slightly in order to avoid this condition.

PISTON PINS

1956-61 V8s & Overhead Valves 6 Cyl.

Pins are a press fit in the connecting rod, thus requiring no locking device. The pin should be a palm press fit in the piston with parts at normal room temperature (70°F.). And with parts clean and dry, the pin must support its weight in a vertical position over its entire length in either of the two piston bosses.

Rambler & Nash Side Valve Sixes 1953-55

The pin is locked in place in the rod by means of a lock bolt. To fit a pin, first hone the rod to fit the pin. Then hone the piston to allow a thumb press fit with the parts at normal room temperature.

1958-61 Side Valve 6's

The piston pins are a press fit into the connecting rod, thus requiring no locking device. The procedure for installing pins is the same as that given previously for 1956-61 overhead valve sixes.

1953-55 Rambler & Nash Overhead Valve Sixes

The pin is full-floating and held in position by lock rings in the piston bosses. To fit a pin, first hone the pin bushing in the rod to allow a thumb press fit with the parts at normal room temperature. Then hone the pin holes in the piston bosses to allow a palm push fit with the piston heated.

Hudson 6-Cyl.

When replacing piston pins, they should be selected so that they can be pushed into the piston bosses with the heel of the hand after the piston has been heated in boiling water. After the proper pin size has been selected, replace the connecting rod upper bushing and ream or burnish to .0003″ larger than the pin. If this fit is correct, the connecting rod will just turn on the pin under its own weight when the rod is held in a horizontal position.

ROD BEARINGS

Service bearings are furnished in standard size and several undersizes, including undersizes for reground crankshafts.

The clearance for connecting rod (and main) bearings may be checked with Plastigage which is available at any auto parts jobber and full instructions for its

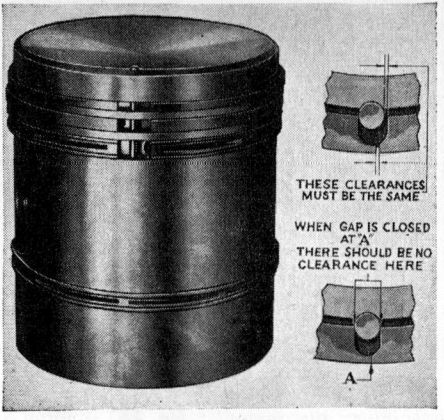

Fig. 14 Piston and rings. Hudson 1955-56 Six

use are furnished with the envelope in which it is contained.

Lacking Plastigage, however, clearance may be checked with a .002 in. test shim, ¾ in. square. Place the shim between the bearing and shaft journal. Install the bearing cap and tighten the nuts to the recommended torque. A locked bearing or drag when the rod is moved endwise on the crankshaft indicates the clearance is correct providing the rod moves endwise freely without the test shim installed. Do not overlook removing the test shim.

MAIN BEARINGS

Main bearings are the shell type and can be removed and replaced without removing the crankshaft. The bearings are made to size and do not require line reaming or readjustment.

When it is necessary to install new bearing shells, it is advisable to measure the shaft journals with a micrometer for being out-of-round. If an out-of-round condition exists in excess of the standard running clearance of the bearings (either main or connecting rod) a satisfactory bearing replacement cannot be made and it will be necessary to replace or regrind the crankshaft.

Use a rifle brush to clean the oil passages in both the shaft and crankcase. If possible, blow out the oil holes with compressed air. Be sure the journals are not nicked or scored and that all parts are thoroughly clean.

After installing the bearings, check the running clearance to be sure it is standard (see *Engine Bearing Data* chart). Use Plastigage or a .002 in. test shim about one inch square. Place the shim between the shaft and bearing and tighten the bearing cap nuts to the recommended torque. The shaft should be locked if the clearance is at the low limit or show a drag if at the high limit when turned, proving that the clearance is correct. Do not overlook removing the test shim.

CRANKSHAFT END PLAY

V8 Engines

Crankshaft end thrust is taken on the

front or No. 1 main bearing insert which is flanged for this purpose. Whenever new bearings are fitted the clearance should be carefully checked by forcing the crankshaft forward and inserting feeler gauges between the bearing flange and crankshaft cheek. End play should be .003″ to .007″. If excessive, install a new front main bearing.

A dial indicator may also be used to check crankshaft end play.

Six-Cylinder Engines

On Nash and Rambler overhead valve engines, end play is controlled by flanges on the center main bearing; on side valve engines the flanges on the front main bearing control end play. Hudson six-cylinder engines also have the end play control on the center main bearing. On all engines, check the end play in the same manner as outlined for V8 engines.

CRANKSHAFT REAR OIL SEAL

V8 Engines

A braided oil seal is pressed into the upper and lower grooves behind the rear main bearing. Directly in front of this seal is an oil slinger which deflects the oil back into the oil pan. Should the braided seal require replacement, the installation of the lower half is accomplished as follows:

With the bearing cap and lower bearing half removed, install a new seal so that both ends protrude above the cap. Tap the seal down into position or roll it snugly in its groove with a smooth rounded tool. Then cut off the protruding ends of the seal with a sharp knife or razor blade.

Installing Upper Seal

Although the usual practice is to remove the crankshaft when the upper half of the seal is to be replaced it is possible to do the job without removing the crankshaft as follows:

To remove the seal, use needle-nose pliers to grasp the end of the seal which is most accessible. Pull the seal downward while rotating the crankshaft slowly in the direction that the seal is being removed.

To install the new seal, fasten a length of wire or strong string such as fishing line securely to one end of the new seal. See that the point of fastening is not bulky and that it is not over ⅝″ from the end of the seal. Coat the seal with Lubriplate. Pass the free end of the wire or string up over the crankshaft at the point where the seal is to be installed. Then exert a firm, steady pull on the wire or string and at the same time rotate the crankshaft slowly in the direction of the pull. This will help to move the seal into position. When the installation is completed, trim the ends of the seal flush with the engine block.

1953-55 Ambassador Six

The threaded oil return has a steel-backed rubber seal. The seal is in halves and fits closely over the edge of the rear bearing oil return groove. It bears firmly on the smooth area of the crankshaft.

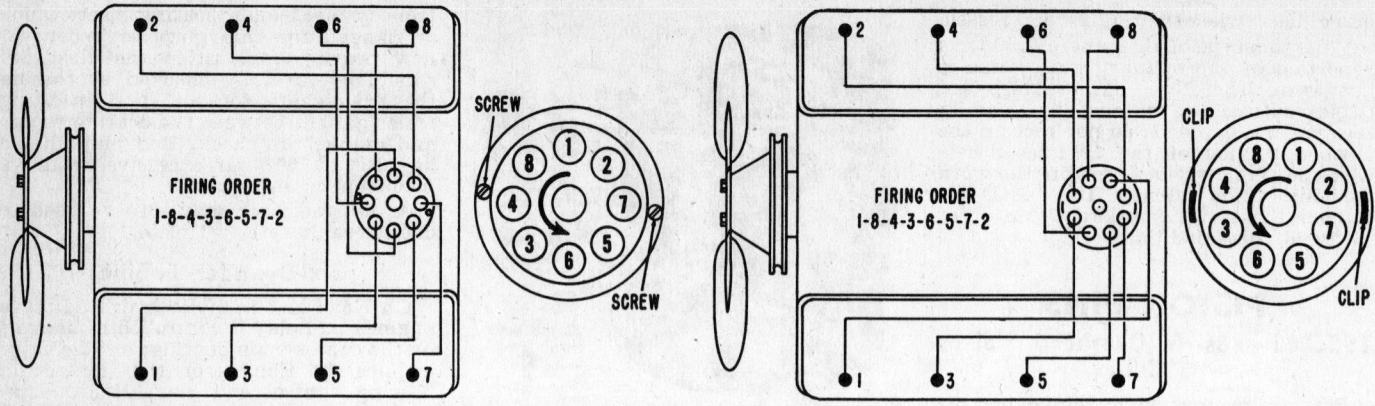

Fig. 16 Ignition details. V8 engines with Delco-Remy distributor   **Fig. 15 Ignition details. Rambler V8 with Auto-Lite distributor**

1953-61 Six (Except 1953-55 Ambassador 6)

Oil sealing at the rear main bearing is similar to that used on V8 engines, and installation of the seal is accomplished in the same manner.

OIL PAN
V8 Engines

If the steering linkage hampers the oil pan's removal, disconnect it and allow it to settle away from the bottom of the engine. Then unfasten and remove the oil pan.

Rambler & Nash 6-Cyl.

In order to remove the pan it will be necessary to remove the steering linkage cross tie rod. And on 1953-56 Statesman and Ambassador, the front suspension pivot bar brace will also have to be removed.

Hudson 6-Cyl. Engines

Disconnect the steering arm support bracket from the crossmember, allowing the steering linkage to drop. Remove flywheel housing lower cover and remove oil pan.

OIL PUMP
V8 Engines

Oil pump removal or replacement will not affect distributor timing as the distributor drive gear remains in mesh with the camshaft gear.

Upon disassembly of the oil pump, locate a straight edge across the pump body and gears in the body and check the gear-to-cover clearance, which should not exceed .004". A clearance of .008" maximum should exist between gears and walls of pump body.

The pump cover should be installed with the pump out of the engine and pump checked for freedom of operation before installation.

The oil pressure relief valve, which is built into the pump, is not adjustable, the correct pressure being built into the relief valve spring.

1953-56 Ambassador Six

The oil pump drive gear which meshes with the camshaft gear is splined to the top end of the oil pump shaft. The spline is a free fit so that it may be removed from below after the oil pump is dropped. The oil pump drive gear is installed from above after the distributor bracket and gear have been removed.

Since the oil pump is driven from a separate gear from the distributor drive gear, no particular attention is necessary in engaging the oil pump drive gear with the camshaft gear.

1953-61 Rambler & Nash 6-Cyl. (Except Ambassador)

The oil pump on these models consist of a drive and driven gear. The drive shaft being keyed to the drive gear at the lower end, is driven by a gear at the upper end which engages with the camshaft gear. The distributor drive is taken from the top end of the oil pump drive shaft. A wire snap ring is used on the undercut on the lower end of the shaft to prevent the shaft from disengaging the lower gear when the oil pump is removed.

Hudson 6-Cyl. Engines

A centrifugal operating rotor type pressure pump is used. To remove the pump and still maintain the correct ignition timing, lift off the distributor cap and rotate the crankshaft until the distributor rotor is in the firing position for No. 1 cylinder. Keep the engine in this position while the pump is removed. Unfasten the pump from the engine and lift it off.

To disassemble, remove the cover. Hold a hand over the cover opening and with the pump upside down, turn the drive shaft until the outer rotor slips out. Drive out the straight pin which holds the drive gear to the shaft. Press the shaft out of the gear. The inner rotor and shaft may then be taken out of the pump housing.

When assembling the pump, press on the drive gear so that there is from .004" and .008" clearance between the hub of the gear and the pump housing.

Note—If the crankshaft has been moved from the No. 1 firing position while the pump was off, turn the engine over to

this position and set the distributor rotor on No. 1 and install the pump, maintaining the same position for the rotor. Then reset the ignition timing.

RADIATOR, REPLACE

To remove, drain cooling system and disconnect hose. Unfasten radiator from its support and lift it out.

WATER PUMP
Front Mounted Type

1. To remove the water pump, drain cooling system.
2. Remove fan belt, fan and pulley.
3. Unfasten and remove water pump from water manifold.
4. To disassemble, remove the bearing lock ring. Place pump in an arbor press and push hub, shaft and bearing out of impeller and cover. Then press shaft and bearing out of hub.
5. If the thrust seal surface in the housing has become rough, it should be refaced with a water pump facing tool. Use a new fan hub to insure a tight fit on the shaft. Press the hub on the shaft so it is flush with the end of the shaft. Insert the shaft in the housing and install the bearing lock ring. Then install a new seal assembly in the impeller and press the impeller on shaft so it is flush with end of shaft. Clearance between impeller and cover should not exceed .090".
6. Install pump in reverse order of removal.

DISTRIBUTOR

1. Disconnect distributor primary wire from coil terminal.
2. Remove distributor cap and rotor. *Mark position of rotor arm on distributor housing so distributor can be installed in same position.*
3. Remove vacuum line from distributor.
4. Remove distributor hold-down clamp.
5. Note relative position of distributor in block, then work it out of the engine.

Installation

1. Turn rotor about ⅛ of a turn counterclockwise past the mark previously placed on the distributor housing.
2. Push the distributor down into the block with the housing in the normal "installed" position. *On gear-driven distributors, it may be necessary to move the rotor slightly to start gear into mesh with camshaft gear, but rotor should line up with mark when distributor is down in place.*
3. Tighten distributor clamp screw snugly and connect vacuum line, primary wire to coil, and install cap.

If spark plug wires were removed from cap on V8's, refer to Figs. 15 and 16 for correct installation.

V8 Service Note

If the engine was disturbed while the distributor was removed from the engine, first crank the engine to bring No. 1 piston up on its compression stroke and continue cranking until the timing mark is adjacent to the timing indicator. Then rotate the distributor cam until the rotor is in position to fire No. 1 cylinder. Install the distributor as outlined above and set the ignition timing as directed below.

IGNITION TIMING

With the breaker points adjusted to the proper clearance, crank the engine to bring No. 1 piston up on its compression stroke and stop when the mark on the vibration damper lines up with the timing tab attached to the chain cover. Loosen the distributor clamp and rotate the distributor until the points just break. Tighten the distributor clamp.

When a timing light is used the engine should be run at hot idling speed for if it is turning faster the spark may be advanced by the centrifugal weights in the distributor and the timing will not be correct.

Carburetor Section

Performance Complaints

Flooding, stumble on acceleration or other performance complaints are in many instances caused by the presence of dirt, water or other foreign matter in the carburetor. To aid in diagnosing the cause of the complaint, the carburetor should be carefully removed from the engine without draining the fuel from the bowl. The contents of the fuel bowl may then be examined for contamination as the carburetor is disassembled.

Check the fuel in the bowl for contamination by dirt, water, gum or other foreign matter. A magnet moved through the fuel in the bowl will pick up and identify any iron oxide dust that may have caused intake needle and seat leakage.

Inspect gasketed surfaces between body and air horn. Small nicks or burrs should be smoothed down to eliminate air or fuel leakage. On carburetors having a vacuum piston, be especially particular when inspecting the top surface of the inner wall of the bowl around the vacuum piston passage. A poor seal at this location may contribute to a "cutting-out" on turns complaint.

Fill the carburetor bowl with clean fuel before installing on manifold. This will help prevent dirt trapped in the fuel system from being dislodged by the free flow of fuel as the carburetor is primed. The operation of the floats and intake needle and seats may be checked under pressure if a fuel pump is used at the bench to fill the carburetor bowl. Operate the throttle several times and visually check the discharge from pump jets.

Poor Mileage and Engine Loading Complaints

Cases of poor mileage and engine loading may be due in many instances to sluggish choke valve opening during cold driveaway, caused by insufficient vacuum in choke housing, a plugged or restricted heat pipe or inlet in choke cover. To check for this condition, have engine warm and running at slow idle. Remove choke heat pipe and hold a finger over the heat inlet hole (hole is on choke housing on some carburetors). If there is little or no vacuum pull on the finger, check the choke housing for gasket leaks or plugged vacuum passages. If these are OK, check choke vacuum passages in carburetor between choke housing and manifold.

Dirty or Rusty Choke Housing

In cases where it is found that the interior of the choke housing is dirty, gummed or rusty while the carburetor itself is comparatively clean, look for a punctured or eroded manifold heat tube (if one is used).

Manifold Heat Control Valve

An engine equipped with a manifold heat control valve can operate with the valve stuck either in the open or closed position. Because of this, an inoperative valve is frequently overlooked at vehicle lubrication or tune-up.

A valve stuck in the "heat-off" position can result in slow warm up, deposits in combustion chamber, carburetor icing, flat spots during acceleration, low gas mileage and spark plug fouling.

A valve stuck in the "heat-on" position can result in power loss, engine knocking, sticking or burned valves and spark plug burning.

To prevent the possibility of a stuck valve, check and lubricate the valve each time the vehicle is lubricated or tuned-up. Check the operation of the valve manually. To lubricate the valve, place a few drops of penetrating oil on the valve shaft where it passes through the manifold. Move the valve up and down a few times to work in the oil. *Never use engine oil for this purpose as it will leave a residue which hampers valve operation.*

CARTER NOTES

METERING ROD

AS—Metering rod should just bottom at wide open throttle. Adjust by bending metering rod arm.

WCD, WCFB and WCD—Metering rod adjustment must be made after the pump setting. Back out throttle lever set screw to seat throttle valves in carburetor bores. Loosen metering rod arm clamp screw. With metering rods in place, press down on vacumeter link until metering rods bottom in casting. Holding rods down, revolve metering rod arm until finger on arm contacts lip of vacumeter link. Hold in place and tighten clamp screw.

YF—With throttle valve seated in carburetor bore, press down on upper end of diaphragm shaft until diaphragm bottoms in vacuum chamber. Metering rod should contact bottom of metering rod well, and metering rod arm should contact lifter link between springs and at supporting lug. Adjust by bending lip up or down.

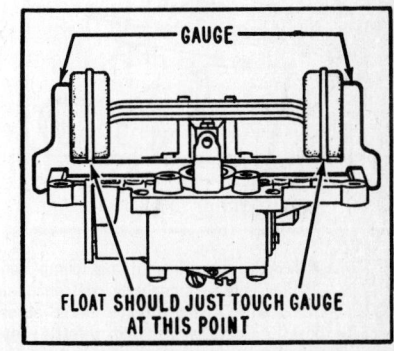

FLOAT SHOULD JUST TOUCH GAUGE AT THIS POINT

Fig. ①—WCD float level. To adjust bend float lever.

CARTER CARBURETOR ADJUSTMENTS

Year	Carburetor Model	Idle Adjustments				Float Level		Float Drop		Pump Travel Setting	Choke Unloader Setting	Choke Setting
		Mixture Screws Turns Open	Hot Idle Speed Neutral	Fast Idle Speed	Dashpot Plunger Clearance	Primary	Secondary	Primary	Secondary			
RAMBLER												
1961	AS-3169S	¼-1¼	475	.035 [10]	None	¼ [8]	None	None	None	[9]	⅛ [11]	Index
	WCD-3170S	½-1½	475	.020 [3]	None	5/32 [1]	None	None	None	[2]	3/16 [4]	Index
1959-60	WCD-2887S, SA	½-2	475	.023 [3]	None	5/32 [1]	None	None	None	[2]	3/16 [4]	Index
1955-60	YF-2014S	½-1½	475	.054 [6]	None	½ [5]	None	None	None	None	9/32 [7]	1 Lean
1957-60	WCD-2586S	½-1½	475	.020 [3]	None	5/32 [1]	None	None	None	[2]	3/16 [4]	Index
1958-60	YF-2757S	½-1½	475	.054 [6]	None	½ [5]	None	None	None	None	9/32 [7]	1 Lean
1958	AS-2748S	¼-1¼	475	.030 [10]	None	¼ [8]	None	None	None	[9]	3/16 [11]	2 Rich
	AS-2749S	¼-1¼	475	.030 [10]	None	¼ [8]	None	None	None	[9]	3/16 [11]	2 Rich
1957	AS-2664S	¼-1¼	475	.030 [10]	None	¼ [8]	None	None	None	[9]	3/16 [11]	2 Rich
	AS-2665S	¼-1¼	475	.030 [10]	None	¼ [8]	None	None	None	[9]	3/16 [11]	2 Rich
	AS-2564S	¼-1¼	475	.030 [10]	None	¼ [8]	None	None	None	[9]	9/64 [11]	2 Rich
	AS-2580S	¼-1¼	475	.030 [10]	None	¼ [8]	None	None	None	[9]	9/64 [11]	2 Rich
	WGD-2352S-A	1-2	475	.023 [6]	None	7/32 [12]	None	None	None	[13]	3/16 [14]	Index
1956	AS-2349S	¼-1½	475	.043 [10]	None	¼ [8]	None	None	None	[9]	3/16 [11]	1 Lean
NASH & HUDSON												
1957	WCFB-2593S-A	¼-1¼	475	.023 [3]	None	⅛ [15]	3/16 [15]	5/8 [16]	11/16 [16]	[13]	9/32 [4]	Index
1956	WGD-2352S-A	1-2	475	.023 [6]	None	7/32 [12]	None	None	None	[13]	3/16 [14]	Index
	WCD-2350S	½-1½	475	.020 [3]	None	5/32 [1]	None	None	None	[2]	3/16 [4]	Index
	YH-2369S	¼-1¾	475	.018 [6]	None	7/16 [5]	None	2⅜ [17]	None	None	5/8 [14]	2 Lean
	YH-2368S	¼-1¾	475	.030 [6]	None	5/16 [5]	None	2⅜ [17]	None	None	½ [14]	1 Rich
1955-56	WGD-2252S	1¾-2¾	475	.030 [6]	None	¼ [12]	None	None	None	[13]	7/32 [14]	Index
	WGD-2231S-A	½-1½	475	.030 [6]	None	¼ [12]	None	None	None	[13]	3/16 [14]	1 Rich
	WCD-2061S	½-1½	475	.026 [3]	None	5/32 [1]	None	None	None	[2]	11/64 [4]	Index

CARTER NOTES
continued

Fig. ②—With throttle valves closed and pump connector link in outer hole of pump arm, flat on pump should be parallel with a straightedge placed across dust cover boss. Adjust by bending throttle connector rod.

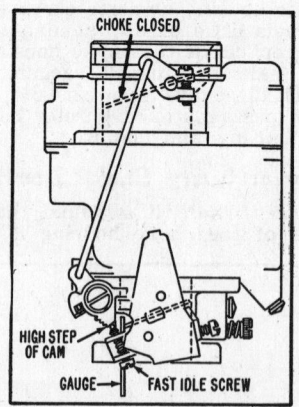

Fig. ③—With choke valve closed, tighten fast idle screw on high step of fast idle cam until there is the clearance specified between throttle valve and carburetor bore.

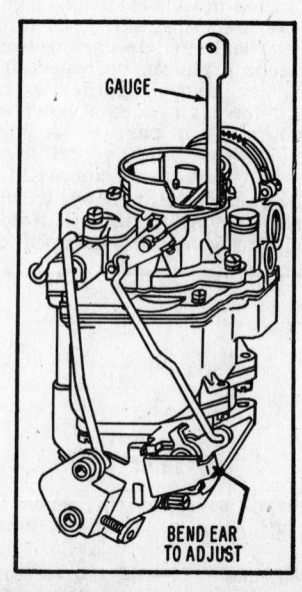

Fig. ④—With throttle wide open there should be the clearance specified between upper edge of choke valve and inner wall of air horn. Adjust by bending ear on throttle shaft lever.

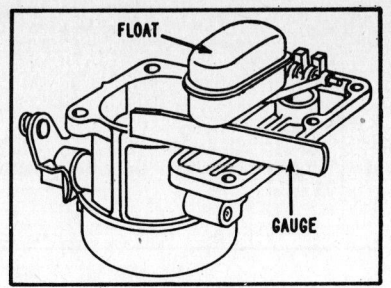

Fig. ⑤—YF and YH float level. Adjust by bending float lever.

⑥—With choke valve closed and fast idle cam in fast idle position, there should be the clearance specified between throttle valve and carburetor bore (side opposite idle port). Adjust by bending choke connector link.

CARTER NOTES
continued

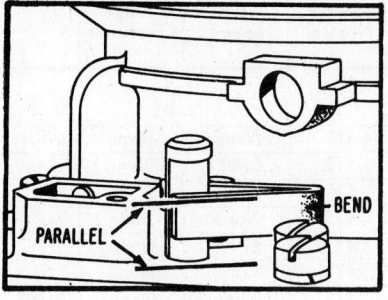

Fig. ⑨—Pump arm on lifter link should parallel top of casting. Adjust by bending pump arm.

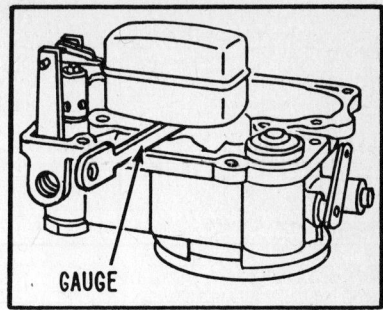

Fig. ⑫—WGD float level. Adjust by bending float lever.

⑬—See ②. With throttle valves closed, flat on pump arm should parallel a straightedge placed across dust cover boss. Adjust by bending throttle connector rod.

⑭—With throttle valves wide open, there should be the clearance specified between upper edge of choke valve and inner wall of air horn. Adjust by bending choke shaft unloader arm.

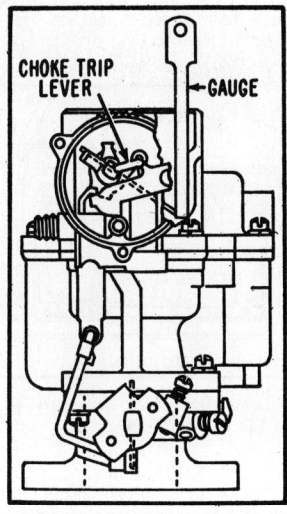

Fig. ⑦—With throttle valve wide open there should be the clearance specified between lower edge of choke valve and inner wall of air horn. Adjust by bending arm of choke trip lever.

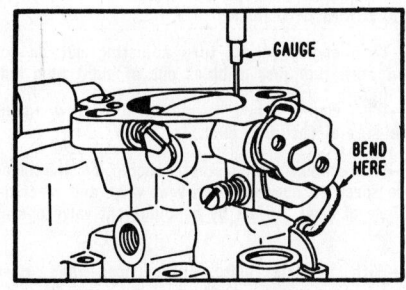

Fig. ⑩—There should be the clearance specified between lower edge of throttle valve and carburetor bore with fast idle link on high step of cam. Adjust by bending choke connector rod.

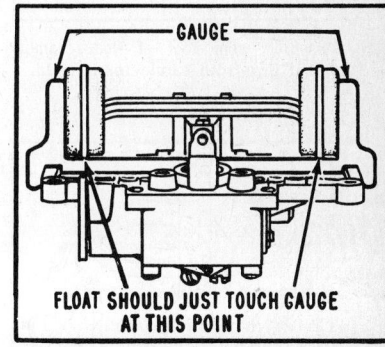

Fig. ⑮—WCFB float level. Adjust by bending float lever.

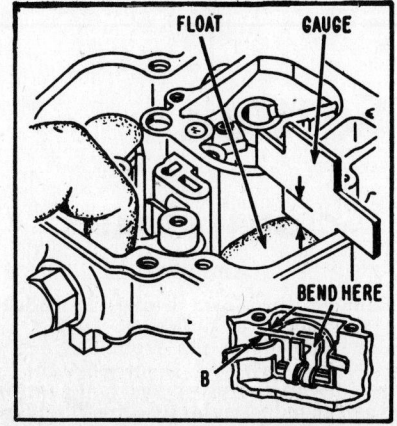

Fig. ⑧—AS float level. Adjust by bending float lip.

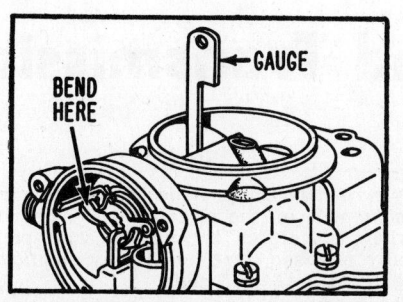

Fig. ⑪—With throttle wide open there should be the clearance specified between top edge of choke valve and inner wall of air horn. Adjust by bending arm on choke trip lever.

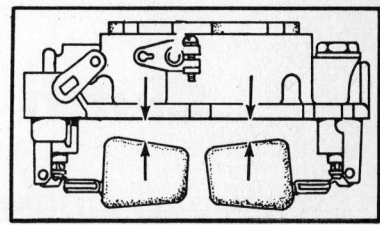

Fig. ⑯—WCFB float drop. Adjust by bending stop tabs on float bracket.

⑰—Measured from bowl cover to bottom of float at free end. Adjust by bending stop tab on float arm.

HOLLEY CARBURETOR ADJUSTMENTS

Year	Model	Carb. Type	Idle Adjustments					Float Level	Fuel Level	Float Bowl Vent Valve	Pump Override Spring	Choke Unloader	Choke Setting
			Mixture Screws Turns Open	Air Bypass Turns Open	Hot Idle Speed Neutral	Fast Idle Speed	Dashpot Plunger Clearance						
RAMBLER													
1961	Six	1 Bore	1	None	475	None	None	⑭	¾②	None	None	5/16③	Index
	V8	2 Bore	1	None	475	1700⑥	None	④	⑤	.060⑦	⑧	3/16⑨	1 Rich
	V8	4 Bore	1	None	475	1700⑥	None	④	⑤	.060⑦	⑧	3/16⑨	1 Lean
1960	Six	1 Bore	1¼	None	475	None	None	3/16①	23/32②	None	None	7/16③	Index
	V8	2 Bore	1	None	475	1700⑥	None	④	⑤	.060⑦	⑧	3/16⑨	1 Rich
	V8	4 Bore	1	None	475	1700⑥	None	④	⑤	.060⑦	⑧	3/16⑨	1 Lean
1959	Six	1 Bore	1¼	None	475	None	None	3/16①	23/32②	None	None	7/16③	Index
	V8	4 Bore	1	None	475	1700⑥	None	⑩	⑪	.060⑦	⑧	3/16⑨	1 Lean
1958	V8	4 Bore	1	None	475	⑬	None	⑫	⑪	.060⑦	⑧	None	1 Lean

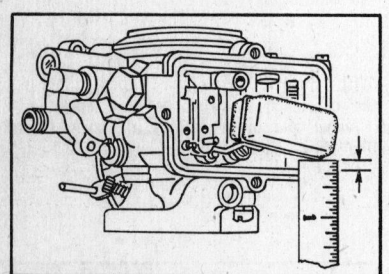

Fig. ①—Measured from roof of float chamber to lowest point of float with carburetor inverted.

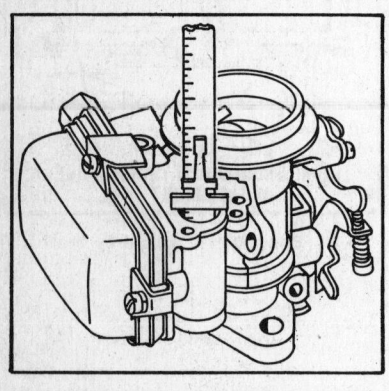

←

Fig. ②—Measured with scale through power valve mounting hole from outside surface of main body to level of fuel. Take measurement with engine idling.

HOLLEY NOTES

③—With throttle lever in wide open position and choke plate closed against unloader lever, opening of choke plate should be as specified between edge of choke plate and venturi. Adjust by bending unloader lever.

④—With carburetor inverted, adjust float level by means of adjusting nut on fuel bowl so float is parallel with bowl floor.

⑤—With engine idling, turn adjusting nut on fuel bowl until fuel just dribbles out of sight plug hole.

⑥—With engine idling, turn fast idle screw against high step of fast idle cam.

⑦—With engine idling, there should be the clearance specified between bowl vent valve and machined surface of bowl. Adjust by bending vent valve operating rod.

⑧—With throttle plates fully open and pump lever in compressed position, turn override spring screw until it just touches pump lever; then tighten screw ¼ turn.

⑨—With throttle plates wide open, clearance between top edge of choke plate and inner wall of air horn should be as specified. Adjust by bending tab on throttle shaft lever where it contacts fast idle cam.

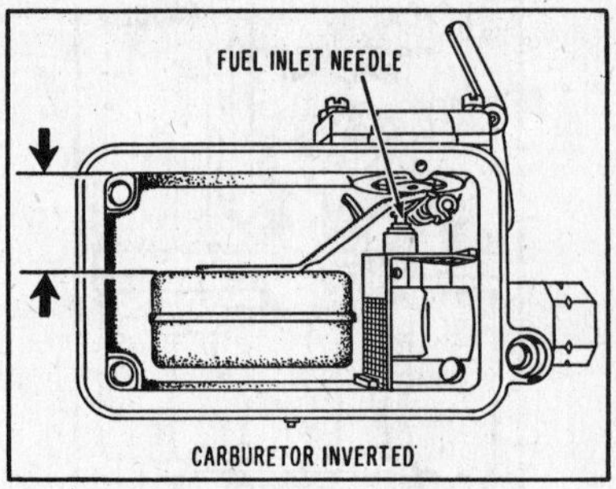

FUEL INLET NEEDLE

CARBURETOR INVERTED

Fig. ⑩—Primary float ⅞″, secondary 1 1/16″. Adjust by bending tab on float lever.

⑪—With engine idling, fuel should just dribble out of sight plug hole. If not, adjust float level.

⑫—See Fig. ⑩. Primary float 1 3/16″, secondary ¾″.

⑬—With engine idling, turn fast idle screw so that it just touches lowest step on fast idle cam.

⑭—Use Gauge J-10231.

Clutch and Transmission Section

CLUTCH PEDAL, ADJUST

1953-54

Adjustment for free pedal play is made by varying the length of the throwout lever rod. Lengthening this rod reduces the pedal play, and shortening it, increases the play. Free play of from ½ to ¾″ should be maintained at all times.

1955-60

In order to provide sufficient free movement of the clutch release bearing when the clutch is engaged and pedal fully released, free pedal play should be ½ to ¾″ at all times.

Adjustment for free pedal play is made by varying the length of the beam or link to the release lever rod. Lengthening this rod reduces pedal travel; shortening it increases pedal play.

CLUTCH REPAIRS

Removal

Remove the floor board. Disconnect the release fork pull-back spring and remove the clevis pin from the end of the release fork rod. Disconnect the release fork at the pivot and pull the fork out as far as possible. Remove the transmission as described under *Transmission, Remove & Replace.*

Remove the clutch housing pan and mark the clutch cover and flywheel so that the clutch may be installed in the same relative position. Loosen the clutch cover bolts gradually and evenly until the clutch spring pressure is entirely relieved. Remove the bolts, and the clutch assembly may be removed from below.

Service Note

Unless special clutch rebuilding equipment is available, it is recommended that the clutch assembly be exchanged for a rebuilt unit should the clutch require rebuilding. The driven disc, however, may be replaced without special equipment. If clutch rebuilding equipment is available, follow the equipment manufacturer's instructions, Fig. 1.

Clutch, Install

1. Very sparingly apply front wheel bearing lubricant to the clutch shaft pilot bearing in the crankshaft. If too much lubricant is used, it will run out of face of flywheel when hot and ruin driven plate facings. Make certain that flywheel surface is clean and dry.
2. Make sure that splines in driven plate hub are clean, and apply a light coating of lubriplate. Driven plate facings must be clean and dry.
3. Place driven plate on pressure plate, then place clutch assembly in position on flywheel, being sure to align marks made on flywheel and cover before removal.
4. Install cover bolts with washers but do not tighten.
5. Insert a spare clutch shaft through hub of driven plate and into pilot bearing.
6. Tighten each clutch cover bolt several turns at a time to draw

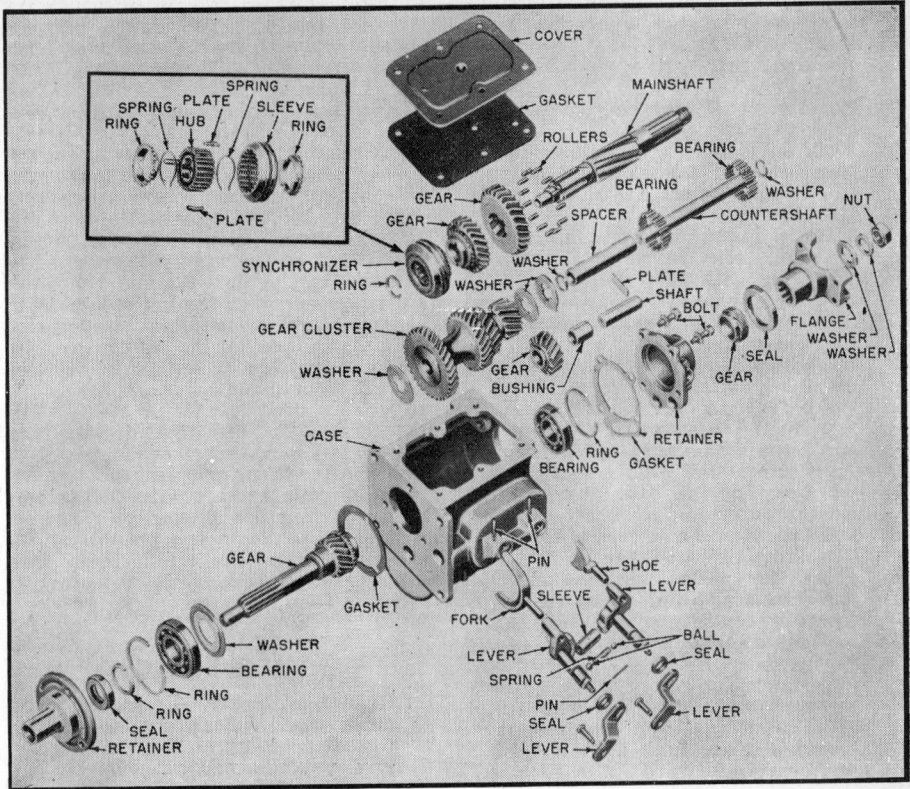

Fig. 2 Manual shift transmission (type with top cover)

cover evenly to flywheel and avoid distortion of cover.
7. While tightening cover bolts, move clutch shaft from side to side to center driven plate with pilot bearing. If driven plate is not centered, it will be difficult to slide the transmission into place. Make sure all cover bolts are uniformly tightened.
8. Remove aligning clutch shaft and install transmission, clutch linkage and adjust clutch pedal free play.

TRANSMISSION, REPLACE

1953-55 Ambassador & Statesman & All 1956-61 (Except American)

1. To remove the transmission, disconnect the brake tube bracket from the underside of the body floor pan.
2. Disconnect torque tube from rear of transmission.
3. Disconnect hand brake cable at bell crank and the brake cable housing at the bell crank bracket.
4. Move rear axle to the rear to permit the front universal joint to be taken off the transmission mainshaft.
5. Disconnect speedometer cable and shifter rods from transmission.
6. If equipped with overdrive, disconnect wires at solenoid and overdrive control cable at the lever on the overdrive housing.
7. Remove the two upper bolts from the transmission and insert guide pins in their place. Remove the two

lower bolts and slide the transmission straight back on the guide pins until it is clear of the clutch disc.
8. To install, reverse the foregoing procedure.

1953-55 Rambler and 1958-61 American

To remove the transmission on 100″ wheelbase models, disconnect rear spring front eye brackets from the underside of the body floor pan, rear shock absorbers at axle tube, rear brake hose bracket, and hand brake cable at equalizer. Then slide rear axle to the rear to remove the front universal joint from the transmission mainshaft.

To remove the transmission on 108″ wheelbase models, remove the propeller shaft coupling nut from the coupling. Tap the coupling off the pinion shaft splines with a soft-faced hammer. Disconnect the crossmember from the support brackets at the side sills. Then remove the crossmember and both front and rear propeller shafts by sliding them from the transmission mainshaft.

On all models, after removing the two top bolts holding the transmission to the bell housing, install guide studs in these holes to avoid any possibility of damaging the clutch shaft or pilot bearing while removing the transmission.

TRANSMISSION REPAIRS

Type With Top Cover

1. Take off cover and gasket, Fig. 1.
2. Pull off companion flange.

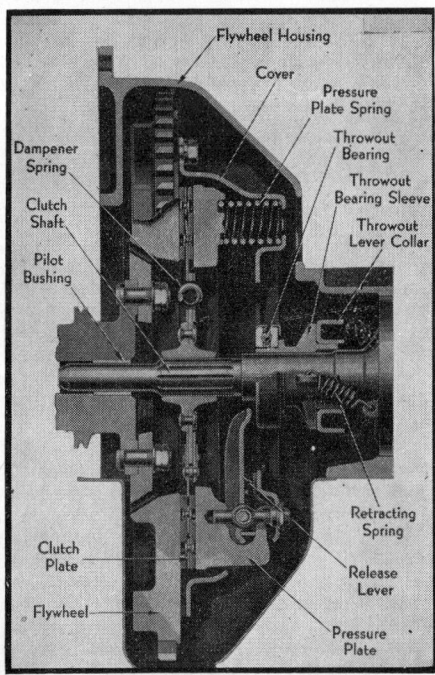

Fig. 1 Sectional view of Borg and Beck clutch

3. Remove mainshaft rear bearing retainer and speedometer drive gear from mainshaft.

4. Remove main drive gear bearing retainer.

5. Remove small snap ring from main drive gear.

6. With brass drift and hammer, move countershaft rearward just enough to free up lock plate in shaft groove at rear end.

7. Make a dummy countershaft of ¾" diameter cold rolled steel *exactly* 7$\frac{5}{64}$" long with a $\frac{3}{16}$" hole drilled 1" deep at each end. The purpose of the dummy shaft is to retain in position the needle rollers, sleeve and thrust washers when removing and installing the countershaft gear cluster.

8. Place the end of the dummy shaft against the front end of the countershaft and with a soft hammer, carefully drive the countershaft rearward out of the case, leaving the cluster gear, dummy shaft and related parts in the bottom of the case.

9. With a small brush, paint a fine line across the synchronizer rings, sleeve and second and high mainshaft gear to insure replacement of these parts in their original position.

10. To remove the main drive gear, place a brass bar or drift against the rear face of the drive gear teeth at the top (not synchronizer gear teeth) and carefully drive the gear and bearing forward out of the case.

11. With a brass bar placed against the front end of the mainshaft, drive the mainshaft rear bearing out through the rear of the case.

12. Using snap ring pliers, remove the snap ring from the front end of the mainshaft.

13. Holding the synchronizer parts and mainshaft gears together as a unit, move the mainshaft to the right and disengage the shifter fork and shoe from the grooves in the shifter sleeve and low gear. Then twist and withdraw the mainshaft through rear of case.

14. With a long brass drift, drive the reverse idler gear shaft out of the rear of the case and lift out the idler gear.

15. Lift the countershaft gear cluster and related parts straight out of the case to prevent the needle rollers from spilling. Then carefully remove the thrust washers and note the position of each to insure exact replacement.

16. With a punch, drive out the taper pins securing the shift shafts in position, upward out of the case.

17. Remove the nuts, washers and levers from the shift shafts and take shafts out of case. Also remove the interlock sleeve, detent balls, spring and pin.

Assembly Details — Regardless of appearance, all gaskets and oil seals should be replaced. When installing oil seals, coat the outside of the seal and inside of housing with red or white lead or gasket sealer to insure leak-tight joints. Leather seals should be soaked for 24 hours before installing them.

After installing the shift shaft levers, move either one into any in-gear position and with one end of the interlock con-

tacting a shift shaft cam, measure the clearance with a feeler gauge between the opposite end of the sleeve and the cam of the other shift shaft. This clearance should be .001" to .007". If not within these limits, remove the sleeve and replace with one of the proper length, available in five different lengths.

When installing the countershaft cluster gear, install the front washer with bronze face to the gear and lug at top. The rear inner (bronze) washer should be installed so the lugs will engage the slots in the cluster gear and the outer (steel) washer with the lug at top. With the countershaft installed temporarily, check the end play of the cluster gear. Do this by inserting a feeler gauge between the rear thrust washers. End play should range from .006" to .016" on 1952-54 and .003" to .006" on 1955-57. If greater than this, install new thrust washers.

With correct end play established, remove the countershaft with the dummy shaft, allowing the cluster gear and related parts to lie in the bottom of the case until after the main drive gear, mainshaft and reverse idler gears are installed. Then raise the cluster gear and install the countershaft.

Type With Side Cover

1. Referring to Fig. 3, remove overdrive assembly as outlined in the *Overdrive Chapter*.

2. Remove transmission cover.

3. Remove clutch shaft bearing.

4. Pull clutch shaft as far forward as possible.

5. Grasp mainshaft and its components and separate mainshaft from clutch shaft.

6. Slide mainshaft assembly out through rear of case.

7. Strip mainshaft of its parts.

8. Remove clutch shaft from rear of transmission.

9. The countershaft and reverse idler gear shaft are a press fit in the case and are locked in position at the rear by Woodruff keys. To maintain the position of the 80 needle bearings in the countershaft gear, drive the countershaft out of the rear of the case, using a dummy shaft machined to .870" x 8$\frac{1}{16}$".

10. With countershaft removed, lift countergear assembly out through rear of case.

11. Knock out reverse idler shaft through rear of case.

Assembly Notes

Whenever any transmission gear requires replacement, the gear with which it meshes should also be replaced. To assemble the transmission, reverse the order of disassembly, referring to Fig. 3, and observe the following:

1. Use the dummy shaft to assemble the needle bearings in the countershaft. When assembling the thrust washers, the two small projections on the face of the bronze rear thrust washer must index with the grooves in the countershaft gear. The front thrust washer must index with the transmission case. Position the large thrust washer and place the assembly in the bottom of the case.

2. Install the reverse idler and shaft. Then align the countershaft gear

assembly but before installing the shaft, check the washers for proper alignment.

3. To assemble the mainshaft, install mainshaft snap ring. This ring is furnished in four different sizes ranging from .087" to .096". Select the thickest snap ring that will fit into the retaining groove. Proper snap ring selection will reduce end play to a minimum.

4. Place oil baffle in overdrive adapter case with concave side facing forward.

5. Tap mainshaft and center bearing into housing.

6. Install large snap ring into retaining groove of adapter housing. Select the thickest snap ring (four sizes available) which will fit into groove.

7. Install sliding gear on mainshaft with shifting collar to front.

8. Install second speed gear on shaft with tapered cone to front.

9. Install synchronizer on shaft.

10. Install lock ring and spacer on mainshaft.

11. Insert 14 pilot bearing rollers in rear of clutch shaft.

12. Insert clutch shaft in transmission from rear.

13. Insert mainshaft assembly through rear of case. Place clutch shaft on mainshaft. Place both shafts into proper position in case.

14. Check synchronizer friction rings for proper location and freeness.

Service Note

An excessive amount of grease used to retain the needle bearings in the clutch shaft when assembling a standard or overdrive transmission may lead to a failure. This results from insufficient lubrication when the grease plugs the three oil holes in the shaft and shuts off the oil supply.

A light coating of petroleum jelly or oil on the rollers will hold them in place until all are installed. Once installed, they will remain in place.

GEARSHIFT, ADJUST
Synchromesh Trans.

To adjust the gearshift linkage, place the shift lever in neutral. Disconnect the rods from the shift levers on the transmission and place the transmission levers in neutral position. Install an aligning tool (or a $\frac{3}{16}$" rod) in the small holes in the gearshift operating levers and the grooves in the bearing housing on the lower end of the steering column.

With the aligning tool in position and transmission shift levers in neutral, adjust shift rods at transmission end. After adjustment, remove aligning tool.

On 1960-61 models (except American) the shift gate must be pried downward to align the lever pins. This will lock both lever pins in the slot of the shift gate. Then move the operating levers down to the neutral position and adjust the trunnions on the gear shift rods so they will enter freely into the transmission shift levers while the shift levers are in neutral position.

HYDRA-MATIC

Linkage, Adjust
1955 All; 1956-57 Rambler

1. Place selector lever in D-3 position.
2. Disconnect control rod at transmission lever.
3. Place transmission shift lever in D-3 position (3rd detent from front).
4. Adjust clevis so its pin passes freely through hole in shift lever.
5. After adjustment is made, lengthen control rod by turning clevis two full turns and connect clevis to shift lever.
6. To adjust gearshift selector pointer on Ambassador and Statesmen, remove Phillips screw from lower end of shroud on steering gear jacket tube. Pointer can then be moved on shaft by holding shaft with pliers and turning pointer by hand. Pointer is press fit on shaft.
7. The pointer on the 1955 Rambler is located on the selector shift lever. Adjustment is made by setting the lever in D-3 position and loosening the retaining screw and setting the pointer to correspond with the numeral 3. The pointer on the 1956-57 Rambler is a press fit on a split shaft and may be moved to any position.

1956-57 Ambassador, 1956 Statesman

1. Adjust idle speed to 450 rpm (with air conditioning 500 rpm, compressor running) with engine and transmission at operating temperature and selector lever in Neutral.
2. On Ambassador models, disconnect TV rod at carburetor throttle shaft lever. With carburetor off fast idle, adjust TV rod to fit freely in hole of throttle shaft lever. Then shorten TV rod three full turns and attach it.
3. On Statesman models, remove upper end of throttle rod at bell crank and disconnect carburetor to bell crank rod at carburetor throttle rod. Insert a $\frac{3}{16}$" diameter rod in the holes of the bell crank and bracket. With carburetor set off fast idle, adjust

carburetor to bell crank rod and fasten in place. Then adjust TV rod at the bell crank to fit freely with the hole in the lever. Shorten TV rod three full turns and connect to bell crank. Remove aligning pin.

Hydra-Matic, Replace

The Hydra-Matic transmission, rear flywheel housing, torus cover and torus members are removed as an assembly. The procedure is as follows:

1. Raise and support rear of car at body side sills. Support rear axle assembly with hydraulic jack.
2. Drain fluid from transmission.
3. Disconnect hand brake cable at bell crank and brake cable housing at bell crank bracket.
4. Disconnect speedometer cable and housing at transmission adapter.
5. Disconnect throttle rod from lever at transmission.
6. Disconnect control rod from transmission shift lever.
7. Remove rear brake hose bracket from floor pan to prevent damage to hose.
8. Disconnect torque tube from rear bearing retainer and separate by sliding the universal joint to the rear off the splines of the output shaft.
9. Support rear end of engine to relieve weight from rear engine support cross member.
10. Remove rear engine support cross member, cushion and bracket.
11. Remove flywheel housing lower cover.
12. Drain fluid from torus cover.
13. Remove throttle control lever from transmission to prevent bending it while removing and replacing transmission.
14. Remove 30 torus cover-to-flywheel attaching bolts.
15. Lower engine *slightly* to remove flywheel housing attaching bolts.
16. Place hydraulic jack under transmission and lift transmission slightly to take strain off rear flywheel housing bolts.
17. Remove rear housing-to-front housing attaching bolts. The lower studs on each side of rear housing also hold rear engine supports in housing.

18. Remove the upper rear stud on each side of housing and enter two $\frac{9}{16}$" studs approximately 2 inches long into the rear flywheel housing (one on each side) just above the dowel pins. Thread the bolts into the housing to force the dowel pins from the front flywheel housing. After dowel pins are free, remove the two studs.
19. Move the transmission to the rear of the car and lower the assembly after the mainshaft has been withdrawn from the crankshaft pilot bushing. To prevent end of mainshaft from striking the flywheel-to-crankshaft bolts when lowering the transmission, turn the flywheel so the end of the mainshaft will pass between the two bolts.
20. Reverse the foregoing procedure to install the transmission and adjust the linkage as previously outlined.

ULTRAMATIC DRIVE

Linkage Adjustments, 1955-56

1. Place selector lever in Reverse.
2. Disconnect control rod at transmission.
3. Place shift lever at transmission all the way to downward position.
4. Adjust clevis on control rod so that clevis pin fits freely in hole of transmission shift lever. This adjustment will insure proper detent location in transmission.

FLASHOMATIC TRANSMISSION

1959-61 Push Buttons

To adjust the gear selector push button control, disconnect the cable at the transmission lever. Push the "L" button in and move the selector lever at the transmission all the way to the rear which is low gear.

Adjust the cable linkage clevis, aligning holes in clevis and lever. Install clevis pin and washer and tighten clevis securely. Check adjustment in all positions.

1958 Push Buttons

To adjust the gear selector push button control, disconnect the cable at the transmission lever. Push the "N" button in and move selector lever on transmis-

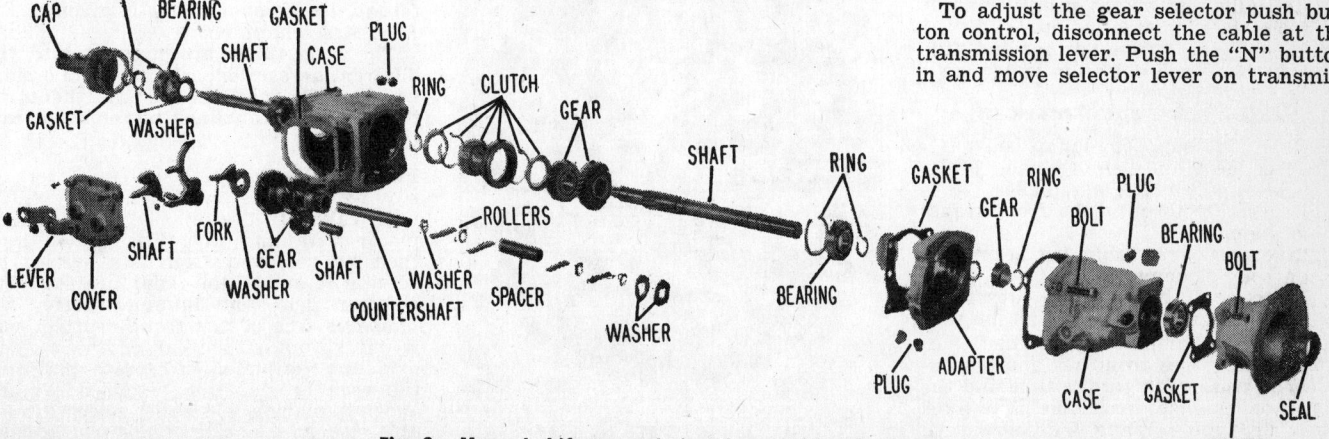

Fig. 3   Manual shift transmission (type with side cover)

sion all the way forward. Then set lever into first notch which is Neutral.

Adjust cable linkage clevis, aligning holes in clevis and lever. Install clevis pin and washer and tighten to clevis securely. Check adjustment in all five positions on the shift quadrant.

Selector Lever Linkage 1957 Rambler

1. To adjust the linkage, set the selector in Reverse.
2. Disconnect clevis at transmission lever and set transmission lever in Reverse position.
3. Adjust clevis to transmission lever so that the pin passes freely through hole in lever.

4. Check selector lever pointer in all positions. If pointer does not line up properly, remove bottom half of jacket tube and adjust pointer to line up with center of letter N.

Transmission Removal 1957-61 Rambler

1. Disconnect battery cable.
2. Drain transmission.
3. Disconnect vacuum line and wire terminal at vacuum unit at rear of transmission.
4. Disconnect speedometer cable.
5. Disconnect rear brake hose bracket from floor panel.
6. Disconnect linkage from transmission lever.

7. Disconnect rear shock absorbers from rear axle.
8. Disconnect torque tube, propeller shaft and hand brake cable.
9. Lower rear axle and move rearward to separate torque tube and propeller shaft from transmission.
10. Support transmission with suitable hoist or jack.
11. Remove transmission-to-converter housing upper cap screws and install two guide pins in the cap screw holes.
12. Remove lower cap screws.
13. Remove transmission from converter assembly.
14. Reverse the foregoing procedure to install the transmission and adjust the shift linkage as outlined above.

Rear Axle and Brake Section

Refer To Hydraulic Brakes Chapter For Brake Adjustments

REAR AXLE, REPLACE

1953-54 Series 40, 60

1. Disconnect the brake tube bracket from the underside of the body floor pan.
2. Disconnect torque tube from rear of transmission.
3. Disconnect hand brake cable at bell crank and brake cable housing at bell crank bracket.
4. Move rear axle to rear and slide from under car.

1953-55 Rambler & 1958-61 American

1. Disconnect rear shocks at axle tubes.
2. Disconnect rear brake hose bracket.
3. Disconnect hand brake cable at equalizer.
4. Disconnect rear spring front eye brackets from underside of body floor pan.
5. Loosen coupling nut and remove propeller shaft. The coupling nut dust shield will serve as a puller to partially remove the propeller shaft from the rear axle pinion.
6. Separate axle from springs and slide axle back and out from under car.

1956-61 Except American

1. Raise and support rear of body.
2. Disconnect and remove hand brake cables from brake assemblies.
3. Disconnect torque tube from transmission.
4. Disconnect rear brake hoe at bracket on body floor pan.
5. Disconnect rear shock absorbers from mounting bracket, and the rear stabilizer bar at the axle tube.
6. Roll axle free from car and disconnect truss rods, torque tube and the propeller shaft from the rear axle. A slip type coupling is used between the propeller shaft and rear axle.

7. Reverse the foregoing procedure to install the axle.

1955-57 Ambassador & Statesman

1. Raise and support rear of body.
2. Disconnect hand brake cable at bell crank and hand brake cable housing at bracket.
3. Disconnect torque tube from transmission.
4. Disconnect rear brake hose at bracket on body floor pan.
5. Disconnect rear springs and shock absorbers from axle tube.

Fig. 1 1953-61 Rambler and Statesman rear axle

6. Disconnect stabilizer bar at axle tube (Ambassador & Statesman).
7. Roll rear axle free of car and disconnect truss rods, torque tube and propeller shaft from rear axle.

REAR AXLE REPAIRS

1953-57 Series 10, 40 & All 1958-61

Fig. 1. In this type axle, the drive pinion is held in position by the shoulders in the differential carrier upon which the pinion bearing cups seat. The pinion position is maintained by a washer located between the rear bearing and the rear shoulder in the differential carrier. Shims between the bearing spacer and the front bearing cone are used to adjust pinion bearings.

The shimmed type of differential bearing adjustment is employed. The procedure for making this adjustment, as well as the assembly of the differential case, replacing the ring gear, checking ring gear and pinion backlash, and other differential case operations, is given in the *Rear Axle* chapter.

The axle tubes are pressed into the differential carrier to form a one-piece housing. To overhaul the unit, therefore, the axle assembly must be removed from the chassis.

Pinion & Bearings, Replace—After removing the axle shafts and differential unit, take off the oil seal retainer and pinion retaining nut. The pinion may then be removed from the carrier by driving it out of the front bearing with a brass drift and hammer. After the pinion is free of the front bearing, pull it out through the rear of the carrier.

Mount the pinion in a press and force the rear bearing cone from the shaft. When replacing the cone, select a suitable sleeve or length of pipe of the same diameter as the cone so the rollers or cage will not be damaged when being pressed on the shaft. Drive the front bearing cup out of the carrier toward the front. If the rear bearing cup is to be replaced, remove it also.

Pinion Bearings, Adjust—The only occasion for adjusting the drive pinion bearings is when a new pinion or differential carrier is installed. To make the adjustment, install sufficient shims between the bearing spacer and the front bearing so that when the pinion retaining nut is tightened, all rollers in the bearings are tight, but still permit rotating the pinion by hand.

Pinion, Adjust—After adjusting the pinion bearings, the position of the pinion should be checked. If a pinion setting gauge is available, check the pinion depth as outlined in the *Rear Axle Chapter*. If a correction is necessary, disassemble the pinion and, if the pinion is to be moved toward the center of the axle, install a thicker washer. If the pinion has to be moved away from the center of the axle, install a thinner washer.

If no pinion setting gauge is available, assemble the differential unit in the carrier and check the tooth contact by painting the ring gear teeth as described in the *Rear Axle Chapter*. After satisfactory tooth contact has been established, lock the adjustment with the pinion shaft nut.

1953-57 Series 60, 80

Figs. 2, 3. The differential unit is the same as that shown in Fig. 1 except

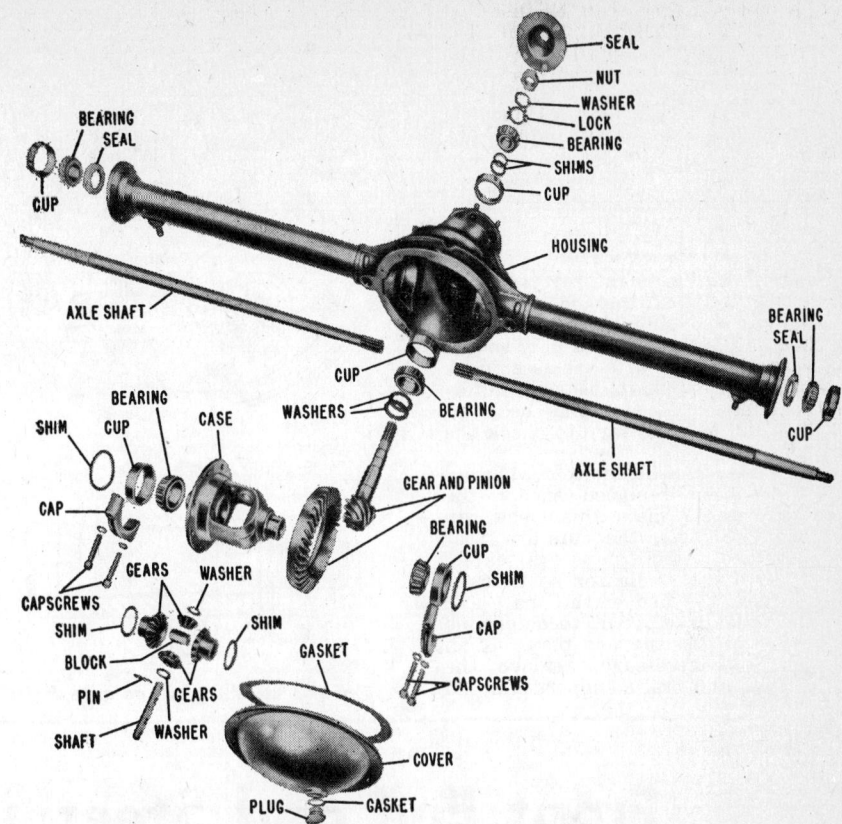

Fig. 3   Rear axle.   1953-57 Nash, 1953-61 Rambler and 1955-57 Hudson

that on the left side, shims are used between the differential case hub and the bearing to control ring gear and pinion backlash. The differential bearings are adjusted by means of the conventional type adjusting nut on the right side of the differential case.

Follow the procedure outlined in the *Rear Axle Chapter* for the assembly of the differential case, replacing the ring gear, checking ring and pinion backlash, and other differential case operations. However, when adjusting differential bearings, draw up the nut until there is no side movement in the bearings, then tighten the nut two more notches.

When checking backlash between the ring gear and pinion, the bearing cap must be tight and the differential bearings properly adjusted. Check the backlash in three or four places to secure an average and, if more than .007 inch, add shims; if less than .005 inch, remove shims.

AXLE SHAFTS

Removal, 1953-56 & Early 1957 Six

The rear wheel hub and drum are a one piece unit. The axle shaft is removed as follows:

1. Remove the wheel and use a puller to take off the hub and drum.
2. Block the brake pedal so it cannot be depressed and disconnect the

brake line from the wheel cylinder.
3. Remove the nuts and take off the outer oil seal, shims and brake support.
4. Pull out the axle shaft and bearing and inner oil seal with a suitable puller.

1957 Six (Late) & 1958-61

The hub and drum are separate units. The drum is attached to the hub by cap screws on V8s and by speed nuts on sixes. Also, the hub and axle shaft are serrated to mate and fit together on the taper. Both are punch marked to insure correct assembly, Fig. 3A. The axle shaft is removed as follows:

1. Remove the wheel and then remove the brake drum which is retained by cap screws on V8s and speed clips on Sixes.
2. Remove the hub with a suitable puller. *Do not use a knock-out type puller as damage to the wheel bearings or thrust block may result.*
3. Remove brake support plate, oil seal and shims.
4. Remove axle shaft with a puller

Service Caution

Do not use an original hub on a replacement axle shaft; use a new hub. A new hub may be installed on an original axle shaft providing the serrations on the shaft are not worn or damaged. Be certain that the hub and axle shaft are punch marked to insure proper alignment on installation. A replacement hub,

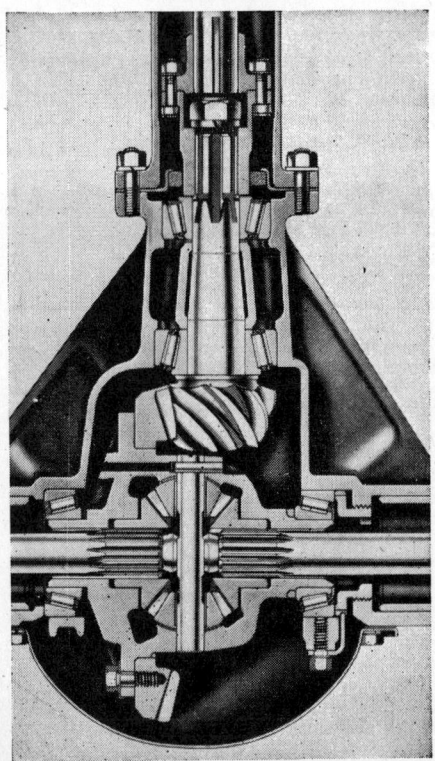

Fig. 2   1953-57 Ambassador rear axle

which is not serrated, can be installed and serrations will be cut in the hub when installed on the shaft due to the difference in hardness of the shaft and the hub.

When installing the hub onto the axle shaft tighten the axle nut to 150-200 lbs. ft. A measurement of $\frac{3}{16}''$ should exist between the face of the hub and the outer taper of the axle shaft, Fig. 3A.

Assembly

Replace the parts in the reverse order of their removal. If the old parts are replaced and the shims have not been disturbed, the axle shaft end play should be correct when the parts are assembled. However, if a new shaft, bearing, differential carrier or housing has been installed, it will be necessary to check the end play.

The end play can be checked when all parts have been replaced except the wheel and hub. To make this check, rap each axle shaft after the nuts are tight to be sure the bearing cups are seated. Then place a dial indicator so that its stem contacts the end of the shaft and work the shaft in and out to determine the amount of existing end play. If an adjustment is necessary, remove the outer oil seal and brake support and add

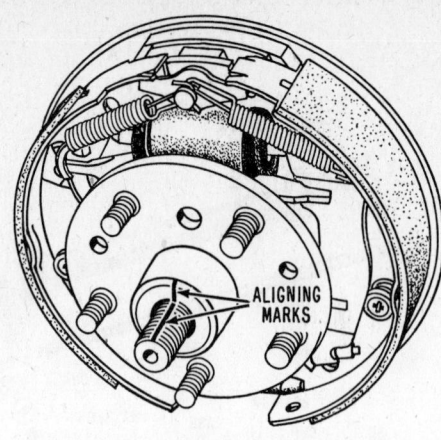

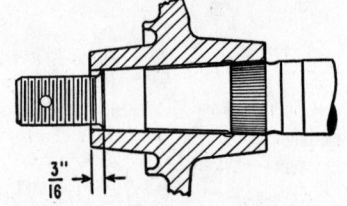

Fig. 3A Installing hub on axle shaft

or remove shims as required. When making this adjustment, an equal thickness of shims should be removed or added on each side of the axle housing to maintain a central position of the differential thrust block.

Service Note

The application of a bead of sealing material such as "Pliobond" or "Permatex" to the outer diameter of axle tube flange and the brake support contact area is recommended. Late production 1960 and 1961 models have a gasket installed at this location. On these models the sealing material will be used in addition to the gasket for improved sealing.

BRAKE MASTER CYLINDER, REPLACE

To remove the master cylinder, unhook the brake pedal return spring. Disconnect the master cylinder push rod from the brake pedal. Disconnect the brake lines from the connections on the master cylinder. Unfasten the cylinder from its mounting and remove from the car.

Install in the reverse order of removal and bleed the brake system.

Front End and Steering Section

CASTER & CAMBER

1953-55 Rambler & 1953-54 Statesman & Ambassador & 1958-60 American

Fig. 1. To adjust caster, loosen the nuts at the inner end of the lower control arm pivot bar mounting screws and insert additional spacer shims at either point "A" or "B" as required. Adding shims at "A" increases caster and adding them at "B" decreases caster.

To increase camber angle, add an equal number of shims at both points "A" and "B". To decrease camber, remove an equal number of shims.

1955 Hudson & Nash, 1956-61 Nash, Hudson & Rambler

To adjust caster on these models, loosen the lower control arm attaching bolt nut. This will permit turning the bolt and eccentric to provide the necessary adjustment.

TOE-IN, ADJUST

To adjust toe-in, loosen the clamps at both ends of the adjustable tubes on each tie rod. Turn the tubes an equal amount until the toe-in is correct. Turning the right tube in the direction the wheels revolve when the car is going forward increases the toe-in and turning the left tube in the opposite direction increases toe-in. To decrease toe-in turn the right tube backward and the left tube forward.

It is important that both tubes be turned an equal amount in order to maintain the correct position of the steering wheel. When adjustment is complete, tighten all clamp bolts.

Service Note

If a shimmy occurs at low speeds on a 1957 Series 10 or 30 or on a 1958 Series

Fig. 1 Showing caster and camber adjusting shims at the lower control arm pivot bar mounting. 1953-55 Rambler and 1958-61 American

20 or 80, a Teflon type thrust bearing kit is available for correction. The shimmy may result from chuck-hole contact or on driving over a rough railroad crossing. The parts in the kit replace the original upper control arm trunnion thrust ball bearing assembly. The Teflon bearing should be coated with a light film of chassis lubricant before installing it in between the two races.

Check wheel balance and alignment and correct any excessive looseness in the steering gear and front suspension parts when the kit is installed.

Service Note, Series 01, 10, 80

In performing service operations on the steering linkage or when adjusting toe-in, be sure to square the tie rod ball sockets on the studs and align the tie rod stud in the center, or slightly above center, of the cross tube opening, before tightening the steering linkage adjusting tube. This will prevent the stud from contacting the side of the cross tube opening, which would otherwise result in noise problems or damage.

FRONT END REPAIRS

In contrast to the conventional type knee action, this design, Fig. 2, has the springs located above the upper control arms and can be removed and replaced with the use of a special spring compressor. To do this, support the front end of the car with a stationary jack under the frame and place an adjustable jack under the suspension unit. Take off the wheel and lower the suspension so the spring is distended. Then install the special spring compressor on the coils of the spring Fig. 3, and compress the spring by means of the turnbuckle. When sufficiently compressed, lift the spring from its lower seat and take it out of its upper seat.

On Rambler models, the upper and lower control arms are interchangeable from right to left suspension units. However, the front and rear horizontal arms have been provided with a two-degree twist at the inner ends and are identified with a stamping "R" and "L". Therefore, when assembling either an upper or lower control arm, the front and rear horizontal arms must be installed in pairs, one stamped "R" and one stamped "L".

On all models except Rambler, only the upper control arms are interchangeable between sides.

Fig. 4 is a layout of the steering knuckle assembly. Prior to installing the knuckle pin into the upper control arm trunnion, the spring seat must be bolted to the trunnion. Then install the knuckle pin, turn it up tight, and loosen it one complete turn. This will prevent the end of the pin bottoming when the front wheels are turned.

When installing a steering knuckle pin into a lower control arm trunnion, a clearance of approximately ¼ in. must be provided between the upper edge of the seal seat and the trunnion.

HORN BUTTON

1953-61 With Full Horn Ring—The horn button or cap is rubber loaded and is removed by twisting it out the steering wheel hub.

1953-61 With Half Horn Ring—The horn button on these models is removed by twisting it out of the steering wheel hub.

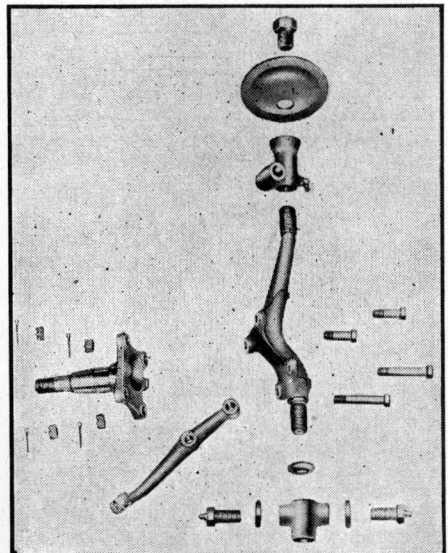

Fig. 4 Layout of steering knuckle and pin parts.

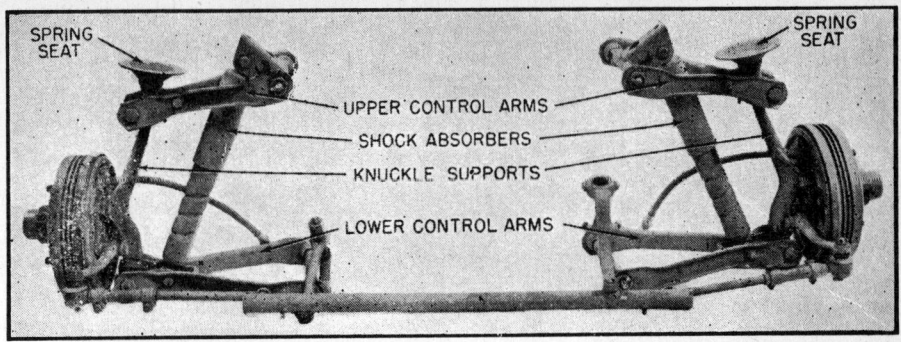

Fig. 2 1953-61 Rambler front suspension. Coil springs (not shown) act directly at steering knuckle supports. Control arms serve only for alignment purposes. Front suspension cross member is eliminated—suspension units are connected directly to body structure. Design typical of 1953-57 Statesman and Ambassador

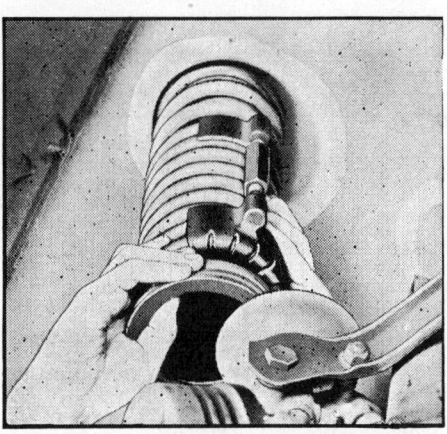

Fig. 3 Removing front spring with special spring compressor. 1953-56

STEERING GEAR, REPLACE

1953-57 Rambler & 1958-61 American

Pull off the steering wheel. Disconnect the pitman arm from the steering gear and the tie rod from the steering arm.

On 1953-55 and 1958-60 American, after raising front of car, drain the radiator and remove the radiator-to-water pump tube.

On 1956-57 models, support the engine at the front and remove front engine support crossmember.

Remove steering gear to body sill mounting bolts and remove the steering gear from the bottom without removing the jacket tube.

1958-61 (Except American)

The steering gear is removed from the bottom of the car on all series as follows:
1. Disconnect battery.
2. Remove steering wheel.
3. Remove toe board plate screws.
4. Loosen four lower-to-upper steering jacket tube screws.
5. On Series 10 and 20, remove pitman arm. Support engine at front and remove front engine support cross

member. Mark location of turning radius stop plate, then remove plate. Unfasten steering gear from its mounting and remove from under car.
6. On Series 80, remove left front wheel. Mark location of turning radius stop plate and remove plate. Remove pitman arm nut. Loosen steering gear housing attaching screws and then remove pitman arm with a puller. Remove left exhaust manifold. Remove power steering hose bracket at left front engine support. Support engine at front and remove left front engine support mounting bracket. Remove front cross member with stabilizer bar attached. Unfasten steering gear and lower to floor.

MANUAL STEERING GEAR REPAIRS

1958-61 (Except American) Disassemble, Fig. 5

1. Rotate steering worm until nut is in center of travel.
2. Remove sector shaft nut.
3. Use puller to remove pitman arm.
4. Remove side cover screws and remove side cover and sector shaft from housing.
5. To remove side cover from sector shaft, turn adjuster screw in end of sector shaft down through cover.
6. Remove screws and take out end cover with worm bearing, outer race and thrust washer.
7. To remove lower worm bearing, outer race and thrust washer from cover, loosen worm bearing adjuster screw lock nut and turn screw in through cover.
8. Grasp lower end of steering worm and draw steering shaft and nut out of steering housing. *Be sure to keep shaft in horizontal position so that nut does not move against stops at any time, causing damage to ball return mechanism. Disassembly of worm nut is not recommended.*

Assemble

1. Install worm shaft and nut assembly

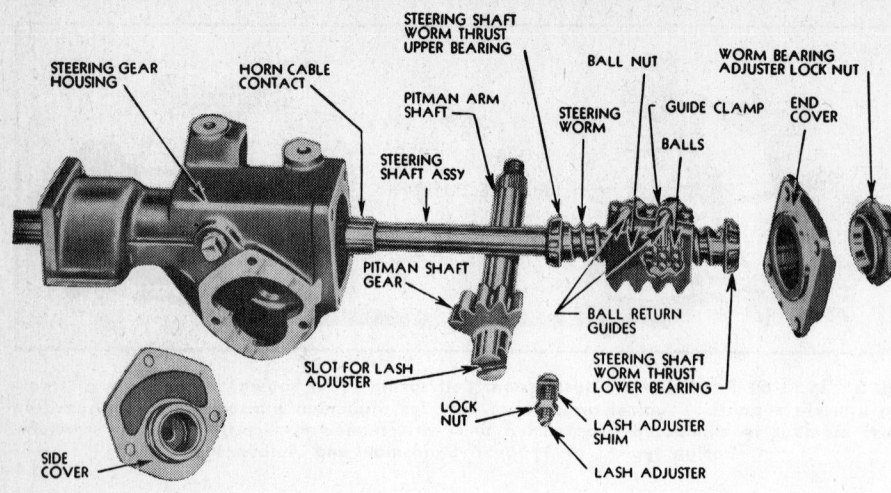

Fig. 5 Steering gear (typical). 1958-61 (Except American)

in gear housing, keeping ball nut away from stops on worm.

2. Install worm bearing adjusting screw with lower worm bearing, outer race and thrust washer in end cover.

3. Install end cover and attaching parts on gear housing, making sure bearings seat properly.

4. Tighten worm bearing adjusting screw until a slight drag is felt on bearings. Do not tighten lock nut.

5. Install pitman arm.

6. Install sector shaft and adjusting screw inside cover.

7. Rotate steering column until ball nut is in center of travel so that center tooth on sector shaft will enter space on nut.

8. Install side cover and sector shaft in gear housing.

9. Tighten sector shaft adjusting screw until a slight drag is felt on bearing but do not tighten lock nut.

10. After steering gear is installed in car, adjust as outlined below:

Adjustments

1. Disconnect steering relay rod from pitman arm.

2. Loosen sector shaft lash adjuster screw a few turns to relieve load from bearings.

3. Turn steering wheel in one direction until stopped by gear, then back away about one turn.

4. With a spring scale hooked to rim of steering wheel, measure pull required to keep wheel in motion; this should be ¼ to ¾ lb. If not within these limits, adjust worm bearings as follows:

5. Loosen worm bearing adjuster lock nut and turn adjuster until there is no perceptible end play in worm. Check pull at wheel rim, readjusting as required to obtain proper pull. Tighten lock nut and recheck pull.

6. After worm bearing adjustment is completed and all mounting bolts tightened, adjust sector shaft end play.

7. With steering wheel in straight-ahead position, turn lash adjuster screw clockwise to remove all lash and tighten lock nut.

8. Check pull at rim of steering wheel, taking highest reading on scale as wheel is turned through the central or straight-ahead position. This should be between ⅞ and 1½ lbs. *If more than 1½ lb., turn lash adjuster screw counterclockwise, then come up on the adjustment in a clockwise motion.*

9. Tighten lock nut and recheck pull.

1953-57

In this type steering gear, Fig. 6, the worm is integral with the steering shaft and is supported on each end by opposed tapered roller bearings. The triple tooth roller is attached to the roller shaft by means of a steel shaft. Two needle bearing assemblies are installed between this shaft and the roller. (Some models have a two tooth roller shaft).

The roller shaft is mounted in the steering gear housing on two needle bearing assemblies which are pressed into the housing. The housing cover is attached to the housing by four cap screws. An adjustment screw, mounted in the cover, controls roller shaft end play and worm and roller mesh adjustment.

The steering wheel and roller shaft arm (pitman arm) are splined to the steering shaft and roller shaft respectively. Both the pitman arm and steering wheel have master splines to insure correct installation.

Worm End Play, Adjust

1. Free the steering gear of all load by disconnecting the drag link and loosening the steering column braces.

2. Loosen four cover screws about ⅛".

3. Use a knife to separate the top shim, passing the blade all the way around between the shims, being careful not to damage the remaining shims.

4. Remove one shim at a time between inspections to remove the end play.

5. The adjustment is correct when there is no end play and no stiffness in the steering gear throughout the complete range of its travel.

Roller Shaft End Play, Adjust

1. Turn the steering gear to either extreme and back off ⅛ of a turn.

2. Gripping the pitman arm at the hub, the roller shaft should rotate freely without a particle of end play.

3. If end play exists, adjust as required by means of the roller shaft adjusting screw in the side cover.

4. Be sure to tighten the lock nut securely and inspect for end play and free rotation throughout the entire range of steering gear travel.

Worm & Roller Mesh, Adjust

1. Loosen the roller shaft adjusting screw lock nut.

2. With the steering gear in its central position (drag link disconnected) tighten the roller shaft adjusting screw just enough to remove play between the roller shaft roller tooth and worm.

3. Check this by the amount of play felt at the pitman arm. It is better to leave a slight amount of play at this point than to tighten too much.

4. If tightened beyond the point where the lash is removed, serious results will occur which will cause poor steering operation.

5. Tighten the adjusting screw lock nut.

POWER STEERING

On Car Adjustments

Adjustment of belt tension and bleeding of the system are the only two "on the ear" adjustments which can be made.

Belt Tension

Adjust the belt so it does not deflect more than ¼". This is done by loosening the belt pivot and adjusting bolts on the pump mounting bracket to allow movement of the bracket in its adjusting slot.

Bleeding Systems

To bleed the system, raise front wheels and run engine at idling speed until normal operating temperatures are obtained. Then accelerate the engine and turn front wheels to right and left several times until bubbles in reservoir disappear. *Do not hold wheels against stops.* Always recheck and replenish fluid in reservoir after bleeding.

Fluid Pressure Test

A fluid pressure test will show whether the pump or some other unit in the power steering system is causing trouble. Connect an oil pressure gauge in the main oil line at the control valve assembly. Start the engine and allow the oil to circulate for several minutes to warm the oil.

1. Turn the wheels against the curbing or other obstacle and hold tension on the wheel. The oil pressure should be 500-800 psi on 1956-57 models, 650-900 psi on 1958-59 models, 800-900 psi on 1960-61 models with Roll type pump and 850-950 psi on 1960-61 models with Slipper type pump.

2. Turn the wheel in the opposite

direction and note the reading. If there is a variation between the left and right turns, internal leakage is evident. If the pressure is low, stop the engine and disconnect the gauge from the valve and cap the pressure line.

3. Restart the engine and note the reading. If the pump is operating properly the pressures will be as noted in Step 1. If the pressure is low the pump belt or fan belt may be slipping. With belt tension correct and there is low pressure, the trouble exists in the pump. *Do not run the last check for a period longer than is necessary to obtain a steady pressure reading.*

Pump Removal

Remove the fan belt and place a suitable container under the pump. Disconnect the pressure and return hoses, capping the outlets to prevent loss of oil in the power steering unit. Unfasten and remove pump from engine.

Pump, Install

Position the pump on the engine and install and tighten the bolts securely. Connect the pressure and return hoses, taking care to tighten the pressure hose evenly when forcing the outlet fitting into place. Tighten the drive belt so that not more than ¼" deflection exists. Fill the reservoir to the bottom edge of the filler neck and bleed the system as described earlier.

Power Cylinder Removal

1. Disconnect the oil hoses, the piston rod from the side sill bracket, and the tie rods from the cylinder and valve assembly.
2. Remove the pitman arm stud nut and roll pin, washer, cushions and spacers.
3. Remove the cylinder and valve assembly from the pitman arm stud.

Power Cylinder, Install

1. Install the valve housing end of cylinder on the pitman arm.
2. Tighten the inner nut on the stud until there is sufficient tension on the rubber cushions to prevent rattles and grease leakage and still permit free movement of the stud. *Overtightening the stud will cause poor recovery from turns and binding when steering. Looseness may result in shimmy.*

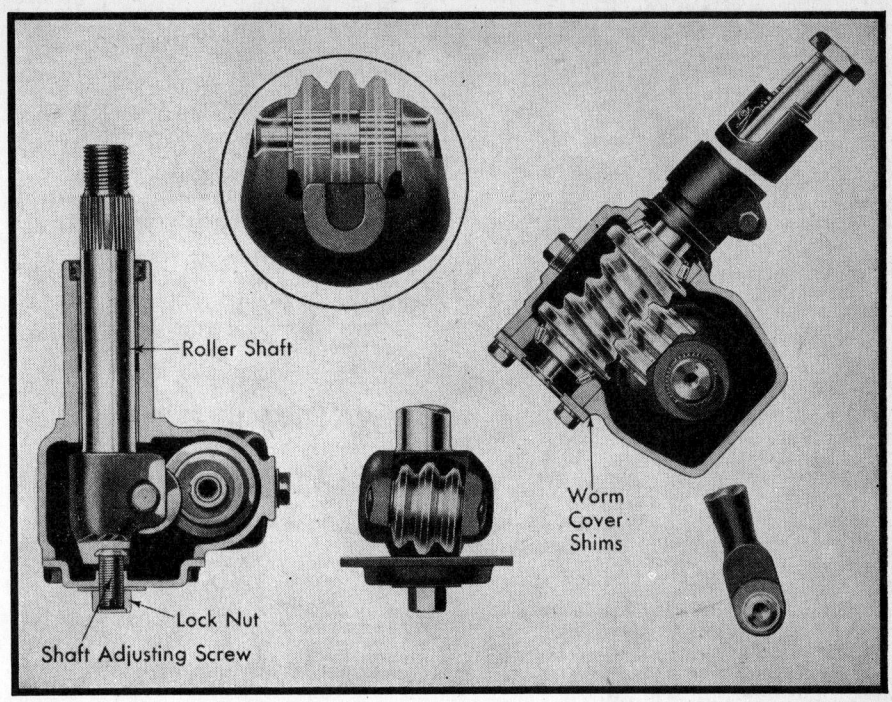

Fig. 6   Steering gear adjustments.   1953-57

3. When the stud nut is correctly adjusted, the locking roll pin should be installed.
4. After the cylinder has been installed in the car, and the hoses connected, fill the pump reservoir and bleed the system as outlined previously.

Control Valve, 1956-58

If the control valve has been disassembled the centering adjustment is made as follows:

The screw plug in the valve housing may be turned in or out 1/6 of a turn at a time, road testing after each adjustment. The plug should not be adjusted more than ½ turn in either direction. If the adjustment can not be made with a ½ turn, the cylinder and valve should be replaced.

Turn the plug *IN* if:
Left turn is too hard
Right turn is too easy
Poor recovery from right turns, but good recovery from left turns
Car wanders to the right

Turn the plug *OUT* if:
Right turn is too hard

Left turn is too easy
Poor recovery from left turns, good recovery from right turns
Car wanders to the left

Control Valve, 1959-61

If necessary to adjust the valve spool assembly for correct centering, turn piston rod end plug *OUT* and turn pitman arm end plug *IN* the same amount about ½ turn at a time for the following conditions:

Left turn is to hard
Right turn is too easy
Poor recovery from right turns, but good recovery from left turns
Car wanders to the right

Turn pitman arm end plug *OUT* and piston rod end plug *IN* the same amount about ½ turn at a time for the following conditions:

Right turn is too hard
Left turn is too easy
Poor recovery from left turns, but good recovery from right turns
Car wanders to the left

After final adjustment, tighten end plugs securely to 50 ft. lbs.

Speedometer, Radio & Windshield Wiper

SPEEDOMETER

1953-55 Series 40, 60; 1956-57 All; 1958-61 Series 10, 20, 80

To remove the speedometer, take off battery ground strap as a precaution against a short circuit. Disconnect speedometer cable at speedometer. Remove speedometer and housing assembly from rear of instrument panel. The speedometer head can then be removed.

1953-55 Rambler; 1958-61 American

Disconnect wiring and speedometer cable from rear of instrument cluster. Then remove three "L" shaped brackets retaining cluster to rear of panel. The speedometer head can then be removed from the instrument cluster by unfastening the lens bezel and removing lens and two screws.

RADIO

1953-55 Series 40-60

1. Disconnect battery.
2. Remove radio control knobs and mounting nuts from shaft.
3. Remove glove box and glove box mounting panel.
4. Disconnect all wires.
5. Remove heater, air conditioning and defroster control knob and shaft from switch; then remove switch.
6. Loosen nuts on both sides of radio. This will permit studs on radio chassis to be lowered in the slots of the brackets and removal of radio.

1953-55 Rambler

1. Disconnect battery.
2. Remove heater switch and light switch mounting bracket.
3. Remove radio knobs and two retaining nuts located behind knobs.
4. Disconnect radio wire to battery at light switch.
5. Remove antenna lead.
6. Remove two screws at sides of radio and remove radio and speaker from under dash.

1956-57 Rambler

1. Disconnect battery.
2. Disconnect radio at fuse.
3. Disconnect antenna lead.
4. Remove radio knobs and shaft mounting nuts.

5. Remove radio mounting bolts and take radio out from under dash.

1958-61 American

1. Unfasten instrument switch panel from lower panel (2 screws).
2. Pull radio knobs off shafts.
3. Remove dial indicator pointer.
4. Disconnect radio power lead at fuse case and the antenna from right side of radio.
5. Remove nuts from radio control shafts.
6. Move radio toward front of car away from instrument panel, and remove.

WINDSHIELD WIPER

1953-55 Rambler; 1958-61 American

1. To remove the wiper motor, unhook the link to the motor retainer and remove link.
2. Release motor from mounting bracket (2 screws) and remove hose.
3. Loosen screw and lift control cable and conduit from motor control valve.
4. *When connecting the cable and conduit to the motor and valve, the conduit must not protrude beyond its mounting to allow for full travel of wire and valve.*

1956-61 Rambler

1. To remove wiper motor, first open heater control valve and drain about two quarts of fluid from radiator to lower coolant level.
2. Remove heater core.
3. Remove rain baffle below motor to make motor mounting screws accessible.
4. Remove link to motor retainer clips and link.
5. Disconnect control conduit and vacuum tube from motor and remove motor attaching screws.
6. *When installing motor, control cable must be checked to insure full travel of valve to open and closed position.*

1955-57 Hudson & Nash

1. To remove wiper motor, disconnect hose from motor.
2. Remove motor access hole cover located under hood in center of cowl top air intake chamber.
3. Disconnect link retainers from wiper motor pivot arms.
4. Slide pivot body links off motor pivot arm studs.
5. Unfasten and remove wiper motor.
6. Disconnect cable and conduit from motor.
7. Upon installation, the motor must be in the "off" position and the left pivot shaft body to motor link must be installed onto the *bottom* stud of the motor pivot arm.

STUDEBAKER

INDEX OF SERVICE OPERATIONS

PAGE NO.

ACCESSORIES
Speedometer Removal 1109
Windshield Wiper 1109
Windshield Wiper Troubles 37

BODY
Air Conditioning 177
Automatic Seat Adjuster Troubles 36
Automatic Top Troubles 36
Automatic Window Lift Troubles 36

BRAKES (Mechanical)
Adjustments 112
Brake Cylinder Sizes 1080
Hydraulic Brake System 112
Master Cylinder, Replace 1104
Trouble Shooting 31

BRAKES (Power)
Power Unit, Replace 1104
Power Unit Repairs 128
Trouble Shooting 32

CLUTCH
Clutch Pedal, Adjust 1095
Clutch, Replace 1095
Trouble Shooting 13

COOLING SYSTEM
Radiator, Replace 1090
Trouble Shooting 8
Water Pump Repairs 1090

ELECTRIC SYSTEM
Dash Gauge Service 85
Distributor, Replace 1091
Distributor Service 46
Distributor Specifications 1079
Generator & Regulator Service 62
Generator & Regulator Specs. 1079
Horn Button or Ring, Replace....... 1106
Ignition System Service 46
Ignition Timing 1091
Starter, Replace 1092
Starter Switch Service 83
Starting Motor Service 77
Starting Motor Specifications........ 1080
Trouble Shooting 10
Turn Signal Troubles 12

ENGINE
Camshaft, Replace 1088
Crankshaft & Bearing Specs. 1078
Crankshaft Oil Seal, Replace 1089
Cylinder Head, Replace 1083
Engine, Replace 1082
Main Bearings, Replace 1089
Piston Pins, Replace 1088
Piston Rings, Replace 1088
Piston, Pin & Ring Specs. 1078
Pistons & Rods, Remove 1088
Piston & Rod, Assemble 1088
Pistons, Replace 1088
Rocker Arms 1084
Rod Bearings, Replace 1089
Timing Cover, Replace 1087
Timing Gears, Replace 1087
Trouble Shooting 4
Valves, Adjust 1084
Valve Arrangement 1084
Valves, Grind 1087
Valve Guides 1086
Valve Lifters 1087
Valves, Remove 1085
Valve Spring Installed Height 1086
Valve Spring Testing 1086
Valve Specifications 1077

ENGINE OILING
Oil Pan, Replace 1089
Oil Pump Repairs 1090
Trouble Shooting 9

FRONT SUSPENSION
Camber, Adjust 1104
Caster, Adjust 1104
Front End Repairs 1104
Toe-in, Adjust 1104
Trouble Shooting 33
Wheel Alignment Specifications 1080

FUEL & EXHAUST SYSTEM
Carburetors 1092
Fuel Pumps 96
Supercharger 1091
Trouble Shooting 4

OVERDRIVE 100
Trouble Shooting 14

REAR AXLE
Axle Shaft, Replace 1104
General Service 102
Non-Slip Differentials 109
Rear Axle Repairs 1103
Rear Axle Assembly, Replace......... 1102
Rear Axle Specifications 1080
Trouble Shooting 31

SPECIFICATIONS
Brake Cylinder Sizes 1080
Capacity Data 1078
Carburetors 1093
Cooling System 1078
Crankshaft & Bearings 1078
Distributors 1079
Engine Tightening 1078
Generator & Regulators 1079
Pistons, Pins & Rings 1078
Rear Axle 1080
Starting Motors 1080
Tune Up 1077
Valve Timing 1087
Valves 1077
Wheel Alignment 1050

STEERING GEARS (Mechanical)
Horn Button or Ring, Replace 1106
Steering Gear Service (Ross)........ 1107
Steering Gear Service (Saginaw)...... 1107
Steering Gear, Replace 1106
Steering Wheel, Replace........... 1106
Trouble Shooting 33

STEERING GEARS (Power)
Steering Gear, Repairs 145
Steering Gear, Replace 1109
Trouble Shooting 34

TRANSMISSIONS (Manual Shift)
Gearshift, Adjust 1098
Transmission, Repairs 1096
Transmission, Replace 1095
Trouble Shooting 14

TRANSMISSIONS (Automatic)
Borg-Warner Automatic Drive—
Linkage, Adjust 1098
Transmission, Replace 1100
Transmission Repairs 179
Trouble Shooting 29
Flightomatic Repairs 240
Linkage, Adjust 1101
Replace 1102
Trouble Shooting 24

TUNE UP 38

GENERAL SPECIFICATIONS

Year	Model Designation	Wheelbase, Inches	Valve Location	Bore and Stroke	Piston Displacement, Cubic Inches	Compression Ratio (Standard)	Maximum Brake H.P. @ R.P.M.	Maximum Torque Lbs. Ft. @ R.P.M.	Normal Oil Pressure Pounds
1953	Champion 6............14G	(2)	In Block	3.0000 x 4.000	169.6	(3)	85 @ 4000	138 @ 2400	40
	Commander V8.........4H	(2)	In Head	3.3750 x 3.250	232.6	7.00	120 @ 4000	190 @ 2000	40
1954	Champion 6............15G	(2)	In Block	3.0000 x 4.000	169.6	7.50	85 @ 4000	138 @ 2400	40
	Commander V8.........5H	(2)	In Head	3.3750 x 3.250	232.6	7.50	127 @ 4000	202 @ 2000	40
1955	Champion 6............16G6	(2)	In Block	3.0000 x 4.375	185.6	7.50	101 @ 4000	152 @ 1800	40
	Commander V8(4).......16G8	(2)	In Head	3.5625 x 2.812	224.3	7.50	140 @ 4500	202 @ 2800	40
	Commander V8(5).......16G8	(2)	In Head	3.5625 x 3.250	259.2	7.50	162 @ 4500	250 @ 2800	40
	President V8(4).........6H	120½	In Head	3.5625 x 3.250	259.2	7.50	175 @ 4500	250 @ 3000	40
	President V8(5).........6H	120½	In Head	3.5625 x 3.250	259.2	7.50	185 @ 4500	258 @ 2800	40
1956	Commander V8.........56B	116½	In Head	3.5625 x 3.250	259	7.80	170 @ 4500	260 @ 2800	40
	Power Hawk V8........56B	120½	In Head	3.5625 x 3.250	259	7.80	170 @ 4500	260 @ 2800	40
	Parkview V8...........56B	116½	In Head	3.5625 x 3.250	259	7.80	170 @ 4500	260 @ 2800	40
	Champion 6............56G	116½	In Block	3.0000 x 4.375	185	7.50	101 @ 4000	152 @ 1800	40
	Flight Hawk 6.........56G	120½	In Block	3.0000 x 4.375	185	7.50	101 @ 4000	152 @ 1800	40
	Pelham 6..............56G	116½	In Block	3.0000 x 4.375	185	7.50	101 @ 4000	152 @ 1800	40
	President V8...........56H	116½	In Head	3.5625 x 3.625	289	7.80	195 @ 4500	286 @ 2800	40
	Classic V8.............56H	120½	In Head	3.5625 x 3.625	289	7.80	195 @ 4500	286 @ 2800	40
	Sky Hawk V8..........56H	120½	In Head	3.5625 x 3.625	289	7.80	195 @ 4500	296 @ 2800	40
	Pinehurst V8...........56H	116½	In Head	3.5625 x 3.625	289	7.80	195 @ 4500	286 @ 2800	40
	Golden Hawk V8.......56J	120½	In Head	4.0000 x 3.500	352	9.50	275 @ 4600	380 @ 2800	45
1957	Scotsman 6............57G	116½	In Block	3.0000 x 4.375	185	7.8	101 @ 4000	152 @ 1800	40
	Champion 6............57G	116½	In Block	3.0000 x 4.375	185	7.8	101 @ 4000	152 @ 1800	40
	Commander V8.........57B	116½	In Head	3.5625 x 3.250	259	8.0	180 @ 4500	260 @ 2800	40
	President V8...........57H	116½(6)	In Head	3.5625 x 3.625	289	8.0	210 @ 4500	300 @ 2800	40
	Silver Hawk 6.........57G	120½	In Block	3.0000 x 4.375	185	7.8	101 @ 4000	152 @ 1800	40
	Silver Hawk V8........57H	120½	In Head	3.5625 x 3.625	289	8.0	210 @ 4500	300 @ 2800	40
	Golden Hawk V8.......57H	120½	In Head	3.5625 x 3.625	289	7.5	275 @ 4500	333 @ 3200	40
1958	Scotsman 6............58G	116½	In Block	3.0000 x 4.375	185	7.8	101 @ 4000	152 @ 1800	40
	Champion 6............58G	116½	In Block	3.0000 x 4.375	185	7.8	101 @ 4000	152 @ 1800	40
	Commander V8.........58B	116½	In Head	3.5625 x 3.250	259	8.3	180 @ 4500	260 @ 2800	40
	President V8...........58H	120½(1)	In Head	3.5625 x 3.625	289	8.3	225 @ 4500	305 @ 3000	40
	Silver Hawk 6.........58G	120½	In Block	3.0000 x 4.375	185	7.8	101 @ 4000	152 @ 1800	40
	Silver Hawk V8........58H	120½	In Head	3.5625 x 3.625	289	8.3	210 @ 4500	300 @ 2800	40
	Golden Hawk V8.......58H	120½	In Head	3.5625 x 3.625	289	7.8	275 @ 4500	333 @ 3200	40
1959	Lark 6................59S	(7)	In Block	3.0000 x 4.000	170	8.3	90 @ 4000	145 @ 2000	40
	Lark V8...............59V	(7)	In Head	3.5625 x 3.250	259	8.8	180 @ 4500	260 @ 2800	40
	Hawk 6................59S	120½	In Block	3.0000 x 4.000	170	8.3	90 @ 4000	145 @ 2000	40
	Hawk V8..............59V	120½	In Head	3.5625 x 3.250	259	8.8	180 @ 4500	260 @ 2800	40
1960	Lark 6................60S	(7)	In Block	3.0000 x 4.000	170	8.3	90 @ 4000	145 @ 2000	Normal
	Lark V8...............60V	(7)	In Head	3.5625 x 3.250	259	8.8	180 @ 4500	260 @ 2800	Oil
	Hawk 6................60S	(7)	In Block	3.0000 x 4.000	170	8.3	90 @ 4000	145 @ 2000	Pressure
	Hawk V8..............60V	120½	In Head	3.5625 x 3.625	289	8.8	210 @ 4500	300 @ 2800	Pounds
1961	Lark 6................61S	(7)	In Head	3.0000 x 4.000	170	8.5	112 @ 4500	154 @ 2000	40
	Lark 8................61V	(7)	In Head	3.5625 x 3.250	259	8.8	180 @ 4500	260 @ 2800	40
	Hawk 8................61V	120½	In Head	3.5625 x 3.625	289	8.8	210 @ 4500	300 @ 2800	40

(1)—Station Wagon 116½".
(2)—Two and four door sedans 116½", coupes and hardtop convertibles 120½", 1953-54 Land Cruiser 120½".
(3)—With synchromesh transmission 7.0-1, with Automatic Drive 7.5-1.
(4)—Prior to Jan. 3, 1955.
(5)—Starting with Jan. 3, 1955.
(6)—Classic 120½.
(7)—Sedans 108½", Station Wagons 113'.

TUNE UP SPECIFICATIONS

★Disconnect vacuum line when using timing light to set timing.

Year	Model	Ground Polarity and Voltage	Spark Plug Type [2]	Spark Plug Gap Inch	Distributor Point Gap Inch	Distributor Cam Angle Degrees	Firing Order [1]	Ignition Timing★ Mark	Ignition Timing★ Location	Idle Speed RPM In Neutral	Compression Pressure @ Cranking Speed Minimum
1953	Champion	P-6	J7	.030	.020	39	153624	IGN	Damper	550	120
	Commander	P-6	H14Y	.035	.013	28–34	18436572	IGN	Damper	550	120
1954	Champion	P-6	J7	.030	.020	39	153624	IGN	Damper	550	120
	Commander	P-6	H14Y	.035	.013	28–34	18436572	IGN	Damper	550	120
1955	Six	P-6	J7	.030	.020	39	153624	IGN	Damper	550	130
	V8	P-6	H14Y	.035	.013	28–34	18436572	IGN	Damper	550	130
1956	Six	N-12	J7	.030	.020	39	153624	IGN	Damper	550	130
	Stude. V8	N-12	H14Y	.035	.016	26–33	18436572	IGN	Damper	550	130
	Pack. V8	N-12	N8-67B	.035	.017	31	18436572	IGN	Damper	400[3]	150
1957–58	Six	N-12	J7	.030	.020	39	153624	IGN	Damper	550	130
	V8 (Ex. G. H.)	N-12	H14Y	.035	.016	26–33	18436572	IGN	Damper	550	130
	Gold. Hawk	N-12	H14Y	.035	.016	26–33	18436572	IGN	Damper	550	130
1959–60	Six	N-12	J7	.030	.020	39	153624	IGN	Damper	550	130
	V8	N-12	H14Y	.035	.016	28–34	18436572	IGN	Damper	550	130
1961	Six	N-12	H14Y	.035	.020	37–41	153624	IGN	Damper	550	140
	V8	N-12	H14Y	.035	.016	28–32	18436572	IGN	Damper	550	140

①—V8 cylinder numbering (front to rear): Left bank 1-3-5-7, right bank 2-4-6-8.
②—Champion.
③—Set with transmission in Drive.

VALVE SPECIFICATIONS

Year	Model	Valve Lash Int.	Valve Lash Exh.	Valve Angles Seat	Valve Angles Face	Valve Spring Installed Height	Valve Spring Pressure Lbs. @ In.	Valve Lift Int.	Valve Lift Exh.	Stem Clearance Intake	Stem Clearance Exhaust	Stem Diameter Int.	Stem Diameter Exh.
1953	Champ.	.016C	.016C	45	45	1²¹/₃₂	98 @ 1⁵/₁₆	.3437	.3437	.0015–.0035	.0015–.0035	.3125	.3125
	Com.	.024C	.024C	45	45	2¹/₃₂	110 @ 1⁴³/₆₄	.3593	.3593	.0015–.0035	.0015–.0035	.3437	.3437
1954	Champ.	.016C	.016C	45	45	1²¹/₃₂	98 @ 1⁵/₁₆	.3437	.3437	.0015–.0035	.0015–.0035	.3125	.3125
	Com.	.024C	.024C	45	45	2¹/₃₂	110 @ 1⁴³/₆₄	.3593	.3593	.0015–.0035	.0015–.0035	.3437	.3437
1955	Champ.	.016C	.016C	45	45	1²¹/₃₂	98 @ 1⁵/₁₆	.3437	.3437	.0015–.0035	.0015–.0035	.3125	.3125
	Com.	.026C	.026C	45	45	2¹/₃₂	110 @ 1⁴³/₆₄	.3593	.3593	.0015–.0035	.0015–.0035	.3437	.3437
	Pres.	.026C	.026C	45	45	2¹/₃₂	110 @ 1⁴³/₆₄	.3593	.3593	.0015–.0035	.0015–.0035	.3437	.3437
1956	Six	.016C	.016C	45	45	1²¹/₃₂	98 @ 1⁵/₁₆	.3437	.3437	.0015–.0035	.0015–.0035	.3125	.3125
	V8-289	.026C	.026C	45	45	2¹/₃₂	110 @ 1⁴³/₆₄	.3593	.3593	.0015–.0035	.0015–.0035	.3437	.3437
	V8-352	Zero	Zero	①	①	1³/₄	180 @ 1³/₈	.398	.388	.001–.002	.002–.003	.3725	.3715
1957	Six	.016C	.016C	45	45	1²¹/₃₂	98 @ 1⁵/₁₆	.3437	.3437	.0015–.0035	.0015–.0035	.3125	.3125
	V8	.026C	.026C	45	45	2¹/₃₂	110 @ 1⁴³/₆₄	.3593	.3593	.0015–.0035	.0015–.0035	.3437	.3437
1958	Six	.016C	.016C	45	45	1²¹/₃₂	98 @ 1⁵/₁₆	.3437	.3437	.0015–.0035	.0015–.0035	.3125	.3125
	V8	.026C	.026C	45	45	2¹/₃₂	110 @ 1⁴³/₆₄	.3593	.3593	.0015–.0035	.0015–.0035	.3437	.3437
1959	Six	.018C[2]	.018C[2]	45	45	1²¹/₃₂	98 @ 1⁵/₁₆	.3437	.3437	.0015–.0035	.0015–.0035	.3125	.3125
	V8	.026C	.026C	45	45	2¹/₃₂	110 @ 1⁴³/₆₄	.3593	.3593	.0015–.0035	.0015–.0035	.3437	.3437
1960	Six	.018C	.018C	45	45	1²¹/₃₂	98 @ 1⁵/₁₆	.3437	.3437	.0015–.0035	.0015–.0035	.3125	.3125
	V8	.026C	.026C	45	45	2¹/₃₂	110 @ 1⁴³/₆₄	.3593	.3593	.0015–.0035	.0015–.0035	.3437	.3437
1961	Six	.026C	.026C	45	45	2¹/₃₂	110 @ 1⁴³/₆₄	.3593	.3593	.0015–.0035	.0015–.0035	.3415	.3415
	V8	.026C	.026C	45	45	2¹/₃₂	110 @ 1⁴³/₆₄	.3594	.3594	.0015–.0035	.0015–.0035	.3437	.3437

①—Intake 29°, exhaust 44.5°.   ②—Disregard early valve covers marked ".016 cold".

STUDEBAKER

PISTONS, PINS, RINGS, CRANKSHAFT & BEARINGS

Year	Model	Fitting Pistons		Ring End Gap ①		Wrist-pin Diameter	Rod Bearings		Main Bearings			
		Shim To Use ②	Pounds Pull On Scale	Comp.	Oil		Shaft Diameter	Bearing Clearance	Shaft Diameter	Bearing Clearance	Thrust on Bear. No.	Shaft End Play
1953-54	Champ.	.002	11-16	.007	.007	.7493	1.812-1.813	.0005-.002	2.437-2.4375	.0005-.0025	③	.003-.006
	Comm.	.002	11-16	.008	.008	.8743	1.999-2.000	.0005-.002	2.4995-2.500	.0006-.0027	③	.003-.006
1955	Six	.002	11-16	.007	.007	.7493	1.812-1.813	.0005-.002	3.0623-3.0628	.0005-.0025	③	.003-.006
	V8	.002	11-16	.008	.008	.8743	1.999-2.000	.0005-.002	2.4995-2.500	.0005-.0025	③	.003-.006
1956-58	Six	.002	11-16	.007	.007	.7493	1.812-1.813	.0005-.002	3.0623-3.0628	.0005-.0025	③	.003-.006
	Stude. V8	.002	8-13	.008	.008	.8743	1.999-2.000	.0005-.002	2.4995-2.500	.0005-.0025	③	.003-.006
1959-61	Six	.002	11-16	.007	.007	.7493	1.812-1.813	.0005-.002	3.0623-3.0628	.0005-.0025	③	.003-.006
	V8	.002	8-13	.008	.008	.8743	1.999-2.000	.0005-.002	2.4995-2.5000	.0005-.0025	③	.003-.006

①—Fit rings in tapered bores for clearance listed in tightest portion of ring travel.
②—Feeler gauge one inch wide.　③—Controlled by shims at front main bearing.

ENGINE TIGHTENING SPECIFICATIONS★

★Torque specifications are for clean and lightly lubricated threads only. Dry or dirty threads produce increased friction which prevents accurate measurement of tightness.

Year	Spark Plugs Ft. Lbs.	Cylinder Head Bolts Ft. Lbs.	Intake Manifold Ft. Lbs.	Exhaust Manifold Ft. Lbs.	Rocker Arm Shaft Bracket Ft. Lbs.	Rocker Arm Cover Ft. Lbs.	Connecting Rod Cap Bolts Ft. Lbs.	Main Bearing Cap Bolts Ft. Lbs.	Flywheel to Crankshaft Ft. Lbs.	Vibration Damper or Pulley Ft. Lbs.
1953-60 Six	25-30	46-50	25-30	25-30	None	None	28-32	85-95	33-35	130-140
1953-55 V8	25-30	46-50	25-30	25-30	13-17	8-10①	52-54	85-95	33-35	130-140
1956-61 V8-259	25-30	55-65	26-30	25-30	13-17	②	52-54	85-95	33-35	130-140
1956-61 V8-289	25-30	55-65	26-30	25-30	13-17	②	52-54	85-95	33-35	130-140
1956 V8-352	26-30	55-60	26-30	25-30	55-60	25-30①	40-45	90-95	55-60	140-150
1961 Six	25-30	46-50	25-30	25-30	13-17	20 In. Lb.	28-32	85-95	33-35	130-140

①—Inch Lbs.　②—1956-59 and 1960 up to Serial No. 60V-13000, 8-10 inch lbs.; Beginning with Serial No. 60V-13001, 20 inch lbs.

COOLING SYSTEM & CAPACITY DATA

Year	Model	Cooling System Data			Thermostat Opening Temp.		Fuel Tank Gals.	Engine Oil			Transmissions			Rear Axle Pints
		Quarts No Heater	Quarts With Heater	Rad. Cap Relief Pressure	①	②		Refill Qts.⑧	Summer Grade	Winter Grade	Std. Pints	With Over-drive Pints	Auto-matic Qts.	
1953-54	Champ.	10	11½	7	180	155	18	5	30	10W	1.6	2¾	9½	2½
	Com.	17½	19	7	180	160	18	6	30	10W	2.4	3.4	9½	3
1955	Champ.	10	11½	13	180	155	18	5	30	10W	1½	2¾	9½	2½
	Com.	17¼	18¾	13	180	160	18	6	30	10W	2.4	3.4	9½	2½⑤
	Pres.	17¼	18¾	13	180	160	18	6	30	10W	2.4	3.4	9½	3
1956-58	Six	11	12½	13	180	170	18	5	30	10W	1.6	2¾	9	2½
	V8	17	18½	13	180	170	18	5	30	10W	2.4	3.4④	9	3
	Pack.V8	25	26½	13	180	170	18	5	30	10W	None	3.7	11	3
1959-60	Six	11	12	13	180	170	18	5	30	10W	2.3	3.15	9	2½
	V8	17	18½	13	180	170	18	5	30	10W	3.8	4.06	9	2½
1961	Six	11	12	13	180	170	18	5	30	10W	2.3	3.15	9	2½
	V8	17	18	13	180	170	18	5	30	10W	3.8	4.06	9	2½

①—For permanent type anti-freeze.　⑧—Add one quart with filter change.　⑤—Station Wagon 3 pints.
②—For alcohol type anti-freeze.　④—Classic 3.7 pints.

DISTRIBUTOR SPECIFICATIONS

Year and Model	Part No. ①	Rotation ②	Cam Angle, Degrees	Breaker Point Opening, Inch	Condenser Capacity, Mfds.③	Breaker Arm Spring Tension, Ounces	Centrifugal Advance Data Degrees @ R.P.M. of Dist.		Vacuum Advance Data		
							Advance Starts	Full Advance	Inches of Vacuum to Start Plunger Movement	Inches of Vacuum for Full Plunger Travel	Maximum Vacuum Advance, Dist. Degrees
AUTO-LITE											
1953–58 Six	1AT-4201	CC	39	.020	.21–.25	17–20	1 @ 400	7 @ 1400	4	12	9
1956 V8	1BJ-4001C	CC	31	.017	.25–.28	17–20	1 @ 300	14 @ 2000	7	13	10
1959–60 Six	1AT-4403	CC	39	.020	.21–.25	17–20	0 @ 400	7 @ 1400	4	12	8.5
DELCO-REMY											
1953–55 V8	1110839	CC	28–34	.013	.20–.25	17–21	1 @ 350	16 @ 1450	4–6	10–11½	8
1956–60 V8	1110864	CC	26–33	.016	.20–.25	17–21	1 @ 350	12 @ 1125	4–6	10–11½	8
1959 Six	1110229	CC	31–37	.022	.20–.25	17–21	1 @ 550	7 @ 1400	3–5	12½	9
1960 V8	1110969	CC	26–33	.016	.20–.25	17–21	1 @ 300	12 @ 1150	5	12	8

①—Stamped on plate riveted to housing. ②—As viewed from top. ③—Microfarads.

GENERATOR AND REGULATOR SPECIFICATIONS

★To Polarize Generator: For internally grounded systems, disconnect field lead from regulator and momentarily flash this wire to regulator battery terminal. For externally grounded systems, connect leads to regulator; then momentarily connect a jumper wire from "Gen" or "Arm" to "Bat" terminals of regulator.

Year	Generator						Regulator					
	Generator Number	Rotation and Ground Polarity ①	Rated Cap. Amps.	Gen. Field Ground Location★	Brush Spring Tension, Ounces	Field Current Amperes	Regulator Number	Cutout Relay		Voltage Regulator Setting Volts	Current Regulator Setting Amperes	Current and Voltage Armature Air Gap, Inch
								Voltage to Close Points	Armature Air Gap, Inch			
AUTO-LITE												
1953	GGW-4801A	C-P	45	External	35–53	1.4–1.5	VBE-6101A	6.5	.032	7.3	45	.050
1953	GGW-4801C	C-P	45	External	35–53	1.4–1.5	VBE-6101A	6.5	.032	7.3	45	.050
1954–55	GGW-4801E	C-P	45	External	35–53	1.4–1.5	VBE-6101A	6.5	.032	7.3	45	.050
1956–59	GJC-7002F	C-N	30	External	18–36	1.2–1.3	VRX-6008A	13.3	.032	14.5	30	.050
1960	GJC-7002F	C-N	30	External	18–36	1.2–1.3	VBO-4202B1	13.3	.032	14.5	30	.050
1960–61	GJP-7102C	C-N	35	External	18–36	1.6–1.7	VBO-6201A	13.0	.027	14.2	35	.050
DELCO-REMY												
1953–55	1102778	C-P	45	External	28	1.87–2.00	1118950	6.3	.020	7.1	45	.075
1956–61	1102003	C-N	30	External	28	1.48–1.62	1119123	12.6	.020	14.3	30	.075

①—C-Clockwise. P-Positive. N-Negative.

STUDEBAKER

STARTING MOTOR SPECIFICATIONS

Car and Model	Part No.	Rotation ①	Brush Spring Tension, Ounces	No Load Test			Torque Test		
				Amperes	Volts	R.P.M.	Amperes	Volts	Torque, Lbs. Ft.
AUTO-LITE									
1953–55 Champ.	MZ-4157	C	42–53	68	5.0	4000	280	2.0	4.4
1956–60 Six	MBG-4103	C	42–53	55	10.0	5200	235	4.0	5.2
1956 V8	MDF-6008	C	42–53	60	10.0	3200	240	4.0	6.5
1960–61	MDU-7005	C	42–53	55	10.0	5200	235	4.0	5.2
DELCO-REMY									
1953–55 V8	1107115	C	24 Min.	70	5.65	5500	550	3.25	11
1952–55 V8	1107116	C	24 Min.	70	5.65	5500	550	3.25	11
1956–60 V8	1107650	C	35 Min.	75	10.3	6900	435	5.8	10.5
1956–60 V8	1107651	C	35 Min.	75	10.3	6900	435	5.8	10.5
1961 V8	1107900	C	35 Min.	75	11.0	5000	435	5.8	14.0

① —As viewed from drive end.   C—Clockwise.

REAR AXLE AND BRAKE CYLINDER SPECIFICATIONS

Year	Model	Ring Gear & Pinion Backlash, Inch	Drive Pinion Adjustment	Drive Pinion Bearing Preload, Inch Lbs.	Drive Pinion Bearing Adjustment	Axle Shaft End Play, Inch	Hydraulic Cylinder Bore Sizes, Inch		
							Wheel Cylinder		Master Cylinder
							Front	Rear	
1953	All	.003–.006	Shims	10–20	Shims	.001–.005	1	7/8	1
1954	Six	.003–.006	Shims	10–20	Shims	.001–.005	1	13/16	1
	V8	.003–.006	Shims	10–20	Shims	.001–.005	1 1/16	7/8	1
1955	Six	.003–.006	Shims	10–20	Shims	.003–.006	1	13/16	1
	V8	.003–.006	Shims	10–20	Shims	.003–.006	1 1/16	7/8	1
1956–61	Six	.003–.006	Shims	10–20	Shims	.001–.006	1	13/16	1
	V8	.003–.006	Shims	10–20	Shims	.001–.006	1 1/16	7/8	1

WHEEL ALIGNMENT SPECIFICATIONS

Year	Model	Caster, Degrees		Camber, Degrees		Toe-In, Inches	Toe-out on Turns, Degrees①		Kingpin Angle, Degrees②
		Limits	Desired	Limits	Desired		Outer Wheel	Inner Wheel	
1952–58	All	— 1 to — 2½	—1¾③	0 to + 1	+½④	1/16 to 1/8	20	22½ to 23½	6 @ 0 Camber
1959–60	All	— 1½ to — 3	—2¼③	0 to + 1	+½④	1/16 to 1/8	20	23½ to 24½	6 @ 0 Camber
1961	All	— 1¼ to + ¼	—½	0 to + 1	+½	1/16 to 1/8	20	24	6 @ 0 Camber

① —Incorrect toe-out, when other adjustments are correct, indicates bent steering arms.
② —Incorrect kingpin angle with correct camber indicates bent suspension arms or steering knuckle support.
③ —Not more than ¾° variation between wheels.
④ —½° more favored on drivers side.

SERIAL NUMBER LOCATION
Left Front Door Pillar

1953

1958 Champion (Except Hawk)

1954

1958 Commander

1955

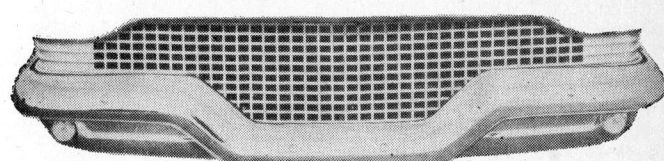

1958 President (Except Hawk)

1956 Except Coupe and Hardtop

1958 Scotsman

1956-57 Coupe and Hardtop

1958 Hawk

1957 Except Coupe and Hardtop

1959-61 Hawk

1959 Lark

1961 Lark With Dual Headlamps

1960 Lark

1961 Lark With Single Headlamps

Engine Section

ENGINE, REPLACE

1953-54

The engine may be lifted out after the transmission and radiator have been removed. Before lifting it out, however, make a careful inspection to see that all wires, pipes, sheet metal and accessories that would hamper the removal of the engine are disconnected and removed.

1955-60 Six-Cylinder

For most service procedures where it is necessary or desirable to remove the engine, it is best to disconnect it at the junction of the engine block and clutch housing or converter housing. The clutch assembly would then be removed as a part of the engine. On models equipped with Automatic Drive, the torque converter should be disconnected from the engine drive plate so that the torque converter will remain on the transmission splines when the engine is removed.

However, if a different cylinder block is to be installed, the clutch housing or converter housing can be removed with the engine after disconnecting the propeller shaft at the transmission and removing the transmission. The clutch housing alignment can then be checked before the housing and engine are reinstalled.

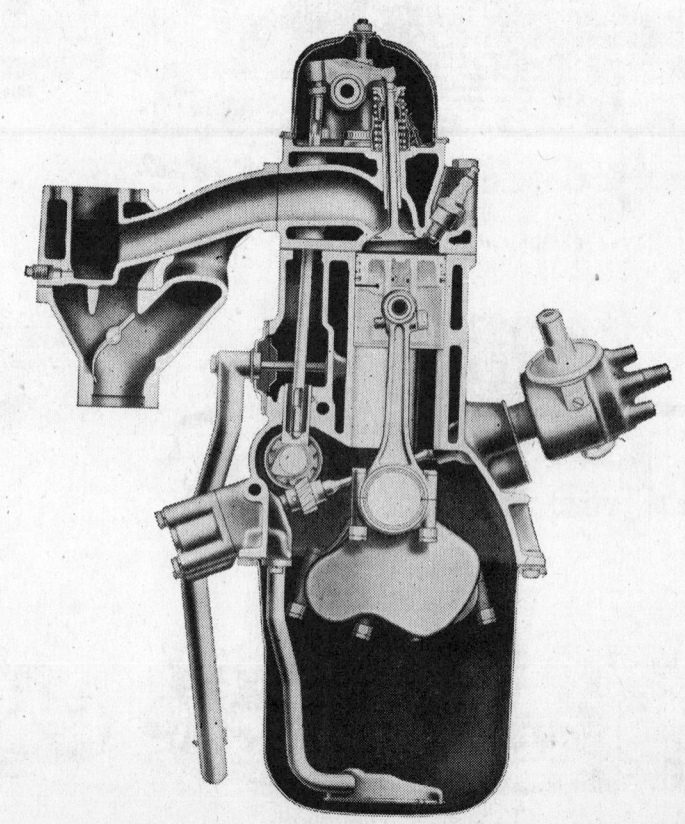

1961 six cylinder engine

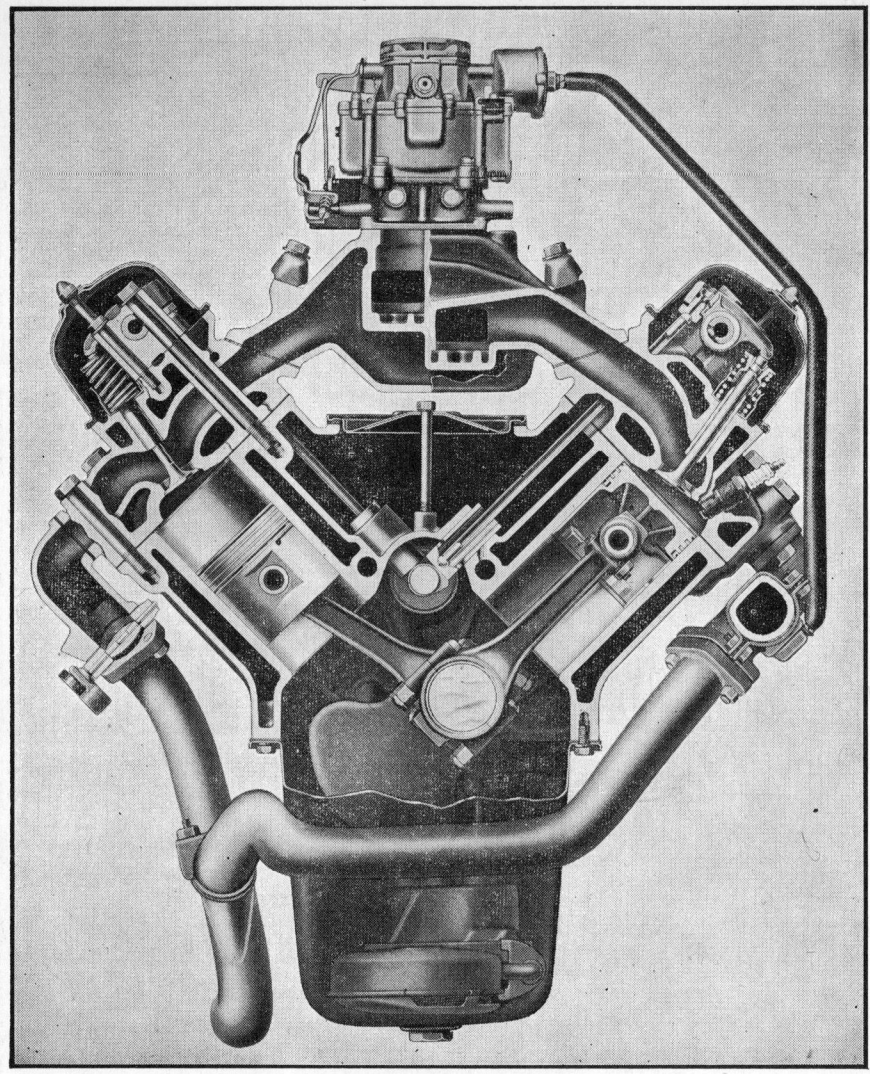

Studebaker V8 engine

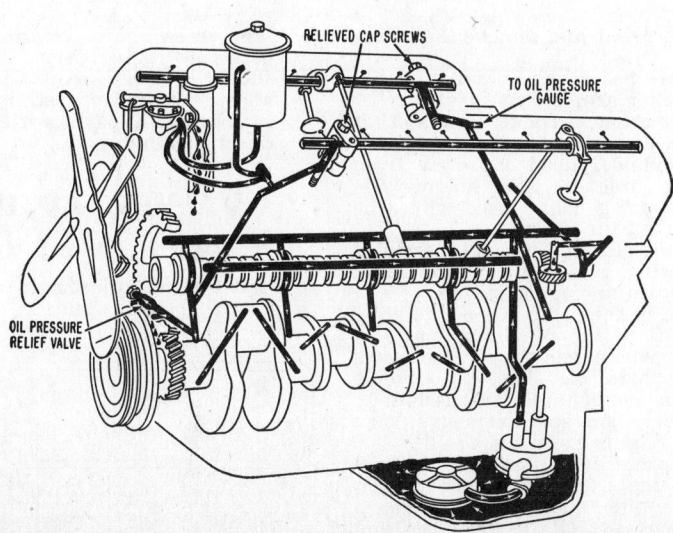

Engine lubrication. V8-232, 259 and 289 engines

1955-61 V8 Engines

For most service procedures where removing the engine from the car is necessary or desirable, it is best to disconnect it at the clutch or torque converter housing. However, if a different cylinder block is to be installed, it will be necessary to recheck the clutch housing alignment, and therefore the clutch housing should be removed with the engine. If the clutch housing is not properly aligned, the car will probably slip out of high gear.

On cars with Air Conditioning, remove the compressor mounting bracket and compressor as an assembly *without disconnecting refrigerant hoses*. Move the assembly to a position on the front of the right front fender, being careful to keep the compressor crankcase lower than the compressor cylinder head so that oil will not leak into the chamber above the compressor pistons.

CYLINDER HEAD, REPLACE

1961 Six

1. Drain cooling system and remove upper radiator hose.
2. Remove rocker arm cover.
3. Remove spark plugs.
4. Remove manifold and carburetor as a unit.
5. Remove rocker arm shaft assembly.
6. Lift out push rods.
7. Unfasten and remove head.
8. Reverse removal procedure to install head and tighten head bolts in the sequence shown in Fig. 1 to the torque listed in the *Engine Tightening Chart.*

1953-60 Six

1. Drain cooling system and remove water outlet, thermostat and upper radiator hose.
2. Remove air cleaner.
3. Remove spark plugs.
4. Disconnect or remove any linkage tubes, wires, etc. attached to head.
5. Unfasten and lift off cylinder head.
6. Reverse removal procedure to install the head and tightening head bolts in the sequence shown in Fig. 2 to the torque listed in the *Engine Tightening Chart.*

1954-61 V8

1. Drain radiator and remove air cleaner.
2. Disconnect linkage, tubes, wires, etc., attached to cylinder head being removed.
3. Remove intake manifold and carburetor as a unit.
4. Remove generator and battery if necessary.
5. If air conditioned, *remove compressor without disconnecting refrigerant hoses.*
6. Remove exhaust manifold bolts and pull manifold away from head.
7. Remove rocker arm shaft assembly and push rods.
8. Unfasten cylinder head and lift off.
9. Reverse removal procedure to install

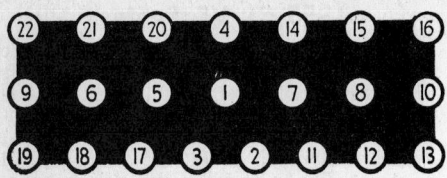

Fig. 2 Head tightening sequence, 1953-60 Six

head and tighten bolts in the sequence shown in Fig. 3 to the torque listed in the *Engine Tightening Chart.*

VALVE ARRANGEMENT

Front to Rear

All Sixes . . . . E-I-I-E-E-I-I-E-E-I-I-E
All V8's . . . . E-I-I-E-E-I-I-E

ROCKER ARMS

1961 Six

1. Before disassembly, mark the rocker arms, brackets and rocker arm shaft so that they can be reassembled in the original positions.
2. Hold rocker assembly and press in on one of the shaft end brackets and remove cylinder head capscrew from the end bracket.
3. Gradually release the compression of the spring and carefully remove the bracket, spacer, first rocker arm, compression spring and the next rocker arm from the shaft.
4. Proceed in the same manner to strip the shaft of the remaining parts.
5. Except when new parts are used, install all rocker arms and brackets on the shaft in the original positions. The two end brackets differ from the center brackets. *To insure correct installation and oil distribution, a flat is located on the front end of the rocker arm shaft.* Make certain that the oil holes and grooves in the shaft and oil holes in rocker arms and adjusting screws are clean. Clearance between rocker arms and shaft should be .0005" to .0025". If clearance is excessive, install new parts. Lubricate all parts with engine oil during assembly.

V8 Engines

1. Before disassembly, mark the rocker arms, brackets and shaft so they can be reassembled in their original positions.
2. Referring to Fig. 4, push in on the outer flat washer at one end of the assembly so that the spring washer

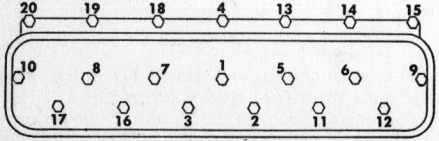

Fig. 1 Cylinder head tightening sequence. 1961 Six

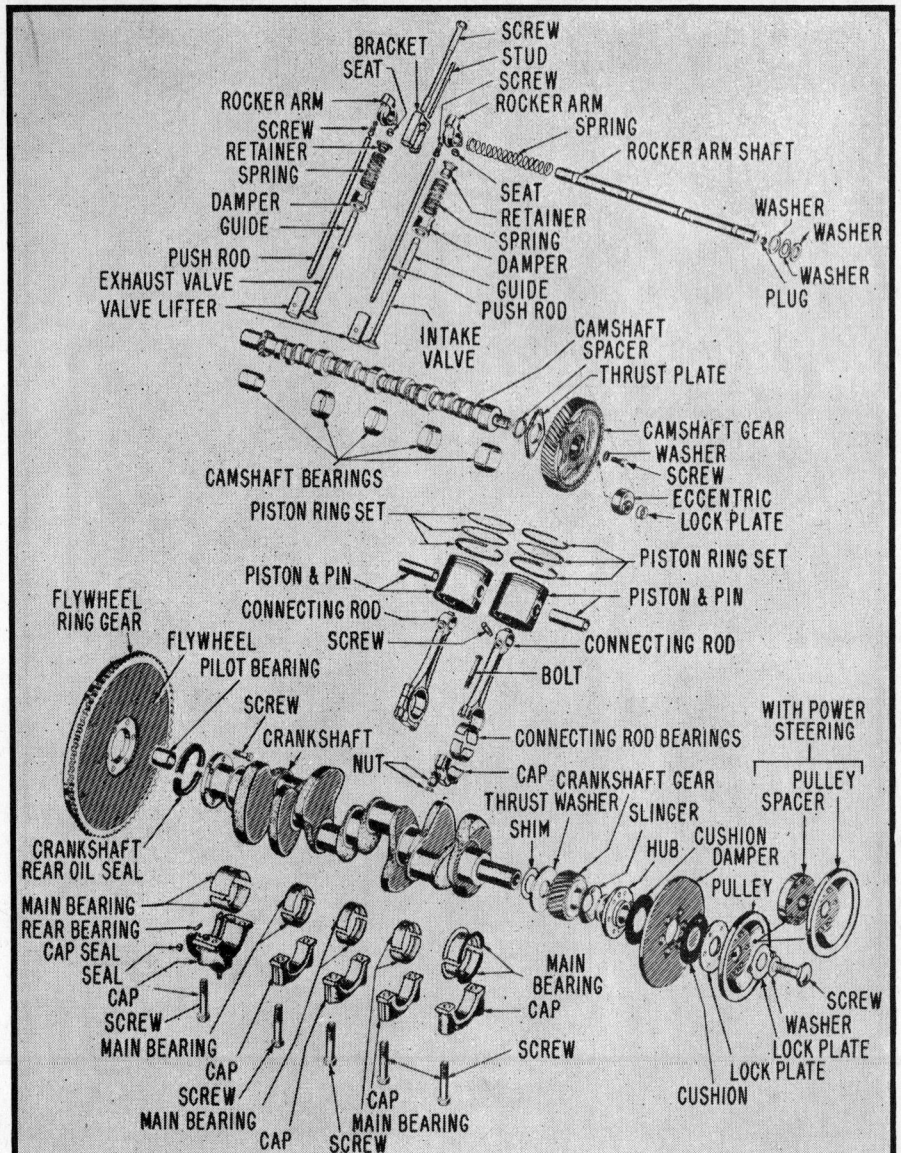

Internal parts of Studebaker V8 engines

is compressed, and remove the cotter pin.
3. Remove the washers and slip the end rocker arm off the shaft.
4. Holding the next rocker arm so that the spacer spring is compressed, remove cylinder head capscrew from the end bracket. Still holding the spacer spring compressed, slide the bracket off the shaft.
5. Gradually release the compression of the spring and remove the next rocker arm and space spring.
6. Proceed in the same manner to strip the shaft of the remaining parts.
7. Except where new parts are used, install parts on shaft in reverse order of removal. Before assembly, test rocker arm spacer springs; they should require from 9½ to 10½ lbs. to compress each spring to 2$\frac{1}{32}$". A spring that does not test within these limits should be replaced. Make certain that the oil holes and grooves in rocker arm shaft and oil holes in rocker arms and adjust-

ing screws are clean. Clearance between rocker arms and shaft should be .0005" to .0025". If clearance is excessive, install new parts. Lubricate all parts with engine oil during assembly.

VALVES, ADJUST

1961 Six & All V8's

A self-locking adjusting screw is used

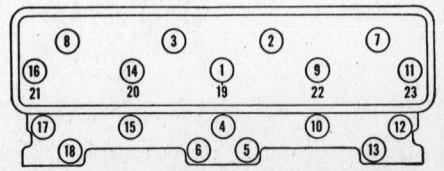

Fig. 3 1953-61 V8 cylinder head tightening sequence

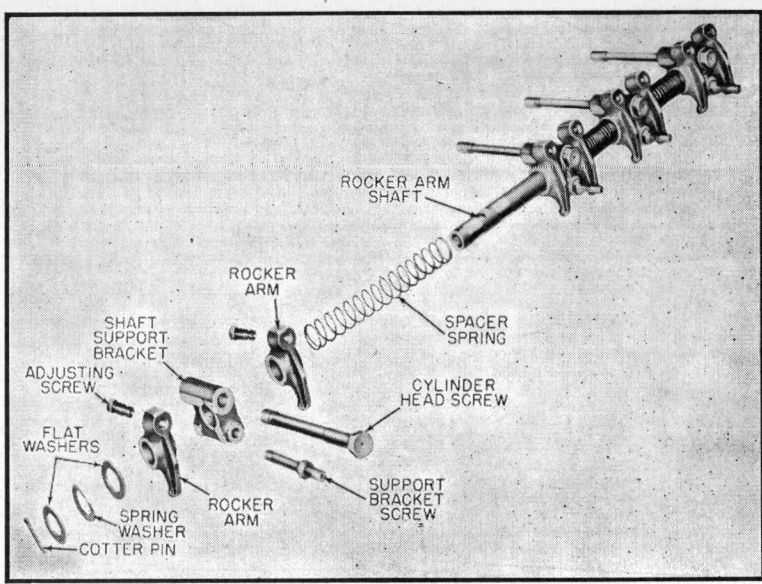

Fig. 4 Rocker arm assembly. V8 Engines

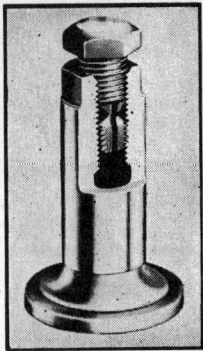

Fig. 6 Self-locking tappet adjusting screw. 1953-60 Six

Fig. 7 Using spring scale to check tension on self-locking tappet adjusting screw. 1953-60 Six

between the rocker arm and push rod for valve clearance adjustment. A torque of at least 30 inch lbs. should be required to turn the screw when the threads are engaged on both sides of the groove. Check with a spring scale in a manner similar to that shown in Fig. 7. The pull on the spring scale should be at least 30 inch lbs.

If the cylinder head cap screws are to be tightened, always complete the tightening process before adjusting valve clearances.

Adjust the clearances to the specifications given in the *Valve Specifications* chart. To set the clearance with the engine cold (at room temperature), turn the crankshaft until No. 1 piston is on the compression stroke and the UDC 1-6 on the vibration damper is directly under the timing pointer. Then adjust the clearance for No. 1 cylinder valves to the specifications listed in the *Valve Specifications Chart*. Then turn over the engine and adjust the remaining valves in accordance with the firing order of the engine, Fig. 5.

1953-60 Sixes

The slotted adjusting screw, Fig. 6, of the valve lifter is self-locking. When an adjusting screw is replaced, the torque required to turn the screw should be measured. A torque of at least 2 lb. ft. should be required to turn the screw. This is approximately a 4-lb. pull at the end of a six-inch wrench with a spring scale attached as shown in Fig. 7.

The valve clearance should be set to the clearances given in the *Valve Specifications* chart and should be set with the engine cold (room temperature of 70°). Turn the crankshaft in the direction of normal engine rotation until the No. 1 piston is on the compression stroke and the ignition timing mark is in line with the timing pointer. Then adjust the valves for No. 1 cylinder.

To be sure that the valve lifter is on the base circle of the cam, remove the distributor cap and connect a single-contact timing light to the primary wire on the distributor and to a ground. Turn on the ignition switch and rotate the distributor until the breaker points open for No. 1 cylinder (bulb lights). Rotate the crankshaft until the bulb lights again and adjust No. 5 valves. Repeat this procedure, following the firing order of the engine.

VALVES, REMOVE

1961 Six & All V8's

1. Use a suitable valve spring compressor to remove the valve spring locks, Fig. 8. *The valve springs must not be compressed more than is required to remove the locks. If they are compressed until the coils bottom, the springs may lose as much as 10 to 15 lbs. tension.*

2. Release the valve spring compressor slowly and remove the parts from the valve.

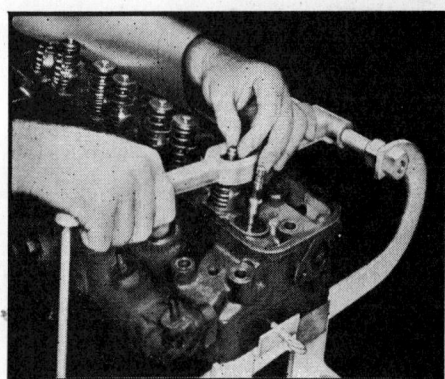

Fig. 8 Removing valve keepers with the aid of special cylinder head holding tool

3. Repeat the operation and strip the remaining valves.

4. Remove the valves from the head and place them in a board with numbered holes so that, if they are to be reused, they can be inserted in the original guide holes.

5. Referring to Fig. 9, install the damper on the closed coil end of the spring. Cupped side of seal goes toward top of valve guide. (On 1953-54 engines, O-ring seals are used

Fig. 5 Adjusting valves on 1961 Six and all V8's

Fig. 9 Location of seal (1) and damper (2) on valve stem (3). 1961 six and 1955-61 V8's. For 1953-54 V8's O-ring seals are used instead of the umbrella type shown

and they are installed on top of the valve spring retainers.)

5. The spring dampers should be inspected to be sure that the fingers are not bent out. The fingers must contact the sides of the springs to be effective.

1953-60 Sixes

To remove valves from these engines, take off the cylinder head and valve covers and use cloth to block off the holes in the valve chamber to prevent the valve locks from falling into the crankcase.

With a suitable valve spring compressor, raise the springs on those valves which are closed and remove the locks. Then turn the crankshaft until those valves which are open are closed and remove the remaining valve locks.

Remove all valves and place them in a board with numbered holes so they can be identified as to the valve port from which they were removed.

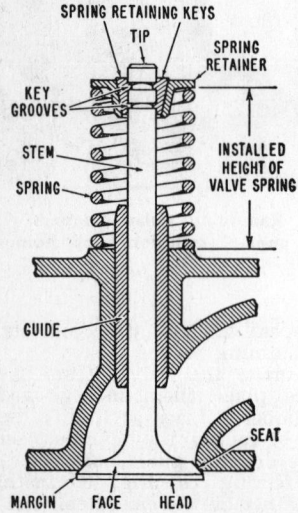

Fig. 10 Checking installed height of valve springs. 1961 six and all V8's

VALVE SPRING INSTALLED HEIGHT

1961 Six & All V8's

When valves and seats are reground the position of the valve in the head is changed so as to lessen the valve spring tension. Without proper valve spring tension the valve does not seat long enough or it may not seat completely. Since the valve is cooled by transferring heat from the valve head to the seat and thence to the coolant, improper valve spring tension will cause worn, pitted and distorted valves which result in loss of compression and power as well as poor gasoline mileage.

When valves, springs, retainers and locks are installed, measure the assembled height of the valve springs from the surface of the cylinder head spring pad to the underside of the spring retainer as shown in Fig. 10. If the assembled height is geater than the dimension given in the *Valve Specifications Chart*, install a spacer or shim of proper thickness between cylinder head spring pad and spring to bring the assembled height to specifications.

Do not install spacers unless necessary. Excessive use of spacers will result in overstressing valve spring and overloading camshaft lobes which could lead to spring breakage and worn camshaft lobes.

VALVE SPRING TESTING

Wash the springs with gasoline or other suitable solvent. Then examine them for damage or corrosion due to acid etching, which will develop into surface cracks and cause spring failure.

Check the valve spring pressure on a spring testing fixture, if one is available, Fig. 11. If a fixture is not available, at least check the free length of each spring by standing it alongside a new one. Any spring that does not conform to the specifications in the *Valve Data* chart within 10 per cent. should be replaced. Likewise, any spring that stands shorter than the new spring used for comparison should be discarded.

VALVE GUIDES

1961 Six & All V8's

Clean the valve guides with a wire guide brush, and clean the valves with a wire wheel brush, making sure that all carbon is removed from the top and bottom of the heads, as well as the gum which might have accumulated on the stems.

Check the valve stem-to-guide clearance with a dial indicator if one is available. Mount the indicator on the valve guide so that the button contacts the valve stem squarely and as near the end of the guide as possible. Then move the valve stem away from the indicator. Note the total clearance reading. If the guides are worn so that the reading exceeds .0035 in., new guides should be installed.

The special Valve Guide Tool shown

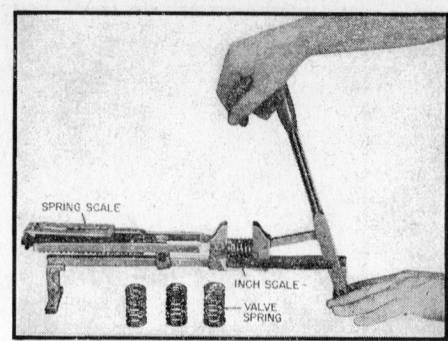

Fig. 11 Checking valve spring tension. All models.

in Fig. 12 should be used to remove and install guides in these engines. When removing a valve guide, use the driver to drive the guide out of the cylinder head from the combustion chamber side.

When installing a guide, first coat the outside of the guide lightly with white lead. Then start the chamfered end of the guide into the head from the combustion chamber side. Place the installing plate on the face of the head as shown in Fig. 12 and drive in the guide until the shoulder of the driver contacts the bottom of the counterbore in the plate. The plate is marked "Intake" on one side and "Exhaust" on the other. Be sure the exposed mark of the plate corresponds to the valve guide being installed.

If the special tool is not available, carefully measure the position of the guides before removing them and drive the new ones in accordingly.

1953-60 Six

To check valve stem-to-guide clearance, take a new valve and place it in each valve guide and feel the clearance by moving the valve stem back and forth. If this check shows excessive clearance (over .0035 in.) it will be necessary to replace the guide. If the clearance is not excessive when checking

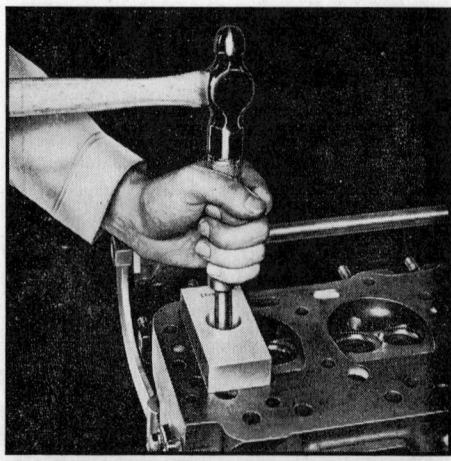

Fig. 12 Showing special tool used to control position of valve guides when driven in place. 1961 Six and all V8's

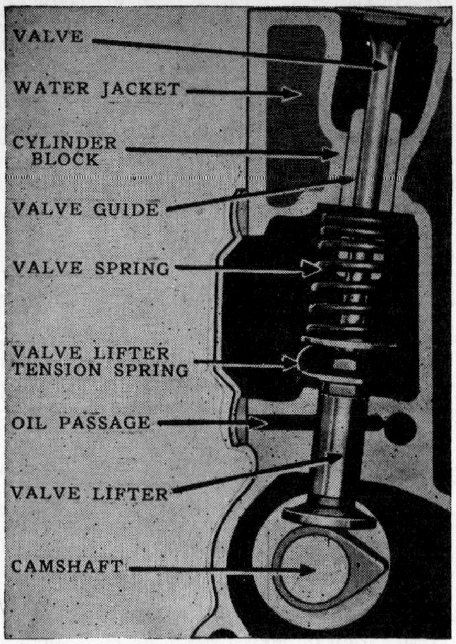

Fig. 13 Valve mechanism. 1953-60 Six

with a new valve but is excessive when checked with the old valve, the old valve stem is worn and a new valve must be installed.

If it is necessary to replace valve guides, the old guides can be driven down and out of the valve chamber. A special driver is available for this work. However, in lieu of the driver, the guides can be pulled out of the block by using a suitable piece of pipe together with a long bolt and suitable washer.

Be sure the new guides are driven to the correct position in the block. This can be determined by measuring the position of the old guides before they are removed.

VALVES, GRIND

In refacing valves, take off only the minimum of metal required to clean up the valve faces. If the outer edge of the valve becomes too thin or sharp due to excessive grinding, the valve must be replaced.

Inspect the valve seats for cracks, burns, pitting, ridges or improper angle. During any general engine overhaul it is advisable to reface the valve seats regardless of their condition. If new valve guides are required, they must be installed before refacing the seats if the equipment used has a valve guide pilot.

The valve seat width after refacing should measure $\frac{1}{16}''$ to $\frac{3}{32}''$. The width may be checked by placing a scale across the face of the seat.

VALVE LIFTERS

1961 Six & All V8's

A straight barrel type lifter is used. To remove the lifters, take off the cylinder heads and push rods as outlined previously. Then remove the three capscrews that retain the valve lifter chamber cover and breather pipe and lift off the cover and pipe.

Take out the valve lifters, keeping them in order so they can be replaced in the same bore from which they were removed.

Wash the lifters with clean gasoline or other solvent. Remove the carbon and sludge deposits from the oil holes. Inspect all lifters for excessive wear and replace where necessary.

1953-60 Six

Mushroom type lifters are used on all Champion engines which means that the oil pan and camshaft must be removed and the lifters taken out from below when lifters require replacement, Fig. 13.

TIMING GEAR COVER

V8 Engines

1. To remove the cover, drain cooling system and remove fan shroud and radiator.
2. Remove fan belt, and power steering belt (if equipped).
3. Remove fan blade assembly.
4. Remove water manifold.
5. Remove fuel pump.
6. Remove vibration damper and fan pulley hub.
7. Remove screws and take off cover.
8. On 1955-58 models, do not remove the self-tapping screws which hold the retainer plate. Remove the felt oil seal with an ice pick or other pointed tool and clean the recess in the cover carefully before installing a new felt seal.
9. Install the new seal and wet it with engine oil in the recess in the cover. Insert the crankshaft pulley hub through the seal to center it.
10. Install the cover but do not tighten the screws. Install the crankshaft pulley hub to locate the seal and cover properly; then tighten the cover screws.
11. Complete the installation in the reverse order of removal.

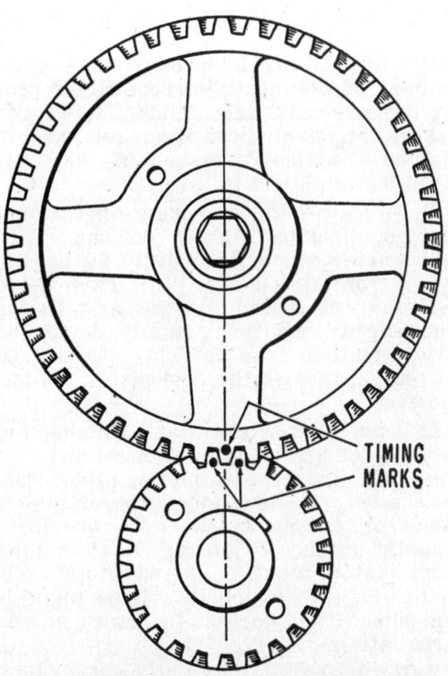

Fig. 14 Valve timing marks for No. 6 cylinder. V8 Engines

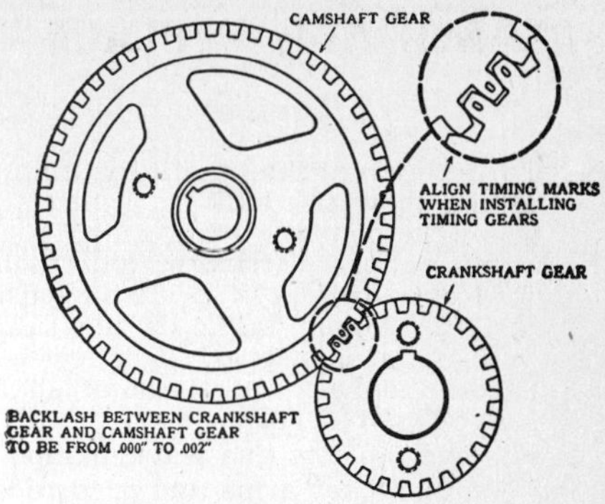

Fig. 15 Timing gear installation. Six-Cylinder Engines

Six-Cylinder Engines

1. Remove radiator.
2. Remove vibration damper.
3. Remove crankshaft fan pulley.
4. Remove screws and take off cover.
5. Pick out the old oil seal and clean out the recess in the cover.
6. Install a new seal in the cover, using the hub of the crankshaft pulley to seat it in the recess.
7. Install the cover, leaving the screws loose enough so that the cover can center itself as the crankshaft pulley is installed.
8. Press crankshaft pulley into position and securely tighten the cover screws.

VALVE TIMING DATA

Year	Model	Intake Opens①	Intake Closes②	Exhaust Opens③	Exhaust Closes④
1953	Six	15	49	54	10
	V8	11	53	50	14
1954	Six	15	49	54	10
	V8	11	53	50	14
1955	Champion	15	49	54	10
	Commander	19	46½	59½	6
	President	11	54½	51½	14
1956	Six	15	49	54	10
	56B, 56H	11	54½	51½	14
	56J	14	62	54	18
1957	Six	15	49	54	10
	V8	11	54½	51½	14
1958	Six	15	49	54	10
	V8	11	54½	51½	14
1959	Six	15	49	54	10
	V8	11	54½	51½	14
1960	Six	15	49	54	10
	V8	11	54⅗	51⅗	14
1961	Six	15	50⅗	55	10
	V8	11	54	51⅗	14

①—Degrees before top dead center.
②—Degrees after bottom dead center.
③—Degrees before bottom dead center.
④—Degrees after top dead center.

TIMING GEARS

For correct valve timing, the gears should be assembled as shown in Figs. 14 and 15. Always use suitable puller and pusher equipment when removing and installing gears. This is particularly important in the case of camshaft gear as there is danger of loosening the welsh plug in back of the camshaft if the gear is driven on with hammer blows.

CAMSHAFT, REPLACE

V8 Engines

1. Turn the crankshaft until the timing marks show the IGN mark directly under the pointer on the timing gear cover and the distributor rotor is in the No. 6 firing position. In this position the timing mark on the camshaft gear is properly aligned between the marks on the crankshaft gear, Fig. 14.
2. Remove radiator and water pump.
3. Remove rocker arms and push rods.
4. Remove carburetor and intake manifold.
5. Remove breather pipe and valve lifter cover and take out valve lifters.
6. Remove fuel pump.
7. Remove timing gear cover.
8. Turn camshaft just enough to expose thrust plate retaining screws and remove the screws. Then turn the gears back to align the marks of the two gears.
9. Remove camshaft and gear as a unit, being careful not to damage the camshaft bearings.
10. Remove the gear from the camshaft with a puller.
11. Install a new camshaft gear on the camshaft, install the assembly in the engine and align the timing gear marks as shown in Fig. 14.
12. Check the gear backlash, which should be .001-.003". Install the camshaft thrust plate screws and complete the installation in the reverse order of removal.

Six-Cylinder Engines

To remove the camshaft, take off the radiator and all necessary sheet metal. Remove vibration damper and pulley. Remove the timing gear cover and screws which fasten the camshaft thrust plate to the cylinder block. Take off the manifolds, cylinder head, fuel pump, oil pump, oil pan, oil pump drive shaft and valve covers.

If removal of the valves is not intended, raise the lifters and keep them up with spring-type clothespins or metal

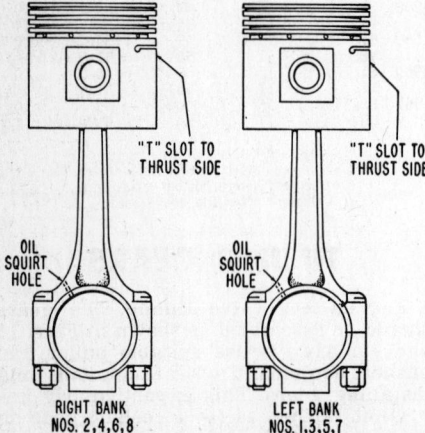

Fig. 16 Correct assembly of pistons to rods. V8 Engines

supports so they won't interfere with the camshaft as it is being withdrawn.

PISTONS & RODS, REMOVE

After removing the cylinder heads and oil pan, examine the cylinder bores above the ring travel area. If the bores are worn so that a shoulder or ridge exists at this point, remove the ridge with a ridge reamer to avoid damaging rings or cracking ring lands of pistons during removal.

Remove the connecting rod caps and push the pistons and rods out through the top of the cylinders, using care to prevent the big end of the rods from damaging the crankshaft or cylinders.

Make sure the rods and pistons are properly numbered so they can be reinstalled in the original locations. It is advisable to install caps on rods to avoid mixing parts.

PISTONS & RODS, ASSEMBLE

V8 Engines

Pistons should be assembled to the connecting rods so that the oil squirt holes are on the same side as the unslotted side of pistons, Fig. 16. And when installed in the cylinders the T-slot side of all pistons should be toward the left side of the engine.

Six-Cylinder Engines

When correctly assembled the oil squirt hole in the connecting rod will be on the camshaft side of the engine with the T-slot side of the piston facing away from the camshaft.

PISTONS

Standard size service pistons are high limit or maximum diameter; therefore, they can usually be used with a slight amount of honing to correct slight scoring or excessive clearances in engines having relatively low mileages. Service pistons are also furnished in .005, .010, .015, .020 and .030 in. oversizes.

Before a honing or boring operation is started, measure all new pistons with a micrometer at points exactly 90 degrees away from the piston pin. Then select the smallest piston for the first fitting. The slight variation usually found between pistons in a set may provide for correction in case the first piston is fitted too free.

It is very important that refinished cylinder bores are trued up to have not more than .0005 in. out-of-round or taper. Each bore must be final honed to remove all stone or cutter marks and provide a smooth surface. During final honing, each piston must be fitted individually to the bore in which it will be installed and should be marked to insure correct installation.

After final honing and before the piston is checked for fit, each bore must be thoroughly washed to remove all traces of abrasive and then dried thoroughly.

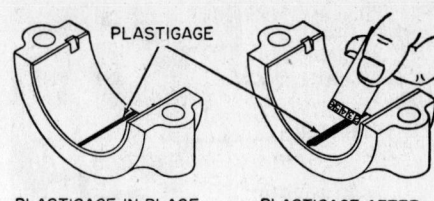

Fig. 17 Checking bearing clearance with Plastigage. All models

The dry bore should then be brushed clean with a power-driven fibre brush.

Both the piston and cylinder block must be at the same temperature (room temperature of 70 degrees) when the piston is checked for fit in the cylinder bore. Therefore, the cylinder should be allowed to cool after boring or honing and before the piston fit is checked. This is important because a difference of 10 degrees between the temperature of parts is sufficient to produce a variation of .0005 in.

PISTON RINGS

When new piston rings are to be installed without reboring cylinders, the glazed cylinder walls should be slightly dulled but without increasing the bore's diameter. This is done with a "Glazebuster" or with a hone equipped with the finest grade of stones.

New rings must be checked for clearance in piston grooves and for gap in cylinder bores. Cylinder bores and piston grooves must be clean, dry and free of carbon and burrs.

Check the clearance of each ring in its piston groove by installing the ring and then inserting feeler gauges *under* the ring. Any wear that occurs in the piston groove forms a step or ridge at the inner portion of the lower land. If gauges are inserted above the ring, the ring may rest on the step instead of on the worn portion of the lower land, and a false measurement of clearance will result.

If the piston grooves have worn to the extent that relatively high steps or ridges exist on the lower lands, the piston should be replaced because the steps will interfere with the operation of the new rings and the ring clearances will be excessive. Piston rings are not furnished in oversize widths to compensate for ring groove wear.

To check the end gap of rings, place the ring in the cylinder in which it will be used. Square it in the bore by tapping with either end of the piston, then measure the gap with feeler gauges. If necessary to increase the gap, file the ends of rings carefully with a smooth file.

PISTON PINS

Service piston pins are available in standard and .0025 and .005 in. oversizes. When fitted correctly in the piston, pins should require a light finger push with parts at room temperature of approximately 70 degrees.

V8 Engines

To remove the piston pin, remove the lock nut and star washer from the clamp screw. Install and tighten the lock nut on the other end of the clamp screw, which will loosen the clamp screw in the rod. Remove the screw from the rod and slide the piston and rod off the pin.

To install the pin, slide the piston and rod into position. But before inserting the clamp screw, be sure the solid side of the piston is to the squirt hole side of the rod.

If the connecting rod is a new one and hasn't been marked, it should be checked to determine whether it is a left or right bank rod. The rods are offset at the crankpin end and can be identified as shown in Fig. 16.

Install the piston pin clamp screw so that the nut will be installed on the T-slot side of all pistons. Be sure the flat surface of the clamp screw mates with the flat surface of the piston pin, otherwise the pin will work loose in service.

Six-Cylinder Engines

On these engines the piston pin is locked in the rod in the same manner as for V8 engines. However, on connecting rods 1, 3 and 5, the clamp screw nut is installed on the T-slot side of the piston. On Nos. 2, 4 and 6, the nut is installed on the solid side of the piston.

When installing the clamp screw regardless of the rod number, hold the rod with its offset to the left and insert the screw from the front. This will locate the lock nut on the correct side with relation to the piston.

ROD BEARINGS

Connecting rod bearings can be replaced without removing the connecting rod assembly by removing the cap and replacing the upper and lower bearing halves. The clearance between the bearing and crankshaft can be measured with Plastigage as follows:

1. Remove bearing cap and wipe oil from crankshaft and bearing.
2. With crankpin at approximately bottom dead center, place a piece of Plastigage in the center of the cap, Fig. 17.
3. Reinstall the cap and tighten to the torque value given in the *Engine Torque Specifications* table.
4. Remove the bearing cap and determine bearing clearance by comparing the width of the flattened Plastigage at its widest point with the graduation on the Plastigage envelope. The number within the graduation on the envelope indicates the clearance in thousandths of an inch, Fig. 17. If clearance is excessive, install a new bearing.

MAIN BEARINGS

Caution—Main bearing clearance can be checked with Plastigage in the same manner described for rod bearings. If bearings are measured with the engine in the chassis, the crankshaft must be supported in order to take up clearance

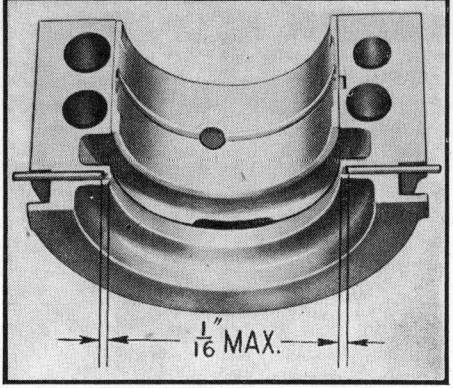

Fig. 18   Installing neoprene seals in bearing cap groove. All models

between the upper bearing insert and crankshaft journal. This can be done by tightening bearing caps of adjacent bearings with .005″ to .015″ cardboard, (such as a calling card) between lower bearing shell and journal. Use extreme care when this is done to avoid unnecessary strain on the crankshaft or bearings or a false reading may be obtained. Do not rotate crankshaft while Plastigage is installed. *Be sure to remove cardboard.* To install new bearings, proceed as follows:

1. Remove bearing cap and worn lower shell.
2. Rotate crankshaft in normal direction to turn upper bearing shell out of crankcase. Use a cotter pin with a flattened head or the special tool made for the purpose in the crankshaft oil hole to contact the bearing and force it out.
3. Place a new upper shell on the crankshaft journal with the locating notch in the correct position and rotate the shaft to turn the bearing in place.
4. Install the lower bearing shell in the cap.
5. Tighten all cap nuts to the torque value given in the *Engine Torque Data* table.

Service Note, 1955-60 Six-Cyl.

The small amount of clearance between the front main bearing cap and the

Fig. 19 Installing crankshaft rear oil seal

crankshaft cheek-to-engine front plate makes it necessary to follow a specific procedure in removing the front main bearing cap.

To remove the bearing cap, first remove the gasket from the engine front plate. Turn the crankshaft until the No. 1 connecting rod bearing journal is at approximately a 5 o'clock position (partly down and toward the camshaft). Unfasten the bearing cap and separate it from the block and swing the end that is away from the camshaft toward the rear of the engine, crossing the crankshaft cheek. Turn the free end of the bearing cap toward the cylinder bore and at the same time bring the other end over the crankshaft.

To install, reverse the procedure.

REAR MAIN BEARING OIL SEAL

Oil sealing at the rear main bearing is controlled by a Brummer oil seal installed around the crankshaft journal, wood filler blocks between the sides of the main bearing cap and block, and Neoprene seals between the bearing cap face and block.

It is not necessary to remove the engine from the chassis to replace the Brummer oil seal.

1. Remove rear main bearing cap and the old seal.
2. Wash bearing, blow dry and wipe clean.
3. Loosen intermediate bearing caps about two turns to give additional clearance between rear journal and block.
4. Insert Neoprene seals in cross grooves of rear bearing cap as shown in Fig. 18.
5. Place cap with seals downward on a flat surface and, while pressing on cap, use a sharp knife or razor blade to cut protruding ends of seals flush with sides of cap.
6. Blunt sharp edge of flange at rear of block on which Brummer seal is mounted, Fig. 19. Use flat side of screwdriver or similar tool.
7. Install new Brummer seal *dry*.
8. Parting line or split of two seal halves should be *assembled horizontally.* This will guard against initial distortion of or damage to seal during completion of the installation.
9. Install bearing cap and tighten screws to specified torque; also torque intermediate bearing caps which were previously loosened.
10. Install two wood filler blocks between sides of bearing cap and block, being sure blocks are not damaged or split during the installation.
11. Complete the job and run engine for 45 minutes and check for oil leaks.

OIL PAN

1953-55 Champ. & 1956-58 Sixes

1. Drain oil and remove level gauge.
2. On long wheelbase models, swing wheels to the right to move the steering bellcrank out of the way.
3. On shorter wheelbase models, dis-

connect tie rods and reach rod from steering bellcrank. Remove retaining pinch bolt and bellcrank from shaft.

4. Remove pan screws and lower oil pan.

1953-58 V8

1. Drain oil and remove level gauge and oil level gauge adapter tube.
2. Disconnect one battery cable and remove starting motor.
3. On 1953-58 models with 120½" wheelbase (except Land Cruisers), swing wheels to the right to move steering bell crank out of the way.
4. On 1953-58 models with 116½" wheelbase and Land Cruisers, remove steering bell crank and exhaust cross-over pipe.
5. On all models, remove attaching screws and drop oil pan.

1959-61 Sixes

1. On Hawk models, swing wheels to the right to move steering bellcrank out of the way. Unfasten oil pan and remove from car.
2. On all models except Hawks, disconnect tie rods and reach rod from bellcrank. Remove retaining pinch bolt and remove bellcrank from shaft. Remove attaching screws and drop oil pan.

1959-61 V8's

1. Remove oil level gauge and adapter tube by removing head bolt which retains tube clamp.
2. Disconnect one battery cable.
3. Drain oil from crankcase.
4. Remove starting motor.
5. On Hawk models, swing wheels to the right to move steering bellcrank out of the way. Then unfasten and remove oil pan.
6. On all models except Hawks, remove steering bellcrank assembly, exhaust crossover pipe and exhaust connection. Unfasten and remove oil pan.

OIL PUMP REPAIRS

Important—On all six-cylinder engines, before removing the oil pump, crank the engine to bring No. 1 piston to its firing position, which is when the ignition mark on the vibration damper or flywheel is in line with the pointer. If possible, leave the engine in this position while the pump is off in order to obtain correct ignition timing. However, if the engine is disturbed while the pump is off, return it to the No. 1 firing position before attempting to install the pump.

1953-54 Champion

Removal of the oil pump in these engines is a piece-by-piece operation. Take off the bottom cover and pick out the "C" washer from the pump shaft. Remove the body and pull out the shaft and gears.

Reverse the operations to assemble, being sure the engine is in the position to fire No. 1 cylinder.

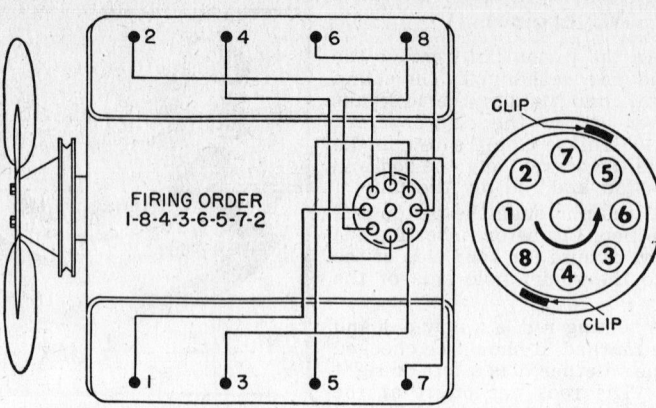

Fig. 20   Ignition details.   Studebaker V8 Engines

FIRING ORDER 1-8-4-3-6-5-7-2

1953-55 Champ. & 1956-61 Sixes

To remove the oil pump and drive gear the crankshaft must be turned away from the No. 1 top dead center position to provide sufficient clearance between the cylinder block and the crankshaft center counterweight. If it is necessary to remove the oil pump drive shaft and gear, the oil pan must be removed. Note the position the crankshaft is in when the oil pump shaft and drive gear is removed because this is the position the crankshaft must be in when the shaft and gear are again installed.

When installing the oil pump shaft and drive gear, first position the crankshaft so the oil pump shaft will enter the block. Then turn the crankshaft to the No. 1 top dead center position and push the oil pump shaft and drive gear out of engagement with the camshaft. Turn the shaft and gear until the keyway in the shaft points toward the bottom of the engine. Then draw the oil pump drive gear into engagement with the camshaft gear. As the two gears engage, the keyway in the oil pump shaft will turn toward the rear of the engine. This provides the correct location for distributor setting and ignition timing.

V8 Engines

Removing the pump from these engines does not effect the ignition timing. After removing the oil pan as previously outlined, remove the two pump retaining nuts and slip the pump from the mounting studs.

RADIATOR

1953-55

1. Drain cooling system and disconnect radiator inlet hose.
2. Remove fan blades.
3. Remove wiring junction block and horn relay from fan shroud.
4. Pry open wiring harness clips and move harness out of the way.
5. Remove four cap screws holding fan shroud to radiator support and remove fan shroud.
6. Unfasten radiator from its support and lift it out.

1956-61

1. Drain cooling system.
2. Disconnect battery.
3. Tie up hood.
4. Remove horn relay and headlamp junction block screws and free wires from top of shroud.
5. On B, H and J models, remove gasoline pipe screw.
6. If car has power steering, free upper hose from hose support.
7. Remove fan blades.
8. Remove upper and lower hose.
9. Unfasten and remove radiator.

WATER PUMP REPAIRS

Six-Cylinder Engines

1. To remove the pump, drain the cooling system.
2. Remove fan shroud (if equipped).
3. Remove fan belt, fan blades and pulley.
4. Disconnect Climatizer hose (if equipped).
5. Remove generator adjusting arm, if necessary.
6. Disconnect radiator outlet hose.
7. Unfasten and remove water pump.
8. To disassemble, remove bearing lock ring. Place pump in arbor press and remove shaft, bearing and hub assembly by pressing arbor through impeller and out through front of housing. Then press shaft out of hub.
9. If the thrust seal surface in the housing has become rough, it should be refaced with a water pump facing tool. In reassembling the pump, always use a new seal assembly and impeller. When installing the impeller, there should be .015" to .031" clearance between the impeller and housing. Rotate the shaft when checking the clearance.
10. Install the pump in the reverse order of removal.

V8 Engines

1. To remove the water pump, drain cooling system.
2. Remove fan belt, fan and pulley and fan shroud.
3. Unfasten and remove water pump from water manifold.
4. To disassemble, remove the bearing

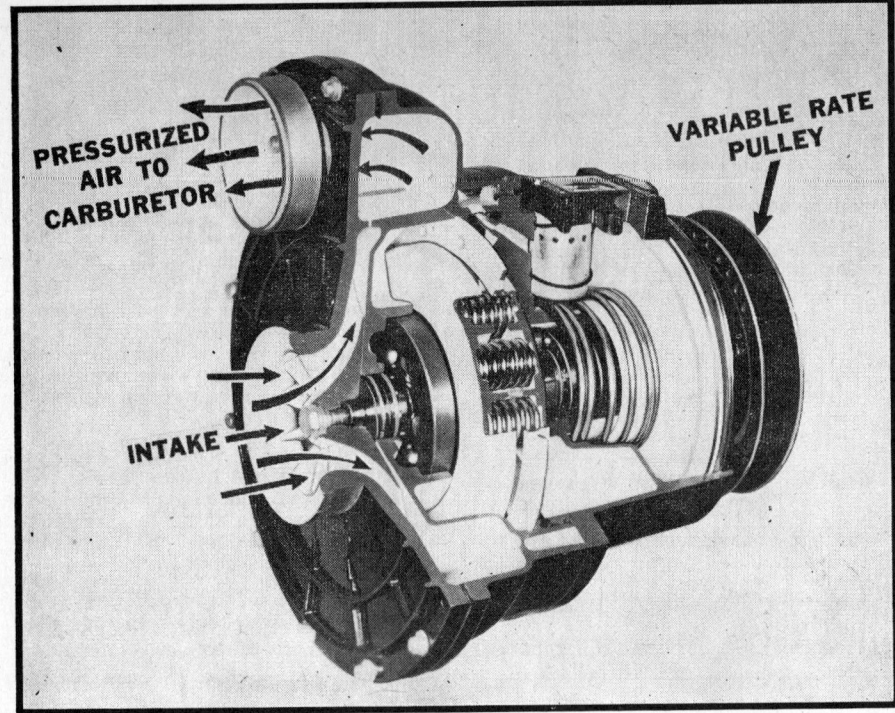

Fig. 21 Cutaway view of supercharger. 1957-58 Golden Hawk

Labels on figure:
PRESSURIZED AIR TO CARBURETOR
VARIABLE RATE PULLEY
INTAKE

IGNITION TIMING

1. When distributor is installed it should be positioned so that the contact points will just start to open and the rotor will be pointing directly at the No. 1 terminal in the distributor cap when the index line nearest the IGN mark on the vibration damper is directly under the pointer on the timing gear cover.
2. Before checking the timing with the engine running, disconnect the vacuum advance pipe at the carburetor and install a temporary plug in the carburetor. This will prevent the possibility of the vacuum advance holding the breaker plate from returning to the full retard position.
3. Use a power timing light and, if rubber caps cover the spark plug terminals, an adapter will have to be used on the No. 1 spark plug to provide a terminal for attaching the timing light.
4. With the engine running at hot idle speed, the timing mark should show the index mark nearest the IGN mark to be directly under the pointer. If it does not, loosen the distributor clamp nut and turn the distributor as required to obtain the correct setting.
5. Remove the temporary plug from the carburetor and connect the vacuum advance pipe.

SUPERCHARGER

1957-58 Golden Hawk

The supercharger, Fig. 21, is of the single-stage, centrifugal type. It is a five-pound boost, full-pressure system which crams about a 30 per cent greater amount of fuel and air mixture into the combustion chamber, resulting in high explosion pressures than under normal operating intake vacuum. The supercharger is driven through a variable rate pulley which produces maximum power during acceleration while permitting normal fuel economy at cruising speeds.

Drive power is taken from the engine crankshaft through a single "V" belt and the variable-ratio pulley fitted to the input shaft of the supercharger.

A planetary drive system is incorporated between the input and output shafts to increase the speed of the impeller. It is a ball bearing, friction-type system which eliminates the use of gears. Spring-loaded ball races automatically take up any wear that might develop in the drive.

The lubrication system is completely self-contained and does not require any connections to the engine lubricating system. An internal oil sump holds 8 ounces of Automatic Transmission Fluid. The piston-type oil pump works off a cam ground into the input shaft. A dipstick oil gauge, located in the bearing housing assembly, is marked to indicate the "safe" operating level and the "add oil" level of the lubricant in the sump.

Supercharger Testing

1. With the engine at rest or idling, the belt should be in the bottom of

---

lock ring. Place pump in an arbor press and push hub, shaft and bearing out of impeller and cover. Then press shaft and bearing out of hub.
5. If the thrust seal surface in the housing has become rough, it should be refaced with a water pump facing tool. Use a new fan hub to insure a tight fit on the shaft. Press the hub on the shaft so it is flush with the end of the shaft. Insert the shaft in the housing and install the bearing lock ring. Then install a new seal assembly in the impeller and press the impeller on shaft so it is flush with end of shaft. Clearance between impeller and cover should not exceed .090".
6. Install pump in reverse order of removal.

DISTRIBUTOR, REPLACE

1. Before removing distributor on V8 models, turn crankshaft until IGN mark on vibration damper is directly beneath pointer, and distributor rotor is in line with No. 1 spark plug terminal of cap.
2. On all models, remove distributor cap.
3. On V8 models, remove air cleaner.
4. On all models, disconnect cable from coil tower. Then remove spark plug cables, cable brackets and distributor cap as a unit.
5. Remove cable from center terminal of distributor.
6. Disconnect vacuum advance pipe.
7. Remove distributor clamp and lift out distributor.

Installation, Six Cylinder

1. Insert distributor shaft in cylinder block opening and engage slot in end of shaft with tongue of oil pump drive shaft.
2. Install distributor clamp. Before tightening clamp screw, position clamp so that center of octane selector scale is aligned with scribe mark on mounting pad.
3. Connect wires, vacuum advance pipe and secure cap.
4. Set timing as outlined below.

Installation, V8 Engines

1. Be sure IGN mark is directly under pointer on gear cover.
2. Position distributor with rotor pointing toward front of engine with vacuum advance unit pointing to front and slightly to the right.
3. Turn rotor approximately 30° clockwise and insert oil pump drive shaft and coupling into cylinder block opening. When teeth on distributor shaft gear contact teeth on camshaft gear, the rotor will be turned counterclockwise and, as the teeth mesh, the tongue on the oil pump drive shaft will enter the groove of the oil pump shaft. This will permit the distributor to seat on the block, and the rotor will have to be turned to point directly at the No. 1 terminal of the distributor cap, Fig. 20. Very slight misalignment may cause difficulty in engaging oil pump drive shaft tongue with groove of oil pump shaft. After gears are meshed, engine may be cranked to secure proper alignment. Maintain light pressure on distributor while cranking engine to facilitate engagement.
4. Complete the installation and time the ignition as outlined below.

STUDEBAKER

the pulley groove (high blower position).

2. With the engine running at approximately 1500 rpm, the belt should start to leave the bottom of the groove and begin to climb up.

3. With the engine running at 3500 rpm (no load) the belt should be running near the top of the pulley (low blower position).

4. With the engine at 3500 rpm (no load) manually operate the regulator kickdown switch. The belt should go immediately to the bottom of the pulley groove (high blower position). Releasing the kickdown switch should allow the belt to return immediately to the top (low blower position).

5. Remove the ⅜" pipe plug, located at the rear of the rear of the cover, (normally used for setting the idle speed) and, using a low reading pressure gauge, connect it to the air chamber cover. Pressure at this point should indicate approximately 5 pounds at 3500 rpm with the kickdown switch closed (in high blower position).

6. Fuel pump pressure should be checked at idle by disconnecting the line at the air chamber base and hooking the gauge on the open line. A reading of 5½ to 7 lbs. should be recorded.

Supercharger Does Not Shift

If the variable-ratio pulley does not shift or operates sluggishly, check the following:

1. Spline may be burred.
2. Spline dirty and sticky.
3. Rough or gummy pulley.
4. Tension arm binding. It should be free on pivot pin and have a slight end play so washers will turn free.
5. Solenoid regulator not operating. An audible click should be heard with the ignition on each time the switch is depressed. The circuit should be connected to the 12-volt side of the ignition coil resistor.

Supercharger Boost Pressure Too Low

If the supercharger shifts okay and the pulley is functioning properly, check the following:

1. Improperly operating solenoid regulator.
2. Hose leakage between supercharger inlet and carburetor air chamber.
3. Carburetor air chamber leaking air—could be gaskets or leaking flapper valves.
4. Dirty air cleaner.
5. Malfunction of supercharger such as air leakage by seals, etc. Necessary to overhaul supercharger.

STARTER REPLACE

1953-58

Before the starter can be removed on Champion models the oil level gauge adapter and distributor must be removed. On 1956 Golden Hawk remove the left exhaust pipe at the flange mounting.

1959-61

1. Disconnect one battery cable.
2. On six cylinder models, remove the oil level gauge and tube. Disconnect wires from starter, unfasten and remove starter from engine.
3. On V8 models, disconnect a cable from battery and the cable at the starter. Unfasten and remove starter from clutch or converter housing.

Carburetor Section

Performance Complaints

Flooding, stumble on acceleration or other performance complaints are in many instances caused by the presence of dirt, water or other foreign matter in the carburetor. To aid in diagnosing the cause of the complaint, the carburetor should be carefully removed from the engine without draining the fuel from the bowl. The contents of the fuel bowl may then be examined for contamination as the carburetor is disassembled.

Check the fuel in the bowl for contamination by dirt, water, gum or other foreign matter. A magnet moved through the fuel in the bowl will pick up and identify any iron oxide dust that may have caused intake needle and seat leakage.

Inspect gasketed surfaces between body and air horn. Small nicks or burrs should be smoothed down to eliminate air or fuel leakage. On carburetors having a vacuum piston, be especially particular when inspecting the top surface of the inner wall of the bowl around the vacuum piston passage. A poor seal at this location may contribute to a "cutting-out" on turns complaint.

Fill the carburetor bowl with clean fuel before installing on manifold. This will help prevent dirt trapped in the fuel system from being dislodged by the free flow of fuel as the carburetor is primed. The operation of the floats and intake needle and seats may be checked under pressure if a fuel pump is used at the bench to fill the carburetor bowl. Operate the throttle several times and visually check the discharge from pump jets.

Poor Mileage and Engine Loading Complaints

Cases of poor mileage and engine loading may be due in many instances to sluggish choke valve opening during cold driveaway, caused by insufficient vacuum in choke housing, a plugged or restricted heat pipe or inlet in choke cover. To check for this condition, have engine warm and running at slow idle. Remove choke heat pipe and hold a finger over the heat inlet hole (hole is on choke housing on some carburetors). If there is little or no vacuum pull on the finger, check the choke housing for gasket leaks or plugged vacuum passages. If these are OK, check choke vacuum passages in carburetor between choke housing and manifold.

Dirty or Rusty Choke Housing

In cases where it is found that the interior of the choke housing is dirty, gummed or rusty while the carburetor itself is comparatively clean, look for a punctured or eroded manifold heat tube (if one is used).

Manifold Heat Control Valve

An engine equipped with a manifold heat control valve can operate with the valve stuck either in the open or closed position. Because of this, an inoperative valve is frequently overlooked at vehicle lubrication or tune-up.

A valve stuck in the "heat-off" position can result in slow warm up, combustion chamber deposits, carburetor icing, flat spots during acceleration, low gas mileage and spark plug fouling.

A valve stuck in the "heat-on" position can result in power loss, engine knocking, sticking or burned valves and spark plug burning.

To prevent the possibility of a stuck valve, check and lubricate the valve each time the vehicle is lubricated or tuned-up. Check the operation of the valve manually. To lubricate the valve, place a few drops of penetrating oil on the valve shaft where it passes through the manifold. Move the valve up and down a few times to work in the oil. *Never use engine oil for this purpose as it will leave a residue which hampers valve operation.*

STROMBERG CARBURETOR ADJUSTMENTS

Year	Carburetor Model	Idle Adjustments				Float Level	Pump Travel	Choke Unloader	Choke Setting
		Mixture Screws Turns Open	Hot Idle Speed Neutral	Fast Idle Speed	Dashpot Plunger Clearance				
1959-61	WW6-123, A	1¼	550	.025②	None	3/16①	None	.192③	Index
1958	WW6-117B, C	1¾	550	④	None	3/16①	None	.228③	1 Lean
	WW6-122A	1¾	550	.030②	None	7/32①	None	.228③	1 Lean
1957	WW6-117A	1¾	550	④	None	3/16①	None	.228③	1 Lean
	WW6-121	1¾	550	④	None	7/32①	None	.228③	1 Lean
1956	WW6-117	1¾	550	④	None	3/16①	None	.228③	1 Lean
1955	WW6-112F	1¾	550	④	None	3/16①	None	.228③	Index
	WW6-115	1¾	550	④	None	3/16①	None	.228③	Index
	WW6-112C	1¾	550	④	None	3/16①	None	.228③	Index
1953-54	WWULV-26	1¾	550	④	None	3/16①	None	.228③	Index

②—Close choke so that high step of fast idle cam contacts fast idle screw. Turn fast idle screw until the clearance specified exists between throttle valve and carburetor bore on idle port side.

STROMBERG NOTES

THROTTLE RETURN DASHPOT

Supercharged Models — Adjust dashpot unit in bracket until plunger just breaks contact with tab on throttle lever. Mark position of dashpot relative to bracket, then turn dashpot 1¾ to 2 turns toward throttle lever.

CARBURETOR BALL CHECKS

Whenever it becomes necessary to dismantle a carburetor be sure to account for the ball check valves that may be found under pump plungers and compensating or power valves.

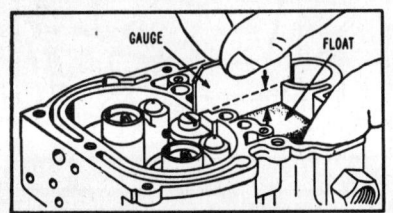

Fig. ①—WW float level. To adjust bend lip of float lever.

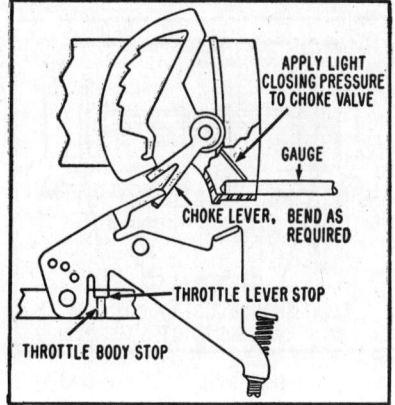

Fig. ③—Hold choke valve lightly closed. Then open throttle until throttle lever stop rests against throttle body stop. Choke should be open the dimension specified between narrow side of choke valve and inner wall of air horn. Adjust by bending throttle lever ear.

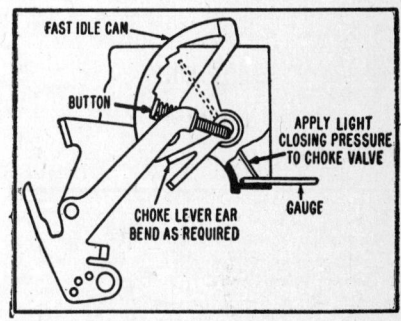

Fig. ④—With choke valve fully closed and fast idle cam in fast idle position, one-half the diameter of the button at the end of the throttle stop screw should rest against the step of the fast idle cam. Adjust by bending choke lever ear.

CARTER NOTES

METERING ROD

AS—Metering rod should just bottom at wide open throttle. Adjust by bending metering rod arm.

WCFB—Metering rod adjustment must be made after pump setting. Back out throttle lever set screw to seat throttle valves in carburetor bores. Loosen metering rod arm clamp screw. With metering rods in place, press down on vacumeter link until metering rods bottom in casting. Holding rods down, revolve metering rod arm until finger on arm contacts lip of vacumeter link. Hold in place and tighten clamp screw.

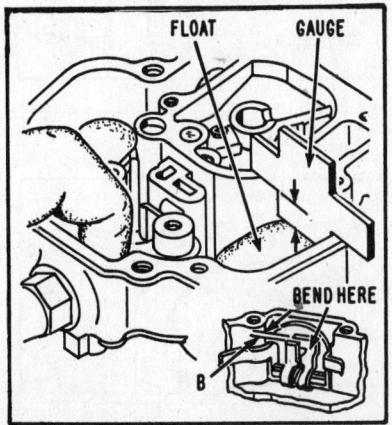

Fig. ①—AS float level. Adjust by bending float lip.

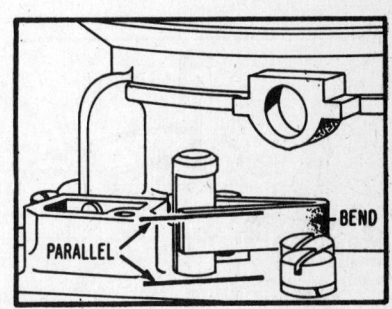

Fig. ②—Pump arm on lifter link should parallel top of casting. Adjust by bending pump arm.

CARTER CARBURETOR ADJUSTMENTS

Year	Carburetor Model	Idle Adjustments				Float Level		Float Drop		Pump Travel Setting	Choke Unloader Setting	Choke Setting
		Mixture Screws Turns Open	Hot Idle Speed Neutral	Fast Idle Speed	Dashpot Plunger Clearance	Primary	Secondary	Primary	Secondary			
1961	AS-3159S	½-1½	550	.065③	None	¼①	None	None	None	②	3/16④	1 Rich
	AS-3161S	½-1½	550	.065③	None	¼①	None	None	None	②	3/16④	1 Rich
	AS-3186S	½-1½	550	.065③	None	¼①	None	None	None	②	3/16④	1 Rich
1960-61	AS-2934S, SA	½-1½	550	.065③	None	¼①	None	None	None	②	3/16④	1 Rich
1959-60	AS-2876S	¼-1¾	550	.045③	None	¼①	None	None	None	②	3/16④	Index
1958-61	WCFB-2574S	½-1½	550	.024⑧	1/16⑯	3/16⑤	3/16⑤	11/16⑥	11/16⑥	⑦	1/8⑨	1 Rich
	WCFB-2575S	½-1½	550	.024⑧	1/16⑯	3/16⑤	3/16⑤	11/16⑥	11/16⑥	⑦	1/8⑨	1 Rich
1958	BBRI-2764S	½-1½	550	None	None	5/64⑩	None	None	None	½⑪	None	None
1957	BBRI-2724S	½-1½	550	None	None	5/64⑩	None	None	None	½⑪	None	None
	WE-2417S	½-1½	550	.046⑭	None	3/8⑫	None	None	None	7/32⑬	3/16⑮	1 Lean
1955-57	WCFB-2219S-A-B	½-1½	550	.024⑧	1/16⑯	3/16⑤	3/16⑤	11/16⑥	11/16⑥	⑦	1/8⑨	1 Rich
	WCFB-2214S-A-B	½-1½	550	.024⑧	1/16⑯	3/16⑤	3/16⑤	11/16⑥	11/16⑥	⑦	1/8⑨	1 Rich
1956	WCFB-2394S	¾-1¾	400⑰	.023⑧	1/16⑯	1/8⑤	3/16⑤	5/8⑥	11/16⑥	⑦	9/32⑮	Index
1954-55	WE-2108S	½-1½	550	.046⑭	None	3/8⑫	None	None	None	7/32⑬	3/16⑮	1 Lean
1954	WE-2190S	½-1½	550	.046⑭	None	3/8⑫	None	None	None	7/32⑬	3/16⑮	1 Lean
1953	WE-989S-A	½-1½	550	.046⑭	None	3/8⑫	None	None	None	7/32⑬	3/16⑮	1 Lean

CARTER NOTES
continued

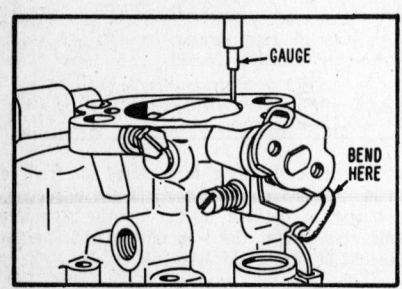

Fig. ③—With choke valve closed there should be the clearance specified between lower edge of throttle valve and carburetor bore with fast idle link on high step of cam. Adjust by bending choke connector rod.

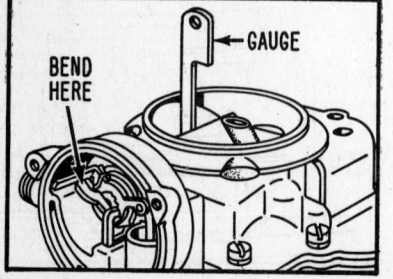

Fig. ④—With throttle valve wide open there should be the clearance specified between top edge of choke valve and inner wall of air horn. Adjust by bending arm on choke trip lever.

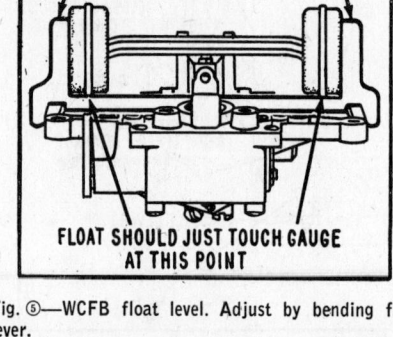

Fig. ⑤—WCFB float level. Adjust by bending float lever.

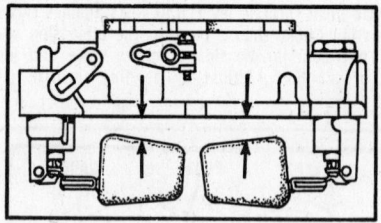

Fig. ⑥—WCFB float drop. Adjust by bending stop tabs on float bracket.

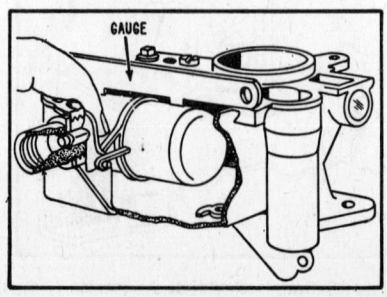

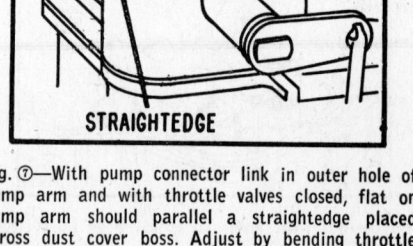

Fig. ⑦—With pump connector link in outer hole of pump arm and with throttle valves closed, flat on pump arm should parallel a straightedge placed across dust cover boss. Adjust by bending throttle connector rod.

⑧—With throttle closed, tighten fast idle adjusting screw on high step of fast idle cam until there is the clearance specified between throttle valve and carburetor bore (side opposite idle port).

⑨—With throttle valve wide open there should be the clearance specified between lower edge of choke valve and inner wall of air horn. Adjust by bending unloader lip on throttle shaft lever.

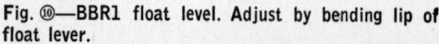

Fig. ⑩—BBR1 float level. Adjust by bending lip of float lever.

⑪—Pump plunger should travel distance specified with pump link in center hole of pump arm. Adjust by bending pump lifter link.

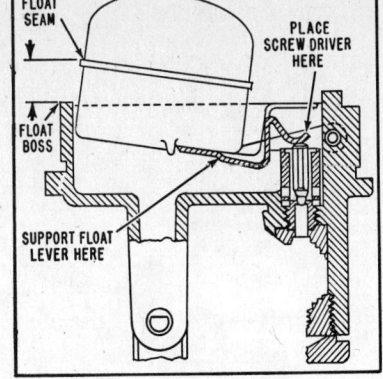

Fig. ⑫—WE float level. Adjust by bending float lever.

⑬—Pump plunger should travel distance specified. Adjust by bending throttle connector rod.

⑭—Hold choke valve closed, then close throttle. There should be the clearance specified between throttle valve and carburetor bore. Adjust by bending choke connector rod.

⑮—With throttle valve wide open there should be the clearance specified between lower edge of choke valve and inner wall of air horn. Adjust by bending arm on choke trip lever.

⑯—With choke valve tightly closed and fast idle screw on highest step of fast idle cam, there should be the clearance specified between throttle lever and lower tip of plunger shaft. Loosen locknut and turn adjusting screw as required.

⑰—In drive range.

Clutch and Transmission Section

CLUTCH PEDAL, ADJUST

1953

Clutch pedal free travel should be maintained at ¾" to 1". To adjust, unhook the pullback spring, Fig. 1, loosen the lock nut and turn the adjustment clevis as required.

1954-58

The clutch pedal should have from ½" to 1" free travel on all models except the Goldenhawk, which has 1½" free travel. On all models except Goldenhawk, adjust by loosening the lock nut on the rod connecting the clutch release shaft lever and remove clevis pin. Turn clevis to shorten or lengthen to obtain the desired result.

On the Goldenhawk, loosen the lock nut on the rod connecting the release shaft lever to operating shaft and turn the nut as required to obtain the desired adjustment.

1959-61

The clutch pedal should have ¾" free travel. A correctly adjusted brake pedal (free travel adjustment of ¼ to ⅜") is used as a reference point when adjusting clutch pedal free travel.

With the brake pedal correctly set (by means of the adjusting stop screw) adjust the clutch pedal to the same height. Turn the clutch pedal stop screw as required to bring the pedal to the same height as the brake pedal. *On cars with power brakes, adjust the clutch pedal pad location with the stop screw so that the distance from the top of the clutch pedal pad to the floor mat or carpet is 6¼ to 6½".*

Adjust length of overcenter clutch return spring by turning the nut so that the overall length of the spring is 10".

Adjust the clutch pedal-to-bellcrank rod to give ½" clearance between top end of bellcrank and body flange on front side of firewall. Loosen lock nut on rod connecting clutch operating bellcrank to the operating shaft lever. Turn the nuts to

shorten or lengthen the rod to decrease or increase the pedal free travel as required to obtain a free travel adjustment of ½ to 1", measured at the pedal pad.

CLUTCH, REPLACE

1953-55

1. Disconnect battery.
2. On 1953-54 six-cylinder models, remove distributor.
3. On all six-cylinder models, remove oil level gauge and tube. Take off starter without disconnecting wires and tie it out of the way.
4. On V8 models, remove starter.
5. On all models, remove floor plate and top clutch housing cap screws.
6. Remove transmission.
7. Remove engine rear support mounting bolts. Raise rear of engine just enough to take weight off rear support and remove crossmember.
8. Loosen exhaust pipe support bracket-to-clutch housing bolts. Loosen clamp and swing support bracket out of the way.
9. On V8 models, remove clutch housing plate.
10. On all models, remove remaining clutch housing bolts and take off clutch housing. On six-cylinder models, remove dowel bolts first.
11. Remove clutch from flywheel.

1956-58

1. Disconnect battery ground strap.
2. On Champion and Flighthawk remove oil level gauge and tube; remove starter without disconnecting cables and tie it out of the way.
3. On Commander, President, Powerhawk and Skyhawk, remove starter.
4. Remove clutch operating shaft.
5. Remove transmission.
6. Remove two bolts which hold rear support insulator cage to crossmember. Jack up rear of engine to relieve weight of engine from crossmember, and remove crossmember.
7. Loosen and swing exhaust pipe sup-

port bracket out of the way.
8. On Commander, President, Powerhawk and Skyhawk, remove clutch housing cover plate.
9. Remove remaining housing mounting bolts or cap screws and remove clutch housing. On Champion and Flighthawk, remove dowel bolts first.

1959-61

1. Disconnect battery ground cable.
2. On 6-cylinder models, remove oil level gauge and tube, remove starter mounting capscrews without disconnecting cables and tie starter out of the way.
3. On V8 models, remove starter.
4. Remove clutch operating shaft.
5. Remove transmission.
6. Remove two bolts or nuts which hold engine rear support insulator to crossmember. Raise engine with a jack under rear of oil pan just enough to relieve weight of crossmember; then remove crossmember.
7. On V8's remove clutch housing cover plate.
8. Unfasten clutch housing and lift out of car. On 6-cylinder engines, remove dowel pins first.
9. Reverse removal procedure to install the clutch and adjust free pedal travel.

TRANSMISSION, REPLACE

1953-61

1. To remove the transmission, drain the case.
2. Disconnect the U-joint from the transmission flange and remove the propeller shaft support stud nuts. Then remove the front propeller shaft and support rearward on the slip yoke splines. Move the end of the shaft to one side as far as possible and tie it in position.
3. Disconnect shift rods from transmission levers, and remove the speedometer cable from the transmission case. If overdrive equipped, disconnect wires and control cable.

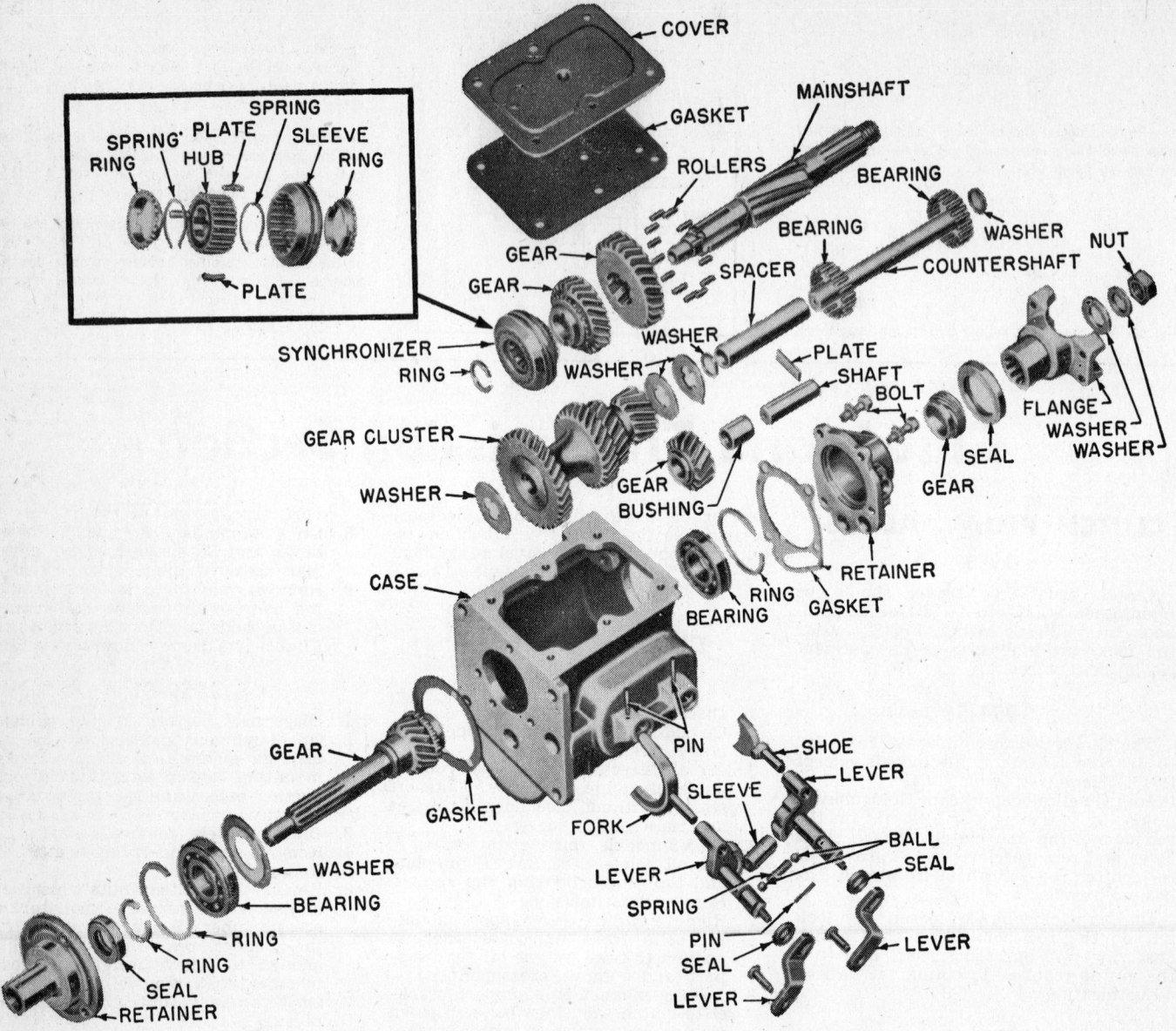

Fig. 1 Exploded view of synchromesh transmission without overdrive. Typical of all Six-cylinder models. The V8 transmission is similar except that the low-reverse mainshaft gear has the shift fork groove facing the front

4. Unfasten the transmission from the clutch housing. Remove the clutch operating shaft, bracket and bearing from the transmission case.

5. Move the transmission rearward until the clutch shaft is free of the clutch and remove the unit from the car.

6. To install, reverse removal procedure.

TRANSMISSION REPAIRS

1953-61 Fig. 1

Note—The following outlines the procedure for conventional transmissions. For repairs on the overdrive unit, see the *Overdrive Chapter*.

Disassemble

1. Take off cover and gasket.
2. Pull off companion flange.
3. Remove mainshaft rear bearing retainer and speedometer drive gear from mainshaft.
4. Remove main drive gear bearing retainer.
5. Remove small snap ring from main drive gear.
6. With brass drift and hammer, move countershaft rearward just enough to free up lock plate in shaft groove at rear end.
7. Make a dummy countershaft exactly the length of the countershaft and thrust washers combined. The purpose of the dummy shaft is to retain in position the needle rollers, sleeve and thrust washers when removing

and installing the countershaft gear cluster.

8. Place the end of the dummy shaft against the front end of the countershaft and with a soft hammer, carefully drive the countershaft rearward out of the case, leaving the cluster gear, dummy shaft and related parts in the bottom of the case.

9. With a small brush, paint a fine line across the synchronizer rings, sleeve and second and high mainshaft gear to insure replacement of these parts in their original position.

10. To remove the main drive gear, place a brass bar or drift against the rear face of the drive gear teeth at the top (not synchronizer gear teeth) and carefully drive the gear and bearing forward out of the case.

11. With a brass bar placed against the

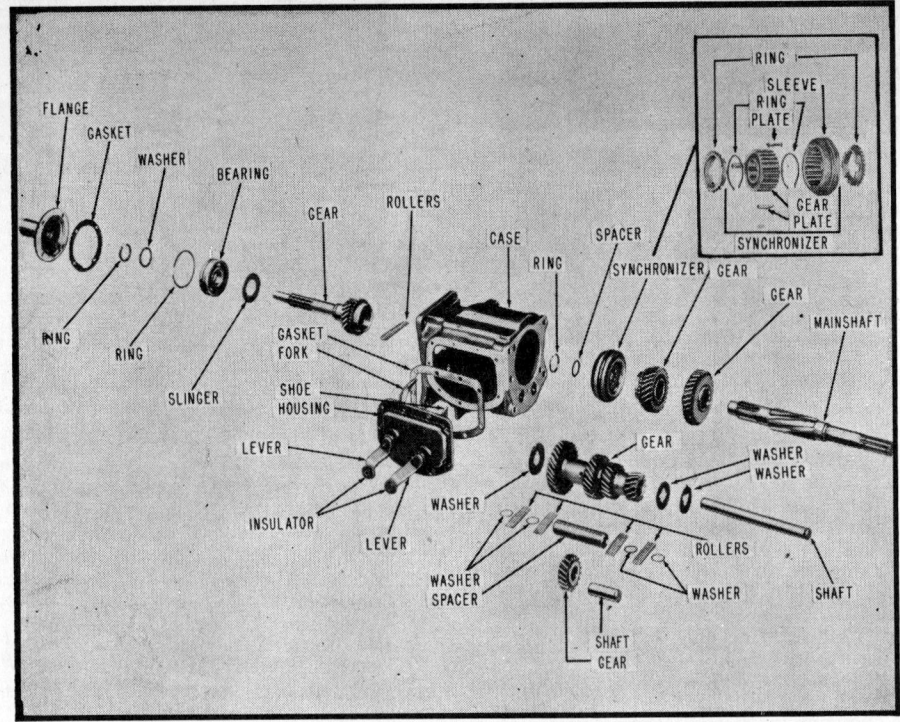

Fig. 2 Synchromesh transmission. 1956-58 President Classic and Golden Hawk

front end of the mainshaft, drive the mainshaft rear bearing out through the rear of the case.

12. Using snap ring pliers, remove the snap ring from the front end of the mainshaft.

13. Holding the synchronizer parts and mainshaft gears together as a unit, move the mainshaft to the right and disengage the shifter fork and shoe from the grooves in the shifter sleeve and low gear. Then twist and withdraw the mainshaft through rear of case.

14. With a long brass drift, drive the reverse idler gear shaft out of the rear of the case and lift out the idler gear.

15. Lift the countershaft gear cluster and related parts straight out of the case to prevent the needle rollers from spilling. Then carefully remove the thrust washers and note the position of each to insure exact replacement.

16. With a punch, drive out the taper pins securing the shift shafts in position, upward out of the case.

17. Remove the nuts, washers and levers from the shift shafts and take shafts out of case. Also remove the interlock sleeve, detent balls, spring and pin.

Assembly Notes

Regardless of appearance, all gaskets and oil seals should be replaced. When installing oil seals, coat the outside of the seal and inside of housing with red or white lead or gasket sealer to insure leak-tight joints. Leather seals should be soaked for 24 hours before installing them.

After installing the shift shaft levers, move either one into any in-gear posi-

tion and with one end of the interlock contacting a shift shaft cam, measure the clearance with a feeler gauge between the opposite end of the sleeve and the cam of the other shift shaft. This clearance should be .001" to .007". If not within these limits, remove the sleeve and replace with one of the proper length, available in five different lengths.

When installing the countershaft cluster gear, install the front washer with bronze face to the gear and lug at top. The rear inner (bronze) washer should be installed so the lugs will engage the slots in the cluster gear and the outer (steel) washer with the lug at top. With the countershaft installed temporarily, check the end play of the cluster gear. Do this by inserting a feeler gauge between the rear thrust washers. End play should range from .006" to .016". If greater than this, install new thrust washers.

With correct end play established, remove the countershaft with the dummy shaft, allowing the cluster gear and related parts to lie in the bottom of the case until after the main drive gear, mainshaft and reverse idler gears are installed. Then raise the cluster gear and install the countershaft.

1956-58 President Classic and Golden Hawk

NOTE—The following outlines the procedure for conventional transmissions. For repairs on the overdrive unit, see the *Overdrive Chapter*.

Disassemble, Fig. 2

1. Remove side cover and shift fork assembly from case.

2. Remove rear housing retainer screws.

3. Move housing rearward about ½" and rotate to expose rear end of countershaft.

4. Tap countershaft rearward and remove Woodruff key in end of shaft.

5. Then, using a suitable bar which is exactly the same length as the cluster gear and thrust washers combined, drive countershaft out with this bar, allowing cluster gear (with bar in cluster) to lie in bottom of case.

6. Raise front end of mainshaft so that the synchronizer sleeve will pass over countershaft cluster gear and remove mainshaft and rear housing assembly from the case.

7. Remove mainshaft front bearing rollers from bore of main drive gear.

8. Remove main drive gear bearing retainer and gasket.

9. Remove small snap ring and washer from main drive gear.

10. Place assembly in arbor press and press main drive gear shaft out of bearing.

11. Remove large bearing snap ring and tap main drive gear bearing out of case.

12. Remove countershaft gear cluster from bottom of case, being careful not to spill the countershaft bearing rollers.

13. To remove the reverse idler gear, tap the shaft rearward out of the case and remove the gear.

14. To disassemble the mainshaft, remove the front bearing spacer from the front end of the shaft. Mark the synchronizer sleeve, gear, blocker rings, second speed gear and low and reverse sliding gear so that they can be reinstalled in their original positions. Remove the synchronizer gear snap ring. Then slip the synchronizer assembly off the shaft. Slip the second speed and low gears off the shaft.

15. To remove the mainshaft from the rear housing, remove the bearing snap ring and tap the shaft and bearing out of the housing.

16. If necessary, remove the thrust washers and bearing rollers from the countershaft gear cluster.

Assembly Notes

Reverse the foregoing procedure to assemble the transmission, being sure to observe the following:

1. The reverse idler gear should be installed with the chamfered ends of the gear teeth and the smaller diameter shoulder to the front of the case. Then after the keyway is placed in the slot, drive the reverse idler shaft in until the end of the shaft is flush with the case.

2. Assemble the bearing rollers in the cluster gear, referring to Fig. 2, and using stiff grease to hold them in place around the assembly bar mentioned in disassembly procedure.

3. When installing the countershaft gear thrust washers, the front (large) thrust washer should be placed so that the lug is up and faces the front when the assembly is installed. The rear washer should be placed against the cluster so the lugs engage the notches in the gear. Place the entire cluster gear assembly in the bottom of the case. Slip

the steel spacer between the case and the rear thrust washer with the tab up.

4. When installing the oil slinger on the main drive gear shaft the concave side should be toward the gear.

5. Main drive gear bearing snap rings are available in six sizes. Be sure to select one which fits snugly in the groove.

6. When installing the mainshaft in the rear housing, make sure the snap ring is in the bore of the rear housing. Then insert the shaft in the housing, tap into position and install the front snap ring.

7. When assembling the mainshaft, align the marks of the low and reverse sliding gear and the mainshaft and install gear on shaft. The gear is installed with the shift fork channel toward the front end of the shaft. Install the second speed gear with the clutch cone forward.

8. When assembling the synchronizer, place the gear on the bench with the long hub up. Insert the shifter plates in the slots of the gear. Then align the marks made at disassembly and slip the sleeve on the gear. The shift fork channel in the sleeve must be down. Install the lock springs so that the identical ends of the springs are hooked in the same shifter plate.

9. When installing the synchronizer on the mainshaft, place the rear blocker

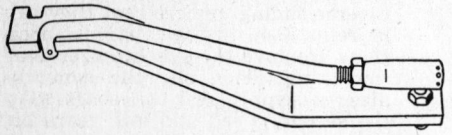

Fig. 3 Special gauge for checking length of hand control bell crank-to-transmission rod. Gauge is marked on either end for the various models

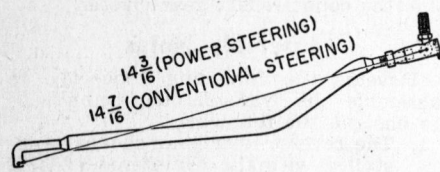

Fig. 4 Correct measurement of bell crank-to-transmission rod on 1953-57 two-door, four-door and Land Cruiser models

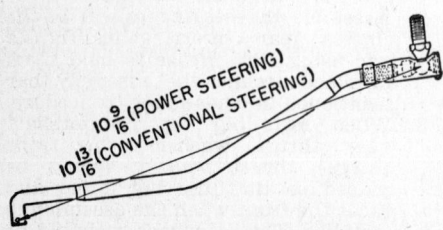

Fig. 5 Correct measurement of bell crank-to-transmission rod on 1953-57 Hardtop convertibles and five-passenger coupe models

ring on the second speed gear. Align the marks of the gear and shaft and install the synchronizer on the mainshaft with the shift fork channel to the rear of the shaft.

10. Before installing the shift cover, shift one of the shafts into an in-gear position and, with one end of the interlock sleeve against the cam of the shaft, measure the clearance between the other end of the sleeve and the cam with a feeler gauge. If the clearance is not within the limits of .001″ to .007″, replace the interlock sleeve with one of sufficient length to establish the correct clearance. Sleeves are available in four different lengths.

GEARSHIFT, ADJUST

To adjust the steering post gearshift control, first disconnect the shift rods from the transmission shift levers, noting the position of each clevis. Check to see that the shift levers on the transmission are in neutral, which can be determined by the action of the interlock.

Remove the back-up light switch (if so equipped). Position the locating bar of the special tool made for the purpose in the opening in the steering post jacket and under the shift levers. Place the other half of the clamp in position, engaging the stud on the locating bar. Install the thumb nut and tighten to hold the levers in position.

By turning the threaded clevis, adjust the length of each shift rod so that the holes in the clevis and shift lever are in alignment. Then insert the clevis pin and secure the clevis with the lock nut. Repeat this procedure with the other shift rod. After adjusting both rods, remove the gauge and check the operation of the gearshift control.

B-W AUTOMATIC DRIVE

The operation, construction and repair procedures on this transmission are given in detail in the *Borg-Warner Automatic Drive* chapter in this manual. The following gives the service adjustments for the various models.

Hand Control Linkage, 1953-56 All Models

1. Disconnect the hand control bell crank-to-transmission rod. Then check the length of the rod, using the gauge shown in Fig. 3. The tool is made to gauge a distance of $7\frac{5}{16}$″ (marked 9G and 17A) on one edge, and a distance of $7\frac{5}{8}$″ (marked 10G and H) on the other edge. The edge marked 10G and H is also used for 1953-56 models. Adjust the rod according to the tool.

2. Then, on 1952 models shorten the rod by one full turn of the ball joint end.

3. On 1953-56 models, measure the diagonal distance from the center of the cotter pin hole at the bell crank end to the center of the ball at the ball joint end as shown in Figs. 4 and 5 and adjust the rod to the

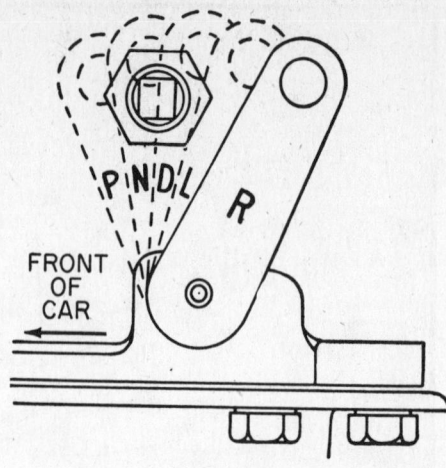

Fig. 6 Transmission selector valve lever shown in Reverse position

dimension shown for the model being serviced.

4. After the rod is correctly adjusted and lock nut tightened, set the transmission selector valve lever in Reverse, Fig. 6, and shift the hand control lever to the R position.

5. Adjust the length of the hand control tube-to-bell crank rod by turning the clevis until the holes in the clevis and bell crank line up so that the cotter pin will slip in easily. Then tighten the lock nut and remove the clevis pin.

6. Shift the hand control lever to the P position and set the transmission selector lever to the Parking position (all the way forward). In this position the propeller shaft should be locked.

7. Check the adjustment of the hand control tube-to-transmission rod by slipping the clevis pin into the assembled clevis and bell crank. If the pin does not slip in easily, change the adjustment of the rod by ½ turn to give a compromise fit for both P and R positions. If ½ turn does not give the proper adjustment, check the entire linkage for wear, looseness, binding or distortion.

8. Connect the rod to the bell crank and check the operation of the transmission.

Throttle Control Linkage, 1953-56 Champion

1. Adjust engine idle speed to 500-550 rpm by means of the idle adjustment screw at the carburetor throttle lever.

2. Remove the wire from the anti-creep switch and remove switch, Fig. 7.

3. Measure the distance between the accelerator cross shaft bracket and the contact plate. This measurement should be ¼″ with the accelerator fully released. If it is not, remove the clevis pin from the accelerator cross shaft-to-bell crank rod clevis, loosen the lock nut and adjust the clevis until the ¼″ measurement is obtained.

4. Then install the anti-creep switch until the plunger of the switch just

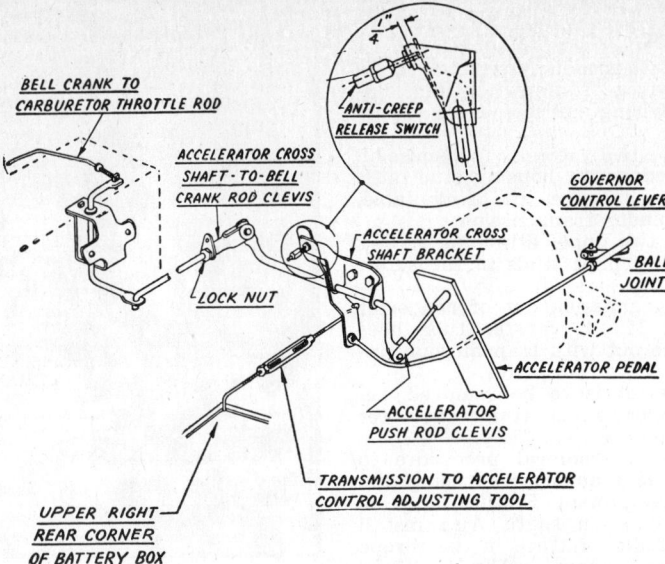

Fig. 7 Transmission control linkage. 1953-56 Champion

contacts the contact plate.

5. Install the wire, turn on the ignition and adjust the release switch as required until an audible click is heard in the solenoid. Then tighten the lock nut.

6. Shift the selector lever to the Park position. With the Accelerator-to-Transmission Control Adjusting Tool, Fig. 7, at its maximum length, hook one end of the tool in the notch of the accelerator cross shaft lever and the other end at the upper right rear corner of the battery box, as shown. In doing so, the accelerator push rod will be pulled forward, causing the bell crank-to-carburetor throttle rod to partially open the carburetor throttle. Adjust the length of the tool by turning the turnbuckle until the accelerator is brought forward far enough to put the throttle valve in its wide open position.

7. Disconnect the accelerator cross shaft-to-transmission rod ball joint from the governor control lever.

8. Turn the governor control lever forward (clockwise) until the resistance of the detent is felt (see Fig. 8).

9. Adjust the length of the rod by turning the ball joint until it can be slipped easily into the governor control lever when the lever is at the point where the resistance of the detent is felt (full throttle position).

10. Remove the accelerator-to-transmission control adjusting tool.

11. Check the linkage operation as follows: (a) With floor mat properly in place and accelerator fully depressed, remove ball joint and check to make sure the governor control lever on the transmission is at the end of its forward travel. (b) With the accelerator fully released, check to make sure there is at least ¼" of free travel of the governor control lever before spring pressure is felt as it is turned forward. If the adjust-

ment is correct, connect the ball joint to the governor control lever. (c) If full forward travel or the proper amount of free travel of the governor control lever are not obtained, recheck the linkage adjustment. If proper travel is still not obtained, check for and eliminate any bind, distortion or interference in the linkage which would affect proper adjustment.

Throttle Control Linkage, 1953-55 V8

1. To adjust, first disconnect the anti-creep release switch wire at the switch. Remove the switch from the bell crank bracket. Leave all three springs attached.

2. With the selector lever in the P or N position, adjust the engine idle speed to 500-550 rpm by means of the idle adjusting screw. Make sure the screw is contacting the lowest step of the fast idle cam. Make sure the throttle return check is functioning properly.

3. Place the idle speed adjusting screw on the 4th step of the fast idle cam (lowest step being the first step). Adjust the throttle check screw until it just contacts the pad on the throttle shaft lever.

4. Loosen the two threaded rod lock nuts. The throttle actuating spring turns and secure with the lock nut. will sag slightly. Hold the cross shaft arm against the bracket and at the same time tighten the forward nut on the threaded rod until the spring is taut. The idle adjusting screw will just start to break contact with the low step of the fast idle cam. Back off the forward threaded rod nut just enough to let the idle adjusting screw lightly contact the low step of the fast idle cam.

5. Install the anti-creep release switch in the cross shaft bracket. Turn it

in until the idle adjusting screw starts to break contact with the low step of the fast idle cam. Back off the anti-creep switch three complete

6. Back off the forward threaded rod nut three complete turns. This will allow approximately ⅛ to $\frac{3}{16}$" sag in the throttle actuating spring. Tighten the rear threaded rod nut.

7. A piece of ½" or ¾" angle iron 15¼" long can be used to hold the accelerator in a position to hold the throttle valve in its wide-open position. Pull the hand brake control handle out about four or five inches. Position the angle iron between the hand brake plunger, just forward of the handle, and the accelerator pedal. Depress the accelerator pedal nearly to the wide-open position and at the same time slide the lower end of the angle iron up near the top of the accelerator pedal. Then slowly push the hand brake in until the carburetor throttle valve is just to its wide-open throttle position. This is the point where any further movement of the accelerator pedal would only result in operating the over-travel spring. The angle iron will now hold the linkage in this position while the accelerator cross shaft-to-governor linkage is adjusted.

Governor Control Linkage, 1953-55 All Models

The throttle control linkage must be adjusted before this adjustment is attempted.

1. Disconnect accelerator rod ball joint from the governor lever. *Note whether it is removed from the inner or outer hole if the governor lever has two holes.*

2. Turn the governor control lever forward (clockwise), Fig. 8, until the resistance of the detent is felt and check the adjustment of the rod. If the linkage is correctly adjusted, the stud of the ball joint can easily be slipped into the proper hole of the governor lever. If adjustment is required, loosen the ball joint lock nut and turn the ball joint until the stud is aligned with the proper hole in the lever. Make sure that the lever is still at the point where the resistance of the detent is felt. After making the adjustment, tighten the lock nut securely. *Do not install the ball joint nut at this time.*

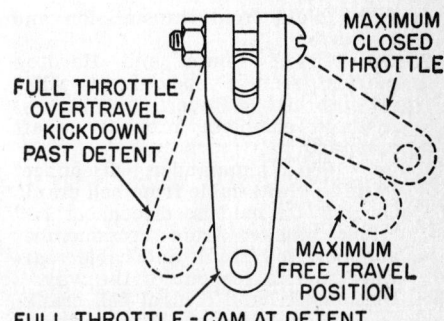

Fig. 8 Governor control lever 1953-55

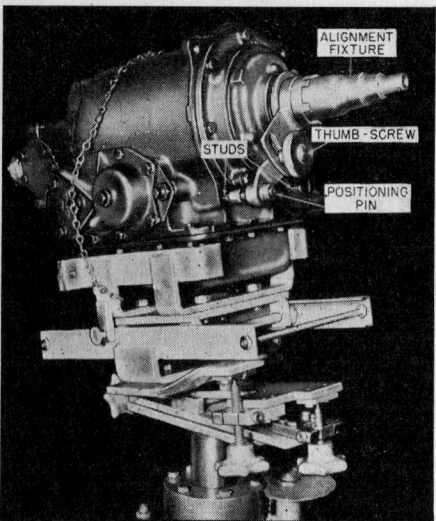

Fig. 9 Transmission mounted on special lift ready for installation. 1953-57

to-transmission rod ball joint from governor control lever.
8. Remove speedometer cable.
9. On 1953-55 models, disconnect anti-creep wires from switch and unfasten wiring harness from transmission.
10. Remove two lower transmission case-to-converter housing stud nuts.
11. Place transmission lift, if available, Fig. 9, under transmission.
12. Remove two upper attaching screws and install pilot studs in the screw holes.
13. Slide transmission out of converter housing. If oil transfer tube does not come out with transmission, remove it from converter.
14. If converter is to be removed, remove pilot studs from converter housing.
15. Reverse the removal procedure to install the transmission, using the Spline Alignment Fixture, Fig. 9, on transmission shaft. Also install the alignment fixture in the torque converter as shown in Fig. 10. When installation is completed, check and adjust the control linkage.

Torque Converter, Replace

1. Remove starter motor.
2. Remove transmission.
3. Disconnect exhaust pipes and muffler as required to provide additional clearance and working space.
4. The engine rear support crossmember must be removed. But before doing so, the engine weight must be lifted off the crossmember. The jack used to lift the engine should not bear against the bottom of the oil pan but rather on the oil pan flanges. A suitable support should be made capable of supporting 600 lbs. The support may be made of wood or channel iron in a U shape so that the weight is taken on the oil pan flanges.
5. Place the engine support saddle 3" to 5" forward of the engine rear plate and up against the oil pan

Fig. 11 Converter aligning flange tool being installed on converter. 1953-57

flange. Then install the jack on the support.
6. Remove rear engine support stud nuts and raise engine just enough to have separation between support and crossmember, and remove crossmember.
7. Remove converter housing front plate, and converter housing from dowels.
8. To facilitate removal of converter housing, lower engine, being careful not to pull off water outlet hose. If additional clearance is required, drain cooling system and disconnect outlet hose.
9. Remove torque converter.
10. Reverse removal procedure to install the converter, using the Converter Aligning Flange, Fig. 11, in the bore of the converter housing and over the pump drive fingers on the converter. Hold flange in place with two transmission attaching screws. Rotate converter through two complete revolutions to center the converter.

Starter Cut-Out Switch

The starter cut-out switch is located at the base of the steering post jacket and acts to break the starter solenoid circuit when the selector lever is in the D, L or R position and also to control the operation of the back-up light if so equipped.

Removal—Remove the two screws holding the switch to the steering post jacket. Lift out the switch and disconnect the hand control-to-switch rod. Disconnect the wiring cable from the switch.

Installation—Align the pin hole in the switch lever with the corresponding hole in the switch body. Install a pin through the holes that maintain alignment of the lever and body. Connect the wiring cable to the switch. Assemble the rod to the switch.
With the selector lever in N position,

3. Remove the angle iron from the accelerator push rod. Then check linkage operation as follows:
4. With the floor mat properly in place and accelerator *fully* depressed, slip the ball joint stud out of the governor lever and check to make sure the governor lever is at the end of its forward travel.
5. With the accelerator fully released, check to make sure there is at least ¼" of free travel of the governor lever before spring pressure is felt as it is turned forward. If the adjustment is correct, install and tighten the ball joint stud nut.
6. If full forward travel or the correct amount of free travel of the governor lever is not obtained, recheck the linkage adjustment. If proper travel is still not obtained, check for and eliminate any bind, distortion or interference in the linkage. A possible point of interference could be between the bell crank-to-transmission rod and the car floor pan. Remove the front splash pan from the frame side rail and check for this condition. If the condition exists, bend the floor pan (not the linkage) out of the way. Also check all linkage mounting bolts for tightness.

Automatic Transmission (Only), Replace

1. Drain fluid from transmission and converter.
2. On 1954-56 Coupe and Hardtop models, remove body front pillar support crossmember.
3. Remove complete propeller shaft assembly.
4. On 1950 Commander, disconnect parking brake cable from bell crank.
5. On 1950-53 models, disconnect bell crank bracket from crossmember and pull bell crank and cable rearward and fasten out of the way.
6. Disconnect hand control bell crank-to-transmission rod from selector control shaft lever.
7. Disconnect accelerator cross shaft-

Fig. 10 Spline alignment fixture inserted in torque converter. 1953-57

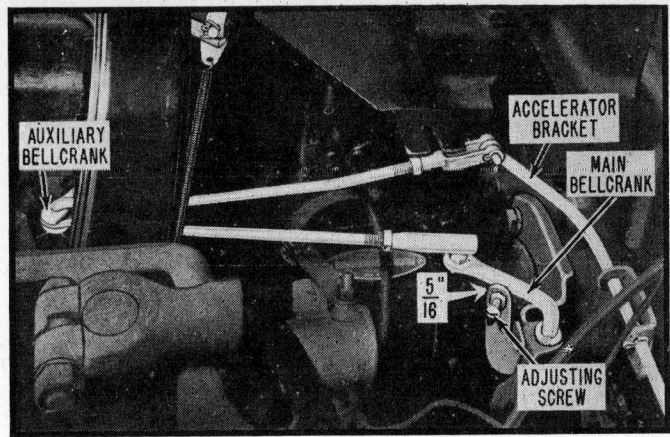

Fig. 12 Flightomatic throttle linkage. 1956-60 six-cylinder models

Fig. 13 Flightomatic throttle linkage. V8's

place the switch in position on the steering post jacket and install the screws. Remove the pin from the switch lever and body and test the operation of the switch.

Idle Adjusting Screw Switch

The idle adjusting screw switch is located on the carburetor throttle lever and acts to release the anti-creep system when the accelerator pedal is depressed to move the car. It replaces the usual idle adjusting screw and the position of the switch determines engine idling speed.

Removal—Disconnect the wire leading to the idle adjusting screw switch. Screw the switch out of the carburetor throttle lever.

Installation—With the lock spring in position on the switch, screw the switch into place in the carburetor throttle lever. Start the engine and, with the selector lever in the N position, set the engine idle at 500-550 rpm by turning the switch in or out as required. Connect the lead-in wire to the switch, and check anti-creep operation.

Anti-Creep Solenoid Control Switch

This switch is located at the rear of the transmission case and acts to prevent operation of the anti-creep system while the car is moving forward. The anti-creep system is not used on 1956 models so the pressure switch is replaced by a $\frac{1}{4}$" pipe plug. However, if anti-creep system is desired, a kit is available for installation on these models.

Removal—Disconnect the two control cables from the switch. Unscrew the switch from the rear of the transmission case.

Installation—Screw the switch into the back of the transmission case. Connect the control cables to the switch and check its operation.

Anti-Creep Solenoid Valve

The anti-creep solenoid valve is fastened to the rear of the brake master cylinder and acts to hold pressure on the rear brakes after the brakes have been applied to stop the car with the accelerator fully released.

Removal—With the ignition off, disconnect the cables at the connectors. Disconnect the brake tube from the solenoid valve to the adapter and take off the valve.

Installation—Insert the solenoid valve into the adapter and fasten the valve in place with the attaching screw. Connect the brake tube to the solenoid valve outlet. Bleed the brake system. Connect the control cables. Check operation of valve as follows:

With rear wheels stationary, ignition on and accelerator fully released, depress the brake pedal firmly and release. Rear wheel brakes should now be set, preventing the rear wheels from turning. The rear wheel brakes should release when the ignition is turned off or the accelerator is depressed.

FLIGHTOMATIC TRANSMISSION

A detailed service procedure on this transmission may be found in the *Automatic Transmission Section* of this Manual. The following covers the removal of the transmission and converter, and linkage adjustments.

Throttle Linkage, 1958-60 Six

1. Set selector lever in P or N position and operate engine until automatic choke is in wide open position.
2. Disconnect rod which connects accelerator bracket, Fig. 12, to auxiliary bellcrank.
3. Connect tachometer to engine and set engine idle speed to 550 rpm.
4. Disconnect rod which connects main bellcrank to auxiliary bellcrank.
5. Adjust the screw to provide 5/16" gap between bellcrank and pad as shown. A 5/16" drill may be used as a gauge.
6. Adjust ball joint on the main bellcrank-to-auxiliary bellcrank rod until ball joint stud freely enters hole in main bellcrank lever. During this

adjustment the carburetor idle speed screw must be against its stop and the 5/16" gap must be maintained.

7. Disconnect and adjust length of main bellcrank-to-throttle valve outer lever rod, Fig. 13, so that the ball joint stud freely enters throttle valve outer lever. During this adjustment, the throttle valve must be held against its internal stop (outer lever held to rear of transmission).
8. Remove ball joint stud from throttle valve outer lever and shorten rod four complete turns of the ball joint assembly.
9. Reinstall stud and tighten nut securely.
10. Hold accelerator bracket arm approximately 3⅞" from the firewall and adjust accelerator bracket-to-auxiliary bellcrank rod clevis until clevis pin freely enters clevis and bracket arm.

1959-60 Lark 6 Service Note

It is essential that the trottle control rod from bellcrank to carburetor be properly adjusted. The correct adjustment provides for a dimension of $11\frac{1}{16}$" between

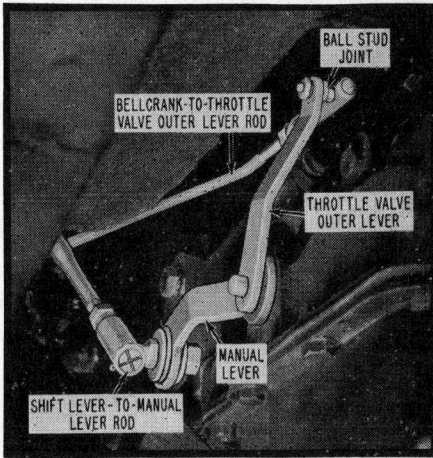

Fig. 14 Flightomatic throttle linkage at transmission. All 1956-61

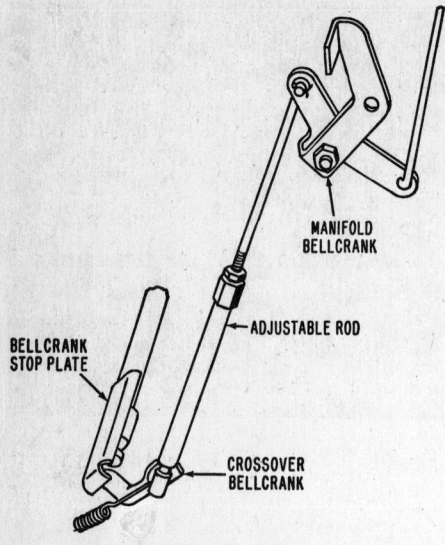

Fig. 15 Throttle linkage at right side of engine. 1961 Six

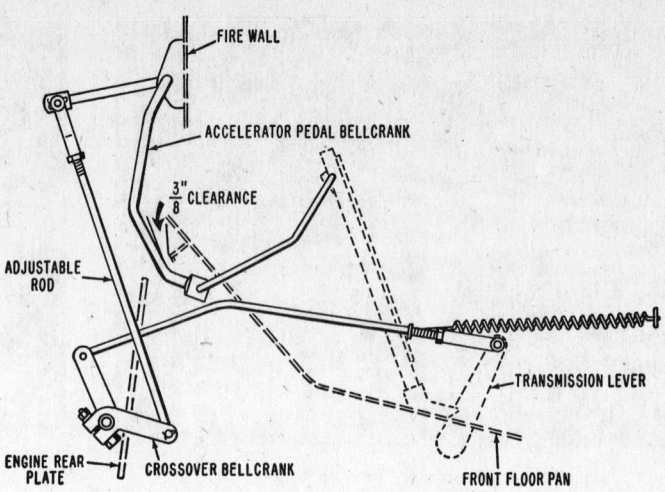

Fig. 16 Throttle linkage at left side of engine. 1961 Six

the centerline of the cotter pin hole and the centerline of the ball stud. After the rod has been adjusted to this length, it should not be changed in any subsequent adjustment operation.

1958-61 V8's

1. Set selector lever in P or N position and operate engine until the automatic choke is in wide open position.
2. Make sure throttle return check (dashpot) is operating correctly.
3. Connect tachometer to engine and set idle speed to 550 rpm.
4. Set stop on bellcrank to provide 17/64" gap between bellcrank pads, Fig. 13. A $\frac{17}{64}$" drill may be used as a gauge.

1961 Six

1. On right side of engine, Fig. 15, disconnect adjustable rod from manifold bellcrank.
2. With engine idling at 550 rpm in N or P, and with crossover bellcrank against bellcrank stop plate, adjust length of adjustable rod so end of rod slides freely in hole in manifold bellcrank.
3. On the left side of the engine, Fig. 16, adjust length of adjustable rod to provide ⅜" clearance between rib

of floor pan and accelerator pedal bellcrank arm.

Manual Control Valve Linkage

1. Disconnect shift lever-to-transmission manual valve lever rod, Fig. 14, at the ball joint.
2. Place selector lever in D position, which is the center of the manual valve lever travel.
3. Adjust shift lever-to-manual valve lever rod until the ball joint stud will slip freely through the hole in the manual valve lever.

Transmission, Replace

1. Drain oil from transmission and converter.
2. On Coupe and Hardtop models, remove body front pillar support crossmember.
3. On cars equipped with dual exhaust system, remove left exhaust system.
4. Remove complete propeller shaft assembly.
5. Disconnect rods from transmission levers.
6. Remove speedometer cable.
7. Support the transmission on a suitable lift. Then unfasten the transmission from the converter and remove from converter housing.
8. Installation is made in the reverse order of removal.

Converter, Replace

1. Remove the transmission and starting motor.
2. Disconnect rear exhaust pipe from front exhaust pipe and pull muffler and pipe assembly rearward.
3. The rear engine support crossmember must be removed to permit removal of the converter housing. But before removing the crossmember, the engine weight must be lifted off the crossmember. The jack used to lift the engine should not bear against the bottom of the oil pan; the engine should be supported at the oil pan flanges. A suitable support should be made capable of supporting 600 lbs. The support may be made of wood or channel iron in a U shape so that the weight is taken on the oil pan flanges.
4. Remove the rear engine stud nuts and raise the engine just enough to have separation between insulators and crossmember.
5. Remove crossmember.
6. Remove converter bell housing. To facilitate removal, lower rear of engine, being careful not to pull off the water outlet hose. If additional clearance is necessary, drain cooling system and remove this hose.
7. Unfasten and remove converter from the drive plate.
8. To install, reverse removal procedure.

Rear Axle and Brake Section

Refer To Hydraulic Brakes Chapter For Brake Adjustments

REAR AXLE ASSEMBLY, REPLACE

1. Remove axle nuts.
2. Raise car and support on two stands

placed under frame directly in front of rear springs.
3. Remove rear wheels.
4. Pull off hubs and drums.
5. Disconnect brake pipes at wheel cylinders.

6. Remove bolts from backing plates.
7. Remove brake pipe from axle housing.
8. Remove backing plates and adjusting shims and suspend them from frame.

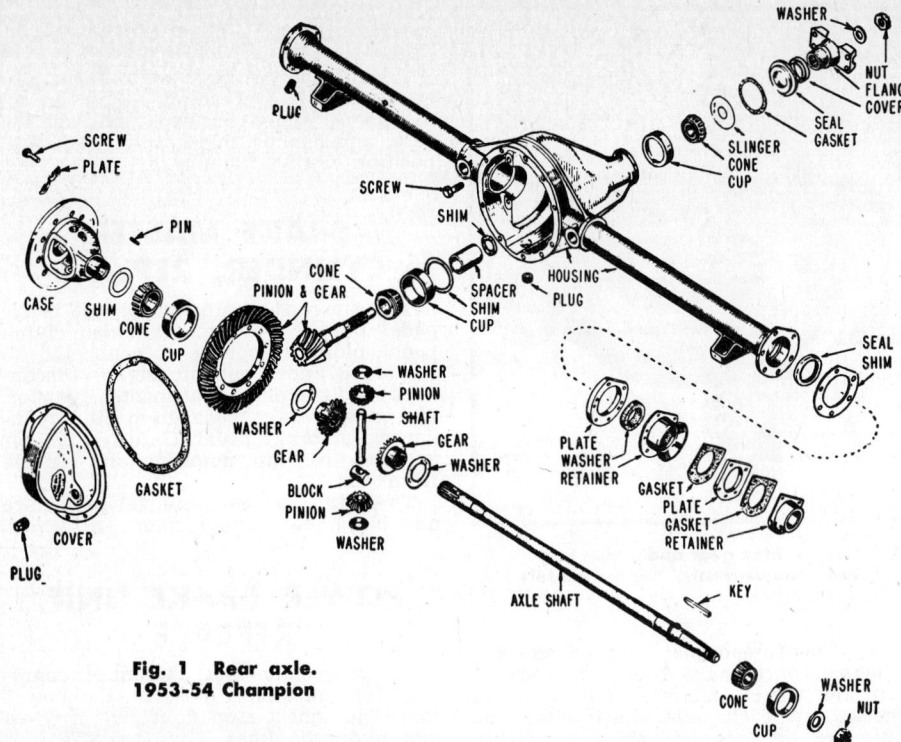

**Fig. 1   Rear axle.
1953-54 Champion**

9. Disconnect propeller shaft at axle housing and move to one side.
10. Remove spring U bolts from axle housing and disconnect shock absorbers from spring plates. On models so equipped, disconnect stabilizer shaft from spring plates.
11. Move axle assembly from under car.
12. Reverse removal procedure to install and, after connecting brake pipes, bleed the brake system.

REAR AXLE REPAIRS

In these units, Figs. 1 and 2, the drive pinion is held in position by shoulders in the differential carrier upon which the pinion bearing cups seat. The pinion position is maintained by shims located between the rear bearing and the rear shoulder in the differential carrier. Shims between the bearing spacer and the front bearing cone are used to adjust pinion bearings.

The shimmed type of differential bearing adjustment is employed, Fig. 3. The procedure for making this adjustment, as well as the assembly of the differential case, replacing the ring gear, checking ring gear and pinion backlash, and other differential case operations, is given in the *Rear Axle Chapter*.

The axle tubes are pressed into the differential carrier to form a one-piece housing. To overhaul the unit, therefore, the rear axle assembly must be removed from the chassis.

Pinion & Bearings, Replace

After removing the axle shafts and differential unit, unscrew the pinion flange retaining nut and pull off the flange. The pinion may then be removed from the carrier by driving it out of the front bearing with a brass drift and hammer. After the pinion is free of the

front bearing, pull it out through the rear of the carrier.

Mount the pinion in a press and press the pinion shaft out of the bearing. When replacing the bearing, select a suitable sleeve or length of pipe of the same diameter as the cone so the rollers or cage will not be damaged when being forced on the shaft.

Drive the front bearing cup and oil seal out of the forward end of the carrier. If the rear bearing cup is to be replaced or if the pinion setting is to be changed, remove the rear bearing cup.

To change the pinion setting, the shims behind the rear bearing cup should be measured with a micrometer. The necessary shims may then be removed or added to obtain the proper pinion setting as indicated when a pinion setting gauge is used (see *Rear Axle Chapter*). After the required shims have been added or subtracted, replace the rear bearing cup.

When making a pinion adjustment, the same thickness of pinion bearing adjusting shims should be added or removed at the rear bearing cup to retain the proper pinion bearing adjustment.

To install the pinion, support it under the head with a wood block while the pinion flange is reinstalled. The pinion oil seal should not be replaced until after the pinion setting has been checked.

Pinion Bearings, Adjust

The only occasion for adjusting the drive pinion bearings is when a new pinion or differential carrier is installed. To make the adjustment, install sufficient shims between the bearing spacer and front bearing so that when the pinion retaining nut is tightened against the pinion flange, all rollers in the bearing are tight, but still permit rotating the pinion by hand.

Pinion, Adjust

After adjusting the pinion bearings, the position of the pinion may be checked. If a pinion setting gauge is available, check the pinion depth as outlined in the *Rear Axle Chapter*. If a correction is necessary, disassemble the pinion and,

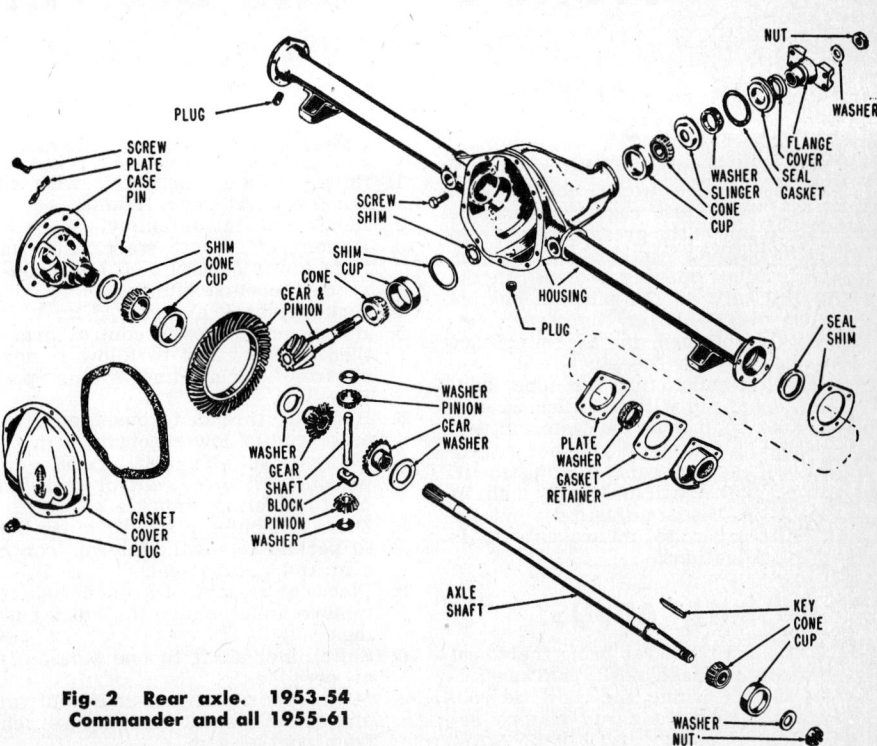

**Fig. 2   Rear axle.   1953-54
Commander and all 1955-61**

if it is to be moved toward the center of the axle, add shims between the rear bearing and rear shoulder in the carrier. If the pinion has to be moved away from the center of the axle, remove shims from this point.

If no pinion setting gauge is available, assemble the differential unit in the carrier and check the tooth contact by painting the ring gear teeth as described in the *Rear Axle Chapter*. After satisfactory tooth contact has been established, remove the pinion flange to make the installation of the oil seal. Using a compressing collar and the pinion flange retaining nut, press the new oil seal in place. Install the pinion flange, tighten the nut solidly in place and lock it with a new cotter pin.

AXLE SHAFTS

To remove an axle shaft, jack up the wheel and pull off the hub and brake drum. Block the brake pedal in such a manner that it cannot be depressed. Disconnect the hydraulic brake line from the wheel cylinder. Remove the mounting screws and take off the outer oil seal, shims and brake support. The shaft and bearing may then be pulled out of the housing. The inner oil seal may be removed at this time.

Replace the shaft and bearings in the reverse order. If the old parts are replaced and the shims have not been disturbed, the end play should be correct when the parts are assembled. However, if a new axle shaft, bearing, differential carrier or housing has been installed, it will be necessary to check the end play.

Fig. 3 Ring gear and pinion backlash adjustments. All models

To Decrease Backlash, Remove Shims Here and Install on Opposite Side

To Increase Backlash, Remove Shims Here and Install on Opposite Side

Axle shaft end play can be checked when all parts have been replaced except the wheel and hub. To make the check, rap each axle shaft after the nuts are tight to be sure the bearing cups are seated. Then mount a dial indicator on the axle housing with its contact button touching the end of the shaft. Work the shaft in and out by hand and note the reading on the indicator. If an adjustment is necessary, remove the oil seal and brake support

and add or remove shims as required to bring the end play within the limits shown in *Rear Axle and Brake* chart.

When making this adjustment, an equal thickness of shims should be removed or added on each side of the axle housing to maintain the central position of the axle shafts.

BRAKE MASTER CYLINDER, REPLACE

To remove the unit, unhook the brake pedal pullback spring, and also clutch pedal pullback spring if connected to master cylinder support strap. Disconnect fluid line or lines at master cylinder. Disconnect brake pedal-to-master cylinder rod at brake pedal. Unfasten master cylinder from its mounting and remove from car.

To install, reverse removal procedure and bleed the brake system.

POWER BRAKE UNIT, REPLACE

To remove the unit, disconnect manifold vacuum supply hose at the power unit. Disconnect stop light switch wires and hydraulic lines. Unfasten the unit from its mounting and remove from car.

If necessary, repairs to the power unit may be accomplished in the manner described in the *Power Brakes Chapter*. To install the unit, reverse the removal procedure and bleed the system as outlined in the *Power Brakes Chapter*.

Front End and Steering Section

CASTER & CAMBER, ADJUST

Caster and camber adjustments are both made at the upper control arm outer pin. To adjust caster, loosen the lock bolt. Remove the grease fitting from the front bushing and insert an Allen wrench into the opening provided in the pin. A full turn of the pin will change caster ½ degree. After the correct adjustment is obtained, install the grease fitting and tighten the pinch bolt.

To adjust camber, turn the upper control arm outer pin with an Allen wrench in the same manner as for caster adjustment. One half turn of the pin covers the entire range of camber adjustment. Adjusting camber will make only a slight change in the caster adjustment but recheck the caster to make sure it is within specifications.

TOE-IN, ADJUST

Turn the left tie rod to bring the wheel in the straight-ahead position. Then adjust toe-in by turning the right tie rod. Be sure to tighten tie rod clamps securely.

FRONT END REPAIRS

Lower Control Arm Removal

1. Raise car and support it with stationary jacks under frame.
2. Remove wheel assembly.
3. Disconnect front stabilizer shaft from lower control arm and remove rubber rebound bumper.
4. Remove shock absorber, Fig. 1.
5. Inner end of lower control arm is then disconnected to allow removal of front spring and spring pads, Fig. 2.
6. Remove threaded bushings from outer end of lower control arm.
7. Using a suitable drift, remove pin which locks lower control arm outer pin to steering knuckle support.
8. Drive out outer pin with brass drift to permit removal of lower control arm and grease seals.
9. Place lower control arm in vise and remove inner shaft threaded bushings.
10. Shift inner shaft to one side as far as possible.
11. Move opposite end of shaft outward and remove shaft and grease seals from control arm.

Lower Control Arm Install

1. Place control arm in vise.
2. Install seals on inner shaft.
3. Insert one end of inner shaft in one member of control arm, push in as far as possible, swing opposite end into position and insert it in other member of arm.
4. It is necessary to spread ends of control arm .015" to prevent bind at threaded bushings. Install Spreader Tool, Fig. 3, and tighten threaded tip of tool finger tight, then turn one-half turn more to spread ends .015".
5. With spreader in position, place inner shaft in center between ends of control arm, being sure control arm does not bind on shaft.
6. It is also necessary to spread outer ends of lower control arm .015". Determine outer dimension by adjusting a pair of calipers, Fig. 4, so setting includes a .015" feeler gauge which is inserted between outside edge of control arm and on prong of calipers.
7. After setting calipers, position outer end of lower control arm at lower steering knuckle support and install

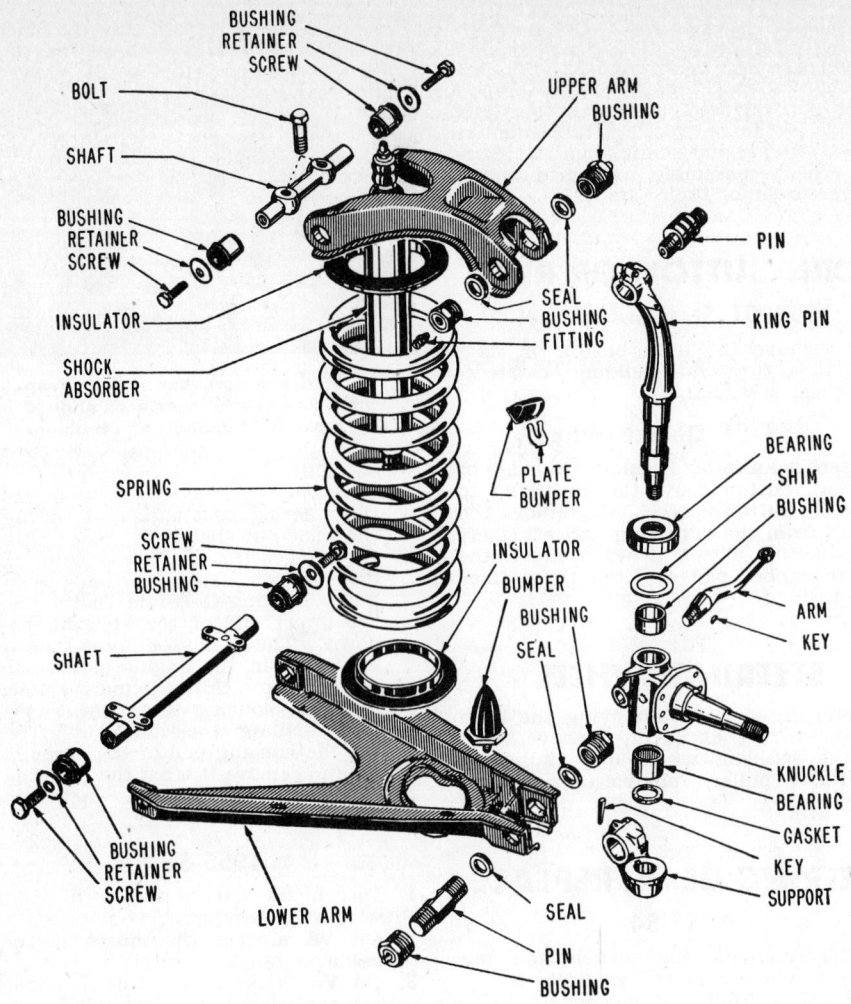

Fig. 1 Front suspension. 1953-61

BUSHING RETAINER SCREW
BOLT
SHAFT
BUSHING RETAINER SCREW
INSULATOR
SHOCK ABSORBER
UPPER ARM BUSHING
SEAL BUSHING FITTING
PIN
KING PIN
SPRING
SCREW RETAINER BUSHING
SHAFT
PLATE BUMPER
INSULATOR BUMPER BUSHING SEAL
BEARING
SHIM
BUSHING
ARM KEY
BUSHING RETAINER SCREW
LOWER ARM
SEAL
PIN
BUSHING
KNUCKLE BEARING
GASKET
KEY
SUPPORT

5. Remove grease seals from shaft.
6. To assemble, install seals on inner shaft.
7. Insert one end of shaft into control arm, bring opposite end in position and insert in control arm.
8. It is necessary to spread inner ends of upper control arm .015″. Using calipers and .015″ feeler gauge, determine outside dimension of control arm.
9. Then with Spreader Tool, Fig. 5, spread inner ends of control arm until outside dimension is equal to setting of calipers.
10. With spreader tool in place, centralize inner shaft with ends of control arm and install bushings. Make sure shaft is free.
11. The outer end of the upper control arm must also be spread .015″.
12. Using calipers and .015″ feeler gauge, determine outside dimension.
13. Position upper control arm at kingpin and insert outer pin, with hex opening in pin toward front through one of control arm ends.
14. Install grease seal on pin, push pin through end of kingpin and install other grease seal.
15. Center outer pin in kingpin by aligning groove of outer pin with hole in kingpin and install pinch bolt.
16. Install Spreader Tool and spread ends of control arm to setting of calipers, Fig. 6.
17. Center end of kingpin in control arm and, with spreader still in place, install bushings.
18. On 1950 Commander, install shock absorber and cork grease seal on control arm.
19. With marked side of inner shaft up, align holes of inner shaft and holes of frame bracket and install retaining bolts.
20. On 1950 Commander, connect shock absorber arm link to frame bracket.
21. Install wheel.
22. Check and adjust camber and caster as outlined previously.

Steering Knuckle Service

1. Raise car and support it at outer end of lower control arm.
2. Remove front wheel assembly.
3. Remove brake plate from knuckle flange without disturbing brake hose and suspend brake assembly in an out of the way position. Do not al-

outer pin, with a seal on each side of steering knuckle support.
8. Using a screwdriver in slot provided in end of outer pin, turn pin and align slot at center of outer pin and hole of knuckle support and install lock pin.
9. Then install Spreader Tool, Fig. 4, between inner surfaces of outer ends and spread ends until outside dimension is equal to setting of calipers.
10. Centralize outer end of control arm on outer pin.
11. Install bushings and tighten them securely. Then remove spreader tool, and make sure control arm turns freely on outer pin.
12. Install front spring and spring pads and complete installation of control arm.
13. On 1952-58, install shock absorber.
14. Connect stabilizer shaft, install rebound bumper and wheel assembly.

Upper Control Arm Removal

1. Raise car and support it at outer end of lower control arm.
2. Remove front wheel.
3. On 1950 Commander, disconnect shock absorber arm from frame bracket.
4. Remove pinch bolt which holds up-

per control arm in head of kingpin.
5. Remove threaded bushings and outer pin and grease seals.
6. Mark top front of control arm inner shaft so that position of shaft can be noted after assembly is removed.
7. Remove bolts and nuts which hold inner shaft to frame bracket and remove upper control arm.

Caution — Note position of inner shaft as identified by the mark which was made during removal of arm. The holes in the inner shaft are drilled off the centerline of the shaft and turning the shaft over will increase or decrease the camber slightly less than ¾ degree. Therefore, on assembly, it is important that the shaft be installed in the original position.

Upper Control Arm Repair & Install

1. Place upper control arm in vise.
2. Remove shock absorber and grease seal from 1950 Commander control arm.
3. Remove bushings from inner shaft.
4. Shift shaft as far as possible to one side, move opposite end of shaft out of control arm end and remove shaft and seals from arm.

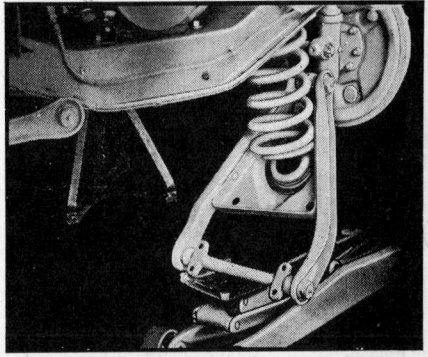

Fig. 2 Lower control arm disconnected to allow removal of front spring

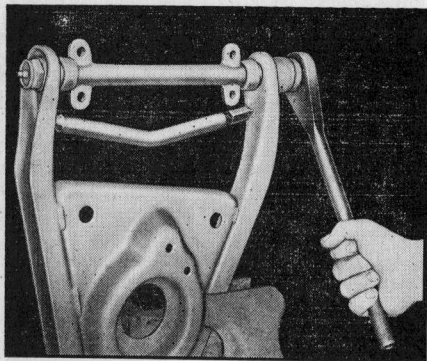

Fig. 3 Using spreader tool to keep lower control arm members aligned to prevent binding of threaded bushings

the thrust bearing and lower shoulder of the kingpin and press down on the thrust bearing. If the surface of the thrust bearing is not flush with the shoulder of the kingpin, remove or add shims as required. After proper end play is obtained, remove the knuckle, thrust bearing and shims from the kingpin. Then reassemble the parts in the reverse order of their removal.

HORN BUTTON OR RING

1953-61 Standard Wheel

To remove the horn button or ring, twist it ⅓ turn while holding the steering wheel stationary.

1953-61 Deluxe Wheel

Insert a knife blade under the edge of the horn button above the horn ring to force the button up and out. Remove the screws from the horn ring and lift it off the steering wheel. Then remove the sponge rubber pad and the three fiber spacers.

STEERING WHEEL

All Models — After removing the horn button or ring as outlined above, take off the steering wheel nut and, with a suitable puller, remove the steering wheel.

STEERING GEAR, REPLACE

1953-54

After removing the horn button and steering wheel, proceed as follows:
1. Remove front seat cushion.
2. Remove battery.
3. Disconnect quadrant light cable and starter cut-out switch cable, if car is equipped with Automatic Drive. Disconnect shift lever rod or rods and loosen the jacket clamp bolt.
4. Remove the jacket bracket retaining bolts from the instrument panel. Loosen the bracket clamp screw and turn the bracket to avoid hitting the instrument panel when removing the jacket. Then slip the jacket off

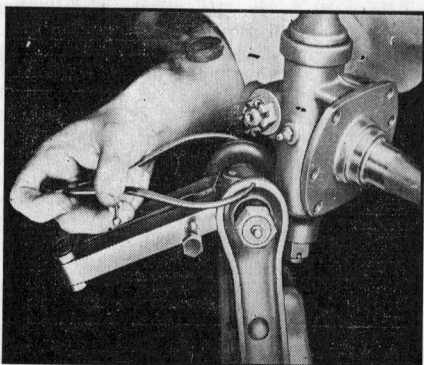

Fig. 4 Using calipers and spreader tool to establish proper spread of outer ends of lower control arm

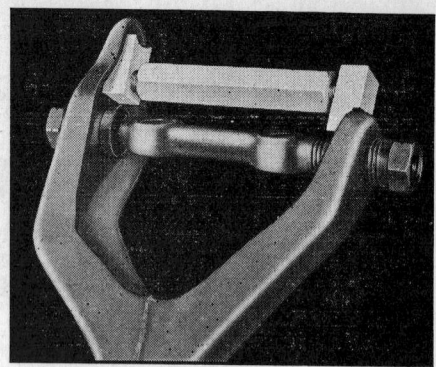

Fig. 5 Using spreader tool to keep upper control arm inner ends aligned to prevent binding of bushings

the steering post as a unit through the inside of the car.
5. Disconnect the reach rod from the pitman arm. Remove the steering gear housing-to-frame bolts. Tip the upper end of the steering post down. The gear asembly is then removed from the engine side of the cowl. Wrap a cloth around the steering gear housing top cover to prevent spilling the lubricant. Then lift the housing end of the assembly up and remove it from the chassis.
6. Reverse the foregoing to install the gear.

1955-58

1. Disconnect battery and horn switch wire at connector.
2. On V8 models, disconnect battery cable at starter switch.
3. On V8 Coupe and Hardtop models, remove battery and battery box.
4. Remove steering gear housing, steering post jacket and steering wheel as an assembly.
5. On V8 Coupe and Hardtop models, remove left front engine support cushion and raise this corner of engine about 2".
6. Pull off pitman arm.
7. Unfasten steering gear from frame and take it out through hole in dash and into car. Wrap a cloth around the gear housing top cover to prevent spilling lubricant during removal.
8. To install, reverse removal procedure.

1959-61

1. Remove battery.
2. Disconnect horn switch wire at connector.
3. Disconnect battery cable at starter switch.
4. Remove battery box on Sport Coupe.
5. Remove steering column jacket.
6. On V8's (except Sport Coupe) remove left front engine support cushion stud nut and raise engine about 1½". *Before raising engine, remove distributor cap.*
7. Remove reach rod from pitman arm.
8. Unfasten steering gear from frame and roll gear over so that it is upside down. Then lift and remove it through engine compartment.

low assembly to hang on hose.
4. Disconnect tie rod from knuckle arm.
5. Remove kingpin retaining nut. Then use a lead mallet to drive kingpin upward out of lower support.
6. Lift upper control arm and kingpin assembly and swing kingpin outward.
7. Remove Woodruff key from kingpin, then remove steering knuckle, shim and thrust bearing.
8. Remove cork gasket from lower end of knuckle.

To service the knuckle, proceed as follows:
1. First remove needle bearing at lower end of knuckle.
2. Insert removal adapter in knuckle and place it on upper surface of bearing.
3. Place knuckle in arbor press. Then, using the bushing of the knuckle as a pilot, insert arbor and press bearing out of knuckle.
4. To remove bushing, invert steering knuckle, insert removal adapter and place it on inner end of bushing.
5. Insert pilot in bearing end of knuckle and, using the arbor, press bushing out of knuckle.
6. To remove kingpin, remove bushings and outer pin as outlined under Upper Control Arm.
7. If necessary to replace the steering knuckle arm, remove arm retaining nut and, using a suitable drift, drive the arm out of the knuckle and remove the Woodruff key from the arm.

Assembly Notes

Assemble the steering knuckle in the reverse order. However, when pressing the bearing into the steering knuckle, be sure that the pressure is applied to the lettered end of the bearing. Then, to determine the steering knuckle end play on the kingpin, first place the kingpin in a vise and place the steering knuckle on the kingpin without the cork gasket which is normally installed on the bottom of the knuckle. Place the thrust bearing and shims on the kingpin. Insert a .003" to .006" feeler gauge between the shoulder of the kingpin and steering knuckle. Place a straightedge or small scale across the top surface of

Fig. 6 Using calipers and spreader tool to establish proper spread of outer ends of upper control arm

ROSS STEERING GEAR

This type steering gear, Fig. 7, can be identified by the location of the filler hole plug which is at the upper end of the housing.

Two adjustments are provided for the steering gear assembly: steering post end play and cam lever shaft stud clearance. Before making adjustments, free the steering gear of all load by disconnecting the steering gear from the steering linkage.

Steering Post End Play

Loosen the cam lever shaft adjusting screw lock nut, Fig. 8, and back off the adjusting screw. Using a spring scale that is calibrated in ounces, measure the amount of pull required to turn the steering wheel. The scale should be hooked to a tag wire or string which is wrapped around the rim of the steering wheel at the spoke. A steady pull of 4 to 7 ounces should turn the steering wheel smoothly. If the pull is not within limits, loosen the steering post jacket clamp, remove the top cover cap screws and add or remove shims as required to secure the proper scale reading, Fig. 9.

Cam Lever Shaft Stud Clearance

With the steering post end play adjusted correctly, locate the center of travel (high spot) of the steering gear. While turning the steering wheel back and forth over the high spot, turn the lever shaft adjusting screw, Fig. 8. Keep the lock nut snug until a slight drag is felt. Then tighten the lock nut.

To check the adjustment, hook the spring scale to the steering wheel rim and check the amount of effort required to turn the wheel in either direction through the high spot. The scale reading should be 16 to 24 ounces.

Steering Gear Repairs

If repairs are required on the steering post or its bearings, remove the steering gear assembly from the car as outlined previously. But if only the cam lever shaft requires service, it may be removed from the gear housing without removing the entire steering gear from the car.

SAGINAW STEERING GEAR
1953-60

This steering gear may be identified by the location of the filler hole plug which is on a boss located near the center of the housing. It can also be identified by the large lock nut at the lower end of the housing, Fig. 10.

There are two adjustments for the steering gear assembly: worm shaft end play, and the clearance adjustment between the worm shaft and roller. Although there are but two adjustments, the complete procedure outlined below must be followed. Before making adjustments, free the steering gear of all load by disconnecting the steering gear from the steering linkage.

Worm Shaft Bearings

Loosen the lock nut, Fig. 11, and turn the adjusting screw a few turns in a counterclockwise direction. This releases the worm shaft bearings from the load caused by the close meshing of the worm and roller. Turn the steering wheel gently in one direction until stopped by the gear, then back away one turn.

Attach a spring scale to the rim of

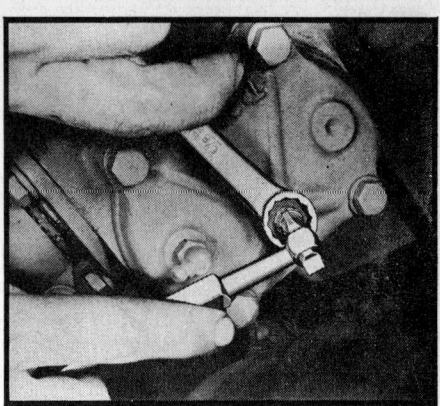

Fig. 8 Adjusting cam lever stud clearance. Ross steering gear

the steering wheel and measure the pull required to turn the wheel. The spring scale reading should be between 6 and 10 ounces. If not within these limits, loosen the lock nut and turn the bearing adjuster, Fig. 10, as required to bring it within limits (clockwise to increase drag; counterclockwise to decrease it). Tighten lock nut and recheck the adjustment.

Tighten the jacket bracket-to-instru-

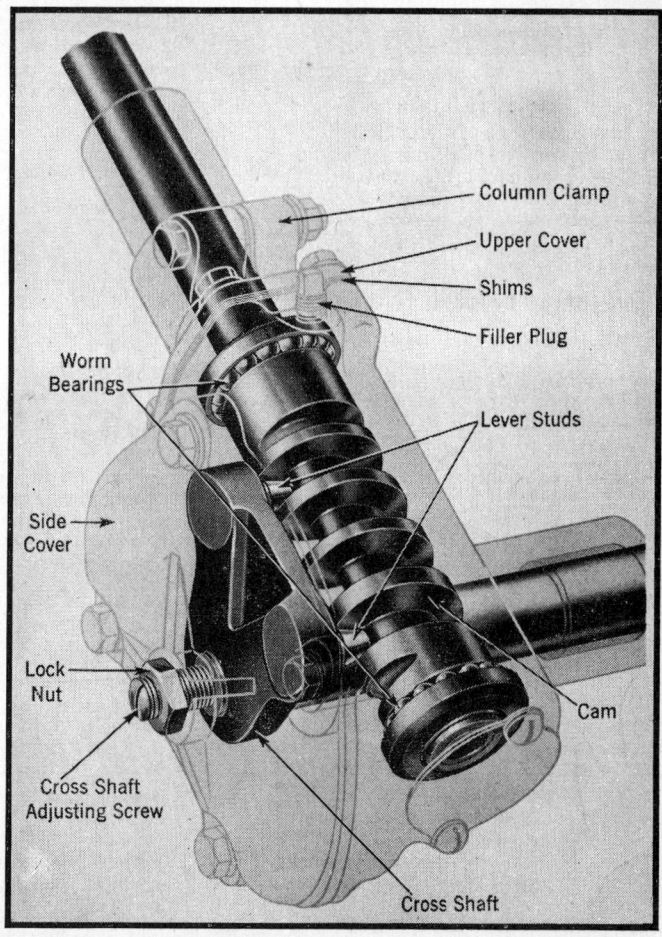

Fig. 7 Ross cam and twin lever steering gear. A gear with a single cam lever is used on 1957-60 V8 models

Column Clamp
Upper Cover
Shims
Filler Plug
Worm Bearings
Lever Studs
Side Cover
Cam
Lock Nut
Cross Shaft Adjusting Screw
Cross Shaft

Fig. 9 Removing shim to eliminate steering post end play. Ross steering gear

ment panel bolts and recheck the worm shaft end play adjustment to make sure a bind is not imposed on the gear. If the scale readings are not now within specified limits, it will be necessary to loosen the gear housing mounting bolts and slightly shift or shim the assembly to correct the binding condition.

Worm Shaft & Roller Clearance

After proper adjustment of the worm shaft end play is obtained, adjust the roller-to-worm clearance. First turn the steering wheel gently through the entire range of travel, carefully counting the total number of turns. Then turn the wheel back exactly halfway, to the center position.

Turn the adjusting screw, Fig. 11, clockwise to take out all the lash and tighten lock nut. Then check the pull at the wheel as in the first adjustment. Take the highest reading on the scale as the wheel is pulled through the center position. This should be 14 to 30 ounces. After setting the lock nut, recheck the adjustment.

Steering Gear Repairs

If repairs are required on the worm shaft and bearings, the steering gear assembly will have to be removed from the car. But if only the cross shaft assembly requires service it may be re-

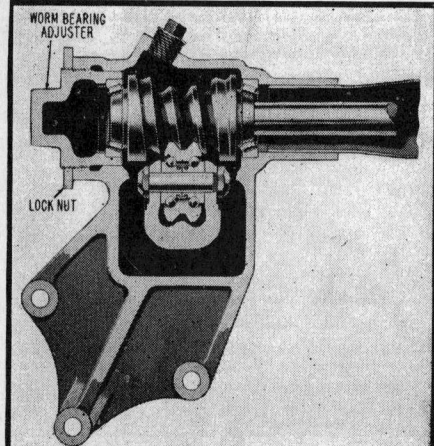

Fig. 10 Worm shaft end play adjustment. Saginaw steering gear. 1953-60

moved from the gear housing without removing the entire steering gear from the car.

STEERING GEAR REPAIRS, 1961

Disassemble

1. Rotate steering worm until nut is in center of travel, Fig. 12.
2. Remove sector shaft nut.
3. Remove side cover and sector shaft from housing.
4. Turn adjuster screw in end of sector shaft down through cover.
5. Remove end cover with worm bearing, outer race and thrust washer.
6. To remove lower worm bearing, outer race and thrust washer from cover, loosen worm bearing adjuster screw lock nut and turn screw in though cover.
7. Grasp lower end of steering worm and draw steering shaft and nut assembly out of steering housing. *Be sure too keep shaft in horizontal position so that nut does not move against stops at any time, thereby causing damage to ball return mechanism. Disassembly of worm nut is not recommended.*

Assemble

1. Install steering shaft and nut assembly in steering housing, keeping ball nut away from stops on worm.
2. Install worm bearing adjusting

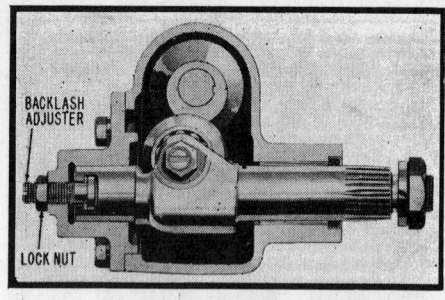

Fig. 11 Adjusting backlash between worm shaft and roller. Saginaw steering gear. 1953-60

screw with lower worm bearing, outer race, and thrust washer in end cover.
3. Install end cover and attaching parts on gear housing, making sure bearings seat properly.
4. Tighten worm bearing adjusting screw until a slight drag is felt on bearings. Do not tighten lock nut.
5. Install pitman arm.
6. Install sector shaft and adjuster screw inside cover.
7. Rotate steering column until ball nut is in center of travel so that center tooth on sector shaft will enter center space on nut.
8. Install side cover and sector shaft in gear housing.
9. Tighten sector shaft adjusting screw until a slight drag is felt on bearing but do not tighten lock nut.
10. After steering gear has been installed in car, adjust gear as outlined below.

Steering Gear, Adjust

The recirculating ball type steering gear has two adjustments: the worm bearing adjustment and cross shaft end play adjustment.

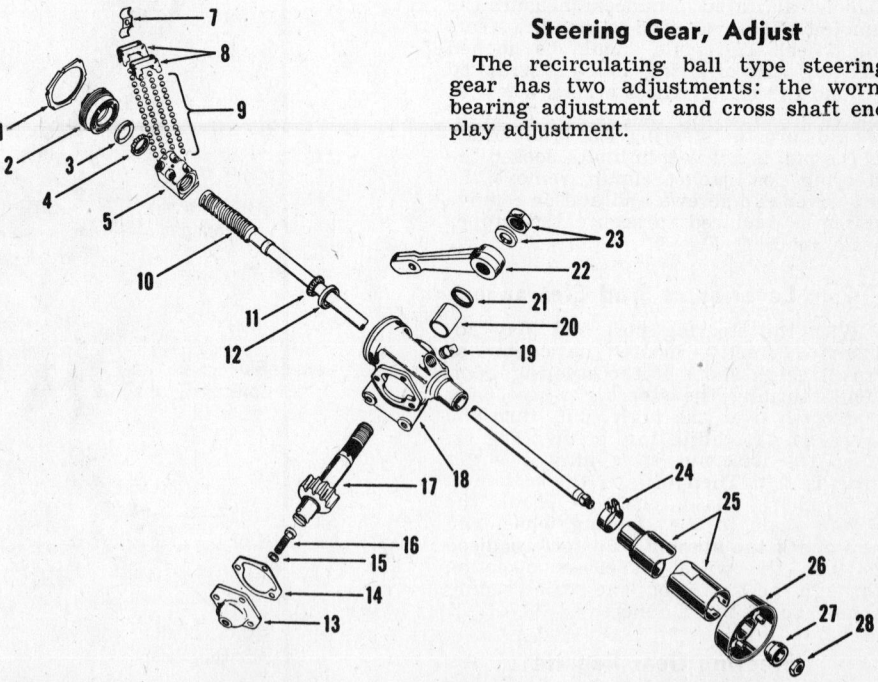

1. Bearing adjuster lock nut	8. Ball guides	15. Adjusting shim	22. Pitman arm
2. Bearing Adjuster nut	9. Balls	16. Adjusting screw	23. Lock washer and nut
3. Bearing cap	10. Steering post	17. Sector shaft	24. Clamp
4. Bearing	11. Bearing	18. Housing	25. Post jacket
5. Ball nut	12. Bearing cap	19. Filler plug	26. Upper bracket
6. Clamp screw	13. Sector shaft cover	20. Bushing	27. Upper post bearing
7. Guide clamp	14. Gasket	21. Seal	28. Nut

Fig. 12 Saginaw recirculating ball nut type steering gear. 1961

Worm Bearing Adjustment—Disconnect steering connecting rod at pitman arm. Turn steering wheel to either right- or left-hand stop. Then check load to pull steering wheel back to a point not less than 90° from the straight-ahead position of the steering wheel. The load should be between 2¼ to 6¾ inch pounds. Load is checked with a spring scale hooked to the rim of the steering wheel. To adjust, loosen lock nut and turn the worm bearing adjusting screw as required. Tighten the lock nut and recheck the adjustment.

Cross Shaft End Play—Turn the steering wheel about 90° each way through center. The pull through center should be between 8 and 9 inch pounds. If an adjustment is required, loosen the lock nut and turn the cross shaft adjusting screw in the direction required to obtain the desired result. Tighten the lock nut when the adjustment is correct and recheck the adjustment.

POWER STEERING, REPLACE

1953-58

1. Disconnect and remove battery.
2. On C and K models, remove battery box.
3. Unfasten and slip steering post collar up out of the way.
4. If equipped with automatic transmission, disconnect quadrant light and starter cut-out switch cables.
5. If equipped with turn signals, disconnect cables.

6. Disconnect shift lever rod or rods.
7. Loosen jacket clamp bolt at lower end of jacket.
8. Remove steering wheel.
9. Unfasten and slip steering jacket off steering post.
10. Separate steering coupling, keeping collector ring and insulators intact, and remove steering post assembly. Tape coupling studs to prevent damaging threads when removing the unit.
11. On W, F and D Commander and President Sedan models, remove left rocker arm cover.
12. Disconnect reach rod from pitman arm.
13. Remove pitman arm pinch bolt.
14. Move fender gravel deflector out of the way and remove steering gear-to-mounting bracket bolts.
15. On W, F and D Commander and President Sedan models, it may be necessary to shift the unit against the fender apron to gain clearance to remove the pitman arm. Then remove pitman arm.
16. Disconnect flexible hoses from pump. Tape openings of pump fittings and hoses or install suitable plugs.
17. Shift unit rearward, inserting its top end through opening in firewall. Lift lower end of unit, turning it as necessary to gain clearance past fender apron and battery box on W, F, D and Y models. Then lift unit from car.
18. To install, reverse removal procedure. Then after connecting the hoses, fill gear housing to the proper level and bleed system as outlined in the *Power Steering Chapter*.

1959-61

1. Remove battery.
2. Remove steering post collar screws and slip collar up out of the way.
3. Remove horn wire brush terminal and bracket.
4. If equipped with automatic transmission, disconnect quadrant light and starter cutout switch cables.
5. If equipped, disconnect turn signal cables.
6. Disconnect shift lever rod or rods.
7. Loosen jacket clamp bolt at lower end of jacket.
8. Remove steering wheel.
9. Remove column jacket spring.
10. Loosen column jacket-to-instrument panel bracket clamp screw and remove screws and shims (if present). Then slip jacket off steering post.
11. Remove four steering post coupling nuts, separate coupling (keeping insulators intact) and remove post assembly.
12. Remove left rocker arm cover.
13. Disconnect reach rod from pitman arm.
14. Remove pitman arm pinch bolt.
15. Move fender gravel deflector out of the way and remove three steering gear housing-to-frame bolts. *It may be necessary to shift the unit against the fender apron to gain clearance when removing pitman arm.*
16. Disconnect hoses from pump.
17. Shift power steering unit rearward, inserting its top end through opening in firewall. Then lift lower end as necessary to gain clearance past fender apron and lift out of car.

Speedometer and Windshield Wiper

SPEEDOMETER REMOVAL

1953-54 Champion

Disconnect battery ground cable. Uncouple drive cable and lamps from speedometer. Remove two auxiliary circuit breaker retaining screws. Remove speedometer after taking out four screws.

1953-54 Commander and Land Cruiser

Disconnect battery ground cable and speedometer cable. Remove speedometer case clamps. Push speedometer out of instrument panel toward rear of car.

1955

Disconnect battery ground cable. On models with flat windshield remove left lower panel cover (4 screws). On all models, remove retaining clamps, disconnect speedometer cable and pull speedometer forward out of panel.

1956-61

Disconnect speedometer cable and lamp. Remove speedometer from panel (4 screws).

WINDSHIELD WIPER

The parking position of the wiper blades is adjustable by means of a lever on the front of the wiper drive. Loosen the three screws slightly and turn the lever a short distance toward "advance" or "retard" whichever is required. Then tighten the screws and test the operation.

To remove the wiper motor on 1958-61 models, remove the radio, if so equipped. On electric motors, swing the cover to one side and remove the main link nut and main link. Remove the attaching parts and take out the motor.

WILLYS JEEP

INDEX OF SERVICE OPERATIONS

PAGE NO.

BRAKES

Adjustments 112
Brake Cylinder Sizes 1114
Hydraulic Brake System 112
Master Cylinder, Replace 1130
Trouble Shooting 31

CLUTCH

Clutch Pedal, Adjust 1123
Clutch, Replace 1123
Trouble Shooting 13

COOLING SYSTEM

Radiator, Replace 1121
Trouble Shooting 8
Water Pump Repairs 1121
Water Pump, Replace 1121

ELECTRIC SYSTEM

Dash Gauge Service 85
Distributor, Replace 1121
Distributor Service 46
Distributor Specifications 1113
Generator & Regulator Service 62
Generator & Regulator Specs. 1112
Horn Button or Ring, Replace 1131
Ignition System Service 46
Ignition Timing 1122
Starter Switch Service 83
Starting Motor Service 77
Starting Motor Specifications 1113
Trouble Shooting 10
Turn Signal Troubles 12

ENGINE

Camshaft, Replace 1118
Crankshaft & Bearing Specs. 1111
Crankshaft Oil Seal, Replace 1121
Cylinder Head, Replace 1115
Engine, Replace 1114

PAGE NO.

ENGINE continued

Main Bearings, Replace 1120
Piston Pins, Replace 1120
Piston Rings, Replace 1120
Piston, Pin & Ring Specs. 1111
Pistons & Rods, Remove 1119
Piston & Rod, Assemble 1119
Pistons, Replace 1120
Rocker Arms 1116
Rod Bearings, Replace 1120
Timing Case Cover, Replace 1118
Timing Chain, Replace 1119
Timing Gears, Replace 1119
Trouble Shooting 4
Valves, Adjust 1116
Valves, Grind 1118
Valve Guides, Replace 1118
Valve Lifters 1118
Valves, Remove 1117
Valve Spring Installed Height 1118
Valve Spring Testing 1118
Valve Specifications 1112

ENGINE OILING

Oil Pan, Replace 1121
Oil Pump Repairs 1121
Trouble Shooting 9

FRONT SUSPENSION

Camber, Adjust 1130
Caster, Adjust 1130
Front End Repairs 1131
Toe-in, Adjust 1130
Trouble Shooting 33
Wheel Alignment Specifications 1114

FUEL SYSTEM

Carburetors 1122
Fuel Pumps 96
Trouble Shooting 4

"LIVE" FRONT AXLE 1129

PAGE NO.

OVERDRIVE 100

Trouble Shooting 14

REAR AXLE

Axle Shaft, Replace 1127
General Service 102
Rear Axle Repairs 1128
Rear Axle Assembly, Replace 1127
Rear Axle Specifications 1114
Trouble Shooting 31

SPECIFICATIONS

Brake Cylinder Sizes 1114
Capacity Data 1112
Carburetors 1123
Cooling System 1112
Crankshaft & Bearings 1111
Distributors 1113
Engine Tightening 1113
Generator & Regulators 1112
Pistons, Pins & Rings 1111
Rear Axle 1114
Starting Motors 1113
Tune Up 1111
Valve Timing 1119
Valves 1112
Wheel Alignment 1114

STEERING GEARS

Horn Button or Ring, Replace 1131
Steering Gear Repairs 1131
Steering Gear, Replace 1131
Steering Wheel, Replace 1131
Trouble Shooting 33

TRANSFER CASE 1127

TRANSMISSIONS

Gearshift, Adjust 1127
Transmission Repairs 1126
Transmission, Replace 1124
Trouble Shooting 14

TUNE UP 38

GENERAL SPECIFICATIONS

Year	Model Designation	Wheelbase, Inches	Valve Location	Bore and Stroke	Piston Displacement, Cubic Inches	Compression Ratio (Standard)	Maximum Brake H.P. @ R.P.M.	Maximum Torque Lbs. Ft. @ R.P.M.	Normal Oil Pressure Pounds
JEEPS									
1953–61	Jeep 4..............CJ-3B	80	①	3.1250 x 4.375	134	6.90	72 @ 4000	114 @ 2000	35
1955–61	Jeep 4..............CJ-5	81	①	3.1250 x 4.375	134	6.90	72 @ 4000	114 @ 2000	35
1955–61	Jeep 4..............CJ-6	101	①	3.1250 x 4.375	134	6.90	72 @ 4000	114 @ 2000	35
1956–61	Jeep Dispatcher.......DJ-3A	80	In Block	3.1250 x 4.375	134	6.48	60 @ 4000	105 @ 2000	35
STATION WAGONS									
1953	4 Cyl.....................	104½	①	3.1250 x 4.375	134	7.40	72 @ 4000	114 @ 2000	35
1953	6 Cyl.....................	104	In Block	3.1250 x 3.500	161	6.90	75 @ 4000	117 @ 1600	35
1953–61	4 Cyl.....................	104	①	3.1250 x 4.375	134	7.40	72 @ 4000	114 @ 2000	35
1953	6 Cyl.....................	104	In Block	3.1250 x 3.500	161	6.90	75 @ 4000	117 @ 1600	35
1954–61	6 Cyl..........4 x 4-226	104	In Block	3.3125 x 4.375	226	7.30	115 @ 3650	190 @ 1800	35
1954–61	6 Cyl..............6–85	104	①	3.1250 x 3.500	161	6.90	75 @ 4000	117 @ 1600	35

①—Intake valves in head; exhaust valves in block.

TUNE UP SPECIFICATIONS

Year	Model	Ground Polarity and Voltage	Spark Plug Type	Spark Plug Gap Inch	Distributor Point Gap Inch	Distributor Cam Angle Degrees	Firing Order	Ignition Timing Mark	Ignition Timing Location	Idle Speed RPM In Neutral	Compression Pressure @ Cranking Speed Minimum
1953	L-Head 4	N-6	AN7②	.030	.020	④	1342	5°BTDC	Flywheel	600	90
	L-Head 6	N-6	J8③	.030	.020	39	153624	5°BTDC	Damper	550	105
1953–61	F-Head 6	N-6	①	.030	.020	39	153624	5°BTDC	Damper	550	115
1953–61	F-Head 4	N-6	J8③	.030	.020	42	1342	5°BTDC	Pulley	600	100
1954–61	6–226	N-6	J8③	.030	.020	39	153624	4°BTDC	Damper	450	120
1956–61	L-Head 4	N-6	J8③	.030	.020	42	1342	5°BTDC	Flywheel	600	100

①—Champion J7 on passenger cars, J8 on other models.   ②—Auto-Lite.   ③—Champion.
④—Cam angle varies according to distributor used.

PISTONS, PINS, RINGS, CRANKSHAFT & BEARINGS

Year	Model	Fitting Pistons Shim To Use	Fitting Pistons Pounds Pull On Scale	Ring End Gap ① Comp.	Ring End Gap ① Oil	Wrist-pin Diameter	Rod Bearings Shaft Diameter	Rod Bearings Bearing Clearance	Main Bearings Shaft Diameter	Main Bearings Bearing Clearance	Thrust on Bear. No.	Shaft End Play
1953–61	L-Head 4	.003	5–10	.008	.008	.8119	1.9375–1.9385	.0005–.0025	2.333–2.334	.0015–.003	1	.006 Max.
1953–61	F-Head 4	.003	5–10	.008	.008	.8119	1.9375–1.9385	.0005–.0025	2.333–2.334	.0015–.003	1	.006 Max.
1953	L-Head 6	.0025	7–12	.008	.008	.7497	1.875	.0001–.0025	2.250	.001–.003	1	.006 Max.
1953–61	F-Head 6	.003	5–10	.007	.007	.7497	1.875	.0001–.0025	2.250	.001–.003	1	.006 Max.
1954–61	6–226	.0015	5–10	.008	.008	.8592	2.062–2.063	.0005–.002	2.374–2.375	.0007–.002	1	.006 Max.

①—Fit rings in tapered bores for clearance listed in tightest portion of ring travel.

WILLYS JEEP

VALVE SPECIFICATIONS

Year	Model	Valve Lash Int.	Valve Lash Exh.	Valve Angles Seat	Valve Angles Face	Valve Spring Installed Height	Valve Spring Pressure Lbs. @ In.	Valve Lift Int.	Valve Lift Exh.	Stem Clearance Intake	Stem Clearance Exhaust	Stem Diameter Int.	Stem Diameter Exh.
WILLYS JEEP													
1953	L-Head 4	.016C	.016C	45	45	2⁷⁄₆₄	110 @ 1¾	.384	.300	.0015–.0032	.0025–.0045	.3411	.3400
1953–61	F-Head 6	.018C	.016C	45	45	⑤	①	.260	.300	.0007–.0022	.0025–.0045	.3735	.3400
1953–61	F-Head 4	.018C	. ②	45	45	⑤	③	.260	.351	.0007–.0022	.0025–.0045	.3735	.3715
1954–61	6-226	.014C	.014C	④	④	1²¹⁄₃₂	98 @ 1⅜	.352	.3315	.001–.003	.0032–.005	.3706	.3386
1956–61	L-Head 4	.016C	.016C	45	45	2⁷⁄₆₄	110 @ 1¾	.351	.351	.0007–.0022	.0025–.0045	.3735	.3715

①—Intake 153 @ 1¹³⁄₃₂″, exhaust 105 @ 1²¹⁄₆₄″.
②—Eaton face valve .012C, Thompson Roto Valve .016C.
③—Intake 140 @ 1¹³⁄₃₂″, exhaust 110 @ 1¾″.
④—Intake 30°, exhaust 45°.
⑤—Intake 1²¹⁄₃₂″, exhaust 2⁷⁄₆₄″.

GENERATOR AND REGULATOR SPECIFICATIONS

★To Polarize Generator: For internally grounded systems, disconnect field lead from regulator and momentarily flash this lead to regulator battery terminal. For externally grounded systems, reconnect the leads to the regulator, then momentarily connect a jumper wire from the "Arm" to the "Bat" terminals of the regulator.

Year	Generator Number	Rotation and Ground Polarity ①	Rated Cap. Amps.	Gen. Field Ground Location ★	Brush Spring Tension, Ounces	Field Current Amperes	Regulator Number	Cutout Relay Voltage to Close Points	Cutout Relay Armature Air Gap, Inch	Voltage Regulator Setting Volts	Current Regulator Setting Amperes	Current and Voltage Armature Air Gap, Inch
1953	GDZ-6001D	C-N	35	2000	35–53	1.3–1.5②	VRP-4007C-2	6.5	.032	7.3	35	.050
1953–60	GGW-4801D	C-N	45	2125	35–53	1.4–1.5②	VBE-6105A	6.5	.032	7.3	45	.050
1955–60	GGW-4801EN	C-N	45	2125	35–53	1.4–1.5②	VBE-6105A	6.5	.032	7.3	45	.050
1958–59	GJC-7002J	C-N	30	External	18–36	1.2–1.3③	VRX-6009B	13.1	.032	14.2	30	.050
1960–61	GJP-7202A	C-N	35	Internal	18–36	1.6–1.7③	VBO-4201E	13.1	.032	14.2	35	.050
1958–59	GJC-7002K	C-N	30	External	18–36	1.2–1.3③	VRX-6009B	13.1	.032	14.2	30	.050
1960–61	GJP-7202B	C-N	35	Internal	18–36	1.6–1.7③	VBO-4201E	13.1	.032	14.2	35	.050

①—C-Clockwise. N-Negative.   ②—At 5 volts.   ③—At 10 volts.

COOLING SYSTEM & CAPACITY DATA

Year & Model	Quarts No Heater	Quarts With Heater	Rad. Cap Relief Pressure	Thermostat Opening Temp. ①	Thermostat Opening Temp. ②	Fuel Tank Gals.	Engine Oil Refill Qts. ③	Engine Oil Summer Grade	Engine Oil Winter Grade	Std. Pints	With Over-drive Pints	Auto-matic Qts.	Rear Axle Pints
1953–55 4 Cyl.	11	12	7	180	160	15	4	30	10W	1½④	2¼	None	2
1953 L-Head 6	11	12	7	180	160	15	5	30	10W	1½	2¼	None	2
1953–61 F-Head 6	11	12	7	180	160	15	5	30	10W	1½	2¼	11	2
1954 6-226	12	13	7	180	160	18	5	30	10W	2½	3½	11	3
1955–61 6-226-A	13	14	7	180	160	19	5	30	10W	2½	3½	11	3
1953–61 Jeep	11	12	7	180	160	10½	4	30	10W	6½⑤	None	None	2¾
1956–61 DJ-3A	11	12	7	180	160	12	4	30	10W	1½	None	4¼	2

①—For permanent type anti-freeze.   ②—For alcohol type anti-freeze.   ③—Add one quart with filter change.
④—Models with transfer case 6½.   ⑤—Includes transfer case.

ENGINE TIGHTENING SPECIFICATIONS★

★Torque specifications are for clean and lightly lubricated threads only. Dry or dirty threads produce increased friction which prevents accurate measurement of tightness.

Year	Spark Plugs Ft. Lbs.	Cylinder Head Bolts Ft. Lbs.	Intake Manifold Ft. Lbs.	Exhaust Manifold Ft. Lbs.	Rocker Arm Shaft Bracket Ft. Lbs.	Rocker Arm Cover Ft. Lbs.	Connecting Rod Cap Bolts Ft. Lbs.	Main Bearing Cap Bolts Ft. Lbs.	Flywheel to Crankshaft Ft. Lbs.	Vibration Damper or Pulley Ft. Lbs.
1953–61 L-Head 4	25–30	60–70	31–35	31–35	....	....	①	65–75	36–40	100–130
1953–61 F-Head 4	25–30	60–70	29–35	29–35	30–35	....	35–40	65–75	36–40	100–130
1953 L-Head 6	25–30	60–70	29–35	29–35	....	....	②	65–75	36–40	100–130
1953–61 F-Head 6	25–30	60–70	29–35	29–35	30–35	....	②	65–75	36–40	100–130
1954–61 6-226	25–30	30–35	30–35	30–35	....	....	40–45	85–95	35–40	100–130

①—For $\frac{7}{16}''$ bolts 50–55; for $\frac{3}{8}''$ bolts 35–40.
②—For $\frac{7}{16}''$ bolts 50–55; for $\frac{11}{32}''$ bolts 33–38.

DISTRIBUTOR SPECIFICATIONS

Year	Model	Part No. ①	Rotation ②	Cam Angle, Degrees	Breaker Point Opening, Inch	Condenser Capacity, Mfds. ③	Breaker Arm Spring Tension, Ounces	Centrifugal Advance Data Degrees @ R.P.M. of Dist. Advance Starts	Full Advance	Vacuum Advance Data Inches of Vacuum to Start Plunger Movement	Inches of Vacuum for Full Plunger Travel	Maximum Vacuum Advance, Dist. Degrees
1953–59	Four	1AT-4204A	CC	42	.020	.21–.25	17–20	1 @ 300	11 @ 1700	5⅛	14	6
1953	675	1AT-4007	CC	39	.020	.21–.25	17–20	1 @ 350	12 @ 1500	3½	15	6
1953	685	1AT-4007A	CC	39	.020	.21–.25	17–20	1 @ 300	9½ @ 1300	5⅛	14	6
1953–54	Four	1AD-4008A	CC	42	.020	.23–.26	17–20	1 @ 300	11 @ 1700	None	None	None
1953–54	685	1AT-4205A	CC	39	.020	.21–.25	17–20	1 @ 300	9½ @ 1300	5⅛	14	6
1955–56	Four	1AD-4041	CC	42	.020	.23–.26	17–20	1 @ 300	11 @ 1700	None	None	None
1955–57	6-226	1AT-4206	CC	39	.020	.21–.25	17–20	1 @ 325	9 @ 1675	10	15	5
1956–59	DJ-3A	1AY-4012	CC	39	.020	.21–.25	17–20	1 @ 300	11 @ 1700	None	None	None
1957–59	6-226	1AT-4206B	CC	39	.020	.21–.25	17–20	1 @ 375	7½ @ 1700	10	15	5
1960–61	Four	1AY-4401	CC	42	.020	.25–.28	17–20	1 @ 425	11 @ 1700	None	None	None

①—Stamped on plate riveted to side of distributor housing.
②—As viewed from the top. CC—Counter Clockwise.
③—Microfarads—as indicated on a condenser tester.

STARTING MOTOR SPECIFICATIONS

Year	Model	Part No.	Rotation ①	Brush Spring Tension, Ounces	No Load Test Amperes	Volts	R.P.M.	Torque Test Amperes	Volts	Torque, Lbs. Ft.
1953–54	675, 685	MCH-6203	C	42–53	65	5.0	4300	335	2.0	6
1953–57	Four	MCH-6207	C	42–53	65	5.0	4300	335	2.0	6
1955–60	6-226	MCH-6210	C	42–53	65	5.0	4300	335	2.0	6
1956–60	Four	MCH-6203	C	42–53	65	5.0	4300	335	2.0	6
1958–61	Four	MDM-6005	C	31–47	50	10.0	4400	210	4.0	5
1958–61	6-226	MDM-6006	C	31–47	50	10.0	4400	210	4.0	5

①—As viewed from the drive end. C—Clockwise.

REAR AXLE AND BRAKE CYLINDER SPECIFICATIONS

Year	Model	Ring Gear & Pinion Backlash, Inch	Drive Pinion Adjustment	Drive Pinion Bearing Preload, Inch Lbs.	Drive Pinion Bearing Adjustment	Axle Shaft End Play, Inch	Hydraulic Cylinder Bore Sizes, Inch: Wheel Cylinder Front	Wheel Cylinder Rear	Master Cylinder
1953–61	Jeep	①	Shims	③	Shims	.003–.007	1	3/4	1
1953–61	Station Wagons	.004–.009	Shims	12–18	Shims	.003–.007	②	②	1
1953–61	675, 685	.004–.008	Shims	③	Shims	.003–.007	1 1/8	1	1
1954–61	6–226	.004–.008	Shims	③	Shims	.003–.007	1 1/8	13/16	1
1956–61	DJ-3A		Shims	③	Shims		1 1/8	13/16	1

①—Backlash is .005–.007″ on CJ-2A up to serial No. 13453. After serial No. 13453 and on all later models the setting is .004–.008″.

②—Effective with Model 4x473 Serial No. 19523; Model 473 SW Serial No. 24122; Model SD Serial No. 14653; Model 673 SW Serial No. 17499 the front wheel cylinders were increased from 1″ to 1 1/8″ and the rear wheel cylinders from 7/8″ to 1″.

③—Drive pinion should turn with a slight drag only but with no end play.

WHEEL ALIGNMENT SPECIFICATIONS

Year	Model	Caster, Degrees: Limits	Caster, Degrees: Desired	Camber, Degrees: Limits	Camber, Degrees: Desired	Toe-In, Inches	Toe-out on Turns, Degrees: Outer Wheel	Toe-out on Turns, Degrees: Inner Wheel①	Kingpin Angle, Degrees②
1953–61	Jeep	+ 3	+ 3	+ 1 1/2	+ 1 1/2	3/64 to 3/32	20	20	7 1/2
1953–61	Sta. Wagon	+ 1	+ 1	+ 1	+ 1	1/16 to 1/8	18 1/2	20	5
1953–55	675, 685	+ 1/2 to + 1 1/2	+ 1	+ 3/4 to + 1 1/4	+ 1	3/32 to 5/32	19	20	8
1954–55	6–226	+ 1/2 to + 1 1/2	+ 1	+ 3/4 to + 1 1/4	+ 1	3/32 to 5/32	19	20	7 1/2
1956–61	DJ-3A	+ 3	+ 3	+ 1	+ 1	3/64 to 3/32	20	22	7 1/2

①—Incorrect toe-out, when other adjustments are correct, generally indicates bent steering arms.

②—Incorrect kingpin or knuckle support angle with correct camber indicates bent suspension arms or knuckle support.

Engine Section

ENGINE MARKINGS

Current production engines are marked with a letter following the serial number when the engine is not strictly standard.

The letter "A" means crankshaft journals are .010″ undersize.

The letter "B" means the bores are .010″ oversize.

The letter "C" means .010″ oversize bores and .010″ undersize crankshaft journals.

ENGINE, REPLACE

Jeeps

1. Disconnect one battery cable.
2. Drain cooling system.
3. Remove radiator stay bar on CJ-3B.
4. Remove radiator and heater hoses.
5. Remove fan and fan hub.
6. Remove radiator and shroud.
7. Disconnect fuel line at pump.
8. Disconnect windshield wiper hoses.
9. Remove air cleaner and two breather hoses.
10. Disconnect choke and throttle controls.
11. Remove starting motor.
12. Disconnect generator wires.
13. Disconnect primary wire at coil.
14. Disconnect heat indicator and oil pressure gauge tubes.
15. Disconnect exhaust pipe from manifold.
16. Remove front engine supports. This will allow engine to drop slightly and will permit access to the two top bolts on the bell housing.
17. Install a suitable lifting sling on engine. Attach sling to hoist and take up slack.
18. Pull engine forward or roll vehicle backward until clutch clears bell housing, and lift engine from vehicle.
19. To install, reverse procedure.

Four-Cylinder Station Wagons

1. Disconnect one battery cable.
2. Drain cooling system.
3. Remove hood and radiator brace rods.
4. Remove heater and radiator hoses.
5. Remove radiator.
6. Disconnect fuel line at pump.
7. Disconnect windshield wiper hose.
8. Remove carburetor air cleaner.
9. Disconnect throttle controls.
10. Remove starting motor.
11. Disconnect generator wires.
12. Disconnect primary wire at coil.
13. If equipped with overdrive, disconnect overdrive control wires. (To avoid possibility of error when connecting overdrive wires, mark or tag them.)
14. Disconnect heat indicator and oil gauge wires.
15. Disconnect exhaust pipe from manifold.
16. Remove engine support bolts.
17. Unfasten bell housing from engine.
18. Install a suitable lifting sling on engine. Raise engine high enough to relieve weight from front engine supports and pull engine forward, or roll vehicle backward, until clutch clears bell housing. Then remove engine from vehicle.
19. To install, reverse procedure.

F-Head 6-Cyl. Station Wagons

1. Remove hood and radiator stay bar.
2. Drain cooling system.
3. Disconnect one battery cable.
4. Remove air cleaner.
5. Disconnect wires from temperature sender, coil primary and secondary at distributor, starter solenoid, generator, oil sender.
6. Remove coil.

Six cylinder 148" and 161" L-Head Engine

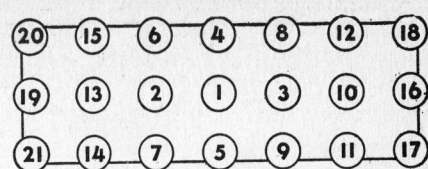

Fig. 2 Six cylinder head tightening. 1953-55 L-Head

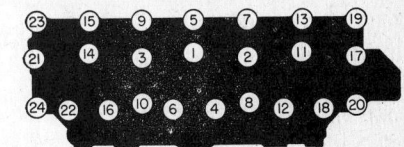

Fig. 3 Six-cylinder F-head engine head tightening

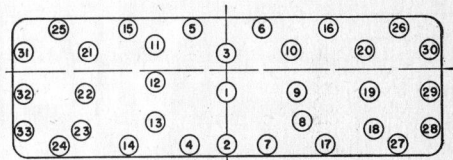

Fig. 4 Cylinder head tightening sequence. 226" engine

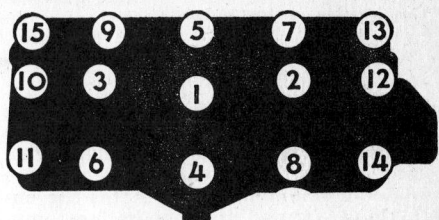

Fig. 5 Cylinder head tightening. Four-cylinder F-head engines

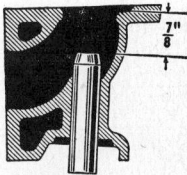

Fig. 6 Position of valve stem guides in six cylinder 148" and 161" L-Head engines

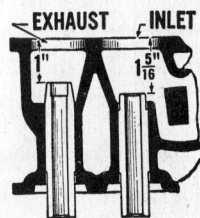

Fig. 7 Position of valve stem guides in four cylinder L-Head engine

7. Disconnect heater hoses at engine.
8. Disconnect throttle link and remove choke control from carburetor.
9. Disconnect accelerator pedal link from throttle bell crank and push back into vehicle.
10. Disconnect fuel line at pump.
11. Disconnect windshield wiper hose from vacuum booster tube.
12. Remove radiator and hoses.
13. Remove exhaust pipe from manifold.
14. Remove bolts from engine front supports.
15. Disconnect ground strap at left front engine support.
16. Remove bell housing-to-rear engine plate bolts and remove battery ground strap from bell housing if so attached.
17. The engine is now free of connections and can be lifted from vehicle.
18. To install, reverse procedure.

"6-226" Station Wagons

1. Drain cooling system.
2. Remove hood and radiator stay bars.
3. Remove radiator hoses and heater hoses.
4. Remove radiator and shroud.
5. Disconnect battery ground cable.
6. Disconnect wires from temperature sender, oil pressure sender, starter, generator, coil and secondary at distributor.
7. Remove air cleaner.
8. Disconnect accelerator pedal linkage from bell crank.
9. Disconnect vacuum line from wiper motor.
10. Disconnect fuel line from pump.
11. Disconnect engine ground strap from front engine support.
12. Disconnect clutch linkage.
13. Disconnect exhaust pipe at manifold.
14. Disconnect front engine supports.
15. The engine is now free of connections and can be lifted from vehicle.
16. To install, reverse foregoing procedure.

CYLINDER HEAD

Before the cylinder head is installed, make certain that all dirt and carbon is removed from both the head and block. File or hone all high spots.

Use a torque wrench when tightening down cylinder heads. Uneven or excessive tightening of nuts may distort cylinder bores, causing compression loss and excessive oil consumption.

Tighten cylinder heads in the sequence

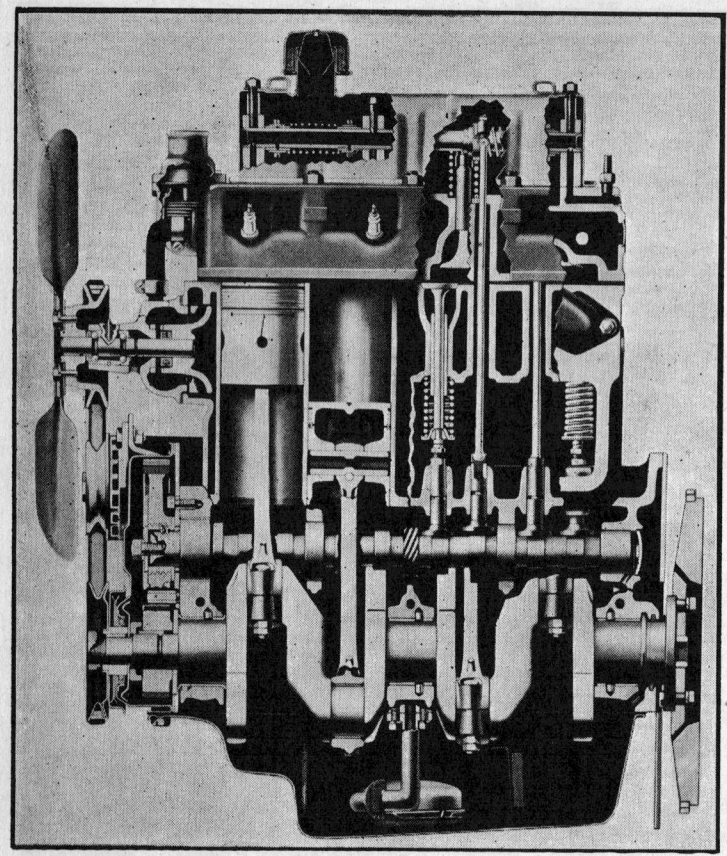

F-Head four cylinder engine

F-Head four cylinder engine

shown in Figs. 2 to 5, tightening them a little at a time in the proper order a couple of times around before final tightening to the torque values given in the *Engine Tightening Chart*. After the engine has warmed up to operating temperature, recheck the torque and tighten as required.

On F-Head engines, be sure to check intake valve operating clearances after the final tightening.

Note—Tightening cylinder heads on F-

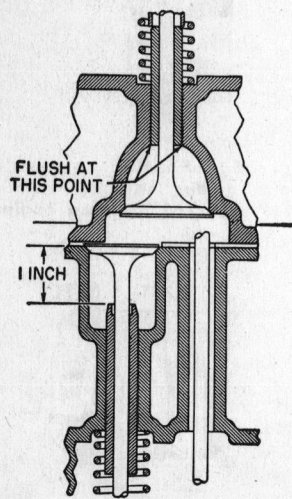

Fig. 8 Position of valve guides in F-head engines

head engines without removing rocker arms may be accomplished with a wrench having an 11/16" box on one end and a 1/2" square box on the other end. This, together with a torque wrench will do the job.

Service Note

Accurate alignment of the cylinder head, gasket and block on L6-226 engines is required to prevent gasket failure. Two cylinder head bolt holes, at opposite corners of the head (positions 24 and 26 in Fig. 4) have a slightly smaller diameter than the other holes and can be used for guide pins.

The guide pins can be made by cutting the heads off two cylinder head bolts. Cut slots in the end from which the heads were removed to install and then remove the guide pins.

The torquing sequence for the head bolts is shown in Fig. 4.

ROCKER ARMS

F-Head Engines

To remove the rocker arm assembly, proceed as follows:
1. Remove carburetor air cleaner.
2. Disconnect spark plug wires.
3. Drain cooling system.
4. Remove rocker arm cover.
5. Remove rocker arm bracket screws and lift off rocker arm assembly.

Before disassembly, mark rocker arms, brackets and shaft so they can be reassembled in the original positions.

VALVES, ADJUST

L-Head Engines

The valves may be adjusted when the engine is at normal room temperature. Crank the engine over until the valve to be adjusted is fully closed. Hold the lifter body with a tappet wrench to prevent it from turning. Then turn the tappet adjusting screw until the proper clearance is obtained. Measure the clearance with a feeler gauge and, after adjusting one tappet, proceed in like manner with the others, being certain that the valve being adjusted is fully closed.

In addition to the conventional method of adjusting tappets by locating the distributor rotor and then adjusting the tappets by following the firing order of the engine, the following method may also be used:

Four-Cylinder Engines

Valves Fully Raised	Adjust Tappets
1 and 3	6 and 8
2 and 5	4 and 7
6 and 8	1 and 3
4 and 7	2 and 5

Six-Cylinder 148" & 161" Engines

Valves Fully Raised	Adjust Tappets
1 and 3	10 and 12
7 and 9	4 and 6
2 and 5	8 and 11
10 and 12	1 and 3
4 and 6	7 and 9
8 and 11	2 and 5

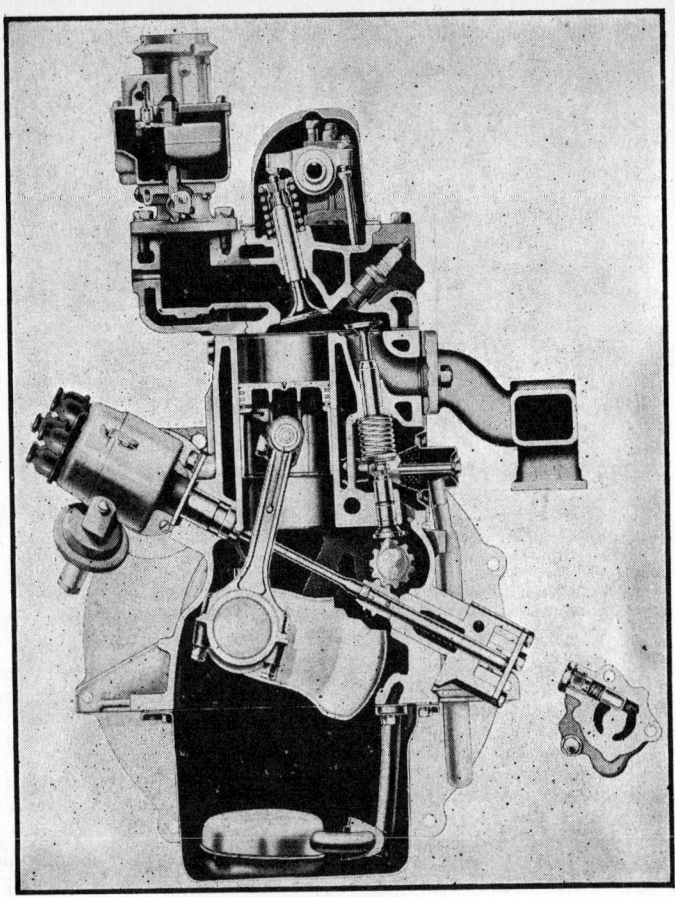

Six-cylinder F-Head engine

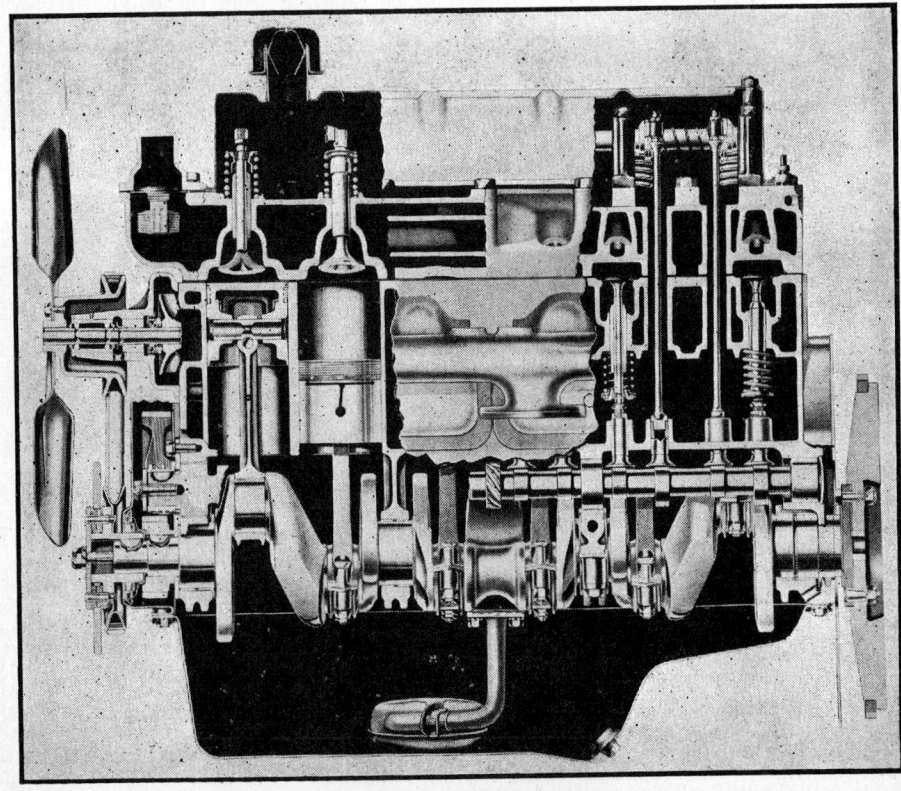

Six-cylinder F-Head engine

Six-Cylinder 226" Engine

Valves Fully Raised	Adjust Tappets
1 and 3	10 and 12
8 and 9	4 and 5
2 and 6	7 and 11
10 and 12	1 and 3
4 and 5	8 and 9
7 and 11	2 and 6

F-Head Engines

The exhaust valves (in block) may be adjusted in the same manner as outlined for L-head engines. However, the intake valves may best be adjusted with the engine running after it has warmed up to operating temperature.

If the cylinder head has been tightened, be sure to recheck intake valve clearances and adjust as required.

VALVES, REMOVE

L-Head Engines

After removing the cylinder head, take off the valve chamber covers and use cloth to block off the holes in the valve chamber to prevent the valve locks from falling into the crankcase.

With a suitable valve spring compressor, raise the springs on those valves which are closed and remove the valve locks. Then turn the crankshaft until those valves which are open are closed and remove the remaining valve locks.

Remove all valves and place them in a board with numbered holes so they can be identified as to the valve port from which they were removed.

F-Head Engines

Follow the same procedure in removing the exhaust valves from these engines as outlined for L-head engines.

In removing the intake valves from the head a suitable fixture is available which holds the valves closed and compresses the spring at the same time.

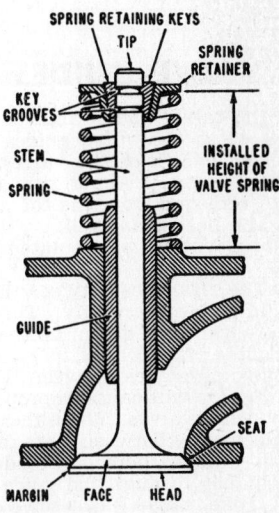

Fig. 5A Checking valve spring installed height

VALVE SPRING INSTALLED HEIGHT

When valves and seats are reground the position of the valve in the head is changed so as to lessen the valve spring tension. Without proper valve spring tension the valve does not seat long enough or it may not seat completely. Since the valve is cooled by transferring heat from the valve head to the seat and thence to the coolant, improper valve spring tension will cause worn, pitted and distorted valves which result in loss of compression and power as well as poor gasoline mileage.

When valves, springs, retainers and locks are installed, measure the assembled height of valve springs from the surface of the cylinder head spring pad to the underside of the spring retainer as shown in Fig. 5A. If the assembled height is greater than the dimension given in the *Valve Specifications Chart*, install a spacer or shim of proper thickness between cylinder head spring pad and spring to bring the assembled height to specifications.

Do not install spacers unless necessary. Excessive use of spacers will result in overstressing valve springs and overloading camshaft lobes which could lead to spring breakage and worn camshaft lobes.

VALVE SPRING TESTING

After taking out the valves, remove the springs and wash them with gasoline or other suitable solvent. Examine the springs for damage or corrosion due to acid etching, which will develop into surface cracks and cause spring failure.

Check valve spring pressure on a spring testing fixture if one is available. If a fixture is not available, at least check the free length of each spring by standing it alongside a new spring. Any spring that does not conform to the pressure specifications given in the *Valve Data* chart within 10 per cent should be replaced. Likewise, any spring that stands shorter than the new spring used for comparison should be discarded.

VALVE GUIDES

After the valves and springs have been removed, clean the valve guides with a wire brush, and clean the valves with a wire wheel brush, making sure that all carbon is removed from the top and bottom of the heads, as well as the gum which might have accumulated on the stems.

Check the clearance between the valve stems and guides carefully. The standard clearances are given in the *Valve Data* chart.

Excessive clearance between the valve stem and guide will cause improper seating and burned valves. When there is too much clearance between intake valve stems and guides, there is a tendency to draw oil vapor through the guide on the suction stroke, causing excessive oil consumption, fouled spark plugs and poor low speed performance.

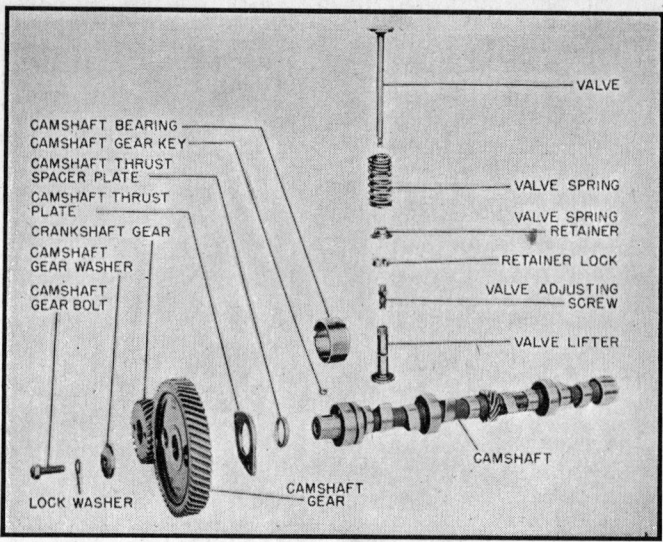

Fig. 9 Layout of valve system. Four cylinder L-head engine. This is typical of the F-head engine except that the intake valve mechanism is contained in the cylinder head

To check valve stem-to-guide clearance, take a new valve and place it in each valve guide and feel the clearance by moving the valve stem back and forth. If this check shows excessive clearance, it will be necessary to replace the valve guide. If the clearance is not excessive when checking with a new valve but is excessive when checked with the old valve, the old valve stem is worn and a new valve must be installed.

If it is necessary to replace the valve guides, the old guides can be driven out with a special driver which is available for the purpose. However, in lieu of the driver, the guides can be pulled out by using a suitable piece of pipe together with a long bolt and suitable washers.

When replacing the guides, maximum engine performance can only be secured when the guides are installed correctly (see Figs. 6, 7 and 8).

VALVES, GRIND

In refacing valves, take off the minimum of metal required to clean up the valve faces. If the outer edge of the valve becomes too thin or sharp due to excessive grinding, the valve must be replaced.

Inspect the valve seats in the block and head for cracks, burns, pitting, ridges or improper angle. During any general engine overhaul it is advisable to reface the valve seats regardless of their condition. If new valve guides are required, they must be installed before refacing the seats if the equipment used has a valve guide pilot.

The valve seat width after refacing should measure not more than $\frac{5}{64}$ in. The width may be checked by placing a scale across the face of the seat.

A simple check can be made to prove the fit of the valve in the valve seat by spreading a thin film of Prussian Blue on the valve face and then inserting the valve into the valve seat.

With hand pressure, rotate the valve ¼ turn and then remove it and observe the transfer of Prussian Blue to the valve seat. An uneven transfer of Prussian Blue will indicate an inaccurate valve and valve seat refacing operation.

VALVE LIFTERS

These lifters are of the mushroom type operating in guide holes cast in the block. This means that the camshaft will have to be removed from the engine if valve lifters require replacement.

Whenever the camshaft is removed, inspect the faces of the lifters where they contact the cams and replace any that are scored, rough or cracked. Check the clearance of the lifters in the guides, replacing those that have worn excessively. Oversize available is .004 in. and the guides must be reamed to accommodate them.

CAMSHAFT & GEAR COVER, REPLACE

All Engines (Except 6-226)

1. Drain cooling system.
2. Remove radiator and grille or guard.
3. Remove cylinder head, valves and springs.
4. On L-head engines, remove manifolds.
5. Remove fuel and oil pumps.
6. Remove oil pan.
7. Remove crankshaft pulley (and vibration damper on 6-cyl.).
8. Remove fan assembly.
9. On CJ-2A and CJ-3A, remove nuts from front engine support.
10. Remove engine front cover.
11. Remove camshaft gear and thrust plate.
12. Tie valve lifters up to their highest point of travel with string wrapped around the adjusting screws and

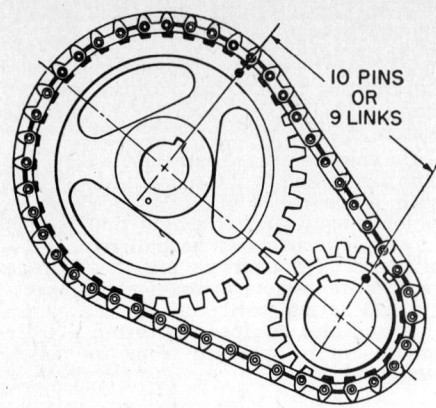

Fig. 10 Valve timing. Six-cyl. 226" engine

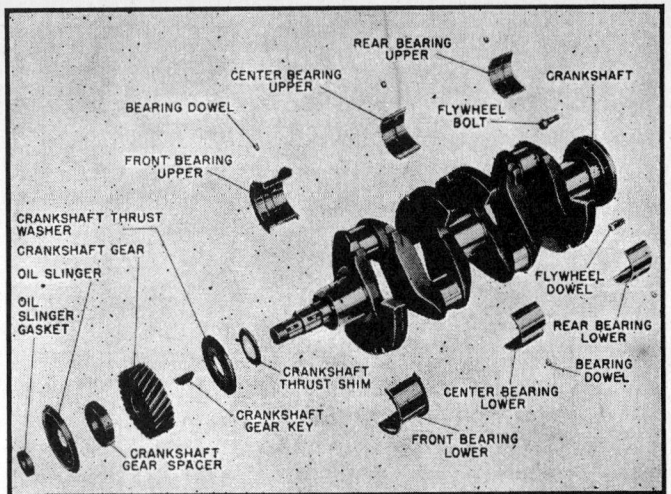

Fig. 12 Layout of crankshaft and related parts. Four cylinder engine

attach to manifold studs. Spring clip type clothespins or small "C" clamps may also be used.

13. On CJ-2A and CJ-3A, raise front of engine until camshaft will clear front crossmember.
14. Remove camshaft from engine.
15. To install, reverse foregoing procedure and set valve timing as shown in Fig. 10.

"6-226" Engines

1. Drain cooling system.
2. Remove radiator.
3. Remove vibration damper.
4. Remove timing chain cover.
5. Remove timing gears and chain.
6. Remove fuel pump.
7. Remove cylinder head.
8. Remove oil pan and oil pump.
9. Remove valves and springs.
10. Hold valve lifters up with spring type clothespins or string to prevent them from interfering with camshaft as it is being withdrawn.
11. Unfasten camshaft thrust plate from cylinder block and withdraw the camshaft.
12. To install, reverse removal procedure and set valve timing as shown in Fig. 11.

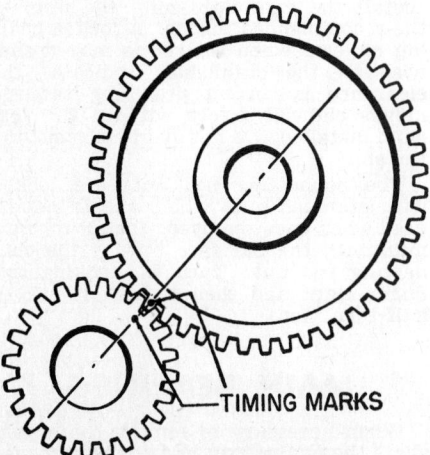

TIMING MARKS

Fig. 11 Valve timing for timing gear driven engines

VALVE TIMING DATA

Year Model	Intake Opens①	Intake Closes②	Exhaust Opens③	Exhaust Closes④
1953-61 6-226 Eng.	10	60	55	10
Others	9	50	47	12

① —Degrees before top dead center.
② —Degrees after bottom dead center.
③ —Degrees before bottom dead center.
④ —Degrees after top dead center.

TIMING CHAIN

"6-226" Engines

For correct valve timing on this engine, install the chain so there are 10 pins between the sprocket timing marks, Fig. 10.

TIMING GEARS

All Except "6-226"

The camshaft is driven by a steel gear on the crankshaft and a fibre gear on the camshaft. Lubrication is positive through a jet pressed into the crankcase directly back of the contact point of the gears. When the gears are removed, check both the jet and oil passage to make sure they are clear.

When it becomes necessary to replace the timing gears, due attention must be given to the end play of both shafts and running clearance of the gears. End play of the crankshaft is controlled by the running clearance between the crankshaft gear and gear thrust plate, Fig. 11. The end play is adjusted by shims placed between the thrust plate and the end of the front main bearing. Shims .002 in. thick are available for this adjustment. When the thrust plate or washer is removed, be sure it is reinstalled with the beveled inner edge toward the crankcase.

End play of the camshaft is determined by the running clearance between the camshaft gear and thrust plate. The standard clearance is .003 to .0055 in. which is determined by the thickness

of the camshaft gear thrust plate spacer, Fig. 9. Should a check indicate not enough clearance, place a thin shim between the thrust plate spacer and the shoulder on the camshaft. Clearance may be reduced by dressing off the spacer slightly. Whenever the spacer is installed, make sure that the beveled inner edge is toward the rear.

End play of both the camshaft and crankshaft can best be measured with a dial indicator.

Standard running clearance between the gears is .000 to .002 in., which should be checked with a dial indicator.

To set the valve timing, install the crankshaft gear followed by the camshaft gear with the camshaft positioned to allow installation with the timing gear marks meshed, Fig. 11.

PISTONS & RODS, REMOVE

After removing the cylinder head and oil pan, examine the cylinder bores above the ring travel area. If the bores are worn so that a shoulder or ridge exists at this point, remove the ridge with a ridge reamer to avoid damaging rings or cracking ring lands of pistons during removal.

Remove the connecting rod caps and push pistons and rods out of cylinders, using care to prevent rod bolts from contacting and nicking crankshaft journals.

Make sure the rods and pistons are properly numbered so they can be reinstalled in original locations. It is advisable to install caps on rods to avoid mixing parts.

PISTONS & RODS, ASSEMBLE

All Except "6-226" Engine

As shown in Fig. 13, pistons should be assembled to the connecting rods so that the oil spray hole in the rod *faces* away from the camshaft side of the engine with the vertical slot in the piston facing the camshaft side.

"6-226" Engine

When correctly assembled, the oil spray hole in the rod *faces* the camshaft side of the engine with the vertical slot in the piston facing away from the camshaft side.

PISTONS

Standard size service pistons are high limit or maximum diameter; therefore, they can usually be used with a slight amount of honing to correct slight scoring or excessive clearances in engines having relatively low mileages. Service pistons are also furnished in .005, .010, .015, .020 and .030 in. oversizes.

Before a honing or boring operation is started, measure all new pistons with a micrometer at points exactly 90 degrees away from the piston pin. Then select the smallest piston for the first fitting. The slight variation usually found between pistons in a set may provide for correction in case the first piston is fitted too free.

It is very important that refinished cylinder bores are trued up to have not more than .0005 in. out-of-round or taper. Each bore must be final honed to remove all stone or cutter marks and provide a smooth surface. During final honing, each piston must be fitted individually to the bore in which it will be installed and should be marked to insure correct installation.

After final honing and before the piston is checked for fit, each bore must be thoroughly washed to remove all traces of abrasive and then dried thoroughly. The dry bore should then be brushed clean with a power-driven fibre brush.

Both the piston and cylinder block must be at the same temperature (room temperature of 70 degrees) when the piston is checked for fit in the cylinder bore. Therefore the cylinder should be allowed to cool after boring or honing and before the piston fit is checked. This is important because a difference of 10 degrees between the temperature of parts is sufficient to produce a variation of .0005 in.

To check the fit of pistons, use a feeler ribbon gauge ¾ in. wide and the thickness listed in the *Piston & Ring Data* chart. Insert the piston upside down in the cylinder bore with rings removed. Locate the feeler 90 degrees from the piston pin hole, between the thrust face of the piston and cylinder wall. Hook the feeler to a spring scale. If the force required to pull the feeler out of the cylinder with the scale is as specified in the chart, the piston fit is correct. If too tight, the cylinder must be honed out until the proper clearance is obtained.

PISTON RINGS

When new piston rings are to be installed without reboring cylinders, the glazed cylinder walls should be slightly dulled, but without increasing the bore diameter. This is done with a "Glaze-

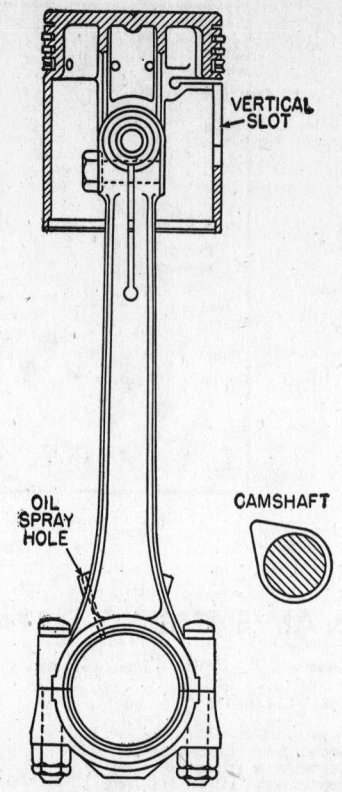

Fig. 13 Assemble pistons and rods as shown. All except "6-226" engine. On. "6-226" the oil spray hole faces the camshaft side with the vertical piston slot away from the camshaft side

buster" or with a hone equipped with the finest grade of stones.

New piston rings must be checked for clearance in piston grooves and for gap in cylinder bores. Cylinder bores and piston grooves must be clean, dry and free of carbon and burrs.

Check the clearance of each ring in its piston groove by installing the ring and then inserting feeler gauges *under* the ring. Any wear that occurs in the piston groove forms a step or ridge at the inner portion of the lower land. If gauges are inserted above the ring, the ring may rest on the step instead of on the worn portion of the lower land, and a false measurement of clearance will result.

If the piston grooves have worn to the extent that relatively high steps or ridges exist on the lower lands, the piston should be replaced because the steps will interfere with the operation of the new rings and the ring clearances will be excessive. Piston rings are not furnished in oversize widths to compensate for ring groove wear.

See the *Piston & Ring Data* chart for ring groove clearances and end gap clearances.

To check the end gap of rings, place the ring in the cylinder in which it will be used. Square it in the bore by tapping with either end of the piston, then measure the gap with feeler gauges. If necessary to increase the gap, file the ends with a smooth file.

PISTON PINS

On "6-226" engine the pins are of the full-floating type, being retained by snap rings which fit in grooves cut into the piston bosses.

On engines other than the "6-226", the pins are locked in the rods and are fitted with a clearance of .0001 to .0005 in. which is equivalent to a light thumb push fit with the parts at normal room temperature. No oversize pin is available as it is impossible to ream the connecting rod satisfactorily due to the clamp slot, and also because the piston plating should not be removed from the piston pin bore.

ROD BEARINGS

Insert type bearings consist of two half shells, the upper shell having an oil spray hole which communicates with the oil hole in the rod.

When the shells are placed in the rod and cap the ends extend slightly beyond the parting faces so that when the rod bolts are tightened the shells will be clamped tightly in place to insure positive seating and to prevent turning. *The ends of the shells must never be filed flush with the parting faces of the rod and cap.*

If this type bearing becomes noisy or is worn so that clearance on the crankpin is excessive, a new bearing of proper size must be selected and installed since no provision is made for adjustment. Under no circumstances should the rod or cap be filed to adjust bearing clearance.

Service bearings are furnished in standard sizes and several undersizes, including undersizes for reground crankshafts.

The clearances of connecting rod (and main) bearings may be checked with Plastigage which is available at any auto parts jobber and full instructions for its use are furnished with the envelope in which it is contained.

Lacking Plastigage, however, clearance may be checked with a .002 in. test shim, ¾ in. square. Place the shim between the bearing and shaft journal. Install the cap, tightening the nuts to the recommended torque. A locked bearing or drag when the rod is moved endwise on the crankshaft indicates the clearance is correct providing the rod moves endwise freely without the test shim installed. Do not overlook removing the shim.

The connecting rod nuts are locked with stamped nuts which should not be used when once removed. Install the new nuts with the flat face toward the connecting rod nut. Turn the locking nut finger tight and then tighten it only a half-turn more.

MAIN BEARINGS

When necessary to remove the crankshaft the engine will have to be removed from the chassis. And since the main bearings on all four-cylinder engines are

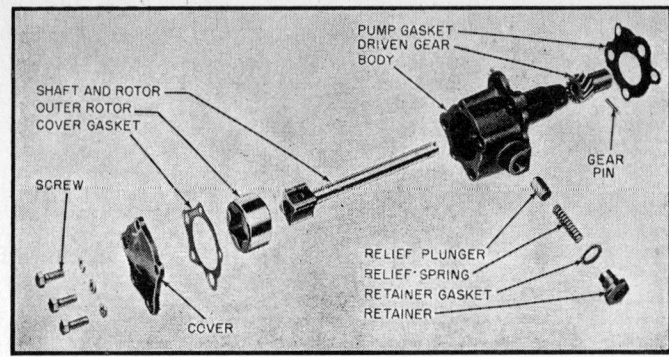

Fig. 14 Rotor type oil pump. All except "6-226" engine

held in place by dowels, the engine will have to be removed when their replacement becomes necessary.

Main bearings on six-cylinder engines may be removed and installed without removing the engine.

The bearings are made to size and do not require line reaming or adjustment.

When it is necessary to install new bearing shells it is advisable to measure the shaft journals with a micrometer for being out-of-round. If an out-of-round condition exists in excess of the standard running clearance of the bearings (either main or rod) a satisfactory bearing replacement cannot be made and it will be necessary to replace or regrind the crankshaft. Undersize bearings of .010 and .020 in. are available.

Before installing the shaft and bearings, use a rifle brush to clean the oil passages thoroughly in both the shaft and crankcase. If possible, blow out the holes with compressed air. Be sure the journals are not nicked or scored and that all parts are thoroughly clean.

After installing the bearings, check the running clearance to be sure it is standard (see *Engine Bearing Data* chart). Use Plastigage or a .002 in. test shim about one inch square. Place the shim between the shaft and bearing and tighten the bearing cap nuts to the recommended torque. The shaft should be locked if the clearance is at the low limit or show a drag if at the high limit when turned, proving that the clearance is correct. Do not overlook removing the test shim.

CRANKSHAFT OIL SEAL

The rear main bearing is sealed against external leakage by a lip type neoprene seal with a metal core. The seal has the advantage of being able to be slipped into place without removing the crankshaft.

For easy installation, give the seal a coat of grease. Be careful not to coat the ends of the seal as they have sealing compound applied to them.

OIL PAN

The floating oil intake is attached to the crankcase with two cap screws. Whenever the oil pan is removed, the float, screen and tube should be cleaned thoroughly in a suitable cleaning fluid

to remove any accumulation of dirt. If the screen has been crushed, it is better to replace it rather than attempt to make a repair.

OIL PUMP
All Except "6-226" Engines

The oil pump is located externally on the left side of the engine. When necessary to remove the pump, first take off the distributor cap and note the position of the rotor so that the pump may be reinstalled without disturbing the ignition timing.

To install the pump without disturbing the timing, the pump gear must be correctly meshed with the camshaft driving gear to allow engagement of the driving key on the distributor shaft in the pump shaft driving slot without moving the distributor rotor. Assembly can be made only in one position because the slot and driving key are machined off center.

To disassemble the pump, Fig. 14, remove the cover and gasket. Hold a hand over the cover opening and, with the pump upside down, turn the shaft until the outer rotor slips out. Drive out the pin securing the drive gear to the shaft. Press the shaft out of the gear and slide the shaft and inner rotor out of the body.

Failure of the pump to operate at full efficiency may usually be traced to excessive end play in the rotor or excessive clearance between the rotors. The clearance between the outer rotor and pump body should also be checked.

End play of the rotors is controlled by the thickness of the cover gasket which is made of special material which can only be slightly compressed. Never use other than a standard factory gasket.

"6-226" Engines

The oil pump is of the positive gear type, located at the bottom of the vertical shaft which also drives the distributor.

To disassemble the oil pump, take off the screen float. Drive out the pin which secures the drive gear to the shaft and take off the gear. Remove pump cover and gasket. Position the pump with the drive shaft end up and allow the gears to drop from the pump body. Do not remove the idler gear shaft unless worn or damaged.

Assemble the pump with new parts, using a new gasket. When replacing the upper drive gear, position it on the shaft and use a feeler gauge to measure clearance between gear and end of pump body, allowing a clearance of .002 to .004". When proper clearance has been obtained, drill a $\frac{3}{16}$" pin hole through the drive shaft, install the pin and peen it securely.

RADIATOR, REMOVE

Raise the hood, disconnect the upper and lower hose, unfasten the core from its mounting and lift it off.

WATER PUMP, REPLACE

Remove the fan belt and blades, unfasten the pump from the cylinder block and lift it off. On some models, it may be necessary to loosen the radiator core and pull it forward in order to remove the water pump assembly.

WATER PUMP REPAIRS

To disassemble the pump, take out the bearing retaining wire and press the shaft through the impeller and pump body. Remove the seal washer and seal. Place the pump shaft and fan pulley on the press in such a position that the bearing will clear the opening and press the shaft from the pulley.

To reassemble the pump, install the long end of the shaft in the pump body from the front end until the outer end of the bearing is flush with the front end of the pump body.

Dip the seal and seal washer in brake fluid and install in the impeller. Place the impeller on the bed of the press and press the long end of the shaft into the impeller until the end of the shaft is flush with the impeller.

Support the assembly on the impeller end of the shaft and press the fan pulley on the shaft so that the end of the shaft is flush with the face of the fan pulley. Move the shaft in the body so that the grooves in the bearing and pump body line up, then lock in position with the bearing retaining wire.

DISTRIBUTOR, REPLACE
All Except "6-226" Engines

The distributor is mounted on the right side of the engine and is operated by a coupling on the oil pump shaft which is driven by a spiral gear on the camshaft.

1. Remove wires from the distributor cap, noting the order in which they are assembled to assure correct reassembly.
2. Remove primary lead from terminal post at side of distributor.
3. Disconnect vacuum tube.
4. Remove distributor cap.
5. Note position of rotor in relation to the distributor housing. Mark housing to facilitate installing and timing.
6. Remove screw holding distributor to

crankcase and lift unit from engine.

7. Reinstall in the reverse order of removal and set the timing as outlined below.

"6-226" Engines

To remove the distributor, disconnect the vacuum tube and low tension wire and remove distributor cap. Remove bolt and washer that holds advance arm to adapter and lift out distributor. Install the distributor in the reverse order of removal and set the ignition timing as outlined below.

IGNITION TIMING

Crank engine to bring No. 1 piston up on its compression stroke and stop when the timing mark is in the center of the hole in the flywheel housing or when the pointer on the timing gear cover lines up with the specified timing mark on the crankshaft pulley or vibration damper (see *Tune Up Chart*). Loosen the distributor body clamp and rotate the distributor until the points close. Then turn it in the opposite direction until the points just begin to open and tighten the clamp bolt. Check the timing with a timing light.

When using a timing light, *it is advisable to disconnect the distributor vacuum line before checking timing,* otherwise the timing may be affected due to the fact that the centrifugal advance may operate if the engine is idling too fast, thus obtaining incorrect timing.

Connect the timing light according to the manufacturer's instructions. Start the engine and operate at idle speed. Direct the light on the timing mark. It should flash just as the timing mark lines up with the pointer, indicating correct timing. If the pointer and timing mark does not line up, rotate the distributor as required to bring them in alignment.

Carburetor Section

Performance Complaints

Flooding, stumble on acceleration or other performance complaints are in many instances caused by the presence of dirt, water or other foreign matter in the carburetor. To aid in diagnosing the cause of the complaint, the carburetor should be carefully removed from the engine without draining the fuel from the bowl. The contents of the fuel bowl may then be examined for contamination as the carburetor is disassembled.

Check the fuel in the bowl for contamination by dirt, water, gum or other foreign matter. A magnet moved through the fuel in the bowl will pick up and identify any iron oxide dust that may have caused intake needle and seat leakage.

Inspect gasketed surfaces between body and air horn. Small nicks or burrs should be smoothed down to eliminate air or fuel leakage. On carburetors having a vacuum piston, be especially particular when inspecting the top surface of the inner wall of the bowl around the vacuum piston passage. A poor seal at this location may contribute to a "cutting-out" on turns complaint.

Fill the carburetor bowl with clean fuel before installing on manifold. This will help prevent dirt trapped in the fuel system from being dislodged by the free flow of fuel as the carburetor is primed. The operation of the float and intake needle and seat may be checked under pressure if a fuel pump is used at the bench to fill the carburetor bowl. Operate the throttle several times and visually check the discharge from pump jets.

Poor Mileage and Engine Loading Complaints

Cases of poor mileage and engine loading may be due in many instances to sluggish choke valve opening during cold driveaway, caused by insufficient vacuum in choke housing, a plugged or restricted heat pipe or inlet in choke cover. To check for this condition, have engine warm and running at slow idle. Remove choke heat pipe and hold a finger over the heat inlet hole (hole is on choke housing on some carburetors). If there is little or no vacuum pull on the finger, check the choke housing for gasket leaks or plugged vacuum passages. If these are OK, check choke vacuum housing and manifold.

Dirty or Rusty Choke Housing

In cases where it is found that the interior of the choke housing is dirty, gummed or rusty while the carburetor itself is comparatively clean, look for a punctured or eroded manifold heat tube (if one is used).

Manifold Heat Control Valve

An engine equipped with a manifold heat control valve can operate with the valve stuck either in the open or closed position. Because of this, an inoperative valve is frequently overlooked at vehicle lubrication or tune-up.

A valve stuck in the "heat-off" position can result in slow warm-up, combustion chamber deposits, carburetor icing, flat spots during acceleration, low gas mileage and spark plug fouling.

A valve stuck in the "heat-on" position can result in power loss, engine knocking, sticking or burned valves and spark plug burning.

To prevent the possibility of a stuck valve, check and lubricate the valve each time the vehicle is lubricated or tuned-up. Check the operation of the valve manually. To lubricate the valve, place a few drops of penetrating oil on the valve shaft where it passes through the manifold. Move the valve up and down a few times to work in the oil. *Never use engine oil for this purpose as it will leave a residue which hampers valve operation.*

Rough Idle & Low Speed Stalling

These engines are equipped with positive sealed type crankcase ventilation which reduces to a minimum condensation and the formation of sludge. The correct operation of the system depends upon the free flow of air from the carburetor air cleaner through the oil filler tube and engine to the control valve mounted in the intake manifold.

Be sure there is no air leakage at the tube connection, and that the oil filler tube cap gasket is in good condition. Always keep the cap locked securely.

Be sure that the ventilator valve, mounted in the intake manifold, operates at all times. Should the valve become clogged with carbon the ventilating system will not operate and a pressure will build up in the engine crankcase which may cause oil loss at the rear main bearing or by the piston rings.

Should the valve fail to seat it will be impossible to make the engine idle satisfactorily. When the valve operates correctly, a slight vacuum is present in the crankcase which is of material assistance in oil control.

Clean the ventilator valve each time the valves are ground or the engine tuned.

CARTER CARBURETOR ADJUSTMENTS

Year	Carburetor Model	Float Level	Float Drop	Idle Screw Turns Open	Pump Travel Setting	Fast Idle Setting	Choke Unloader Setting	Choke Setting
1956-61	YF-2467S	9/32①	1¼②	1 — 2½	③	④	None	None
1956-61	YF-2392S	9/32①	None	½ — 2	None	④	None	None
1954-61	WCD-2204S	3/16⑤	None	1 — 2	11/32⑥	.016⑦	⅛⑧	Index
1954-55	WGD-2052S	⑨	None	½ — 1½	½⑩	.020⑪	9/64⑫	2 Rich
1954-55	WGD-2052SA	⑨	None	½ — 1½	½⑩	.020⑪	9/64⑫	Index
1953-61	YF-938S-A-B-C	5/16①	None	¾ — 1¾	None	④	None	None
1953-61	YF-951S-A	5/16①	None	¾ — 1¾	None	④	None	None

CARTER NOTES

METERING ROD

YF—This adjustment must be checked after adjusting pump and each time the carburetor is reassembled. With throttle valve closed, press down on upper end of diaphragm shaft until diaphragm bottoms in vacuum chamber. Metering rod should contact bottom of metering rod well and metering rod arm should contact lifter link at outer end nearest springs and at supporting lug. Adjust by bending lip of metering rod arm to which metering rod is attached.

WGD and WCD—This adjustment must be made after pump adjustment. With throttle valves closed, press down on vacumeter link until metering rods bottom. With rods held down, revolve metering rod arm until lip contacts vacumeter link. Hold in place and tighten set screw.

②—With bowl cover held upright, distance between free end of float and bowl cover should be as listed. Adjust by bending stop tabs on float arm.

③—With throttle valve closed, press down on upper end of diaphragm shaft until it reaches bottom. Metering rod arm should now contact pump lifter link at outer end and nearest springs. Adjust by bending pump connector link at lower angle.

④—With choke held wide open, lip of fast idle cam should contact boss on body casting. Adjust by bending at offset portion of choke connector link.

⑥—With throttle valves closed, distance from top of plunger shaft to top of dust cover boss should be as listed. Adjust by bending throttle connector rod.

⑦—With choke valve closed, tighten fast idle screw on high step of fast idle cam until the clearance listed exists between throttle valve and carburetor bore.

⑧—With throttle wide open, there should be the clearance listed between upper edge of choke valve and inner wall of air horn. Adjust by bending unloader lip on throttle shaft lever.

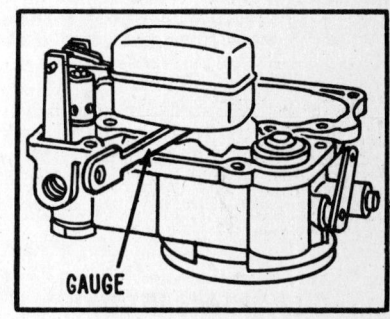

Fig. ⑨—WGD float level. With solid needle 9/32", with spring loaded needle 7/32".

⑩—With throttle valves closed, distance from dust cover boss to top of plunger shaft should be as listed. Adjust by bending throttle connector rod.

⑪—Hold choke valve closed, then close throttle. There should now be the clearance listed between throttle valve and carburetor bore. Adjust by bending choke connector rod.

⑫—With throttle valves wide open, close choke valve as far as possible without forcing. There should now be the clearance listed between upper edge of choke valve and inner wall of air horn. Adjust by bending arm on choke trip lever.

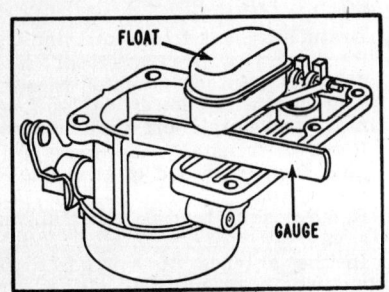

Fig. ①—YF float level.

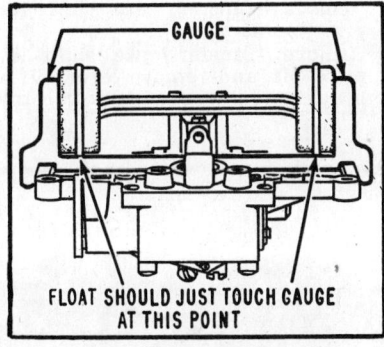

Fig. ⑤—WCD float level.

Clutch, Transmission and Transfer Case

CLUTCH PEDAL, ADJUST

Jeeps

To adjust the clutch pedal free travel, which should be 1½", lengthen or shorten the clutch control cable as required.

Station Wagons (Except "6-226")

To adjust clutch pedal free travel, which should be 1", turn the threaded connection between the clutch control lever and the clutch control tube lever as required to obtain the desired result.

"6-226"

To adjust the clutch free pedal travel on these models, loosen the two lock nuts on the pedal adjusting rod. Turn the nuts forward to increase or backward to decrease the free travel. After pedal free travel of 1" is obtained, tighten both lock nuts against the adjusting trunnion, being careful not to change the adjustment.

CLUTCH, REPLACE

Both the Auburn and Rockford clutches, Figs. 1 and 2, are used. They are of the single plate, dry disc type, the difference between them being that the Auburn clutch has three springs while the Rockford clutch has six.

When it becomes necessary to replace the clutch assembly or just the driven disc, follow the procedure outlined for removing the transmission or transmission and transfer case from the vehicle.

Note that labor will be saved on all models except "6-226" if the engine is removed from the chassis without the bell housing. Then remove the clutch from the flywheel.

On "6-226" models, which are equipped with a split bell housing, it is advisable to disconnect both the front and rear propeller shafts, pull the transmission and transfer case to the rear sufficiently to clear the shaft from the clutch. Remove the bottom pan from the bell housing and remove the clutch from the flywheel with the engine still in the vehicle.

If only a new driven disc is to be installed, mark both the pressure plate and flywheel so that the assembly may be installed in the same position to maintain clutch balance. When removing the clutch from the flywheel, loosen the attaching screws a turn or two at a time in progression to prevent distortion of the clutch bracket (cover).

Installation is made in the reverse order, being sure to turn the screws a little at a time in progression until all are tight. When installation is complete, adjust the clutch pedal free travel as outlined above.

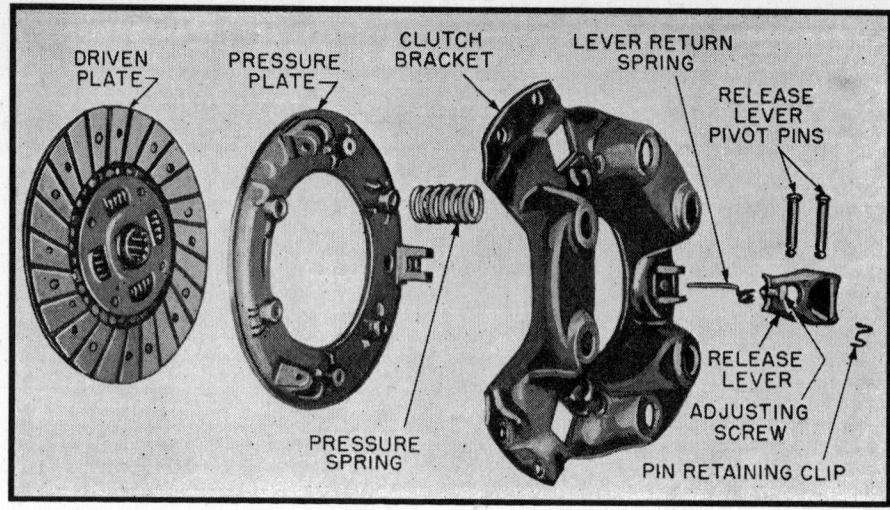

Fig. 1   Layout of Rockford clutch parts

TRANSMISSION, REPLACE

Jeeps & 4-Wheel Drive Station Wagons

1. Remove front and rear propeller shafts.
2. If vehicle is equipped with a power take-off, disconnect transfer case end of power take-off drive shaft.
3. Disconnect speedometer cable at transfer case.
4. Disconnect brake cable.
5. Support transmission and engine with jacks.
6. Remove nuts holding rear mounting to frame crossmember.
7. Remove transfer case snubbing rubber bolt nut at crossmember.
8. Remove shift lever or remote control rods.
9. Disconnect clutch release cable at bell crank at yoke end.
10. Remove floor board inspection plate.
11. Remove transfer case shift lever pivot pin screw.
12. Remove transfer case shift lever pivot pin and remove levers. If vehicle is equipped with power take-off, remove shift lever plate screws and lift out lever.
13. Remove frame center crossmember.
14. Remove bolts holding transmission to bell housing.
15. Force transmission to right to disengage clutch control lever tube ball joint.
16. Lower jacks under engine and transmission and slide transmission and transfer case toward rear of vehicle until clutch shaft clears bell housing.

Separate Transmission From Transfer Case

1. Drain lubricant from both units.
2. Remove five screws from cover on rear face of transfer case (if equipped with power take-off, remove power take-off shift housing).
3. Remove transfer case main drive gear from rear end of transmission mainshaft.
4. Remove shift tower from transmission.
5. In the absence of a transmission mainshaft retaining plate, loop a piece of wire around the mainshaft just back of the second speed gear, twist the wire and attach one end to right hand front cover screw and the other end to left hand cover screw.
6. Draw wire tightly to prevent mainshaft from pulling out of transmission case when transfer case is removed.
7. Separate the two housings, using care to see that the transmission mainshaft bearing, which bears in both housings, remains in the transmission case.
8. Reverse the removal procedure to attach the transmission to the transfer case and install the assembly in the vehicle.

Two-Wheel Drive Station Wagons

The following outline covers removal of transmission and overdrive. If not so

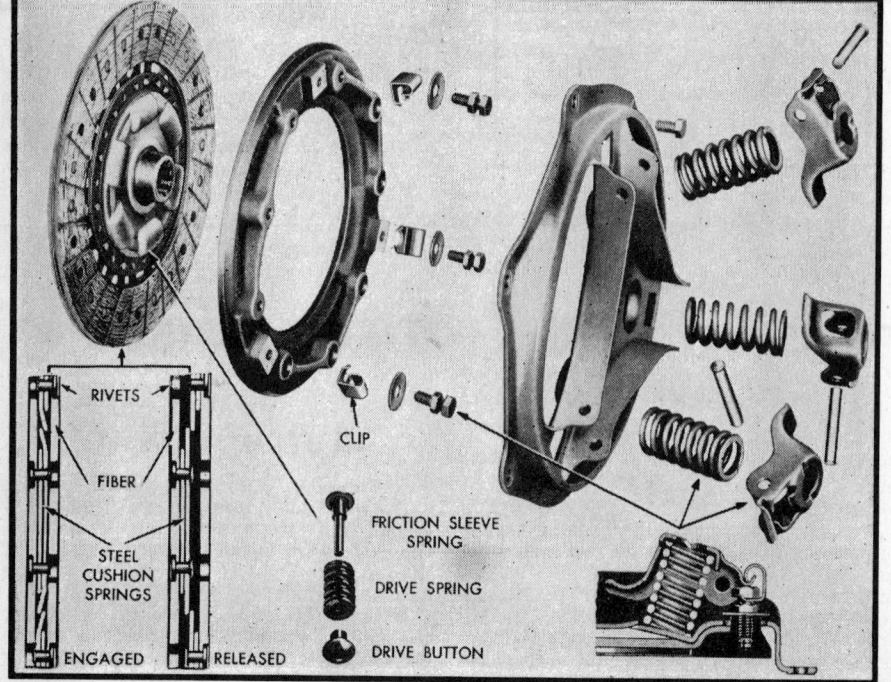

Fig. 2   Layout of Auburn clutch parts

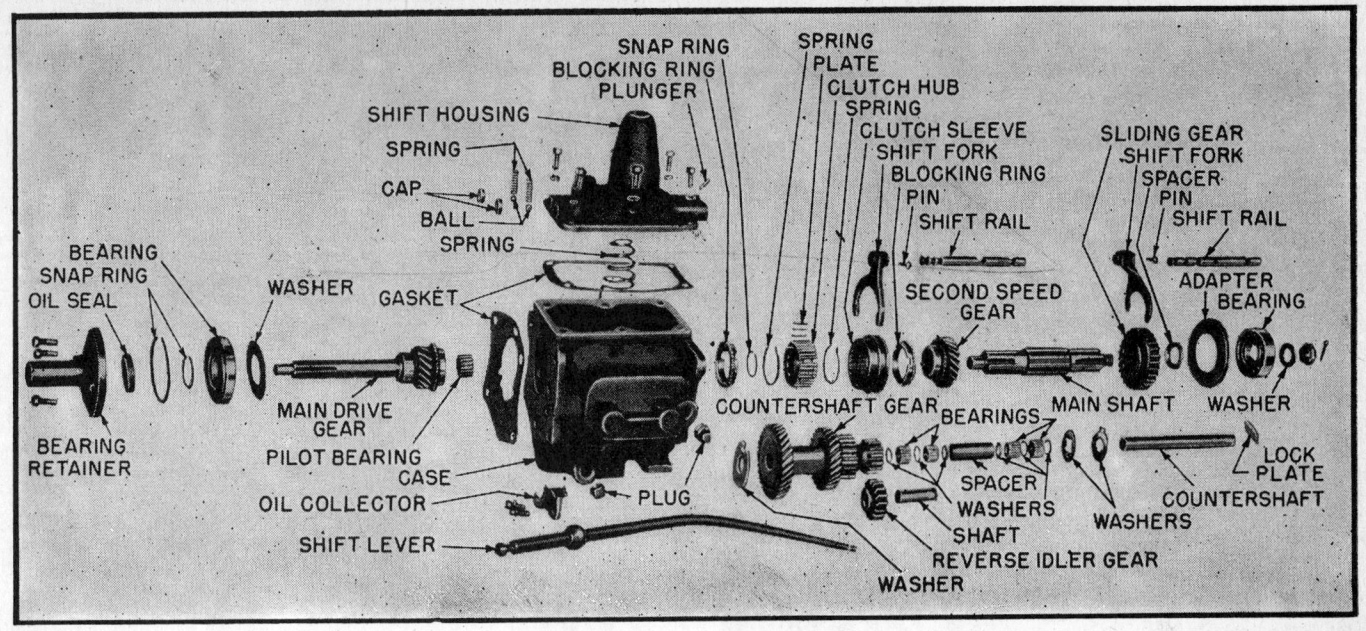

Fig. 3   Exploded view of transmission.   Jeeps and four-wheel drive Station Wagons

equipped, disregard operations pertaining to overdrive.

1. Disconnect remote control rods at transmission.
2. Disconnect two wires from overdrive solenoid. *Tag wires and terminals to assure correct assembly.*
3. Disconnect two wires at overdrive rail switch. *Tag wires and terminals to assure correct assembly.*

4. Disconnect front universal joint, and speedometer cable at transmission. Have available an ordinary cork of correct size to close cable opening to prevent leakage of lubricant.
5. Disconnect overdrive control cable and conduit.
6. Remove rubber mounted saddle support at rear end of overdrive. Use care not to lose spacers. Remove overdrive governor.

7. Place jack under flywheel bell housing and raise it to support weight of housing.
8. Remove frame cross member with rubber insulators attached.
9. Place jack under engine to support engine when transmisson is removed.
10. Thread out four screws attaching transmission to bell housing as far

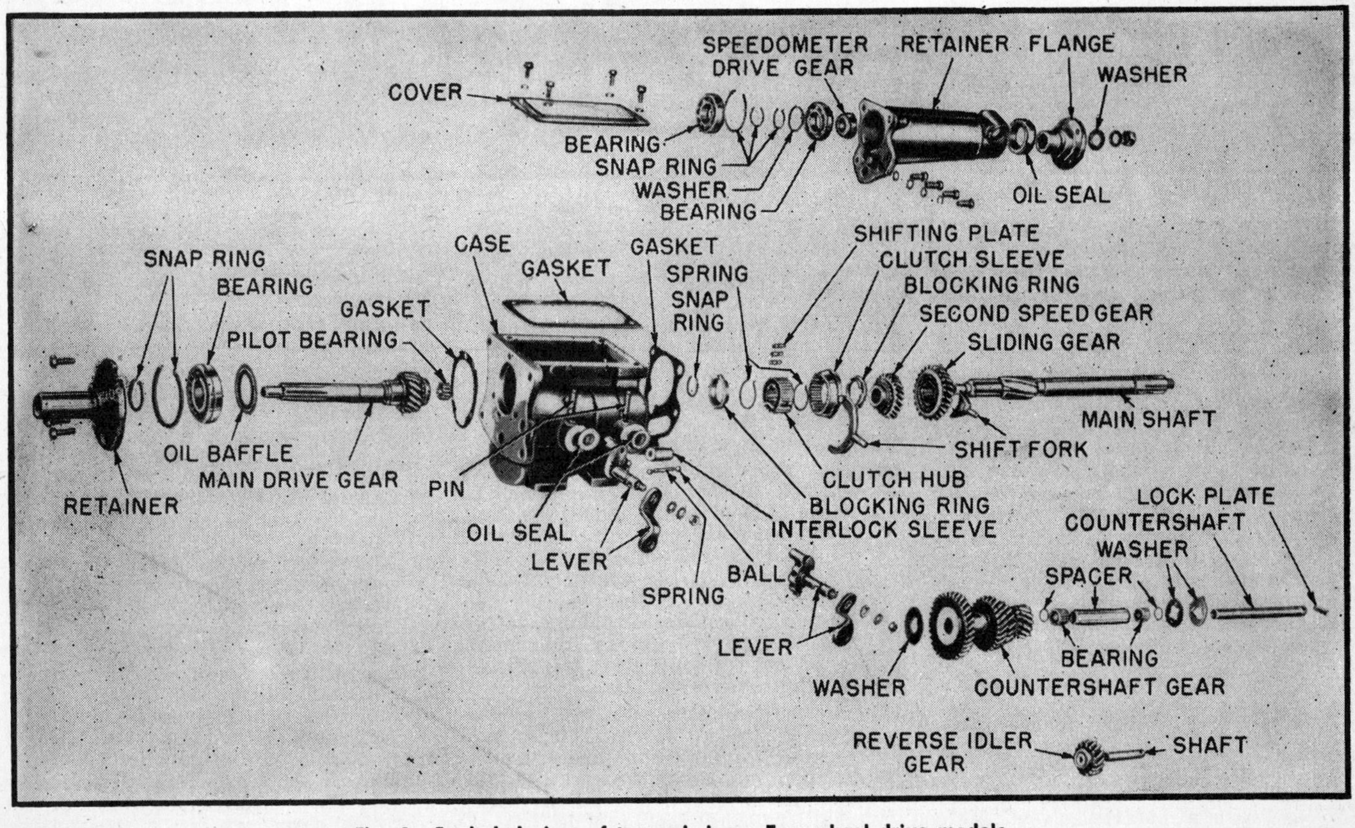

Fig. 4   Exploded view of transmission.   Two-wheel drive models

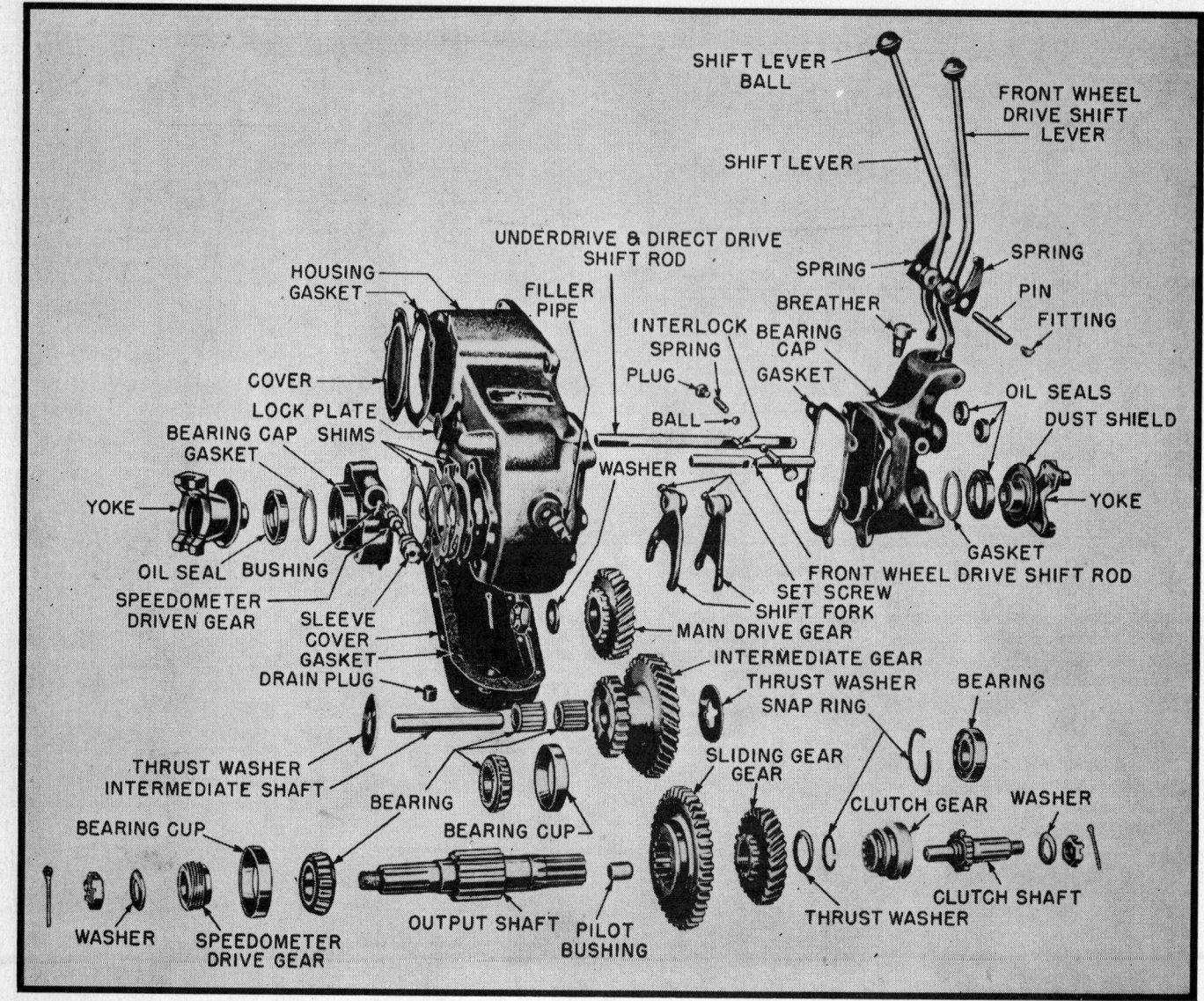

Fig. 5 Exploded view of transfer case. Jeeps and four-wheel drive Station Wagons

as possible and yet support weight of transmission. Pull transmission back to bolt heads which will provide approximately ¾" opening between the two housings and at the same time relieve pressure on clutch release fork in bell housing.

11. Use a long screwdriver through opening in side of bell housing to pry clutch release fork from engagement with clutch release bearing carrier.

12. Complete removal of four transmission attaching screws and pull transmission back until clutch shaft clears bell housing and remove the assembly with release bearing carrier attached.

TRANSMISSION REPAIRS

Four Wheel Drive, Fig. 3

1. Drain lubricant from case and clean case with a suitable solvent.

2. If transfer case is attached, remove its rear cover.

3. If equipped with a power take-off, remove the shift unit which replaces the cover.

4. Remove transfer case main drive gear.

5. Remove transmission cover.

6. Loop a piece of wire around mainshaft directly back of mainshaft second speed gear. Twist wire and attach one end to right hand front cover screw and other end to left front screw. Draw wire tightly to prevent mainshaft from pulling out of transmission case when transfer case is removed. Should mainshaft come out, synchronizer parts will drop into bottom of case.

7. Support transfer case and with a rawhide mallet or brass drift and hammer, tap lightly on end of transmission mainshaft to separate the two units. The transmission mainshaft bearing should slide out of

transfer case and remain in transmission.

8. Remove drive gear bearing retainer.

9. Remove lock plate and drive countershaft out through rear.

10. Remove mainshaft rear bearing adapter.

11. Remove mainshaft and gear assembly through transfer case opening.

12. Remove countershaft gearset and thrust washers, noting position of washers.

13. Drive reverse idler shaft out rearward and lift out gear.

Assembly Notes

Reverse the order of the above procedure to assemble the transmission, being sure to observe the following precautions:

The countershaft gearset should have from .012" to .018" end play when assembled in the case. This clearance is obtained by selective thickness of the rear steel thrust washer, which is available in two thicknesses. Assemble the larger bronze washer at the front of the case with the lip entered in the slot in the case. The bronze faced steel washer goes next to the gear at the rear end, and the steel washer next to the case. Use a loading sleeve to assemble the countershaft roller bearings.

Two Wheel Drive, Fig. 4

1. Remove cover, front flange and snap rings from pinion bearing.
2. Use puller to remove pinion bearing, using a suitable synchronizer ring protector to take up the thrust and prevent possible damage to the synchronizer.
3. Pull off the companion flange, remove the rear bearing retainer and oil seal, and slide the speedometer drive gear off the shaft.
4. Mark the synchronizer blocker rings, gear and sleeve so that these parts may be reassembled in their original position.
5. Raise the drive pinion over the countershaft gear, pull the mainshaft and bearing rearward and remove the drive gear from the case.
6. Cock the mainshaft to the side as far as possible, disengage and remove the shift forks.
7. Release the mainshaft front snap ring. Grasp the mainshaft parts and slide the shaft through these parts and out through the rear.
8. Remove the lock plate and drive the countershaft out rearward.
9. Lift out the cluster gear and washers, noting the position of these parts.
10. Drive out the shaft and lift out the reverse idler gear.
11. Remove the shift shaft locating pins and take out the shift levers and shafts and oil seals.

12. Assembly may be made in the reverse order, being sure to use new gaskets and oil seals.

TRANSFER CASE

Four Wheel Drive, Fig. 5

In removing the transfer case, follow the procedure outlined under transmission removal. Then dismantle the case as follows:

1. Remove propeller shaft flange, brake assembly and linkage.
2. Remove lower cover.
3. Remove lock plate.
4. Drive intermediate shaft to rear of case, being careful not to lose thrust washers.
5. Remove intermediate gear, thrust washers and roller bearings through bottom of case.
6. Shift front wheel drive to engaged position (shaft forward) and remove poppet plugs, springs and balls on both sides of output bearing cap.
7. Remove output bearing cap together with the universal joint end yoke, clutch shaft, bearing, clutch gear, fork and shift rod. Use care not to lose the interlock.
8. Remove output shaft snap ring and thrust washer.
9. Use a rawhide mallet to drive against the front end of the mainshaft to start the rear bearing from the case. As the shaft is removed, the gears will remain in the case and can be taken out through the bottom, also the snap ring and thrust washer.
10. Remove set screw in sliding gear shift fork and take out the shift rod.
11. Disassemble the front and rear bearing caps as required.

Assembly Notes

Reverse the order of the above procedure to assemble the transfer case. But when rear bearing cap assembly is installed, check the end movement of the mainshaft which determines the adjustment of the tapered roller bearings. For correct bearing adjustment, the shaft should have from .004" to .008" end play. Adjustment is made by selective shim installation between the cap and case. Shims .003", .010" and .031" thicknesses are available for this adjustment. Do not install the rear cap oil seal until the bearings are properly adjusted.

GEARSHIFT, ADJUST

Remote Control Models

To make an adjustment, shift the hand control lever to its neutral position. Align the pin holes in the levers at the bottom of the main shifting rod to hold them in their neutral positions. Disconnect the control rods from the levers at the transmission and place the transmission levers in neutral. Finally, adjust the length of the control rods so that they will just slip into their respective levers on the transmission without moving the levers from their neutral positions.

Service Note

Difficult shifting on two-wheel drive utility vehicles and station wagons may be due to improper installation of the second and high shift rod on the shift lever.

The shift lever, mounted on the lower end of the remote control shift shaft, is provided with two holes. The shift rod should be placed in the outer hole of the lever on six cylinder models and in the inner hole on four cylinder models.

Rear Axle, "Live" Front Axle and Brakes

Refer To Hydraulic Brakes Chapter For Brake Adjustments

REAR AXLE

This rear axle is of the semi-floating, hotchkiss drive type. The drive pinion is the over-hung type, mounted on preloaded taper roller bearings. Sealing of the pinion shaft is accomplished at the front end by a spring-loaded leather seal bearing on the companion flange, which is splined and secured to the pinion shaft by a nut, Fig. 1.

Axle Shaft, Remove

To remove an axle shaft, jack up the wheel and pull off the hub and brake drum. Block the brake pedal in such a manner that it cannot be depressed. Disconnect the hydraulic brake line from the wheel cylinder. Remove the mounting screws and take off the outer oil seal, shims and brake support. The shaft and bearing may then be pulled out of the

housing. The inner oil seal may be removed at this time.

Axle Shaft, Install

Replace the shaft and bearings in the reverse order. If the old parts are replaced and the shims have not been disturbed, the end play should be correct when the parts are assembled. However, if a new axle shaft, bearing, differential carrier or housing has been installed, it will be necessary to check the end play.

Axle Shaft End Play, Adjust

Axle shaft end play can be checked when all parts have been replaced except the wheel and hub. To make the check, rap each axle shaft after the nuts are tight to be sure the bearing cups are seated. Then mount a dial indicator on the axle housing with its contact

button touching the end of the shaft. Work the shaft in and out by hand and note the reading on the indicator. If an adjustment is necessary, remove the oil seal and brake support and add or remove shims as required to bring the end play to .001" to .005".

When making this adjustment, an equal thickness of shims should be removed or added on each side of the axle housing to maintain the central position of the axle shafts.

Rear Axle Assembly, Replace

Inasmuch as the axle tubes are pressed into the differential carrier to form a one-piece housing, the rear axle assembly must be removed from the chassis when it becomes necessary to overhaul the unit.

1. Raise vehicle from floor and support

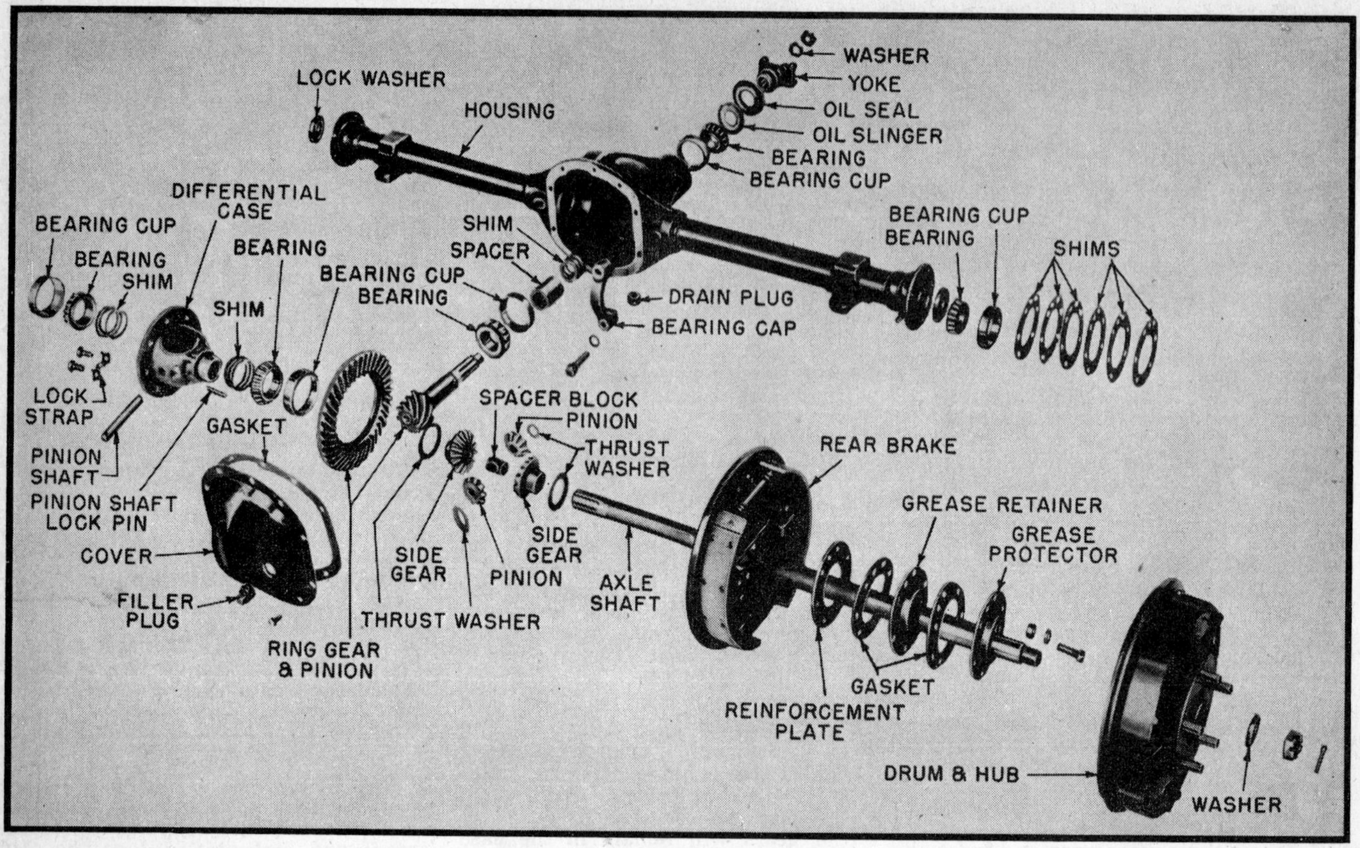

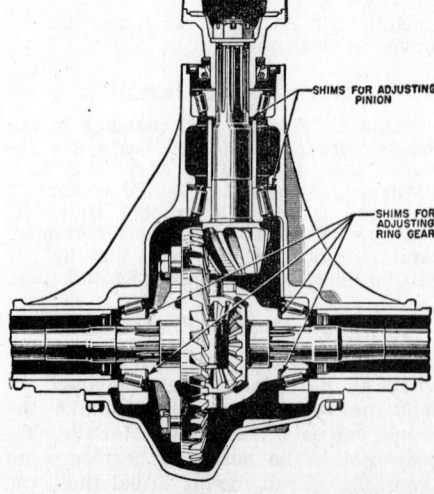

Fig. 1   Exploded view of rear axle assembly.   All Models

with stand jacks under frame side rails.
2. Remove rear wheels.
3. Split rear universal joint.
4. Disconnect parking brake cable (if equipped) from operating lever and from brake backing plates.
5. Disconnect hydraulic brake line connection at rear axle housing.
6. Loosen and move shock absorbers out of the way.
7. While supporting axle housing with hydraulic jack, remove spring clips and lower axle assembly to the floor.
8. Reverse the foregoing procedure to install the rear axle assembly, being sure to bleed the brake system when the installation is completed.

Differential Carrier, Disassemble

1. Remove axle shafts as outlined previously. Axle shafts may be pulled out only far enough to clear differential side gears.
2. Drain lubricant and remove rear cover.
3. Make sure differential side bearing caps and axle housing are marked, then remove the side bearing caps.
4. Pry differential from housing.
5. Remove side bearing cups.
6. Pull off side bearings and adjusting shims, tagging the shims for identification on reassembly.
7. Unfasten ring gear from case.
8. Drive out differential pinion shaft pin and pull out the shaft, pinions and side gears.
9. Hold companion flange from turning and remove flange nut.

10. Pull flange from pinion shaft.
11. Remove pinion from carrier by tapping on front end with soft hammer.
12. Remove pinion shaft bearing oil seal and bearings from carrier, keeping separate the shim pack at each bearing.

Pinion & Bearings, Replace

If the original ring gear and pinion are being used in the original carrier, use the original shim packs at each

Fig. 2   Rear axle adjustments.   All models

bearing, Fig. 2. If a new pinion or differential carrier is installed, note the markings on the end of the pinion gear and on the differential carrier to obtain the correct thickness of shimming to be used with these parts from your supplier. The shims behind the rear bearing establishes the correct pinion depth.

1. Press the rear pinion bearing cup in the housing with the proper thickness of shims. Press the rear pinion bearing on the shaft.
2. Install the front bearing cup and shims, and front bearing.
3. Install the companion flange and, while holding the flange from turning, tighten the nut to a torque load of 200-220 lb. ft.
4. Check the pinion bearing pre-load with a spring scale and heavy cord wrapped around the companion flange. Pull on the spring scale. The torque required to rotate the pinion is 10-30 inch lbs. If not within these limits, add or remove shims from behind the front bearing to obtain the proper pre-load.
5. Remove the companion flange and install a new oil seal (well soaked). Reinstall the companion flange and tighten the nut.

Ring Gear, Replace

1. Install guide pins in every other hole in the ring gear. These pins can be made from 1½" long capscrews with heads cut off and ends slotted.
2. Make sure back face of ring gear and face of case are free of dirt and

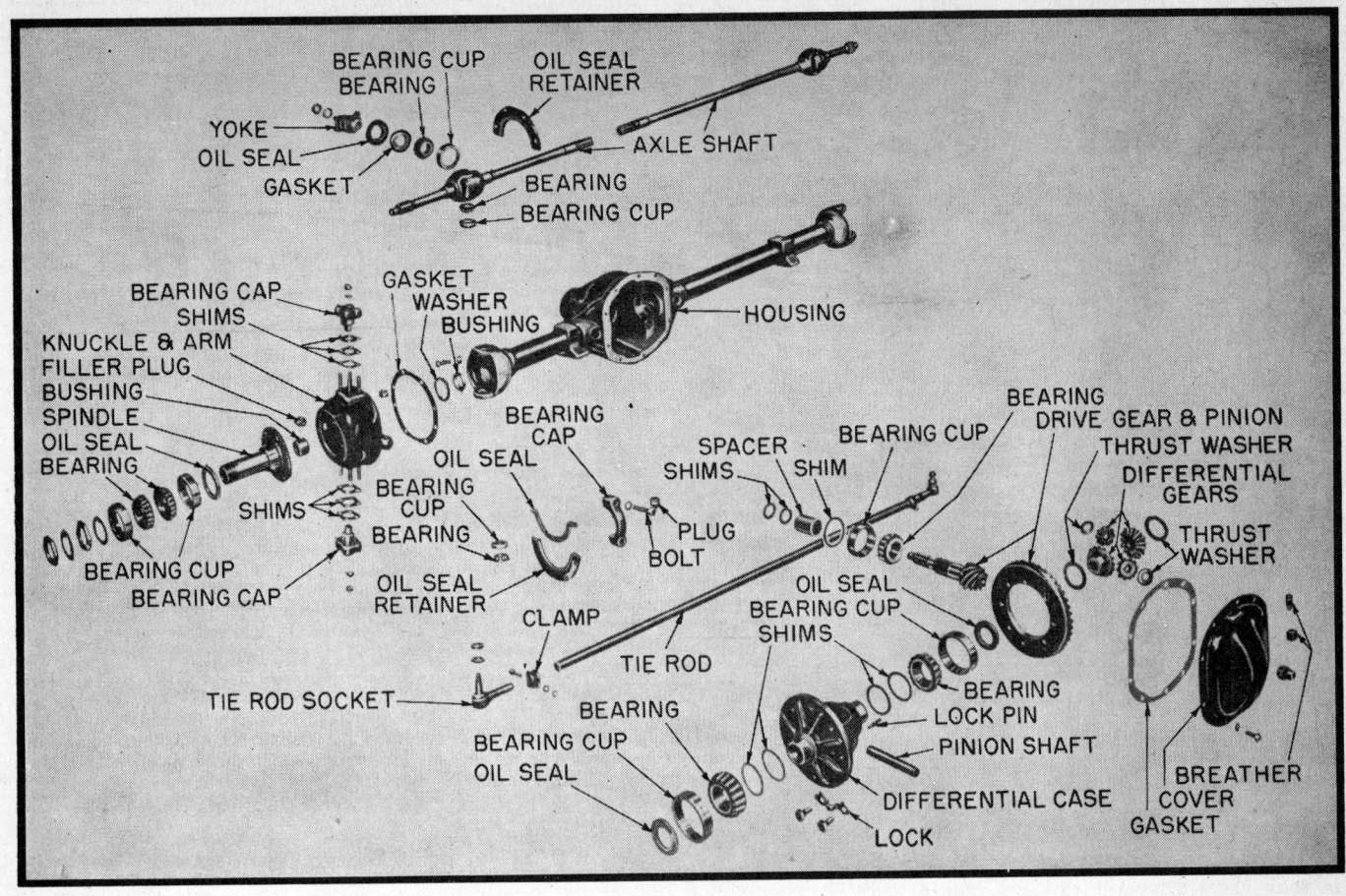

Fig. 3 "Live" front axle. Jeeps and four-wheel drive Station Wagons

burrs and slip gear over pilot diameter of case.

3. Install every other ring gear bolt. Draw them up evenly and snugly so ring gear face is flush with case.

4. Remove guide pins and install remaining bolts.

Differential Carrier, Assemble

The differential bearings are adjusted by shims, Fig. 2. These shims also establish the ring gear position with the pinion. Therefore, backlash must be checked whenever a bearing adjustment is made.

The correct bearing adjustment is one which will provide a .008" pinch fit when the differential unit is assembled into the carrier. To make the adjustment, install the bearing cones without shims and place the assembly in the housing with the bearing cups. Force the unit to one side and check the clearance between the bearing cup and differential case with a feeler gauge. When the clearance is determined, select shims of this amount plus .008" extra to establish the proper pre-load.

Remove the differential bearings again and divide the shims into two packs of equal thickness and install on each side and replace the bearings. Reinstall the unit in the carrier. This operation is made easier by cocking the bearing cups slightly when the differential is placed in the housing and then tapping them lightly with a mallet. However, when installing the differential in the housing,

be sure the ring gear teeth mesh with the pinion teeth before tapping the bearings in place.

After the bearing cups are firmly in place, install the bearing caps. The bearing caps and gasket surface of the housing are marked with a horizontal numeral and on the other side by a vertical numeral. The position of the numerals should correspond when reinstalling the bearing caps.

Ring Gear & Pinion Backlash, Adjust

Mount a backlash gauge indicator on the carrier and start checking for the correct backlash between the ring gear and pinion. If the backlash is not within the limits of .004" to .009", it will be necessary to change the arrangement of the shims back of the bearings. Make corrections in backlash, as described for this type axle in the *Rear Axle Chapter*, bearing in mind that shims removed from one side must be installed on the opposite side so that the total shim thickness of the right and left side will remain unchanged, and the bearing adjustment undisturbed.

Gear Tooth Contact Pattern

Allowable variations in the carrier or drive pinion may cause the pinion to be too far in or out even when shimmed properly. Thus, the tooth contact must be tested and corrected as necessary or the gears may be noisy.

Paint the ring gear teeth with a light coating of red lead, white lead or prussian blue. Revolve the gears and observe the contact, referring to the illustrations shown in the *Rear Axle Chapter* for this operation.

Installation in Vehicle

To install the axle under the vehicle, have the end of the vehicle securely supported with a chain hoist or a support under the frame just ahead of the rear springs. Place the axle assembly in position and raise it so the spring clips and front spring bolts may be installed. Connect the brake line hose at the frame, install lock clip and attach brake line. Connect the propeller shaft at the rear universal joint. The wheels may then be installed and the vehicle lowered to the floor. Bleed the brakes to remove any air from the lines.

"LIVE" FRONT AXLE
Four-Wheel Drive Models, Fig. 3

The front axle on these models is a live driving unit with hypoid driving gears and spherical steering knuckles mounted on pivot pins which ride on tapered roller bearings for ease of steering. The drive is of the full-floating type through axle shafts built integrally with constant velocity universal joints which revolve in the steering knuckles.

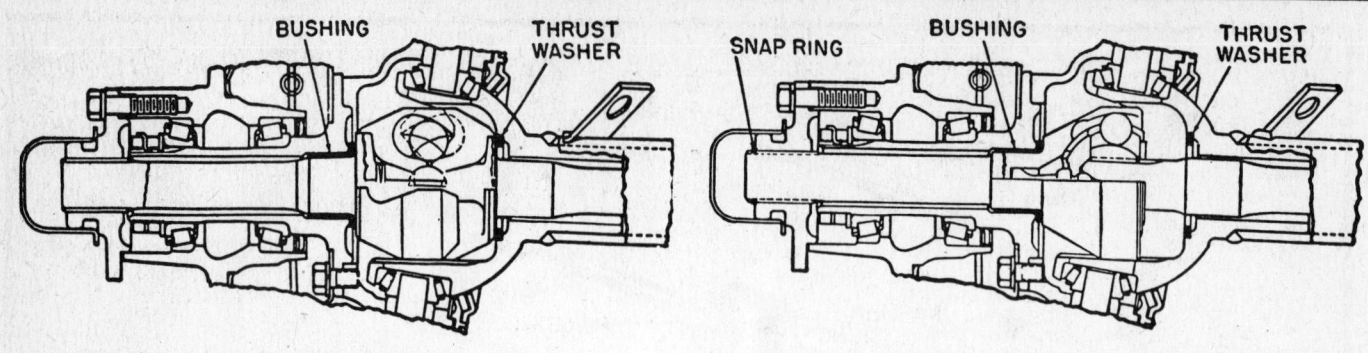

Fig. 4 Bendix type axle shaft and universal joint. For "live" front axles

Fig. 5 Rzeppa type axle shaft and universal joint. For "live" front axles

Front Axle Service

The differential is mounted in a housing similar to that used in the rear axle except that the pinion shaft faces toward the rear instead of to the front and to the right of the center of the axle. This design allows the placing of the front propeller shaft along the right side of the engine oil pan to avoid reducing road clearance under the engine.

The axle is of the full floating type and the axle shafts can be removed without dismantling the steering knuckle housing.

Overhaul of this axle unit is the same as the rear axle.

Service Note (Axle Shafts)

A change in design of the front axle on four-wheel drive vehicles was placed in production effective with the following serial numbers:

No. 37549 on CJ-3A
No. 44070 on 4WD
No. 14284 on 4x463

In the new design the front axle shaft outer splined end floats in the wheel driving flange and is not retained by a nut and lockwasher as originally used. With this construction it is no longer necessary to install shims between the driving flange and wheel hub to provide the correct end float of the axle shaft universal joint.

The new construction, when using the Bendix type axle shaft, is shown in Fig. 4. Note that the end float of the

Bendix type joint is predetermined in manufacture by the position and flange thickness of the bushing and thrust washer. These parts are so positioned and of the correct thickness to provide .088" maximum end float of the universal joint to operate at the centerline of the spindle pivot pins. With the correct joint end float controlled by the bushing flange and thrust washer, it is no longer necessary to install shims between the driving flange and wheel hub, a gasket only being used.

The new type Bendix axle shaft and universal joint may be readily installed in an old type axle by installing the new type flanged bushing. When this is done, discard the shims previously installed between the flange and hub, installing a gasket only. The flanged bushing requires no reaming and is so designed that when it is pressed into the spindle it will be compressed to provide correct running clearance. Coat the inner surface of the bushing with chassis grease before installing the spindle.

The axle construction is similar for installation of the Rzeppa joint, Fig. 5. The thrust washer is not necessary although it is installed in all axles to allow installation of the Bendix type shaft if so desired. As the thrust washer is not effective, a snap ring is installed at the outer end of the shaft to control end float.

Steering Knuckle Pivot Pins

When reinstalling a steering knuckle, sufficient shims must be installed under

the bearing caps so the proper tension will be obtained on the bearings. The shims are available in thicknesses of .003", .005", .010" and .030".

Install one each of the shims over the studs on the steering knuckle at the top and bottom. Install the bearing caps, lock washers and nuts and tighten securely. Check the tension of the bearings by hooking a spring scale in the hole in the arm for the tie rod socket. The load should be 6-9 lbs. without the oil seal in position and is secured by adding or removing shims as required. Make sure there are the same thickness of shims between the upper cap and the knuckle as between the lower cap and knuckle.

Service Note (Lower Shims)

On models CJ-3A, 473-4WD and 4x473, .058" was added to the bottom face of the king pin boss on the steering knuckles. This eliminated the shims for the lower kingpin bearing and the adjustment of the bearing is now made by shims at the top only.

BRAKE MASTER CYLINDER, REPLACE

To remove the master cylinder, disconnect the fluid lines and stop light wires from the cylinder. Unfasten the cylinder from its mounting. Remove the eye bolt from the shaft and drop the cylinder from its mounting.

Front End and Steering Section

CAMBER & CASTER

Two-Wheel Drive Station Wagons

Camber is adjusted by adding or removing shims as required from behind the upper control arm frame bracket, Fig. 1.

Caster is controlled by the relationship between the position of the front spring and its location in the frame cross member channel. If caster is out, examine the suspension for worn or damaged parts.

TOE-IN, ADJUST

Two-Wheel Drive Station Wagons

Load the front end of the vehicle by weights or persons so that the front spring main leaf is flat. Flatness of the front spring main leaf may be checked by holding a straight edge or string below the main leaf, and parallel with it.

Roll the vehicle backward and forward so that all parts will attain a normal position. With suitable trams or gauge, measure the distance between

the wheels at the rear and then at the front. These measured distances should be equal (for zero toe-in).

If the distances are not equal, readjust the tie rods as required to make the distance equal.

When the load is removed from the front of the vehicle, it will be found that the wheels will attain a slight toe-in, ranging from $\frac{1}{8}$ to $\frac{3}{16}$ in., depending upon the arch of the front spring. This is normal and will give satisfactory results in respect to tire wear and proper handling of the vehicle.

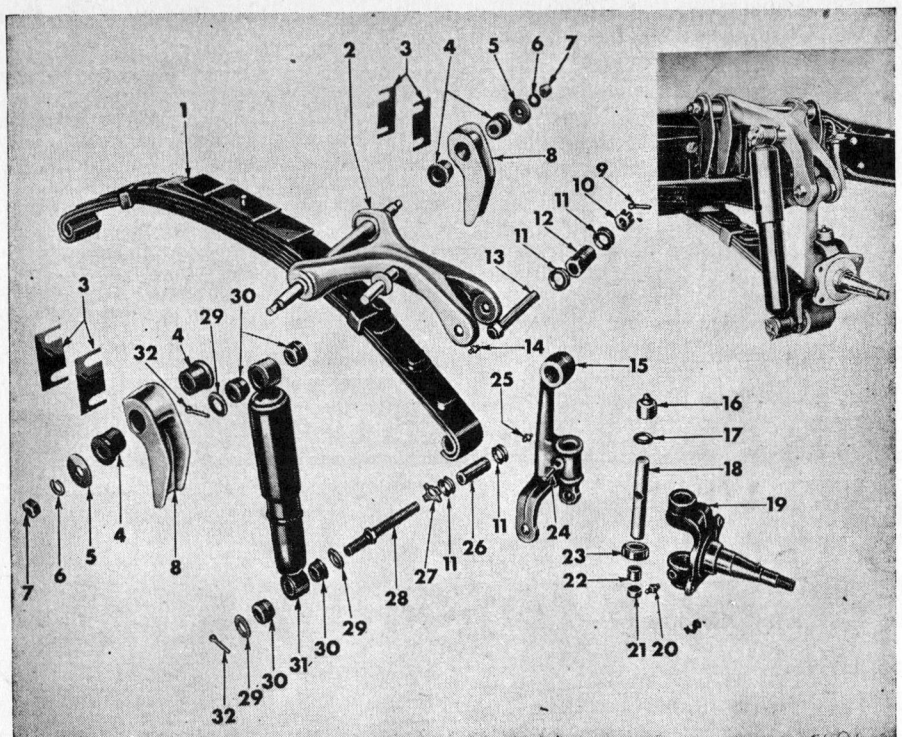

Fig. 1 Front Suspension. Two-Wheel Drive Station Wagons

1 — Front spring	12 — Arm pin bushing	23 — Thrust bearing
2 — Control arm	13 — Control arm pin	24 — Kingpin lock pin
3 — Camber shims	14 — Grease fitting	25 — Grease fitting
4 — Rubber bushing	15 — Knuckle support	26 — Spring bushing
5 — Control arm washer	16 — Knuckle bearing	27 — Bolt lock
6 — Lock washer	17 — Bearing washer	28 — Pivot bolt
7 — Nut	18 — Kingpin	29 — Pin washer
8 — Frame bracket	19 — Knuckle	30 — Rubber bushing
9 — Cotter pin	20 — Grease fitting	31 — Shock absorber
10 — Nut	21 — Expansion plug	32 — Cotter pin
11 — Dust seal	22 — Knuckle bushing	

FRONT END REPAIRS

Two-Wheel Drive Station Wagons Kingpins & Bushings

The following text applies to earlier models insofar as this operation is concerned.

1. Remove wheel hub and dust caps.
2. Take off wheel and hub, bearings and oil seal.
3. Disconnect hydraulic brake tube and remove brake backing plate with brake assembly attached.
4. Drive out kingpin lock pin.
5. Use a sharp drift to remove the kingpin lower expansion plug.
6. Use a brass drift to drive the kingpin up until the upper needle bearing is removed.
7. Use a brass drift to drive the kingpin out through the bottom.
8. Remove the bushing from the lower part of the spindle.

Assembly is the reverse of the above. When reaming the bushing to size, use a pilot type reamer to be sure that the bushing is square with the upper needle bearing. Examine the ball thrust bearing and replace it if worn or damaged. Do not overlook bleeding the brakes.

Steering Knuckle Supports

Should it be necessary to disassemble the front suspension, be sure that the steering knuckle supports are reinstalled on the proper side. The left support will interchange with the right but the wheel camber will be incorrect, resulting in unstable steering. The supports have the part number on the forging for identification—641026 left side, 641027 right side. Later production parts may be identified by the letter L for left and R for right.

When mounting the upper control arm pin bushing in the steering knuckle support, tighten it to 175 lbs. ft. torque. Centralize the control arm over the knuckle support before starting to thread the pivot pin through the support. This is necessary to provide the proper caster effect and equal clearance at each side of the support for the rubber dust seals. Also for the same reasons centralize the spring eye in the lower end of the knuckle support before starting the spring pivot bolt.

HORN BUTTON OR RING

Remove the horn button or steering wheel hub cover by turning it about ⅛ turn to the left and disengaging.

STEERING WHEEL

After removing the horn button and ring, use a suitable puller to pull off the steering wheel.

STEERING GEAR, REPLACE

Jeeps & Station Wagons

It is necessary to pass the steering gear down through the floor pan. The procedure is as follows:

1. Remove left front fender on CJ-2A.
2. Disconnect remote control rods from levers on steering column if equipped with steering post shift.
3. Remove horn button and steering wheel.
4. Remove steering post bracket at instrument panel.
5. Remove steering post hand lever.
6. Remove exhaust pipe from manifold.
7. Remove steering column cover plate on toe board.
8. Remove two screws attaching remote control housing to steering column.
9. Remove horn wire contact brush (CJ-2A) or disconnect horn wire.
10. Remove remote control gearshift assembly down through floor pan.
11. Remove pitman arm from steering gear.
12. Unfasten steering gear from frame and bring it down through the floor pan and over the outside of the frame side rail.

STEERING GEAR REPAIRS

This steering gear, Fig. 2, is the cam and twin lever type in which the cam is

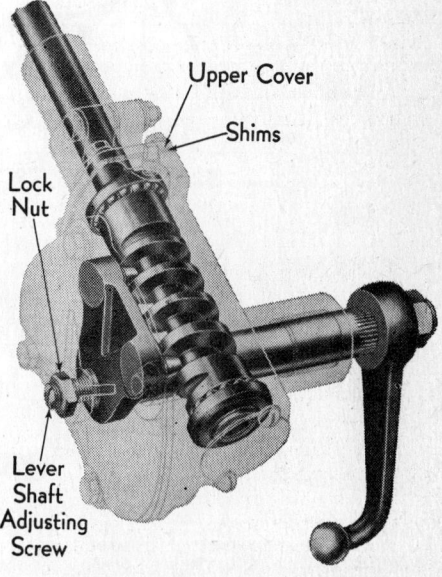

Fig. 2 Steering gear adjustments

mounted on ball bearings and the lever shaft turns on steel backed bronze bushings.

As the cam is turned by the wheel tube, the follower studs are pulled along the cam groove, causing the lever arm to rotate the lever shaft. The groove in the cam is cut shallower in the straight-ahead driving position to provide closer adjustment between the studs and the cam where most of the steering action occurs.

Cam End Play, Adjust

1. Free the steering gear of all load by disconnecting the drag link and loosening the steering column braces.

2. Loosen the lock nut adjusting screw in the side cover to free the studs in the cam groove.

3. Remove the upper cover stud nuts and raise the housing upper cover to permit removal of the adjusting shims, which are .002", .003" and .010" thickness.

4. Clip and remove one thin shim, tighten down the cover and check the adjustment. There should be a slight drag but the steering wheel should turn freely with the thumb and forefinger lightly gripping the rim. If necessary, remove or replace shims until the adjustment is correct.

Lever Shaft Backlash, Adjust

1. Centralize the steering gear by turning the wheel all the way to the right. Then, starting from this point, count the number of turns required to reach end of travel to the left. Turn the wheel back half this number of turns to the mid-position.

2. Tighten the side cover adjusting screw until a very slight drag is felt through the mid-position when turning the steering wheel slowly from one side to the other. The gear should not bind in any position but a slight drag should be felt in the mid-position only.

3. After proper adjustment is secured, tighten the lock nut and give the gear a final check for binding.

THREE SPEED HYDRAMATIC
1961 OLDSMOBILE & PONTIAC

For Linkage Adjustments See Car Chapter

CONTENTS

Description 1133
Trouble Shooting 1144

Maintenance

Adding Oil 1133
Changing Oil 1133

"In Car" Repairs

Pressure Regulator Valve 1133
Line Boost Pressure Check 1133
Coupling Feed Limit Valve 1133
Rear Seal and Bushing 1133
Control Valve Body 1133
Governor 1134
Servo and Accumulator 1134

Repairs Requiring Transmission Removal

Transmission, Disassemble 1135
Unit Repairs 1136
Transmission, Reassemble 1141

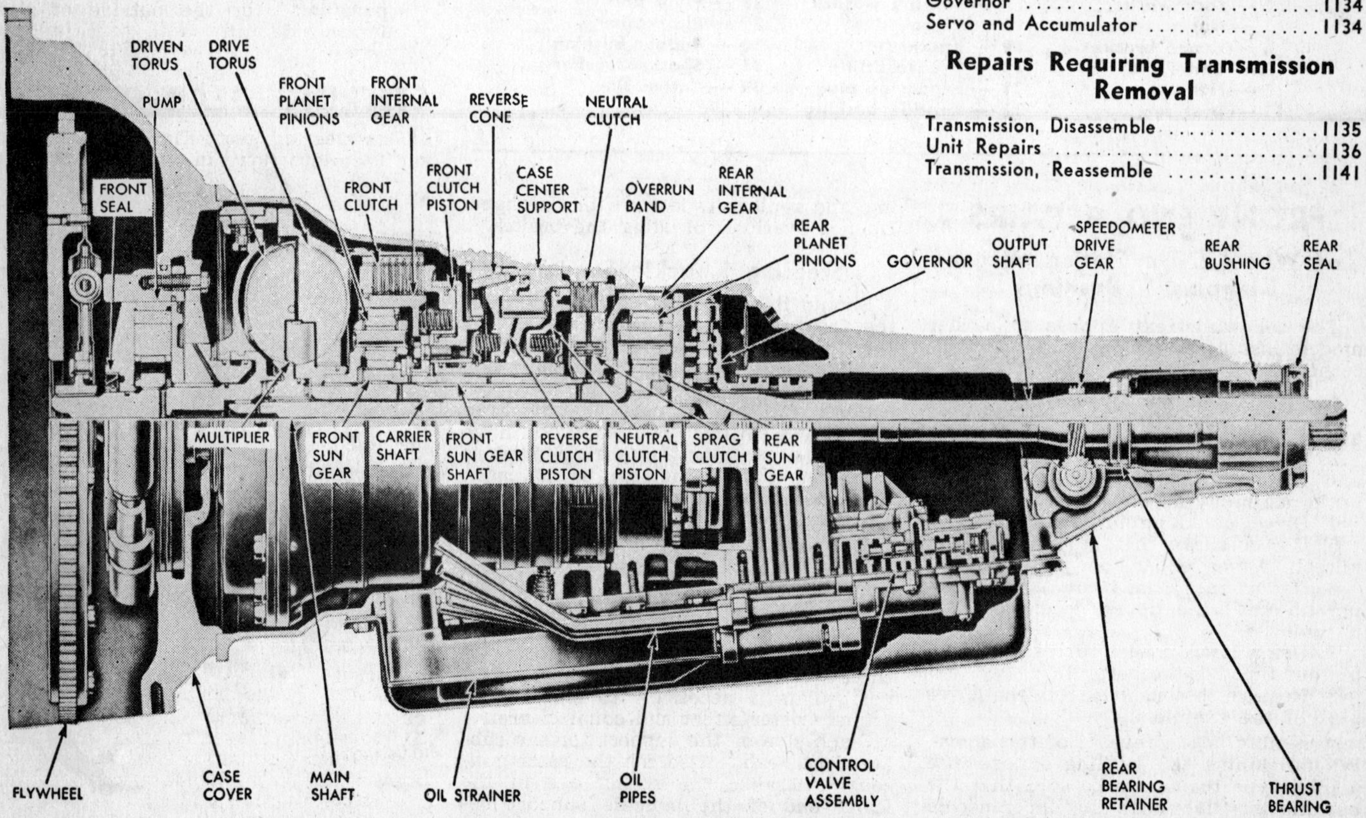

Fig. 1 Cross section of transmission

DESCRIPTION

This transmission, Fig. 1, consists of a fluid coupling combined with a hydraulically controlled automatic transmission having three speeds forward and one reverse. The fluid coupling incorporates a torque multiplier. The torque multiplier actually is a stator which converts the fluid coupling into a mild torque converter with maximum torque multiplication of 1.3 to 1. Stator rotation is prevented through the use of a one-way (sprag) clutch attached to the output shaft.

Gears are changed by dumping and filling the main coupling. In first speed, the rear planetary is in reduction, the coupling is full and the gear ratio of the planetary is multiplied by the ratio of the converter.

In second speed, the coupling is emptied and the front clutch engages. The drive is now entirely mechanical through the front planetary, which is in reduc-tion. The rear planetary transmits no power.

In third speed, the coupling again fills, both planetaries are in direct drive and there is no gear reduction.

MAINTENANCE

Adding Oil

With engine idling and warmed up to normal operating temperature and with selector lever in Park position, check oil level on dipstick. Add automatic transmission fluid to bring the level up to the "Full" mark on dipstick.

Since this transmission is very sensitive to oil level, special precautions should be taken when checking the level, otherwise valve buzz or shift malfunctions may be experienced.

Changing Oil

1. Remove flywheel housing bottom cover.
2. Remove hex head pipe plug from torus cover. Disconnect filler pipe from right side of oil pan.
3. Remove oil pan and discard strainer.
4. Install new strainer using new "O" ring on pump intake pipe if necessary.
5. Install oil pan with new gasket.
6. Connect filler pipe and install torus cover drain plug.
7. Install flywheel housing bottom cover.
8. Pour 8 quarts of Hydra-Matic fluid into transmission.
9. Set selector lever in Park position and set hand brake. Run engine at a fast idle for about 1½ minutes to fill fluid coupling.
10. Reduce engine speed to slow idle and add fluid to bring the oil level up to the "Full" mark. *Do not overfill as foaming will result.*

"In Car" Repairs

PRESSURE REGULATOR VALVE

1. To remove, take off left-hand inspection cover on case cover.
2. Remove valve plug, stop, spring and valve from pump body.

Installation

1. Replace "O" ring on plug, if necessary.
2. Place line boost plug in valve plug with hollow end facing out, and then set valve stop on top of plug.
3. With spring attached to regulator valve, place spring through plug stop and into plug.
4. Feed assembly through inspection hole and into pump. Some manipulation may be required to get valve and plug stop properly into their bores. Torque plug to 15-20 ft. lbs. and replace inspection cover.

LINE BOOST PRESSURE CHECK

The line boost plug in the pressure regulator valve is supplied in three different bore depths which provide different line boost pressures. The plugs are distinguished by either a plain side, a ring, or a groove on the side of the cap at the end of the plug. The plain side plug creates normal pressure, the ring plug a higher pressure, and the groove plug creates the highest pressure. If replacement of a plug is necessary, the same size should be used unless a pressure test shows otherwise. To check line boost pressure:

1. Disconnect control rod at T.V. outer lever.
2. Secure T.V. lever in full T.V. position with a length of wire.
3. Install oil pressure gauge in upper of two test holes in rear bearing retainer.
4. Start engine and run at 1500 rpm in Park position. Main line pressure should be 176-183 psi.
5. Change line boost plug if necessary to obtain correct pressure.

COUPLING FEED LIMIT VALVE

1. To remove, take off inspection plate on right-hand side of case cover.
2. Coupling feed valve plug is located in lower portion of pump and may be removed with a ¾" socket and suitable extension.
3. The valve plug and pin will come out with the socket. The spring and valve will usually remain in the pump body and may be removed with long nose pliers.

Installation

1. Using long nose pliers, carefully insert spring and valves together into pump.
2. Replace "O" ring on plug if necessary.
3. Place valve plug into wrench socket and then place pin into plug.
4. Insert plug and pin into inspection hole and, with pin in center of spring, screw plug into pump. A speed handle wrench works best for starting the plug. Torque to 15-20 ft. lbs. and replace inspection plate.

REAR SEAL & BUSHING

To remove the rear seal it is necessary only to remove the propeller shaft and then the seal from the rear bearing retainer with a screwdriver.

To replace the seal, coat the outer casing with gasket sealing compound and drive it into the rear extension housing.

If removal of both the rear bushing and sleeve assembly and the rear seal is necessary, remove the bushing retaining bolt from the left side of the rear bearing retainer and remove the propeller shaft. Bushing remover (J-8845) with slide hammer (J-2619) is then fitted into the bushing and tightened. The slide hammer will then remove the bushing and seal in one operation.

To replace the bushing, install it, chamfered end first, into rear bearing retainer, aligning retaining bolt slot with bolt hole. Install with a soft hammer and drift. Coat the casing of the seal with gasket sealing compound and install it. Then replace propeller shaft.

CONTROL VALVE BODY

1. Remove filler pipe and drain transmission.
2. Remove outer throttle lever from shaft.
3. Remove throttle lever seal, using a small screwdriver behind flange.
4. Remove oil pan and gasket.
5. Unfasten valve body from rear bearing retainer (5 bolts).
6. Slide valve body off pipe assembly and remove from transmission. *Do not let manual valve drop out of valve body during removal.*

Installation

1. Install manual valve in valve body.
2. Apply petrolatum (vaseline) to valve body pipe ports to prevent damage to "O" rings during assembly.
3. Install valve body in rear bearing retainer by guiding throttle shaft through its opening and then positioning manual valve on pick-up pin (detent lever). Guide valve body over pipe assembly and slide forward to seat seals. Attach with five screws.

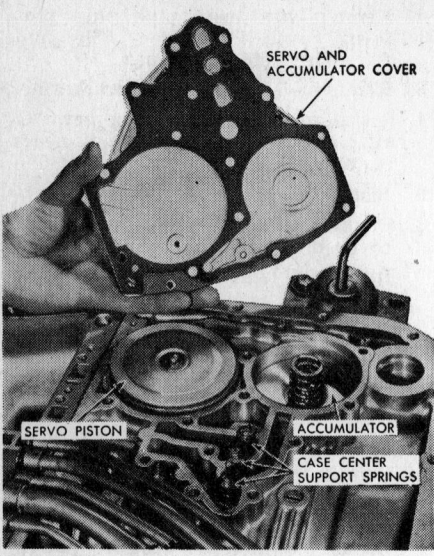

SERVO AND
ACCUMULATOR **COVER**

SERVO PISTON

ACCUMULATOR

CASE CENTER
SUPPORT SPRINGS

Fig. 2 Servo and accumulator cover

4. Install seal over throttle shaft and into case. Install oil pan gasket, using petrolatum and torque pan bolts to 12-15 ft. lbs.
5. Install oil filler pipe and refill transmission.

GOVERNOR

1. To remove, take off oil filler tube and drain transmission.
2. Remove oil pan.
3. Remove T.V. lower control rod from T.V. outside lever, remove T.V. outside lever and gearshift control rod from outside shift lever.
4. Remove speedometer cable.
5. Remove hand brake cable guide rod and return spring from frame crossmember.
6. Remove propeller shaft.
7. Place jack under front of transmission.
8. Remove crossmember.
9. Remove control valve (5 bolts).
10. Remove breather pipe.

CASE CENTER
SUPPORT SPRING

CASE CENTER
SUPPORT SEAL

Fig. 3 Case center support seals and springs

11. Reach into rear bearing retainer and remove the four governor and output shaft attaching bolts. Hold outside manual lever forward to engage parking brake when loosening bolts. Rotate shaft as necessary to remove all four bolts.
12. Mark edge of output shaft flange and a corresponding spot on inside of case with a grease pencil to match output shaft with planet carrier when reassembling. *Do not rotate carrier after removing output shaft or guide marks will become meaningless.*
13. Remove rear bearing retainer-to-case attaching bolts (2 are inside) and remove retainer from transmission.
14. Remove bearing retainer cover (4 bolts).
15. Reach through access hole with 90° snap ring pliers and unseat snap ring from output shaft. Remove output shaft from front of retainer. *Do not strike inner sleeve of rear bearing retainer with speedometer drive gear when removing shaft.*
16. Press off speedometer drive gear and remove governor.

Installation—Reverse removal procedure to install the governor, observing the following:
1. Install speedometer drive gear on shaft so that its rear side is $6\frac{9}{32}''$ from end of shaft.
2. Be sure to align guide marks on output shaft flange and case.
3. When installing rear bearing retainer, use a short bolt in the center hole on each side and one inside rear bearing retainer.
4. Install and tighten governor attaching bolts to 19-23 ft. lbs.
5. When installing frame crossmember, brake cables go above crossmember.

SERVO & ACCUMULATOR

1. To remove, take off filler pipe and drain transmission.
2. Remove oil pan and compensator valve body (3 screws and 1 bolt).
3. Remove servo and accumulator cover, Fig. 2. *The servo release spring pushes the servo piston against the cover, so care is required to prevent dropping servo piston when cover is removed.* Accumulator lower spring and possibly case center support springs will be removed with cover, Figs. 3 and 4.
4. Use accumulator pin to remove both accumulator pistons and remaining spring, Fig. 5.
5. Remove case center support seal springs and seals if they did not previously fall free.

Installation
1. It will be necessary to make a retainer to hold servo piston in place while cover is being installed. *A rectangular piece of sheet metal can be cut so it will hold servo piston in its bore when bolted to right rear oil pan bolt hole.*
2. Place upper accumulator piston on pin and place tapered spring over pin with large end of spring against

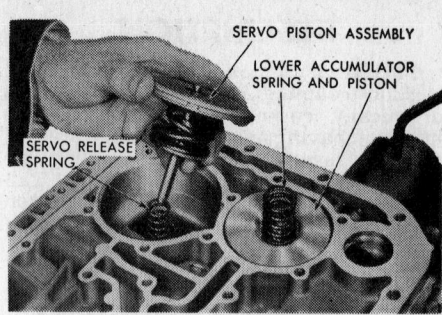

SERVO PISTON ASSEMBLY
LOWER ACCUMULATOR
SPRING AND PISTON
SERVO RELEASE
SPRING

Fig. 4 Servo and accumulator pistons

piston and seal facing away from spring, Fig. 5.
3. Install tapered spring, pin and upper piston into case with small end of spring up. Hold these parts in case and install lower accumulator piston with pocket side down, Fig. 4.
4. Screw ends of case center support seal springs into seals far enough so they will not fall off easily and install seals into case so springs are suspended below them. Petrolatum may be needed to help hold seals and springs in place, Fig. 3.
5. Place servo return spring over servo pin and install assembly in case. Retain it in bore using previously mentioned retaining tool bolted to an oil pan hole.
6. Place remaining accumulator spring in position over pin and hold in place while installing servo and accumulator cover, Fig. 2. Attach cover with three bolts and leave just loose enough to remove servo retaining tool. Make sure three seal springs enter case straight.
7. Remove servo retaining tool and install remaining cover bolts except strainer attaching bolt. Torque to 6-8 ft. lbs.
8. Install compensator, oil strainer, oil pan (with new gasket), oil filler pipe and refill transmission.

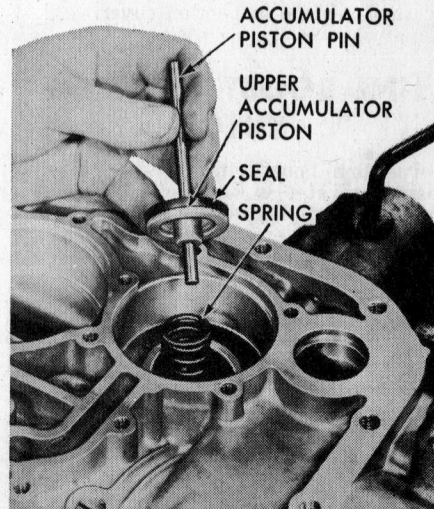

ACCUMULATOR
PISTON PIN

UPPER
ACCUMULATOR
PISTON

SEAL

SPRING

Fig. 5 Accumulator piston

Repairs Requiring Transmission Removal

TRANSMISSION, DISASSEMBLE

1. Remove outer shift lever and T.V. lever.
2. Remove oil pan and strainer. Pry throttle shaft seal from side of rear bearing retainer with small screwdriver.
3. Remove control valve body.
4. Remove manual valve from control valve.
5. Remove compensator valve body from valve body (3 screws and 1 bolt).
6. Remove servo and accumulator cover and related parts as outlined previously.

Front Unit End Play Check

1. Attach a dial indicator to one case cover bolt hole so that indicator stem contacts input shaft of torus cover.
2. With a screwdriver behind flange on output shaft, gently pry forward on output shaft to position units forward. At the same time, record end play indicated on dial gauge.
3. End play should be .006-.018". If not within these limits, inspect thrust washers, thrust bearings and bearing races when removing units from case to determine source of end play error and replace as required.
4. Remove pipe assembly and seals.

Rear Bearing Retainer & Governor

Follow procedure for removal of these parts as previously outlined, bearing in mind that some of the steps described do not apply as the transmission is now removed from the vehicle.

Case Cover, Pump and Torus Cover

1. Remove case cover and pump by lifting straight up. Slight tapping with a plastic hammer may be necessary. Remove thrust bearing race from torus cover if it did not remain with case cover.
2. If replacement is necessary, remove and discard front seal by bending entire outer edge of seal in toward center with punch. Seal can then be removed with pliers or by prying out with a long screwdriver.
3. Unfasten and remove torus cover from torus by lifting input shaft straight up.
4. Remove thrust bearing and two races from either torus cover or torus member as parts may have remained with either unit.

Torus, Front and Rear Units

1. From front of transmission, remove driven torus member-to-mainshaft spiral snap ring with pointed tool.
2. Push mainshaft through driven torus member and remove member.
3. Remove thrust bearing and two races from drive torus member.
4. Remove mainshaft and sun gear.
5. Remove bearing from rear carrier.
6. Remove sun gear from mainshaft by pushing toward splined end of shaft.
7. From front of transmission, remove drive torus member and torque multiplier as a unit.
8. Remove torque multiplier by pushing from rear of drive torus member.
9. If necessary, remove oil seal rings from driven torus member and torque multiplier (3 rings).
10. Remove front carrier-to-carrier shaft snap ring.
11. Remove front unit carrier.
12. Remove thrust bearing and two races.
13. Remove rear carrier and shaft.
14. Remove roller thrust bearing and race from rear unit carrier.
15. Remove snap ring and remove internal gear and sprag assembly including retainer. Make certain parking pawl is disengaged.
16. With front of transmission up, remove front unit sun gear, thrust bearing and two races.
17. Remove front unit internal gear and clutch.
18. Remove bronze thrust washer from front unit drum.

Reverse Clutch and Center Support

1. Remove snap ring and, using puller J-8768, remove reverse cone and reverse stationary cone. Remove stationary cone key from case.
2. Remove reverse and neutral piston and support assembly. If tight in case, tap gently with soft hammer from rear.

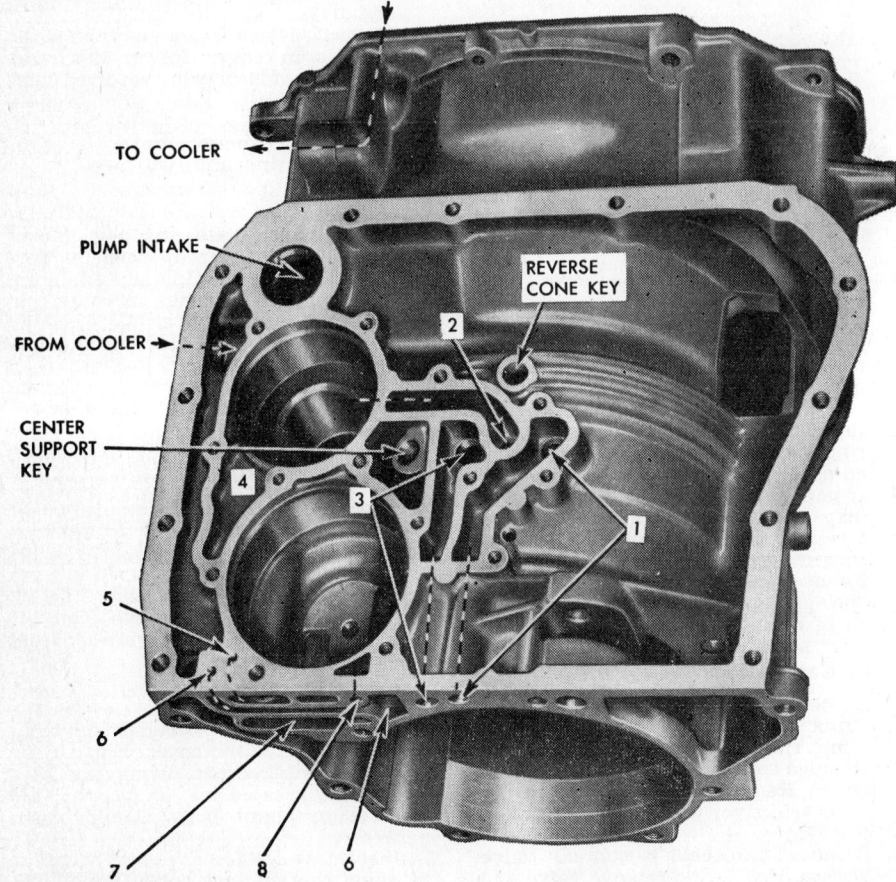

Fig. 6 Case oil passages

1. Neutral clutch	5. Drive
2. Front clutch	6. Throttle valve
3. Reverse clutch	7. Front clutch
4. Compensator	8. Overrun band

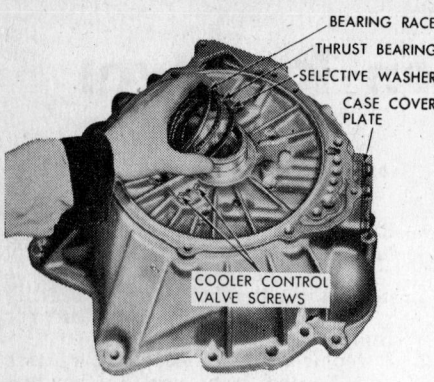

Fig. 7 Case cover thrust bearing and selective washer

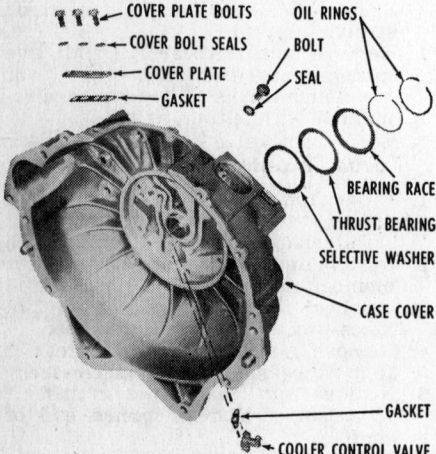

Fig. 8 Case cover components

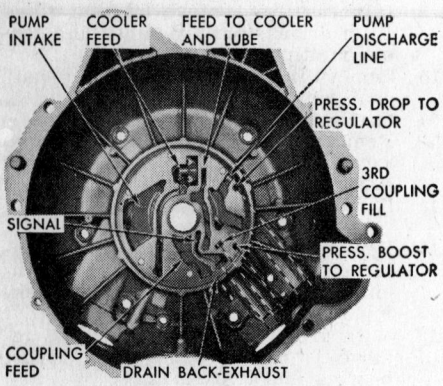

Fig. 9 Case cover oil passages

3. Remove center support key from case.
4. Remove neutral clutch plates and clutch backing plate.
5. With rear end of transmission up, remove band by unhooking from anchor and lifting upward.

Parking Linkage

1. If necessary, remove parking pawl pin from case.

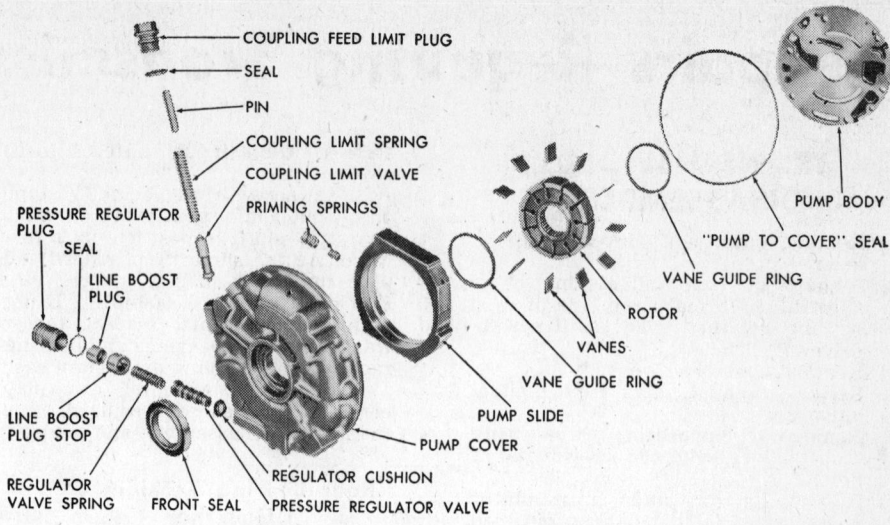

Fig. 10 Pump components

2. Remove parking linkage assembly by lifting parking bracket shaft and entire assembly out of hole in rear of case.
3. Remove pawl spacer from case.

UNIT REPAIRS

Transmission Case

Clean and make a thorough inspection of all parts to determine which should be replaced. It is important to distinguish between "worn in" parts and those worn to the extent that they affect the operation of the unit.

1. Blow out all case passages with suitable air nozzle. Inspect bolt threads for cross-threading.
2. Inspect case for leaks or inter-connected passages, Fig. 6, by using air gun or smoke.
3. Inspect case for hair line cracks.
4. Inspect case-to-strainer neck "O" ring seal for cuts, hardness or pinched seal.
5. If parking linkage was not removed, inspect parking pawl pin and links for excessive wear or bind.
6. Inspect center support-to-case seals for hardness or cracks. Inspect seal springs for collapsed coils and good fit of seals on spring ends.

Case Cover and Pump

1. Loosen six cover-to-pump bolts 4 turns. Tap loosened bolts to remove pump from cover.
2. Remove two hook-type oil rings from cover. Remove race, thrust bearing and selective washer from cover, Fig. 7.
3. Remove two cooler control valve screws, Fig. 7, and remove valve and gasket. Do not disassemble valve.
4. Remove 3 cover plate-to-cover bolts and seals, Fig. 8. Remove plate and remaining bolt and seal from cover.

Inspection

1. Clean and inspect all oil passages for inter-connected passages or re-

strictions. Use air gun and smoke, Fig. 9.
2. Inspect bushing for tight fit or excessive wear.
3. Inspect cover for cracks or porosity.
4. Inspect rings and grooves for nicks or burrs.
5. Inspect cooler passage connection threads in cover for cross-thread. Worn threads may be repaired with thread repair kits commercially available.
6. Inspect cover-to-coupling cover thrust bearing and two races.

Assemble

1. Install cover plate and new gasket with 3 bolts and seal washers. Torque 18-20 ft. lbs. Install remaining bolts and seal washer in cover and torque to 18-20 ft. lbs.
2. Attach cooler control valve and torque screws 2½-3½ ft. lbs.
3. Install remaining parts as shown in Fig. 8 and assemble pump to case.

Pump

To disassemble, remove pump-to-cover "O" ring seal if necessary to replace. Remove attaching screws and remove pump cover from pump over roll pin (do not pry to remove). Referring to Fig. 10, disassemble pump components. Only if necessary, remove rubber cushion from pressure regulator valve.

Inspection

1. Inspect all oil passages in pump body, Fig. 11, and cover, Fig. 12, for dirt or restrictions, using tag wire and compressed air.
2. Slide in pump body should move freely.
3. Inspect vanes for excessive wear at guide ring contact point. Vanes will slow bright spots at the two wear points. This is normal and should not be considered unusable. Abnormal wear will usually indicate that foreign matter has found its way into pump and other related parts and will be indicated by score marks.
4. Inspect rotor for scoring; check

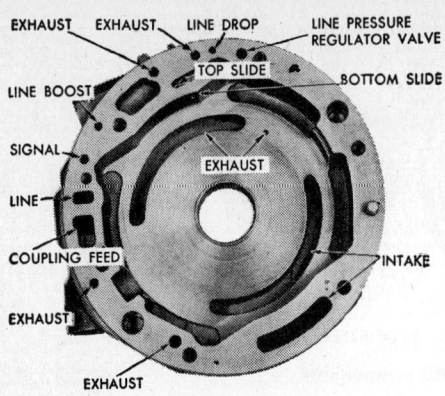

Fig. 11   Pump body oil passages

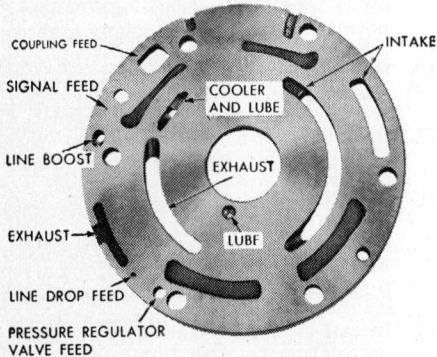

Fig. 12   Pump cover oil passages

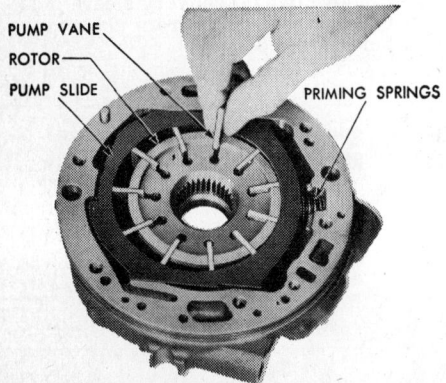

Fig. 13   Pump vanes

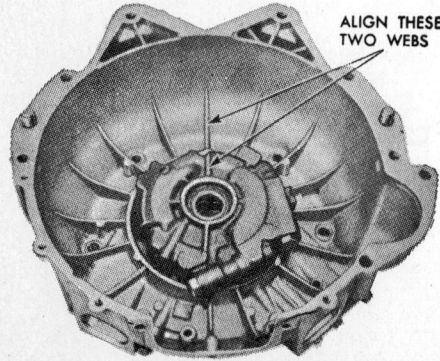

Fig. 14   Aligning pump in case cover

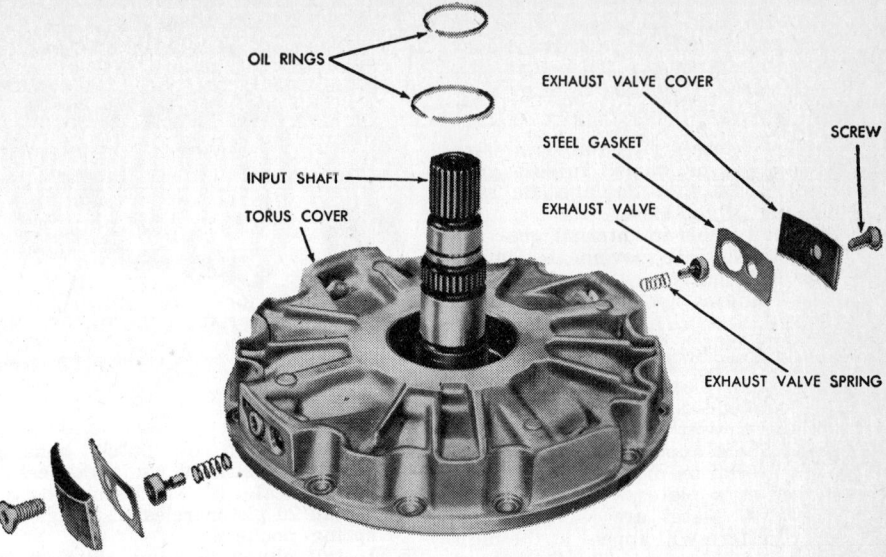

Fig. 15   Torus cover components

splines for nicks and burrs.

5. Inspect pressure regulator valve for scoring, nicks or burrs. Be sure valve moves freely in bore.

6. Inspect coupling feed limit valve for nicks or burrs. Be sure valve moves freely in bore.

7. Inspect pressure regulator valve spring for distortion or collapsed coil; likewise inner and outer primary spring, and coupling feed limit valve spring.

8. Replace pump-to-case cover "O" ring.

9. Inspect coupling feed limit valve plug for cross thread, and seal for cuts or damage.

Assemble—Reverse the disassembly procedure to assemble the pump, referring to Figs. 10 to 13, noting the following:

1. After installing the coupling feed limit valve parts, torque plug to 15-20 ft. lbs.

2. When assembling slide to pump body, compress slide against priming springs at lower end until slide can be fully installed into pump.

3. Install pump rotor with shoulder side down in pump pocket over guide ring.

4. When installing vanes, see that ring wear pattern on edge of vane is against guide ring.

5. Install pump cover over roll pin and torque retaining screw to 6-8 ft. lbs.

6. When assembling pump to case cover, lay pump in recess with coupling feed limit plug and pressure regulator plug facing their access holes. Align webs as shown in Fig. 14. Then start one pump attaching bolt from underside of cover to assure proper alignment before pushing pump to bottom of its recess in cover. Install and torque attaching bolts to 15-18 ft. lbs.

Torus Cover

1. Inspect and remove, if necessary, two hook-type oil rings from input shaft, Fig. 15.

2. Remove the two exhaust valves and related parts. Discard old and install new gaskets.

Inspection

1. Inspect splines and snap ring grooves for nicks or burrs. Check for broken rings.

2. Use tag wire and check coupling signal passages for restrictions.

3. Inspect exhaust valves for nicks or burrs. Be sure valves move freely in bores.

4. Check exhaust valve springs for distortion or collapsed coils.

5. Inspect cover for cracks or porosity.

6. Inspect thrust bearing and race.

7. Inspect mainshaft pilot bushing for excessive wear and tight fit.

Assemble—Reverse disassembly procedure to assemble. Use a clutch head socket when installing exhaust valve screws and torque to 19-23 ft. lbs.

Front Clutch

1. Remove bronze thrust washer, Fig. 16.

2. Install assembly in vise with internal gear up and vise engaging large teeth on opposite side of assembly.

Fig. 16   Thrust washer in front clutch housing

3. Remove four internal gear attaching bolts and gently tap a dowel pin with a drift to remove internal gear from clutch housing. Then dismantle the unit as suggested by Fig. 17.

Inspection

1. Inspect internal gear for tooth damage, nicks or burrs. Inspect gear bushing wear or damage. Be sure bushing is not loose.
2. Inspect splines in internal gear for free clutch plate movement; remove any obstruction.
3. Check lubrication ports for restriction.
4. Inspect clutch backing plate for nicks, burrs or foreign material.
5. Inspect all plates for foreign particles embedded in plates. Check for excessive wear on plates such as metal spots appearing through facing material on drive plates or deep cuts in steel plates.
6. The steel plates are waved and a wear pattern will appear at the high points of the wave. This is normal and plates should not be replaced because of these bright spots.
7. The faced plates will appear discolored after a few hundred miles, which is a normal reaction from oil-absorbing characteristics of the facing material. Faced plates are flat and an even wear pattern will appear over the entire area.
8. Inspect front clutch apply piston for scores, nicks or burrs, and for cracks in casting.
9. Replace inner and outer piston rubber lip-type seals. Be sure seal is not nicked or pinched during installation. The inner seal should be installed first, using the clutch piston without the outer seal to seat the inner seal snug in the ring groove by rotating piston back and forth.
10. Inspect clutch housing for foreign material. Check clutch apply oil passages for restrictions or off location oil passages.
11. Inspect thrust washer for damage.

Assemble

1. Install new inner piston seal on clutch housing with seal lip facing down.
2. Install new outer seal on piston with lip facing away from spring pockets.

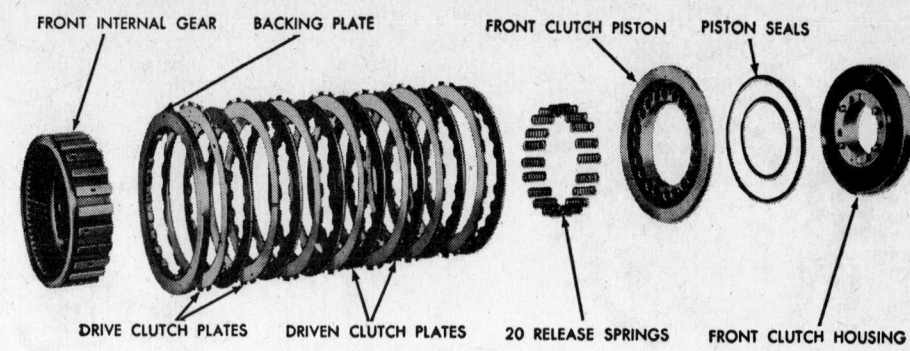

Fig. 17 Front clutch components

FRONT INTERNAL GEAR — BACKING PLATE — FRONT CLUTCH PISTON — PISTON SEALS — DRIVE CLUTCH PLATES — DRIVEN CLUTCH PLATES — 20 RELEASE SPRINGS — FRONT CLUTCH HOUSING

3. Install piston in clutch housing, rotating assembly while depressing piston seal with small screwdriver.
4. Install 20 piston release springs into spring pockets.
5. Install clutch backing plate on internal gear with undercut facing flange on internal gear.
6. Install 7 faced plates and 7 steel plates alternately over internal gear, starting with a faced plate. The steel plates must be assembled in an un-nested position as follows:
7. Place a faced plate and first steel plate over internal gear, noticing location of slight half-moon notch in edge of steel plate.
8. Install another faced plate and then the second steel plate so that the notch is located 2 drive lugs on the internal gear away from notch in first steel plate.
9. Continue in this alternating manner so that the notches in the odd numbered steel plates are one above the other and the notches in the even numbered steel plates are one above the other.
10. Holding assembly together, position internal gear with plates on clutch release springs, aligning dowels.
11. Place entire assembly in vise with vise engaging large teeth on clutch housing.
12. Install four attaching bolts and alternately tighten bolts to properly seat internal gear on dowels. Check bottom steel plate for freedom after tightening bolts. Torque to 22-27 ft. lbs.
13. Install thrust washer, Fig. 16, using petrolatum to hold in place.

Case Center Support

1. Remove two oil delivery sleeve hook-type oil seal rings from center support, Fig. 18.

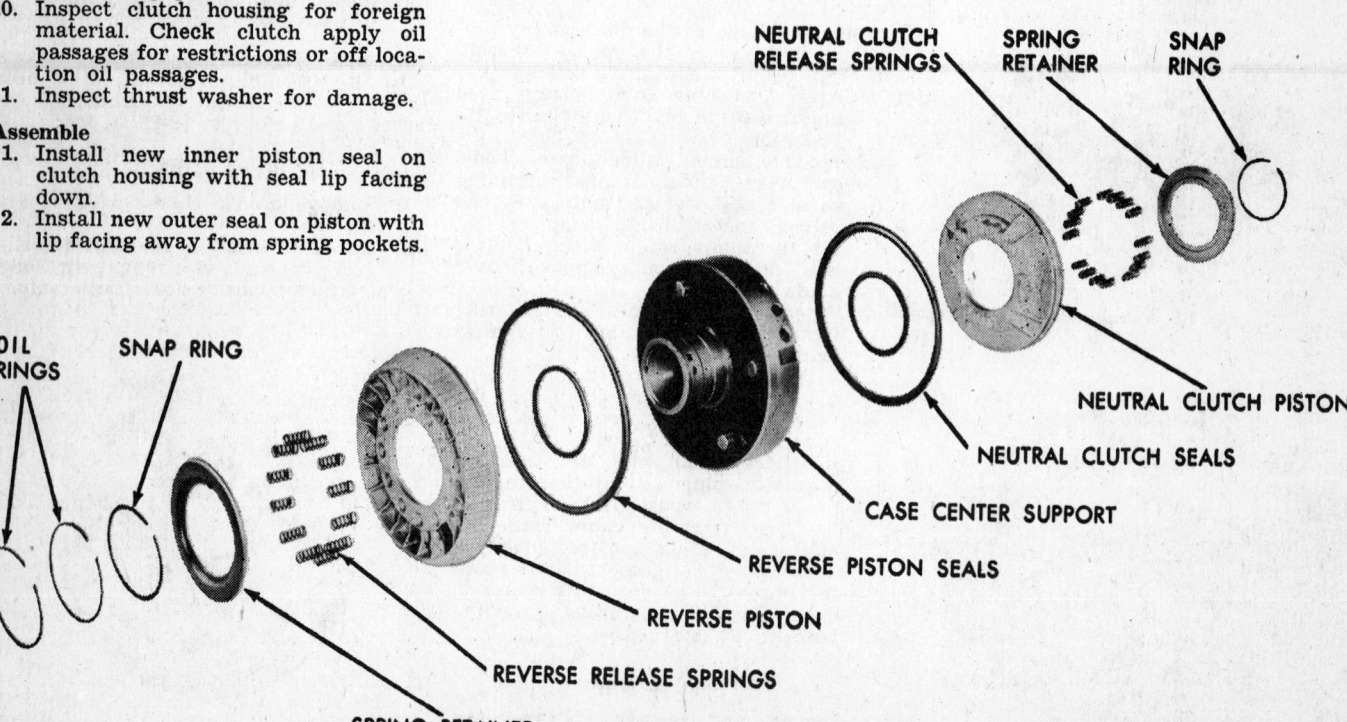

NEUTRAL CLUTCH RELEASE SPRINGS — SPRING RETAINER — SNAP RING — NEUTRAL CLUTCH PISTON — NEUTRAL CLUTCH SEALS — CASE CENTER SUPPORT — REVERSE PISTON SEALS — REVERSE PISTON — REVERSE RELEASE SPRINGS — SPRING RETAINER — OIL RINGS — SNAP RING

Fig. 18 Case center support components

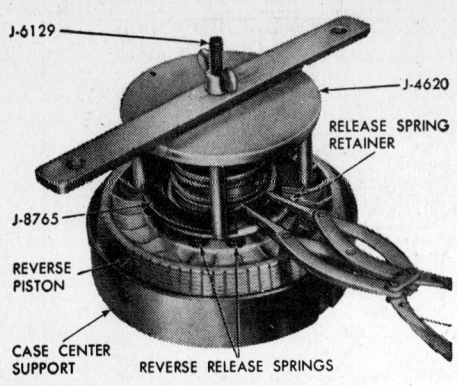

Fig. 19 Removing reverse release spring retainer snap ring

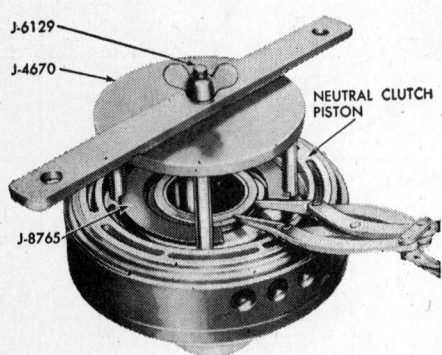

Fig. 20 Removing neutral clutch spring retainer snap ring

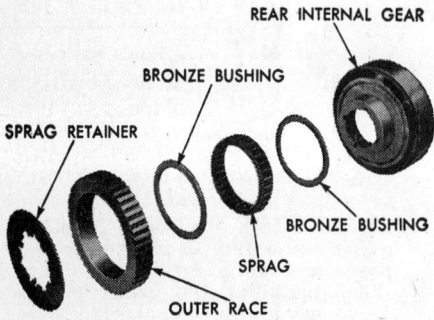

Fig. 21 Sprag components

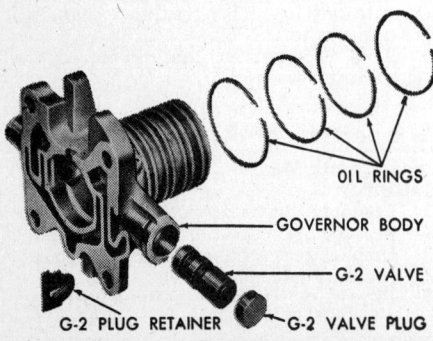

Fig. 22 Governor components

2. Using tools shown in Fig. 19, remove release spring retainer snap ring. Remove tools and take out retainer, 12 piston release springs and reverse clutch piston. It may be necessary to tap housing gently. Remove piston seal rings and discard.
3. With tools shown in Fig. 20, disassemble neutral clutch in same manner as reverse piston parts. *Do not mix the 16 neutral clutch release springs with the 12 reverse piston release springs.*

Inspection

1. Inspect case center support for nicks, burrs, damaged or excessive wear on bushing. Make certain bushing is not loose.
2. Check reverse apply and clutch apply oil passages with air and tag wire. Check for inter-connected or restricted passages.
3. Check hook-type seal rings for damage.
4. Inspect clutch and reverse pistons for cracks or distortion and springs for distorted or collapsed coils.
5. Replace clutch inner and outer piston seals.
6. Inspect clutch and reverse spring retainers and snap ring grooves.

Assemble—Reverse disassembly procedure to assemble, referring to Figs. 18, 19 and 20, noting the following:
1. When installing inner and outer clutch seals, have lip of seal facing away from spring pockets.
2. When installing clutch piston, use small screwdriver to depress lip of outer seal into case center support.
3. When installing seal rings on reverse piston, have lip of seals facing dowel pin holes in piston. Install reverse piston, aligning piston to index with dowel pins.

Rear Internal Gear and Sprag

1. Disassemble as suggested by Fig. 21, and inspect all parts for excessive wear or damage.
2. To assemble, place one bronze bushing over inner race of internal gear with cup side facing up.
3. Place sprag into sprag outer race. With shoulder side of sprag up, start sprag and outer race over internal gear and down against gear.
4. Install second bushing with cup side down against sprag.
5. Apply petrolatum on sprag retainer and install retainer on internal gear, aligning tangs with gear slots. *Check to make certain sprag is properly installed by rotating outer race counterclockwise; outer race should not turn clockwise.*

Governor

1. Disassemble governor as suggested by Fig. 22.
2. Inspect rings and grooves. Rings should fit freely in grooves.
3. Use tag wire and check oil passages for restrictions.
4. Inspect bushing for scores, nicks or burrs.
5. Inspect valves for free movement in bores.
6. Use air gun to be certain governor

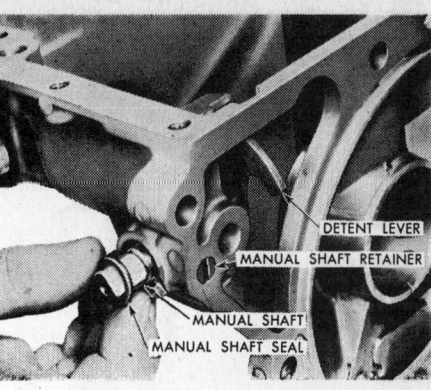

Fig. 23 Manual shaft seal

casting is free from dirt and chips.
7. Assemble governor. Install G-2 plug retainer with finger side out as shown.

Rear Bearing Retainer

1. To disassemble, remove inside detent lever and shaft assembly by removing manual shaft retaining pin from case side of retainer, Fig. 23. *This is not a screw.*
2. Rotate lever and shaft to remove from rear bearing retainer. If necessary, remove manual shaft seal from retainer bore.
3. Remove snap ring through access hole in retainer, Fig 24, and remove rear thrust bearing and two races.

Inspection

1. Inspect retainer for hair line cracks or leaks. Use air gun or smoke to check for inter-connected oil passages, Fig. 25.
2. Check air vent passage for restriction, and anti-syphoning valve for proper movement.
3. Inspect detent lever for nicks, burrs and replace shaft "O" ring. seal Clean thoroughly with air gun.

Assemble

1. Install thrust bearing and two races.
2. Install snap ring, concave side toward rear (identification side away from race) and align ear on snap ring with top slot in retainer.
3. If removed, install bushing and sleeve, chamfered end first. Align short slot in bushing with retaining bolt hole in rear bearing retainer. Torque bushing bolt to 12-15 ft. lbs.
4. Install inside detent lever and shaft assembly.
5. Install detent shaft retainer into hole in retainer, aligning key with annular groove in detent shaft. If removed, install new manual shaft seal over detent shaft with grooved side toward retainer.

Servo and Accumulator Pistons

1. Disassemble servo piston as shown in Fig. 26. Referring to Fig. 27, inspect parts as follows:
2. Inspect piston ring and ring groove for nicks or burrs.
3. Check release springs for collapsed coils or broken spring.
4. Check piston stem for scoring.

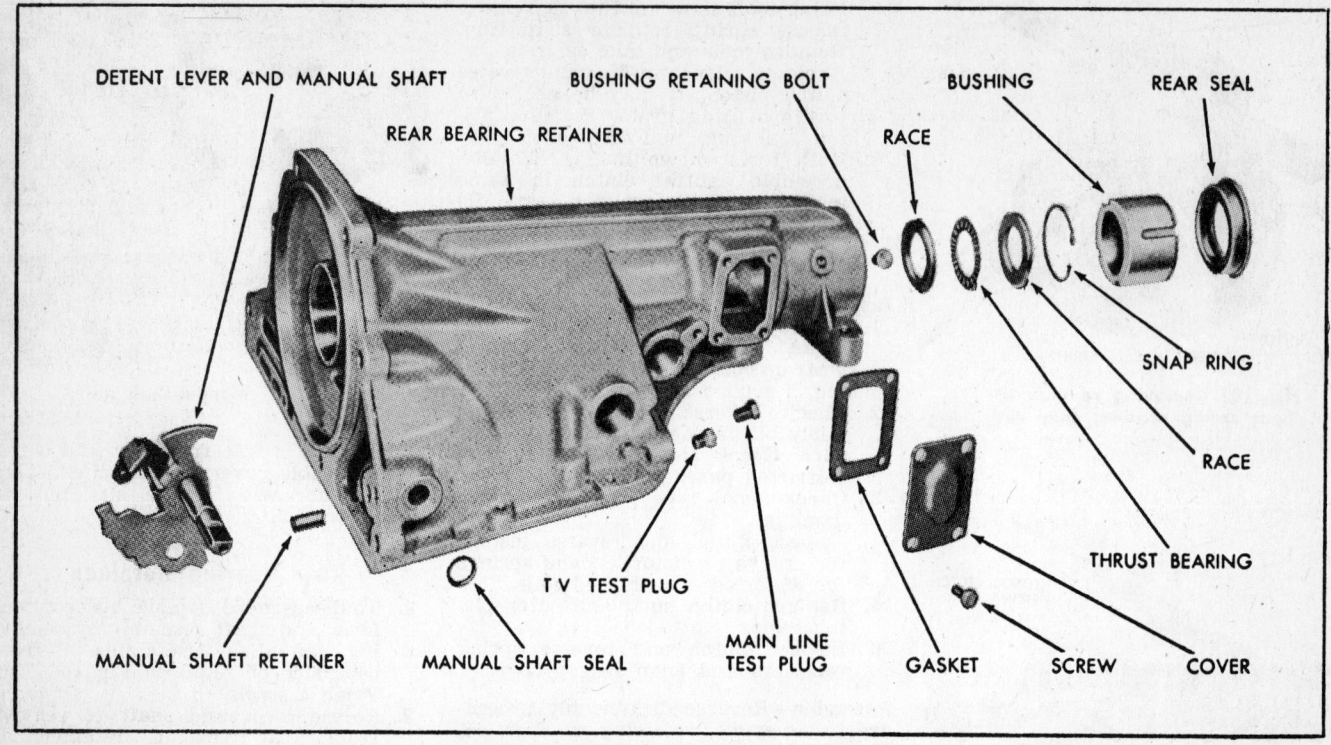

Fig. 24 Rear bearing retainer components

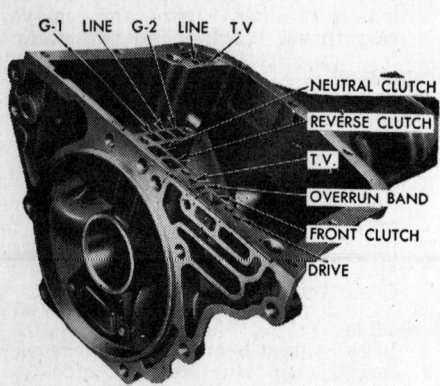

Fig. 25 Rear bearing retainer oil passages

5. Use tag wire and check oil passages in piston.
6. Inspect lower accumulator piston ring and ring grooves for nicks or burrs.
7. Replace rubber lip-type seal on upper accumulator piston. Inspect release springs for collapsed coils or broken ring.
8. Inspect accumulator piston pin for scoring.
9. Assemble by referring to Figs. 26 and 27.

Control Valves

Refer to Figs. 28 to 32 when disassembling and assembling the control valves. When disassembled, inspect for the following.
1. Inspect each valve in valve body for free movement in valve bore. It may be necessary to stone lands of valve

lightly to remove small burrs. The valves will have sharp edges to perform a cleaning action within the valve bore. *Do not remove edges.*
2. Inspect springs for distortion or collapsed coils.
3. Be sure check ball seats are not pitted or chipped.
4. Inspect spacer plates for restrictions, dents or distortion.
5. Clean valve body thoroughly with air gun.

Assemble—When assembling the control valve body, refer to the illustrations. All attaching screws should be torqued to 2½-3½ ft. lbs. and bolts to 6-8 ft. lbs. Also be sure to observe the following:
1. When installing the T.V. shaft through hole in valve body, be sure T.V. lever will index between T.V. plunger and throttle adjusting screw. Install washer and "C" ring secur-

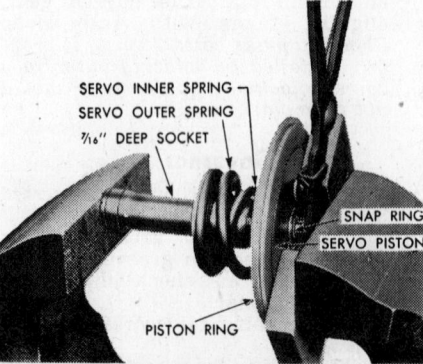

Fig. 26 Removing snap ring from servo piston pin

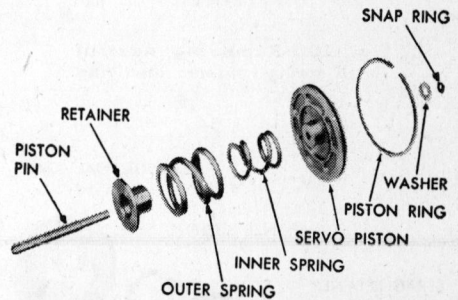

Fig. 27 Servo piston components

ing lever to valve body. *Turn T.V. adjusting screw back to original position, exactly 5 turns.*
2. When installing the pressure boost valve, use a brass rod to guide valve into bore (long land first). Install retaining pin through same bore.
3. When installing valve bore plug in valve body, compress and partially install multiple plug retainer. Install retainer in such a manner that only one corner of plug will be retained. This will permit installation of remaining valves.

Inspection of Remaining Units
Drive Torus Member and Torque Multiplier
1. Inspect drive torus member for porosity, chipped or damaged vanes.
2. Inspect torus bushing for good staking and excessive wear.
3. Check for damaged splines on torque multiplier and bent or damaged vanes. Check oil seal ring on torque multiplier for broken ring and free

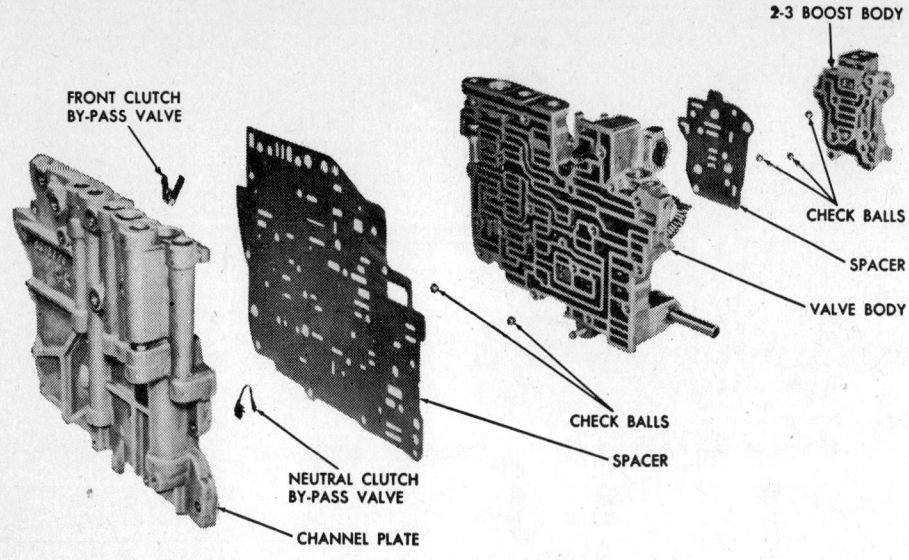

Fig. 28 Control valve assembly

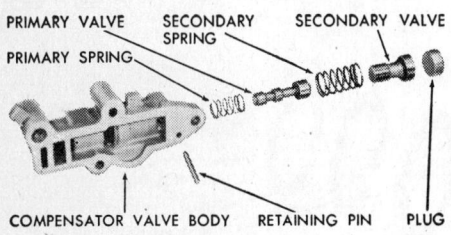

Fig. 29 Compensator valve components

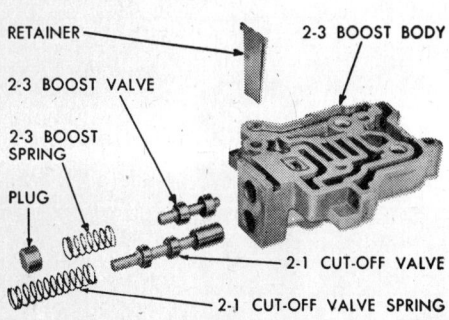

Fig. 30 2-3 boost plug components

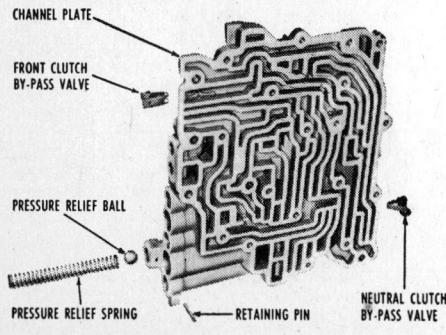

Fig. 31 Channel plate components

movement in ring groove.
4. Check for burrs or restrictions on clutch plate drive lugs.

Driven Torus Member

1. Inspect for bent or damaged vanes.
2. Check splines in hub for nicks or burrs.
3. Check two oil seal rings and ring grooves for broken rings and oil seal grooves for nicks or burrs. When locked, rings should turn freely in grooves.
4. If balance weight is present, inspect for good weld.
5. Inspect driven coupling-to-torque multiplier thrust bearing race for distorted bearing surface or excessive wear on thrust race. Check for foreign particles on thrust race and clean thoroughly. *A slight distortion or bend on thrust bearing could cause a side loading effect and cause part of rollers to dislodge from cage.*

Front Unit Carrier

1. Inspect planet pinions for damaged gears, chipped teeth, nicks or burrs.
2. Check for free movement of pinion gears on pinion pins; be sure pins are well staked.
3. Check splines on carrier hub for nicks or burrs.
4. Inspect front sun gear-to-carrier thrust washer for damage or foreign particles embedded on thrust race.

Mainshaft and Sun Gear

1. Inspect for damaged splines, teeth or thrust washer surface.
2. Remove sun gear from mainshaft and inspect damper for cracks, peeling or foreign material.

Output Shaft

1. Inspect shaft splines for damage.
2. Inspect snap ring groove on shaft for good machine cut and see that it is free of dirt and chips.
3. Inspect pilot bushing for excessive wear and tight fit.
4. Inspect parking sprocket lugs for burred edges.

5. Inspect speedometer drive gear for misalignment and tight fit on shaft.

Rear Planet Carrier

1. Inspect planet pinions for damaged gear and free movement on pinion pins. Be sure pinion pins are well staked. Check 8 planet pinion thrust washers, being sure washers have not cut a pocket in carrier.
2. Inspect shaft splines for damage.
3. Inspect carrier-to-internal gear thrust bearing and race. Check for foreign particles embedded in race.
4. Handle thrust bearings with care. A slight distortion or bend caused by dropping or careless handling could cause a side loading effect which may not be visible and cause some of rollers to dislodge from cage.
5. Inspect sun gear-to-carrier thrust washer and race.
6. Use tag wire and check 6 lubrication ports for restrictions.

TRANSMISSION, ASSEMBLE

Neutral Clutch, Case Center Support and Reverse Clutch

1. With transmission case front end up, install neutral clutch backing plate in case with flat side up. Install clutch plates as follows:
2. Install faced plate on clutch backing plate and then a steel plate with notched lug of plate in slot adjacent to one of wide lugs in case.
3. Install second faced plate and then another steel plate with its notched lug on opposite side of wide case lug from the first. The steel plates must be installed in this manner to properly un-nest the clutch pack.
4. Install alternately faced plates and steel plates so that notches on first and third plates are on one side of wide lug and the second and fourth steel plate notches are on the opposite side.
5. Install long case center support key with longer lip toward front of case, Fig. 33. Hold in place with petrolatum.
6. Mark the case to indicate sides of the key to assist in alignment of case center support, Fig. 33.
7. Install clutches and center support assembly into case, aligning key into keyway. Make sure oil rings did not come unhooked during installation.
8. Install reverse stationary cone key into case with rounded side toward front of case, Fig. 34.
9. Install reverse cone (steel) into reverse piston.
10. Install reverse stationary cone (plastic), aligning cone key with keyway in cone, lightly tapping into place if necessary.
11. Install large reverse cone snap ring with flat ends up and ring gap at open segment of ring groove in case.
12. Position transmission with rear end up and install overrun band over anchor in case.

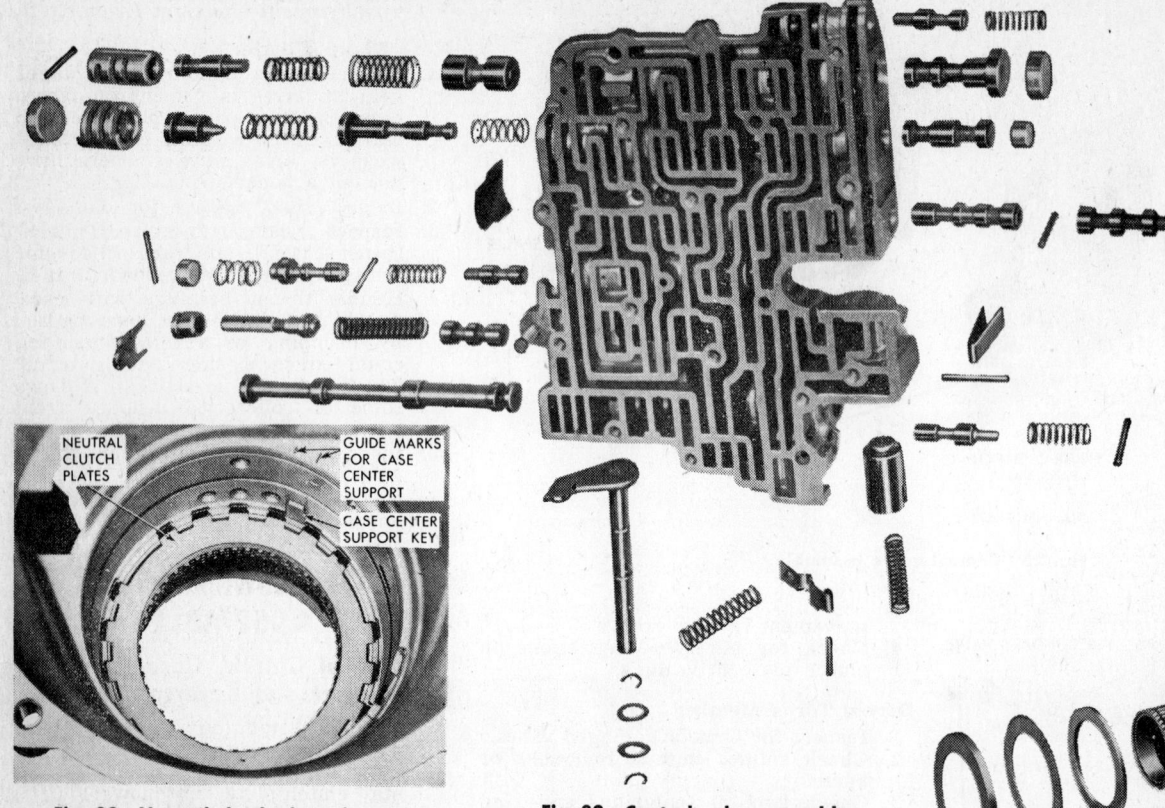

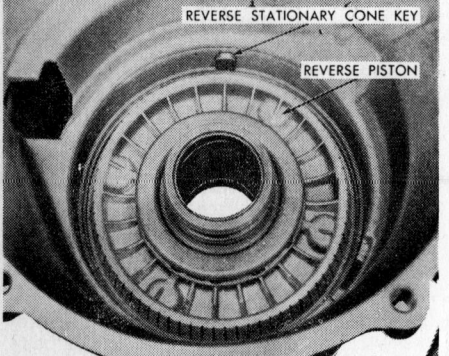

Fig. 33 Neutral clutch plates in case

Fig. 32 Control valve assembly

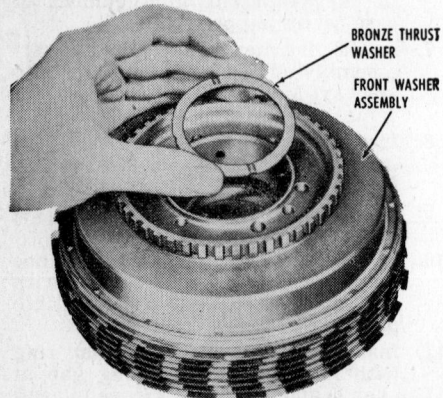

Fig. 34 Reverse piston in case

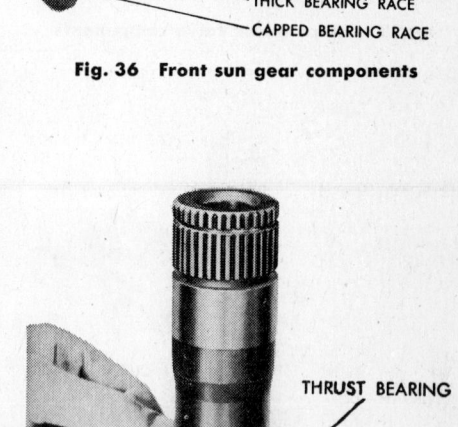

FRONT SUN GEAR
THRUST BEARING
THICK BEARING RACE
CAPPED BEARING RACE

Fig. 36 Front sun gear components

13. Install rear unit internal gear, sprag and sprag retainer, aligning neutral clutch plates with sprag outer race. Be sure sprag retainer bottoms against case center support to insure engagement of all plates.

Front and Rear Units

1. With transmission bottom side up, install front clutch, engaging teeth in front clutch hub with reverse cone. Be sure bronze washer is positioned in counterbore of front unit clutch drum, Fig. 35.
2. Install thick bearing race, thrust bearing and thin cupped bearing race on front sun gear and shaft, Fig. 36.
3. Install front sun gear and shaft through case center support, aligning splines of sun gear shaft with rear internal gear and cutaway splines with sprag retainer. *Be sure to hold rear unit internal gear forward during this operation.*
4. Install front sun gear shaft-to-rear unit internal gear snap ring.
5. Install bearing race (flange up) and bearing on rear planet carrier. Retain with petrolatum, Fig. 37.
6. Install rear planet carrier through front unit sun gear shaft from rear of case.
7. Install front carrier thrust bearing race onto rear carrier shaft (inner flange out) Fig. 38.
9. Install front carrier thrust bearing into race.
10. Install thrust bearing race over front thrust bearing (outer flange inward).

BRONZE THRUST
WASHER

FRONT WASHER
ASSEMBLY

Fig. 35 Bronze thrust washer in front clutch

THRUST BEARING

BEARING RACE

REAR PLANET
CARRIER

Fig. 37 Thrust bearing on rear planet carrier

Fig. 38 Thrust bearing and races on rear sun gear

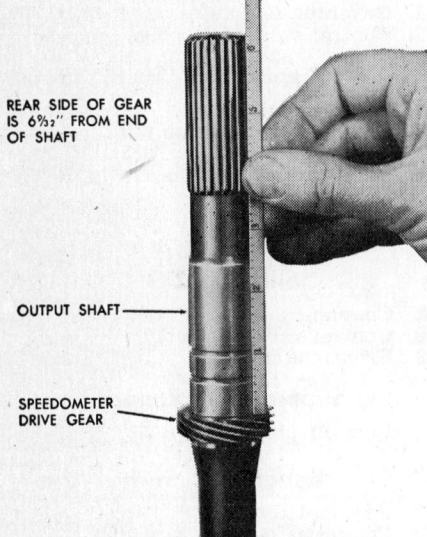

Fig. 39 Locating speedometer gear on output shaft

11. Holding rear planet carrier forward, install front unit carrier.
12. Install front unit carrier-to-rear plant carrier shaft snap ring while holding rear carrier forward.

Parking Linkage

1. With rear of transmission up, install pawl spacer in case.
2. Install parking assembly, pawl first, through hole in rear of case so that pawl tooth faces inside of case.
3. Install pawl pin in case through pawl and spacer.
4. Push parking bracket shaft to bottom of its bore.
5. Move pawl to its disengaged position.

Output Shaft and Governor

1. Install rear unit sun gear-to-rear carrier bearing race into rear carrier with flange up and retain with petrolatum.
2. Install rear unit sun gear-to-rear carrier thrust bearing into bearing race.
3. Assemble rear unit sun gear to mainshaft (if removed) and install through rear carrier.
4. Install governor with gasket on output shaft.
5. Install speedometer drive gear, Fig. 39.
6. Install output shaft to rear carrier, using alignment marks.
7. Engage parking pawl.
8. Install 4 governor attaching bolts and torque to 19-23 ft. lbs.
9. Install snap ring on front output shaft groove.

Rear Bearing Retainer

1. Stick a new gasket on rear bearing retainer.
2. Start retainer down over output shaft and install rear output shaft snap ring through access hole and over end of output shaft while re-

tainer is being lowered over governor.
3. Align parking linkage pin and manual detent lever as rear bearing retainer is aligned with dowel pin and case.
4. It may be necessary to move output shaft rearward to locate rear bearing snap ring by positioning transmission to horizontal position.
5. Install two retaner bolts at center location at each side. Install remaining short bolt inside retainer. Install 5 long bolts and torque all bolts to 20-25 ft. lbs.
6. Install new rear seal, if necessary.
7. Install rear bearing retainer cover plate and gasket.

Torus

1. With front of transmission up, install drive torus, aligning front unit clutch plates with drive slots in torus. Looking through vent port in bottom of case, see that all clutch plates are engaged.
2. Install hook-type oil ring on torque multiplier hub (if removed) Fig. 40.
3. Install hook-type oil ring on front and rear hubs of driven torus member (if removed).
4. Install torque multiplier into drive torus, aligning splines, and position torque multiplier so that the I.D. of hub of multiplier is flush with planet carrier shaft.
5. Install driven torus-to-torque multiplier rear bearing race into multiplier.
6. Install flanged race with flange up into driven torus, Fig. 41.
7. Install bearing into flange race and retain with petrolatum.
8. Install driven torus over mainshaft.
9. Position transmission 90° so bottom is up (do not rotate more than 90° or parts will fall out of front).
10. While moving mainshaft forward with small tool inserted in hole of mainshaft, if necessary, install driven torus-to-mainshaft spiral retaining ring, Fig. 42.
11. Position transmission with front end up. Then install new gasket on torus drive member.
12. Install flat bearing race into torus cover, Fig. 43. Install bearing into flanged race. Install bearing and flanged race into torus cover with flange down, using petrolatum.
13. Install torus cover to drive torus, aligning to dowel pins.
14. Install 12 torus cover bolts and torque to 17-20 ft. lbs.

Case Cover

1. Stick a new gasket on case cover and install cover and pump on transmission.
2. Install 5 of the 6 large attaching bolts, leaving one hole into which to install dial indicator. Torque bolts to 30-35 ft. lbs.

Front Unit End Play Check

1. With bottom of transmission up, install dial indicator in to remaining hole in case.
2. With dial indicator zeroed, use a large screwdriver through case behind flange on output shaft. Pry

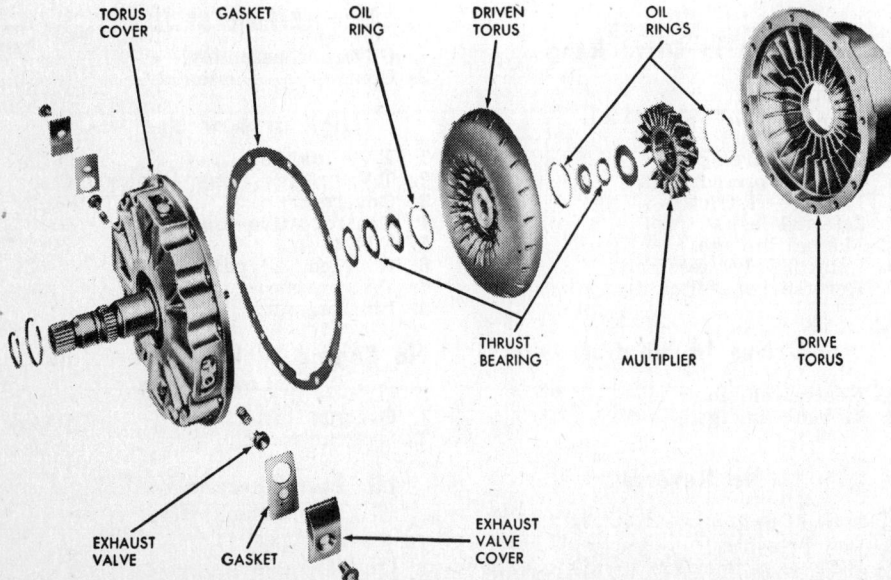

Fig. 40 Torus and torque multiplier components

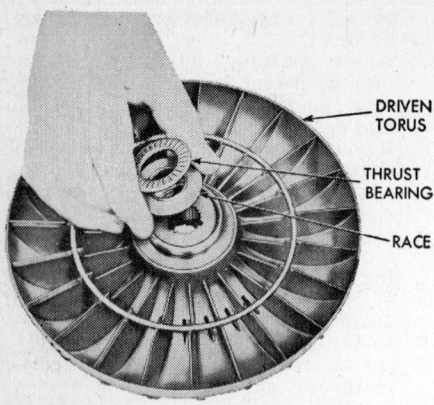

Fig. 41   Thrust bearing in driven torus

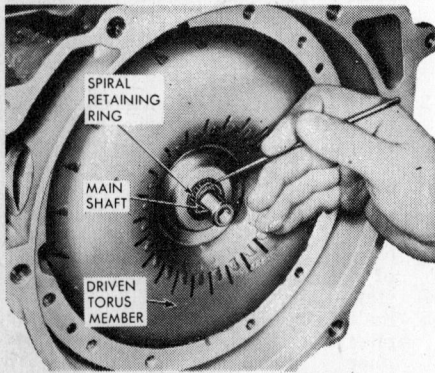

Fig. 42   Spiral retaining ring on mainshaft

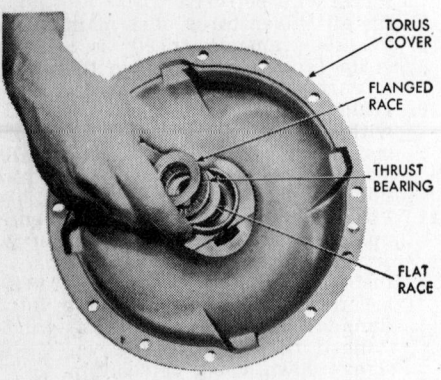

Fig. 43   Thrust bearing and race in torus cover

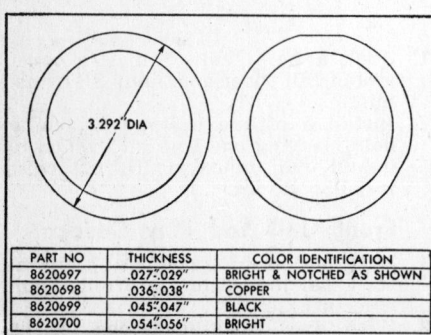

PART NO	THICKNESS	COLOR IDENTIFICATION
8620697	.027".029"	BRIGHT & NOTCHED AS SHOWN
8620698	.036".038"	COPPER
8620699	.045".047"	BLACK
8620700	.054".056"	BRIGHT

Fig. 44   Table of selective washers

forward on output shaft to position units forward and at the same time record end play, which should be .006-.018".

3. If end play is not within limits, remove case cover and install proper thrust washer or combination of washers between case cover and torus cover to obtain desired end play, Fig. 44.

4. Remove tools and install and tighten remaining bolts to 30-35 ft. lbs.

5. With front of transmission up, install front seal with rubber lip down.

Final Assembly

Install servo and accumulator as outlined at the beginning of this chapter, referring to Figs. 2, 3, 4 and 5. Then install control valve body and oil pan as directed also at the beginning of this chapter.

TROUBLE SHOOTING

Low Oil Pressure

1. Low oil level.
2. Incorrect or stuck boost plug.
3. Pressure regulator valve.
4. Strainer and "O" ring.
5. Manual valve misaligned with quadrant.
6. Foaming or cavitation.
7. Internal leak.
8. Control valve assembly (stuck valve).
9. Front pump slide stuck (low output).

High Oil Pressure

1. Pressure regulator valve stuck.
2. Incorrect or stuck boost plug.
3. Manual valve misaligned with quadrant.
4. Control valve assembly (valve stuck).
5. Front pump slide stuck (high output).

No Drive In Drive Range

1. Neutral clutch.
2. Sprag assembly (or race).
3. Coupling.
4. Low oil level.
5. Low oil pressure.
6. Passage restricted.
7. Internal leak.
8. Manual linkage.
9. Control valve assembly.
10. Reverse cone sticking.

Drives In Neutral

1. Neutral clutch.
2. Manual linkage.

No Reverse

1. Manual linkage.
2. Low pressure.
3. Reverse cone clutch.
4. Restricted passage.
5. Neutral clutch.

Drive in "Right Drive" or Low Range Only

1. Sprag assembly.
2. Neutral clutch.

Forward Drive In Reverse

1. Manual linkage.
2. Neutral clutch.

Reverse Drive In Neutral

1. Reverse cone clutch.

Drive In 2nd and 3rd Only

1. Control valve assembly.

Drive In 1st and 3rd Only

1. Control valve only.
2. Coupling.

Drive In 1st and 2nd Only

1. Governor G-2 valve.
2. Control valve assembly.

Slipping 1-2 Shift

1. Front clutch.
2. Control valve assembly.
3. Accumulator.
4. Compensator body assembly.
5. Low oil pressure.
6. T.V. linkage.
7. 1-2 oil passages.

Slipping 2-3

1. Coupling.
2. Control valve assembly.
3. Front clutch.

Slipping All Ranges

1. Low oil pressure.

Rough 1-2 Shift

1. Accumulator.
2. Compensator body assembly.
3. Front clutch.
4. Front clutch passage.
5. Control valve assembly.
6. T.V. linkage.
7. Coupling.

Erratic Shifts

1. Governor assembly.
2. Control valve assembly.

High or Low Upshifts

1. T.V. linkage (short, high upshifts).
2. T.V. linkage (long, low upshifts).
3. Governor.
4. Control valve assembly.
5. T.V. lever.
6. Governor oil passage.
7. T.V. pressure.
8. Line pressure.

No Engine Braking Intermediate or Low Range

1. Overrun band.
2. Overrun servo.

No Part Throttle or Detent Downshifts

1. T.V. Linkage.
2. Control valve assembly.
3. Accelerator travel.
4. Governor.

Selector Lever Won't Go Into Reverse

1. Manual linkage.
2. Reverse blocker valve.
3. Governor.

Selector Lever Won't Go Into Park

1. Parking linkage.
2. Manual linkage.

Noise Diagnosis

1. Oil pump moan, all ranges, more pronounced with hot oil. Also in 1st gear from 1000 to 1200 rpm.
2. Oil pump whine at 2-1 and 2-3 shifts.
3. Reverse and 2nd gear noise at low rpm only indicates defective front unit gear set.
4. Gear noise 1st to 2nd, reverse and neutral at high rpm indicates defective rear unit gear set.
5. Noise in 2nd during 2-3 shift:
   a. Coupling fill pump whine, hot oil, low rpm.
   b. All except 2nd indicates defective coupling.
   c. Buzzing indicates T.V. valves and governor.
   d. Rattle in 3rd, light load, indicates defective damper.

Foreign Car Data

ALFA-ROMEO

Year	Model	Spark Plug Gap, In.	Breaker Gap, In.	Firing Order	Ignition Timing: Timing Mark	Ignition Timing: Location	Valve Lash (C-Cold, H-Hot): Intake	Valve Lash (C-Cold, H-Hot): Exhaust	Engine Oil, Qts. Refill	Cooling Capacity, Qts.: No Heater	Cooling Capacity, Qts.: With Heater	Alignment: Caster	Alignment: Camber	Alignment: Toe-In
1957–58	1900	.019	.013–.015	1342	P.M.S.	Flywheel	.015C	.017C	5½①	..	11	2	½	⅛
1957–58	1900C	.019	.013–.015	1342	P.M.S.	Flywheel	.017C	.025C	5½①	..	11	2	½	⅛
1957–60	Spider	.021	.015	1342	P.M.S.	Flywheel	.017C	.019C	4½①	..	8	1½	0	⅛
1957–60	Super Spider	.024	.015	1342	P.M.S.	Flywheel	.017C	.019C	4½①	..	8	1½	0	⅛
1957–60	Sprint	.024	.015	1342	P.M.S.	Flywheel	.017C	.019C	4½①	..	8	...	..	..
1957–60	Veloce	.024	.015	1342	P.M.S.	Flywheel	.016C	.022C	4½①	..	8	...	..	..
1959–60	2000	.024	.015	1243	Mark	Pulley	.017C	.021C	8	..	12½	2	½	⅛

① Add 1¾ pints if filter is changed.

AUSTIN

Year	Model	Spark Plug Gap, In.	Breaker Gap, In.	Firing Order	Ignition Timing: Timing Mark	Ignition Timing: Location	Valve Lash (C-Cold, H-Hot): Intake	Valve Lash (C-Cold, H-Hot): Exhaust	Engine Oil, Qts. Refill	Cooling Capacity, Qts.: No Heater	Cooling Capacity, Qts.: With Heater	Alignment: Caster	Alignment: Camber	Alignment: Toe-In
1954	Somerset	.018	.015	1342	TDC	Pulley	.015C	.015C	4½	..	7¼	1¾	1	3/32
1957–59	A35	.018	.015	1342	TDC	Flywheel	.012C	.012C	4	..	5½	1½	½	1/16
1956–57	A40	.018	.015	1342	TDC	Flywheel	.012C	.012C	4½	..	7¼	2¼	1	3/32
1958–60	A40	.025	.015	1342	5° BTDC	Pulley	.012C	.012C	4¼	..	4.8	3	1	1/16–⅛
1956–57	A50	.018	.015	1342	5° BTDC	Pulley	.015C	.015C	4½	..	7¼	1½	1	⅛
1958–59	A55	.020	.015	1342	5° BTDC	Pulley	.015C	.015C	4½	..	7¼	1½	1	1/16
1959–60	A55MKII	.025	.015	1342	5° BTDC	Pulley	.015H	.015H	4.8	..	7	3	¾	1/16
1957–58	A95	.025	.015	153624	5° BTDC	Pulley	.015C	.015C	6½	..	12	...	..	..
1960	A99	.025	.015	153624	7° BTDC	Pulley	.012H	.012H	8	..	12½	1¼	1	⅛
1957–58	A105	.025	.015	153624	5° BTDC	Pulley	.015C	.015C	6½	..	12	...	..	..
1960	A850	.025	.015	1342	3° BTDC	Pulley	.012C	.012C	5½	..	..	3¼	1	1/16①

① Toe-out.

AUSTIN-HEALEY

Year	Model	Spark Plug Gap, In.	Breaker Gap, In.	Firing Order	Ignition Timing: Timing Mark	Ignition Timing: Location	Valve Lash (C-Cold, H-Hot): Intake	Valve Lash (C-Cold, H-Hot): Exhaust	Engine Oil, Qts. Refill	Cooling Capacity, Qts.: No Heater	Cooling Capacity, Qts.: With Heater	Alignment: Caster	Alignment: Camber	Alignment: Toe-In
1954–56	100	.025	.014–.016	1342	6° BTDC	Flywheel	.012C	.012C	6	..	12	1¾	1	3/32
1956–57	100S	.025	.014–.016	1342	6° BTDC	Flywheel	.012C	.012C	6	..	12	1¾	1	3/32
1957–59	100–6	.025	.014–.016	153624	6° BTDC	Pulley	.012H	.012H	7	..	12	1¾	1	3/32
1959–60	Sprite	.024–.026	.014–.016	1342	5° BTDC	Pulley	.012C	.012C	6 Pts.①	..	12	...	..	..
1959–60	3000	.024	.015	153624	5° BTDC	Pulley	.012H	.012H	7	..	12	2	1¾	1/16–⅛

① Add 1 pint if filter is changed.

BMW

Year	Model	Spark Plug Gap, In.	Breaker Gap, In.	Firing Order	Ignition Timing: Timing Mark	Ignition Timing: Location	Valve Lash (C-Cold, H-Hot): Intake	Valve Lash (C-Cold, H-Hot): Exhaust	Engine Oil, Qts. Refill	Cooling Capacity, Qts.: No Heater	Cooling Capacity, Qts.: With Heater	Alignment: Caster	Alignment: Camber	Alignment: Toe-In
1957–60	300 Isetta	.024	.016	1	①	①	.006C	.008C	3.6 Pts.	None	None	2 7/16	1½	11/64
1957–60	600	.024	.016	1–2	①	①	.006C	.008C	4.2 Pts.	None	None	5	1½	11/64
1960	700	.028	.016	1–2	①	①	.006C	.008C	4.2 Pts.	None	None	14	½	3/32
1957–59	501	.036	.014	15486372	8° BTDC	Damper	.010H	.010H	6	..	8	5	1	⅛
1957–59	502	.036	.014	15486372	8° BTDC	Damper	.010H	.010H	6	..	8	5	1	⅛
1960	502	.036	.014	15486372	Mark	Damper	.010H	.010H	7	..	8	1	1	5/64
1957–59	503	.035	.016	15486372	8° BTDC	Damper	.010H	.010H	7	..	11½	5	1	⅛
1960	503	.036	.016	15486372	Mark	Damper	.010H	.010H	7	..	12	3⅓	1	5/64
1957–59	507	.035	.016	15486372	8° BTDC	Damper	.010H	.010H	7	..	11½	5	1	⅛
1960	507	.036	.016	15486372	Mark	Damper	.010H	.010H	7	..	11	3½	1	5/64

① Red fin of blower wheel to line up with "S" mark on engine housing.

BORGWARD

Year	Model	Spark Plug Gap, In.	Breaker Gap, In.	Firing Order	Ignition Timing: Timing Mark	Ignition Timing: Location	Valve Lash (C-Cold, H-Hot): Intake	Valve Lash (C-Cold, H-Hot): Exhaust	Engine Oil, Qts. Refill	Cooling Capacity, Qts.: No Heater	Cooling Capacity, Qts.: With Heater	Alignment: Caster	Alignment: Camber	Alignment: Toe-In
1957	Isabella 1500	.028	.016	1342	TDC	Flywheel	.008H	.008H	4¾①	..	8½	3	½	0
1958–60	Isabella 60	.028	.016	1342	TDC	Flywheel	.008H	.008H	4¾①	..	8½	3	½	0
1958–60	Isabella TS75	.028	.016	1342	TDC	Flywheel	.008H	.008H	4¾①	..	8½	3	½	0

① Includes filter drain.

CITROEN

Year	Model	Spark Plug Gap, In.	Breaker Gap, In.	Firing Order	Ignition Timing: Timing Mark	Ignition Timing: Location	Valve Lash (C-Cold, H-Hot): Intake	Valve Lash (C-Cold, H-Hot): Exhaust	Engine Oil, Qts. Refill	Cooling Capacity, Qts.: No Heater	Cooling Capacity, Qts.: With Heater	Alignment: Caster	Alignment: Camber	Alignment: Toe-In
1955–60	2CV	.024	.016	1–2	12° BTDC	Flywheel	.008H	.008H	2⅛	..	..	¼	1½	3/16①
1955–56	11B	.024	.016	1342	12° BTDC	Flywheel	.008C	.010C	4¼	..	9	1½	1	⅛①
1957–60	1D19	.024	.016	1342	12° BTDC	Flywheel	.008C	.010C	4¼	..	10½	1½	0	7/64
1956–60	DS19	.024	.016	1342	12° BTDC	Flywheel	.008C	.010C	4¼	..	12	1½	0	7/64
1958	Truckette	.024	.016	1–2	12° BTDC	Flywheel	.008H	.008H	2⅛	..	..	...	..	..

① Negative.

Year	Model	Spark Plug Gap, In.	Breaker Gap In.	Firing Order	Ignition Timing Timing Mark	Location	Valve Lash C-Cold H-Hot Intake	Exhaust	Engine Oil, Qts. Refill	Cooling Capacity, Qts. No Heater	With Heater	Alignment Caster	Camber	Toe-In
FIAT														
1958-60	500	.027–.031	.016–.019	1342	10° BTDC	③	.006C	.006C	1.42	①	①	9	1	⅛
1957-60	600	.027–.031	.016–.019	1342	10° BTDC	③	.004C	.004C	3.15	②	..	9	1	3/32④
1957-60	1100	.027–.031	.016–.019	1342	TDC	③	.004C	.004C	3.15	5.25	5.95	2	½	⅛
1957-60	1200	.027–.031	.016–.019	1342	3° BTDC	③	.006C	.006C	2.57	5.25	5.95	2	½	⅛
1960	2100	.020–.024	.014	153624	5° BTDC	..	.008C	.008C	5.3	..	9	1½	1	⅛

① Air cooled. ② Sedan 4.3 Multipla 6.9 ③ Mark on timing chain cover. ④ Toe out.

FORD														
1954-59	Anglia	.025	.015	1243	Notch	Pulley	.013C	.013C	2.0	7.2	7.7	3	1½	3/32①
1960	Anglia	.030	.015	1243	Notch	Pulley	.010H	.017H	2.5	6.2	6.8	3	1	3/32②
1954-59	Prefect	.025	.015	1243	Notch	Pulley	.013C	.013C	2.0	7.2	7.7	3	1½	3/32①
1960	Prefect	.030	.015	1243	Notch	Pulley	.010H	.017H	2.5	6.9	7.5	1¾	1½	3/32②
1954-55	Consul	.032	.015	1243	Notch	Pulley	.014H	.014H	4.0	10.0	10.5	0	1¼	1/16①
1956	Consul	.032	.015	1243	Notch	Pulley	.014H	.014H	3.5	11.8	12.5	¼	1¾	3/32②
1957-60	Consul	.032	.015	1243	Notch	Pulley	.014H	.014H	3.5	11.8	12.5	¼	1¾	3/32②
1954-60	Escort	.025	.015	1243	Notch	Pulley	.013C	.013C	2.0	7.2	7.7	2	1½	3/32②
1954-60	Squire	.025	.015	1243	Notch	Pulley	.013C	.013C	2.0	7.2	7.7	2	1½	3/32②
1954-55	Zephyr	.032	.015	153624	Notch	Pulley	.014H	.014H	5.0	13.2	13.9	¼	1¼	3/32②
1956	Zephyr	.032	.015	153624	Notch	Pulley	.014H	.014H	4.0	13.2	13.9	¼	1½	3/32
1957-60	Zephyr	.032	.015	153624	Notch	Pulley	.014H	.014H	4.0	13.2	13.9	¼	1½	3/32
1954-56	Zodiac	.032	.015	153624	Notch	Pulley	.014H	.014H	5.0	13.2	13.9	¾	1¼	3/32②
1957-60	Zodiac	.032	.015	153624	Notch	Pulley	.014H	.014H	4.0	13.2	13.9	¼	1½	3/32
1957-60	Thames 5 Cwt.	.025	.015	1243	Notch	Pulley	.013C	.013C	2.0	7.2	7.7	3	1½	3/32①
1957-60	Thames 7 Cwt.	.025	.015	1243	Notch	Pulley	.013C	.013C	2.0	7.2	7.7	3	1½	3/32①
1958-60	Thames 800	.032	.015	1243	Notch	Pulley	.014H	.014H	3.5	9.0	10.0	½	1½	3/32
1960	Taunus 12M⑤	.030	.017	1243	Notch	Pulley	.012H	.014H	2.5	6.9	7.4	1½	½	¼
1958-60	Taunus 17M	.030	.017	1243	Notch	Pulley	.012H	.014H	3.2	7.4	8.7	⅓	1⅓	3/32

① Toe (on 20° turn) out, 4°. ② Toe (on 20° turn) out, 2½°. ③ Toe (on 20° turn) out, 5°. ④ Toe (on 20° turn) out, ¾°.
⑤ Applies to 12M Super Models.

GOGGOMOBIL														
1958-60	T400	.025	.008	1-2	...	...	None	None	2	...	..	...	..	..
1958-60	TS400	.025	.008	1-2	...	...	None	None	2	..	..	...	..	..
1959-60	T700	.025	.010	1-2	...	...	...	...	3	..	..	...	..	..

HILLMAN														
1954	Mark VII	.030	.012	1342	Notch	Pulley	.010C	.015C	4¼	6½	7½	3¾⑤	¾⑤	⅛⑤
1955-57	Mark VIII	.030	.016	1342	①	Pulley	.014C	.014C	5	7½	8	3¾⑤	¾⑤	⅛⑤
1955-57	Husky	.030	.016	1342	③	Pulley	.010C	.015C	4¼	6½	7½	3¾⑤	¾⑤	⅛⑤
1958-59	Husky Series I	.025	.015	1342	③	Pulley	.012H	.014H	4¼	7½	8	2¾⑤	¾⑤	3/16⑤
1957	Minx Series I	.030	.016	1342	①	Pulley	.012H	.014H	5	7½	8	3½⑤	¾⑤	⅛⑤
1958	Minx Series II	.030	.016	1342	④	Pulley	.012H	.014H	5	7½	8	3½⑤	¾⑤	⅛⑤
1959	Minx Series III	.030	.016	1342	①	Pulley	.012H	.014H	5	7½	8	1¾⑤	¾⑤	3/16⑤
1960	Minx Series IIIA	.030	.016	1342	7° BTDC⑥	Pulley	.012H	.014H	5	7½	8	⑦⑤	¾⑤	3/16⑤
1960	Husky	.030	.016	1342	7° BTDC⑥	Pulley	.012H	.014H	5	7½	8	2°53'⑤	¾⑤	3/16⑤

① 7/16" before TDC mark. ② ⅜" before TDC mark. ③ 19/64" before TDC mark. ④ 7/32" before TDC mark.
⑤ Car fully laden. ⑥ Timing mark indicates TDC. ⑦ Sedan and Conv. Cpe. 1¾°, Estate Car 3°.

JAGUAR														
1954	XK-120	.022	.015	153624	7° BTDC	Flywheel	.004C	.006C	12½	15	15½	5	1⅞	5/32
1954	Mark VII	.022	.015	153624	3° BTDC	Flywheel	.004C	.006C	11½	13¼	13¾	0	1	1/16
1955-57	Mark VII	.022	.015	153624	TDC	Damper	.004C	.006C	11½	13½	14	0	1	1/16
1955-57	XK-140	.022	.015	153624	10° BTDC	Damper	.004C	.006C	11½	15	15½	1¾	¾	1/16
1956-58	2.4 Litre	.025	.015	153624	6° BTDC	Damper	.004C	.006C	8	11½	12	¾	¾	1/32
1957-58	Mark VIII	.022	.015	153624	6° BTDC	Damper	.004C	.006C	11½	13½	14	0	1	5/32
1958-60	3.4 Litre	.025	.015	153624	2° BTDC	Flywheel	.004C	.006C	6½	12½	13	¾	¾	1/32
1958-60	XK-150	.025	.015	153624	6° BTDC	Damper	.004C	.006C	7¾	13	13½	1¾	¾	1/16
1959-60	Mark IX	.022	.016	153624	4° BTDC	Damper	.004C	.006C	11½	13½	14	...	..	..
1959-60	XK-150-S	.025	.015	153624	9° BTDC	Damper	.004C	.006C	11½	13½	14	..	..	..
1960	3.8 Litre	.025	.016	153624	4° BTDC	Damper	.004C	.006C	13¼	12½	13¼	0	¾	1/16

Year	Model	Spark Plug Gap, In	Breaker Gap, In	Firing Order	Ignition Timing Timing Mark	Ignition Timing Location	Valve Lash C-Cold H-Hot Intake	Valve Lash C-Cold H-Hot Exhaust	Engine Oil, Qts. Refill	Cooling Capacity, Qts. No Heater	Cooling Capacity, Qts. With Heater	Alignment Caster	Alignment Camber	Alignment Toe-In
LANCIA														
1959–60	Appia	.022	.016–.019	1342	8° BTDC	①	.006C	.008C	①	..	6	0	1	³⁄₁₆
1959	Aurelia	.022	.016–.019	143652	12° BTDC	①	.010C	.014C	5¼	..	11	1	1¾	³⁄₁₆
1959–60	Flaminia	.022	.016–.019	143652	11° BTDC	①	.006C	.010C	7¼	..	11	1	2	³⁄₁₆

① Second series 4, third series 3¾.

Year	Model	Spark Plug Gap, In	Breaker Gap, In	Firing Order	Timing Mark	Location	Intake	Exhaust	Oil Refill	No Heater	With Heater	Caster	Camber	Toe-In
MERCEDES BENZ														
1957–59	180A	.038	.017	1342	8° BTDC	Damper	.004C	.008C	4.2	..	9½	3¼	½	¹⁄₁₆
1957–59	180D①	..	..	1342	..	..	.007C	.006C	4	8	9	3¼	½	¹⁄₁₆
1958–59	190	.038	.017	1342	8° BTDC	Damper	.004C	.008C	4.2	..	9¾	3¼	½	¹⁄₁₆
1959	190D①	..	..	1342	..	..	.006C	.008C	4	..	9¾	3¼	½	¹⁄₁₆
1957–59	190SL	.030	.013	1342	②	Damper	.004C	.008C	4.2	..	10½	3½	½	¹⁄₁₆
1957–58	219	.038	.014	153624	5 BTDC	Damper	.004C	.008C	6¼	..	12	3¼	½	¹⁄₁₆
1958–59	219③	.030	.014	153624	1° BTDC	Damper	.004C	.008C	6¼	..	12	3¼	½	¹⁄₁₆
1957–58	220S	.038	.014	153624	8° BTDC	Damper	.004C	.008C	6¼	..	12	3¼	½	¹⁄₁₆
1958–59	220S③	.030	.014	153624	2° BTDC	Damper	.004C	.008C	6¼	..	12	3¼	½	¹⁄₁₆
1959	220SE	.022	.014	153624	2° BTDC	Damper	.005C	.008C	6¼	..	12	3¼	½	¹⁄₁₆
1958–59	300D	.022	.014	153624	④	Damper	.003C	.008C	7	..	22	2½	½	¹⁄₁₆
1957	300SL Cpe.	.022	.013	153624	④	Damper	.003C	.008C	12	..	16¼	5	½	⁷⁄₆₄
1958–59	300SL Rdst.	.022	.012	153624	④	Damper	.003C	.008C	12	19¼	21	5	½	⁷⁄₆₄

① Diesel engine.   ② With distributor No. VJ4BR11 9° BTDC; with VJUR4BR11 and VJ4BR12 1° BTDC.   ③ With 8.7:1 Compression Ratio.
④ Set to 4500 RPM to specs. on cylinder head or intake manifold.

Year	Model	Spark Plug Gap, In	Breaker Gap, In	Firing Order	Timing Mark	Location	Intake	Exhaust	Oil Refill	No Heater	With Heater	Caster	Camber	Toe-In
MG														
1955–56	TF-1500	.024	.015	1342	Notch	Pulley	.012H	.012H	6	6	7	2	1	0
1955–59	Magnette	.025	.015	1342	Notch	Pulley	.015H	.015H	4.8	6.3	7	3	1	0
1957–59	MG-A	.025	.015	1342	Notch	Pulley	.017H	.017H	4.25	6.3	7	4	1	0
1959–60	MGA-1600	.025	.015	1342	6° BTDC	Pulley	.015H	.015H	4¼	..	6	4	1	0
1959–60	Magnette III	.025	.015	1342	6° BTDC	Pulley	.015H	.015H	4.8	..	7	3	¾	0–⅛

Year	Model	Spark Plug Gap, In	Breaker Gap, In	Firing Order	Timing Mark	Location	Intake	Exhaust	Oil Refill	No Heater	With Heater	Caster	Camber	Toe-In
MORGAN														
1957–60	4–4 Series 2	.025	.015	1243	5° BTDC	Pulley	.012C	.014C	3¼	7	..	4	2	⁵⁄₃₂
1957–60	Plus Four	.032	.015	1342	4° BTDC	Pulley	.010H	.012H	5½	8	..	4	2	⁵⁄₃₂

Year	Model	Spark Plug Gap, In	Breaker Gap, In	Firing Order	Timing Mark	Location	Intake	Exhaust	Oil Refill	No Heater	With Heater	Caster	Camber	Toe-In
MORRIS														
1957–60	Minor 1000	.025	.014–.016	1342	TDC	Pulley	.012C	.012C	4¼	..	5½	3	0	³⁄₃₂
1960	Mini-Minor	.025	.015	1342	3° BTDC	Pulley	.012C	.012C	5½	..	3¼	..	1	¹⁄₁₆①
1960	Oxford V	.025	.015	1342	5° BTDC	Pulley	.015H	.015H	4.8	..	7	3	¾	0–⅛

① Toe-out.

Year	Model	Spark Plug Gap, In	Breaker Gap, In	Firing Order	Timing Mark	Location	Intake	Exhaust	Oil Refill	No Heater	With Heater	Caster	Camber	Toe-In
NASH METROPOLITAN														
1955	551, 552	.024	.015	1342	Notch	Pulley	.015C	.015C	4	7	8	2½	1	¹⁄₃₂
1956–57	561, 562	.024	.015	1342	Notch	Pulley	.015C	.015C	4	7	8	2½	1	¹⁄₃₂
1958–59	561, 562	.025	.015	1342	7° BTDC	Pulley	.015C	.015C	4	7	8	2½	1	¹⁄₃₂
1960	561, 562	.025	.015	1342	7° BTDC①	Pulley	.015C	.015C	4	7	8	2½	1	¹⁄₃₂

① Engine prefix 15-CNH 5° BTDC, prefix IH 11° BTDC.

Year	Model	Spark Plug Gap, In	Breaker Gap, In	Firing Order	Timing Mark	Location	Intake	Exhaust	Oil Refill	No Heater	With Heater	Caster	Camber	Toe-In
NSU PRINZ														
1959–60	2 Dr. Sed.	.024	.014	1–2	TDC	Flywheel①	.004	.004	3½	..	..	...	..	³⁄₆₄
1960	Sport Coupe	.024	.014	1–2	TDC	Flywheel①	.004	.004	3½	..	..	..	..	³⁄₆₄

① Remove rubber cap left side of dipstick.

Year	Model	Spark Plug Gap, In	Breaker Gap, In	Firing Order	Timing Mark	Location	Intake	Exhaust	Oil Refill	No Heater	With Heater	Caster	Camber	Toe-In
OPEL														
1957–60	Rekord	.036–.040	.014–.016	1342	Ball	Flywheel	.008H	.012H	3⅙	8	8½	1½	1¾	³⁄₃₂
1958–60	Caravan	.036–.040	.014–.016	1342	Ball	Flywheel	.008H	.012H	3⅙	8	8½	1½	1¾	³⁄₃₂

Year	Model	Spark Plug Gap, In	Breaker Gap, In	Firing Order	Timing Mark	Location	Intake	Exhaust	Oil Refill	No Heater	With Heater	Caster	Camber	Toe-In
PANHARD														
1956–60	Dyna	.025	.016	1–2	12° BTDC	Flywheel	.006C	.006C	2⅓	..	..	1½	0	⅛①

① Negative.

Year	Model	Spark Plug Gap, In	Breaker Gap, In	Firing Order	Timing Mark	Location	Intake	Exhaust	Oil Refill	No Heater	With Heater	Caster	Camber	Toe-In
PEUGEOT														
1957–60	203	.024	.016	1342	Mark	Flywheel	.010C	.020C	4¼	..	10	2½	⅛	¹⁄₁₆
1957–60	403	.024	.016	1342	Mark	Flywheel	.010C	.020C	4¼	..	10	2½	⅛	¹⁄₁₆

Year	Model	Spark Plug Gap, In.	Breaker Gap, In.	Firing Order	Ignition Timing Timing Mark	Location	Valve Lash C-Cold H-Hot Intake	Exhaust	Engine Oil, Qts. Refill	Cooling Capacity, Qts. No Heater	With Heater	Alignment Caster	Camber	Toe-In
PORSCHE														
1956	356–1600	.027	.016	1432	TDC	Pulley	.004C	.004C	4½	..	..	2¾	¾	¼
1956	356–1600S	.027	.016	1432	TDC	Pulley	.006C	.004C	4½	..	..	2¾	¾	¼
1956-58	356A-1600	.027	.016	1432	TDC	Pulley	.004C	.004C	4½	..	..	5	½	⅛
1956-57	356A-1600S	.027	.016	1432	TDC	Pulley	.006C	.004C	4½	..	..	5	½	⅛
1959	356AT2-1600	.027	.016	1432	TDC	Pulley	.006C	.004C	4½	..	..	5	½	⅛
1959	356AT2-1600S	.027	.016	1432	TDC	Pulley	.006C	.004C	4½	..	..	5	½	⅛
1957-60	Carrera	.016	.015	1432	25° BTDC	Pulley	.006C	.006C	8½-11	..	..	...	..	..
1960	356B-1600	.027	.016	1342	TDC	Pulley	.004C	.006C	4½	..	..	5	½	⅛
1960	356B-1600S	.027	.016	1342	TDC	Pulley	.006C	.004C	4½	..	..	5	½	⅛
RENAULT														
1957-60	750 (4CV)	.020	.018	1342	Notch	Pulley	.006	.008C	2½	4½	5	10	1	⅛-3/16
1957-60	Dauphine	.020	.018	1342	Notch	Pulley	.006C	.008C	2½	4½	5	10	1	⅛-3/16
1960	Caravelle	.020	.018	1342	Notch	Pulley	.006C	.008C	2½	4½	5	10	1	⅛-3/16
1960	Petitruck	.020	.018	1342	Notch	Pulley	.006C	.008C	2½	4½	5	0	2	⅛①

① Toe-out.

Year	Model	Spark Plug Gap, In.	Breaker Gap, In.	Firing Order	Timing Mark	Location	Intake	Exhaust	Engine Oil Refill	No Heater	With Heater	Caster	Camber	Toe-In
SAAB														
1956-58	93, 93B	.028	.012-.016	1-2-3	①	①	None	None	...	..	7	...	..	..
1959-60	93B, 93F	.028	.012-.016	1-2-3	①	①	None	None	...	..	9	1	¾	1/16

① Checked by special timing gauge fitted to No. 2 cylinder. 8° BTDC. Standard, 6° BTDC G. T. Model.

Year	Model	Spark Plug Gap, In.	Breaker Gap, In.	Firing Order	Timing Mark	Location	Intake	Exhaust	Engine Oil Refill	No Heater	With Heater	Caster	Camber	Toe-In
SIMCA														
1956-60	Aronde	.025	.017-.019	1342	①	①	.004C	.006C	5	6½	7½	2	1¼	⅛②
1956-60	Vedette	.027	.015-.016	15486372	3° BTDC	Pulley	.011C	.011C	4½	17	18	—½	1	1/16

① Flash engine 4° BTDC, Super Flash engine TDC. ② Toe-out.

Year	Model	Spark Plug Gap, In.	Breaker Gap, In.	Firing Order	Timing Mark	Location	Intake	Exhaust	Engine Oil Refill	No Heater	With Heater	Caster	Camber	Toe-In
SKODA														
1958-60	Sedan 440	.027	.012	1342	Groove	Flywheel	.006H	.010H	4	..	..	...	..	..
1958-60	Sedan 445	.027	.012	1342	Groove	Flywheel	.006C	.008C	5	..	..	...	..	..
1958-60	Convertible 450	.027	.012	1342	Groove	Flywheel	.006H	.010H	4	..	..	...	..	..
SUNBEAM														
1955-58	Mark III	.030	.016	1342	TDC	Flywheel	.007H	.009H	6½	12	13	3	¾	⅛
1956-58	Rapier	.030	.015	1342	①	Pulley	.012H	.014H	5	7¼	8	3¾	¾	⅛
1958-59	Rapier Series II	.025	.016	1342	②	Pulley	.012H	.014H	5	7¼	8	1¾	¾	3/16
1960	Rapier Series III	.025	.016	1342	7° BTDC④	Damper	.012H	.014H	5	7½	8	½②	¾③	⅛②
1960	Alpine Series I	.025	.016	1342	7° BTDC④	Damper	.012H	.014H	5	8½	9	4°41'②	¾③	3/16②

① Set timing 10°-12° before TDC (⅜" before TDC). ② Set timing 7°-9° BTDC (11/32" BTDC). ③ Car fully laden. ④ Timing mark indicates TDC.

Year	Model	Spark Plug Gap, In.	Breaker Gap, In.	Firing Order	Timing Mark	Location	Intake	Exhaust	Engine Oil Refill	No Heater	With Heater	Caster	Camber	Toe-In
TRIUMPH														
1956-60	TR3	.025	.015	1342	4° BTDC	Pulley	①	①	6	8.4	8.7	0	2	③
1958-60	Sedan	.032	.015	1342	10° BTDC	Pulley	.010C	.010C	3½	4½	5.1	1¾	2	1/32②
1958-60	Station Wagon	.032	.015	1342	10° BTDC	Pulley	.010C	.010C	3½	4½	5.1	0	2	1/16

① With cast iron rocker arm pedestals .015C, with aluminum pedestals .010C. ② Toe-out. ③ Dunlop tires ⅛", Michelin "X" tires 1/16".

Year	Model	Spark Plug Gap, In.	Breaker Gap, In.	Firing Order	Timing Mark	Location	Intake	Exhaust	Engine Oil Refill	No Heater	With Heater	Caster	Camber	Toe-In
VAUXHALL														
1958-60	Victor	.030	.020	1342	9° BTDC	Flywheel	.013H	.013H	3.6	6.3	6.9	1½	0°38'	⅛
VOLKSWAGEN														
1955-57	Car	.026	.016	1432	7½° BTDC	Pulley	.004C	.004C	2½	..	..	2	1	1/16
1958-60	Car	.026	.016	1432	7½° BTDC	Pulley	.004C	.004C	2½	..	..	2½	⅔	3/32
1955-57	Truck, Bus	.026	.016	1432	7½° BTDC	Pulley	.004C	.004C	2½	..	..	2	1	1/16
1958-60	Truck, Bus	.026	.016	1432	7½° BTDC	Pulley	.004C	.004C	2½	..	..	2½	⅔	3/32
VOLVO														
1957-59	B16	.028	.016	1342	4 BTDC	Flywheel	.020H	.020H	3½	..	8	¼①	⅛	1/16
1960	P-544	.028	.019	1342	7 BTDC	Flywheel	.020H	.020H	3½	..	8	—¼	+⅛	1/16

① Negative.